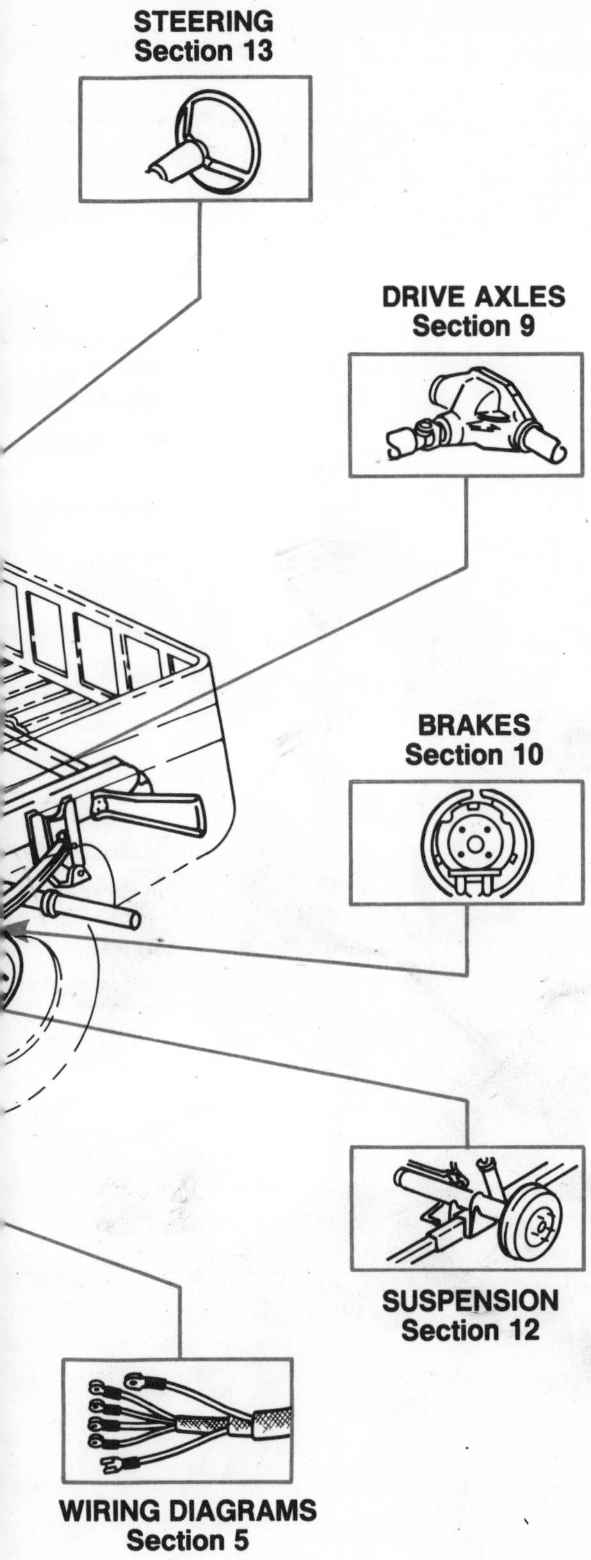
STEERING
Section 13
DRIVE AXLES
Section 9
BRAKES
Section 10
SUSPENSION
Section 12
WIRING DIAGRAMS
Section 5

PREFACE

This is the 1985 edition of Mitchell Information Services' Light Trucks & Vans Service and Repair Manual. This manual, like the many Mitchell publications which have preceded it, represents our commitment to professionalism in the automotive service market.

The automotive industry advances every year, and Mitchell Information Services pledges to advance and improve its products as we maintain the quality and usefulness of all Mitchell publications.

We cordially acknowledge the good will and mutual goals that exist in the automotive business, and it is in this spirit that we thank the automotive manufacturers, distributors, dealers and the entire automotive industry for their fine cooperation and assistance which have made this publication possible.

1985 DOMESTIC LIGHT TRUCKS & VANS TUNE-UP MECHANICAL SERVICE & REPAIR

MANUALS FOR THE AUTOMOTIVE PROFESSIONAL

Published By:
MITCHELL INFORMATION SERVICES
A Cordura Company
P.O. BOX 26260
SAN DIEGO, CALIFORNIA 92126

ISBN 0-8470-6745-9

MITCHELL™
information services inc.
a Cordura Company

PUBLISHER
Barry A. Norton, President

SALES
James E. Lown, Vice President

EDITORIAL
Vice President
Editor-in-Chief
Kenneth A. Young

Managing Editor
Daniel M. Kelley

Ass't. Managing Editor
Terry L. Blomquist

Art Director
Eloise S. Stiverson

Detroit Editors
Lynn D. Meeker
Andy Henry

Coordinating Editors
Daryl F. Visser
Philip G. Wallan
Thomas L. Landis
Daniel D. Fleming

ACKNOWLEDGEMENT

Mitchell Information Services, Inc. thanks the domestic manufacturers, distributors, and dealers for their generous cooperation and assistance which makes this manual possible.

Chrysler Corporation
Ford Motor Company
General Motors Corporation
Jeep Corporation

Technical Editors
Eddie Santangelo
Patrick T. Rice
David L. Skora
Thomas G. Meyer
Richard Langley
Chuck Ackerman
David R. Koontz
Ramiro Gutierrez
David R. Costantino
John von Euen
James Anas
Chuck Vedra
Randy S. Russell
Paul Nutt
Leonard A. St. Amand
Roger Leftridge

IN MEMORY OF
Jeffrey C. Wedeking
1957-1985

PUBLISHED BY

MITCHELL INFORMATION SERVICES, INC.
9889 Willow Creek Road
P.O. Box 26260
San Diego, California 92126

a subsidiary of
CORDURA PUBLICATIONS, INC.
George C. Evanoff, President
John Opelt, Senior Vice President of Finance & Administration
Peter B. Jones, Vice President of Business Development
Robert W. Ladd, Vice President of Manufacturing

For Subscription Information:
CALL TOLL FREE 800-854-7030. In California CALL TOLL FREE 800-421-0159. Or WRITE: P.O. Box 26260, San Diego, CA 92126

ISBN 0-8470-6745-9

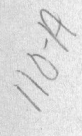

DISCLAIMER OF WARRANTIES: Although the information contained within this volume has been obtained from sources generally believed to be reliable, no warranty (express or implied) can be made as to its accuracy or completeness, nor is any responsibility assumed by the publisher or anyone connected with it for loss or damages suffered through reliance on any information contained in this volume. Specifically, no warranty of merchantability, fitness for a particular purpose or any other warranty is made or to be implied with respect to this volume, and no person has the authority to modify such limitation except in a writing signed by a corporate officer of the publisher. The acceptance of this manual is conditional on the acceptance of this disclaimer. If the buyer does not accept the terms of this disclaimer, return the manual within fifteen (15) days and the publisher will refund any money advanced by the buyer toward the purchase of this manual.

Introduction

You now have the most complete and up to date Service and Repair Manual currently available to the professional mechanic. Our staff of experts has spent many hundreds of hours gathering and processing service and repair information from sources throughout the automotive industry. More than 200 separate articles provide specific step-by-step Testing, Adjusting and Repair procedures for 1985 Domestic Light Trucks and Vans.

To use this manual in the most efficient and profitable way possible, please take the time to read the following instructions, "How To Find the Information." This will enable you to quickly locate the car model and the mechanical procedure you need, without wasting time thumbing through unnecessary pages.

HOW TO FIND THE INFORMATION

3 Quick Steps

(1) On the inside cover, you'll find the contents of this manual. Locate the section you want, and notice that it has a black square next to it.

THUMB INDEX SPOT

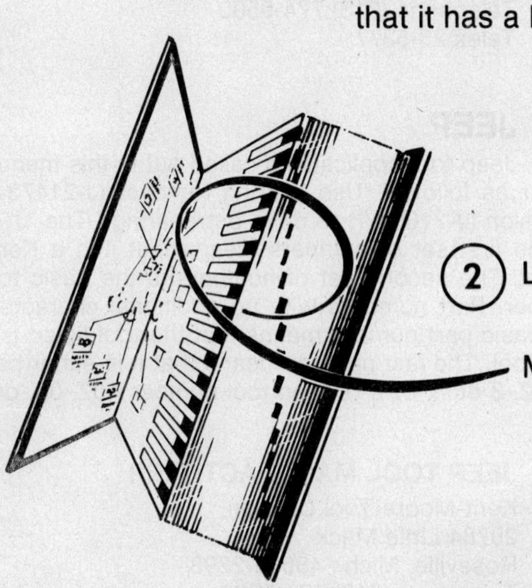

(2) Looking along the right edge of the book, you'll notice additional black squares.

Match the black square of the section listed on the cover with the black square in line with it on the book's edge, then turn directly to that section.

(3) Review the section contents page.

After locating the specific article and starting page needed, turn to the beginning of the article.

OR ...

Go directly to the GENERAL INDEX located at the front of this manual. Use this alphabetical guide as you would any type of reference index.

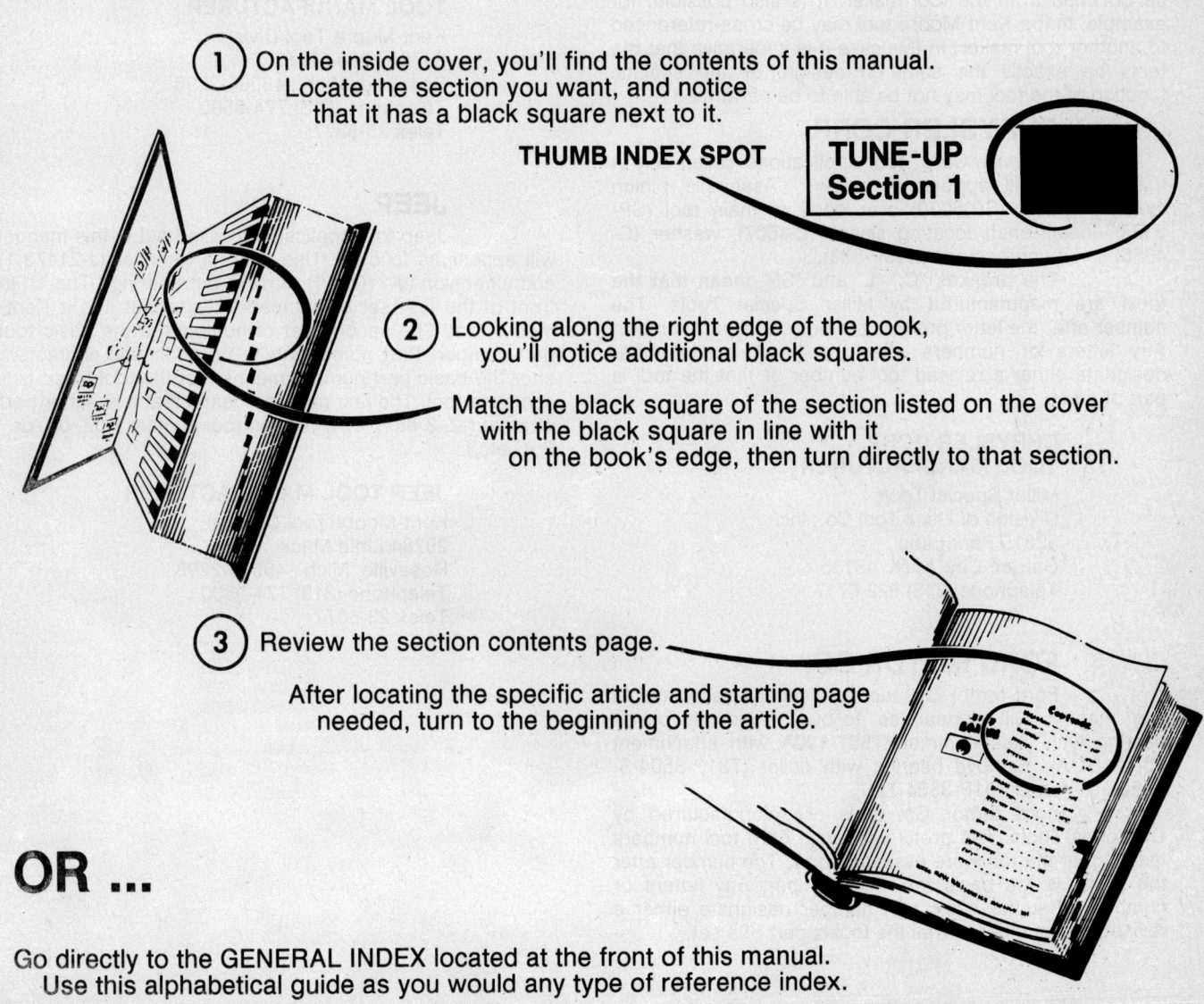

Tool Applications

ALL MANUFACTURERS

DESCRIPTION

Tool applications used in this manual are noted in the text of all articles where applicable. These tools are usually specific tools that must be used to perform a specific function in Removal, Installation, Overhaul or Testing of a component.

For example; "Using Spline Adapter (J-28513) and Holding Wrench (J-28514), tighten pinion nut until end play is taken up." Although other tools could possibly be substituted, the tool references in text are those that are recommended by the vehicle manufacturer. These tools should be used whenever possible. In cases where a non-specific tool is called for, no tool number will be given.

For example; "Place bearing insert in rod and install guides on rod bolts. Compress piston rings using ring compressor." Since just about any ring compressor that works and does not damage the components can be used, no specific tool number will be called out.

The following descriptions show an example of the reference in text, the maker of the tools recommended by the manufacturer and the tool maker address. Further information on tools and local suppliers of the tools can be obtained from the tool maker. It is also possible, for example, that a Kent-Moore tool may be cross-referenced to another tool maker. In this case it is imperative that the tools be exactly the same in design, or the specific function of the tool may not be able to be performed.

CHRYSLER CORP.

Chrysler Corp. tool applications called out in this manual will appear as follows: "Assemble pinion locating spacer (SP-6030) over body of main tool (SP-5385). Install shaft locating sleeve (L-4507), washer (C-4656) and compression nut (SP-533)."

The prefixes "C," "L" and "SP" mean that the tools are manufactured by Miller Special Tools. The number after the letter prefix is the basic tool part number. Any letters or numbers after the basic part number designate either a revised tool number or that the tool is part of a set.

**CHRYSLER CORP.
TOOL MANUFACTURER**

Miller Special Tools
Division of Utica Tool Co., Inc.
32615 Park Lane
Garden City, Mich. 48135
Telephone (313) 522-6717

FORD MOTOR CO.

Ford Motor Co. tool applications called out in this manual will appear as follows: "Remove pinion bearing with slide hammer (T50T-100A with attachment T58L-101-A). Remove bearing with puller (T81P-3504-S, T58L-101-A and T81P-3504-T)."

Ford Motor Co. tools are manufactured by Owatonna Tools. The prefix used with Ford tool numbers means that the tools are essential tools. The number after the prefix is the basic tool part number. Any letters or numbers after the basic part number designate either a revised tool number or that the tool is part of a set.

**FORD MOTOR CO.
TOOL MANUFACTURER**

Owatonna Tool Co. Inc.
Owatonna, Minn. 55060
Telephone (507) 455-2626
Telex 29-0876

GENERAL MOTORS

General Motors tool applications called out in this manual will appear as follows; "Install pivot pin remover (J-21854-1) and remove pins. Using pin punch (J-22635), drive out lever pin."

The "J" in front of the first set of numbers means that it is a Kent-Moore tool. The second set of numbers is the basic tool part number. Part numbers with no additional characters after the basic part number means that the tool listed is a complete tool. The last number means that it is either part of a set (-2,-3 etc.), or a revised tool number (-02,-03, or -B,-C etc,).

**GENERAL MOTORS
TOOL MANUFACTURER**

Kent-Moore Tool Division
29784 Little Mack
Roseville, Mich., 48066-2298
Telephone (313) 774-9500
Telex 23-5377

JEEP

Jeep tool applications called out in this manual will appear as follows: "Use bearing remover (J-21473-1) and extension (J-21054-1) to drive out bearing." The "J" in front of the first set of numbers means that it is a Kent-Moore tool. The second set of numbers is the basic tool part number. Part numbers with no additional characters after the basic part number means that the tool listed is a complete tool. The last number means that it is either part of a set (-2,-3 etc.), or a revised tool number (-02,-03, or -B,-C etc,).

JEEP TOOL MANUFACTURER

Kent-Moore Tool Division
29784 Little Mack
Roseville, Mich., 48066-2298
Telephone (313) 774-9500
Telex 23-5377

1985 Light Truck Model Identification

In this manual, Light Truck models will be referred to by the manufacturer's model and/or series designation. When a specific model does not have a designated model or series designation, it will be referred to by model name.

NOTE: **When General Motors is referred to within this manual (rather than Chevrolet or GMC), the Chevrolet numerical vehicle series designations will be abbreviated for common reference to both Chevrolet and GMC models. The GMC counterpart models will be identified as follows: 10 = 1500 (except S15); 20 = 2500; 30 = 3500.**

CHEVROLET

MODEL IDENTIFICATION

Model	Description
C10	[1] 1/2 Ton Conventional Cab 2WD
C20	[1] 3/4 Ton Conventional Cab 2WD
C30	1 Ton Conventional Cab 2WD
K10	[1] 1/2 Ton Conventional Cab 4WD & Blazer
K20	[1] 3/4 Ton Conventional Cab 4WD
K30	1 Ton Conventional Cab 4WD
G10	1/2 Ton Van
G20	3/4 Ton Van
G30	[2] 1 Ton Van
M	Astro Panel & Passenger Van
P20	3/4 Ton Parcel Delivery Van
P30 (42)	1 Ton Parcel Delivery Van
S10	1/2 Ton Conventional Cab 2WD & Blazer
T10	1/2 Ton Conventional Cab 4WD & Blazer

[1] – Includes Suburban models.
[2] – Includes Front Section and Hi-Cube models.

DODGE

MODEL IDENTIFICATION

Model	Description
AD150	Ramcharger 2WD
AW150	Ramcharger 4WD
B150	1/2 Ton Van/Wagon
B250	3/4 Ton Van/Wagon
B350	1 Ton Van/Wagon
D100	Light Duty 1/2 Ton Conventional Cab 2WD
D150	Heavy Duty 1/2 Ton Conventional Cab 2WD
D250	3/4 Ton Conventional Cab 2WD
D350	1 Ton Conventional Cab 2WD
K	Caravan & Mini Ram Van
W100	Light Duty 1/2 Ton Conventional Cab 4WD
W150	Heavy Duty 1/2 Ton Conventional Cab 4WD
W250	3/4 Ton Conventional Cab 4WD
W350	1 Ton Conventional Cab 4WD

FORD

MODEL IDENTIFICATION

Model	Description
Aerostar	Trim-Sized Panel & Passenger Van
Bronco	Full-Sized Family 4WD Wagon
Bronco II	Trim-Sized Family 4WD Wagon
E150	1/2 Ton Van
E250	3/4 Ton Van

FORD (Cont.)

MODEL IDENTIFICATION

Model	Description
E350	[1] 1 Ton Van
F150	1/2 Ton Conventional Cab 2WD & 4WD
F250	3/4 Ton Conventional Cab 2WD & 4WD
F350	1 Ton Conventional Cab 2WD & 4WD
Ranger	1/2 Ton Conventional Cab 2WD & 4WD

[1] – Includes Front Section models.

GMC

MODEL IDENTIFICATION

Model	Description
C1500	[1] 1/2 Ton Conventional Cab 2WD
C2500	[1] 3/4 Ton Conventional Cab 2WD
C3500	1 Ton Conventional Cab 2WD
K1500	[1] 1/2 Ton Conventional Cab 4WD & Blazer
K2500	[1] 3/4 Ton Conventional Cab 4WD
K3500	1 Ton Conventional Cab 4WD
G1500	1/2 Ton Van
G2500	3/4 Ton Van
G3500	[2] 1 Ton Van
M	Safari Panel & Passenger Van
P2500	3/4 Ton Parcel Delivery Van
P3500 (42)	1 Ton Parcel Delivery Van
S15	1/2 Ton Conventional Cab 2WD & Blazer
T15	1/2 Ton Conventional Cab 4WD & Blazer

[1] – Includes Suburban models.
[2] – Includes Front Section and Hi-Cube models.

JEEP

MODEL IDENTIFICATION

Model	Description
Cherokee (77)	Cherokee 4WD (2-Door)
Cherokee (78)	Cherokee 4WD (4-Door)
CJ7 (87)	94" Wheelbase Utility Vehicle 4WD
Grand Wagoneer (15)	Heavy Duty Fam. Wagon 4WD
J10 (25)	119" Wheelbase 1/2 Ton Conv. Cab 4WD
J10 (26)	131" Wheelbase 1/2 Ton Conv. Cab 4WD
J20 (27)	3/4 Ton Conventional Cab 4WD
Scrambler (88)	104" Wheelbase Utility Vehicle 4WD
Wagoneer (75)	Wagoneer 4WD (4-Door)

PLYMOUTH

MODEL IDENTIFICATION

Model	Description
H	Voyager

1985 Engine Size Conversion Charts

CHRYSLER CORP. ENGINES

Liters	Cubic Inches
4-Cylinder	
2.2	135
2.6	159
6-Cylinder	
3.7	225
V8	
5.2	318
5.9	360

FORD MOTOR CO. ENGINES

Liters	Cubic Inches
4-Cylinder	
2.0	122
2.3 EFI	140
2.3 Turbo Diesel	143.2
V6	
2.8	170
6-Cylinder	
4.9	300
V8	
5.0	302
5.8	351
6.9 Diesel	420
7.5	460

GENERAL MOTORS ENGINES

Liters	Cubic Inches
4-Cylinder	
1.9	119
2.2 Diesel	135
2.5	151
V6	
2.8	173
4.3	262
6-Cylinder	
4.8	292
V8	
5.0	305
5.7	350
6.2 Diesel	378
7.4	454

JEEP ENGINES

Liters	Cubic Inches
4-Cylinder	
2.1 Turbo Diesel	126
2.5	150
V6	
2.8	171
6-Cylinder	
4.2	258
V8	
6.0	360

GENERAL INDEX

The first step in using these pages is to locate the listed components you require information on. Go down the list under the component headings to the model or engine size of the vehicle you have. On the right-hand side of the column you will find the page number of the article, specification, or wiring diagram you need.

1985 General Index

1985 General Index

1985 General Index

1985 General Index

1985 General Index

G

I

J

1985 General Index

1985 General Index

T

1985 General Index

U

V

W

1985 General Index

SECTION T

QUICK-CHECK TUNE-UP SPECIFICATIONS

NOTE: ALSO SEE GENERAL INDEX.

1985 Light Truck Tune-Up

TUNE-UP SPECIFICATIONS

ENGINE	IGNITION TIMING *		SPARK PLUGS		FUEL SYSTEM	No.
	Man. Trans.	Auto. Trans.	Type	Gap In. (mm)	Make & Type	
CHRYSLER CORP.						
2.2L (135") 4-Cyl.						
Fed.	10@800	10@900	CH RN-12Y	.035 (.9)	Holley 5220 2-Bbl.	1
Calif. & High Alt.	10@900	10@800	RN-12Y	.035 (.9)	Holley 6520 2-Bbl.	2
2.6L (156") 4-Cyl.						
Fed.	.....	7@800	CH RN-12Y	.037 (1)	Mikuni 2-Bbl.	3
Calif.	.....	7@850	CH RN-12Y	.037 (1)	Mikuni 2-Bbl.	4
3.7L (225") 6-Cyl.						
Fed.	12@725	16@750	CH RBL-16Y	.035 (.9)	Holley 1945 1-Bbl.	5
Calif.	12@775	16@775	CH RBL-16Y	.035 (.9)	Holley 6145 1-Bbl.	6
5.2L (318") V8						
Fed.	12@700	12@700	CH RN-12YC	.035 (.9)	Holley 2280 2-Bbl.	7
Calif.	8@725	8@650	CH RN-12YC	.035 (.9)	Holley 6280 2-Bbl.	8
High Alt.	8@650	8@650	CH RN-12YC	.035 (.9)	Holley 6280 2-Bbl.	9
5.9L (360") V8						
Fed.	16@800 [3]	16@800 [3]	CH RN-12YC	.035 (.9)	Rochester M4ME 4-Bbl.	10
Calif.	6@800	6@800	CH RN-12YC	.035 (.9)	Rochester M4ME 4-Bbl.	11
High Alt.	.....	16@750	CH RN-12YC	.035 (.9)	Rochester M4ME 4-Bbl.	12
FORD MOTOR CO.						
2.0L (122") 4-Cyl.	6@800	6@800	MC AWSF-42	.044 (1.1)	Carter YFA 1-Bbl.	13
2.3L (140") 4-Cyl.	10@800 [1]	10@800 [1]	MC AWSF-44C	.044 (1.1)	Ford EFI	14
4.9L (300") 6-Cyl.						
Light Duty	10@750	10@600	MC BSF-42	.044 (1.1)	Carter YFA Feedback	15
Heavy Duty	12@800	12@800	MC BSF-42	.044 (1.1)	Carter YFA 1-Bbl.	16
2.8L (170") V6	10@750 [1]	10@850 [1]	MC AWSF-42	.044 (1.1)	Motorcraft 2150A Feedback	17
5.0L (305") V8 EFI	8@Idle [1]	10@Idle [1]	MC ASF-32C	.044 (1.1)	Ford EFI	18
5.0L (305") V8 2-Bbl.	10@575 [1]	10@575 [1]	MC ASF-42	.044 (1.1)	Motorcraft 2150A Feedback	19
5.8L (351") V8 2-Bbl.						
Light Duty	10@Idle	10@Idle [2]	MC ASF-42	.044 (1.1)	Motorcraft 2150A Feedback	20
Heavy Duty	8@700	8@800	MC ASF-42	.044 (1.1)	Motorcraft 2150 2-Bbl.	21
5.8L (351") V8 4-Bbl.	10@600	10@600	MC ASF-32C	.044 (1.1)	Holley 4180C 4-Bbl.	22
7.5L (460") V8	8@800	8@800	MC ASF-42	.044 (1.1)	Holley 4180C 4-Bbl.	23

Spark Plugs – **AC** = Delco; **CH** = Champion; **MC** = Motorcraft.
* – All specifications are BTDC; Auto. Trans. in "D" unless otherwise noted.

1985 Light Truck Tune-Up

TUNE-UP SPECIFICATIONS (Cont.)

No.	HOT IDLE • Man. Trans.	HOT IDLE • Auto. Trans.	FAST IDLE + M/T RPM	FAST IDLE + Cam Step	FAST IDLE + A/T RPM	REMARKS
1	800	800	1700	Low	1850	[1] – High Alt. – 900 RPM.
2	900	800 [1]	1700	Low	1850	[2] – Use cam follower spacing tool (C-4812).
3	.....	800/900	.....	[2]	1300	[3] – Fed. Heavy Duty – 6@800 RPM.
4	.....	800/900	.....	[2]	950	
5	725/825	750/850	1600	2nd	1600	
6	775/850	775/850	1600	2nd	1600	
7	700	700	1600	2nd	1600	
8	725/850	650/800	1625	2nd	1450	
9	650/780	650/780	1400	2nd	1400	
10	800	800/900	1350	2nd	1350	
11	800	800	1350	2nd	1350	
12	.....	750	.....	2nd	1600	
13	775/825	775/825	1700	High	1700	[1] – Controlled by EEC-IV system.
14	575-725 [1]	625-775 [1]	[1]	.....	[1]	[2] – Fed. High Alt. – 14°@Idle.
15	600-700	550-650	1600	2nd (KD)	1600	
16	700	550	1600	2nd (KD)	1600	
17	800-900 [1]	700-800 [1]	3000	High	3000	
18	775 [1]	675 [1]	[1]	.....	[1]	
19	575 [1]	575 [1]	2000 [1]	High	2000 [1]	
20	750 [1]	600 [1]	2000 [1]	High	2000 [1]	
21	650	650	1500	2nd (KD)	1500	
22	650	650	2000	High	2000	
23	800	650	1600	2nd (KD)	1600	

• – When idle solenoid is used, lower RPM is with solenoid disconnected; higher RPM is with solenoid connected.

\+ – All specifications are with transmission in Neutral unless otherwise noted.

1985 Light Truck Tune-Up

TUNE-UP SPECIFICATIONS (Cont.)

ENGINE	IGNITION TIMING *		SPARK PLUGS		FUEL SYSTEM	
	Man. Trans.	Auto. Trans.	Type	Gap In. (mm)	Make & Type	No.
GENERAL MOTORS						
1.9L (119") 4-Cyl.	6@800 [1]	6@900	AC R42CXLS	.041 (1.0)	Hitachi DCH340/DFP340	24
2.5L (151") 4-Cyl.	[5]	[5]	AC R43TSX	.060 (1.5)	GM Model 300 TBI	25
4.8L (292") 6-Cyl.	8@700	8@700	AC R44T	.035 (.9)	Rochester 1ME 1-Bbl.	26
2.8L (173") V6						
Fed.	8@700	12@700	AC R43CTS	.045 (1.2)	Rochester 2SE 2-Bbl.	27
Calif.	10@750	10@650	AC R43CTS	.045 (1.2)	Rochester E2SE 2-Bbl.	28
High Alt.	10@700	12@700	AC R43CTS	.045 (1.2)	Rochester 2SE 2-Bbl.	29
4.3L (262") V6 4-Bbl.						
Fed.	0@600	0@500	AC R43CTS	.045 (1.2)	Rochester M4ME 4-Bbl.	30
Calif.	4@600	4@500	AC R43CTS	.045 (1.2)	Rochester E4ME 4-Bbl.	31
High Alt.	0@600	0@500	AC R43CTS	.045 (1.2)	Rochester M4ME 4-Bbl.	32
5.0L (305") V8						
Fed.	4@700	4@550 [7,8]	AC R45TS	.045 (1.2)	Rochester M4ME 4-Bbl.	33
Calif.	.....	6@550	AC R45TS	.045 (1.2)	Rochester E4ME 4-Bbl.	34
5.7L (350") V8						
Light Duty						
Fed.	8@700	8@550 [7,8]	AC R45TS	.045 (1.2)	Rochester M4ME 4-Bbl.	35
Calif.	.....	6@550	AC R45TS	.045 (1.2)	Rochester E4ME 4-Bbl.	36
Heavy Duty						
Fed.	4@800	4@700	AC R44T	.045 (1.2)	Rochester M4MC 4-Bbl.	37
Calif.	6@700	6@700	AC R44T	.045 (1.2)	Rochester M4MC 4-Bbl.	38
7.4L (454") V8	4@700	4@800	AC R44T	.045 (1.2)	Rochester M4MC 4-Bbl.	39
JEEP						
2.5L (150") 4-Cyl.	12@1600	12@1600	CH RFN14LY	.035 (.9)	Carter YFA 1-Bbl.	40
4.2L (258") 6-Cyl.	17-21@2000	17-21@2000	CH RFN14LY	.035 (.9)	Carter BBD 2-Bbl.	41
2.8L V6						
Fed.	10@700	10@700	AC R43CTS	.041 (1.0)	Rochester 2SE 2-Bbl.	42
Calif.	10@700	10@700	AC R43CTS	.041 (1.0)	Rochester E2SE 2-Bbl.	43
6.0L (360") V8	12@600	12@600	CH RN12LY	.035 (.9)	Motorcraft 2150 2-Bbl.	44

Spark Plugs – AC = Delco; **CH** = Champion; **MC** = Motorcraft.
★ – All specifications are BTDC; Auto. Trans. in "D" unless otherwise noted.

1985 Light Truck Tune-Up

TUNE-UP SPECIFICATIONS (Cont.)

No.	HOT IDLE •		FAST IDLE +		
	Man. Trans.	Auto. Trans.	M/T RPM	Cam Step	A/T RPM
24	900/900 [2]	900/900 [3]	3200 [4]	1st	3200 [4]
25	475-525 [6]	750-800 [6]	[6]	.....	[6]
26	450/700	450/700	2400	High	2400
27	700/850	650/850	2100	High	2100
28	750/950	650/850	2100	High	2100
29	700/850	700/850	2100	High	2100
30	600	500	1800 [7]	[5]	[5]
31	600	500	1800	[5]	[5]
32	600	500	1800	[5]	[5]
33	700/800	500 [8]/650	1700 [9]	High	1800 [10]
34	.....	550/650	.....	High	1800
35	700/800	550 [8]/650	1300 [11]	High	1600 [11]
36	.....	550/650	.....	High	1800
37	600/800	700	1900	High	1900
38	600/800	700	1900	High	1900
39	700	700	1900	High	1900

REMARKS

[1] – Calif. Man. Trans – 6@900.
[2] – Fed. & High Alt. Man. Trans. – 800 RPM.
[3] – Calif. Auto. Trans. – 1900 RPM (N).
[4] – Approx.; Throttle angle must be 15-17° for Man. Trans., 17-19° for Auto. Trans.
[5] – Information not available.
[6] – Controlled by CCC system.
[7] – Low Alt. – 2200 RPM
[8] – High Alt. – 600 RPM.
[9] – All High Alt. Man. Trans. – 1500 RPM; All "G" Series – 1500 RPM.
[10] – High Alt. Auto. Trans. – 1500 RPM.
[11] – High Alt. – 1400 RPM.

No.	HOT IDLE •		FAST IDLE +		
	Man. Trans.	Auto. Trans.	M/T RPM	Cam Step	A/T RPM
40	750/950	700/850	2000	2nd	2300
41	680/900 [1]	600/800 [2]	1700	2nd	1850
42	700	700	2100	High	2300
43	700	700	2100	High	2300
44	600	600	1500	High	1600

REMARKS

[1] – High Alt. – 700 RPM.
[2] – High Alt. – 650 RPM.

• – When idle solenoid is used, lower RPM is with solenoid disconnected; higher RPM is with solenoid connected.
\+ – All specifications are with transmission in Neutral unless otherwise noted.

SECTION 1

TUNE-UP

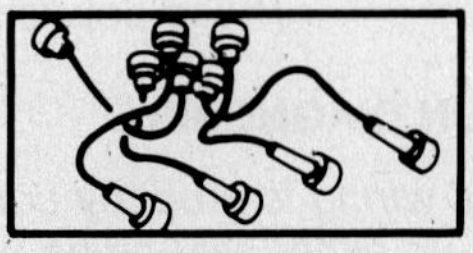

CONTENTS

TROUBLE SHOOTING **Page**

TUNE-UP

NOTE: **ALSO SEE GENERAL INDEX.**

IMPORTANT: **Because of the many model names used by vehicle manufacturers, accurate identification of models is important. See Model Identification at the front of this publication.**

Tune-Up

TUNE-UP TROUBLE SHOOTING

CONDITION	POSSIBLE CAUSE	CORRECTION
	SPARK PLUG DIAGNOSIS	
Normal Spark Plug Condition	Light Tan or Gray deposits on insulator Electrode not burned or fouled Gap tolerance not changed	
Cold Fouling or Carbon Deposits	Over-rich air/fuel mixture Faulty choke Clogged air filter Incorrect idle speed or dirty carburetor Faulty ignition wiring Prolonged operation at idle Sticking valves or worn valve guide seals	Adjust air/fuel mixture, see TUNE-UP Replace choke assembly, see FUEL Clean and/or replace air filter Reset idle speed and/or clean carburetor Replace ignition wiring Shut engine off during long idle Check valve train
Wet Fouling or Oil Deposits	Worn rings and pistons Excessive cylinder wear Worn or loose bearings	Install new rings and pistons Rebore or replace block Tighten or replace bearings
Gap Bridged	Deposits in combustion chamber becoming fused to electrode	Clean combustion chamber of deposits
Blistered Electrode	Engine overheating Wrong type of fuel Loose spark plugs Over-advanced ignition timing	Check cooling system Replace with correct fuel Re-tighten spark plugs Reset ignition timing, see TUNE-UP
Pre-Ignition or Melted Electrodes	Incorrect type of fuel Incorrect ignition timing Burned valves Engine overheating Wrong type of spark plug, too hot	Replace with correct fuel Reset ignition timing, see TUNE-UP Replace valves Check cooling system Replace with correct spark plug, see TUNE-UP
Chipped Insulators	Severe detonation Improper gapping procedure	Check for over-advanced timing or combustion chamber deposits Re-gap spark plugs
Rust Colored Deposits	Additives in unleaded fuel Water in combustion chamber	Try different fuel brand These deposits do not affect plug performance
	ELECTRONIC IGNITION DIAGNOSIS	
Before diagnosing an electronic ignition system, ensure that all wiring is properly connected between distributor, wiring connector and spark plugs. Ignition problems will show up either as: Engine Will Not Start or Engine Runs Rough.		
Engine Won't Start	Open circuits in the following locations: Between distributor and bulkhead connector Between bulkhead connector and ignition switch Between ignition switch and starter solenoid	 Repair circuit Repair circuit Repair circuit
Engine Runs Rough	Fuel lines leaking or clogged Ignition timing incorrect Centrifugal advance malfunction Defective spark plugs, or wiring	Tighten fitting, remove restriction Reset ignition timing, see TUNE-UP Check distributor advance, see ELECTRICAL Replace plugs or plug wiring
Component Failure	Spark arc-over on rotor, coil or cap Defective pick-up coil Defective ignition coil Defective vacuum unit Defective control module	Replace rotor, cap or coil Replace pick-up coil, see ELECTRICAL Replace ignition coil Replace vacuum unit, see ELECTRICAL Replace control module

TUNE-UP TROUBLE SHOOTING (Cont.)

CONDITION	POSSIBLE CAUSE	CORRECTION
ELECTRONIC IGNITION DIAGNOSIS BY OSCILLOSCOPE PATTERN		
Firing Voltage Lines are the Same, But Abnormally High	Retarded ignition timing	Reset ingition timing, see TUNE-UP
	Fuel mixture too lean	Re-adjust carburetor, see TUNE-UP
	High resistance in coil wire	Replace coil wire
	Corrosion in coil tower terminal	Clean and/or replace coil
	Corrosion in distributor coil terminal	Clean or replace distributor cap
Firing Voltage Lines are the Same, But Abnormally Low	Fuel mixture too rich	Re-adjust carburetor, see TUNE-UP
	Breaks in coil wire causing arcing	Replace coil wire
	Cracked coil tower causing arcing	Replace coil
	Low coil output	Replace coil
	Low engine compression	Determine cause and repair
One or More, But Not All Firing Voltage Lines Are Higher Than the Others	Carburetor idle mixture not balanced	Re-adjust idle mixture, see TUNE-UP
	EGR valve stuck open	Inspect and/or replace EGR valve
	High resistance in spark plug wire	Replace spark plug wires
	Cracked or broken spark plug insulator	Replace spark plugs
	Intake vacuum leak	Repair leak
	Defective spark plugs	Replace spark plugs
	Corroded spark plug terminals	Replace spark plugs
One or More, But Not All Firing Voltage Lines Are Lower	Curb idle mixture not balanced.	Re-adjust idle mixture, see TUNE-UP
	Breaks in plug wires causing arcing.	Replace spark plug wires
	Cracked coil tower causing arcing.	Replace coil
	Low compression.	Determine cause and repair
	Defective or fouled spark plugs	Replace spark plugs
Cylinders Not Firing	Cracked distributor cap terminals.	Replace distributor cap
	Shorted spark plug wire.	Determine cause of short and replace wire
	Mechanical problem in engine.	Determine problem and correct
	Defective spark plugs.	Replace spark plugs
	Spark plugs fouled.	Replace spark plugs
GENERAL DIAGNOSIS		
Hard Starting	Binding carburetor linkage	Eliminate binding
	Binding choke linkage	Eliminate binding
	Binding choke piston	Eliminate binding
	Restricted choke vacuum	Check vacuum lines for blockage
	Worn or dirty needle valve and seat	Clean carburetor, see FUEL
	Float sticking	Re-adjust or replace float, see FUEL
	Incorrect choke adjustment.	Reset choke adjustment, see TUNE-UP
	Defective coil.	Replace coil
	Improper spark plug gap.	Re-gap spark plugs
	Incorrect ignition timing.	Reset ignition timing, see TUNE-UP
Detonation	Over-advanced ignition timing	Reset ignition timing, see TUNE-UP
	Defective spark plugs	Replace spark plugs
	Fuel lines clogged	Clean out fuel lines
	EGR system malfunction	Check EGR system
	PCV system malfunction	Check PCV system
	Vacuum leaks	Check and repair vacuum system
	Loose fan belts	Tighten or replace fan belts, see TUNE-UP
	Restricted air flow	Remove restriction
	Vacuum advance malfunction	Check distributor operation, see ELECTRICAL
Dieseling	Binding carburetor linkage	Free carburetor linkage
	Binding throttle linkage	Free throttle linkage
	Binding choke linkage or fast idle cam	Free binding linkage
	Defective idle solenoid	Replace solenoid, see FUEL
	Improper base idle speed	Reset idle speed, see TUNE-UP
	Incorrect ignition timing	Reset ignition timing, see TUNE-UP
	Incorrect idle mixture setting	Reset idle mixture setting, see TUNE-UP

TUNE-UP TROUBLE SHOOTING (Cont.)

GENERAL DIAGNOSIS (Cont.)

CONDITION	POSSIBLE CAUSE	CORRECTION
Faulty Acceleration	Incorrect ignition timing	Reset ignition timing, see TUNE-UP
	Engine cold and choke too lean	Adjust choke and allow engine to warm-up
	Defective spark plugs	Replace spark plugs
	Defective coil	Replace coil
Faulty Low Speed Operation	Clogged idle transfer slots	Clean idle transfer slots, see FUEL
	Restricted idle air bleeds and passages.	Disassemble carburetor and clean, see FUEL
	Clogged air cleaner filter	Replace air cleaner
	Defective spark plugs	Replace spark plugs
	Defective ignition wires	Replace ignition wires, see TUNE-UP
	Defective distributor cap	Replace distributor cap
Faulty High Speed Operation	Incorrect ignition timing	Reset ignition timing, see TUNE-UP
	Defective distributor centrifugal advance.	Replace mechanism, see ELECTRICAL
	Defective distributor vacuum advance	Replace advance unit, see ELECTRICAL
	Incorrect spark plugs or plug gap	Check gap and/or replace spark plugs
	Faulty choke operation	Check choke and repair as required
	Clogged vacuum passages	Remove restrictions
	Improper size or clogged main jet	Check jet size and clean, see FUEL
	Restricted air cleaner	Check filter and replace as required
	Defective distributor cap, rotor or coil	Replace cap, rotor or coil
	Worn distributor shaft	Replace distributor
Misfire At All Speeds	Defective spark plugs	Replace spark plugs
	Defective spark plug wires	Replace spark plug wires
	Defective distributor cap, rotor or coil	Replace cap, rotor, or coil
	Cracked or broken vacuum hoses	Replace vacuum hoses
	Vacuum leaks	Seal leaks
	Fuel lines clogged	Remove restriction
Hesitation	Cracked or broken vacuum hoses	Replace vacuum hoses
	Vacuum leaks	Repair leaks
	Binding carburetor linkage	Eliminate binding
	Binding throttle linkage	Eliminate binding
	Binding choke linkage or fast idle cam	Eliminate binding
	Improper float setting	Re-adjust float setting, see FUEL
	Cracked or broken ignition wires	Replace ignition wires
Rough Idle, Missing or Stalling	Incorrect curb idle or fast idle speed.	Reset idle speeds, see TUNE-UP
	Incorrect basic timing	Reset ignition timing, see TUNE-UP
	Improper idle mixture adjustment	Reset idle mixture adjustment, see TUNE-UP
	Improper feedback system operation	Check feedback system, see FUEL
	Incorrect spark plug gap	Reset spark plug gap, see TUNE-UP
	Moisture in ignition components	Dry components
	Loose or broken ignition wires	Replace ignition wires
	Damaged distributor cap or rotor	Replace cap or rotor
	Faulty ignition coil	Replace coil
	Fuel filter clogged or worn	Replace fuel filter
	Damaged idle mixture screw	Replace idle mixture screw, see FUEL
	Improper fast idle cam adjustment	Reset fast idle cam adjustment, see TUNE-UP
	Improper EGR valve operation	Replace EGR valve
	Faulty PCV valve air flow	Replace PCV valve
	Choke binding, or improper setting	Reset choke and eliminate binding
	Vacuum leak	Eliminate leak
	Improper float bowl fuel level	Reset float adjustment, see FUEL
	Clogged air bleed or idle passages	Clean carburetor passages, see FUEL
	Clogged or worn air cleaner filter	Replace air filter
	Faulty choke vacuum diaphragm	Replace diaphragm, see FUEL
	Exhaust manifold heat valve inoperative	Replace heat valve
	Improper distributor spark advance	Check distributor operation, see ELECTRICAL

TUNE-UP TROUBLE SHOOTING (Cont.)

CONDITION	POSSIBLE CAUSE	CORRECTION
	GENERAL DIAGNOSIS (Cont.)	
Rough Idle, Missing or Stalling (Cont.)	Leaking valves or valve components	Check valve train
	Improper carburetor mounting	Remove and remount carburetor
	Excessive play in distributor shaft	Replace distributor, see ELECTRICAL
	Loose or corroded wiring connections	Repair or replace as required
Engine Surges	Improper PCV valve air flow	Replace PCV valve
	Vacuum leaks	Eliminate leaks
	Clogged main jets	Remove restriction
	Clogged air bleeds	Remove restriction
	EGR valve malfunction	Replace EGR valve
	Restricted air cleaner filter	Replace air filter
	Cracked or broken vacuum hoses	Repair or replace hoses
	Cracked or broken ignition wires	Replace ignition wires
	Vacuum advance malfunction	Check unit and replace if required
	Defective or fouled spark plugs	Replace spark plugs
Ping or Spark Knock	Incorrect ignition timing	Reset ignition timing, see TUNE-UP
	Distributor centrifugal or vacuum advance malfunction	Check operation amd replace as required
	Carburetor setting too lean	Re-adjust mixture setting, see TUNE-UP
	Vacuum leak	Eliminate leak
	EGR valve malfunction	Replace EGR valve
Poor Gasoline Mileage	Cracked or broken vacuum hoses	Replace vacuum hoses
	Vacuum leaks	Eliminate leaks
	Defective ignition wires	Replace wires
	Incorrect choke setting	Re-adjust setting, see FUEL
	Defective vacuum advance	Replace vacuum advance, see ELECTRICAL
	Defective spark plugs	Replace spark plugs
	Binding carburetor power piston	Eliminate binding
	Dirt in carburetor jets	Clean jets and/or replace, see FUEL
	Incorrect float adjustment	Re-adjust float setting, see FUEL
	Defective power valves	Replace power valve, see FUEL
Engine Stalls	Incorrect idle speed	Re-adjust idle speed, see TUNE-UP
	Improper float level	Re-adjust float level, see FUEL
	Leaking needle valve and seat	Replace needle valve and seat, see FUEL
	Vacuum Leaks	Eliminate leaks

1985 Chrysler Corp. 4 Tune-Up

TUNE-UP

ENGINE IDENTIFICATION

VEHICLE IDENTIFICATION NUMBER CODE

Engine can be identified by the 8th character of Vehicle Identification Number (VIN). VIN number is located on a plate attached to top left corner of instrument panel and is visible through windshield.

Engines also carry an engine identification number (EIN). On 2.2L engines, the number is located on the left rear face of block, directly under cylinder head. On 2.6L engines, the number is located on the left side of the block, between the core plug and rear face of block (on radiator side of engine).

VIN ENGINE CODES

Application	Code
2.2L (135") 2-Bbl.	C
2.6L (156") 2-Bbl.	G

TUNE-UP NOTES

NOTE: **When performing tune-up procedures described in this article, the following notes and precautions must be followed:**

Due to late changes and corrections, always refer to Engine Tune-Up Decal in engine compartment before attempting tune-up. If manual and decal differ, always use decal specifications.

On vehicles equipped with catalytic converters, do not allow or create an engine misfire in more than one cylinder for an extended period of time. Damage to converter may occur due to loading converter with unburned air/fuel mixture.

Also on vehicles equipped with catalytic converters, do not add fuel system cleaning agents to fuel tank or carburetor as cleaning agents may damage the catalytic converter.

Before making a compression test or cranking engine using a remote starting switch, disconnect coil wire from distributor and secure to a good ground.

ENGINE COMPRESSION

Check compression pressure at cranking speed (250 RPM) with engine warm, spark plugs removed and throttle valve wide open.

COMPRESSION SPECIFICATIONS

Compression Ratio	
2.2L	9.6:1
2.6L	8.7:1
Compression Pressure	
2.2L	130-150 psi (9-10.4 kg/cm²)
2.6L	149 psi (10.3 kg/cm²)
Max. Variation Between Cylinders	
2.2L	20 psi (1.4 kg/cm²)
2.6L	15 psi (1.0 kg/cm²)

VALVE CLEARANCE

VALVE CLEARANCE SPECIFICATIONS (HOT)

Application	Intake In. (mm)	Exhaust In. (mm)
2.2L (Hydraulic)	Zero Lash	Zero Lash
2.6L	[1] .006 (.15)	.010 (.25)

[1] - Jet valve is .010" (.25 mm).

VALVE ARRANGEMENT

2.2L

E-I-E-I-E-I-E-I (Front-to-rear).

2.6L

Right side - All exhaust.
Left side - All intake.

SPARK PLUGS

SPARK PLUG TYPE

Application	Champion No.
All Models	RN12Y

SPARK PLUG SPECIFICATIONS

Application	Gap In. (mm)	Torque Ft. Lbs. (N.m)
2.2L	.035 (.9)	20 (28)
2.6L	.035-.040 (0.9-1.0)	20 (28)

HIGH TENSION WIRE RESISTANCE

1) Carefully remove spark plug wire from spark plug. Remove distributor cap with spark plug wires attached.

2) Connect one ohmmeter lead to coil or spark plug end of wire. Connect other ohmmeter lead to electrode inside distributor cap.

3) If resistance is more than 7200 ohms per foot, remove wire from distributor cap and connect ohmmeter lead to wire. If resistance is still not to specifications, replace with electronic suppression type wire.

NOTE: **When replacing spark plug wires on 2.2L engines, do not pull on wires. These models are equipped with spark plug wires with positive locking terminals, which must be released from inside distributor cap.**

IGNITION COIL WIRE

Carefully remove ignition coil wire without bending it. Check terminals for corrosion and clean if necessary. Check coil wire resistance. Replace wire if resistance is excessive.

TUNE-UP (Cont.)

HIGH TENSION WIRE RESISTANCE (OHMS)

Application	Specification
Spark Plug Wires	3000-7200 per ft.
Ignition Coil Wire	22,000 max.

DISTRIBUTOR

The 2.2L engine is equipped with Chrysler Corp. Hall Effect Electronic Spark Advance (ESA) Ignition system. The 2.6L engine is equipped with Mitsubishi Electronic Ignition system.

The only adjustments that can be made to either system are initial ignition timing (changing distributor position) and spark plug gap.

Fig. 1: 2.2L Firing Order and Timing Marks

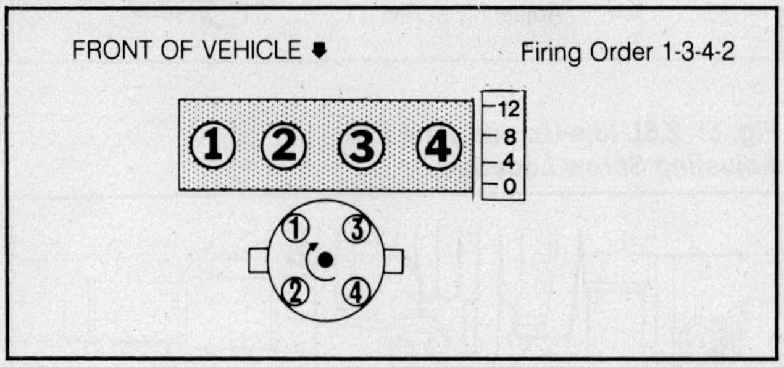

Fig. 2: 2.6L Firing Order and Timing Marks

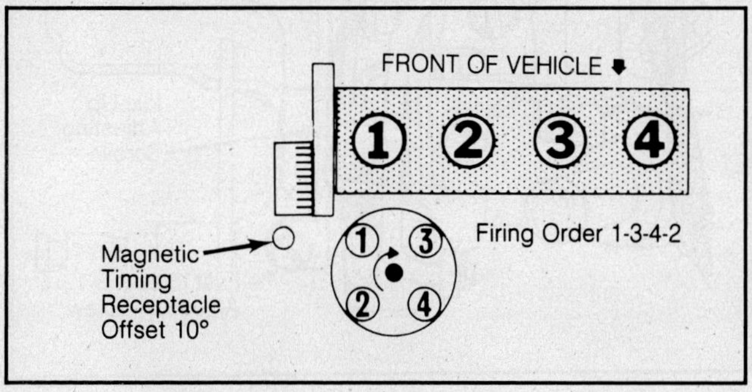

IGNITION TIMING

CAUTION: Use proper adapters for timing light connections. Do not puncture cables, boots or nipples with test probes.

1) If using a magnetic probe timing light, refer to equipment manufacturer's instruction for proper hook-up. If using a conventional timing light, connect it to No. 1 cylinder.

2) Connect a tachometer to engine. Start engine and warm to normal operating temperature. Momentarily open throttle and release to ensure linkage does not bind and idle speed screw is against its stop.

3) If vehicle is equipped with carburetor switch, connect a jumper wire between switch and ground. Disconnect and plug vacuum line at Spark Control Computer on 2.2L engines or at distributor on 2.6L engines.

4) Ensure engine is operating at or below curb idle RPM. If not, adjust curb idle. See HOT (SLOW) IDLE RPM in this article. Check timing. If timing is within 2° of specifications, do not adjust.

5) If timing is not correct, loosen distributor hold-down bolt and turn distributor housing until specified timing is reached. Recheck timing after distributor hold-down bolt has been tightened.

IGNITION TIMING SPECIFICATIONS (Degrees BTDC@RPM)

Application	Man. Trans.	Auto. Trans.
2.2L		
Federal	10 @ 800	[1] 10 @ 800
Calif.	10 @ 900	10 @ 800
2.6L		
Federal		7 @ 800
Calif.		7 @ 850

[1] – Set High Altitude idle speed to 900 RPM.

HOT (SLOW) IDLE RPM

2.2L

NOTE: 2.2L engines with A/C are equipped with a solenoid kicker. It is not necessary to adjust A/C idle speed but kicker operation should be checked.

A/C Solenoid Kicker Check

1) Start engine and warm to normal operating temperature. Set temperature control lever in coldest position and turn on A/C. Kicker plunger should move in and out as A/C compressor clutch cycles on and off. Air cleaner may be removed to inspect kicker operation.

2) If kicker does not move in and out, check kicker system for vacuum leaks or electrical problems. If kicker still does not operate, replace kicker and check again.

Curb Idle Speed

1) Ensure ignition timing is properly adjusted. Disconnect and plug vacuum connector at Coolant Vacuum Switch Cold Closed (CVSCC). Unplug connector at radiator fan and install a jumper wire so fan runs continuously.

2) Disconnect PCV valve from rubber connector and let valve draw in fresh air. Connect tachometer to engine. Ground carburetor switch (if equipped) with a jumper wire.

3) Disconnect oxygen system test connector, located on left fender shield of vehicles with Holley 6520 carburetors. Start engine and warm to normal operating temperature. Adjust idle speed to specified RPM using idle speed screw. *See Fig. 3*.

4) Turn engine off and remove tachometer. Reconnect cooling fan connector and oxygen connector. Remove jumper wire grounding carburetor switch. Reinstall PCV valve. Reconnect connector to CVSCC.

2.2L IDLE SPEED (RPM)

Application	Man. Trans.	Auto. Trans.
2.2L		
Federal	800	[1] 800
Calif.	900	800

[1] – High Altitude is 900 RPM.

TUNE-UP (Cont.)

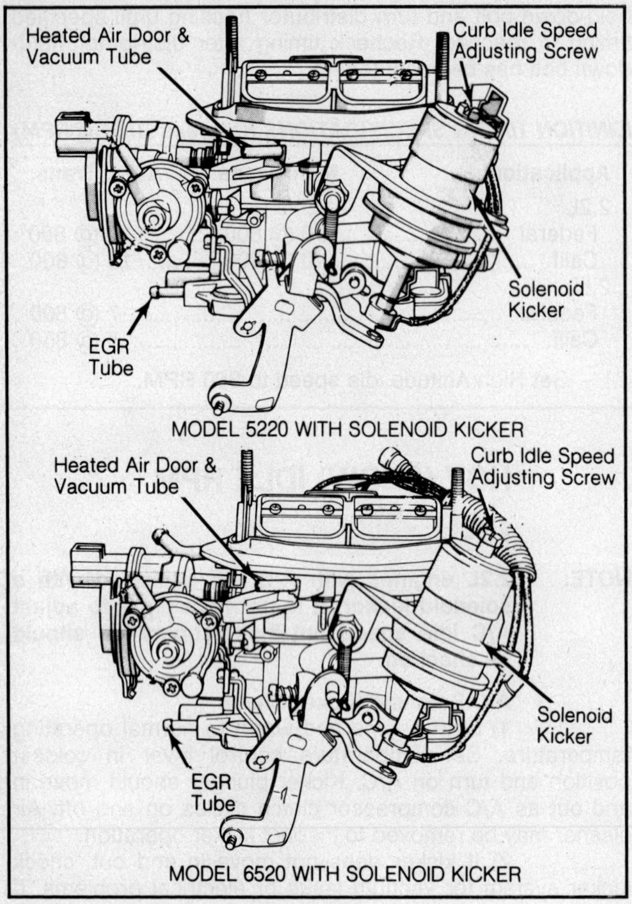

Fig. 3: 2.2L Curb Idle Speed Adjustment Locations

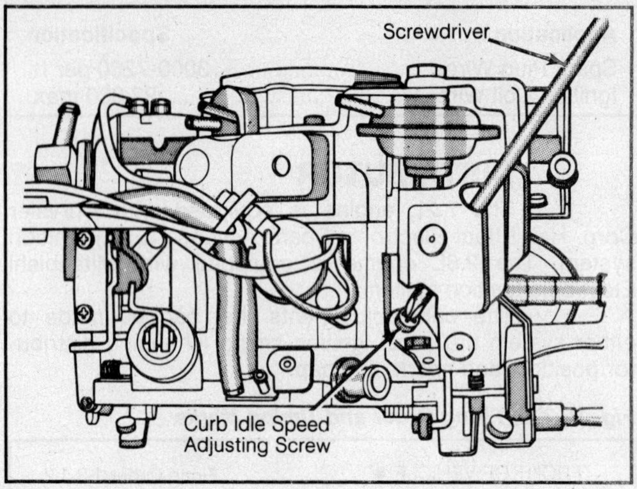

Fig. 4: 2.6L Curb Idle Speed Adjusting Screw Location

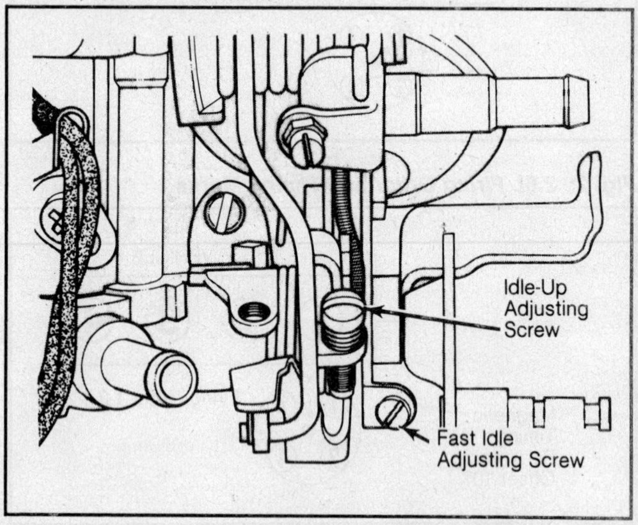

Fig. 5: 2.6L Idle-Up and Fast Idle Adjusting Screw Location

2.6L IDLE SPEED (RPM)

Application	Curb Idle RPM	A/C On RPM
2.6L	800	900

2.6L

1) Ensure engine timing is correctly set. Set parking brake and place transaxle in Neutral. Turn all lights and accessories off. Disconnect radiator cooling fan. Connect tachometer to engine.

2) Start engine and warm to normal operating temperature. Open throttle and let engine run at 2500 RPM for 10 seconds, then return to idle.

3) After 2 minutes at idle, check idle speed. Adjust idle speed screw to obtain specified curb idle RPM. *See Fig. 4*.

4) On models with A/C, start engine and run for 2 minutes. Set to coldest temperature and turn on A/C. With compressor running, adjust engine speed by turning idle-up screw. *See Fig. 5*. Shut off engine, disconnect tachometer, reconnect fan and idle switch connector.

IDLE MIXTURE ADJUSTMENT

NOTE: Idle mixture adjustment is not part of a regular tune-up. DO NOT adjust mixture unless carburetor has been diassembled or vehicle fails emissions testing.

MIXTURE SCREW PLUG REMOVAL

2.2L

1) Remove air cleaner crossover. Remove canister purge and air pump diverter valve vacuum hoses from carburetor. Locate and center punch a mark 1/4" from end of mixture screw housing. *See Fig. 6*.

TUNE-UP (Cont.)

Fig. 6: 2.2L Mixture Screw Plug Removal

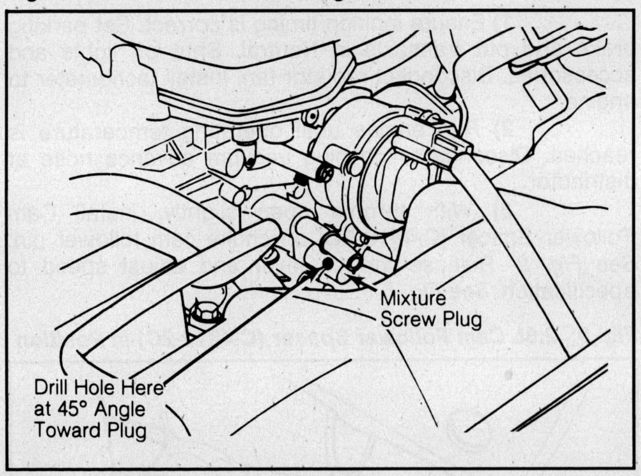

Drill hole at 10 o'clock position.

2) Drill through outer section of housing using a 3/16" drill bit. Concealment plug should drop out. If not, use a small drift punch to remove plug. DO NOT allow drift to contact mixture screw.

3) Reinstall vacuum hoses and air cleaner crossover. Perform propane idle mixture adjustment and reinstall plug.

2.6L

1) Remove impact plate (if equipped). Remove vacuum connector (if equipped) from high altitude compensator (HAC) fitting.

2) Using 8" long, 1/4" diameter drill bit, drill out concealment plug as shown in *Fig. 7*.

3) After removing plug, reinstall vacuum connector and impact plate.

Fig. 7: 2.6L Mixture Screw Plug Removal

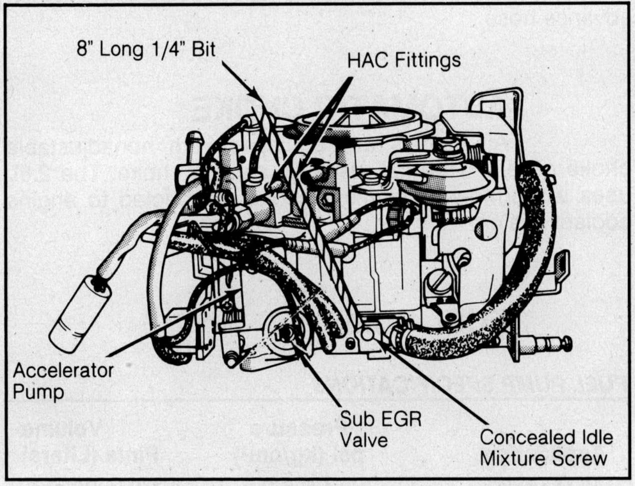

PROPANE MIXTURE ADJUSTMENT (RPM)

2.2L

1) Set parking brake and place transaxle in Neutral. Turn off all lights and accessories. Connect tachometer to engine. Remove concealment plug. Start engine and warm it to normal operating temperature with fast idle cam on second highest step. Return engine to curb idle.

2) Disconnect and plug vacuum connector at CVSCC. Disconnect vacuum hose from heated air door at 3-way connector. In its place, install supply hose from a propane bottle. Ensure valves are closed, bottle is upright and in a safe place.

3) Disconnect connector at radiator fan and install a jumper wire so fan will run continuously. Remove PCV valve from valve cover so valve can draw fresh air.

4) Connect a jumper wire between carburetor switch and ground. On vehicles with Holley 6520 carburetor, disconnect oxygen test connector on left fender shield.

5) Open propane bottle main valve. With air cleaner installed, slowly open propane metering valve until maximum engine RPM is reached. Carefully adjust metering valve to obtain maximum steady RPM. If too much propane is added, engine speed will drop.

6) While propane is flowing, adjust idle speed screw on top of solenoid to specified RPM. Fine tune propane metering valve and idle adjustment screw to specified RPM.

7) Turn off main valve and allow engine speed to stabilize. With air cleaner in place, slowly adjust idle mixture screw to specified idle set RPM. *See Fig. 6*. Let engine stabilize between adjustments.

8) Turn on propane main valve and note maximum RPM reading. If highest engine speed is not within 25 RPM of specified propane RPM, repeat steps **5)** through **8)** until proper propane idle RPM is obtained.

9) Turn off both propane bottle valve. Remove test equipment and jumper wires. Reconnect vacuum lines and install new concealment plug.

MIXTURE ENRICHMENT (RPM)

Application	RPM
2.2L	
Man. Trans.	875
Auto. Trans.	975
2.6L	
Federal	875
Calif.	850

2.6L

1) Remove concealment plug. Place transaxle in Neutral. Turn off all lights and accessories. Connect tachometer to engine. Start engine and warm to normal operating temperature. Ensure engine timing is correct. Disconnect radiator fan.

2) Start engine and run it at 2500 RPM for 10 seconds. Return engine to idle for 2 minutes. Detach air duct from air cleaner. Place propane supply hose 4" into air cleaner snorkel. Ensure propane bottle is upright, in a safe place and both valves are fully closed.

3) Open propane main valve. Slowly open metering valve of propane until highest engine RPM is reached. Engine speed will decrease if too much propane is added. Fine tune for highest RPM. While propane is flowing, adjust idle speed screw to specified propane RPM.

4) With propane main valve turned off, let engine speed stabilize. To achieve specified idle RPM, slowly adjust mixture screw. Let engine speed stabilize between adjustments.

TUNE-UP (Cont.)

5) Open propane main valve to obtain highest engine RPM. If highest speed is not within 25 RPM of specified propane RPM, repeat steps **3)** through **5)**.

6) Turn off both propane valves. Remove propane hose and reinstall air duct. Install new concealment plug and impact plate.

7) If vehicle has A/C, set to lowest temperature and turn on system. With compressor running, set engine speed to 900 RPM by adjusting idle-up screw. *See Fig. 5*.

COLD (FAST) IDLE RPM

2.2L

1) Ensure ignition timing is correct. Disconnect connector from radiator fan and connect a jumper wire to fan so it will run continuously. Remove PCV valve from valve cover and let it draw fresh air.

2) Disconnect and plug vacuum connector at CVSCC. Connect tachometer to engine. Using a jumper wire, ground carburetor switch.

3) On models with Holley 6520 carburetors, disconnect oxygen system test connector on left fender shield.

4) Start engine and warm to normal operating temperature. Open throttle slightly. Place fast idle adjusting screw on lowest step of fast idle cam. *See Fig. 8*. Let engine speed stabilize.

Fig. 8: 2.2L Fast Idle Speed Adjusting Screw Location

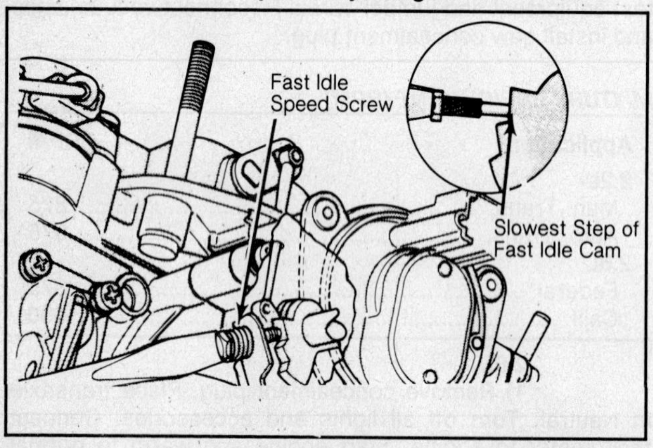

5) With choke fully open, adjust fast idle speed to specified RPM using fast idle adjusting screw. Return to idle. Replace adjusting screw on lowest step of fast idle speed cam to verify fast idle speed. Readjust if necessary.

6) Turn off engine and remove tachometer. Unplug and reconnect vacuum connector. Remove jumper wires and reconnect all connectors.

FAST IDLE SPEED (RPM)

Application	Man. Trans.	Auto. Trans.
2.2L		
All Models	1700	1850
2.6L		
Federal	.....	1300
Calif. & High Alt.	.....	950

2.6L

1) Ensure ignition timing is correct. Set parking brake and put transaxle in Neutral. Shut off lights and accessories. Disconnect radiator fan. Install tachometer to engine.

2) Run engine until operating temperature is reached. Disconnect and plug vacuum advance hose at distributor.

3) With throttle open slightly, install Cam Follower Spacer (C-4812-2C) on choke cam follower pin. *See Fig. 9*. Release throttle lever and adjust speed to specification. *See Fig. 5*.

Fig. 9: 2.6L Cam Follower Spacer (C-4812-2C) in Position

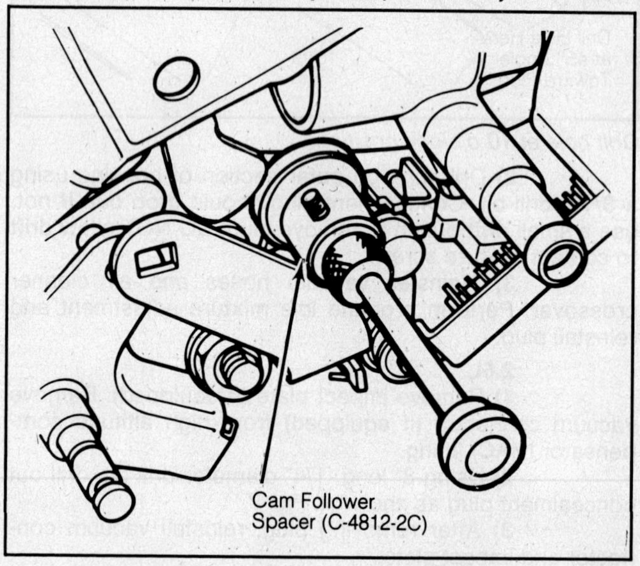

4) Remove spacer and tachometer. Turn off engine, reconnect fan, unplug and reconnect vacuum advance hose.

AUTOMATIC CHOKE

All models are equipped with nonadjustable choke covers. The 2.2L uses an electric choke. The 2.6L uses a thermo-wax element choke, connected to engine coolant system.

FUEL PUMP

FUEL PUMP SPECIFICATIONS

Application	Pressure psi (kg/cm²)	Volume Pints (Liters)
All Models	4.5-6.0	1.0 in 30 sec.
	(.32-.42)	(.5L) in 30 sec.

TUNE-UP (Cont.)

2.2L ELECTRONIC SPARK ADVANCE (ESA) CHECK

1) Set ignition basic timing. Start engine and warm to normal operating temperature. Temperature sensor must be connected and operating properly.

2) Remove and plug vacuum hose at vacuum transducer. Connect an auxiliary vacuum supply to vacuum transducer and set for 16 in. Hg.

3) Raise engine speed to 2000 RPM, wait 1 minute and check specifications. Advance specifications are in addition to basic advance. If specified readings are not obtained, replace computer.

ELECTRONIC SPARK ADVANCE TEST (Engine at 2000 RPM & 16 in. Hg Vacuum to Computer)

Application	[1] Degrees BTDC
2.2L	
Federal & Calif.	
Man. Trans.	35-43
Auto. Trans.	38-46
High Alt. (Auto. Trans.)	35-43

[1] – In addition to basic timing.

GENERAL SERVICING

IGNITION SYSTEM

DISTRIBUTOR

All 2.2L engines are equipped with Chrysler Corp. Hall Effect Electronic Spark Advance (ESA) Ignition systems. All 2.6L engines are equipped with Mitsubishi Electronic Ignition systems.

The only adjustments that can be made to either system are initial ignition timing (changing distributor position) and spark plug gap.

DISTRIBUTOR PICK-UP COIL RESISTANCE

Application	Ohms
2.2L	[1]
2.6L	920-1120

[1] – Cannot be measured.

TOTAL SPARK ADVANCE @ 3000 RPM

Application	W/Vacuum Advance	W/O Vacuum Advance
2.2L	[1]	[1]
2.6L		
Federal	20°	10°
Calif.	17.5°	10°

[1] – Computer-controlled.

IGNITION COIL

IGNITION COIL RESISTANCE – OHMS @ 75°F (24°C)

Application	Primary	Secondary
Prestolite	1.60-1.79	9400-11,700
Essex	1.41-1.62	9000-12,200
Mitsubishi	.70-.85	9000-11,000

FUEL SYSTEMS

CARBURETORS

Application	Model
2.2L	
Federal	Holley 5220 2-Bbl.
Calif. & High Altitude	Holley 6520 2-Bbl.
2.6L	Mikuni 2-Bbl.

ELECTRICAL SYSTEM

BATTERY SPECIFICATIONS

Application [1]	Cold Cranking Amps @ 0°F (-18°C)	Reserve Capacity Minutes
Standard	335	62
Standard [2]	400	86
Optional	500	110

[1] – Any battery listed may be used, depending on model and optional equipment.

[2] – With models equipped with electric heated rear window.

STARTER

The 2.2L engine uses Bosch or Nippondenso direct drive starter. The 2.6L engine uses a Nippondenso gear reduction starter.

STARTER SPECIFICATIONS

Application	Volts	Amps	Test RPM
2.2L	11	47	6600
2.6L	11	85	3700

GENERAL SERVICING (Cont.)

ALTERNATOR

The 2.2L engine uses Chrysler Corp. or Bosch alternator. The 2.6L engine uses a Mitsubishi alternator.

ALTERNATOR SPECIFICATIONS

Application	Field Current [1] Draw @ 12 Volts	Rated Amp Output
2.2L		
Yellow Tag	2.5-5.0 Amps	60
Brown Tag	2.5-5.0 Amps	78
2.6L	[2]	75

1 – While rotating alternator by hand.
2 – Information not available from manufacturer.

ALTERNATOR REGULATOR

2.2L models have a Chrysler Corp. Electronic Voltage Regulator. 2.6L models have a Mitsubishi IC Regulator, integral with alternator.

REGULATOR OPERATING VOLTAGE

Application	Voltage
2.2L [1]	13.9-14.4
2.6L [2]	14.1-14.7

1 – Measured at 68°F (20°C).
2 – Measured at 80°F (27°C).

ADJUSTMENTS

BELT ADJUSTMENT
Deflection In. (mm) with 10 lbs. (4.5 kg) Pressure

Application	New Belt	Used Belt
2.2L		
A/C Compressor	5/16 (7.5)	7/16 (10.5)
Air Pump	3/16 (4.5)	1/4 (6.0)
Alternator	1/8 (3.0)	1/4 (6.0)
Power Steering	1/4 (6.0)	7/16 (10.5)
2.6L		
A/C Compressor	1/4 (6.0)	5/16 (7.5)
Alternator	3/16 (4.5)	1/4 (6.0)
Power Steering	1/4 (6.0)	3/8 (9.0)
Water Pump	5/16 (7.5)	3/8 (9.0)

SERVICE INTERVALS

REPLACEMENT INTERVALS

Component	Interval (Miles)
Oil Filter	15,000
Air Filter	
2.2L	52,500
2.6L	30,000
PCV Filter	52,500
Fuel Filter	52,500
Spark Plugs	30,000

CAPACITIES

FLUID CAPACITIES

Application	Quantity
Crankcase (Includes Filter)	
2.2L	4.0 qts. (3.8L)
2.6L	5.0 qts. (4.8L)
Fuel Tank	
Standard	15.0 gals. (56.8L)
Optional	20.0 gals. (75.7L)
Cooling System	
2.2L	8.5 qts. (8.0L)
2.6L	9.5 qts. (8.0L)
Transaxle	
Man. Trans. (Dexron II)	
A-460 4-Speed	2.0 qts. (1.9L)
A-525 & A-465 5-Speed	2.3 qts. (2.2L)
Auto. Trans. (Dexron II)	
A-413 & A-470	
Fleet Models	9.2 qts. (8.7L)
Except Fleet Models	8.9 qts. (8.4L)

SYSTEM REFRIGERANT CAPACITIES

Application	Ounces
2.2L & 2.6L	38

TUNE-UP

ENGINE IDENTIFICATION

The engine can be identified by a number stamped on right side of block below No. 6 spark plug. The first digit indicates model year. The next 3 digits indicate cubic inch displacement.

The engine can also be identified by the eighth character of the Vehicle Identification Number (VIN). The VIN is located on a label on upper left corner of instrument panel, near windshield.

VIN ENGINE CODES

Application	VIN Code
3.7L (225") 1-Bbl.	H

TUNE-UP NOTES

NOTE: When performing tune-up procedures, the following notes and precautions must be followed.

Due to late changes and corrections, always refer to Engine Tune-Up Decal in engine compartment before attempting tune-up. If manual and decal differ, always use decal specifications.

When performing tune-up on vehicles equipped with catalytic converters, do not allow or create a condition of engine misfire in more than 1 cylinder for an extended period of time. Damage to converter may occur due to loading converter with unburned air/fuel mixture.

ENGINE COMPRESSION

Before making compression test or cranking engine using remote starting switch, disconnect coil wire from distributor and secure to good ground. Check compression with engine warm, spark plugs removed and throttle wide open.

COMPRESSION SPECIFICATIONS

Compression Ratio	8.4:1
Compression Pressure	Min. 100 psi (7.0 kg/cm²)
Maximum Pressure Variation	25 psi (1.8 kg/cm²)

VALVE ARRANGEMENT

E-I-E-I-E-I-I-E-I-E-I-E (Front-to-rear).

VALVE CLEARANCE

All engines are equipped with hydraulic valve lifters. Lifters should be adjusted to zero lash.

SPARK PLUGS

SPARK PLUG TYPE

Application	Champion No.
All Models	RBL-16Y

SPARK PLUG SPECIFICATIONS

Application	Gap In. (mm)	Torque Ft. Lbs. (N.m)
All Models	.035 (0.9)	10 (14)

HIGH TENSION WIRE RESISTANCE

1) Carefully remove spark plug wire from spark plug. DO NOT remove wire from distributor cap. Connect an ohmmeter between spark plug end terminal and corresponding electrode inside cap.

2) If resistance is not within specifications, remove wire from distributor cap and test wire. Replace wire if not to specification. To check coil wire resistance, remove distributor cap from distributor without removing wire from cap or coil. Connect an ohmmeter between center contact in cap and other end of wire.

3) If resistance is not within specifications, remove wire at coil tower and repeat test. If resistance is not within specifications, replace wire.

HIGH TENSION WIRE RESISTANCE

Application	Ohms
All Wires	
Minimum	3000 per ft.
Maximum	7200 per ft.

DISTRIBUTOR

All models use Chrysler Electronic Spark Advance (ESA) system. Automatic transmission models have dual pick-up distributors. Manual transmission models have single pick-up distributors. No adjustments are necessary.

Fig. 1: Timing Marks and Firing Order

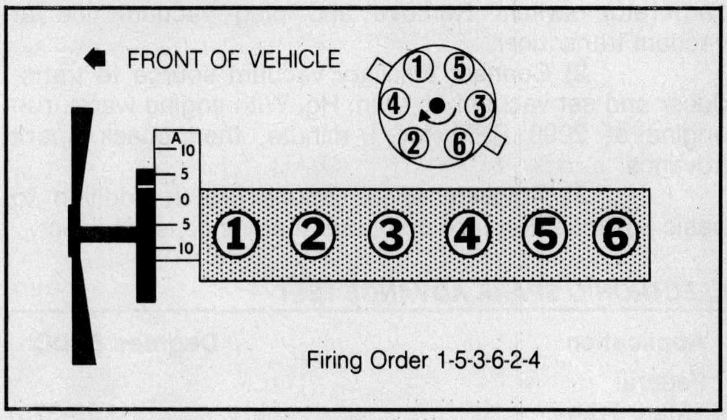

Magnetic probe located at 10° ATDC.

TUNE-UP (Cont.)

IGNITION TIMING

NOTE: **All models are equipped with socket for magnetic timing equipment, located at 10° ATDC. Do not use this location for timing with a conventional timing light.**

1) Connect power timing light to number 1 plug wire. Connect tachometer to engine. Start engine, set parking brake and place transmission in Neutral. With engine at normal operating temperature, momentarily open throttle and make sure idle speed screw returns against its stop.

2) Ground carburetor switch (if equipped) with jumper wire. On models without Spark Control Computer (SCC), disconnect and plug vacuum line at distributor. Engine idle speed should be at or below specification. If idle is too high, turn idle speed screw to adjust. Aim timing light at timing plate on chain case cover or read magnetic timing unit.

3) If timing is not within 2° of specification, loosen distributor hold-down arm screw and rotate distributor housing to obtain correct timing. Tighten distributor hold-down screw when timing is correct.

4) Recheck idle speed and timing. If curb idle is not within 50 RPM of specification, readjust idle. Do not reset timing. Turn engine off, reconnect vacuum lines, and remove jumper wire and tachometer.

IGNITION TIMING SPECIFICATIONS (Degrees BTDC@RPM)

Application	Man. Trans.	Auto. Trans.
Federal	12@725	16@750
California	12@725	16@775

ELECTRONIC SPARK ADVANCE (ESA) CHECK

1) Set ignition basic timing. Place thin insulating material between curb idle adjusting screw and carburetor switch. Remove and plug vacuum line at vacuum transducer.

2) Connect auxiliary vacuum source to transducer and set vacuum at 10 in. Hg. With engine warm, run engine at 2000 RPM for 1 minute, then check spark advance.

3) Advance specifications are in addition to basic advance. Replace computer if advance is incorrect.

ELECTRONIC SPARK ADVANCE TEST

Application	[1] Degrees BTDC
Federal	
Man. Trans.	[2] 29-37
Auto. Trans.	34-42
California	
Man. Trans.	33-41
Auto. Trans.	26-34

[1] – In addition to basic timing.
[2] – 26-34 with Fuel Miser.

HOT (SLOW) IDLE RPM

SOLENOID IDLE STOP RPM

1) Ensure that ignition timing is properly adjusted. Disconnect and plug vacuum hose at EGR valve. Disconnect and plug 3/16" control hose at canister.

2) Remove PCV valve from cylinder head cover and allow to draw underhood air. Prop up air cleaner for access to carburetor. Ground carburetor switch (if equipped) with jumper wire.

3) Install tachometer. Start and warm engine to normal operating temperature. Turn A/C on and set blower on "LOW". Disconnect A/C clutch wire. On non-A/C models, connect a jumper wire between battery positive post and solenoid idle stop lead wire. Be sure to jumper proper wire or harness damage could result.

4) Open throttle slightly to allow solenoid plunger to extend. Remove adjusting screw and spring from solenoid. Insert a 1/8" Allen wrench into solenoid and adjust to correct RPM.

5) Turn off A/C and replace A/C clutch wire (or remove jumper wire). Replace solenoid screw and spring. Perform CURB IDLE SPEED adjustment.

SOLENOID IDLE STOP RPM [1]

Application	Solenoid Energized
Federal	
Man. Trans.	825
Auto. Trans.	850
Calif.	850

[1] – Subtract 75 RPM on vehicles with less than 300 miles.

CURB IDLE SPEED

1) Ensure that ignition timing is properly adjusted. Disconnect and plug vacuum hose at EGR valve. Disconnect and plug 3/16" control hose at canister.

2) Remove PCV valve from cylinder head cover and allow to draw underhood air. Prop up air cleaner for access to carburetor. Ground carburetor switch (if equipped) with jumper wire.

3) On California models, disconnect vacuum hose from heated air temperature sensor and plug hose. Disconnect and plug vacuum hose at distributor. Disconnect and ground oxygen sensor lead.

NOTE: **DO NOT pull on oxygen sensor lead. Connector is located about 4" from oxygen sensor.**

4) Remove and plug vacuum hose at vacuum transducer on computer. Connect auxiliary vacuum supply to vacuum transducer and apply 16 in. Hg vacuum. On all models, install tachometer. Start and warm engine to normal operating temperature.

5) Allow engine to run at least 2 minutes to stabilize idle, then check idle speed. Adjust idle speed screw on solenoid to obtain correct idle RPM.

6) Reconnect oxygen sensor. Remove auxiliary vacuum supply and reconnect all vacuum lines and hoses. Remove jumper wire from carburetor switch. Idle speed may vary under normal operating conditions (all wires and hoses connected). This is normal and does not require readjustment.

TUNE-UP (Cont.)

CURB IDLE SPEED (RPM)

Application	Man. Trans.	Auto. Trans.
Federal	725	750
California	775	775

IDLE MIXTURE

NOTE: Idle mixture adjustment is not part of a regular tune-up. DO NOT adjust mixture unless carburetor has been disassembled or vehicle fails emissions testing.

MIXTURE SCREW PLUG REMOVAL

Remove air cleaner and disconnect all vacuum hoses from front of carburetor. Center punch idle mixture screw housing 1/4" from end of housing. Drill through outer section of housing at punch mark with 3/16" drill. Pry plug out of housing and save for reassembly. Reconnect vacuum hoses and install air cleaner.

Fig. 2: Mixture Screw Plug Location

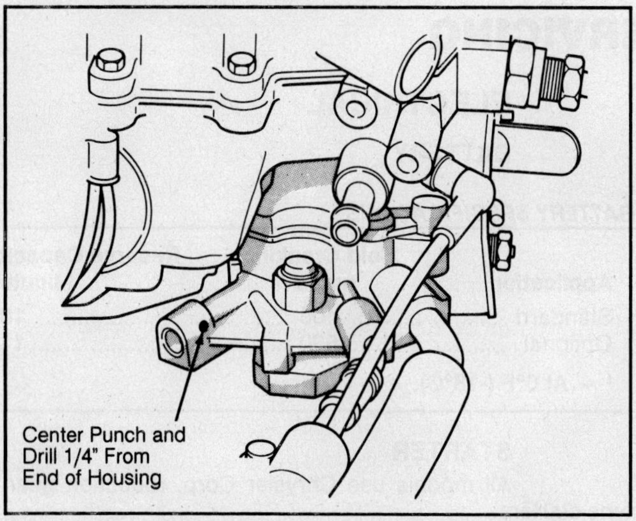

Drill through outer section of housing and pry out plug.

PROPANE ENRICHMENT PROCEDURE

1) Remove concealment plug. Set parking brake and place transmission in Neutral. Turn all lights and accessories off. Connect tachometer to engine. Start engine and allow to warm up on 2nd highest step of fast idle cam until normal operating temperature is reached. Return to idle.

2) Disconnect and plug vacuum hose at EGR valve. Prop up air cleaner for access to carburetor. Ground carburetor switch (if equipped) with jumper wire.

3) Disconnect vacuum supply hose from choke diaphragm at "T" and install propane supply hose. Other connections at "T" must remain in place.

4) With propane bottle held upright and in a safe location, remove PCV valve from rocker cover and allow valve to draw underhood air. Disconnect and plug 3/16" control hose from canister.

5) On California models, disconnect and ground oxygen sensor lead. Remove and plug vacuum hose at vacuum transducer on computer. Using auxiliary vacuum supply, apply 16" Hg to vacuum transducer.

NOTE: Do not pull on oxygen sensor wire when disconnecting connector. Also be careful not to touch exhaust manifold.

6) On all models, allow engine to run for 2 minutes to stabilize idle. Open main propane valve. Slowly open the metering valve until maximum RPM is reached. With propane flowing, adjust idle speed screw on solenoid to reach specified RPM.

7) Adjust metering valve again to reach maximum RPM. If there has been a change in maximum RPM, readjust idle speed screw to specified RPM. Turn off propane and allow engine speed to stabilize. Adjust idle mixture screw 1/16 turn at a time, waiting 30 seconds between adjustments, until smoothest idle at specified RPM is reached.

8) Turn on propane main valve and "fine tune" metering valve to obtain highest engine RPM. If RPM is more than 25 RPM different from specified RPM, repeat steps **6)** and **7)**.

9) Turn off propane valves. Remove propane supply hose and carburetor switch ground wire. Reconnect oxygen sensor lead and all vacuum hoses. Remove test equipment. Install concealment plug. Perform all idle speed adjustments.

PROPANE MIXTURE ADJUSTMENT (RPM)

Application	Man. Trans.	Auto. Trans.
Federal	750	775
California	850	825

COLD (FAST) IDLE RPM

1) Ensure that ignition timing is properly adjusted. Disconnect and plug vacuum hose at EGR valve. Disconnect and plug 3/16" control hose at canister.

2) Remove PCV valve from cylinder head cover and allow to draw underhood air. Prop up air cleaner for access to carburetor. Ground carburetor switch (if equipped) with jumper wire.

3) On California models, disconnect vacuum hose from heated air temperature sensor and plug hose. Disconnect and plug vacuum hose at distributor. Disconnect and ground oxygen sensor lead.

NOTE: DO NOT pull on oxygen sensor wire. Oxygen sensor connector is about 4" from sensor.

4) On all models, install tachometer. Start and warm engine to normal operating temperature. Allow engine to run at least 2 minutes to stabilize idle, then open throttle slightly and place fast idle adjustment screw on 2nd highest step of fast idle cam. With choke fully open, adjust fast idle speed by turning screw.

5) Return to idle speed, then recheck fast idle speed with fast idle speed screw on 2nd highest step of fast idle cam. Readjust if required. Remove test equipment and reconnect all components.

6) Idle speed may fluctuate under normal operating conditions (all wires and vacuum lines connected). This is normal and does not require readjustment.

1985 Chrysler Corp. 6 Tune-Up

TUNE-UP (Cont.)

FAST IDLE SPEED (RPM)

Application	Man. Trans.	Auto. Trans.
All Models	1600	1600

AUTOMATIC CHOKE SETTING

Vehicles over 6000 lbs. GVW are equipped with a nonadjustable thermostatically-controlled automatic choke using engine heat only in positioning valve. All other models use an electric assist choke which requires no adjustment.

FUEL PUMP

Measure fuel pump output and pressure with engine running at idle.

FUEL PUMP SPECIFICATIONS

Application	Pressure psi (kg/cm^2)	Volume Quarts (Liters)
All Models	3.0-4.5 (.21-.32)	1.0 in 1 min. (.95 in 1 min.)

MANIFOLD HEAT CONTROL VALVE

Apply solvent to both ends of valve shaft where it rotates in bushing every 18,000 miles. Work valve back and forth several times.

CAUTION: Apply solvent only when manifold is cold.

EMISSION CONTROL SYSTEMS

NOTE: See appropriate article in EMISSION CONTROL section.

GENERAL SERVICING

IGNITION

DISTRIBUTOR

Automatic transmission models have dual pick-up distributors. Manual transmission models have single pick-up distributors. No adjustments are necessary.

DISTRIBUTOR PICK-UP COIL RESISTANCE (Ohms)

All Models	150-900

IGNITION COIL

IGNITION COIL RESISTANCE – Ohms @ 75°F (24°C)

Application	Primary	Secondary
Essex	1.34-1.55	9000-12,200
Prestolite	1.34-1.55	9400-11,700

FUEL SYSTEMS

CARBURETORS

Application	Model
Federal	Holley 1945
California	Holley 6145

ELECTRICAL

BATTERY

BATTERY SPECIFICATIONS

Application	Cold Cranking Amps [1]	Reserve Capacity Minutes
Standard	400	100
Optional	500	110

[1] – At 0°F (-18°C).

STARTER

All models use Chrysler Corp. reduction gear type starters.

STARTER SPECIFICATIONS

Application	Volts	Amps	Test RPM
All Models	11	90	3700

ALTERNATORS

All models use Chrysler Corp. alternators.

ALTERNATOR SPECIFICATIONS

Tag Color	Field Current Draw @ 12 Volts	Rated Amp Output
Violet	[1] 2.5-5.0	41
Yellow		
Standard	[1] 2.5-5.0	60
Optional	[1] 2.5-5.0	114
Brown	[1] 2.5-5.0	78

[1] – While rotating alternator by hand.

GENERAL SERVICING (Cont.)

ALTERNATOR REGULATOR

All models use Chrysler Corp. Electronic Voltage Regulator. Unit is nonadjustable.

REGULATOR OPERATING VOLTAGE @ 80°F (27°C)

Application	Volts
All Models	13.9-14.6

ADJUSTMENTS

BELT ADJUSTMENT
Deflection In. (mm) with 10 lbs. (4.5 kg) Pressure

Application	Deflection In. (mm)
New Belts	1/4-1/2 (6.0-12.0)
Used Belts [1]	1/4-5/16 (6.0-7.5)

[1] – Used belts are any operated more than 15 minutes.

SERVICE INTERVALS

REPLACEMENT INTERVALS

Component	Interval (Miles)
Oil Filter	15,000
Fuel Filter	18,000
PCV Valve	24,000
Air Filter	30,000
Spark Plugs	
With Cat. Converter	30,000
Without Cat. Converter	15,000

CAPACITIES

COOLING SYSTEM CAPACITIES

Application	Quantity
All Models	[1] 12.0 qts. (11.4L)

[1] – Add 2 quarts (1.9L) with A/C or increased cooling.

ENGINE OIL & FUEL CAPACITIES

Application	Quantity
Crankcase (Includes Filter)	6.0 qts. (5.7L)
Fuel Tank	
Pickup Models [1]	
Standard (Sport Utility)	35 gals. (132L)
Standard (Light Duty)	20 gals. (75L)
Optional	30 gals. (113L)
Van Models	
Standard	22 gals. (83L)
Optional	36 gals. (136L)

[1] – Includes Ramcharger.

TRANSMISSION, TRANSFER CASE & DIFFERENTIAL CAPACITIES

Application	Pts. (L)
Auto. Trans. (Dexron II)	
A-727	[1] 7.7 pts. (3.6L)
All Others	17.1 pts. (8.1L)
Man. Trans.	
A-833 4-Speed Overdrive (Dexron II)	7.5 pts. (3.5L)
N. P. 435 4-Speed (SAE 90)	7.0 pts. (3.3L)
Transfer Case	
N. P. 205 (SAE 90)	4.5 pts. (2.1L)
N. P. 208 (Dexron II)	6.0 pts. (2.8L)
Rear Axle (SAE 80W-90)	
8 1/4" Ring Gear	4.5 pts. (2.1L)
8 3/8" Ring Gear	4.5 pts. (2.1L)
9 1/4" Ring Gear	4.5 pts. (2.1L)
Spicer Model 60	6.0 pts. (2.8L)
Front Axle (SAE 80W-90)	
Model 44	5.6 pts. (2.7L)
Model 60	6.5 pts. (3.1L)

[1] – Without torque converter drain.

SYSTEM REFRIGERANT CAPACITIES

Application	Ounces
Pickup Models [1]	42
Van Models	
Front	48
Front & Rear	64

[1] – Includes Ramcharger.

TUNE-UP

ENGINE IDENTIFICATION

Engine identification number is stamped on a pad located at rear of the right engine mount. First digit indicates model year. The next 3 digits indicate engine size in cubic inches.

Engine can also be identified by the eighth character in the Vehicle Identification Number (VIN). VIN is located on a plate attached to upper left corner of instrument panel, near windshield.

VIN ENGINE CODES

Application	VIN Code
5.2L (318") 2-Bbl.	T
5.9L (360") 4-Bbl.	
Federal	W
California	I
Heavy Duty	V

TUNE-UP NOTES

NOTE: **When performing tune-up procedures described in this article, the following notes and precautions must be followed.**

When performing tune-up on vehicles equipped with a catalytic converter, do not allow or create a condition of engine misfire in one or more cylinders for an extended period of time. Damage to converter may occur due to loading with unburned air/fuel mixture.

Due to production changes, always refer to Engine Tune-Up Decal in engine compartment before attempting tune-up. In the event of a conflict between specifications given in this manual and decal specifications, use the decal specifications.

On vehicles equipped with catalytic converters do not add fuel system cleaning agents to fuel tank or carburetor as their use may be detrimental to the catalytic converter.

For tune-up purposes, "Light Duty" refers to vehicles 8500 lbs. GVW or less and "Heavy Duty" refers to vehicles over 8500 lbs. GVW.

ENGINE COMPRESSION

Disconnect coil wire from distributor and secure to a good ground. Check compression pressure at cranking speed (250 RPM) with engine warm, spark plugs removed, and throttle valve wide open.

COMPRESSION SPECIFICATIONS

Compression Ratio	
5.2L	9.0:1
5.9L	8.5:1
Compression Pressure	Min. 100 psi (7.0 kg/cm^2)
Maximum Pressure Variation	25 psi (2.8 kg/cm^2)

VALVE ARRANGEMENT

E-I-I-E-E-I-I-E (Front-to-rear, both banks).

VALVE CLEARANCE

All engines are equipped with hydraulic lifters. Lifters should be adjusted to zero lash.

SPARK PLUGS

SPARK PLUG TYPE

Application	Champion No.
All Models	RN-12YC

SPARK PLUG SPECIFICATIONS

Application	Gap In. (mm)	Torque Ft. Lbs. (N.m)
All Models	.035 (0.9)	30 (41)

HIGH TENSION WIRE RESISTANCE

1) Carefully remove spark plug wire from spark plug. DO NOT remove wire from distributor cap. Connect an ohmmeter between spark plug end terminal and corresponding electrode inside cap. If resistance is not within specifications, disconnect wire from cap and test wire.

2) To check coil wire resistance, remove disributor cap from distributor without removing wire from cap or coil. Connect an ohmmeter between center contact in cap and other end of wire.

3) If resistance is not within specifications, remove wire at coil tower and repeat test. If resistance of any wire is not to specification, replace wire.

HIGH TENSION WIRE RESISTANCE

Application	Ohms
All Wires	
Minimum	3000 per foot
Maximum	7200 per foot

DISTRIBUTOR

California and High Altitude 5.2L models are equipped with Chrysler Electronic Spark Advance (ESA). All other models are equipped with Chrysler Electronic Ignition (EI) system. No adjustments are required.

Models with 5.9L engine use a dual pick-up distributor. A single pick-up distributor is used on models with 5.2L engine.

TUNE-UP (Cont.)

Fig. 1: Chrysler Corp. V8 Timing Marks and Firing Order

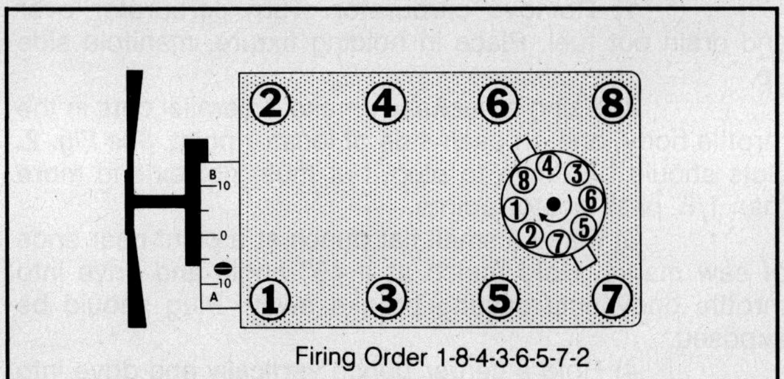

Magnetic probe socket located at 10° ATDC.

IGNITION TIMING

NOTE: All models are equipped with socket for magnetic timing equipment, located at 10° ATDC. Do not use this location for timing with a conventional timing light.

1) Connect power timing light to number 1 plug wire. Connect tachometer to engine. Start engine, set parking brake and place transmission in neutral. With engine at normal operating temperature, momentarily open throttle and make sure idle speed screw returns against its stop.

2) Ground carburetor switch (if equipped) with jumper wire. On models without ESA computer, disconnect and plug vacuum line at distributor. Engine idle speed should be at or below specification. If idle is too high, turn idle speed screw to adjust. Aim timing light at timing plate on chain case cover or read magnetic timing unit.

3) If timing is not within 2° of specification, loosen distributor hold-down arm screw and rotate distributor housing to obtain correct timing. Tighten distributor hold-down screw when timing is correct.

4) Recheck idle speed and timing. If curb idle is not within 50 RPM of specification, readjust idle. Do not reset timing. Turn engine off, reconnect vacuum lines, and remove jumper wire and tachometer.

CAUTION: DO NOT use distributor vacuum advance unit as a handle when turning distributor housing.

TIMING SPECIFICATIONS (Degrees BTDC @ RPM)

Application	Man. Trans.	Auto Trans.
5.2L 2-Bbl.		
Federal	12@700	12@700
Calif.	8@725	8@650
High Alt.	8@650	8@650
5.9L 4-Bbl.		
Light Duty		
Federal		16@800
High Alt.		16@750
Heavy Duty		
Federal	6@800	6@800
California	6@800	6@800

HOT (SLOW) IDLE RPM

SOLENOID IDLE STOP RPM

1) Ensure that ignition timing is properly adjusted. Disconnect and plug vacuum hoses at ESA module (5.2L) and EGR valve. Disconnect and plug vacuum hose at heated air temperature sensor.

2) Remove air cleaner. Disconnect and plug 3/16" control hose (5.2L Federal models) or canister purge hose (all other models) at canister.

3) Remove PCV valve from rocker cover and allow to draw underhood air. Install tachometer. Disconnect carburetor switch (if equipped). DO NOT ground switch.

4) Start engine and allow to reach normal operating temperature. Turn engine off. Disconnect lead from oxygen sensor (if equipped). Ground sensor lead from engine harness.

NOTE: DO NOT pull on oxygen sensor lead. Connector is located about 4" from sensor.

5) Start and run engine for 5 minutes to stabilize idle. Connect jumper wire from battery positive post to solenoid idle stop lead wire (solenoid coil terminal of carburetor connector on Rochester). Be sure to jumper proper wire or harness damage could result.

6) Open throttle slightly to allow solenoid plunger to extend. On 5.9L models, adjust solenoid plunger screw to specified speed. Remove jumper wire.

7) On 5.2L models, remove adjusting screw and spring from solenoid. Insert a 1/8" Allen wrench into solenoid and adjust to correct RPM. Install solenoid screw and spring until screw lightly bottoms. Remove jumper wire. Adjust idle speed by turning screw out. See CURB IDLE SPEED table.

8) On all models, remove tach. Unplug and reconnect all hoses and wires. Reinstall PCV valve and air cleaner.

9) Idle speed may vary under normal operating conditions (all wires and hoses connected). This is normal and does not require re-adjustment.

SOLENOID IDLE STOP RPM [1]

Application	Solenoid Energized
5.2L 2-Bbl.	
Federal	700
High Alt.	780
California	
Man. Trans.	850
Auto. Trans.	800
5.9L 4-Bbl.	
All Models	900

[1] – Subtract 75 RPM on vehicles with less than 300 miles.

CURB IDLE SPEED

1) Ensure that ignition timing is properly adjusted. Disconnect and plug vacuum hose at EGR valve. Disconnect and plug vacuum hose at heated air temperature switch. Remove air cleaner.

TUNE-UP (Cont.)

2) Disconnect and plug 3/16" control hose (5.2L Federal models) or canister purge hose (all other models) at canister. Remove PCV valve from rocker cover and allow to draw underhood air.

3) Disconnect and plug vacuum line to distributor (5.2L). Install tachometer. Start and run engine until normal operating temperature is reached.

4) Turn idle speed screw to adjust curb idle. Stop engine, remove test equipment and reconnect all hoses.

5) Idle speed may vary under normal operating conditions (all wires and hoses connected). This is normal and does not require readjustment.

CURB IDLE SPEED (RPM)

Application	Man. Trans.	Auto. Trans.
5.2L 2-Bbl.		
Federal	700	700
High Alt.	650	650
California	725	650
5.9L 4-Bbl.		
Federal	800	800
High Alt.		750
California	800	800

IDLE MIXTURE

NOTE: Idle mixture adjustment is not part of a normal tune-up. DO NOT adjust mixture unless carburetor has been disassembled or vehicle fails emissions testing.

MIXTURE SCREW CONCEALMENT PLUG REMOVAL

Holley Carburetors

Center punch each idle mixture screw housing about 1/4" from end of housing. *See Fig. 2.* Drill through outer section of housing at punch mark with 3/16" drill. Pry plug out of housing and save for reassembly.

Rochester Carburetors

1) Remove carburetor. Turn carburetor over and drain out fuel. Place in holding fixture, manifold side up.

2) Using a hacksaw, make 2 parallel cuts in the throttle body, one on each side of locator point. *See Fig. 2.* Cuts should be down to plug, but must not extend more than 1/8" past locator points.

3) Place a small flat punch at a point near ends of saw marks. Hold punch at a 45° angle and drive into throttle body until casting breaks away. Plug should be exposed.

4) Hold a center punch vertically and drive into plug. Change punch angle to 45° and drive plug out of casting. Plug will shatter. It is not necessary to remove plug completely, only enough of it to allow access to idle mixture screw. Repeat procedure for other plug.

PROPANE ENRICHMENT PROCEDURE

1) Remove concealment plug. Set parking brake and place transmission in Neutral. Turn all lights and accessories off. Connect tachometer. Start engine and allow to warm up on the second highest step of fast idle cam. Return to idle.

2) On 5.9L models and 5.2L models with Holley 2280 carbs, disconnect and plug vacuum hoses at EGR valve, distributor and heated air temperature sensor. Remove air cleaner.

3) On vehicles with Holley 6280 carbs, turn engine off. Disconnect and plug vacuum hoses at EGR valve and ESA computer. Disconnect and plug canister purge hose at canister.

4) Disconnect carburetor ground switch (do not ground switch). Disconnect lead from oxygen sensor and ground lead from engine harness. Start and run engine for at least 4 minutes.

NOTE: Do not pull on oxygen sensor lead. Connector is located about 4" from sensor.

Fig. 2: Removing Mixture Screw Concealment Plugs

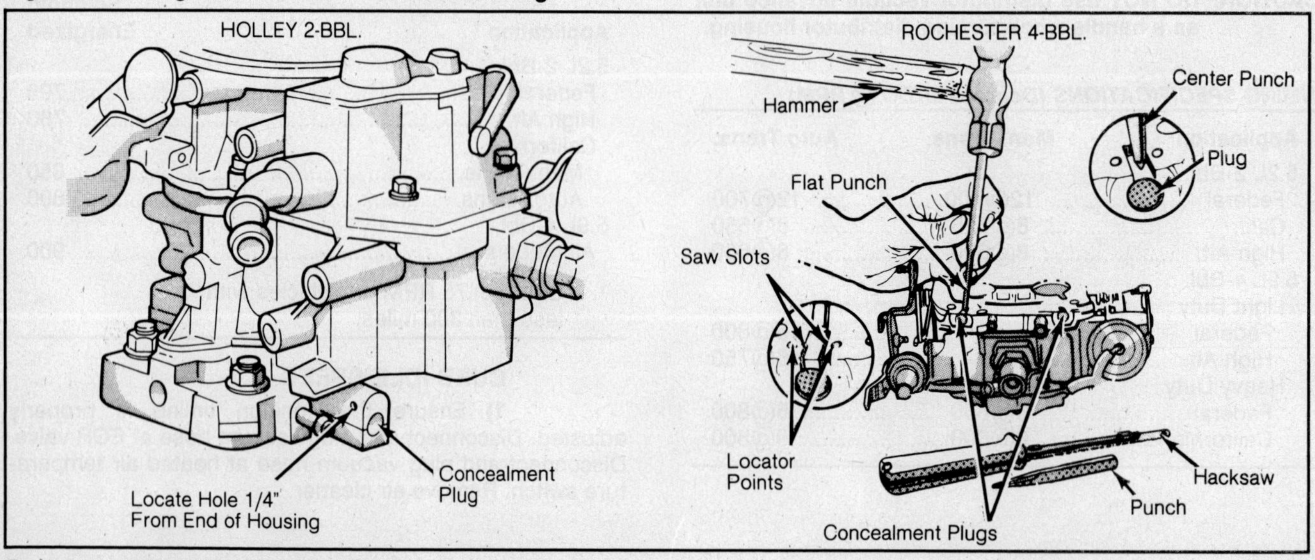

Rochester carburetors must be removed from vehicle to remove plugs.

TUNE-UP (Cont.)

5) On all models, disconnect vacuum supply hose from choke diaphragm at "T" and install propane supply hose. Other connections at "T" must remain in place.

6) With propane bottle upright and in a safe location, remove PCV valve from rocker cover and allow to draw underhood air. On 5.9L models and 5.2L models with Holley 2280 carbs, disconnect and plug 3/16" control hose from canister.

7) On all models, open propane main valve. Slowly open propane metering valve to obtain maximum RPM. With propane still flowing, adjust idle speed screw until propane RPM is reached. See PROPANE MIXTURE ADJUSTMENT table.

8) Again, adjust propane metering valve to obtain highest engine speed. If maximum RPM has changed, readjust idle speed screw to specified propane RPM.

9) Turn off propane main valve and allow engine speed to stabilize. Adjust idle mixture screws, 1/16 turn at a time, to obtain smoothest idle at curb idle speed. Wait 30 seconds between adjustments.

10) Turn on propane main valve. Adjust propane metering valve to highest RPM. If maximum speed is more than 25 RPM different than propane RPM, repeat steps **7)** through **10)**.

11) Turn off propane main and metering valves. Remove propane supply hose and reinstall choke vacuum hose. Install mixture screw concealment plugs. Reinstall all vacuum hoses and electrical connections. Perform all idle speed adjustments.

NOTE: **Idle speeds may vary from set speeds when hoses and wiring are reconnected. DO NOT readjust.**

PROPANE MIXTURE ADJUSTMENT (RPM)

Application	Propane RPM (Man. Trans.)	Propane RPM (Auto. Trans.)
5.2L 2-Bbl.		
Holley 2280		
Federal	800	800
Holley 6280		
High Altitude	710	710
California	775	740
5.9L 4-Bbl.		
Rochester M4ME		
Federal	840	900
High Altitude	.....	750
California	860	860

COLD (FAST) IDLE RPM

1) Ensure that ignition timing is properly adjusted. Disconnect and plug vacuum hose at EGR valve. On 5.2L models, disconnect and plug vacuum hose at heated air temperature switch. On all models, remove air cleaner.

2) Disconnect and plug 3/16" control hose at canister. Remove PCV valve from rocker cover and allow to draw underhood air.

3) Disconnect and plug vacuum line to distributor (5.2L). Install tachometer. Start and run engine until normal operating temperature is reached. Plug heated air hose (5.9L).

4) Place fast idle adjusting screw on second highest step of fast idle cam. With choke fully open, turn fast idle adjusting screw to obtain correct fast idle speed.

5) Return to curb idle, then reposition fast idle speed screw on second step of cam. Readjust fast idle speed as needed. Remove test equipment and reconnect all components.

NOTE: **Idle speeds may vary from set speeds when hoses and wiring are reconnected. DO NOT readjust.**

FAST IDLE SPEED

Application	RPM
5.2L 2-Bbl.	
Holley 2280	
Federal	1600
Holley 6280	
High Altitude	1400
California	[1]1450
5.9L 4-Bbl.	
Federal	1350
High Altitude	1600
California	1350

[1] – 1625 with manual transmission.

AUTOMATIC CHOKE SETTING

Vehicles over 6000 lbs. GVW are equipped with a non-adjustable thermostatically-controlled automatic choke, using engine heat only in positioning valve. All other models use an electric assist choke which requires no adjustment.

FUEL PUMP

Measure fuel pump pressure and volume with engine running at idle.

FUEL PUMP SPECIFICATIONS

Application	Pressure psi (kg/cm²)	Volume Quarts (Liters)
All Models	4.75-6.25 (.33-.44)	1.0 in 1 min. (.95 in 1 min.)

ELECTRONIC SPARK ADVANCE (ESA) CHECK

1) Set ignition basic timing. Place thin insulating material between curb idle adjusting screw and carburetor switch. Remove and plug vacuum line at vacuum transducer.

2) Connect auxiliary vacuum source to transducer and set vacuum at 10 in. Hg. With engine warm, run engine at 2000 RPM for 1 minute, then check spark advance.

3) Advance specifications are in addition to basic advance. Replace computer if advance is incorrect.

TUNE-UP (Cont.)

ELECTRONIC SPARK ADVANCE TEST (Engine at 2000 RPM & 16 in. Hg Vacuum to Computer)

Application	[1] Degrees BTDC
Federal & High Alt.	30-38
California	
Man. Trans.	
With Overdrive	30-38
Without Overdrive	26-34
Auto. Trans.	30-38

[1] – In addition to basic timing.

MANIFOLD HEAT CONTROL VALVE

Apply solvent to both ends of valve shaft where it rotates in bushing every 18,000 miles. Work valve back and forth several times.

CAUTION: Apply solvent only when manifold is cold.

EMISSION CONTROL SYSTEMS

NOTE: Refer to appropriate article in EMISSION CONTROL section.

GENERAL SERVICING

IGNITION

DISTRIBUTOR

California and High Altitude 5.2L models are equipped with Chrysler Electronic Spark Advance (ESA). All other models are equipped with Chrysler Electronic Ignition (EI) system. No adjustments are required.

Models with 5.9L engine use a dual pick-up distributor. A single pick-up distributor is used on models with 5.2L engine.

DISTRIBUTOR PICK-UP COIL RESISTANCE (Ohms)

All Models	150-900

IGNITION COIL

IGNITION COIL RESISTANCE – Ohms @ 75°F (24°C)

Application	Primary	Secondary
Essex	1.3-1.6	9000-12,200
Prestolite	1.6-1.8	9400-11,700

FUEL SYSTEMS

CARBURETORS

Application	Model
5.2L 2-Bbl.	
Federal	Holley 2280
California & High Alt.	Holley 6280
5.9L 4-Bbl.	Rochester M4ME

ELECTRICAL

BATTERY

BATTERY SPECIFICATIONS

Application	Cold Cranking Amps [1]	Reserve Capacity Minutes
Standard	400	100
Optional	500	110

[1] – At 0°F (-18°C).

STARTER

All models use a Chrysler Corp. reduction gear type starter.

STARTER SPECIFICATIONS

Application	Volts	Amps.	Test RPM
All Models	11	90	3700

ALTERNATORS

All models use Chrysler Corp. alternators.

ALTERNATOR SPECIFICATIONS

Tag Color	Field Current Draw @ 12 Volts [1]	Rated Amp. Output
Violet	2.5-5.0 Amps	41
Yellow		
Standard	2.5-5.0 Amps	60
Optional	2.5-5.0 Amps	114
Brown	2.5-5.0 Amps	78

[1] – While rotating alternator by hand.

ALTERNATOR REGULATOR

All models use Chrysler Corp. Electronic Voltage Regulator, which are non-adjustable.

REGULATOR OPERATING VOLTAGE @ 80°F (27°C)

All Models	13.9-14.6

ADJUSTMENTS

BELT ADJUSTMENT Deflection In. (mm) with 10 lbs. (4.5 kg) Pressure

Application	Deflection In. (mm)
New Belts	1/4-1/2 (6.0-12.0)
Used Belts [1]	1/4-5/16 (6.0-7.5)

[1] – Used belts are any operated more than 15 minutes.

GENERAL SERVICING (Cont.)

SERVICE INTERVALS

REPLACEMENT INTERVALS

Component	Interval (Miles)
Oil Filter	15,000
Fuel Filter	18,000
PCV Valve	24,000
Air Filter	30,000
Spark Plugs	
With Cat. Converter	30,000
Without Cat. Converter	15,000

CAPACITIES

COOLING SYSTEM CAPACITIES

Application	Quantity
Cooling System [1]	
5.2L	16 qts. (15.2L)
5.9L	14.5 qts. (13.8L)

[1] – Add 1 quart (1.9L) with A/C or increased cooling.

ENGINE OIL & FUEL CAPACITIES

Application	Quantity
Crankcase (Includes Filter)	6.0 qts. (5.7L)
Fuel Tank	
Pickup Models [1]	
Standard (Sport Utility)	35 gals. (132L)
Standard (Light Duty)	20 gals. (75L)
Optional	30 gals. (113L)
Van Models	
Standard	22 gals. (83L)
Optional	36 gals. (136L)

[1] – Includes Ramcharger.

TRANSMISSION, TRANSFER CASE & DIFFERENTIAL CAPACITIES

Application	Pts. (L)
Auto. Trans. (Dexron II)	
A-727	[1] 7.7 pts. (3.6L)
All Others	17.1 pts. (8.1L)
Man. Trans.	
4-Speed Overdrive	
A-833 (Dexron II)	7.5 pts. (3.5L)
N.P. 435 4-Speed	
(SAE 80W-90)	7.0 pts. (3.3L)
Transfer Case	
N.P. 205 (SAE 80W-90)	4.5 pts. (2.1L)
N.P. 208 (Dexron II)	6.0 pts. (2.8L)
Rear Axle (SAE 80W-90)	
Spicer Model 60	6.0 pts. (2.8L)
All Others	4.5 pts. (2.1L)
Front Axle (SAE 80W-90)	
Model 44	5.6 pts. (2.7L)
Model 60	6.5 pts. (3.1L)

[1] – Without torque converter drain.

SYSTEM REFRIGERANT CAPACITIES

Application	Ounces
Pickup Models [1]	42
Van Models	
Front	48
Front & Rear	64

[1] – Includes Ramcharger.

1985 Ford 4 Tune-Up

TUNE-UP

ENGINE IDENTIFICATION

Eighth character of Vehicle Identification Number (VIN) identifies engine. VIN is stamped on metal tab, attached to upper left side of instrument panel and is visible through windshield. VIN can also be found on Safety Standard Certification Label attached to left door lock edge.

VIN ENGINE CODES

Engine	Code
2.0L (122") 1-Bbl.	C
2.3L (140") EFI	A

TUNE-UP NOTES

NOTE: **When performing tune-up procedures described in this article, following notes and precautions must be followed.**

When performing tune-up on vehicles equipped with catalytic converter, do not allow or create condition of engine misfire in one or more cylinders for an extended period of time. Damage to converter may occur due to loading with unburned air/fuel mixture.

When connecting a tachometer to Dura-Spark ignition coil, install the alligator clip on tachometer into the "DEC" (Tach Testing) cavity. If any spark plug wire is disconnected with this system, connection must be first greased with silicone grease before it is reattached.

Due to production changes, always refer to Engine Tune-Up Decal in engine compartment before attempting tune-up. In the event of conflict between specifications given in this manual and decal specifications, use decal specifications.

SPARK PLUGS

SPARK PLUG TYPE

Application	Motorcraft No.
2.0L	AWSF-42
2.3L	AWSF-44C

SPARK PLUG SPECIFICATIONS

Application	Gap In. (mm)	Torque Ft. Lbs. (N.m)
All Models	.042-.046 (1.1-1.2)	5-10 (7-13)

HIGH TENSION WIRE RESISTANCE

1) Remove wire from ignition coil. Loosen wires from spark plugs by twisting spark plug boot carefully to loosen seal on spark plug. Remove wires by pulling on plug boot. Remove distributor cap from distributor, leaving wires connected to cap.

NOTE: **DO NOT disconnect wires from distributor cap unless replacement is necessary.**

2) Using an ohmmeter, check resistance of each wire by connecting one ohmmeter lead to coil or spark plug terminal and other lead to distributor cap insert. If more than 5000 ohms resistance per INCH, remove wire and test again. If still over 5000 ohms per INCH, replace wire. New wires should have resistance of 7000 ohms per FOOT.

NOTE: **Whenever high tension wire is disconnected, interior of spark plug terminal boot must be coated with silicone grease before reconnection.**

HIGH TENSION WIRE RESISTANCE (OHMS)

Application	Maximum Resistance
Spark Plug Wires	
Used	5000 per INCH
New	7000 per Foot

DISTRIBUTOR

All 2.0L models are equipped with Dura-Spark II ignition system. All 2.3L EFI models are equipped with TFI-IV ignition system. No adjustments are required.

Fig. 1: 2.0L and 2.3L Timing Marks and Firing Order

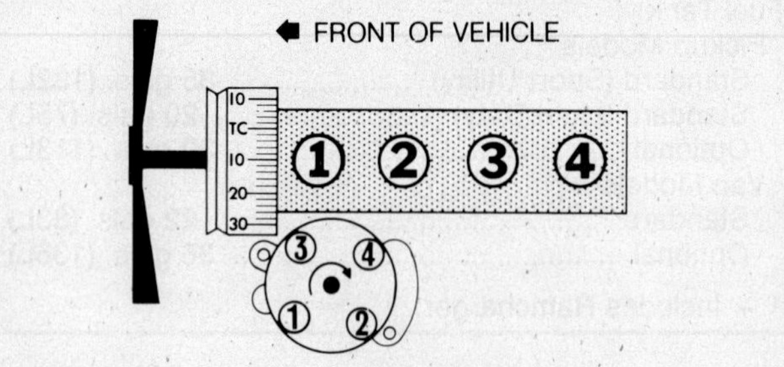

ENGINE COMPRESSION

Test compression pressure with engine at normal operating temperature, all spark plugs removed, and throttle wide open. Crank engine through at least 5 compression strokes before recording pressure.

COMPRESSION SPECIFICATIONS

Application	Specification
Compression Ratio	
2.0L	9.0:1
2.3L	9.5:1
Max. Variation Between Cyl.	less than 25%

VALVE ARRANGEMENT

E-I-E-I-E-I-E-I (Front-to-rear).

TUNE-UP (Cont.)

VALVE CLEARANCE

All engines have hydraulic lifters. Lifters should be adjusted to zero lash.

IGNITION TIMING

NOTE: **Timing instrument should be connected to number one spark plug wire using an adapter or snap-on connector. Do not puncture spark plug wire or boot to make connection.**

2.0L

1) Place transmission in Neutral. Turn A/C and heater off. Disconnect and plug vacuum lines at distributor. Connect inductive-type timing light and tachometer to engine.

2) Warm engine to normal operating temperature. With engine running at specified RPM, adjust ignition timing. Remove test equipment and reconnect all components.

2.3L

1) Warm engine to normal operating temperature and shut off engine. Turn all accessories off and place transmission in Neutral. Disconnect single wire (Black) connector near distributor.

2) Attach timing light. Start engine and check ignition timing. Adjust as needed.

IGNITION TIMING SPECIFICATIONS (Degrees BTDC@RPM)

Application	Specification
2.0L	6@800
2.3L [1]	10@800

[1] – Idle speed and timing are controlled be the EEC-IV system and no adjustments are required.

HOT (SLOW) IDLE RPM

CAUTION: **Do not idle engine for over 3 minutes at a time. If idle adjustment is not completed within 3 minutes, run engine at 2200-2800 RPM for 30 seconds before continuing. Repeat as required.**

2.0L 1-BBL.

Curb Idle Checking

1) Place transmission in Neutral. Warm engine to normal operating temperature. Turn ignition off. Turn A/C, lights and accessories off. Leave all vacuum hoses connected.

2) Ensure curb idle RPM is at specification with transmission in Neutral. Turn ignition off. Disconnect engine coolant temperature switch. Switch has 2 wire (Light Green/Yellow and Black/Light Green) connector.

3) Restart engine. Idle speed should be 1125-1275 RPM. If not to specification, see the Electronic Idle Speed Control Article in the EXHAUST EMISSION SYSTEMS SECTION of this manual. Turn ignition off. Reconnect engine coolant temperature switch. Recheck idle RPM.

Fig. 2: Carburetor Adjustment Screw Locations

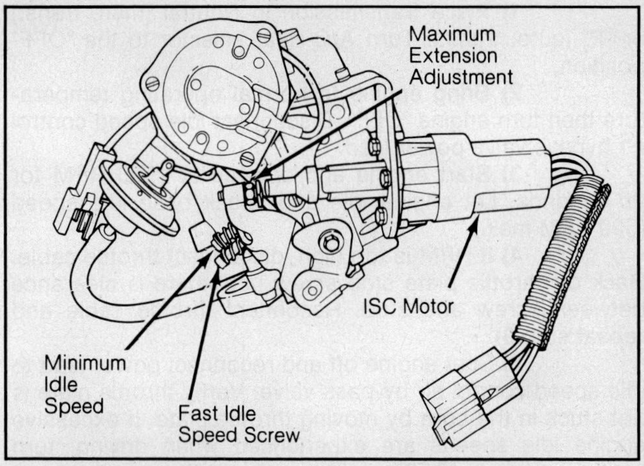

IDLE SPEED (RPM)

Application	Curb Idle
2.0L	775-825

Minimum and Maximum Idle

1) Turn ignition switch off. Disconnect Idle Speed Control (ISC) motor connector. Disconnect EGR valve vacuum hose and plug. Connect insulated jumper wires from battery terminals to ISC motor terminals.

2) Motor should retract. If not, reverse jumper leads. Disconnect jumper leads when motor is fully retracted. If motor did not move in or out, replace ISC motor.

3) Start engine and adjust minimum idle speed (kill speed) to 700 RPM or less. Reverse jumper leads on ISC motor terminals. Disconnect terminals after ISC motor fully extends.

4) Check and adjust maximum idle speed to 1800-2200 RPM. Reconnect ISC motor connector. Remove plug from EGR vacuum hose and reconnect.

Fig. 3: Extending & Retracting ISC Motor

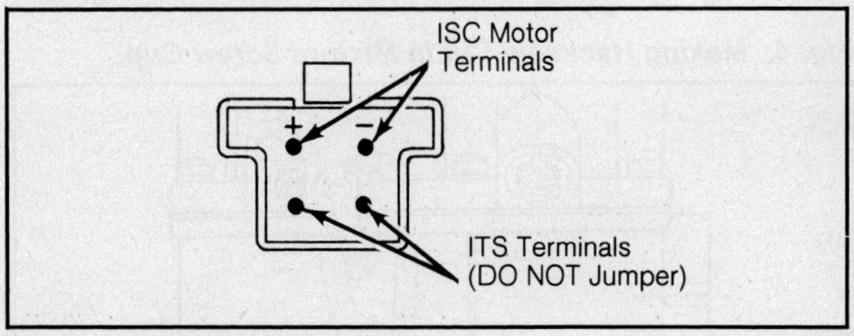

Do not jumper ITS terminals.

2.3L EFI

NOTE: **This procedure is only performed if the curb idle is not 625-775 RPM (auto. trans.) or 575-725 RPM (man. trans.). Curb idle speed (RPM) is controlled by the EEC-IV processor and the idle speed control air by-pass valve assembly. If engine curb idle RPM is not within specification after performing this procedure, it will be necessary to perform the appropriate EEC-IV diagnostics.**

1985 Ford 4 Tune-Up

TUNE-UP (Cont.)

Curb Idle

1) Place transmission in Neutral (man. trans.) or "P" (auto. trans.). Turn A/C-Heat selector to the "OFF" position.

2) Bring engine to normal operating temperature then turn engine "OFF". Disconnect idle speed control air bypass valve power lead.

3) Start engine and operate at 1500 RPM for 20 seconds. Let engine idle and check base idle speed (600 RPM max.).

4) If RPM is too high, disconnect throttle cable. Back off throttle plate stop screw until there is clearance between screw and stop. Reconnect throttle cable and repeat step **3)**.

5) Shut engine off and reconnect power lead to idle speed control air by-pass valve. Verify throttle plate is not stuck in the bore by moving throttle plate. If excessive engine idle speeds are experienced when driving, turn ignition switch to "OFF" position and restart.

IDLE MIXTURE ADJUSTMENT

CAUTION: **Do not idle engine for over 3 minutes. If idle adjustment is not completed within 3 minutes, run engine at 2200-2800 RPM for 30 seconds before continuing. Repeat as required. Prolonged idling can result in catalyst overheating and excessive underbody temperatures.**

MIXTURE SCREW PLUG REMOVAL

NOTE: **Mixture adjustment is not a normal tune-up procedure. DO NOT remove idle mixture plugs unless vehicle fails emissions testing or carburetor has been disassembled.**

1) Remove carburetor from engine. Drain fuel from carburetor. Using hacksaw, carefully cut lengthwise slot through metal cup around mixture screw. *See Fig. 4*.

Fig. 4: Making Hacksaw Cut in Mixture Screw Cup

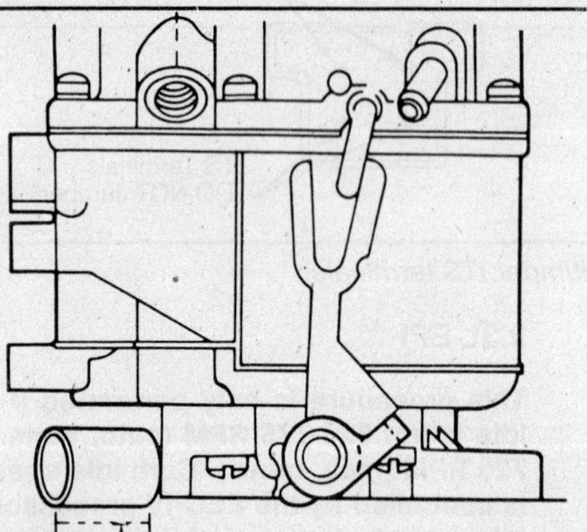

Do not contact carburetor body with hacksaw blade.

2) Insert screwdriver into hacksaw slot and twist screwdriver to spread outer cap. Spread cap just enough to remove inner cap. Count number of turns required to seat mixture screw needle lightly. Remove mixture screw and cup.

3) When adjustment is completed, install idle mixture screw and spring. Install new tamper resistant cup. Turn screw in until it lightly seats. Turn screw out to same number of turns noted when disassembling. Reinstall carburetor on engine.

PROPANE ENRICHMENT PROCEDURE

1) Apply parking brake and block drive wheels. Disconnect automatic brake release (if equipped) and plug vacuum connection. Connect tachometer to engine.

2) Disconnect fresh air duct from air cleaner. Insert propane supply hose 3/4 way into air cleaner duct, securing it with tape. Leave all vacuum hoses connected to air cleaner. Air cleaner may be positioned aside for adjustments, but must be in place during speed checks.

3) Disconnect and plug hose at air by-pass valve. Disconnect and plug hose between purge valve and spacer at purge valve. Verify timing and adjust if necessary. Turn A/C and all lights and accessories off. Remove PCV valve from its grommet. Disconnect crankcase hose at air cleaner.

4) Place transmission in Neutral and run engine approximately 2500 RPM for 15 seconds before each mixture check. If check is not completed within 1 minute, repeat 15-second acceleration.

5) With engine idling at normal operating temperature, place transmission in Neutral. Gradually open propane valve and watch for engine speed gain. When engine speed reaches maximum and begins to drop off, note amount of speed gain.

NOTE: **Propane bottle must be in vertical position. If engine speed will not drop off, check propane cartridge gas supply.**

6) If measured speed gain is higher than specification, turn mixture screw counterclockwise (rich) slightly, then repeat steps **4)** and **5)** until gain matches "Reset RPM".

NOTE: **After turning idle mixture screw, wait 15 seconds for idle to stabilize before turning screw again.**

7) If measured speed gain is lower than specification, turn mixture screw clockwise (lean) slightly, and repeat steps **4)** and **5)** until gain matches "Reset RPM".

8) Reconnect PCV valve and other disconnected components. Readjust curb idle speed if necessary. Remove test equipment.

PROPANE MIXTURE ADJUSTMENT (RPM)

Application	Gain RPM	Reset RPM
2.0L	10-40	20

COLD (FAST) IDLE RPM

1) Place transmission in Neutral. Start engine and warm to normal operating temperature. Stop engine and turn ignition and A/C off. Disconnect and plug vacuum hose at EGR valve.

TUNE-UP (Cont.)

2) Place fast idle speed adjusting screw on highest step of fast idle cam. Start engine without touching acclerator pedal. Check fast idle speed. Adjust to specification by turning fast idle speed adjusting screw. *See Fig. 2*.

3) Momentarily increase engine speed and let it return to idle. Turn ignition off. Reconnect vacuum hose at EGR and remove test equipment.

FAST IDLE SPEED (RPM)

Application	RPM
2.0L	1700

AUTOMATIC CHOKE

NOTE: Although automatic choke is of tamper-proof design, these steps are used if automatic choke is damaged or when carburetor is rebuilt.

1) Choke housing is non-adjustable. Setting is fixed by an index plate located between carburetor and choke cover. Color of index plate indicates calibration setting.

2) To replace index plate, loosen choke thermostat cover. Remove 2 rivets and retaining screw. Separate cover from carburetor and exchange index plates. Replace cover. Install and tighten new rivets and screw.

FUEL PUMP

Make all tests with engine idling at normal operating temperature, and transmission in Neutral.

FUEL PUMP SPECIFICATIONS

Application	Pressure psi (kg/cm²)	Volume Pints (Liters)
Mechanical		
2.0L	5.0-7.0 (34.5-41.5)	1 in 25 sec. (.47 in 25 sec.)
Electrical		
2.3L EFI	[1]	[1]

[1] – Information not available from manufacturer.

GENERAL SERVICING

FUEL SYSTEMS

CARBURETORS

Application	Model
2.0L	Carter YFA 1-Bbl.
2.3L EFI	Ford EFI

ELECTRICAL

BATTERY SPECIFICATIONS

Application	Capacity Amps	Discharge Rate (Amps)
All Models		
Standard	45	190
Optional	63	260

STARTER

All models use Motorcraft positive engagement type starter.

STARTER SPECIFICATIONS

Application	Volts	Amps	Test RPM
All Models			
4" Armature	12	80	180-250
4 1/2" Armature	12	80	150-290

ALTERNATORS

All models use Motorcraft rear-terminal alternators with external regulators.

ALTERNATOR SPECIFICATIONS

Stamp Color	Field Curent Draw@12 Volts	Rated Amp Output
Orange	4.0	40
Green	4.0	60

ALTERNATOR REGULATOR

All models use Motorcraft Solid State Electronic Regulator, calibrated and preset by manufacturer. No adjustment is required or possible. Two models are used. Though similar in appearance, they are different and must never be interchanged.

REGULATOR IDENTIFICATION

Application	Color Coding
All with Ammeter	Gray
All with Indicator Light	Black

ADJUSTMENTS

BELT ADJUSTMENT

BELT ADJUSTMENT
Tension in Lbs. (Kg) Using Strand Tension Gauge

Application	New Belt	Used Belt
All Models		
Standard V-Belts	50-90 (23-41)	40-60 (18-27)
Ribbed V-Belts	150-190 (68-86)	140-160 (64-73)

1985 Ford 4 Tune-Up

GENERAL SERVICING (Cont.)

IGNITION

DISTRIBUTOR

All 2.0L models are equipped with Dura-Spark II ignition system. All 2.3L EFI models are equipped with TFI-IV ignition system. No adjustments are required.

DISTRIBUTOR PICK-UP COIL RESISTANCE

Application	Ohms
Dura-Spark II	400-1000
TFI-IV	650-1300

TOTAL SPARK ADVANCE @ 2500 RPM

Application	W/Vacuum Advance	W/O Vacuum Advance
2.0L	34-41	11-15

IGNITION COIL

IGNITION COIL RESISTANCE – OHMS @ 75°F (24°C)

Application	Primary	Secondary
Dura-Spark II	0.8-1.6	7700-10,500
TFI-IV	0.3-1.0	8,000-11,000

SERVICE INTERVALS

REPLACEMENT INTERVALS

Component	Interval (Miles)
Oil Filter	7500
Air Filter	30,000
Fuel Filter	50,000
PCV Filter	30,000
Spark Plugs	30,000

CAPACITIES

FLUID CAPACITIES

Application	Quantity
Cooling System	
Without A/C	6.5 qts. (6.2L)
With A/C	7.4 qts. (7.0L)
Crankcase	
2.0L Engine	[1] 4.0 qts. (3.8L)
2.3L Engine	[1 2 3] 4.0 qts. (3.8L)
Auto. Trans.	
C-3 (Dexron II)	8.0 qts. (7.6L)
C-5 (Motorcraft Type H)	
2WD Ranger	7.5 qts. (7.1L)
4WD Ranger	7.9 qts. (7.5L)
AOD (Dexron II)	
2WD Aerostar & Ranger	9.5 qts. (9.0L)
4WD Ranger	10.3 qts. (10.0L)
Man. Trans.	
4-Speed	3.0 pts. (1.4L)
5-Speed	3.6 pts. (1.7L)
Transfer Case (Dexron II)	3.0 pts. (1.4L)
Rear Axle (Hypoid Gear Lube)	
6 3/4" Ring Gear	3.0 pts. (1.4L)
7 1/2" Ring Gear	5.0 pts. (2.4L)
8.8" Ring Gear	5.5 pts. (2.6L)
Front Axle (Hypoid Gear Lube)	
Model 28	1.0 pts. (0.5 L)
Fuel Tank	
Standard	
Short Wheelbase	15.0 gals. (57.5L)
Long Wheelbase	17.0 gals. (64.0L)
Optional Auxiliary	
Aerostar	15.0 gals. (57.5L)
All Others	13.0 gals. (49.0L)

[1] – Add 1 qt. (.95L) with filter change.
[2] – 2.3L engine with cast aluminum oil pan has 6 qt. (5.7L) capacity with filter change.
[3] – Add .5 qt. (.45L) on Aerostar with oil cooler.

SYSTEM REFRIGERANT CAPACITY

Application	Ounces
All Models	40

TUNE-UP

ENGINE IDENTIFICATION

Engine can be identified by the eighth character of Vehicle Identification Number. Number is located on Safety Compliance label on left front door pillar. It also is located on metal plate, riveted to the driver's side of dash and visible through windshield.

VIN ENGINE CODE

Application	Code
4.9L (300") 1-Bbl.	Y

TUNE-UP NOTES

NOTE: **When performing tune-up procedures described in this article, the following notes and precautions must be followed:**

For tune-up purposes, "Light Duty" refers to vehicles up to 8500 lbs. GVW. "Heavy Duty" refers to vehicles exceeding 8500 lbs. GVW.

Due to late changes and corrections, always refer to Engine Tune-Up Decal in engine compartment before performing tune-up procedures. If manual specifications and decal specifications are differ, always use specifications on Engine Tune-Up Decal.

Do not allow or create a condition of engine misfire in more than 1 cylinder for an extended time. Damage to converter may result due to loading converter with unburned air/fuel mixture.

If Dura-Spark 2-piece distributor cap must be removed, first remove top portion, then rotor, then bottom portion (adapter). If any spark plug wire is disconnected with this system, connection must be first greased with silicone grease before it is reattached.

When connecting a tachometer to Dura-Spark ignition coil, install the alligator clip on tachometer into the "DEC" (Tach Testing) cavity.

ENGINE COMPRESSION

Test compression with all spark plugs removed and engine at normal operating temperature. Crank engine through at least 5 compression strokes before recording reading.

COMPRESSION SPECIFICATIONS

Application	Specification
Compression Ratio	
All Models	8.9:1
Max. Variation Between Cyl.	less than 25%

VALVE ARRANGEMENT

E-I-E-I-E-I-E-I-E-I-E-I (Front-to-rear).

VALVE CLEARANCE

VALVE CLEARANCE SPECIFICATIONS

Application	Clearance
All Models	[1] .100-.200" (2.5-5.1 mm)

[1] – Allowable clearance with tappet collapsed. Desired clearance is .125-.175" (3.2-4.5 mm).

SPARK PLUGS

SPARK PLUG TYPE

Application	Motorcraft No.
All Models	BSF-42

SPARK PLUG SPECIFICATIONS

Application	Gap In. (mm)	Torque Ft. Lbs. (N.m)
All Models	.044 (1.15)	15-22 (20-30)

HIGH TENSION WIRE RESISTANCE

1) Loosen wires from spark plugs by twisting spark plug boot carefully to loosen seal on spark plug. Remove wires by pulling on plug boot. Remove distributor cap from distributor, leaving wires connected to cap.

2) Using an ohmmeter, check resistance of each wire. Connect one ohmmeter lead to spark plug terminal and other lead to distributor cap insert.

3) Replace any wire with over 5000 ohms resistance per INCH. New wires should have a resistance of 7000 ohms per FOOT.

HIGH TENSION WIRE RESISTANCE (OHMS)

Application	Maximum Resistance
New Wires	7000 per Foot
Used Wires	5000 per INCH

NOTE: **Whenever a high tension wire is disconnected, spark plug terminal boot interior must be coated with dielectric silicone grease before reconnection.**

DISTRIBUTOR

All Light Duty models are equipped with TFI-IV (Thick Film Integrated) ignition system. All Heavy Duty models are equipped with Dura-Spark II ignition system. No adjustments are required.

TUNE-UP (Cont.)

Fig. 1: Timing Mark and Firing Order

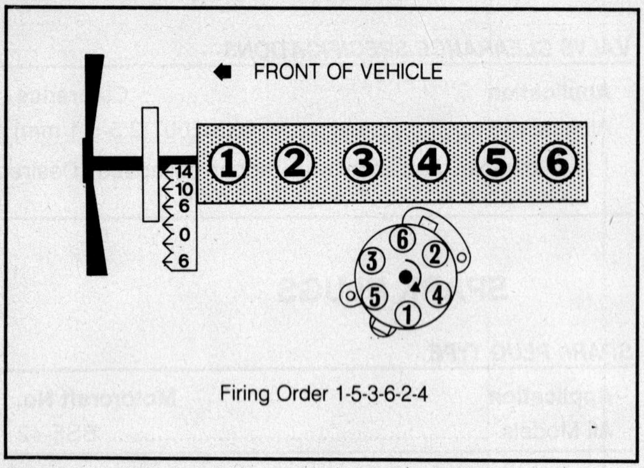

Receptacle for magnetic pick-up timing light is located at 135° ATDC.

IGNITION TIMING

CAUTION: Engines are equipped with a receptacle for use with magnetic pick-up timing lights, located at 135° ATDC. Do not use this location for timing with a conventional timing light.

1) Place transmission in Neutral (man. trans.) or "P" (auto. trans.). Turn A/C and heater off. Remove vacuum hose from distributor vacuum advance connection, and plug hose.

2) Place mark on proper degree line of damper (or of pointer and damper notch). Connect timing light using inductive pick-up or adapter. Do not puncture spark plug leads.

3) Connect an accurate tachometer. On EEC-IV equipped models, disconnect single Black lead connector near distributor. Start engine and warm engine to normal operating temperature. With engine idling in Neutral, check timing.

4) If timing is not correct, loosen distributor hold-down bolt and rotate distributor to set timing. Recheck after tightening bolt.

IGNITION TIMING SPECIFICATIONS (Degrees BTDC@RPM)

Application	Auto. Trans.	Man. Trans.
All Models		
Light Duty	[1] 10@600	10@750
Heavy Duty	12@800	12@800

[1] – With parking brake on, wheels blocked and transmission in "D".

HOT (SLOW) IDLE RPM

LIGHT DUTY

1) Place transmission in Neutral (man. trans.) or "P" (auto. trans.) with engine at normal operating temperature. Turn off all accessories. Remove air cleaner. Disconnect and plug vacuum line at bottom of air cleaner. Allow engine speed to stabilize and measure curb idle speed.

2) With engine off, disconnect Engine Coolant Temperature (ECT) sensor connector. Start engine and open throttle momentarily 3 times. Adjust the maximum Idle Speed Control (ISC) extension speed by turning the ISC extension screw. *See Fig. 2.*

Fig. 2: Adjustment Points for YFA 1-Bbl. Carburetor on Light Duty Engines

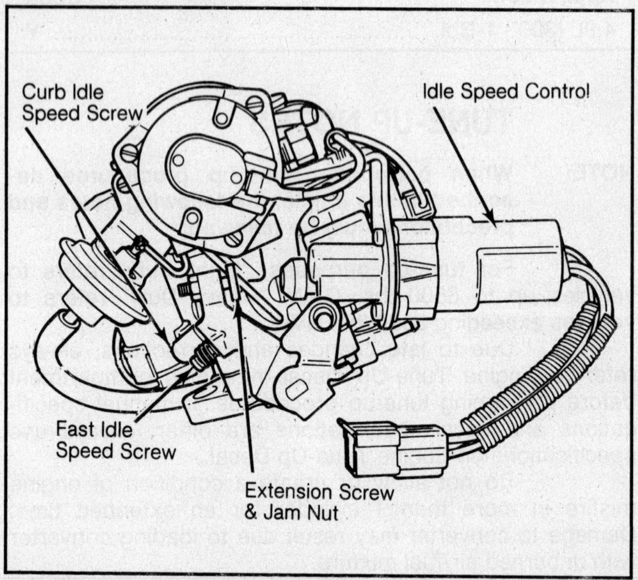

Use Allen wrench to adjust idle speeds.

3) Place transmission in Neutral. Reconnect ECT sensor wire connector. Increase engine RPM momentarily. Allow ISC to adjust idle speed, then recheck idle RPM.

4) Turn engine off. Connect a jumper wire between STI connector and single pin return pin on self-test input connector. *See Fig. 3.* Turn ignition key to run position, but do not start engine. Allow ISC motor to retract.

5) Disconnect jumper wire and ISC motor connector. Start engine. Check anti-diesel RPM with ISC off. If necessary, adjust anti-diesel RPM to 500-550 RPM. If the idle speed or ISC motor does not operate correctly, see the EEC-IV article in the EXHAUST EMISSION SECTION.

Fig. 3 Jumper STI and Self-Test Connectors

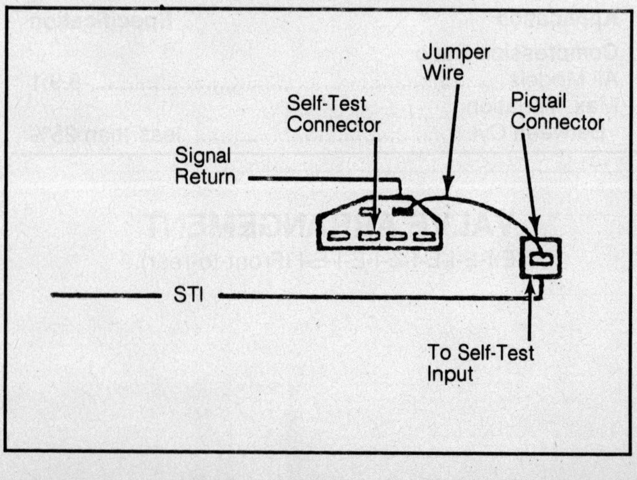

TUNE-UP (Cont.)

LIGHT DUTY IDLE SPEED (RPM)

Application	ECT Off	Curb Idle ECT On
All Models		
Auto. Trans.	1550	[1] 550-650
Man. Trans.	1550	600-700

[1] – Transmission in "D".

HEAVY DUTY

1) Place transmission in Neutral (man. trans.) or "P" (auto trans.) with engine at normal operating temperature. Turn A/C heat selector off.

2) Turn engine on to activate Throttle Speed Positioner (TSP). Set curb idle to specification by turning solenoid in or out. *See Fig. 4.*

Fig. 4: Adjustment Points for YFA 1-Bbl. Carburetor on Heavy Duty Engines

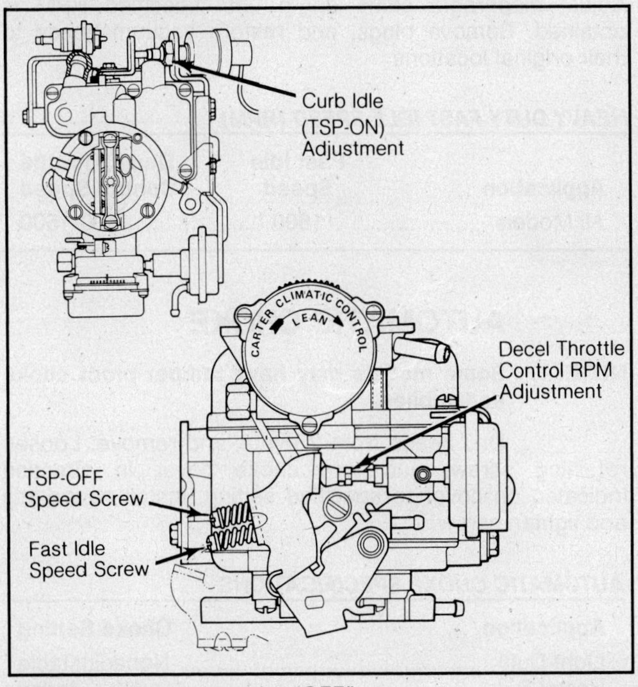

A/C heat selector must be "OFF".

3) With transmission selector in Neutral (man. trans.) or "P" (auto. trans.), increase engine speed momentarily, letting it return to normal curb idle. Check RPM and readjust if necessary.

4) If final curb idle speed adjustment is required, bowl vent setting must be checked. Stop engine and turn ignition key "ON". Secure choke plate in wide open position.

5) Open throttle so that throttle vent lever does not touch fuel bowl vent rod. Close throttle and measure travel of fuel bowl vent rod at point "A" from open position. *See Fig. 5.*

6) Travel should be within .10-.15" (2.5-3.8 mm). If out of specification, bend vent lever to obtain required travel. To set TSP-Off RPM, run engine to normal operating temperature. Turn A/C heat selector to "OFF". Disconnect TSP wire. Place transmission in Neutral. Using TSP-Off adjusting screw, set TSP-Off RPM to specifications. Reconnect TSP wire to terminal.

Fig. 5: Setting Fuel Bowl Vent

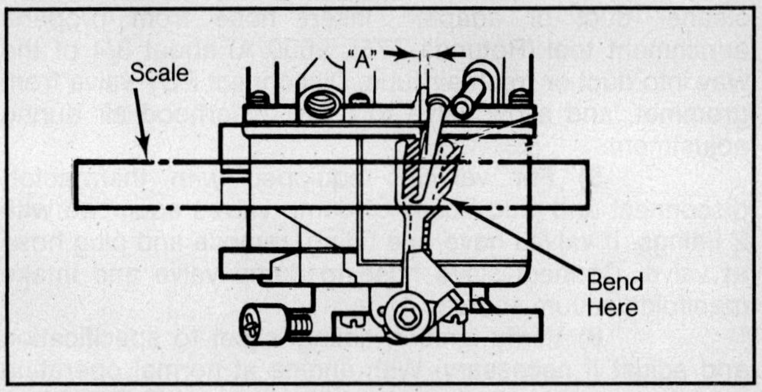

HEAVY DUTY IDLE SPEED (RPM)

Application	Curb Idle TSP-On	TSP-Off
All Models		
Auto. Trans.	[1] 550	[2] 500
Man. Trans.	700	500

[1] – Transmission in "D".
[2] – Transmission in Neutral.

IDLE MIXTURE ADJUSTMENT

NOTE: **This procedure is not part of normal tune-up procedure. Idle mixture should be adjusted only during carburetor repair or when necessary as a result of government inspection laws.**

MIXTURE SCREW PLUG REMOVAL

1) Remove carburetor from engine. Drain fuel from carburetor. Using a hacksaw, carefully cut a lengthwise slot through metal cup around mixture screw. Do not cut throttle body.

2) Insert a screwdriver into hacksaw slot and twist screwdriver to spread cap. Spread cap just enough to remove inner cap. Count number of turns needed to lightly seat mixture screw needle. Remove mixture screw and cup.

3) When adjustment is complete, install idle mixture screw and spring. Install new tamper-resistant cup. Turn screw in until it lightly seats. Turn screw out same number of turns noted during disassembly. Reinstall catburetor in engine.

PROPANE ENRICHMENT PROCEDURE

NOTE: **Propane enrichment procedure is for Light Duty Vehicles only.**

1) Leave all vacuum signal hoses attached to air cleaner assembly when relocating air cleaner for carburetor adjustments. Air cleaner must be installed for engine speed checks.

2) Apply parking brake and block wheels. Disconnect automatic brake release, and plug vacuum connection, if equipped. Connect tachometer.

3) Disconnect and plug fuel evaporative purge valve signal hose at engine. Disconnect purge hose at air cleaner and plug nipple.

1985 Ford 6 Tune-Up

TUNE-UP (Cont.)

4) Disconnect flexible fresh air tube from air cleaner duct or adapter. Insert hose from propane enrichment tool (Rotunda T75L 9600 A) about 3/4 of the way into duct or fresh air tube. Disconnect PCV valve from grommet, and allow valve to draw underhood air during adjustment.

5) For vehicles equipped with thermactor, disconnect and plug hoses of dump valves equipped with 2 fittings. If valves have one fitting, remove and plug hose at valve. Connect slave hose to dump valve and intake manifold vacuum source.

6) Verify ignition timing is set to specification and adjust if necessary. With engine at normal operating temperature, check curb idle speed or A/C-Off RPM. Adjust as necessary. Run engine at 2500 RPM for 15 seconds before each mixture check.

7) With engine idling in Neutral, gradually open propane tool valve and watch for engine speed gain on tachometer. When speed reaches maximum and begins to drop off, note amount of speed gain.

NOTE: **Propane cartridge must be in vertical position. If engine speed will not drop off, check bottle gas supply. If necessary, repeat test with new bottle.**

8) Compare measured speed gain with specifications. If mixture adjustment is necessary, adjust so gain is within "Reset RPM" specifications. If propane enrichment speed gain is within "RPM Gain" specifications, proceed to step **11)**.

9) If measured speed gain is greater than specification, turn mixture screw counterclockwise, and recheck until measured speed rise is within "Reset RPM" specifications. Proceed to step **11)**.

10) If measured speed gain is less than specification, turn mixture screw clockwise, and recheck until measured speed rise is within "Reset RPM" specifications. Proceed to step **11)**.

11) Check curb idle, and remove all test equipment. Reconnect hoses in original positions, and connect PCV valve.

PROPANE MIXTURE ADJUSTMENT (RPM)

Application	RPM Gain	Reset RPM
Light Duty	10-90	40

COLD (FAST) IDLE RPM

LIGHT DUTY

1) Place transmission in Neutral. Bring engine to normal operating temperature. Disconnect vacuum hoses at EGR, purge valve or purge solenoid valve, and plug hoses.

2) Disconnect and plug vacuum hose from cold start vacuum switch (Orange vacuum switch on valve cover). Using a slave vacuum hose, connect manifold vacuum to cold start vacuum switch.

3) Place fast idle screw on 2nd step (kickdown) of fast idle cam. Adjust fast idle speed to specifications. *See Fig. 2*. Remove plugs from vacuum hoses, and restore all hoses to their original locations.

LIGHT DUTY FAST IDLE SPEED (RPM)

Application	RPM	Cam Step
All Models	1600	2nd (Kickdown)

HEAVY DUTY

NOTE: **Procedure includes setting Decel Throttle Control.**

1) Place transmission in Neutral. Bring engine to normal operating temperature. Disconnect and plug vacuum hose at EGR valve, decel throttle control diaphragm and purge valve (if equipped).

2) Place fast idle adjusting screw on second step (kickdown) of fast idle cam. Adjust fast idle speed to specifications. Momentarily depress throttle to rotate fast idle cam.

3) Using a slave vacuum hose, connect manifold vacuum to decel throttle control diaphragm. Adjust diaphragm shaft length until specified RPM is obtained. Remove plugs, and restore vacuum hoses to their original locations.

HEAVY DUTY FAST IDLE SPEED (RPM)

Application	Fast Idle Speed	Decel Throttle Control Speed
All Models	1600	1400-1500

AUTOMATIC CHOKE

NOTE: **Some models may have tamper-proof choke assemblies.**

Drill heads from 2 rivets, and remove. Loosen retaining screw, and turn choke cover in direction indicated on cover to specified setting. Install new rivets and tighten screw.

AUTOMATIC CHOKE SPECIFICATIONS

Application	Choke Setting
Light Duty	Nonadjustable
Heavy Duty	Index

FUEL PUMP

Check fuel pump at idle RPM with engine at normal operating temperature.

FUEL PUMP SPECIFICATIONS

Application	Pressure psi (kg/cm²)	Volume Pints (Liters)
All Models	5.0-7.0	1 in 20 sec.
	(.35-.50)	(.47 in 20 sec.)

GENERAL SERVICING

IGNITION SYSTEM

DISTRIBUTOR

All Light Duty models are equipped with TFI-IV (Thick Film Integrated) ignition system. All Heavy Duty models are equipped with Dura-Spark II ignition system. Both systems require no outside adjustments.

DISTRIBUTOR PICK-UP COIL RESISTANCE

Application	Ohms
Light Duty (TFI-IV) Models	650-1300
Heavy Duty (Dura-Spark) Models	400-1000

TOTAL SPARK ADVANCE @ 2500 RPM

Distributor No.	W/Vac. Advance	W/O Vac. Advance
Light Duty	[1]	[1]
Heavy Duty		
D5TE-12127-FA	29-40°	16-21°
D9TE-12127-AEA	24-34°	18-23°
D9TE-12127-ADA	24-34°	18-23°

[1] – Spark advance is computer-controlled.

IGNITION COIL

IGNITION COIL RESISTANCE – OHMS @ 75°F (24°C)

Application	Primary	Secondary
Dura-Spark II	0.8-1.6	7700-10,500
TFI-IV	0.3-1.0	8000-11,500

FUEL SYSTEMS

CARBURETORS

Application	Model
Light Duty	Carter YFA 1-Bbl. Feedback
Heavy Duty	Carter YFA 1-Bbl.

ELECTRICAL

BATTERY

BATTERY SPECIFICATIONS

Application	Capacity (Amp Hours)	Discharge Rate (Amps)
Standard		
Manual	36	155
Automatic	45	190
Optional	63, 81	260, 175

STARTER

All models use Motorcraft positive engagement type starters with either a 4" or 4 1/2" armature.

STARTER SPECIFICATIONS

Application	Volts	Amps	Test RPM
4" Armature	12	80	6700 Min.
4 1/2" Armature	12	80	7380-9356

ALTERNATOR

All models use Motorcraft alternators.

ALTERNATOR SPECIFICATIONS

I.D. Tag Color	Field Current Draw@12 Volts	Rated Amp Output
Rear Terminal		
Orange	2.8	40
Green	4.0	60
Side Terminal		
Black	4.25	70
Red	4.25	100

ALTERNATOR REGULATOR

Two Motorcraft electronic voltage regulators are used. Although they look alike, they are not interchangeable.

REGULATOR IDENTIFICATION

Application	Color Coding
Used with Ammeter	Blue Label
Used with Indicator Lamp	Black Label

ADJUSTMENTS

BELT ADJUSTMENT

BELT ADJUSTMENT
Tension in Lbs. (Kg) Using Strand Tension Gauge

Application	New Belt	Used Belt
All Models		
1/4" Belt	50-80 (23-36)	40-60 (18-27)
All Others	120-160 (54-72)	110-130 (49-58)

SERVICE INTERVALS

REPLACEMENT INTERVALS

Application	Miles
Oil Filter	7500
Air Filter	30,000
PCV Filter	30,000
PCV Valve	60,000
Spark Plugs	30,000
Spark Plug Wires	60,000

GENERAL SERVICING (Cont.)

CAPACITIES

FLUID CAPACITIES (EXCEPT FUEL & COOLING)

Application	Quantity
Crankcase	[1] 6.0 qts. (5.6L)
Rear Axle (Hypoid Gear Lube)	
Ford Standard & Traction-Lok	[2] 6.5 pts. (3.0L)
Dana 60, 61-1 & 61-2	[2] 6.0 pts. (2.8L)
Dana 70	
Standard	[2] 6.5 pts. (3.0L)
Heavy Duty	[2] 7.4 pts. (3.5L)
Front Axle (Hypoid Gear Lube)	
Dana 44-IFS & 50-IFS	[3] 4.0 pts. (1.8L)
Transfer Case (Dexron II)	
Warner 1345	6.5 pts. (3.0L)
New Process 208	9.0 pts. (4.3L)
Auto. Trans. (Dexron II)	
C-5 3-Speed	22 pts. (10.4L)
C-6 3-Speed	
2WD	24 pts. (11.2L)
4WD	27 pts. (12.7L)
AOT 4-Speed	24 pts. (11.7L)
Man. Trans. (SAE 80W-90)	
Ford 3.03 3-Speed	3.5 pts. (1.6L)
T-18 4-Speed	7.0 pts. (3.3L)
New Process 435 4-Speed W/Ext.	7.0 pts. (3.3L)
New Process 435 4-Speed W/O Ext.	6.5 pts. (3.0L)
4-Speed Overdrive	4.5 pts. (2.1L)

[1] – Includes 1 qt. (.95L) for filter change.
[2] – Add 4 ozs. friction modifier to limited slip axles.
[3] – Add 2 ozs. friction modifier to limited slip axles.

FUEL TANK CAPACITIES

Application	Quantity
F150 (Short W.B.)	
Standard	16.5 gals. (62.5L)
Auxiliary	19.0 gals.(72.0L)
F150/F250/F350 (Long W.B.)	
Standard	19.0 gals. (72.0L)
Auxiliary	19.0 gals. (72.0L)
E150, Club Wagon (124" W.B.)	18.0 gals. (68.0L)
E150/E250/E350 (138" & 158" W.B.)	
Standard	22.0 gals. (83.0L)
Auxiliary	18.0 gals. (68.0L)
Bronco	32.0 gals. (121.0L)

COOLING CAPACITIES

Application	Quantity
"E" Models	
With Heater	15.0 qts. (14.2L)
With Heater & A/C	18.0 qts. (17.0L)
Bronco & "F" Models	
With Heater	13.0 qts. (12.2L)
With Heater & A/C	14.0 qts. (13.2L)

SYSTEM REFRIGERANT CAPACITIES

Application	Ounces
Bronco & F150-350	48
E150-350	
Standard	52
Auxiliary	64

1985 Ford V6 Tune-Up

TUNE-UP

ENGINE IDENTIFICATION

The eighth character of the Vehicle Identification Number (VIN) identifies engine. The VIN is stamped on a metal plate located at upper left corner of dash.

VIN ENGINE CODES

Application	VIN Code
2.8L (170") V6	S

TUNE-UP NOTES

NOTE: When performing tune-up procedures described in this article, the following notes and precautions must be followed:

Due to late changes and corrections, always refer to Engine Tune-Up Decal in engine compartment before attempting tune-up. If manual and decal differ, always use decal specifications.

Do not allow or create a condition of engine misfire in one or more cylinders for an extended time. Damage to converter may occur due to loading converter with unburned air/fuel mixture.

ENGINE COMPRESSION

Test compression with spark plugs removed, engine at normal operating temperature and throttle wide open. Crank engine through at least 5 compression strokes before recording reading.

COMPRESSION SPECIFICATIONS

Application	Specification
Compression Ratio	
2.8L	8.7:1
Max. Variation	
Between Cyl.	less than 25%

VALVE ARRANGEMENT

Right Bank – I-E-I-E-E-I (Front-to-rear).
Left Bank – I-E-E-I-E-I (Front-to-rear).

VALVE CLEARANCE

VALVE CLEARANCE ADJUSTMENT

Application	Intake In. (mm)	Exhaust In. (mm)
2.8L	[1] .014 (.35)	[1] .016 (.40)

[1] – Engine cold.

SPARK PLUGS

SPARK PLUG TYPE

Application	Motorcraft No.
2.8L	AWSF-42C

SPARK PLUG SPECIFICATIONS

Application	Gap In. (mm)	Torque Ft. Lbs. (N.m)
All Models	.042-046 (1.1-1.2)	20 (28)

HIGH TENSION WIRE RESISTANCE

1) Remove wire from ignition coil. Remove wires from spark plugs by twisting spark plug boot carefully to loosen seal on plug. Remove wires by pulling on plug boot. Remove distributor cap from distributor, leaving wires connected to cap.

2) Using an ohmmeter, check resistance of each wire. Connect one ohmmeter lead to coil wire or spark plug wire terminal and other lead to distributor cap insert.

3) Replace any wire with over 5000 ohms resistance per INCH. New wires should have a resistance of 7000 ohms per FOOT.

HIGH TENSION WIRE RESISTANCE (OHMS)

Application	Maximum Resistance
Spark Plug Wires	
Used	5000 per INCH
New	7000 per Foot

DISTRIBUTOR

All 2.8L engines are equipped with the TFI-IV EEC-IV ignition system. No adjustments are required on any of these systems.

Fig. 1: 2.8L V6 Timing Mark and Firing Order

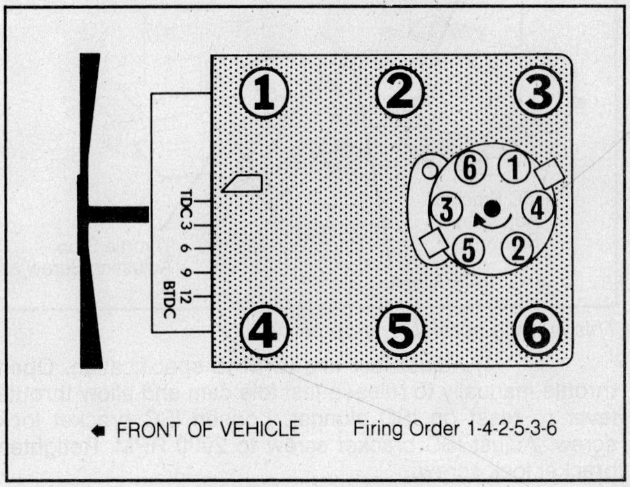

IGNITION TIMING

1) Warm engine to normal operating temperature and shut off engine. Turn all accessories off and place transmission in Neutral. Disconnect single Black lead connector near distributor.

2) Attach timing light. Start engine and check ignition timing. Adjust as needed.

1985 Ford V6 Tune-Up

TUNE-UP (Cont.)

IGNITION TIMING SPECIFICATIONS (Degrees BTDC@RPM)

Application	Auto. Trans.	Man. Trans.
2.8L [1]	[2] 10@850	[2] 10@750

[1] – Idle speed and timing are controlled by EEC-IV system and are not adjustable.
[2] – Except Calif. man. trans. models; 14@Idle.

HOT (SLOW) IDLE RPM

NOTE: The 2.8L engine is equipped with automatic idle speed control and adjustment is not a normal tune-up procedure. If idle speed is not correct, perform the following EEC-IV diagnostic procedure.

1) Place transmission in Neutral (man. trans.) or "D" (auto. trans.). Turn all accessories off. Warm engine to normal operating temperature. Set parking brake and block wheels.

2) Remove Air Charge Temperature (ACT) sensor and adapter from air cleaner tray, keeping wiring harness connected. Remove air cleaner. Disconnect and plug vacuum line at bottom of air cleaner.

3) Turn ignition off. Within 10 seconds, Idle Speed Control (ISC) plunger should move to maximum extension. Disconnect and plug EGR vacuum hose. With engine running, manually open throttle and set fast idle adjusting screw on highest step of cam. *See Fig. 2.*

Fig. 2: Idle Speed Control Adjustment

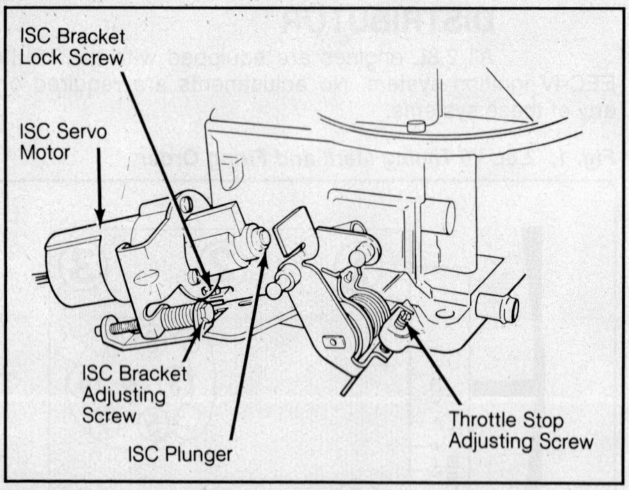

This is not a normal tune-up procedure.

4) Adjust fast idle RPM to specification. Open throttle manually to release fast idle cam and allow throttle lever to reset on ISC plunger. Loosen ISC bracket lock screw. Adjust ISC bracket screw to 2000 RPM. Retighten bracket lock screw.

5) Reconnect ISC. RPM will automatically be adjusted to curb idle. At the same time, manually hold throttle above 1000 RPM, push ISC plunger until it retracts fully, and then release throttle. Quickly unplug connection. Adjust anti-dieseling speed throttle stop screw to specification.

6) Reconnect ISC and EGR vacuum hose. Shut engine off. Restart engine and verify curb idle speed.

IDLE SPEED SPECIFICATIONS (RPM)

Application	Curb Idle Speed	Anti-Diesel Speed
Man. Trans.	800-900	750 ("N")
Auto Trans.	700-800	650 ("D")

IDLE MIXTURE ADJUSTMENT

NOTE: Idle mixture adjustment is not part of a normal tune-up. DO NOT adjust mixture unless carburetor has been disassembled or vehicle fails emissions testing.

MIXTURE SCREW CAP REMOVAL

Before any idle mixture adjustment can be made, idle mixture limiter caps must be removed. If adjustment is required, use the following procedure to remove caps. *See Fig. 3.*

1) Remove carburetor from vehicle and drain fuel. Turn carburetor over and locate locking tab on limiter cap. Use a blunt punch and light hammer to tap tab in until locking detent is cleared. Remove cap.

CAUTION: Support area under limiter cap when removing to prevent bending adjustment needle.

2) Repeat step **1)** for other limiter cap. Install carburetor. After adjustments have been made, install new caps on both adjusting screws. To install caps, position locking tab in line with detent in locking plug and press cap into plug.

Fig. 3: Removing Idle Mixture Limiter Caps

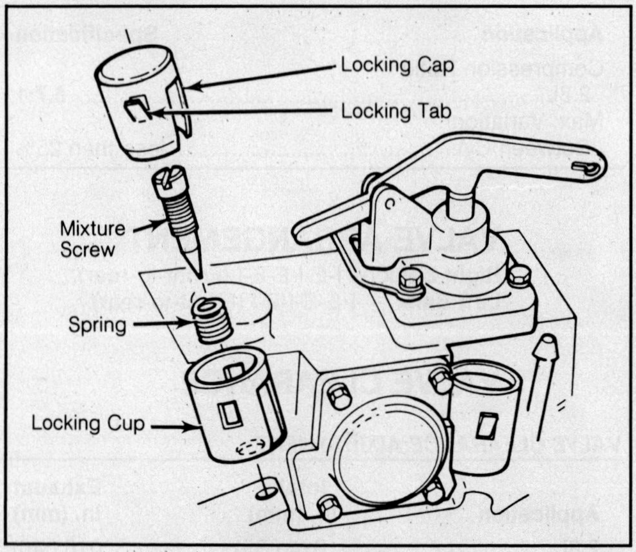

PROPANE ENRICHMENT PROCEDURE

Vehicle Preparation

1) Apply parking brake and block wheels. Check ignition timing. Remove air cleaner assembly. Disconnect wiring harness from carburetor feedback solenoid at rear of carburetor.

2) Remove PCV valve from valve cover and allow it to draw fresh air. Disconnect fuel evaporating purge line at purge solenoid. Install adapter into end of

TUNE-UP (Cont.)

purge line, (line is still connected to intake manifold spacer).

3) Disconnect ISC motor from wiring harness. Connect a tachometer to engine, start engine and manually hold throttle above 1000 RPM. Push ISC plunger until it retracts fully. After plunger retracts, release throttle and quickly unplug connection.

4) Be sure throttle lever is resting on speed screw. Install air cleaner assembly, but do not connect flexible fresh air tube to air cleaner duct and valve assembly.

5) Insert hose from propane enrichment tool (Rotunda T75L 9600 A) about 3/4 of the way into duct or fresh air tube, securing with tape.

Propane Enrichment Method

1) Leave all vacuum signal hoses attached to air cleaner assembly when relocating air cleaner for carburetor adjustments. Air cleaner must be installed and the air charge temperature switch must be connected for engine speed checks.

CAUTION: Do not let engine idle for extended periods, as catalyst overheating may cause excessive underbody temperatures.

2) Disconnect crankcase vent hose (filler cap to air cleaner) from air cleaner. Allow hose to vent to underhood air. With transmission in Neutral, run engine at 2500 RPM for 15 seconds before each mixture check.

3) With engine idling at normal operating temperature, gradually open propane tool valve and watch for engine speed gain on tachometer. When speed reaches maximum and begins to drop off, note amount of speed gain.

NOTE: Propane cartridge must be in vertical position. If engine speed will not drop off, check bottle gas supply. If necessary, repeat test with new bottle.

4) Compare measured speed gain with specifications. If mixture adjustment is required, limiter caps must first be removed. Refer to MIXTURE SCREW CAP REMOVAL procedure. With caps removed and carburetor installed, adjust mixture until RPM gain is within "Reset RPM" specifications. If adjustment is not required, go to step **7)**.

5) If measured speed gain is greater than specification, turn mixture screws counterclockwise (rich) in equal amounts, and recheck until measured speed rise is within "Reset RPM" specifications. Then go to step **7)**.

6) If measured speed gain is less than specification, turn mixture screws clockwise (lean) in equal amounts, But do not exceed 2 1/4 turns from fully seated position. Recheck until measured speed rise is within "Reset RPM" specification.

7) Restore carburetor tamper-resistant features. Reconnect hoses in original positions and connect PCV valve. Reconnect wiring harnesses to feedback solenoid and ISC motor.

8) Remove adapter from fuel purge line and reconnect line to purge solenoid. Reinstall air cleaner if removed. Check and adjust curb idle as needed.

IDLE MIXTURE SPECIFICATIONS (PROPANE ENRICHMENT)

Application	Gain RPM (Check)	Reset RPM (Adjust)
2.8L	160-240	210

COLD (FAST) IDLE RPM

NOTE: Before performing Cold (Fast) Idle RPM adjustment, perform Hot (Slow) Idle RPM preliminary adjustments.

1) With transmission in Neutral (man. trans.) or "P" (auto. trans.) and engine at normal operating temperature, disconnect and plug EGR vacuum line. Place fast idle screw on highest step of fast idle cam. *See Fig. 4.*

2) Adjust idle speed to specifications. Remove plug from vacuum line and reconnect to EGR valve.

FAST IDLE (RPM)

Application	Man. Trans.	Auto. Trans.
2.8L		
Calif. Man. Trans.	3200	3200
All Others	3000	3000

Fig. 4: Adjusting Fast Idle Speed

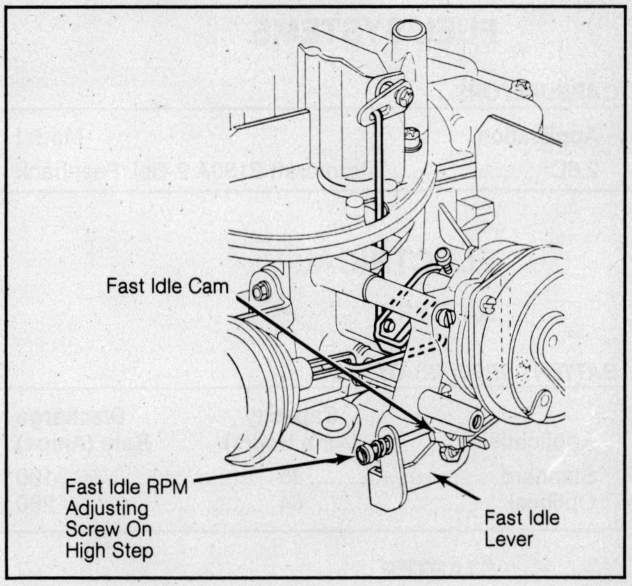

AUTOMATIC CHOKE

Loosen choke thermostat cover screws and turn cover in direction indicated on cover to specified setting. Tighten screws.

AUTOMATIC CHOKE SPECIFICATIONS

Application	Choke Setting
2.8L	3 Rich or "V" Notch

TUNE-UP (Cont.)

FUEL PUMP

Check fuel pump with engine idling at normal operating temperature. Pinch off fuel return line during test.

FUEL PUMP SPECIFICATIONS

Application	Pressure psi (kg/cm²)	Volume Pints (Liters)
2.8L	4.5-6.5	1 in 30 sec.
	(.32-.46)	(.47 in 30 sec.)

GENERAL SERVICING

IGNITION

DISTRIBUTOR

All models with the 2.8L engine are equipped with the TFI-IV EEC-IV ignition system. All ignition advance is computer controlled. No vacuum or mechanical advance mechanisms are used. No pickup coil is used on this system. No resistance measurements can be made.

IGNITION COIL

IGNITION COIL RESISTANCE – OHMS @ 75°F (24°C)

Application	Primary	Secondary
TFI-IV	0.3-1.0	8000-11,500

FUEL SYSTEMS

CARBURETORS

Application	Model
2.8L	Motorcraft 2150A 2-Bbl. Feedback

ELECTRICAL

BATTERY

BATTERY SPECIFICATIONS

Application	Capacity (Amp Hours)	Discharge Rate (Amps)
Standard	45	190
Optional	64	260

STARTER

Motorcraft positive engagement type with either a 4" or 4.5" armature.

STARTER SPECIFICATIONS

Application	Volts	Amps.	Test RPM
4" Armature	12	80	6700 Min.
4 1/2" Armature	12	80	7380-9356

ALTERNATOR

All models use Motorcraft rear-terminal alternators.

ALTERNATOR SPECIFICATIONS

Stamp Color	Field Current Draw@12 Volts	Rated Amp Output
Orange	4.0	40
Green	4.0	60

ALTERNATOR REGULATOR

Two models of Motorcraft electronic voltage regulators are used. No adjustment is required or possible. They are similar in appearance, but different internally and must not be interchanged.

REGULATOR IDENTIFICATION

Application	Color Coding
With Ammeter	Gray
With Indicator Light	Black

ADJUSTMENTS

BELT ADJUSTMENT
Tension in Lbs. (Kg) Using Strand Tension Gauge

Application	New Belt	[1] Used Belt
2.8L	120-160 (55-73)	110-130 (50-59)

[1] – Any belt operated 10 minutes or more.

SERVICE INTERVALS

REPLACEMENT INTERVALS

Application	Miles
Oil Filter	7500
Air Filter	30,000
Fuel Filter	5000
PCV Filter	30,000
Spark Plugs	30,000

GENERAL SERVICING (Cont.)

CAPACITIES

FLUID CAPACITIES

Application	Quantity
Cooling System	
Aerostar	8.0 qts. (7.6L)
All Other Models	
With A/C	7.8 qts. (7.4L)
Without A/C	7.2 qts. (6.8L)
Crankcase [1]	5.0 qts. (4.7L)
Auto. Trans.	
C-3 (Dexron II)	8.0 qts. (7.6L)
C-5 (Motorcraft ATF Type H)	
2WD Ranger	7.5 qts. (7.1L)
Bronco II & 4WD Ranger	7.9 qts. (7.5L)
AOD (Dexron II)	
2WD	9.5 qts. (9.0L)
4WD	10.3 qts. (9.7L)
Man. Trans.	
4-Speed	3.0 pts. (1.4L)
5-Speed	4.0 pts. (1.7L)
Transfer Case (Dexron II)	
Bronco II & Ranger w/Warner 1350	3.0 pts. (1.4L)
Front Axle (Hypoid Gear Lube)	
Model 28	1.0 pts. (.5L)
Rear Axle (Hypoid Gear Lube)	
Dana Model 30	2.5 pts. (1.2L)
6 3/4" Ring Gear	3.0 pts. (1.4L)
7 1/2" Ring Gear	5.0 pts. (2.4L)
Fuel Tank	
Aerostar	
Standard	17.0 gals. (64.0L)
Optional	15.0 gals. (57.5L)
Bronco II	23.0 gals. (87.0L)
Ranger	
Standard Short Bed	15.0 gals. (57.5L)
Standard Long Bed	17.0 gals. (64.0L)
Optional Auxiliary	13.0 gals. (49.0L)

[1] – Includes 1 qt. (.9L) for filter change.

SYSTEM REFRIGERANT CAPACITY

Application	Ounces
All Models	40

1985 Ford V8 Tune-Up

TUNE-UP

ENGINE IDENTIFICATION

Engine can be identified by the eighth character of Vehicle Identification Number. Number is stamped on a metal plate, which is riveted to upper left corner of instrument panel and visible through left side of windshield.

VIN ENGINE CODE

Application	Code
5.0L (302") 2-Bbl.	F
5.0L (302") EFI	N
5.8L (351") 2-Bbl.	G
5.8L (351") 4-Bbl.	H
7.5L (460") 4-Bbl.	L

TUNE-UP NOTES

NOTE: **When performing tune-up procedures described in this article, the following notes and precautions must be followed.**

For Tune-Up purposes "Light Duty" refers to vehicles up to 8500 lbs. GVW. "Heavy Duty" refers to vehicles exceeding 8500 lbs. GVW.

If Dura-Spark 2-piece distributor cap must be removed, first remove top portion, then rotor, then bottom portion (adapter). If any spark plug wire is disconnected with this system, connection must be first greased with silicone grease before it is reattached.

When connecting a tachometer to Dura-Spark ignition coil, install the alligator clip on tachometer into the "DEC" (Tach Testing) cavity.

When connecting tachometer to SSI ignition coil, install the alligator clip on tachometer into the "DEC" (TACH TEST) cavity.

Due to changes and corrections, always refer to Engine Tune-Up Decal in engine compartment before performing tune-up. If manual and decal differ, always use decal specifications.

Do not allow or create a condition of engine misfire in one or more cylinders for an extended period of time. Damage to converter from overheating may occur due to loading with unburned fuel.

ENGINE COMPRESSION

Test compression with all spark plugs removed and engine at normal operating temperature. Crank engine through at least 5 compression strokes before recording reading.

COMPRESSION SPECIFICATIONS

Application	Specification
Compression Ratio	
5.0L 2-Bbl.	8.4:1
5.0L EFI	9.0:1
5.8L	8.3:1
7.5L	8.0:1
Max. Variation	
Between Cyl.	less than 25%

VALVE ARRANGEMENT

Right Bank – I-E-I-E-I-E-I-E (Front-to-rear).
Left Bank – E-I-E-I-E-I-E-I (Front-to-rear).

VALVE CLEARANCE

All engines are equipped with hydraulic lifters. Adjust all valves to zero lash.

SPARK PLUGS

SPARK PLUG TYPE

Application	Motorcraft No.
All Engines [1]	ASF-42

[1] – 5.0L EFI and 5.8L 4-Bbl. use ASF-32C.

SPARK PLUG SPECIFICATIONS

Application	Gap In. (mm)	Torque Ft. Lbs. (N.m)
5.0L & 5.8L	.044 (1.1)	10-15 (14-20)
7.5L	.044 (1.1)	5-7 (7-14)

HIGH TENSION WIRE RESISTANCE

1) Loosen wires from spark plugs by twisting spark plug boot carefully to loosen seal on spark plug. Remove wires by pulling on plug boot. Remove distributor cap from distributor, leaving wires connected to cap.

NOTE: **DO NOT disconnect wires from distributor cap unless replacement is necessary.**

2) Using an ohmmeter, check resistance of each wire by connecting one ohmmeter lead to spark plug terminal and other lead to distributor cap insert. Replace any wire with over 5000 ohms resistance per INCH. New wires should have a resistance of 7000 ohms per FOOT.

NOTE: **Whenever a high tension wire is disconnected, the interior of spark plug terminal boot must be coated with dielectric silicone grease before connection.**

HIGH TENSION WIRE RESISTANCE (OHMS)

Application	Maximum Resistance
New Wires	7000 per Foot
Used Wires	5000 per INCH

DISTRIBUTOR

Light Duty models with 5.0L and 5.8L Calif. (man. trans.) engines are equipped with EEC-IV TFI-IV (Thick Film Integrated) ignition system. All other models are equipped with Dura-Spark II ignition system. No adjustments are required.

TUNE-UP (Cont.)

Fig. 1: 5.0L & 7.5L Timing Marks and Firing Order

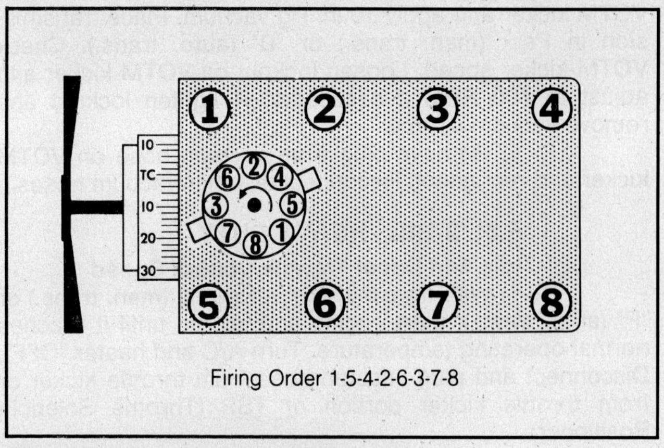

Magnetic probe located at 135° ATDC.

Fig. 2: 5.8L Timing Marks and Firing Order

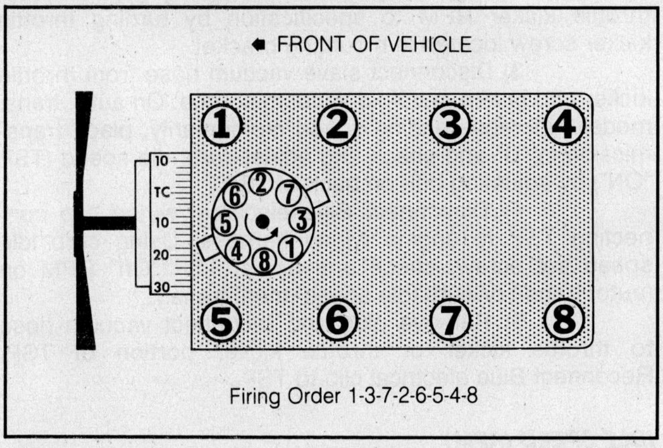

Magnetic probe located at 135° ATDC.

IGNITION TIMING

NOTE: **Magnetic probe timing device may be used if instrument is available and engine is so equipped. Timing probe offset is 135° ATDC.**

1) Determine specified timing and mark degree line on damper (on some vehicles mark both pointer and damper notch). Disconnect and plug vacuum line(s) at distributor.

IGNITION TIMING SPECIFICATIONS (Degrees BTDC@RPM)

Application	Man. Trans.	Auto. Trans.
5.0L [1]		
2-Bbl.	10@575	10@575
EFI	8@Idle	10@Idle
5.8L [1]		
Light Duty	[2] 10@Idle[1]	[2] [3] 10@Idle
Heavy Duty	8@700	8@800
7.5L	8@800	8@800

[1] - Engines are equipped with Electronic Engine Control (EEC-IV) system. Ignition timing is not a normal adjustment.

[2] - Federal light duty trucks with 5.8L use Dura-Spark II ignition system.

[3] - Set Federal High Alt. to 14°@Idle.

2) Connect tachometer. Connect timing light to No. 1 spark plug wire. If vehicle is equipped with a barometric sensor, disconnect the sensor from module. Connect Black and Yellow wires in module connector. If vehicle is equipped with EEC-IV, disconnect single wire Black connector near distributor. Set timing to specifications.

HOT (SLOW) IDLE RPM

NOTE: **After engine adjustments are complete, reconnect all vacuum lines or hoses to their original positions. Reinstall air cleaner assembly. Run engine at 2500 RPM for 15 seconds and recheck curb idle speed. Final curb idle speed check must be made with air cleaner installed. Adjust as necessary and recheck dashpot clearance.**

5.0L 2-BBL.

Idle Speed

1) Set the parking brake and block wheels. Place transmission in Neutral or "P". With engine at normal operating temperature, disconnect EVAP purge solenoid connector. Disconnect and plug vacuum line to Vacuum Operated Throttle Modulator (VOTM) kicker.

2) Place transmission in Drive. Check curb idle speed. If adjustment is necessary, loosen TSP-dashpot mounting bracket hold-down screw. Use the saddle bracket adjusting screw to adjust curb idle speed.

3) Place transmission in Neutral or Park. Increase engine speed momentarily. Place transmission in Drive and recheck curb idle. Adjust if required. Retighten TSP-dashpot mounting bracket hold-down screw. Reconnect VOTM kicker and EVAP purge soleniod.

4) Whenever idle speed is adjusted more than 50 RPM on automatic overdrive transmission (AOT) equipped vehicles, adjustment screw on the linkage lever at the carburetor should also be adjusted.

5) Place shift lever in Neutral position, and set parking brake. With engine off, back out linkage adjusting screw completely. Turn adjusting screw in to obtain .005" (.13 mm) clearance between end of screw and throttle lever. Turn screw in an additional 4 turns. Recheck curb idle.

IDLE SPEED (RPM)

Application	RPM
5.0L 2-Bbl.	575

5.0L EFI

Idle Speed Check

NOTE: **Curb idle speed is controlled by the EEC-IV processor and the Idle Speed Control (ISC) device. If the control system is operating properly, these speeds are self-compensating and cannot be changed by traditional adjustment techniques.**

1) Set parking brake and block wheels. Bring engine to normal operation temperature and turn off. Place transmission in Neutral or "P". Turn A/C-Heat selector to the off position.

TUNE-UP (Cont.)

2) Ensure throttle linkage is free and travel is unobstructed. Ensure cruise control cable (if so equipped) is not holding the throttle open. Check for vacuum leaks.

3) Operate engine at 1800 RPM for at least 30 seconds. Place transmission in "D" (auto. trans.) or Neutral (man. trans.). Allow engine to stabilize. Check idle speed.

4) If curb idle speed is equal to or less than 675 RPM (auto. trans.), 775 RPM (man. trans.) do not adjust. If speeds exceed specifed RPM turn engine off and disconnect the positive terminal of the battery and then reconnect. Repeat step **3)**.

5) If speeds still exceed specifications, perform EEC-IV Diagnosis/Repair then repeat step **3)**.

6) If idle speed is still not correct, back out idle air set screw until speed reaches 580-620 RPM (auto. trans.) or 680-720 RPM (man. trans.). Then back out the curb idle screw one-half additional turn to bring the throttle plate linkage into the nominal operating range of the ISC system.

5.8L 2-BBL. LIGHT DUTY

Idle Speed

1) With transmission in Neutral (man. trans.) or "P" (auto. trans.), start engine and let run until it reaches normal operating temperature. Disconnect and plug the vacuum hose to the VOTM kicker (leave connected on vehicles operating at elevations above 4000 ft.). Disconnect the EVAP purge soleniod electrical connector.

2) Run engine in Neutral at 2000 RPM for 120 seconds. Return engine to idle and place transmission in Neutral (man. trans.) or in "D" (auto. trans.).

3) Check/adjust curb idle RPM. If adjustment is required, loosen saddle bracket locking screw. Adjust idle speed using saddle bracket adjusting screw. Adjustment must be made within 90 seconds. Tighten saddle bracket locking screw.

4) Remove plug from VOTM vacuum hose and connect to VOTM (if disconnected). Connect EVAP purge solenoid electrical connector. Increase engine speed momentarily. Check idle speed. Readjust if necessary.

CURB IDLE (RPM)

Application	Curb Idle
5.8L 2-Bbl.	
Light Duty	
Auto. Trans. (In Drive)	600
Man. Trans.	750
Heavy Duty	650

5.8L 4-BBL. LIGHT DUTY

Idle and VOTM Speed

1) Place transmission in Neutral (man. trans.) or "P" (auto. trans.). With engine at normal operating temperature, turn A/C and heater selector switch off. Disconnect and plug vacuum hoses at air control valve, EGR valve and purge control valves. Disconnect EVAP purge solenoid connector. Disconnect and plug vacuum line to VOTM kicker.

2) Place transmission in Park (man. trans.) or "D" (auto. trans.). Check curb idle. If adjustment is necessary, use curb idle screw.

3) Place transmission in Neutral or Park, and increase engine speed momentarily. Place transmission in specified position, recheck curb idle. Adjust if required.

4) Connect an external vacuum source to the VOTM kicker and apply 10 in. Hg vacuum. Place transmission in Park (man. trans.) or "D" (auto. trans.). Check VOTM kicker speed. Loosen locknut on VOTM kicker and adjust to 700 RPM if necessary. Retighten locknut and remove vacuum source.

5) Remove plug from vacuum hose on VOTM kicker and reconnect. Reconnect all other vacuum hoses.

5.8L 2-BBL. HEAVY DUTY

Idle and Decel Throttle Control Speed

1) With transmission in Neutral (man. trans.) or "P" (auto. trans.), start engine and let run until it reaches normal operating temperature. Turn A/C and heater "OFF". Disconnect and plug vacuum hose from throttle kicker or from throttle kicker portion of TSP (Throttle Solenoid Positioner).

2) Install a slave vacuum hose from throttle kicker portion of TSP to intake manifold vacuum. Speed up engine momentarily. Check and adjust the decel throttle kicker RPM to specification by turning throttle kicker screw located in mounting bracket.

3) Disconnect slave vacuum hose from throttle kicker and intake manifold vacuum source. On auto. trans. models, increase engine speed momentarily, place transmission in "D" and check and adjust curb idle speed (TSP "ON") by adjusting bolt on back of TSP.

4) Disconnect Blue electrical wiring clip connecting TSP to engine wiring harness. Using curb idle speed set screw, check and adjust TSP "Off" RPM on (auto. trans.) or curb idle speed (man. trans.).

5) Remove plug and reconnect vacuum hose to throttle kicker or throttle kicker portion of TSP. Reconnect Blue electrical clip to TSP.

IDLE SPEED (RPM)

Application	Curb Idle TSP "On"	TSP "Off"
5.8L 2-Bbl.		
Heavy Duty	650	525

DECEL THROTTLE KICKER IDLE (RPM)

Application	RPM
5.8L Heavy Duty	1750-1950

7.5L VEHICLES

Idle and Decel Throttle Control Speed

1) With transmission in Neutral (man. trans.) or "P" (auto. trans.), and A/C off, start engine. Operate engine until it reaches normal operating temperature. Remove air cleaner. Disconnect and plug decel throttle control kicker diaphragm vacuum hose.

2) Connect a slave vacuum hose from intake manifold vacuum to decel throttle control kicker. Run engine at 2500 RPM for 15 seconds. Release throttle. If decel throttle control kicker RPM is not within 50 RPM of specifications, adjust to proper RPM.

3) Disconnect slave vacuum hose and allow engine to return to idle. Check and adjust curb idle if necessary, using curb idle speed adjusting screw. Unplug, and reconnect vacuum hose to decel throttle control kicker diaphragm. Reinstall air cleaner.

TUNE-UP (Cont.)

IDLE SPEED (RPM)

Application	Curb Idle
7.5L	
Auto. Trans.	650
Manual Trans.	800

DECEL THROTTLE KICKER (RPM)

Application	RPM
7.5L	1650-1750

IDLE MIXTURE ADJUSTMENT

NOTE: **Idle mixture adjustment is not part of a normal tune-up. DO NOT adjust mixture unless carburetor has been disassembled or vehicle fails emissions testing.**

PROPANE ENRICHMENT PROCEDURE

NOTE: **This procedure is for Carbureted Light Duty Vehicles only.**

1) Leave all vacuum signal hoses attached to air cleaner assembly when relocating air cleaner for carburetor adjustments. Air cleaner MUST be installed for engine speed checks.

CAUTION: **Do not let engine idle for extended periods, as catalyst overheating may cause excessive underbody temperatures.**

2) Apply parking brake and block wheels. Disconnect automatic brake release, and plug vacuum connection. Remove the crankcase vent hose at the air cleaner, and allow hose to vent air from under hood. Connect tachometer.

3) Disconnect flexible fresh air tube from air cleaner duct or adapter. Insert hose from propane enrichment tool (Rotunda T75L 9600 A) about 3/4 of the way into duct or fresh air tube. Disconnect PCV valve from grommet, and allow valve to draw underhood air during adjustment.

4) For light duty trucks equipped with thermactor, disconnect and plug hoses of dump valves equipped with 2 vacuum fittings. If valves have one fitting or combination air by-pass/air control valve, remove and plug hose at valve. Connect slave hose to dump valve and intake manifold vacuum source.

5) For 5.0L and 5.8L vehicles equipped with 2-Bbl. carburetors, disconnect battery negative cable for 10 seconds and reconnect. Disconnect electrical connector from engine coolant temperature sensor. Remove and plug hose from the VOTM hose. Disconnect and plug hose from Manifold Absolute Pressure (MAP) sensor. Connect vacuum pump to MAP and apply 20 in. Hg. vacuum.

6) Check and adjust ignition timing if necessary. With engine at normal operating temperature, check curb idle speed or A/C "OFF" idle. Adjust as necessary. Run engine at 2500 RPM for 15 seconds before each mixture check.

7) With engine idling and transmission in Neutral, gradually open propane tool valve and watch for engine speed gain on tachometer. When speed reaches maximum and begins to drop off, note amount of speed gain.

NOTE: **Propane cartridge must be in vertical position. If engine speed will not drop off, check bottle gas supply. If necessary, repeat test with new bottle.**

8) Compare measured speed gain with specifications. If mixture adjustment is necessary, adjust so gain is within "Reset RPM" specifications. If propane enrichment speed gain is within "RPM Gain" specifications, proceed to step **11)**.

9) If measured speed gain is greater than specification, turn mixture screws counterclockwise in equal amounts, and recheck until measured speed rise is within "Reset RPM" specifications. Proceed to step **11)**.

10) If measured speed gain is less than specification, turn mixture screws clockwise in equal amounts, and recheck until measured speed rise is within "Reset RPM" specifications.

11) Check curb idle, and remove all test equipment. Reconnect hoses and wiring to original locations, and connect crankcase vent hose.

PROPANE MIXTURE ADJUSTMENT (RPM)

Application	RPM Gain (Check)	Reset RPM (Adjust)
5.0L		
Light Duty		
Calif.	30-150	80
Federal		
Man. Trans.	40-80	60
Auto. Trans.	20-100	60
5.8L		
Light Duty		
Man. Trans.	40-170	100
Auto. Trans.	70-180	120

[1] – Idle mixture is controlled by the EEC-IV system and no adjustments are required.

COLD (FAST) IDLE RPM

NOTE: **Before adjusting Cold (Fast) Idle RPM, perform Hot (Slow) Idle RPM preliminary adjustments.**

5.0L 2-BBL. ONLY

1) With transmission in Neutral (man. trans.) or "P" (auto. trans.), warm engine to operating temperature. Disconnect and plug hoses at both EGR valve and thermactor air by-pass valve. Disconnect vacuum hose and electrical connector on EVAP purge solenoid.

3) Place fast idle adjusting screw on highest step of fast idle cam. Check and adjust (if necessary) fast idle by turning fast idle adjusting screw. Reconnect vacuum hoses and electrical connector.

1985 Ford V8 Tune-Up

TUNE-UP (Cont.)

FAST IDLE SPEED (RPM)

Application	Man. Trans.	Auto. Trans.
5.0L	2000	2000

5.8L LIGHT DUTY

1) With transmission in Neutral (man. trans.) or "P" (auto. trans.), warm engine to operating temperature.

2) Disconnect and plug vacuum hose at EGR valve and purge valve. Disconnect electrical connector at EVAP purge solenoid (2-Bbl. models). Disconnect and plug vacuum hose at purge valve (4-Bbl. models).

3) Place fast idle adjusting screw on highest step of fast idle cam. Check and adjust (if necessary) fast idle by turning fast idle adjusting screw. Unplug and connect vacuum hoses. Connect electrical connector on 2-Bbl. models.

FAST IDLE SPEED (RPM)

Application	Man. Trans.	Auto. Trans.
5.8L		
Light Duty		
2-Bbl.	2000	2000
4-Bbl.	.....	1900

5.8L HEAVY DUTY

1) With transmission in Neutral (man. trans.) or "P" (auto. trans.), warm engine to normal operating temperature. Disconnect and plug the hose between carburetor spacer and purge valve at carburetor spacer and plug nipple on the carburetor spacer. Disconnect and plug vacuum hose at EGR valve. Disconnect and plug vacuum hose at throttle kicker or at throttle kicker portion of TSP.

2) Place fast idle adjusting screw on 2nd step of fast idle cam and adjust fast idle to specified RPM by turning fast idle adjusting screw. Unplug and reconnect vacuum hoses.

FAST IDLE SPEED (RPM)

Application	Man. Trans.	Auto. Trans.
5.8L		
Heavy Duty	1500	1500

7.5L VEHICLES

1) With transmission in Neutral (man. trans.) or "P" (auto. trans.) and A/C "OFF", start engine and let run until it reaches normal operating temperature. Remove the air cleaner. Disconnect and plug throttle decel control diaphragm vacuum hose.

2) Disconnect and plug evaporative emission purge valve hose (if equipped) and EGR valve vacuum hose. Depress throttle lever and turn fast idle cam, by hand, until fast idle adjusting screw sets on the 2nd step of fast idle cam. Adjust fast idle to specified RPM by turning fast idle adjusting screw.

3) Unplug and reconnect all vacuum hoses. Reinstall air cleaner.

FAST IDLE SPEED (RPM)

Application	Man. Trans.	Auto. Trans.
7.5L	1600	1600

DASHPOT ADJUSTMENT

1) Ensure idle speed and mixture are properly adjusted. Remove air cleaner and loosen dashpot lock nut. With choke open, hold throttle plate closed (idle position).

2) Check clearance between throttle lever pad and dashpot plunger tip. Plunger MUST be completely collapsed to check clearance. Turn dashpot in or out to obtain .090-.140 (2.3-3.6 mm) clearance. Tighten lock nut.

SOLENOID BOWL VENT VALVE TEST

5.0L & 5.8L MODELS

1) Remove air cleaner. Turn ignition on and off. Solenoid should click if it is operating properly.

2) If not, disconnect electrical lead and connect a voltmeter between lead and ground. Turn ignition on and check for battery voltage. If not present, repair wiring as required.

3) If 12 volts are present at lead connector, check valve for binding and/or plugged condition. Repair as required. If valve is not binding and/or plugged, replace solenoid valve assembly. Reinstall air cleaner.

AUTOMATIC CHOKE

Loosen choke thermostat cover screws and turn choke cover in direction indicated on cover to specified setting.

AUTOMATIC CHOKE SPECIFICATIONS

Application	Setting
5.0L	3 Rich or "V" Notch
5.8L	
Light Duty	
2-Bbl.	3 Rich or "V" Notch
4-Bbl.	Spacer Index
Heavy Duty	3 Rich or "V" Notch
7.5L	3 Rich

FUEL PUMP

MECHANICAL

Check mechanical fuel pump at curb idle RPM, with engine at normal operating temperature, and transmission in Neutral.

1985 Ford V8 Tune-Up

TUNE-UP (Cont.)

ELECTRICAL

Electric fuel pump system used with the 5.0L EFI engine consists of two fuel pumps; low pressure pump mounted in the fuel tank and a high pressure fuel pump mounted on the frame rail.

Electric fuel pump used with the 7.5L engine is a low pressure pump located in the fuel tank.

FUEL PUMP SPECIFICATIONS

Application	Pressure psi (kg/cm²)	Volume Pints (Liters)
Mechanical	6.0-8.0 (.45-.56)	1.0 in 20 sec. (.47 in 20 sec.)
Electrical		
5.0L	[1] 39.0 (2.7)	[2] 16/Hr. [3] (60/Hr.)
7.5L	[1] 4.50 (.32)	[2] 25/Hr [3] (95/Hr.)

[1] – Working pressure.
[2] – Gallons per hour.
[3] – Liters per hour.

GENERAL SERVICING

IGNITION

DISTRIBUTOR

5.0L and Light Duty 5.8L Calif. (man. trans.) models are equipped with Motorcraft TFI-IV EEC-IV ignition system. All other models are equipped with Motorcraft Dura-Spark II ignition system. Units are self-contained and require no outside adjustments.

DISTRIBUTOR PICK-UP COIL RESISTANCE

Application	Ohms
5.0L & Light Duty 5.8L (man. trans.) (TFI-IV)	650-1300
All Other Models (Dura-Spark II)	400-1000

TOTAL SPARK ADVANCE @ 2500 RPM

Engine & Calibration No.	W/O Vacuum Advance	W/Vacuum Advance
Light Duty		
5.0L	[1]	[1]
5.8L	[1]	[1]
Heavy Duty		
5.8L		
2-75J-R20	13-16	19-25
2-76J-R20	13-16	19-25
4-64G-R00	23-27	35-44
4-64G-R02	23-27	35-44
4-64Z-R10	24-29	39-48
7.5L		
3-97J-R10	23-27	39-49
3-97J-R11	23-27	39-49
4-98S-R00	18-23	26-34
4-98S-R10	18-23	26-34

[1] – Engines equipped with EEC-IV TFI-IV have computerized spark advance.

IGNITION COIL

COIL RESISTANCE – OHMS @ 75°F (24°C)

Application	Primary	Secondary
Dura-Spark II Models	0.8-1.6	7700-10,500
TFI-IV Models	0.3-1.0	8000-11,500

FUEL SYSTEMS

CARBURETORS

Application	Model
5.0L & 5.8L 2-Bbl.	Motorcraft 2150A 2-Bbl.
5.8L & 7.5L 4-Bbl.	Holley 4180C 4-Bbl.

FUEL INJECTION

Application	Model
5.0L EFI	Ford EFI

ELECTRICAL

BATTERY

BATTERY SPECIFICATIONS

Application	Capacity (Amp Hours)	Discharge Rate (Amps)
Standard		
Federal	36	155
California	45	190
Optional	63, 81	260, 175

STARTER

All models use Motorcraft positive engagement type starters with either a 4" or 4 1/2" armature.

STARTER SPECIFICATIONS

Application	Volts	Amps	Test RPM
4" Armature	12	80	6700 Min.
4 1/2" Armature	12	80	7380-9356

ALTERNATOR

All models use Motorcraft alternators.

1985 Ford V8 Tune-Up

GENERAL SERVICING (Cont.)

ALTERNATOR SPECIFICATIONS

I.D. Tag Color	Field Current Draw @ 12 Volts	Rated Amp Output
Rear Terminal		
Orange	4.0	40
Green	4.0	60
Side Terminal		
Black	4.25	70
Red	4.25	100

ALTERNATOR REGULATOR

Two Motorcraft electronic voltage regulators are used. Although both look alike, they are not interchangeable.

REGULATOR IDENTIFICATION

Application	Color Coding
Used with Ammeter	Gray Label
Used with Indicator Lamp	Black Label

ADJUSTMENTS

BELT ADJUSTMENT

BELT ADJUSTMENT
Tension in Lbs. (Kg) Using Strand Tension Gauge

Application	New	[1] Used
Thermactor		
Belt	90-130 (40-58)	80-100 (35-45)
All Others	120-160 (54-72)	90-120 (41-54)

[1] – Any belt in operation 10 minutes or more.

SERVICE INTERVALS

REPLACEMENT INTERVALS

Component	Interval (Miles)
Oil Filter	
Light Duty	7500
Heavy Duty	5000
Air Filter	[1] 30,000
Fuel Filter	15,000
PCV Valve	60,000
Spark Plugs	30,000
Spark Plug Wires	60,000

[1] – 15,000 miles on 5.8L 4-Bbl. engine.

CAPACITIES

SYSTEM REFRIGERANT CAPACITIES

Application	Ounces
Bronco & F150-350	48
E150-350	
Standard	52
Auxiliary	64

COOLING SYSTEM CAPACITIES

Application	Quantity
5.0L	
E150/250	
Standard or Extra Cooling	17.5 qts. (16.6L)
Super Cooling	18.5 qts. (17.5L)
F150/350 & Bronco	
Standard or Extra Cooling	13.0 qts. (12.3L)
Super Cooling	14.0 qts. (13.2L)
5.8L	
E150/350 All	
Standard or Extra Cooling	20.0 qts. (19.2L)
Super Cooling	21.0 qts. (19.9L)
F150/350 & Bronco	
Standard or Extra Cooling	15.0 qts. (14.2L)
Super Cooling	16.0 qts. (15.1L)
7.5L	
F250 HD, F350	18.0 qts. (17.1L)
E350	28.0 qts. (26.5L)

FLUID CAPACITIES (EXCEPT COOLING)

Application	Quantity
Crankcase (All, Including Filter)	6.0 qts. (5.6L)
Man. Trans. (SAE 80W-90)	
3.03 3-Speed	3.5 pts. (1.6L)
New Process 435 4-Speed	
W/Extension	7.0 pts. (3.3L)
W/O Extension	6.5 pts. (3.1L)
T-18 4-Speed	7.0 pts. (3.3L)
4-Speed Overdrive	4.5 pts. (2.1L)
Auto. Trans. (Dexron II)	
C-5 3-Speed	22.0 pts. (10.4L)
AOT 4-Speed	25.0 pts. (11.7L)
C-6 3-Speed 2WD	23.8 pts. (11.2L)
C-6 3-Speed 4WD	26.8 pts. (12.7L)
Rear Axle (Hypoid Gear Lube)	
Ford Standard & Traction-Lok	
8.8"	5.5 pts. (2.6L)
9.0"	6.5 pts. (3.1L)
Dana 60, 61-1 & 61-2	6.3 pts. (3.0L)
Dana 70	
Standard	6.5 pts. (3.1L)
Heavy Duty	7.4 pts. (3.5L)
Front Axle (Hypoid Gear Lube)	
Dana 44-IFS & 50-IFS	4.0 pts. (1.8L)
Dana 60 Monobeam	5.8 pts. (2.8L)
Transfer Case (Dexron II)	
Warner 1345	6.5 pts. (3.1L)
New Process 208	9.0 pts. (4.3L)
Fuel Tank	
F150 Models	
116.8" Wheel Base	
Standard	16.5 gals. (62.5L)
Auxiliary	19.0 gals. (72.0L)
All Other F150/350 Models	[1] 19.0 gals. (72.0L)
Bronco	32.0 gals. (121.0L)
E150 Van & Club Wagon	[1] 18.0 gals. (68.0L)
All Other "E" Models	
Standard	22.0 gals. (83.6L)
Auxiliary	18.0 gals. (68.0L)

[1] – Auxiliary tank is same capacity. F350 optional tank capacity is 20.0 gals. (75.0L).

1985 Ford Diesel Tune-Up

TUNE-UP

ENGINE IDENTIFICATION

Engine is identified by eighth character of Vehicle Identification Number (VIN). The VIN is stamped on a metal tab, attached to upper left side of instrument panel and is visible through windshield.

The VIN can also be found on Safety Standard Certification Label attached to left door lock edge.

VIN ENGINE CODES

Application	VIN Code
2.3L (140") 4-Cyl. Turbo Diesel	E
6.9L (420") V8 Diesel	1

TUNE-UP NOTES

NOTE: When performing tune-up procedures described in this article, the following notes and precautions must be followed:

Due to late changes and corrections, always refer to engine compartment Emission Control Tune-Up Decal before attempting tune-up procedures. In the event manual specifications and decal specifications are different, always use decal specifications.

Ensure all diesel injection lines and fittings are thoroughly cleaned before removing. Cap all lines, nozzles and fittings when removed. Dirt in system may damage injection pump or engine.

Some models are equipped with water separator units. Check periodically for presence of water and drain off if needed or when "WATER-IN-FUEL" indicator light glows (if equipped).

ENGINE COMPRESSION

1) Prior to checking compression, be sure batteries are fully charged. Do not add oil to cylinders. Adding oil may cause hydrostatic lock and extensive engine damage.

2) Start and warm engine to normal operating temperature. Turn ignition off. Remove air cleaner and/or intake opening cover. Disconnect injection pump solenoid leads.

3) Remove all glow plugs and insert compression gauge in No. 1 cylinder glow plug hole. With ignition off, crank engine through at least 6 compression strokes. Note number of strokes required to obtain highest reading.

4) Repeat check on each cylinder, cranking engine same number of compression strokes.

COMPRESSION SPECIFICATIONS

Application	Specification
Compression Ratio	
2.3L	21.0:1
6.9L	20.7:1
Compression Pressure	
2.3L	384-341
6.9L	[1]
Maximum Pressure Variation	
2.3L	43
6.9L	25%

[1] - Information not available.

VALVE ARRANGEMENT

2.3L
E-I-E-I-E-I-E-I (Front-to-rear).
6.9L
Right Bank - I-E-I-E-I-E-I-E (Front-to-rear).
Left Bank - E-I-E-I-E-I-E-I (Front-to-rear).

VALVE CLEARANCE

VALVE CLEARANCE SPECIFICATIONS (HOT)

Application	Intake In. (mm)	Exhaust In. (mm)
2.3L	.010 (.25)	.010 (.25)
6.9L (Hydraulic)	Zero Lash	Zero Lash

GLOW PLUGS

Each cylinder has a glow plug screwed into the cylinder head. Tip of the glow plug projects into the combustion chamber to preheat cylinder and to aid in cold engine starting.

On 2.3L engine, the glow plug system provides for quicker starting with a cold engine. The system consists of 4 glow plugs, a control module, 2 relays, a dropping resistor, a coolant temperature sensor (CTS) and wiring harness.

When the engine is cranked, the control module cycles on preglow relay No. 1 for 1-6 seconds. After the engine starts, alternator output signals the module to stop relay No. 1 and an afterglow function takes over.

If coolant temperature is below 86°F (30°C), afterglow relay No. 2 remains closed. This applies 6-6.7 volts to the glow plugs through the dropping resistor. When coolant temperature is above 86°F (30°C), the control module opens No. 2 relay, cutting off all current to glow plugs.

On 6.9L engines, full system voltage is supplied to glow plugs when ignition is turned on. Depending on coolant temperature, glow plug voltage is cycled between 12 and 4 volts or is maintained at a reduced voltage of 4-5 volts for a short period of time after engine start.

Glow plugs are 6-volt heaters, which are activated when ignition switch is turned on. Glow plugs are controlled by a control switch, based upon coolant temperature. Control switch allows glow plug operation only when coolant temperature is below 165°F (91°C).

GLOW PLUG TYPE

Application	Motorcraft Part No.	Torque Ft. Lbs. (N.m)
2.3L	[1]	12 (16)
6.9L	E3TZ-12A342-A	12 (16)

[1] - Information not available.

1985 Ford Diesel Tune-Up

TUNE-UP (Cont.)

Fig. 1: 2.3L Diesel Firing Order

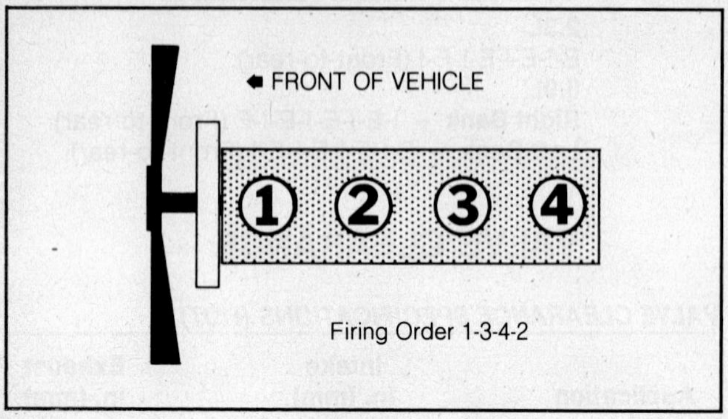

Fig. 2: 6.9L Diesel Firing Order

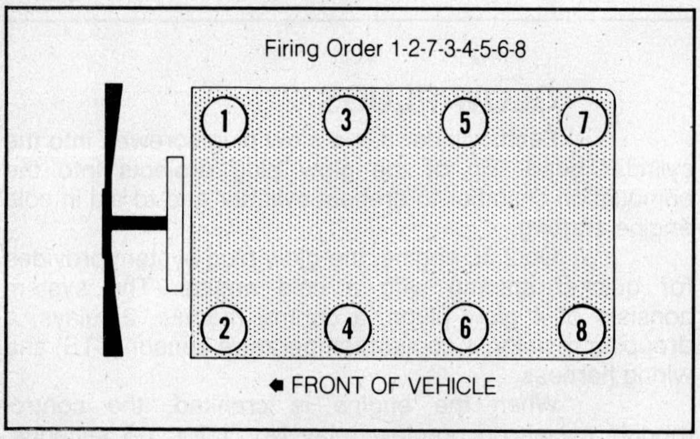

Fig. 3: 2.3L Engine and Injection Timing Marks

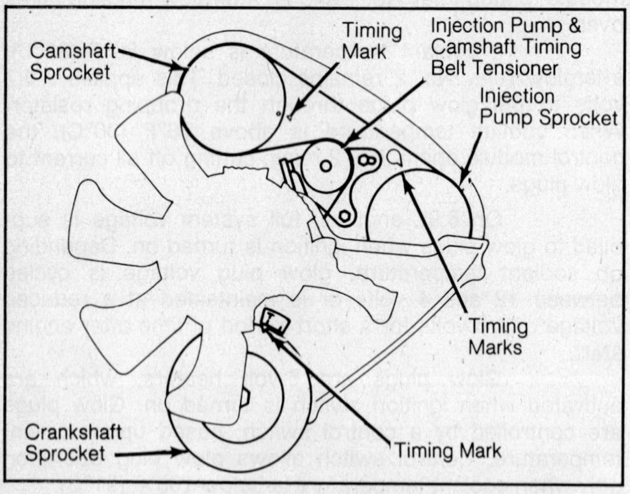

INJECTION TIMING

2.3L ENGINE

1) Remove upper timing belt cover. Turn crankshaft in normal direction of rotation to bring No. 1 piston to TDC on compression stroke. Verify piston position by checking timing marks. *See Fig. 3.*

2) If coolant temperature is above 122°F (50°C), go to step **3)**. If temperature is below 122°F (50°C), by-pass cold start mechanism by rotating fast idle lever and inserting a spacer or wrench at least .27" (7 mm) thick between cold start advance lever and cold start device. *See Fig. 4.*

Fig. 4: By-Passing Injection Pump Cold Start Device

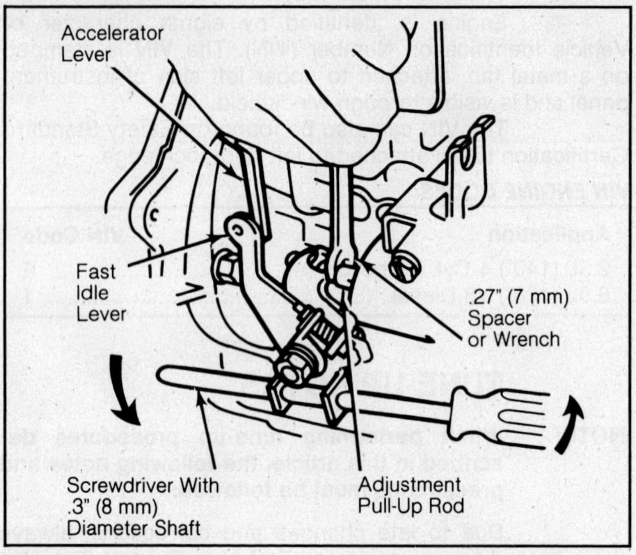

By-pass cold start device if coolant temperature is below 122°F (50°C).

3) Loosen injection pump-to-front cover and injection pump-to-mounting bracket nuts. Using back-up wrench, loosen fuel injection line nuts at pump. Remove plug bolt from timing port at center of pump hydraulic head.

4) Install Timing Adapter (014-00303) in timing port and mount dial indicator in adapter. *See Fig. 5.* Preload dial indicator to at least .10" (.25 mm). Rotate crankshaft about 30° counterclockwise and zero indicator dial.

Fig. 5: Timing Adapter and Dial Indicator Installed

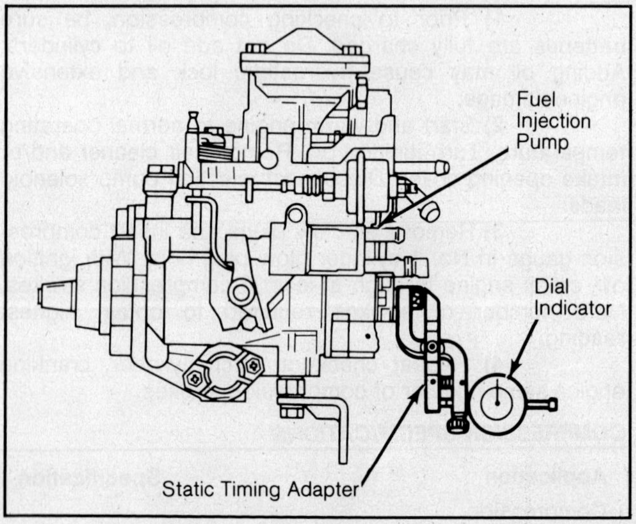

5) Rotate crankshaft clockwise to 5° ATDC. Dial indicator should read .0383-.0405" (.97-1.03 mm). Rotate injection pump body as needed to obtain correct reading. Rotate pump clockwise to decrease value, counterclockwise to increase value.

6) Tighten injection pump mounting nuts and repeat steps **4)** and **5)** to ensure timing is correct. Tighten fuel injection line nuts. Install timing port plug bolt with new copper gasket. Remove spacer and screwdriver (if used). Install timing belt cover, start engine and check for leaks.

1985 Ford Diesel Tune-Up

TUNE-UP (Cont.)

6.9L ENGINE

NOTE: Models with C-6 transmissions and late production models with manual transmissions are equipped with a pump-mounted fast idle bracket and solenoid. Bracket and solenoid must be removed on these models to provide access for pump wrench and rotating tool during timing procedure.

Static Timing (With Engine Stopped)

1) Using injector pump wrench (T83T 9000 B), loosen (but keep snug) 3 nuts attaching fuel injection pump to pump mounting adapter.

2) Install injection pump rotating tool (T83T 9000 C) on front of pump. Rotate pump to align injection pump mounting flange timing mark with pump mounting adapter timing mark. *See Fig. 6.*

Fig. 6: 6.9L Static Timing Mark Alignment

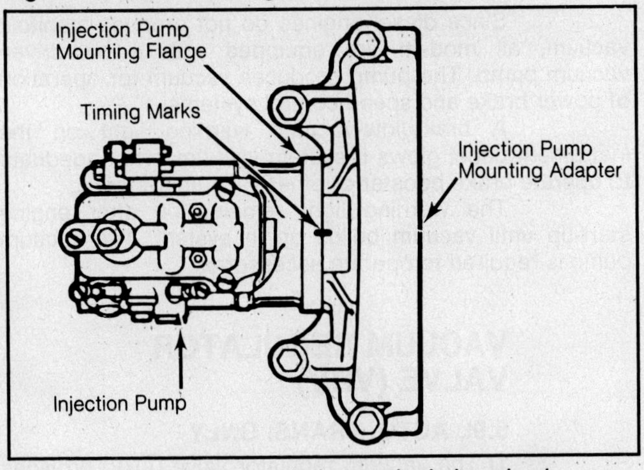

Keep mounting nuts snug during static timing check.

3) Remove tools and tighten mounting nuts to specifications. Visually recheck timing to ensure that marks are still aligned after tightening nuts.

Dynamic Timing (With Engine Running)

1) Start and warm engine to normal operating temperature. Coolant temperature MUST be above 192°F (89°C) to perform dynamic timing procedure. Stop engine and install magnetic pick-up probe of dynamic timing meter (78 0100) into timing pointer probe hole. *See Fig. 7.*

Fig. 7: 6.9L Magnetic Pick-Up Probe Installation

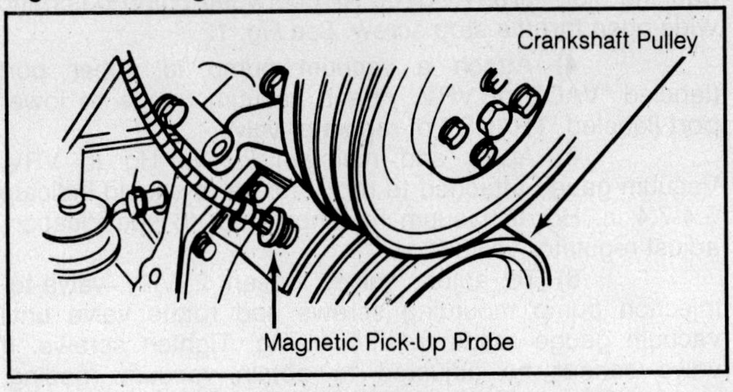

2) Remove No. 1 cylinder glow plug. Install luminosity probe in place of glow plug, and tighten to 12 ft. lbs. (16 N.m). *See Fig. 8.* Connect photocell over luminosity probe and connect to dynamic timing meter. Connect dynamic timing meter to battery and set to 20° offset.

Fig. 8: 6.9L Luminosity Probe Installation

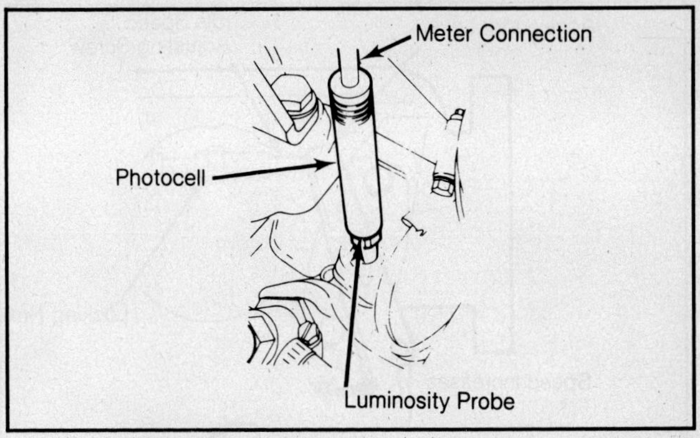

3) Raise vehicle and support rear axle. Place transmission in Neutral and start engine. Using throttle control tool (14-0302), set engine speed at 1400 RPM with no accessory load. Observe injection timing on meter. Timing should be 2-4° ATDC. Add 1° for altitudes over 3000 feet.

4) If timing is not within specifications, stop engine and loosen pump retaining nuts (keep nuts snug).

5) As viewed from front of engine, rotate top of pump to right to retard timing or to left to advance timing with pump rotating tool. Moving timing mark .030" (.75 mm) is equal to 2° of timing. Retighten nuts.

CAUTION: Engine should not be restarted with pump retaining nuts loose. Torquing action could cause pump to break off from mounting flange.

6) Recheck timing using meter. If still not to specifications, repeat steps **4)** and **5)**. When timing is correct, tighten retaining nuts to specification. Remove timing meter and other test equipment. Reinstall glow plug using anti-seize compound on threads.

LINKAGE ADJUSTMENT

With engine off, check that throttle lever contacts injection pump stop at full accelerator depression. Adjust stop screw on throttle lever if necessary.

HOT (SLOW) IDLE RPM

2.3L ENGINE

1) With transmission in Neutral and all lights and accessories off, bring engine to normal operating temperature. Connect tachometer to engine. Ensure idle speed adjusting screw is against its stop.

2) Run engine at 2000-3000 RPM for about 5 seconds, then let it idle for 2 minutes. Check idle speed. Adjust idle speed to specification as indicated on Emission Tune-Up Decal in engine compartment. Use idle speed adjustment screw on side of pump for adjustment.

TUNE-UP (Cont.)

Fig. 9: 2.3L Idle Speed Adjusting Screw

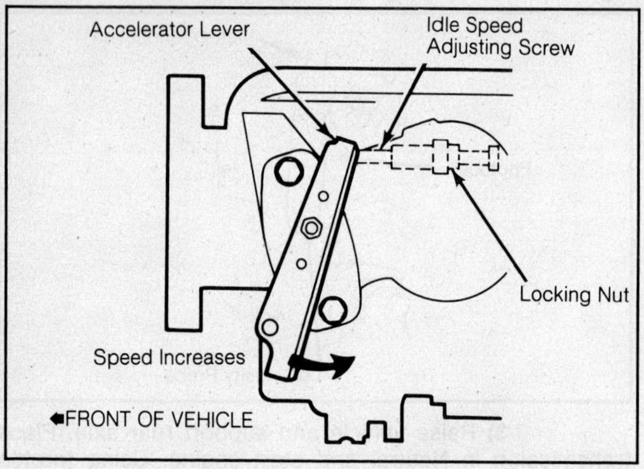

6.9L ENGINE

1) Apply reflective tape to rear flange rim of the crankshaft pulley. Start and run engine to normal operating temperature. Connect a photoelectric tachometer (99 0001) to engine and check idle speed. Measure idle speed with transmission in Neutral (man. trans.) or "D" (auto. trans.).

2) Turn idle speed adjusting screw to adjust idle speed. *See Fig. 10.* Shift transmission out of gear, and momentarily accelerate engine. Shift back into specified gear and recheck idle speed. Readjust if necessary.

Fig. 10: 6.9L Idle Adjusting Locations

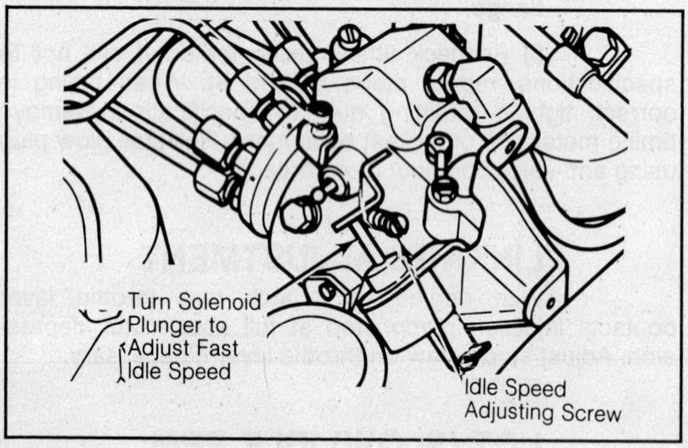

SLOW IDLE SPEED (RPM)

Application	RPM
6.9L	
Early Models	725-775
Late Models	650-700

COLD (FAST) IDLE SPEED

NOTE: **Fast idle speed on 2.3L engine is not adjustable.**

6.9L ENGINE

1) Apply reflective tape to rear flange rim of crankshaft pulley. Attach photoelectric tachometer to engine. Disconnect wiring harness from fast idle solenoid. Apply battery voltage to solenoid to activate it. Momentarily accelerate engine to set solenoid plunger.

2) Check fast idle speed. Adjust fast idle speed by turning solenoid plunger in or out. *See Fig. 10.* Momentarily accelerate engine and recheck fast idle speed. Readjust if necessary.

3) Stop engine. Remove battery voltage from solenoid and reconnect wiring harness to solenoid. Remove tachometer.

FAST IDLE SPEED (RPM)

Application	RPM
6.9L	850-900

VACUUM PUMP

ALL MODELS

Since diesel engines do not produce manifold vacuum, all models are equipped with a belt-driven vacuum pump. The pump produces vacuum for operation of power brake and speed control systems.

A brake/low-vacuum warning light on the instrument panel glows if system vacuum is not adequate to operate brake booster or other vacuum systems.

The warning light remains on after engine start-up until vacuum builds up in system. The vacuum pump is required to operate accessories.

VACUUM REGULATOR VALVE (VRV)

6.9L AUTO. TRANS. ONLY

1) The vacuum regulator valve (VRV) provides vacuum signals to control transmission shift points. Vacuum setting of valve should be checked periodically, using the following procedure. Engine must not be running during this procedure.

2) Disconnect 2-port vacuum connector from VRV, located on left side of pump. *See Fig. 11.* Remove throttle cable from pump throttle lever, located on right side of pump.

3) Remove and reposition throttle return spring. Place one end of spring over throttle lever ball stud and other end over throttle cable support bracket. Insert gauging block (T83T 7B200 AH) between pump boss and wide open throttle stop screw. *See Fig. 12.*

4) Attach a vacuum pump to upper port (labeled "VAC") of VRV. Attach vacuum gauge to lower port (labeled "TRANS") of regulator valve.

5) Apply and maintain 20 in. Hg to VRV. Vacuum gauge attached to regulator valve should indicate 6.4-7.4 in. Hg. If vacuum reading is not to specification, adjust regulator valve.

6) To adjust valve, loosen 2 VRV valve-to-injection pump mounting screws and rotate valve until vacuum gauge reads 6.4-7.4 in. Hg. Tighten screws. If valve cannot be adjusted to obtain vacuum reading, replace regulator valve.

7) Release vacuum and remove gauging block. Reconnect throttle return spring in original position and make sure fuel injection pump lever returns and stays at idle position.

TUNE-UP (Cont.)

Fig. 11: Location of Vacuum Regulator Valve on 6.9L Fuel Injection Pump

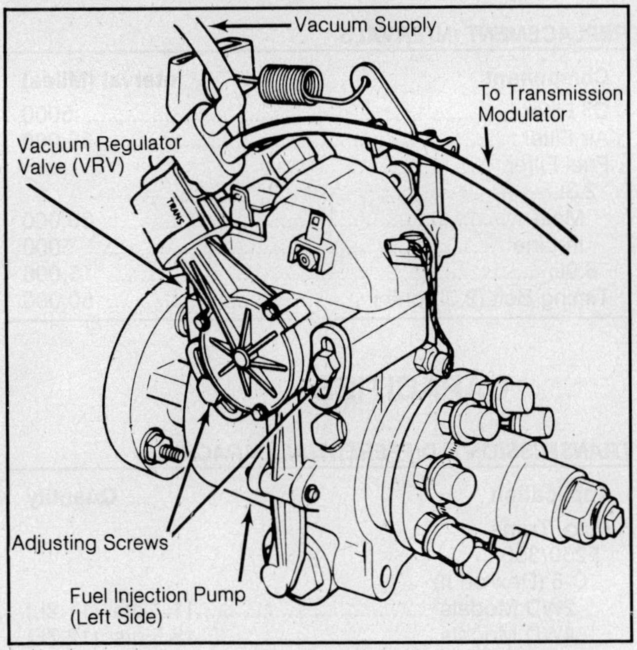

Fig. 12: Repositioning Throttle Return Spring on 6.9L

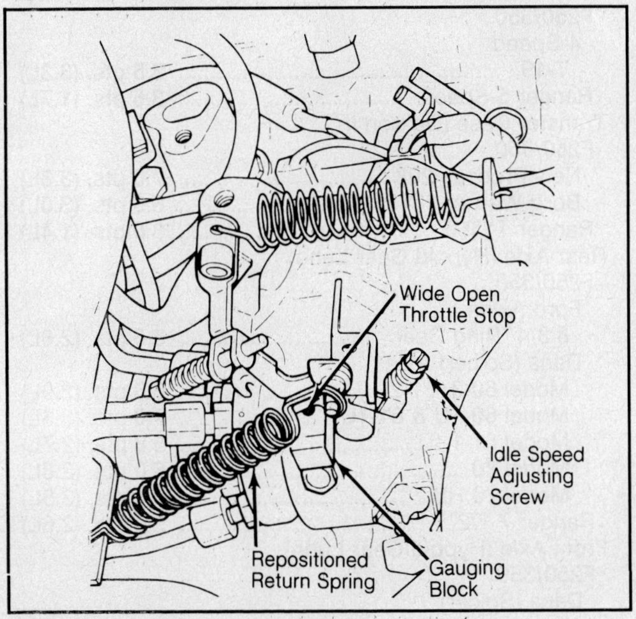

Insert gauging block between pump boss and wide open throttle stop screw.

8) Apply and maintain 20 in. Hg to VRV again. Vacuum gauge MUST indicate 13 in. Hg. If vacuum reading is less than 13 in. Hg, replace VRV and adjust new valve using above procedure.

9) Remove vacuum pump and gauge. Reconnect all disconnected components in their original positions.

TRANSFER PUMP PRESSURE

2.3L ENGINE

1) Remove banjo fitting from injection pump fuel return line. Install adapter connector (10356). Install connect pressure tester (19-0002) onto adapter connector.

2) Place transmission in Neutral and run engine at 800 RPM. Pressure should be 27-40 psi (1.9-2.8 kg/cm²). Operate engine at 4400 RPM with no accessory load. Pressure should be 91-104 psi (6.4-7.3 kg/cm²). If not to specification, replace fuel injection pump.

6.9L ENGINE

1) Remove screw from transfer pump pressure port cover, and install transfer pump pressure connector (T83T-9000-A). Connector should go through cover and into pressure port. Install adapter (5650) onto connector and connect pressure tester (19-0002).

2) Connect photoelectric tachometer to engine. Place transmission in Neutral and run engine at 3300 RPM with no accessory load. Pressure should be 95-110 psi (6.8-7.7 kg/cm²). If not to specification, replace fuel injection pump.

WATER SEPARATOR

Water should be drained from the water separator whenever the warning lamp comes on or every 5000 miles. More frequent drain intervals may be required depending on fuel quality and vehicle useage.

DRAINING

1) Shut engine off. Place an empty container under the water separator. On E-Series, the water separator is located inside the driver's side frame rail in line with the front wheel. On F-Series and Ranger, the separator is located in the engine compartment.

2) Raise the plastic cover on the drain handle (if equipped). Turn ignition swith to the "ON" position (Ranger only). Grasp the handle or ring and pull out until liquid flows.

3) Release the drain handle or ring and ensure the liquid has stopped flowing. Start engine and ensure the "WATER-IN-FUEL" indicator lamp has gone out.

GENERAL SERVICING

FUEL INJECTION

DIESEL FUEL INJECTORS

Application	Opening Pressure
2.3L	1707-1850 psi (120-130 kg/cm²)
6.9L	1800-1950 psi (126-136 kg/cm²)

ADJUSTMENTS

BELT ADJUSTMENT

Using a strand tension gauge, measure belt tension midway between pulleys. Used belts are any operated for more than 10 minutes.

GENERAL SERVICING (Cont.)

BELT ADJUSTMENT
Tension in Lbs. (Kg) Using Strand Tension Gauge

Application	New Belt	Used Belt
All Models		
Thermactor	90-130 (41-59)	80-100 (36-45)
All Others	120-160 (54-73)	110-130 (50-59)

ELECTRICAL SYSTEM

BATTERY

BATTERY SPECIFICATIONS

Application	Capacity (Amp Hours)	Discharge Rate (Amps)
2.3L	63	[1] 260
6.9L	83	[2] 350

[1] – 520 cold cranking amps total.
[2] – 700 cold cranking amps total.

STARTER

The 2.3L engine uses a Mitsubishi starter. The 6.9L engine uses a Delco-Remy starter.

STARTER SPECIFICATIONS

Application	Volts	Amps	Test RPM
2.3L	12	90-130	150-220
6.9L	12	[1] 120-200	170-230

[1] – Under no load; 430-530 under normal load.

GLOW PLUGS

GLOW PLUG RESISTANCE @ 68°F (20°C)

Application	Ohms Resistance
2.3L	.23 or less
6.9L	2.0 or less

ALTERNATORS

All models use Motorcraft external regulator alternators.

ALTERNATOR SPECIFICATIONS

I.D. Tag Color	Field Current Draw @ 12 Volts	Rated Amp Output
Rear Terminal		
Orange	2.8	40
Green	4.0	60
Side Terminal		
Black	4.25	70
Red	4.25	100

ALTERNATOR REGULATOR

All models use Motorcraft Solid State Electronic Regulator, calibrated and preset by manufacturer. No adjustment is required or possible.

SERVICE INTERVALS

REPLACEMENT INTERVALS

Component	Interval (Miles)
Oil Filter	5000
Air Filter	30,000
Fuel Filter	
2.3L	
Main	30,000
In-Line	5000
6.9L	15,000
Timing Belt (2.3L only)	50,000

CAPACITIES

TRANSMISSION & DIFFERENTIAL CAPACITIES

Application	Quantity
Auto. Trans.	
F250/350	
C-6 (Dexron II)	
2WD Models	11.7 qts. (11.2L)
4WD Models	13.5 qts. (12.7L)
Ranger AOD (Dexron II)	9.0 qts. (7.4L)
Man. Trans.	
F250/350	
4-Speed	
T-19	3.5 qts. (3.3L)
Ranger 5-Speed	3.6 pts. (1.7L)
Transfer Case (Dexron II)	
F250/350	
New Process 208	7.0 pts. (3.3L)
Borg-Warner 1345	6.5 pts. (3.0L)
Ranger T1350	3.0 pts. (1.4L)
Rear Axle (Hypoid Gear Lube)	
F250/350	
Ford Axles	
8 3/4" Ring Gear	5.5 pts. (2.6L)
Dana (Spicer) Axles	
Model 60-3, 61-2	6.3 pts. (2.9L)
Model 60-1U & 61-1U	7.0 pts. (3.3L)
Model 61-1	5.8 pts. (2.7L)
Model 70	6.0 pts. (2.8L)
Model 70 HD	7.4 pts. (3.5L)
Ranger 7 1/2"	5.5 pts. (2.6L)
Front Axle (Hypoid Gear Lube)	
F250/350	
Dana (Spicer)	
Model 44 IFS HD	3.9 pts. (1.8L)
Model 50 IFS	4.1 pts. (2.0L)
Ranger Dana 28	1.0 pts. (.45L)

COOLING SYSTEM CAPACITIES

Application	Quantity
2.3L	
Without A/C	12.0 qts. (11.4L)
With A/C	13.0 qts. (12.3L)
6.9L	31.0 qts. (29.0L)

1985 Ford Diesel Tune-Up

GENERAL SERVICING (Cont.)

SYSTEM REFRIGERANT CAPACITY

Application	Ounces
Bronco & F150-350	48
E150-350	
Standard	52
With Auxiliary	64
Ranger	40

ENGINE OIL & FUEL CAPACITIES

Application	Quantity
Crankcase (Including Filter)	
2.3L	7.0 qts. (6.6L)
6.9L	10.0 qts. (9.3L)
Fuel Tank	
2.3L	
Short Wheel Base	15.0 gals. (57.0L)
Long Wheel Base	17.0 gals. (64.0L)
Auxiliary	13.0 gals. (49.0L)
6.9L	
"E" Series Vans	
Rear Tank	22.0 gals. (84.0L)
Auxiliary Tank	18.0 gals. (68.0L)
F250 2WD Super Cab Short Wheelbase	
Front Tank	17.0 gals. (64.0L)
Auxiliary Tank	19.0 gals. (72.0L)
All Other Models	
Main Tank	19.0 gals. (72.0L)
Auxiliary Tank	19.0 gals. (72.0L)

TUNE-UP

ENGINE IDENTIFICATION

The 8th character of the Vehicle Identification Number (VIN) identifies the engine. The VIN number is stamped on a plate attached to the left top side of dash.

VIN ENGINE CODES

Application	VIN Code
1.9L (119") 2-Bbl.	A
2.5L (151") TBI	E

TUNE-UP NOTES

NOTE: **When performing tune-up procedures described in this article, these notes and precautions must be followed.**

Due to changes and corrections, always refer to Engine Tune-Up Decal in engine compartment before attempting tune-up. If manual and decal specifications differ, use decal specifications.

When performing tune-up on vehicles equipped with a catalytic converter, do not allow or create an engine misfire in one or more cylinders for an extended period of time. Damage to converter from overheating may occur due to loading with unburned fuel.

ENGINE COMPRESSION

When making compression checks, disconnect ignition switch connector (Pink wire) from High Energy Ignition (HEI) system. With air cleaner removed, throttle and choke wide open, crank engine through at least 4 compression strokes.

COMPRESSION SPECIFICATIONS

1.9L	
Compression Ratio	
1.9L	8.4:1
2.5L	9.0:1
Compression Pressure	
1.9L	170 psi (12 kg/cm²)
2.5L	140 psi (10 kg/cm²)
Minimum Pressure	
1.9L & 2.5L	100 psi (7 kg/cm²)
Maximum Variation	
1.9L	10 psi (0.7 kg/cm²)
2.5L	30 psi (2 kg/cm²)

VALVE ARRANGEMENT

1.9L

Left Side - All intake.
Right Side - All exhaust.

2.5L

I-E-I-E-E-I-E-I (Front-to-rear).

VALVE CLEARANCE

Check rocker arm bracket nuts for looseness and retighten as necessary before adjusting valves. Adjust valves with engine cold.

VALVE ADJUSTMENT

Application	Clearance
1.9L	
Intake	.006" (.15 mm)
Exhaust	.010" (.25 mm)
2.5L	
All (Hydraulic Lifters)	Zero lash

SPARK PLUGS

SPARK PLUG TYPE

Application	AC Number
1.9L	R42CXLS
2.5L	R43TSX

SPARK PLUG SPECIFICATIONS

Application	Gap In. (mm)	Torque Ft. Lbs. (N.m)
1.9L	.039-.043 (1.0-1.1)	7-19 (9-26)
2.5L	.060 (1.5)	15 (20)

HIGH TENSION WIRE RESISTANCE

Carefully remove ends of wire from spark plug and distributor cap. Using an ohmmeter, check resistance while gently twisting wire. If resistance is not within specifications or fluctuates from infinity to any value, replace cable.

IGNITION COIL WIRE

Remove ignition coil wire from coil and distributor cap. Check terminals for corrosion and clean if necessary. Check coil wire resistance. Replace wire if resistance is excessive.

HIGH TENSION WIRE RESISTANCE

Application	Ohms per Foot
All Models	31,500-73,500

DISTRIBUTOR

All 1.9L engines are equipped with a Nippondenso electronic ignition distributor. Some 2.5L engines use Delco-Remy High Energy Ignition (HEI) distributor and some use Delco-Remy HEI with Electronic Spark Timing (EST). No adjustments other than timing are necessary.

IGNITION TIMING

1) Install timing light with adapter between No. 1 spark plug and No. 1 spark plug wire, or use inductive type pick-up. Do not puncture wire.

2) Run engine until it reaches normal operating temperature. Disconnect and plug distributor advance, EGR and canister purge vacuum hoses. Place transmission in Neutral (man. trans.) or Drive (auto. trans.). Check ignition timing and adjust if necessary. Reconnect all hoses.

TUNE-UP (Cont.)

Fig. 1: 1.9L 4-Cylinder Firing Order

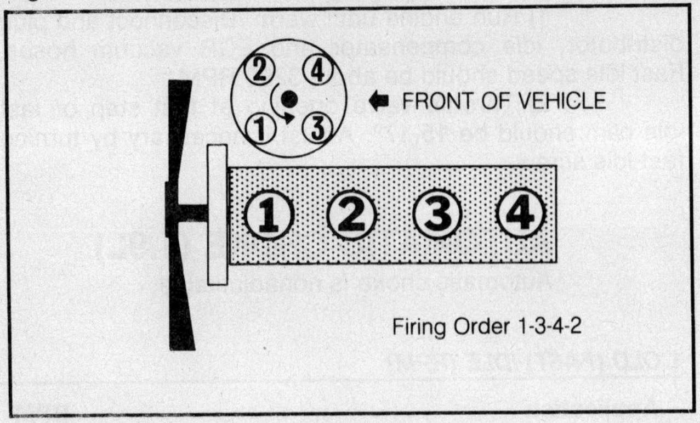

Fig. 2: 2.5L 4-Cylinder Firing Order

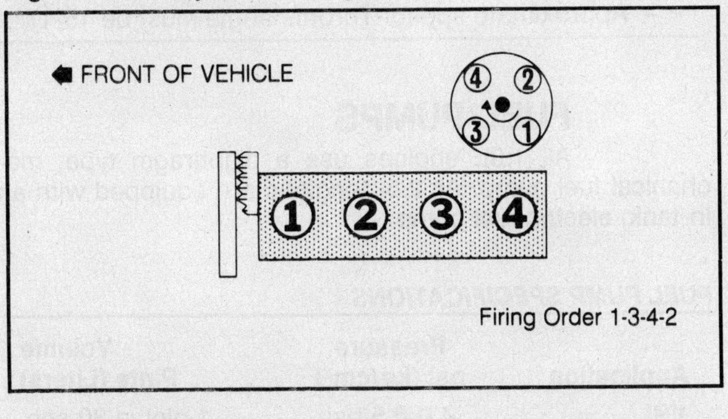

IGNITION TIMING SPECIFICATIONS (Degrees BTDC@RPM)

Application	Man. Trans.	Auto. Trans.
1.9L	[1] 6 @ 900	6 @ 900
2.5L	[2]	[2]

1 – Federal and high alt. models: 6° @ 800 RPM.
2 – Use engine tune-up decal specifications.

HOT (SLOW) IDLE RPM

1.9L

1) Warm engine to normal operating temperature and place transmission in Neutral. California models must be in closed loop operation before checking or adjusting. Disconnect and plug distributor vacuum hose, canister purge line and EGR vacuum line.

2) Pinch off idle compensator vacuum hose by bending rubber hose. Adjust throttle adjusting screw to obtain specified idle RPM. If vehicle is equipped with A/C, turn A/C on maximum cold and high blower.

3) Open throttle momentarily to assure solenoid is fully extended, then let it close. Adjust screw on throttle lever to obtain solenoid RPM. Reconnect wires and hoses.

IDLE SPEED (RPM)

Application	Idle RPM	Solenoid RPM
1.9L	[1] 900	[2] 900

1 – Fed. and high alt. man. trans. models: 800 RPM.
2 – Calif. auto. trans. models: 1900 RPM in Neutral.

2.5L

1) Remove air cleaner and gasket. Plug TBI unit vacuum port for THERMAC (Thermostatic Air Cleaner). Remove T.V. cable from throttle control bracket. Connect tachometer to engine.

2) Disconnect Idle Air Control (IAC) connector. Start engine and warm to normal operating temperature with transmission in Park (auto. trans.) or Neutral (man. trans.).

3) Install Air Passage Plug (J-33047) into throttle body idle air passage, ensure plug seats air tight. *See Fig. 3.*

Fig. 3: Installing Throttle Body Air Passage Plug

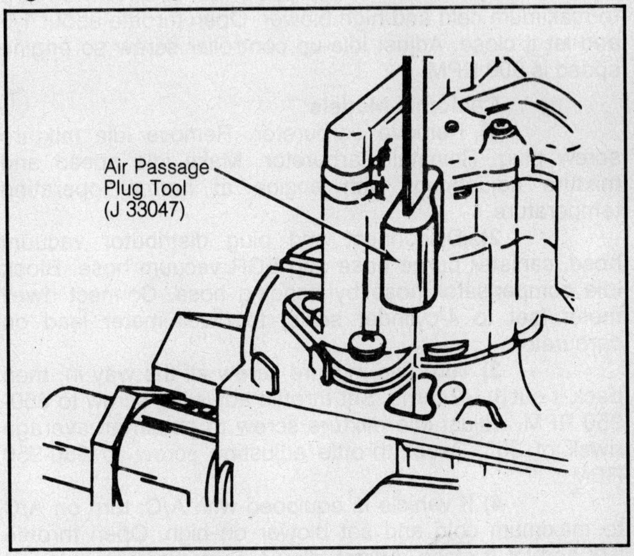

4) If plug covers throttle stop screw hole, remove plug by drilling 5/32" hole through casting into plug. Using 1/16" punch, remove plug.

5) Using Torx Bit No. 20, turn throttle stop screw to adjust slow idle to specifications. Turn off engine and remove plug tool from throttle body air passage.

6) Install T.V. cable into throttle control bracket. Install IAC connector. Seal throttle stop screw with silicone sealant. Install air cleaner and gasket.

IDLE SPEED (RPM)

Application	Man. Trans.	Auto. Trans.
2.5L	475-525	750-800

IDLE MIXTURE

NOTE: **On 2.5L, idle mixture is controlled by Electronic Control Module (ECM) and is nonadjustable. On 1.9L, do not adjust mixture unless carburetor has been disassembled or vehicle fails emissions testing.**

MIXTURE SCREW PLUG REMOVAL (1.9L)

Remove carburetor from vehicle. Drill hole into idle mixture screw plug. Insert screw into plug and pull plug out.

TUNE-UP (Cont.)

MIXTURE ADJUSTMENT (1.9L)

Federal Models

1) Remove carburetor. Remove idle mixture screw plug. Reinstall carburetor. Block drive wheels and place transmission in Neutral.

2) Disconnect and plug distributor vacuum hose, idle compensator and EGR vacuum hoses. With engine at normal operating temperature, turn idle mixture screw all the way in, then back it out 1 1/2 turns. Adjust throttle screw to 850 RPM.

3) Adjust idle mixture screw to obtain maximum speed. Reset throttle screw to 850 RPM. Turn idle mixture screw clockwise to obtain 800 RPM.

4) If vehicle is equipped with A/C, turn on A/C to maximum cold and high blower. Open throttle about 1/3 and let it close. Adjust idle-up controller screw so engine speed is 900 RPM.

California Models

1) Remove carburetor. Remove idle mixture screw plug. Reinstall carburetor. Make idle speed and mixture adjustment with engine at normal operating temperature.

2) Disconnect and plug distributor vacuum hose, canister purge hose and EGR vacuum hose. Block idle compensator hose by bending hose. Connect dwell meter (set to 4-cylinder scale) to dwell meter lead on carburetor.

3) Turn idle mixture screw all the way in, then back it out 1 1/2 turns. Set throttle adjusting screw to 850-950 RPM. Adjust idle mixture screw to obtain an average dwell of 36°. Reset throttle adjusting screw to 850-950 RPM.

4) If vehicle is equipped with A/C, turn on A/C to maximum cold and set blower on high. Open throttle 1/3 and let it close. Adjust idle-up controller screw to set idle at 900 RPM.

COLD (FAST) IDLE RPM

NOTE: **On 2.5L engines, fast idle is controlled by Electronic Control Module (ECM) and is nonadjustable.**

1.9L

1) Run engine until warm. Disconnect and plug distributor, idle compensator and EGR vacuum hoses. Fast idle speed should be about 3200 RPM.

2) Throttle valve opening at first step of fast idle cam should be 15-17°. Adjust if necessary by turning fast idle screw.

AUTOMATIC CHOKE (1.9L)

Automatic choke is nonadjustable.

COLD (FAST) IDLE (RPM)

Application	RPM
1.9L	[1] 3200

[1] – Approximate speed. Throttle angle must be 15-17°.

FUEL PUMPS

All 1.9L engines use a diaphragm type, mechanical fuel pump. All 2.5L engines are equipped with an in-tank, electric fuel pump.

FUEL PUMP SPECIFICATIONS

Application	Pressure psi (kg/cm^2)	Volume Pints (Liters)
1.9L	4.0-6.5 psi (.28-.46 kg/cm^2)	1 pint in 30 sec. (.5 in 30 sec.)
2.5L	9.0-13.0 psi (.63-.91 kg/cm^2)	1 pint in 30 sec. (.5 in 30 sec.)

GENERAL SERVICING

IGNITION

DISTRIBUTOR

All 1.9L engines are equipped with a Nippondenso solid state distributor. All 2.5L engines are equipped with a Delco-Remy HEI solid state distributor. No adjustments are necessary.

DISTRIBUTOR PICK-UP COIL RESISTANCE

Application	Ohms
All Models	500-1500

IGNITION COIL

IGNITION COIL RESISTANCE – OHMS @ 75°F (24°C)

Application	Primary	Secondary
All Models	0.9-1.4	7300-11,100

FUEL SYSTEMS

All 1.9L engines use Hitachi model DCH340 carburetor. All 2.5L engines use General Motors Model 300 Throttle Body Injection (TBI).

ELECTRICAL SYSTEM

BATTERY

BATTERY SPECIFICATIONS

Application	Cold Crank Amps @ 0°F (18°C)	Reserve Capacity Minutes
Standard	315	75
Optional	405	75

GENERAL SERVICING (Cont.)

STARTER

All 1.9L and 2.5L engines use a Delco-Remy 5MT solenoid-actuated starter with overrunning clutch.

STARTER SPECIFICATIONS

Application	Volts	Amps	Test RPM
All Models	10	50-75	6000-11,900

ALTERNATOR

All models use a Delco-Remy alternator with integral voltage regulator.

ALTERNATOR SPECIFICATIONS

Application	Field Current Draw @ 12 Volts [1]	Rated Amp Output
Standard	4.0-5.0 Amps	37
Optional	4.0-5.0 Amps	66
Optional	4.0-5.0 Amps	78

[1] – At 80°F (27°C).

ALTERNATOR REGULATOR

All models are equipped with Delco-Remy nonadjustable voltage regulator, integral with alternator.

REGULATOR OPERATING VOLTAGE

Application	Voltage
All Models	13.5-16.0

ADJUSTMENTS

BELT ADJUSTMENT

Using a tension gauge, measure belt tension midway between pulleys. If tension is not as specified in table, adjust tension or replace belt.

BELT ADJUSTMENT
Tension in Lbs. (Kg) Using Tension Gauge

Application	New Belt	Used Belt
1.9L		
A/C	157 (71)	90 (41)
Alternator	135 (61)	67 (30)
Power Steering	135 (61)	67 (30)
Vacuum Pump	135 (61)	67 (30)
2.5L		
A/C	169 (77)	90 (41)
Alternator		
Without A/C	146 (66)	67 (30)
With A/C	169 (77)	90 (41)
Power Steering	146 (66)	67 (30)
Vacuum Pump	146 (66)	67 (30)

SERVICE INTERVALS

REPLACEMENT INTERVALS

Component	Interval (Miles)
Air Filter	30,000
Fuel Filter	15,000
Oil Filter	
Normal Service	7500
Severe Service	3000
PCV Valve & Filter	30,000
Spark Plugs	30,000

CAPACITIES

FLUID CAPACITIES

Application	Quantity
Cooling System	
1.9L	9.5 qts. (9.0L)
2.5L	
Astro/Safari	[1] 10.0 qts. (9.5L)
All Others	12.0 qts. (11.5L)
Crankcase	
1.9L	4.0 qts. (3.8L)
2.5L	3.0 qts. (2.8L)
Automatic Transmission (Dexron II)	
Overhaul	
3-Speed	19.0 pts. (8.9L)
4-Speed	23.0 pts. (10.9L)
Refill	
3-Speed	7.0 pts. (3.3L)
4-Speed	10.0 pts. (4.7L)
Manual Transmission (Dexron II)	[2]
Front Axle	2.5 pts. (1.2L)
Transfer Case (Dexron II)	4.6 pts. (2.2L)
Fuel Tank	
Standard	
Astro/Safari	17.0 gals. (64L)
Blazer/Jimmy	13.5 gals. (51L)
All Others	13.0 gals. (49L)
Optional (1.9L)	20.0 gals. (76L)
Optional (2.5L)	27.0 gals. (102L)

[1] – Add 3 qts. (2.7L) with rear heater.
[2] – Add fluid to bottom of filler plug hole.

SYSTEM REFRIGERANT CAPACITIES

Application	Ounces
Astro/Safari	
C-60 System	32
C-69 System	48
Pickup Models	40

TUNE-UP

ENGINE IDENTIFICATION

Engines can be identified by the eighth character of the Vehicle Identification Number (VIN). The VIN number is stamped on a plate located at the base of the steering column on "P" (Van conversion) models, and on a plate at the upper left corner of the dash on all other models.

VIN ENGINE CODE

Application	VIN Code
4.8L (292") 1-Bbl.	T

TUNE-UP NOTES

NOTE: **When performing tune-up procedures described in this article, the following notes and precautions must be observed:**

Due to changes and corrections, always refer to Engine Tune-Up Decal in engine compartment before attempting tune-up. In the event of a conflict between specifications given in this manual and decal specifications, follow decal specifications.

When performing tune-up on vehicles equipped with a catalytic converter, do not allow or create a condition of engine misfire in one or more cylinders for an extended period of time. Damage to converter from overheating may occur due to loading with unburned fuel.

For tune-up purposes, "Light Duty" refers to vehicles up to 8500 lbs. GVW. "Heavy Duty" refers to vehicles exceeding 8500 lbs. GVW.

ENGINE COMPRESSION

When making compression checks, disconnect ignition switch Pink wire from High Energy Ignition (HEI) system. With air cleaner removed and throttle and choke wide open, crank engine through at least 4 compression strokes.

COMPRESSION SPECIFICATIONS

Compression Ratio	8.0:1
Compression Pressure	130 psi (9.1 kg/cm²)
Maximum Pressure Variation	30 psi (2.1 kg/cm²)

VALVE ARRANGEMENT

E-I-I-E-E-I-I-E-E-I-I-E (Front-to-rear).

VALVE CLEARANCE

All engines have hydraulic lifters which should be adjusted to 1 turn down from zero lash.

SPARK PLUGS

SPARK PLUG TYPE

Application	AC No.
All Models	R44T

SPARK PLUG SPECIFICATIONS

Application	Gap In. (mm)	Torque Ft. Lbs. (N.m)
All Models	.035 (.90)	17-27 (23-37)

HIGH TENSION WIRE RESISTANCE

Carefully remove ends of wire from spark plug and distributor. Using an ohmmeter, check resistance while gently twisting wire. If resistance is incorrect, or fluctuates from infinity to any value, replace cable.

HIGH TENSION WIRE RESISTANCE (OHMS)

Wire Length	Maximum
Under 24"	30,000
Over 24"	50,000

DISTRIBUTOR

All models are equipped with High Energy Ignition (HEI) systems and no adjustments are required.

Fig. 1: Firing Order and Timing Marks

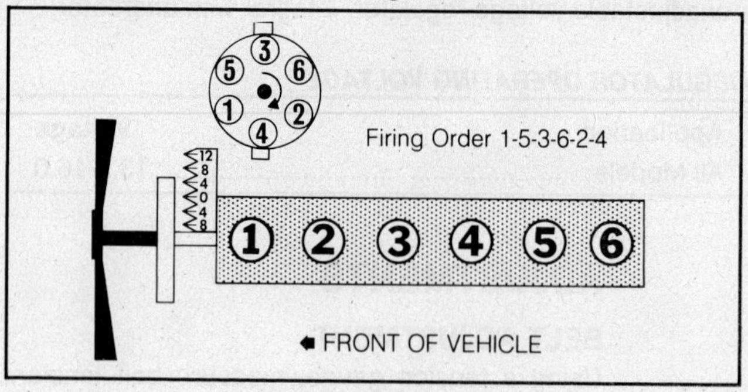

Magnetic probe located at 10° ATDC.

IGNITION TIMING

NOTE: **Engines are equipped with a receptacle for magnetic probe timing equipment, located 10° ATDC. Do not use this location for timing with a conventional light.**

1) Install timing light with an adapter between No. 1 spark plug and No. 1 spark plug wire, or use an inductive type pickup. Do not puncture wire.

2) With engine at normal operating temperature, choke fully open, air cleaner installed and A/C off (if equipped). Disconnect and plug vacuum hose at distributor. Set ignition timing at specified engine speed.

IGNITION TIMING SPECIFICATIONS (Degrees BTDC@RPM)

Application	Man. Trans.	Auto. Trans.
4.8L	8@700	8@700

1985 General Motors 6 Tune-Up

TUNE-UP (Cont.)

HOT (SLOW) IDLE RPM

1) With engine at normal operating temperature, choke fully open, air cleaner installed, A/C off (if equipped) and transmission in "D" (auto. trans.) or Neutral (man. trans.). Disconnect and plug canister purge hose, and disconnect canister signal hose. Disconnect solenoid wire and set base idle speed with hex head screw in rear of solenoid.

2) Reconnect solenoid wire. Set curb idle speed by turning solenoid assembly in or out. Ensure solenoid is energized and fully extended. Reconnect all hoses.

Fig. 2: Hot (Slow) Idle RPM Adjustment

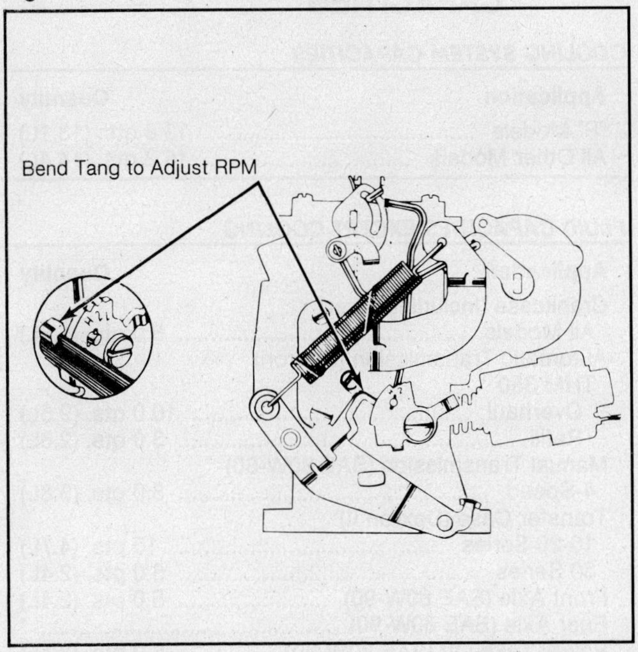

IDLE SPEED (RPM)

Application	Base Idle	Curb Idle
All Models	450	700

IDLE MIXTURE

NOTE: Mixture adjustment is not a normal tune-up procedure. DO NOT remove limiter cap unless vehicle fails emissions testing or carburetor has been disassembled.

1) Set parking brake and block drive wheels. Remove air cleaner for access to carburetor, but keep vacuum hoses connected. Disconnect and plug other hoses, as directed by Engine Tune-Up Decal under hood.

2) Place transmission in "P" (auto. trans.) or Neutral (man. trans.). Warm engine to normal operating temperature. Make sure choke is open and A/C is off (if equipped). Connect a tachometer to engine. Disconnect and plug distributor vacuum advance hose.

3) Check ignition timing and adjust if necessary. Connect distributor vacuum advance hose. Remove limiter cap from idle mixture screw. Lightly seat mixture screw and back out just enough so engine will run.

4) Connect vacuum gauge to port "B" of carburetor. Turn idle mixture screw until maximum vacuum reading is obtained at idle. Remove vacuum gauge, check and adjust fast idle speed. Connect vacuum hoses, install air cleaner and recheck idle speed.

COLD (FAST) IDLE RPM

Place cam follower on high step of fast idle cam. Support lever with pliers and bend tang in or out to adjust fast idle RPM.

NOTE: On models with manual choke, rotate fast idle cam clockwise to farthest "UP" position.

Fig. 3: Cold (Fast) Idle RPM Adjustment

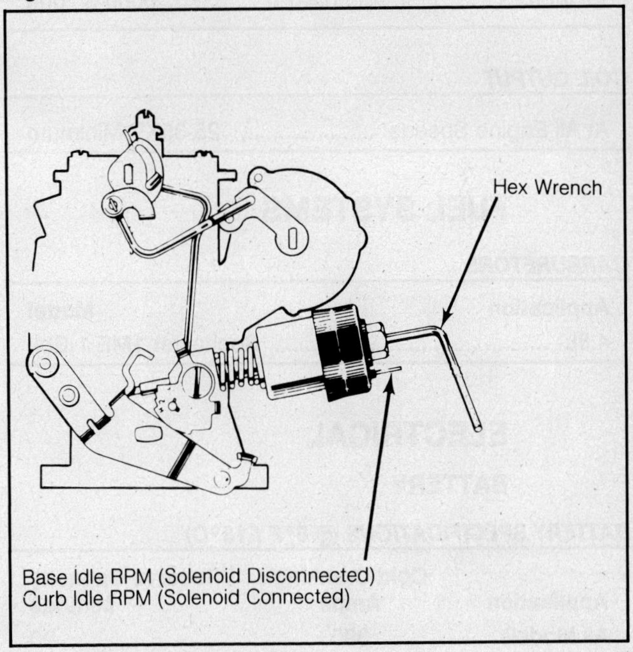

FAST IDLE SPEED (RPM)

Application	RPM
All Models	2400

AUTOMATIC CHOKE

All choke caps are retained with rivets and are non-adjustable.

FUEL PUMP

All models use mechanical fuel pumps.

FUEL PUMP SPECIFICATIONS

Application	Pressure psi (kg/cm²)	Volume Pints (Liters)
All Models	4.5-6.0 (.3-.4)	1.0 in 30 sec. (.5 in 30 sec.)

1985 General Motors 6 Tune-Up

GENERAL SERVICING

IGNITION

DISTRIBUTOR

All models are equipped with High Energy Ignition (HEI) systems and no adjustments are required.

DISTRIBUTOR PICK-UP COIL RESISTANCE

Application	Ohms
All Models	500-1500

IGNITION COIL

IGNITION COIL RESISTANCE – OHMS @ 75°F (24°C)

Application	Primary	Secondary
All Models	0.4-1.0	6000-30,000

COIL OUTPUT

At All Engine Speeds	25-35KV Minimum

FUEL SYSTEMS

CARBURETORS

Application	Model
4.8L	Rochester 1ME 1-Bbl.

ELECTRICAL

BATTERY

BATTERY SPECIFICATIONS @ 0°F (-18°C)

Application	Cold Cranking Amps	Reserve Capacity Minutes
All Models	390	90

STARTER

All models are equipped with Delco-Remy overrunning clutch models.

STARTER SPECIFICATIONS

Application	Volts	Amps	Test RPM
All Models	10	60-90	6500-10,500

ALTERNATOR

All models are equipped with Delco-Remy Integral Regulator Alternators.

ALTERNATOR SPECIFICATIONS @ 80°F (27°C)

Application	Field Current Draw @ 12 Volts	Rated Amp Output
Standard	4.0-4.5	37, 42
Optional	4.0-4.5	66, 80

ALTERNATOR REGULATOR

All models are equipped with Delco-Remy non-adjustable regulator, integral with alternator.

REGULATOR SPECIFICATIONS @ 85°F (29°C)

Operating Voltage	13.5-16

BELT ADJUSTMENT
Tension in Lbs. (Kg) Using Strand Tension Gauge

Application	New Belt	[1] Used Belt
Air Conditioning	145 (66)	65-100 (29-45)
All Others	130 (59)	50-80 (23-36)

[1] – Any belt in operation 10 minutes or more.

CAPACITIES

COOLING SYSTEM CAPACITIES

Application	Quantity
"P" Models	13.8 qts. (13.1L)
All Other Models	15.2 qts. (14.4L)

FLUID CAPACITIES EXCEPT COOLING

Application	Quantity
Crankcase (Including Filter)	
All Models	6.0 qts. (5.8L)
Automatic Transmission (Dexron)	
THM 350	
Overhaul	10.0 qts. (9.5L)
Refill	3.0 qts. (2.8L)
Manual Transmission (SAE 80W-90)	
4-Speed	8.0 pts. (3.8L)
Transfer Case (Dexron II)	
10-20 Series	10 pts. (4.7L)
30 Series	5.0 pts. (2.4L)
Front Axle (SAE 80W-90)	5.0 pts. (2.4L)
Rear Axle (SAE 80W-90)	[1]
Power Take-Off (SAE 80W-90)	5.0 pts. (2.4L)
Fuel Tank	
Pickup Models	
Short Wheelbase (Each Tank)	16.0 gals. (61.0L)
Long Wheelbase (Each Tank)	20.0 gals. (76.0L)
"P" Models	
School Bus	30.0 gals. (114.0L)
All Others	40.0 gals. (151.0L)

[1] – Fill to bottom of filler hole.

SERVICE INTERVALS

REPLACEMENT INTERVALS

Components	Interval (Miles)
Oil Filter	
Normal Use	12,000
Heavy Use	3000
Spark Plugs	30,000
PCV Valve and Filter	30,000
Air Filter	30,000

SYSTEM REFRIGERANT CAPACITIES

Application	Ounces
All Models	48

1985 General Motors V6 Tune-Up

TUNE-UP

ENGINE IDENTIFICATION

Engines can be identified by the eighth character of the Vehicle Identification Number (VIN). The VIN number is stamped on a plate attached to the left top side of dash.

VIN ENGINE CODES

Application	VIN Code
2.8L (173") 2-Bbl.	B
4.3L (262") 4-Bbl.	N

TUNE-UP NOTES

NOTE: **When performing tune-up procedures described in this article, these notes and precautions must be observed.**

Due to changes and corrections, always refer to Engine Tune-Up Decal in engine compartment before attempting tune-up. In the event of a conflict between specifications given in this manual and decal specifications, decal specifications prevail.

When performing tune-up on vehicles equipped with a catalytic converter, do not allow or create a condition of engine misfire in one or more cylinders for an extended period of time. Damage to converter from overheating may occur due to loading with unburned fuel.

ENGINE COMPRESSION

When making compression checks, disconnect the ignition switch connector Pink wire from high energy ignition system. With air cleaner removed and throttle and choke wide open, crank engine through at least 4 compression strokes.

COMPRESSION SPECIFICATIONS

Compression Ratio	
2.8L	8.5:1
4.3L	9.3:1
Minimum Pressure	100 psi (7.0 kg/cm²)
Maximum Pressure Variation	30%

VALVE ARRANGEMENT

2.8L

E-I-I-E-I-E (Left bank, front-to-rear).
E-I-E-I-I-E (Right bank, front-to-rear).

4.3L

E-I-E-I-I-E (Left bank, front-to-rear).
E-I-I-E-I-E (Right bank, front-to-rear).

VALVE CLEARANCE

All engines use hydraulic lifters.

VALVE CLEARANCE ADJUSTMENT

Application	Turns from zero lash
2.8L	1 1/2
4.3L	1

SPARK PLUGS

SPARK PLUG TYPE

Application	AC Number
All Engines	[1] R43CTS

[1] – Use R42CTS on S-10 for Heavy Duty use.

SPARK PLUG SPECIFICATIONS

Application	Gap In. (mm)	Torque Ft. Lbs. (N.m)
2.8L	.045 (1.2)	7-15 (9-20)
4.3L	.035 (.9)	22 (30)

HIGH TENSION WIRE RESISTANCE

Carefully remove ends of wire from spark plug and distributor. Using an ohmmeter, check resistance while gently twisting wire. Twist spark plug boot 1/2 turn before removing. If resistance is not within specifications, or fluctuates from infinity to any value, replace cable.

HIGH TENSION WIRE RESISTANCE (Ohms)

Wire Length	Maximum
Under 24"	30,000
Over 24"	50,000

DISTRIBUTOR

Federal models with 2.8L and 4.3L engines are equipped with Delco High Energy Ignition (HEI) distributors. California models with 2.8L engines have Delco HEI-Electronic Spark Timing (HEI-EST) distributors.

California models with 4.3L engines are equipped with Delco HEI-EST distributors with Electronic Spark Control (ESC).

Fig. 1: 2.8L Firing Order and Timing Marks

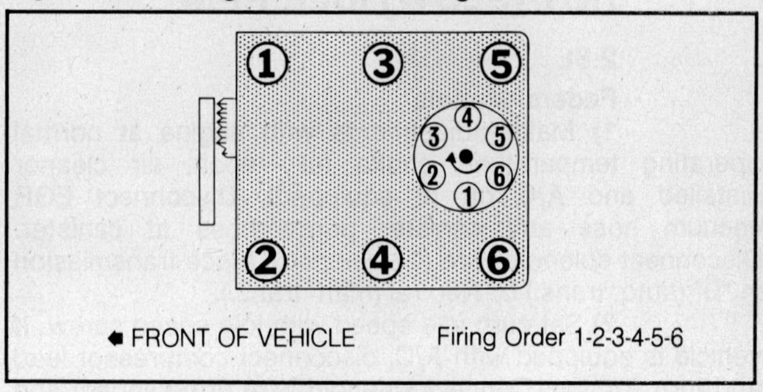

Magnetic probe located at 9.5°ATDC.

IGNITION TIMING

2.8L & 4.3L

Federal Models

1) Install timing light with an adapter between No. 1 spark plug and No. 1 spark plug wire or use an inductive type pickup. Do not puncture wire.

1985 General Motors V6 Tune-Up

TUNE-UP (Cont.)

Fig. 2: 4.3L Firing Order and Timing Marks

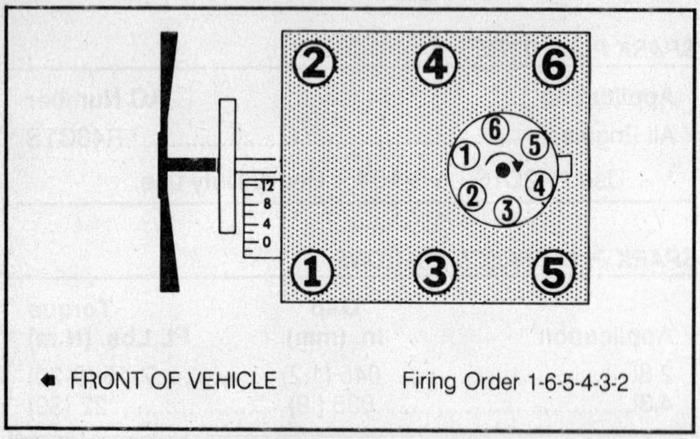

2) Check/adjust ignition timing with engine at normal operating temperature, distributor advance line disconnected and plugged, and transmission in "D" (auto. trans.) or Neutral (man. trans.).

California Models

1) Install timing light with an adapter between No.1 sprark plug and No. 1 spark plug wire or use an inductive type pickup. Do not puncture wire. Disconnect 4-wire connector at distributor.

2) Check/adjust ignition timing with engine at normal operating temperature and transmission in "D" (auto. trans.) or Neutral (man. trans.). Connect 4-wire connector. Clear trouble code by removing ECM power fuse for 10 seconds.

IGNITION TIMING SPECIFICATIONS (Degrees BTDC@RPM)

Application	Man. Trans.	Auto. Trans.
2.8L		
Federal	8@700	12@700
California	10@750	10@650
High Altitude	10@700	12@700
4.3L		
Federal	0@600	0@500
Cal. & Hi. Alt.	4@600	4@500

HOT (SLOW) IDLE RPM

2.8L

Federal Models

1) Make adjustments with engine at normal operating temperature, choke fully open, air cleaner installed and A/C off (if equipped). Disconnect EGR vacuum hose and canister purge hose at canister. Disconnect solenoid wire (if equipped). Place transmission in "D" (auto. trans.) or Neutral (man. trans.).

2) Set curb idle speed with idle speed screw. If vehicle is equipped with A/C, disconnect compressor lead and turn A/C on. Connect solenoid wire (if equipped) and all hoses. Open throttle slightly to allow solenoid to extend. Adjust solenoid idle by turning screw in back of solenoid.

California Models

1) Make adjustments with engine at normal operating temperature, choke fully open, air cleaner installed and A/C off (if equipped). Disconnect vacuum hose from carburetor port "C" (to EGR/Canister Purge TVS) and cap port.

2) Disconnect solenoid wire (if equipped). Place transmission in "D" (auto. trans.) or Neutral (man. trans.). Set curb idle speed with idle speed screw.

3) If vehicle is equipped with A/C, disconnect compressor lead and turn A/C on. Connect solenoid wire (if equipped) and all hoses. Open throttle slightly to allow solenoid to extend. Adjust solenoid idle by turning screw in back of solenoid.

IDLE SPEED (RPM)

Application	Solenoid Idle	Curb Idle
2.8L 2-Bbl.		
Federal		
Man. Trans.	850	700
Auto. Trans.	850	650
High Altitude	850	700
California		
Man. Trans.	950	750
Auto. Trans.	850	650
4.3L		
Man. Trans.	[1]	600
Auto. Trans.	[1]	500

[1] – Controlled by Stepped Speed Control Actuator.

4.3L

Federal Models

1) Set ignition timing to specifications. Disconnect and plug vacuum hose at EGR valve, canister purge and purge signal. Place transmission in "D" (auto. trans.) or Neutral (man. trans.). Adjust curb idle speed using idle speed screw.

2) Disconnect and plug vacuum hose from Stepped Speed Control Actuator (SSCA). Connect a 12 in. Hg vacuum source to SSCA. Ensure throttle opens and SSCA is fully extended. Adjust SSCA idle speed by turning screw.

3) Remove vacuum source and connect vacuum hose. Stop engine and reconnect all hoses.

STEPPED SPEED CONTROL ACTUATOR SPECIFICATIONS

Application	RPM
Federal	
Auto. Trans. (in Drive)	[1] 750
Man. Trans	[1] 850
California	
Auto. Trans. (in Drive)	700
Man. Trans.	800

[1] – On Models without A/C, subtract 50 RPM.

California Models

NOTE: **On California models, ISC and SSCA are controlled by ECM. Adjustment is not usually necessary.**

1) Check identification letter on ISC plunger. *See Fig. 3.* If no letter appears, remove plunger from unit using adjustment tool (J-29607 or BT-8022).

2) Measure and record length of plunger from back side of plunger head to end of screw. This is dimension "A". *See Fig. 3.* Install plunger so that distance measured from back side of plunger to ISC nose piece is less than dimension "B".

TUNE-UP (Cont.)

3) Remove air cleaner, disconnect and plug EGR and canister purge hoses. Connect tachometer to engine. Connect dwell meter (set on 6-cylinder scale) to mixture control solenoid dwell lead. Turn A/C off. Start engine and run until meter starts to vary.

Fig. 3: Idle Speed Control (ISC) Adjustment

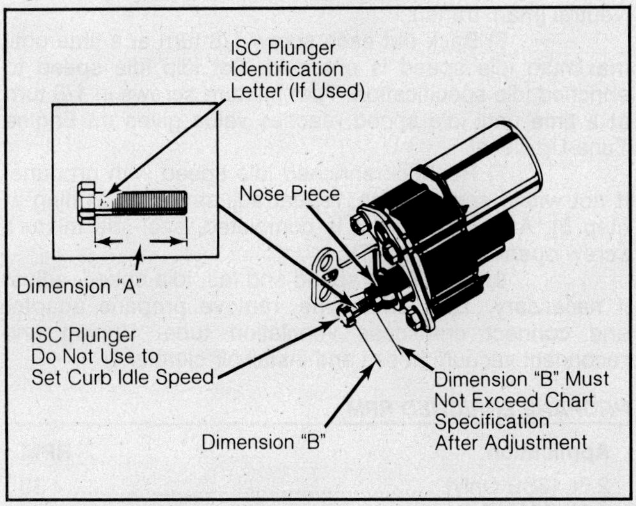

NOTE: **Do not disconnect or connect ISC connector with ignition on as damage to ECM may occur.**

4) Turn igniton off and unplug connector from ISC motor. Retract plunger by applying 12V to terminal "C" of ISC motor connection and ground lead to terminal "D" of ISC motor connection. *See Fig. 4.*

5) Start engine and wait until dwell meter begins to vary. Set parking brake, block drive wheels and place transmission in "D" (auto. trans.) or Neutral (man. trans.). With plunger fully retracted, adjust idle stop screw to curb idle specification.

Fig. 4: ISC Motor Connections

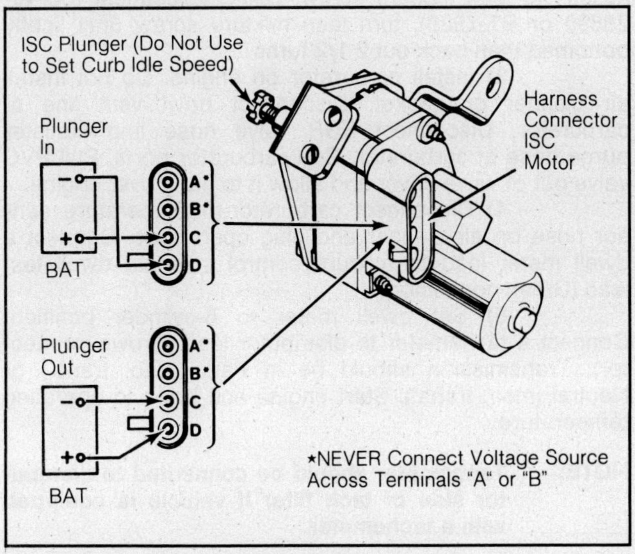

6) Place transmission in "P" (auto. trans.). Fully extend plunger by applying 12V to terminal "D" and ground terminal "C". Leave power applied only long enough to extend plunger.

7) Using adjustment tool (J-29607 or BT-8022), adjust solenoid idle speed on vehicles with manual transmissions. Preset plunger to 1500 RPM on vehicles with automatic transmissions, place transmission in "D", then adjust solenoid idle speed using adjustment tool.

8) Recheck solenoid idle speed with voltage applied to motor. After adjustment of plunger, measure distance from back side of plunger to ISC nose piece. Dimension "B" must not exceed specification shown.

9) Fully retract plunger and turn ignition off. Disconnect battery leads, tachometer and dwell meter. Connect 4-terminal connector.

10) Disconnect and plug vacuum hose from Stepped Speed Control Actuator (SSCA). Connect a 12 in. Hg vacuum source to SSCA. Ensure throttle opens and SSCA is fully extended. Adjust SSCA idle speed by turning screw.

11) Remove vacuum source and connect vacuum hose. Stop engine and reconnect all hoses.

IDLE SPEED CONTROL PLUNGER SPECIFICATIONS

Letter	Dimension "A" In. (mm)	Dimension "B" In. (mm)
None	9/16 (14.3)	7/32 (5.6)
None	41/64 (16.3)	5/16 (8.0)
X	47/64 (18.7)	25/64 (10.0)
A	49/64 (19.4)	27/64 (10.7)
Y	51/64 (20.2)	15/32 (12.0)
S	27/32 (21.4)	1/2 (12.7)
Z	7/8 (22.2)	35/64 (14.0)
G	29/32 (23.0)	37/64 (14.7)
E	1 (25.4)	43/64 (17.1)
L	1 3/32 (27.8)	3/4 (19.0)
J	1 3/16 (30.2)	27/32 (21.4)
N	1 17/64 (32.0)	59/64 (23.4)
T	1 11/32 (34.0)	1 (25.4)

IDLE MIXTURE

NOTE: **Idle mixture adjustment is not a normal tune-up procedure. Idle mixture should be checked only if vehicle fails emissions testing or carburetor has been disassembled.**

MIXTURE SCREW PLUG REMOVAL

1) Remove carburetor from engine and drain fuel. Invert carburetor. Make 2 parallel cuts, one on each side of locator point(s) with a hacksaw. Cuts should not extend more than 1/8" beyond locator point(s). *See Fig. 5.*

2) Place a flat punch near end of saw marks. Hold punch at a 45° angle. Drive it into throttle body until casting breaks away, exposing steel plug.

3) Hold a center punch in a vertical position and drive it into plug. Now hold punch at a 45° angle, and drive plug out of casting.

PROPANE ENRICHMENT PROCEDURE

2.8L Federal Models (2SE Only)

1) Engine must be at normal operating temperature and A/C off. Set parking brake and block drive wheels. On vehicles equipped with vacuum parking brake release, disconnect and plug hose at brake.

TUNE-UP (Cont.)

Fig. 5: Idle Mixture Plug Removal

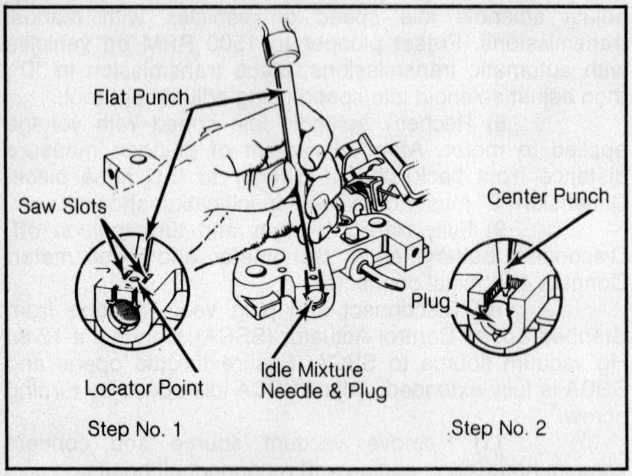

Idle mixture plug removal for 2.8L engines shown.

2) Disconnect and plug vacuum advance hose. Connect tachometer to engine. Adjust timing and reconnect vacuum advance hose. Set idle speed.

3) Disconnect crankcase ventilation tube from air cleaner. Using adapter (J-26911), insert hose with rubber stopper (from propane valve) into air cleaner snorkel. Be sure propane cartridge is vertical.

4) With engine idling in "D" (auto. trans.) or Neutral (man. trans.), open propane supply control valve slowly. Engine speed will increase. Add propane until engine speed begins to drop from over-richness. Note maximum enriched idle RPM.

5) The maximum enriched idle RPM is the idle RPM plus propane enrichment RPM. Engine speed should rise above normal idle by amount specified. If so, mixture is correct. Go to step **9**).

6) If speed is incorrect, remove idle mixture screw plugs. Carburetor must be removed and a punch driven through bottom of throttle body to remove plug. Seat screws, then back out 3 turns.

7) Place transmission in "D" (auto. trans.) or Neutral (man. trans.). Back out screw slowly until maximum idle speed is reached. Set maximum enriched idle speed.

8) Turn each mixture screw in (clockwise) 1/8 turn at a time until idle speed is correct. Recheck maximum enriched speed with propane. If incorrect, repeat step **7**).

9) Check and adjust fast idle speed. Turn off engine. Remove propane tool, connect crankcase ventilation tube and reconnect all vacuum hoses.

4.3L Federal Models (M4ME Only)

1) Warm engine to normal operating temperature and turn A/C off. Set parking brake and block drive wheels. Disconnect and plug vacuum advance hose. Connect tachometer to engine. Adjust timing and reconnect vacuum advance hose. Set idle speed.

2) Disconnect crankcase ventilation tube from air cleaner. Using adapter (J-26911), insert hose with rubber stopper (from propane valve) into air cleaner snorkel. Be sure propane cartridge is vertical.

3) With engine idling in "D" (auto. trans.) or Neutral (man. trans.), open propane supply control valve slowly. Engine speed will increase. Add propane until engine speed begins to drop from over-richness. Note maximum enriched idle RPM.

4) If enriched idle speed is within specifications, idle mixture is correct. Go to step **8**). If enriched idle speed is not correct, remove carburetor and remove idle mixture plugs.

5) Install carburetor on engine, lightly seat idle mixture screws then back out equally, just enough so that engine will run. Place transmission in "D" (auto. trans.) or Neutral (man. trans.).

6) Back out each screw 1/8 turn at a time until maximum idle speed is obtained. Set idle idle speed to enriched idle specification. Turn mixture screws in 1/8 turn at a time until idle speed reaches value given on Engine Tune-Up Decal.

7) Recheck enriched idle speed with propane. If not within specification, repeat adjustment beginning at step **5**). After adjustment is completed, seal idle mixture screw openings using RTV.

8) Check idle speed and fast idle speed, adjust if necessary. Turn off engine, remove propane adapter and connect crankcase ventilation tube. Unplug and reconnect vacuum hoses and install air cleaner.

PROPANE ENRICHED RPM

Application	RPM
2.8L (2SE Only)	[1] 30
4.3L (M4ME Only)	
Auto. Trans.	[2] 10
Man. Trans	50

[1] – 40 RPM on High Altitude models.
[2] – 20 RPM on High Altitude models.

IDLE MIXTURE ADJUSTMENT

2.8L California Models (E2SE Only)

1) Remove carburetor from engine, and remove idle mixture screw plug. Turn mixture screw in until lightly seated and back out 4 turns. If plug in air horn (covering idle air bleed) has been removed, replace air horn.

2) Remove vent stack screen assembly to gain access to lean mixture screw. Using adjustment tool (J-28696 or BT-7928), turn lean mixture screw until lightly bottomed then back out 2 1/2 turns.

3) Install carburetor on engine. Do not install air cleaner or gasket. Disconnect bowl vent line at carburetor. Disconnect EGR valve hose and canister purge hose at carburetor. Cap carburetor ports. Pull PVC valve out of valve cover and allow it to hang over engine.

4) Disconnect carburetor-to-temperature sensor hose on air cleaner and plug open hose. Connect a dwell meter lead to mixture control solenoid dwell test lead (Green connector).

5) Set dwell meter to 6-cylinder position. Connect a tachometer to distributor lead (Brown connector). Transmission should be in Park (auto. trans.) or Neutral (man. trans.). Start engine and bring to operating temperature.

NOTE: **Tachometer should be connected to distributor side of tach filter if vehicle is equipped with a tachometer.**

6) Run engine on high step of fast idle cam for at least 3 minutes, until engine is in closed loop operation (dwell meter varying). Push TPS down and insert a 1/8" (3 mm) spacer between plunger and lever.

TUNE-UP (Cont.)

7) Run engine at 3000 RPM and adjust lean mixture screw slowly to allow time for dwell to stabilize. Turn screw to obtain an average dwell of 35°. If unable to adjust, inspect main metering circuit for leaks or restrictions. Return engine to idle.

8) Adjust idle mixture screw to obtain average dwell of 25° with cooling fan in off cycle, if equipped. Adjustment is very sensitive, make final check with adjusting tool removed. If unable to adjust, inspect idle system for leaks or restrictions.

9) Disconnect mixture control solenoid when cooling fan is in off cycle. Check for an RPM change of at least 50 RPM. If RPM does not change, check idle air bleed circuit for leaks or restrictions.

10) Run engine at 3000 RPM for a few moments and note dwell reading. Dwell should show an average of 35°. If not, reset lean mixture screw. Then reset idle mixture screw to obtain 25° dwell. *See Fig. 6.*

11) When dwell has been set, connect all hoses, install vent screen and air cleaner. Set idle speed and remove 1/8" (3 mm) spacer.

Fig. 6: 2.8L E2SE Idle Mixture Adjustment

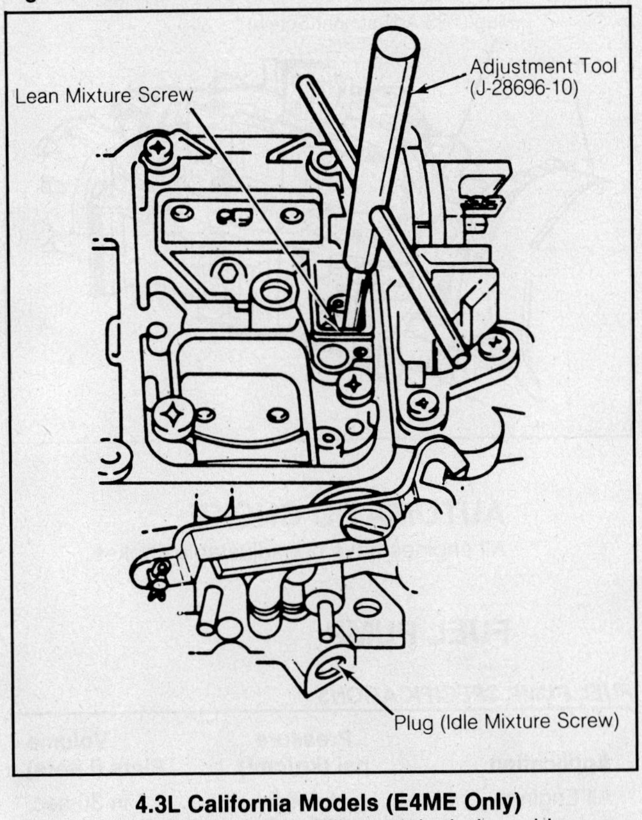

4.3L California Models (E4ME Only)

1) With engine idling and choke wide open, insert float gauge (J-34935-1 or BT-8420-A) in vent hole (slot) and allow gauge to float freely. Do not press down on gauge as flooding may occur.

2) Observe mark on gauge that lines up with top of air horn casting. Float setting should be within 2/32" of specified float level. If not within specifications, remove air horn and adjust float.

3) Insert float gauge in "D" shaped vent hole of air horn casting, next to Idle Air Bleed cover. It may be necessary to file material off gauge to allow it to enter vent hole.

4) With engine off and air cleaner and gasket removed. Lightly press down on gauge and release, observe that gauge moves freely. With gauge released, observe mark on gauge that lines up with top of air horn casting. Record reading.

E4ME FLOAT LEVEL SPECIFICATIONS

GM Carburetor No.	Float Level
17085202	11/32" (8.7 mm)
17085203	11/32" (8.7 mm)
17085204	11/32" (8.7 mm)
17085207	11/32" (8.7 mm)
17085218	11/32" (8.7 mm)
17085502	7/16" (11 mm)
17085503	7/16" (11 mm)
17085506	7/16" (11 mm)
17085508	7/16" (11 mm)
17085524	7/16" (11 mm)
17085526	7/16" (11 mm)

5) Lightly press down on gauge until it bottoms, and record reading of gauge mark that lines up with top of air horn casting. Total plunger travel must be within 1/16" and 3/16" (1.6 mm and 4.8 mm).

6) If plunger travel is within specifications and dwell reading at 3000 RPM is 10°-50°, go to step **7)**. If travel is incorrect, carburetor must be disassembled and travel adjusted.

7) Stop engine and remove air cleaner and gasket. cover internal bowl vents and air inlets to air bleed valve with masking tape. Carefully drill pop rivets retaining air bleed valve cover. Drive out shanks with a drift and small hammer.

8) Remove and discard air bleed valve cover along with masking tape. Install air bleed valve gauging tool (J-33815-2 or BT-8253-B) in "D" shaped vent hole of air horn casting. Upper end of tool should be positioned over open cavity, next to idle air bleed valve.

9) Lightly press down on gauging tool so that solenoid plunger is against idle stop. Adjust idle air bleed valve so that gauging tool will pivot over and just contact top of valve.

10) Remove carburetor from engine and remove idle mixture plugs. Using adjustment tool (J-29030 or BT-7610-B), turn each idle mixture adjustment screw clockwise until lightly seated. Back out idle mixture screws 3 turns.

11) Install carburetor on engine, but do not install air cleaner or gasket. Disconnect vacuum hose to canister purge valve and plug it. Start engine and warm to operating temperature.

12) Place transmission in "D" (auto. trans.) or Neutral (man. trans.). Adjust both idle mixture screws equally and in 1/8 turn increments until dwell reading varies within 25°-35°. Bring dwell reading as close as possible to 30°.

13) If reading is too high, turn idle mixture screws clockwise. If reading is too low, turn idle mixture screws counterclockwise. After adjustment is completed, seal idle mixture screw openings using RTV. Check idle speed and fast idle speed, adjust if necessary.

COLD (FAST) IDLE RPM

NOTE: Procedures listed are for carbureted engines with adjustable fast idle.

Warm up vehicle. Remove and plug EGR and purge control vacuum lines. Place fast idle screw on

TUNE-UP (Cont.)

highest step of fast idle cam. Start engine. On ECM controlled engines, wait until engine enters closed loop operation. Adjust fast idle screw to obtain fast idle RPM.

FAST IDLE RPM

Application	Man. Trans.	Auto. Trans.
2.8L	2100	2100
4.3L	1800	[1] 1800

[1] – Set Fed. Low Altitude at 2200 RPM.

THROTTLE POSITION SENSOR (TPS) ADJUSTMENT

NOTE: **DO NOT remove TPS adjustment screw plug unless TPS is not adjusted correctly or it is necessary to replace air horn assembly, float bowl, TPS sensor, or TPS adjustment screw.**

2.8L (E2SE Only)

1) Using a 5/64" (2 mm) drill, carefully drill a hole in steel cup plug covering TPS adjustment screw. Use care not to damage screw head. Remove steel plug using a small slide hammer.

2) Disconnect TPS connector and jumper all 3 terminals. Connect a digital voltmeter from TPS connector center terminal "B" to bottom terminal "C".

3) With ignition on, engine stopped, turn TPS screw with flat-bladed screwdriver to obtain specified voltage at curb idle position and A/C off.

4) After adjustment, a new cup plug or RTV must be inserted in air horn. If cup plug is used, cup should face outward and must be flush with air horn.

Fig. 7: 2.8L E2SE TPS Adjustment Screw Location

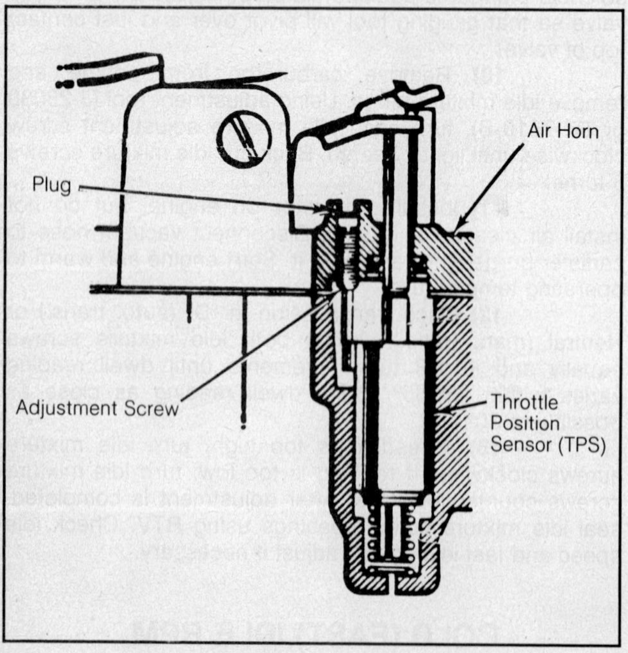

4.3L (E4ME Only)

1) Using a 5/64" (2 mm) drill, drill a 1/16" to 1/8" deep hole in aluminum plug covering TPS adjustment screw. Use care not to damage screw head. *See Fig. 8.*

2) Start a No. 8 1/2" long self-tapping screw in drilled hole, turning screw in only far enough to ensure good thread engagement. Using a screwdriver between screw head and air horn, pry out plug.

3) Using tool (J-28696), remove TPS adjustment screw. Connect a digital voltmeter from TPS connector center terminal "B" to bottom terminal "C". With ignition on, engine stopped, install TPS adjustment screw to obtain specified voltage with A/C off and throttle at idle.

4) After adjustment, install new plug in air horn. If new plug not available, use Delco Threadlock Adhesive X-10 on screw threads then adjust voltage, as in step **3)**. Clear trouble code memory after adjustment.

THROTTLE POSITION SENSOR SPECIFICATIONS

Application	Volts@Idle
2.8L E2SE	.26
4.3L E4ME	.25

Fig. 8: 4.3L E4ME TPS Adjustment Screw Location

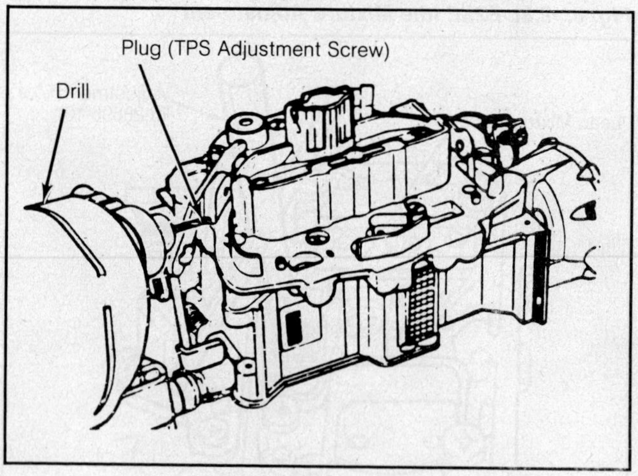

AUTOMATIC CHOKE

All engines have nonadjustable chokes.

FUEL PUMP

FUEL PUMP SPECIFICATIONS

Application	Pressure psi (kg/cm²)	Volume Pints (Liters)
All Engines	4.0-6.5 (.28-.46)	1 in 30 sec. (.5 in 30 sec.)

1985 General Motors V6 Tune-Up

GENERAL SERVICING

IGNITION

DISTRIBUTOR

Federal models with 2.8L and 4.3L engines are equipped with Delco High Energy Ignition (HEI) distributors. California models with 2.8L engines have Delco HEI-Electronic Spark Timing (HEI-EST) distributors.

California models with 4.3L engines are equipped with Delco HEI-EST distributors with Electronic Spark Control (ESC).

DISTRIBUTOR PICK-UP COIL RESISTANCE

Application	Ohms
All Models	500-1500

IGNITION COIL

COIL RESISTANCE - Ohms @ 75°F (24°C)

Application	Primary	Secondary
All Models	0.9-1.4	7300-11,100

FUEL SYSTEMS

All models are equipped with carburetors.

CARBURETORS

Application	Model
2.8L	
Federal	Rochester 2SE
California	Rochester E2SE
4.3L	
Federal	Rochester M4ME
California	Rochester E4ME

ELECTRICAL

BATTERY

BATTERY SPECIFICATIONS @ 0°F (-18°C)

Application	Cold Cranking Amps	Reserve Capacity Minutes
2.8L		
Standard	315	75
Optional	515	115
4.3L		
Standard	315	75
Optional	630	90

STARTER

All engines are equipped with Delco overrunning clutch starters.

STARTER SPECIFICATIONS

Application	Volts	Amps	Test RPM
All Engines	10.0	50-75	6000-11,900

ALTERNATOR

All engines are equipped with Delco alternators with integral voltage regulator.

ALTERNATOR SPECIFICATIONS @ 80°F (27°C)

Application	Field Current Draw @ 12 Volts	Rated Amp Output
2.8L		
Standard	4.0-5.0	66
Optional	4.0-5.0	78
4.3L		
Standard	4.0-5.0	56
Optional	4.0-5.0	66, 78

ALTERNATOR REGULATOR

All engines are equipped with Delco non-adjustable voltage regulators, integral with alternator.

ADJUSTMENTS

BELT ADJUSTMENT

Using a strand tension gauge, measure belt tension midway between pulleys. If tension is not as specified, adjust tension or replace belt.

BELT ADJUSTMENT
Tension in Lbs. (Kg) Using Strand Tension Gauge

Application	New Belt	[1] Used Belt
A/C Belt	145 (66)	65-100 (23-36)
All Others	130 (59)	50-80 (23-36)

[1] - Any belt in operation 10 minutes or more.

SERVICE INTERVALS

REPLACEMENT INTERVALS

Component	Interval (Miles)
Oil Filter	
Normal Use	7500
Heavy Use	3000
Fuel Filter	15,000
Spark Plugs	30,000
PCV Valve & Filter	30,000
Air Filter	30,000

CAPACITIES

SYSTEM REFRIGERANT CAPACITIES

Application	Ounces
Astro Van/Safari	[1]
Pickup & Van	48

[1] - Information not available.

GENERAL SERVICING (Cont.)

FLUID CAPACITIES

Application	Quantity
Cooling System [1]	
2.8L	12.0 qts. (11.4L)
4.3L	
Pickup & Van	11.0 qts. (10.4L)
All Others	13.5 qts. (13.0L)
Crankcase (Including Filter)	
2.8L	4.0 qts. (3.8L)
4.3L	5.0 qts. (4.8L)
Auto. Trans. (Dexron II)	
3-Speed	
Overhaul	20.0 pts. (9.5L)
Refill	6.0 pts. (2.8L)
4-Speed	
Overhaul	22.0 pts. (10.4L)
Refill	7.0 pts. (3.3L)
Man. Trans. (Dexron II)	[2]
Rear Axle	4.5 pts. (1.9L)
Front Axle	3.0 pts. (1.4L)
Transfer Case (Dexron II)	4.6 pts. (2.2L)
Fuel Tank	
Standard	
Astro Van/Safari	17.0 gals. (64L)
Blazer/Jimmy	13.0 gals. (50L)
All Others	13.0 gals. (40L)
Optional	
Astro Van/Safari	27.0 gals. (102L)
All Others	20.0 gals. (76L)

[1] – Add 3 qts. (2.7L) if equipped with rear heater.
[2] – Fill to bottom of filler hole.

TUNE-UP

ENGINE IDENTIFICATION

Engines can be identified by 8th character of Vehicle Identification Number (VIN). Number is located on plate at top left corner of dashboard and at base of steering column on van models.

Engine code numbers are located at front of block, at right cylinder head on 5.0L and 5.7L engines and in front of intake manifold on 7.4L engines.

VIN ENGINE CODES

Application	VIN Code
5.0L (305") 4-Bbl.	
Federal	H
Calif.	F
5.7L (350") 4-Bbl.	
Light Duty	L
Heavy Duty	M
7.4L (454") 4-Bbl.	W

TUNE-UP NOTES

NOTE: **When performing tune-up procedures described in this article, the following notes and precautions must be observed.**

Due to changes and corrections, always refer to Engine Tune-Up Decal in engine compartment before attempting tune-up. In the event of a conflict between specifications given in this manual and decal specifications, decal specifications prevail.

For tune-up purposes, "Light Duty" refers to vehicles up to 8500 lbs. "Heavy Duty" refers to vehicles exceeding 8500 lbs.

When performing tune-up on vehicles equipped with a catalytic converter, do not allow or create a condition of engine misfire in one or more cylinders for an extended period of time. Damage to converter from overheating may occur due to loading with unburned fuel.

ENGINE COMPRESSION

When making compression checks, disconnect ignition switch connector Pink wire from high energy ignition system. With air cleaner removed and throttle and choke wide open, crank engine through at least 4 compression strokes.

COMPRESSION SPECIFICATIONS

Compression Ratio	
5.0L	
Federal	9.2:1
Calif.	8.6:1
5.7L	
Light Duty	8.2:1
Heavy Duty	8.3:1
7.4L	8.0:1
Compression Pressure	150 psi (10.5 kg/cm²)
Maximum Pressure Variation	[1] 30%

[1] – Minimum reading of 100 psi.

VALVE ARRANGEMENT

5.0L & 5.7L
Both Banks – E-I-I-E-E-I-I-E (Front-to-rear).

7.4L
Left Bank – E-I-E-I-E-I-E-I (Front-to-rear).
Right Bank – I-E-I-E-I-E-I-E (Front-to-rear).

VALVE CLEARANCE

All vehicles are equipped with hydraulic lifters. Lifters should be adjusted to one turn down from zero lash.

SPARK PLUGS

SPARK PLUG TYPE

Application	AC No.
Light Duty Emissions	
5.0L Federal	R44TS
All Others	R45TS
Heavy Duty Emissions	R44T

SPARK PLUG SPECIFICATIONS

Application	Gap In. (mm)	Torque Ft. Lbs. (N.m)
All Models	.045 (1.14)	17-27 (23-37)

HIGH TENSION WIRE RESISTANCE

Carefully remove ends of wire from spark plug and distributor. Using an ohmmeter, check resistance while gently twisting wire. If resistance is not to specifications, or fluctuates from infinity to any value, replace cable.

HIGH TENSION WIRE RESISTANCE (OHMS)

Wire Length	Ohms
0-24"	30,000 Max.
Over 24"	50,000 Max.

DISTRIBUTOR

California 5.0L and 5.7L engines are equipped Delco-Remy High Energy Ignition with Electronic Spark Timing (HEI-EST).

Federal 5.0L high compression (9.2:1) engines use Electronic Spark Control (ESC) ignition system with detonation sensor.

All other engines are equipped with High Energy Ignition (HEI) systems and no adjustments are required.

TUNE-UP (Cont.)

Fig. 1: Firing Order and Timing Mark

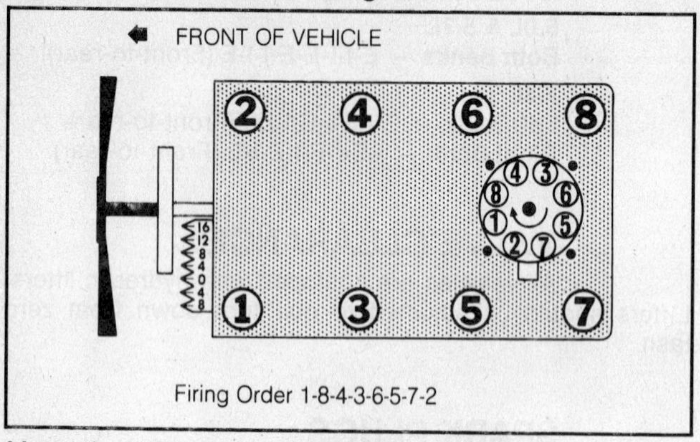

Magnetic timing pick-up is located at 10° ATDC.

IGNITION TIMING

NOTE: Engines are equipped with a receptacle for magnetic probe timing lights, located 10° ATDC. Do not use this location for timing with a conventional light.

1) Connect an adapter between No. 1 spark plug wire or use an inductive type pick-up. Do not puncture wires. Connect timing light according to manufacturer's instructions.

2) Check or adjust ignition timing with engine at normal operating temperature, distributor vacuum line (if equipped) disconnected and plugged. Light duty models with automatic transmission should be in Drive; all others in Neutral.

3) On California Models with HEI-EST and HEI-ESC distributors, disconnect 4-wire plug connector at distributor when checking ignition timing. Once timing has been set, reconnect connector and clear trouble code from computer.

IGNITION TIMING SPECIFICATIONS (Degrees BTDC@RPM)

Application	Man. Trans.	Auto. Trans
5.0L		
Federal	4@700	[1] 4@550
Calif.	...	6@550
5.7L		
Light Duty		
Federal	8@700	[2] 8@550
Calif.	...	6@550
Heavy Duty		
Federal	4@800	4@700
Calif.	6@700	6@700
7.4L	4@700	4@800

[1] – High altitude specification is 4@600.
[2] – High altitude specification is 10@600.

HOT (SLOW) IDLE RPM

M4MC, M4ME, M4MED & M4MEF CARBURETORS

Curb Idle and Throttle Return Control (TRC)

1) Set ignition timing to specifications. Disconnect lead from idle solenoid (if equipped). Adjust curb idle speed to specifications using idle speed screw. Transmission should be in Drive for light duty models with automatic transmission, and in Neutral on all others.

2) Disconnect lead from A/C compressor. Reconnect lead at idle solenoid. Turn A/C on. Open throttle slightly to allow solenoid to fully extend. Adjust solenoid idle speed by turning solenoid screw.

3) On heavy duty engines equipped with TRC, connect a hand vacuum pump to control diaphragm. With engine idling, apply sufficient vacuum to extend plunger fully.

4) Open throttle slightly to allow plunger to fully extend. Screw plunger in or out as necessary to obtain specified RPM.

IDLE SPEED (RPM)

Application	Curb Idle	Solenoid Energized
Light Duty		
5.0L		
Calif.		
Man. Trans.	....	....
Auto. Trans.	550	650
Federal		
Man. Trans.	700	800
Auto. Trans.	500	650
High Alt.		
Man. Trans.	700	....
Auto. Trans.	600	....
5.7L		
Calif.		
Man. Trans.	....	....
Auto. Trans.	550	650
Federal		
Man. Trans.	700	800
Auto. Trans.	550	650
High Alt.		
Man. Trans.	700	....
Auto. Trans.	600	....
Heavy Duty		
5.7L		
Man. Trans.	600	800
Auto. Trans.	700	....
7.4L		
Man. Trans.	600	800
Auto. Trans.	700	....

THROTTLE RETURN CONTROL (RPM)

Application	Federal	Calif.
Heavy Duty		
5.7L	1600	1600
7.4L	1500	1600

E4ME CARBURETOR

Idle Speed Control (ISC)

1) Check identification letter on ISC plunger. *See Fig. 2.* If no letter appears, remove plunger from unit using Wrench (J-29607 or BT-8022).

2) Measure and record length of plunger from back side of plunger head to end of screw. This is dimension "A". *See Fig. 2.* Install plunger so that distance measured from back side of plunger to ISC nose piece is less than dimension "B".

TUNE-UP (Cont.)

3) Remove air cleaner, disconnect and plug EGR and canister purge hoses. Connect tachometer to engine. Connect dwell meter (set on 6-cylinder scale) to mixture control solenoid dwell lead. Turn A/C off. Start engine and run until meter starts to vary.

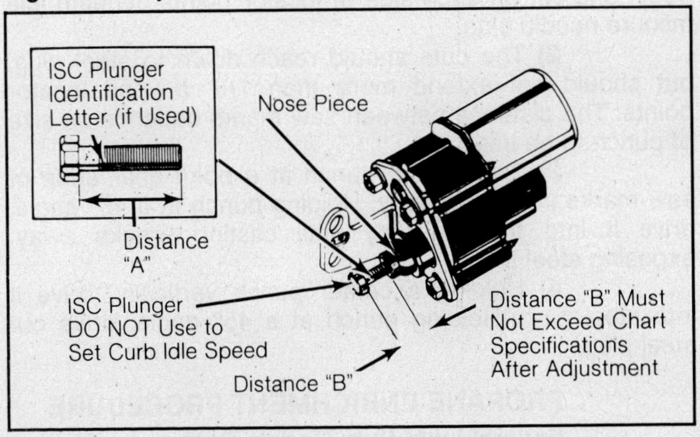

Fig. 2: Idle Speed Control (ISC) Adjustment

NOTE: **Do not disconnect or connect ISC connector with ignition on as damage to ECM may occur.**

4) Turn ignition off and unplug connector from ISC motor. Retract plunger by applying 12V to terminal "C" of ISC motor connection and ground lead to terminal "D" of ISC motor connection. *See Fig. 3.*

5) Start engine and wait until dwell meter begins to vary. Set parking brake, block drive wheels and place transmission in "D" (auto. trans.) or Neutral (man. trans.). With plunger fully retracted, adjust idle stop screw to curb idle specification.

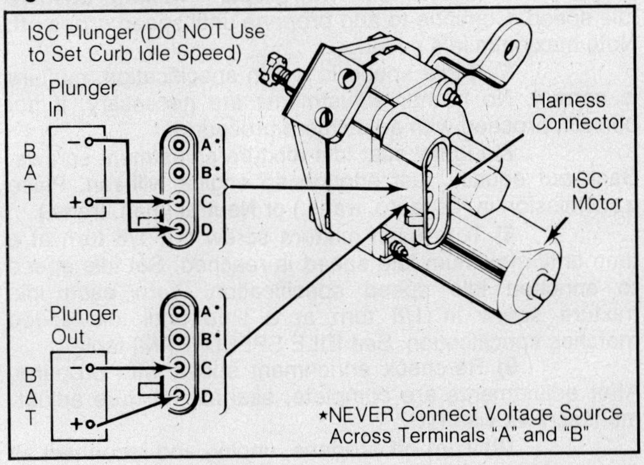

Fig. 3: ISC Motor Connections

6) Place transmission in "P" (auto. trans.). Fully extend plunger by applying 12V to terminal "D" and ground terminal "C". Leave power applied only long enough to extend plunger.

7) Using Adjuster (J-29607 or BT-8022), adjust solenoid idle speed on vehicles with manual transmissions. Preset plunger to 1500 RPM on vehicles with automatic transmissions. Place transmission in "D", then adjust solenoid idle speed using adjuster.

IDLE SPEED (RPM)

Application	Curb Idle	Solenoid Idle Speed
Calif. Light Duty		
5.0L & 5.7L	550	650

8) Recheck solenoid idle speed with voltage applied to motor. After adjustment of plunger, measure distance from back side of plunger to ISC nose piece. Dimension "B" must not exceed specification shown.

9) Fully retract plunger and turn ignition off. Disconnect battery leads, tachometer and dwell meter. Connect 4-terminal connector.

IDLE SPEED CONTROL PLUNGER SPECIFICATIONS

Letter	Dimension "A" In. (mm)	Dimension "B" In. (mm)
None	9/16 (14.3)	7/32 (5.6)
None	41/64 (16.3)	5/16 (8.0)
X	47/64 (18.7)	25/64 (10.0)
A	49/64 (19.4)	27/64 (10.7)
Y	51/64 (20.2)	15/32 (12.0)
S	27/32 (21.4)	1/2 (12.7)
Z	7/8 (22.2)	35/64 (14.0)
G	29/32 (23.0)	37/64 (14.7)
E	1 (25.4)	43/64 (17.1)
L	1 3/32 (27.8)	3/4 (19.0)
J	1 3/16 (30.2)	27/32 (21.4)
N	1 17/64 (32.0)	59/64 (23.4)
T	1 11/32 (34.0)	1 (25.4)

Idle Load Compensator (ILC)
(M4MC Carburetor Only)

1) Place transmission in "P", set brakes and block drive wheels. Connect tachometer to engine. Remove air cleaner and plug hose to thermal vacuum valve (TVV). Disconnect and plug hoses to EGR, canister purge port and idle load compensator (ILC).

2) Back out idle stop screw 3 turns. Turn A/C off. With engine running and transmission selector in "D", check that ILC plunger is fully extended. Adjust plunger to obtain 725 RPM. Hold jam nut on plunger to avoid damage to ILC.

3) Remove plug from vacuum hose, reconnect hose to ILC. Idle speed should be 500 RPM in "D". If speed is correct, no further adjustment is necessary. If speed is not correct, proceed to next step.

4) Stop engine and remove ILC. Plug vacuum hose to ILC. With ILC removed, remove rubber cap or metal plug from center outlet tube.

Fig. 4: Adjusting Idle Load Compensator

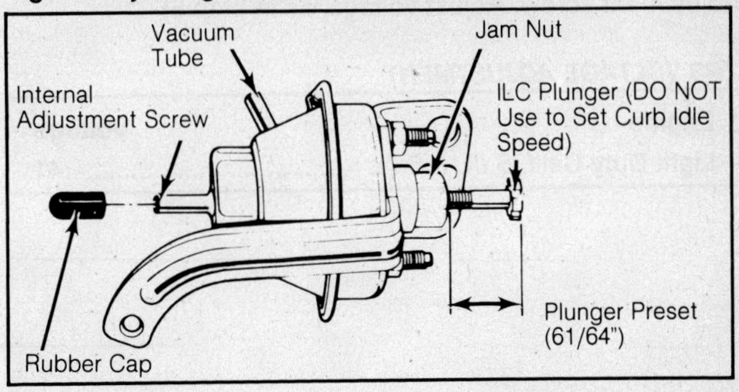

TUNE-UP (Cont.)

5) Install ILC and related parts on carburetor. Remove plug from vacuum hose and reconnect to ILC. Using a spare rubber cap with a hole punched to accept a 3/32" Allen wrench, install cap on center outlet tube.

6) Start engine and turn adjusting screw to obtain 500 RPM in "D". Remove wrench and cap. Install new rubber cap.

7) With engine running and transmission in "D", measure distance from jam nut to tip of plunger. This distance must not exceed 1" (25.4 mm). *See Fig. 4.*

8) Disconnect and plug vacuum hose to ILC. Apply vacuun to ILC inlet tube to fully retract plunger. Adjust idle stop screw on carburetor float bowl to obtain 500 RPM in "D". Stop engine, reconnect all hoses and remove test equipment.

Throttle Position Sensor (TPS)

1) Adjust TPS only if it is not adjusted correctly, or if it is necessary to replace air horn assembly, float bowl, TPS sensor or TPS adjustment screw.

2) Using a 5/64" drill bit, drill a 1/16" to 1/8" deep hole in aluminum plug covering TPS adjustment screw. Use care not to damage screw head. *See Fig. 5.*

Fig. 5: TPS Adjustment Screw Location for E4ME

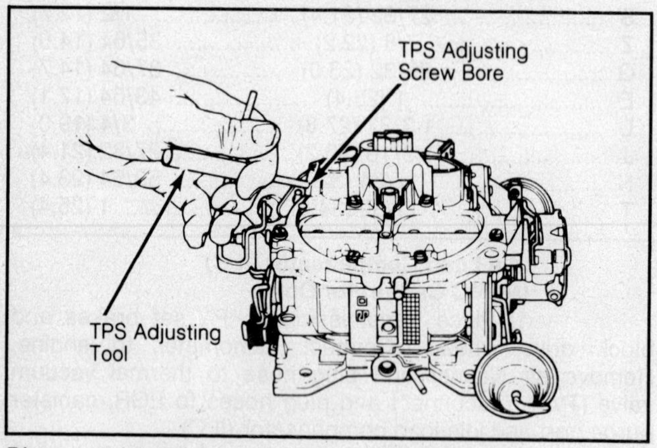

Plug must be drilled out to adjust screw.

3) Start a No. 8-1/2" long self-tapping screw in drilled hole, turning screw in only far enough to ensure good thread engagement. Using a screwdriver between screw head and air horn, pry out plug.

4) Using TPS Adjuster (J-28696), remove TPS adjusting screw. Connect digital voltmeter from TPS connector center terminal "C" to bottom terminal "C".

5) With ignition on, engine stopped, install TPS adjustment screw to obtain specified TPS voltage with A/C off.

6) Install new plug in air horn. If new plug not available, use Delco Threadlock Adhesive X-10 on TPS adjustment screw. Adjust voltage, as in step **5)**.

TPS VOLTAGE ADJUSTMENT

Engine	Voltage
Light Duty Calif. 5.0L & 5.7L	.41

IDLE MIXTURE

MIXTURE SCREW PLUG REMOVAL

1) Remove carburetor from engine and drain fuel. Invert carburetor. Make 2 parallel cuts in throttle body, one cut on each side of locator points beneath idle mixture needle plug.

2) The cuts should reach down to steel plug, but should not extend more than 1/8" beyond locator points. The distance between saw marks depends on size of punch to be used.

3) Place a flat punch at a point near ends of saw marks in throttle body. Holding punch at a 45° angle, drive it into throttle body until casting breaks away, exposing steel plug.

4) Holding a center punch vertically, drive it into steel plug. Holding punch at a 45° angle, drive out steel plug.

PROPANE ENRICHMENT PROCEDURE

Federal Light Duty Models Only

1) With engine at normal operating temperature, choke fully open and A/C off (if equipped), set parking brake and block drive wheels.

2) Connect tachometer to engine. Disconnect vacuum advance and set timing to specification. Reconnect vacuum advance. Disconnect crankcase ventilation tube from air cleaner.

3) Insert hose with rubber stopper from propane valve into PCV tube opening in air cleaner. Propane bottle must be in vertical position.

4) Slowly open control valve until maximum engine speed is reached with transmission in "D" (auto. trans.) or Neutral (man. trans.).

5) Observe propane flow meter to ensure propane cartridge is full. With propane flowing, observe idle speed. Continue to add propane until speed drops off. Note maximum idle speed.

6) If idle speed is within specification, mixture is correct. No further adjustments are necessary. If not correct, proceed with adjustment procedure.

7) Lightly seat idle mixture adjustment screws. Back out equally, just enough so engine will run. Place transmission in "D" (auto. trans.) or Neutral (man. trans.).

8) Turn each mixture screw out 1/8 turn at a time until maximum idle speed is reached. Set idle speed to enriched idle speed specification. Turn each idle mixture screw in 1/8 turn at a time until idle speed matches specification. See IDLE SPEED (RPM) table.

9) Re-check enrichment speed with propane. After adjustments are complete, seal idle mixture adjustment screws with RTV.

10) Turn off propane, unplug and reconnect all vacuum hoses. Install air cleaner. Recheck idle speed and repeat procedure if necessary.

PROPANE ENRICHED RPM (Federal Light Duty)

Application	Man. Trans.	Auto. Trans.
5.0L 4-Bbl.		
Federal	75	30
High Alt.	40	20
5.7L 4-Bbl.		
Federal	100	30
High Alt.	80	.....

TUNE-UP (Cont.)

BEST IDLE PROCEDURE

Heavy Duty Models Only

1) Set parking brake and block drive wheels. Warm engine to normal operating temperature. Remove air cleaner. Place transmission in Neutral and connect tachometer.

2) Turn idle mixture screws in lightly to seat them, then back out 2 turns. Do not turn screws tightly against seat or damage may result.

3) With engine running, choke open, and transmission in Neutral, adjust idle speed to specification. Adjust mixture screws to obtain maximum RPM.

4) Readjust idle speed screw to specification, and readjust mixture screws to obtain highest RPM. Turn ignition off, and install air cleaner.

E4ME & E4MED MIXTURE ADJUSTMENT

Mixture Control Solenoid Plunger Travel

1) Idle mixture control solenoid plunger travel should be checked before mixture adjustment or disassembly. Use Float Gauge (J-9789-130 or BT-7720) to check float level externally.

2) Insert gauge in "D" shaped vent hole in air horn casting, next to Idle Air Bleed cover. It may be necessary to file material off gauge to allow it to enter vent hole.

3) Turn engine off. Remove air cleaner and gasket. Check that gauge moves freely in vent hole. With gauge released, record reading of gauge mark that lines up with top of air horn casting.

4) Lightly press down on gauge and record reading of gauge mark that lines up with top of air horn casting. Total plunger travel must be between 1/8" (3.2 mm) and 3/8" (9.5 mm).

5) If plunger travel is within specifications, proceed to Idle Air Bleed Valve Adjustment. If plunger travel is incorrect, carburetor must be disassembled and adjusted.

Idle Air Bleed Valve Adjustment

1) Mixture must not be adjusted unless carburetor has been disassembled for cleaning or parts replacement or a systems performance check indicates that carburetor is cause of malfunction.

2) If adjustment is necessary, check ignition timing. Connect tachometer to engine. Connect dwell meter to Green wire of mixture control solenoid on carburetor.

3) Set dwell meter to 6-cylinder scale. Bring engine to operating temperature and check idle speed. Adjust idle and curb idle speed if necessary. On models with ILC or ISC, curb idle is controlled by ECM.

4) With engine idling in "D" (auto. trans.) or Neutral (man. trans.), observe dwell reading. If varying within 10-50°, adjustment is correct and no further checks are necessary. If not, perform the following procedure.

5) Turn engine off. Cover internal bowl vents, air inlets to bleed valve and carburetor air inlets with masking tape to prevent metal chips from entering carburetor.

6) Use a No. 35 (.110") drill bit to drill out rivet heads on either side of idle air bleed valve cover. Lift off idle air bleed valve cover and remove rivet pieces from carburetor. On models without rivets, pry cover off.

7) Look for letter identification code on top of idle air bleed valve. Not all valves will have an identification code.

NOTE: **On idle air bleed valves WITHOUT a letter code, the following procedure (setting valve to gauge dimension) is not necessary unless the idle air bleed valve was serviced prior to on-vehicle adjustment.**

8) To set idle air bleed valve to gauge dimension, install Air Bleed Valve Gauge (J-33815-2 or BT-8253-B) in throttle side "D" shaped hole in air horn casting. *See Fig. 7.*

Fig. 6: Idle Air Bleed Valve Identification

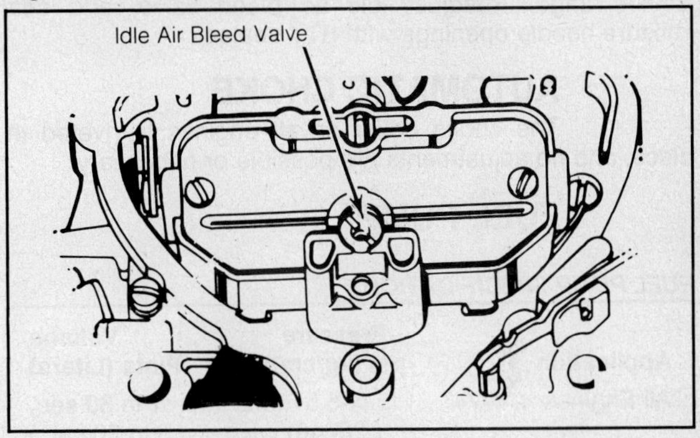

Check for letter identification code on top of valve.

Fig. 7: Positioning Idle Air Bleed Valve

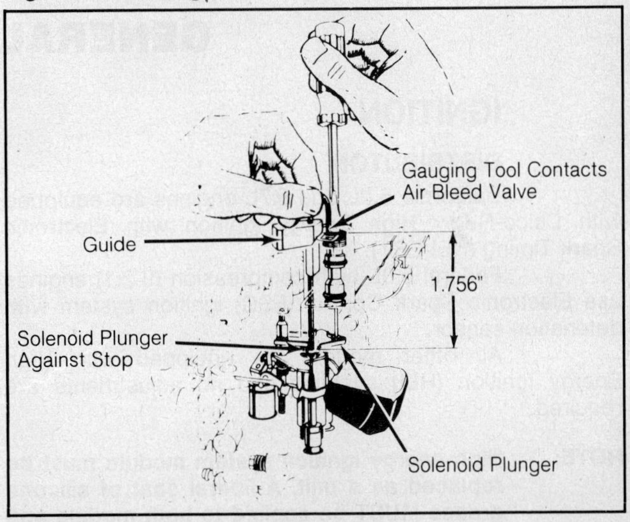

Hold gauging tool down lightly.

9) Upper end of gauge should be positioned over open cavity, next to air bleed valve. Hold gauge down lightly against solenoid stop.

10) Adjust idle air bleed valve so that gauge will pivot over and just contact top of valve. Valve is now ready for adjustment.

NOTE: **If idle air bleed valve HAS a letter code, air bleed valve does NOT have an adjustment. Proceed to Adjusting Idle Mixture Needles.**

11) Start engine and bring to operating temperature. While idling in "D" (auto. trans.) or Neutral (man. trans.), use a screwdriver to adjust valve until a dwell reading of 25-35° is obtained.

12) If dwell reading is not within 25-35°, remove mixture needle plugs and adjust idle mixture needles.

TUNE-UP (Cont.)

Adjusting Idle Mixture Needles

1) Turn each needle clockwise until lightly seated. Back out needles 3 turns. Bring engine to operating temperature.

2) For valves WITH letter code, adjust both needles equally, in or out, until dwell meter reads as close to 30° as possible. After adjustment is complete, seal mixture needle openings with RTV sealant.

3) For valves WITHOUT letter code, readjust air bleed valve. If unable to set dwell to 25-35° range, turn mixture needles equally in or out to bring dwell reading within range. Readjust idle air bleed valve, and seal mixture needle openings with RTV sealant.

AUTOMATIC CHOKE

The choke cover on all engines is riveted in place, and no adjustments are possible or necessary.

FUEL PUMP

FUEL PUMP SPECIFICATIONS

Application	Pressure psi (kg/cm²)	Volume Pints (Liters)
All Engines	4-6.5	1 in 30 sec.
	(.28-.46)	(.5 in 30 sec.)

COLD (FAST) IDLE RPM

1) Place transmission in "P" (auto. trans.) or Neutral (man. trans.). Place cam follower on highest step of fast idle cam. On light duty vehicles; disconnect and plug vacuum hose to EGR valve, canister purge hose and purge signal hose at canister.

2) Start engine without touching throttle. Turn fast idle speed screw to adjust speed to specification.

FAST IDLE SPEED (RPM)

Application	Man. Trans.	Auto. Trans.
Light Duty		
Federal		
5.0L		
"C" & "K" Series	[1] 1700	[2] 1800
"G" Series	1500	[1] 1800
5.7L		
"C" & "K" Series	[3] 1300	[3] 1600
"G" Series		[3] 1600
Calif.		1800
Heavy Duty	1900	1900

1 – Set high altitude models to 1500 RPM.
2 – Set high altitude models to 1600 RPM.
3 – Set high altitude models to 1400 RPM.

GENERAL SERVICING

IGNITION

DISTRIBUTOR

California 5.0L and 5.7L engines are equipped with Delco-Remy High Energy Ignition with Electronic Spark Timing (HEI-EST).

Federal 5.0L high compression (9.2:1) engines use Electronic Spark Control (ESC) ignition system with detonation sensor.

All other models are equipped with High Energy Ignition (HEI) systems and no adjustments are required.

NOTE: **High energy ignition system module must be replaced as a unit. A liberal coat of silicone grease MUST be applied to both module and its mounting surface.**

DISTRIBUTOR PICK-UP COIL RESISTANCE

Application	Ohms
All Models	500-1500

ELECTRICAL

BATTERY SPECIFICATIONS @ 0°F (-18°C)

Application	Cold Cranking Amps	Reserve Capacity Minutes
"C" & "K"	405	75
"G" & "P"	390	90
"P" Heavy Duty	475	130

STARTER

All models are equipped with Delco-Remy overrunning clutch starters.

STARTER SPECIFICATIONS

Application	Volts	Amps	Test RPM
5.0L			
"C" & "K"			
Man. Trans.	10	50-75	6000-11,900
Auto. Trans.	10	70-110	6500-10,700
"G" Series	10	70-110	6500-10,700
5.7L & 7.4L	10	70-110	6500-10,700

IGNITION COIL

IGNITION COIL RESISTANCE – OHMS @ 75°F (24°C)

Application	Primary	Secondary
All Models	0.4-1.0	6000-30,000

COIL OUTPUT

Application	Output
At All Engine Speeds	30 KV Min.

1985 General Motors V8 Tune-Up

GENERAL SERVICING (Cont.)

FUEL SYSTEMS

CARBURETORS

Application	Model
Light Duty	
5.0L & 5.7L	
Fed.	Rochester M4MC/ME/MED/MEF 4-Bbl.
Calif.	Rochester E4ME/E4MED 4-Bbl.
Heavy Duty	
All Models	Rochester M4MC 4-Bbl.

ALTERNATOR

All models are equipped with Delco-Remy alternators with integral voltage regulators. No adjustments are possible.

ALTERNATOR SPECIFICATIONS @ 80°F (27°C)

Application	Field Current Draw @ 12 Volts	Rated Amp Output
Standard		
"P" Models	4.0-4.5	42
All Others	4.0-4.5	37
Optional		
All Models	4.0-4.5	66
All Models	4.0-4.5	78

ALTERNATOR REGULATOR

Regulators are Delco nonadjustable, integral with alternator.

REGULATOR SPECIFICATIONS

Application	Operating Voltage
All Models	13.5-16.0

SERVICE INTERVALS

REPLACEMENT INTERVALS

Components	Intervals (Miles)
Air Filter	30,000
Oil Filter	
Heavy Duty	3000
Light Duty	12,000
PCV Valve and Filter	30,000
Spark Plugs	30,000

ADJUSTMENTS

BELT ADJUSTMENT
Tension in Lbs. (Kg) Using Strand Tension Gauge

Application	New Belt	Used Belt
Air Conditioning	145 (66)	65-100 (29-45)
All Others	130 (59)	50-80 (22-36)

CAPACITIES

FLUID CAPACITIES

Application	Quantity
Cooling System	
"P" Models	
5.7L	15.5 qts. (14.5L)
7.4L	22.5 qts. (21.2L)
All Other Models	
5.0 & 5.7L	
With A/C	18.0 qts. (17.0L)
Without A/C	17.5 qts. (16.5L)
7.4L	
With A/C	24.5 qts. (23.0L)
Without A/C	23.0 qts. (22.0L)
Crankcase (Including Filter)	
5.0 & 5.7L	5.0 qts. (3.8L)
7.4L	7.0 qts. (5.7L)
Automatic Transmission (Dexron II)	
THM 350 (Refill)	6.0 pts. (2.8L)
THM 400 (Refill)	7.0 pts. (3.8L)
THM 700-R4 (Refill)	10.0 pts. (4.7L)
Manual Transmission (SAE 80W-90)	
3-Speed	3.0 pts. (1.4L)
4-Speed	8.0 pts. (3.8L)
Transfer Case (Dexron II)	
205	5.0 pts. (2.4L)
208	10.0 pts. (4.8L)
Front Axle (SAE 80W-90)	5.0 pts. (2.4L)
Rear Axle (SAE 80W-90)	[1]
Power Take-Off (SAE 80W-90)	5.0 pts. (2.4L)
Fuel Tank	
Blazer & Suburban	
Standard	25.0 gals. (95L)
Optional	31.0 or 40.0 gals. (117L or 151L)
Caballero & El Camino	
Standard	18.0 gals. (68L)
Optional	22.0 gals. (83L)
Pickup Models	
Short Wheelbase (Each Tank)	16.0 gals. (61L)
Long Wheelbase (Each Tank)	20.0 gals. (76L)
Van Models	
Standard	22.0 gals. (83L)
Optional	33.0 gals. (125L)
"P" Models	
Standard [2]	40.0 gals. (151L)
Optional [3]	60.0 gals. (227L)

[1] – Fill to bottom of filler hole.
[2] – School bus has 30.0 gals. (114L)
[3] – Motor home chassis only.

SYSTEM REFRIGERANT CAPACITIES

Application	Specification
C-60	
All Models	3 lbs.
Overhead System	
"C" & "K" Models	5.25 lbs.
"G" Models	4.5 lbs.

TUNE-UP

ENGINE IDENTIFICATION

Engines can be identified by the eighth character of Vehicle Identification Number (VIN) which is stamped on a tag at the top left corner of dashboard. The 2.2L engine VIN number also appears on left front of cylinder block above crankshaft pulley.

The 6.2L engine is also identified by code letters, located on a label at rear of left valve cover and also stamped into block on left front corner

VIN ENGINE CODES

Application	Code
2.2L (136") 4-Cylinder	S
6.2L (379") V8 (Light Duty)	C
6.2L (379") V8 (Heavy Duty)	J

TUNE UP NOTES

NOTE: **When performing tune-up procedures described in this article, these notes and precautions must be followed.**

Due to late changes and corrections, always refer to Engine Tune-Up Decal in engine compartment before attempting tune-up. If decal specifications are different than specifications given in this manual, use decal specifications.

Adjustment of injectors or internal adjustment of injection pump must be done in a properly equipped injector shop with clean environment.

Prior to checking compression, be sure battery is fully charged to avoid battery run down. When turning engine over during test, 6 "puffs" per cylinder should be used to obtain reading.

ENGINE COMPRESSION

NOTE: **Do not add oil to cylinders during compression check as extensive engine damage will result.**

2.2L

1) Start engine and bring coolant temperature to 176°F (80°C). Remove sensing resistor, glow plug connector and fuel cut solenoid connector. Disconnect fusible link wire of glow plug system. Remove all glow plugs.

COMPRESSION SPECIFICATIONS

Compression Ratio	
2.2L	21.0:1
6.2L	21.3:1
Compression Pressure	
2.2L	
Standard	[1] 441 psi (31 kg/cm²)
Minimum	[1] 398 psi (28 kg/cm²)
6.2L	300 psi (21 kg/cm²)
Max. Pressure Variation	
6.2L	20%

[1] – Measured at 200 RPM.

2) Install adapter (J-26999-20) and compression gauge. Turn starter motor and read compression for individual cylinders.

6.2L

1) Remove air cleaner. Disconnect electrical wire from fuel injection pump solenoid terminal.

2) Disconnect glow plug wiring, and remove all glow plugs. Use compression gauge (J-26999-10) to test individual cylinders.

VALVE ARRANGEMENT

2.2L

E-I-I-E-E-I-I-E (Front-to-rear).

6.2L

I-E-I-E-I-E-I-E (Left bank, front-to-rear).
E-I-E-I-E-I-E-I (Right bank, front-to-rear).

VALVE CLEARANCE

2.2L

1) Tighten rocker arm shaft bolts to 9-17 ft. lbs. (12-23 N.m). Bring No. 1 piston to TDC of compression stroke. Adjust intake and exhaust valves on No. 1 cylinder. Adjust intake valves on No. 2 and No. 3 cylinders.

2) Turn crankshaft one revolution and adjust intake and exhaust valves on No. 4 cylinder. Adjust exhaust valves on No. 2 and No. 3 cylinders.

VALVE CLEARANCES

Application	Cold In. (mm)	Hot In. (mm)
2.2L		
All Valves	.016 (.40)	.015 (.37)

6.2L

The 6.2L engine uses hydraulic lifters with roller followers. Adjust to zero lash.

GLOW PLUGS

2.2L

Glow plugs are of the fast glow type (fast warm-up). During start and warm-up modes, engine is electronically controlled to provide fast cold starts and good cold driveaway.

The glow plug system consists of an electronic control module, glow plug relays 1 and 2, a dropping resistor, sensing resistor, thermo switch and fusible links.

A fast chamber preheat is provided if engine coolant temperature at thermo switch is below 122°F (50°C). Relay 1 is then energized and the glow plugs indicator lamp is on for a period of 3.5 seconds or more, before going out. Chamber preheat temperatures permit starting the engine.

At engine coolant temperatures above 122°F (50°C), relay 1 is inoperative and relay 2 turns on to provide stabilizing heat during starting.

TUNE-UP (Cont.)

6.2L

Glow plugs are small 6-volt heaters operated by an electronic relay. They cycle on and off, powered by 12 volts to give rapid heating. Glow plug light on dash should lit as plugs cycle on and off.

If test lamp is connected to glow plugs and ground, it should flash on and off. Relay can be heard clicking on and off after ignition has been on for approximately 25 seconds.

GLOW PLUG SPECIFICATIONS

Application	GM Part No.
2.2L	
California	94110792
Federal	94241449
6.2L	[1] 5613738

[1] - Tighten to 8-12 ft. lbs. (11-16 N.m).

Fig. 1: 2.2L Firing Order

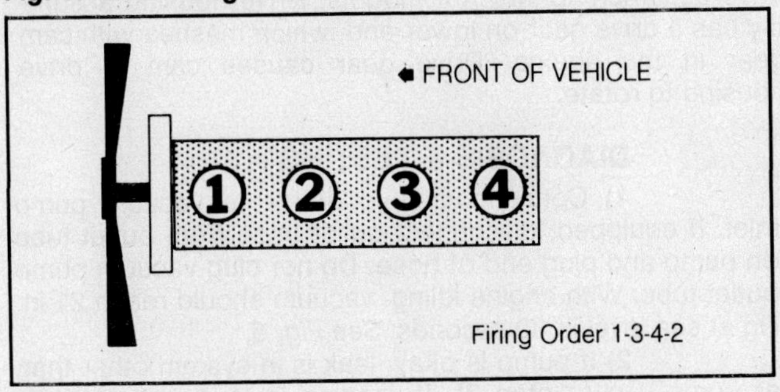

Fig. 2: 6.2L Firing Order

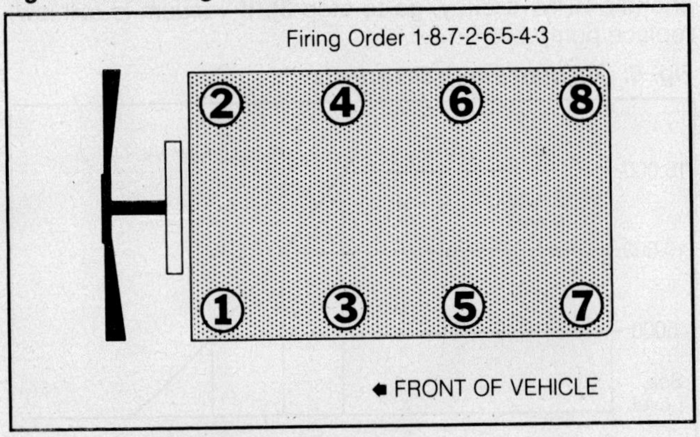

INJECTION PUMP TIMING

2.2L

1) Check that notched line on injection pump flange is in alignment with notched line on injection pump front bracket. Bring No. 1 piston to TDC of compression stroke.

2) Remove upper fan shroud. Check that timing belt is properly tensioned and that timing marks are aligned. If not, remove belt and readjust. Remove injection lines and remove distributor head screw and washer.

3) Install dial indicator (J-29763) and set lift to 0.04" (1 mm) from plunger. Bring piston in No. 1 cylinder to a point 45-60° BTDC by turning crankshaft. *See Fig. 3.* Calibrate dial indicator to zero.

Fig. 3: 2.2L Injection Pump Timing

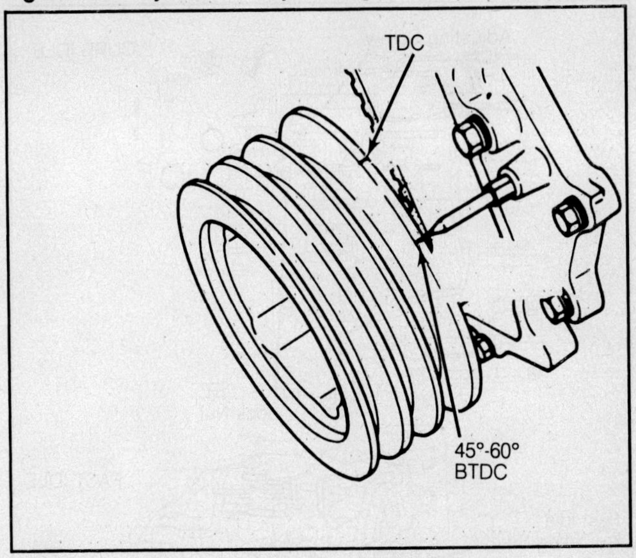

4) Turn crankshaft pulley slightly in both directions and check that gauge indication is stable. Turn crankshaft in normal direction of rotation and take reading when timing mark on crankshaft pulley is aligned with pointer.

5) Dial indicator should read .020" (0.5 mm). If reading is not as specified, hold crankshaft in place (15° BTDC) and loosen 2 nuts on injection pump flange.

6) Move injection pump to a point where dial indicator reading is .020" (0.5 mm) and tighten pump flange nuts. Recheck dial indicator reading and readjust if necessary.

7) Install distributor screw and washer into injection pump. Install injection lines. Connect wires and hoses previously removed. Install upper dust cover. Install timing belt, if removed. Install fan shroud. Adjust engine idle speed and fast idle speed.

6.2L

1) Check alignment of injection pump timing marks on top of engine front cover and injection pump flange. Half circles on California models, scribe marks on Federal models.

2) If timing marks are not aligned, loosen 3 retaining nuts, and align mark on injection pump with mark on front cover. Tighten nuts to 30 ft. lbs. (41 N.m) and adjust throttle linkage.

IDLE SPEED (RPM)

2.2L

1) Set parking brake and block drive wheels. Place transmission in Neutral. Connect tachometer. Start engine and warm to normal operating temperature. Loosen lock nut on idle speed adjusting screw. *See Fig. 4.*

2) Turn adjusting screw to obtain curb idle speed. Tighten lock nut. Apply vacuum to fast idle actuator. Loosen lock nut on fast idle actuating screw. Adjust knurled nut to obtain fast idle speed. Tighten lock nut.

TUNE-UP (Cont.)

Fig. 4: 2.2L Idle Speed Adjustment

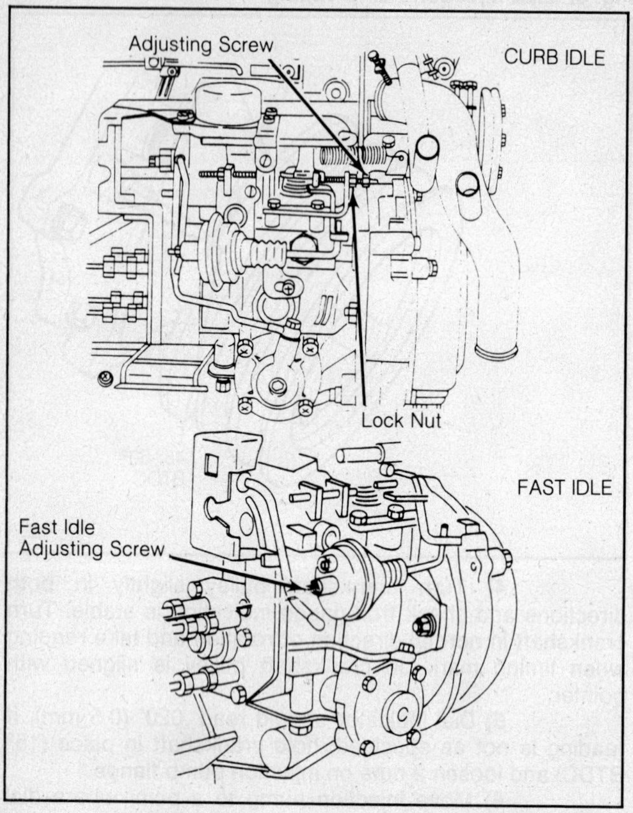

IDLE SPEED (RPM)

Application	Curb Idle	Fast Idle
2.2L	800	925

6.2L

1) Set parking brake and block drive wheels. Warm engine to normal operating temperature and install tachometer (J-26925). Adjust low idle speed screw on pump to obtain curb idle speed. *See Fig. 5.*

2) Remove connector from fast idle solenoid. Run an insulated jumper wire from battery positive terminal to solenoid terminal to energize solenoid. Open throttle to ensure plunger is fully extended.

Fig. 5: 6.2L Idle Speed Adjustment

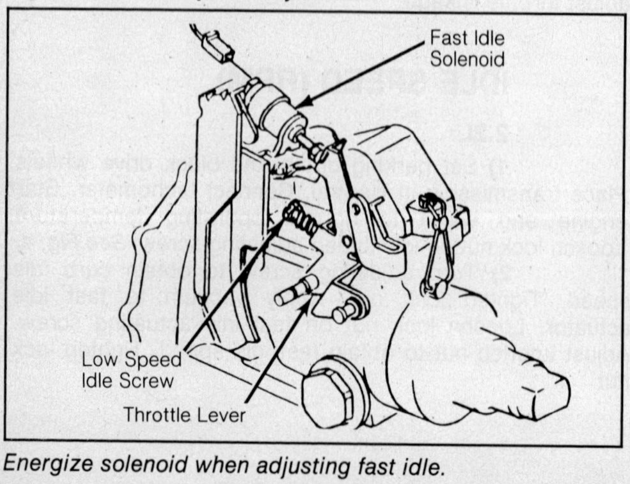

Energize solenoid when adjusting fast idle.

3) Adjust fast idle speed by turning plunger hex head. Turn off engine, remove jumper wire and test equipment. Install fast idle solenoid connector.

IDLE SPEED (RPM)

Application	Curb Idle	Fast Idle
6.2L	650	800

VACUUM PUMP

The vacuum pump is designed to aid the engine in maintaining a proper vacuum level for the power brake system and other vacuum operated accessories. The vacuum pump is a diaphragm type pump which requires no periodic maintenance.

The vacuum pump on 2.2L engines is belt-driven. Vacuum pump on 6.2L engines are either belt-driven or gear-driven.

Gear-driven pump is driven by a cam inside drive assembly to which it mounts. Drive housing assembly has a drive gear on lower end, which meshes with cam gear in the engine. Drive gear causes cam in drive housing to rotate.

DIAGNOSIS & TESTING

1) Connect vacuum gauge to vacuum pump inlet. If equipped, disconnect outlet hose from outlet tube on pump and plug end of hose. Do not plug vacuum pump outlet tube. With engine idling, vacuum should reach 21 in. Hg at sea level in 30 seconds. *See Fig. 6.*

2) If pump is okay, leak is in system other than at pump. Go to step **3)**. If reading is low or fluctuates, check gauge and connections for leaks. Check drive belt and idle RPM. If okay, go to step **3)**. If vacuum is still low, replace pump.

Fig. 6: Vacuum Pump Diagnosis

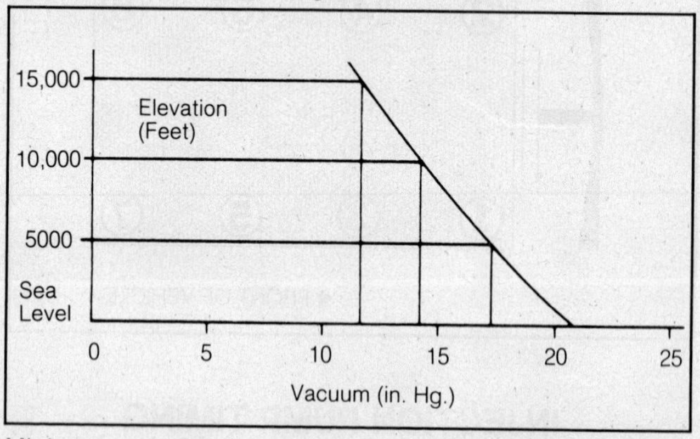

Minimum acceptable vacuum shown at specified altitude.

3) Where applicable, remove plug from outlet hose and reconnect hose to pump outlet tube. Reconnect vacuum hose with a "T" and vacuum gauge located near pump inlet.

4) With engine idling, vacuum may be 3 in. Hg less than measured in step **1)**. If vacuum is okay, problems are not within vacuum system. If vacuum is low, check all attaching hoses and accessories for leaks.

TUNE-UP (Cont.)

INJECTION NOZZLES

2.2L

Opening Pressure

1) Using a reliable nozzle tester and SAE J9670 calibrating oil at room temperature, check opening pressure. Connect test line to nozzle holder assembly and tighten fittings.

2) Close gauge valve and operate tester handle sharply several times. Check for proper nozzle position. Spray should be injected into a clean container. Open gauge valve and operate tester handle slowly to determine injection opening pressure.

3) Observe gauge reading just before oil is sprayed from tip. A buzzing noise will occur when spray is injected. Minimum opening pressure is 1493 psi (105 kg/cm²).

Spray Pattern

Close pressure gauge. Check spray pattern by operating handle one stroke every 2 seconds. Observe spray pattern. Spray should be uniform and injected at correct angle of nozzle being tested.

Leakage

Apply 284 psi (20 kg/cm²) pressure to nozzle. Nozzle tip should remain dry without an accumulation of fuel at spray holes. A slight wetting is allowed after 10 seconds if no droplets are formed.

6.2L

Opening Pressure

1) Using a reliable nozzle tester and ISO 3104 testing oil at room temperature, check opening pressure. Connect test line to nozzle holder assembly and tighten fittings.

2) Close shutoff valve at pressure gauge and operate tester handle sharply several times. Check for proper nozzle position. Spray should be injected into a clean container.

3) Open shutoff valve at pressure gauge 1/4 turn. Operate tester handle slowly to determine injection opening pressure. Observe gauge reading just before oil is sprayed from tip. Minimum opening pressure is 1500 psi (105 kg/cm²).

Leakage

Open shutoff valve at pressure gauge 1 turn. Apply 1400 psi (98 kg/cm²) pressure to nozzle. Tip should remain dry. A drop is allowed after a period of 10 seconds if no droplets are formed.

ADJUSTMENTS

THROTTLE POSITION SWITCH (TPS)

6.2L Federal Engine Only

1) Loosely assemble throttle position switch to fuel injection pump with throttle lever in closed position. Attach a continuity meter across terminals (Pink wire and Yellow wire on light duty engines).

2) Insert proper "switch-closed" gauge block, between gauge boss on injection pump and wide open stop screw on throttle shaft. Rotate and hold throttle lever against gauge block.

3) Rotate throttle switch clockwise (facing throttle switch) until continuity pivot occurs (high meter reading) across terminals. Hold switch body at this position and tighten mounting bolts to 48-50 INCH lbs. (5-7 N.m).

NOTE: Switch point must be set only while rotating switch body in clockwise direction.

4) Release throttle lever and allow it to return to idle position. Remove "switch-closed" gauge block and insert "switch-open" gauge block. Rotate throttle lever against "switch-open" gauge block. There should be no continuity across terminals.

5) If no continuity exists, switch is set properly. However, if there is continuity, then switch must be reset by returning to step **1)** and repeating entire procedure. *See Fig. 7.*

TPS GUAGE BLOCK SPECIFICATIONS

Application	Dimension
Switch Closed	
Auto. Trans.	.646" (16.4 mm)
Man. Trans.	.602" (15.3 mm)
Switch Open	
Auto. Trans.	.668" (16.9 mm)
Man. Trans.	.624" (15.8 mm)

Fig. 7: 6.2L Throttle Position Switch Adjustment

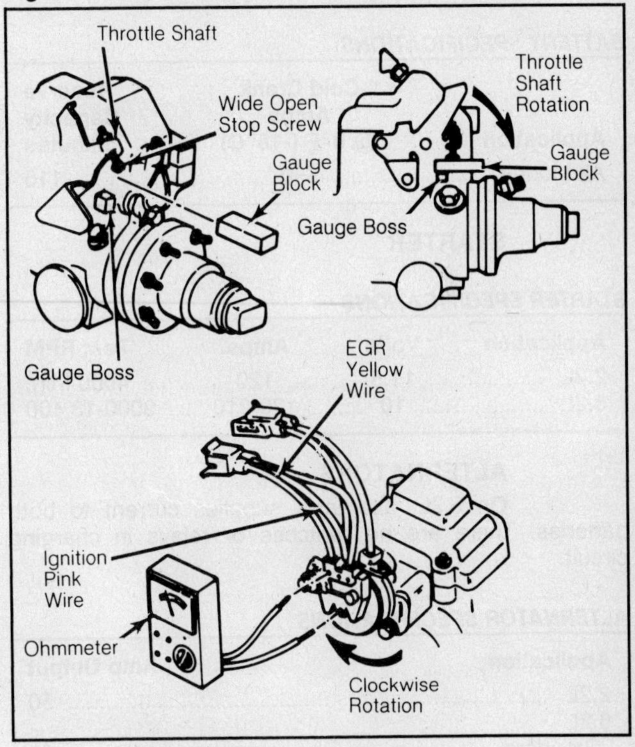

Rotate clockwise until continuity occurs.

VACUUM REGULATOR VALVE

6.2L Heavy Duty (VIN J)

1) Attach vacuum regulator valve snugly, but loosely to fuel injection pump. The valve body must be free to rotate on pump. Attach a vacuum source of 18-21 in. Hg to bottom of vacuum nipple.

2) Attach vacuum gauge to top vacuum nipple. Insert vacuum regulator gauge bar (.646") between gauge boss on injection pump and wide open throttle valve stop screw on throttle lever.

TUNE-UP (Cont.)

3) Rotate and hold throttle shaft against gauge bar. Slowly rotate vacuum regulator valve clockwise (facing valve) until vacuum gauge reads 7.4-8.6 in. Hg. Hold valve body in this position, and tighten mounting screws to 48-60 INCH lbs. (5-7 N.m).

4) Valve must be set while rotating valve body in a clockwise direction only. Check by releasing throttle shaft, allowing it to return to idle stop position. Rotate throttle shaft back against gauge bar and determine if vacuum gauge reads within 7.4-8.6 in. Hg. If vacuum is outside limits, reset valve.

GENERAL SERVICING

FUEL INJECTION

All 2.2L engines are equipped with Kiki diesel fuel injection. All 6.2L engines are equipped with General Motors diesel fuel injection.

ELECTRICAL

BATTERIES

All models use Delco "Freedom" type batteries. All V8 diesel vehicles use two 12-volt, negative ground, sealed-top batteries. One battery is located on each side of engine compartment and they are wired in parallel. The 2.2L uses one 12-volt battery.

BATTERY SPECIFICATIONS

Application	Cold Crank Amps @ 0°F (-18°C)	Reserve Capacity Minutes
All Models	550	115

STARTER

STARTER SPECIFICATIONS

Application	Volts	Amps.	Test RPM
2.2L	11.5	120	4000 Min.
6.2L	10	120-210	9000-13,400

ALTERNATORS

On 6.2L, alternator supplies current to both batteries. There are no switches or relays in charging circuit.

ALTERNATOR SPECIFICATIONS

Application	Amp Output
2.2L	50
6.2L	
Standard	66
Optional	78, 85

ALTERNATOR REGULATOR

All models are equipped with Delco non-adjustable regulators, integral with alternator.

REGULATOR SPECIFICATIONS @ 85°F (29°C)

Application	Volts
All Models	13.5-16.0

BELT ADJUSTMENTS

BELT ADJUSTMENT
Tension in Lbs. (Kg) Using Strand Tension Gauge

Application	New Belt	[1] Used Belt
2.2L (ALL)	135 (79)	35 (79)
6.2L		
Air Conditioning	145 (66)	65-100 (29-45)
All Others	130 (59)	50-80 (23-36)

[1] – Any belt in operation 10 minutes or more.

SERVICE INTERVALS

REPLACEMENT INTERVALS

Component	Interval (Miles)
Oil Filter	
2.2L	
Normal Use	7500
Heavy Use	3000
6.2L	
Normal Use	5000
Heavy Use	2500
Air Cleaner Element	30,000
Fuel Filter	
2.2L	30,000
6.2L	15,000
Auto. Trans. Filter (Heavy Use)	15,000
EGR Pressure Valve	[1] 15,000

[1] – Check every 5000 miles.

CAPACITIES

SYSTEM REFRIGERANT CAPACITIES

Applicaton	Ounces
Blazer & Pickups	48
Suburban	
Front System Only	48
Front & Rear System	84
Vans	
Front System Only	48
Front & Rear System	72

GENERAL SERVICING (Cont.)

FLUID CAPACITIES

Application	Quantity
Crankcase (Includes Filter)	
2.2L	[1] 5.5 qts. (5.2L)
6.2L	[2] 7.0 qts. (6.6L)
Auto. Trans. (Dexron)	
6.2L	[3] 6.0 pts. (2.8L)
Manual Transmission	
4-Speed OD (Dexron II)	[4]
S10 (Dexron II)	[4]
All Others (SAE 80W-90)	[4]
Rear Axle (SAE 80W-90) [5]	
"S" Series	3.0 pts. (1.4L)
All Others	[4]
Transfer Case (Dexron II)	
10 & 20 Series	5.0 qts. (4.8L)
30 Series	2.5 qts. (2.4L)
Cooling System	
"S" Series	
Without A/C	11.5 qts. (11.0L)
With A/C	12.0 qts. (11.3L)
All Others	25.0 qts. (23.7L)
Fuel Tank	
"S" Series	
Standard	14.0 gals. (53L)
Optional	20.0 gals. (76L)
Blazer	
Standard	27.0 gals. (102L)
Optional	32.0 gals. (121L)
Motor Home	
Standard	40.0 gals. (151L)
Optional	60.0 gals. (227L)
Pickup	
Short W.B. (Main or Aux.)	16.0 gals. (61L)
Long W.B. (Main or Aux.)	20.0 gals. (76L)
"P" Series	40.0 gals. (151L)
School Bus	30.0 gals. (114L)
Suburban	
Standard	27.0 gals. (102L)
Optional	41.0 gals. (155L)
Van	
Standard	22.0 gals. (83L)
Optional	33.0 gals. (125L)

1 – Use oil designated BOTH SF and CD or BOTH SF and CC.
2 – Oil MUST be designated BOTH SE & CC. If CD appears anywhere on can, do not use.
3 – Total fill is 10.0 qts. (9.5L).
4 – Fill to bottom of filler hole.
5 – Use G.M. (1052271) on locking type.

1985 Jeep 4 Tune-Up

TUNE-UP

ENGINE IDENTIFICATION

Engine can be identified by the 4th character of the Vehicle Identification Number (VIN). The VIN is stamped on a plate attached to top left corner of instrument panel.

VIN ENGINE CODE

Application	Code
2.5L (150") 1-Bbl.	U

TUNE-UP NOTES

NOTE: **When performing tune-up procedures described in this article, the following notes and precautions must be followed.**

Due to late changes and corrections, always refer to Engine Tune-Up Decal in engine compartment before attempting tune-up. If manual and decal differ, always use decal specifications.

EPA high altitude emission standards apply to vehicles sold in certain areas outside California which have an elevation above 4,000 feet.

When performing tune-up on vehicles equipped with catalytic converters, do not allow or create an engine misfire in one or more cylinders for an extended period of time. Damage to converter may occur due to loading converter with unburned air/fuel mixture.

ENGINE COMPRESSION

Test compression with all spark plugs removed and engine at normal operating temperature. Crank engine through at least 5 compression strokes before recording reading.

COMPRESSION SPECIFICATIONS

Application	Specification
Compression Ratio	9.2:1
Compression Pressure	170 psi (11.7 kg/cm²)
Max. Variation Between Cyls.	30 psi (2.1 kg/cm²)

VALVE ARRANGEMENT

E-I-I-E-E-I-I-E (Front-to-rear).

VALVE CLEARANCE

All models are equipped with hydraulic lifters, which should be adjusted to zero lash.

SPARK PLUGS

SPARK PLUG TYPE

Application	Champion No.
2.5L	RFN14LY

SPARK PLUG SPECIFICATIONS

Application	Gap In. (mm)	Torque Ft. Lbs. (N.m)
2.5L	.035 (.9)	27 (37)

HIGH TENSION WIRE RESISTANCE

Do not puncture spark plug wires with any type of probe. Remove spark plug wire and check resistance with an ohmmeter.

IGNITION COIL WIRE

Remove ignition coil wire from coil and distributor cap. Check terminals for corrosion and clean if necessary. Check coil wire resistance. Replace wire if resistance is excessive.

HIGH TENSION WIRE RESISTANCE (OHMS)

Wire Length (In.)	Minimum	Maximum
0-15	3,000	10,000
15-25	4,000	15,000
25-35	6,000	20,000
Over 35	8,000	25,000

DISTRIBUTOR

Jeep 2.5L engines are equipped with a Motorcraft SSI ignition system. No adjustments are required on system.

Fig. 1: 2.5L Firing Order

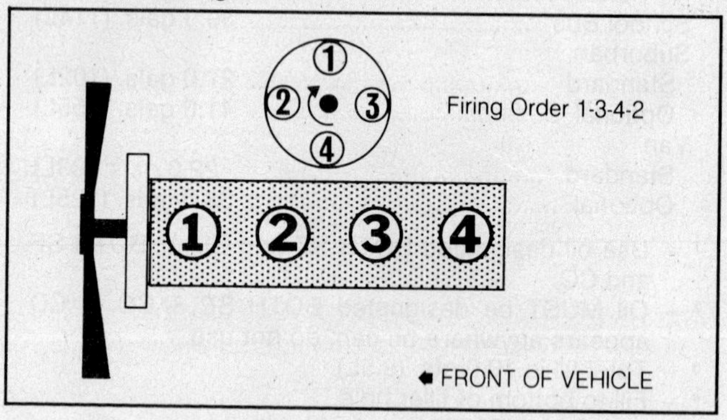

IGNITION TIMING

Check and adjust ignition timing with engine at normal operating temperature, 3-wire connector to vacuum input switch disconnected, and distributor vacuum advance hose disconnected and plugged.

IGNITION TIMING SPECIFICATIONS (Degrees BTDC@RPM)

Application	Man. Trans.	Auto. Trans.
2.5L	12@1600	12@1600

TUNE-UP (Cont.)

HOT (SLOW) IDLE RPM

SOLE-VAC VACUUM ACTUATOR ADJUSTMENT

1) Start engine and allow it to reach normal operating temperature. Turn all accessories off. Connect a tachometer to engine.

Fig. 2: 2.5L Sole-Vac Idle Adjusting Screw Location

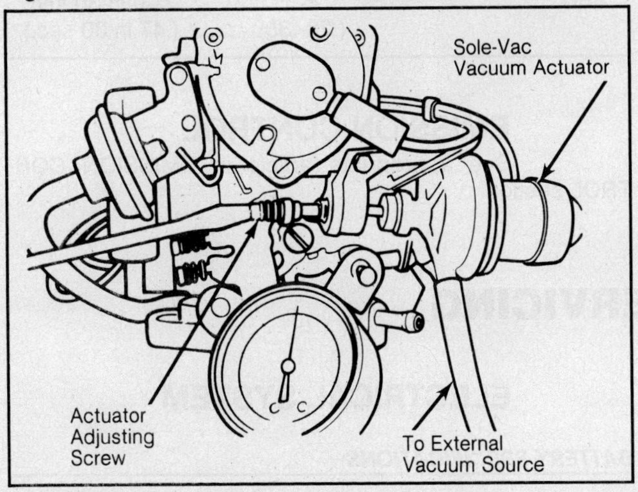

Always adjust curb idle speed after adjusting Sole-Vac vacuum actuator.

2) Disconnect vacuum hose from Sole-Vac vacuum actuator valve. Connect an external vacuum source. Apply 10-15 in. Hg vacuum to actuator. Adjust idle speed using vacuum actuator adjustment screw on throttle lever. *See Fig. 2.*

SOLE-VAC IDLE SPEED (RPM)

Application	Vacuum Applied
2.5L	
Auto. Trans. [1]	850
Man. Trans. [2]	950

[1] – Transmission in Drive.
[2] – Transmission in Neutral.

Fig. 3: Sole-Vac Actuator Hex Screw Location

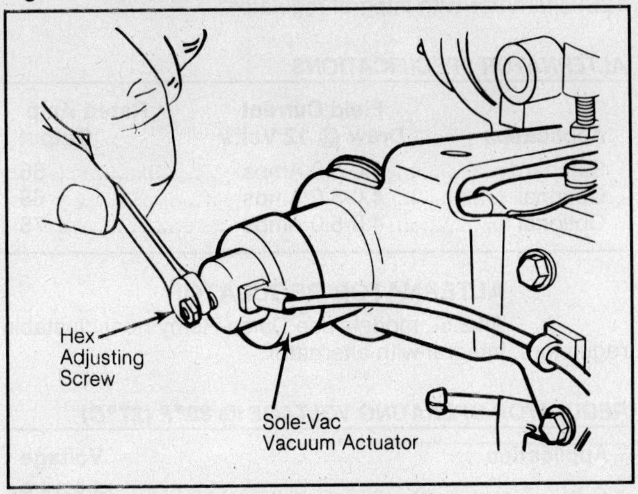

Use a 1/4" wrench to adjust curb idle speed.

CURB IDLE SPEED ADJUSTMENT

Warm engine to normal operating temperature, turn all accessories off. Disconnect and plug vacuum hose at Sole-Vac vacuum actuator. Adjust curb idle speed with 1/4" wrench. *See Fig. 3.* Reconnect vacuum hose at Sole-Vac vacuum actuator.

NOTE: Engine idle speed will vary 10-30 RPM during adjustment, due to closed loop fuel feedback operation.

IDLE SPEED (RPM)

Application	Curb Idle
2.5L	
Auto. Trans. [1]	700
Man. Trans. [2]	750

[1] – Transmission in Drive.
[2] – Transmission in Neutral.

ANTI-DIESEL ADJUSTMENT

1) With engine at normal operating temperature and all accessories off, disconnect and plug hose at Sole-Vac vacuum actuator. Disconnect wire at Sole-Vac electrical connector.

2) Using adjusting screw on throttle lever, adjust engine speed to 500 RPM in Neutral. *See Fig. 4.* Reconnect Sole-Vac vacuum actuator hose and wire connector. Disconnect tachometer from engine.

Fig. 4: Throttle Lever Adjusting Screw Location

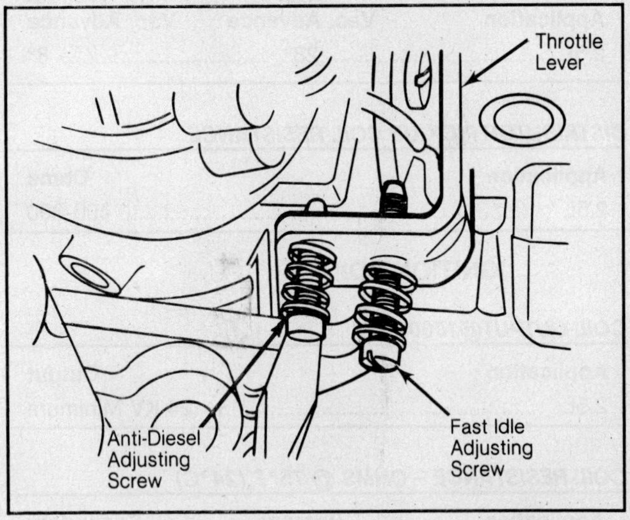

IDLE MIXTURE ADJUSTMENT

NOTE: The 2.5L is equipped with a Carter YFA 1-Bbl. carburetor. Air/Fuel mixture is controlled by a Microcomputer Unit (MCU). No idle mixture adjustments are required or possible.

COLD (FAST) IDLE RPM

Warm engine to normal operating temperature. Disconnect and plug EGR valve vacuum hose. Place transmission in Neutral. Position fast idle screw on 2nd

1985 Jeep 4 Tune-Up

TUNE-UP (Cont.)

step of fast idle cam and turn fast idle screw to obtain specified RPM. *See Fig. 4.* After adjustment, return throttle to idle position and reconnect EGR valve vacuum hose.

FAST IDLE SPEED (RPM)

Application	RPM
2.5L	
Auto. Trans.	2300
Man. Trans.	2000

AUTOMATIC CHOKE

The YFA 1-Bbl. carburetor uses a nonadjustable choke. This choke is preset at the factory and setting should not be changed.

FUEL PUMP

The 2.5L engine uses a mechanical fuel pump located on right side of engine.

FUEL PUMP SPECIFICATIONS

Application	Pressure psi (kg/cm²)	Volume Pints (Liters)
2.5L	4-5	1.0 in 30 sec.
	(.28-.35)	(.47 in 30 sec.)

EMISSION CONTROL

See appropriate article in EMISSION CONTROL section.

GENERAL SERVICING

IGNITION

DISTRIBUTOR

All 2.5L engines are equipped with Motorcraft SSI distributors.

TOTAL SPARK ADVANCE@2500 RPM

Application	With Vac. Advance	Without Vac. Advance
2.5L	28°	8°

DISTRIBUTOR PICK-UP COIL RESISTANCE

Application	Ohms
2.5L	400-800

IGNITION COIL

COIL OUTPUT@1000 RPM

Application	Output
2.5L	24 KV Minimum

COIL RESISTANCE – OHMS @ 75°F (24°C)

Application	Primary	Secondary
2.5L	1.13-1.23	7700-9300

FUEL SYSTEMS

CARBURETOR

Application	Model
2.5L	Carter YFA 1-Bbl.

ELECTRICAL SYSTEM

BATTERY SPECIFICATIONS

Application	Cold Cranking Amps [1]	Reserve Capacity Minutes
Standard	370	65
Optional	450	72

[1] – At 0°F (-18°C).

STARTER

2.5L engines use a Motorcraft positive engagement starter.

STARTER SPECIFICATIONS

Application	Volts	Amps	Test RPM
2.5L	12	67	7380-9356

ALTERNATOR

All 2.5L engines use a Delco-Remy 10SI or 12SI alternator with integral regulator.

ALTERNATOR SPECIFICATIONS

Application	Field Current Draw @ 12 Volts	Rated Amp Output
Standard	4.0-5.0 Amps	56
Optional	4.0-5.0 Amps	68
Optional	4.0-5.0 Amps	78

ALTERNATOR REGULATOR

All 2.5L models use Delco-Remy nonadjustable regulators, integral with alternator.

REGULATOR OPERATING VOLTAGE @ 80°F (27°C)

Application	Voltage
2.5L	13.9-14.9

GENERAL SERVICING (Cont.)

ADJUSTMENTS

BELT ADJUSTMENT

BELT ADJUSTMENT
Tension Using Strand Tension Gauge

Application	Lbs. (Kg)
New Belts	120-160 (53-71)
Used Belts	90-115 (40-51)
Serpentine Belts	180-200 (80-90)

SERVICE INTERVALS

REPLACEMENT INTERVALS

Component	Interval (Miles)
Oil Filter	7500
Air Filter	30,000
Fuel Filter	30,000
PCV Valve	30,000
Spark Plugs	30,000

CAPACITIES

FLUID CAPACITIES

Application	Quantity
Crankcase (Includes Filter)	4.0 qts. (3.3L)
Cooling System	
CJ7, Scrambler	9.0 qts. (8.5L)
Cherokee, Wagoneer	10.0 qts. (9.5L)
Man. Trans.	
CJ7, Scrambler (P/N 8983 000 000)	
4-Speed	3.5 pts. (1.7L)
5-Speed	4.0 pts. (1.9L)
Cherokee, Wagoneer (75W-90)	
4-Speed	3.7 qts. (3.5L)
5-Speed	3.5 qts. (3.3L)
Auto. Trans. (Dexron II)	
CJ7, Scrambler	17.0 pts. (8.0L)
Cherokee, Wagoneer	7.9 qts. (7.5L)
Transfer Case	
CJ7, Scrambler (75W-90)	4.0 pts. (1.9L)
Cherokee, Wagoneer (Dexron II)	
207	2.25 qts. (2.1L)
229	3.0 qts. (2.8L)
Front Axle (75W-90)	2.5 pts. (1.2L)
Rear Axle (75W-90) [1]	4.8 pts. (2.3L)
Fuel Tank	
Standard	13.5 gals. (51.0L)
Optional	20.2 gals. (76.5L)

[1] – Cherokee and Wagoneer rear axle capacity is same as front.

SYSTEM REFRIGERANT CAPACITIES

Application	Ounces
Cherokee & Wagoneer	36

1985 Jeep 6 Tune-Up

TUNE-UP

ENGINE IDENTIFICATION

Engine can be identified by the 4th character of engine Build Date Code number, located on a tag attached to right side of block between No. 2 and 3 cylinders.

The same code letter is also the 4th character in the Vehicle Identification Number (VIN), located at top left corner of dashboard.

VIN ENGINE CODE

Application	Code
4.2L (258") 2-Bbl.	C

TUNE-UP NOTES

NOTE: **When performing tune-up procedures described in this article, the following notes and precautions must be observed:**

When performing tune-up on vehicles equipped with a catalytic converter, do not allow or create a condition of engine misfire in one or more cylinders for an extended period of time. Damage to converter from overheating may occur, due to loading with unburned air/fuel mixture.

Due to production changes, always refer to Engine Tune-Up Decal in engine compartment before attempting tune-up. In the event of a conflict between specifications given in this manual and decal specifications, use the decal specifications.

ENGINE COMPRESSION

Check compression pressure with engine at normal operating temperature, all spark plugs removed, throttle and choke valves wide open and engine at cranking speed.

COMPRESSION SPECIFICATIONS

Compression Ratio	9.2:1
Compression Pressure	120-150 psi (8.4-10.5 kg/cm²)
Maximum Variation Between Cylinders	30 psi (2.1 kg/cm²)

VALVE ARRANGEMENT

E-I-I-E-I-E-E-I-E-I-I-E (Front-to-rear).

VALVE CLEARANCE

All engines are equipped with hydraulic lifters. Valve clearance is not adjustable.

SPARK PLUG TYPE

Application	Champion No.
All Models	RFN14LY

SPARK PLUG SPECIFICATIONS

Application	Gap In. (mm)	Torque Ft. Lbs. (N.m)
All Models	.035 (0.9)	7-15 (10-20)

HIGH TENSION WIRE RESISTANCE

Do not puncture spark plug wires with any type of probe. Remove spark plug wire and check resistance using an ohmmeter.

IGNITION COIL WIRE

Remove ignition coil wire from coil and distributor cap. Check terminals for corrosion and clean if necessary. Check coil wire resistance. Replace wire if resistance is excessive.

HIGH TENSION WIRE RESISTANCE (OHMS)

Wire Length	Minimum	Maximum
0-15"	3000	10,000
15-25"	4000	15,000
25-35"	6000	20,000
Over 35"	8000	25,000

DISTRIBUTOR

All models are equipped with Motorcraft Solid State Ignition (SSI) systems. No adjustments are required.

Fig. 1: Timing Marks and Firing Order

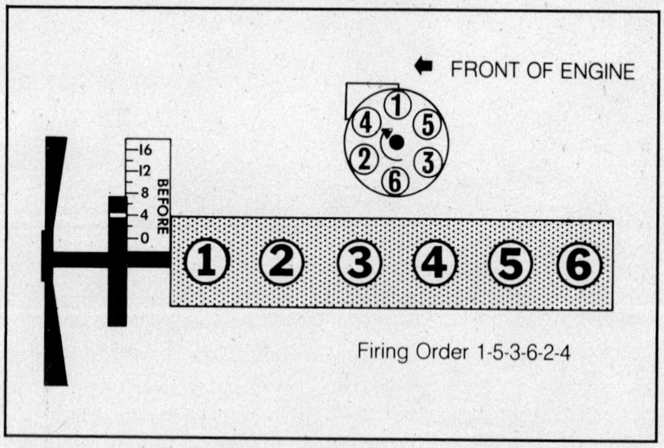

Magnetic probe located at 9.5° ATDC.

IGNITION TIMING

NOTE: **Engines are equipped with a receptacle for a magnetic probe timing light, located 9.5° ATDC. Do not use this location to check timing with a conventional light.**

TUNE-UP (Cont.)

MAGNETIC TIMING PROCEDURE

1) Set parking brake, and place transmission in Neutral. Start engine and run at idle to obtain normal operating temperature. Turn ignition off and connect timing light, using inductive pick-up or adapter. Do not puncture spark plug wire.

NOTE: If timing light has an adjustable advance control feature, turn the control to the "OFF" position.

2) Connect tachometer. Disconnect and plug vacuum hose at distributor. Disconnect vacuum switch assembly wire connector, located on top of valve cover. Start engine and increase engine speed to 1600 RPM.

3) Adjust timing. To set timing, loosen distributor clamp bolt and turn distributor. Recheck timing after clamp bolt is tightened.

MAGNETIC IGNITION TIMING SPECIFICATIONS

Application	Specification
4.2L	16.5-21.5° BTDC

NON-MAGNETIC TIMING PROCEDURE

1) Set parking brake and place transmission in Neutral (Drive for automatic transmissions). Start engine and run at idle to obtain normal operating temperature. Turn ignition off, and using inductive pick-up or adapter, connect timing light. Do not puncture spark plug wire.

NOTE: If timing light has an adjustable advance control feature, turn the control to the "OFF" position.

2) Disconnect and plug 4 in. Hg vacuum switch hose (Red and Black wires connected to switch). Disconnect distributor vacuum advance hose, and connect hose to 4 in. Hg vacuum switch. Disconnect wire connector from knock sensor, located in cylinder head. Using a jumper wire, ground knock sensor wire connector to engine block. Start engine.

3) With engine at idle speed (solenoid energized), check timing. If required, adjust timing to specification.

NON-MAGNETIC IGNITION TIMING SPECIFICATIONS

Application	Man. Trans.	Auto. Trans.
4.2L	9° BTDC	9° BTDC

HOT (SLOW) IDLE RPM

1) Warm engine to normal operating temperature. Set parking brake and place automatic transmission selector in Drive (Neutral on manual transmissions). Disconnect and plug vacuum hose from vacuum actuator. Disconnect solenoid wire connector.

2) Adjust curb idle screw to obtain correct curb idle. Apply 10-15 in. Hg vacuum to vacuum actuator. When throttle positioner is fully extended, adjust screw on throttle lever to set vacuum actuator RPM. Disconnect vacuum source.

3) Apply battery voltage to solenoid with a jumper wire. Turn A/C on (if equipped), and open throttle to allow solenoid to extend fully. Adjust hex-head screw to obtain solenoid RPM. Reconnect solenoid connector and vacuum hose.

CURB IDLE SPEED (RPM)

Application	Man. Trans.	Auto. Trans.
4.2L		
50 State	680	600
High Altitude	700	650

VACUUM ACTUATOR & SOLENOID IDLE (RPM)

Application	Vacuum Actuator	Solenoid Energized
All Models		
Man. Trans.	1100	900
Auto. Trans.	900	800

Fig. 2: Adjustment Points for Carter BBD Carburetor

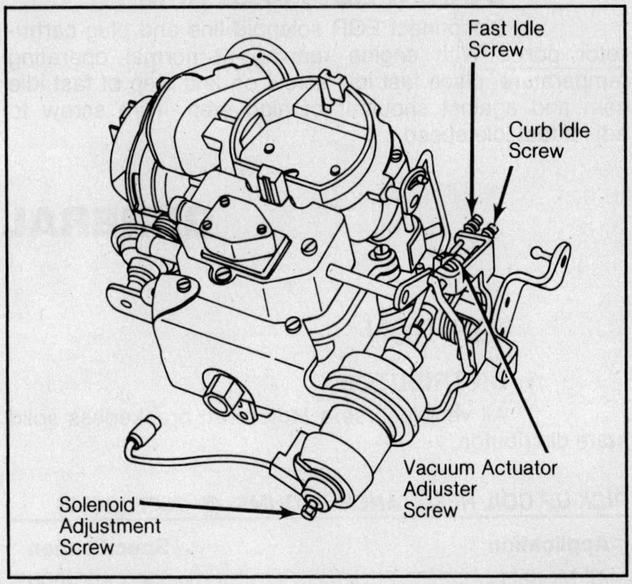

Holding solenoid maintains throttle position.

IDLE MIXTURE

NOTE: Be sure idle speed and timing are set before performing idle mixture adjustment. If mixture setting takes more than 3 minutes, run engine at 2000 RPM in Neutral for 1 minute, and resume adjustment.

TACHOMETER (LEAN DROP) PROCEDURE

NOTE: Idle mixture adjustment is not part of a normal tune-up. DO NOT adjust mixture unless carburetor has been disassembled or vehicle fails emissions testing.

1) Remove carburetor and locate roll pins blocking idle mixture screws. Drill through throttle body on closed end of roll pin hole. Drive pins out with punch. Reinstall carburetor.

1985 Jeep 6 Tune-Up

TUNE-UP (Cont.)

2) Warm vehicle to operating temperature, and adjust idle speed. Place automatic transmission selector in Drive (Neutral for manual transmissions). Turn mixture screws in (lean) until RPM drops. Turn screw out until highest RPM is reached.

3) Turn mixture screws in until specified "Lean Drop" is obtained. Adjust both screws equally. When mixture is correctly adjusted, replace roll pin to block adjustment screws.

NOTE: **If final RPM differs more than 30 RPM from specified curb idle speed, reset curb idle, and repeat mixture adjustment.**

LEAN DROP (RPM)

Application	Man. Trans.	Auto. Trans.
All Models	50	50

COLD (FAST) IDLE RPM

Disconnect EGR solenoid line and plug carburetor ports. With engine running at normal operating temperature, place fast idle screw on 2nd step of fast idle cam and against shoulder of high step. Turn screw to adjust fast idle speed.

FAST IDLE SPEED (RPM)

Application	Man. Trans.	Auto. Trans.
All Models	1700	1700

AUTOMATIC CHOKE SETTING

Choke coil cover is riveted in place and no adjustment is necessary or possible.

FUEL PUMP

Perform fuel pump test with air cleaner removed and fuel inlet line or filter disconnected at carburetor. Disconnect fuel return line at fuel filter and plug nipple on filter. Make all tests at idle speed.

FUEL PUMP SPECIFICATIONS

Application	Pressure psi (kg/cm²)	Volume Pts. (Liters)
All Models	4.0-5.0 (.28-.35)	1.0 in 30 sec. (.47 in 30 sec.)

GENERAL SERVICING

IGNITION

DISTRIBUTOR

All vehicles use a Motorcraft breakerless solid state distributor.

PICK-UP COIL RESISTANCE – OHMS @ 75°F (24°C)

Application	Specification
All Models	400-800

TOTAL SPARK ADVANCE @ 2000 RPM

Application	With Vac. Advance	Without Vac. Advance
All Models	30.5°	7.5-12.5°

IGNITION COIL

COIL OUTPUT @ 1000 RPM

Application	Output
All Models	24KV Minimum

IGNITION COIL RESISTANCE - OHMS @ 75°F (24°C)

Application	Primary	Secondary
All Models	1.13-1.23	7700-9300

FUEL SYSTEMS

CARBURETORS

Application	Model
All Models	Carter BBD 2-Bbl.

ELECTRICAL SYSTEM

BATTERY

BATTERY SPECIFICATIONS

Application	Cold Cranking [1] Amps	Reserve Capacity Minutes
CJ7 & Scrambler		
Standard	421	75
Optional	452	81
Grand Wagoneer & Truck		
Standard	421	75
Optional	450	80
Optional	440	135

[1] – At 0°F (-18°C).

GENERAL SERVICING (Cont.)

STARTER

All models are equipped with Motorcraft positive engagement starters.

STARTER SPECIFICATIONS

Application	Volts	Amps	Test RPM
All Models	12	67	7380-9356

ALTERNATOR

All models use Delco-Remy solid state alternators with internal voltage regulator.

ALTERNATOR SPECIFICATIONS

Application	Field Current Draw @ 12 Volts	Rated Amp Output
Standard	[1] 4.0-5.0	42
Optional	[1] 4.0-5.0	56
Optional	[1] 4.0-5.0	78

[1] – At 80°F (27°C).

ALTERNATOR REGULATORS

All models use Delco-Remy solid state regulators, integral with alternator. Regulator is nonadjustable.

ADJUSTMENTS

BELT ADJUSTMENT

BELT ADJUSTMENT
Tension in Lbs. (Kg) Using Strand Tension Gauge

Application	New Belts	Used Belts
P/S Belt	120-140 (54-63)	90-115 (40-52)
Other Belts	120-160 (54-72)	90-115 (40-52)
Serpentine	180-200 (82-90)	140-160 (63-72)

SERVICE INTERVALS

REPLACEMENT INTERVALS

Component	Interval (Miles)
Air Filter	30,000
Fuel Filter	30,000
Oil & Filter	7500
PCV Valve	30,000
Spark Plugs	30,000

CAPACITIES

FLUID CAPACITIES

Application	Capacity
Cooling System (Includes Heater)	
Grand Wagoneer & Truck	12.5 qts. (11.8L)
CJ7 & Scrambler	10.5 qts. (9.9L)
Crankcase (Includes Filter)	6.0 qts. (5.7L)
Man. Trans. [1]	
T4 4-Speed	3.5 pts. (1.7L)
T176 4-Speed	3.5 pts. (1.7L)
T5 5-Speed	4.0 pts. (1.9L)
Auto. Trans. (Dexron II)	
Refill	8.5 pts. (4.0L)
Overhaul	17.0 pts. (8.0L)
Transfer Case	
CJ7 & Scrambler [1]	4.0 pts. (1.9L)
All Others (Dexron II)	6.0 pts. (2.8L)
Drive Axles (SAE 75W-90)	
CJ7 & Scrambler	
Front	2.5 pts. (1.2L)
Rear	4.8 pts. (2.3L)
Grand Wagoneer & Truck	
Front w/o Selec-trac	3.0 pts. (1.4L)
Front with Selec-trac	4.5 pts. (2.1L)
Rear Model 44	4.8 pts. (2.3L)
Rear Model 60	6.0 pts. (2.8L)
Fuel Tank	
CJ7 & Scrambler	
Standard	14.8 gals. (56.0L)
Optional	20.0 gals. (76.0L)
Grand Wagoneer	20.3 gals. (76.8L)
Truck	18.2 gals. (68.8L)

[1] – Use transmission lubricant (8983 000 000) only.

SYSTEM REFRIGERANT CAPACITIES

Application	Ounces
CJ7 & Scrambler	40
All Other Models	36

1985 Jeep V6 Tune-Up

TUNE-UP

ENGINE IDENTIFICATION

Engines can be identified by the 4th character of the VIN. The VIN number is stamped on a plate attached to the left top side of dash.

VIN ENGINE CODE

Application	VIN Code
2.8L (173") 2-Bbl.	W

TUNE-UP NOTES

NOTE: **When performing tune-up procedures described in this article, these notes and precautions must be observed.**

Due to changes and corrections, always refer to Engine Tune-Up Decal in engine compartment before attempting tune-up. In the event of a conflict between specifications given in this manual and decal specifications, decal specifications prevail.

When performing tune-up on vehicles equipped with a catalytic converter, do not allow or create a condition of engine misfire in one or more cylinders for an extended period of time. Damage to converter from overheating may occur due to loading with unburned fuel.

ENGINE COMPRESSION

Disconnect 2-wire connector at ignition coil. With air cleaner removed and throttle and choke wide open, crank engine through at least 4 compression strokes.

COMPRESSION SPECIFICATIONS

Compression Ratio	8.5:1
Compression Pressure	Min. of 100 psi (7.0 kg/cm²)
Maximum Pressure Variation	30%

VALVE ARRANGEMENT

Left Bank – E-I-I-E-I-E (Front-to-rear).
Right Bank – E-I-E-I-I-E (Front-to-rear).

VALVE CLEARANCE

All engines have hydraulic lifters. Lifters should be adjusted to 1 1/2 turns down from zero lash.

SPARK PLUGS

SPARK PLUG TYPE

Application	AC Number
2.8L	R43CTS

SPARK PLUG SPECIFICATIONS

Application	Gap In. (mm)	Torque Ft. Lbs. (N.m)
2.8L	.041 (1.0)	7-15 (9-20)

HIGH TENSION WIRE RESISTANCE

Carefully remove ends of wire from spark plug and distributor. Using an ohmmeter, check resistance while gently twisting wire. Spark plug boot should be turned 1/2 turn before removing. If resistance is not within specifications, or fluctuates from infinity to any value, replace cable.

HIGH TENSION WIRE RESISTANCE

Application	Specification
All Models	31,500-73,500

DISTRIBUTOR

Federal models are equipped with a Delco High Energy Ignition (HEI) distributor. California models have Delco HEI-EST distributors. No adjustments are required.

Fig. 1: Firing Order and Timing Mark

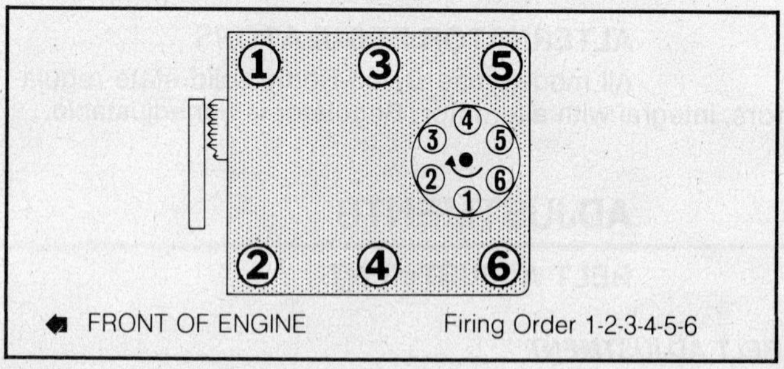

Magnetic probe located at 9.5°ATDC.

IGNITION TIMING

1) Install timing light with an adapter between No. 1 spark plug and No. 1 spark plug wire, or use an inductive type pick-up. Do not puncture wire.

2) Check or adjust ignition timing with engine at normal operating temperature, distributor advance line disconnected and plugged, and automatic transmission in Drive (if equipped).

IGNITION TIMING SPECIFICATIONS (Degrees BTDC@RPM)

Application	Man. Trans.	Auto. Trans.
2.8L	10@700	10@700

HOT (SLOW) IDLE RPM

1) Make adjustments with engine at normal operating temperature, choke fully open, air cleaner installed and A/C off. Set base idle speed with idle speed screw.

2) If vehicle is equipped with A/C, disconnect electrical lead from compressor and turn on A/C switch. Open throttle slightly to allow solenoid to extend. Adjust solenoid idle by turning screw in back of solenoid.

3) Disconnect vacuum hose from idle kick solenoid and connect vacuum pump to solenoid. Apply 15 in. Hg vacuum to solenoid. Adjust hex-head adjustment screw to the specified solenoid RPM.

TUNE-UP (Cont.)

SLOW IDLE SPEED (RPM)

Application	Curb Idle
2.8L	700

IDLE MIXTURE

NOTE: Mixture adjustment is not a normal tune-up procedure. DO NOT remove idle mixture plugs unless vehicle fails emissions testing or throttle body has been disassembled.

MIXTURE SCREW PLUG REMOVAL

1) Remove carburetor from engine. Invert carburetor. Make 2 parallel cuts, one on each side of the locator point with a hacksaw. Cuts should not extend more than 1/8" beyond the locator point. *See Fig. 2.*

Fig. 2: Removing Idle Mixture Plug

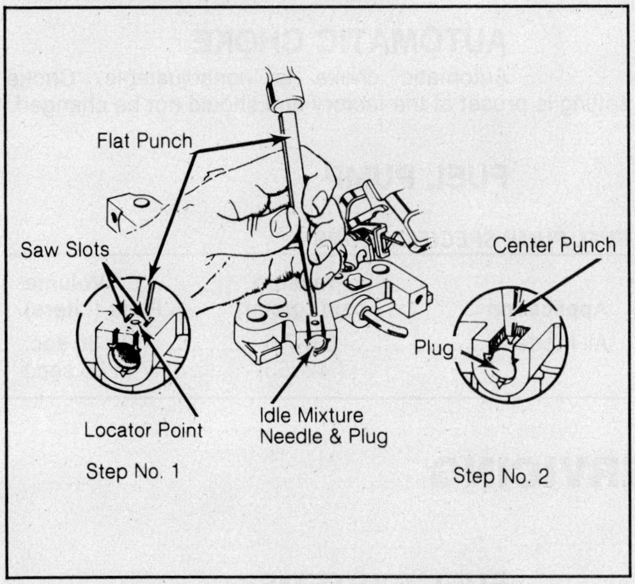

Distance between saw cuts depends on the size of the punch to be used.

2) Place a flat punch near the end of the saw marks. Hold the punch at a 45° angle. Drive it into the throttle body until the casting breaks away, exposing the steel plug.

3) Hold a center punch in a vertical position and drive it into the plug. Now hold punch at a 45° angle, and drive plug out of casting.

PROPANE ENRICHMENT PROCEDURE

Federal Models (HEI)

1) Engine must be at normal operating temperature and A/C off. Set parking brake and block drive wheels. If vehicles are equipped with vacuum parking brake release, disconnect and plug hose at brake.

2) Disconnect and plug vacuum advance hose. Connect tachometer to engine. Adjust timing and reconnect vacuum advance hose. Set idle speed.

3) Disconnect crankcase ventilation tube from air cleaner. Using Propane Enrichment Adapter J-26911, insert hose with rubber stopper (from propane valve) into air cleaner snorkel. Ensure propane cartridge is vertical.

4) With engine idling in Drive (auto. trans.) or Neutral (man. trans.), open propane supply control valve slowly. Engine speed will increase. Add propane until engine speed begins to drop from over-richness. Note maximum enriched idle RPM.

5) The maximum enriched idle RPM is the idle RPM plus propane enrichment RPM. Engine speed should rise above normal idle by amount specified. If so, mixture is correct. Proceed to step **9)**.

6) If speed is incorrect, remove idle mixture screw plug. Carburetor must be removed and a punch driven through bottom of throttle body to remove plug. Seat screw, then back out 3 turns.

7) Place transmission in Drive (auto. trans.) or Neutral (man. trans.). Back out screw slowly until maximum idle speed is reached. Set maximum enriched idle speed.

8) Turn mixture screw in (clockwise) 1/8 turn at a time until idle speed is correct. Recheck maximum enriched speed with propane. If incorrect, repeat step **7)**. Check and adjust fast idle speed.

9) Turn off engine. Remove propane, connect crankcase ventilation tube and reconnect all vacuum hoses.

PROPANE ENRICHED RPM

Application	RPM
Federal	20

IDLE MIXTURE ADJUSTMENT

California Models (HEI-EST)

1) Modify Carburetor Adjuster (J-29030-B) by grinding off 1/4" from front of tool. Remove carburetor from engine, and remove idle mixture screw plug. Turn mixture screw in until lightly seated and back out 4 turns. If plug in air horn (covering idle air bleed) has been removed, replace air horn.

2) Remove vent stack screen assembly to gain access to lean mixture screw. Turn lean mixture screw until lightly bottomed and back out 2 1/2 turns. Some resistance should be felt. If there is no resistance, remove screw and check for spring.

3) Install carburetor on engine with modified Carburetor Adjuster (J-29030-B) installed on mixture adjustment screw. Do not install air cleaner. Disconnect bowl vent line at carburetor. Disconnect the EGR valve hose and canister purge hose at carburetor. Cap carburetor ports.

4) Disconnect carburetor-to-temperture sensor hose on air cleaner and plug open hose. Connect a dwell meter lead to the mixture control solenoid dwell test lead (Green connector).

5) Set dwell meter to 6-cylinder position. Connect a tachometer to distributor lead (Brown connector). Transmission should be in Park (auto. trans.) or Neutral (man. trans.). Start engine and bring to operating temperature.

6) Run engine at 3000 RPM for at least 3 minutes with fast idle screw on high step of cam, and until engine is in closed loop operation. Adjust the lean mixture screw slowly to allow time for dwell to stabilize.

7) It is normal for dwell to vary over a narrow range of approximately 5°. Turn screw to obtain an average dwell of 35°. If unable to adjust, inspect main metering circuit for leaks or restrictions. Return engine to idle.

TUNE-UP (Cont.)

8) Adjust idle mixture screw to obtain average dwell of 25° with cooling fan in off cycle. Adjustment is very sensitive. Make final check with carburetor adjuster removed.

9) If unable to adjust, inspect idle system for leaks or restrictions. Disconnect mixture control solenoid when cooling fan is in off cycle. Check for an RPM change of at least 50 RPM. If RPM does not change, check idle air bleed circuit.

10) Run engine at 3000 RPM for a few moments and note dwell reading. Dwell should show an average of 35°. If not, reset lean mixture screw. Then reset idle mixture screw to obtain 25° dwell.

11) When dwell readings have been set, reconnect all hoses and install vent screen and air cleaner. Set idle speed.

COLD (FAST) IDLE RPM

Warm up vehicle. Remove and plug EGR valve hose. Place fast idle screw on highest step of fast idle cam. Adjust fast idle screw to obtain fast idle RPM.

FAST IDLE SPEED (RPM)

Application	Man. Trans.	Auto. Trans.
2.8L	2000-2200	2200-2400

THROTTLE POSITION SENSOR (TPS) ADJUSTMENT

CALIFORNIA ONLY

1) DO NOT remove the TPS adjustment screw plug unless the TPS is not adjusted correctly or it is necessary to replace the air horn assembly, float bowl, TPS sensor, or TPS adjustment screw.

2) Using a 5/64" drill, carefully drill a hole in the steel cup plug covering the TPS adjustment screw. Plug is located next to the TPS plunger bore. Remove steel plug using a small slide hammer.

3) Disconnect the TPS connector and jumper all 3 terminals. Connect a digital voltmeter from TPS connector center terminal (B) to bottom terminal (C).

4) With ignition on and engine stopped, turn the TPS screw with flat bladed screwdriver to obtain specified voltage at curb idle position. Air conditioner must be off and Idle Speed Control fully retracted.

5) After adjustment, a new cup plug or silicone sealant rubber RTV must be inserted in the air horn.

THROTTLE POSITION SENSOR SPECIFICATIONS

Application	Volts@Idle
California Models	.26

AUTOMATIC CHOKE

Automatic choke is nonadjustable. Choke setting is preset at the factory and should not be changed.

FUEL PUMP

FUEL PUMP SPECIFICATIONS

Application	Pressure psi (kg/cm²)	Volume Pints (Liters)
All Models	6.0-7.5	1 in 30 sec.
	(.42-.53)	(.47 in 30 sec.)

GENERAL SERVICING

IGNITION

DISTRIBUTOR

California models use Delco High Energy Ignition Electronic Spark Timing (HEI-EST) system with 5-pin module and a detonation sensor. All other models use a standard HEI system with 4-pin module.

DISTRIBUTOR PICK-UP COIL RESISTANCE

Application	Ohms
All Models	500-1500

IGNITION COIL

IGNITION COIL RESISTANCE – OHMS @ 75°F (24°C)

Application	Primary	Secondary
All Models	0.9-1.4	7300-11,100

FUEL SYSTEMS

CARBURETORS

Application	Model
2.8L V6	
Federal	Rochester 2SE 2-Bbl.
California	Rochester E2SE 2-Bbl.

ELECTRICAL SYSTEM

BATTERY

Application	Cold Cranking [1] Amps	Reserve Capacity Minutes
2.8L		
Standard	390	75
Optional	425	82

[1] – At 0°F (-18°C).

GENERAL SERVICING (Cont.)

STARTER

All 2.8L V6 engines are equipped with Delco-Remy overrunning clutch starters.

STARTER SPECIFICATIONS

Application	Volts	Amps	Test RPM
All Models	9.0	45-70	7000-11,900

ALTERNATOR

All 2.8L V6 engines are equipped with Delco-Remy alternators with integral voltage regulator.

ALTERNATOR SPECIFICATIONS

Application	Field Current Draw @ 12 Volts	Rated Amp Output
Standard	[1] 4.0-5.0 Amps	56
Optional	[1] 4.0-5.0 Amps	66
Optional	[1] 4.0-5.0 Amps	78

[1] – At 80°F (27°C).

ALTERNATOR REGULATOR

All 2.8L V6 engines are equipped with Delco-Remy nonadjustable voltage regulators, integral with alternator.

ADJUSTMENTS

BELT ADJUSTMENT

Using a strand tension gauge, measure belt tension midway between pulleys. If tension is not as specified, adjust tension or replace belt. Used belts are any that have been rotated at least 1 complete revolution by engine pulley.

BELT ADJUSTMENT
Tension in Lbs. (Kg) Using Strand Tension Gauge

Application	New Belts	Used Belts
P/S Belt	120-140 (54-63)	90-115 (40-52)
Other Belts	120-160 (54-72)	90-115 (40-52)
Serpentine	180-200 (82-90)	140-160 (63-72)

SERVICE INTERVALS

REPLACEMENT INTERVALS

Component	Interval (Miles)
Air Filter	30,000
Fuel Filter	30,000
Oil & Filter	7,500
PCV Valve & Filter	30,000
Spark Plugs	30,000

CAPACITIES

FLUID CAPACITIES

Application	Quantity
Cooling System	[1] 12.0 qts. (11.4L)
Crankcase	[2] 4.0 qts. (3.8L)
Auto. Trans. (Dexron II)	15.8 pts. (7.5L)
Man. Trans. (75W-90) [3]	
4-Speed	3.7 qts. (3.5L)
5-Speed	3.5 qts. (3.3L)
Differentials (75W-90)	1.25 qts. (1.2L)
Transfer Case (Dexron II)	
W/Full-Time 4WD	6.0 pts. (2.8L)
W/Part-Time 4WD	4.5 pts. (2.1L)
Fuel Tank	
Standard	13.5 gal. (51.1L)
Optional	20.2 gal. (76.5L)

[1] – Includes 2.3 qts. (2.2L) in recovery system.
[2] – With or without filter.
[3] – Fill to bottom of filler hole.

SYSTEM REFRIGERANT CAPACITIES

Application	Ounces
Cherokee & Wagoneer	36

1985 Jeep V8 Tune-Up

TUNE-UP

ENGINE IDENTIFICATION

Engine can be identified by the 4th character of engine Build Date Code, located on a tag attached to the right cylinder head valve cover.

The same code letter is also the 4th character of Vehicle Identification Number (VIN), located on a plate attached to top left corner of instrument panel.

VIN ENGINE CODE

Application	Code
5.9L (360") 2-Bbl.	N

TUNE-UP NOTES

NOTE: When performing tune-up procedures described in this article, the following notes and precautions must be observed.

Due to production changes, always refer to Engine Tune-Up Decal in engine compartment before attempting tune-up. In the event of a conflict between specifications given in this manual and decal specifications, use the decal specifications.

When performing tune-up on vehicles equipped with a catalytic converter, do not allow or create a condition of engine misfire in one or more cylinders for an extended period of time. Damage to converter may occur due to loading with unburned air/fuel mixture.

ENGINE COMPRESSION

Measure compression pressure with engine at normal operating temperature, spark plugs removed, throttle and choke valves wide open and engine at cranking speed.

COMPRESSION SPECIFICATIONS

Compression Ratio	8.25:1
Compression Pressure	120-140 psi (8.4-9.8 kg/cm²)
Maximum Pressure Variation	30 psi (2.1 kg/cm²)

VALVE ARRANGEMENT

Both Banks – E-I-I-E-E-I-I-E (Front-to-rear).

VALVE CLEARANCE

All engines are equipped with hydraulic lifters. Valve clearance is not adjustable.

SPARK PLUGS

SPARK PLUG TYPE

Application	Champion No.
All Models	RN12LY

SPARK PLUG SPECIFICATIONS

Application	Gap In. (mm)	Torque Ft. Lbs. (N.m)
All Models	.035 (0.9)	22-33 (30-45)

HIGH TENSION WIRE RESISTANCE

Do not puncture spark plug wires with any type of probe. Remove spark plug wire and check resistance using an ohmmeter.

IGNITION COIL WIRE

Remove ignition coil wire from coil and distributor cap. Check terminals for corrosion and clean if necessary. Check coil wire resistance. Replace wire if resistance is excessive.

HIGH TENSION WIRE RESISTANCE (OHMS)

Wire Length	Minimum	Maximum
0-15"	3000	10,000
15-25"	4000	15,000
25-35"	6000	20,000
Over 35"	8000	25,000

DISTRIBUTOR

All models are equipped with Solid State Ignition (SSI) systems. No adjustments are required.

Fig. 1: Timing Mark and Firing Order

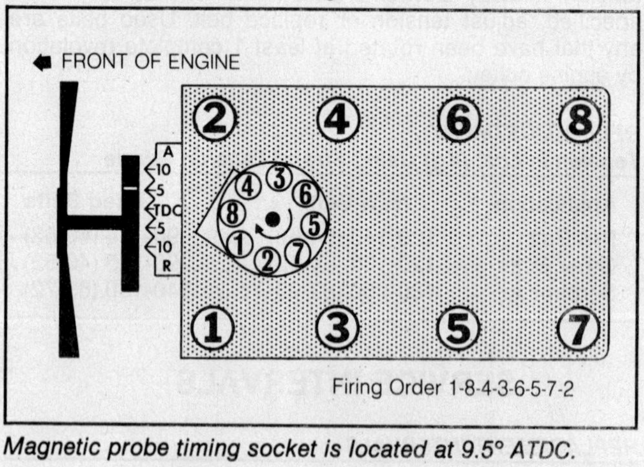

Magnetic probe timing socket is located at 9.5° ATDC.

IGNITION TIMING

NOTE: Engines are equipped with a receptacle for a magnetic probe timing light, located 9.5° ATDC. Do not use this location for timing with a conventional light.

Warm engine and allow to idle. Disconnect and plug distributor vacuum line. Check ignition timing. To adjust, loosen distributor clamp bolt and turn distributor. Check timing again after distributor bolt is tightened.

TUNE-UP (Cont.)

IGNITION TIMING SPECIFICATIONS (Degrees BTDC)

Application	Man. Trans.	Auto. Trans.
5.9L	12@600	12@600

HOT (SLOW) IDLE RPM

1) Set parking brake and block drive wheels. Connect tachometer to engine. Warm engine to operating temperature and place in Neutral (manual) or Drive (automatic).

2) Turn hex head screw on solenoid carriage to adjust solenoid RPM. Disconnect solenoid wire and adjust idle speed screw to obtain curb idle.

3) If equipped with dashpot, depress stem fully, and measure clearance between stem and throttle lever. Turn dashpot to adjust to .093" (2.4 mm) clearance. Tighten lock nut and remove test equipment.

IDLE SPEED (RPM) WITH SOLENOID ENERGIZED

Application	Specification
5.9L	600

IDLE MIXTURE

NOTE: **Idle mixture adjustment is not part of a regular tune-up. DO NOT adjust mixture unless carburetor has been disassembled or vehicle fails emissions testing.**

TACHOMETER (LEAN DROP) PROCEDURE

NOTE: **Ensure idle speed and timing are set before performing idle mixture adjustment. If mixture setting takes more than 3 minutes, run engine at 2000 RPM in Neutral for 1 minute. Resume adjustment.**

1) Warm engine to normal operating temperature. Note position of idle mixture screw slot, and remove limiter caps. If screw moved during cap removal, adjust to prior position.

2) Start engine and run in Neutral (man. trans.) or Drive (auto. trans.). Adjust idle to specified RPM.

3) Turn mixture screws clockwise (leaner) until engine speed begins to drop. Then turn screws counterclockwise (richer) until highest RPM reading is obtained. This is lean best idle. Finally, turn screws clockwise until specified "Lean Drop" (RPM) is obtained.

NOTE: **If final RPM differs more than 30 RPM from specified curb idle speed, reset curb idle and repeat mixture adjustment.**

4) Carefully install new limiter caps with tabs positioned against full rich stop. Press caps fully into place.

LEAN DROP (RPM)

Application	Man. Trans.	Auto. Trans.
All Models	50	20

COLD (FAST) IDLE RPM

Disconnect EGR vacuum line and plug carburetor port. Let engine run at idle in Neutral until it reaches normal operating temperature. Place fast idle screw on 2nd step of fast idle cam and against shoulder of high step. Adjust screw to set fast idle RPM.

FAST IDLE SPEED (RPM)

Application	Man. Trans.	Auto. Trans.
All Models	1500	1600

AUTOMATIC CHOKE SETTING

To adjust automatic choke, grind-off choke cover retaining rivets or loosen cover retaining screws. Rotate cover in direction indicated by arrow on face of cover. Adjust to specified setting.

AUTOMATIC CHOKE SETTING

50-State (Auto. Trans.)	2NR

FUEL PUMP

Perform fuel pump test with air cleaner removed and fuel inlet line or filter disconnected at carburetor. Disconnect fuel return line at fuel filter and plug nipple on filter. Make all tests at idle speed.

FUEL PUMP SPECIFICATIONS

Application	Pressure psi (kg/cm^2)	Volume Pints (Liters)
All Models	5.0-6.5	1.0 in 30 sec.
	(.35-.46)	(.47 in 30 sec.)

GENERAL SERVICING

IGNITION

DISTRIBUTOR

All models are equipped with Motorcraft breakerless solid state distributors. No adjustments are required.

DISTRIBUTOR PICK-UP COIL RESISTANCE

Application	Ohms
All Models	400-800

1985 Jeep V8 Tune-Up

GENERAL SERVICING (Cont.)

TOTAL SPARK ADVANCE @ 2000 RPM

Application	With Vac. Advance	Without Vac. Advance
All Models	30°	6-10.5°

IGNITION COIL

COIL OUTPUT @ 1000 RPM

Application	Output
All Models	24 KV min.

IGNITION COIL RESISTANCE – Ohms @ 75°F (24°C)

Application	Primary	Secondary
All Models	1.13-1.23	7700-9300

FUEL SYSTEMS

CARBURETORS

Application	Model
All Models	Motorcraft 2150 2-Bbl.

ELECTRICAL SYSTEM

BATTERY

BATTERY SPECIFICATIONS

Application	Cold Cranking [1] Amps	Reserve Capacity Minutes
Standard	421	75
Optional	450	80
Optional	440	135

[1] – At 0°F (-18°C).

STARTER

All models are equipped with Motorcraft positive engagement starters.

STARTER SPECIFICATIONS

Application	Volts	Amps	Test RPM
All Models	12	67	7380-9356

ALTERNATORS

All models are equipped with Delco-Remy solid state alternators with integral voltage regulator.

ALTERNATOR REGULATORS

All models use Delco-Remy solid state regulators, integral with alternator. Regulator is nonadjustable.

ALTERNATOR SPECIFICATIONS

Application	Field Current Draw @ 12 Volts	Rated Amp Output
Standard	[1] 4.0-5.0	42
Optional	[1] 4.0-5.0	56
Optional	[1] 4.0-5.0	78
Optional	[1] 4.0-5.0	85

[1] – At 80°F (27°C).

ADJUSTMENTS

BELT ADJUSTMENT

BELT ADJUSTMENT
Tension in Lbs. (Kg) Using Strand Tension Gauge

Application	New Belt	Used Belt
New Belts	125-155	90-115 (41-52)

SERVICE INTERVALS

REPLACEMENT INTERVALS

Component	Interval (Miles)
Air Filter	30,000
Fuel Filter	30,000
Oil & Filter	7500
PCV Valve	30,000
Spark Plugs	30,000

CAPACITIES

FLUID CAPACITIES

Application	Capacity
Cooling System (Includes Heater)	15.5 qts. (14.7L)
Crankcase (Includes Filter)	5.0 qts. (4.7L)
Man. Trans. [1]	
T176 4-Speed	3.5 pts. (1.7L)
Auto. Trans. (Dexron II)	
Refill	8.5 pts. (4.0L)
Overhaul	17.0 pts. (8.0L)
Transfer Case (Dexron II)	6.0 pts. (2.8L)
Drive Axles (75W-90)	
Front w/o Selec-Trac	3.0 pts. (1.4L)
Front with Selec-Trac	4.5 pts. (2.1L)
Rear Model 44	4.8 pts. (2.3L)
Rear Model 60	6.0 pts. (2.8L)
Fuel Tank	
Grand Wagoneer	20.3 gals. (76.8L)
Truck	18.2 gals. (68.9L)

[1] – Use transmission lubricant (8983 000 000) only.

SYSTEM REFRIGERANT CAPACITIES

Application	Ounces
Grand Wagoneer & Truck	36

1985 Jeep 4 Turbo Diesel Tune-Up

TUNE-UP

ENGINE IDENTIFICATION

Engine can be identified by the 4th character of the Vehicle Identification Number (VIN), located on a plate attached to top left corner of instrument panel.

The engine identification plate is attached to the front, right side of cylinder block. The first three characters of the engine code denote engine family, indirect fuel injection, and displacement.

VIN ENGINE CODE

Application	Code
2.1L Turbo Diesel	B

TUNE-UP NOTES

NOTE: **When performing tune-up procedures described in this article, these notes and precautions must be followed.**

Due to late changes and corrections, always refer to Engine Tune-Up Decal in engine compartment before attempting tune-up. If the decal specifications are different than the specifications presented here, use decal specifications.

Adjustment of injectors or internal adjustment of injection pump must be done in a properly equipped injector shop with clean environment.

Prior to checking compression, ensure battery is fully charged to avoid battery run down. Crank engine through at least 6 compression strokes before recording reading.

ENGINE COMPRESSION

Disconnect fuel shut-off solenoid wire. Remove injectors. Install Compression Gauge and Adapter (J-35129) into injector hole. Install injector retaining clamps. Crank engine until no further rise in pressure is indicated on gauge.

If piston rings and valves are in good condition, the highest pressure increase will be seen on the 1st full compression stroke. Compression will build up to maximum on subsequent strokes.

If compression increases only gradually on each compression stroke, this indicates that burnt valve seats or worn valve guides. If maximum pressure is low on all cylinders, this indicates worn pistons, rings or valves.

CAUTION: **DO NOT add oil to the cylinders for a wet compression test. The high compression ratio could cause the oil to ignite and cause serious bodily harm.**

COMPRESSION SPECIFICATIONS

Application	Specification
Compression Ratio	21.5:1

VALVE ARRANGEMENT

E-I-E-I-E-I-E-I (Rear-to-front)

VALVE CLEARANCE

NOTE: **The number 1 (one) cylinder is located at the flywheel/drive plate end of the engine.**

CAUTION: **As each adjustment screw is tightened, ensure that the bottom of the screw is aligned with the valve stem. If the adjustment screw is not aligned with the stem when tightened, it can cause the stem to bend.**

1) Rotate crankshaft clockwise (viewed from front of engine) until No. 1 exhaust valve is wide open. Adjust clearances for number 3 intake and number 4 exhaust.

2) With No. 3 exhaust valve wide open, adjust No. 4 intake and No. 2 exhaust. With No. 4 exhaust valve wide open, adjust No. 2 intake and No. 1 exhaust. With No. 2 exhaust valve wide open, adjust No. 1 intake and No. 3 exhaust.

VALVE CLEARANCE ADJUSTMENT

Application	[1] Clearance
Intake	.008" (.20 mm)
Exhaust	.010" (.25 mm)

[1] - Cold.

GLOW PLUGS

Glow plugs protrude into precombustion chambers in the cylinder head. The glow plugs heat precombustion chambers to aid cold weather start-ups. A temperature controlled timer determines the heating duration of the glow plugs by controlling the glow plug relays.

Fig. 1: 2.1L 4-Cylinder Diesel Firing Order

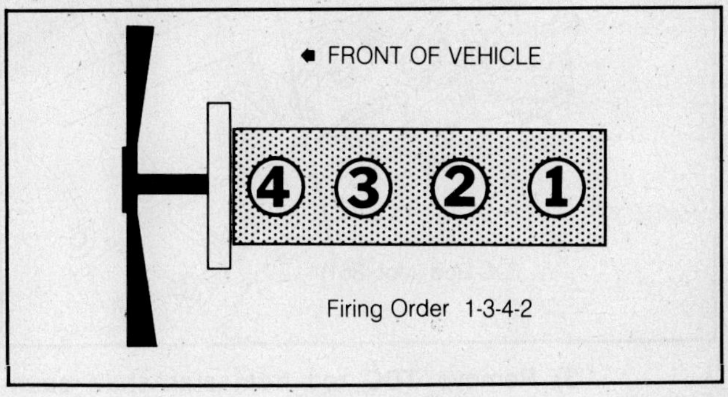

INJECTION TIMING

STATIC TIMING

1) Loosen control cable screw at injection pump and turn control cable clevis pin 1/4 turn to disengage cold start system control. Rotate crankshaft clockwise 2 revolutions and align camshaft and injection pump sprocket timing marks with indexes on timing belt cover. *See Fig. 2.*

TUNE-UP (Cont.)

Fig. 2: Location of Timing Belt Cover Indexes

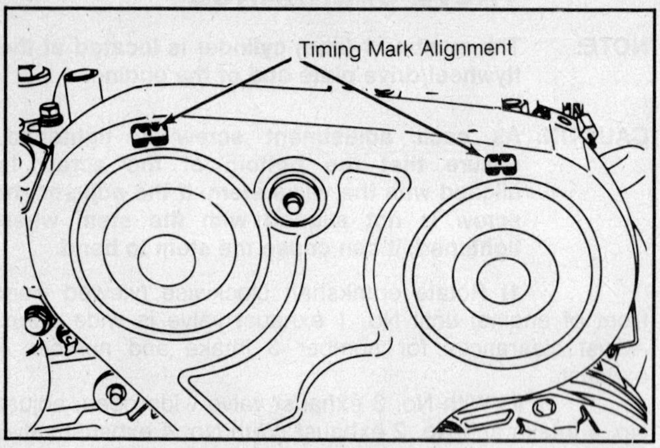

Align sprocket timing marks with indexes.

2) Install TDC Rod (Mot. 861) in crankshaft counterweight TDC slot. *See Fig. 3*. Remove screw plug and copper washer located between 4 high pressure fuel outlets on rear of injection pump. Install Dial Indicator Support (Mot. 856) in place of screw plug. Insert dial indicator tip into support.

Fig. 3: Installation of TDC Rod

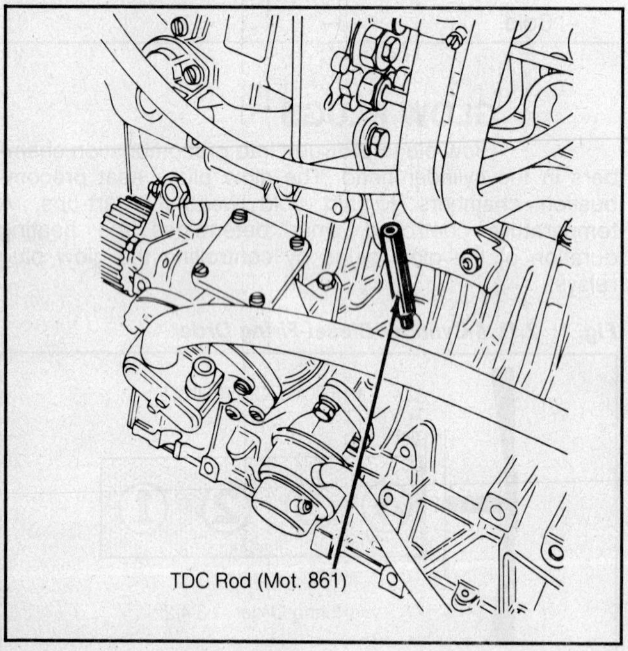

3) Remove TDC rod from crankshaft counterweight TDC slot. Slowly rotate crankshaft counterclockwise until dial indicator pointer stops moving. Zero dial indicator. Slowly rotate crankshaft clockwise until TDC rod can be inserted into slot in crankshaft counterweight.

4) At TDC, dial indicator pointer should indicate a piston travel distance of .031-.033" (.80-.84 mm). If fuel injection pump piston lift travel distance is not correct, pump piston must be adjusted.

5) To adjust pump piston, loosen pump adjustment bolts. Observe dial indicator. To increase piston lift, rotate pump toward engine and then away from engine. To decrease piston lift, rotate pump away from engine.

NOTE: **Always adjust piston by rotating pump away from engine. This is normal direction of pump rotation. When increasing piston lift, rotate pump toward engine until piston lift is greater than specified tolerance and then rotate pump away from engine until correct piston lift is indicated on dial indicator.**

6) Tighten injection pump adjustment bolts. Remove TDC rod from crankshaft counterweight. Observe dial indicator and rotate crankshaft clockwise 2 complete revolutions until TDC rod can be inserted into crankshaft counterweight TDC slot.

7) Dial indicator pointer should return to zero and then move to .031-.033" (.80-.84 mm). This will indicate that fuel injection pump static timing is correct. Remove TDC rod from crankshaft counterweight and install plug in cylinder block.

8) Remove dial indicator and support tool. Install washer and screw plug in fuel injection pump. Connect high pressure fuel pipes to fuel injection pump and injectors. Engage cold start system control by returning clevis pin to its original position and tightening screw.

IDLE SPEED RPM

IDLE SPEED

Application	RPM
Auto. Trans. [1]	800
Man. Trans. [2]	800

[1] – Transmission in Drive.
[2] – Transmission in Neutral.

COLD START THERMOSTAT CAPSULE

When the engine is stationary and cold, the spring inside the capsule applies tension to the control cable. This moves the timing control lever to the advance position and the throttle lever to the fas idle position.

When engine starts and coolant temperature rises, the thermostat in the capsule slowly expands and compresses the spring. The control cable is relaxed, allowing the timing control lever and piston to move forward. The throttle lever returns to its original position.

INJECTION NOZZLES

If engine starts but idles roughly, check injection nozzles as described:

1) Start engine. Loosen injection line fitting at each nozzle, one at a time. Ensure fuel is directed away from soures which could cause fire. If, when an injection line fitting is loosened, idle speed or quality does not change, replace that nozzle and repeat test.

TUNE-UP (Cont.)

2) Disconnect fuel return system from nozzles on one bank of engine at a time. Start engine and observe fuel seepage from each nozzle. Replace any nozzle that leaks excessively. Torque nozzle clamp bolt to 25 ft. lbs. (34 N.m).

REFERENCE PULSE REGULATOR

The reference pulse regulator is located on the firewall above the engine. The regulator automatically compensates for changes in height above sea level.

GENERAL SERVICING

FUEL INJECTION

All Jeep Cherokee and Wagoneer 2.1L turbo diesel engines are equipped with Bosch Fuel Injection. The injection pump No. is (VE 4/9 f 2200 R 183 0460 494 160).

TURBOCHARGER

All 2.1L turbo diesel engines are equipped with Garrett T-2 turbochargers. Check turbocharger boost pressure at 2500 RPM. See TURBOCHARGER BOOST PRESSURE table.

TURBOCHARGER BOOST PRESSURE

Application	Pressure
2.1L Turbo Diesel	8.7 psi (.6 kg/cm²)

ELECTRICAL SYSTEM

BATTERY SPECIFICATIONS

Application	Cold Cranking Amps [1]	Reserve Capacity Minutes
Standard	815	135

[1] – At 0°F (-18°C).

STARTER

All 2.1L engines use a Paris-Rhone starter.

ALTERNATOR

All 2.1L engines use a Paris-Rhone alternator with intergral regulator.

ALTERNATOR SPECIFICATIONS

Application	Field Current Draw @ 12 Volts	Rated Amp. Output
Standard	[1]	60
Optional	[1]	70

[1] – Information not available from manufacturer.

ALTERNATOR REGULATOR

All 2.1L models use a Paris-Rhone nonadjustable regulator, integral with alternator.

REGULATOR OPERATING VOLTAGE @ 80°F (27°C)

Application	Voltage
2.1L	13.9-14.9

ADJUSTMENT

BELT ADJUSTMENT

BELT ADJUSTMENT
Tension Using Strand Tension Gauge

Application	Lbs. (Kg.)
New Belts	125-155 (56-69)
Used Belts	90-115 (40-51)

SERVICE INTERVALS

REPLACEMENT INTERVALS

Component	Interval (Miles)
Air Filter	30,000
Auto. Trans. Fluid	30,000
Coolant	25,000
Differential Fluid	30,000
Fuel Filter	15,000
Transfer Case Fluid	30,000
Man. Trans. Fluid	30,000
Oil & Filter	5000

CAPACITIES

FLUID CAPACITIES

Application	Quantity
Crankcase (Includes Filter)	6.3 qts. (6.0L)
Cooling System	9.0 qts. (8.5L)
Man. Trans. (75W-90)	3.5 qts. (3.3L)
Auto. Trans.(Dexron II)	7.9 qts. (7.5L)
Transfer Case	
Cherokee, Wagoneer (Dexron II)	
207	2.25 qts. (2.1L)
229	3.0 qts. (2.8L)
Differential (75W-90)	1.25 qts. (1.2L)

SYSTEM REFRIGERANT CAPACITIES

Application	Ounces
Cherokee & Wagoneer	36

SECTION 1a

COMPUTERIZED ENGINE CONTROLS

CONTENTS

NOTE: **ALSO SEE GENERAL INDEX.**

IMPORTANT: Because of the many model names used by vehicle manufacturers, accurate identification of models is important. See Model Identification at the front of this publication.

CHRYSLER CORP. FWD ELECTRONIC FUEL CONTROL

Dodge Caravan & Mini Ram Van,
Plymouth Voyager (2.2L Engine)

NOTE: **All 2.2L models use the Spark Control Computer with Spark Advance and Throttle Control systems. Only models with Holley 6520 carburetors use oxygen sensor feedback system.**

DESCRIPTION

The Electronic Fuel Control (EFC) system is an electronically controlled system that closely controls ignition timing and, on models with oxygen sensor feedback system, air/fuel ratio. The Spark Control Computer (SCC) is the heart of the system.

The SCC provides the capability of igniting a lean air/fuel mixture under various engine operating conditions. Also, during closed loop operation on models with feedback system, the computer maintains an air/fuel ratio close to the ideal 14.7:1.

OPERATION

The EFC system consists of 7 sub-systems: fuel control, spark control, throttle control, data sensors, Spark Control Computer (SCC), catalytic converter and self-diagnostic system.

FUEL CONTROL

Some models are equipped with a Holley 6550 carburetor. This model contains an electrically operated duty cycle solenoid. This solenoid meters the main fuel system of the carburetor and operates in parallel with conventional fixed main metering jets. The computer controls operation of the solenoid in response to signals received from data sensors, particularly the oxygen sensor. *See Fig. 1.*

Fig. 1: Sectional View of Feedback Carburetor With Duty Cycle Solenoid

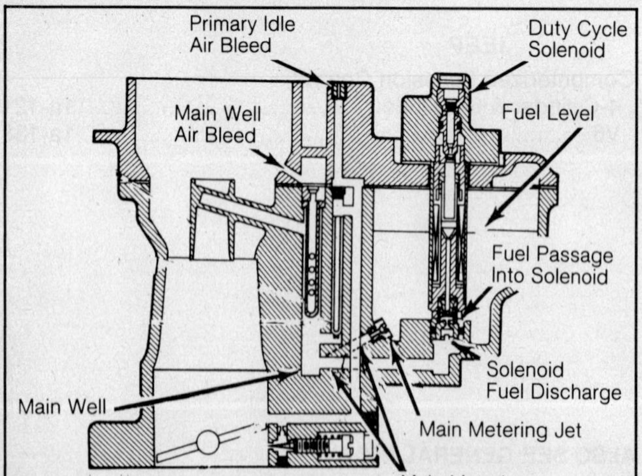

When the solenoid is de-energized by the computer, the solenoid valve spring pushes upward through main system fuel valve. When de-energized, the solenoid main metering orifice is fully uncovered, providing the richest mixture for any given air flow.

When the solenoid is energized by the computer, the solenoid main metering orifice is fully sealed. This solenoid position offers the leanest mixture within the carburetor for any given air flow.

Main system fuel may be regulated between richest and leanest conditions by controlling the amount of time that the solenoid is energized and de-energized. The computer controls the duration of time that the solenoid is energized in comparison to total time of solenoid operation and in response to engine operating conditions and/or oxygen sensor signals. In this manner, the ideal air/fuel ratio can be constantly maintained.

SPARK CONTROL

Spark control allows the computer to determine the exact instant that ignition is required, then signals ignition coil to produce electrical impulses to fire the spark plugs. The computer eliminates the need for either vacuum advance units or centrifugal advance weights. Spark control operates in one of the following modes:

Start Mode

During cranking, an electrical signal from the distributor is fed into the computer, which causes the computer to fire the spark plugs at a fixed amount of advance.

Run Mode

Once the engine starts and is operating normally, timing will be controlled by the computer, based upon information received from the data sensors.

Total spark advance is determined by three factors: coolant temperature, engine speed and manifold vacuum.

In a cold or warm engine, as indicated by coolant temperature sensor, RPM has no affect on advance. Under these conditions, advance curve is determined by vacuum signal only. In a hot engine, computer is programmed to consider engine speed in addition to manifold vacuum, to determine total spark advance.

THROTTLE CONTROL

The throttle control system is used to maintain or raise engine speed for certain conditions. The conditions when engine speed is raised are during A/C operation, or during timer operation. There are 2 timers used in this system. When the engine is started, one timer provides a 2 second delay, during which engine speed is raised. Also, when throttle is closed, another timer prevents the throttle from immediately closing all the way.

DATA SENSORS

Hall Effect Pickup Assembly

This device is located in the distributor to supply a basic timing signal to the computer. The computer determines engine speed (RPM) based on this signal. *See Fig. 2.*

CHRYSLER CORP. FWD ELECTRONIC FUEL CONTROL (Cont.)

Fig. 2: Location of Hall Effect Pickup Assembly in Distributor

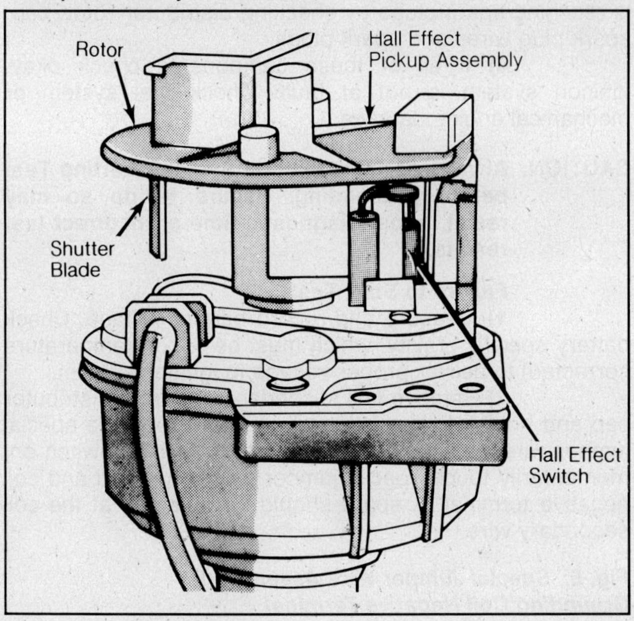

Coolant Sensor

This sensor is located on the thermostat housing and supplies a signal to the computer. Sensor resistance is inversely proportional to coolant temperature.

This information is required to prevent air/fuel ratio from changing until engine reaches normal operating temperature. The computer also controls the amount of spark advance with a cold engine. *See Fig. 3*.

Fig. 3: Location of Coolant Sensor

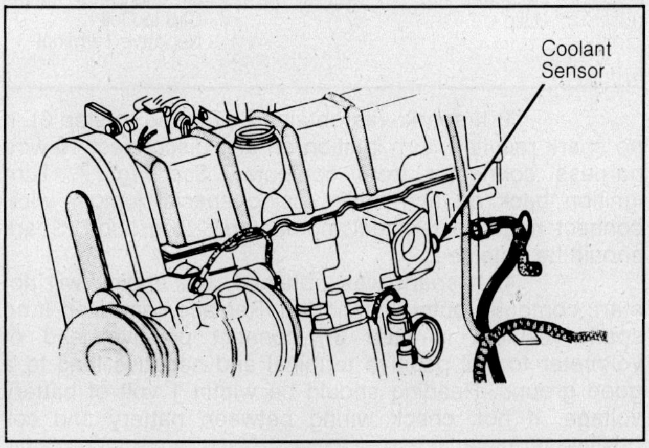

Vacuum Transducer

The vacuum transducer is mounted on the computer and provides the computer with a signal of the amount of engine vacuum. Engine vacuum is used by the computer to determine how much to advance or retard ignition timing and to change air/fuel mixture.

Carburetor Switch

This switch is located on the end of the idle stop to signal the computer when the engine is at idle. *See Fig. 4*.

Fig. 4: Location of Carburetor Switch

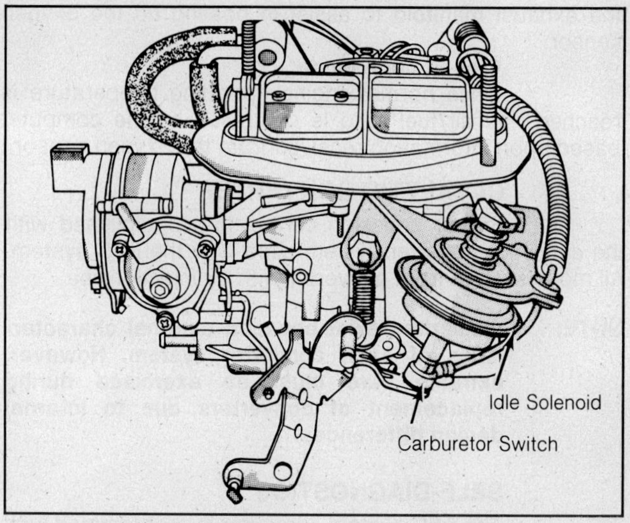

Oxygen Sensor

This sensor, used with feedback system only, is located in the exhaust manifold to signal the computer of oxygen content of exhaust gases. The voltage output of the oxygen sensor is proportional to oxygen content of exhaust gases. The computer will adjust the air/fuel mixture (vary duty cyle solenoid timing) to a level which will maintain operating efficiency of the 3-way catalyst system and engine.

SPARK CONTROL COMPUTER

The computer is located on the left inner fender well, near battery. The computer consists of a printed circuit board which simultaneously receives signals from all data sensors and analyzes these signals to determine correct ignition timing and, on models with feedback system, air/fuel mixture. Air/fuel mixture is controlled in one of the following modes:

Fig. 5: Location of Spark Control Computer

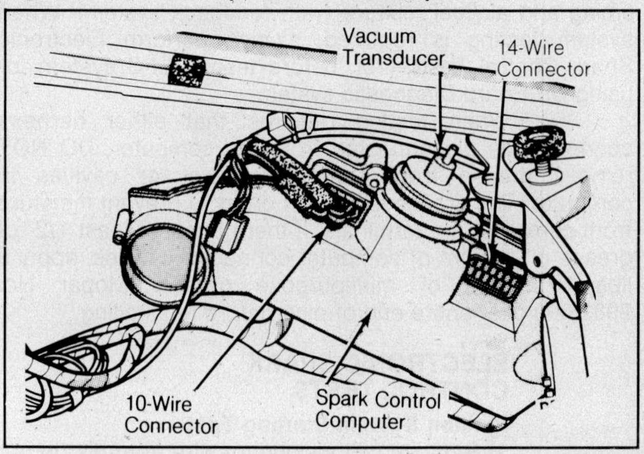

Open Loop Mode

During cold engine operation, the air/fuel ratio is controlled by information programmed into the computer by the manufacturer. Until normal operating temperature is obtained, the air/fuel mixture will be fixed at a rich level to allow proper engine warm-up. During this mode of

CHRYSLER CORP. FWD ELECTRONIC FUEL CONTROL (Cont.)

operation, air from the AIR pump is injected "upstream" in the exhaust manifold to assist in heating up the oxygen sensor.

Closed Loop Mode

Once normal engine operating temperature is reached, the air/fuel ratio is controlled by the computer based upon information received from the oxygen sensor.

CATALYTIC CONVERTER

Proper emission control is accomplished with the catalytic converter system used with the EFC system. All models use a front converter with air injection line.

NOTE: **Similarites exist between external characteristics of each converter system. However, extreme care must be exercised during replacement of converters due to internal design differences.**

SELF-DIAGNOSTICS

The EFC system computer is programmed with self-diagnostic capabilities. The SCC constantly monitors the various engine systems and components. If a problem is detected in any monitored system, a "Fault Code" will be stored as an aid to system diagnosis. If a detected problem is repaired, or fails to repeat within 30 ignition on/off cycles, the computer cancels the code.

Stored fault codes may be recalled as an aid to complete system diagnosis by using a special diagnostic readout box (C-4805).

TESTING

A malfunction in the EFC system may result in engine surge, hesitation, rough idle and/or poor fuel economy. Before making any tests, check all vacuum and electrical wiring for proper routing and connections, and check for exhaust and intake manifold leaks. If these are in order, testing may begin.

The Spark Control Computer controls ignition timing and air/fuel mixture (with feedback system). When system testing is required, always perform Electronic Spark Control Tests first, before testing EFC system, or using On-Board Diagnostic system.

When testing requires that either harness connector be disconnected from the computer, DO NOT remove grease from either connector or cavities in computer. The grease is used in order to prevent moisture from corroding the terminals. If there is not at least 1/2" of grease on bottom of computer connector cavities, apply a liberal amount of multipurpose grease (Mopar No. 2932524) over entire end of plug before reinstalling.

ELECTRONIC SPARK CONTROL TESTS

Ignition System Starting Test

1) Remove coil secondary wire from distributor cap. Hold end of wire 1/4" away from good engine ground. Have assistant crank engine, while you watch for spark at secondary wire. Spark should be constant and bright blue.

2) If spark is constant and bright blue, have assistant continue to crank engine and watch for arcing at coil tower while slowly moving coil secondary wire away from good ground. If arcing occurs, replace coil. If spark is weak or inconsistent, or there is no spark, proceed to Failure to Start Test.

3) If spark is good and there is no arcing at the coil tower, secondary voltage is satisfactory. Make sure it is reaching spark plugs by checking distributor rotor, cap, spark plug wires and spark plugs.

4) If all of these components check okay, ignition system is not at fault. Check fuel system or mechanical engine damage.

CAUTION: **Always perform Ignition System Starting Test before proceeding. Failure to do so may result in lost diagnostic time or incorrect test results.**

Failure to Start Test

1) Measure and record battery voltage. Check battery specific gravity, which must be 1.220 (temperature corrected) to deliver proper voltage to ignition system.

2) Remove coil secondary wire from distributor cap and hold 1/4" from a good ground. Prepare a special jumper wire assembly. *See Fig. 6*. With ignition switch on, momentarily touch special jumper wire to ground and coil negative terminal. A spark should be obtained at the coil secondary wire.

Fig. 6: Special Jumper Wire Assembly for Grounding Coil Negative Terminal

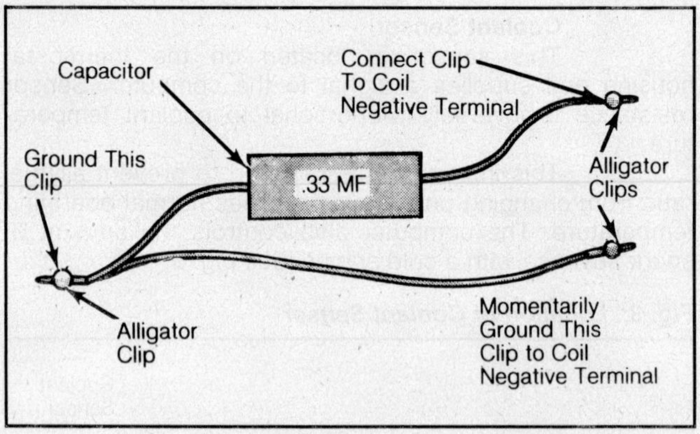

3) If spark was obtained, proceed to step **6)**. If no spark resulted, turn ignition off and disconnect 10-wire harness connector from computer. *See Fig. 7*. Turn ignition back on and again, using special jumper wire, connect negative terminal momentarily to ground. Spark should be obtained.

4) If spark was obtained, but engine will not start, computer output is shorted. Replace computer. If no spark resulted in step **3)**, connect positive lead of voltmeter to coil positive terminal and negative lead to a good ground. Reading should be within 1 volt of battery voltage. If not, check wiring between battery and coil positive terminal.

5) If correct voltage was recorded in step **4)**, measure voltage between ground and coil negative terminal. Again, it should be within 1 volt of battery voltage. Replace ignition coil if there is either no voltage present, or if voltage is present but no spark results when shorting negative coil terminal.

6) If spark was obtained in step **2)**, or if in step **5)**, voltage was obtained but engine would not start, hold carburetor switch open with a thin cardboard insulator. Measure voltage between carburetor switch and ground. Reading should again be within 1 volt of battery voltage. If so, go to step **10)**.

CHRYSLER CORP. FWD ELECTRONIC FUEL CONTROL (Cont.)

Fig. 7: Distributor and Computer Harness Connectors Used in Testing Electronic Spark Control System

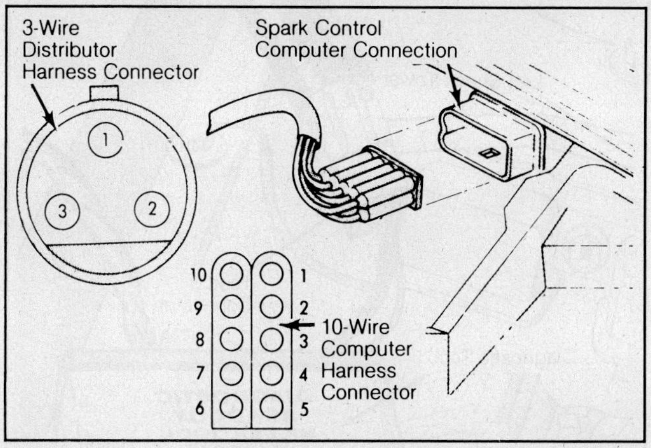

7) If voltage was incorrect in step **6)**, turn ignition off and disconnect 10-wire harness connector from computer. Turn ignition on. Connect positive lead of voltmeter to cavity 2 of connector and negative lead to ground. Reading should be within 1 volt of battery voltage.

8) If no battery voltage is present, check wire from battery to ignition switch to cavity 2. Use an ohmmeter if necessary, to check continuity of wires. Correct problem and repeat step **7)**. If voltage was present in step **7)**, turn ignition off and connect ohmmeter leads to carburetor switch terminal and cavity 7 of 10-wire connector.

9) If no continuity is found, check for open wire between cavity 7 and carburetor switch. If continuity was indicated, connect ohmmeter leads to cavity 10 and to a good ground. If continuity exists, replace computer, as correct power is entering computer, but not leaving it. Repeat step **6)**. If no continuity existed between cavity 10 and ground, check for an open wire in the ground system.

10) Reconnect 10-wire harness connector to computer. Turn ignition on and hold secondary coil wire 1/4" from a good ground. Disconnect 3-wire distributor connector from distributor. Attach jumper wire between cavities 2 and 3 of harness connector. A good spark should jump from coil wire to ground.

11) If spark resulted, but engine will not start, replace Hall Effect Pickup. If no spark resulted in step **10)**, connect voltmeter positive lead to distributor harness connector cavity 1 and negative lead to ground. Reading should be within 1 volt of battery voltage. If no battery voltage is present, proceed to step **14)**. If voltage was correct, turn ignition off and disconnect 10-wire harness connector from computer.

12) Connect ohmmeter leads between cavity 2 (Black/Light Blue wires) of distributor harness connector and cavity 9 of 10-wire connector. Then connect leads to cavity 3 (Gray wire) of distributor harness connector and cavity 5 of 10-wire connector.

13) If no continuity is present, repair open wires. If continuity exists, replace computer (power going into computer, but not coming out). Repeat step **10)**.

14) If there was no battery voltage in step **11)**, turn ignition off. Disconnect 10-wire connector and connect ohmmeter leads to cavity 1 of distributor harness and cavity 3 of 10-wire connector. If no continuity exists, repair wire and repeat step **10)**.

15) If continuity existed in step **14)**, turn ignition on and check for battery voltage with voltmeter positive lead in cavity 2 of 10-wire connector and negative lead in cavity 10. If battery voltage is present, but vehicle will not start, replace computer and repeat step **10)**. If no battery voltage is present, check ground wire and repeat step **10)**.

Spark Control Computer Spark Test

1) Bring engine to normal operating temperature ensure that basic ignition timing is properly adjusted. Be sure coolant temperature sensor is connected and working properly.

2) Remove and plug vacuum hose at vacuum transducer. Connect an auxiliary vacuum supply to vacuum transducer and apply 16 in. Hg. Increase engine speed to 2000 RPM and wait 1 minute before checking specifications. *See Spark Advance Test Specifications table*. Specifications given in table are TOTAL advance (initial advance is included).

3) If computer fails to obtain settings, replace computer.

SPARK ADVANCE TEST SPECIFICATIONS [1]

Application	Computer Part No.	Advance [2]
2.2L		
High Altitude		
(Auto)	5226499	39°
Federal		
Automatic	5226497	42°
4-Spd Manual	5226589	39°
5-Spd Manual	5226587	39°
California		
Automatic	5226465	42°
Manual	5226591	42°

[1] – Engine speed of 2000 RPM and 16 in. Hg applied.
[2] – All readings ±4°. If amount of advance differs from emission label, use label as accurate listing.

ELECTRONIC THROTTLE CONTROL SYSTEM TEST

1) Connect a tachometer to engine. Start and run engine until it reaches normal operating temperature. Depress accelerator, then release. Engine speed should not immediately return to idle. On vehicles equipped with A/C, a slight increase in idle speed should be observed while A/C is in operation.

2) Turning off A/C will return idle speed to normal. As the A/C clutch cycles on and off, the throttle kicker solenoid (solekicker) plunger should extend and retract. If plunger does not move with clutch cycling, or after engine starts, check the kicker system for vacuum leaks. If engine speed does not increase as specified, disconnect the 6-way connector at carburetor.

3) Connect ohmmeter leads from ground to solenoid terminal that was connected to Black wire. Resistance should be 20-100 ohms. If not, replace solenoid. Reconnect solenoid. Start vehicle and immediately (before 2 second time delay times out) measure voltage across vacuum solenoid terminals.

4) Voltage should be within 2 volts of charging system voltage. If not, replace computer. Turn on A/C after time delay has timed out. Charging voltage should once again be present at solenoid. If not, check wiring back to instrument panel for open circuit.

CHRYSLER CORP. FWD ELECTRONIC FUEL CONTROL (Cont.)

ELECTRONIC FUEL CONTROL SYSTEM TESTS

NOTE: The Spark Control Computer Spark Test should be made prior to beginning any test on EFC system. The following tests should be performed in the sequence given. Ensure basic timing and hot curb idle speed are set to specifications before testing.

Carburetor Switch Test

1) Turn ignition off and disconnect 10-wire connector from computer. With throttle completely closed, check continuity with ohmmeter leads connected to cavity 7 and ground.

NOTE: Grounding carburetor switch eliminates spark advance on most systems and provides fixed air/fuel ratio on feedback carburetor systems.

2) If no continuity is read, check wire from cavity 7 to carburetor switch terminal. Also check carburetor switch for proper operation.

3) Open throttle and check for continuity from cavity 7 to ground. There should be no continuity. If readings are not as outlined, replace carburetor switch.

Coolant Sensor Test

1) Turn ignition off and disconnect wire connector from sensor. Connect one ohmmeter lead to one sensor terminal and the other lead to remaining sensor terminal.

2) An engine at 70°F (21°C), should show 5000-6000 ohms. An engine at 200°F (93°C), should show 700-800 ohms. If not, replace sensor.

ON-BOARD DIAGNOSTICS

A diagnostic readout box (C-4805) is used to recall stored codes. The readout tool can be used to check three different system modes. These are: Diagnostic Test Mode, Circuit Actuation Test Mode (ATM test), and Switch Test Mode.

The Diagnostic Test Mode is used to retrieve fault codes that may be stored in the computer; the Circuit Actuation Test Mode (ATM Test) is used to check out specific component systems; the Switch Test Mode is used to check certain switch circuits.

Diagnostic Test Mode

1) Connect diagnostic readout tool (C-4805) to connector at left shock tower and move read/hold switch on tool to "READ" position. *See Fig. 8.*

2) Ensure that carburetor switch is open by placing fast idle screw on highest step. Turn ignition switch to run position. Wait for code "00" to appear on readout tool.

3) Move hold/read switch to "HOLD" position and record any codes that are displayed. Readout may be stopped at any time by moving switch to "READ" position, then back to "HOLD" position when ready to continue readout.

4) Before using indicated trouble code charts, perform a careful visual check of all wiring and vacuum connections in the indicated system (many problems are the result of loose, disconnected, or misconnected wires or vacuum hoses). If these components are in good condition and properly connected, use respective charts to complete diagnosis of system fault. Refer to *EFC Fault Code Identification* table to interpret stored codes.

Fig. 8: Diagnostic Readout Tool – C-4805

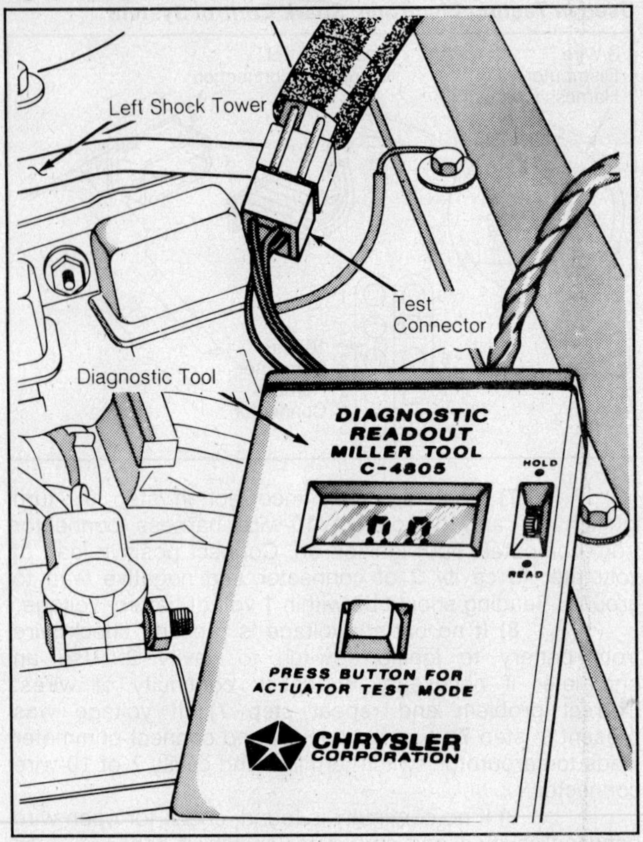

EFC FAULT CODE IDENTIFICATION

Code	Circuit/System Affected
00	Readout tool receiving power.
11	O² Solenoid Circuit.
13	Canister Purge Solenoid Circuit.
14	Stored when battery has been disconnected.
16	Radiator Fan Control Relay (Disregard with A/C).
17	Electronic Throttle Control Vacuum Solenoid.
18	Vacuum Operated Secondary Control Solenoid.
21	Distributor Pick-Up system.
22	O² System Full Rich or Full Lean.
24	SCC
25	Radiator Fan Coolant Sensor.
26	Engine Temperature Sensor.
28	Distance Sensor System (Man. Trans. only).
31	Stored when engine has not cranked since battery last disconnected.
32 & 33	SCC
55	Indicates end of message.
88	First code displayed. Indicates start of message.

Circuit Actuation Test Mode (ATM)

1) Run system through Diagnostic Test Mode and wait for code "55" to display. Press ATM button on readout tool to activate display. ATM test codes will

CHRYSLER CORP. FWD ELECTRONIC FUEL CONTROL (Cont.)

Fig. 9: Chrysler Corp. 2.2L EFC System Wiring Diagram

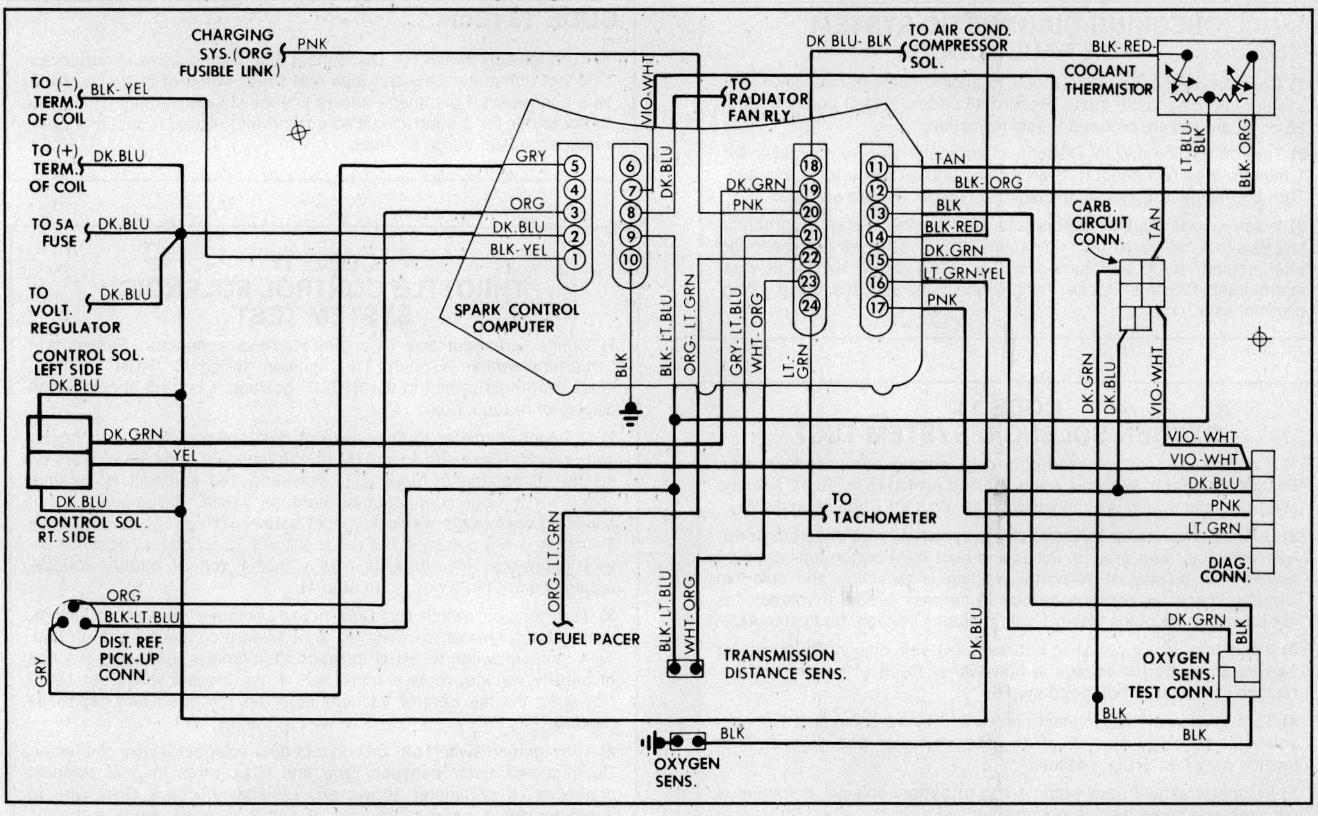

appear on readout tool. Hold button down until desired display appears.

2) The SCC will turn selected circuit on and off for up to 5 minutes, or until ATM button is pressed again (or ignition switch turned off). If ATM button is not pressed again, SCC will shut system off after 5 minutes.

ATM TEST DISPLAY CODES

Code	System Tested
91	O² Feedback Solenoid.
92	Shift Indicator Light (Man Trans. only).
93	Canister Purge Solenoid.
96	Fan Relay.
97	Electronic Throttle Control Solenoid.
98	Vacuum Operated Secondary Control Solenoid.

Switch Test Mode

1) Run system through Diagnostic Test Mode and wait for code "55" to display. Check that both air conditioning and rear window defogger are off. Press ATM button and immediately move read/hold switch to "READ" position.

2) Wait for code "00" to display. Turn A/C switch on. If computer is receiving input, display will change to "88" when switch is turned on and back to "00" when switch is turned off.

CHECKING DIAGNOSTIC SYSTEM FOR FAULT CODES

1) Connect diagnostic readout box to engine harness connector. Put system into "Diagnostic Mode". Record all codes.

NOTE: If fault codes 22, 28, 25 or 26 are stored, proceed to test indication.

2) Turn ignition switch off. Disconnect computer 14-wire connector for 1 minute, then reconnect it. Start engine and run for 2 minutes. Turn engine off. Put system into "Diagnostic Mode". Record all codes.

3) If same code appears before and after engine is started, problem still exists. Proceed to test indications. If a code does not reappear after engine is run and turned off, code no longer exists (was intermittent). Check for loose or corroded wiring connections in circuit. Use wiring diagram as a guide.

CHRYSLER CORP. FWD ELECTRONIC FUEL CONTROL (Cont.)

CHECKING DIAGNOSTIC SYSTEM FOR FAULT CODES

1) Connect diagnostic readout box to engine harness connector. Put system into diagnostic mode. Record all codes. If fault codes 22, 25, 26 or 28 are stored, proceed to test indication.

2) Turn off ignition switch. Disconnect computer 14-wire connector for 1 minute, then reconnect it. Start engine and let it run for 2 minutes. Turn off engine. Put system in diagnostic mode. Record all codes.

3) If same code appears before and after engine is started, problem still exists. Proceed to test indications. If a code does not reappear after engine is run and turned off, code no longer exists. (It was intermittent.) Check for loose wiring connections in circuit, using wiring diagram as a guide.

CODE 11 OXYGEN SOLENOID SYSTEM TEST

1) Connect diagnostic readout box to engine harness connector. Ensure carburetor switch is open, ignition switch is in "RUN" position and read/hold switch is in "Hold" position. Wait for Code 55 to display.

2) Connect a voltmeter to Green oxygen solenoid wire at carburetor 6-wire connector and ground. Press and hold ATM button until code 91 appears on display. If voltmeter reading is pulsating and solenoid clicking, check for poor connection in harness circuit. If voltmeter is not pulsating but reads within 1 volt of battery voltage, go to step **4)**.

3) If voltmeter is not pulsating but reads 0-1 volt, disconnect computer 14-wire connector. If voltage is now within 1 volt of battery voltage, replace computer. If not, go to step **6)**.

4) Turn ignition off. Disconnect computer 14-wire connector. Connect voltmeter to cavity No. 12 of 14-wire connector and ground. Turn ignition switch to "RUN" position.

5) Voltmeter should read within 1 volt of battery voltage. If voltage is OK, replace computer. If not, inspect wire from cavity No. 12 to oxygen solenoid for open circuit and repair as needed.

NOTE: Before replacing computer, make sure that terminals in cavity No. 12 are not spread apart so that they cannot touch the computer pin.

6) Turn ignition switch off. Disconnect carburetor 6-wire connector. Connect an ohmmeter between Tan and Green wires of carburetor 6-wire connector. Ohmmeter should show resistance. Amount of resistance is not important as long as some resistance is present. If resistance is present, go to step **7)**. If not (open circuit), replace oxygen solenoid.

7) With carburetor 6-wire connector disconnected, connect voltmeter to Blue wire of 6-wire connector and ground. Turn ignition switch to run position. If voltmeter reads within 1 volt of battery voltage, check Green wire of oxygen solenoid to computer for a short circuit to ground. Repair as needed. If voltmeter reads zero volts, inspect Blue wire for open circuit to ignition switch and repair.

CODE 13 CANISTER PURGE SOLENOID CONTROL SYSTEM TEST

1) Connect diagnostic readout box to engine harness connector. Ensure that carburetor switch is open. With ignition in "RUN" position, place read/hold switch in "HOLD" position.

2) If voltmeter is pulsating and clicking, check for poor connection in harness circuit. If voltmeter is not pulsating but reads within 1 volt of battery voltage, go to step **3)**. If voltmeter is not pulsating but reads 0-1 volt, disconnect computer 14-wire connector. If voltage is now within 1 volt of battery voltage, replace computer. If not, go to step **4)**.

3) Turn ignition switch off. Disconnect computer 14-wire connector. Connect voltmeter to cavity No. 13 of 14-wire connector and ground. Turn ignition switch to "RUN" position. If voltmeter reads within 1 volt of battery voltage, replace computer. If voltage is not okay, inspect wire from cavity 13 to canister purge control solenoid for open and repair as needed.

CODE 13 (Cont.)

4) Turn ignition switch off. Disconnect dual solenoid 3-wire connector. Connect ohmmeter between Blue and Green wires of dual solenoid 3-wire connector. If ohmmeter shows any resistance, inspect Green wire to computer for a short circuit to ground and repair. If circuit is open, replace canister purge solenoid.

CODE 17 THROTTLE CONTROL SOLENOID SYSTEM TEST

1) Connect readout box to engine harness connector. Ensure that carburetor switch is open. Turn ignition switch to "RUN" position. Place read/hold switch in the "HOLD" position. Code 55 should be on display of readout box.

2) Connect voltmeter to Gray wire of dual solenoid 3-wire connector and ground. Press and hold ATM button until test code 97 appears on display. If voltemeter reading is pulsating and solenoid is clicking, check for a poor connection in harness circuit. If voltmeter is not pulsating buts reads within 1 volt of battery voltage, go to step **3)**. If voltmeter is not pulsating but reads 0-1 volt, disconnect computer 14-wire connector. If voltage is now within 1 volt of battery voltage, replace computer. If not, go to step **4)**.

3) Turn ignition switch off. Disconnect computer 14-wire connector. Connect a voltmeter to cavity No. 6 of 14-wire connector and ground. Turn ignition switch to "RUN" position. If voltmeter reads within 1 volt of battery voltage, replace computer. If not, inspect wire from cavity No. 6 to throttle control vacuum solenoid for open and repair as needed.

4) Turn ignition switch off. Disconnect dual solenoid 3-wire connector. Connect ohmmeter between Blue and Gray wires in dual solenoid connector. If ohmmeter shows any resistance, check Gray wire to computer for a short to ground. If circuit is open, replace throttle control solenoid.

CODE 18 VOS CONTROL SOLENOID SYSTEM TEST

1) Connect diagnostic readout box to engine harness connector. With carburetor switch open and ignition switch in "RUN" position, place read/hold switch in "HOLD" position. Wait for Code 55 to appear on display of readout box.

2) Connect voltmeter to Black wire of carburetor 6-wire connector and ground. Press and hold ATM button until test code 98 appears on display. If voltmeter reading is pulsating and solenoid is clicking, check for poor connection in harness circuit.

3) If voltmeter is not pulsating buts reads within 1 volt of battery voltage, go to step **4)**. If voltmeter is not pulsating but reads 0-1 volt, disconnect computer 14-wire connector. If voltage is now within 1 volt of battery, replace computer. If not, go to step **5)**.

4) Turn ignition switch off. Disconnect computer 14-wire connector. Connect voltmeter to cavity No. 8 of 14-wire connector and ground. Turn ignition to "RUN" position. If voltmeter reads within 1 volt of battery voltage, replace computer. If not, inspect wire from cavity No. 8 to VOS control solenoid for open and repair as needed.

5) With carburetor 6-wire connector disconnected, connect a voltmeter to Blue wire of harness 6-wire connector and ground. Turn ignition switch to "RUN" position. If voltmeter reads within 1 volt of battery voltage, inspect Black/White wire from VOS solenoid to computer for short circuit to ground and repair as needed. If zero volts, check Blue wire for open circuit to ignition switch.

CHRYSLER CORP. FWD ELECTRONIC FUEL CONTROL (Cont.)

CODE 22
OXYGEN FEEDBACK SYSTEM TEST

1) Turn ignition switch off. Connect a voltmeter to Green oxygen solenoid wire at carburetor 6-wire connector and ground. Disconnect and plug vacuum line at computer. Connect auxiliary vacuum supply to computer and apply 14 in. Hg vacuum.

2) Connect a tachometer to engine. Disconnect oxygen system test connector and then reconnect Green/White wire only. If equipped with manual transaxle, disconnect speed sensor connector. Stick a straight pin into wire from cavity No. 5 of computer 10-wire connector.

3) Connect a jumper wire between straight pin and White/Orange tracer wire of speed sensor harness connector. Start engine and wait 1 minute. Raise engine speed to 2000 RPM. Hold oxygen system test connector (open terminal) with one hand and touch battery positive terminal with other hand. If voltmeter reading drops to zero volts, go to step **4)**. If voltage does not decrease, go to step **6)**.

4) With voltmeter connected to oxygen solenoid Green wire, disconnect and plug vacuum line at computer. Apply 14 in. Hg of vacuum to computer. Connect tachometer to engine and run engine to 2000 RPM.

5) Reconnect oxygen test connector. Wait a few seconds for oxygen system to start working. If voltmeter reading pulsates between 7 and 14 volts, go to step **6)**. If voltage is below 7 volts, go to step **7)**.

6) Connect voltmeter to oxygen solenoid Green wire. Disconnect and plug vacuum line to computer. Apply 14 in. Hg of vacuum to computer. Connect tachometer to engine and raise engine speed to 2000 RPM. Disconnect oxygen test connector. If voltmeter reading drops to zero volt, oxygen system is okay. If voltage does not decrease, check oxygen sensor wire for an open circuit to test connector. Repair as needed. If there is no open circuit, replace oxygen sensor.

7) Run engine at 2000 RPM with 14 in. Hg of vacuum applied to computer. Disconnect hose from PCV valve and cover orifice. Allow air to slowly enter orifice. If voltmeter reading increases towards 14 volts, oxygen system is okay. If voltage does not increase, check oxygen sensor wire for a short circuit to test connector and repair as needed. If there is no short, replace oxygen sensor.

8) With oxygen system test connector still disconnected (Green/White wire reconnected, let engine return to idle speed and then turn off engine. Disconnect computer 14-wire connector. Connect ohmmeter between test connector (Black wire) on computer side and cavity No. 10 of 14-wire connector. If ohmmeter shows continuity, replace computer. If there is no continuity, repair open wire to test connector.

CODE 25 OR 26
COOLANT SENSOR CIRCUIT TEST

1) Disconnect coolant sensor connector. Connect one lead of ohmmeter to terminal No. 1 of coolant sensor. Connect other lead of ohmmeter to terminal No. 2 and then terminal No. 3 of coolant sensor. If there is some resistance at both terminals, go to step **2)**. If resistance at one terminal and not at the other, replace coolant sensor.

2) Make sure sensor connector is disconnected. Disconnect computer 14-wire connector. Connect ohmmeter between cavity No. 9 of 14-wire connector and terminal No. 3 of coolant sensor connector. If ohmmeter shows continuity, go to step **3)**. If there is no continuity, check wire for open circuit and repair.

3) Disconnect computer 14-wire connector and coolant sensor connector. Connect ohmmeter between cavity No. 11 of 14-wire connector and terminal No. 2 of coolant sensor connector. If ohmmeter shows continuity, replace computer. If there is no continuity, inspect wire for open circuit and repair as needed.

CODE 28
SPEED SENSOR SYSTEM TEST

1) Turn ignition switch off. Remove speed sensor from transaxle. Disconnect speed sensor connector. Connect ohmmmeter between terminals of speed sensor connector. Slowly rotate speed sensor 1 turn. Ohmmeter should show approximately 8 pulses for every turn of the speed sensor. If ohmmeter reading is okay, go to step **2)**. If not, replace speed sensor.

2) Disconnect speed sensor connector. Connect positive lead of voltmeter to White/Orange wire of speed sensor connector. Connect negative lead of voltmeter to Black/Blue wire of speed sensor harness connector. Turn ignition to "RUN" position.

3) Voltmeter should read at least 8.5 volts. If voltage is okay, inspect transaxle drive gear-to-speed sensor drive gear for proper contact. If zero volts, move voltmeter negative lead to a good engine ground. If voltmeter now reads correct voltage, inspect speed sensor ground wire for an open circuit and repair. If voltmeter still reads zero, go to step **4)**.

4) Turn ignition switch off. Disconnect computer 14-wire connector. Connect ohmmeter between cavity No. 2 of 14-wire connector and White/Orange wire of speed sensor harness connector. If ohmmeter shows continuity, replace computer. If no continuity, inspect wire for open circuit and repair.

NO CODE 88

1) Disconnect diagnostic readout box from harness connector. Connect voltmeter between cavity No. 4 of engine harness connector and ground. Turn ignition switch to "RUN" position. Voltmeter should read 4-5 volts. Go to step **2)**. If voltage is not okay, go to step **2)**.

2) Turn ignition switch off. Disconnect 14-wire connector from computer. Connect ohmmeter between cavity No. 2 of engine harness diagnostic connector and cavity No. 14 of computer 14-wire connector. If ohmmeter shows continuity, replace computer. If no continuity, inspect wire from cavity No. 14 to harness connector for open and repair.

3) Disconnect diagnostic readout box. Turn ignition switch off. Disconnect 14-wire connector from computer. Connect ohmmeter between cavity No. 4 of engine harness connector and cavity No. 1 of computer 14-wire connector. If ohmmeter shows continuity, replace computer. If no continuity, inspect wire from cavity No. 1 to engine harness for an open circuit and repair.

CARBURETOR CHOKE SYSTEM TEST

NOTE: **Engine MUST be dead cold before starting this test.**

1) Set accelerator linkage to proper start position. Remove air cleaner. Check choke plate and fast idle cam position.

2) Choke plate should be in fully closed position and fast idle screw should be on highest step of fast idle cam. If choke and cam position are okay, go to step **3)**. If choke is not fully closed or cam is not in position, check for choke plate sticking or binding. Repair choke and linkage as required.

3) Remove air cleaner. Set fast idle speed screw on highest step of fast idle cam. Remove vacuum line from choke diaphragm. Connect auxiliary vacuum supply to choke diaphragm. Apply 15 in. Hg of vacuum. Measure clearance between top of choke plate and air horn wall.

4) Vacuum should hold at applied setting and choke plate should be in proper position of vacuum kick specifications. If vacuum holds and choke vacuum kick is within specifications, go to Heated Air Intake System Test. If vacuum does not hold, replace choke vacuum kick diaphragm.

CHRYSLER CORP. FWD ELECTRONIC FUEL CONTROL (Cont.)

HEATED AIR INTAKE SYSTEM TEST

1) Disconnect air duct from air cleaner snorkel. Disconnect vacuum line to heated air intake system air temperature sensor. Apply 15 in. Hg of vacuum.

2) Vacuum should close heated air door when air temperature is below 76°F (25°C) and then slowly bleed down, opening the heated air door.

3) If vacuum builds up, closes heated air door and then bleeds down, go to Engine Coolant Sensor Calibration Test. If vacuum builds up but heated air door does not close, repair or replace door as necessary. If vacuum does not build up or does not bleed down, replace air temperature sensor. If vacuum builds up and bleeds down, but heated air door does not open, repair or replace door as required.

ENGINE COOLANT SENSOR CALIBRATION TEST

1) Disconnect coolant sensor. Connect ohmmeter between terminals 1 and 3 of coolant sensor. Ohmmeter reading should be as follows: Below 150°F (66°C), 20-200 ohms; 150-200°F (66-93°C), 100-150 ohms; Above 200°F (93°C), 400-6000 ohms. If resistance is correct, go to step **9)**. If not, replace coolant sensor.

2) With coolant sensor connector disconnected and ohmmeter connected between terminals 1 and 2 of sensor, ohmmeter should read as follows: -40-20°F (-60-6.7°C), 382K-22K ohms; 50-100°F (10-38°C), 36K-3300 ohms; 140-245°F (60-118°C), 3.9-176 ohms. If resistance is okay, go to go to EGR System CVSCC Valve Test. If not, replace coolant sensor.

EGR SYSTEM CVSCC VALVE TEST

1) Disconnect CVSCC valve at vacuum line connector. Connect auxiliary vacuum supply to valve. Apply at least 10 in. Hg of vacuum. Vacuum should hold with coolant temperature below 125°F (52°C). If vacuum is okay, go to step **2)**. If vacuum does not hold, replace CVSCC valve.

2) Remove air cleaner. Start engine. Check position of choke plate. Choke plate should open from a fully closed position. If choke plate is in proper position, system is okay. If not, adjust choke.

CARBURETOR SWITCH TEST

NOTE: Engine MUST be dead cold when starting this test.

1) Disconnect computer 10-wire connector. Connect ohmmeter between cavity No. 7 of 10-wire connector and ground. Open and close throttle while watching at ohmmeter.

2) Ohmmeter should show continuity with no resistance when throttle is closed and no continuity when throttle is open. If okay, go to step **4)**.

3) If no continuity is present with throttle closed, inspect wire from cavity No. 7 to carb. switch for open circuit and repair as needed. If there is continuity with resistance when throttle is closed, clean corrosion from carb. switch. If there is continuity with throttle open, inspect wire from cavity No. 7 for a short to ground and repair.

4) Disconnect coolant sensor connector. Connect ohmmeter between terminals 1 and 3 of coolant sensor. Resistance should be between 400 and 6000 ohms. If resistance is okay, go to next test. If resistance is not okay, replace coolant sensor.

CHOKE SYSTEM TEST

1) Remove air cleaner and start engine. Choke should be fully open. If choke position is okay, go to step **3)**. If choke position is not okay, go to step **2)**.

2) With engine running, connect voltmeter to choke feed wire and ground. Voltmeter should read within 1 volt of battery voltage. If voltage is okay, check for binding linkage. If okay, replace choke thermostat housing. If voltage is not okay, go to step **3)**.

3) Turn off engine. Disconnect oil pressure switch connector. Connect voltmeter to terminal C of oil pressure switch connector and ground. Turn ignition switch to "RUN" position. Voltage should be within 1 volt of battery voltage. If voltage is okay, go to step **4)**. If voltage is not okay, repair open circuit in harness to ignition switch.

4) Dicsonnect oil pressure switch connector. Connect ohmmeter between terminal A of connector and choke connector. Ohmmeter should show continuity with no resistance. If there is continuity, replace oil pressure switch. If there is no continuity, repair open circuit in harness.

CARBURETOR IDLE CIRCUIT TEST

1) Connect tachometer to engine. Remove air cleaner. If equipped, disconnect and plug vacuum line at solenoid kicker. Start engine, momentarily raise engine speed above 1100 RPM and then wait 2 minutes for idle speed to stabilize. Plug idle air bleed hole.

2) Engine speed should drop. If so, go to step EGR System Check. If not, or if engine speed increases, check carburetor for plugged circuit and repair as needed.

EGR SYSTEM TEST

1) Connect tachometer to engine. Disconnect vacuum line from EGR valve. Connect auxiliary vacuum supply to EGR valve. If equipped, disconnect and plug vacuum line at solenoid kicker. Start engine, momentarily raise engine speed above 1100 RPM and wait 2 minutes for idle speed to stabilize. Very slowly apply vacuum to EGR valve.

2) Engine speed should begin to drop when applied vacuum reaches 2 to 5 in. Hg of vacuum and continue to drop as more vacuum is applied. Engine may stall before 5 in. Hg of vacuum is applied. If engine speed drop is okay, go to step **3)**. If engine speed does not drop or engine speed does not drop until 5 in. Hg or more vacuum, replace EGR valve.

3) Connect tachometer to engine. If equipped, plug vacuum line at solenoid kicker. Run engine at idle for at least 2 minutes. Disconnect EGR hose. Connect vacuum gauge to EGR vacuum line. Slowly increase engine speed.

4) As engine speed increases, so should reading on vacuum gauge. If vacuum reading is okay, go to next test. If vacuum is not okay, go to step **6)**.

5) Turn engine off. Remove connector from EGR CVSCC valve. Connect vacuum pump to either port of valve. Try to apply vacuum. Vacuum should not hold with coolant temperature above 125°F (52°C). If vacuum does not hold, check EGR signal hose from carburetor for leaks or restrictions. If vacuum holds, replace EGR CVSCC valve.

AIR SWITCHING SYSTEM TEST

1) Remove air cleaner. Disconnect downstream air hose from switch/relief valve. Start engine. With engine coolant above 150°F (67°C), air should be coming from downstream air port of switch/relief valve.

2) If air is coming from downstream port, go to Solenoid Kicker Circuit Test. If not, go to step **3)**.

3) With air cleaner removed and engine running, disconnect vacuum line from air switch/relief valve. Connect a vacuum gauge to line. There should be no vacuum reading. If so, replace air switch/relief valve. If vacuum is present, replace CVSCC valve.

CHRYSLER CORP. FWD ELECTRONIC FUEL CONTROL (Cont.)

SOLENOID KICKER CIRCUIT TEST

1) Remove air cleaner cover. Turn ignition key to "RUN" position while looking at solenoid plunger. Slowly open throttle. Plunger should move out when key is turned on or when throttle is opened. If plunger movement is okay, go to step **3)**.

2) If plunger movement is not okay, check solenoid adjusting screw to be sure that it is not turned in all the way (preventing plunger movement). If not, replace solenoid kicker.

3) With ignition key in "RUN" position, disconnect vacuum line from solenoid kicker. Connect auxiliary vacuum supply to solenoid kicker. Apply 15 in. Hg of vacuum and then release vacuum. Plunger should move out when vacuum is applied and return when vacuum is released. If plunger movement is as described, go to Carburetor Bowl Vent System Test. If not, replace solenoid kicker.

CARBURETOR BOWL VENT SYSTEM TEST

1) Remove bowl vent hose from carburetor and canister. Blow lightly into hose. Air should pass through. If so, go to step **2)**. If air does not pass through, clear hose or replace bowl vent valve. Look for liquid in hose near canister. If liquid is found, check routing of hose.

2) With bowl vent hose removed from carburetor and canister, start engine and blow lightly into hose. Air should not pass through hose. If so, check for blockage and repair as necessary. If air passes through hose, check air pressure in hose from air switch relief valve. Repair as required. If okay, replace bowl vent valve.

COMPUTER CONTROLLED COMPONENT TESTS

Check Procedure

Connect diagnostic readout box to engine harness connector. Put system in ATM test mode. Press and hold ATM button until test codes appear as follows: with oxygen feedback system – Code 92. Oxygen feedback system with manual transaxle – Code 92. Without oxygen feedback system, with automatic transaxle – Code 93.

Code 91

Should hear oxygen solenoid clicking. If oxygen solenoid is clicking, press and hold ATM button until next test code appears. If oxygen solenoid does not click, replace unit.

Code 92

Shift indicator light (SIL) should be blinking on instrument panel. If SIL light is blinking, press and hold ATM button until next test code appears. If SIL light does not blink, repair circuit as necessary.

Code 93

Canister purge solenoid should be clicking. If canister purge solenoid is clicking, press and hold ATM button until next test code appears. If canister purge solenoid does not click, replace unit.

Code 96

Radiator fan should be turning on and off. If so, press and hold ATM button until next test code appears. If fan does not turn on and off, check fan relay. If relay is clicking, repair circuit from relay to fan motor. If relay does not click, go to Radiator Fan Relay Circuit Test.

Code 97

Electronic throttle control solenoid should be clicking. If so, press and hold ATM button until next test code appears. If electronic throttle control solenoid does not click, replace unit.

Code 98

The VOS control solenoid should be clicking. If so, turn ignition switch off and go to Solenoid Kicker Operation Test. If VOS control solenoid does not click, replace unit.

RADIATOR FAN RELAY CIRCUIT TEST

1) Connect diagnostic readout box to engine harness connector. Ensure that carburetor switch is open. Turn ignition switch to "RUN" position. Place read/hold switch in "HOLD" position and wait for Code 55 to display. Connect voltmeter to terminal No. 2 of radiator fan relay and ground. Press and hold ATM button until Code 96 appears on display.

2) Voltmeter reading should be pulsating and relay should be clicking. If so, check for poor connection in circuit. If voltmeter is not pulsating but reads within 1 volt of battery voltage, go to step **3)**. If voltmeter is not pulsating but reads 0-1 volt, disconnect computer 10-wire connector. If voltage is now within 1 volt of battery voltage, replace computer. If not within 1 volt, go to step **5)**.

3) Turn ignition switch off. Disconnect computer 10-wire connector. Connect voltmeter to cavity No. 8 of 10-wire connector and ground. Turn ignition switch to "RUN" position.

4) Voltmeter should read within 1 volt of battery voltage. If voltage is okay, replace computer. If voltage is not okay, inspect wire from cavity No. 8 to radiator fan relay for open circuit and repair as needed.

5) Turn ignition switch off. Disconnect smaller of two 3-wire connectors from radiator fan relay. Connect ohmmeter between terminals No. 1 and 2 of radiator fan relay. Ohmmeter should show resistance.

6) If there is resistance, turn ignition switch to "RUN" position. Check for battery voltage at wire that connects to terminal No. 1 of relay. If there is voltage, inspect wire from cavity No. 8 of computer 10-wire connector for short to ground. If there is no voltage, check for open in wire to fuse No. 2. If there is an open circuit, replace radiator fan relay.

SOLENOID KICKER OPERATION TEST

1) Remove air cleaner cover. Look at plunger of solenoid kicker diaphragm while starting engine. Vacuum diaphragm plunger should move out and hold throttle open for at least 5 minutes and then return throttle to curb idle position.

NOTE: Some systems may hold throttle open for less than 5 minutes.

2) If plunger movement is okay, go to step **3)**. If no plunger movement, go to step **4)**.

3) Press A/C button and look at plunger for solenoid kicker vacuum diaphragm. Vacuum plunger should move out and hold throttle open while A/C compressor clutch is engaged. If plunger movement is okay, go to Ignition System Test. If no plunger movement, go to step **4)**.

4) Connect diagnostic readout box to engine harness connector. Put system in "Switch Test Mode". Make sure A/C control is in "OFF" position. Press A/C button on and off.

5) Code 88 should appear on display when A/C button is pressed on and then return to 00 when turned off. If code 88 appears when A/C button is turned on, replace computer. If code 88 does not appear, go to step **6)**.

6) Turn ignition switch off. Disconnect computer 14-wire connector. Connect voltmeter to cavity No. 7 of 14-wire connector and ground. Make sure A/C button is off. Turn ignition switch to "RUN" position.

7) Voltmeter should read within 1 volt of battery voltage. If voltage is okay, replace computer. If voltage is not okay, inspect wire from cavity No. 7 to A/C push button switch for an open circuit and repair as needed.

8) Turn engine off. Disconnect vacuum supply line from solenoid kicker and connect a vacuum gauge to it. Start engine. Vacuum gauge should indicate intake manifold vacuum. If vacuum is okay, replace computer. If there is no vacuum, repair vacuum supply from carburetor.

CHRYSLER CORP. FWD ELECTRONIC FUEL CONTROL (Cont.)

IGNITION SYSTEM TEST

Checking Secondary Ignition System

Connect engine analyzer to engine. Start engine and let engine speed stabilize for 2 minutes. Follow equipment manufacturer's procedure for secondary ignition testing and pattern analysis. If secondary igniton system is okay, go to next test. If secondary ignition not to specifications, repair as required.

Checking Basic Ignition Timing

1) Connect a tachometer and timing light to engine. Ground carburetor switch. Start engine and run until normal operating temperature is reached. Momentarily raise engine speed above 1100 RPM. If equipped, disconnect and plug vacuum line at solenoid kicker. Disconnect and plug vacuum line at computer (engine RPM will drop when line is disconnected).

2) Engine idle speed should be below curb idle specifications. If necessary, turn idle screw to lower engine RPM. Basic timing should be within 2° of specifications shown on emissions label. If basic timing is okay, go to step **3)**. If timing not, adjust as necessary.

Checking Ignition Spark Advance

1) Connect tachometer and timing light to engine. Plug vacuum line to computer and solenoid kicker. With engine running at operating temperature, remove jumper wire from carburetor ground switch.

2) Connect auxiliary vacuum supply to computer. Apply 16 in. Hg vacuum to system. Raise engine speed to 2000 RPM. Timing should be within 4° of specification. If spark is okay, go to next test. If spark is not okay, replace computer.

Checking Vacuum Supply To Computer

1) With engine running at normal operating temperature, allow RPM to drop to normal idle speed. Unplug hose to computer and connect vacuum gauge. Gauge should read manifold vacuum. If vacuum is okay, go to Engine Idle System Test. If vacuum is not okay, check vacuum supply from carburetor.

ENGINE IDLE SYSTEM TEST

Checking Engine Idle RPM

1) Turn off all lights and accessories. Connect tachometer to engine. Disconnect and plug vacuum connector at EGR CVSCC valve. Jumper radiator fan connector so fan will run continuously.

2) If equipped, disconnect oxygen system test connector. Remove PCV valve and allow it to draw outside air. Ground carburetor switch. If equipped, disconnect and plug vacuum line at solenoid kicker.

3) Start engine and momentarily raise engine speed above 1100 RPM. Wait 2 minutes for engine speed to stabilize. Tachometer should indicate same RPM as shown on emission label.

4) If idle speed is okay, go to Checking Idle Mixture. If idle speed is not okay, turn idle speed screw until engine RPM is the same as shown on emission label.

Checking Idle Mixture

1) Remove hose to heated air sensor from 3-wire connector and install propane supply hose in its place. Open propane main valve. Meter propane until maximum RPM is reached.

2) Engine speed should increase by 90 RPM. If so, go to next test. If engine speed increase is not okay, adjust according to propane assisted idle set procedure.

Checking Fast Idle RPM

1) If equipped, disconnect oxygen system test connector. With engine running at normal operating temperature, turn propane valve off. Open throttle and set fast idle adjustment screw on slowest speed step of fast idle cam.

2) Fast idle speed should be within specifications as shown on emission label. If idle speed is okay, go to Checking Throttle Stop RPM. If fast idle speed is not okay, adjust to specifications.

Checking Throttle Stop RPM

1) With engine running at normal operating temperature, reconnect vacuum connector at EGR CVSCC valve. Reinstall PCV valve. Remove jumper wire from radiator fan and reconnect connector.

2) Remove power feed wire to SIS or solenoid kicker from carburetor 6-wire connector. Tachometer should read 600 RPM or less. If engine speed is okay, test is complete. If speed is greater than 600 RPM, adjust to specifications.

REMOVAL & INSTALLATION

SPARK CONTROL COMPUTER

Removal & Installation

1) Remove battery. Disconnect 10-wire and 14-wire connectors from computer. Disconnect air duct and vacuum hose from vacuum transducer.

NOTE: **Do not remove grease from harness connectors or connector cavities in computer. Grease is used to prevent moisture from corroding terminals. If not at least 1/2" of grease on bottom of computer connector cavities, apply liberal amount of multi-purpose grease (Mopar No. 2932524) over entire end of connector plug before reinstallation.**

2) Remove 3 mounting screws holding computer to fender well. Remove computer. To install, reverse removal procedure.

NOTE: **Computer is not serviceable. Do not attempt disassembly for any reason. If vacuum transducer is defective, replace entire computer.**

COOLANT SENSOR

Removal & Installation

Disconnect electrical connector and remove sensor. To install, coat sensor with anti-seize compound and reverse removal procedure.

CARBURETOR SWITCH

Removal & Installation

Remove bracket and idle solenoid assembly from carburetor. Disconnect electrical connector. To install, reverse removal procedure.

DUTY CYCLE SOLENOID

Removal

1) Remove 2 solenoid retaining screws and gently lift solenoid from air horn. Remove anti-rattle spring, 2 retaining screws and idle solenoid.

2) Remove 2 WOT cut-out switch mounting screws, if equipped. Mark location for proper assembly. Remove harness mounting screws and open retaining clip. Remove wires from connector and thread through clip.

Installation

1) Install idle solenoid and anti-rattle spring. Install wide open throttle cut-out switch, if equipped. Adjust switch so A/C clutch circuit is open in throttle position of 10° before wide open throttle.

2) Install new duty cycle solenoid gasket on air horn. Install new "O" ring on solenoid tip. Lightly lubricate solenoid with petroleum jelly. Install solenoid into carburetor. Install and tighten mounting screws. Route wiring through clamp and connect to harness. Install and tighten harness mounting screw.

OXYGEN SENSOR

Removal

Disconnect negative battery cable. Disconnect electrical lead from oxygen sensor and remove sensor.

Installation

Clean threads in exhaust manifold with 18mm x 1.5 x 16E tap. If old sensor is reinstalled, coat threads with anti-seize compound. New sensors have compound already applied. Hand start sensor, then tighten to 20 ft. lbs. (27 N.m). Connect electrical connector and battery cable.

CHRYSLER CORP. RWD ELECTRONIC FUEL CONTROL

3.7L & 5.2L RWD Light Trucks

NOTE: **All 3.7L and some 5.2L models use the Spark Control Computer with Spark Advance and Throttle Control systems. Only 3.7L models with Holley 6145 feedback carburetor use oxygen sensor feedback system.**

DESCRIPTION

The Electronic Fuel Control (EFC) system is an electronically controlled system that closely controls ignition timing and, on 3.7L models with feedback system, air/fuel ratio. The Spark Control Computer (SCC) is the heart of the system.

The SCC provides the capability of igniting a lean air/fuel mixture under various engine operating conditions. Also, during closed loop operation on models with feedback system, the computer maintains an air/fuel ratio close to the ideal 14.7:1.

OPERATION

The EFC system consists of the following sub-systems: fuel control (models with feedback system), electronic throttle control, spark control, data sensors, Spark Control Computer (SCC), electronic exhaust gas recirculation (EGR), electronic air switching, and catalytic converter.

FUEL CONTROL

Some 3.7L models are equipped with the Holley 6145 1-bbl. feedback carburetor. This carburetor contains an electronically operated duty cycle solenoid. This solenoid meters air flow of the carburetor fuel circuit and operates in parallel with the conventional fixed main metering jets. The computer controls the operation of the solenoid with electrical signals, in response to input from data sensors. *See Fig. 1.*

Fig. 1: Sectional View of Holley 6145 Feedback Carburetor With Duty Cycle Solenoid

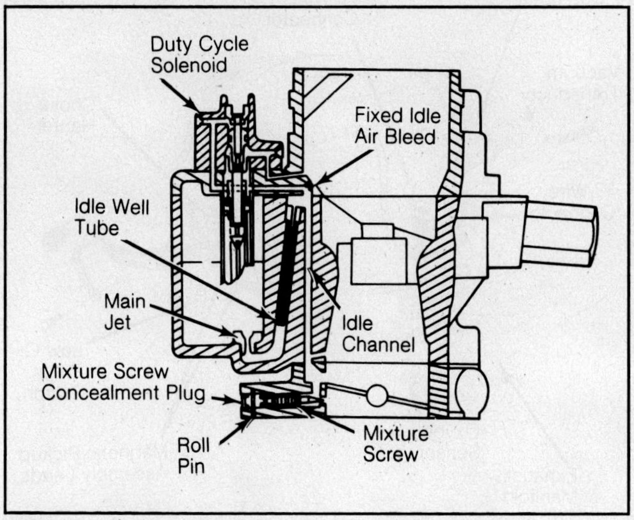

Used on some 3.7L models.

When the solenoid is de-energized by the computer, the solenoid valve spring pushes upward through the main system fuel valve. When de-energized, the solenoid main metering orifice is fully uncovered, providing the richest mixture for any given air flow.

When the solenoid is energized by the computer, the solenoid main metering orifice is fully sealed. This solenoid position offers the leanest mixture within the carburetor for any given air flow.

Main system fuel may be regulated between richest and leanest mixture conditions by controlling the amount of time that the solenoid is energized and de-energized. The computer controls the length of time that the solenoid is energized relative to total solenoid operation time.

This time interval is determined by engine operating conditions and/or oxygen sensor signals. In this manner, the ideal air/fuel ratio can be constantly maintained.

ELECTRONIC THROTTLE CONTROL

The Electronic Throttle Control system and 2 electric timers are incorporated within the SCC. A solenoid, mounted on the carburetor, is energized whenever the air conditioning, heater, rear window defogger or electric timers are activated. The 2 timers operate when the throttle is closed, providing a 2 second time delay, or after engine is started.

SPARK CONTROL

Spark Control allows the computer to determine the exact instant that ignition is required; then signals ignition coil to produce electrical impulses which fire the spark plugs. The computer eliminates the need for either vacuum advance units or centrifugal advance weights. Spark control operates in one of the following modes:

Start Mode

During cranking, an electrical signal from the distributor is fed into the computer. The computer determines spark timing based on this signal. Spark timing while in "start" mode does not vary as it is dependent upon distributor position.

Run Mode

With the engine started and operating normally, spark timing is controlled by the computer, based upon information received from the data sensors.

Spark timing and dwell cannot be adjusted in the run mode. If the computer fails, the system will go into "start" mode. This enables vehicle to be driven in for repair; but performance and fuel economy will be poor. If start mode fails, engine will not start or run.

The amount of spark advance in "run" mode is determined by engine speed, temperature and engine vacuum. When advance occurs is dependent upon the following conditions:

Advance From Vacuum

Advance based upon engine vacuum is allowed by the computer when the carburetor switch is open. The amount of advance is programmed into the computer and is proportionate to vacuum, temperature and engine speed (RPM).

Advance From Speed

Advance based upon engine speed (RPM) is controlled by the computer when the carburetor switch is open. If carburetor switch closes, advance from speed will be cancelled.

CHRYSLER CORP. RWD ELECTRONIC FUEL CONTROL (Cont.)

DATA SENSORS

Each sensor furnishes electrical impulses to the SCC. The SCC computes ignition timing and air/fuel mixture ratio necessary to maintain proper engine operation. The function of each sensor is closely related to each of the other sensors. Operation of each sensor is as follows:

Magnetic Pickup Assembly

The magnetic pickup assembly consists of 2 pickup coils: start pickup coil and run pickup coil. Both are located in the distributor and operate as follows:

- **Start Pickup Coil** - Supplies a signal to SCC which will cause the spark plugs to fire at a fixed amount of advance during cranking only. This coil is permanently attached to distributor and the amount of advance is determined by distributor position. *See Fig. 2.*
- **Run Pickup Coil** - Once engine begins to run, the start pickup coil signal is by-passed and the run pickup coil supplies advance information to the SCC. The SCC then modifies advance in response to engine operating conditions as reported by other sensors.

Fig. 2: View of Distributor with Cap & Rotor Removed

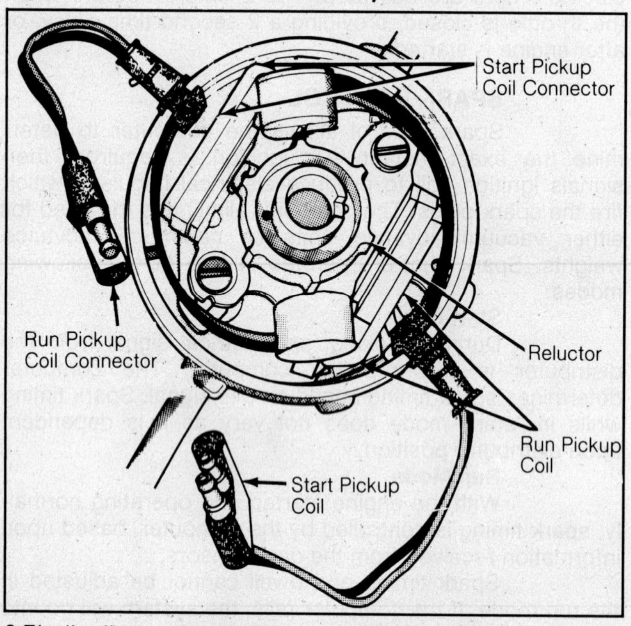

3.7L distributor shown. 5.2L distributor similar.

Coolant Temperature Sensor/Switch

The coolant sensor and switch inform the SCC when engine has reached normal operating temperature. Coolant temperature information is used to control ignition timing while engine is cold.

Vacuum Transducer

This sensor is mounted on the computer and provides the computer with a signal indicating the amount of engine vacuum. Engine vacuum is used by the computer to determine how much to advance or retard ignition timing and when to adjust air/fuel mixture.

Carburetor Switch

Located on the end of idle stop, the carburetor switch informs the computer when the engine is at idle. When carburetor switch contacts throttle lever ground, the computer will cancel spark advance and prevent air/fuel ratio adjustment.

Fig. 3: Location of Data Sensors on 3.7L Engine

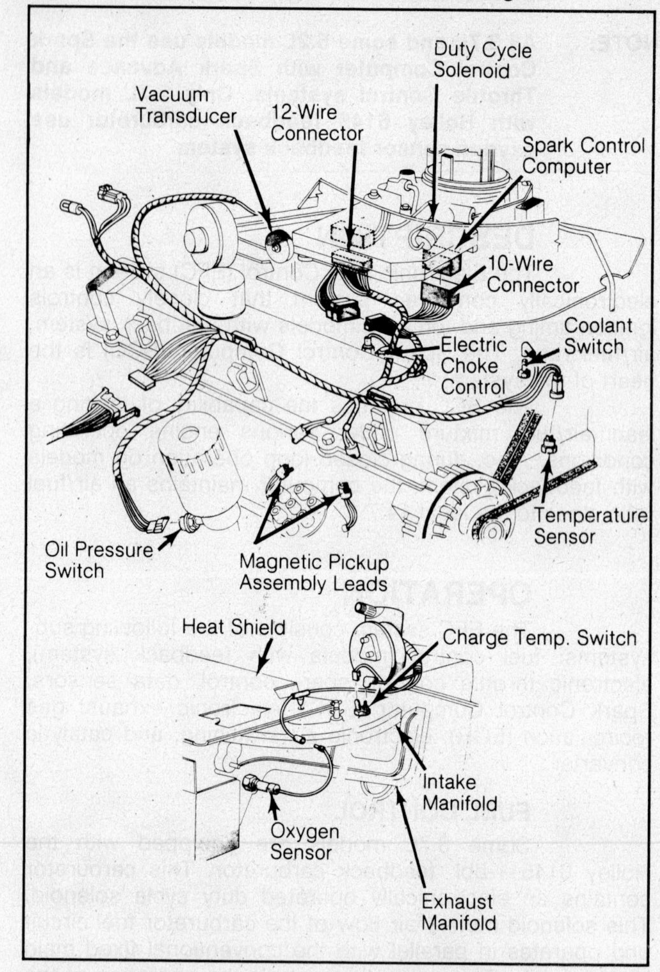

Fig. 4: Location of Data Sensors on 5.2L Engine (Rear View)

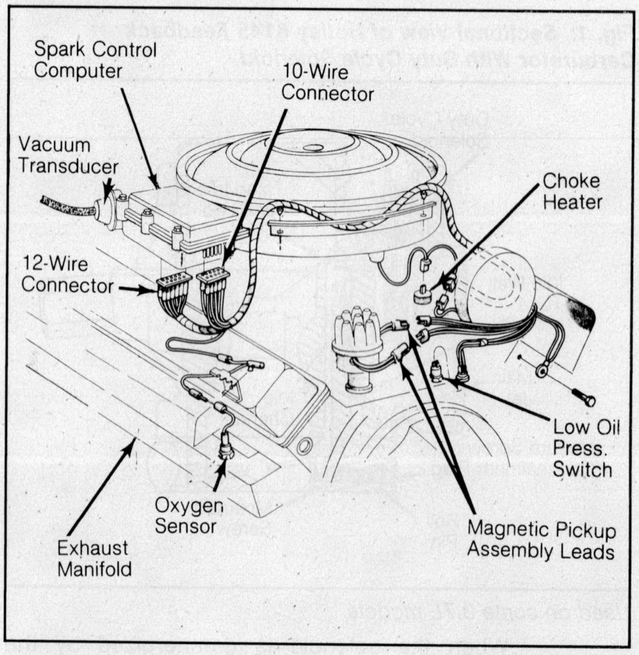

CHRYSLER CORP. RWD ELECTRONIC FUEL CONTROL (Cont.)

Fig. 5: Location of Data Sensors on 5.2L Engine (Front View)

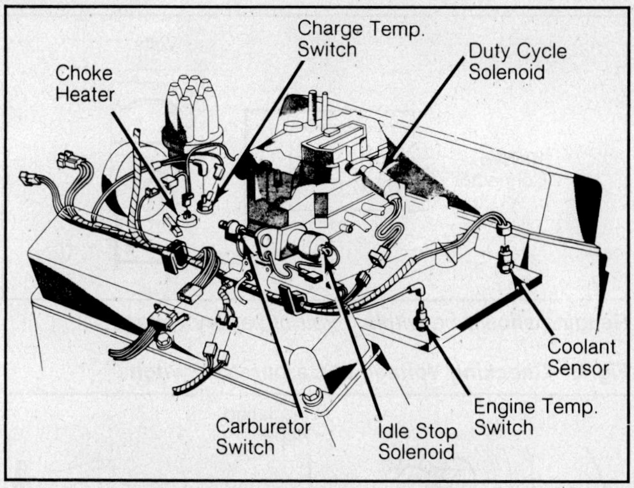

Oxygen Sensor

The oxygen sensor is only used on vehicles with feedback carburetors. The sensor is located in the exhaust manifold. Sensor informs the computer of the amount of oxygen present in exhaust gases. The amount is proportional to mixture strength. The computer adjusts air/fuel ratio to maintain ideal operating conditions and optimum efficiency of the 3-way catalyst system.

Charge Temperature Switch

This sensor is located in the intake manifold. The switch is closed when intake charge (air/fuel mixture) is below 60°F (16°C). This prevents EGR timer function and EGR valve operation. When temperature is above 60°F (16°C), the switch opens, allowing EGR timer to time out and EGR valve to operate.

Fig. 6: Internal View of Spark Control Computer

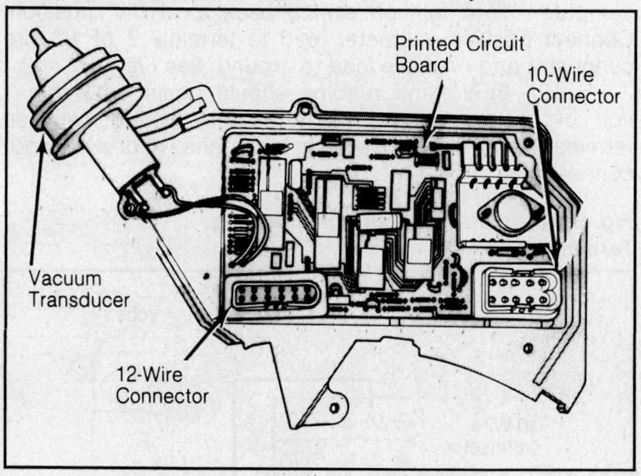

SPARK CONTROL COMPUTER

The Spark Control Computer (SCC) is mounted on the air cleaner housing and consists of a printed circuit board which simultaneously receives signals from all data sensors and analyzes these signals to determine spark advance and, on models with feedback carburetor, air/fuel mixture. Incorporated within the computer are the electronics for throttle control, EGR and air switching systems. After determining spark advance, the computer operates the engine feedback system (on models so equipped) in one of the following modes:

Open Loop

During cold engine operation, the air/fuel ratio is controlled by information programmed into the computer by the manufacturer. Until normal operating temperature is reached, the air/fuel mixture will be fixed at a rich level to allow proper engine warm-up. During this mode of operation, air from the air pump is injected "upstream" in the exhaust manifold to assist in heating up the oxygen sensor.

Closed Loop

Once normal engine operating temperature is achieved, the air/fuel ratio is controlled by the computer based upon information received from the oxygen sensor.

ELECTRONIC EXHAUST GAS RECIRCULATION (EGR)

The electronic EGR system is incorporated within the SCC and is used on all models equipped with Electronic Spark Advance (ESA). This system prevents EGR flow until engine has reached normal operating temperature (after a predetermined length of time).

ELECTRONIC AIR SWITCHING

The electronic air switching system is incorporated within the SCC and is used only on Calif. and High Altitude models. This system directs the flow of air from the air pump either "upstream" or "downstream" after engine has reached operating temperature and a specified period of time has elapsed.

CATALYTIC CONVERTER

All models are equipped with one or two catalytic converters to reduce emissions of all three major polutants: HC, CO and NOx. In addition to the main converter, some models are equipped with a "mini-ox" converter. The mini-ox is located immediately below the exhaust manifold-to-exhaust pipe connection (left side on V8) and is significantly smaller than the main converter, which is located farther downstream.

NOTE: External similarities exist between converter systems. However, extreme care must be exercised during replacement of converters due to internal design differences.

TESTING

A malfunction in the EFC system may result in engine surge, hesitation, rough idle and/or poor fuel economy. Before performing any tests, check all vacuum and electrical wiring for proper routing and connections and check for exhaust and intake manifold leaks. If these are OK, proceed with testing.

The Spark Control Computer controls ignition timing and air/fuel mixture (on models so equipped). When system testing is required, always perform Electronic Spark Control Tests first, before testing EFC system.

When testing requires that either harness connector be disconnected from computer, DO NOT remove grease from either connector or cavities in computer. The grease is used in order to prevent moisture from corroding the terminals. If there is not at least 1/2" of grease on bottom of computer connector cavities, apply a liberal amount of multipurpose grease (Mopar No. 2932524) over entire end of plug before reinstalling.

CHRYSLER CORP. RWD ELECTRONIC FUEL CONTROL (Cont.)

ELECTRONIC SPARK CONTROL TESTS

Ignition System Starting Test

1) Measure and record battery voltage. Check battery specific gravity, which must be 1.220 (temperature corrected) to deliver proper voltage to ignition system.

2) Turn ignition on and remove coil wire from distributor cap. Hold end of wire 1/4" from a good engine ground. Intermittently jump coil negative terminal to ground, while watching for spark at coil wire. If there is a spark, it must be constant and bright blue.

3) If there is a good spark, continue jumping negative coil terminal to ground while slowly moving secondary wire away from ground. Look for arcing at coil tower. If arcing occurs, replace coil. If spark is weak or inconsistent, or if there is no spark, go to Failure to Start Test.

4) If spark is good and there is no arcing at coil tower, secondary voltage is okay. Make sure spark is reaching spark plugs by checking distributor cap, rotor, plug wires and plugs.

5) If all components check okay, ignition system is not at fault. Check fuel system or mechanical engine damage.

CAUTION: Always perform Ignition System Starting Test before proceeding. Failure to do so may result in lost diagnostic time or incorrect test results.

Failure to Start Test

1) If a strong spark was obtained in step **2)** of Ignition System Starting Test, go directly to step **5)**. If spark was weak or intermittent, turn ignition switch off and disconnect 10-way connector from SCC. Repeat Ignition System Starting Test, step **2)**. If spark results, replace computer.

2) If no spark is obtained, check voltage at coil positive terminal. With ignition switch on, connect positive voltmeter lead to coil positive terminal and negative lead to a good ground. Reading should be within 1 volt of battery voltage. If not, check wiring between battery and coil positive terminal.

3) If voltage at positive coil terminal was correct, connect positive voltmeter lead to coil negative terminal and negative lead to a good ground. Again, voltage should be within 1 volt of battery voltage. If not, replace ignition coil.

4) If voltage was correct at negative coil terminal, but no spark was obtained in step **2)** of Ignition System Starting Test, replace ignition coil.

5) If spark results, but engine will not start, turn ignition switch to "RUN" position. Connect positive voltmeter lead to terminal 1 of 10-wire connector and negative lead to a good ground. *See Fig. 7*. Reading should be within 1 volt of battery voltage. If not, check wire for open and repair it. Repeat this step after repairing wire. Reconnect 10-wire connector to computer.

6) If battery voltage was recorded in step **5)**, place a thin insulator (paper or thin cardboard) between curb idle adjusting screw and carburetor switch or make sure screw does not touch switch. *See Fig. 8*. Connect negative lead of voltmeter to a good ground.

7) Turn ignition switch to "RUN" position and touch positive voltmeter lead to carburetor switch terminal. Reading should be about 5 volts. If so, proceed to step **13)**.

Fig. 7: Voltmeter Hookup for Checking Terminal 1 Voltage

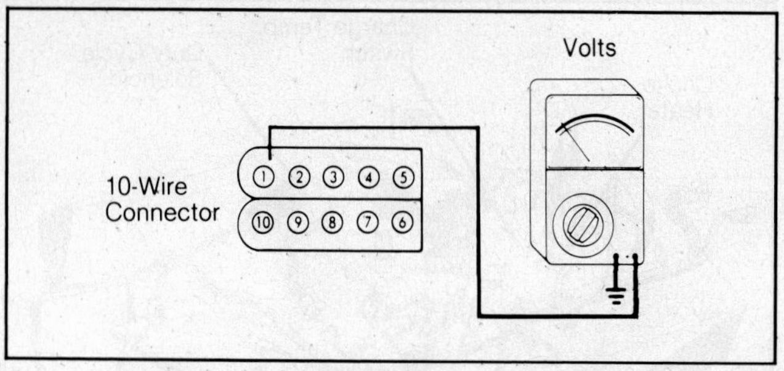

Reading should be within 1 volt of battery voltage.

Fig. 8: Checking Voltage at Carburetor Switch

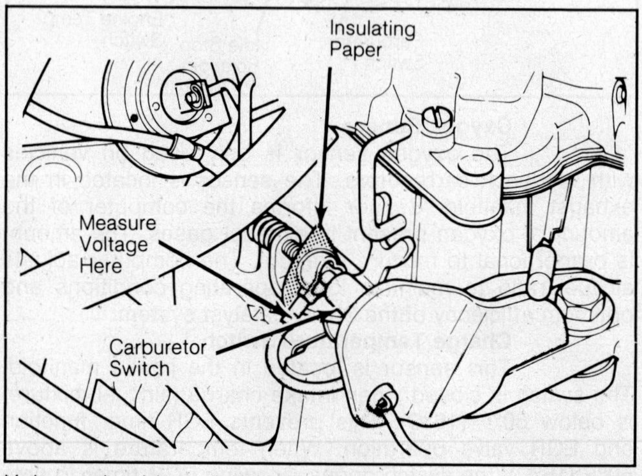

Voltage should read about 5 volts

8) If voltage in step **7)** was not at least 5 volts, turn ignition switch off. Disconnect 10-wire connector from computer. Turn ignition switch back to "RUN" position. Connect positive voltmeter lead to terminal 2 of 10-wire connector and negative lead to ground. *See Fig. 9*.

9) Voltage reading should again be within 1 volt of battery voltage. If not, check wiring between terminal 2 and ignition switch for opens, shorts or poor connections.

Fig. 9: Voltmeter Hookup for Checking Terminal 2 Voltage

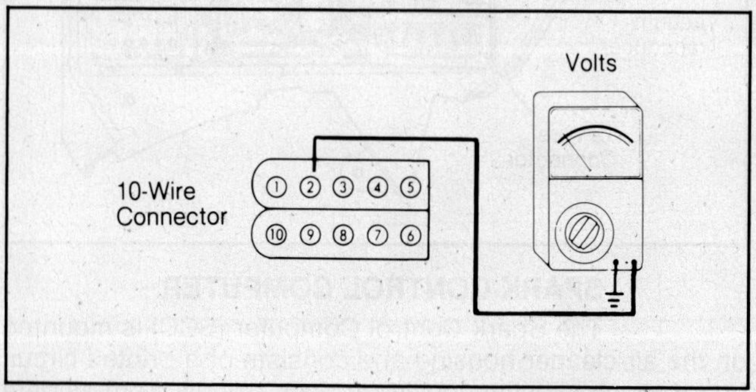

Voltage should be within 1 volt of battery voltage.

10) If voltage at terminal 2 was correct, turn ignition switch off. Using an ohmmeter, check continuity between terminal 7 of 10-wire connector and carburetor switch terminal. *See Fig. 10*. Continuity should exist.

CHRYSLER CORP. RWD ELECTRONIC FUEL CONTROL (Cont.)

11) If not, check wire between connections for opens, shorts or poor connections. If continuity is present, use an ohmmeter with leads attached to terminal 10 and engine ground to check continuity of ground circuit. *See Fig. 11*.

12) If there is continuity, replace computer. If there is no continuity, check wire from terminal 10 to ground. Recheck continuity between terminal 7 of 10-wire connector and carburetor switch. Try to start engine. If engine fails to start, go to next step.

Fig. 10: Ohmmeter Hookup for Checking Carburetor Switch Wiring Harness

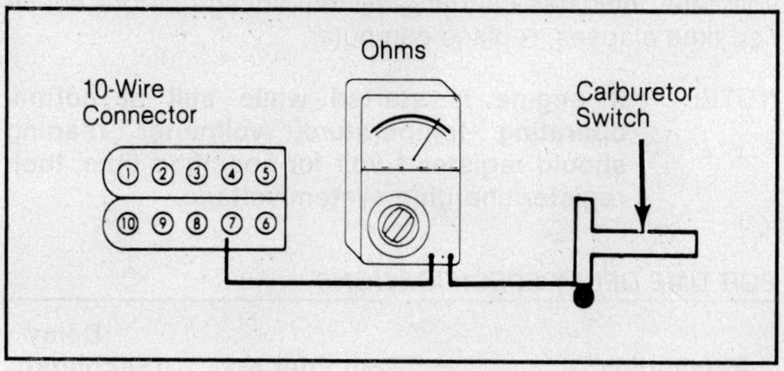

Fig. 11: Ohmmeter Hookup for Checking Computer Ground Circuit

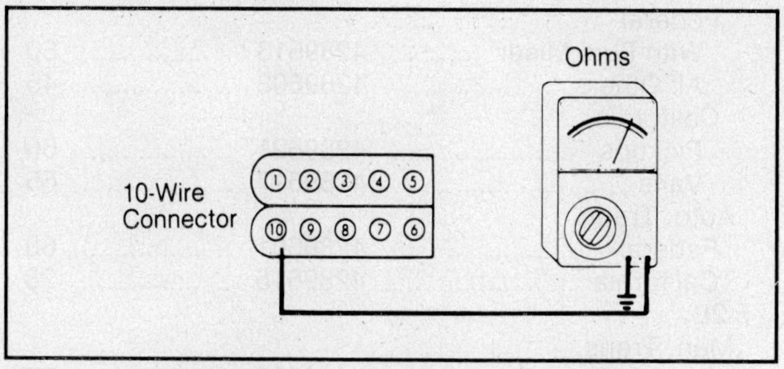

Fig. 12: Ohmmeter Hookup for Checking Pick-Up Coil Resistance

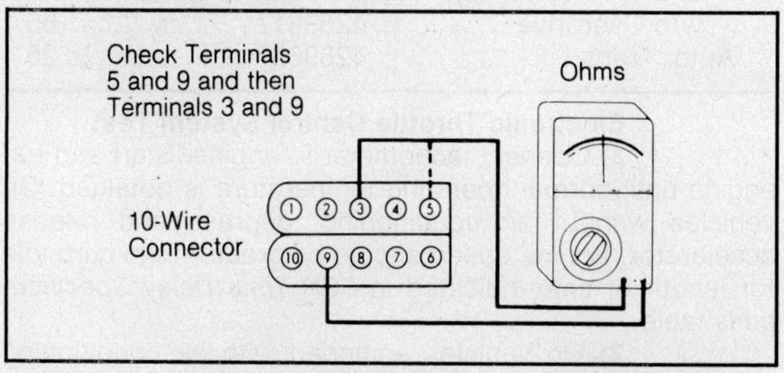

Resistance should be between 150 and 900 ohms.

13) Turn ignition switch off. Attach ohmmeter leads to terminals 5 and 9 of 10-wire harness connector to check run pickup coil resistance and to terminals 3 and 9 to check start pickup coil resistance. *See Fig. 12*. Resistance should be 150-900 ohms. If so, go to step **15)**.

14) If resistance of either pickup coil is incorrect, disconnect distributor connectors and attach ohmmeter leads to run pickup coil leads and then to start pickup coil leads coming from distributor. If resistance is now okay, wiring harness is defective. If resistance is still not 150-900 ohms, replace pickup coils, as necessary.

15) Connect one lead of an ohmmeter to engine ground and touch other lead to each terminal of leads coming from 2 distributor pickup coils. There should be no continuity. If continuity is indicated, replace pickup coil.

16) Remove distributor cap and rotor and check reluctor-to-pickup coil(s) air gap. Air gap for single pickup coil distributor should be .006" (.15 mm). On dual pickup distributors, air gap should be .006" (.15 mm) for start pickup coil and .012" (.30 mm) for run pickup coil.

17) If gap is incorrect, adjust gap using a non-magnetic feeler gauge. *See Fig. 13*. To adjust, loosen pickup coil hold-down screws. With gauge between coil and reluctor tooth, move coil against gauge. Tighten hold-down screw, remove feeler gauge and recheck gap.

Fig. 13: Checking Distributor Pickup Air Gap

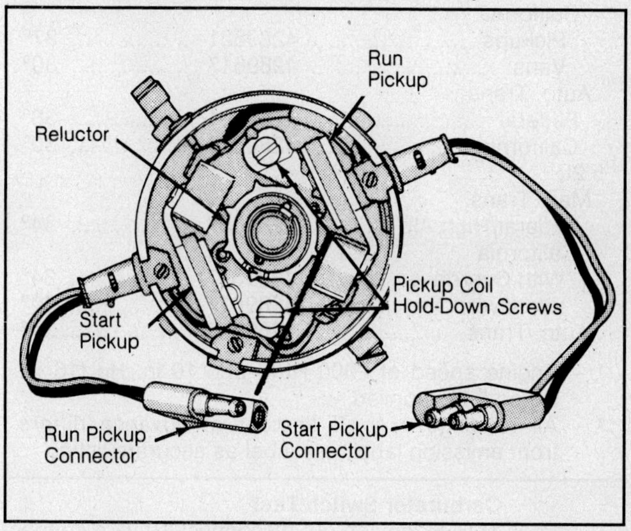

A non-magnetic feeler gauge must be used when checking and/or adjusting air gap.

18) Install distributor cap and reinstall all wiring. If engine fails to start, replace SCC. If engine fails to start with new computer, re-install original computer and repeat testing procedure.

SCC Spark Test

NOTE: Ensure basic timing is properly set before performing test.

1) Warm engine to normal operating temperature. Connect adjustable timing light or magnetic timing probe to engine.

2) Ensure that carburetor switch is not grounded by placing a thin insulator (paper or thin cardboard) between curb idle adjusting screw and switch or make sure curb idle adjusting screw does not contact switch. Be sure coolant temperature sensor is connected and working properly.

3) Remove vacuum hose from vacuum transducer. Attach an outside vacuum source (pump) to transducer and apply 10 in. Hg (16 in. Hg on 5.2L engine) of vacuum. Increase engine speed to 2000 RPM and wait 1 minute before checking spark advance. *See Spark Advance Test Specifications table*. Specifications given in table are TOTAL advance (initial advance is included).

4) If computer fails to obtain settings, replace computer.

NOTE: The 3.7L engine is equipped with an accumulator (timer). The carburetor switch MUST be

CHRYSLER CORP. RWD ELECTRONIC FUEL CONTROL (Cont.)

ungrounded until accumulator times out before checking specified spark advance schedule.

SPARK ADVANCE TEST SPECIFICATIONS [1]

Application	Computer No.	Spark Advance [2]
3.7L		
Man. Trans.		
Federal		
With Fuel Miser	4289613	30°
All Others	4289603	33°
California		
Pickups	4289621	37°
Vans	4289617	30°
Auto. Trans.		
Federal	4289601	38°
California	4289615	30°
5.2L		
Man. Trans.		
Federal/High Alt.	4289637	34°
California		
With Overdrive	4289637	34°
w/o Overdrive	4289617	30°
Auto. Trans.	4289637	34°

[1] – Engine speed of 2000 RPM and 10 in. Hg (16 in. Hg on 5.2L) applied.

[2] – All readings ±4°. If amount of advance differs from emission label, use label as accurate listing.

Carburetor Switch Test

1) With ignition off, disconnect 10-wire connector from SCC. With throttle completely closed, check for continuity between pin 7 of disconnected connector and good ground.

NOTE: Grounding carburetor switch eliminates all spark advance on most systems.

2) If no continuity exists, check wiring and carburetor switch. Recheck basic ignition timing.

3) Open throttle and again check continuity between pin 7 and ground. There should be no continuity.

Coolant & Charge Temperature Switch Test

1) Turn ignition off and disconnect wire from temperature switch. Connect 1 lead of ohmmeter to center terminal of temp. switch. Connect other end to good ground (coolant switch) or ground terminal (charge switch). Check for continuity.

2) On a cold engine, continuity should be present (resistance less than 100 ohms). If not, replace switch. The charge temperature switch must be cooler than 60°F (16°C) to obtain this reading. On an engine at normal operating temperature, there should be no continuity. If there is, replace switch.

Coolant Sensor Test

Turn ignition switch off and disconnect wire connector from sensor. Connect ohmmeter leads to sensor terminals. With engine cold and air temperature below 90°F (32°C), resistance should be 500-1100 ohms. With engine at normal operating temperature, resistance should be greater than 1300 ohms. If resistance in either case is not as indicated, replace sensor.

NOTE: Coolant sensor resistance will vary with changes in engine temperature.

Electronic EGR System Test

1) Ensure that engine temperature sensors are working properly. With engine cold and ignition switch off, connect voltmeter between Gray wire on EGR solenoid and ground. Start engine. Voltage should read less than 1 volt. Reading should be maintained until normal operating temperature is reached and specified time has elapsed as indicated in *EGR Time Delay Specifications* table.

2) After normal operating temperature is reached and specified time has elapsed, voltmeter should register charging system voltage. If readings are not as indicated, replace EGR solenoid and repeat test. If voltmeter indicates charging system voltage before specified time elapses, replace computer.

NOTE: If engine is started while still at normal operating temperature, voltmeter reading should register 1 volt for specified time, then register charging system voltage.

EGR TIME DELAY SPECIFICATIONS

Application	Computer No.	Delay (Seconds)
3.7L		
Man. Trans.		
Federal		
With Fuel Miser	4289613	60
All Others	4289603	45
California		
Pickups	4289621	60
Vans	4289617	65
Auto. Trans.		
Federal	4289601	60
California	4289615	28
5.2L		
Man. Trans.		
Federal/High Alt.	4289637	25
California		
With Overdrive	4289637	25
w/o Overdrive	4289617	65
Auto. Trans.	4289637	25

Electronic Throttle Control System Test

1) Connect tachometer to engine. Start and run engine until normal operating temperature is obtained. On vehicles without air conditioning, depress and release accelerator. Engine speed should be greater than curb idle for length of time indicated in *EGR Time Delay Specifications* table.

2) On vehicles equipped with air conditioning or rear window defogger, turning on the air conditioner or defogger and depressing accelerator for a moment should give an RPM higher than curb idle speed. Turning off the air conditioner or rear window defogger will result in normal idle speed.

NOTE: The air conditioning clutch will cycle on and off as it is running. Do not mistake this for electronic throttle control operation.

3) On all vehicles, if speed increases do not occur as indicated, turn engine off and disconnect six-wire connector at carburetor. Using an ohmmeter, check resistance of solenoid by measuring from terminal which contained black wire, to ground. Resistance should be 15-35 ohms. If not, replace solenoid.

CHRYSLER CORP. RWD ELECTRONIC FUEL CONTROL (Cont.)

4) On vehicles without air conditioning or rear window defogger, start vehicle and, before specified time has elapsed, measure voltage at Black wire of 6-wire connector. Voltmeter reading should equal charging system voltage. If not, replace computer (5.2L High Alt., all 3.7L models), or Gray starter timer (all other models).

5) Start engine and turn A/C and/or rear window defogger on (if equipped). Measure voltage at Black wire of 6-wire connector. Voltmeter reading should equal charging system voltage AFTER specified time has elapsed. If not, check wiring back to instrument panel for an open circuit.

ELECTRONIC FUEL CONTROL SYSTEM TESTS

NOTE: **The Spark Control Computer Spark Test should be performed before any test on EFC system. The following tests should be performed in the sequence given.**

Before beginning test procedures, check all vacuum hose connections and routing (see vacuum diagram in engine compartment). Check resistance in all related wiring, with specific attention to connectors at output devices and at SCC.

Remove hose from vacuum transducer on SCC and attach an outside vacuum source (pump). Apply 16 in. Hg. vacuum, set parking brake, start engine and bring to normal operating temperature. Throughout testing procedures, any time engine is started hot, maintain engine speed of 1500 RPM for at least 2 minutes before proceeding. Do not ground carburetor switch.

Air Switching System Diagnosis (Vacuum Supply)

1) Remove vacuum hose from air switching/diverter valve and connect a vacuum gauge to hose. Set parking brake. Start engine and observe gauge reading.

2) On cold engine, vacuum should be present until coolant and intake charge reach normal operating temperature. When temperature is reached and time delay has elapsed, vacuum should drop to zero.

3) If no vacuum is present on gauge, check vacuum supply, air switching solenoid, coolant switch, charge temperature switch and computer wiring and connections. If all check okay, computer may be defective, preventing air switching function. Proceed to step **5)**.

4) On a warm engine, vacuum should be present after engine starts until time delay has elapsed, then drop to zero. If there is no vacuum, check vacuum supply, air switching solenoid, coolant switch, charge temperature switch and computer wiring and connections. If all check okay, computer may be defective, preventing air switching function. Proceed to step **5)**.

5) If no vacuum was recorded in step **3)** and **4)**, and all components are operating properly, check voltage at Light Green wire on air switching solenoid (engine off). With engine at normal operating temperature, start engine. Voltage should be less than 1 volt.

6) After time delay has elapsed, voltmeter should read charging system voltage. If not, replace solenoid and repeat test. If voltmeter reads charging system voltage before time delay has elapsed, replace computer.

Air Switching Diagnosis (Air Switching Valve)

1) Remove air supply hose from air switching valve. Remove vacuum hose from valve and attach outside vacuum source (pump).

2) Set parking brake. Start engine. Air should blow out of side port. Apply vacuum to valve. Air should blow out bottom port.

Temperature Sensor/Switch Tests

Refer to test procedures in Electronic Spark Control System Tests section. If sensors are okay, proceed to Carburetor Duty Cycle Solenoid Test.

Carburetor Duty Cycle Solenoid Test

1) Connect tachometer to engine. Disconnect duty cycle solenoid connector at solenoid. Average engine speed should increase a minimum of 50 RPM. Reconnect solenoid connector. Engine speed should slowly return to 1500 RPM.

2) Disconnect 12-pin connector at computer. Connect a ground to harness connector pin 11. Engine speed should decrease 50 RPM (minimum). If speed does not change as indicated, service carburetor (check for air leaks).

Electronic Fuel Control Computer Test

1) With tachometer still connected and parking brake set, start engine. Warm to normal operating temperature and maintain engine speed of 1500 RPM. Connect voltmeter to duty cycle solenoid output wire going to carburetor (Green wire). Do not separate solenoid connector from wiring harness.

2) Separate connector from oxygen sensor and connect jumper wire from connector to good ground. Engine speed should increase at least 50 RPM and voltmeter should indicate more than 9 volts.

3) With jumper still attached to sensor harness, touch other end to battery positive cable. Engine speed should decrease at least 50 RPM and voltmeter should indicate less than 3 volts. If computer fails both tests, replace it. Reconnect oxygen sensor harness.

REMOVAL & INSTALLATION

SPARK CONTROL COMPUTER

Removal

1) Remove negative battery terminal. Disconnect 10-wire and 12-wire connectors from computer. Remove vacuum hose from vacuum transducer. Remove mounting screws from inside air cleaner and remove computer.

2) Do not remove grease from harness connectors or connector cavities in computer. Grease is used to prevent moisture from corroding terminals.

Installation

1) If there is not at least 1/2" of grease on bottom of computer connector cavities, apply a liberal amount of multipurpose grease (Mopar No. 2932524) over entire end of plug before reinstalling.

2) Reverse removal procedures to complete installation.

NOTE: **Computer is not serviceable. Do not attempt to take it apart for any reason. If vacuum transducer is defective, entire computer must be replaced.**

CHRYSLER CORP. RWD ELECTRONIC FUEL CONTROL (Cont.)

CARBURETOR SWITCH

Removal & Installation

Remove bracket and switch assembly from carburetor. Disconnect electrical connector. To install, reverse removal procedure and adjust if necessary.

OXYGEN SENSOR

Removal & Installation

Disconnect battery cable and electrical lead at sensor. Remove sensor. If old sensor is to be reinstalled, coat threads with anti-seize compound. New sensors are manufactured with compound already applied. Hand start sensor, then tighten to 20 ft. lb. (27 N.m). Connect electrical connector and battery cable.

Fig. 14: Wiring Diagram for RWD Truck EFC System

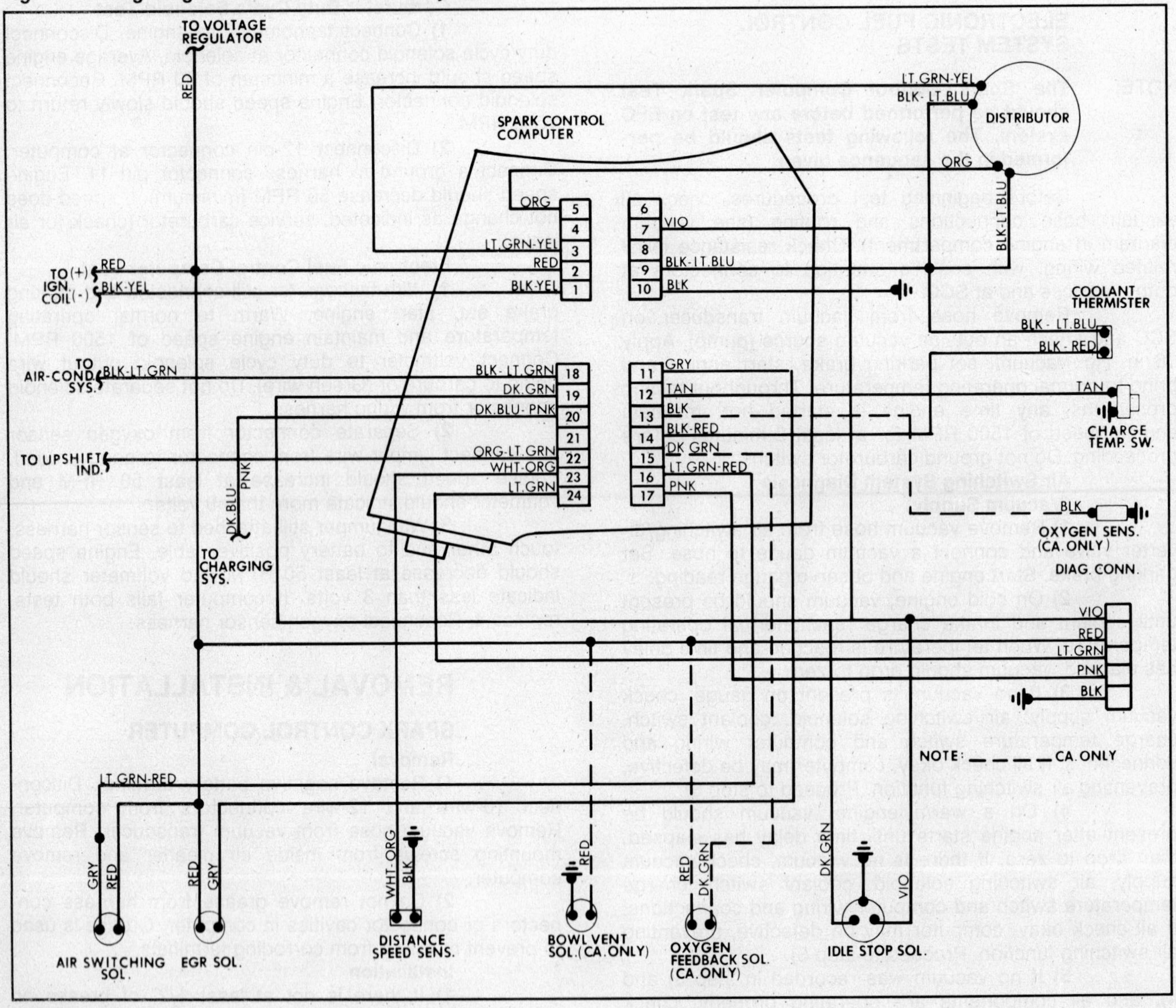

3.7L 6-cylinder engines.

CHRYSLER CORP. RWD ELECTRONIC FUEL CONTROL (Cont.)

Fig. 15: Wiring Diagram for RWD Truck EFC System

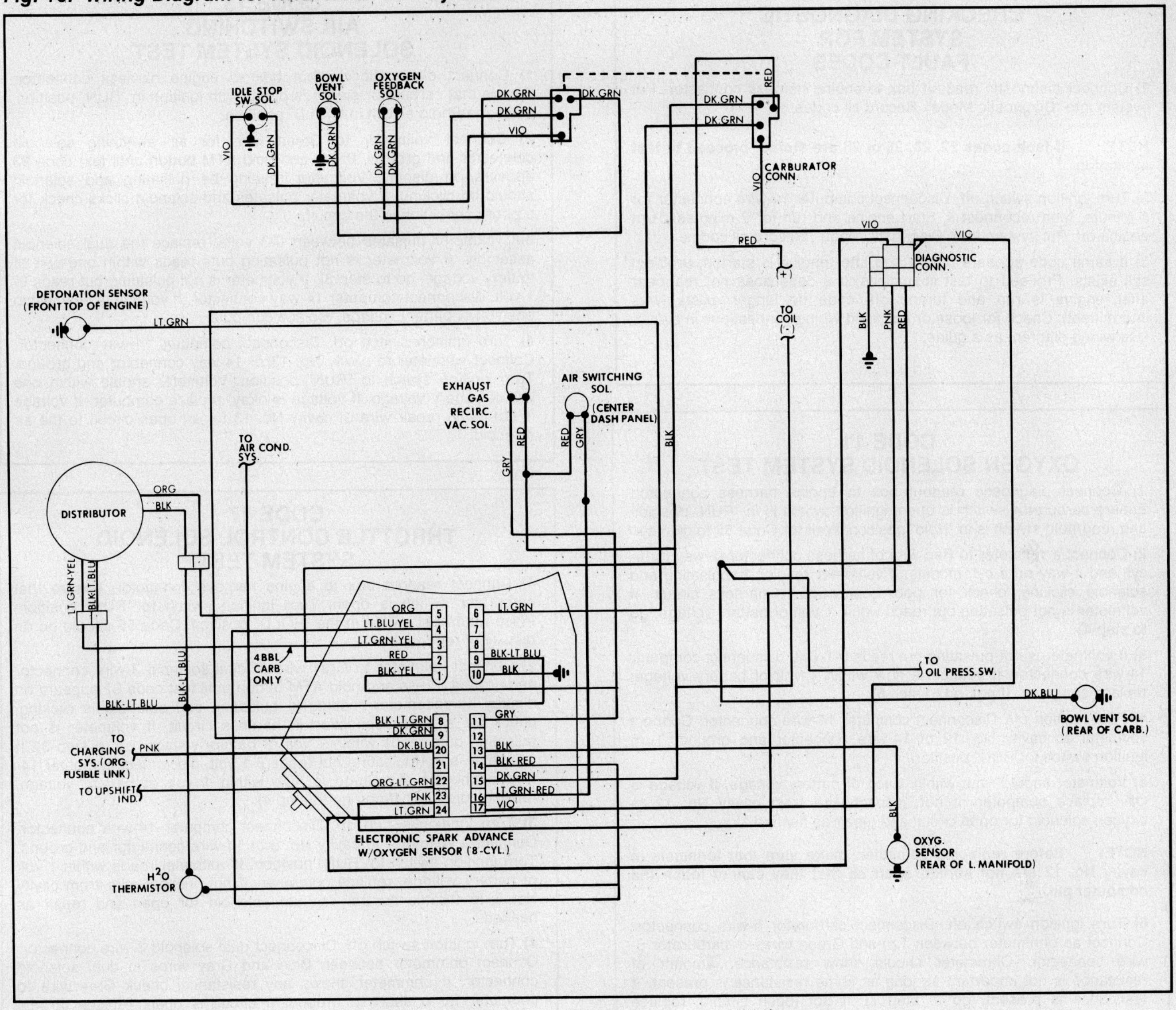

5.2L V8 engines.

CHRYSLER CORP. RWD ELECTRONIC FUEL CONTROL (Cont.)

CHECKING DIAGNOSTIC SYSTEM FOR FAULT CODES

1) Connect diagnostic readout box to engine harness connector. Put system into "Diagnostic Mode". Record all codes.

NOTE: If fault codes 22, 28, 25 or 26 are stored, proceed to test indication.

2) Turn ignition switch off. Disconnect computer 14-wire connector for 1 minute, then reconnect it. Start engine and run for 2 minutes. Turn engine off. Put system into "Diagnostic Mode". Record all codes.

3) If same code appears before and after engine is started, problem still exists. Proceed to test indications. If a code does not reappear after engine is run and turned off, code no longer exists (was intermittent). Check for loose or corroded wiring connections in circuit. Use wiring diagram as a guide.

CODE 11 OXYGEN SOLENOID SYSTEM TEST

1) Connect diagnostic readout box to engine harness connector. Ensure carburetor switch is open, ignition switch is in "RUN" position and read/hold switch is in "Hold" position. Wait for Code 55 to display.

2) Connect a voltmeter to Red wire of harness connector (2-way for 6-cyl. and 4-way on 8 cyl. models) If voltmeter reading is pulsating and solenoid clicking, check for poor connection in harness circuit. If voltmeter is not pulsating but reads within 1 volt of battery voltage, go to step **4)**.

3) If voltmeter is not pulsating but reads 0-1 volt, disconnect computer 14-wire connector. If voltage is now within 1 volt of battery voltage, replace computer. If not, go to step **6)**.

4) Turn ignition off. Disconnect computer 14-wire connector. Connect voltmeter to cavity No. 12 of 14-wire connector and ground. Turn ignition switch to "RUN" position.

5) Voltmeter should read within 1 volt of battery voltage. If voltage is OK, replace computer. If not, inspect wire from cavity No. 12 to oxygen solenoid for open circuit and repair as needed.

NOTE: Before replacing computer, make sure that terminals in cavity No. 12 are not spread apart so that they cannot touch the computer pin.

6) Turn ignition switch off. Disconnect carburetor 6-wire connector. Connect an ohmmeter between Tan and Green wires of carburetor 6-wire connector. Ohmmeter should show resistance. Amount of resistance is not important as long as some resistance is present. If resistance is present, go to step **7)**. If not (open circuit), replace oxygen solenoid.

7) With carburetor 6-wire connector disconnected, connect voltmeter to Blue wire of 6-wire connector and ground. Turn ignition switch to run position. If voltmeter reads within 1 volt of battery voltage, check Green wire of oxygen solenoid to computer for a short circuit to ground. Repair as needed. If voltmeter reads zero volts, inspect Blue wire for open circuit to ignition switch and repair.

CODE 13 AIR SWITCHING SOLENOID SYSTEM TEST

1) Connect diagnostic readout box to engine harness connector. Ensure that carburetor switch is open. With ignition in "RUN" position, place read/hold switch in "HOLD" position.

2) Connect voltmeter to Green wire for air switching solenoid connector and ground. Press and hold ATM button until test code 93 appears on display. Voltmeter reading be pulsating and solenoid should be clicking. If voltmeter pulsates and solenoid clicks check for a poor connection in the circuit.

3)If voltmeter pulsates between 0-3 volts, replace the dual solenoid assembly. If voltmeter is not pulsating buts reads within one volt of battery voltage, go to step **3)**. If voltmeter is not pulsating but reads 0-1 volt, disconnect computer 14-way connector. If voltage is now within one volt of battery voltage, replace computer.

4) Turn ignition switch off. Disconnect computer 14-way connector. Connect voltmeter to cavity No. 13 of 14-way connector and ground. Turn ignition switch to "RUN" position. Voltmeter should within one volt of battery voltage. If voltage is okay, replace computer. If voltage is not okay, repair wire of cavity No. 13 for an open circuit to the air solenoid.

CODE 17 THROTTLE CONTROL SOLENOID SYSTEM TEST

1) Connect readout box to engine harness connector. Ensure that carburetor switch is open. Turn ignition switch to "RUN" position. Place read/hold switch in the "HOLD" position. Code 55 should be on display of readout box.

2) Connect voltmeter to Gray wire of dual solenoid 3-wire connector and ground. Press and hold ATM button until test code 97 appears on display. If voltemeter reading is pulsating and solenoid is clicking, check for a poor connection in harness circuit. If voltmeter is not pulsating buts reads within 1 volt of battery voltage, go to step **3)**. If voltmeter is not pulsating but reads 0-1 volt, disconnect computer 14-wire connector. If voltage is now within 1 volt of battery voltage, replace computer. If not, go to step **4)**.

3) Turn ignition switch off. Disconnect computer 14-wire connector. Connect a voltmeter to cavity No. 6 of 14-wire connector and ground. Turn ignition switch to "RUN" position. If voltmeter reads within 1 volt of battery voltage, replace computer. If not, inspect wire from cavity No. 6 to throttle control vacuum solenoid for open and repair as needed.

4) Turn ignition switch off. Disconnect dual solenoid 3-wire connector. Connect ohmmeter between Blue and Gray wires in dual solenoid connector. If ohmmeter shows any resistance, check Gray wire to computer for a short to ground. If circuit is open, replace throttle control solenoid.

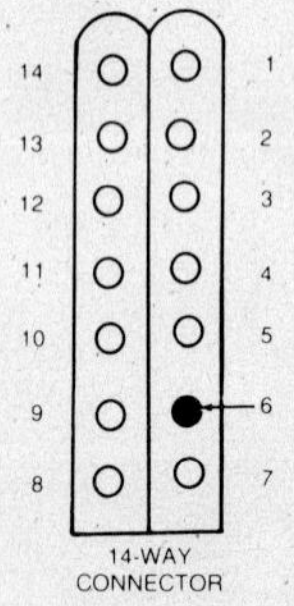

CHRYSLER CORP. RWD ELECTRONIC FUEL CONTROL (Cont.)

CODE 18
EGR CONTROL SOLENOID SYSTEM TEST

1) Connect diagnostic readout box to engine harness connector. With carburetor switch open and ignition switch in "RUN" position, place read/hold switch in "HOLD" position. Wait for Code 55 to appear on display of readout box.

2) Connect voltmeter to Gray wire of EGR solenoid 3-way connector and ground. Press and hold ATM button until test code 98 appears on the display. If voltmeter pulsates and solenoid clicks, check for a poor connection in the EGR circuit. If voltmeter pulsates between 0-3 volts, replace dual solenoid assembly.

3) If voltmeter is not pulsating but reads within one volt of battery voltage, go to step **4)**. If voltmeter is not pulsating but reads 0-1 volt, disconnect computer 14-way connector. If voltage is now within one volt of battery voltage, replace computer.

4) Turn ignition switch off. Disconnect computer 14-way connector. Connect voltmeter to cavity No. 8 of 14-way connector and ground. Turn ignition switch to the run position. Voltmeter should read within one volt of battery voltage. If voltage is okay, replace computer. If voltage is not okay, repair wire of cavity No. 8 for an open circuit to EGR solenoid.

5) Turn ignition switch off. Disconnect dual solenoid 3-way connector. Connect ohmmeter to solenoid 3-way connector. If ohmmeter shows some resistance, repair gray wire to computer for a short circuit to ground. If the circuit is open, replace dual solenoid assembly.

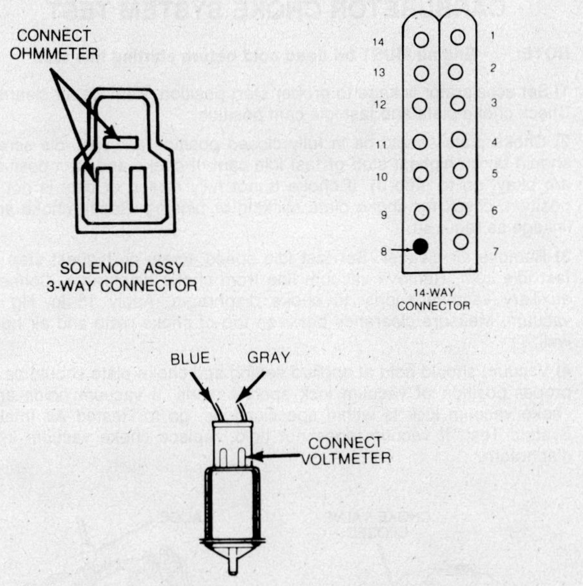

CODE 22
OXYGEN FEEDBACK SYSTEM TEST

1) Turn ignition switch off. Connect a voltmeter to Green oxygen solenoid wire at carburetor connector (2-way for 6 cyl.and 4-way for 8 cyl. models) and ground. Disconnect and plug vacuum line at computer. Connect auxiliary vacuum supply to computer and apply 14 in. Hg vacuum.

2) Connect a tachometer to engine. Disconnect oxygen system test connector. Start engine and wait 1 minute. Raise engine speed to 2000 RPM. Hold oxygen system test connector (open terminal) with one hand and touch battery positive terminal with other hand. If voltmeter reading drops to zero volts, go to step **3)**. If voltage does not decrease, go to step **5)**.

3) With voltmeter connected to oxygen solenoid Green wire, disconnect and plug vacuum line at computer. Apply 14 in. Hg of vacuum to computer. Connect tachometer to engine and run engine to 2000 RPM.

4) Reconnect oxygen test connector. Wait a few seconds for oxygen system to start working. If voltmeter reading pulsates between 7 and 14 volts, go to step **5)**. If voltage is below 7 volts, go to step **6)**.

5) Connect voltmeter to oxygen solenoid Green wire. Disconnect and plug vacuum line to computer. Apply 14 in. Hg of vacuum to computer. Connect tachometer to engine and raise engine speed to 2000 RPM. Disconnect oxygen test connector. If voltmeter reading drops to zero volt, oxygen system is okay. If voltage does not decrease, check oxygen sensor wire for an open circuit to test connector. Repair as needed. If there is no open circuit, replace oxygen sensor.

6) Run engine at 2000 RPM with 14 in. Hg of vacuum applied to computer. Disconnect hose from PCV valve and cover orifice. Allow air to slowly enter orifice. If voltmeter reading increases towards 14 volts, oxygen system is okay. If voltage does not increase, check oxygen sensor wire for a short circuit to test connector and repair as needed. If there is no short, replace oxygen sensor.

7) With oxygen system test connector still disconnected (Green/White wire reconnected, let engine return to idle speed and then turn off engine. Disconnect computer 14-wire connector. Connect ohmmeter between test connector (Black wire) on computer side and cavity No. 10 of 14-wire connector. If ohmmeter shows continuity, replace computer. If there is no continuity, repair open wire to test connector.

CHRYSLER CORP. RWD ELECTRONIC FUEL CONTROL (Cont.)

CODE 25 OR 26
COOLANT SENSOR CIRCUIT TEST

1) Disconnect center terminal connector from charge temperature switch. Connect a voltmeter to disconnected wire and ground. Turn ignition switch to the "RUN" position. If voltmeter shows some voltage, go to step **2)**. If there's no voltage, go to step **3)**.

2) Disconnect side terminal connector from the charge temperature switch. Connect an ohmmeter between the disconnected wire from the side terminal and ground. If ohmmeter shows continuity, replace the charge temperature switch. If there's no continuity, repair open in circuit.

3) With charge temperature switch center terminal disconnected, turn ignition switch off. Disconnect computer 14-way connector. Connect ohmmeter between disconnected wire of the charge temperature switch and cavity No. 9 of the 14-way connector. If ohmmeter shows continuity, replace computer. If there's no continuity, repair wire for an open circuit.

4) Code 26. Disconnect engine temperature sensor connector. Connect an ohmmeter between the terminals of the sensor. If ohmmeter shows some resistance, go step **5)**. If there's no resistance or open circuit, replace sensor.

5) Reconnect connector to engine temperature sensor. Disconnect both computer connectors. Connect ohmmeter between cavity No. 9 of the 10-way connector and cavity No. 11 of the 14-way connectors. If ohmmeter shows resistance, replace computer. If there's an open circuit, repair wire of cavity No. 11 of the 14-way connector for an open circuit.

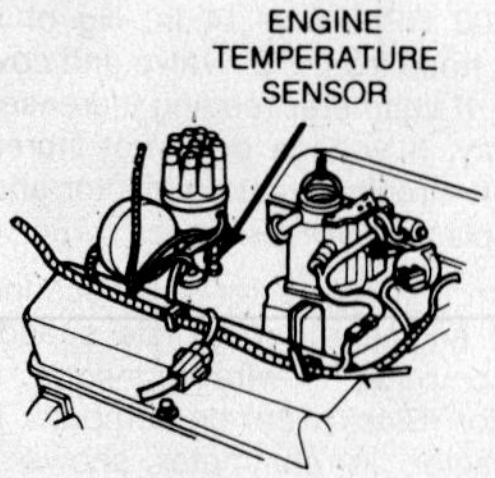

CODE 28
SPEED SENSOR SYSTEM TEST

1) Turn ignition switch off. Remove speed sensor from transaxle. Disconnect speed sensor connector. Connect ohmmmeter between terminals of speed sensor connector. Slowly rotate speed sensor one turn. Ohmmeter should show approximately 8 pulses for every turn of the speed sensor. If ohmmeter reading is okay, go to step **2)**. If not, replace speed sensor.

2) Disconnect speed sensor connector. Connect positive lead of voltmeter to White/Orange wire of speed sensor connector. Connect negative lead of voltmeter to Black/Blue wire of speed sensor harness connector. Turn ignition to "RUN" position.

3) Voltmeter should read at least 8.5 volts. If voltage is okay, inspect transaxle drive gear-to-speed sensor drive gear for proper contact. If zero volts, move voltmeter negative lead to a good engine ground. If voltmeter now reads correct voltage, inspect speed sensor ground wire for an open circuit and repair. If voltmeter still reads zero, go to step **4)**.

4) Turn ignition switch off. Disconnect computer 14-wire connector. Connect ohmmeter between cavity No. 2 of 14-wire connector and White/Orange wire of speed sensor harness connector. If ohmmeter shows continuity, replace computer. If no continuity, inspect wire for open circuit and repair.

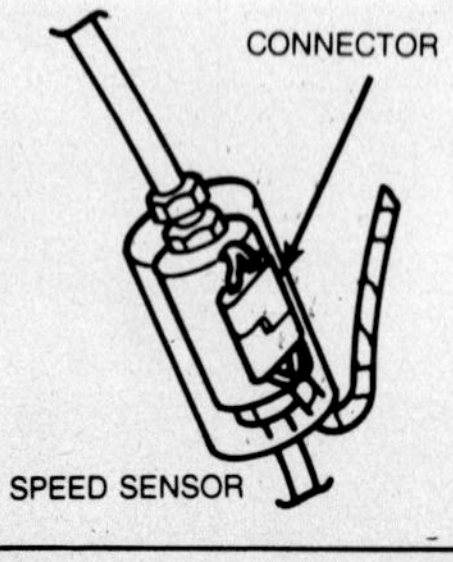

NO CODE 88

1) Disconnect diagnostic readout box from harness connector. Connect voltmeter between cavity No. 4 of engine harness connector and ground. Turn ignition switch to "RUN" position. Voltmeter should read 4-5 volts. Go to step **2)**. If voltage is not okay, go to step **2)**.

2) Turn ignition switch off. Disconnect 14-wire connector from computer. Connect ohmmeter between cavity No. 2 of engine harness diagnostic connector and cavity No. 14 of computer 14-wire connector. If ohmmeter shows continuity, replace computer. If no continuity, inspect wire from cavity No. 14 to harness connector for open and repair.

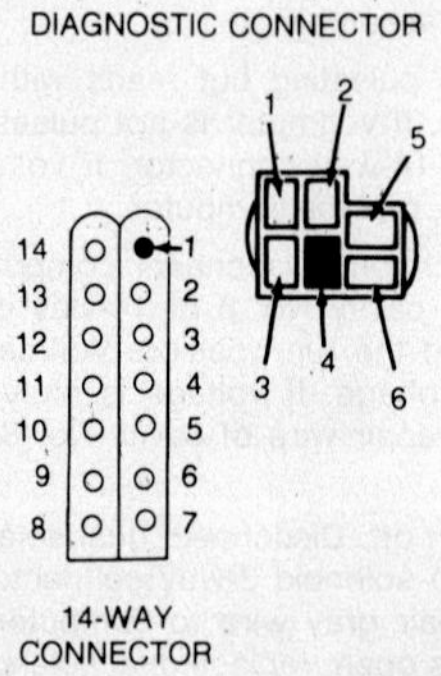

CARBURETOR CHOKE SYSTEM TEST

NOTE: **Engine MUST be dead cold before starting this test.**

1) Set accelerator linkage to proper start position. Remove air cleaner. Check choke plate and fast idle cam position.

2) Choke plate should be in fully closed position and fast idle screw should be on highest step of fast idle cam. If choke and cam position are okay, go to step **3)**. If choke is not fully closed or cam is not in position, check for choke plate sticking or binding. Repair choke and linkage as required.

3) Remove air cleaner. Set fast idle speed screw on highest step of fast idle cam. Remove vacuum line from choke diaphragm. Connect auxiliary vacuum supply to choke diaphragm. Apply 15 in. Hg of vacuum. Measure clearance between top of choke plate and air horn wall.

4) Vacuum should hold at applied setting and choke plate should be in proper position of vacuum kick specifications. If vacuum holds and choke vacuum kick is within specifications, go to Heated Air Intake System Test. If vacuum does not hold, replace choke vacuum kick diaphragm.

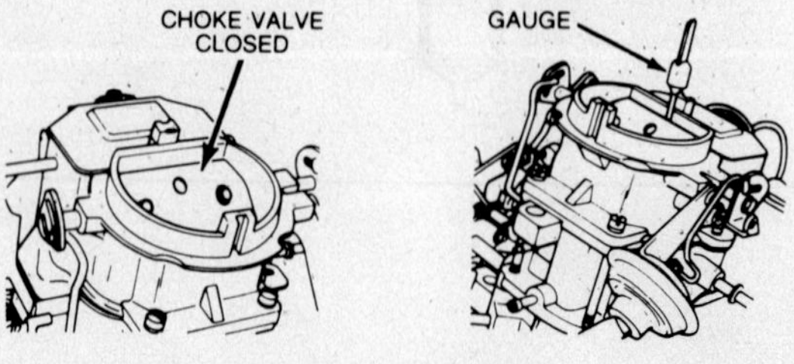

CHRYSLER CORP. RWD ELECTRONIC FUEL CONTROL (Cont.)

HEATED AIR INTAKE SYSTEM TEST

1) Disconnect air duct from air cleaner snorkel. Disconnect vacuum line to heated air intake system air temperature sensor. Apply 15 in. Hg of vacuum.

2) Vacuum should close heated air door when air temperature is below 76°F (25°C) and then slowly bleed down, opening the heated air door.

3) If vacuum builds up, closes heated air door and then bleeds down, go to Engine Coolant Sensor Calibration Test. If vacuum builds up but heated air door does not close, repair or replace door as necessary. If vacuum does not build up or does not bleed down, replace air temperature sensor. If vacuum builds up and bleeds down, but heated air door does not open, repair or replace door as required.

ENGINE COOLANT SENSOR CALIBRATION TEST

1) Disconnect coolant sensor. Connect ohmmeter between terminals 1 and 3 of coolant sensor. Ohmmeter reading should be as follows: Below 150°F (66°C), 20-200 ohms; 150-200°F (66-93°C), 100-150 ohms; Above 200°F (93°C), 400-6000 ohms. If resistance is correct, go to step **2)**. If not, replace coolant sensor.

2) With coolant sensor connector disconnected and ohmmeter connected between terminals 1 and 2 of sensor, ohmmeter should read as follows: -40-20°F (-60-6.7°C), 382K-22K ohms; 50-100°F (10-38°C), 36K-3300 ohms; 140-245°F (60-118°C), 3.9-176 ohms. If resistance is okay, go to go to EGR System CVSCC Valve Test. If not, replace coolant sensor.

EGR SYSTEM CVSCC VALVE TEST

1) Disconnect CVSCC valve at vacuum line connector. Connect auxiliary vacuum supply to valve. Apply at least 10 in. Hg of vacuum. Vacuum should hold with coolant temperature below 125°F (52°C). If vacuum is okay, go to step **2)**. If vacuum does not hold, replace CVSCC valve.

2) Remove air cleaner. Start engine. Check position of choke plate. Choke plate should open from a fully closed position. If choke plate is in proper position, system is okay. If not, adjust choke.

CARBURETOR SWITCH TEST

NOTE: Engine MUST be dead cold when starting this test.

1) Disconnect computer 10-wire connector. Connect ohmmeter between cavity No. 7 of 10-wire connector and ground. Open and close throttle while watching at ohmmeter.

2) Ohmmeter should show continuity with no resistance when throttle is closed and no continuity when throttle is open. If okay, go to step **4)**.

3) If no continuity is present with throttle closed, inspect wire from cavity No. 7 to carb. switch for open circuit and repair as needed. If there is continuity with resistance when throttle is closed, clean corrosion from carb. switch. If there is continuity with throttle open, inspect wire from cavity No. 7 for a short to ground and repair.

4) Disconnect coolant sensor connector. Connect ohmmeter between terminals 1 and 3 of coolant sensor. Resistance should be between 400 and 6000 ohms. If resistance is okay, go to next test. If resistance is not okay, replace coolant sensor.

CHOKE SYSTEM TEST

1) Remove air cleaner and start engine. Choke should be fully open. If choke position is okay, go to step **3)**. If choke position is not okay, go to step **2)**.

2) With engine running, connect voltmeter to choke feed wire and ground. Voltmeter should read within 1 volt of battery voltage. If voltage is okay, check for binding linkage. If okay, replace choke thermostat housing. If voltage is not okay, go to step **3)**.

3) Turn off engine. Disconnect oil pressure switch connector. Connect voltmeter to terminal C of oil pressure switch connector and ground. Turn ignition switch to "RUN" position. Voltage should be within 1 volt of battery voltage. If voltage is okay, go to step **4)**. If voltage is not okay, repair open circuit in harness to ignition switch.

4) Dicsonnect oil pressure switch connector. Connect ohmmeter between terminal A of connector and choke connector. Ohmmeter should show continuity with no resistance. If there is continuity, replace oil pressure switch. If there is no continuity, repair open circuit in harness.

CARBURETOR IDLE CIRCUIT TEST

1) Connect tachometer to engine. Remove air cleaner. If equipped, disconnect and plug vacuum line at solenoid kicker. Start engine, momentarily raise engine speed above 1100 RPM and then wait 2 minutes for idle speed to stabilize. Plug idle air bleed hole.

2) Engine speed should drop. If so, go to step EGR System Check. If not, or if engine speed increases, check carburetor for plugged circuit and repair as needed.

EGR SYSTEM TEST

1) Connect tachometer to engine. Disconnect vacuum line from EGR valve. Connect auxiliary vacuum supply to EGR valve. If equipped, disconnect and plug vacuum line at solenoid kicker. Start engine, momentarily raise engine speed above 1100 RPM and wait 2 minutes for idle speed to stabilize. Very slowly apply vacuum to EGR valve.

2) Engine speed should begin to drop when applied vacuum reaches 2 to 5 in. Hg of vacuum and continue to drop as more vacuum is applied. Engine may stall before 5 in. Hg of vacuum is applied. If engine speed drop is okay, go to step **3)**. If engine speed does not drop or engine speed does not drop until 5 in. Hg or more vacuum, replace EGR valve.

3) Connect tachometer to engine. If equipped, plug vacuum line at solenoid kicker. Run engine at idle for at least 2 minutes. Disconnect EGR hose. Connect vacuum gauge to EGR vacuum line. Slowly increase engine speed.

4) As engine speed increases, so should reading on vacuum gauge. If vacuum reading is okay, go to next test. If vacuum is not okay, go to step **6)**.

5) Turn engine off. Remove connector from EGR CVSCC valve. Connect vacuum pump to either port of valve. Try to apply vacuum. Vacuum should not hold with coolant temperature above 125°F (52°C). If vacuum does not hold, check EGR signal hose from carburetor for leaks or restrictions. If vacuum holds, replace EGR CVSCC valve.

FORD ELECTRONIC ENGINE CONTROL IV THEORY & OPERATION

2.3L, 5.0L EFI (Under 8500 GVW), 2.8L, 4.9L FBC (Under 8500 GVW) 5.0L FBC (Calif. Under 8500 GVW), 5.8L FBC (Under 8500 GVW High Alt. Bronco, "E" & "F" Series Auto. Trans. Only).

DESCRIPTION

The center of the EEC-IV system is the Electronic Control Assembly (ECA). The ECA receives information from various sensors and switches. Based on information received and the operation program in the ECA's memory, the ECA generates output signals to control engine operation. The calibration module for EEC-IV system is mounted inside the ECA. The ECA is located in the passenger compartment, in one of the following locations: under the center console, under dash on left side of steering column, under passenger seat, or under dash behind right kick panel.

The 2.3L and 5.0L EFI models use the Bosch/Ford Electronic Fuel Injection system (EFI). The EFI system is classified as a multi-point, pulse time, speed density, fuel injection system. The EEC-IV computer accepts inputs from various engine sensors to compute the required fuel flow rate necessary to maintain a prescribed air/fuel ratio throughout the entire engine operational range. The computer then outputs a command to the fuel injectors to meter the appropriate quanity of fuel.

The EEC-IV system controls 3 major areas of engine operation: Air/fuel mixture, ignition, and emission control. Additionally the system can control A/C compressor clutch operation and idle speed. The system provides self-diagnostic capabilities.

On all other models, the air/fuel mixture control is accomplished by use of a feedback carburetor (FBC). The ignition system is controlled by the ECA through a Thick Film Ignition (TFI-IV) module. Ignition timing (advance or retard) and dwell are controlled with this system to improve ignition system performance.

Emission control components controlled by this system include EGR and canister purge. These systems are normally off, but are turned on when the engine is ready to operate with the mixture change caused by EGR and canister purge operation.

OPERATION

The engine control system consists of the ECA, sensors and switches, and actuators. In order for the ECA to properly perform its function, it must be kept constantly informed of engine operating conditions.

It is the task of the engine sensors to supply the ECA, via electrical signal, with specific information required to determine engine operating conditions. The ECA can then send out electrical signals of its own to control air/fuel ratio, emission controls, idle speed, and ignition timing. Individual component operation is as follows:

INPUTS

Airflow Meter Assembly
(2.3L & 5.0L EFI Models)

The airflow meter consists of 2 sensors in a single housing, mounted between the air cleaner and throttle body assembly. An air flow sensor and an air temperature sensor are both exposed to intake airflow. The combined information from these sensors allows ECA to determine the mass and temperature of air entering engine.

Air By-Pass Solenoid

The Air By-pass Solenoid (ABS) is used to control engine idle speed and is operated by the EEC-IV module. The ABS allows air to pass around the throttle plates to control:

- Cold engine fast idle.
- No touch start.
- Dashpot operation.
- Over temperature idle boost.
- Engine idle load correction.

Air Charge Temperature (ACT) Sensor
(2.8L FBC Models Only)

The ACT is threaded into cylinder runner of intake manifold or attached to air cleaner. ACT provides ECA with air/fuel mixture temperature information. The ECA uses this information for correcting fuel flow and to control fuel flow during cold enrichment (cold starts).

A/C Compressor Clutch Signal (ACC)
(5.0L & 5.8L FBC Models)

When battery voltage is applied to compressor clutch, a signal is sent to ECA. ECA uses signal to increase engine idle speed to compensate for added load created by A/C compressor.

EGR Valve Position Sensor
(All Except 4.9L FBC Models)

This sensor is located on top of the EGR valve. It informs the ECA of EGR valve position.

Engine Coolant Temperature (ECT) Sensor

This sensor, threaded into heater supply tube, monitors engine coolant temperature. The ECA interprets this as either cold or normal operating temperature. This influences ECA control of fuel mixture enrichment, ignition timing, and EGR operation.

Fuel Injectors
(2.3L & 5.0L EFI Models)

On EFI equipped engines, each cylinder has a solenoid-operated injector which sprays fuel toward back of each inlet valve. Each injector is energized through ignition circuit and grounded through ECA to complete circuit. Injectors deliver 1/2 the amount of fuel required for an operating cycle each time they open (twice per cycle).

Idle Tracking Switch (ITS)
(2.8L & 4.9L FBC Models Only)

The ITS is a mechanically operated electric switch held open by throttle linkage when throttle is closed. When throttle stop lever is against switch, ITS is open. The ITS is integral with the idle speed control motor.

Key Power

This is simply the test input for Quick Test using Key On-Engine Off Self-Test. These tests are to detect hard faults only, not intermittent problems.

Knock Sensor
(2.8L FBC Models Only)

This is a piezoelectric device designed to vibrate at about the same frequency as engine vibration. The sensor informs the ECA of engine knock and the ECA retards ignition timing until knock stops. The ECA will then go back to previous advance schedule, until knock is detected or engine operating conditions change.

FORD ELECTRONIC ENGINE CONTROL IV THEORY & OPERATION (Cont.)

Manifold Absolute Pressure (MAP) Sensor

Mounted on left or right inner fender, sensor measures absolute pressure of mixture in intake manifold and sends a signal to ECA that is proportional to absolute pressure in manifold.

Oxygen Sensor

This sensor is threaded into exhaust manifold where it constantly monitors oxygen content of exhaust gases. A voltage signal is produced which varies according to difference in oxygen content between exhaust gases and surrounding atmosphere.

This signal is sent to the ECA which translates exhaust gas oxygen content to air/fuel ratio. It then alters air/fuel ratio to hold the ideal ratio for current engine operating conditions.

Park/Neutral Switch

Automatic transmission 2.8L models use a park/neutral switch. Switch indicates whether engine is loaded or unloaded and ensures that vehicle cannot be started in gear. ECA uses signal generated by switch to maintain same idle speed regardless of engine load.

Profile Ignition Pick-Up (PIP)

The PIP informs the ECA of crankshaft position and speed. PIP assembly is integral with distributor. PIP has an armature with 4 windows and 4 metal tabs that rotate past a stator assembly (Hall-Effect Switch). Ignition distributor does not have any mechanical or vacuum advance. Distributor is adjustable for resetting base timing, if necessary.

Self-Test Input

Self-test input is a wire (pigtail) in Self-Test connector used to start the Quick Test. Self-Test procedures are built into EEC-IV control module so system can display continous Self-Test codes for diagnosis of intermittent problems.

Throttle Air By-Pass Valve (TABV)
(2.3L & 5.0L EFI Models)

The TABV is a solenoid-operated valve controlled by ECA. The TABV operates a variable-area metering valve. Responding to commands from ECA, valve controls both cold and warm idle air flow. Valve causes air to by-pass throttle plate, thereby adjusting idle speed.

Throttle Position Sensor (TPS)

The TPS is mounted on side of throttle body and connected directly to throttle shaft. The TPS senses throttle movement and position and transmits an electrical signal to the ECA. These signals keep the ECA informed of wide open throttle, closed throttle, or normal cruise conditions.

OUTPUTS

EEC Power Relay

This relay is activated by ignition switch. Relay supplies battery voltage to ECA when switch is on. Some power relays incorporate a time delay of 5-10 seconds. If time delay is used, a throttle control activator assembly is also used.

Canister Purge Solenoid

This solenoid switches manifold vacuum to operate canister purge valve when a signal is received from ECA. Vacuum opens purge valve when solenoid is energized.

EGR Control Solenoid

Solenoid switches manifold vacuum to operate EGR valve on command from ECA. Vacuum opens EGR valve when solenoid is energized.

EGR Shut-Off Solenoid

EGR shut-off solenoid is an electrically-operated vacuum valve located between manifold vacuum source and EGR valve. A controlled vacuum bleed is located between solenoid and EGR valve. This vacuum bleed is a Backpressure Variable Transducer. These 2 devices operate EGR for optimum performance. Vacuum switched by solenoid is also supplied to canister purge solenoid valve.

EGR Vent Solenoid

Solenoid vents EGR control solenoid vacuum line. When vent solenoid is energized, control solenoid can open EGR valve.

Feedback Control Solenoid (FCS)

Feedback control is accomplished by this solenoid which regulates idle, off idle and main system air/fuel ratios according to ECA signals. The solenoid is mounted on the carburetor.

Idle Speed Control (ISC) Motor

This DC motor is used to provide idle speed control according to signals from ECA.

Self-Test Output

Part of the Self-Test connector, service codes are transmitted through the output in the form of timed pulses. These pulses are read as diagnostic codes.

Shift Indicator Lamp
(2.8L & 4.9L FBC Models Only)

This lamp indicates to driver when to shift gears for optimum fuel economy. ECA signals lamp to light according to information received on engine speed and manifold vacuum levels.

TFI Ignition Module

The TFI module triggers ignition coil and determines dwell. Module is mounted on side of distributor. ECA uses signal from Profile Ignition Pick-Up to determine crankshaft position. Ignition timing is determined within ECA. ECA then signals TFI module when to fire coil.

Thermactor Air By-Pass (TAB) Solenoid

Solenoid provides a vacuum signal to by-pass valve in response to ECA signals. The TAB valve then bypasses thermactor pump air to atmosphere.

Thermactor Air Diverter (TAD) Solenoid

Solenoid provides a vacuum signal to diverter valve in response to ECA signals. The TAD valve then diverts thermactor pump air to either exhaust manifold or catalytic converter.

Throttle Kicker Solenoid

This is a 2-port valve with an atmospheric vent. A vacuum diaphragm is used to maintain nominal idle speed on command from ECA.

Variable Voltage Choke (VVC)
(2.8L Models Only)

The ECA controls the choke rate by controlling voltage "on-time" supplied to the choke. The voltage supplied to the choke is switched by the choke relay.

Temperature Compensated
Accelerator Pump (TCP)
(2.8L Models Only)

The ECA controls the TCP solenoid, which provides a vacuum signal to the carburetor. This vacuum

FORD ELECTRONIC ENGINE CONTROL IV THEORY & OPERATION (Cont.)

signal is used to increase the accelerator pump shot when the engine is cold.

TESTING & DIAGNOSIS

DIAGNOSTIC PROCEDURE

The checks, codes and test charts for each engine are in separate sections of this article. Use the directory at the front of the article to locate the correct page. The headings at the top of the pages will also help you find the tests for your engine. Follow this sequence when testing:

1) Make sure all NON-EEC problems are solved first. Loose wires, low compression, fouled plugs, etc. can cause problems that waste valuable time.

2) Connect test equipment (as described later in this article) to the engine.

3) Perform Key On-Engine Off Self-Test for your engine. This checks input and output circuits. If any codes appear, refer to the proper test shown in the reference table for that engine. Start with the first code displayed. If the tests refer you to other checks, perform them as instructed.

4) Perform the Computed Timing Check. This checks the system's spark timing ability.

5) Do the Engine Running Self-Test. This is a system check with sensors and output devices. If any codes appear, refer to the proper test shown in the reference table.

6) To check for intermittent problems, perform the Continuous Self-Test. This monitors the inputs for shorts and open circuits as you wiggle wires and connectors.

PREPARATION

Correct test results for this system are dependent on the correct operation of several related non-EEC components and systems. All non-EEC problems should be corrected before attempting to diagnose the EEC system.

Before hooking up any equipment to diagnose the EEC system, make the following checks:

- Verify the condition of the air cleaner and air ducting.
- Check all vacuum hoses for leaks, restrictions and proper routing.
- Check the EEC system wiring harness electrical connections for loose or detached connectors, wires or terminals, and proper routing.
- Check the ECA, sensors and actuators for physical damage.
- Perform all necessary safety precautions to prevent personal injury or vehicle damage.
- Set parking brake and place shift lever in "Park" (Neutral for manual transmission). Do not move shift lever during testing unless specifically directed to do so.
- Turn off all lights and accessories, and make sure that vehicle doors are closed when making readings.
- Check coolant level and correct as necessary.
- Start engine and idle until upper radiator hose is hot and pressurized and throttle is off fast idle. Check for leaks around exhaust manifold, oxygen sensor and vacuum connections
- Turn ignition off.

NOTE: **If vehicle is towed in or is suspected of having intermittent problems, do not turn the ignition key off. Diagnostic codes may be stored in the continuous testing memory.**

READING SELF-TEST CODES

Service codes are transmitted to the Self-Test Output connector. They are shown as voltage pulses on a Volt-Ohmmeter (VOM), or as numbers on the STAR tester.

Key On-Engine Off Self-Test

The first code shown is the On Demand code, the second code is a Separator code and the third code is the Continuous code. The On Demand first digit is indicated by a pulse, then the needle drops to zero for 2 seconds, then the second digit of the code is displayed. After 6-9 seconds, the Separator code (single digit) will be displayed for 1/2 second. After 6-9 seconds, the first digit of the Continuous code will be displayed, the needle will drop to zero for 2 seconds, then the second digit of the Continuous code will display. *See Fig. 2.*

Engine Running Self-Test

The codes shown are an Engine ID code, a Dynamic Response Code and an On Demand code. On Demand codes are the same as Continuous codes in Key On-Engine Off Self-Test. Dynamic Response code is the same as a Separator code in Key On-Engine Off Self-Test. The Engine ID code has no application in the field, and is for factory use only. The codes will be displayed in the same manner as Key On-Engine Off Self-Test codes. *See Fig. 3.*

EQUIPMENT HOOK-UP

With ignition off, connect a timing light to engine. Connect a jumper wire from the Self-Test input to ground. Connect a DC voltmeter (0-20V range) to battery positive terminal and Self-Test output terminal No. 4. *See Fig. 1.*

Fig. 1: Meter Hook-Up for Reading Codes

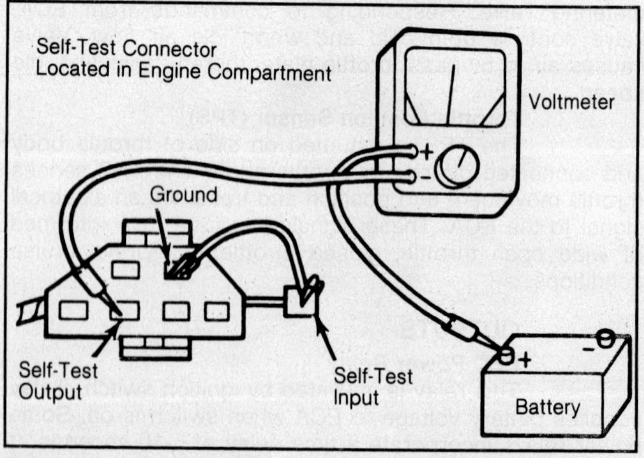

This applies to all models.

TEST EQUIPMENT

The following equipment is recommended to diagnose and test EEC-IV systems. Some equipment is REQUIRED to perform tests. DO NOT attempt to test this system without proper equipment. Damage to vehicle components will result if improper equipment is used.

FORD ELECTRONIC ENGINE CONTROL IV THEORY & OPERATION (Cont.)

- Self-Test Automatic Read-Out (STAR) Tester. This tool is recommended, but not required. It is specially built for the EEC-IV system and is used to display the 2-digit service codes that are programmed into the control module.
- Analog Volt-Ohmmeter with 0-20V DC range. This can be used as an alternate to the STAR tester.
- Breakout Box. This is a jumper wire assembly which connects between the vehicle harness and the ECA. The Breakout Box is REQUIRED to perform certain tests on the system. Ford Motor Co. DOES NOT recommend using a DVOM to probe the ECA pins as permanent damage to the pins will result.
- Digital Volt-Ohmmeter (DVOM) with 10 megohm minimum input impedance.
- Vacuum Gauge with 0-30 in. Hg range, and resolution in the 1 in. Hg. range.
- Tachometer with 0-6000 RPM range, accuracy ± 40 RPM and resolution within 20 RPM.
- Vacuum Pump with 0-25 in. Hg range.
- Timing light.
- Spark tester. A modified spark plug with side electrode removed and alligator clip attached may be used.
- Non-powered test light.
- Jumper wire about 15" long.

NOTE: **A small, portable tester for 1983-85 models is available from Hickok Electrical Instrument Co., 10514 Dupont Ave., Cleveland, OH 44106. This tester (STAR; Self Test Automatic Readout) provides a built-in capability to locate intermittents within the EEC-IV system.**

QUICK TESTS (ALL VEHICLES)

KEY ON–ENGINE OFF SELF–TEST

Connect voltmeter and insert jumper wire to self-test input terminal and output terminal No. 2. This activates the self-test. Turn ignition switch to "Run" position. Do not depress throttle during test. Observe and record On Demand and Continuous codes. When more than 1 code is displayed, always repair problems in the order that codes were displayed. Repair codes as follows:

KEY ON-ENGINE OFF SELF-TEST RESULTS

On Demand Codes	Continuous Codes	Go To
11	11	TIMING CHECK
Any	11	On Demand Code Table
Any	Any	On Demand Code Table
11	Any	TIMING CHECK
None	None	Test D

Fig. 2: Key-On Engine Off Code Format

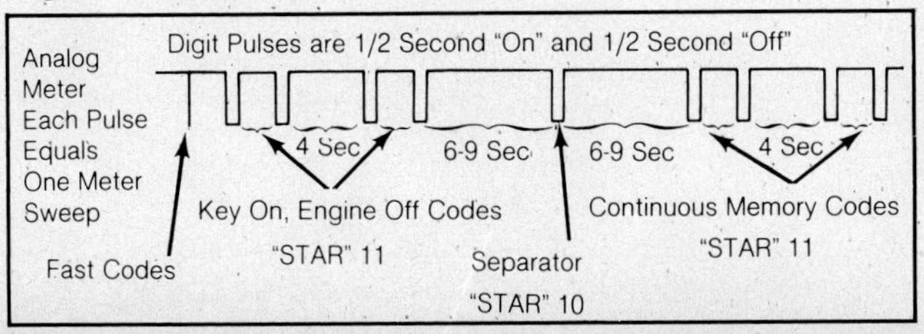

TIMING CHECK

Disconnect grounded jumper wire from self-test input. Start engine and reconnect grounded jumper wire to self-test input. Check timing within 2 minutes after display of last code. If timing is 27-33° BTDC, proceed to Engine Running Self-Test. If timing is not 27-33° BTDC, proceed to Test T.

NOTE: **If engine stalls while testing, proceed to Test D, step 10).**

ENGINE RUNNING SELF-TEST

This test checks sensors under actual operating conditions and at normal operating temperature. Any faults must be present at time of test to be detected.

NOTE: **If engine will not start, perform Test A.**

Connect jumper wire or STAR tester to activate test. This test will display an Engine ID code, a Dynamic Response code and an On Demand Service code. After a Dynamic Response code (single digit) is received, quickly press and release accelerator once only.

Deactivate the self-test. Start and run engine at more than 2000 RPM for 2 minutes. Turn engine off and wait 10 seconds. Activate self-test. Start engine. Test will proceed with Engine ID code, Dynamic Response code and Engine Running On Demand Service codes. If a 10 or 1 pulse occurs during Dynamic Response code, open throttle wide open momentarily. Record codes and proceed as follows:

Fig. 3: Self-Test Engine Running Code Format

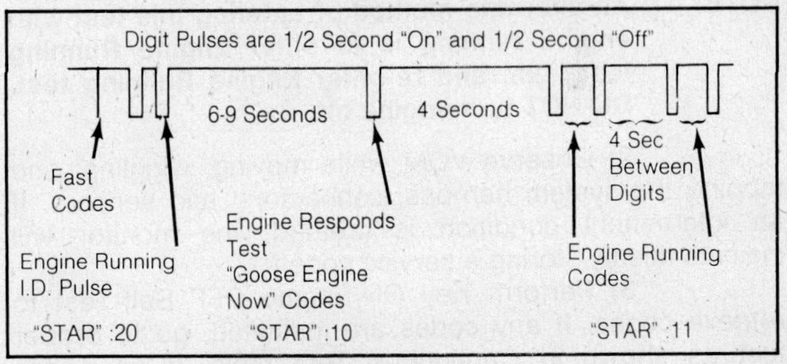

NOTE: **If engine stalls while testing, proceed to Test D, step 10).**

CONTINUOUS TEST

1) Codes shown in this test are intermittent service codes. Unless instructed otherwise, do not disconnect any sensor with ignition on, or a service code may be stored.

2) Verify that previous self-tests indicated a pass (code 11). If an On Demand code is detected during this test, repair it first, as some hard failures will set a code in the continuous test.

3) Perform Key On-Engine Off Self-Test. When the first service code is appears, exit self-test by removing jumper wire from self-test input. This clears ECA of all codes stored in continuous memory. *See Fig. 4.*

4) Check your list of Continuous codes that were recorded in Key On-Engine Off and Engine Running self-tests. Disregard any codes you already repaired. To confirm remaining codes, perform Continuous Monitor Test.

FORD ELECTRONIC ENGINE CONTROL IV THEORY & OPERATION (Cont.)

Fig. 4: Continuous Memory Service Codes

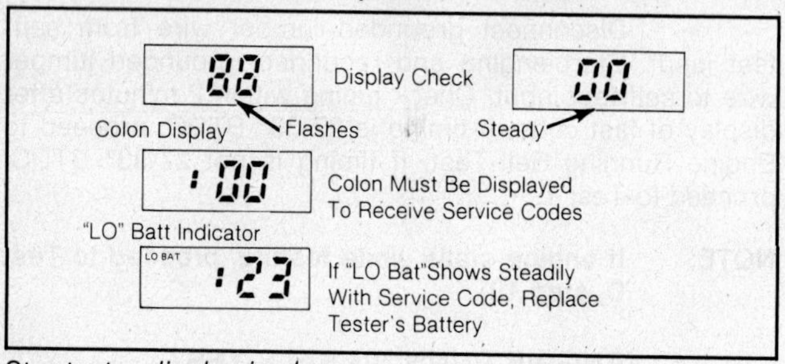

Star tester display is shown.

CONTINUOUS MONITOR (WIGGLE) TEST

NOTE: Make sure that Self-Test is deactivated. Do not activate Self-Test unless specifically instructed to do so.

1) This test monitors ECA inputs for shorts and opens. Self-Test output will be activated when a fault is detected. A detected fault is indicated by a 10.5 volt or greater deflection on VOM. One or both of the following modes may be used to find the intermittent fault.

- **Key ON/Engine OFF**: Self-Test deactivated and ignition switch ON.
- **Engine Running**: Self-Test activated. After service code output has finished, do not turn engine off or deactivate Self-Test. About 2 minutes after code 11 has been displayed, Continuous Monitor test mode will start. It will run until Self-Test is deactivated or engine is turned off.

NOTE: An alternate method of entering this test with engine running is to enter Engine Running test, exit, and re-enter Engine Running test. DO NOT turn engine off.

2) Observe VOM while moving, wiggling, and tapping the system harness, connectors, and sensors. If an intermittent condition is created, the monitor will indicate this by storing a service code.

3) Perform Key ON/Engine OFF Self-Test to retrieve codes. If any codes are indicated, go to proper test as shown in Continuous Test table. If no codes appear, the fault is not in a monitored EEC sensor circuit. EEC testing is complete. Refer to *Diagnosis By Symptom Test* for additional testing information.

NOTE: Continuous test can only be run once without turning ignition off. Do not miss any of the service codes.

HOW TO USE THE CIRCUIT TESTS

1) DO NOT run any test unless codes have been set. Make sure all non-EEC related faults are corrected. Do not replace any part unless directed to do so. When more than one service code is received, start with lowest code first.

2) DO NOT measure voltage or resistance at ECA or connect any test lamps to it, unless specified. All measurements are made by probing the REAR of the connector. Isolate both ends of a circuit and turn ignition off whenever checking for shorts or continuity, unless specified.

3) Disconnect solenoids and switches from harness before measuring continuity, resistance or applying 12 volts. Follow each step in order until fault is found. After any repairs, check all component connections and repeat Quick Test.

Output State Test

1) These checks are specified in the testing charts. Output State Test is used to diagnose each actuator. Test is performed in the Key On-Engine Off Self-Test mode after service codes have been sent. Do not disable self-test, but momentarily depress throttle and release. All auxiliary EEC outputs will be activated at this time. Another throttle depression will turn them off.

2) Connect DVOM to self-test output pin 4. Start the Key On-Engine Off Self-Test. When Continuous codes are completed, DVOM will read 0 volts. Depress accelerator to turn on actuators.

3) Disconnect DVOM from pin 4 and connect to appropriate actuator. Measure voltage at actuator. Readings above 10.5 volts indicate actuators are on, readings below 2 volts indicate actuators are off. Each test will tell what action to take according to voltage shown on DVOM.

Fig. 5: 2.3L EFI Fuel Injection System

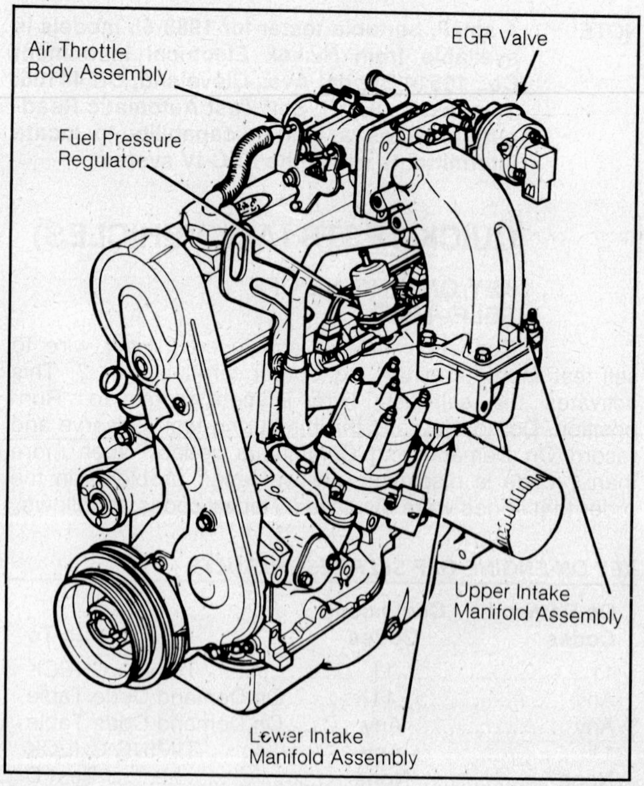

FORD ELECTRONIC ENGINE CONTROL IV (Cont.)

Fig. 6: 2.8L FBC EEC-IV System Inputs/Outputs & Component Locations

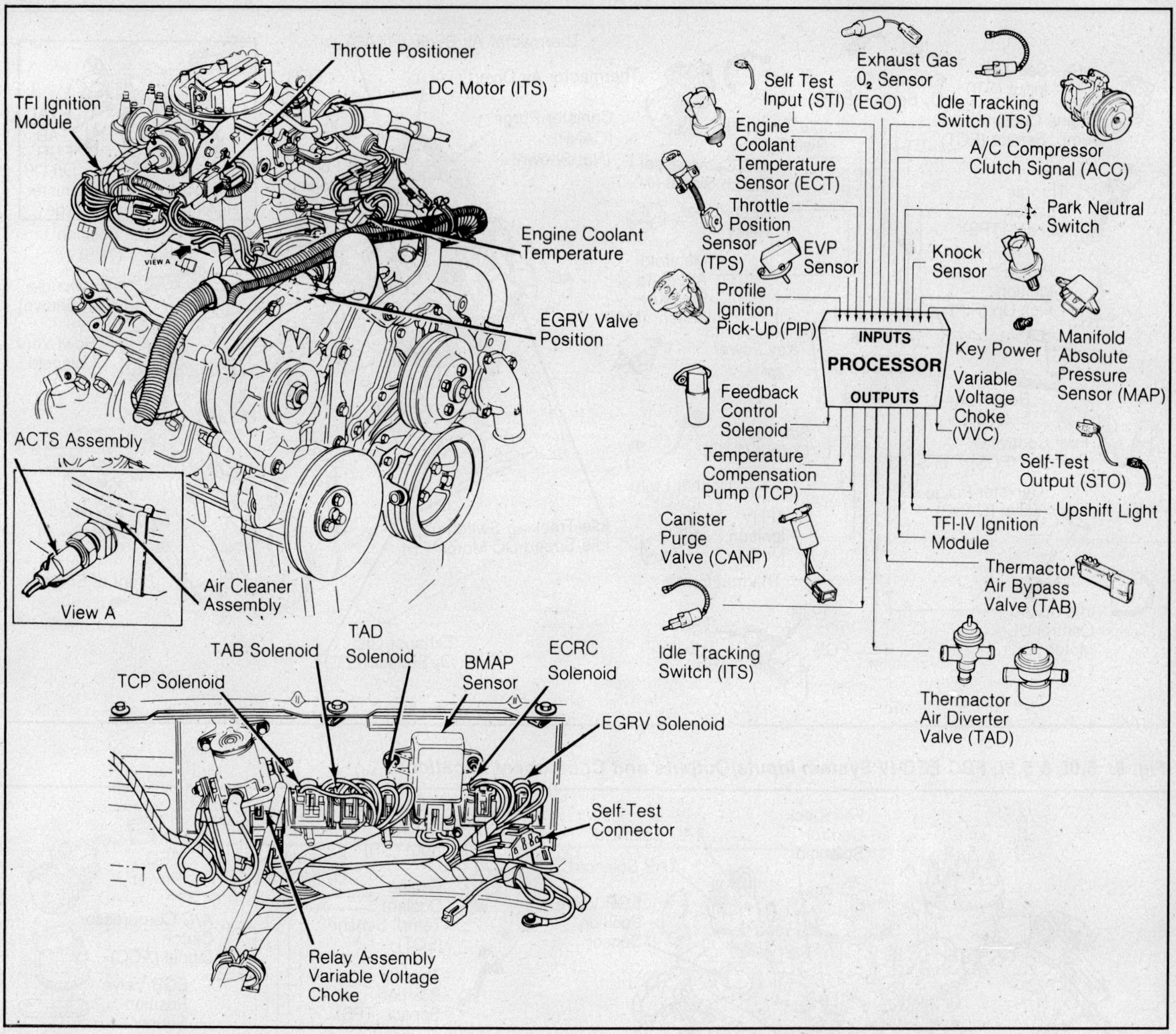

FORD ELECTRONIC ENGINE CONTROL IV (Cont.)

Fig. 7: 4.9L FBC EEC-IV System Inputs/Outputs and Component Locations

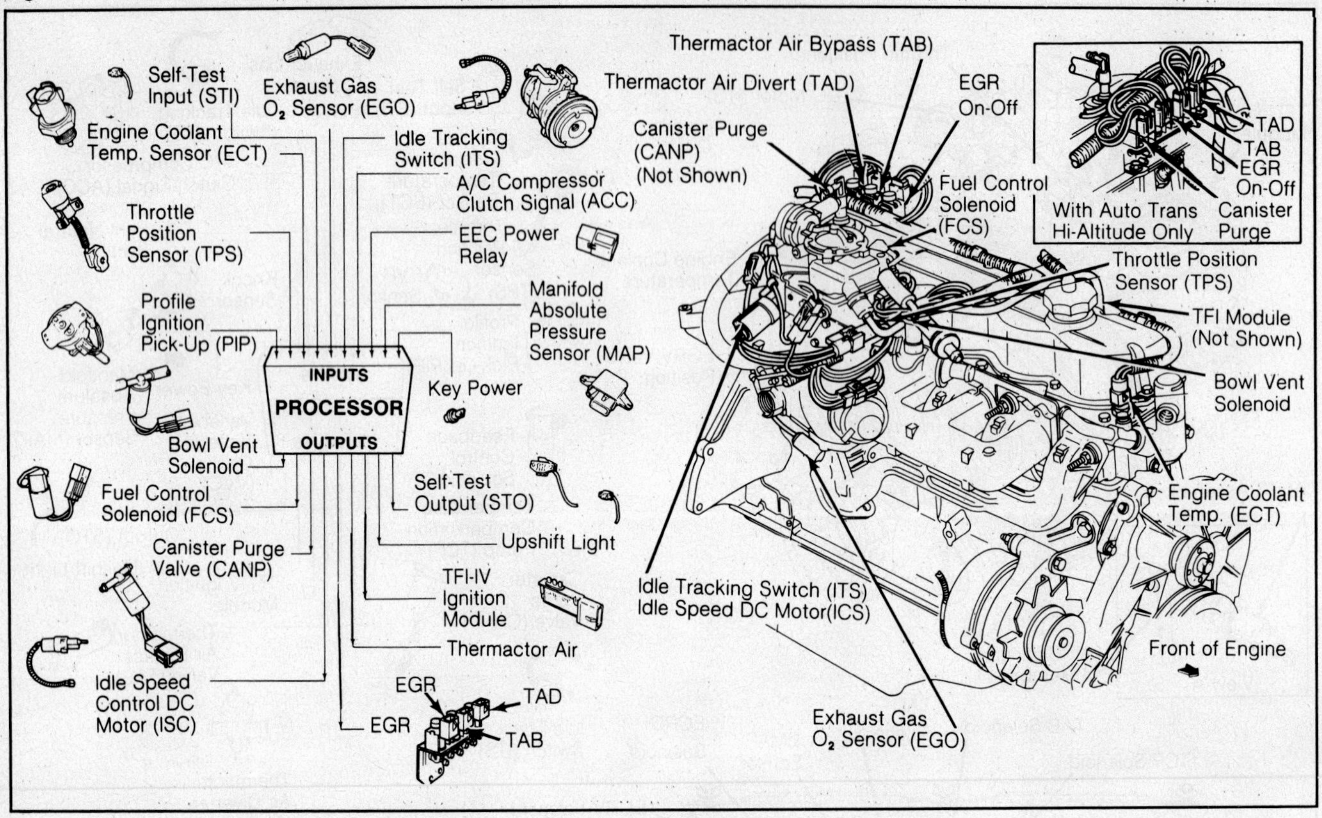

Fig. 8: 5.0L & 5.8L FBC EEC-IV System Inputs/Outputs and Component Locations

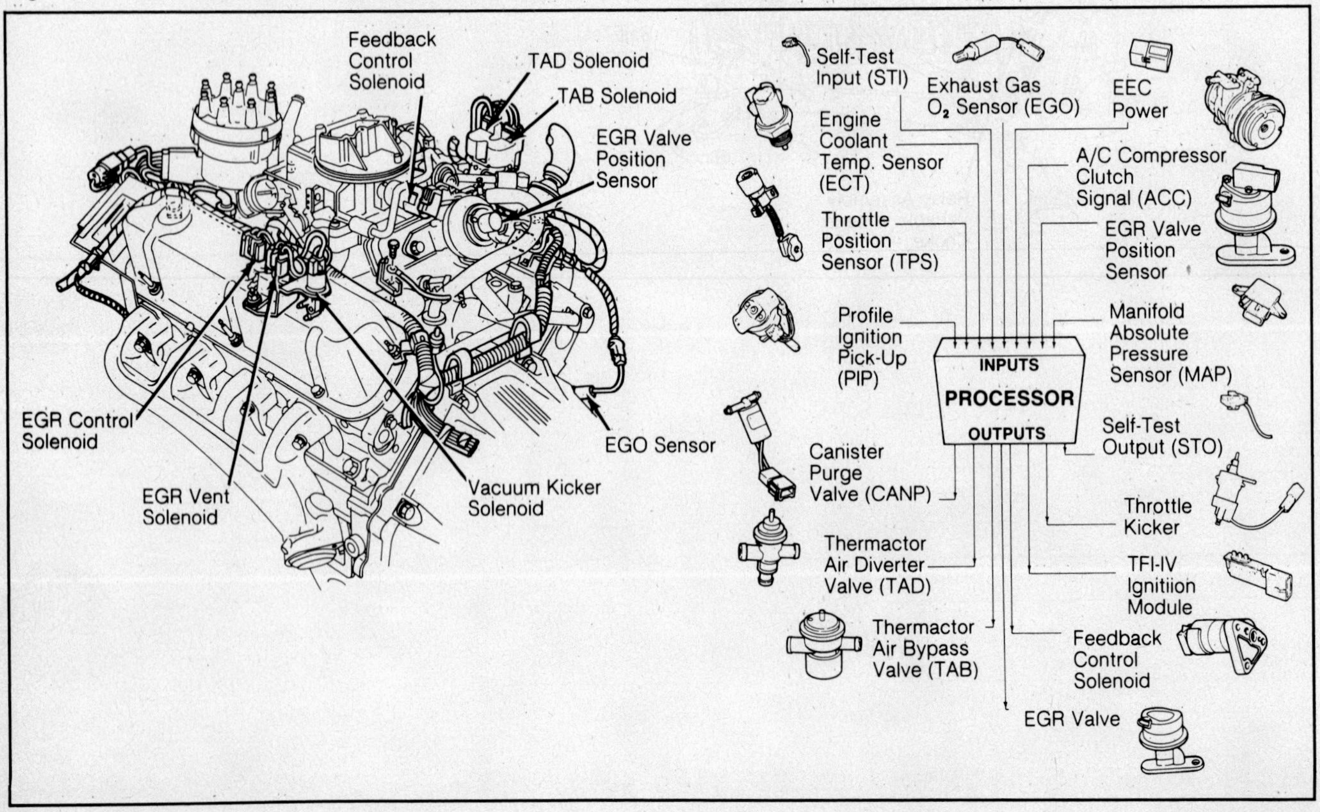

FORD ELECTRONIC ENGINE CONTROL IV (Cont.)

Fig. 9: 2.3L EFI EEC-IV Wiring Diagram

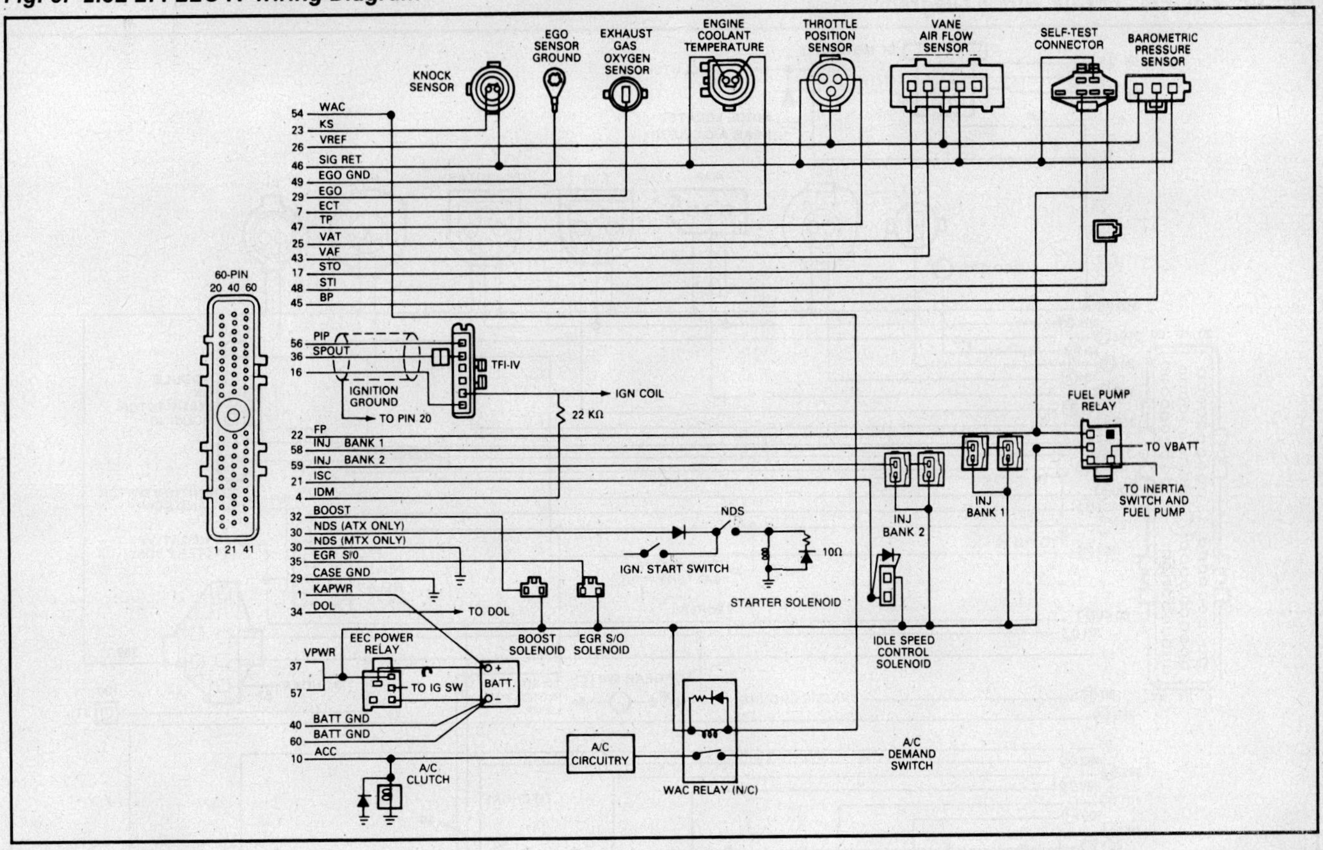

FORD ELECTRONIC ENGINE CONTROL IV (Cont.)

Fig. 10: 2.8L FBC EEC-IV Wiring Diagram

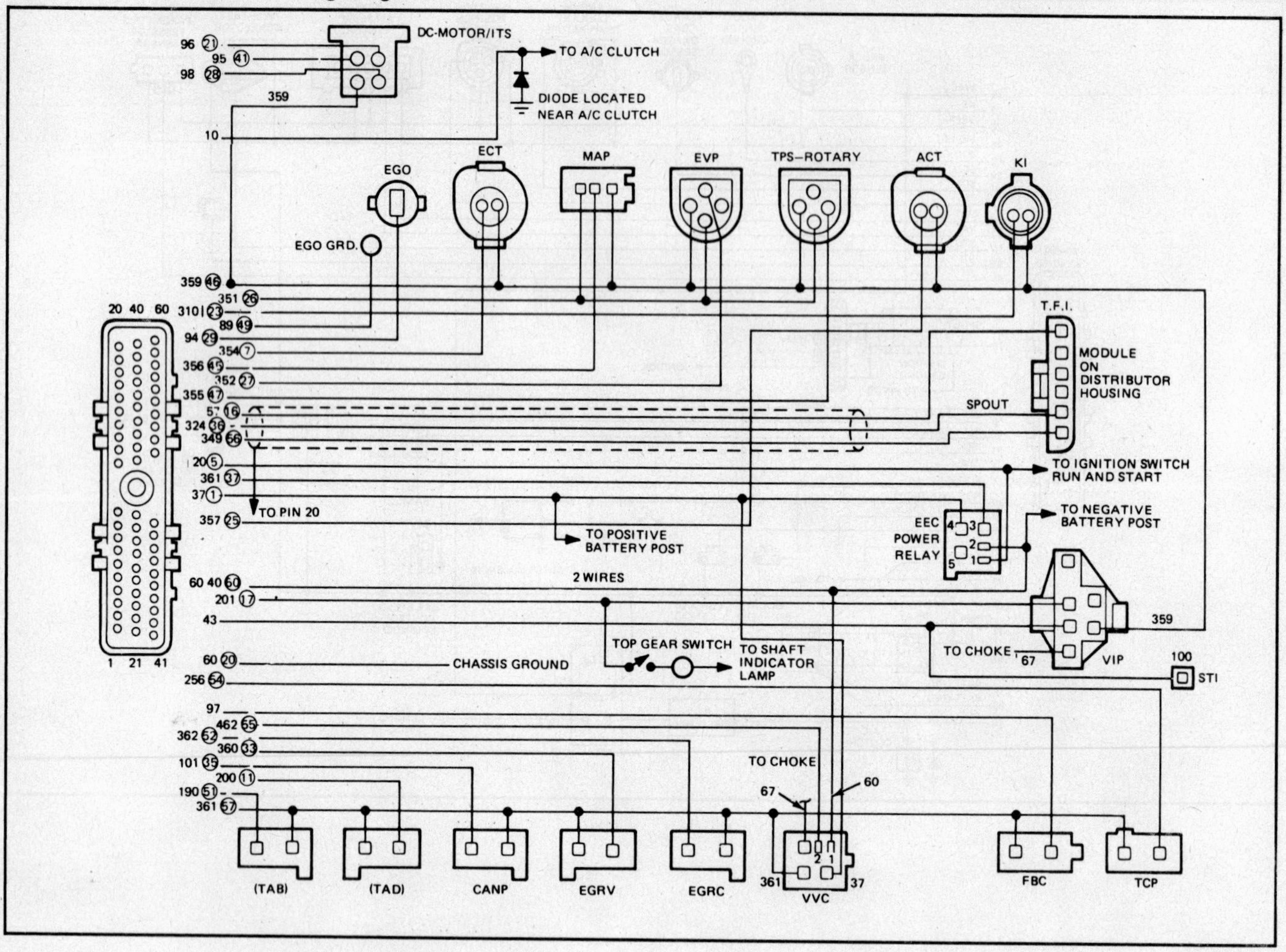

FORD ELECTRONIC ENGINE CONTROL IV (Cont.)

Fig. 11: 4.9L FBC EEC-IV Wiring Diagram (All Exc. Van Models)

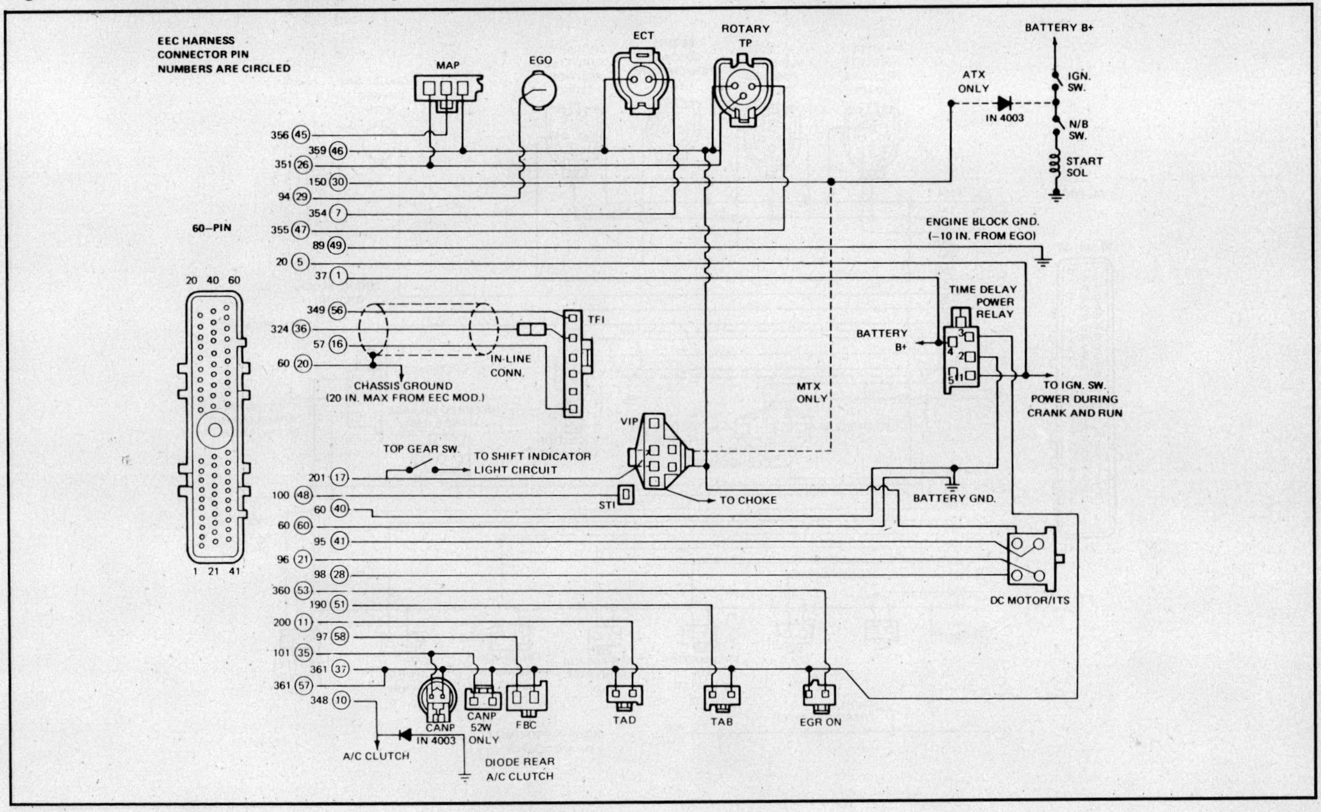

Fig. 12: 4.9L FBC EEC-IV Wiring Diagram (Van Models)

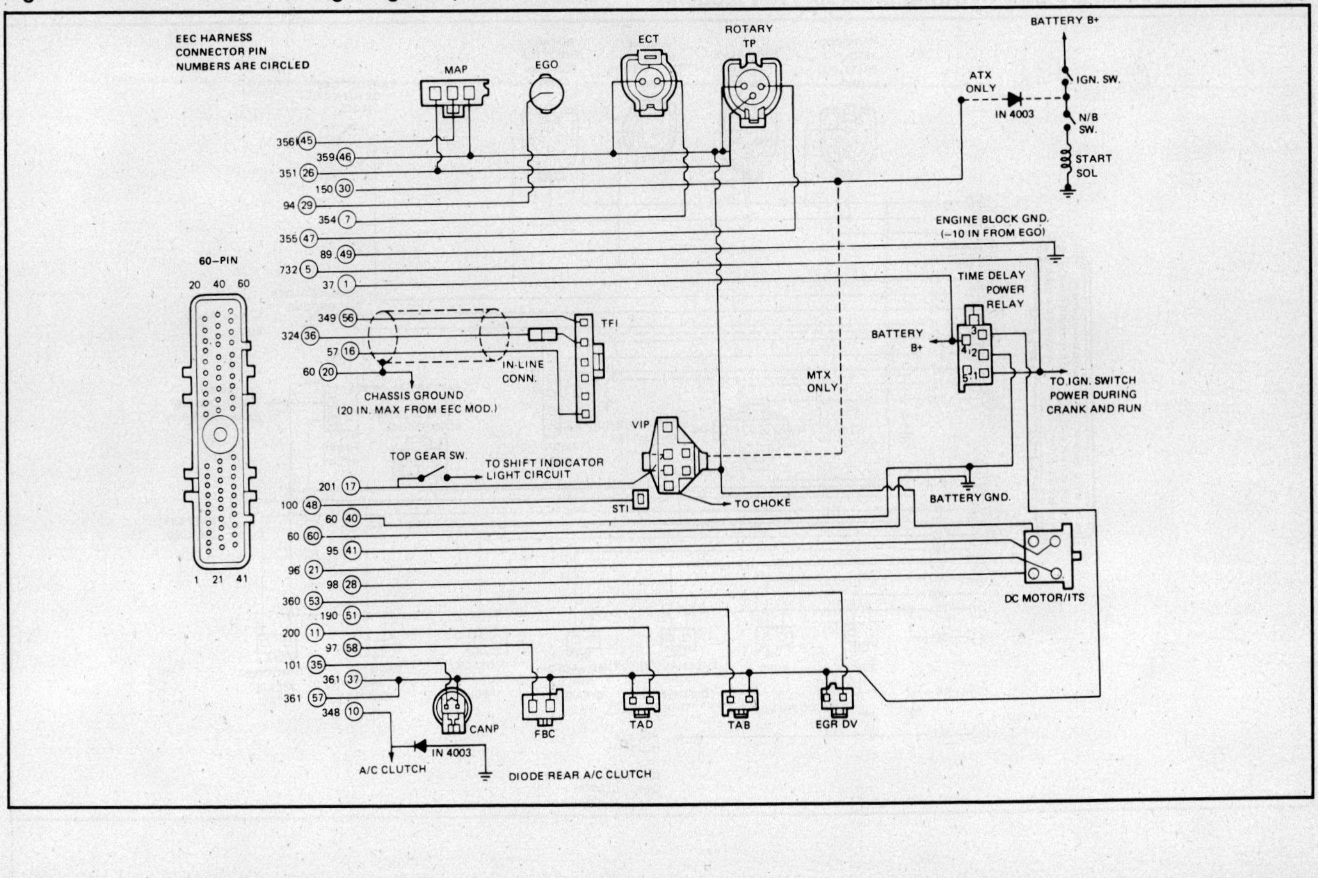

FORD ELECTRONIC ENGINE CONTROL IV (Cont.)

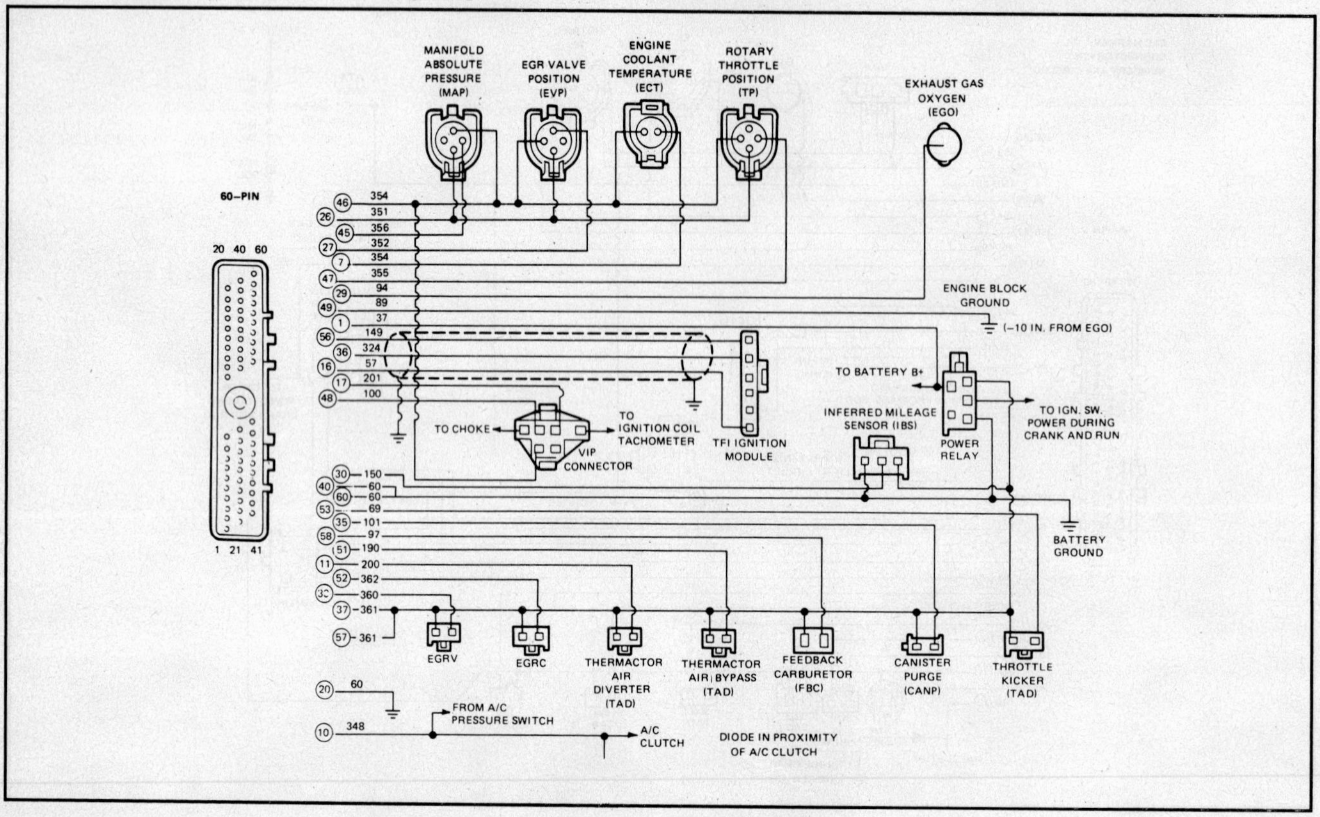

Fig. 13: 5.0L & 5.8L FBC EEC-IV Wiring Diagram (All Exc. Van Models)

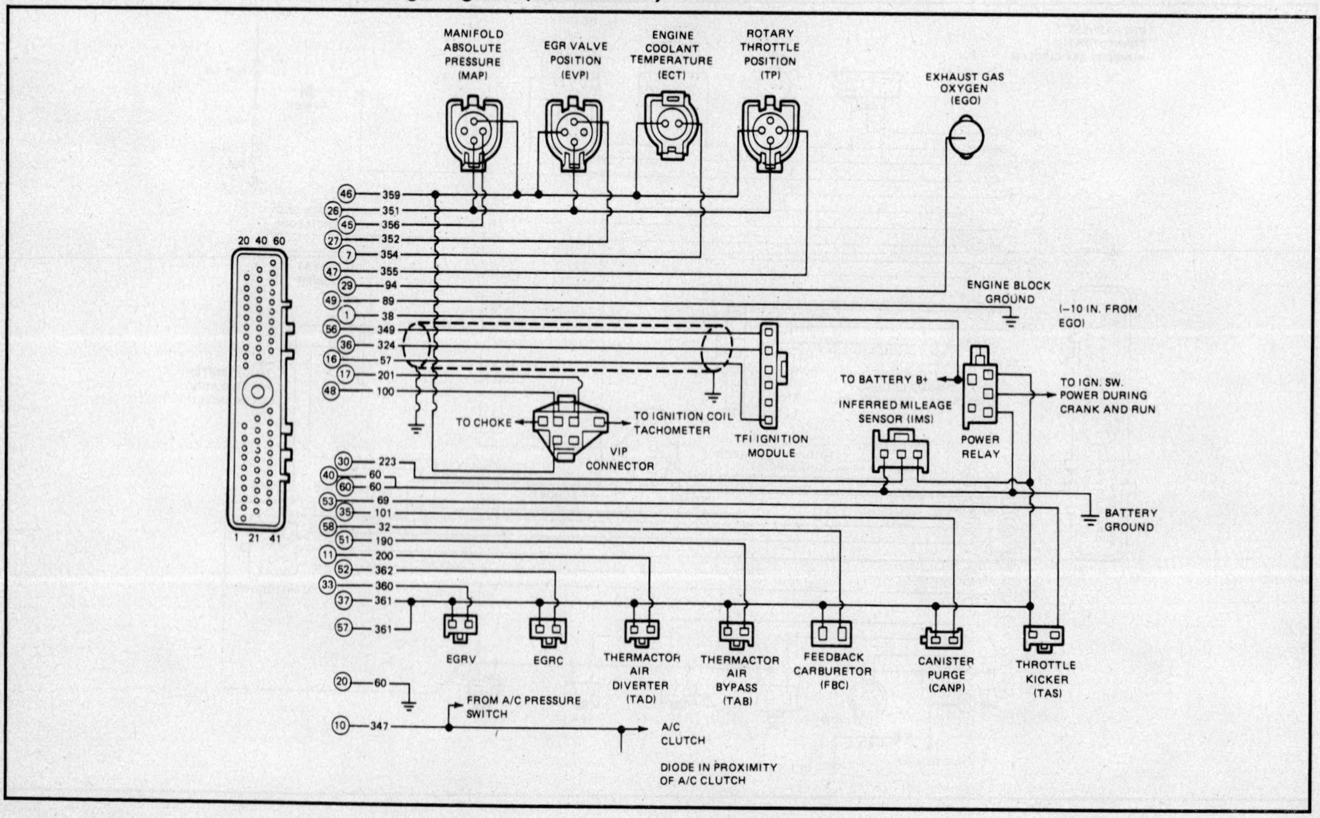

Fig. 14: 5.0L & 5.8L FBC EEC-IV Wiring Diagram (Van Models)

FORD ELECTRONIC ENGINE CONTROL IV (Cont.)

Fig. 15: 5.0L EFI EEC-IV Wiring Diagram

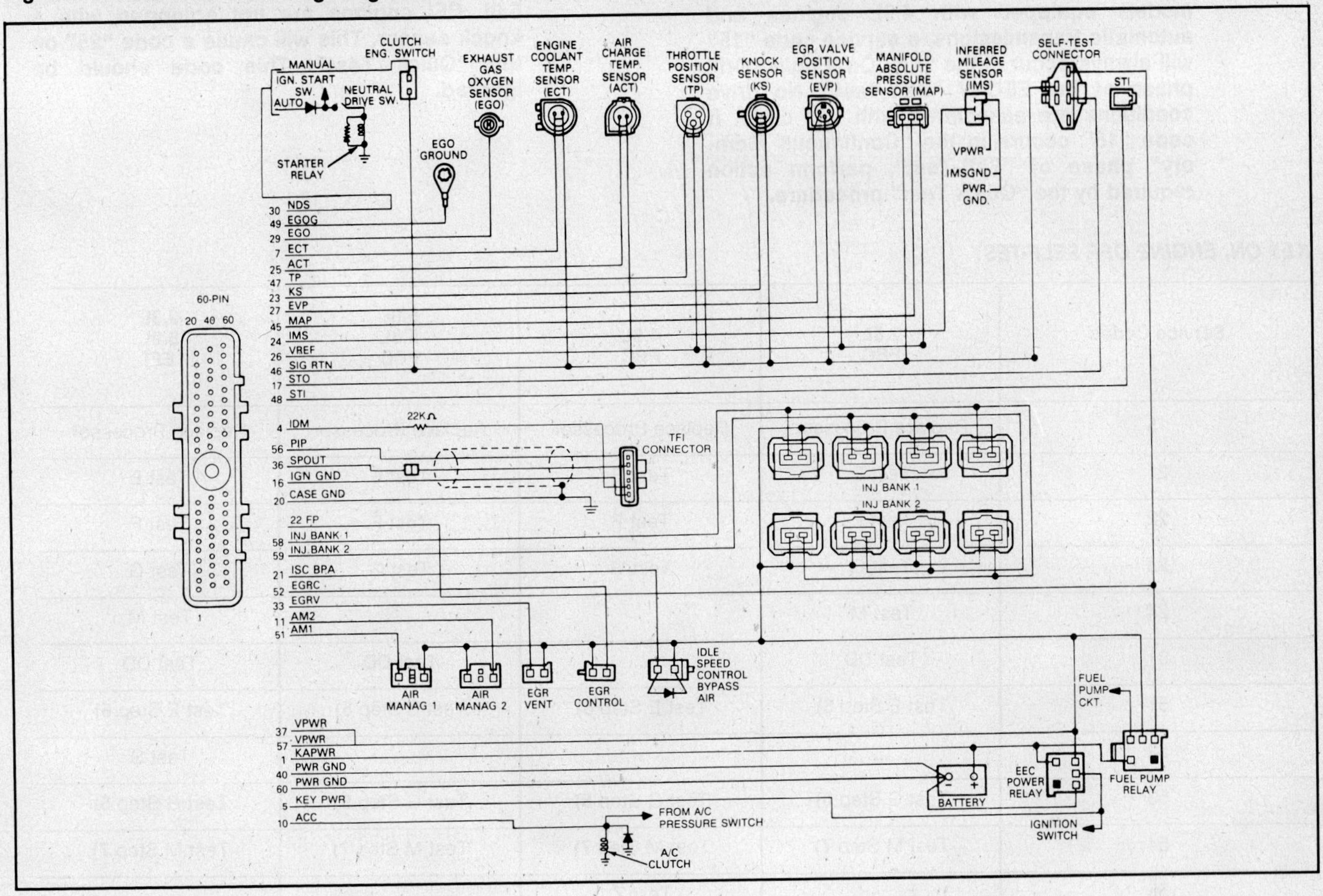

1985 Computerized Engine Controls

FORD ELECTRONIC ENGINE CONTROL IV (Cont.)

NOTE: On early production "E, F" series and Bronco models equipped with 4.9L engines and automatic transmissions, a service code "15" will always occur in the "Key On, Engine Off" phase of the EEC-IV "Self-Test". No drive conditions are associated with this code. If code "15" occurs in the "Continuous Memory" phase of "Self-Test", perform action required by the "Quick Test" procedure.

NOTE: Bronco and "F" series models equipped with 5.0L EFI engines are not equipped with a knock sensor. This will cause a code "25" on the "Quick Test". This code should be ignored.

KEY ON, ENGINE OFF SELF-TEST

Service Codes	2.8L FBC	4.9L FBC	5.0L 5.8L FBC	2.3L 5.0L EFI
15	Replace Processor	Replace Processor	Replace Processor	Replace Processor
21	Test E	Test E	Test E	Test E
22	Test F	Test F	Test F	Test F
23	Test G	Test G	Test G	Test G
24	Test M	...	...	Test M
31	Test DD	...	Test DD	Test DD
51	Test E Step **6)**	Test E Step **6)**	Test E Step **6)**	Test E Step **6)**
52	...	...	...	Test S
53	Test G Step **5)**	Test G Step **5)**	Test G Step **5)**	Test G Step **5)**
54	Test M Step **7)**	Test M Step **7)**	Test M Step **7)**	Test M Step **7)**
55	...	Test Z	...	...
61	Test E Step **8)**	Test E Step **8)**	Test E Step **8)**	Test E Step **8)**
63	Test G Step **10)**	Test G Step **10)**	Test G Step **10)**	Test G Step **10)**
64	Test M Step **9)**	...	...	Test M Step **9)**
67	Test N	Test N	...	Test N
68	Test H Step **5)**	Test H Step **5)**	...	...
81	Test O	...	...	Test O
82	Test O	...	...	Test O
83	Test P	...	...	Test P
84	Test P	...	...	Test P
85	Test Q	...	...	...
87	Test R	...	...	Test R
88	Test S	...	...	...
89	Test CC	...	...	Test CC

FBC - Feedback Carburetor
EFI - Electronic Fuel Injection

FORD ELECTRONIC ENGINE CONTROL IV (Cont.)

KEY ON, ENGINE RUNNING SELF-TEST

Service Codes	2.8L FBC	4.9L FBC	5.0L 5.8L FBC	2.3L 5.0L EFI
12	Test J	Test J	Test FF	Test FF
13	Test K	Test K	...	...
16	Test D	Test D	Test D	...
21	Test E	Test E	Test E	Test E
22	Test F	Test F	Test F	Test F
23	Test G	Test G	Test G	Test G
24	Test M	...	...	Test M
25	Test U	...	...	Test U
31	Test I	...	Test I	Test I
32	Test DD Step **9)**	...	Test DD Step **9)**	Test DD Step **9)**
33	Test DD Step **9)**	...	Test DD Step **9)**	Test DD Step **9)**
34	Test DD Step **9)**	...	Test DD Step **9)**	Test DD Step **9)**
35	Test I Step **19)**	...	Test I Step **19)**	Test I Step **19)**
41	Test I	Test I	Test I	...
42	Test I Step **14)**	Test I Step **14)**	Test I Step **14)**	Test J
43	Test I	Test I	Test I	...
44	Test O	Test O	Test O	Test O
45	Test O	Test O	Test O	Test O
46	Test O	Test O	Test O	Test O
47	Test J Step **14)**	Test J Step **14)**	Test J Step **14)**	...
55	Test Z	...	...	...
58	Test H	Test H	...	...
65	Test Z	...	...	...
72	Test F	Test F	Test F	Test F
73	Test G Step **14)**	Test G Step **14)**	Test G Step **14)**	Test G Step **14)**
74	Test EE	...	...	Test EE
75	Test EE	...	...	Test EE
77	Test W	Test W	Test W	Test W

FBC – Feedback Carburetor
EFI – Electronic Fuel Injection

1985 Computerized Engine Controls

FORD ELECTRONIC ENGINE CONTROL IV (Cont.)

NOTE: **On early production "E, F" series and Bronco models equipped with 4.9L engines and automatic transmissions, a service code "15" will always occur in the "Key On, Engine Off" phase of the EEC-IV "Self-Test". No drive conditions are associated with this code. If code "15" occurs in the "Continuous Memory" phase of "Self-Test", perform action required by the "Quick Test" procedure.**

NOTE: **Bronco and "F" series models equipped with 5.0L EFI engines are not equipped with a knock sensor. This will cause a code "25" on the "Quick Test". This code should be ignored.**

KEY ON, ENGINE OFF SELF-TEST (OFF TEST)

Service Codes	2.8L FBC	4.9L FBC	5.0L 5.8L FBC	2.3L 5.0L EFI
15	Replace Processor	Replace Processor	Replace Processor	Replace Processor
21	Test E	Test E	Test E	Test E
22	Test F	Test F	Test F	Test F
23	Test G	Test G	Test G	Test G
24	Test M	...	...	Test M
31	Test DD	...	Test DD	Test DD
51	Test E Step **6)**	Test E Step **6)**	Test E Step **6)**	Test E Step **6)**
52	...	...	...	Test S
53	Test G Step **5)**	Test G Step **5)**	Test G Step **5)**	Test G Step **5)**
54	Test M Step **7)**	Test M Step **7)**	Test M Step **7)**	Test M Step **7)**
55	...	Test Z	...	...
61	Test E Step **8)**	Test E Step **8)**	Test E Step **8)**	Test E Step **8)**
63	Test G Step **10)**	Test G Step **10)**	Test G Step **10)**	Test G Step **10)**
64	Test M Step **9)**	...	...	Test M Step **9)**
67	Test N	Test N	...	Test N
68	Test H Step **5)**	Test H Step **5)**	...	...
81	Test O	...	...	Test O
82	Test O	...	...	Test O
83	Test P	...	...	Test P
84	Test P	...	...	Test P
85	Test Q	...	...	...
87	Test R	...	...	Test R
88	Test S	...	...	...
89	Test CC	...	...	Test CC

FBC - Feedback Carburetor
EFI - Electronic Fuel Injection

FORD ELECTRONIC ENGINE CONTROL IV (Cont.)

KEY ON, ENGINE RUNNING SELF-TEST (RUN TEST)

Service Codes	2.8L FBC	4.9L FBC	5.0L 5.8L FBC	2.3L 5.0L EFI
12	Test J	Test J	Test FF	Test FF
13	Test K	Test K	...	...
16	Test D	Test D	Test D	...
21	Test E	Test E	Test E	Test E
22	Test F	Test F	Test F	Test F
23	Test G	Test G	Test G	Test G
24	Test M	...	...	Test M
25	Test U	...	...	Test U
31	Test I	...	Test I	Test I
32	Test DD Step 9)	...	Test DD Step 9)	Test DD Step 9)
33	Test DD Step 9)	...	Test DD Step 9)	Test DD Step 9)
34	Test DD Step 9)	...	Test DD Step 9)	Test DD Step 9)
35	Test I Step 19)	...	Test I Step 19)	Test I Step 19)
41	Test I	Test I	Test I	...
42	Test I Step 14)	Test I Step 14)	Test I Step 14)	Test J
43	Test I	Test I	Test I	...
44	Test O	Test O	Test O	Test O
45	Test O	Test O	Test O	Test O
46	Test O	Test O	Test O	Test O
47	Test J Step 14)	Test J Step 14)	Test J Step 14)	...
55	Test Z	...	...	...
58	Test H	Test H	...	...
65	Test Z	...	...	...
72	Test F	Test F	Test F	Test F
73	Test G Step 14)	Test G Step 14)	Test G Step 14)	Test G Step 14)
74	Test EE	...	...	Test EE
75	Test EE	...	...	Test EE
77	Test W	Test W	Test W	Test W

FBC – Feedback Carburetor
EFI – Electronic Fuel Injection

FORD ELECTRONIC ENGINE CONTROL IV (Cont.)

CONTINUOUS SELF-TEST RESULTS

Service Codes	2.8L FBC	4.9L FBC	5.0L 5.8L FBC	2.3L 5.0L EFI
11	Test Complete	Test Complete	Test Complete	Test Complete
14	Test FF	Test FF	Test FF	Test FF
18	Test GG	Test GG	Test GG	Test GG
21	Test E Step **10)**	Test E Step **10)**	Test E Step **10)**	Test E Step **10)**
22	Test F Step **12)**	Test F Step **12)**	Test F Step **12)**	Test F Step **12)**
31	Test DD Step **4)**	...	Test DD Step **4)**	Test DD Step **4)**
41	Test I	Test I	Test I	...
42	Test I Step **14)**	Test I Step **14)**	Test I Step **14)**	Test J
51	Test E Step **11)**	Test E Step **11)**	Test E Step **11)**	Test E Step **11)**
53	Test G Step **5)**	Test G Step **5)**	Test G Step **5)**	...
54	Test M Step **7)**	...	...	Test M Step **7)**
61	Test E Step **11)**	Test E Step **11)**	Test E Step **11)**	Test E Step **11)**
63	Test G Step **19)**	Test G Step **19)**	Test G Step **19)**	Test G Step **19)**
64	Test M Step **11)**	...	...	Test M Step **11)**

TEST A

NO START TEST

1) Try to start engine. If engine does not crank, check for excess fuel in cylinders (hydraulic lock) and check the starting/charging system. If engine cranks, but does not start or continue to run, proceed with test.

2) Disconnect spark plug wire to any cylinder. Connect spark tester between plug wire and engine ground. Crank engine and check for spark. If spark is produced, go to step **13)**. If not, go to next step. Reconnect spark plug wire to plug.

3) Remove high tension coil wire from distributor and install spark tester. Check for spark while cranking. If spark is produced, service or repair TFI ignition system. If no spark, go to next step.

TFI Module Circuit Diagram

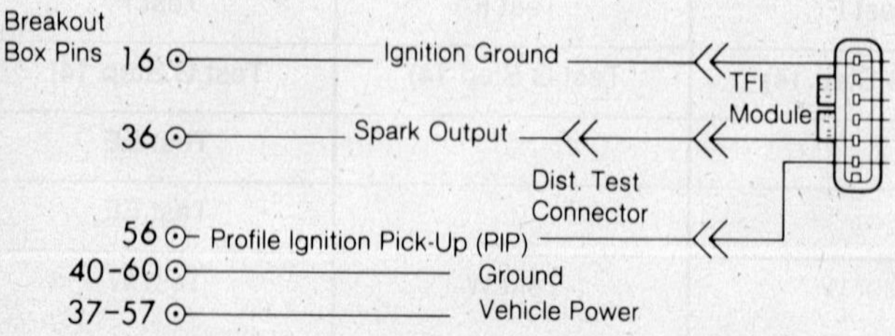

4) Turn ignition off and wait for 10 seconds. Disconnect 60-pin harness connector at ECA. Inspect for damaged pins, corrosion, or loose wires. Repair as required. Install breakout box (timing switch in "Computed" position). Turn ignition on (engine off). With DVOM on 20 volt scale, measure voltage from box pin 37 to box pins 40, 57 and 60 in turn. If either voltage reading is less than 10.5 volts, perform Test B. If voltage readings are 10.5 volts or greater, continue test.

5) Turn ignition off and wait 10 seconds. With DVOM on 200 ohm scale, measure between box pin 16 to TFI connector (ignition ground). If resistance is 5 ohms or greater, repair harness and repeat Quick Test. If resistance is less than 5 ohms, go to next step.

6) Reconnect 60-pin harness at ECA. With breakout box still connected, set timing switch to "Dist" position. Try to start vehicle. If vehicle starts, go to step **10)**. If not, go to next step.

7) Turn timing switch to "Computed" position. Set DVOM on 20 volt scale and measure from box pin 36 to chassis ground while cranking engine. If voltage is between 3-6 volts, EEC system is okay. Service TFI ignition system. If voltage is less than 3 volts or greater than 6 volts, continue test.

8) Turn ignition off and wait 10 seconds. Disconnect 60-pin harness at ECA. Disconnect TFI. With DVOM set on 200,000 ohm scale, measure resistance from box pin 36 to pins 16, 20, 26, 40 and 60 in turn, for short to ground; from box pin 36 to pins 37 and 57 in turn, for short to power; from box pin 36 to 56 for short to PIP. If any reading is less than 10,000 ohms, repair short and repeat test if vehicle does not start. If all readings are 10,000 ohms or more, go to next step.

9) Turn ignition off and wait 10 seconds. Reconnect 60-pin harness at ECA (TFI still disconnected). With DVOM on 200 ohm scale, measure resistance from box pin 36 to pins 37 and 57 for short to power; from box pin 36 to pins 40 and 60 for short to ground. If any reading is less than 5 ohms, replace ECA and repeat Quick Test. If all readings are 5 ohms or more, continue test.

10) With DVOM on 20 volt scale, measure voltage from box pin 56 to pin 16 while cranking engine. If voltage is between 3-6 volts, remove breakout box and replace ECA. Repeat Quick Test. If voltage is less than 3 volts or more than 6 volts, go to next step.

11) Turn ignition off and wait 10 seconds. Disconnect 60-pin harness at ECA. With DVOM on 200 ohm scale, measure resistance from box pin 56 to PIP circuit of TFI connector. If resistance is 5 ohms or greater, repair open and repeat Quick Test. If resistance is less than 5 ohms, continue to next step.

TEST A (Cont.)

12) With ECA and TFI harnesses still disconnected and ignition off, set DVOM on 200,000 ohm scale. Measure resistance from box pin 56 to pins 16, 20, 40 and 60 in turn, for short to ground; from box pin 56 to pins 37 and 57 in turn, for short to power; from box pin 56 to pin 36 for short to spark output. If any resistance is less than 10,000 ohms, service PIP circuit. If all resistances are greater than 10,000 ohms, service TFI ignition system.

13) Turn ignition off and wait 10 seconds. Disconnect 60-pin connector at ECA and check for damaged pins, corrosion and loose wires. Service as required. Install breakout box (timing switch at "Computed" position). Reconnect 60-pin connector at ECA. With DVOM on 20 volt scale, measure voltage from box pin 36 to chassis ground while cranking engine. If voltage is less than 3 volts or greater than 6 volts, go to step **10)**. If voltage is 3-6 volts, check fuel system.

TEST B

VEHICLE BATTERY

1) Turn ignition on, engine off. With DVOM on 20 volt scale, measure voltage across battery terminals. If more than 10.5 volts, go to next step. If less than 10.5 volts, service discharged battery.

2) Ignition on, engine off. With DVOM on 20 volt scale, measure voltage between battery negative post to signal return circuit in self-test connector. If less than .5 volts, go to next step. If more than .5 volts, go to step **4)**.

3) Connect breakout box, ECA connected. Turn ignition on, engine off. With DVOM on 20 volt scale, measure voltage from battery positive post to pin box 37 and pin 57. If both readings are less than .5 volts, go to Test C. If either is more than .5 volts, go to step **7)**.

4) With breakout box and ECA connected, turn ignition on (engine off). With DVOM on 20 volt scale, measure voltage from battery negative post to box pin 40 and pin 60. If both readings are less than .5 volts, go to next step. If either is .5 volts or more, circuit has high resistance or open. Correct faulty ground circuit and repeat Quick Test.

5) With breakout box and ECA connected, place DVOM on 200 ohm scale. Turn ignition off and wait 10 seconds. Measure resistance between box pins 40 and 46, and between box pins 46 and 60. If both readings are less than 5 ohms, go to next step. If either is 5 ohms or more, disconnect ECA connector and inspect for damaged pins and corrosion. Repair as required and repeat Quick Test. If fault is still present, replace ECA and repeat Quick Test.

6) With breakout box and ECA connected, place DVOM on 200 ohm scale. Turn ignition off and wait 10 seconds. Measure resistance between box pin 46 and signal return circuit in self-test connector. If less than 5 ohms, system okay, repeat Quick Test. If 5 ohms or greater, excessive resistance in signal return circuit is indicated. Correct fault and repeat Quick Test.

Battery Test Circuits

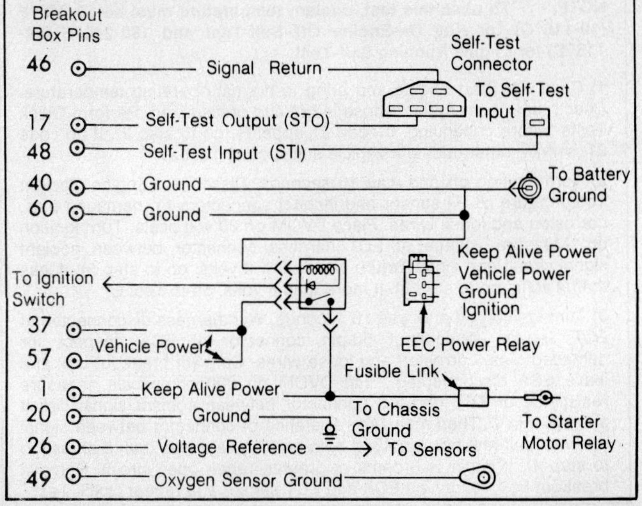

TEST B (Cont.)

7) Place DVOM on 20 volt scale. With ECA connected, turn ignition on. Connect DVOM negative lead to battery negative post and make the following voltage checks with DVOM positive lead. Ignition must remain on for these checks.

- Keep alive power circuit at EEC power relay. If 10.5 volts or greater, continue checks. If less than 10.5 volts, check keep alive power and vehicle power circuits for shorts to ground. Check keep alive power circuit from power relay to battery positive post for opens.
- Ignition circuit at EEC power relay. If 10.5 volts or greater, continue checks. If less than 10.5 volts, check 10 amp fuse in location 18. Check for opens in ignition switch circuits. Service as required and repeat Quick Test.
- Ground circuit at EEC power relay. If less than .5 volt, go to next check. If .5 volt or more, correct open or ground in ground circuit. Repeat Quick Test.
- Vehicle power circuit at EEC power relay. If 10.5 volts or more, correct short to ground or open in vehicle power circuit from relay to ECA connector pins 37 and 57. Repeat Quick Test. If less than 10.5 volts, replace power relay and repeat Quick Test.

TEST C

REFERENCE VOLTAGE

1) Turn ignition off and connect breakout box (ECA connected). Turn ignition on. With DVOM on 20 volt scale, connect positive lead to box pin 37 and negative lead to signal return in self-test connector. If 10.5 volts or greater, go to next step. If less than 10.5 volts, go to Test B.

2) With ignition still on, measure voltage between box pins 26 and 46. If 4-6 volts; reference voltage okay, repeat Quick Test. If 4 volts or less, go to step **4)**. If 6 volts or more, go to next step.

3) Turn ignition off and wait 10 seconds. Disconnect ECA (breakout box connected). Place DVOM on 20 volt scale. Measure voltage from box pin 26, then box pin 46 to battery ground. If less than .5 volt, replace ECA and repeat Quick Test. If .5 volt or more, service short to battery power in EEC harness. Repeat Quick Test.

4) Turn ignition off and wait 10 seconds. Reconnect ECA to breakout box. Disconnect throttle position sensor (TPS) from vehicle harness. Turn ignition on. With DVOM on 20 volt scale, measure voltage between box pins 26 and 46. If less than .4 volt, go to next step. If .4 volt or more, replace TPS and repeat Quick Test.

5) Turn ignition off and wait 10 seconds. With breakout box and ECA connected, disconnect EGR valve position sensor from harness. Turn ignition on. With DVOM on 20 volt scale, measure voltage between box pins 26 and 46. If less than 4 volts, go to next step. If more than 4 volts, replace EGR valve position sensor and repeat Quick Test.

6) Turn ignition off and wait 10 seconds. With breakout box and ECA connected, disconnect MAP (manifold absolute pressure) sensor from harness. Turn ignition on and place DVOM on 20 volt scale. Measure voltage between box pins 26 and 46. If less than 4 volts, go to next step. If 4 volts or more, replace MAP sensor and repeat Quick Test.

Reference Voltage Test Circuits

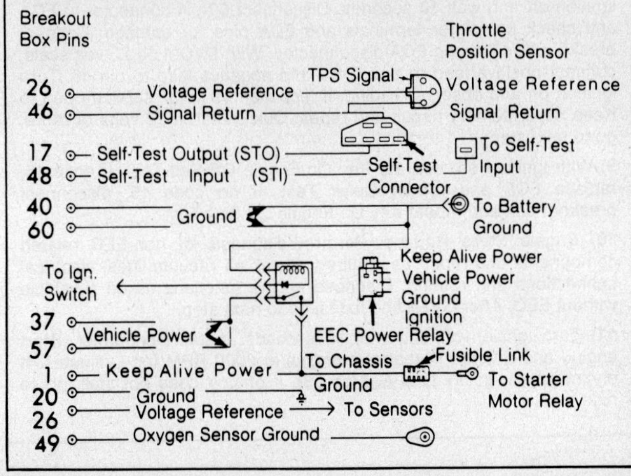

FORD ELECTRONIC ENGINE CONTROL IV (Cont.)

TEST C (Cont.)

7) With ignition off, disconnect ECA (breakout box connected). Turn ignition off and wait 10 seconds. Disconnect throttle position, barometric pressure and EGR valve position sensors from vehicle harness. With DVOM on 200 ohm scale, measure continuity from box pin 26 to box pins 20, 40, 46 and 60 in turn. If less than 5 ohms, service short to ground in voltage reference circuit and repeat Quick Test. If 5 ohms or greater, go to next step.

8) With breakout box connected, leave ECA and sensors listed in step **7)** disconnected. Turn ignition off. With DVOM on 200 ohm scale, measure continuity on sensors listed in step **7)** from box pin 26 to voltage reference circuit on sensor harness connectors. If all readings are less than 5 ohms, reconnect sensors and replace ECA. Repeat Quick Test. If any reading is 5 ohms or greater, repair open in voltage reference circuit and repeat Quick Test.

TEST D

NO CODES
IMPROPER CODES

1) Turn ignition off and wait 10 seconds. Place DVOM on 20 volt scale. Disconnect throttle position sensor (TPS). Turn ignition on. Measure voltage at TPS harness connector between voltage reference signal circuit and signal return circuit. If 6 volts or more, to to Test C, step **2)**. If less than 4 volts, to to Test C, step **1)**. If between 4-6 volts, reconnect TPS and go to next step.

2) With ignition on, measure voltage between battery negative post and signal return circuit in Self-Test connector. If less than .5 volt, go to next step. If .5 volt or more, go to Test B, step **4)**.

3) Turn ignition off and wait 10 seconds. Disconnect 60-pin connector at ECA and inspect. Repair as required. Connect breakout box and reconnect ECA. Place DVOM on 200 ohm scale. Measure resistance of Self-Test input connector from Self-Test pigtail to box pin 48. If less than 5 ohms, go to next step. If 5 ohms or more, repair open circuit and repeat Quick Test.

4) Measure resistance of Self-Test output between Self-Test connector and box pin 17. If less than 5 ohms, go to next step. If 5 ohms or more, repair open circuit and repeat Quick Test.

5) Turn ignition off. Connect DVOM between oxygen sensor ground point on engine and box pin 49. If 5 ohms or more, repair oxygen sensor ground wire or open circuit bad connection and repeat Quick Test. If less than 5 ohms, disconnect ECA and inspect connector. If okay, reconnect and repeat Quick Test. If problem still present, replace ECA.

6) Continuous Code 15. Code 15 is recorded any time power is lost to Keep Alive Memory circuit. Clear continuous codes and repeat Key On-Engine Off Self-Test. If code 15, go to next step. If no code 15, test complete.

7) Ensure EEC components are properly connected and wiring does not contact ignition components or wires. Service as required and repeat Key On-Engine Off Self-Test. If code 15, go to next step. If no code 15, test complete.

8) Check power circuit to Keep Alive Memory circuit for voltage. Turn ignition off and wait 10 seconds. Disconnect 60-pin connector at ECA and check connector terminals and ECA pins for damage. Connect breakout box, leaving ECA disconnected. With DVOM on 20 volt scale, connect positive lead to box pin 1 and negative lead to pin 46. Turn ignition on and observe reading. If less than 10 volts, service open to Keep Alive Memory circuit and repeat Quick Test. If 10 volts or more, go to next step.

9) With ignition on, activate Key On-Engine Off Self-Test. If code 15, replace ECA and repeat Quick Test. If no code 15, disconnect breakout box and repeat Key On-Engine Off Self-Test.

10) Engine Stalls Routine. Perform diagnosis of non-EEC related components and repair as required. Check all vacuum lines, electrical connections and routing. Diagnose engine functions as on a vehicle without EEC. After correcting faults, go to next step.

11) Turn ignition off and wait 10 seconds. Install tachometer. Start engine and attempt to maintain engine at 2000 RPM for 2 minutes. If engine stalls, go to Test A, step **13)**. If engine does not stall, go to next step.

TEST D (Cont.)

12) With engine at operating temperature and tachometer installed, turn ignition off and wait 10 seconds. Activate Quick Test and perform Engine Running Self-Test while maintaining engine at 2000 RPM. If engine passes test or any codes are recorded, service codes as described for Engine Running Self-Test. If no codes are recorded, go to step **1)**.

13) Output State Check Not Functioning. Turn ignition off and wait 10 seconds. Perform Key On-Engine Off Self-Test and leave ignition on to enter Output State Check. If codes 23, 53, 63, or 68 are present in On Demand Test results, service codes as described for Key On-Engine Off Self-Test. If no codes 23, 53 or 63, leave ignition on and go to next step.

14) While in Output State Check, set DVOM on 20 volt scale. Measure voltage between Self-Test output circuit of Self-Test connector and battery positive terminal. Depress throttle to wide open position and release. Verify throttle is in closed position and note voltage reading. If greater than 10 volts, check throttle and linkage for sticking or binding and repeat Quick Test. If less than 10 volts, replace throttle position sensor (TPS) and repeat Quick Test.

No Codes/Invalid Codes Circuit Diagram

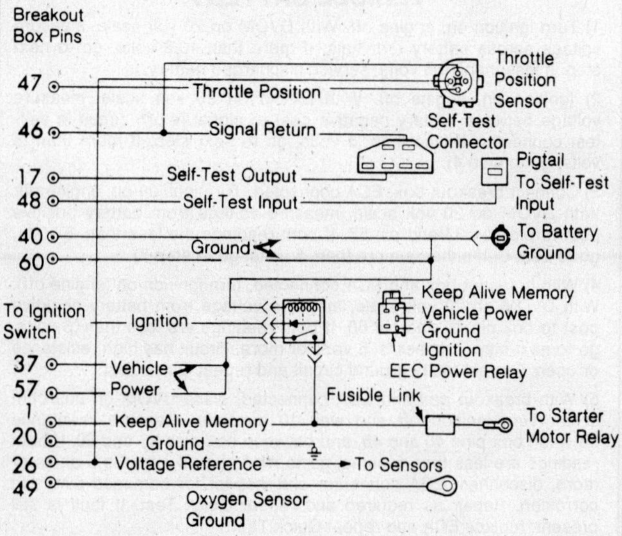

TEST E

ENGINE COOLANT
TEMPERATURE SENSOR

NOTE: To pass this test, coolant temperature must be 50-240°F (10-116°C) for Key On-Engine Off Self-Test and 180-240°F (82-116°C) for Engine Running Self-Test.

1) Code 21. Start engine and bring to normal operating temperature. Check that upper radiator hose is hot and pressurized. Perform Quick Tests before continuing. If code 21 appears, go to step **2)**. If no code 21, service other codes. If vehicle stalls, go to Test X.

2) Turn ignition off and wait 10 seconds. Disconnect Engine Coolant Temperature (ECT) sensor and inspect connectors for damaged pins, corrosion and loose wires. Place DVOM on 20 volt scale. Turn ignition on. Measure voltage at ECT harness connector between coolant signal circuit and signal return circuit. If 4-6 volts, go to step **5)**. If less than 4 volts, go to step **3)**. If more than 6 volts, go to Test C.

3) Turn ignition off and wait 10 seconds. With harness disconnected at ECT sensor, disconnect 60-pin connector at ECA. Inspect for damaged pins, corrosion and loose wires. Connect breakout box and leave ECA disconnected. With DVOM on 200 ohm scale, measure resistance of ECT harness connector between coolant signal circuit and box pin 7. Then measure resistance of connector between signal return circuit and box pin 46. If both readings are less than 5 ohms, go to step **4)**. If either is 5 ohms or greater, repair open circuit. Remove breakout box, reconnect ECA and ECT sensor and repeat Quick Test.

TEST E (Cont.)

4) Turn ignition off and connect breakout box. Disconnect ECA and ECT sensor. With DVOM on 200K ohm scale, measure resistance between box pin 7 and pins 40 and 60. If either reading is less than 10K ohms, service short circuit. Remove breakout box, reconnect ECA and ECT sensor and repeat Quick Test. If both readings are 10K ohms or more, go to step **5)**.

5) Reconnect ECA and ECT sensor. Remove breakout box. Warm engine to normal operating temperature, turn ignition off and wait 10 seconds. Disconnect harness at ECT sensor. With DVOM on 200K ohm scale, measure resistance of ECT sensor. In Key On-Engine Off Self-Test, reading should be 1300-7700 ohms. In Engine Running Self-Test, reading should be 1550-4550 ohms. If both are within limits, replace ECA, reconnect sensor and repeat Quick Test. If not within limits, replace ECT sensor and repeat Quick Test.

6) Code 51 Turn ignition off and wait 10 seconds. Reconnect 60-pin connector at ECA and remove breakout box. Disconnect ECT sensor harness and inspect for damaged pins, corrosion and loose wires. Insert jumper wire in ECT sensor harness between coolant signal circuit and signal return circuit. Run Key On-Engine Off Self-Test. If code 61 appears, replace ECT sensor, remove jumper wire, reconnect harness and repeat Quick Test. If no code 61, go to step **7)**.

7) Turn ignition off and wait 10 seconds. Remove jumper. Disconnect 60-pin connector at ECA and inspect for damaged pins, corrosion and loose wires. Connect breakout box, leaving ECA disconnected. With DVOM on 200 ohm scale, measure resistance of ECT harness between coolant signal circuit and box pin 7 and signal return circuit and box pin 46. If either is 5 ohms or more, repair open in harness, remove breakout box, reconnect ECA and ECT sensor and repeat Quick Test. If both are less than 5 ohms, replace ECA, remove breakout, reconnect ECA and ECT sensor and repeat Quick Test.

8) Code 61 Turn ignition off and wait 10 seconds. Disconnect 60-pin connector at ECA and inspect for damaged pins, corrosion and loose wires. Perform Key On-Engine Off Self-Test. If code 51 appears, replace ECT and repeat Quick Test. If no code 51, go to step **9)**.

9) Turn ignition off and wait 10 seconds. With ECT disconnected, install breakout box and leave ECA disconnected. With DVOM on 200K ohm scale, measure resistance between box pin 7 to pins 40 and 60. If any less than 10K ohms, repair short in harness and repeat Quick Test. If both 10K ohms or more, replace ECA and repeat Quick Test.

10) Continuous Monitor Code 21. Turn ignition off and wait 10 seconds. Remove breakout box, reconnect ECA and ECT sensor and prepare vehicle for test drive (all test equipment removed). During test drive, try to simulate complaint and keep complaint active for at least one minute. After test drive, perform Key On-Engine Off Self-Test. If code 21 present, ensure thermostat is operating properly. If okay, replace ECT sensor and repeat Quick Test. If no code 21, unable to duplicate fault at this time. Continuous Code 21 test complete.

11) Continuous Monitor Codes 51 and 61. Enter Continuous Monitor mode and observe volt/ohmmeter for fault indication while doing the following: Lightly tap on ECT sensor to simulate road shock. Wiggle sensor connector. If fault is indicated or voltage reading exceeds 5 volts, disconnect harness connectors at ECT and ECA. If connectors and terminals are okay, replace sensor and repeat Quick Test. If no fault indicated, go to step **12)**.

Engine Coolant Temperature Sensor Circuits

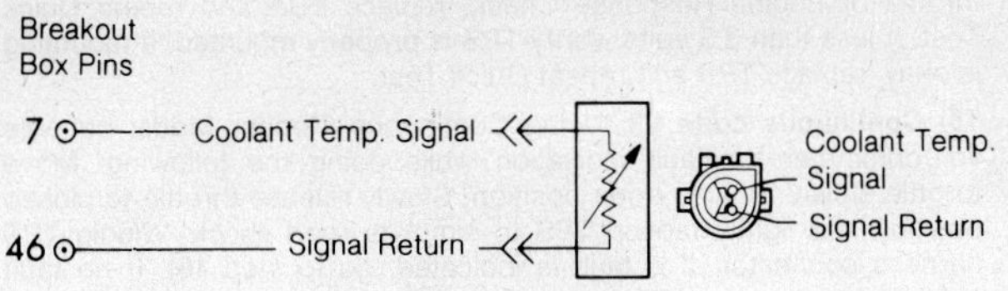

58,750 ohms at 50°F (10°C)
40,500 ohms at 65°F (18°C)
3600 ohms at 180°F (82°C)
1840 ohms at 220°F (104°C)

TEST E (Cont.)

12) Observe volt/ohmmeter while performing the following: Beginning at ECT, wiggle, shake or bend small sections of harness while working way to dash panel. Then repeating process from panel to ECA. If fault is indicated, isolate and repair problem and repeat Quick Test. If no fault indicated, go to step **13)**.

13) Turn ignition off and wait 10 seconds. Disconnect 60-pin connector at ECA and inspect connector and terminals for damage. If damaged, service as required and repeat Quick Test. If okay, fault cannot be duplicated at this time. Continuous Code 51 and 61 testing is complete.

TEST F

MANIFOLD ABSOLUTE PRESSURE (MAP) SENSOR/ BAROMETRIC PRESSURE (BP) SENSOR

1) Key On/Engine Off Code 22 Displayed. Turn key OFF. Disconnect MAP/BP sensor from wire harness. Connect MAP/BP tester bewteen wire harness and MAP/BP sensor. Set DVOM to 20 volt scale and connect banana plugs from tester to DVOM. Go to step **2)**.

2) Turn key ON. If ONLY Green light of tester comes on, VREF is correct. Go to step **4)** of this test. If Red light (less than 4 volts) or no lights come on, VREF is too low. Go to step **3)**. If Red light (greater than 6 volts) comes on, VREF is too high. Go to step **3)**.

3) With MAP/BP tester connected, turn key ON. Disconnect MAP/BP sensor and repeat step **2)**. If ONLY Green light comes on, VREF is correct. Replace MAP/BP sensor and repeat Quick Test. If Red light (less than 4 volts) or no lights come on, VREF is too low. If Red light (greater than 6 volts) comes on, VREF is too high. Remove MAP/BP tester and go to Test B.

4) Connect MAP/BP tester and turn ignition switch to "ON" position. Check output reading of sensor. Measure several known good MAP/BP sensors on other vehicles. Average of readings will be typical for date and location of testing. See chart in circuit diagram for correct output voltage readings. If readings are out of range, go to step **6)** of this test. If readings are within range, go to step **5)**.

5) Turn key OFF and wait 10 seconds. Disconnect MAP/BP sensor and 60-pin ECA connector. Inspect for and repair any damaged wiring. Install breakout box, leaving ECA disconnected. Set DVOM to 200 ohm scale. Measure resistance between MAP/BP signal at connector and test pin 45. If reading is less that 5 ohms, replace ECA. Connect wiring and MAP/BP sensor. Repeat Quick Test. If reading is 5 ohms or more, repair open in circuit. Remove breakout box. Connect ECA and MAP/BP sensor. Repeat Quick Test.

6) Turn key OFF and wait 10 seconds. Disconnect 60-pin ECA connector. Inspect for and repair any damaged wiring. Install breakout box, leaving ECA disconnected. Disconnect MAP/BP sensor and set DVOM to 200K ohm scale. Measure resistance between test pin 45 and test pins 26, 40, 46, and 60. If any reading is less than 10K ohms, repair short circuit. Remove breakout box and reconnect ECA. Reconnect MAP/BP sensor and repeat Quick Test. If all readings are 10K ohms or more, replace MAP/BP sensor. Remove breakout box and connect all wiring. Repeat Quick Test.

7) Engine Running Code 22 Displayed. Turn key OFF and wait 10 seconds. Disconnect vacuum line from MAP/BP sensor and connect vacuum pump to sensor pipe. Apply 18 in. Hg to sensor and check for vacuum leak. If sensor does not hold vacuum, replace it. Reconnect vacuum hose and repeat Quick Test. If MAP/BP sensor holds vacuum, release vacuum and go to step **8)**.

8) Turn key OFF and wait 10 seconds. Plug MAP/BP vacuum supply hose and start engine. While holding 1400-1600 RPM, slowly apply 15 in. HG to MAP/BP sensor. Repeat Engine Running Quick Test while holding RPM level. Ignore all other codes during this step. If code 22 is still displayed, replace MAP/BP sensor. Connect vacuum line to MAP/BP sensor and repeat Quick Test. If code 22 is not displayed, check vacuum supply hose and repair. If hose is good, repair other service codes if any are displayed. If no other codes are displayed, check engine and vacuum supply for cause of low vacuum.

TEST F (Cont.)

9) Code 72 Displayed. Turn key OFF and wait 10 seconds. Connect vacuum gauge with "Tee" in line between intake manifold and MAP/BP sensor. Repeat Engine Running Quick Test and record service codes while observing vacuum reading. If vacuum decrease is 10 in. Hg or more and code 72 is NOT present, disconnect vacuum gauge and repair other codes. If vacuum decrease is 10 in. Hg or more and code 72 is displayed, replace MAP/BP sensor and repeat Quick Test. If vacuum decrease is less than 10 in. Hg, go to step **10)**.

10) Make sure that vacuum lines are routed correctly. Refer to VECI decal. Check hoses for kinks or blockage. If lines are good, EEC-IV system is good. Repair any mechanical causes of poor engine vacuum. If vacuum lines are bad, repair and repeat step **10)**.

11) Turn key OFF and disconnect MAP/BP sensor from harness. Connect MAP/BP tester between harness and sensor. Connect tester plugs to DVOM and set DVOM to 20 volt scale. Go to step **12)**.

12) Repeat voltage output as done in step **4)**. If reading is in range, go to Test L. If reading is out of range, replace MAP/BP sensor.

13) Continuous Code 22 Displayed. While in Continuous Monitor mode, attach vacuum pump to MAP/BP sensor. Slowly apply 25 in. Hg to sensor and then slowly bleed vacuum off. Tap MAP/BP sensor lightly and wiggle connector. If fault is indicated, inspect for and repair any damaged wiring. If wiring is good, replace MAP/BP sensor and repeat Quick Test. If no fault is indicated, go to step **14)** .

14) While still in monitor mode, wiggle and bend EEC-IV harness from MAP/BP sensor connector to firewall. Also wiggle and bend EEC-IV wiring from firewall to ECA. If fault is indicated, repair wiring and repeat Quick Test. If no fault is indicated, go to step **15)**.

15) Turn key OFF and wait 10 seconds. Disconnect ECA. Inspect for and repair any damaged wiring. If wiring is repaired, repeat Quick Test. If wiring is good and fault cannot be duplicated, test is complete.

Manifold Absolute Pressure (MAP/BP) Sensor Circuit

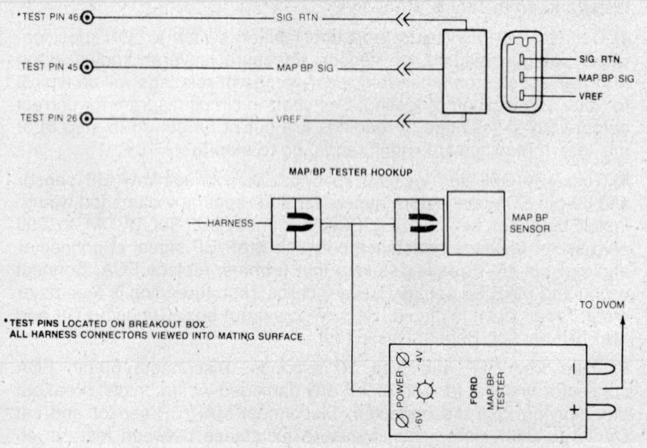

TEST G

THROTTLE POSITION SENSOR (TPS)

1) Code 23 (from Key On-Engine Off Self-Test). If code 68 is present, go to Test H. If no code 68, proceed with test. Before continuing with test, lightly press throttle lever toward actuator tip of idle speed motor while performing Key On-Engine Off Self-Test. If code 23, go to step **3)**. If no code 23, TPS is a little out of adjustment. DO NOT adjust TPS, EEC system is operating properly.

2) Code 23 (from Engine Running Self-Test). If code 58 is present, go to Test H. If no code 58, proceed with test. Before continuing with test, check for code 31 and/or 41 after performing Engine Running Self-Test. If code 31, go to Test I. If code 41, go to Test J. If no code 31 and/or 41, go to step **3)**.

3) Inspect carburetor and throttle linkage for binding. Check that throttle linkage is at mechanical closed throttle. Check for binding speed control linkage and vacuum line or electrical harness interference. If throttle is not stuck, go to step **4)**. If stuck, repair as required and repeat Quick Test.

TEST G (Cont.)

4) Turn ignition off and wait 10 seconds. Disconnect TPS and inspect for damaged pins, corrosion, and loose wires. Repair as required. Perform Key On-Engine Off Self-Test and record codes. If code 63, replace TPS and repeat Quick Test. If no code 63, replace ECA and repeat Quick Test.

5) Code 53. Turn ignition off and wait 10 seconds. Disconnect TPS and inspect. With DVOM on 20 volt scale, connect test leads to battery positive terminal and signal return circuit of TPS harness. If voltage is 10 volts or more, go to next step. If less than 10 volts, go to step **8)**.

6) Ignition off, TPS disconnected and DVOM on 20 volt scale. Connect test leads to TPS harness between throttle position signal circuit and signal return circuit. Turn ignition on and note voltage. If less than 4 volts, go to step **7)**. If 4 volts or more, go to step **9)**.

7) Turn ignition off and wait 10 seconds. With TPS disconnected, perform Key On-Engine Off Self-Test. If code 63 appears, replace TPS and repeat Quick Test. If no code 63, replace ECA and repeat Quick Test.

8) Turn ignition off and wait 10 seconds. With TPS disconnected, set DVOM on 200 ohm scale. Disconnect 60-pin connector at ECA and inspect for damage. Connect breakout box and leave ECA disconnected. Check continuity of TPS harness between signal return circuit and box pin 46. If less than 5 ohms, replace ECA and repeat Quick Test. If 5 ohms or more, repair open circuit and repeat Quick Test.

9) Turn ignition off and wait 10 seconds. With same connections as in step **8)**, set DVOM on 200K ohm scale. Measure resistance between box pin 47 to pins 26 and 57. If either is less than 10K ohms, repair short in harness and repeat Quick Test. If both 10K ohms or more, replace ECA and repeat Quick Test.

10) Code 63. ECA connected and breakout box disconnected. Turn ignition off and wait 10 seconds. Disconnect TPS and inspect. Place DVOM on 20 volt scale. Turn ignition on. Measure voltage of TPS harness from voltage reference circuit to throttle position circuit. If reading is 4-6 volts, go to step **11)**. If less than 4 volts, go to step **13)**. If 6 volts or more, go to Test C.

11) Turn ignition off and wait 10 seconds. TPS disconnected. Disconnect 60-pin connector at ECA, inspect and repair as required. With DVOM on 200K ohm scale, connect 1 lead to throttle position signal circuit of TPS harness and other lead to ground. If reading less than 10K ohms, repair short circuit and repeat Quick Test. If 10K ohms or more, go to step **12)**.

12) Turn ignition off and wait 10 seconds. TPS disconnected. Insert jumper wire into TPS harness between voltage reference circuit and throttle position signal circuit. Perform Key On-Engine Off Self-Test. If code 53, replace throttle position sensor and repeat Quick Test. If no code 53, replace ECA.

13) Turn ignition off and wait 10 seconds. Disconnect 60-pin connector at ECA and inspect. Connect breakout box and connect ECA to breakout box (TPS disconnected). With DVOM on 200 ohm scale, measure continuity of TPS harness from throttle position signal circuit to box pin 47 and from voltage reference signal circuit to box pin 26. If either is 5 ohms or more, repair circuit, reconnect TPS, remove breakout box and repeat Quick Test. If less than 5 ohms, replace ECA, reconnect TPS, remove breakout box and repeat Quick Test.

14) Code 73. Code 73 indicates sensor did not exceed 25 percent of its rotation during Engine Response Check. Turn ignition off. Connect breakout box (TPS and ECA connected). With DVOM on 20 volt scale, measure voltage between box pins 47 and 46. Perform Engine Running Self-Test. If DVOM exceeds 3.5 volts during wide open throttle of Engine Response Check, replace ECA and repeat Quick Test. If less than 3.5 volts, verify TPS is properly mounted. If mounting is okay, replace TPS and repeat Quick Test.

15) Continuous code 53. Using Continuous Monitor Mode, observe volt/ohmmeter for fault indication while doing the following: Move throttle slowly to wide open position. Slowly release throttle to closed position and lightly tap on TPS to simulate road shock. Wiggle TPS harness connector. If a fault is indicated, go to step **16)**. If no fault indicated, go to step **19)**.

16) Turn ignition off and wait 10 seconds. Disconnect 60-pin connector at ECA and inspect. Connect breakout box and reconnect ECA. With DVOM on 20 volt scale, connect leads between box pins 47 and 46. Turn ignition on. While observing DVOM, repeat step **15)**. If fault is indicated below 4.25 volts, disconnect and inspect harness connectors. If okay, replace TPS and repeat Quick Test. If fault does not occur, TPS overtravel may have caused Continuous Code 53. Sensor service not required. Proceed to step **17)** to verify harness integrity.

TEST G (Cont.)

17) Turn ignition off and wait 10 seconds. Remove breakout box, reconnect ECA and TPS. Watch volt/ohmmeter while doing the following: Beginning at TPS, wiggle, shake or bend small sections of harness while working way to dash panel. Then repeating process from panel to ECA. If fault is indicated, isolate and repair problem and repeat Quick Test. If no fault indicated, go to step **18)**.

18) Turn ignition off and wait 10 seconds. Disconnect 60-pin connector at ECA and inspect both harness connector and ECA connector for damage or faults. If damaged, repair as required and repeat Quick Test. If no damage or fault, unable to duplicate fault at this time. Continuous Code 53 test complete.

19) Continuous Monitor Code 63. Using Continuous Monitor Mode, observe volt/ohmmeter for fault indication while doing the following: Move throttle slowly to wide open position. Slowly release throttle to closed position and lightly tap on TPS to simulate road shock. Wiggle TPS harness connector. If a fault is indicated, disconnect and inspect harness connectors. If connectors and terminals okay, replace TPS and repeat Quick Test. If no fault indicated, go to step **20)**.

20) Turn ignition off and wait 10 seconds. Watch volt/ohmmeter while doing the following: Beginning at TPS, wiggle, shake or bend small sections of harness while working way to dash panel. Then repeating process from panel to ECA. If fault is indicated, isolate and repair problem and repeat Quick Test. If no fault indicated, go to step **21)**.

21) Turn ignition off and wait 10 seconds. Disconnect 60-pin connector at ECA and inspect for damage or fault. If terminals and pins are damaged, repair as required and repeat Quick Test. If no damage, fault cannot be duplicated at this time. Continuous Code 63 test complete.

Throttle Position Sensor (TPS) Circuit

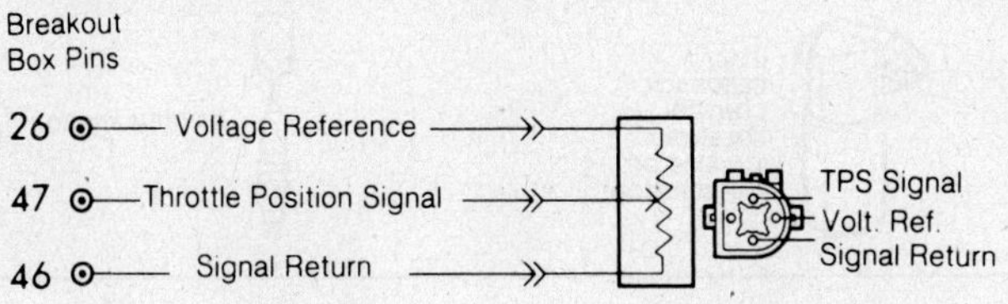

TEST H

IDLE TRACKING SWITCH (ITS)

1) If code 58 is present, go to step **2)**. If code 68 is present, go to step **5)**.

2) Code 58. Turn ignition off and wait 10 seconds. Press on ISC motor shaft to simulate throttle contact. With pressure on ISC motor shaft, perform Key On-Engine Off Self-Test and note codes. If code 68 is present, go to Test K, step **4)**. If code 68 is not present, go to step **3)**. Ignore all other codes at this time.

3) Turn ignition off and wait 10 seconds. Disconnect harness at ISC motor. Perform Key On-Engine Off Self-Test. If code 68 is present, replace ISC DC motor and repeat Quick Test. If code 68 is not present, go to step **4)**.

4) Turn ignition off and wait 10 seconds. Disconnect 60-pin connector at ECA and inspect. Connect breakout box and leave ECA disconnected. With harness disconnected at ISC, place DVOM on 200K ohm scale. Measure resistance from box pin 28 to pins 40, 46 and 60 in turn. If any resistance less than 10K ohms, service short to ground and repeat Quick Test. If all are 10K ohms or more, replace ECA and repeat Quick Test.

5) Code 68. Turn ignition off and wait 10 seconds. Move throttle away from ISC DC motor shaft. Perform Key On-Engine Off Self-Test. If code 68 present, go to step **6)**. If no code 68, go to Test K, step **4)**. Ignore all other codes at this time.

6) Turn ignition off and wait 10 seconds. Disconnect harness at ISC motor. Connect jumper wire between pins 3 and 4 of ISC harness connector (signal return and idle tracking switch circuits). DO NOT short any other pins. Perform Key On-Engine Off Self-Test. If code 68 is present, go to next step. If no code 68, replace ISC DC motor and repeat Quick Test.

TEST H (Cont.)

7) Turn ignition off and wait 10 seconds. Disconnect 60-pin connector at ECA and inspect. Connect breakout box and leave ECA disconnected. With DVOM on 200 ohm scale, measure continuity from box pin 46 to pin 28. If either is 5 ohms or more, service faulty circuit and repeat Quick Test. If both less than 5 ohms, replace ECA and repeat Quick Test.

Idle Tracking Switch Circuit

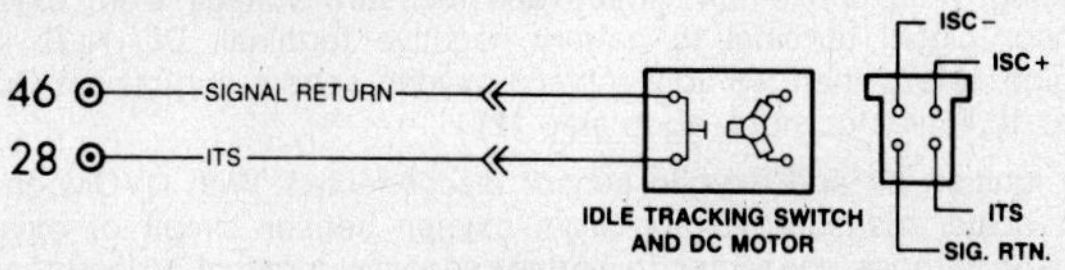

TEST I

FUEL CONTROL TEST (FBC)

1) Code 41. If engine ran for more than 2 minutes before performing Engine Running Self-Test, go to next step. If engine did not run for more than 2 minutes, prepare vehicle and perform Engine Running Self-Test.

2) Before continuing test, check oxygen sensor connection and ground for good connections. Check intake and exhaust manifolds for leaks. If all okay, go to step **3)**. If not okay, repair problem and repeat Engine Running Self-Test.

3) Turn ignition off and wait 10 seconds. Disconnect 60-pin connector at ECA and inspect. Disconnect oxygen sensor harness. With DVOM on 200K ohm scale, measure resistance from oxygen sensor signal circuit of oxygen sensor harness connector to vehicle battery negative terminal. If less than 10K ohms, repair short circuit and repeat Quick Test. If 10K ohms or more, go to step **3)**.

4) Turn ignition off. Reconnect ECA and oxygen sensor. Disconnect thermactor and cap air supply hose at air pump. Perform Engine Running Self-Test. Because thermactor hose is disconnected, code 11 does not indicate a pass. Treat code 11 as a code 44. If code 41 is present, leave thermactor hose disconnected and go to step **5)**. If code 44 is present, perform Engine Running Self-Test. Ignore all other codes at this time.

5) Turn ignition off and wait 10 seconds. With thermactor hose disconnected, disconnect harness at FCS. Perform Engine Running Self-Test. If no code 41, go to step **7)**. If code 41, go to step **6)**. Ignore all other codes at this time.

6) Turn ignition off and wait 10 seconds. With FCS and thermactor hose disconnected, start and run engine at part throttle for 2 minutes. Turn ignition off and wait 10 seconds. Perform Engine Running Self-Test while holding choke 3/4 closed. DO NOT stall engine. If code 41, reconnect all disconnected components and go to step **10)**. If no code 41, replace FCS and repeat Engine Running Self-Test. If code 41 still present, service carburetor.

7) Turn ignition off and wait 10 seconds. Reconnect thermactor hose and FCS. Disconnect 60-pin connector at ECA and inspect. Connect breakout box and leave ECA disconnected. With DVOM on 200K ohm scale, measure resistance from box pin 58 to pins 20, 40 and 46 in turn. If any less than 10K ohms, repair short circuit and repeat Quick Test. If all readings 10K ohms or more, go to step **8)**.

8) Turn ignition off. With breakout box installed, connect ECA to breakout box. Start and run vehicle at part throttle for 2 minutes. Turn ignition off and wait 10 seconds. Perform Engine Running Self-Test while holding choke 3/4 closed. DO NOT stall engine. If no code 41, go to step **9)**. If code 41, replace FCS. Remove breakout box, reconnect FCS and ECA and repeat Quick Test.

9) Turn ignition off and wait 10 seconds. With breakout box installed and ECA connected, disconnect harness at FCS. With DVOM on 2K ohm scale, measure resistance from feedback circuit of FCS harness connector to battery negative terminal. Then measure from vehicle power circuit of FCS harness connector to battery negative terminal. If either reading is less than 1,000 ohms, replace FCS and repeat Quick Test. If both readings are 1,000 ohms or more, remove breakout box, replace ECA, and repeat Quick Test.

FORD ELECTRONIC ENGINE CONTROL IV (Cont.)

TEST I (Cont.)

10) Turn ignition off and wait 10 seconds. With thermactor and FCS connected, disconnect harness at oxygen sensor. With DVOM on 200K ohm scale, measure resistance from oxygen sensor circuit of oxygen sensor harness connector to battery negative terminal. If less than 10K ohms, replace ECA and repeat Quick Test. If 10K ohms or more, go to step **11)**.

11) Turn ignition off. With oxygen sensor disconnected, start and run engine for 2 minutes. Place DVOM on 20 volt scale. With engine running, hold choke 3/4 closed and measure voltage from oxygen sensor pigtail terminal to battery negative terminal. DO NOT stall engine. If less than .45 volt, replace oxygen sensor and repeat Quick Test. If .45 volt or more, go to step **12)**.

12) Ignition on and oxygen sensor disconnected. With DVOM on 20 volt scale, measure voltage from oxygen sensor circuit of oxygen sensor harness connector to battery negative terminal. If less than 2 volts, go to step **13)**. If 2 volts or more, repair short circuit and repeat Quick Test.

13) Turn ignition off and wait 10 seconds. Disconnect 60-pin connector at ECA and inspect. Connect breakout box and leave ECA disconnected. Disconnect oxygen sensor. With DVOM on 200 ohm scale, measure resistance from oxygen sensor circuit of oxygen sensor harness connector to box pin 29. Then measure from box pin 49 to pins 40 and 60. If all readings less than 5 ohms, replace ECA and repeat Quick Test. If any 5 ohms or more, repair open circuit and repeat Quick Test.

14) Code 42. If choke functions properly without sticking or binding, go to step **14)**. If not, service choke assembly and repeat Quick Test.

15) Start and run engine at part throttle for 2 minutes. Turn ignition off and wait 10 seconds. Disconnect harness at oxygen sensor and jumper oxygen sensor circuit of oxygen sensor harness connector to ground. Perform Engine Running Self-Test. If code 41, go to step **16)**. If no code 41, go to step **22)**. Ignore all other codes.

16) Turn ignition off and wait 10 seconds. Reconnect oxygen sensor. Disconnect 7/32" vacuum line at intake manifold vacuum tree. Perform Engine Running Self-Test. If engine stalls, repeat test while manually maintaining engine speed at about 1500 RPM. If code 42 still present, replace oxygen sensor and repeat Quick Test. If code 42 not present, go to step **17)**. Ignore all other codes.

17) Turn ignition off and wait 10 seconds. Reconnect vacuum hose at intake manifold vacuum tree. Disconnect FCS and place DVOM on 200 ohm scale. Measure resistance between terminals on FCS. If resistance is 15-30 ohms, reconnect FCS and go to next step. If not 15-30 ohms, replace FCS and repeat Quick Test.

18) Turn ignition off and wait 10 seconds. Enter Output State Check. Place DVOM on 20 volt scale. Perform Key On-Engine Off Self-Test until end of Continuous code display. DVOM will indicate 0 volts. Depress and release throttle. If DVOM indicated high voltage, remain in Output State Check and go to next step. If DVOM did not indicate high voltage, depress throttle to wide open position and release. If voltage still does not go high, go to Test D, step **13)**.

19) While in Output State Check, turn ignition on and place DVOM on 20 volt scale. Connect DVOM between feedback circuit of FCS connector and battery negative terminal. While observing DVOM, depress and release throttle several times to cycle output on and off. If FCS cycles on and off, go to Test K. If FCS does not cycle on and off, exit Output State Check and go to step **20)**.

20) Turn ignition off and wait 10 seconds. Deactivate Quick Test and disconnect harness at FCS. With DVOM on 20 volt scale, turn ignition on. Measure voltage from voltage power circuit of FCS harness connector to battery negative terminal. If less than 10 volts, reconnect FCS, repair open circuit and repeat Quick Test. If 10 volts or more, go to step **21)**.

21) Turn ignition off and wait 10 seconds. Disconnect harness at FCS. Disconnect 60-pin connector at ECA and inspect. Connect breakout box and leave ECA disconnected. With DVOM on 200 ohm scale, measure resistance from feedback circuit of FCS harness to box pin 58. If less than 5 ohms, replace ECA and repeat Quick Test. If 5 ohms or more, repair open circuit and repeat Quick Test.

22) Turn ignition off and wait 10 seconds. Reconnect oxygen sensor. Disconnect 60-pin connector at ECA and inspect. Connect breakout box and leave ECA disconnected. Turn ignition on. With DVOM on 20 volt scale, measure voltage from box pin 29 to battery negative terminal. If less than .4 volt, replace ECA and repeat Quick Test. If

TEST I (Cont.)

code 42 still present, go to Test K. If .4 volt or more, repair short circuit and repeat Quick Test.

23) Code 43. Start and run engine at 2000 RPM for 2 minutes. Perform Engine Running Self-Test. If code 43, go to step **24)**. If no code 43, service other codes as necessary.

24) If there are any leaks at intake manifold or inlet pipe, repair as required and repeat Quick Test. If okay, go to step **25)**.

25) Start engine and allow to idle. If idle quality weakens and remains poor during and after Quick Test, service carburetor. If not, replace oxygen sensor and repeat Quick Test.

EGR Valve Position (EVP) Sensor Circuit

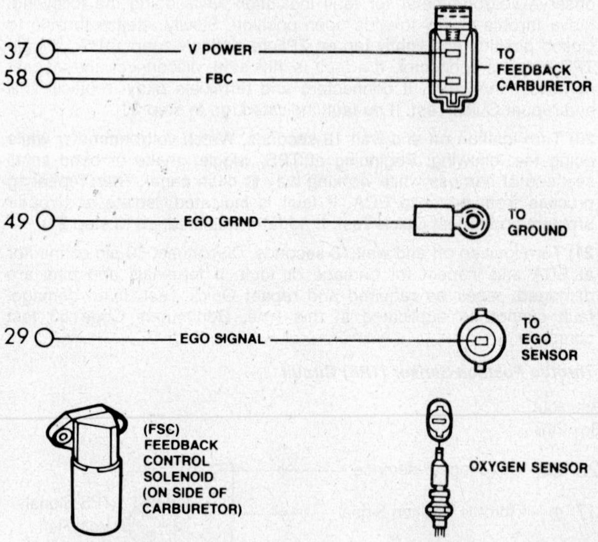

TEST J

FUEL CONTROL TEST (EFI)

1) Code 41. Connect tachometer and run engine at 2000 rpm. Disconnect ISC and use throttle body stop screw to set engine speed. Disconnect and reconnect injectors one at a time. Note rpm drop for each injector. Each injector should drop 150 rpm for 2.3L EFI models and a 50 rpm drop for 5.0L EFI models.

2) If okay, problem is with area common to all cylinders (air leak, vacuum leak etc.). Repair injection system as necessary. If test is not okay, replace faulty injector and repeat Quick Test. Reset curb idle. Check VECI decal for proper specifications.

3) Code 42. Turn key off and wait 10 seconds. If code does not set, go to step **4)**. Check for fuel contamination in engine oil, ignition caused misfire or CANP problems. Disconnect vehicle harness at EGO sensor. Using a jumper wire, ground EGO harness at EGO sensor-to-engine block. Repeat Engine Running Self-Test.

4) Code 41 EGO Harness Check. Turn key off and wait 10 seconds. Install breakout box and measure resistance between test pin 49 and EGO ground at engine block. Measure resistance between test pin 29 and EGO harness connector. If both circuits are less than 5 ohms, disconnect processor connector. Inspect for damage or corrosion. If okay, replace processor and repeat Quick Test. If not okay, repair harness circuit and repeat Quick Test.

5) Code 41. Place DVOM on 20 volt scale. With EGO sensor disconnected from harness, connect DVOM from EGO sensor to engine ground. Disconnct PCV hose and run engine at approximately 2000 rpm. If DVOM reads less than .4 volt within one minute, EGO sensor is okay. Go to step **1)**. If reading is more than .4 volt, replace EGO sensor and repeat Quick Test.

TEST J (Cont.)

6) Code 41. Check for vacuum/air leaks first. If okay, turn key off and place DVOM on 20 volt scale. Disconnect EGO sensor from vehicle harness. Connect DVOM to EGO sensor and engine ground. Disconnect ACT sensor. Start engine and run at approximately 2000 rpm. If DVOM reading is greater than .5 volt in one minute, go to step **7)**. If reading is less than .5 volt in one minute, replace EGO sensor and repeat Quick Test.

7) Turn key off. Install breakout box and disconnect processor. Measure resistance between test pin 49 and engine block ground. Check resistance between EGO connector and test pin 29. If both circuits have than 5 ohms resistance, go to step **8)**. If circuits have more than 5 ohms resistance, repair harness as necessary and repeat Quick Test.

8) Turn key off. Install breakout box and disconnect processor. Set DVOM to 200k ohms range. Measure resistance between test pin 29 and test pin 40. If reading is more than 10K ohms, go to step **9)**. If reading is less than 10K ohms, correct cause of resistance to ground. Repeat Quick Test.

9) To eliminate code 41, turn key off. Reconnect EGO sensor. Make certain that ACT sensor is still disconnected. Start engine and run at approximately 2000 rpm for one minute. Allow engine to return to idle. Perform Engine Running Self-Test. If code is still present, inspect for corrosion or damaged connector pins. If okay, replace processor and repeat Quick Test.

10) Continuous Testing: Code 41/42. If code 41 is displayed, EGO indicated the fuel system was lean for more than 15 seconds when the system should have been in "Closed Loop" fuel control. When system is in "Closed Loop", the fuel control is under the influence of the EGO sensor. When system is in "Open Loop", fuel control is not under the influence of the EGO sensor.

11) Check the following areas for a continuous code 41 or 42:
- Check for unmetered air (vacuum or intake leaks, canister purge system, PCV system etc.).
- EGO is fuel fouled.
- Check fuel pressure. Perform step **1)** test.
- Check ignition system.
- Check TP sensor. Connect DVOM to test pin 47 and to pin 46. Turn ignition switch to "RUN" position. Observe DVOM while moving throttle. Reading must increase in throttle opening. If not correct, replace components as necessary.

12) Turn key off. Set DVOM on 200 ohm scale. Measure resistance between run circuit and ground on heated EGO (HEGO) connector (at room temperature). If reading is between 2.5 and 5.0 ohms, go to step **13)**. If reading is less than 2.5 or greater than 5.0 ohms, replace HEGO sensor.

14) Check continuity of ground to HEGO connector. Turn key off, wait 10 seconds. Set DVOM on 200 ohm scale. Measure resistance of ground cicuit from HEGO connector to battery ground. If reading is less than 5.0 ohms, repair open in run circuit. If reading is more than 5.0 ohms, repair open in ground circuit.

If engine ran for more than 2 minutes before performing Engine Running Self-Test, go to next step. If engine did not run for more than 2 minutes, prepare vehicle and perform Engine Running Self-Test.

Fuel Control Circuit

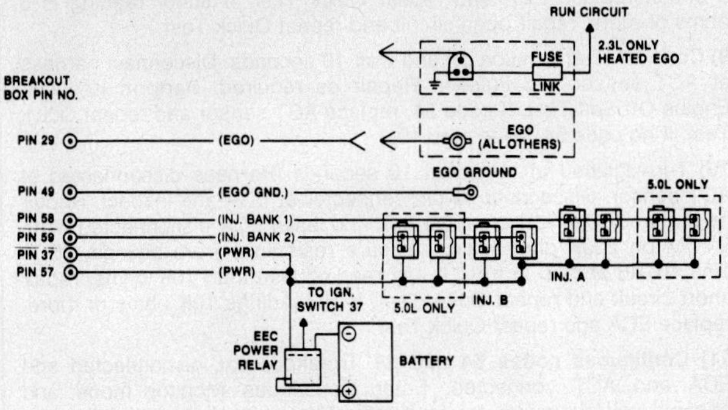

TEST K

IDLE SPEED CONTROL (ISC DC MOTOR)

1) Code 12. If code 58 is also present, go to Test H. If code 58 is not present, go to next step.

2) If code 31 present, go to Test I. If code 41 present, go to Test J. If no code 31 and/or 41, go to step **3)**.

3) Check throttle plates and linkage for binding. Check speed control (if equipped) for binding. If okay, go to step **4)**. If not okay, service as required and repeat Quick Test.

4) Turn ignition off and wait 10 seconds. Disconnect 60-pin connector at ECA and inspect. Connect breakout box and leave ECA disconnected. Disconnect harness at ISC motor. With DVOM on 200 ohm scale, check continuity from box pin 41 to negative ISC circuit and from box pin 21 to positive ISC circuit at ISC harness connector. If both are less than 5 ohms, go to step **5)**. If either 5 ohms or more, repair faulty circuit and repeat Quick Test.

5) Turn ignition on. Breakout box connected and ECA and ISC disconnected. With DVOM on 20 volt scale, measure voltage from box pin 41 to pins 40 and 60. Then measure from box pin 21 to pins 40 and 60. If all less than one volt, go to step **6)**. If one volt or more, repair short circuit and repeat Quick Test. If code 12 still present, replace ECA.

6) Turn ignition off and wait 10 seconds. Breakout box connected and ECA and ISC disconnected. With DVOM on 200K ohm scale, measure resistance from box pin 41 to pins 40, 46 and 60 in turn. Then measure resistance from box pin 21 to pins 40, 46 and 60 in turn. If all 10K ohms or more, go to next step. If any 10K ohms or less, repair faulty circuit and repeat Quick Test. If code 12 still present, replace ECA.

7) Turn ignition off and wait 10 seconds. Breakout box connected and ECA and ISC disconnected. With DVOM on 20 volt scale, connect positive lead to box pin 1 and negative lead to ground. If 10.5 volts or more, go to step **8)**. If less than 10.5 volts, repair open in circuit No. 37 and repeat Quick Test. If code 12 still present, go to step **8)**.

8) Turn ignition off and wait 10 seconds. Breakout box connected and ECA disconnected. Connect harness at ISC DC motor. Insert jumper wires between box pins 21 and 1 and between box pin 41 and ground. If ISC motor shaft extends 2" (51 mm), go to step **9)**. If not, replace DC motor and repeat Quick Test.

9) Turn ignition off and wait 10 seconds. Breakout box connected and ECA disconnected. Insert jumper wires between box pins 41 and 1 and between box pin 21 and ground. If ISC motor shaft retracts, go to step **10)**. If not, replace DC motor and repeat Quick Test.

10) Turn ignition off and wait 10 seconds. Breakout box connected and ECA disconnected. Insert jumper wires as outlined in step **8)**. If motor shaft extends, replace ECA and repeat Quick Test. If not, replace DC motor and repeat Quick Test.

11) Code 13. Deactivate Self-Test and prepare vehicle for normal engine operation. Turn A/C on, if equipped. Start engine. Run for 3 minutes while alternating between idle for 30 seconds and part throttle for 5 seconds. If idle speed is erratic, check and repair vacuum leaks and service codes 22, 31, 41 and 58 before continuing. If idle speed is not erratic, go to next step.

12) Connect test equipment and perform Engine Running Self-Test. If code 13, go to step **13)**. If no code 13, repair other codes as required.

13) Check choke and throttle linkage for sticking or binding. Check to ensure throttle is not stuck on high step of cam. Repair as required and repeat Quick Test. If no binding or sticking, go to step **14)**.

14) Perform Key On-Engine Off Self-Test. Record On Demand codes. If code 68, go to Test H, step **5)**. If no code 68, check anti-diesel speed adjustment.

Idle Speed Control (DC Motor) Circuit

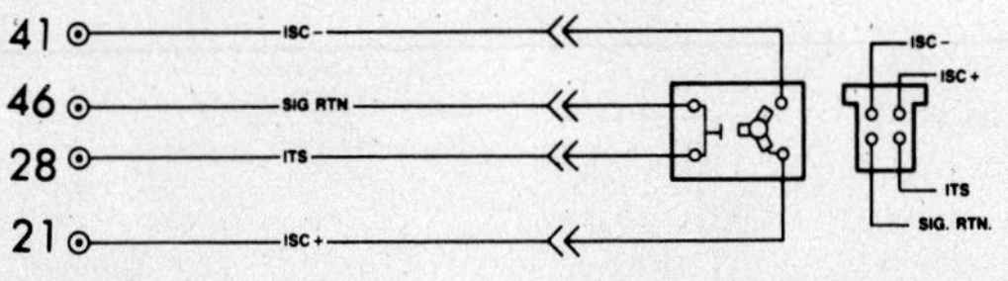

TEST L

CANISTER PURGE TEST

1) With ignition key off, wait 10 seconds. Set DVOM on 200 ohm scale, disconnect CANP solenoid connector and measure solenoid resistance. If resistance is between 40-90 ohms, connect CANP solenoid and proceed to step **2)**. If resistance is less than 40 ohms or greater than 90 ohms, replace CANP solenoid and repeat test.

2) With ignition key off, wait 10 seconds. Set DVOM on 20 volt scale, connect negative lead to STO and positive lead to battery positive. Jumper STI to signal return. Enter Output State Check (Perform Key On-Engine Off Self-Test until completion of the continuous test codes). DVOM will indicate 0 volts, depress and release throttle. If a high voltage reading was obtained, remain in output state check and go to step **3)**. If a high voltage reading was not obtained, depress throttle to WOT and release. If STO voltage does not go to a high reading, go to test D, step **13)**.

3) Leave equipment hooked up and DVOM on 20 volt scale. Connect positive test lead to VPWR on CANP solenoid and negative lead to CANP output circuit. Depress and release the throttle several times while watching DVOM, this will cycle output on and off. If CANP output cycles on and off, go to step **4)**. If CANP does not cycle on and off, remove jumper and go to step **5)**.

4) With ignition key off, wait 10 seconds. Remove jumper wire from STI to signal return. Disconnect vacuum hose at canister purge solenoid at PCV side and apply 16 in. Hg vacuum to CANP solenoid. If CANP solenoid holds vacuum for 20 seconds, EEC-IV system is OK, check fuel system. If the CANP solenoid does not hold vacuum for 20 seconds, replace CANP solenoid and repeat test. If code 42 is still present, check fuel system.

5) With key on, engine off, connect DVOM (scale set on 20 volts) positive test lead to VPWR and negative lead to ground. If CANP solenoid voltage is less than 10.5 volts, service harness open circuit and repeat Quick Test. If CANP solenoid voltage is 10.5 volts or greater go to step **6)**.

6) With key off, wait 10 seconds. Disconnect ECA, inspect both 60-pin connectors, and service as necessary. Connect breakout box to harness and leave ECA disconnected. Measure continuity from test pin 35 to CANP at harness connector with DVOM on 200 ohm scale. If reading is 5 ohms or greater, service open circuit and repeat Quick Test. If reading is less than 5 ohms go to step **7)**.

7) With key off, wait 10 seconds. Breakout box installed (ECA disconnected). With DVOM on 200K ohm scale and CANP solenoid disconnected, measure resistance from test pin 35 to test pins 37 and 57. If resistance is 10K ohms or greater go to next step. If resistance is less than 10K ohms, service short to power and repeat Quick Test.

8) With key off, wait 10 seconds. Leave breakout box installed and ECA disconnected. With DVOM on 200K ohm scale, measure resistance of test pin 35 to test pins 40, 46, and 60. If resistance is less than 10K ohms, service short to ground and repeat Quick Test. If resistance is 10K ohms or greater, remove breakout box, replace ECA and repeat Quick Test.

Canister Purge Solenoid Circuit

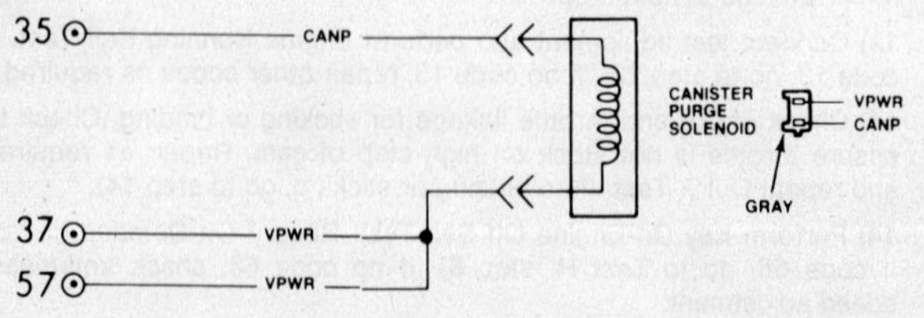

TEST M

AIR CHARGE TEMPERATURE (ACT) SENSOR

NOTE: Ambient air temperature must be greater than 50°F (10°C) for this test.

1) Code 24. For vehicles with ACT sensor mounted in intake manifold, go to step **2)**. On all other models, if sensor is properly mounted in air cleaner, go to step **2)**. If sensor is not properly mounted, install properly and repeat Quick Test.

2) Turn ignition off and wait 10 seconds. Disconnect harness at ACT and check for damaged pins or corrosion. Repair as required. Turn ignition on (engine off). With DVOM on 20 volt scale, measure voltage from ACT signal circuit and signal return circuit of sensor harness. If reading is 4-6 volts, go to step **5)**. If reading is less than 4 volts, go to step **3)**. If reading is greater than 6 volts, go to Test C.

3) Turn ignition off and wait 10 seconds. Harness disconnected at ACT sensor. Disconnect 60-pin connector at ECA. Connect breakout box and leave ECA disconnected. With DVOM on 200 ohm scale, measure resistance from box pin 26 to ACT signal circuit of sensor connector. Then measure resistance from box pin 46 to signal return circuit of sensor connector. If both readings less than 5 ohms, go to step **4)**. If either reading 5 ohms or more, repair open circuit and repeat Quick Test.

4) Turn ignition off. Breakout box connected and ECA and ACT disconnected. With DVOM on 200K ohm scale, measure resistance from box pin 25 to pins 40, 46 and 60 in turn. If any reading less than 10K ohms, repair short circuits and repeat Quick Test. If all readings are 10K ohms or more, go to step **5)**.

5) Remove breakout box and reconnect all connectors. Warm engine to normal operating temperature. Turn ignition off and wait 10 seconds. Disconnect harness at ACT sensor. With DVOM on 200K ohm scale, measure resistance of sensor. If 1100-58K ohms (at about 50°F/10°C), go to next step. If less than 1100 ohms or more than 58K ohms, check heat stove duct valve operation. If duct valve operation is okay, replace sensor and repeat Quick Test.

6) Turn ignition off. With harness disconnected at ACT sensor, start and run engine for 2 minutes. With DVOM on 200K ohm scale, measure resistance of sensor while engine is running. If reading is 2400-29K ohms, replace ECA and repeat Quick Test. If reading is less than 2400 ohms or greater than 29K ohms, check heat stove duct valve operation. If duct valve operation is okay, replace sensor and repeat Quick Test.

7) Code 54. Turn ignition off and wait 10 seconds. Disconnect harness at ACT sensor and inspect for damage. Repair as required. Insert jumper wire between ACT signal circuit and signal return circuit of harness. Perform Key On-Engine Off Self-Test. If code 64 present, replace sensor and repeat Quick Test. If no code 64, remove jumper wire and go to step **8)**.

8) Turn ignition off and wait 10 seconds. ACT connector disconnected. Disconnect 60-pin connector at ECA and inspect for damage. Repair as required. Connect breakout box and leave ECA disconnected. With DVOM on 200 ohm scale, measure resistance between box pin 25 and ACT signal circuit of ACT harness. Then measure between box pin 46 and signal return circuit of ACT harness. If both readings are less than 5 ohms, replace ECA and repeat Quick Test. If either reading is 5 ohms or more, repair open circuit and repeat Quick Test.

9) Code 64. Turn ignition off and wait 10 seconds. Disconnect harness at ACT sensor and inspect. Repair as required. Perform Key On-Engine Off Self-Test. If code 54, replace ACT sensor and repeat Quick Test. If no code 54, go to step **10)**.

10) Turn ignition off and wait 10 seconds. Harness disconnected at ACT sensor. Disconnect 60-pin connector at ECA and inspect. Repair as required. Connect breakout box and leave ECA disconnected. With DVOM on 200K ohm scale, measure resistance from box pin 25 to pins 40, 46 and 60 in turn. If any reading less than 10K ohms, repair short circuit and repeat Quick Test. If all readings 10K ohms or more, replace ECA and repeat Quick Test.

11) Continuous codes 54 and 64. Breakout box disconnected and ECA and ACT connected. Enter Continuous Monitor mode and observe volt/ohmmeter for fault indication while doing the following: Lightly tap on ACT sensor to simulate road shock. Wiggle sensor connector. If fault is indicated, disconnect harness connectors at ACT and ECA. If connectors and terminals are okay, replace sensor and repeat Quick Test. If no fault indicated, go to step **12)**.

FORD ELECTRONIC ENGINE CONTROL IV (Cont.)

TEST M (Cont.)

12) Observe volt/ohmmeter while performing the following: Beginning at ACT, wiggle, shake or bend small sections of harness while working way to dash panel. Then repeating process from panel to ECA. If fault is indicated, isolate and repair problem and repeat Quick Test. If no fault indicated, go to step **13)**.

13) Turn ignition off and wait 10 seconds. Disconnect 60-pin connector at ECA and inspect connector and terminals for damage. If damaged, service as required and repeat Quick Test. If okay, fault cannot be duplicated at this time. Continuous Code 54 and 64 testing is complete.

Air Charge Temperature (ACT) Sensor Circuit

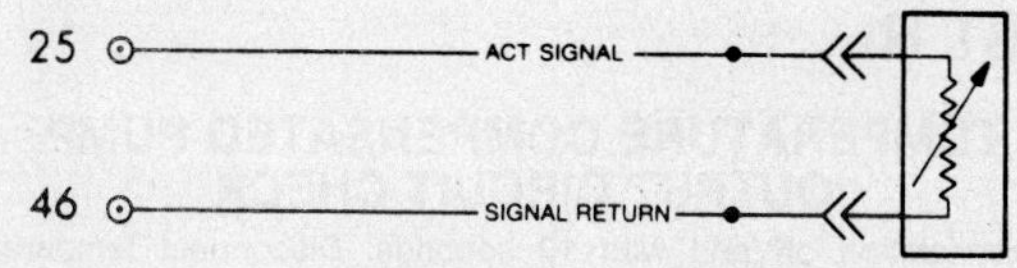

TEST N

NEUTRAL SWITCH-A/C INPUT TEST

4.9L Models Only

1) Turn ignition off and wait 10 seconds. Ensure heater and A/C off. Transmission in Neutral or "P". Disconnect 60-pin connector at ECA and inspect. Install breakout box and reconnect ECA. Turn ignition on and place DVOM on 200 ohm scale. Measure resistance test pin 30 (neutral input circuit) and VIP connector. If less than 5 ohms, proceed to step **3)**. If not, proceed to step **2)**.

2) Turn ignition off and wait 10 seconds. Disconnect processor 60 pin connnector and inspect for damaged pins, corrosion, loose wires. Repair as necessary. With breakout box installed and ECA connected. Reconnect processor and set DVOM on 20 volt scale. Connect positive test lead to test pin 30 and negative test lead to pin 46. Turn key on. Cycle octane switch several times while observing DVOM. If voltage changes from 0 to 5 volts, replace processor. Repeat Quick Test. If voltage does not change, EEC-IV system is okay.

3) Install breakout box. Turn key on. Set DVOM on 20 volt scale. Turn A/C control off. Measure voltage between test pin 10 (A/C clutch circuit) and chassis ground. If less than one volt, replace processor. Repeat Quick Test. If more than one volt, service short to power in A/C clutch circuit. Repeat Quick Test.

Neutral Drive-A/C Input Circuit

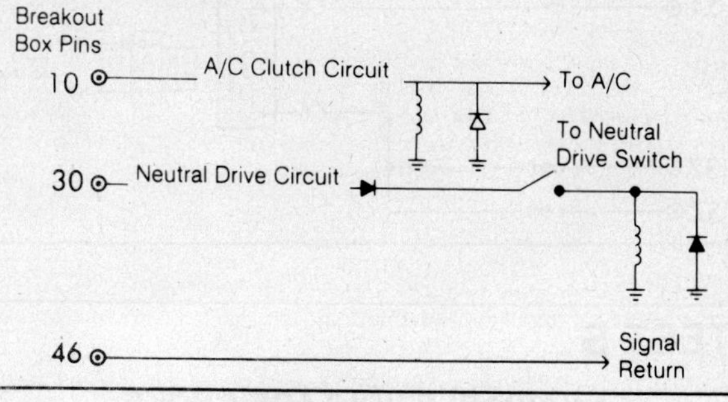

TEST O

AIR MANAGEMENT SYSTEM TEST

1) Codes 81 and 82. Check air and vacuum lines to TAB/TAD solenoids and by-pass diverter valve for blockage, leaks, restrictions and proper routing. Repair as required and repeat Quick Test. If lines okay, go to step **4)** for code 44; next step for code 45 and step **3)** for code 46.

TEST O (Cont.)

2) Disconnect and plug vacuum line at diverter valve. Turn ignition off and wait 10 seconds. Perform Engine Running Self-Test and record codes. If code 45 present, EEC system okay, repair diverter valve or check valve. If no code 45, go to step **3)**.

3) Disconnect and plug vacuum line at by-pass valve. Turn ignition off and wait 10 seconds. Perform Engine Running Self-Test and record codes. If code 46 present, EEC system okay, repair by-pass valve. If no code 46, go to step **4)**.

4) Turn ignition off and wait 10 seconds. Enter Output State Check and perform Key On-Engine Off Self-Test until end of Continuous code display. DVOM will indicate zero volts. Depress and release throttle and observe DVOM. If DVOM indicates high reading, remain in Output State Check and go to step **5)**. If DVOM does not indicate high reading, depress throttle to wide open position and release. If DVOM still does not indicate high reading, go to Test D, step **13)**. Leave equipment connected.

5) Disconnect vacuum line at TAB solenoid supply port and install vacuum pump. Disconnect vacuum line at TAB solenoid output port and install vacuum gauge. While maintaining vacuum on TAB solenoid, depress and release throttle to cycle output on and off and observe vacuum gauge. Repeat procedure for TAD solenoid. If both vacuum outputs cycled on and off, go to next step. If either vacuum output does not cycle on and off, replace TAB/TAD solenoid assembly and repeat Quick Test.

6) Disconnect TAB solenoid-to-thermactor valve vacuum hose. Connect vacuum pump and gauge and test hose for blockage and leaks. Repeat procedure for TAD solenoid-to-thermactor valve vacuum hose. Repair as required and repeat Quick Test. If vacuum lines okay, go to next step.

7) Disconnect vacuum lines at TAB/TAD solenoids and start engine. If vacuum is present, EEC system okay, service air pump or thermactor valve. If vacuum is not present, repair source of vacuum leak or blockage and repeat Quick Test.

Air Management System Circuit

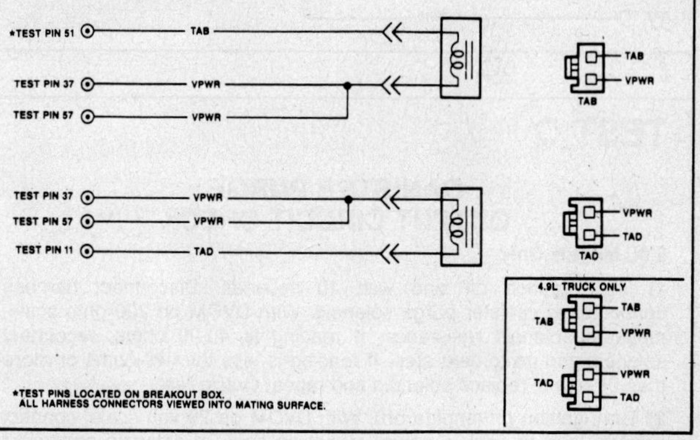

TEST P

EGR VENT & EGR CONTROL VALVE OUTPUT CIRCUIT CHECK

1) Codes 83 and 84. Turn ignition off and wait 10 seconds. Disconnect harness at EGR vent solenoid and EGR control solenoid. With DVOM on 200 ohm scale, measure resistance of solenoids. If both readings are 30-70 ohms, reconnect solenoids and go to next step. If either reading is less than 30 ohms or greater than 70 ohms, replace solenoid assembly and repeat Quick Test.

2) Turn ignition on (engine off). With DVOM on 20 volt scale, connect positive lead to vehicle power circuit of EGR vent solenoid harness and negative lead to good ground. Repeat test on EGR control solenoid harness. If both readings greater than 10.5 volts, go to next step. If either reading less than 10.5 volts, repair open circuit and repeat Quick Test.

FORD ELECTRONIC ENGINE CONTROL IV (Cont.)

TEST P (Cont.)

3) Turn ignition off and wait 10 seconds. Disconnect 60-pin connector at ECA and inspect. Repair as required. Connect breakout box and leave ECA disconnected. With DVOM on 200 ohm scale, measure continuity from box pin 33 to EGR vent circuit at EGR vent solenoid harness. Then measure from box pin 52 to EGR control circuit at EGR control solenoid harness. If both readings less than 5 ohms, go to step **4)**. If either reading 5 ohms or more, repair open circuit and repeat Quick Test.

4) Turn ignition off and wait 10 seconds. Disconnect harness at EGR vent solenoid and EGR control solenoid. Breakout box installed and ECA disconnected. With DVOM on 200K ohm scale, measure resistance from box pin 33 to pins 37 and 57. Then measure from box pin 52 to same pins. If any reading less than 10K ohms, repair short to power and repeat Quick Test. If any reading 10k ohms or more, go to step **5)**.

5) Turn ignition off and wait 10 seconds. Breakout box installed and ECA and EGR vent and EGR control solenoids disconnected. With DVOM on 200K ohm scale, measure resistance from box pin 33 to pins 40, 46 and 60 in turn. Then measure from box pin 52 to same pins. If any reading less than 10K ohms, repair short to ground and repeat Quick Test. If any reading 10K ohms or more, replace ECA and repeat Quick Test.

EGR Vent Solenoid & EGR Control Solenoid Circuits

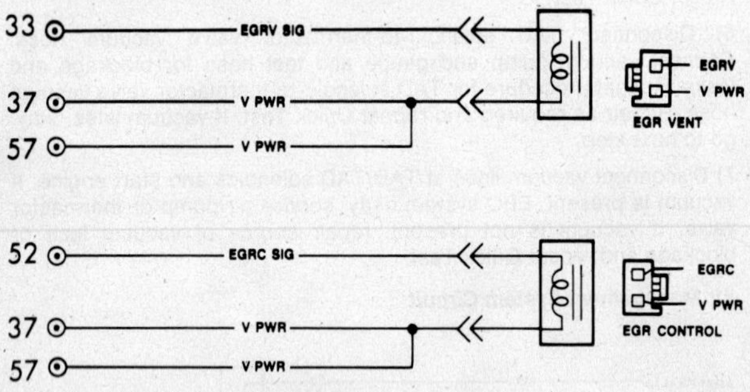

TEST Q

CANISTER PURGE OUTPUT CIRCUIT CHECK

2.8L Models Only

1) Turn ignition off and wait 10 seconds. Disconnect harness connector at canister purge solenoid. With DVOM on 200 ohm scale, measure solenoid resistance. If reading is 40-90 ohms, reconnect solenoid and go to next step. If reading is less than 40 ohms or more than 90 ohms, replace solenoid and repeat Quick Test.

2) Turn ignition on (engine off). With DVOM on 20 volt scale, connect positive lead to vehicle power circuit on back of solenoid connector and negative lead to ground. If reading is less than 10.5 volts, repair open circuit and repeat Quick Test. If reading is 10.5 volts or more, go to step **3)**.

3) Turn ignition off and wait 10 seconds. Disconnect 60-pin connector at ECA and inspect ECA and harness terminals. Repair as required. Connect breakout box and leave ECA disconnected. With DVOM on 200 ohm scale, measure continuity from box pin 35 to canister purge circuit on back of solenoid connector. If reading is 5 ohms or more, repair open circuit and repeat Quick Test. If reading is less than 5 ohms, go to step **4)**.

4) Turn ignition off and wait 10 seconds. Breakout box connected and ECA and canister purge solenoid disconnected. With DVOM on 200K ohm scale, measure resistance from box pin 35 to pins 37 and 57. If reading is 10K ohms or more, go to next step. If reading is less than 10K ohms, repair short to power and repeat Quick Test.

5) Turn ignition off and wait 10 seconds. Breakout box connected and ECA and canister purge solenoid disconnected. With DVOM on 200K ohm scale, measure resistance from box pin 35 to pins 40, 46 and 60 in turn. If readings are less than 10K ohms, repair short to ground and repeat Quick Test. If readings are 10K ohms or more, replace ECA and repeat Quick Test.

TEST Q (Cont.)

Canister Purge Output Circuit

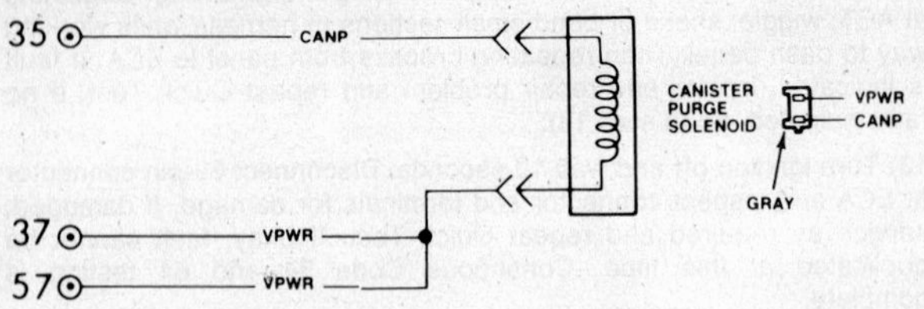

TEST R

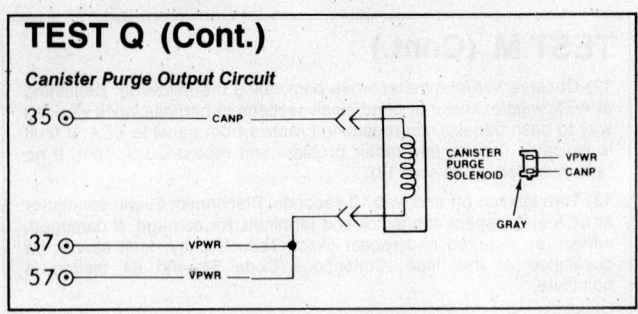

TEMPERATURE COMPENSATED PUMP OUTPUT CIRCUIT CHECK

1) Turn ignition off and wait 10 seconds. Disconnect temperature compensated accelerator pump solenoid harness connector. With DVOM on 200 ohm scale, measure resistance of solenoid. If resistance is between 50-100 ohms, reconnect solenoid and go to next step. If less than 50 ohms or greater than 100 ohms, replace solenoid and repeat Quick Test.

2) Turn ignition on (engine off). With DVOM on 20 volt scale, connect positive lead to vehicle power circuit of solenoid harness connector and negative lead to ground. If voltage is less than 10.5 volts, repair open circuit in harness and repeat Quick Test. If greater than 10.5 volts, go to step **3)**.

3) Turn ignition off and wait 10 seconds. Disconnect 60-pin connector at ECA and inspect for damage. Connect breakout box and leave ECA disconnected. With DVOM on 200 ohm scale, measure continuity from box pin 54 to TCP circuit at solenoid harness connector. If 5 ohms or greater, repair open circuit in harness and repeat Quick Test. If less than 5 ohms, go to next step.

4) Turn ignition off and wait 10 seconds. Breakout box installed (ECA and TCP solenoid disconnected). With DVOM on 200K ohm scale, measure resistance from box pin 54 to box pins 37 and 57. If resistance is 10K ohms or greater, go to next step. If less than 10K ohms, repair short circuit and repeat Quick Test.

5) Turn ignition off and wait 10 seconds. Breakout box installed (ECA and TCP solenoid disconnected). With DVOM on 200K ohm scale, measure resistance from box pin 54 to box pins 40, 46, and 60. If readings are less than 10K ohms, repair short to ground and repeat Quick Test. If readings are 10K ohms or greater, replace ECA and repeat Quick Test.

Temperature Compensated Accelerator Pump Output Circuit

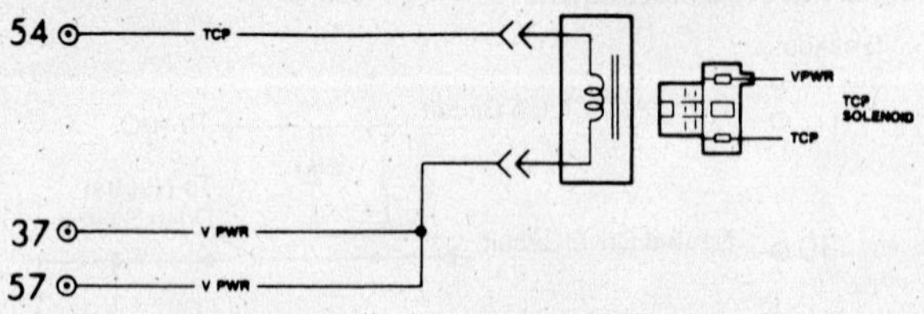

TEST S

VARIABLE VOLTAGE CHOKE OUTPUT CIRCUIT CHECK

1) With DVOM on 20V scale, perform Engine Running Self-Test. Measure choke voltage. If voltage is 10.5 volts or greater, check choke plates for binding and sticking (EEC-IV system operating properly). If choke voltage is less than 10.5 volts, go to step **2)**.

2) Turn ignition off and wait 10 seconds. With DVOM on 20V scale, connect negative test lead to STO and positive lead to battery positive. Jumper STI to signal return. Enter Output State Check (Perform Key On, Engine Off Self-Test until the completion of continuous test codes). DVOM will indicate zero volts. Depress and release throttle. If DVOM reading changed to high voltage, remain in Output State Check

TEST S (Cont.)

and go to next step. If not, depress throttle to wide open position and release. If voltage still does not go high, go to test D, step **13)**.

3) Ignition on (engine off). With DVOM on 20V scale, connect positive lead to V PWR on VCV relay and negative lead to VVC output circuit VVC. Depress and release throttle several times to cycle output on and off. If output cycles on and off, go to next step. If output does not cycle on and off, remain in Output State Check and go to step **5)**.

4) Turn ignition off and wait 10 seconds. DVOM should be on 200 ohm scale. Measure resistance of ground circuit from relay harness connector. Measure resistance of choke circuit from the relay harness connector to the choke. If either resistance is 5 or more ohms, service harness circuit and repeat Quick Test. If both resistances are 5 ohms or greater, replace choke relay and repeat Quick Test.

5) Ignition on (engine off). With DVOM on 20 volt scale, connect DVOM positive lead to vehicle power circuit at relay harness connector and negative lead to ground circuit at relay harness connector. If voltage is less than 10.5 volts, service open in choke power circuit and repeat Quick Test. If voltage is 10.5 volts or greater, go to step **6)**.

6) Turn ignition off and wait 10 seconds. Disconnect 60-pin connector at ECA and inspect. Connect breakout box and leave ECA disconnected. With DVOM on 200 ohm scale, measure continuity from box pin 55 to VVC circuit at harness relay connector. If resistance is 5 ohms or greater, repair harness circuit and repeat Quick Test. If resistance is less than 5 ohms, go to step **7)**.

7) Turn ignition off and wait 10 seconds. With DVOM on 200K ohm scale, leave breakout box installed and ECA disconnected. With VVC relay disconnected, measure resistance from box pin 55 to box pins 1, 37 and 57. If resistance is less than 10K ohms, repair short to power and repeat Quick Test. If greater than 10K ohms, go to step **8)**.

8) Turn ignition off and wait 10 seconds. Turn DVOM to 200K ohm scale. VVC relay should be connected. Leave breakout box installed and ECA disconnected. Measure resistance from box test pin 55 to pins 40, 46 and 60. If any resistance values are less than 10K ohms, replace ECA and repeat Quick Test. If readings are greater than 10K ohms, go to step **9)**.

9) Turn ignition off and wait 10 seconds. Leave breakout box installed and ECA disconnected. With DVOM on 200K scale, disconnect VVC relay. Measure resistance from box pin 55 to pins 40, 46 and 60. If all resistances are greater than 10K ohms, replace choke relay and repeat Quick Test. If any resistances are less than 10K ohms, repair harness short and repeat Quick Test.

Variable Voltage Choke Circuit Diagram

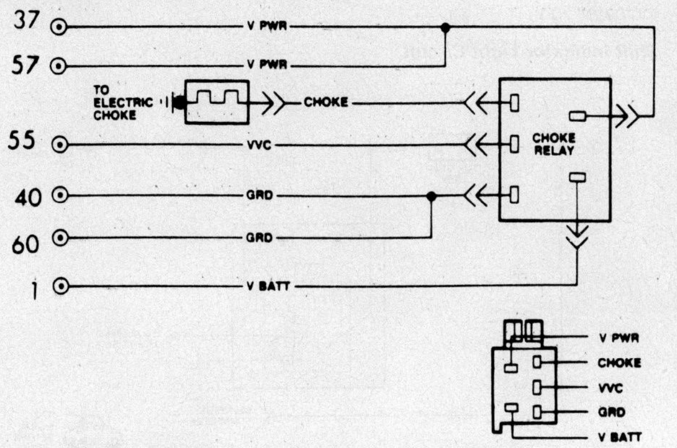

TEST T

SPARK TIMING CHECK

1) If spark advance was not 27-33° in Engine Running Self-Test, place system in Self-Test. After last Self-Test service code is displayed, system returns to normal after 2 minutes and spark timing will no longer be locked at 30°.

TEST T (Cont.)

2) Connect timing light to engine. Locate spark output circuit to TFI module and open the connection. Start engine and check base timing. Base timing is 7-13° BTDC. If timing is correct, go to step **3)**. If timing is not correct, reconnect spark output circuit and set base timing. After timing is adjusted, repeat Quick Test.

3) Turn ignition off and wait 10 seconds. Disconnect 60-pin connector at ECA and inspect. Connect breakout box. Turn ignition on. With DVOM on 20 volt scale, measure voltage from box pin 37 to pin 40 and from box pin 57 to pin 60. If either reading is less than 10.5 volts, perform Test B. If both readings are 10.5 volts or more, go to step **4)**.

4) Turn ignition off and wait 10 seconds. Disconnect harness connector at TFI module. With DVOM on 200 ohm scale, measure spark output circuit from spark output pin (pin 2) on TFI harness connector to box pin 36. If 5 ohms or less, continue to next step. If more than 5 ohms, repair open circuit. Check timing as described in step **1)**.

5) Install breakout box, leave TFI harness disconnected. With ignition off, place DVOM on 200 ohm scale. Measure resistance from box pin 16 to TFI harness connector ignition ground pin (pin 6). If less than 5 ohms, go to Test A, step **7)**. If 5 ohms or more, repair harness as required and repeat Quick Test.

Spark Advance Test Circuit

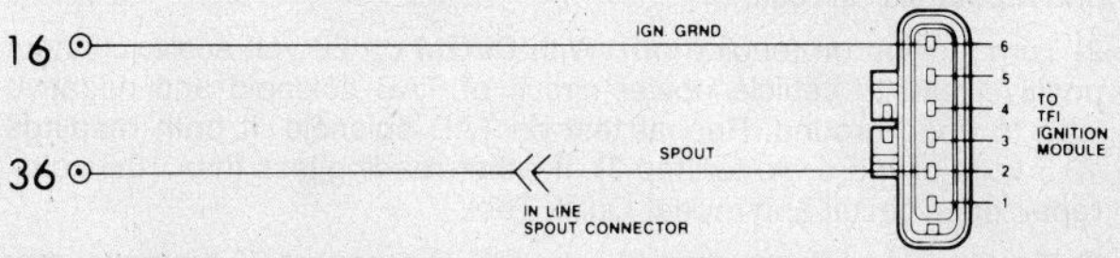

TEST U

KNOCK SENSOR

1) Code 25. Prepare vehicle for Engine Running Self-Test and have 4 oz. hammer ready. Tap on exhaust manifold above knock sensor when Dynamic Response Signal appears. Perform Engine Running Self-Test. Again tap on exhaust manifold when Dynamic Response Signal appears. Check for code 25 in about 15 seconds. If code 25, go to step **2)**. If no code 25, knock system okay. Repeat Engine Running Self-Test and service other codes.

2) Turn ignition off and wait 10 seconds. Disconnect knock sensor and inspect. With DVOM on 20 volt scale, turn ignition on and measure voltage at knock sensor harness between sensor signal circuit and signal return circuit. If voltage is 1-4 volts, go to step **6)**. If less than 1 volt, go to step **3)**. If greater than 4 volts, go to step **5)**.

3) Turn ignition off and wait 10 seconds. Disconnect 60-pin connector at ECA and inspect for damaged pins, corrosion and loose wires. Connect breakout box and leave ECA and knock sensor disconnected. With DVOM on 200 ohm scale, measure continuity of knock sensor harness between sensor signal circuit and box pin 23 and between signal return circuit and box pin 46. If both less than 5 ohms, go to step **4)**. If either 5 ohms or more, repair open circuit and repeat Self Test.

4) Turn ignition off and wait 10 seconds. Breakout box installed and ECA and knock sensor disconnected. With DVOM on 200K ohm scale, measure resistance from sensor signal circuit of knock sensor harness to box pins 40, 46 and 60, in turn. If all 10K ohms or greater, go to step **6)**. If any less than 10K ohms, repair harness short and repeat Self Test.

5) Turn ignition off and wait 10 seconds. With equipment connected as in step **4)**, set DVOM on 20 volt scale. Measure voltage from box pin 23 to pin 40. If .5 volt or more, repair knock sensor harness short to power and repeat Self Test. If less than .5 volt, go to step **6)**.

6) Turn ignition off and wait 10 seconds. Remove breakout box and reconnect ECA. Connect equivalent knock sensor (same part number) into harness but do not install in engine. Perform Engine Running Self-Test. When Dynamic Response Signal appears, lightly tap knock sensor with 4 oz. hammer. If code 25 appears after about 15 seconds, replace ECA, remove substitute knock sensor and repeat Self Test with original sensor. If code 25 does not appear within 15 seconds, install new sensor and repeat Self Test.

TEST U (Cont.)

Knock Sensor Circuits

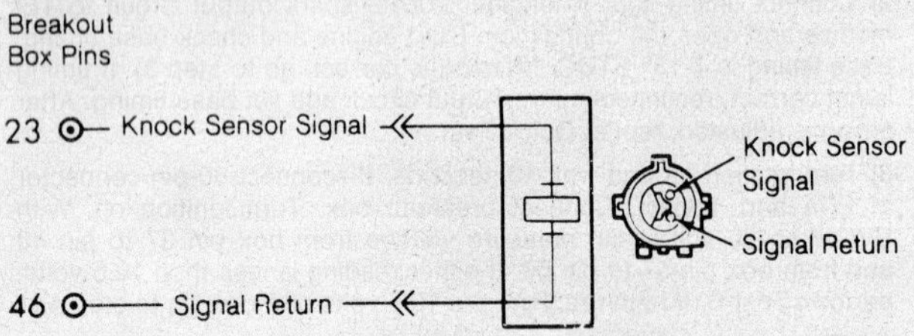

TEST V

THERMACTOR OUTPUT CIRCUIT CHECK

1) Turn ignition off and wait 10 seconds. Disconnect harness at TAB and TAD solenoids. With DVOM on 200 ohm scale, measure resistance oi TAB and TAD solenoids. If both readings 50-100 ohms, reconnect solenoids and go to next step. If either reading less than 50 ohms or more than 100 ohms, replace TAB/TAD solenoid assembly and repeat Quick Test.

2) Turn ignition on (engine off). With DVOM on 20 volt scale, connect positive lead to vehicle power circuit of TAB solenoid and negative lead to good ground. Repeat test on TAD solenoid. If both readings 10.5 volts or more, go to step **3)**. If either reading less than 10.5 volts, repair open circuit and repeat Quick Test.

3) Turn ignition off and wait 10 seconds. Disconnect 60-pin connector at ECA and inspect. Repair as required. Connect breakout box and leave ECA disconnected. With DVOM on 200 ohm scale, measure continuity from box pin 51 to TAB circuit at TAB harness. Then measure from box pin 11 to TAD circuit at TAD harness. If both readings less than 5 ohms, go to next step. If either reading 5 ohms or more, repair open circuit and repeat Quick Test.

4) Turn ignition off and wait 10 seconds. Breakout box installed and ECA and TAB/TAD solenoid disconnected. With DVOM on 200K ohm scale, measure resistance from box pin 51 to pins 37 and 57. Then from box pin 11 to same pins. If all readings 10K ohms or more, go to step **5)**. If any reading less than 10K ohms, repair short to power and repeat Quick Test.

5) Turn ignition off and wait 10 seconds. Breakout box installed and ECA and TAB/TAD solenoid disconnected. With DVOM on 200K ohm scale, measure resistance from box pin 51 to pins 40, 46 and 60 in turn. Then from box pin 11 to same pins. If all readings less than 10K ohms, repair short to ground and repeat Quick Test. If any reading 10K ohms or more, replace ECA and repeat Quick Test.

Thermactor Circuit

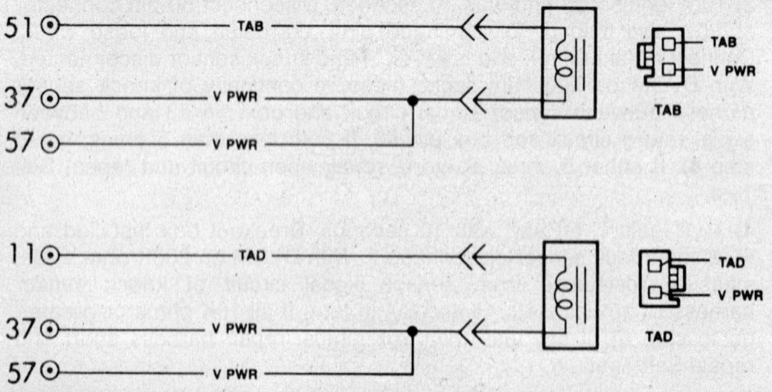

TEST W

DYNAMIC RESPONSE TEST

Code 77. This code appeared because the system failed to recognize a brief wide open throttle. Repeat Engine Running Self-Test. After Dynamic Response Code is received, perform a wide open throttle. If code 77 is still present, replace ECA and repeat Self Test. If no code 77, Dynamic Response Test is passed. Repair any service codes received as required.

TEST X

DIAGNOSTICS BY SYMPTOM

1) If engine stalls, stalls in Self-Test, runs rough or misses, check the following: Poor power/ground connections, ignition system problem, engine internal problem (valves, cam timing, compression, etc.), EGR valve or fuel system.

2) If shift indicator light is alway on or always off, go to Test Y. If A/C does not cut off during wide open throttle operation, or is not functioning, go to test K. If there is high or low idle speed on start up, or engine diesels, go test Z.

3) If gasoline fumes accumulate under hood, check fuel system and canister purge system. If there is a lack of fast idle with A/C on, go to test K.

TEST Y

SHIFT INDICATOR LIGHT

1) Code 11. Pass must be present for Key On-Engine Off and Engine Running Self-Tests before proceeding with this test. Verify shift indicator light fault by drive evaluating vehicle. If light is always off, go to next step. If light is not always off, go to step **4)**.

2) Turn ignition off and wait 10 seconds. Disconnect harness from top gear switch and inspect for damaged pins, corrosion, loose wires, etc. Service as necessary. Set DVOM on 200 ohm scale and measure resistance of top gear switch harness connector STO circuit to self-test connector. If reading is less than 5 ohms, go to next step. If reading is 5 ohms or greater, repair open circuit, reconnect top gear switch and re-evaluate shift indicator light function.

3) With ignition off, disconnect harness from top gear switch and place transmission in first gear. Set DVOM on 200 ohm scale and measure resistance of top gear switch. If less than 5 ohms, check fuse and bulb. If both are OK, repair open circuit. Reconnect top gear switch and re-evaluate shift indicator light. If reading is 5 ohms or greater, replace top gear switch and re-evaluate shift indicator light.

4) Turn ignition off and wait 10 seconds. Disconnect harness from top gear switch. Inspect for damaged pins, corrosion, loose wires, etc. Service as necessary. Place transmission in top gear. Set DVOM on 200,000 ohm scale and measure resistance of top gear switch. If reading is less than 10,000 ohms, replace top gear switch and re-evaluate shift indicator light. If reading is 10,000 ohms or greater, repair short in SIL circuit, reconnect switch and re-evaluate shift indicator light.

Shift Indicator Light Circuit

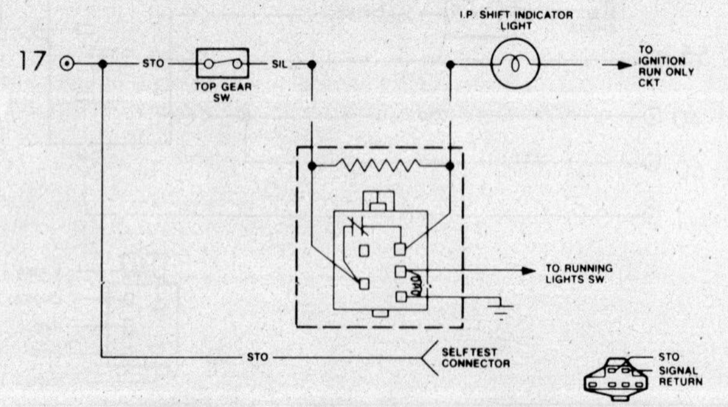

TEST Z

KEY POWER TEST

1) Turn ignition off and wait 10 seconds. Install breakout box with ECA connected. With DVOM on 20V range, connect leads to pins 5 and 60. Perform Engine Running Self-Test. If DVOM reading exceeds 17.5V during Self Test, repair charging system. If reading remains below 17.5 volts and code 65 is present, replace ECA and repeat Self Test. If DVOM remains below 17.5V and code 65 is not present, go to next step.

2) Perform Key On-Engine Off Self-Test. If code 65 is not present, charging system is okay, test complete. If code 65 is present, check charging system.

Key Power Circuit

TEST AA

VARIABLE VOLTAGE CHOKE TEST

1) Perform Engine Running Self-Test. With DVOM on 20 volt scale, measure choke voltage. If voltage is 10.5 volts or greater, check choke plates for binding and sticking. If choke plates are not binding or sticking, EEC-IV system is operating properly, service choke system. If voltage is less than 10.5 volts, go to next step.

2) Turn ignition on (engine off). With DVOM on 20 volt scale, connect positive lead to vehicle battery circuit at relay harness connector and negative lead to ground at relay harness connector. If voltage is less than 10.5 volts, repair open circuit and repeat Self Test. If voltage is 10.5 volts or greater, go to next step.

3) Turn ignition off and disconnect 60-pin connector at ECA. Install breakout box and reconnect ECA. Turn ignition on (engine off). With DVOM on 20 volt scale, measure voltage from box pins 40 and 60 to negative battery terminal. If both are less than 1 volt, ground circuit is okay, go to next step. If voltage is 1 volt on one or both circuits, repair ground circuit and repeat Self Test.

4) Turn ignition off and wait 10 seconds. Enter Output State Check and perform Key On-Engine Off Self-Test until end of Continuous code display. DVOM will indicate zero volts. Depress and release throttle and observe DVOM. If DVOM registered high voltage, remain in Ouput State Check and go to next step. If DVOM did not register high voltage, depress throttle to wide open position and release. If voltage still does not register high reading, go to Test D, step **13)**.

5) Remain in Output State Check. Turn ignition on, engine off. With DVOM on 20 volt scale, connect positive lead to vehicle battery circuit on choke relay and negative lead to variable voltage choke output circuit at choke. While observing DVOM, depress and release throttle several times to cycle output on and off. If output cycles on and off, EEC-IV system is operating properly, repair choke system. If output does not cycle on and off, replace choke relay and repeat Self Test.

Variable Voltage Choke Circuit

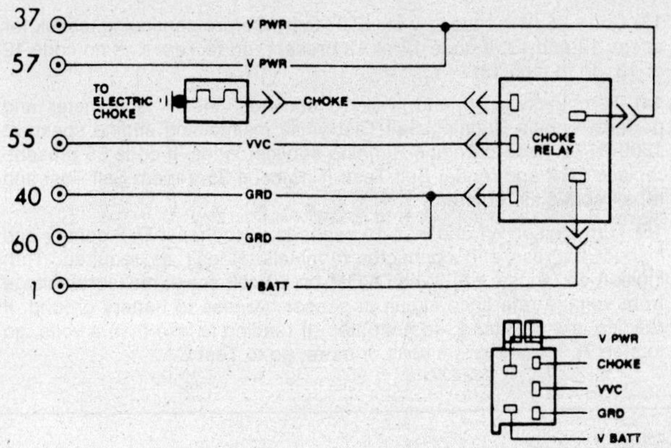

TEST BB

TEMPERATURE COMPENSATED ACCELERATOR PUMP TEST

1) Turn ignition off and wait 10 seconds. Disconnect temperature compensated accelerator pump solenoid harness connector. With DVOM on 200 ohm scale, measure resistance of solenoid. If resistance is between 50-100 ohms, reconnect solenoid and go to next step. If less than 50 ohms or greater than 100 ohms, replace solenoid and repeat Self Test.

2) Turn ignition off and wait 10 seconds. Enter Output State Check and perform Key On-Engine Off Self-Test until end of Continuous code display. DVOM will indicate zero volts. Depress and release throttle and observe DVOM. If DVOM registered high voltage, remain in Ouput State Check and go to next step. If DVOM did not register high voltage, depress throttle to wide open position and release. If voltage still does not register high reading, go to Test D, step **13)**.

3) Remain in Output State Check. Turn ignition on, engine off. With DVOM on 20 volt scale, connect positive lead to vehicle battery circuit on solenoid and negative lead to temperature compensated pump output circuit at solenoid. While observing DVOM, depress and release throttle several times to cycle output on and off. If output cycles on and off, go to next step. If output does not cycle on and off, go to step **6)**.

4) Remain in Output State Check. Install vacuum pump to solenoid vacuum supply port and vacuum gauge to solenoid output port. Apply and maintain a minimum of 6 in. Hg. Depress and release throttle several times to cycle output on and off and observe vacuum gauge. If vacuum output cycles on and off, go to next step. If vacuum does not cycle on and off, replace solenoid and repeat Self Test.

5) Remove all test equipment and vacuum source. Disconnect vacuum lines at temperature compensated accelerator pump solenoid. Start engine and check for vacuum. If vacuum is present, EEC-IV system is operating properly, check fuel system. If no vacuum is present, repair vacuum leak or blockage and repeat Self Test.

6) Turn ignition on (engine off). With DVOM on 20 volt scale, connect positive lead to vehicle power circuit at solenoid connector and negative lead to ground. If voltage is 10.5 volts or less, repair open circuit and repeat Self Test. If voltage is 10.5 volts or greater, go to next step.

7) Turn ignition off and wait 10 seconds. Disconnect 60-pin connector at ECA and inspect connectors for damage. Repair as required. Connect breakout box and leave ECA disconnected. With DVOM on 200 ohm scale, measure continuity from box pin 54 to temperature compensated pump circuit at harness connector. If resistance is 5 ohms or greater, repair open circuit and repeat Self Test. If less than 5 ohms, go to next step.

8) Turn ignition off and wait 10 seconds. Disconnect harness at pump solenoid. Breakout box installed (ECA disconnected). With DVOM on 200,000 ohm scale, measure resistance from box pin 54 to box pins 37 and 57. If resistance is 10,000 ohms or greater, go to next step. If resistance is less than 10,000 ohms, repair short and repeat Self Test.

9) Turn ignition off and wait 10 seconds. Breakout box installed (ECA and solenoid disconnected). With DVOM On 200,000 ohm scale, measure resistance from box pin 54 to pins 40, 46, and 60. If readings are less than 10,000 ohms, repair short to ground and repeat Self Test. If readings are 10,000 ohms or greater, replace ECA and repeat Self Test.

Temperature Compensated Accelerator Pump Output Circuit

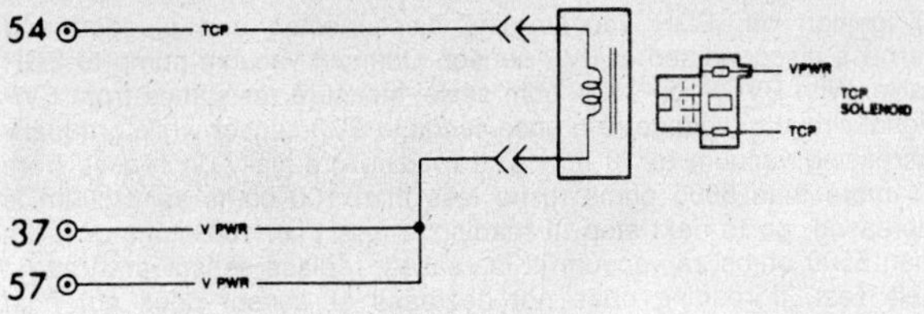

FORD ELECTRONIC ENGINE CONTROL IV (Cont.)

TEST CC

CONVERTER CLUTCH OVERRIDE (CCO)

1) Code 89. Turn key on. Set DVOM on 20 volt scale. Measure voltage at the CCO solenoid connector between VPWR and ground. If voltage reading is less than 10.5 volts, repair open circuit in harness. Repeat Self-Test. If voltage reading is more than 10.5 volts, go to step **2)**.

2) Turn key off and wait 10 seconds. Disconnect processor 60-pin connector and inspect for damaged pins, corrosion, loose wires, etc. Repair as necessary and go to step **3)**.

3) Connect breakout box to harness. Leave processor disconnected. Set DVOM on 200 ohm scale. Measure resistance between test pin 53/22 and CCO circuit at the solenoid harness connector. If resistance readings are 5 ohms or greater, repair harness circuit. Repeat Quick Test. If resistance reading is less than 5 ohms, go to step **4)**.

4) Turn key off and wait 10 seconds. Leave breakout box installed and processor disconnected. Disconnect CCO solenoid. Set DVOM on 200K ohm scale. Measure resistance between test pin 55 and test pins 40, 46 and 60. If resistance readings are less than 10K ohms, repair short to ground. Repeat Self Test. If resistance readings are 10K ohms or greater, go to step **5)**.

5) Turn key off and wait 10 seconds. Set DVOM on 200K ohm scale. Leave breakout box installed and processor disconnected. Disconnect CCO solenoid. Measure resistance between test pin 55 and pins 37 and 57. If resistance reading is 10K ohms or greater, replace processor. Repeat Self Test. If resistance reading is less than 10K ohms, repair short to power supply. Repeat Self Test. If code is still present, replace processor.

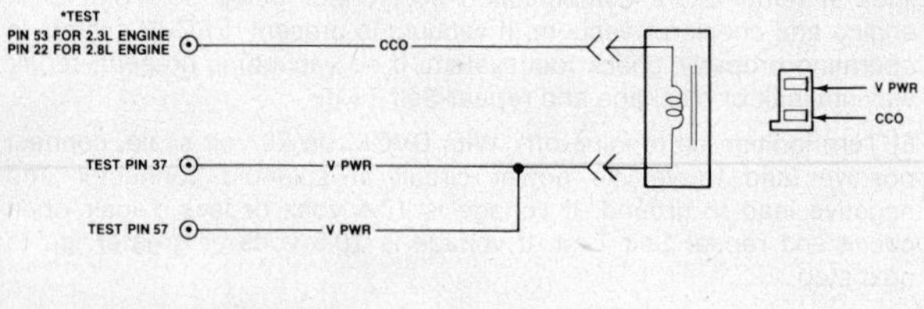

*TEST PINS LOCATED ON BREAKOUT BOX.
ALL HARNESS CONNECTORS VIEWED INTO MATING SURFACE.

TEST DD

EGR VALVE POSITION (EVP) SENSOR

1) Code 31. Turn ignition off and wait 10 seconds. Disconnect and plug EGR vacuum line at EGR valve. Perform Engine Running Self-Test. If code 31, go to step **2)**. If no code 31, but codes 32 and/or 34 present, go to step **9)**.

2) Turn ignition off and wait 10 seconds. EGR vacuum line disconnected and plugged at EGR valve. Disconnect harness connector at EGR valve position (EVP) sensor and inspect terminals for damage. Repair as required. With DVOM on 200,000 ohm scale, measure resistance from EVP signal circuit to voltage reference circuit at EVP sensor. Then measure resistance from signal return circuit to voltage reference circuit at sensor. If both readings are 100-5500 ohms, go to next step. If either reading is less than 100 ohms or more than 5500 ohms, replace sensor and repeat Self Test.

3) Ignition off, EGR vacuum line disconnected and plugged and harness disconnected at EVP sensor. Connect vacuum pump to EGR valve. With DVOM on 200K ohm scale, measure resistance from EVP signal circuit to voltage reference circuit at EVP sensor while gradually increasing vacuum to 10 in. Hg. If reading gradually decreases from no more than 5500 ohms to no less than 100 ohms as vacuum is increased, go to next step. If reading is less than 100 ohms or more than 5500 ohms as vacuum is increased, replace sensor and repeat Self Test. If reading does not decrease or sensor does not hold vacuum, go to step **12)**.

4) Turn ignition on (engine off). EGR vacuum line disconnected and plugged and harness disconnected at EVP sensor. With DVOM on 20 volt scale, measure voltage from voltage reference circuit to signal return circuit at sensor harness. If reading is 4-6 volts, go to next step.

TEST DD (Cont.)

If reading is less than 4 volts, go to step **7)**. If reading is greater than 6 volts, go to Test C.

5) Ignition on (engine off). Reconnect EGR vacuum line at EGR valve and leave harness disconnected. With DVOM on 20-volt scale, measure voltage from voltage reference circuit to EVP signal circuit at sensor harness. If reading is 4-6 volts, go to step **6)**. If reading is less than 4 volts, go to step **7)**.

6) Turn ignition off and wait 10 seconds. Harness disconnected at EVP sensor. Disconnect 60-pin connector at ECA and inspect for damaged terminals. Repair as required. With DVOM on 200K ohm scale, measure resistance from EVP signal circuit to signal return circuit at sensor harness and from EVP signal circuit to battery negative terminal. If either reading is less than 10K ohms, repair short circuit and repeat Self Test. If both readings are 10K ohms or more, replace ECA and repeat Self Test.

7) Turn ignition off and wait 10 seconds. Harness disconnected at EVP and ECA. Connect breakout box and leave ECA disconnected. With DVOM on 200 ohm scale, measure continuity from box pin 46 to signal return circuit of EVP harness; from box pin 26 to voltage reference circuit of EVP harness and from box pin 27 to EVP signal circuit of EVP harness. If all readings less than 5 ohms, go to step **8)**. If any reading 5 ohms or more, repair open circuit and repeat Self Test.

8) Ignition off, EVP harness disconnected, breakout box installed and ECA disconnected. With DVOM on 200K ohm scale, measure resistance from box pin 27 to pins 37 and 57. If either reading is less than 10K ohms, repair short circuit and repeat Self Test. If both readings are 10K ohms or more, replace ECA and repeat Self Test.

9) Codes 32, 33 and 34. Turn ignition off and wait 10 seconds. Enter Output State Check and perform Key On-Engine Off Self-Test until end of Continuous code display. DVOM will indicate zero volts. Depress and release throttle and observe DVOM. If DVOM registered high voltage, remain in Output State Check and go to next step. If DVOM did not register high voltage, depress throttle to wide open position and release. If voltage still does not register high reading, go to Test D, step **13)**.

10) Turn ignition on (engine off). Remain in Output State Check. Disconnect and plug vacuum line at bottom port of EGR control solenoid and connect vacuum pump. Using a "Tee", connect vacuum gauge in top line at EGR valve. Disconnect but DO NOT plug vacuum vent line at EGR vent solenoid. Apply vacuum and observe vacuum gauge while depressing and releasing throttle (cycling outputs on and off). If vacuum output cycles on and off in less than 2 seconds, reconnect vacuum lines and go to next step. If vacuum ouput does not cycle on and off in less than 2 seconds, replace solenoid assembly and repeat Self Test.

11) Turn ignition off and wait 10 seconds. Remove all test equipment and reconnect all vacuum lines. Check EEC system vacuum lines for proper routing, leaks and obstructions. Repair as required. If vacuum lines are okay, service EGR system.

12) Ignition off and harness disconnected at EVP sensor. Remove EVP sensor from EGR valve. With DVOM on 200K ohm scale, measure resistance from signal return circuit to voltage reference circuit at EVP sensor. Observe DVOM while slowly pushing EVP sensor shaft inward. If reading smoothly decreases from no more than 5500 ohms to no less than 100 ohms, replace EGR valve assembly and repeat Self Test. If reading does not decrease smoothly or changes suddenly, replace EVP sensor and repeat Self Test.

13) Code 35 (RPM too low for EGR test). Before continuing, check for codes 12 and 13. If code 12 or 13 present, go to Test K. If no code 12 or 13, go to step **13)**.

14) Turn ignition off and wait 10 seconds. Install tachometer and perform Engine Running Self-Test while maintaining engine speed at 1500 RPM. Record Engine Running service codes. If code 35 present, replace ECA and repeat Self Test. If no code 35, repeat Self Test and repair codes as required.

15) Turn ignition off and wait 10 seconds. Disconnect EVP sensor and inspect harness and connector terminals. Repair as required. Turn ignition on (engine off). With DVOM on 20 volt scale, measure voltage from voltage reference circuit at sensor harness to battery ground. If reading is 4-6 volts, go to next step. If reading is less than 4 volts, go to step **7)**. If reading is 6 volts or more, go to Test C.

TEST DD (Cont.)

16) Ignition on and EVP sensor disconnected. With DVOM on 20 volt scale, measure voltage from voltage reference circuit to signal return circuit at sensor harness. If reading is 4-6 volts, go to next step. If reading is less than 4 volts, repair open circuit and repeat Key On-Engine Off Self-Test.

17) Turn ignition off and wait 10 seconds. Disconnect 60-pin connector at ECA and inspect. Repair as required. Connect breakout box and reconnect ECA. Connect EVP sensor. Turn ignition on (engine off). With DVOM on 20 volt scale, measure voltage from box pin 27 to pin 46. If less than .5 volt, go to next step. If 1.25 volt or greater, go to step **21)**.

18) Turn ignition off and wait 10 seconds. Disconnect ECA and EVP sensor. Breakout box installed. With DVOM on 200 ohm scale, measure resistance from box pin 27 to pins 20, 40, 46 and 60 in turn. If 5 ohms or more, go to next step. If less than 5 ohms, repair short to ground in EVP signal circuit and repeat Self Test.

19) Turn ignition off. Breakout box installed and ECA and EVP sensor disconnected. With DVOM on 200 ohm scale, measure resistance from box pin 27 to EVP signal circuit at sensor harness. If 5 ohms or more, repair open in EVP signal circuit and repeat Self Test. If less than 5 ohms, go to step **20)**.

20) Turn ignition off. Replace EVP sensor with known good sensor and reconnect harness. Remove breakout box and reconnect ECA. Perform Key On-Engine Off Self-Test. If code 31 present, replace ECA and reinstall original EVP sensor. If no code 31, testing is complete.

21) Turn ignition off and wait 10 seconds. Disconnect 60-pin connector at ECA and connect breakout box. Leave ECA disconnected. Disconnect EVP sensor. With DVOM on 200 ohm scale, measure resistance from box pin 27 to pins 26, 37 and 57 in turn. If 5 ohms or more, go to next step. If less than 5 ohms, repair short to power and repeat Key On-Engine Off Self-Test.

22) Turn ignition off and wait 10 seconds. Connect electrical harness to a known good EVP sensor and EGR valve assembly. Remove breakout box and reconnect ECA. Perform Key On-Engine Off Self-Test. If code 31, replace ECA, reconnect original EVP sensor and EGR valve assembly and repeat Self Test. If no code 31, go to step 23.

23) Turn ignition off and wait 10 seconds. Install original EVP sensor and connect harness. Perform Key On-Engine Off Self-Test. If code 31, install new EVP sensor. If no code 31, testing complete.

24) Continuous Code 31. Disconnect vacuum line at EGR valve and install vacuum pump. Very slowly apply 6 in. Hg vacuum to sensor, then slowly bleed off vacuum. Enter Continuous Monitor mode and observe volt/ohmmeter for fault indication while doing the following: Lightly tap on EVP sensor to simulate road shock. Wiggle sensor connector. If fault is indicated, go to step **25)**. If no fault indicated, go to step **26)**.

EGR Valve Position (EVP) Sensor Circuit

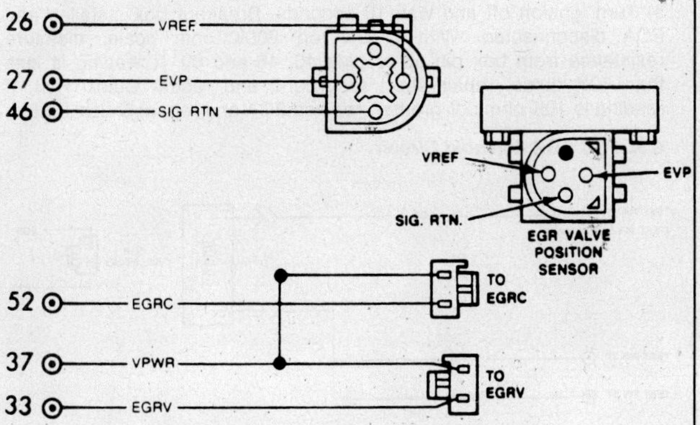

25) Turn ignition off and wait 10 seconds. Disconnect 60-pin connector at ECA and inspect. Repair as required. Connect breakout box and reconnect ECA. With volt/ohmmeter still connected to self-test output as in step **24)**, connect DVOM between box pin 27 and pin 46. Turn ignition on (engine off). With DVOM on 20 volt scale, observe DVOM while repeating step **24)**. If fault occurs below 4.25 volts, disconnect and inspect harness at EVP sensor. If connector and terminals are okay, replace EVP sensor and repeat Self Test. If fault does not occur below 4.25 volts, EGR valve "overshoot" may have caused code 31. Sensor service not required. Go to step **26)** to verify harness integrity.

26) Observe volt/ohmmeter while doing the following: Beginning at EVP, wiggle, shake or bend small sections of harness while working way to dash panel. Then repeating process from panel to ECA. If fault is indicated, isolate and repair problem and repeat Self Test. If no fault indicated, go to step **27)**.

27) Turn ignition off and wait 10 seconds. Disconnect 60-pin connector at ECA and inspect connector and terminals for damage. If damaged, service as required and repeat Self Test. If okay, fault cannot be duplicated at this time. Continuous Code 31 testing is complete.

TEST EE

BRAKE ON/OFF (BOO)

1) Code 74. If brake was pressed during Engine Running Self Test, go to step **2)**. If not, rerun Engine Running Self Test and press brake once during test.

2) Turn key on and wait 10 seconds. Disconnect processor 60 pin connector. Inspect for damage, corrosion, loose wires, etc. Install breakout box and leave processor disconnected. Set DVOM on 20 volt scale. Measure voltage between test pin 2 and test pin 40 while depressing and releasing brake. If voltage cycles, replace processor. Repeat Self Test. If voltage does not cycle, repair brake circuit as necessary.

3) Code 75 Turn key off and wait 10 seconds. Disconnect processor 60 pin connector. Inspect for damaged pins, corrosion, loose wires, etc. Repair as necessary. Install breakout box, leave processor disconnected. Set DVOM on 20 volt scale. Measure voltage between pin 2 and test pin 40 while depressing and releasing brake pedal. If voltage cycles, replace processor. Repeat Self Test. If voltage does not cycle, go to step **4)**.

4) Turn key off. Breakout box installed and processor disconnected. Set DVOM on 200 ohm scale. Disconnect BOO circuit from harness 14290 (12 pin connector). Measure resistance between test pin 2 and ground. If resistance reading is greater than 5 ohms, service BOO circuit short to power. If resistance reading is less than 5 ohms, repair open in BOO circuit.

Brake On/Off Circuit

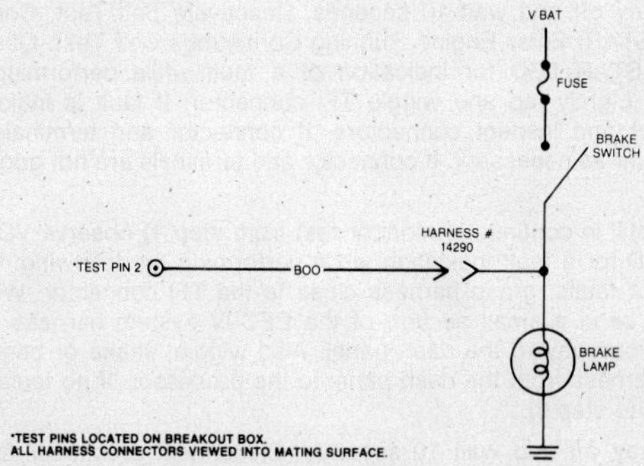

TEST FF

ERRATIC IGNITION

1) Code 14. Check EEC-IV and ignition systems harnesses for: Loose wires and connections. Arcing secondary ignition components (coil, cap, rotor, etc.). Faulty on-board transmitter (CB radio). If any faults are found, repair as necessary and repeat Self Test. If no faults are found, go to step **2)**.

FORD ELECTRONIC ENGINE CONTROL IV (Cont.)

TEST FF (Cont.)

2) Turn key off and wait 10 seconds. Deactivate Self Test. Connect VOM or STAR. Enter Engine Running Continuous Test. Observe VOM or STAR LED display for indication of a fault while performing the following: Lightly tap and wiggle on TFI module and distributor. If fault is indicated, disconnect and inspect connectors. If connector and terminals are good, repair as necessary. If no fault is indicated, go to step **3)**.

3) While still in Continuous Self Test from step **2)** observe VOM or STAR LED for a fault indication while performing the following: While looking for faults grasp the harness close to the TFI connector. Wiggle, shake or bend a small section of the ignition and EEC-IV harness from the dash panel. Also wiggle, shake or bend the EEC-IV harness from the dash panel to the processor. Isolate the PIP circuit if needed for this test. If fault is indicated, isolate fault and repair as necessary. If no fault is found go to step **4)**.

4) Turn key off and wait 10 seconds. Disconnect processor 60 pin connector and inspect for damaged pins, corrosion, loose wires. If any fault is found, repair ignition system as necessary. Repear Self Test.

TEST GG

IGNITION DIAGNOSTIC MONITOR (IDM)

1) Turn key off and wait 10 seconds. Disconnect E-core ignition connector from coil. Disconnect processor and inspect both 60 pin connectors for damaged pins, corrosion, loose wires, etc. If fault is found, repair as necessary and repeat Self Test. If no faults are found, go to step **2)**.

2) Connect breakout box to harness and leave processor disconnected. Leave processor disconnected. Set DVOM on 200K scale. Measure resistance between test pin 4 and ignition coil negative terminal. If resistance reading less than 20K ohms or greater than 24K ohms, repair open circuit and repeat Self Test. If resistance reading is less than 24K ohms but greater than 20K ohms, go to step **3)**.

3) Turn key off and wait 10 seconds. Leave breakout box installed and processor disconnected. Set DVOM on 200K ohm scale. Measure resistance between test pin 4 and test pins 40, 46 and 60. If resistance reading is less than 10K ohms, repair short to ground. Repeat Self Test. If resistance is 10K ohms or greater, go to step **4)**.

4) Turn key off and wait 10 seconds. Deactivate Self Test. Connect VOM or STAR. Enter Engine Running Continuous Self Test. Observe VOM or STAR LED for indication of a fault while performing the following: Lightly tap and wiggle TFI connector. If fault is indicated, disconnect and inspect connectors. If connector and terminals are good, repair as necessary. If connector and terminals are not good, go to step **5)**.

5) While still in continuous monitor test from step **1)** observe VOM or STAR LED for a fault indication while performing the following: While looking for faults, grasp harness close to the TFI connector. Wiggle, shake or bend a small section of the EEC-IV system harness while working your way to the dash panel. Also wiggle, shake or bend the EEC-IV harness from the dash panel to the processor. If no faults can found, go to step **6)**.

6) Turn key off and wait 10 seconds. Disconnect processor 60 pin connector and inspect for damaged pins, corrosion, loose wires. If connectors and terminals are okay and unable to duplicate an IDM fault in the EEC-IV system, testing is complete. If a fault is found, repair system as necessary. Repeat Self Test.

Ignition Diagnostic Monitor Circuit

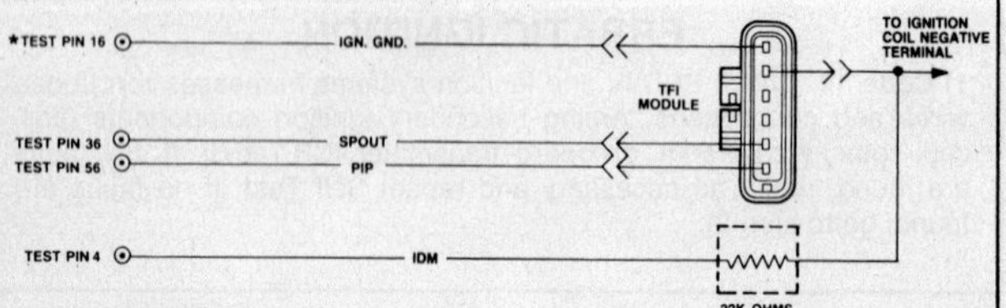

*TEST PINS LOCATED ON BREAKOUT BOX.
ALL HARNESS CONNECTORS VIEWED INTO MATING SURFACE.

TEST HH

EGR ON/OFF CONTROL

1) Turn ignition off and wait 10 seconds. With DVOM on 200 ohm scale, disconnect EGR solenoid connector and measure solenoid resistance. If resistance is 65-110 ohms, connect EGR solenoid and go to next step. If resistance is less than 65 ohms or greater than 110 ohms, replace EGR solenoid and repeat Quick Test.

2) Turn ignition off and wait 10 seconds. Enter Output State Check and perform Key On-Engine Off Self-Test until end of Continuous code display. DVOM will indicate zero volts. Depress and release throttle and observe DVOM. If DVOM registered high voltage, remain in Output State Check and go to next step. If DVOM did not register high voltage, depress throttle to wide open position and release. If voltage still does not register high reading, go to Test D, step **13)**.

3) Remain in Output State Check. With DVOM on 20 volt scale, connect positive test lead to vehicle power circuit on EGR solenoid and negative lead to EGR output circuit. While observing DVOM, depress and release throttle several times to cycle output on and off. If EGR output cycles on and off, go to step **4)**. If EGR does not cycle on and off, go to step **6)**.

4) Install vacuum pump to the solenoid vacuum supply port and install a vacuum gauge to output port. Apply and maintain minimum of 6 in. Hg. While depressing and releasing throttle to cycle output on and off, observe vacuum gauge. If output cycles on and off, go to step **5)**. If vacuum output does not cycle on and off, replace solenoid and repeat Quick Test.

5) Remove all test equipment and disconnect vacuum lines at EGR solenoid. Start engine and check for vacuum at solenoid. If vacuum is present, EEC-IV system is functioning properly. If no vacuum is present, service vacuum source blockage or leak and repeat Quick Test.

6) Turn ignition on (engine off). With DVOM on 20 volt scale, connect positive lead to vehicle power circuit at solenoid and negative lead to ground. Measure voltage. If voltage reading is less than 10.5 volts, repair open circuit and repeat Quick Test. If voltage reading is 10.5 volts or greater, go to step **7)**.

7) Turn ignition off and wait 10 seconds. Disconnect 60-pin connector at ECA and inspect for damaged pins, corrosion or loose wires and service as necessary. Leave ECA disconnected and connect breakout box to harness. With DVOM on 200 ohm scale, measure continuity from box pin 53 to EGR circuit at harness connector. If reading is 5 ohms or greater, repair open circuit and repeat Quick Test. If reading is less than 5 ohms, go to step **8)**.

8) Turn ignition off and wait 10 seconds. Breakout box installed and ECA and EGR solenoid disconnected. With DVOM on 200K ohm scale, measure resistance from box pin 53 to pins 37 and 57. If reading is 10K ohms or greater, go to next step **9)**. If reading is less than 10K ohms, repair short to power and repeat Quick Test.

9) Turn ignition off and wait 10 seconds. Breakout box installed and ECA disconnected. With DVOM on 200K ohm scale, measure resistance from box pin 53 to pins 40, 46 and 60. If reading is less than 10K ohms, repair short to ground and repeat Quick Test. If reading is 10K ohms or greater, replace ECA and repeat Quick Test.

4.9L FBC EGR Solenoid Circuit

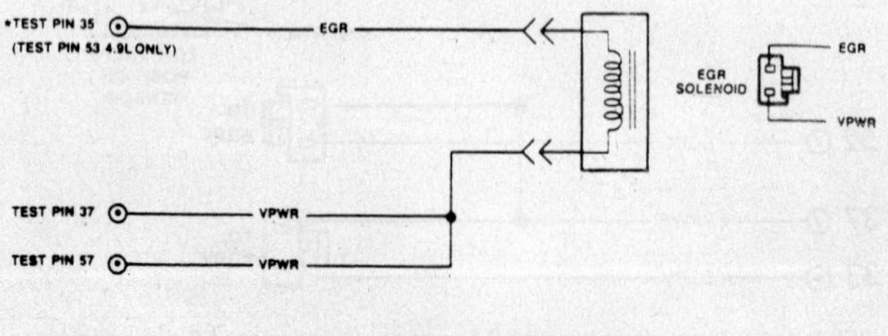

*TEST PINS LOCATED ON BREAKOUT BOX.
ALL HARNESS CONNECTORS VIEWED INTO MATING SURFACE.

FORD ELECTRONIC ENGINE CONTROL IV (Cont.)

TEST II

WOT A/C CUTOFF (WAC) A/C DEMAND

NOTE: This test is intended to diagnose only the following: Harness circuits (WAC and V PWR). WOT A/C cut-off relay. Processor assembly. A/C demand switch. DO NOT use STAR tester for this step, use VOM/DVOM.

1) Turn key off and wait 10 seconds. Set DVOM on 20 volt scale. Connect DVOM negative test lead to STO and positive test lead to battery positive. Jumper STI to signal return. Perform Key On, Engine Off Self-Test until the completion of the Continuous Test Codes. The DVOM will indicate 0 volts. If DVOM reading changed to a high voltage reading, remain in Output state check and go to step **2)**. If not, depress throttle to WOT and release. If STO voltage does not go high, repair system as necessary.

2) Turn key on. Disconnect processor 60-pin connector and inspect for damaged pins, corrosion, loose wires. Repair system as necessary. Connect breakout box to harness and reconnect processor. Turn A/C switch on. Set DVOM on 20 volt scale. Connect DVOM positive test lead to test pin 37 and negative test lead to pin 54. While observing DVOM, depress and release the throttle several times. If A/C clutch output cycled on and off, EEC-IV system is okay. If not, go to step **3)**.

3) Turn key off and wait 10 seconds. Set DVOM on 200 ohm scale. Measure resistance between ground circuit and fan control module connector. If resistance reading is 5 ohms or greater, repair harness circuit. Repeat Quick Test. If resistance reading is less than 5 ohms, go to step **4)**.

4) Turn key on. Set DVOM on 20 volt scale. Measure voltage between ignition circuit and ground circuit on the control module connector. If voltage is less than 10.5 volts, repair open in ignition circuit. Repeat Quick Test. If voltage is 10.5 volts or greater, go to step **5)**.

5) Turn key off and wait 10 seconds. Disconnect processor 60-pin connector and inspect for damaged pins, corrosion, loose wires. Repair system as necessary. Connect breakout box to harness. Leave processor disconnected. Set DVOM on 200 ohm scale. Measure resistance between test pin 54 and WAC circuit at fan control module. If resistance is 5 ohm or greater, repair harness WAC circuit. Repeat Quick Test. If resistance is less than 5 ohms, go to step **6)**.

6) Turn key off and wait 10 seconds. Leave breakout box installed and processor disconnected. Set DVOM on 200K ohm scale. Measure resistance between test pin 54 and test pins 40, 46 and 60. If resistance reading is less than 10k ohms, go to step **7)**. If resistance reading is 10K ohms or greater, replace processor and repeat Quick Test.

7) Turn key off and 10 seconds. Leave breakout box installed and processor disconnected. Set DVOM on 200K ohm scale. Disconnect fan control module. Measure resistance between test pin 54 and test pins 40, 46 and 60. If all resistance readings are 10K ohms or greater, replace fan control module. Repeat Quick Test. If resistance reading is less than 10K ohms, repair harness short. Repeat Quick Test.

8) Turn key off and wait 10 seconds. Set DVOM on 200 ohm scale. Disconnect WAC relay connector and measure relay resistance. If resistance is between 50 and 70 ohms, connect WAC solenoid and go to step **9)**. If resistance is less than 50 ohms or greater than 70 ohms, replace WAC relay. Repeat Quick Test.

9) Turn key on. Set DVOM on 20 volt scale. Connect DVOM positive test lead to V PWR circuit and negative test lead to ground. Measure voltage on WAC relay V PWR circuit. If voltage reading is less than 10.5 volts, repair harness open circuit. Repeat Quick Test. If voltage reading is 10.5 volts or greater, go to step **10)**.

10) Turn key off and wait 10 seconds. Disconnect processor 60-pin connector and inspect for damaged pins, corrosion, loose wires. Repair system as necessary. Connect breakout box to harness. Leave processor disconnected. Set DVOM on 200 ohm scale. Measure resistance between test pin 54 and WAC circuit at harness connector. If resistance readings are 5 ohms or greater, repair harness open circuit. Repeat Quick Test. If resistance readings are 5 ohms or less, go to step **11)**.

11) Turn key off and wait 10 seconds. Leave breakout box installed and processor disconnected. Set DVOM on 200K ohm scale. Measure resistance between test pin 54 and pins 40, 46 and 60. If resistance

TEST II (Cont.)

readings are less than 10K ohms, repair short to ground. Repeat Quick Test. If resistance readings are 10K ohms or greater, go to step **12)**.

12) Turn key off and 10 seconds. Set DVOM on 200K scale. Leave breakout box installed and processor disconnected. Disconnect WAC solenoid. Measure resistance between test pin 54 and pins 37 and 57. If resistance reading is 10K ohms or greater, replace processor. Repeat Quick Test. If resistance reading is less than 10K ohms, service short to power. Repeat Quick Test.

13) Turn key off and wait 10 seconds. Disconnect processor 60 pin connector and inspect for damaged pins, corrosion, loose wires. Repair system as necessary. Connect breakout box to harness. Leave processor disconnected. Set DVOM on 20 volt scale. Measure voltage between test pin 10 (and pin 24 for 2.3L EFI models) and pin 40 on all other models. If output cycles 4-10.5 volts when A/C switch is cycled, replace processor. If not, go to step **14)**.

14) Turn key off and wait 10 seconds. Set DVOM on 200 ohm scale. Measure resistance between AA/ACD test pin 10 (ACD pin 24 on 2.3L EFI models)and A/C clutch and A/C demand switch. If resistance reading is 5 ohms or greater, repair harness circuit. If resistance reading is less than 5 ohms, EEC-IV system is okay. End of test.

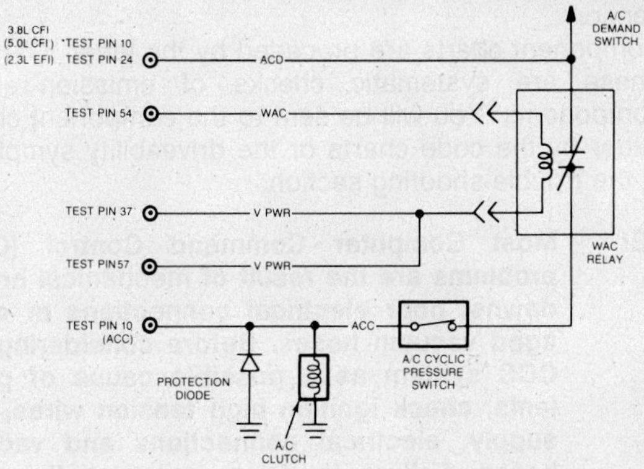

GENERAL MOTORS COMPUTER COMMAND CONTROL THEORY & OPERATION

Calif. 2.8L, 4.3L, 5.0L, 5.7L
All 2.5L

ORGANIZATION

This General Motors CEC article has been divided into sections: the first section describes CEC system operation and includes trouble shooting and diagnostic procedures that apply to all systems.

The last two sections contain all of the trouble code and component charts for diagnosing each individual system – Full Function and Throttle Body Injection (TBI). These sections also include the wiring diagrams and ECM connector pin voltages for each system.

The charts in the last two sections are arranged in the following order:

- Charts that are preceded by the letter "A" (A-2) are used to check engine diagnostics, fuel system and "Engine Cranks But Won't Run" conditions.
- Charts that are called out by a "Code" number (Code 14) are used after a code is stored in memory by the CEC. These codes designate a problem circuit or faulty sensor.
- Component charts are preceded by the letter "C" (C-8). These are systematic checks of emission-related components. You will be sent to the component charts either by the code charts or the driveability symptoms in the trouble shooting section.

NOTE: **Most Computer Command Control (CCC) problems are the result of mechanical breakdowns, poor electrical connections or damaged vacuum hoses. Before considering the CCC system as a possible cause of problems, check ignition high tension wires, fuel supply, electrical connections and vacuum hoses. Failure to do so may result in lost diagnostic time.**

GENERAL MOTORS CEC DIRECTORY

DESCRIPTION

The Computer Command Control (CCC) system controls engine operation and lowers exhaust emissions while maintaining good fuel economy and driveability. The Electronic Control Module (ECM) is the "brain" of the CCC system. The ECM controls as many as 13 different engine related systems to constantly adjust engine operation.

The CCC system is primarily an emission control system, designed to maintain a 14.7:1 air/fuel ratio under all operating conditions. When the ideal air/fuel ratio is maintained, the catalytic converter can control oxides of nitrogen (NOx), hydrocarbon (HC), and carbon monoxide (CO) emissions.

Fig. 1: Electronic Control Module Operating Conditions Sensed & Systems Controlled

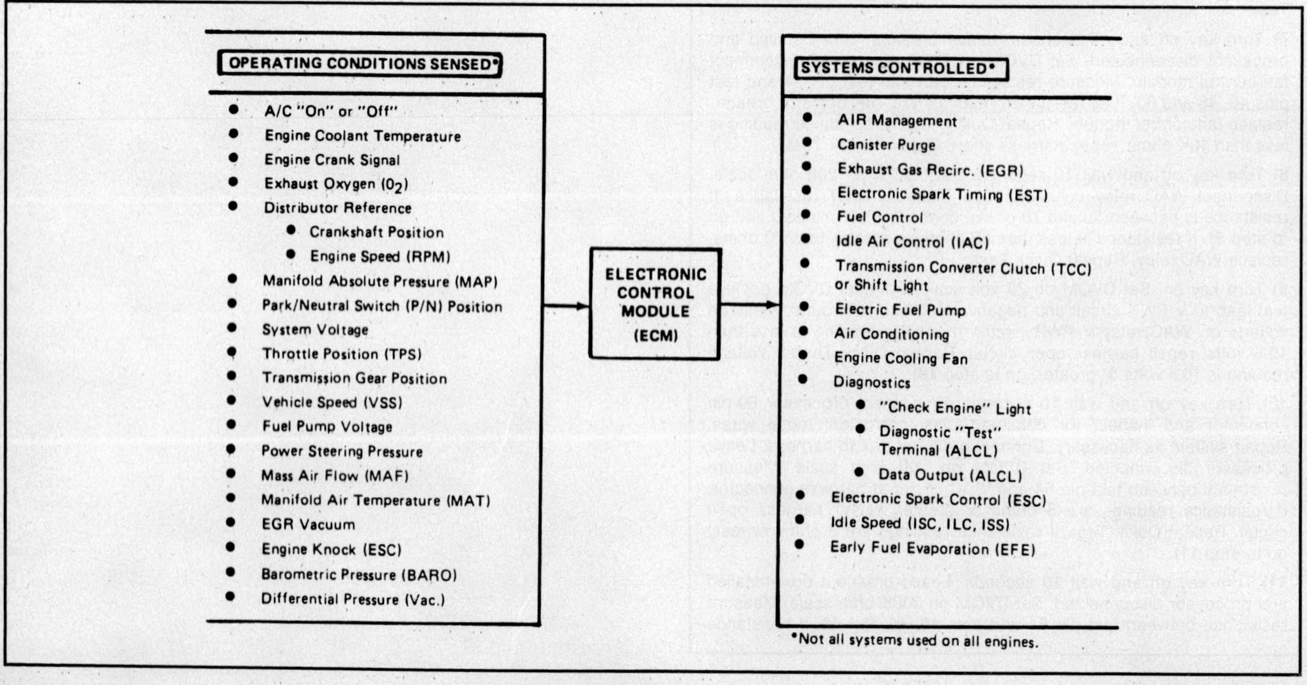

GENERAL MOTORS COMPUTER COMMAND CONTROL THEORY & OPERATION (Cont.)

OPERATION

The CCC system consists of the following subsystems: Fuel Control, Data Sensors, Electronic Control Module (ECM), Spark Timing, AIR Management, Emission Control, Torque Converter Clutch (TCC), Diagnostic System and Catalytic Converter.

FUEL CONTROL

Throttle Body Injection

An electrically pulsed injector is located in the intake manifold throttle body unit. The ECM controls injector "on" time (pulse width) to provide the proper amount of fuel to the engine, resulting in a 14.7:1 air/fuel ratio under most conditions.

Carbureted Models

All carbureted models are equipped with "feedback" carburetors with an electric mixture control (M/C) solenoid. The M/C solenoid operates single or dual metering rods in the float bowl. The metering rod system supplements fuel supplied by the idle and main systems in the carburetor. It varies the air/fuel ratio within a precalibrated range. The M/C solenoid also controls air/fuel ratio through the use of an idle air bleed that operates in conjunction with the metering rod(s).

Fig. 2: Sectional View of Mixture Control Solenoid

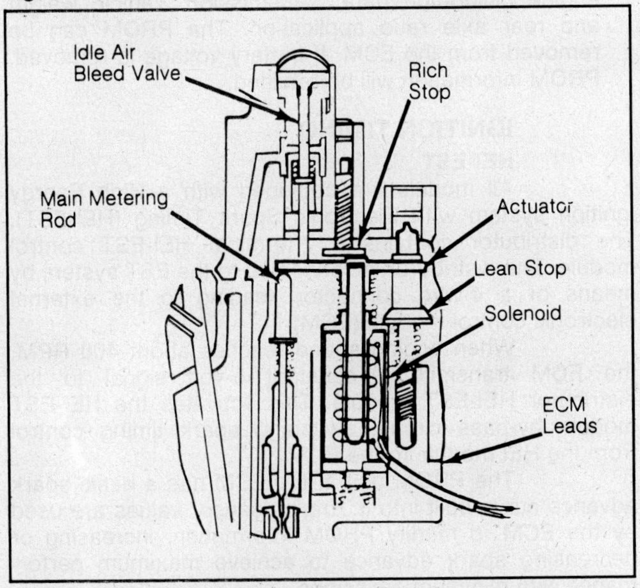

M4ME 4-bbl. carb. shown, E2SE 2-bbl. models similar.

Fig. 3: Throttle Body Injection Unit

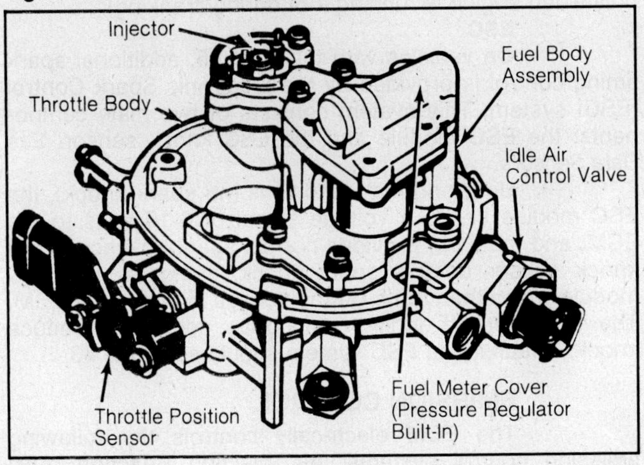

DATA SENSORS

Each sensor furnishes electronic impulses to the ECM. Based on these inputs, the ECM computes spark timing and air/fuel mixture for proper engine operation.

Coolant Temperature Sensor (CTS)

The CTS is located in a coolant passage. The ECM sends a 5 volt signal to the CTS. This 5 volt signal is reduced by the resistance of the CTS and a return signal is sent to the ECM. When coolant temperatures are low, CTS resistance is high (low voltage signal to ECM). When coolant temperatures are high, CTS resistance is low (higher voltage signal to ECM). A coolant sensor problem may set Code 14 or 15.

Manifold Absolute Pressure (MAP) Sensor

Used on fuel injected models only, the MAP sensor measures changes in intake manifold pressure resulting from engine load and speed changes. A 5-volt reference signal is sent to the sensor from the ECM. This signal is modified by the resistance of the sensor and sent back to the ECM.

Sensor resistance changes with manifold pressure. Therefore, sensor output voltage to the ECM is a direct indication of manifold pressure. High voltage indicates a high pressure condition while low voltage indicates a low pressure condition. The ECM uses this information to control fuel delivery and ignition timing.

The MAP sensor is also used to measure barometric pressure under certain conditions, which allows the ECM to automatically adjust for different altitudes.

A failure in the MAP sensor circuit should set a Code 33 or Code 34.

Differential Pressure (Vacuum) Sensor

Used on carbureted models only, this sensor measures the difference between atmospheric pressure (outside air) and manifold pressure (vacuum), i.e. pressure differential. The sensor converts this difference into a voltage output signal to the ECM. A problem in this circuit may set a Code 34.

Gear Select Switch

A gear select switch is used on some 4.3L, 5.0L and 5.7L models with automatic transmissions. This switch sends a signal to the ECM telling it what gear the transmission is in. The ECM uses this information to vary the conditions under which the converter clutch applies or releases. The transmission does not have to be in high gear for the ECM to engage the clutch. Transmissions using gear select switches can be identified by 3 or 4 wires coming out of the TCC connector.

On some models, a third gear switch (normally open) is placed in series on the battery side of the TCC solenoid. This switch prevents TCC application until the transmission is in third gear.

Knock Sensor

A knock sensor is used on all 4.3L engines with the Electronic Spark Control (ESC) system. Mounted in the engine block near the cylinders, this sensor detects abnormal engine vibration due to "detonation" and/or "pre-ignition". This information is sent to the ECM via the ESC

GENERAL MOTORS COMPUTER COMMAND CONTROL THEORY & OPERATION (Cont.)

module. The ECM then alters ignition timing as needed to reduce engine knock.

Oxygen (O_2) Sensor

The O_2 sensor is mounted in the exhaust system where it can monitor oxygen content of exhaust gases. The oxygen content reacts with the sensor to produce a voltage output signal which is sent to the ECM. This voltage signal is always low, varying from a minimum of about .1 volt (lean mixture) to a high of about .9 volt (rich mixture).

Based on this input, the ECM signals the injector (TBI) or M/C solenoid (carb.) to produce a leaner or richer mixture. An open O_2 sensor circuit should set a Code 13. An extended lean or rich mixture signal should set a Code 44 or 45, respectively.

CAUTION: Do not attempt to measure O_2 sensor output voltage. Current drain of voltmeter could damage the sensor. Do not connect any wiring or test equipment to the sensor.

Park/Neutral Switch (P/N)

The P/N switch is connected to the transmission gear selector on 2.5L TBI models, only. The switch indicates when the transmission is in Neutral or Park. Information from the P/N switch is used for TCC and IAC valve operation.

Throttle Position Sensor (TPS)

The TPS is a variable resistor connected to the throttle shaft on TBI units, or mounted in the carburetor. The ECM provides the TPS with a 5-volt reference signal which is modified according to throttle position and returned to the ECM. This return signal varies, being lowest with the throttle closed and highest during wide open throttle conditions.

On carbureted models, an open TPS circuit will cause the ECM to think the vehicle is at wide open throttle, causing the ECM command to go full rich. This should set a Code 21.

On TBI models, an open circuit will cause the ECM to think the throttle is closed, and will normally set a Code 22. If the circuit is shorted, the ECM will think the throttle is at wide open throttle and should set a Code 21.

On all models, once a trouble code is set, the ECM will use an artificial value for the TPS signal, and some vehicle performance will return.

Vehicle Speed Sensor (VSS)

The VSS is used on TBI models, only. It sends a pulsing voltage signal to the ECM which uses it to determine vehicle speed. TCC control is based largely on this information.

ELECTRONIC CONTROL MODULE (ECM)

The ECM is located in the passenger compartment behind the driver's seat on "G" series vans and behind right side of dash (near glove box) on all other models. The ECM consists of input/output devices, a Central Processing Unit (CPU), power supply and memories.

Input/Output Devices

These devices are an integral part of the ECM. They convert electrical signals, received by the ECM from the various engine sensors, into digital signals for use by the CPU.

Central Processing Unit (CPU)

Digital signals received by the CPU are used to perform all mathematical computations and logic functions necessary to deliver proper air/fuel mixture. The CPU also calculates spark timing and idle speed information. The CPU commands operation of emission control, closed loop fuel control and the diagnostic system.

Power Supply

The main source of power for the ECM is from the battery, through the ignition circuit.

Memories

The 3 types of memories in the ECM are: Read Only Memory (ROM), Random Access Memory (RAM), and Programmable Read Only Memory (PROM).

- **Read Only Memory (ROM)** – ROM is programmed information that can only be read by the ECM. The ROM program cannot be changed. If battery voltage is removed, ROM information will be retained.
- **Random Access Memory (RAM)** – This memory is the decision making center for the CPU. It works like a calculator. Data sensor input, diagnostic codes and results of calculations are temporarily stored in RAM. If battery voltage is removed from the ECM, all information stored in this memory is lost.
- **Programmable Read Only Memory (PROM)** – This memory is factory programmed information, including engine calibration data, transmission, vehicle weight and rear axle ratio application. The PROM can be removed from the ECM. If battery voltage is removed, PROM information will be retained.

IGNITION TIMING

HEI-EST

All models are equipped with a High Energy Ignition system with Electronic Spark Timing (HEI-EST). The distributor contains a 7-terminal HEI-EST control module. The distributor is connected to the EST system by means of a 4-wire connector, leading to the external electronic control module (ECM).

When engine speed reaches about 400 RPM, the ECM transmits a constant 5-volt signal to the distributor HEI-EST module. This activates the HEI-EST module by-pass circuit, switching spark timing control from the HEI module to the ECM.

The PROM unit in the ECM has a basic spark advance curve built into it. Engine sensor values are used by the ECM to modify PROM information, increasing or decreasing spark advance to achieve maximum performance with minimum emissions.

Spark timing is calculated by the ECM whenever an ignition pulse is present. Spark advance is controlled only when engine is running (not during cranking).

ESC

On vehicles with the 4.3L V6, additional spark timing control is provided by the Electronic Spark Control (ESC) system. This system consists of two main components: the ESC module and the ESC knock sensor. *See Data Sensors.*

Under normal conditions (no spark knock), the ESC module sends a voltage signal of 8-10 volts to the ECM, and the ECM provides normal spark advance. If the knock sensor detects spark knock, it signals the ESC module which then turns off the voltage signal to the ECM. The ECM retards ignition timing as needed to reduce knock. A fault in the ESC system should set Code 43.

EMISSION CONTROL

The ECM electrically controls the following emission control systems: Air Injection Reaction (AIR)

GENERAL MOTORS COMPUTER COMMAND CONTROL THEORY & OPERATION (Cont.)

Fig. 4: Component Locations for S/T Series Trucks and Astro Vans

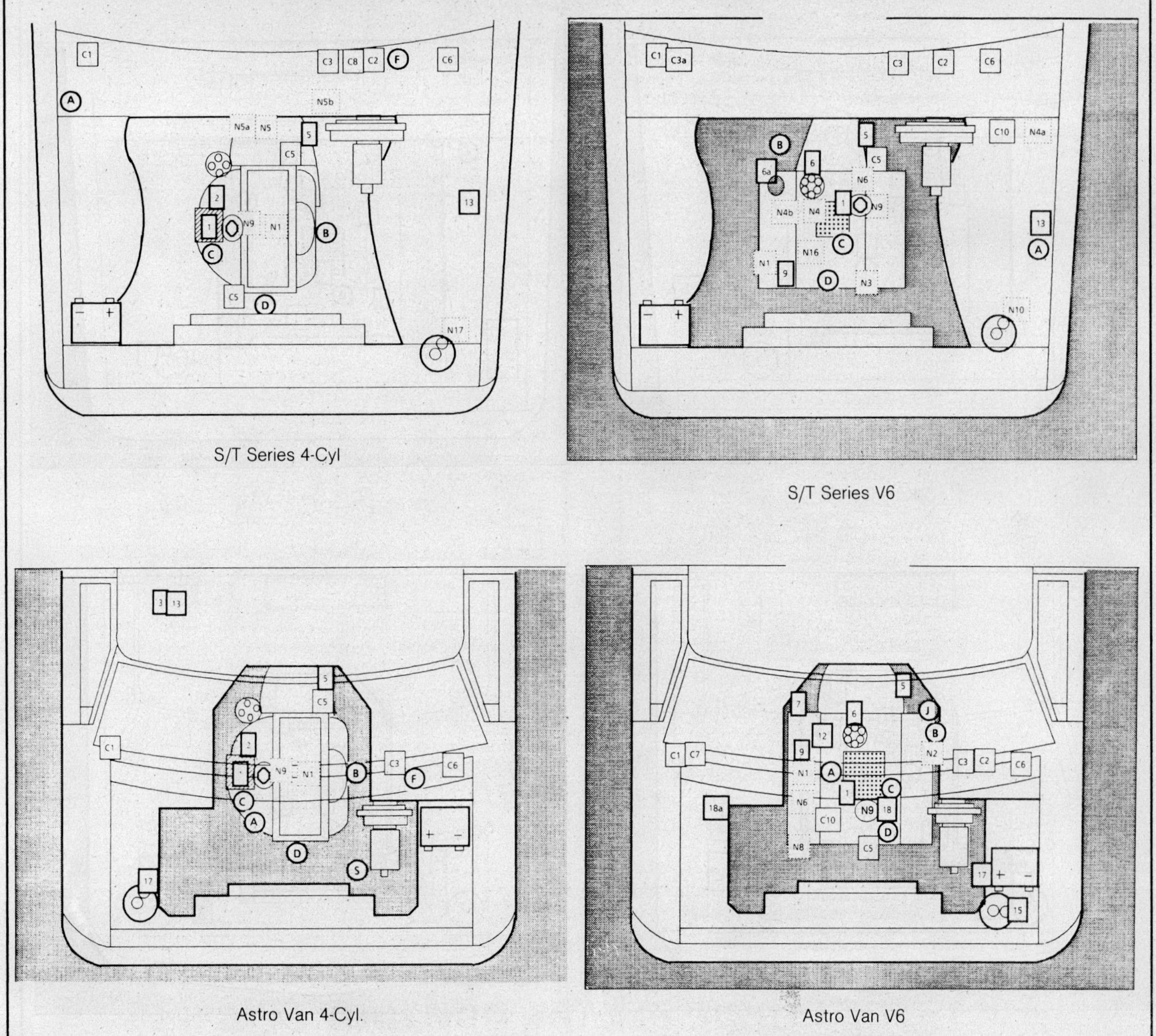

COMPUTER HARNESS

- C1. Electronic Control Module
- C2. ALCL Diagnostic Connector
- C3. "CHECK ENGINE" Light
- C3a. "CHECK ENGINE" Light Driver
- C5. ECM Harness Ground
- C6. Fuse Panel
- C7. "CHECK ENGINE" Light Driver
- C8. Fuel Pump Test Connector
- C10. Diagnostic Dwell Connector

INFORMATION SENSORS

- A. Manifold Pressure (Differential)
- B. Exhaust Oxygen
- C. Throttle Position
- D. Coolant Temperature
- F. Vehicle Speed
- J. ESC Detonation

EMISSION SYSTEMS (Not ECM Controlled)

- N1. PCV Valve
- N2. EFE Valve
- N3. Thermostatic Air Cleaner
- N4. EFE Heated Grid
- N4a. EFE Heated Grid Relay
- N4b. EFE Temperature Switch
- N5. Primary Fuel Cut-Off Relay
- N5a. Trans. Switch, Pri. Fuel Cut-Off
- N5b. Accl. Switch, Pri. Fuel Cut-Off
- N6. Decel Valve
- N8. Air Injection Pump
- N9. EGR Valve
- N10. Fuel Vapor Canister (2.8L)
- N17. Fuel Vapor Canister (2.5L)

CONTROLLED DEVICES

- 1. M/C Solenoid (Carb.) or Fuel Injector (TBI)
- 2. Idle Air Control Motor
- 3. Fuel Pump Relay
- 5. Torque Converter Clutch Connector
- 6. Electronic Spark Timing
- 6a. Ignition Coil
- 7. Electronic Spark Control (ESC) Module
- 9. AIR Divert Valve/Solenoid
- 10. Throttle Kicker Relay
- 12. EGR Solenoid
- 13. A/C Compressor Relay
- 15. Fuel Vapor Canister
- 17. Fuel Vapor Canister Solenoid
- 18. Throttle Kicker
- 18a. Throttle Kicker Solenoid

NOTE: NOT ALL COMPONENTS USED ON ALL MODELS

GENERAL MOTORS COMPUTER COMMAND CONTROL THEORY & OPERATION (Cont.)

Fig. 5: Component Locations for C/K Series Trucks and G Series Vans

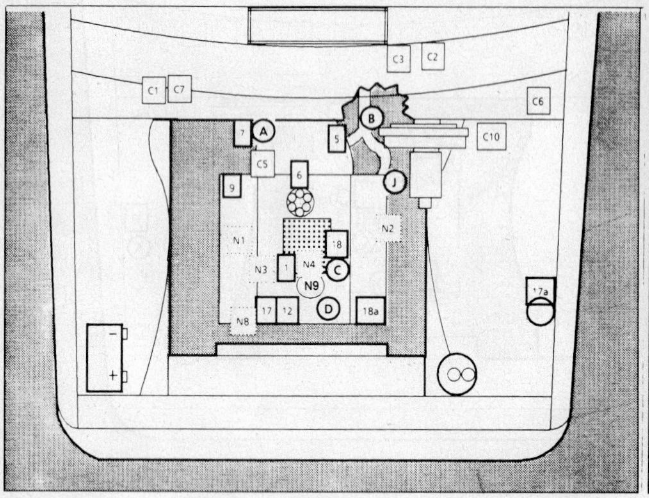

C/K Series V6

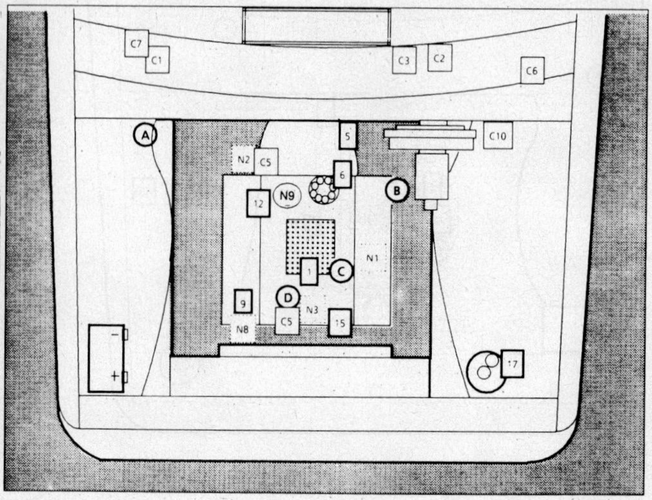

C/K Series V8

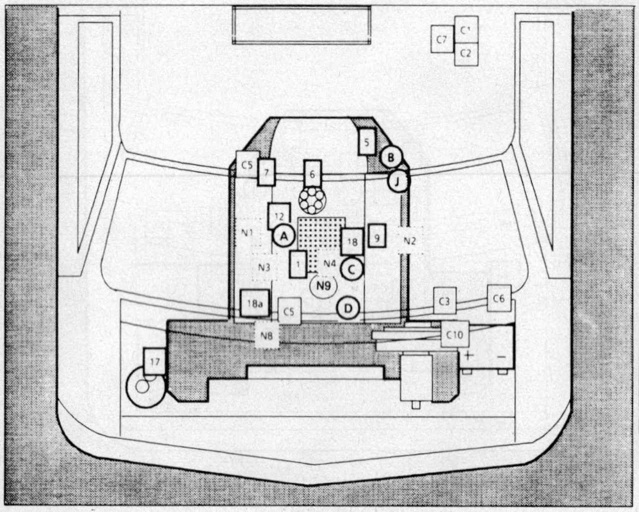

G Series V6

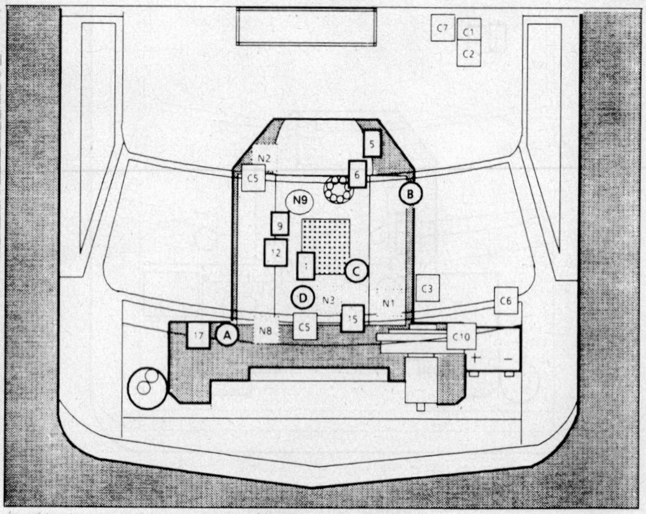

G Series V8

INFORMATION SENSORS

A. Manifold Pressure (Differential)
B. Exhaust Oxygen
C. Throttle Position
D. Coolant Temperature
F. ESC Detonation

EMISSION SYSTEMS (Not ECM Controlled)

N1. PCV Valve
N2. EFE Valve
N3. Deceleration Valve
N4. Accelerator Pump Solenoid
N8. Air Injection Pump
N9. EGR Valve

CONTROLLED DEVICES

1. Mixture Control Solenoid
5. Torque Converter Clutch Connector
6. Electronic Spark Timing
7. Electronic Spark Control (ESC) Module
9. Air Injection Divert Valve
12. EGR Solenoid
15. Fuel Vapor Canister Solenoid
17. Fuel Vapor Canister Solenoid (V6) or Fuel Vapor Canister (V8)
17a. Auxiliary Fuel Vapor Canister
18. Throttle Kicker
18a. Throttle Kicker Solenoid

COMPUTER HARNESS

C1. Electronic Control Module
C2. ALCL Diagnostic Connector
C3. "CHECK ENGINE" Light
C5. ECM Harness Ground
C6. Fuse Panel
C7. "CHECK ENGINE" Light Driver
C10. Diagnostic Dwell Connector (V6) or Air/Fuel Dwell Connector (V8)

NOTE: NOT ALL COMPONENTS USED ON ALL MODELS

GENERAL MOTORS COMPUTER COMMAND CONTROL THEORY & OPERATION (Cont.)

Management (except 2.5L TBI), Exhaust Gas Recirculation (EGR) on 4.3L, 5.0L and 5.7L models, and Evaporative Emission Control (EEC) on 4.3L, 5.0L and 5.7L models.

AIR Management System

This system helps reduce hydrocarbon (HC) and carbon monoxide (CO) exhaust emissions. Air is injected into the exhaust ports, allowing for completion of the combustion process after exhaust gases leave the combustion chamber.

When the ECM energizes the air control valve, air flow from the air pump to the valve is directed to the exhaust ports. During warm engine operation (closed loop), the ECM de-energizes the air control valve, diverting air flow to the air cleaner or atmosphere.

A deceleration valve is used to prevent backfiring on 2.8L and 4.3L V6 engines. During high vacuum conditions (deceleration), this valve allows air flow from the air cleaner to the intake manifold, leaning out the rich air/fuel mixture created by high vacuum when the throttle valve closes.

EGR System

An ECM controlled solenoid valve is used to control EGR valve function. This valve is located in the vacuum line to the EGR valve and is operated by the ECM in response to coolant temperature, throttle position and manifold pressure.

Under conditions of low coolant temperature, engine cranking, wide open throttle, or engine idle, the solenoid valve is energized, blocking vacuum to the EGR valve. At normal operating temperatures, the solenoid valve is de-energized, allowing normal EGR valve function.

EEC System

This system controls purging of the vapor canister. The ECM controls vacuum to the purge valve with a solenoid. When the engine is in open loop, the solenoid valve is energized. This blocks vacuum to the purge valve.

The solenoid is de-energized, allowing the vacuum signal to reach the purge valve, when the engine is at normal operating temperature, above idle speed and the control system is in closed loop (system not in ALCL mode). Fuel vapors are then drawn into the intake manifold and burned.

TORQUE CONVERTER CLUTCH (TCC)

The ECM controls a solenoid valve mounted in the transmission to allow the torque converter to directly connect the engine to the transmission. This reduces slippage and improves fuel economy. The ECM uses information concerning vehicle speed (2.5L TBI), coolant temperature, throttle position and gear position (some models) to determine when to apply the TCC.

When operating conditions indicate that the transmission should function normally, or when the brake pedal is applied, the TCC solenoid is de-energized. This allows the transmission to return to normal automatic operation.

DIAGNOSTIC SYSTEM

NOTE: **A "CHECK ENGINE" lamp driver is installed in the wiring harness from ECM to the "CHECK ENGINE" lamp. This driver amplifies power to the "CHECK ENGINE" lamp to reduce amperage draw on the battery.**

The ECM of the CCC system is equipped with self-diagnostic capabilities which detect system failures or abnormalities. When a malfunction occurs, the ECM will light the "CHECK ENGINE" lamp in the instrument panel. At the same time, a corresponding trouble code is stored in ECM memory. Malfunctions may be recorded as "hard failures" or "intermittent failures".

- "Hard failures" cause the "CHECK ENGINE" lamp to glow and remain on until the malfunction is repaired. If the "CHECK ENGINE" lamp comes on and remains on during vehicle operation, the cause of the malfunction must be determined.
- "Intermittent failures" cause the "CHECK ENGINE" lamp to come on, then flicker or go out after about 10 seconds when the fault goes away. However, the corresponding trouble code will be retained in the ECM memory.

  "Intermittent failures" may be sensor related. If a sensor fails, the ECM will use a substitute value in its calculations to continue engine operation. In this condition, service is not mandatory; but loss of good driveability is likely. If the related fault does not happen again within 50 engine restarts, the related trouble code will be erased from ECM memory.

As a bulb and system check, the "CHECK ENGINE" lamp will glow when the ignition switch is turned on and the engine is not running. When the engine is started, the lamp should go out. If not, a malfunction has been detected in the CCC system.

NOTE: **Trouble codes will be recorded at various operating times. Some codes require operation of that sensor or switch for 5 seconds; others require operation for 5 minutes or longer.**

DIAGNOSIS & TESTING

DIAGNOSTIC PROCEDURE

Diagnosis of the CCC system should be performed in the following order:

1) Make sure that all engine systems not related to the CCC system are operating properly. Do not proceed with testing unless all other problems have been repaired.

2) Go to the Diagnostic Circuit Check chart and follow all instructions given there to verify proper operation of ECM self-diagnostics and to obtain any stored trouble codes.

3) If trouble codes were displayed, determine whether the codes are "intermittent" or "hard". Go to numbered Code Charts for further diagnosis of stored trouble codes.

4) If no trouble codes were displayed, proceed to System Performance Check on carbureted models, or Field Service Mode on TBI models (part of Diagnostic Circuit Check).

5) If no trouble is indicated by any of these charts, use the TROUBLE SHOOTING material in this article. The comments there will send you to the proper component charts or tell you what to fix.

6) After any repairs have been made, always perform System Performance Check. Clear any trouble codes.

GENERAL MOTORS COMPUTER COMMAND CONTROL THEORY & OPERATION (Cont.)

NOTE: Each of the steps listed here are described later in this section. If you are unsure of the proper way to test, read through the following material.

ENTERING OR EXITING DIAGNOSTIC MODE

1) Turn ignition switch on but do not start engine. "CHECK ENGINE" light should glow. Locate assembly line communication link (ALCL) connector attached to ECM wiring harness under instrument panel near steering column (under driver's seat on "G" model vans). Insert spade lug terminal across "TEST" terminal and "GROUND" terminal. *See Fig. 6*.

CAUTION: Inserting spade lug in terminals of ALCL connector grounds "TEST" terminal lead. Do not ground ALCL connector until after ignition is on or engine is started.

Fig. 6: ALCL Connector Terminal Locations

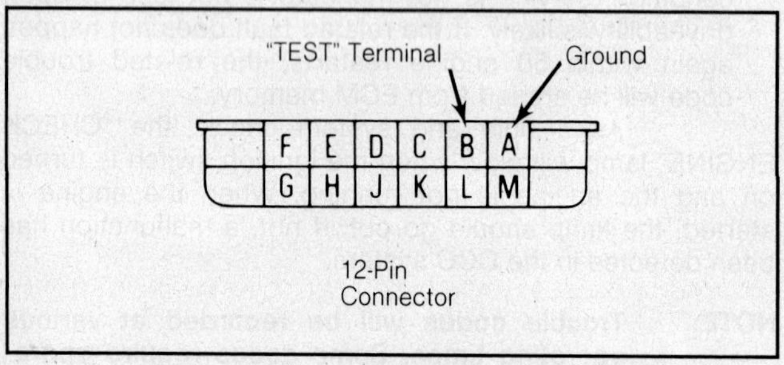

2) "CHECK ENGINE" light should flash code "12" ("FLASH", pause, "FLASH", "FLASH"). Code "12" will be repeated 2 more times. If any trouble codes are stored in the ECM memory, they will be displayed in the same manner.

3) Trouble codes will be displayed from lowest to highest numbered codes (3 times each) and be repeated as long as the "TEST" terminal of the ALCL connector is grounded.

4) To exit diagnostic mode, turn ignition switch off and remove spade lug terminal from ALCL connector.

CLEARING TROUBLE CODES

Trouble codes are cleared by removing battery voltage from the ECM for at least 10 seconds. To do so, be sure ignition switch is "OFF" and remove battery positive terminal, or disconnect ECM harness from positive battery pigtail, or remove ECM fuse from fuse block.

READING TROUBLE CODES

The ECM stores component failure information for the CCC system under a related trouble code which can be recalled for diagnosis and repair. When recalled, these codes will be displayed by flashes of the "CHECK ENGINE" light. Trouble codes are displayed starting with the lowest numbered code. Only codes that represent a definite malfunction will be shown.

Trouble codes are read by counting flashes of the "CHECK ENGINE" light, or by reading output of a diagnostic tool connected to the ALCL connector. These special tools are faster and more accurate, but are not mandatory.

If a special diagnostic tool is not available, read the flashes of the "CHECK ENGINE" light. For example, "FLASH", "FLASH", pause, "FLASH", longer pause, identifies "21". The first flashes are the first digit of the code, second flashes are the second digit.

ECM TROUBLE CODE IDENTIFICATION

Code	Circuit Affected
13	Oxygen sensor circuit.
14	Shorted coolant sensor circuit.
15	Open coolant sensor circuit.
21	Open TPS circuit or TPS misadjusted.
22	Grounded TPS circuit or TPS misadjusted.
23	M/C solenoid open or grounded (carb. models).
24	Vehicle Speed Sensor circuit.
32	Baro sensor circuit signal low (carb. models).
33	MAP sensor voltage low (TBI models).
34	MAP or Vacuum sensor circuit.
35	IAC circuit (TBI models) or ISC control switch (carb. models).
41	No dist. reference pulses to ECM (carb. models).
42	EST circuit.
43	ESC circuit (carb. models).
44	Lean exhaust signal (from oxygen sensor).
45	Rich exhaust signal (from oxygen sensor).
51	Faulty PROM or improper PROM installation.
53	EGR valve vacuum signal (carb. models).
54	Shorted M/C solenoid circuit and/or faulty ECM (carb. models).
55	Faulty ECM (TBI models).

"12" will display only if no reference pulses are received by the ECM; it will never be stored as a malfunction.

TROUBLE CODE DETERMINATION (HARD OR INTERMITTENT)

During any diagnostic procedure, you must decide between "hard" codes and "intermittent" codes. Diagnostic charts will not help analyze intermittent failures.

Proper use of the Diagnostic Circuit Check chart will determine whether a stored code is intermittent or hard. An intermittent code is one which does not reset and is generally not present while diagnosing the vehicle. They are frequently caused by loose connections. A hard code will repeat itself during the circuit check and will reset while diagnosing the vehicle.

DIAGNOSTIC MATERIALS

NOTE: The charts described in the following paragraphs are arranged later in this article by CCC system (TBI or Full Function). See the first page of this article for page numbers of the different charts.

Diagnostic Charts

Diagnostic Charts are used to find and repair problems which On-Vehicle Diagnostics have found. These charts include:

- Charts which fix a problem when the On-Vehicle Diagnostics don't work.
- Charts where a stored trouble code leads you to a particular problem.

GENERAL MOTORS COMPUTER COMMAND CONTROL THEORY & OPERATION (Cont.)

- Charts which are used because the System Performance Check (carbureted models) or the Field Service Mode (TBI models) found a problem.
- "Engine Cranks But Won't Run" charts.

Diagnostic Circuit Check

1) If complaint is "CHECK ENGINE" lamp related, this check will lead to the most likely problem area (if a malfunction exists). Enter diagnostic mode and record stored trouble codes. Begin diagnosis with the lowest numbered code shown and go to the numbered trouble code chart.

2) If code "51" is displayed, see PROM removal and installation in this article. If codes "54" or "55" are displayed with another code, always refer to diagnostic chart for code "54" or "55" first, then proceed to lowest numbered code.

Diagnostic Symptom Check

1) If complaint is not "CHECK ENGINE" lamp related, this check will lead to most likely problem area. However, first make checks that would normally be made for the complaint on a vehicle without CCC system.

2) Follow instructions in diagnostic chart and repair malfunction. After repair, perform System Performance Check (carbureted models) or Field Service Mode check (TBI models).

System Performance Check (Carbureted Models Only)

1) This check verifies that CCC system is functioning correctly. It should always be made after any repair on CCC system.

2) When performing this check, always engage parking brake and block drive wheels.

3) On some engines, the oxygen sensor will cool off after only a short period of time while engine is idling. This will cause engine to go into open loop. To restore closed loop mode, run engine at part throttle for several minutes, accelerating from idle to part throttle several times.

Field Service Mode (TBI Models Only)

1) This test confirms proper operation of fuel system and verifies Closed Loop operation. It is part of the Diagnostic Circuit Check for TBI models. Clear codes and perform this test after any repair is completed.

2) When performing this check, always engage parking brake and block drive wheels.

3) On some engines, the oxygen sensor will cool off after only a short period of time while engine is idling. This will cause engine to go into open loop. To restore closed loop mode, run engine at part throttle for serveral minutes, accelerating from idle to part throttle several times.

NOTE: **Although there are many charts connected with CCC diagnosis, only 2 charts are needed to prove the system is operating properly. Normally, only 3 charts are necessary to find a problem, if one exists.**

DIAGNOSTIC TOOLS

The CCC system does not require special tools for diagnosis. A tachometer, dwell meter, test light, ohmmeter, digital voltmeter with 10 megohms impedance (minimum), vacuum pump, vacuum gauge and 6 jumper wires 6" long (1 wire with female connectors at both ends, 1 wire with male connectors at both ends, 4 wires with male and female connectors at opposite ends) are the only tools necessary for diagnosis.

A test light, rather than a voltmeter, must be used when indicated by a diagnostic chart.

Some brands of dwell meter are not compatible with General Motors CCC systems. If engine operation seems to change as meter is connected, remove dwell meter and use another type.

NOTE: **Special testers can be used to read trouble codes and check voltages in the system. These tools can save a great deal of time, but are not required. Refer to tester manual for operating procedures.**

TROUBLE SHOOTING

HOW TO USE THIS SECTION

The Trouble Shooting section should be used only AFTER the Diagnostic Circuit Check has been performed to verify that:

- On-Vehicle Diagnostics are working.
- There are no trouble codes stored, or only intermittent ones.
- Fuel control system is operating properly as verified by System Performance Check (carbureted models) or Field Service Mode Check (TBI models).

Verify customer complaint and locate the correct symptom below. Check items indicated under that symptom. These procedures will normally lead to a component system on the vehicle, such as EGR, EST, TCC, etc. These are covered in the Component charts. These charts are listed with a "C" before the number of the chart (C-2A, for example).

Several of the following procedures call for a careful visual check. This check should include:

- Vacuum hoses for splits, kinks and proper connections, as shown on Emission Control Information label.
- Air leaks at throttle body or carburetor mounting and intake manifold.
- Ignition wires for cracking, hardness, proper routing, and carbon tracking.
- Wiring for proper connections, pinches, and cuts.

NOTE: **On vehicles with TBI, if engine cranks but will not run, see 2.5L TBI Chart A-3.**

INTERMITTENT "CHECK ENGINE" LIGHT

Symptom Definition

"CHECK ENGINE" light comes on at times, but does not stay on. A stored code may or may not exist.

Possible Cause & Correction

- Check for poor mating of one connector to another. Terminals may not be fully seated. Check for improperly formed or damaged terminals. Check wire to terminal connections.
- If visual check doesn't find cause of problem, drive vehicle with voltmeter connected to suspected circuit and ground. If voltage reading changes as problem occurs, problem is in that circuit.
- Check for poor connection from ignition coil to ground or arcing at spark plug wires or plugs.
- Check wire from "CHECK ENGINE" light to ECM for short to ground.

GENERAL MOTORS COMPUTER COMMAND CONTROL THEORY & OPERATION (Cont.)

- Check diagnostic "Test" terminal wire to ECM for short to ground.
- Check ECM terminals A and U (carbureted engines) or circuits 450R and 450 (TBI engines) for good engine ground connections.
- Check for loss of trouble code memory:
  - On carbureted engines: ground dwell lead for 10 seconds with "test" lead left ungrounded. Code 23 should be stored and retained in memory after engine is stopped and key is turned to "RUN" position. If not, ECM is faulty.
  - On TBI engines: disconnect TPS and idle engine until "CHECK ENGINE" light comes on. Code 22 should be stored when ignition is turned off. If not, ECM is faulty.
- Check for electrical system interference caused by a defective relay or an ECM driven solenoid or switch. They can cause a sharp electrical surge. Problem will usually occur when faulty component is operated.
- Check for improper installation of electrical accessories such as auxiliary lights, 2-way radios, etc.
- Make sure EST wires are kept away from spark plug wires, distributor wires, distributor housing, ignition coil and generator. Make sure wire from ECM to distributor is a good ground.
- Check for open diode across air conditioner compressor clutch, or other open diodes.

NO START – ENGINE CRANKS OK (CARB. MODELS ONLY)

Symptom Definition

Engine cranks properly but does not start. Engine may fire a few times.

Possible Cause & Correction

- Make sure proper starting procedure is being used.
- Perform careful visual check.
- Remove air cleaner and check carburetor choke valve, vacuum break(s), linkage and unloader operation. Choke valve should move smoothly and be closed when cold; open when hot.
- Check for presence of fuel by noting carburetor accelerator pump operation. Look for gas squirt in carburetor bore while quickly opening throttle lever. If no squirt, check for: fuel in tank, carburetor fuel inlet filter dirty or clogged, fuel pump capacity, and float needle for proper operation. If there is a pump squirt, crank engine and check for flooding. If engine is not flooding, check ignition system. *See CHART C-4A (C-4B for 2.8L models).*
- Remove spark plugs, check and replace as necessary.
- Remove distributor cap and check for moisture, dust, cracks, burns, and arcing to coil mounting screws.
- Try to turn distributor shaft by hand. Drive pin may be broken.
- After starting engine, perform "System Performance Check."
- In very cold temperatures, check that proper viscosity oil is used and that the crankcase oil is not contaminated with gasoline.

HARD START (TBI MODELS ONLY)

Symptom Definition

Engine cranks but doesn't start for a long time. Eventually runs. If engine starts but immediately dies (as key is released from "start" position), *see CHART A-3.*

Possible Cause and Correction

- Perform careful visual check.
- Make sure driver is using correct starting procedure.
- Check fuel pump relay: probe fuel pump test terminal with test light to ground. Turn ignition off for 10 seconds, then turn ignition on. Test light should light for 2 seconds. If not, see *CHART A-5 TEST POINT 1.*
- Check TPS for sticking or binding.
- Check injector for leaking. Disconnect injector connector and watch for fuel leakage while cranking.
- Check for high resistance in coolant sensor or sensor circuit. *See CODE 15 CHART.*
- Check for faulty in-tank fuel pump check valve:
  - With ignition off, disconnect fuel line at filter.
  - Remove fuel tank filler cap and connect radiator test pump. Apply 103 kPa (15 psi) pressure in fuel tank. If pressure holds for 60 seconds, check valve is OK.
- Check ignition system for proper operation. Check distributor for:
  - Proper output signal.
  - Worn shaft.
  - Bare and/or shorted wires.
  - Pickup coil resistance and connections.
  - Loose ignition coil ground.
  - Moisture in distributor cap.
- Remove spark plugs. Check for wet plugs, cracks, wear, improper gap, burned electrodes, or heavy deposits. Repair or replace as necessary.
- Fuel pressure should be 9-13 psi (62-90 kPa) at all engine speeds.

HARD START – COLD (CARB. MODELS ONLY)

Symptom Definition

Engine cranks, but does not start for a long time. Eventually, engine does run. If engine starts but immediately dies (as soon as key is released from start position), see *"No Start – Engine Cranks OK."*

Possible Cause & Correction

- Be sure driver is using proper starting procedure.
- Perform careful visual check.
- Check the choke valve, throttle and fast idle cam for sticking. Replace any malfunctioning parts. If caused by foreign material and gum, clean with non-oil base solvent.
- Check choke and vacuum break operation and adjustment. Choke should be closed cold.
- Check EGR valve system for faulty operation that could cause valve to stick open.
- Check float level using external float gauge. Adjust float to specification if required.
- Check carburetor fuel inlet filter, replace if required.
- Check ignition system. *See CHART C-4A (C-4B for 2.8L models).*
  - Check distributor for: Worn shaft, bare and shorted wires, pickup coil resistance and connections, loose ignition coil ground, or moisture in distributor cap.
  - Remove spark plugs and check for wet plugs, wear, improper gap, burned electrodes or heavy deposits. Repair or replace as necessary.
- Check ignition timing and adjust if necessary.

GENERAL MOTORS COMPUTER COMMAND CONTROL THEORY & OPERATION (Cont.)

HARD START – HOT (CARB. MODELS ONLY)

Symptom Definition

Engine cranks, but does not start for a long time. Eventually, engine does run. If the engine starts but immediately dies (as soon as key is released from start position), see *"Ignition System Check."*

Possible Cause & Correction

- Be sure driver is using proper starting procedure.
- Perform careful visual check.
- Check choke valve, throttle linkage and fast idle cam for sticking. Replace any malfunctioning parts. If caused by foreign material and gum, clean with non-oil base solvent.
- Check choke and vacuum break operation and adjustment. Choke should be open hot.
- Check for carb flooding. Check fuel filter and replace as needed.
- Check float level using external float gauge. Adjust float to specification if required.
- On models with 2.8L engine, check EFE electric heater. Heater should be off. *See CHARTS C-9C & E.* On all other models, check EFE valve (if equipped). Valve should be open.
- On all models, check EGR valve system for faulty operation that could cause valve to stick open.
- Check for obvious overheating problems.
- Check ignition system. *See CHART C-4A (C-4B for 2.8L models).*
  - Check distributor for: worn shaft, bare and shorted wires, pickup coil resistance and connections, loose ignition coil ground, and moisture in distributor cap.
  - Remove spark plugs and check for wet plugs, wear, improper gap, burned electrodes or heavy deposits. Repair or replace as necessary.
- Check ignition timing and adjust if necessary.

STALL AFTER START (TBI MODELS ONLY)

Symptom Definition

Engine starts but dies: after brief idle; as soon as any load is place on it (such as A/C turned on or transmission engaged); on initial driveaway.

Possible Cause & Correction

- Perform careful visual check.
- Make sure hot air tube is connected to air cleaner.
- Check proper operation of thermostatic air cleaner.
- Check PCV valve operation by placing finger over inlet hole in valve end several times. Valve should snap back. If not, replace valve.
- Check that EGR valve is not sticking open. *See CHART C-7A.*
- Check for high A/C head pressure (could be caused by inoperative engine cooling fan or overcharged system).
- Check for plugged or restricted fuel lines.
- Check for weak spark from faulty igntion coil.

STALL AFTER START – COLD (CARB. MODELS ONLY)

Symptom Definition

Condition occurs with engine at room or outside temperature. Within three minutes after start, engine either stalls after brief idle, dies as soon as any load is placed on engine (such as A/C turned "ON" or transmission engaged), or dies on initial driveaway. If symptom is present with engine cold and hot, go to *"Stall After Start – Hot."*

Possible Cause & Correction

- Visually check vacuum hoses for splits, kinks and proper connections, as shown on the Vehicle Emission Control Information label.
- Make sure hot air tube is connected to air cleaner.
- Check for proper operation of thermostatic air cleaner.
- Check the choke valve, throttle and fast idle cam for sticking. Replace any malfunctioning parts. If caused by foreign material and gum, clean with non-oil base solvent.
- With engine running, check vacuum break linkage for movement while removing and re-installing vacuum hoses to vacuum breaks. If linkage does not move and vacuum is at hose, check for binding linkage. If linkage OK, replace vacuum break unit.
- With engine "OFF" check all choke adjustments, including vacuum breaks and TVS if used.
- Check fast idle speed (if applicable) and curb idle speed.
- Check carburetor accelerator pump operation.
- On 2.8L models, check EFE electric heater operation. Heater should be "ON" cold. *See CHART C-9E.*
- On all other models, check EFE valve for proper operation. EFE valve should be closed cold. *See CHART C-9C.*
- Check EGR valve system for sticky operation that could cause valve to stick open.
- Check ignition timing and adjust if necessary.
- Check for poor or contaminated gasoline.

STALL AFTER START – HOT (CARB. MODELS ONLY)

Symptom Definition

Engine starts okay, but dies: after brief idle; as soon as any load is placed on it (such as A/C turned on or transmission engaged); or dies on initial driveaway.

Possible Cause & Correction

- Visually check vacuum hoses for splits, kinks and proper connections, as shown on the Vehicle Emission Control Information label.
- Make sure hot air tube is connected to air cleaner.
- Check for proper operation of thermostatic air cleaner.
- Check the choke valve and vacuum breaks for proper operation. Replace any malfunctioning parts. If caused by foreign material and gum, clean with non-oil base solvent.
- Check carburetor accelerator pump operation.
- Check fast idle speed and curb idle speed if applicable.
- Check EFE electric heater for proper operation (2.8L models only). EFE heater should be on. *See CHARTS C-9E.*
- Check EGR valve system for faulty operation that could cause valve to stick open.
- Check for overcharged A/C system or high A/C head pressure.
- Check for obvious overheating problems such as low coolant level, loose water pump belt, restricted air flow to radiator or restricted water flow through radiator.

HESITATION, SAG, STUMBLE

Symptom Definition

Momentary lack of response as accelerator is pushed down. May occur at any vehicle speed. Usually

GENERAL MOTORS COMPUTER COMMAND CONTROL THEORY & OPERATION (Cont.)

most severe when first trying to make vehicle move. Can occasionally cause vehicle to stall.

Possible Cause & Correction – TBI Models

- Perform careful visual check.
- Check thermostatic air cleaner operation.
- Fuel pressure should be a steady 9-13 psi (62-90 kPa) at all engine speeds. Check for water in fuel.
- Check vacuum hose to MAP sensor for leaks or restrictions.
- Check for fouled spark plugs.
- Check for correct PROM number.
- Check TPS for binding or sticking.
- Check ignition timing (See Emission Control Information label).
- Check EGR system for valve sticking open intermittently. *See CHART C-7A.*
- Check fuel injectors:
  - With injector connector disconnected, check for fuel leakage from injector while cranking. Reattach connector.
  - Check for fuel spray from injector. If no spray from injector, see *CHART A-3*.
- Check generator output voltage. Repair if less than 9 or more than 16 volts.
- Check for good HEI ground (circuit 453).
- Check canister purge system for proper operation.

Possible Cause & Correction – Carbureted Models

- Perform careful visual check.
- Make sure hot air tube is connected to air cleaner.
- Check for proper operation of thermostatic air cleaner.
- If symptoms occur on cold engine only, check the following for sticking or faulty operation:
  - Carburetor choke, including vacuum break, throttle linkage and fast idle cam.
  - Choke TVS (if used).
  - All choke adjustments, including vacuum breaks.
- Check float level with external float gage and adjust as needed.
- Check carb accelerator pump operation.
- Check vacuum hose to vacuum sensor for leaks, restrictions and proper connections (should be manifold vacuum).
- Check EGR valve operation.
- Check TPS adjustment.
- Check canister purge system.
- Check for open ignition coil ground and for intermittent ECM ground.
- Check engine ignition timing.
- Poor or contaminated gasoline.

REMOVAL & INSTALLATION

ELECTRONIC CONTROL MODULE (ECM)

Removal

Turn ignition switch off. Disconnect negative battery cable from battery. Locate ECM and remove electrical connectors. Remove ECM from vehicle.

Installation

Reinstall ECM into vehicle. Connect electrical connectors to ECM, install access panels and connect negative battery cable to battery.

PROGRAMMABLE READ ONLY MEMORY

Removal

1) Remove ECM from vehicle as previously described and remove access cover. Note location of reference notches in PROM and ECM for reassembly reference.

2) Engage one end of PROM carrier with hook end of rocker-type PROM removal tool. Press on vertical bar end of tool and rock engaged end of PROM carrier up as far as possible.

3) Engage opposite end of PROM carier in the same manner and rock this end up as far as possible. Repeat process until PROM carrier and PROM are free of PROM socket.

4) PROM carrier and PROM should lift off of PROM socket easily.

NOTE: **PROM carrier should ONLY be removed with special PROM removal tool. Use of any other method may damage PROM or PROM socket.**

Installation

1) Check that new PROM has same service number as replaced PROM. Place new PROM and carrier in ECM. Press on PROM carrier until PROM is firmly seated in ECM.

NOTE: **Make sure that reference notches in ECM and PROM are properly aligned.**

Fig. 7: Replacing PROM in Electronic Control Module

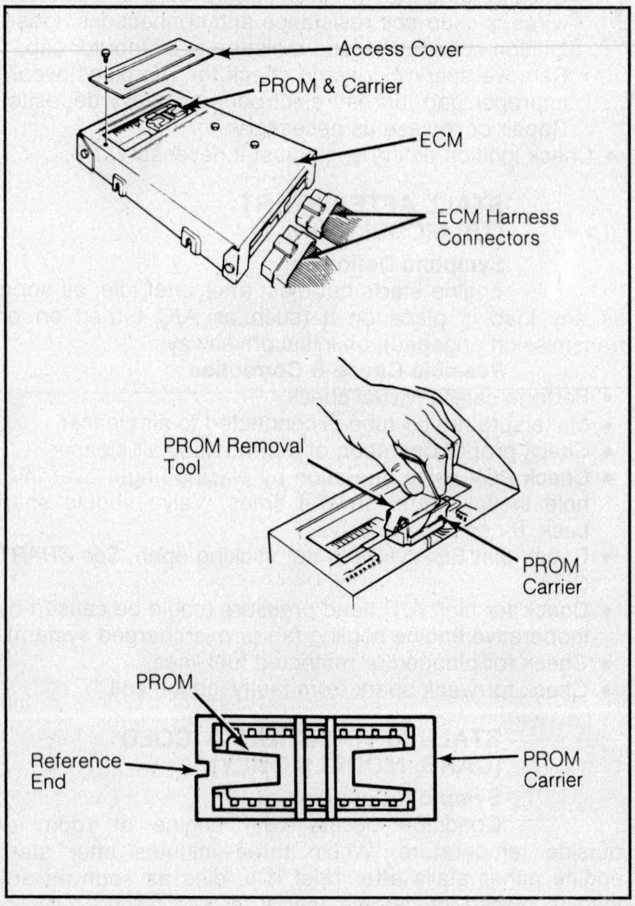

Always use PROM removal tool when replacing PROM.

GENERAL MOTORS COMPUTER COMMAND CONTROL THEORY & OPERATION (Cont.)

2) Reinstall PROM access cover on ECM. Reinstall ECM in vehicle as previously described. Start engine and ground diagnostic test lead.

3) Code 12 should flash at least 4 times, with no other codes stored. This confirms proper PROM installation.

4) If Code 51 is stored, or if CHECK ENGINE light stays on constantly, PROM is not fully seated in ECM, is installed backwards, has bent pins or is defective. If pins are bent and crack when straightened, PROM must be replaced. If PROM is installed backwards or is defective, it must be replaced.

OXYGEN (O_2) SENSOR

Removal

Disconnect negative battery cable at battery. Raise vehicle, if required. Disconnect electrical connector from oxygen sensor. Carefully remove O_2 sensor from exhaust pipe.

NOTE: **O_2 sensor may be difficult to remove when engine temperature is below 120°F (49°C). Excessive removal force may damage threads in exhaust manifold or pipe.**

Installation

1) Whenever an O_2 sensor is removed, its threads must be coated with anti-seize compound before it is reinstalled. New sensors will already have this compound applied to threads.

2) Install O_2 sensor in exhaust pipe and tighten to 30 ft. lbs. (41 N.m). Reconnect electrical connector to sensor. Lower vehicle from hoist. Reconnect negative battery cable to battery.

THROTTLE POSITION SENSOR (TPS)

TBI Models

Removal

Remove air cleaner assembly. Disconnect electrical connector from TPS. Remove 2 TPS attaching screws, lockwashers and retainers. Remove TPS.

Installation

1) With throttle valve in normal closed idle position, install TPS on throttle body. Make sure that TPS lever is located above tang on throttle actuator lever.

2) Apply thread locking compound to TPS screws. Install TPS screws with lock washers and retainers. Reconnect electrical connector to TPS.

Carbureted Models

Removal

1) Disconnect M/C solenoid, TPS and idle speed solenoid electrical connectors.

2) Remove carburetor air horn assembly:

- Remove air horn attaching screws and idle speed solenoid.
- Remove upper choke lever from end of choke shaft by removing retaining screw. Rotate upper choke lever to remove choke rod from slot in lever.
- Remove choke rod from lower lever inside float bowl casting. Remove rod by holding lower lever outward with small screwdriver and twisting rod counterclockwise.
- Remove retainer from pump link, link from pump lever. Do not remove pump lever from air horn.
- Disconnect front vacuum break hose from tube on float bowl.
- Remove air horn-to-bowl screws; then remove two countersunk attaching screws located next to venturi.
- Lift air horn straight up and off of float bowl.

3) Lift air horn gasket from dowel locating pins on float bowl. Discard gasket.

4) TPS is staked in place in bowl. Remove staking as follows:

- Lay a flat tool or metal piece across bowl casting to protect gasket sealing surface.
- Use a small screwdriver to depress TPS sensor lightly and hold against spring tension.
- Use a small chisel (or equivalent) to pry staking upward, making sure prying force is exerted against the metal tool and not against the bowl casting.
- Push up from bottom on electrical connector to remove TPS and connector assembly from bowl.

Installation

1) Install TPS and connector assembly in float bowl by aligning groove in electrical connector with slot in float bowl casting. Push down on connector and sensor assembly so that connector and wires are located below bowl casting surface. Be sure Green TPS actuator plunger is in place in air horn.

2) Install air horn gasket, holding pump plunger assembly down against return spring tension and aligning pump plunger stem with hole in gasket. Align holes in gasket over TPS plunger, solenoid plunger return spring, metering rods, solenoid attaching screw and electrical connector. Position gasket over two dowel locating pins on float bowl.

3) Install solenoid-metering rod plunger, holding down on air horn gasket and pump plunger assembly, and aligning slot in end of plunger with solenoid attaching screw.

4) Carefully lower air horn assembly onto float bowl while positioning TPS adjustment lever over TPS, and guiding pump plunger stem through seal in air horn casting. To ease installation, insert a thin screwdriver between air horn gasket and float bowl to raise TPS adjustment lever, positioning it over the sensor.

5) Install air horn screws and lockwashers, and two countersunk screws (located next to carb. venturi on 4-bbl. models). Tighten all screws evenly and securely, following air horn screw tightening sequence. *See Fig. 8*

6) Install front vacuum break and bracket assembly on air horn, using two attaching screws. Install pump link to pump lever and insert retainer pin.

7) Install choke rod into lower choke lever inside bowl cavity. Install choke rod in slot in upper choke lever, and position lever on end of choke shaft (make sure flats on end of shaft align with flats in lever). Install attaching screw and tighten securely. When properly installed, lever will point to rear of carburetor, and number on lever will face outward.

8) Install M/C solenoid, TPS and idle speed solenoid electrical connectors. Clear trouble code memory and check TPS voltage. Voltage reading, with A/C off and throttle at curb idle position, should be .26 volts for V6 models, or .41 volts for V8s.

Adjustment

1) If voltage reading in step **8)** of installation procedure is incorrect, TPS must be adjusted.

2) Remove tamper-resistant plug covering adjustment screw. Using a 5/64" drill, drill a 1/16" to 1/8" deep hole in plug. Use care in drilling to prevent damage to adjustment screw head.

GENERAL MOTORS COMPUTER COMMAND CONTROL THEORY & OPERATION (Cont.)

Fig. 8: Air Horn Screw Tightening Sequence

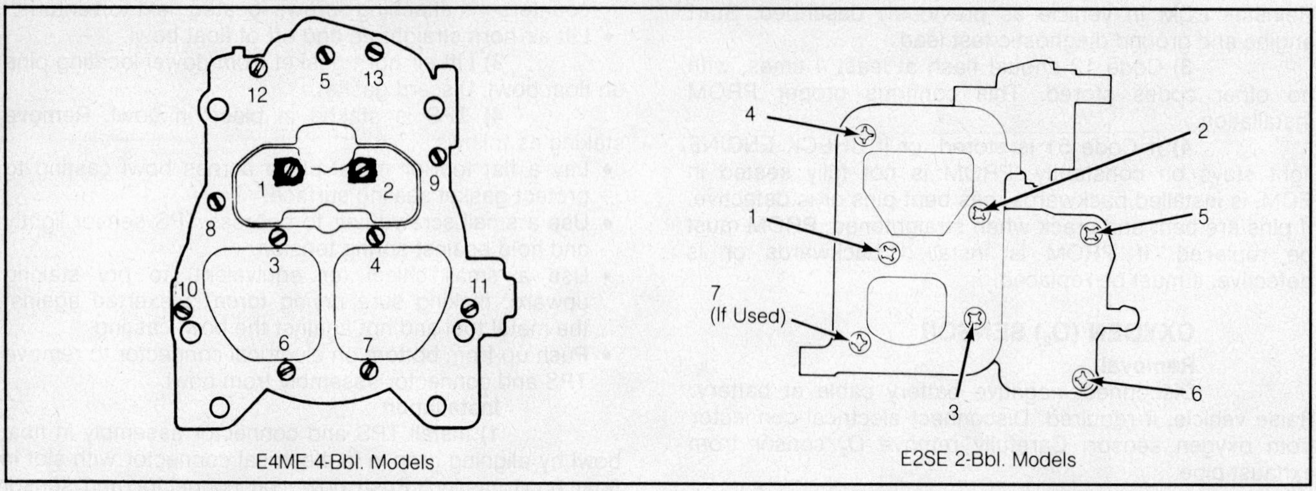

3) Start a No. 8, 1/2" long self-tapping screw in drilled hole turning screw in only enough to ensure good thread engagement in hole.

4) Placing a wide-blade screwdriver between screw head and air horn casting, pry against screw head to remove plug. Discard plug. Remove TPS adjustment screw with TPS adjustment tool (J-28696).

5) Disconnect TPS connector and jumper all three terminals. Connect digital voltmeter from TPS

Fig. 9: ECM Terminal Identification & Voltage Values for 2.5L Engine

WHITE CONNECTOR

	Voltage Key "On" ①	Voltage Engine Run ②	Wire Color	Circuit	Pin	Pin	Circuit	Voltage Key "On"	Voltage Engine Run	Wire Color	
				SPARE	24	1	SPARE				
				NOT USED	23	2	VEHICLE SPEED SENSOR	11.6	13.4	BRN	⑤
				NOT USED	22	3	DIAGNOSTIC TEST ALCL	5.2	5.3	WHT/BLK	
④	0	0	DK. GRN	A/C CLUTCH	21	4	NOT USED				
	0	14.1	BRN/WHT	CHECK ENGINE LIGHT	20	5	PARK/NEUTRAL SWITCH	0	0	ORN/BLK	③
	0	0	TAN/BLK	TCC OR SHIFT LIGHT	19	6	NOT USED				
	0	14.0	DK. GRN/WHT	FUEL PUMP RELAY DRIVE	18	7	SERIAL DATA	5.0 – VARIES –	4.6	ORN	
				NOT USED	17	8	INJECTOR	12.3	14.2	BLU	
	12.3	14.3	PNK/BLK	SWITCHED IGNITION	16	9	NOT USED				
	12.3	14.3	ORN	BATTERY	15	10	BATTERY	12.3	14.3	ORN	
	0	0	BLK/ORN	MAP GROUND	14	11	5 VOLT REFERENCE	5.3	5.3	GRY	
	0	0	BLK/WHT	ECM GROUND	13	12	ECM GROUND	0	0	BLK/WHT	

BACK VIEW OF CONNECTORS

BLACK CONNECTOR

	Voltage Key "On"	Voltage Engine Run	Wire Color	Circuit	Pin	Pin	Circuit	Voltage Key "On"	Voltage Engine Run	Wire Color	
				NOT USED	22	1	CRANK SIGNAL				
				NOT USED	21	2	HEI REFERENCE	0		PPL/WHT	
	5.1	1.5	LT. GRN	MANIFOLD ABSOLUTE PRESSURE SIGNAL	20	3	HEI DIST. GROUND	0	0	BLK/RED	
	0	1.8	WHT	EST SIGNAL	19	4	COOLANT SENSOR SIGNAL	1.3	.6	YEL	
	⑥	⑥	LT. BLU/BLK	I.A.C. COIL "A" LO	18	5	T.P.S. SIGNAL	.81	.81	DK. BLU	
	⑥	⑥	LT. BLU/WHT	I.A.C. COIL "A" HI	17	6	POWER STEERING SIGNAL	12.3	12.3	LT. BLU/ORN	
				NOT USED	16	7	AC CLUTCH RELAY	12.3	14.3	DK. BLU	④
	0	0	TAN	OXYGEN SENSOR GROUND	15	8	OXYGEN SENSOR SIGNAL	.3	VARIES .3 to .7	PPL	
				NOT USED	14	9	COOLING FAN	0	0	LT. BLU/BLK	④
	⑥	⑥	LT. GRN/BLK	I.A.C. COIL "B" LO	13	10	EST BYPASS	0	4.2	TAN/BLK	
	⑥	⑥	LT. GRN/WHT	I.A.C. COIL "B" HI	12	11	COOLANT & TPS GROUND	0	0	BLK	

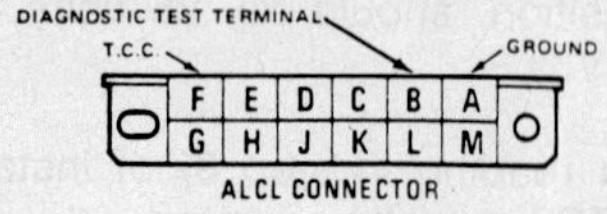

NOTE: This ECM voltage chart can be used with a digital ohmmeter to help save time in diagnosis. Voltages on the car being tested may vary slightly from these due to battery or alternator charging level.

- Engine at operating temperature.
- Engine in closed loop operation.
- Engine idling ("Engine Run" column).
- Test Terminal NOT grounded.
- Scanner or ALCL tool NOT installed.

1 – Engine running in Park, at idle, normal operating temperature, in closed loop.
2 – All voltages shown as "0" should read less than 1.0 volt with a digital volt-ohm meter.
3 – Reads battery voltage in gear.
4 – A/C off.
5 – Varies from 0 to 12 volts depending on position of drive wheels.
6 – Not useable.

GENERAL MOTORS COMPUTER COMMAND CONTROL THEORY & OPERATION (Cont.)

connector center terminal "B" to bottom terminal "C". Reinstall TPS adjustment screw. With ignition on (engine not running), quickly adjust screw to obtain correct TPS voltage.

6) After adjustment, install new tamper-resistant plug (supplied in service kits) in air horn. Drive plug into place until flush with raised pump lever boss on casting. Clear trouble code memory after adjustment.

ALL OTHER SENSORS, SOLENOIDS & SWITCHES

Removal of all other sensors, switches and solenoids is accomplished by removing the electrical and/or vacuum connectors and removing or detaching the component.

Fig. 10: ECM Terminal Identification & Voltage Values for 2.8L Engine

Voltage Key "ON"	Voltage Engine Run	Voltage Circuit Open	Function	Terminal	Terminal	Function	Voltage Key "ON"	Voltage Engine Run	Voltage Circuit Open
0	0	0	SENSOR RETURN	22	1	NOT USED			
5.0	5.0	5.0	5V REFERENCE	21	2	TPS SENSOR SIGNAL	*1.0 +5.0	*1.0	5.0
.5-.65	2-3	*.5	VACUUM SENSOR SIGNAL	20	3	COOLANT TEMP. SENSOR SIGNAL	*2.5	*2.5	5.0
			NOT USED	19	4	AIR CONTROL SOLENOID	12	*1.0	*.5
12	5-10 (var.)	*.5	M/C SOLENOID	18	5	DIAGNOSTIC TEST TERM	5.0	5.0	5.0
			NOT USED	17	6	A/C WOT CUTOUT	12	14	*.5
			NOT USED	16	7	COOLANT TEMP. SENSOR RETURN	0	0	0
			NOT USED	15	8	NOT USED			
*.5	*.5	1.7	OXYGEN SENSOR – LO	14	9	OXYGEN SENSOR – HI	.3-.45	.1-.9 (var.)	.3-.45
*.5	*.5	*1.0	DIST. REF. PULSE – LO	13	10	DIST. REF. PULSE – HI	*.5	1-2 (var.)	*.5
*.5	1-2 (var.)	*.5	EST	12	11	IGN. MODULE BY-PASS	*.5	3.7	*.5
			NOT USED	J	K	NOT USED			
*.5 P/N 12 D/R	*.5 P/N 12 D/R	12	PARK/NEUTRAL SWITCH	H	L	NOT USED			
10	*.5	*.5	"CHECK ENGINE" LAMP	G	M	NOT USED			
			NOT USED	F	N	NOT USED			
			NOT USED	E	P	TRANS CONVERTER CLUTCH SOLENOID	12	14	*.5
			NOT USED	D	R	TROUBLE CODE MEMORY POWER	12	14	*.5
12	14	*.5	IGN. 1 POWER	C	S	NOT USED			
12	14	*.5	AIR SWITCHING SOLENOID	B	T	NOT USED			
0	0	0	GROUND (TO ENGINE)	A	U	GROUND (TO ENGINE)	0	0	0

NOTE:
This ECM voltage chart can be used with a digital ohmmeter to help save time in diagnosis. Voltages on the car being tested may vary slightly from these due to battery or alternator charging level.

- Engine at operating temperature.
- Engine in closed loop operation.
- Engine idling ("Engine Run" column).
- Test Terminal NOT grounded.
- Scanner or ALCL tool NOT installed.
- 2WD

* Value shown or less than that value.
\+ Wide Open Throttle.
(var.) Variable.
P/N Park or Neutral.
D/R Drive or Reverse.

GENERAL MOTORS COMPUTER COMMAND CONTROL THEORY & OPERATION (Cont.)

Fig. 11: ECM Terminal Identification & Voltage Values for 4.3L Engine

Voltage Key "ON"	Voltage Engine Run	Voltage Circuit Open	Circuit	Terminal	Terminal	Circuit	Voltage Key "ON"	Voltage Engine Run	Voltage Circuit Open
0	0	0	SENSOR RETURN	22	1	NOT USED			
5	5	5	5V REFERENCE	21	2	TPS SENSOR SIGNAL	*1.0 +5.0	*2.0	5.0
.5-.65	2-3	*.5	VACUUM SENSOR SIGNAL	20	3	COOLANT TEMP. SENSOR SIGNAL	*3.0	*2.5	5.0
12	14	*.5	EGR	19	4	NOT USED			
12	5-10 (var.)	*.5	M/C SOLENOID	18	5	DIAGNOSTIC TEST TERM	5	5	5
			NOT USED	17	6	NOT USED			
			NOT USED	16	7	COOLANT TEMP. SENSOR RETURN	0	0	0
			NOT USED	15	8	NOT USED			
*.5	*.5	1.7	OXYGEN SENSOR – LO	14	9	OXYGEN SENSOR – HI	.3-.45	.1-.9 (var.)	.3-.45
*.5	*.5	*1.0	DIST. REF. PULSE – LO	13	10	DIST. REF. PULSE – HI	*.5	1-2 (var.)	*.5
*.5	1-2 (var.)	*.5	EST	12	11	IGN. MODULE BY-PASS	*.5	3.7	*.5

Voltage Key "ON"	Voltage Engine Run	Voltage Circuit Open	Circuit	Terminal	Terminal	Circuit	Voltage Key "ON"	Voltage Engine Run	Voltage Circuit Open
			NOT USED	J	K	NOT USED			
			NOT USED	H	L	ESC SIGNAL (4.3L)	7-10	7-10	*.5
10	*.5	*.5	"CHECK ENGINE" LAMP	G	M	NOT USED			
			NOT USED	F	N	4TH GEAR SWITCH	*.5	*.5	12
12	14	*.5	THROTTLE KICKER	E	P	TRANS CONVERTER CLUTCH SOLENOID	12	14	*.5
			NOT USED	D	R	TROUBLE CODE MEMORY POWER	12	14	*.5
12	14	*.5	IGN. 1 POWER	C	S	NOT USED			
12	.14	*.5	AIR DIVERT SOLENOID	B	T	PURGE	12	.12	*.5
0	0	0	GROUND (TO ENGINE)	A	U	GROUND (TO ENGINE)	0	0	0

NOTE:
This ECM voltage chart can be used with a digital ohmmeter to help save time in diagnosis. Voltages on the car being tested may vary slightly from these due to battery or alternator charging level.

- Engine at operating temperature.
- Engine in closed loop operation.
- Engine idling ("Engine Run" column).
- Test Terminal NOT grounded.
- Scanner or ALCL tool NOT installed.
- 2WD.

* Value shown or less than that value.
+ Wide Open Throttle.
(var.) Variable.

Fig. 12: ECM Terminal Identification & Voltage Values for 5.0L & 5.7L Engines

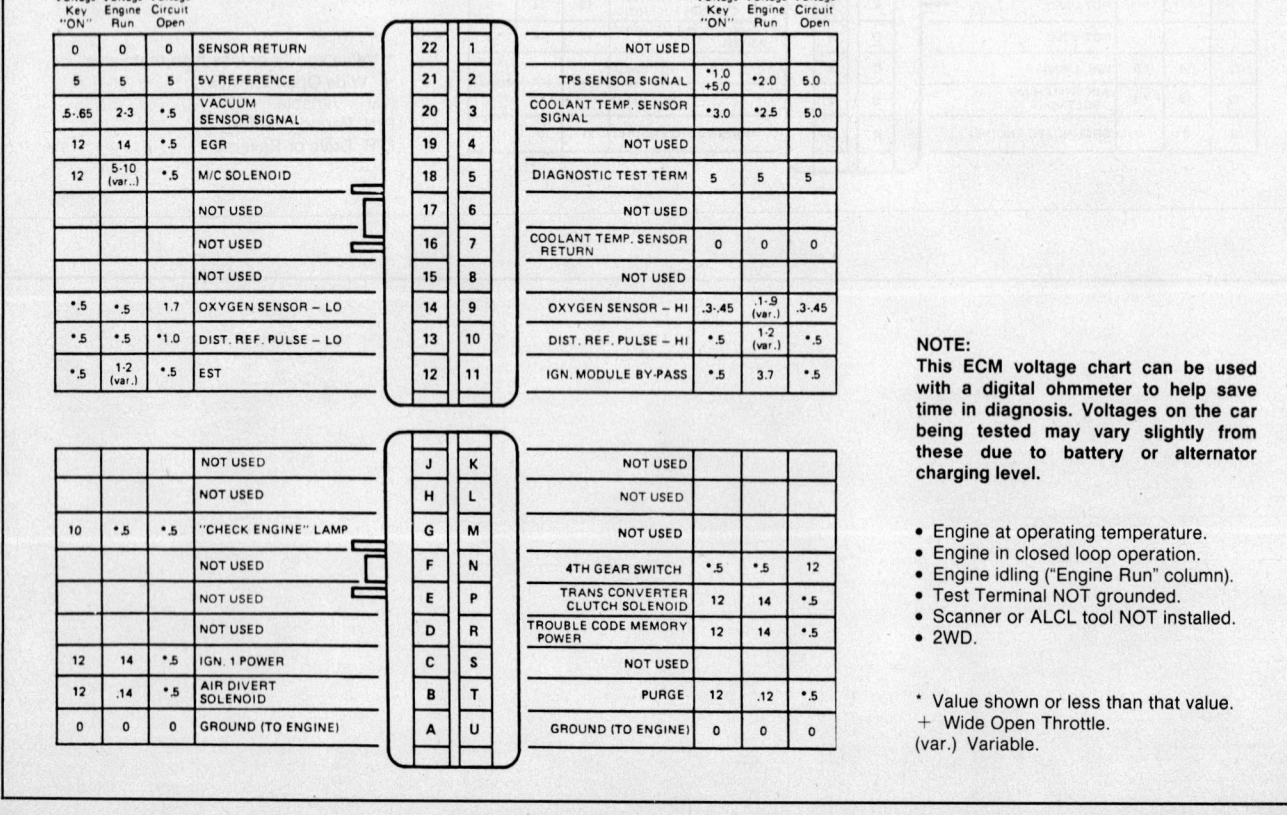

Voltage Key "ON"	Voltage Engine Run	Voltage Circuit Open	Circuit	Terminal	Terminal	Circuit	Voltage Key "ON"	Voltage Engine Run	Voltage Circuit Open
0	0	0	SENSOR RETURN	22	1	NOT USED			
5	5	5	5V REFERENCE	21	2	TPS SENSOR SIGNAL	*1.0 +5.0	*2.0	5.0
.5-.65	2-3	*.5	VACUUM SENSOR SIGNAL	20	3	COOLANT TEMP. SENSOR SIGNAL	*3.0	*2.5	5.0
12	14	*.5	EGR	19	4	NOT USED			
12	5-10 (var.)	*.5	M/C SOLENOID	18	5	DIAGNOSTIC TEST TERM	5	5	5
			NOT USED	17	6	NOT USED			
			NOT USED	16	7	COOLANT TEMP. SENSOR RETURN	0	0	0
			NOT USED	15	8	NOT USED			
*.5	*.5	1.7	OXYGEN SENSOR – LO	14	9	OXYGEN SENSOR – HI	.3-.45	.1-.9 (var.)	.3-.45
*.5	*.5	*1.0	DIST. REF. PULSE – LO	13	10	DIST. REF. PULSE – HI	*.5	1-2 (var.)	*.5
*.5	1-2 (var.)	*.5	EST	12	11	IGN. MODULE BY-PASS	*.5	3.7	*.5

Voltage Key "ON"	Voltage Engine Run	Voltage Circuit Open	Circuit	Terminal	Terminal	Circuit	Voltage Key "ON"	Voltage Engine Run	Voltage Circuit Open
			NOT USED	J	K	NOT USED			
			NOT USED	H	L	NOT USED			
10	*.5	*.5	"CHECK ENGINE" LAMP	G	M	NOT USED			
			NOT USED	F	N	4TH GEAR SWITCH	*.5	*.5	12
			NOT USED	E	P	TRANS CONVERTER CLUTCH SOLENOID	12	14	*.5
			NOT USED	D	R	TROUBLE CODE MEMORY POWER	12	14	*.5
12	14	*.5	IGN. 1 POWER	C	S	NOT USED			
12	.14	*.5	AIR DIVERT SOLENOID	B	T	PURGE	12	.12	*.5
0	0	0	GROUND (TO ENGINE)	A	U	GROUND (TO ENGINE)	0	0	0

NOTE:
This ECM voltage chart can be used with a digital ohmmeter to help save time in diagnosis. Voltages on the car being tested may vary slightly from these due to battery or alternator charging level.

- Engine at operating temperature.
- Engine in closed loop operation.
- Engine idling ("Engine Run" column).
- Test Terminal NOT grounded.
- Scanner or ALCL tool NOT installed.
- 2WD.

* Value shown or less than that value.
+ Wide Open Throttle.
(var.) Variable.

GENERAL MOTORS COMPUTER COMMAND CONTROL THEORY & OPERATION (Cont.)

Fig. 13: Wiring Diagram for 2.5L 4-Cylinder Engines

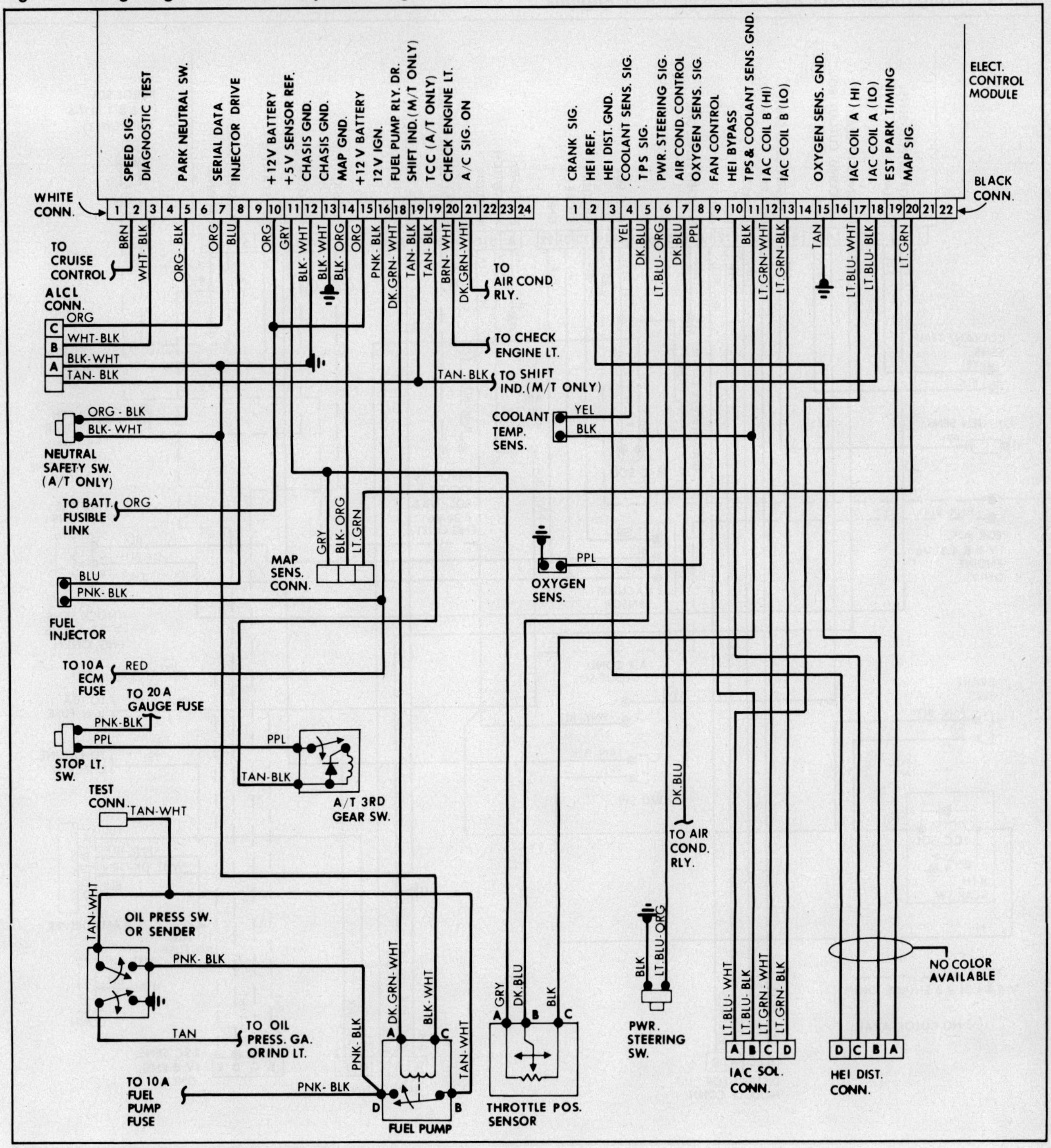

GENERAL MOTORS COMPUTER COMMAND CONTROL
THEORY & OPERATION (Cont.)

Fig. 14: Wiring Diagram for 2.8L, 4.3L, 5.0L & 5.7L Engines

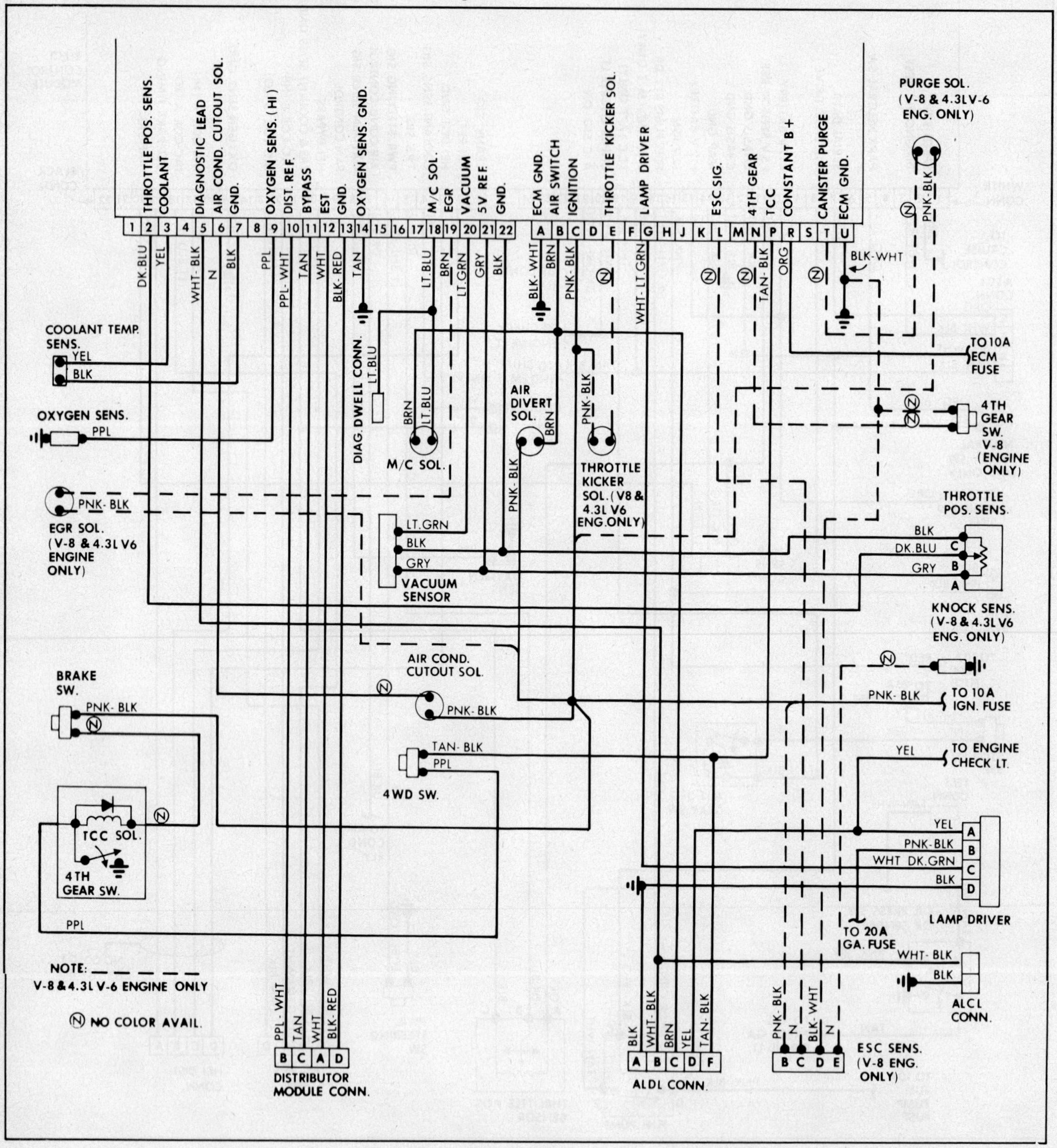

GENERAL MOTORS COMPUTER COMMAND CONTROL 2.5L THROTTLE BODY FUEL INJECTION

DIAGNOSTIC CIRCUIT CHECK

The diagnostic circuit check is an organized approach for identifying a problem caused by the Fuel Injection System. Driver complaints fall into 3 catagories: Steady "CHECK ENGINE" light, driveability problems, and engine "CRANKS BUT WON'T RUN".

1) A steady "CHECK ENGINE" light, with ignition on and engine not running, confirms battery and ignition voltage to ECM.

2) Code 12 should flash 3 times, followed by any other trouble codes stored in memory.

3) Record all stored codes except Code 12.

4) With engine running and diagnostic terminal grounded, ECM will respond to O_2 sensor signal voltage and use the "CHECK ENGINE" light to display this information as follows:

A) Closed loop confirms that O_2 sensor voltage is being used to control fuel delivery. Signal voltage will vary from .35-.55 volt.

B) Open loop confirms that O_2 sensor voltage to ECM is unusable. Signal voltage is a fixed value between .35 and .55 volt. System will flash open loop for 30 seconds to 2 minutes or until O_2 sensor reaches operating temperature.

C) O_2 sensor signal voltage will be less than .35 volt. See Code 44.

D) O_2 sensor signal voltage will be more than .55 volt. See Code 45.

5) Road test of system in field service mode must be done at steady speeds. In this mode the following conditions may be observed and should be considered normal: Light on too long under acceleration (due to acceleration enrichment); Light off too long under deceleration (due to decel leaning of fuel mixture or fuel cut-off); light on too long at idle with idle below 1200 RPM.

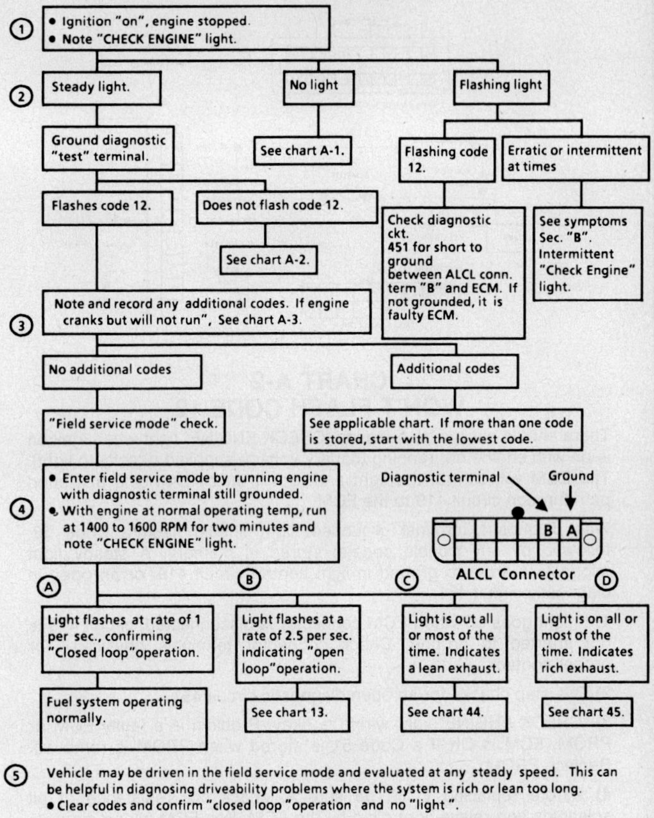

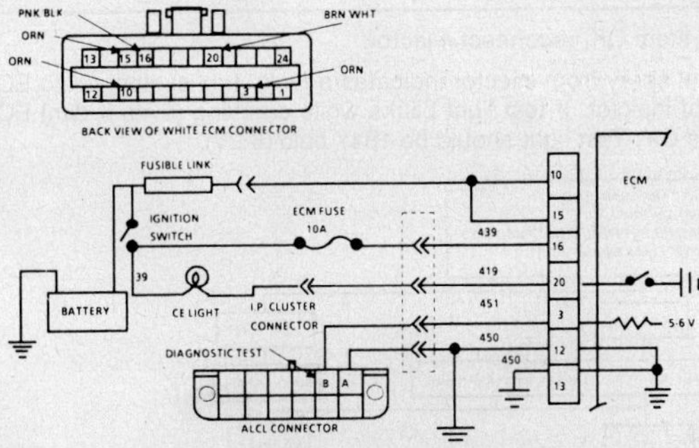

CHART A-1
NO "CHECK ENGINE" LIGHT

There should always be a steady "CHECK ENGINE" light when ignition is on with engine not running (battery voltage supplied directly to light). The ECM will control the light and turn it on by providing a ground path through circuit 419 to the ECM.

If engine runs okay, check for: Faulty light bulb; Circuit 419 open; Gage fuse blown (resulting in no stop lights, oil or generator lights, seat belt reminder, etc).

If engine cranks but will not run, check: Continuous battery (fuse or fusible link open); ECM ignition fuse open; Battery circuit 340 to ECM open; Ignition circuit 439 to ECM open; Poor connector to ECM.

Solenoids and relays are turned on or off by the ECM. Solenoid and relay coil resistance must measure more than 20 ohms. Less resistance will cause early failure of the ECM "driver". Before replacing the ECM, be sure to check the coil resistance of all solenoids and relays controlled by the ECM. See ECM wiring diagram for solenoids, relays and coil terminal identification.

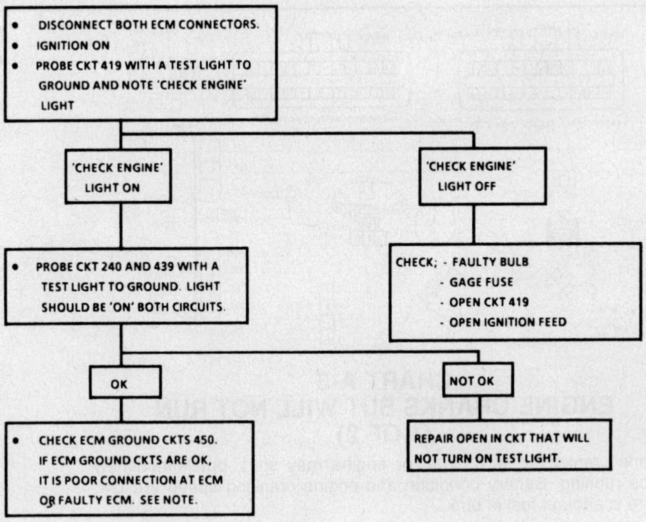

NOTE:
BEFORE REPLACING ECM, USE AND OHMMETER AND CHECK RESISTANCE OF EACH ECM CONTROLLED RELAY AND SOLENOID COIL.
SEE ECM WIRING DIAGRAM FOR COIL TERMINAL IDENTIFICATION FOR SOLENOID(S) AND RELAY(S) TO BE CHECKED.
REPLACE ANY RELAY OR SOLENOID IF THE COIL RESISTANCE MEASURES LESS THAN 20 OHMS.

CLEAR CODES AND CONFIRM "CLOSED LOOP" OPERATION AND NO "CHECK ENGINE" LIGHT.

GENERAL MOTORS COMPUTER COMMAND CONTROL 2.5L THROTTLE BODY FUEL INJECTION (Cont.)

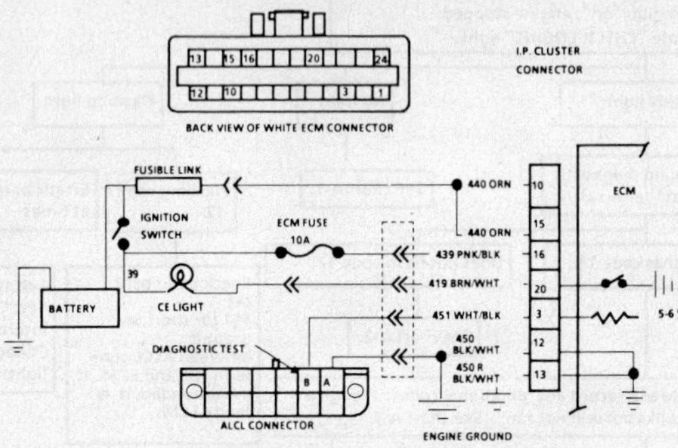

CHART A-2
WON'T FLASH CODE 12

There should always be a steady "CHECK ENGINE" light when ignition is on with engine not running (battery voltage supplied directly to light). The ECM will control the light and turn it on by providing a ground path through circuit 419 to the ECM.

With diagnostic terminal grounded, light should flash a Code 12, followed by any trouble code(s) stored in memory. A steady light suggests a short to ground in light control circuit 419, or an open in diagnostic circuit 451.

1) If light goes off when ECM connector is disconnected, circuit 419 is not shorted to ground. Check connector terminals physically for proper contact.

2) This step checks for an open diagnostic circuit 451.

3) "CHECK ENGINE" light wiring is okay. Problem is a faulty ECM or PROM. ECM is OK if a Code 51 is stored when PROM is removed. Replace PROM.

4) Before replacing ECM, be sure to check coil resistance of all solenoids and relays controlled by the ECM. See ECM wiring diagram for solenoids and relays and coil terminal identification.

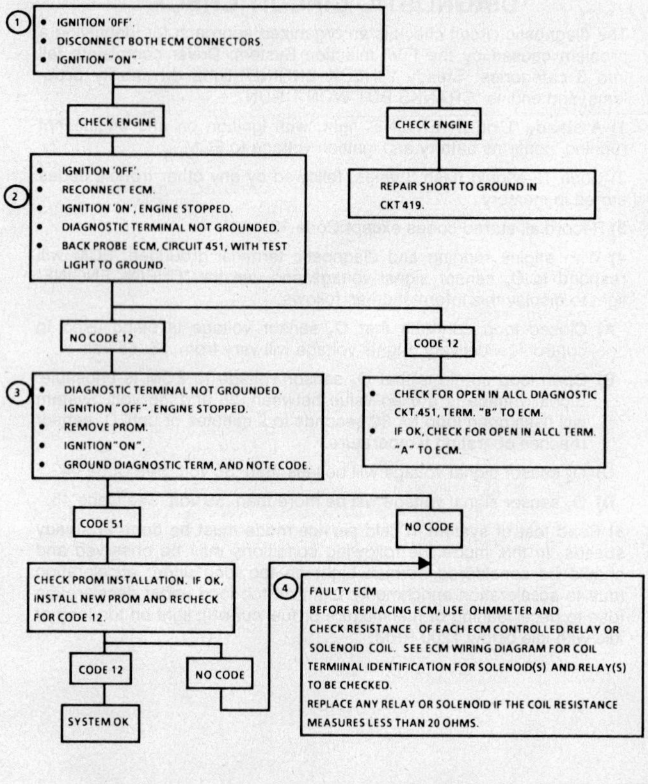

CLEAR CODES AND CONFIRM "CLOSED LOOP" OPERATION AND NO "CHECK ENGINE" LIGHT.

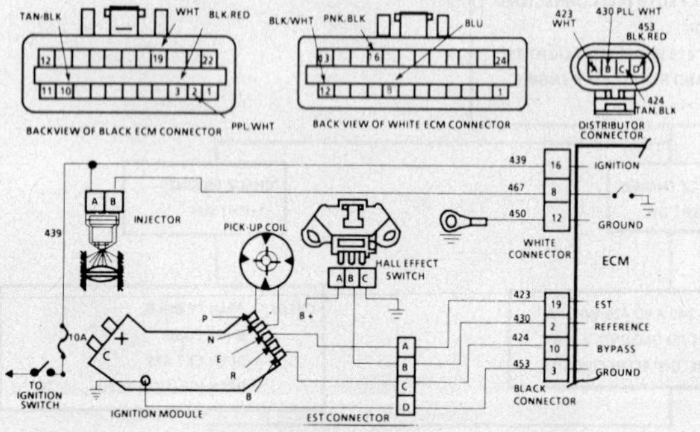

CHART A-3
ENGINE CRANKS BUT WILL NOT RUN
(1 OF 2)

Engine cranks but won't run, or engine may start, but immediately stops running. Battery condition and engine cranking speed are OK. There is enough fuel in tank.

1) "CHECK ENGINE" light "on" is basic check for ignition and battery supply to ECM.

2) Fuel spray from injector indicates that fuel is available. Engine could be flooded due to too much fuel.

3) While cranking, there should be no fuel spray with injector disconnected. Replace injector if it sprays fuel or drips.

4) Check voltage at spark plugs with ST-125 (or equivalent). No spark indicates basic HEI problem. If spark is OK, check for: TPS sticking or binding; open coolant sensor circuit with ignition off (see Code 15); EGR sticking open; open crank signal (may cause a no start during very cold weather); Low fuel pressure or volume (see Chart A-5).

5) EFI system OK, reconnect injector.

6) No fuel spray from injector indicates a faulty fuel system or no ECM control of injector. If test light blinks while cranking (even if dim) ECM control is OK. Test light should be 1847 bulb (6.2V).

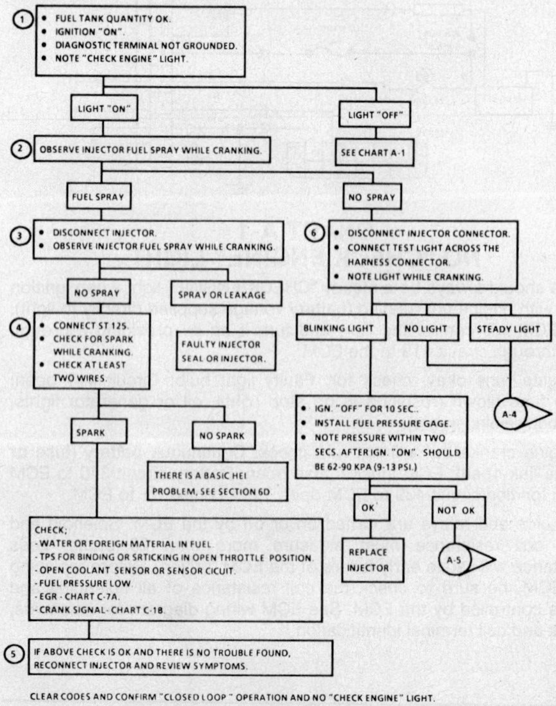

CLEAR CODES AND CONFIRM "CLOSED LOOP" OPERATION AND NO "CHECK ENGINE" LIGHT.

GENERAL MOTORS COMPUTER COMMAND CONTROL 2.5L THROTTLE BODY FUEL INJECTION (Cont.)

CHART A-4 ENGINE CRANKS BUT WILL NOT RUN (2 OF 2)

7) Probe each connector terminal with test light to ground. There should be a light on one terminal, confirming ignition voltage at connector. ECM injector control circuit 467 may be open. Reconnect injector. Using test light connected to ground, check for light at white ECM connector terminal "8". Light at this point indicates that injector drive circuit is OK.

8) No blinking light indicates no ECM control of injector. With voltmeter in "AC Volts" position, and voltage scale switch in 2 volt range, voltage should be greater than .7 volt AC. If voltage is less than .7 volt AC there is an open or short to ground in HEI reference circuit 430. If circuit is OK, there is a basic HEI problem.

8A) ALTERNATE PROCEDURE. Disconnect distributor connector. Momentarily touch ECM side of connector terminal "C" with test light to 12 volts. Note injector as contact is made. Each time test light contacts terminal "C", injector should turn "on". If so, ECM injector control circuit is OK. Contact on ST-125 and check for "spark". If on, it is faulty HEI module. No spark indicates basic HEI problem.

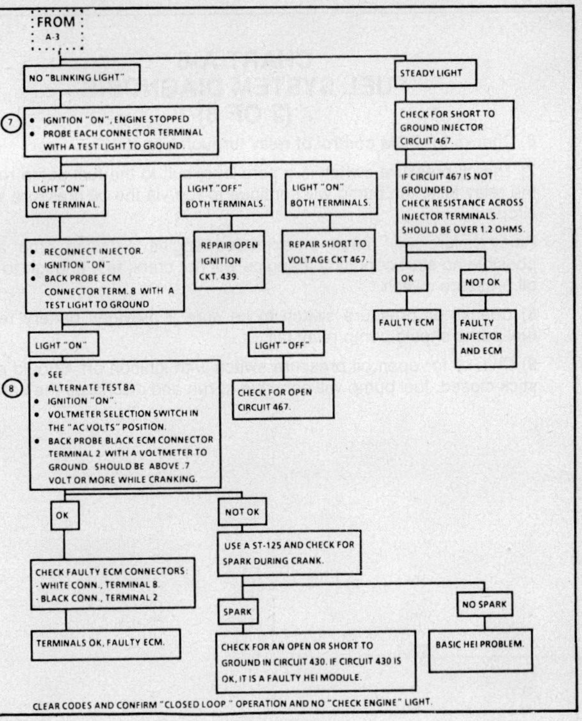

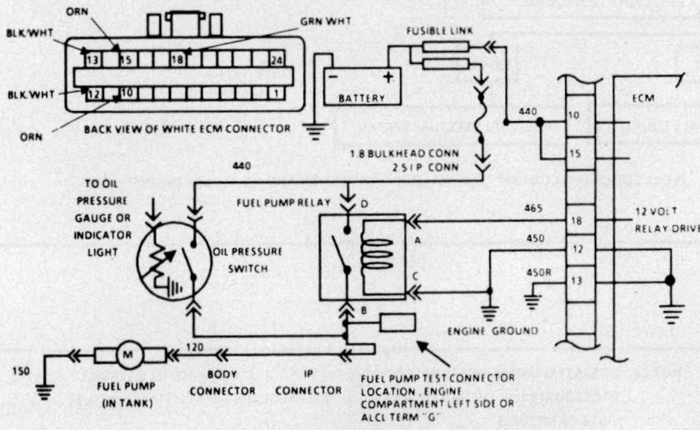

CHART A-5 FUEL SYSTEM DIAGNOSIS (1 OF 3)

When ignition switch is turned on, ECM will turn in-tank fuel pump on. Pump will remain on as long as engine is cranking or running, and ECM is receiving HEI distributor reference pulses.

If there are no reference pulses, ECM will shut off fuel pump within 2 seconds after key is turned on.

Fuel pressure at TBI unit is controlled at 9-13 lbs. Excess fuel is returned to fuel tank.

Fuel pump test terminal is located in ALCL connector terminal "G". When engine is stopped, pump can be turned "ON" by applying battery voltage to test terminal.

Improper fuel system pressure will result in one or all of the following symptoms: Cranks But Won't Run, Code 44, Code 45, cuts out (may feel like ignition problem), poor fuel economy, loss of power, or hesitation.

1) If fuse is blown, test confirms short to ground on circuit 120. Be sure fuel pump is disconnected before test.

2) Determines if pump circuit is ECM controlled. ECM turns pump relay on, then off within 2 seconds since engine is not cranking or running.

3) Fuel pump on if circuit 120 wiring is OK. If pump runs, it is a basic fuel delivery problem which the following steps will locate.

4) Checks for battery voltage at pump relay.

5) Checks relay ground circuit 450.

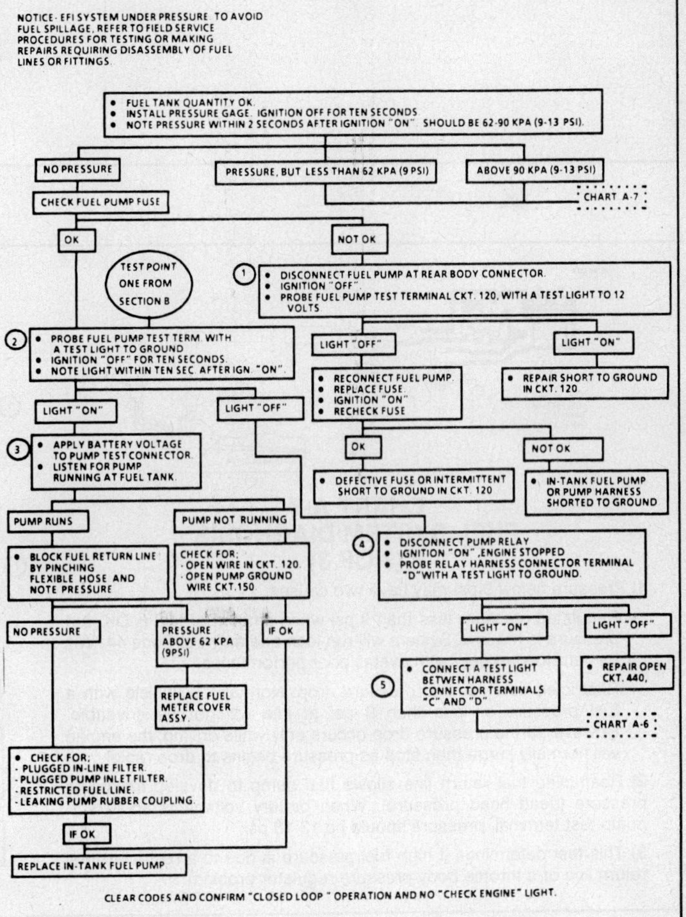

GENERAL MOTORS COMPUTER COMMAND CONTROL
2.5L THROTTLE BODY FUEL INJECTION (Cont.)

CHART A-6
FUEL SYSTEM DIAGNOSIS
(2 OF 3)

6) Checks for ECM control of relay through circuit 465.

7) The oil pressure switch is a parallel circuit to the fuel pump relay. If the relay fails, the pump will continue to run via the oil pressure switch circuit.

Relay failure will result in extended engine cranking time and a possible no start condition if engine will not crank fast enough to close oil pressure switch.

8) Checks oil pressure switch to be sure it provides battery feed to fuel pump should pump relay fail.

9) Checks for open oil pressure switch with ignition off. Should switch stick closed, fuel pump will continue to run and discharge the battery.

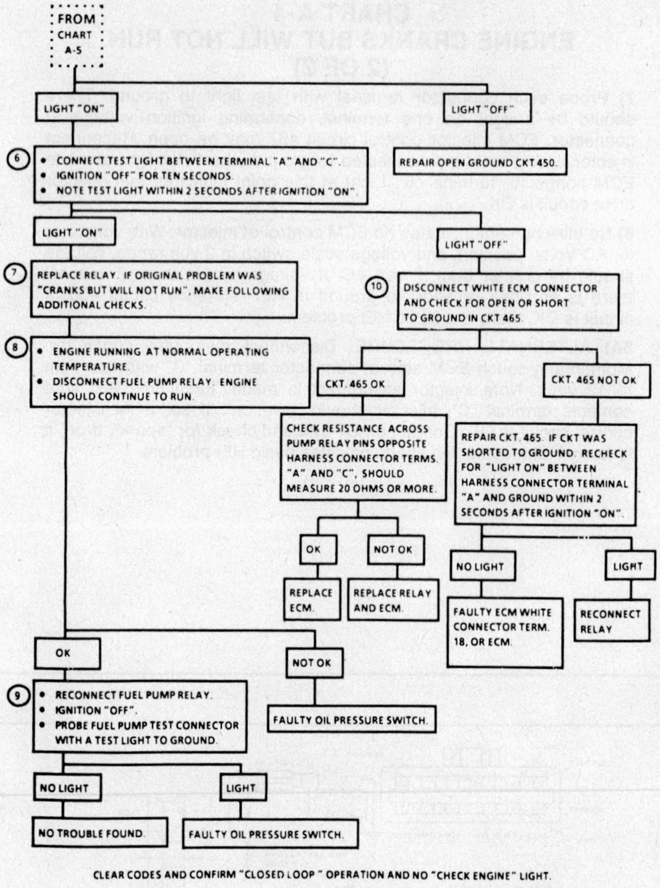

FROM CHART A-5
LIGHT "ON"
LIGHT "OFF"
6
• CONNECT TEST LIGHT BETWEEN TERMINAL "A" AND "C".
• IGNITION "OFF" FOR TEN SECONDS.
• NOTE TEST LIGHT WITHIN 2 SECONDS AFTER IGNITION "ON".
REPAIR OPEN GROUND CKT 450.
LIGHT "ON"
LIGHT "OFF"
7
REPLACE RELAY. IF ORIGINAL PROBLEM WAS "CRANKS BUT WILL NOT RUN", MAKE FOLLOWING ADDITIONAL CHECKS.
10
DISCONNECT WHITE ECM CONNECTOR AND CHECK FOR OPEN OR SHORT TO GROUND IN CKT 465.
8
• ENGINE RUNNING AT NORMAL OPERATING TEMPERATURE.
• DISCONNECT FUEL PUMP RELAY. ENGINE SHOULD CONTINUE TO RUN.
CKT. 465 OK
CKT. 465 NOT OK
CHECK RESISTANCE ACROSS PUMP RELAY PINS OPPOSITE HARNESS CONNECTOR TERMS. "A" AND "C", SHOULD MEASURE 20 OHMS OR MORE.
REPAIR CKT. 465. IF CKT WAS SHORTED TO GROUND, RECHECK FOR "LIGHT ON" BETWEEN HARNESS CONNECTOR TERMINAL "A" AND GROUND WITHIN 2 SECONDS AFTER IGNITION "ON".
OK
NOT OK
REPLACE ECM.
REPLACE RELAY AND ECM.
NO LIGHT
LIGHT
FAULTY ECM WHITE CONNECTOR TERM. 18, OR ECM.
RECONNECT RELAY
OK
NOT OK
9
• RECONNECT FUEL PUMP RELAY.
• IGNITION "OFF".
• PROBE FUEL PUMP TEST CONNECTOR WITH A TEST LIGHT TO GROUND.
FAULTY OIL PRESSURE SWITCH.
NO LIGHT
LIGHT
NO TROUBLE FOUND.
FAULTY OIL PRESSURE SWITCH.
CLEAR CODES AND CONFIRM "CLOSED LOOP" OPERATION AND NO "CHECK ENGINE" LIGHT.

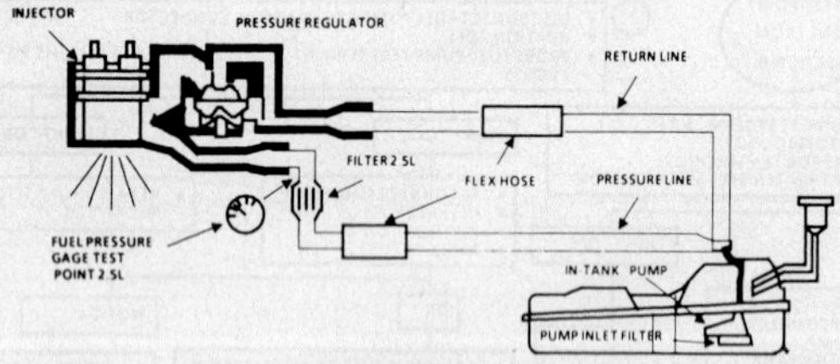

INJECTOR
PRESSURE REGULATOR
RETURN LINE
FILTER 2.5L
FLEX HOSE
PRESSURE LINE
FUEL PRESSURE GAGE TEST POINT 2.5L
IN TANK PUMP
PUMP INLET FILTER

CHART A-7
FUEL SYSTEM DIAGNOSIS
(3 OF 3)

1) Pressure below 9 psi may have two causes:

- Regulated pressure less than 9 psi when amount of fuel is OK, but pressure is too low. System will run lean and may set Code 44. Will be hard to start cold with overall poor performance.
- Restricted flow causing pressure drop. Normally, a vehicle with a fuel pressure of less than 9 psi at idle will not be driveable. However, if the pressure drop occurs only while driving, the engine will normally surge then stop as pressure begins to drop rapidly.

2) Restricting fuel return line allows fuel pump to develop maximum pressure (dead head pressure). When battery voltage is applied to pump test terminal, pressure should be 13-18 psi.

3) This test determines if high fuel pressure is due to a restricted fuel return line or a throttle body pressure regulator problem.

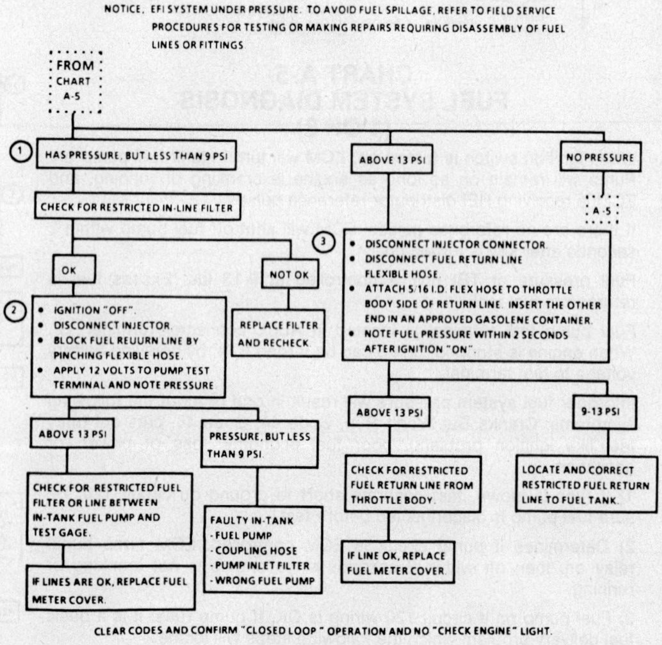

NOTICE, EFI SYSTEM UNDER PRESSURE. TO AVOID FUEL SPILLAGE, REFER TO FIELD SERVICE PROCEDURES FOR TESTING OR MAKING REPAIRS REQUIRING DISASSEMBLY OF FUEL LINES OR FITTINGS
FROM CHART A-5
1
HAS PRESSURE, BUT LESS THAN 9 PSI
ABOVE 13 PSI
NO PRESSURE
CHECK FOR RESTRICTED IN-LINE FILTER
A-5
3
• DISCONNECT INJECTOR CONNECTOR.
• DISCONNECT FUEL RETURN LINE FLEXIBLE HOSE.
• ATTACH 5/16 I.D. FLEX HOSE TO THROTTLE BODY SIDE OF RETURN LINE. INSERT THE OTHER END IN AN APPROVED GASOLENE CONTAINER.
• NOTE FUEL PRESSURE WITHIN 2 SECONDS AFTER IGNITION "ON".
OK
NOT OK
2
• IGNITION "OFF".
• DISCONNECT INJECTOR.
• BLOCK FUEL REUURN LINE BY PINCHING FLEXIBLE HOSE.
• APPLY 12 VOLTS TO PUMP TEST TERMINAL AND NOTE PRESSURE
REPLACE FILTER AND RECHECK
ABOVE 13 PSI
9-13 PSI
ABOVE 13 PSI
PRESSURE, BUT LESS THAN 9 PSI
CHECK FOR RESTRICTED FUEL RETURN LINE FROM THROTTLE BODY.
LOCATE AND CORRECT RESTRICTED FUEL RETURN LINE TO FUEL TANK.
CHECK FOR RESTRICTED FUEL FILTER OR LINE BETWEEN IN-TANK FUEL PUMP AND TEST GAGE.
FAULTY IN-TANK
- FUEL PUMP
- COUPLING HOSE
- PUMP INLET FILTER
- WRONG FUEL PUMP
IF LINE OK, REPLACE FUEL METER COVER.
IF LINES ARE OK, REPLACE FUEL METER COVER.
CLEAR CODES AND CONFIRM "CLOSED LOOP" OPERATION AND NO "CHECK ENGINE" LIGHT.

GENERAL MOTORS COMPUTER COMMAND CONTROL 2.5L THROTTLE BODY FUEL INJECTION (Cont.)

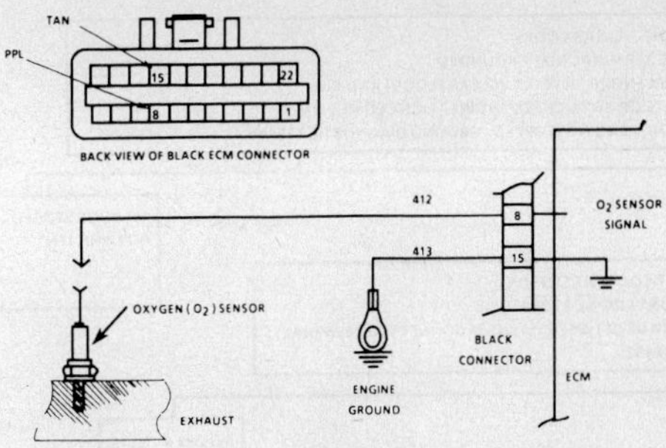

CODE 13
OXYGEN SENSOR CIRCUIT

Code 13 will set: at least 2 minutes after engine starts, with O_2 sensor signal voltage between .35 and .55 volts for more than one minute, and TPS signal above 6% (.8 to 1.2 volts). ECM supplies voltage of about .45 volt between terminals "8" and "15". (If measured with a 10 megohm digital voltmeter, this may read as low as .32 volts.) The O_2 sensor varies the voltage from about 1 volt (exhaust rich) down to about .10 volt (exhaust lean).

The sensor is like an open circuit and produces no voltage when it is below about 600°F (310°C). An open sensor circuit or cold sensor causes open loop operation.

1) Grounding diagnostic terminal with engine running activates "Field Service Mode", which allows ECM to confirm either open or closed loop operation using the "CHECK ENGINE" light.

2) Verifies no additional codes stored, and that Code 13 is intermittent.

3) Simulates lean exhaust. If ECM and wiring are OK, ECM will see lean condition and turn "CHECK ENGINE" light off for at least 15 seconds after engine start, then flash "open loop". Light remaining off for a longer period of time before flashing open loop is normal.

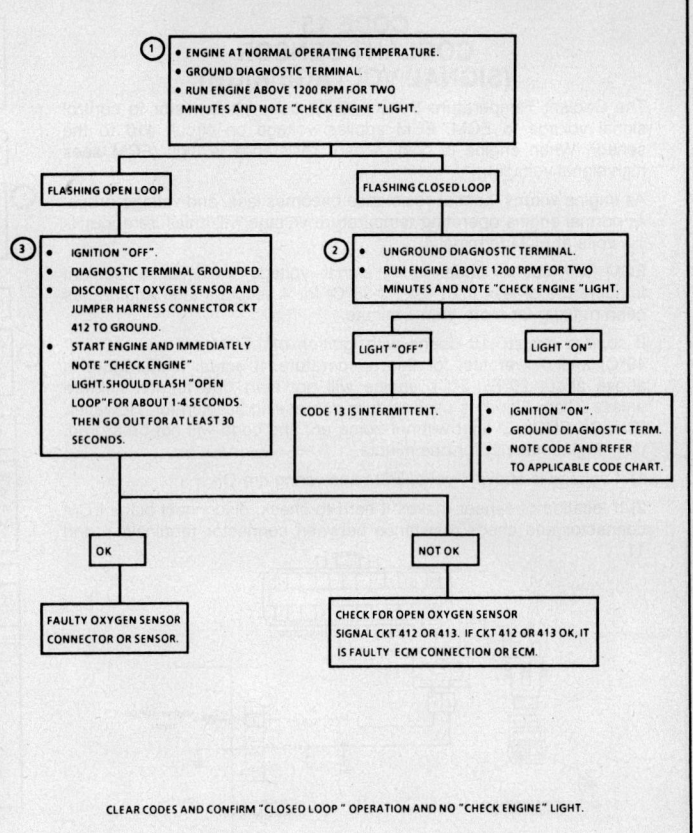

(1)
- ENGINE AT NORMAL OPERATING TEMPERATURE.
- GROUND DIAGNOSTIC TERMINAL.
- RUN ENGINE ABOVE 1200 RPM FOR TWO MINUTES AND NOTE "CHECK ENGINE" LIGHT.

FLASHING OPEN LOOP

(3)
- IGNITION "OFF".
- DIAGNOSTIC TERMINAL GROUNDED.
- DISCONNECT OXYGEN SENSOR AND JUMPER HARNESS CONNECTOR CKT 412 TO GROUND.
- START ENGINE AND IMMEDIATELY NOTE "CHECK ENGINE" LIGHT. SHOULD FLASH "OPEN LOOP" FOR ABOUT 1-4 SECONDS. THEN GO OUT FOR AT LEAST 30 SECONDS.

OK → FAULTY OXYGEN SENSOR CONNECTOR OR SENSOR.

NOT OK → CHECK FOR OPEN OXYGEN SENSOR SIGNAL CKT 412 OR 413. IF CKT 412 OR 413 OK, IT IS FAULTY ECM CONNECTION OR ECM.

FLASHING CLOSED LOOP

(2)
- UNGROUND DIAGNOSTIC TERMINAL.
- RUN ENGINE ABOVE 1200 RPM FOR TWO MINUTES AND NOTE "CHECK ENGINE" LIGHT.

LIGHT "OFF" → CODE 13 IS INTERMITTENT.

LIGHT "ON" →
- IGNITION "ON".
- GROUND DIAGNOSTIC TERM.
- NOTE CODE AND REFER TO APPLICABLE CODE CHART.

CLEAR CODES AND CONFIRM "CLOSED LOOP" OPERATION AND NO "CHECK ENGINE" LIGHT.

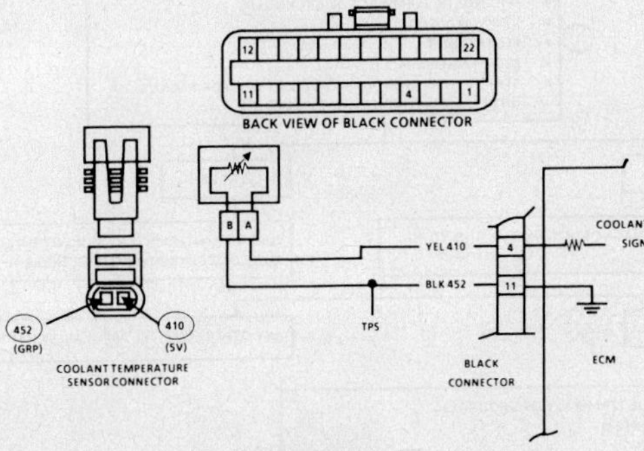

CODE 14
COOLANT SENSOR
(SIGNAL VOLTAGE LOW)

The Coolant Temperature Sensor (CTS) uses a thermistor to control signal voltage to ECM. ECM applies voltage on circuit 410 to the sensor. When engine is cold, sensor resistance is high (ECM sees high signal voltage).

As engine warms, sensor resistance becomes less, and voltage drops. At normal engine operating temperature voltage will measure about 1-1.5 volts at ECM terminal 4.

Code 14 will set if signal voltage indicates coolant temperature above 275°F (135°C) for more than two seconds.

Coolant temperature influences control of fuel delivery, engine timing, idle speed and transmission converter clutch.

1) If voltage is above 4 volts, ECM and wiring are OK.

2) If checking resistance at coolant sensor is difficult because of sensor location, disconnect black ECM connector and check resistance between harness connector terminals 4 and 11.

- IGNITION "OFF", CLEAR CODES.
- DIAGNOSTIC TERMINAL NOT GROUNDED.
- START WARM ENGINE AND RUN FOR 1 MINUTE OR UNTIL CHECK ENGINE" LIGHT COMES ON.
- IGNITION "ON", ENGINE STOPPED. GROUND DIAGNOSTIC TERMINAL AND NOTE CODE.

CODE 14

(1)
- DISCONNECT COOLANT SENSOR.
- IGNITION "ON" ENGINE STOPPED.
- CHECK VOLTAGE BETWEEN HARNESS CONNECTOR TERMINALS, CKT 410 AND 452.

OVER 4 VOLTS

(2) CHECK RESISTANCE ACROSS COOLANT SENSOR TERMINALS. SHOULD BE MORE THAN 185 OHMS. SEE TABLE FOR APPROXIMATE TEMPERATURE TO SENSOR RESISTANCE VALUES.

OK → INTERMITTENT FAULT IN SENSOR CIRCUIT OR CONNECTION. IF ADDITIONAL CODES WERE STORED, SEE APPLICABLE CHART.

NOT OK → REPLACE SENSOR

BELOW 4 VOLTS

- DISCONNECT ECM CONNECTORS.
- CHECK SIGNAL CKT 410 FOR SHORT TO CKT 452 OR CHASSIS GROUND.

IF CKT 410 IS OK, IT IS A FAULTY ECM.

NO CODE STORED. PROBLEM IS INTERMITTENT.

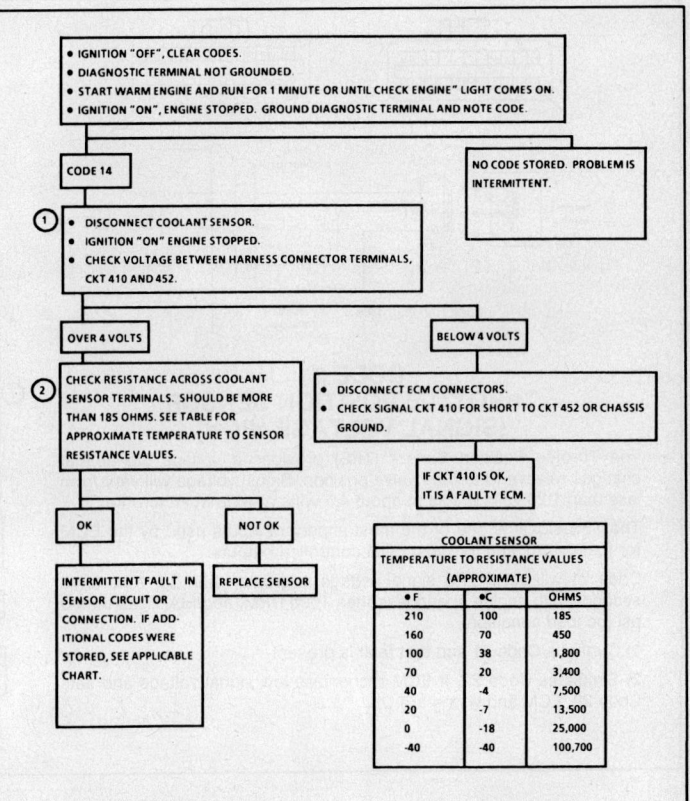

COOLANT SENSOR
TEMPERATURE TO RESISTANCE VALUES (APPROXIMATE)

°F	°C	OHMS
210	100	185
160	70	450
100	38	1,800
70	20	3,400
40	-4	7,500
20	-7	13,500
0	-18	25,000
-40	-40	100,700

CLEAR CODES AND CONFIRM "CLOSED LOOP" OPERATION AND NO "CHECK ENGINE" LIGHT.

GENERAL MOTORS COMPUTER COMMAND CONTROL 2.5L THROTTLE BODY FUEL INJECTION (Cont.)

CODE 15 COOLANT SENSOR (SIGNAL VOLTAGE HIGH)

The Coolant Temperature Sensor (CTS) uses a thermistor to control signal voltage to ECM. ECM applies voltage on circuit 410 to the sensor. When engine is cold, sensor resistance is high (ECM sees high signal voltage).

As engine warms, sensor resistance becomes less, and voltage drops. At normal engine operating temperature voltage will measure about 1-1.5 volts at ECM terminal 4.

ECM will set a Code 15 if signal voltage indicates a coolant temperature of less than -24°F (-35°C) for 4 seconds after engine has been running for more than 1 minute.

If coolant circuit 410 opens with ignition off, ECM will see -40°F (-40°C) and deliver fuel for this temperature. If actual temperature is above about 20°F (-7°C), engine will not start due to rich mixture unless "Clear Flood" is used by fully depressing accelerator. However, "CHECK ENGINE" light will not come on, and code will not be stored, until engine has run for one minute.

1) If voltage is above 4 volts, ECM and wiring are OK.

2) If location of sensor makes it hard to check, disconnect black ECM connector and check resistance between connector terminals 4 and 11.

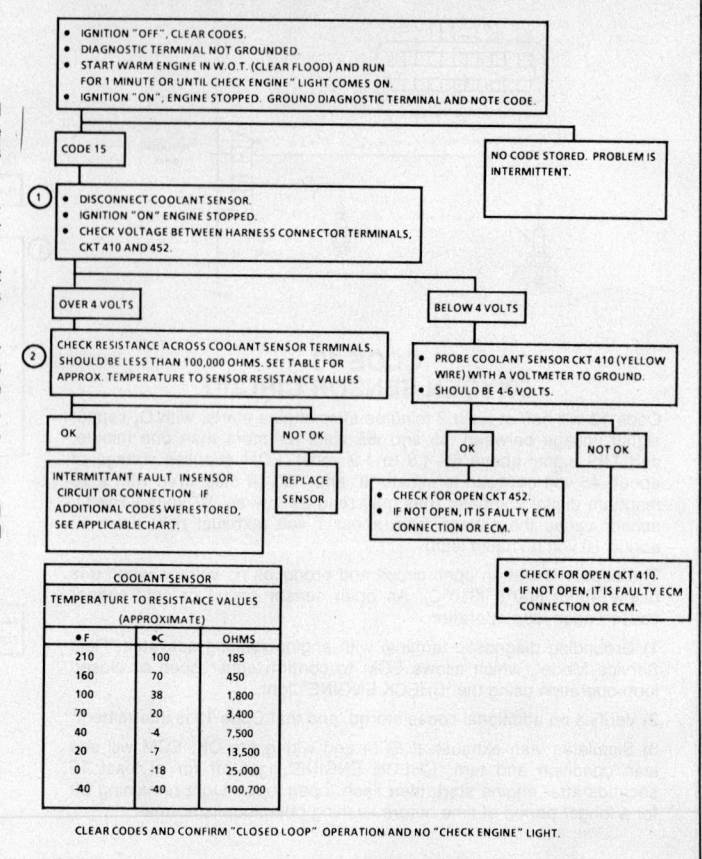

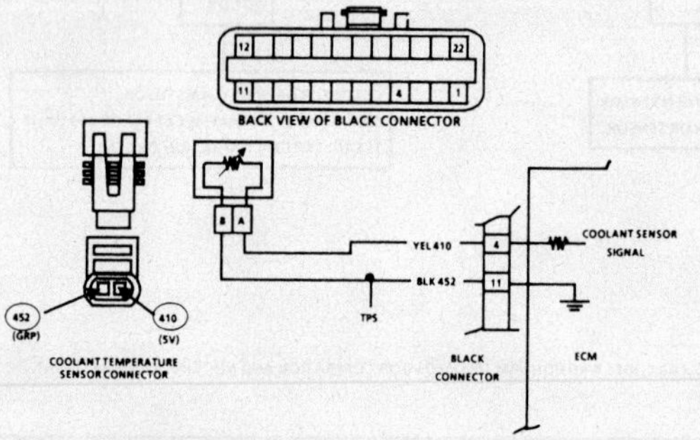

BACK VIEW OF BLACK CONNECTOR
12
22
11
4
1
B
A
YEL 410
BLK 452
4
11
COOLANT SENSOR SIGNAL
TPS
452 (GRD)
410 (5V)
COOLANT TEMPERATURE SENSOR CONNECTOR
BLACK CONNECTOR
ECM

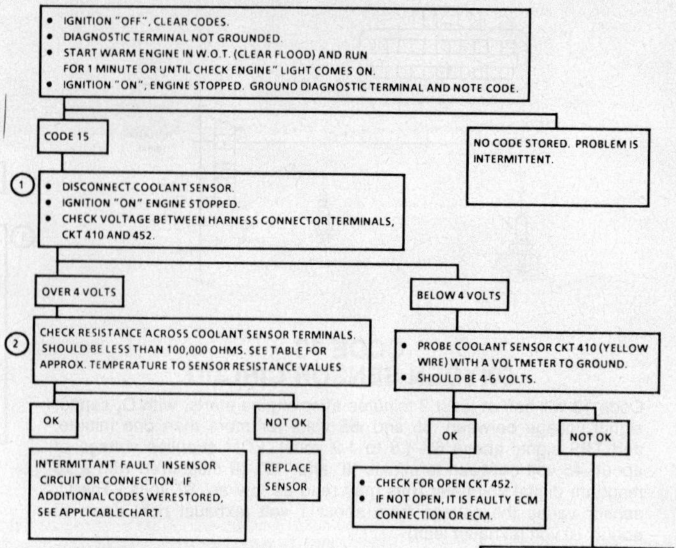

• IGNITION "OFF", CLEAR CODES.
• DIAGNOSTIC TERMINAL NOT GROUNDED.
• START WARM ENGINE IN W.O.T. (CLEAR FLOOD) AND RUN FOR 1 MINUTE OR UNTIL CHECK ENGINE" LIGHT COMES ON.
• IGNITION "ON", ENGINE STOPPED. GROUND DIAGNOSTIC TERMINAL AND NOTE CODE.
CODE 15
NO CODE STORED. PROBLEM IS INTERMITTENT.
1
• DISCONNECT COOLANT SENSOR.
• IGNITION "ON" ENGINE STOPPED.
• CHECK VOLTAGE BETWEEN HARNESS CONNECTOR TERMINALS, CKT 410 AND 452.
OVER 4 VOLTS
BELOW 4 VOLTS
2
CHECK RESISTANCE ACROSS COOLANT SENSOR TERMINALS. SHOULD BE LESS THAN 100,000 OHMS. SEE TABLE FOR APPROX. TEMPERATURE TO SENSOR RESISTANCE VALUES
• PROBE COOLANT SENSOR CKT 410 (YELLOW WIRE) WITH A VOLTMETER TO GROUND.
• SHOULD BE 4-6 VOLTS.
OK
NOT OK
OK
NOT OK
INTERMITTANT FAULT INSENSOR CIRCUIT OR CONNECTION. IF ADDITIONAL CODES WERESTORED, SEE APPLICABLECHART.
REPLACE SENSOR
• CHECK FOR OPEN CKT 452.
• IF NOT OPEN, IT IS FAULTY ECM CONNECTION OR ECM.
• CHECK FOR OPEN CKT 410.
• IF NOT OPEN, IT IS FAULTY ECM CONNECTION OR ECM.

COOLANT SENSOR TEMPERATURE TO RESISTANCE VALUES (APPROXIMATE)

°F	°C	OHMS
210	100	185
160	70	450
100	38	1,800
70	20	3,400
40	4	7,500
20	-7	13,500
0	-18	25,000
-40	-40	100,700

CLEAR CODES AND CONFIRM "CLOSED LOOP" OPERATION AND NO "CHECK ENGINE" LIGHT.

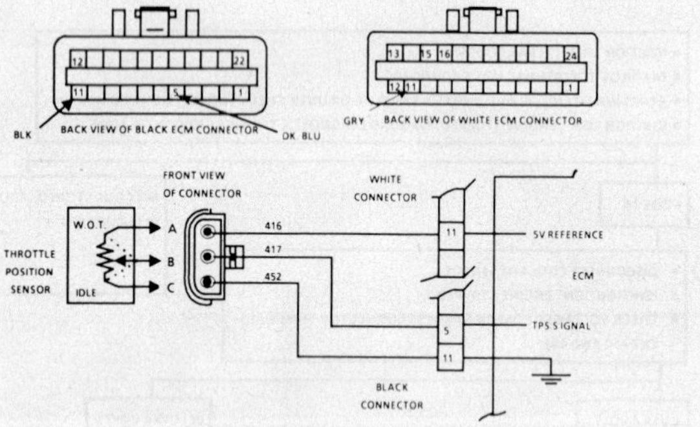

12
22
11
5
1
BLK
BACK VIEW OF BLACK ECM CONNECTOR
DK BLU
13
15
16
24
1
GRY
BACK VIEW OF WHITE ECM CONNECTOR
FRONT VIEW OF CONNECTOR
WHITE CONNECTOR
W.O.T.
THROTTLE POSITION SENSOR
IDLE
A
B
C
416
417
452
11
5V REFERENCE
ECM
5
TPS SIGNAL
11
BLACK CONNECTOR

CODE 21 THROTTLE POSITION SENSOR (SIGNAL VOLTAGE HIGH)

The Throttle Position Sensor (TPS) provides a voltage signal that changes relative to throttle valve position. Signal voltage will vary from less than 1.25 volts at idle to about 4.5 volts at wide open throttle.

The TPS signal is one of the most important inputs used by the ECM for fuel control and for most ECM controlled outputs.

Code 21 will set if TPS signal voltage is greater than 2.5 volts for 2 seconds with engine speed less than 1600 RPM, and MAP less than 9 psi (no load condition).

1) Confirms Code 21 and that fault is present.

2) Simulates Code 22. If ECM recognizes low signal voltage and sets Code 22, ECM and wiring are OK.

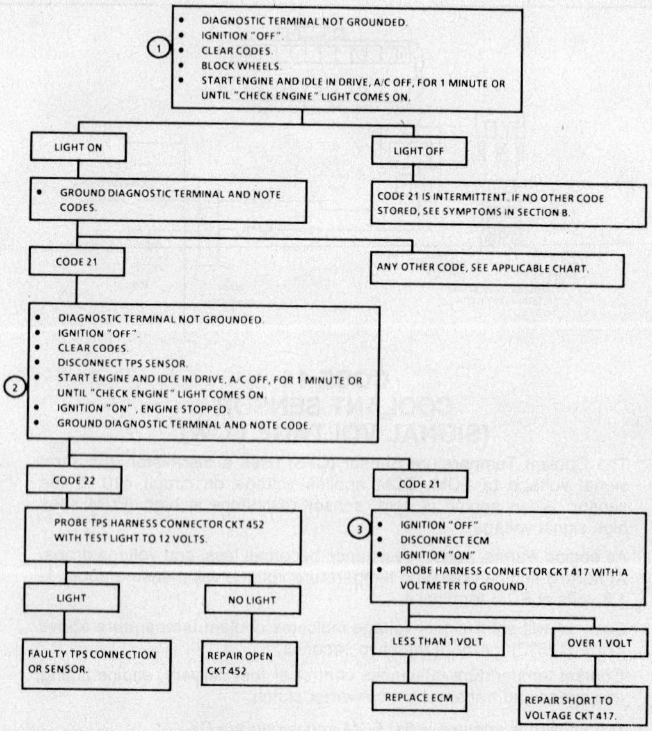

1
• DIAGNOSTIC TERMINAL NOT GROUNDED.
• IGNITION "OFF".
• CLEAR CODES.
• BLOCK WHEELS.
• START ENGINE AND IDLE IN DRIVE, A/C OFF, FOR 1 MINUTE OR UNTIL "CHECK ENGINE" LIGHT COMES ON.
LIGHT ON
LIGHT OFF
• GROUND DIAGNOSTIC TERMINAL AND NOTE CODES.
CODE 21 IS INTERMITTENT. IF NO OTHER CODE STORED, SEE SYMPTOMS IN SECTION B.
CODE 21
ANY OTHER CODE, SEE APPLICABLE CHART.
2
• DIAGNOSTIC TERMINAL NOT GROUNDED.
• IGNITION "OFF".
• CLEAR CODES.
• DISCONNECT TPS SENSOR.
• START ENGINE AND IDLE IN DRIVE, A.C OFF, FOR 1 MINUTE OR UNTIL "CHECK ENGINE" LIGHT COMES ON.
• IGNITION "ON", ENGINE STOPPED.
• GROUND DIAGNOSTIC TERMINAL AND NOTE CODE.
CODE 22
CODE 21
PROBE TPS HARNESS CONNECTOR CKT 452 WITH TEST LIGHT TO 12 VOLTS.
3
• IGNITION "OFF"
• DISCONNECT ECM
• IGNITION "ON"
• PROBE HARNESS CONNECTOR CKT 417 WITH A VOLTMETER TO GROUND.
LIGHT
NO LIGHT
LESS THAN 1 VOLT
OVER 1 VOLT
FAULTY TPS CONNECTION OR SENSOR.
REPAIR OPEN CKT 452
REPLACE ECM
REPAIR SHORT TO VOLTAGE CKT 417.

CLEAR CODES AND CONFIRM "CLOSED LOOP" OPERATION AND NO "CHECK ENGINE" LIGHT.

GENERAL MOTORS COMPUTER COMMAND CONTROL 2.5L THROTTLE BODY FUEL INJECTION (Cont.)

CODE 22
THROTTLE POSITION SENSOR (SIGNAL VOLTAGE LOW)

The Throttle Position Sensor (TPS) provides a voltage signal that changes relative to throttle valve position. Signal voltage will vary from less than 1.25 volts at idle to about 4.5 volts at wide open throttle.

The TPS signal is one of the most important inputs used by the ECM for fuel control and for most ECM controlled outputs.

Code 22 will set if TPS signal is less than .2 volts for 2 seconds and engine speed is less than 1600 RPM.

1) Confirms Code 22 and that fault is present.

2) Simulates Code 21. If ECM recognizes high signal voltage and sets code 21, ECM and wiring are OK.

3) Checks for reference voltage from ECM. To prevent damage to ECM, disconnect white connector when checking circuit wiring for open or shorts to ground.

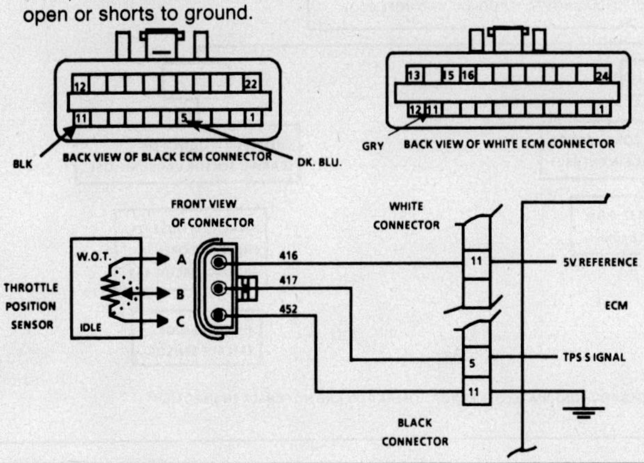

①
- DIAGNOSTIC TERMINAL NOT GROUNDED.
- IGNITION "OFF", CLEAR CODES.
- BLOCK WHEELS.
- START ENGINE AND IDLE IN DRIVE, A/C "OFF", FOR 1 MINUTE OR UNTIL "CHECK ENGINE" LIGHT COMES ON.

LIGHT ON
- IGNITION "ON", ENGINE STOPPED.
- GROUND DIAGNOSTIC TERMINAL AND NOTE CODE.

CODE 22 | ANY OTHER CODE, SEE APPLICABLE CHART.

LIGHT OFF
CODE 22 IS INTERMITTENT.

②
- DIAGNOSTIC TERMINAL NOT GROUNDED.
- IGNITION OFF, CLEAR CODES.
- DISCONNECT TPS AND JUMPER CKTS 416 TO 417.
- BLOCK WHEELS.
- START ENGINE AND IDLE IN DRIVE FOR 1 MINUTE OR UNTIL "CHECK ENGINE" LIGHT COMES ON.
- IGNITION "ON", ENGINE STOPPED.
- GROUND DIAGNOSTIC TERMINAL AND NOTE CODE.

CODE 22
- REMOVE JUMPER FROM 416 AND 417.
- CHECK VOLTAGE BETWEEN HARNESS CONN. CIRCUIT 452 AND 416 USING DIGITAL VOLTMETER (J-29125).

CODE 21
REPLACE TPS

4-6 VOLTS
③ DISCONNECT ECM CONNECTOR AND CHECK FOR OPEN OR SHORT TO GROUND IN CKT 417. IF CKT 417 OK, IT IS FAULTY ECM CONNECTOR TERMINAL OR ECM.

BELOW 4 VOLTS
- DISCONNECT ECM CONNECTOR.
- CHECK FOR OPEN OR SHORT TO GROUND IN CKT 416. IF CKT 416 OK, IT IS FAULTY ECM CONNECTOR TERMINAL OR ECM.

CLEAR CODES AND CONFIRM "CLOSED LOOP" OPERATION AND NO "CHECK ENGINE" LIGHT.

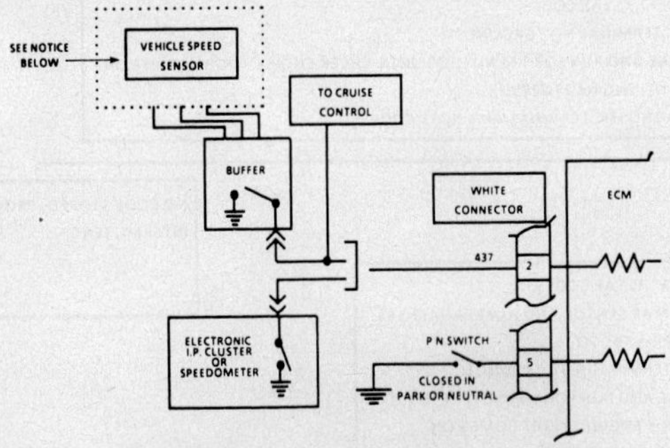

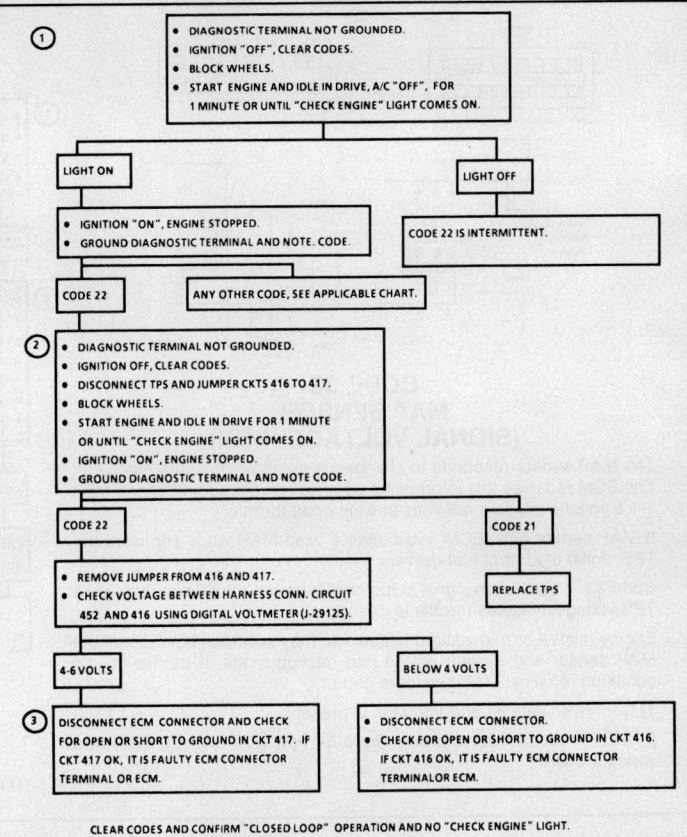

CODE 24
VEHICLE SPEED SENSOR

The ECM supplies a current limited 12 volt signal on circuit 437. The Vehicle Speed Sensor (VSS), located in the instrument panel cluster, senses the speedometer rotating element and furnishes this information to the buffer as a pulsed signal (2 per cable revolution or 2002 pulses per mile).

The buffer assembly switches circuit 437 to ground for each pulse received. The ECM uses the time between pulses to determine vehicle speed.

Code 24 is set when circuit 437 voltage is constant (no rise and fall of voltage for 4 to 10 seconds), with engine speed between 1500 and 4400 RPM, transmission in Drive (as indicated by Park/Neutral switch), and low MAP (indicating engine deceleration).

Loss of VSS will affect Torque Converter Clutch, Idle Air Control, and Fan Control (fan will not shut off above 30 MPH with A/C on).

1) Checks to see if there is a VSS signal to ECM while turning a drive wheel. Voltage should vary from under 3 volts to over 6 volts as wheel is turned. Rotating wheel faster reduces variation.

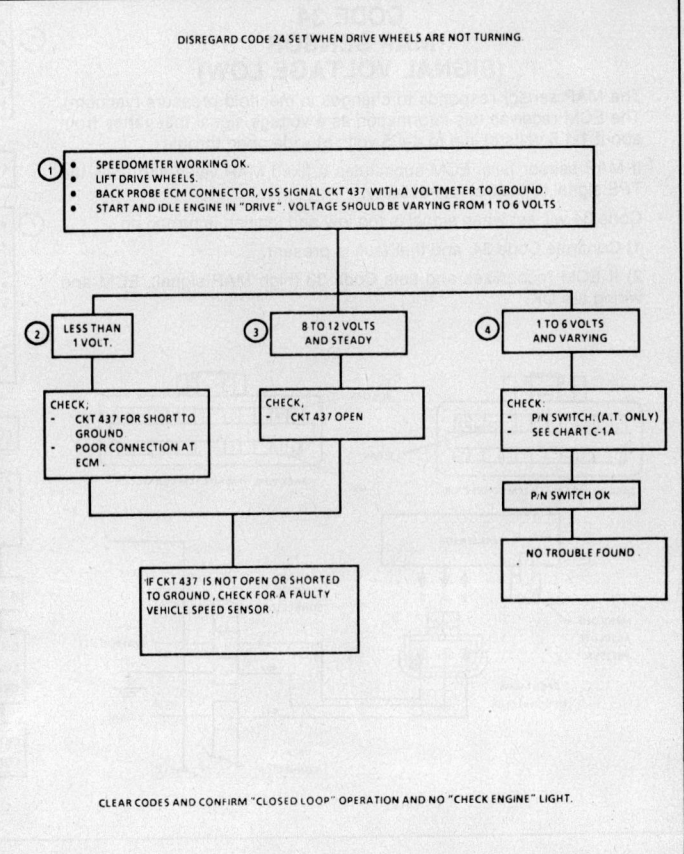

DISREGARD CODE 24 SET WHEN DRIVE WHEELS ARE NOT TURNING.

①
- SPEEDOMETER WORKING OK.
- LIFT DRIVE WHEELS.
- BACK PROBE ECM CONNECTOR, VSS SIGNAL CKT 437 WITH A VOLTMETER TO GROUND.
- START AND IDLE ENGINE IN "DRIVE". VOLTAGE SHOULD BE VARYING FROM 1 TO 6 VOLTS

② LESS THAN 1 VOLT.
CHECK;
- CKT 437 FOR SHORT TO GROUND.
- POOR CONNECTION AT ECM.

③ 8 TO 12 VOLTS AND STEADY
CHECK,
- CKT 437 OPEN

IF CKT 437 IS NOT OPEN OR SHORTED TO GROUND, CHECK FOR A FAULTY VEHICLE SPEED SENSOR.

④ 1 TO 6 VOLTS AND VARYING
CHECK:
- P/N SWITCH. (A.T. ONLY)
- SEE CHART C-1A

P/N SWITCH OK
NO TROUBLE FOUND.

CLEAR CODES AND CONFIRM "CLOSED LOOP" OPERATION AND NO "CHECK ENGINE" LIGHT.

GENERAL MOTORS COMPUTER COMMAND CONTROL
2.5L THROTTLE BODY FUEL INJECTION (Cont.)

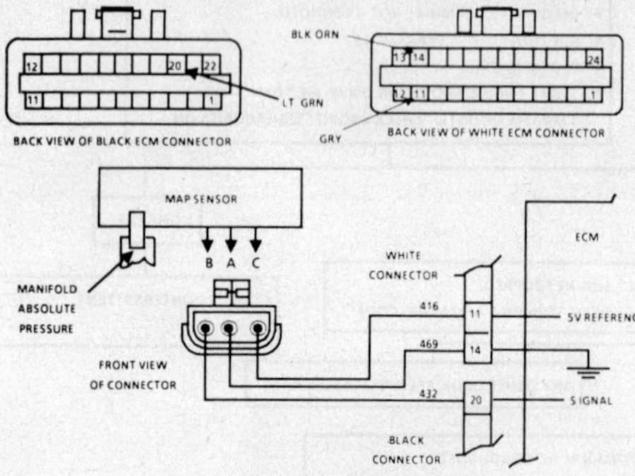

CODE 33
MAP SENSOR
(SIGNAL VOLTAGE HIGH)

The MAP sensor responds to changes in manifold pressure (vacuum). The ECM receives this information as a signal voltage that varies from 1-1.5 volts at idle to 4-4.5 volts at wide open throttle.

If MAP sensor fails, ECM substitutes a fixed MAP value and uses the TPS signal to control fuel delivery.

Code 33 will set when signal is too high for more than 8 seconds while TPS voltage indicates throttle is closed.

Engine misfire or a low and unstable idle may set Code 33. Disconnect MAP sensor and system will go into backup mode. If misfire or idle condition remains, MAP sensor is good.

1) Confirms Code 33 and that fault is present.

2) If ECM recognizes and sets Code 34 (low MAP signal), ECM and wiring are OK.

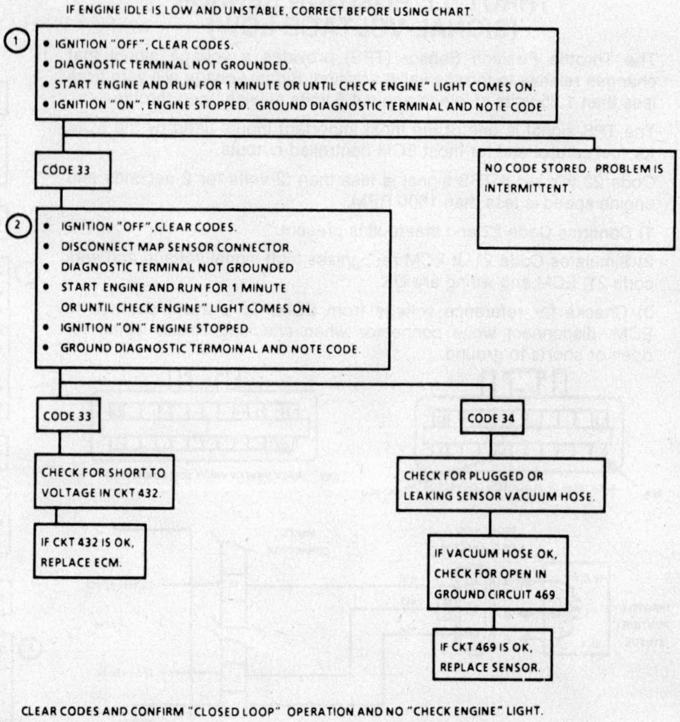

IF ENGINE IDLE IS LOW AND UNSTABLE, CORRECT BEFORE USING CHART.
1
• IGNITION "OFF", CLEAR CODES.
• DIAGNOSTIC TERMINAL NOT GROUNDED.
• START ENGINE AND RUN FOR 1 MINUTE OR UNTIL CHECK ENGINE" LIGHT COMES ON.
• IGNITION "ON", ENGINE STOPPED. GROUND DIAGNOSTIC TERMINAL AND NOTE CODE
CODE 33
NO CODE STORED. PROBLEM IS INTERMITTENT.
2
• IGNITION "OFF",CLEAR CODES.
• DISCONNECT MAP SENSOR CONNECTOR
• DIAGNOSTIC TERMINAL NOT GROUNDED
• START ENGINE AND RUN FOR 1 MINUTE OR UNTIL CHECK ENGINE" LIGHT COMES ON.
• IGNITION "ON" ENGINE STOPPED
• GROUND DIAGNOSTIC TERMOINAL AND NOTE CODE.
CODE 33
CODE 34
CHECK FOR SHORT TO VOLTAGE IN CKT 432.
CHECK FOR PLUGGED OR LEAKING SENSOR VACUUM HOSE.
IF CKT 432 IS OK, REPLACE ECM.
IF VACUUM HOSE OK, CHECK FOR OPEN IN GROUND CIRCUIT 469
IF CKT 469 IS OK, REPLACE SENSOR.
CLEAR CODES AND CONFIRM "CLOSED LOOP" OPERATION AND NO "CHECK ENGINE" LIGHT.

CODE 34
MAP SENSOR
(SIGNAL VOLTAGE LOW)

The MAP sensor responds to changes in manifold pressure (vacuum). The ECM receives this information as a voltage signal that varies from about 1-1.5 volts at idle to 4-4.5 volts at wide open throttle.

If MAP sensor fails, ECM substitutes a fixed MAP value and uses the TPS signal to control fuel delivery.

Code 34 will set when signal is too low and ignition is turned on.

1) Confirms Code 34, and that fault is present.

2) If ECM recognizes and sets Code 33 (high MAP signal), ECM and wiring are OK.

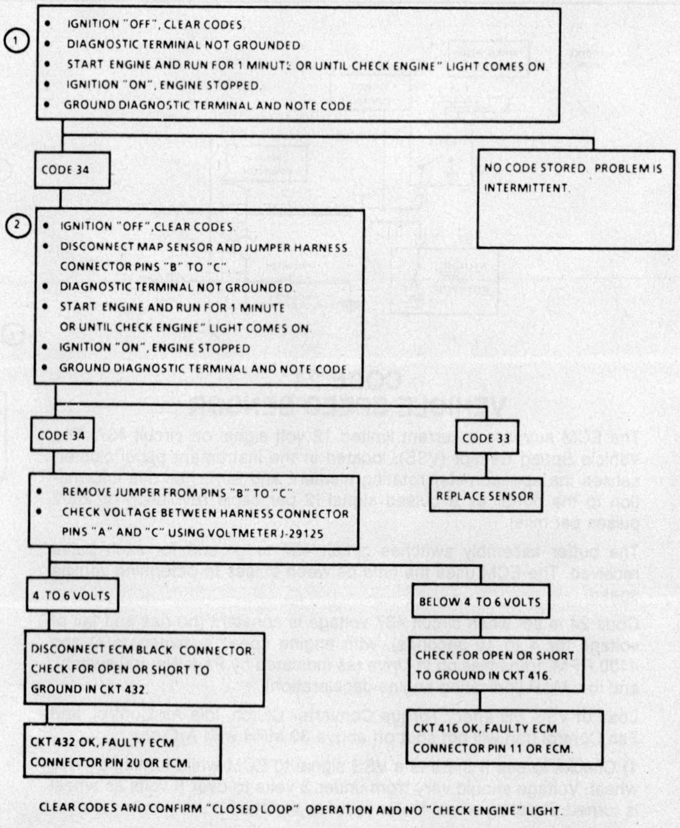

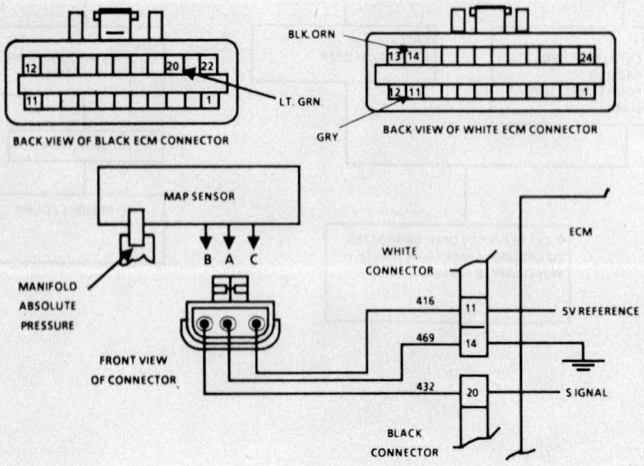

GENERAL MOTORS COMPUTER COMMAND CONTROL 2.5L THROTTLE BODY FUEL INJECTION (Cont.)

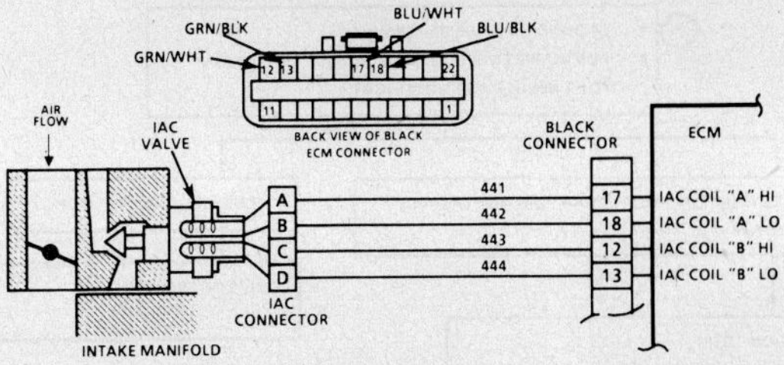

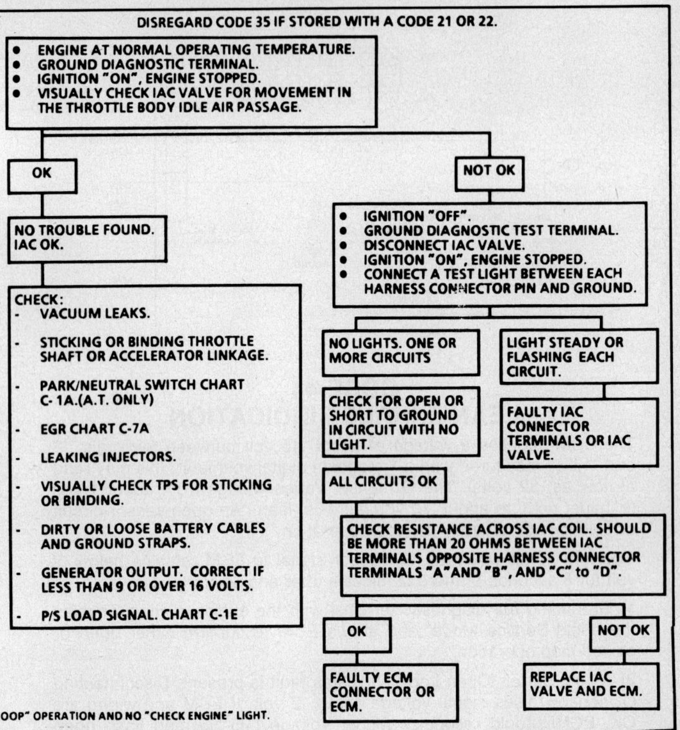

CODE 35
IDLE AIR CONTROL

The ECM controls engine idle speed by moving the Idle Air Control (IAC) valve to control air flow around the throttle plate. Voltage pulses are sent to the proper motor winding. The motor shaft and valve move a given distance for each pulse received.

To increase idle speed, the ECM signals the IAC valve to retract, allowing more air flow and increasing RPM. To decrease idle speed, ECM signals the valve to extend, reducing air flow and engine RPM.

The ECM "learns" correct valve position to maintain proper idle RPM. If "learned" IAC valve position is incorrect, ECM will command a reset. Reset occurs after next engine start when vehicle speed exceeds 35-45 MPH.

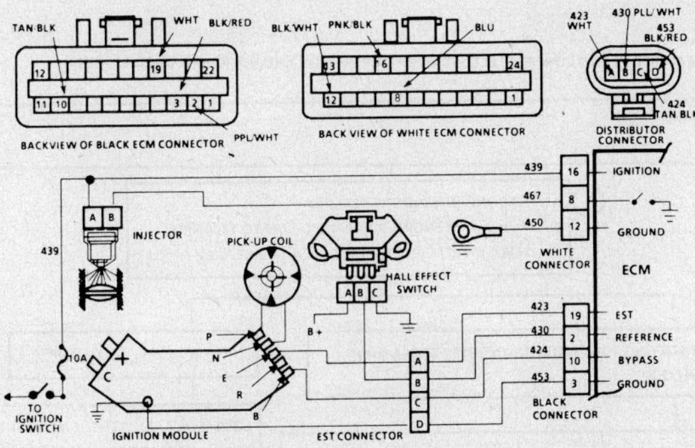

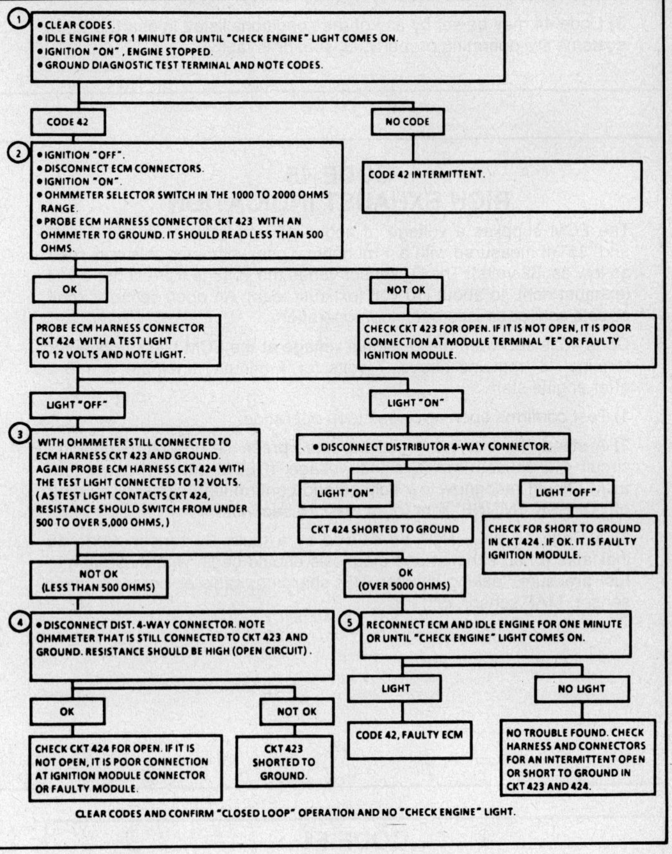

CODE 42
ELECTRONIC SPARK TIMING

Code 42 means ECM has seen an open or short to ground in the Electronic Spark Timing (EST) or bypass circuits.

1) Confirms Code 42 and that fault causing code is present.

2) Checks for normal EST ground path through ignition module. An EST circuit 423 shorted to ground will also read less than 500 ohms (will be checked later).

3) As test light voltage touches terminal 10, module should switch, causing ohmmeter to "overrange" (meter is in the 1000-2000 ohms position). Selecting 10-20,000 ohms position will indicate above 5000 ohms. The important thing is that the module "switched".

4) The module did not switch and this step checks for:
- EST circuit 423 shorted to ground.
- Bypass circuit 424 open.
- Faulty ignition module connection or module.

5) Confirms that Code 42 is a faulty ECM and not an intermittent in circuits 423 or 424.

GENERAL MOTORS COMPUTER COMMAND CONTROL 2.5L THROTTLE BODY FUEL INJECTION (Cont.)

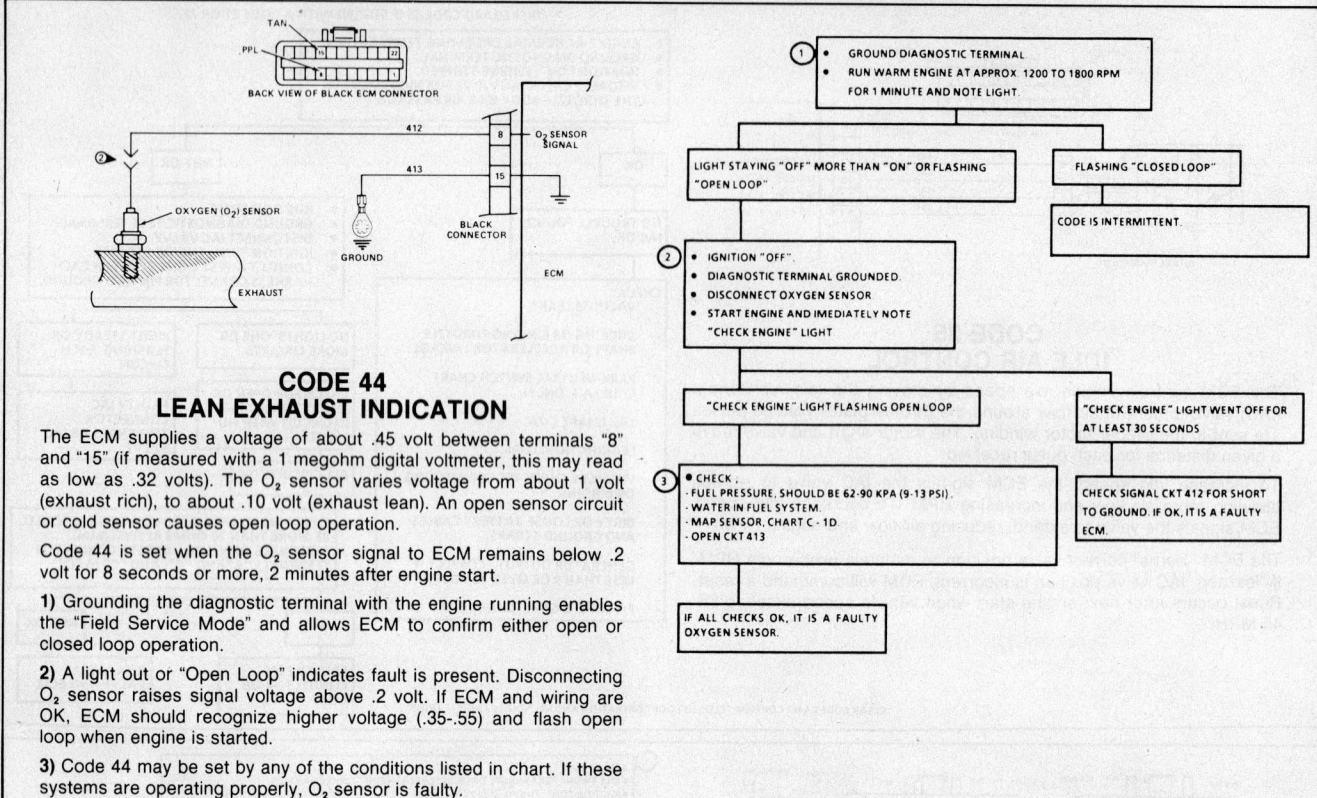

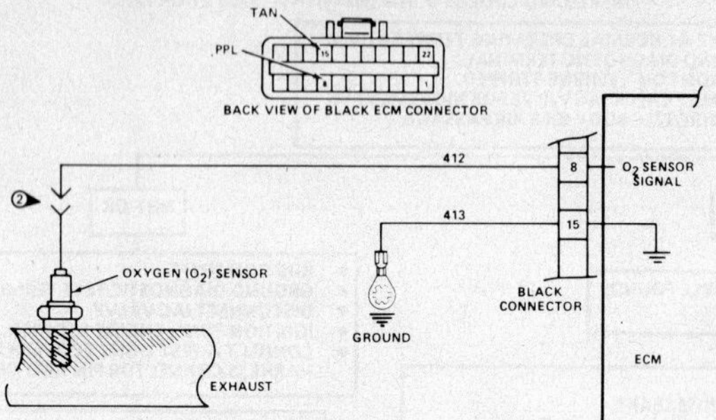

CODE 44
LEAN EXHAUST INDICATION

The ECM supplies a voltage of about .45 volt between terminals "8" and "15" (if measured with a 1 megohm digital voltmeter, this may read as low as .32 volts). The O_2 sensor varies voltage from about 1 volt (exhaust rich), to about .10 volt (exhaust lean). An open sensor circuit or cold sensor causes open loop operation.

Code 44 is set when the O_2 sensor signal to ECM remains below .2 volt for 8 seconds or more, 2 minutes after engine start.

1) Grounding the diagnostic terminal with the engine running enables the "Field Service Mode" and allows ECM to confirm either open or closed loop operation.

2) A light out or "Open Loop" indicates fault is present. Disconnecting O_2 sensor raises signal voltage above .2 volt. If ECM and wiring are OK, ECM should recognize higher voltage (.35-.55) and flash open loop when engine is started.

3) Code 44 may be set by any of the conditions listed in chart. If these systems are operating properly, O_2 sensor is faulty.

(1)
- GROUND DIAGNOSTIC TERMINAL
- RUN WARM ENGINE AT APPROX 1200 TO 1800 RPM FOR 1 MINUTE AND NOTE LIGHT.

LIGHT STAYING "OFF" MORE THAN "ON" OR FLASHING "OPEN LOOP"

(2)
- IGNITION "OFF".
- DIAGNOSTIC TERMINAL GROUNDED.
- DISCONNECT OXYGEN SENSOR
- START ENGINE AND IMEDIATELY NOTE "CHECK ENGINE" LIGHT

"CHECK ENGINE" LIGHT FLASHING OPEN LOOP

(3)
- CHECK ;
  - FUEL PRESSURE, SHOULD BE 62-90 KPA (9-13 PSI).
  - WATER IN FUEL SYSTEM.
  - MAP SENSOR, CHART C - 1D.
  - OPEN CKT 413

IF ALL CHECKS OK, IT IS A FAULTY OXYGEN SENSOR.

"CHECK ENGINE" LIGHT WENT OFF FOR AT LEAST 30 SECONDS

CHECK SIGNAL CKT 412 FOR SHORT TO GROUND. IF OK, IT IS A FAULTY ECM.

FLASHING "CLOSED LOOP"

CODE IS INTERMITTENT.

CLEAR CODES AND CONFIRM "CLOSED LOOP" OPERATION AND NO "CHECK ENGINE" LIGHT.

CODE 45
RICH EXHAUST INDICATION

The ECM supplies a voltage of about .45 volt between terminals "8" and "15" (if measured with a 1 megohm digital voltmeter, this may read as low as .32 volts). The O_2 sensor varies the voltage from about 1 volt (exhaust rich), to about .10 volt (exhaust lean). An open sensor circuit or cold sensor causes open loop operation.

Code 45 is set when the O_2 signal voltage at the ECM black connector terminal "8" remains above .7 volts for 1 minute, 1 minute or more after engine start.

1) Test confirms open or closed loop operation.

2) A steady light or open loop indicates presence of fault. Grounding circuit 412 causes low O_2 signal voltage. If ECM and wiring are OK, ECM should recognize low voltage and confirm lean signal by turning off "CHECK ENGINE" light for at least 15 seconds.

3) A Code 45 WILL NOT be caused by a faulty O_2 sensor. Code 45 indicates a rich exhaust and diagnosis should begin with these items: fuel pressure, leaking injector, HEI shielding, canister purge, coolant sensor, MAP sensor, or TPS.

(1)
- GROUND DIAGNOSTIC TERMINAL.
- RUN WARM ENGINE AT APPROX. 1200 TO 1800 RPM FOR 1 MINUTE AND NOTE "CHECK ENGINE" LIGHT.

LIGHT STAYING "ON" MORE THAN "OFF" OR FLASHING "OPEN LOOP".

(2)
- IGNITION "OFF".
- DIAGNOSTIC TERMINAL GROUNDED
- DISCONNECT OXYGEN SENSOR AND JUMPER HARNESS CONNECTOR SIGNAL CKT 412 TO GROUND
- START ENGINE AND IMEDIATELY NOTE "CHECK ENGINE" LIGHT.

"CHECK ENGINE" LIGHT WENT OFF FOR AT LEAST 30 SECONDS.

SYSTEM RICH

(3) Check fuel pressure, leaking injector, HEI shielding, canister purge, coolant sensor, MAP sensor or TPS.

STEADY LIGHT

FAULTY ECM.

FLASHING "CLOSED LOOP"

CODE IS INTERMITTENT. IF NO ADDITIONAL CODES WERE STORED, REFER TO SECTION B.

FIELD SERVICE MODE;
- ENGINE RUNNING, DIAGNOSTIC TERMINAL GROUNDED.
- OPEN - LOOP, "CHECK ENGINE" LIGHT FLASHES AT A RATE OF 2.5 TIMES PER SECOND.
- CLOSED LOOP, "CHECK ENGINE" LIGHT FLASHES AT A RATE OF 1 TIME PER SECOND.

CLEAR CODES AND CONFIRM "CLOSED LOOP" OPERATION AND NO "CHECK ENGINE" LIGHT.

CODE 51
PROM

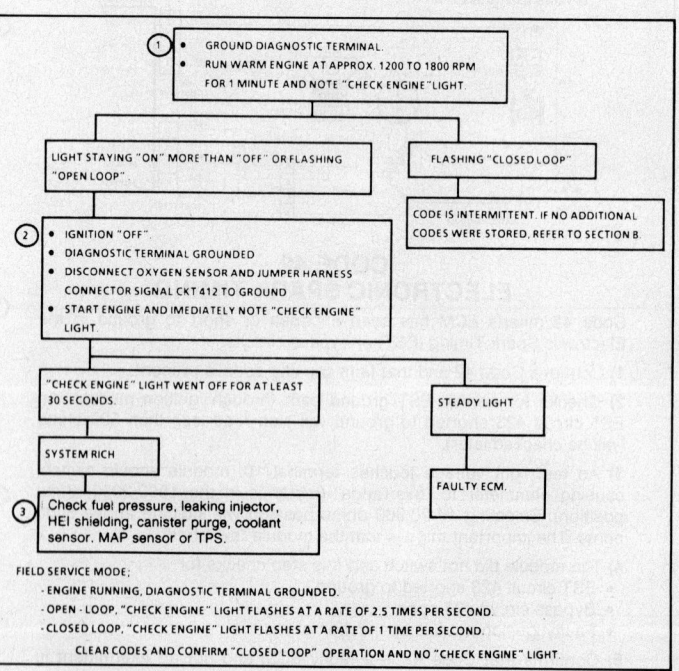

Check that all pins are fully inserted in the socket. If okay, replace PROM, clear memory and recheck. If code 51 reappears, replace ECM.

CODE 55
ECM

Replace Electronic Control Module

Clear codes and confirm "Closed Loop" operation and no "Check Engine"light.

GENERAL MOTORS COMPUTER COMMAND CONTROL CALIF. 2.8L, 4.3L, 5.0L & 5.7L FULL FUNCTION

DIAGNOSTIC CIRCUIT CHECK ALL EXCEPT 2.8L

Diagnostic Circuit Check determines if: 1) the "CHECK ENGINE" light works, 2) the ECM is operating and can recognize a fault, and 3) any codes are stored. It also checks to see if stored codes indicate an intermittent problem. This is the starting point for any diagnosis. If no codes are indicated, go to the System Performance Check. If no additional checks are called out from the System Performance Check, go to the Driveability Symptoms.

1) Check operation of the "CHECK ENGINE" light. Key "ON," engine not running, light should be on steady.

2) Grounding test terminal will flash a Code 12 and any stored trouble codes. The light must go "ON" and "OFF" to indicate a code. The light going from "Bright" to "Dim" is not considered a code. *See CHART A-6.*

3) This step will determine if any codes, other than Code 12, are still present or were intermittent and are no longer stored. Clear memory. Run vehicle for 2 minutes. See if trouble code(s) reset.

4) If the light is "ON," fault is still present. Go to the applicable trouble code chart.

5) If the light is "OFF," the fault is either intermittent, or it is a code that cannot be set with vehicle stationary. For codes that cannot be set during the Diagnostic Circuit Check, the applicable trouble code chart will determine if those codes are intermittent.

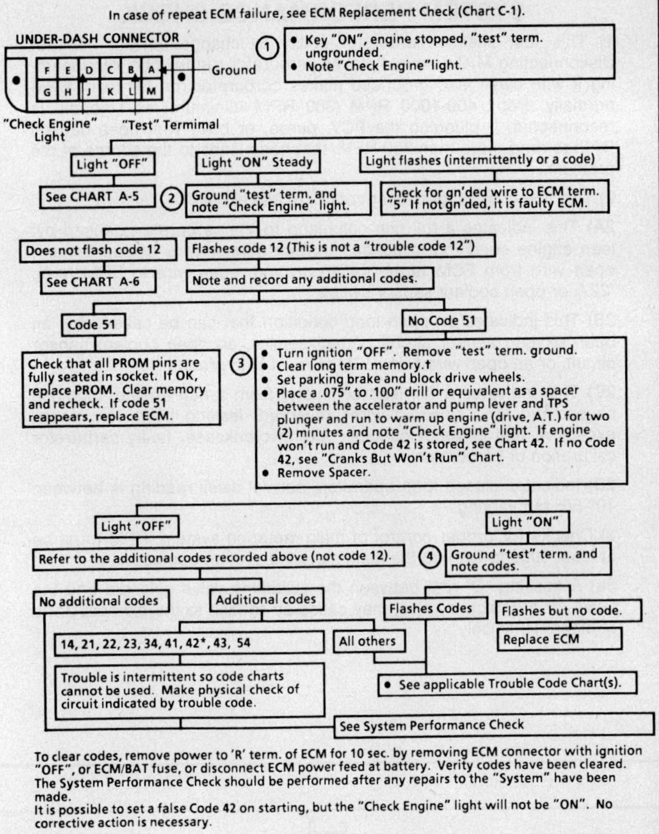

DIAGNOSTIC CIRCUIT CHECK 2.8L ONLY

Diagnostic Circuit Check determines if: 1) the "CHECK ENGINE" light works, 2) the ECM is operating and can recognize a fault, and 3) any codes are stored. It also checks to see if stored codes indicate an intermittent problem. This is the starting point for any diagnosis. If no codes are indicated, go to the System Performance Check. If no additional checks are called out from the System Performance Check, go to the Driveability Symptoms.

1) Check operation of the "CHECK ENGINE" light. Key "ON," engine not running, light should be on steady.

2) Grounding test terminal will flash a Code 12 and any stored trouble codes. The light must go "ON" and "OFF" to indicate a code. The light going from "Bright" to "Dim" is not considered a code. *See CHART A-6.*

3) This step will determine if any codes, other than Code 12, are still present or were intermittent and are no longer stored. Clear memory. Run vehicle for 2 minutes. See if trouble code(s) reset.

4) If the light is "ON," fault is still present. Go to the applicable trouble code chart.

5) If the light is "OFF," the fault is either intermittent, or it is a code that cannot be set with vehicle stationary. For codes that cannot be set during the Diagnostic Circuit Check, the applicable trouble code chart will determine if those codes are intermittent.

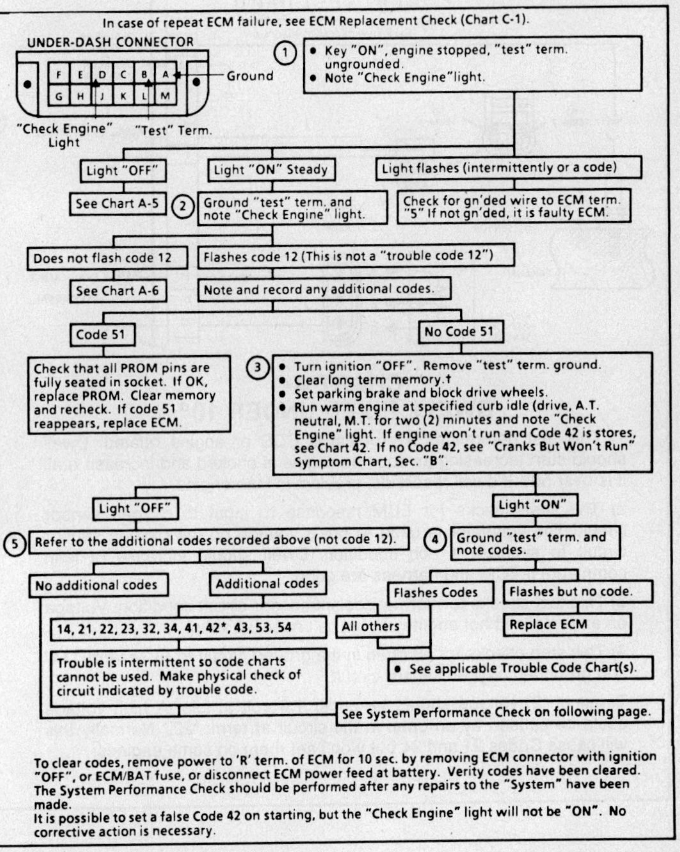

GENERAL MOTORS COMPUTER COMMAND CONTROL CALIF. 2.8L, 4.3L, 5.0L & 5.7L FULL FUNCTION (Cont.)

SYSTEM PERFORMANCE CHECK

1) This test checks carburetor ability to change air/fuel mixture. Disconnecting M/C solenoid makes carburetor run full rich, reconnecting it with dwell lead grounded makes carburetor run full lean. RPM normally drops 400-1000 RPM (300 RPM minimum) as solenoid is reconnected. If plugging the PCV, purge, or bowl vent hose causes RPM to drop more than 300 RPM, that hose leads to the source of the problem.

2) This test checks for proper control of idle circuit.

2A) This indicates a full rich command to the carburetor, caused by: lean engine condition, grounded oxygen sensor wire or bad sensor, open wire from ECM term. "14" to ground, open wire to ECM term. "22.", or open coolant sensor switch.

2B) This indicates an open loop condition that can be caused by: an open oxygen sensor circuit or bad sensor, an open coolant sensor circuit, or an open wire from ECM term. "14" to ground.

2C) This indicates a full lean command from a rich engine condition caused by: M/C solenoid wires reversed, leaking bowl vent valve, excessive fuel in vapor canister, fuel in crankcase, faulty carburetor calibration or carburetor.

2D) Indicates closed loop operation, normal dwell reading is between 10°-50° but varying.

3) Checks for proper control of main metering system. RPM must be at least 3000 to get into the main metering system operation.

3a) A missing "O" ring between the switching valve solenoid and the valve, or a defective valve, may cause air to leak to the exhaust ports at higher RPM only.

(1)
1. Start engine.
2. Ground "test" term. (Must not be grounded before engine is started).
3. Connect tachometer.
4. Disconnect Mixture Control (M/C) Solenoid and ground M/C Solenoid dwell term.
5. Run engine at 3,000 RPM and, while keeping throttle constant, reconnect M/C Solenoid and note RPM. If car is equipped with an electric cooling fan, it may lower RPM when it engages.
6. Remove ground from M/C Solenoid dwell term. before returning to idle.

Less than 300 RPM drop or RPM increases

(1A)
- Check that pink wire is attached to righthand term. of M/C Solenoid Connector, as viewed from harness end (solenoid connected).
- Check evaporator canister for being loaded with fuel and related valves, such as purge and bowl vents for leaks which would cause richness. Also check for fuel in crankcase.

If OK, repair carburetor.

More than 300 RPM drop

(2)
- Connect dwell meter to M/C sol. dwell term. (6 cyl. scale).
- Set carb. on high step of fast idle cam. and run for one (1) minute or until dwell starts to vary, whichever happens first.
- Return engine to idle and note dwell.*

(2A) Fixed under 10° — See Chart A-1

(2B) Fixed 10-50°
- Choke engine.
- Note dwell.

Fixed 10-50° — See Chart A-2

(2D) Varying

(2C) Fixed over 50° — See Chart A-3

(2D) Varying

(3) Check dwell at 3000 RPM

Between 10-50°
- Check air management system.

Under 10°

Over 50°

(3A)
- Check air switching valve leaking to exhaust ports at 3000 RPM.

if not leaking .....

Calibrate Carburetor

- No trouble found in the "System".
- Clear long term memory.**

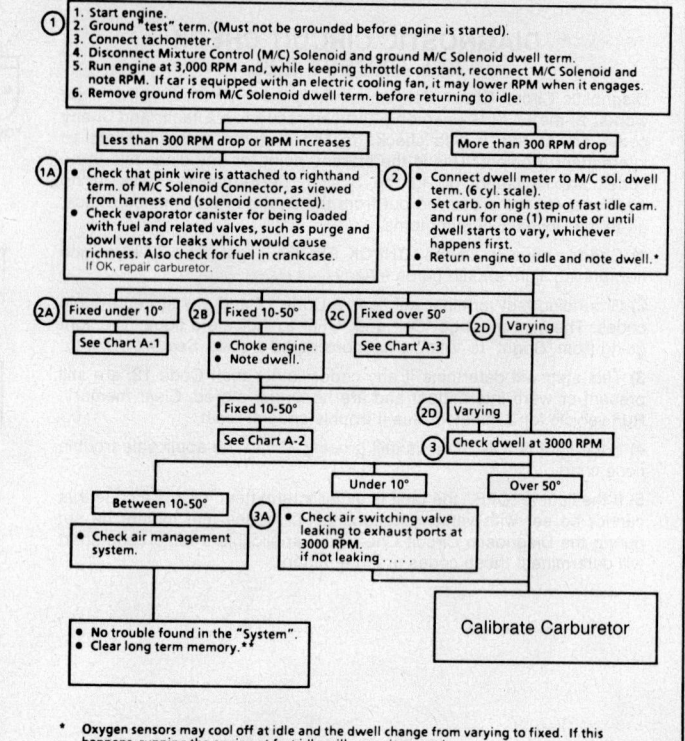

* Oxygen sensors may cool off at idle and the dwell change from varying to fixed. If this happens, running the engine at fast idle will warm it up again.

** See Code(s) Clearing Procedure.

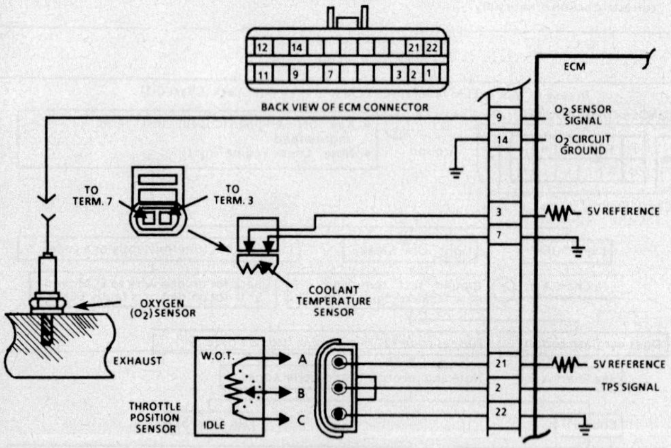

CHART A-1
DWELL FIXED UNDER 10°

1) This test determines if problem is CCC or engine related. Dwell should start increasing as soon as engine is choked and increase until it is over 50°. If dwell responds, problem is lean engine.

2) This test checks for ECM response to input to oxygen sensor circuit. The voltmeter is used to put a voltage on the oxygen sensor circuit to simulate a rich condition. Dwell should increase (a lean command) if ECM and harness are good.

3) This test checks for normal coolant sensor circuit condition. Voltage on a normalized hot engine should be under 2.5 volts.

4) This step checks for an open in the ground circuit to ECM term. "14" and grounded oxygen sensor circuit.

Terminal "2" voltage should be under 1.0 volt at idle. A high voltage could be caused by an open in the circuit at term. "22." Normally this will cause Codes 21 and 34 but won't set them on some engines.

(1)
- Ground "Test" terminal.
- With engine at 2000 rpm, choke engine and note dwell (ignore any variation as throttle position is changed).

Dwell increases to over 50°

(1A)
- Check for air or vacuum leak (including air management system and deceleration valve, if used).
- Check for an exhaust leak.
- Vacuum hose routing.
- Check EGR operation.

No leak
- Repair carburetor.

Leak — Repair

Dwell did not reach 50°

(2)
- Disconnect Oxygen Sensor.
- Connect digital multimeter J29125-A or equivalent and set on the 20 volt scale, from bat. + to purple wire to ECM (not Oxygen Sensor).*
- Note dwell, at part throttle.

Increases
- Check for open from ECM Term. 14 to ground (including ECM connections).
- If not open, replace oxygen sensor.

Under 10°

(3)
- Ignition "On", engine stopped.
- Check voltage from ECM terminals "3" to "7".

Over 3 Volts
- Check for open in coolant sensor circuit.

Under 3 Volts

(4)
- Check for an open from ECM Term. 14 to ground and grounded purple wire to ECM Term. "9".
- If circuits are OK, check ECM terminal "2" to ground

Over 1 volt
- Check for open from ECM term. "22" to TPS term. "C".

open
- Repair Open

not open
- Fault is bad ECM conn. at term. "22" or ECM.

Under 1 volt
- It is a faulty ECM conn. at term. "14" or ECM

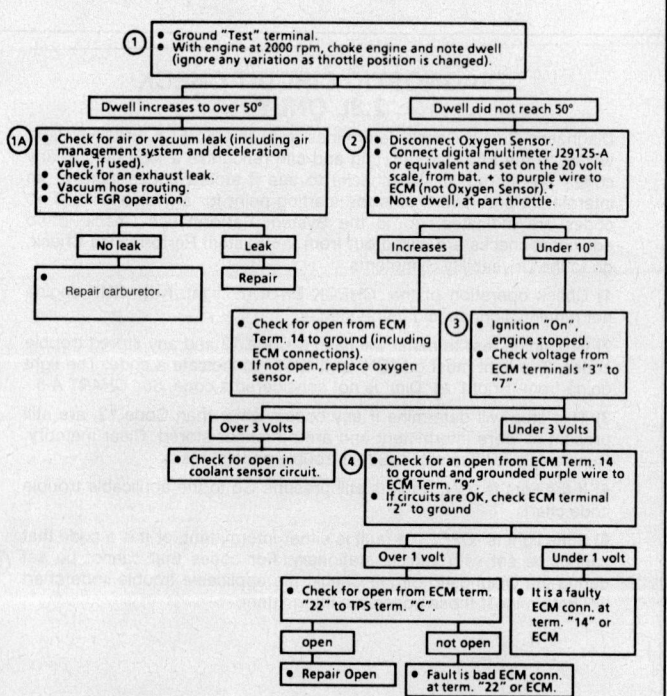

Do Not use an ordinary voltmeter or jumper in place of digital voltmeter, because they have too little resistance. A voltage source of 1.0V to 1.7V (such as a flashlight battery) can be connected with the Positive terminal to the purple wire and the negative terminal to ground as a jumper. If the polarity is reversed, it won't work.

GENERAL MOTORS COMPUTER COMMAND CONTROL CALIF. 2.8L, 4.3L, 5.0L & 5.7L FULL FUNCTION (Cont.)

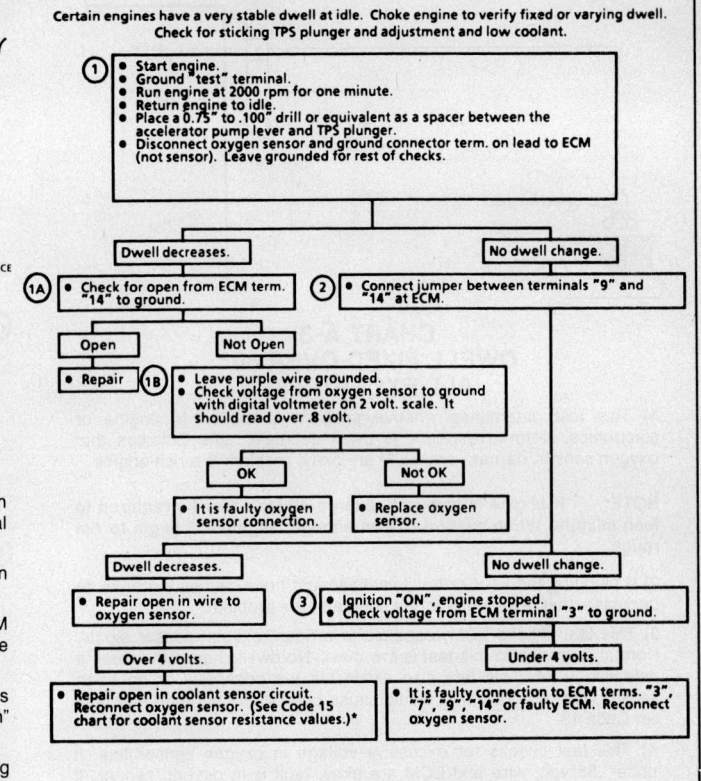

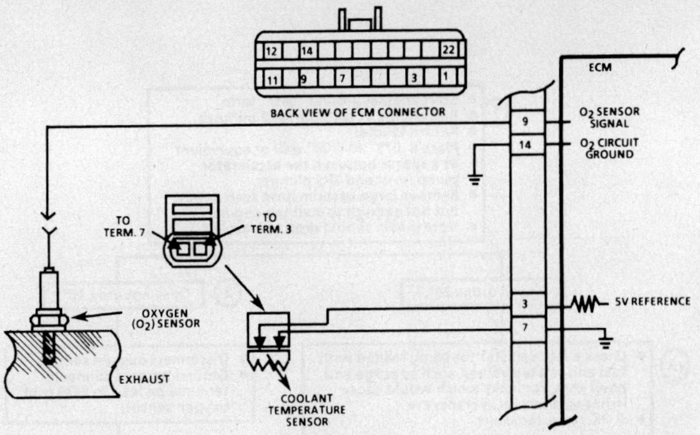

CHART A-2
DWELL FIXED BETWEEN 10°–50°
ALL EXCEPT 2.8L

1) Run engine 1 minute to warm oxygen sensor. Grounding oxygen sensor input checks ECM response to a "lean" signal. Normal response is dwell decreasing to full rich command.

1A) On some ECM's, an open circuit to term. "14" can cause open loop.

1B) Checks output of oxygen sensor with full rich command from ECM caused by grounded oxygen sensor input. Normal response is voltage at oxygen sensor over .8 volt.

2) This step grounds oxygen sensor circuit at ECM to check for opens in wiring to ECM terminals "9" and "14." Normal response to "lean" signal is dwell decrease.

3) This step checks for voltage to the coolant sensor. Normal reading on a warm engine is less than 2.5 volts. An open circuit would cause a reading of approximately 5 volts.

Certain engines have a very stable dwell at idle. Choke engine to verify fixed or varying dwell. Check for sticking TPS plunger and adjustment and low coolant.

(1)
- Start engine.
- Ground "test" terminal.
- Run engine at 2000 rpm for one minute.
- Return engine to idle.
- Place a 0.75" to .100" drill or equivalent as a spacer between the accelerator pump lever and TPS plunger.
- Disconnect oxygen sensor and ground connector term. on lead to ECM (not sensor). Leave grounded for rest of checks.

Dwell decreases.
- **(1A)** • Check for open from ECM term. "14" to ground.
  - **Open** → • Repair
  - **Not Open** → **(1B)** • Leave purple wire grounded. • Check voltage from oxygen sensor to ground with digital voltmeter on 2 volt. scale. It should read over .8 volt.
    - **OK** → • It is faulty oxygen sensor connection.
    - **Not OK** → • Replace oxygen sensor.

No dwell change.
- **(2)** • Connect jumper between terminals "9" and "14" at ECM.
  - **Dwell decreases.** → • Repair open in wire to oxygen sensor.
  - **No dwell change.** → **(3)** • Ignition "ON", engine stopped. • Check voltage from ECM terminal "3" to ground.
    - **Over 4 volts.** → • Repair open in coolant sensor circuit. Reconnect oxygen sensor. (See Code 15 chart for coolant sensor resistance values.)*
    - **Under 4 volts.** → • It is faulty connection to ECM terms. "3", "7", "9", "14" or faulty ECM. Reconnect oxygen sensor.

* Checking coolant sensor resistance may require use of connector and wire assembly No. 12026621 for accessibility.

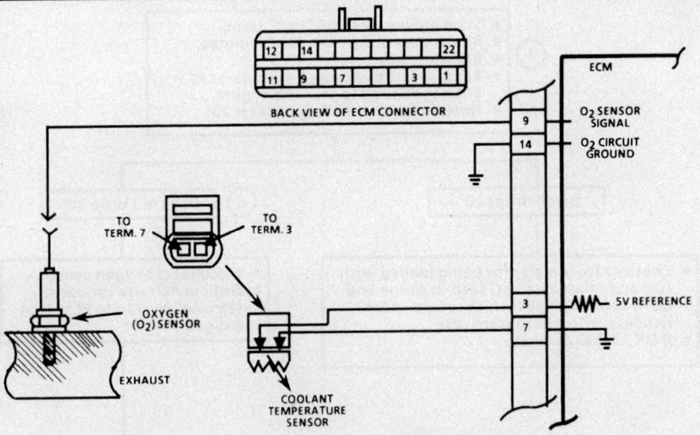

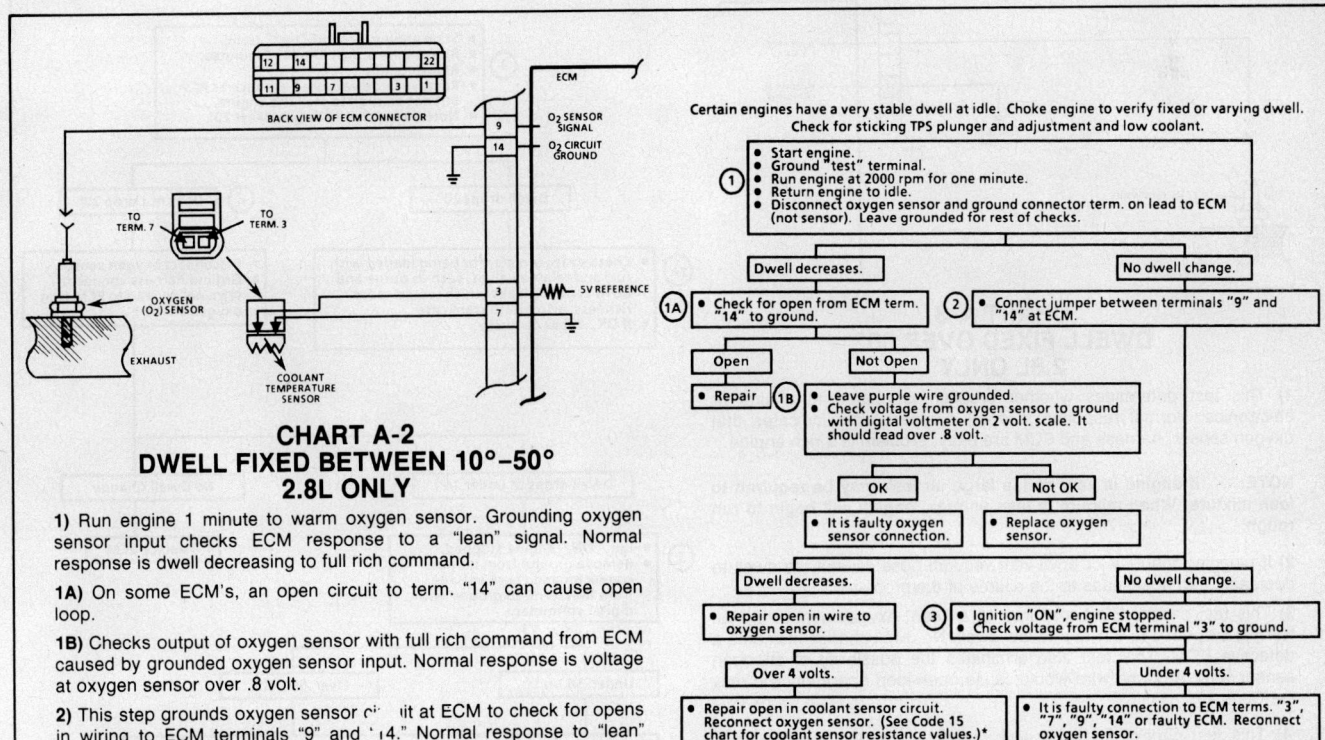

CHART A-2
DWELL FIXED BETWEEN 10°–50°
2.8L ONLY

1) Run engine 1 minute to warm oxygen sensor. Grounding oxygen sensor input checks ECM response to a "lean" signal. Normal response is dwell decreasing to full rich command.

1A) On some ECM's, an open circuit to term. "14" can cause open loop.

1B) Checks output of oxygen sensor with full rich command from ECM caused by grounded oxygen sensor input. Normal response is voltage at oxygen sensor over .8 volt.

2) This step grounds oxygen sensor circuit at ECM to check for opens in wiring to ECM terminals "9" and "14." Normal response to "lean" signal is dwell decrease.

3) This step checks for voltage to the coolant sensor. Normal reading on a warm engine is less than 2.5 volts. An open circuit would cause a reading of approximately 5 volts.

Certain engines have a very stable dwell at idle. Choke engine to verify fixed or varying dwell. Check for sticking TPS plunger and adjustment and low coolant.

(1)
- Start engine.
- Ground "test" terminal.
- Run engine at 2000 rpm for one minute.
- Return engine to idle.
- Disconnect oxygen sensor and ground connector term. on lead to ECM (not sensor). Leave grounded for rest of checks.

Dwell decreases.
- **(1A)** • Check for open from ECM term. "14" to ground.
  - **Open** → • Repair
  - **Not Open** → **(1B)** • Leave purple wire grounded. • Check voltage from oxygen sensor to ground with digital voltmeter on 2 volt. scale. It should read over .8 volt.
    - **OK** → • It is faulty oxygen sensor connection.
    - **Not OK** → • Replace oxygen sensor.

No dwell change.
- **(2)** • Connect jumper between terminals "9" and "14" at ECM.
  - **Dwell decreases.** → • Repair open in wire to oxygen sensor.
  - **No dwell change.** → **(3)** • Ignition "ON", engine stopped. • Check voltage from ECM terminal "3" to ground.
    - **Over 4 volts.** → • Repair open in coolant sensor circuit. Reconnect oxygen sensor. (See Code 15 chart for coolant sensor resistance values.)*
    - **Under 4 volts.** → • It is faulty connection to ECM terms. "3", "7", "9", "14" or faulty ECM. Reconnect oxygen sensor.

* Checking coolant sensor resistance may require use of connector and wire assembly No. 12026621 for accessibility.

GENERAL MOTORS COMPUTER COMMAND CONTROL CALIF. 2.8L, 4.3L, 5.0L & 5.7L FULL FUNCTION (Cont.)

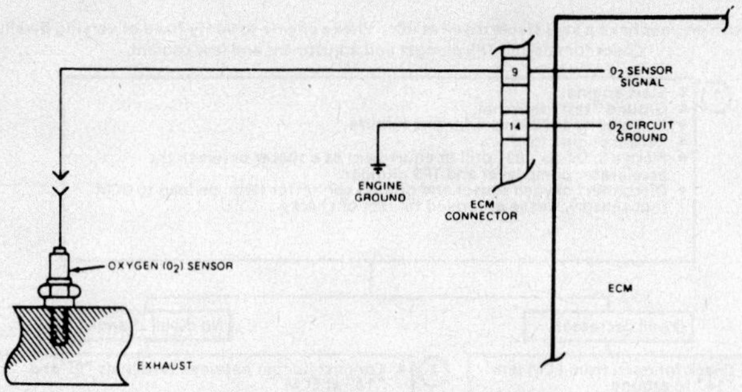

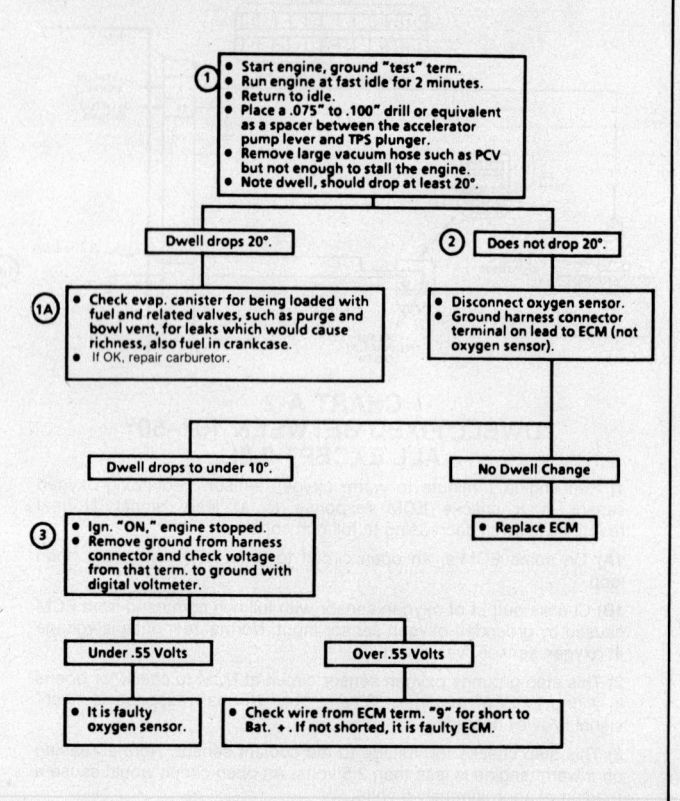

CHART A-3
DWELL FIXED OVER 50°
ALL EXCEPT 2.8L

1) This test determines whether problem is related to engine or electronics. Normal response is dwell decrease, this indicates that oxygen sensor, harness and ECM are okay; problem is a rich engine.

NOTE: If engine is very rich, a large air leak may be required to lean mixture. When mixture is lean enough, engine will begin to run rough.

2) If plugging the PCV or bowl vent vacuum hose causes the dwell to decrease, that hose leads to the source of the problem.

3) This test checks ECM response to a "lean" oxygen sensor signal. Normal response to this test is low dwell. No dwell change indicates a defective ECM. This test also eliminates the possibility of an open sensor wire. An open wire would cause open loop operation and may set Code 13.

4) This test checks for excessive voltage in oxygen sensor line. If under .55 volt, wire and ECM are okay, fault is in oxygen sensor. If over .55 volt, wire is shorted to battery voltage or ECM is faulty.

(1)
- Start engine, ground "test" term.
- Run engine at fast idle for 2 minutes.
- Return to idle.
- Place a .075" to .100" drill or equivalent as a spacer between the accelerator pump lever and TPS plunger.
- Remove large vacuum hose such as PCV but not enough to stall the engine.
- Note dwell, should drop at least 20°.

Dwell drops 20°.

(1A)
- Check evap. canister for being loaded with fuel and related valves, such as purge and bowl vent, for leaks which would cause richness, also fuel in crankcase.
- If OK, repair carburetor.

(2) Does not drop 20°.
- Disconnect oxygen sensor.
- Ground harness connector terminal on lead to ECM (not oxygen sensor).

Dwell drops to under 10°.

(3)
- Ign. "ON," engine stopped.
- Remove ground from harness connector and check voltage from that term. to ground with digital voltmeter.

Under .55 Volts
- It is faulty oxygen sensor.

Over .55 Volts
- Check wire from ECM term. "9" for short to Bat. +. If not shorted, it is faulty ECM.

No Dwell Change
- Replace ECM

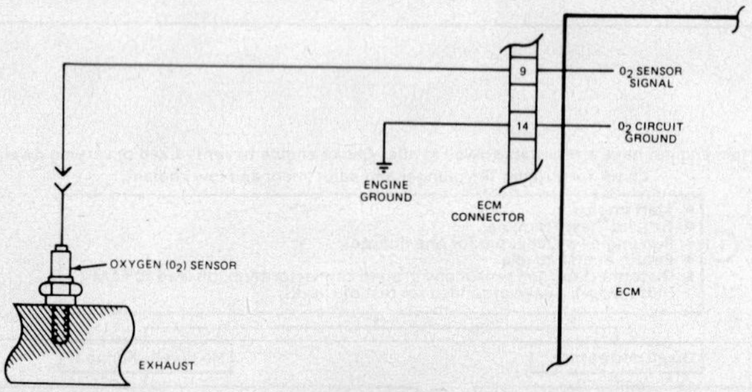

CHART A-3
DWELL FIXED OVER 50°
2.8L ONLY

1) This test determines whether problem is related to engine or electronics. Normal response is dwell decrease, this indicates that oxygen sensor, harness and ECM are okay; problem is a rich engine.

NOTE: If engine is very rich, a large air leak may be required to lean mixture. When mixture is lean enough, engine will begin to run rough.

2) If plugging the PCV or bowl vent vacuum hose causes the dwell to decrease, that hose leads to the source of the problem.

3) This test checks ECM response to a "lean" oxygen sensor signal. Normal response to this test is low dwell. No dwell change indicates a defective ECM. This test also eliminates the possibility of an open sensor wire. An open wire would cause open loop operation and may set Code 13.

4) This test checks for excessive voltage in oxygen sensor line. If under .55 volt, wire and ECM are okay, fault is in oxygen sensor. If over .55 volt, wire is shorted to battery voltage or ECM is faulty.

(1)
- Start engine, ground "test" term.
- Run engine at fast idle for 2 minutes.
- Return to idle.
- Remove large vacuum hose such as PCV but not enough to stall the engine.
- Note dwell, should drop at least 20°.

Dwell drops 20°.

(1A)
- Check evap. canister for being loaded with fuel and related valves, such as purge and bowl vent, for leaks which would cause richness, also fuel in crankcase.
- If OK, Repair carburetor.

(2) Does not drop 20°.
- Disconnect oxygen sensor.
- Ground harness connector terminal on lead to ECM (not oxygen sensor).

Dwell drops to under 10°.

(3)
- Ign. "ON," engine stopped.
- Remove ground from harness connector and check voltage from that term. to ground with digital voltmeter.

Under .55 Volts
- It is faulty oxygen sensor.

Over .55 Volts
- Check wire from ECM term. "9" for short to Bat. +. If not shorted, it is faulty ECM.

No Dwell Change
- Replace ECM

GENERAL MOTORS COMPUTER COMMAND CONTROL CALIF. 2.8L, 4.3L, 5.0L & 5.7L FULL FUNCTION (Cont.)

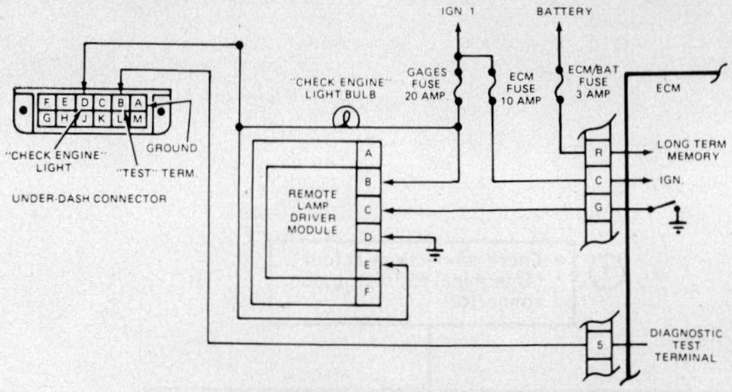
IGN 1
BATTERY
"CHECK ENGINE" LIGHT BULB
GAGES FUSE 20 AMP
ECM FUSE 10 AMP
ECM/BAT FUSE 3 AMP
ECM
F E D C B A
G H J K L M
"CHECK ENGINE" LIGHT
GROUND
"TEST" TERM.
UNDER-DASH CONNECTOR
REMOTE LAMP DRIVER MODULE
A
B
C
D
E
F
R
C
G
LONG TERM MEMORY
IGN.
5
DIAGNOSTIC TEST TERMINAL

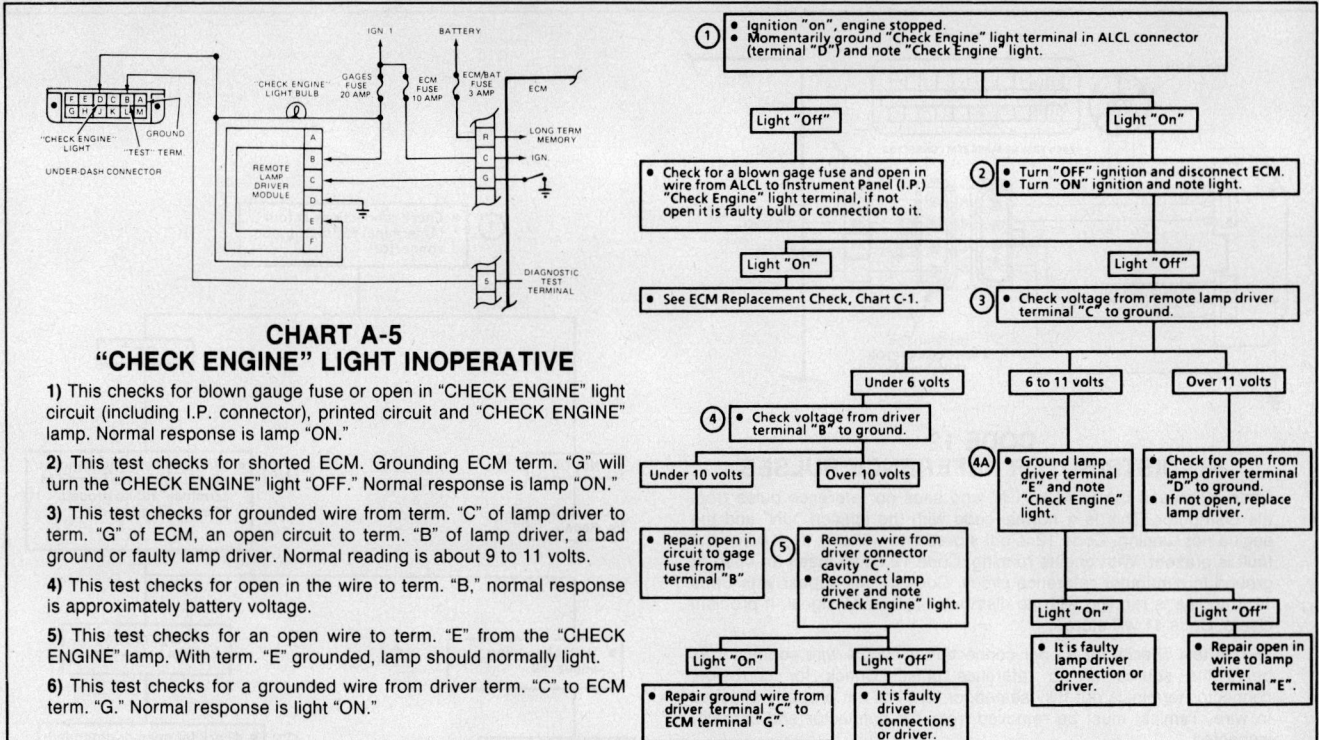

CHART A-5
"CHECK ENGINE" LIGHT INOPERATIVE

1) This checks for blown gauge fuse or open in "CHECK ENGINE" light circuit (including I.P. connector), printed circuit and "CHECK ENGINE" lamp. Normal response is lamp "ON."

2) This test checks for shorted ECM. Grounding ECM term. "G" will turn the "CHECK ENGINE" light "OFF." Normal response is lamp "ON."

3) This test checks for grounded wire from term. "C" of lamp driver to term. "G" of ECM, an open circuit to term. "B" of lamp driver, a bad ground or faulty lamp driver. Normal reading is about 9 to 11 volts.

4) This test checks for open in the wire to term. "B," normal response is approximately battery voltage.

5) This test checks for an open wire to term. "E" from the "CHECK ENGINE" lamp. With term. "E" grounded, lamp should normally light.

6) This test checks for a grounded wire from driver term. "C" to ECM term. "G." Normal response is light "ON."

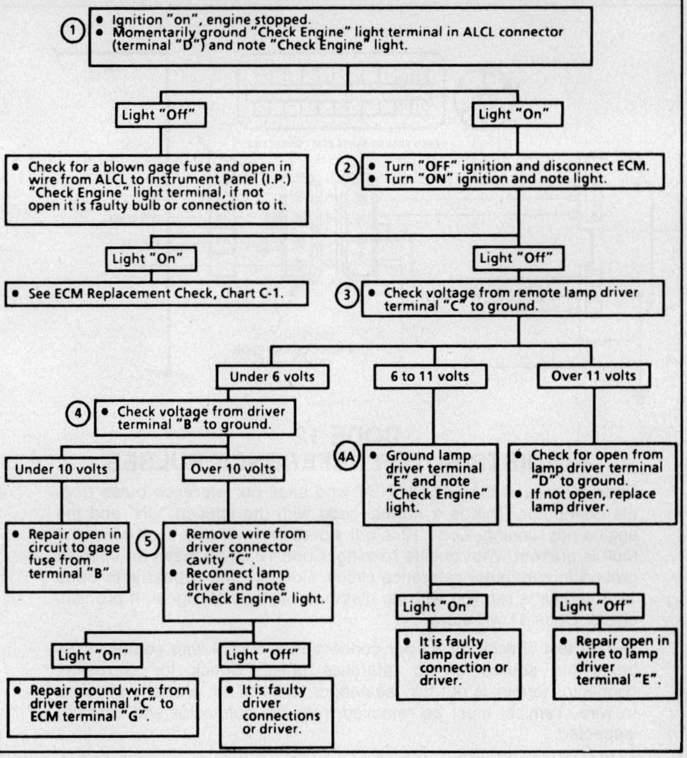
1
• Ignition "on", engine stopped.
• Momentarily ground "Check Engine" light terminal in ALCL connector (terminal "D") and note "Check Engine" light.
Light "Off"
Light "On"
• Check for a blown gage fuse and open in wire from ALCL to Instrument Panel (I.P.) "Check Engine" light terminal, if not open it is faulty bulb or connection to it.
2
• Turn "OFF" ignition and disconnect ECM.
• Turn "ON" ignition and note light.
Light "On"
Light "Off"
• See ECM Replacement Check, Chart C-1.
3
• Check voltage from remote lamp driver terminal "C" to ground.
Under 6 volts
6 to 11 volts
Over 11 volts
4
• Check voltage from driver terminal "B" to ground.
Under 10 volts
Over 10 volts
4A
• Ground lamp driver terminal "E" and note "Check Engine" light.
• Check for open from lamp driver terminal "D" to ground.
• If not open, replace lamp driver.
• Repair open in circuit to gage fuse from terminal "B"
5
• Remove wire from driver connector cavity "C".
• Reconnect lamp driver and note "Check Engine" light.
Light "On"
Light "Off"
• It is faulty lamp driver connection or driver.
• Repair open in wire to lamp driver terminal "E".
Light "On"
Light "Off"
• Repair ground wire from driver terminal "C" to ECM terminal "G".
• It is faulty driver connections or driver.

CHART A-6
WON'T FLASH CODE 12 OR
"CHECK ENGINE" LIGHT ON AT ALL TIMES

1) This step checks for short to battery voltage in wire to term. "C" or faulty lamp driver. Normal reading is 9 to 11 volts.

2) This step checks to see if problem is related to the ECM or lamp driver. Grounding term. "C" should turn lamp "OFF."

3) Grounding term. "G" at ECM and finding light "ON" indicates an open in the wire to term."C" of lamp driver. Grounding term. "G" should turn lamp "OFF."

4) This step checks for open in wire from ECM to test terminal in ALCL connector. The lamp should flash Code 12 when term. "5" is grounded.

5) This checks for proper voltage supply to ECM, both should read over 9 volts. Term. "C" is ignition and term. "R" is constant battery for long term memory.

6) This test checks for bad ground in ECM. Terms. "A" and "U" are connected together in the ECM.

7) This step distinguishes between a faulty ECM and PROM. Normal response is for Code 51 to flash even though the PROM is not installed in the ECM. If no Code 51, ECM is faulty.

NOTE: **See CHART A-5 for wiring schematic.**

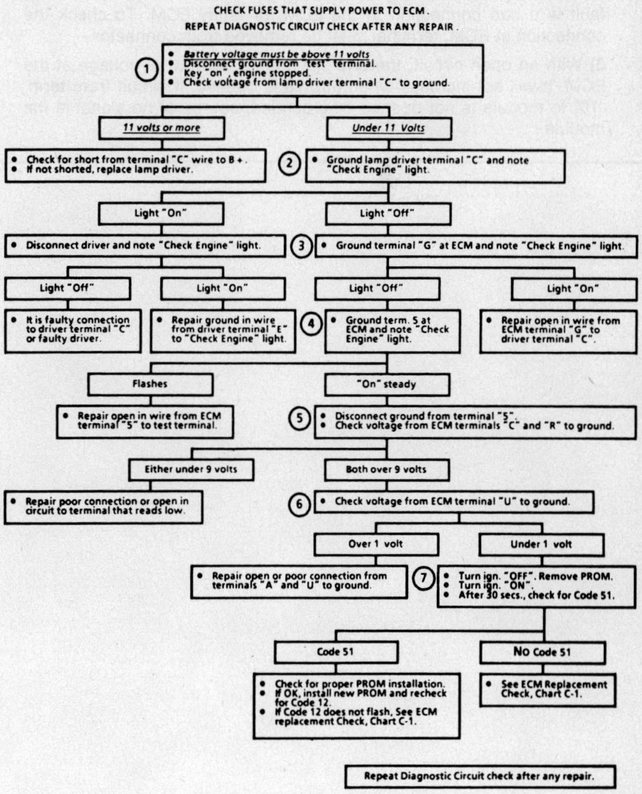
CHECK FUSES THAT SUPPLY POWER TO ECM.
REPEAT DIAGNOSTIC CIRCUIT CHECK AFTER ANY REPAIR.
1
• Battery voltage must be above 11 volts
• Disconnect ground from "test" terminal.
• Key "on", engine stopped.
• Check voltage from lamp driver terminal "C" to ground.
11 volts or more
Under 11 Volts
• Check for short from terminal "C" wire to B+.
• If not shorted, replace lamp driver.
2
• Ground lamp driver terminal "C" and note "Check Engine" light.
Light "On"
Light "Off"
• Disconnect driver and note "Check Engine" light.
3
• Ground terminal "G" at ECM and note "Check Engine" light.
Light "Off"
Light "On"
Light "Off"
Light "On"
• It is faulty connection to driver terminal "C" or faulty driver.
• Repair ground in wire from driver terminal "E" to "Check Engine" light.
4
• Ground term. 5 at ECM and note "Check Engine" light.
• Repair open in wire from ECM terminal "G" to driver terminal "C".
Flashes
"On" steady
• Repair open in wire from ECM terminal "5" to test terminal.
5
• Disconnect ground from terminal "5".
• Check voltage from ECM terminals "C" and "R" to ground.
Either under 9 volts
Both over 9 volts
• Repair poor connection or open in circuit to terminal that reads low.
6
• Check voltage from ECM terminal "U" to ground.
Over 1 volt
Under 1 volt
• Repair open or poor connection from terminals "A" and "U" to ground.
7
• Turn ign. "OFF". Remove PROM.
• Turn ign. "ON".
• After 30 secs., check for Code 51.
Code 51
No Code 51
• Check for proper PROM installation.
• If OK, install new PROM and recheck for Code 12.
• If Code 12 does not flash, See ECM replacement Check, Chart C-1.
• See ECM Replacement Check, Chart C-1.
Repeat Diagnostic Circuit check after any repair.

GENERAL MOTORS COMPUTER COMMAND CONTROL CALIF. 2.8L, 4.3L, 5.0L & 5.7L FULL FUNCTION (Cont.)

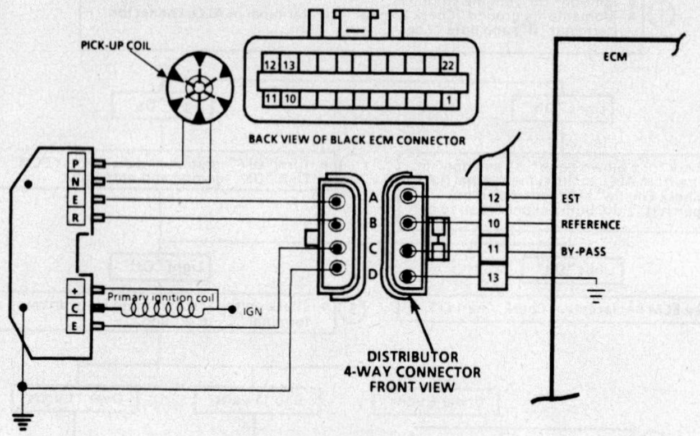

CODE 12
NO DISTRIBUTOR REFERENCE PULSES

Code 12 means the ECM is "ON" and sees no reference pulse from the distributor. This is a normal code with the ignition "ON" and the engine not running. Code 12 is not stored and will only flash when the fault is present. With engine running, Code 12 could mean an open or ground in distributor reference circuit. Code 41 will appear with Code 12 if engine is running with no distributor reference signal. If problem clears, Code 41 will store.

1) This test checks for a poor connection at EST 4-wire connector as being the source of no reference pulse. Check for corrosion, connector terminals not fully seated, or terminal not properly attached to wire. Teminal must be removed from the connector and carefully inspected.

2) This step determines if a reference pulse is being sent to the ECM. Voltage should increase as you go from idle to part throttle. A voltage increase indicates the signal is being generated by the module and fault is a bad connection at the ECM, or faulty ECM. To check the connection at ECM, terminal must be removed from connector.

3) With an open circuit, there is still a small amount of voltage at the ECM. It will not increase when throttle is opened. If circuit from term. "10" to module is not opened or grounded, source of no signal is the module.

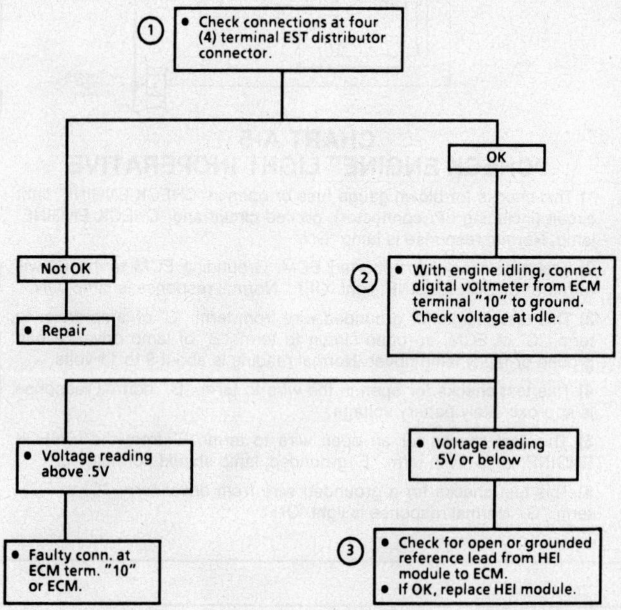

GENERAL MOTORS COMPUTER COMMAND CONTROL CALIF. 2.8L, 4.3L, 5.0L & 5.7L FULL FUNCTION (Cont.)

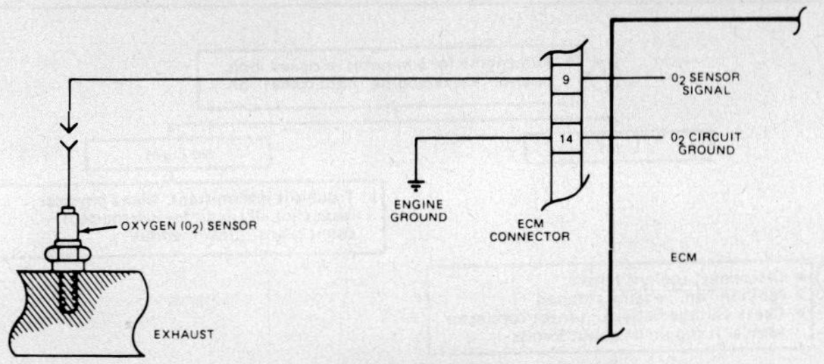

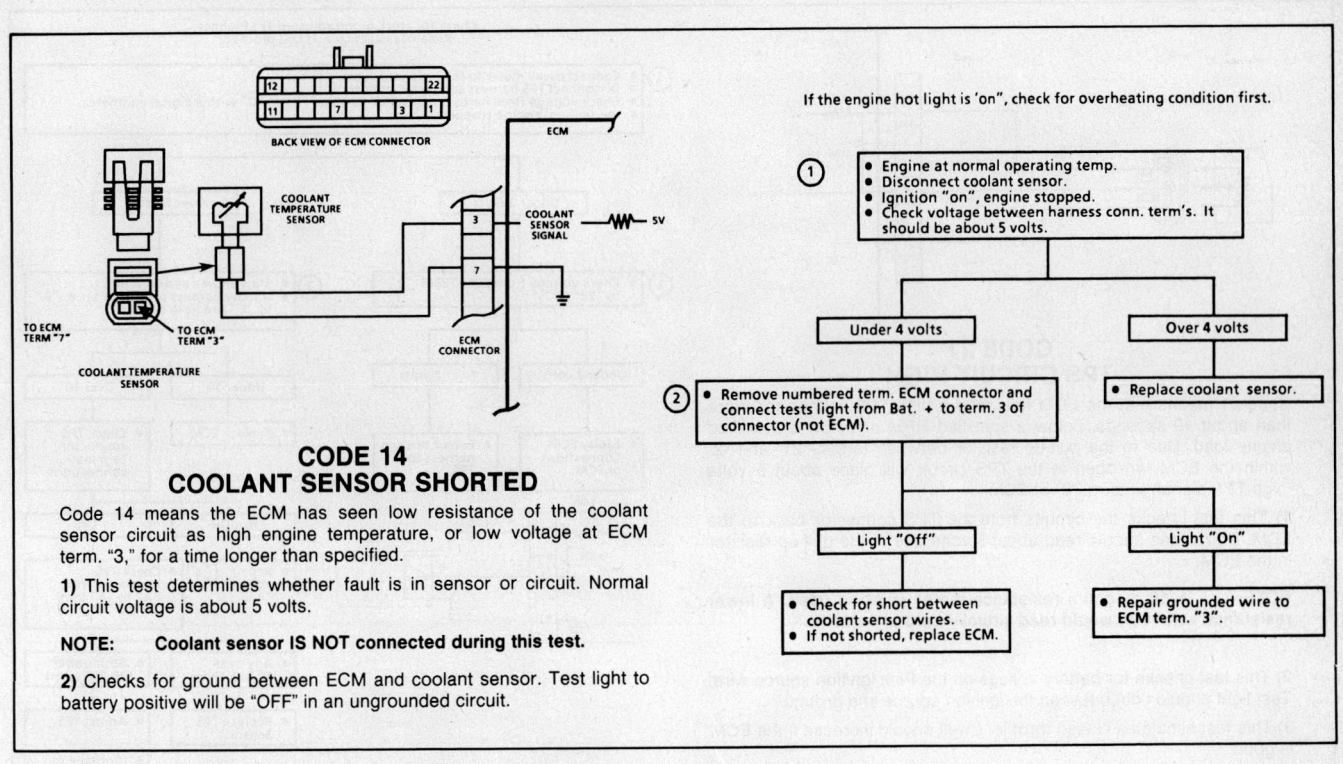

CODE 13
OXYGEN SENSOR CIRCUIT

Code 13 indicates an open in the oxygen sensor circuit with the following conditions:

- Oxygen sensor voltage is within a specified range.
- Above a specified TPS value.
- More than specified time after engine has warmed up.

The ECM supplies about .45 volt between terms. "9" and "14." Voltage may read as low as .32 volt when measured with a 10 megohm digital volt-ohm meter. The oxygen sensor varies the voltage within a range of about 1 volt (rich exhaust) to about .1 volt (lean exhaust).

1) This test checks to see if problem still exists. Fixed dwell indicates fault.

2) By grounding the oxygen sensor circuit to the ECM, a "low voltage (lean) signal" is sent to the ECM. This should result in a "full rich (low dwell) command."

3) This test checks oxygen sensor. With the rich command, the oxygen sensor should read a high voltage, over .8 volt. If the oxygen sensor functions, fault is in the connections to the sensor.

4) Checks for an open in the ECM-oxygen sensor ground circuit. Normal voltage is below 1 volt if the circuit is complete. The worse the connection is, the higher the voltage will read.

5) This grounds the oxygen sensor signal wire at the ECM. Dwell should go to below 10°, since this is a "low voltage signal" inidcating lean exhaust. No change indicates a problem at the ECM connections, or the ECM.

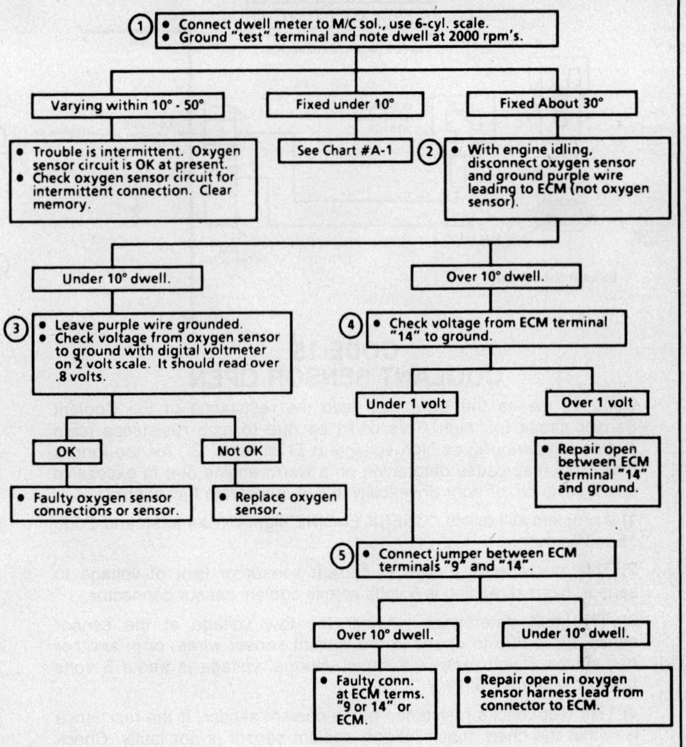

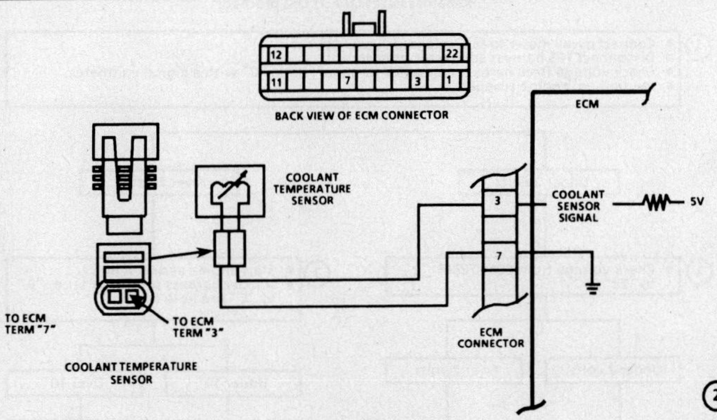

CODE 14
COOLANT SENSOR SHORTED

Code 14 means the ECM has seen low resistance of the coolant sensor circuit as high engine temperature, or low voltage at ECM term. "3," for a time longer than specified.

1) This test determines whether fault is in sensor or circuit. Normal circuit voltage is about 5 volts.

NOTE: Coolant sensor IS NOT connected during this test.

2) Checks for ground between ECM and coolant sensor. Test light to battery positive will be "OFF" in an ungrounded circuit.

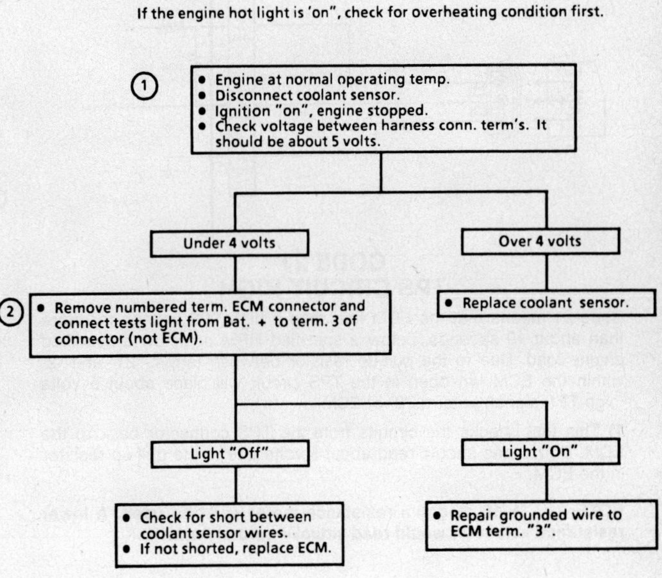

GENERAL MOTORS COMPUTER COMMAND CONTROL
CALIF. 2.8L, 4.3L, 5.0L & 5.7L FULL FUNCTION (Cont.)

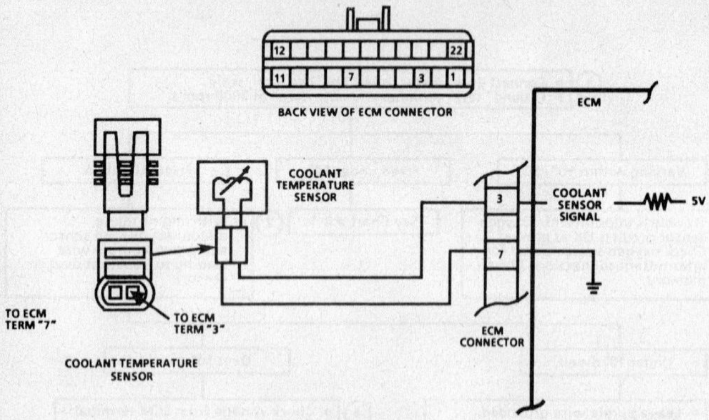

CODE 15
COOLANT SENSOR OPEN

Code 15 means the ECM has seen the resistance of the Coolant Sensor circuit too high. This could be due to high resistance (cold engine temperature) or high voltage at ECM term. "3", for too long a time. This may cause detonation on a warm engine due to excessive spark advance, or poor driveability due to inaccurate fuel control.

1) If problem still exists, "CHECK ENGINE" light will come on and Code 15 will be set.

2) This test checks if fault is coolant sensor or lack of voltage to sensor. Normal reading is 5 volts across coolant sensor connector.

3) This test determines whether the low voltage at the sensor connector is due to opens in the coolant sensor wires, or in another part of the 5 volt reference circuit. Normal voltage is about 5 volts from ECM terms. "3" to "7."

4) This test checks resistance of the coolant sensor. If the resistance is within the chart specifications, coolant sensor is not faulty. Check for corrosion at the connector or low coolant level.

(1) • Run engine for 5 minutes in closed loop, or until "check engine" light comes "on".

- Light → (2)
- No Light → • Trouble is intermittent. Make physical inspection of circuit for intermittent connections. Clear memory.

(2) • Disconnect coolant sensor.
• Ignition "on", engine stopped.
• Check voltage between sensor connector term's. It should be about 5 volts.

- Under 4 volts → (3)
- Over 4 volts → (4)

(3) • Check voltage from ECM term's. "3" to "7" (sensor disconnected).

- Under 4 volts → • It is faulty ECM connection at terminal "3" or "7" or ECM.
- Over 4 volts → • Check for open in wires to ECM term's. "3" and "7".

(4) • Check resistance of coolant sensor. It should be under 1000 ohms on a warm engine. *

- OK → • It is poor sensor connection or low coolant level.
- Not OK → • Replace sensor.

* COOLANT SENSOR

TEMPERATURE TO RESISTANCE VALUES (APPROXIMATE)

°F	°C	OHMS
210	100	185
160	70	450
100	38	1,600
70	-20	3,400
40	-4	7,500
20	-7	13,500
0	-18	25,000
-40	-40	100,700

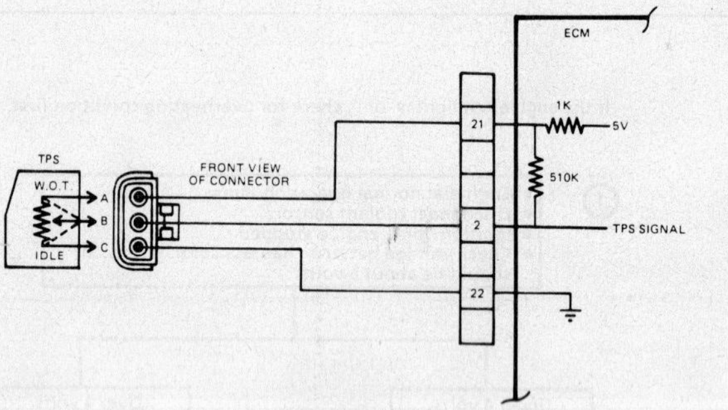

CODE 21
TPS CIRCUIT HIGH

Code 21 means that the ECM has seen a high TPS voltage for more than about 10 seconds, below a specified RPM or below a specified engine load. Due to the pull-up resistor between terms. "21" and "2" within the ECM, an open in the TPS circuit will place about 5 volts (high TPS signal) at term. "2" of ECM.

1) This test checks the circuits from the TPS connector back to the ECM. Both wires should read about 5 volts due to the pull-up resistor in the ECM.

NOTE: A 10 megohm resistance meter must be used. A lower resistance voltmeter would read virtually zero at term. "B."

2) This test checks for battery voltage on the Pink ignition source wire. Test light should light between the ignition source and ground.

3) This test simulates closed throttle. Dwell should increase if the ECM is good.

4) This tests the resistance of the TPS switch. Normal reading is less than 20,000 ohms.

Check for stuck or misadjusted TPS Plunger. Repair as necessary. If OK, proceed:

(1) • Connect dwell meter to M/C solenoid - use 6-cyl. scale.
• Disconnect TPS harness connector from sensor.
• Check voltage from harness connector terminal "B" to "C" with a digital voltmeter.
• Ignition on, engine stopped.

- Under 2 volts. → (2)
- Over 2 volts. → (3)

(2) • Check voltage from ECM TERM. "2" to "22".

- Under 2 volts. → • Faulty ECM Connections or ECM.
- Over 2 volts. → • Repair open in harness to TPS.

(3) • Start engine and let it idle.
• Jumper harness connector term. "B" to "C" and note dwell.

- Under 10° → • Replace ECM
- Over 10° → • Check TPS connector terminal connections.
  - Not OK → • Repair
  - OK → (4) • Check TPS resistance from "A" to "B" then "A" to "C".
    - Any over 20,000 ohms → • Replace TPS Sensor.
    - Both under 20,000 ohms → • Adjust TPS, • If unable to adjust, replace TPS.

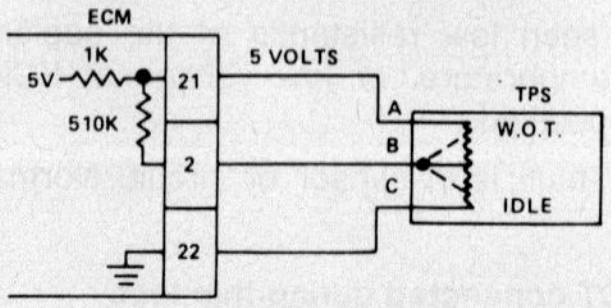

• After any repair, clear long term memory.

GENERAL MOTORS COMPUTER COMMAND CONTROL CALIF. 2.8L, 4.3L, 5.0L & 5.7L FULL FUNCTION (Cont.)

CODE 23
M/C SOLENOID CIRCUIT LOW

Code 23 indicates that the ECM has sensed a low steady voltage at ECM term. "18." Normal voltage at term. "18" is rising and falling as the solenoid is turned "ON" and "OFF." This code could be caused by a ground on the ECM side of the M/C solenoid or an open in the M/C solenoid circuit. A grounded circuit will cause a full lean condition and very poor driveability. An open circuit will cause a full rich condition and poor economy, odor, smoky exhaust or poor driveability.

1) This test checks for a complete circuit from the battery to the M/C solenoid dwell lead. Normal reading should be battery voltage. Battery voltage means there might be an open circuit between dwell connector and ground. No voltage could be either an open between the connector and battery or a ground on the ECM side of the M/C solenoid.

2) This test checks for battery voltage on the Pink ignition source wire. Test light should light between the ignition source and ground.

3) This test checks for an open in the solenoid to ECM circuit. Normal circuit will read about battery voltage at Term. "18" of the ECM.

4) This test determines whether fault is in the M/C solenoid, a ground in the circuit to the ECM or the ECM. A light will indicate a ground in circuit to term. "18" or a faulty ECM.

NOTE: A test light must be used in this step. A voltmeter may give an inaccurate indication.

5) This test checks for ground in wire to ECM term. "18." If wire is grounded, light will stay "ON."

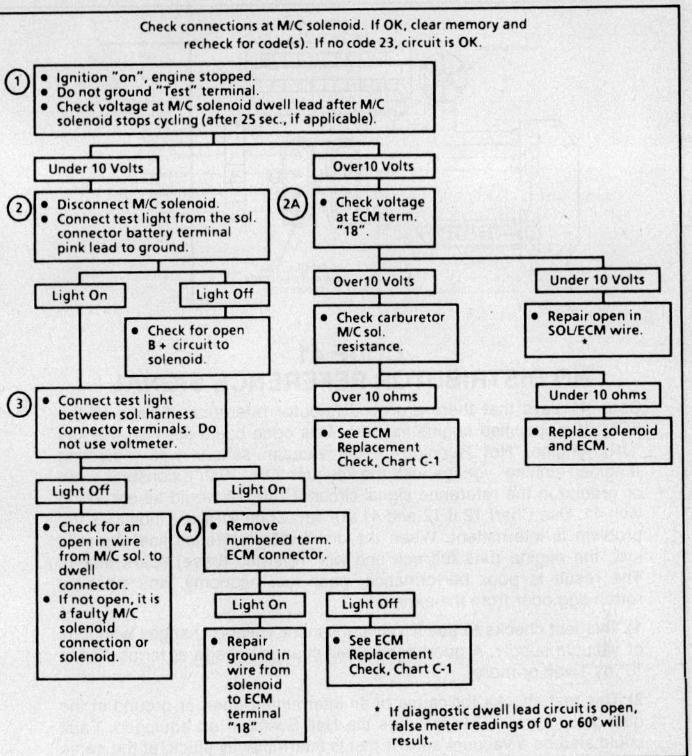

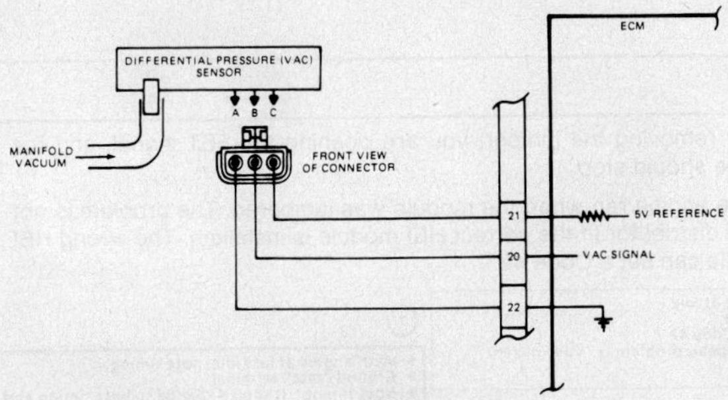

CODE 34
DIFFERENTIAL PRESSURE (VACUUM) SENSOR

Code 34 says that the ECM has seen the following:

- Pressure outside a specified voltage range (seen by ECM as voltage at term. "20").
- Engine RPM less than a given value.
- Engine at operating temperature.
- All the above for a time greater than specified.

The vacuum sensor measures the difference in pressure between atmosphere and manifold. The vacuum sensor supplies high voltage at high vacuum. High voltage increases spark advance.

1) This test checks output of sensor at idle to determine if sensor is within specification. Normal sensor will read less than 1 volt with key "ON," engine "OFF" and over 3 volts with engine idling (15 in. Hg minimum).

2) Normal sensor will drop below 1 volt with no vacuum.

3) This test checks for a ground in wire from term. "B" of vacuum sensor to ECM. Line is open if voltage is over 2 volts.

4) This test checks to see if the fault is in the sensor, the ECM wiring, or the ECM. If the voltage goes over 2 volts with the sensor disconnected, the sensor or sensor connections are faulty.

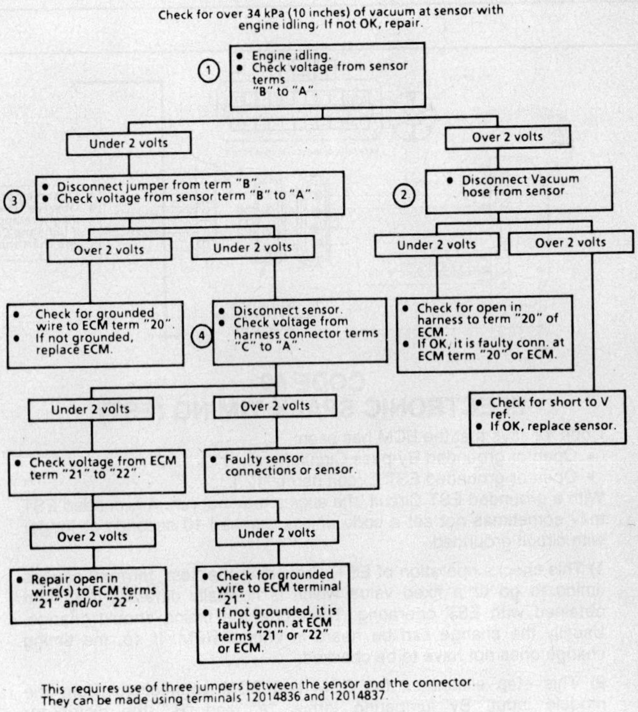

GENERAL MOTORS COMPUTER COMMAND CONTROL CALIF. 2.8L, 4.3L, 5.0L & 5.7L FULL FUNCTION (Cont.)

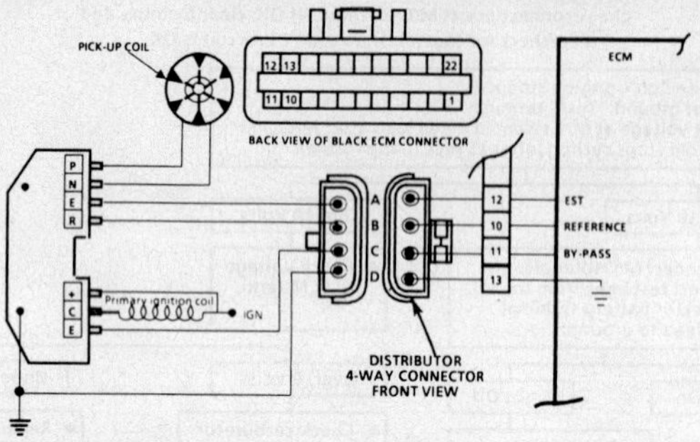

CODE 41
NO DISTRIBUTOR REFERENCE SIGNAL

Code 41 says that there are no distributor references pulses to the ECM at a specified engine vacuum. This code could set with the key "ON," engine "Not Running" if the vacuum sensor was indicating "Engine Running" voltage with the key just "ON." With a constant open or ground in the reference signal circuit, Code 12 would be set along with 41. Use Chart 12 if 12 and 41 are set. Code 41 alone indicates the problem is intermittent. When the distributor reference line signal is lost, the engine runs full rich and with retarded (base) spark timing. The result is poor performance, poor fuel economy, and possibly rotten egg odor from the exhaust.

1) This test checks to see if vacuum sensor voltage changes with loss of vacuum supply. A good sensor will change voltage at terms. "A" to "B" by 1 volt or more.

2) This test checks for cause of an intermittent open or ground in the distributor circuit. This includes the Hall Switch if so equipped. Fault could also be a vacuum sensor that is intermittently stuck, at the same voltage output as an engine "running," when the key is only "ON." This condition will produce no reference signal. Terminals must be removed from connector to properly check them. The distributor pick-up coil should also be checked.

If vacuum has been applied to MAP or VAC sensors with the key 'ON' engine not running, a false Code 41 could be set.

(1) With engine idling, check voltage change of VAC or MAP sensor terminals "B" to "A" as vacuum hose is removed.

(1A) Less than 1.0 volt change → Fault is in the MAP or VAC sensor circuit. See Chart 34.

More than 1.0 volt change → Trouble is intermittent

(2) Make physical check of wires and bad connections for grounds and bad connections. Also check distributor pick-up coil resistance and connections. Fault could be an intermittent MAP or VAC Sensor.

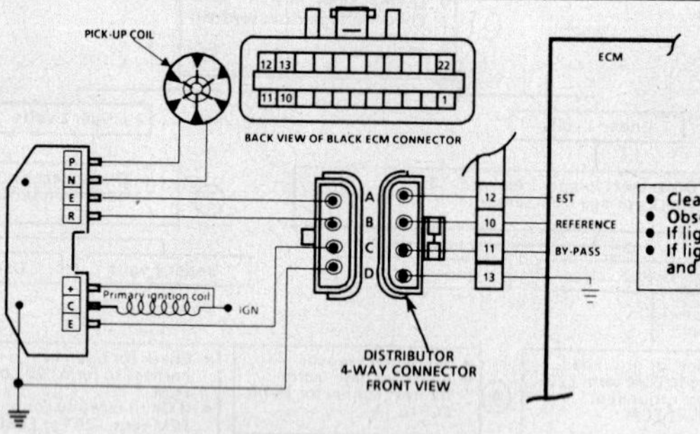

CODE 42
ELECTRONIC SPARK TIMING (EST)

Code 42 says that the ECM has seen:

- Open or grounded By-pass Circuit (term. "11").
- Open or grounded EST Circuit (term. "12").

With a grounded EST Circuit, the engine may not run. A grounded EST may sometimes not set a code unless cranked 10 seconds or longer with circuit grounded.

1) This checks operation of EST. Grounding the "test" terminal causes timing to go to a fixed value which is normally different from that obtained with EST operating. Therefore, the timing should change. Usually the change can be heard in engine RPM. If so, the timing change does not have to be checked.

2) This step eliminates the ECM and ECM connections from the module input. By jumpering terms. "A" and "B," the distributor reference signal is fed directly into the EST line of the module. By putting voltage through the test light on term. "C" of the harness, the module is switched to the EST mode and the vehicle should run. If the engine stops, there is no EST signal reaching the module due to open or poor connections, or the module is faulty.

3) By removing the jumper, you are opening the EST signal, and the engine should stop.

4) The engine ran when the module was jumpered. The problem is not in the distributor (if the correct HEI module is installed). The wrong HEI module can set a Code 42.

- Clear memory and run engine at idle.
- Observe "Check Engine" light.
- If light re-appears, check for Code 42.
- If light and Code do not re-appear, problem is "Intermittent" and chart should not be used

(1)
- With engine at fast idle, note timing.
- Ground "test" terminal.
- Note timing; it should change to base timing and not vary as engine RPM is increased

OK → No trouble found

Not OK →

(2)
- Disconnect 4 terminal EST connector from distributor.
- With engine stopped, connect jumper from "A" to "B" in distributor side of EST connector.
- Start engine, ground "test" terminal and connect test light from Battery + to term. "C" of distributor side of connector.

Engine stops →
- Check for open EST wire to term. "E" of HEI module.
- If wire is OK, it is faulty HEI module conn. or module.

Engine runs →

(3)
- With test light still connected, remove jumper between terminals "A" and "B".

Engine runs →

Check distributor wires for:
- Open or ground to module term. "B".
- Short between module term. "R" & "E".
- If wires are OK, it is faulty HEI module connection or module.

Engine stops →

(4)
- Check for correct HEI module.
- Check for open wire from EST Connector term. "A" to ECM terminal "12".
- Check for open or ground wire from EST Connector terminal "C" to ECM term. "11".

- If not grounded or open →
  - Check for good contact between ECM and terms. "11" and "12". If good term. contact, replace ECM.
- If grounded or open → Repair

GENERAL MOTORS COMPUTER COMMAND CONTROL CALIF. 2.8L, 4.3L, 5.0L & 5.7L FULL FUNCTION (Cont.)

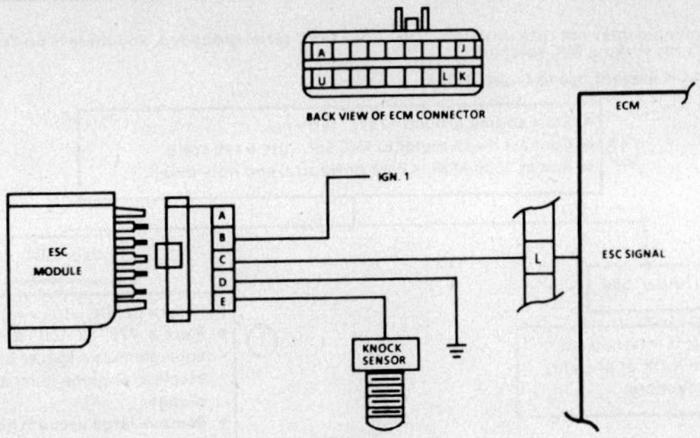

CODE 43
ELECTRONIC SPARK CONTROL
4.3L ONLY

Code 43 says Electronic Spark Control (ESC) retard signal has been seen by ECM for too long. When voltage at Terminal "L" at the ECM is low, spark is retarded. Normal voltage in non-retard mode is about 7.5V or more.

1) Normal voltage would be over 7.5 volts. If 7.5 volts is present at Term. "L", the reason for a Code 43 is a poor connection to ECM or faulty ECM.

2) Over 6 volts indicates an overly sensitive knock sensor or controller, or noise in engine that fools the knock sensor.

3) Checks for grounded ECM.

4) This test checks for an open wire between the ESC and ECM. More than 6 volts at Term. "C" of ESC indicates an open to Term. "L" of ECM.

5) Checks for proper 12V ignition source to ESC Term. "B".

6) Checks to see if spark retard is due to engine knock or a faulty knock sensor. If spark advances when knock sensor is disconnected, fault is result of engine "noise" or sensor.

7) Checks to see if spark retard is due to a faulty ESC controller or "noise" on ESC-to-knock sensor wire. If spark advances when terminal "E" is removed from connector, check for improper routing of knock sensor signal wire.

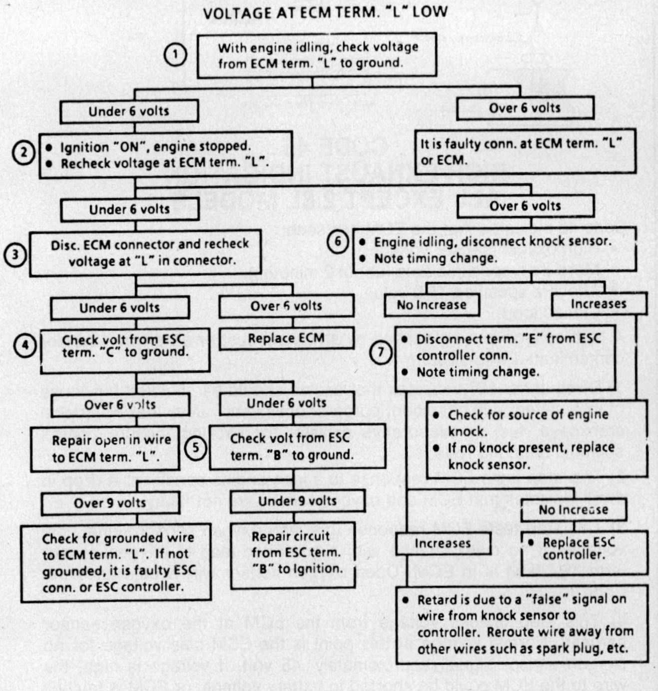

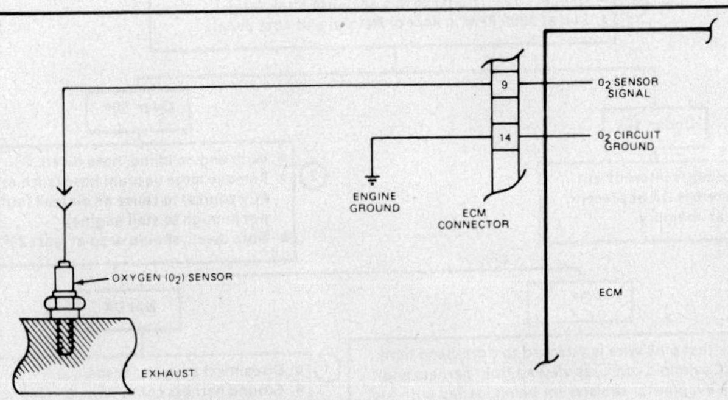

CODE 44
LEAN EXHAUST INDICATION

Code 44 indicates that the ECM has seen oxygen sensor voltage under the following conditions:

- Voltage lower than specified.
- Closed Loop.
- Above a specified TPS value.
- For a time longer than specified.

1) A fixed dwell of under 10° indicates the problem is still present. A fixed dwell under 10° at idle, with dwell varying at 3000 RPM, usually indicates an intake leak. Check this area prior to replacing oxygen sensor.

2) This test checks if the ECM is able to respond to a rich condition caused by choking the engine. If it does, the problem is a lean engine condition, NOT ELECTRICAL.

3) If dwell increases to over 50° with heavy choking, the fault is an air leak. If air is going to exhaust ports, disconnect the solenoid(s) for the air control valve. If air still goes to the ports, air valve is faulty.

4) This step puts a rich oxygen sensor signal (about 1 volt) into term. "9" of the ECM. Dwell should increase (lean command).

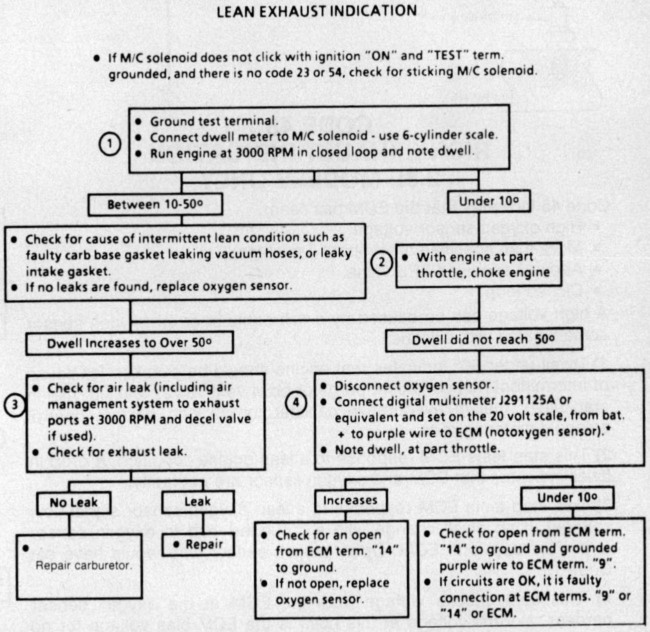

LEAN EXHAUST INDICATION
• If M/C solenoid does not click with ignition "ON" and "TEST" term. grounded, and there is no code 23 or 54, check for sticking M/C solenoid.
1
• Ground test terminal.
• Connect dwell meter to M/C solenoid - use 6-cylinder scale.
• Run engine at 3000 RPM in closed loop and note dwell.
Between 10-50°
Under 10°
• Check for cause of intermittent lean condition such as faulty carb base gasket leaking vacuum hoses, or leaky intake gasket.
• If no leaks are found, replace oxygen sensor.
2
• With engine at part throttle, choke engine
Dwell Increases to Over 50°
Dwell did not reach 50°
3
• Check for air leak (including air management system to exhaust ports at 3000 RPM and decel valve if used).
• Check for exhaust leak.
4
• Disconnect oxygen sensor.
• Connect digital multimeter J291125A or equivalent and set on the 20 volt scale, from bat. + to purple wire to ECM (notoxygen sensor).*
• Note dwell, at part throttle.
No Leak
Leak
Increases
Under 10°
Repair carburetor.
• Repair
• Check for an open from ECM term. "14" to ground.
• If not open, replace oxygen sensor.
• Check for open from ECM term. "14" to ground and grounded purple wire to ECM term. "9".
• If circuits are OK, it is faulty connection at ECM terms. "9" or "14" or ECM.

*Do not use an ordinary voltmeter or jumper in place of the digital voltmeter because they have too little resistance. A voltage of 1.0V to 1.7V (such as a flashlight battery) can be connected with the Positive terminal to the purple wire and the negative terminal to ground as a jumper. If the polarity is reversed, it won't work.

GENERAL MOTORS COMPUTER COMMAND CONTROL
CALIF. 2.8L, 4.3L, 5.0L & 5.7L FULL FUNCTION (Cont.)

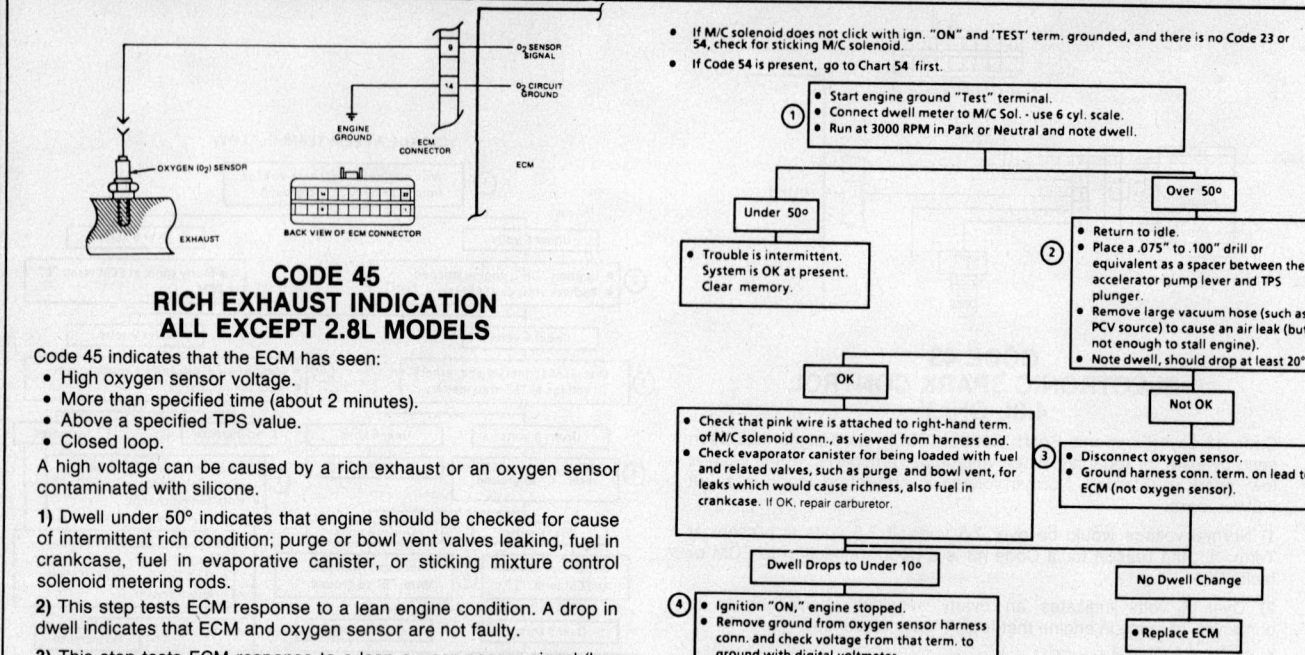

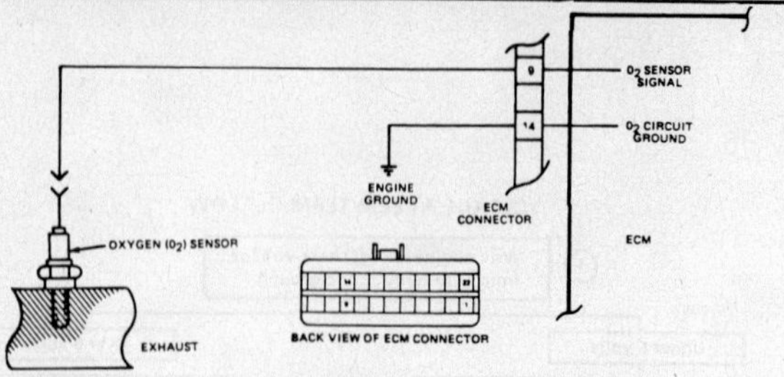

CODE 45
RICH EXHAUST INDICATION
ALL EXCEPT 2.8L MODELS

Code 45 indicates that the ECM has seen:
- High oxygen sensor voltage.
- More than specified time (about 2 minutes).
- Above a specified TPS value.
- Closed loop.

A high voltage can be caused by a rich exhaust or an oxygen sensor contaminated with silicone.

1) Dwell under 50° indicates that engine should be checked for cause of intermittent rich condition; purge or bowl vent valves leaking, fuel in crankcase, fuel in evaporative canister, or sticking mixture control solenoid metering rods.

2) This step tests ECM response to a lean engine condition. A drop in dwell indicates that ECM and oxygen sensor are not faulty.

3) This step tests ECM response to a lean oxygen sensor signal (low voltage). If no dwell change with a grounded lead to oxygen sensor term. "9," fault is in ECM. Open oxygen sensor wire would have set Code 13.

4) This step checks voltage from the ECM at the oxygen sensor harness. Normal voltage at this point is the ECM bias voltage for no oxygen sensor signal, approximately .45 volt. If voltage is high, the wire to the ECM could be shorted to battery voltage, or ECM is faulty.

- If M/C solenoid does not click with ign. "ON" and 'TEST' term. grounded, and there is no Code 23 or 54, check for sticking M/C solenoid.
- If Code 54 is present, go to Chart 54 first.

①
- Start engine ground "Test" terminal.
- Connect dwell meter to M/C Sol. - use 6 cyl. scale.
- Run at 3000 RPM in Park or Neutral and note dwell.

Under 50°
- Trouble is intermittent. System is OK at present. Clear memory.

Over 50°

②
- Return to idle.
- Place a .075" to .100" drill or equivalent as a spacer between the accelerator pump lever and TPS plunger.
- Remove large vacuum hose (such as PCV source) to cause an air leak (but not enough to stall engine).
- Note dwell, should drop at least 20°.

OK
- Check that pink wire is attached to right-hand term. of M/C solenoid conn., as viewed from harness end.
- Check evaporator canister for being loaded with fuel and related valves, such as purge and bowl vent, for leaks which would cause richness, also fuel in crankcase. If OK, repair carburetor.

Not OK

③
- Disconnect oxygen sensor.
- Ground harness conn. term. on lead to ECM (not oxygen sensor).

Dwell Drops to Under 10°

④
- Ignition "ON," engine stopped.
- Remove ground from oxygen sensor harness conn. and check voltage from that term. to ground with digital voltmeter.

Under .55V
- It is faulty oxygen sensor.

Over .55V
- Check wire from ECM term. 9 for short to Bat. +.
- If not shorted, it is faulty ECM.

No Dwell Change
- Replace ECM

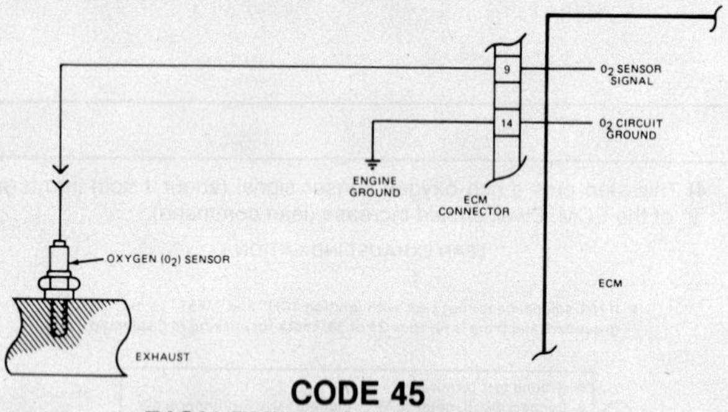

CODE 45
RICH EXHAUST INDICATION
2.8L MODELS ONLY

Code 45 indicates that the ECM has seen:
- High oxygen sensor voltage.
- More than specified time (about 2 minutes).
- Above a specified TPS value.
- Closed loop.

A high voltage can be caused by a rich exhaust or an oxygen sensor contaminated with silicone.

1) Dwell under 50° indicates that engine should be checked for cause of intermittent rich condition; purge or bowl vent valves leaking, fuel in crankcase, fuel in evaporative canister, or sticking mixture control solenoid metering rods.

2) This step tests ECM response to a lean engine condition. A drop in dwell indicates that ECM and oxygen sensor are not faulty.

3) This step tests ECM response to a lean oxygen sensor signal (low voltage). If no dwell change with a grounded lead to oxygen sensor term. "9," fault is in ECM. Open oxygen sensor wire would have set Code 13.

4) This step checks voltage from the ECM at the oxygen sensor harness. Normal voltage at this point is the ECM bias voltage for no oxygen sensor signal, approximately .45 volt. If voltage is high, the wire to the ECM could be shorted to battery voltage, or ECM is faulty.

- If M/C solenoid does not click with ign. "ON" and 'TEST' term. grounded, and there is no Code 23 or 54, check for sticking M/C solenoid.
- If Code 54 is present, go to Chart 54 first.

①
- Start engine ground "Test" terminal.
- Connect dwell meter to M/C Sol. - use 6 cyl. scale.
- Run at 3000 RPM in Park or Neutral and note dwell.

Under 50°
- Trouble is intermittent. System is OK at present. Clear memory.

Over 50°

②
- With engine idling, note dwell.
- Remove large vacuum hose (such as PCV source) to cause an air leak (but not enough to stall engine).
- Note dwell, should drop at least 20°.

OK
- Check that pink wire is attached to right-hand term. of M/C solenoid conn., as viewed from harness end.
- Check evaporator canister for being loaded with fuel and related valves, such as purge and bowl vent, for leaks which would cause richness, also fuel in crankcase. If OK, Repair carburetor.

Not OK

③
- Disconnect oxygen sensor.
- Ground harness conn. term. on lead to ECM (not oxygen sensor).

Dwell Drops to Under 10°

④
- Ignition "ON," engine stopped.
- Remove ground from oxygen sensor harness conn. and check voltage from that term. to ground with digital voltmeter.

Under .55V
- It is faulty oxygen sensor.

Over .55V
- Check wire from ECM term. 9 for short to Bat. +.
- If not shorted, it is faulty ECM.

No Dwell Change
- Replace ECM

GENERAL MOTORS COMPUTER COMMAND CONTROL CALIF. 2.8L, 4.3L, 5.0L & 5.7L FULL FUNCTION (Cont.)

CODE 51 PROM

Code 51 sets if any of the following occur:

- Faulty PROM unit.
- PROM unit improperly installed (may not set a code if installed backward).
- Some PROM pins not making contact (i.e. bent).

Always check to see that the PROM pins are not bent and inserted properly into ECM.

Make sure the PROM is installed in the proper direction as shown in the chart.

Check that all pins are fully inserted in the socket. If OK, replace PROM and recheck. If problem not corrected, replace ECM.

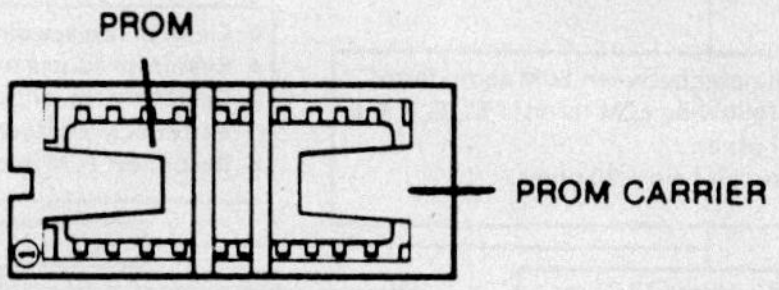

Notch in prom referenced to smaller notch in carrier and pin #1 end.

Small notch of carrier should be aligned with small notch in socket. Press on PROM carrier until it is firmly seated in the socket. Do not press on PROM; only the carrier.

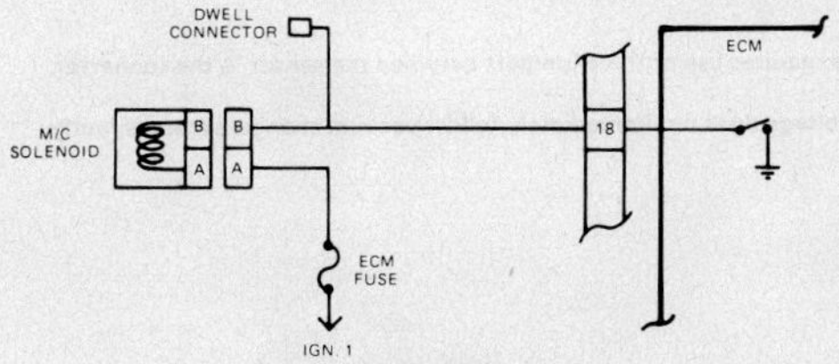

CODE 54 M/C SOLENOID CIRCUIT HIGH

Code 54 will be set if there is constant high voltage at ECM term. "18." A short circuit to 12 volts will cause M/C solenoid to remain in the full rich position.

1) This test checks the M/C solenoid resistance to determine if the fault is in the solenoid or ECM harness/ECM. Normal reading for a solenoid is 18-32 ohms.

NOTE: After replacing a faulty M/C solenoid, a system performance test is necessary to be certain the M/C solenoid was the only faulty part. Solenoid may have caused the ECM to fail, this will reset code.

2) This test checks if reason for high voltage to term. "18" is a faulty ECM or a short to 12 volts on that wire. If the test light to ground lights at the M/C solenoid test lead with both ends of harness disconnected, there is a short to 12 volts in the wire.

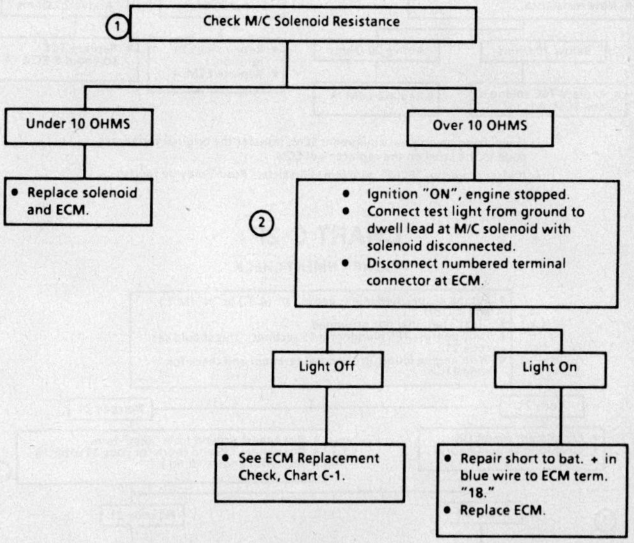

GENERAL MOTORS COMPUTER COMMAND CONTROL CALIF. 2.8L, 4.3L, 5.0L & 5.7L FULL FUNCTION (Cont.)

CHART C-1

ECM REPLACEMENT CHECK

- Always check 'PROM' for the correct application and installation before replacing an "ECM".

1.
- Remove both ECM connectors.
- Check for good connector terminal to ECM contact including foreign material.

Good Terminal Contact

2.
- Conn. ohmmeter between ECM conn. term. "C" & the following ECM terms: "B", E, T, 4, 6 and 19" (if used).
- Note any circuit below 20 ohms.

Poor Terminal Contact

- Clean or replace dirty term.
- Repair for source of foreign material.
- Remove term. w/poor contact & bend term. for better ECM contact.
- Reconnect ECM and retest.

All Above 20 Ohms

3.
- Connect ohm. between ECM conn. terms. "C" and "P".
- Note resistance.

Below 20 Ohms

- Disconnect conn. from solenoid or relay in circuit involved.
- Recheck resistance in circuit.

Below 20 Ohms

- Repair short to ign. & replace ECM. Δ

Above 20 Ohms

- Replace sol. or relay in circuit.
- Replace ECM. Δ

Over 50 Ohms

4.
- Remove TCC solenoid conn.
- Connect ohmmeter across terms. "A" & "D" of solenoid.
- Hoist drive wheels and run vehicle to engage 3rd gear.
- Note resistance.

Below 20 Ohms

- Replace TCC solenoid and ECM. Δ

Above 20 Ohms

- Replace ECM. Δ

20-50 Ohms

- Replace ECM. Δ

Under 20 Ohms

- Disconnect conn. from TCC solenoid.
- Recheck resistance in circuit.

Below 20 Ohms

- Repair short to ignition.
- Replace ECM. Δ

Above 20 Ohms

- Replace TCC solenoid & ECM. Δ

Δ 1. If replacing an original equipment ECM, transfer the original broadcast code to the label on the replacement ECM.
2. If after replacing "ECM", problem still exists, "Prom" may be faulty.

CHART C-1E

If vacuum is applied to VAC sensor with key "ON" engine not running, a false Code 41 could be set.

1.
- Ignition "ON", engine stopped.
- Check voltage from sensor terminal "B" to "A".
- It should be .50-.64 volts.

Not OK

- Replace sensor.

OK

2.
- Apply 34 KPa (10") of vacuum and note voltage.
- It should be 2.25 to 2.95 volts.**

Not OK

- Replace sensor.
- Clear long term memory.

OK

- No trouble found.
- Clear long term memory.

* This requires use of three jumpers between the sensor & the connector.

**If voltage does not immediately follow vacuum change, sensor is faulty.

CHART C-2F

TPS ENRICHMENT CHECK

1.
- Engine at specified idle speed in "D" (A.T.) or "N" (M.T.) and A/C off.
- "Test" terminal not grounded.
- Fully depress TPS plunger for 15 seconds. This should set code 21.
- With engine idling, ground test terminal and check for code 21.

Code 21

- Enrichment circuit OK.
- Clear long term memory.

No code 21

2.
- Disconnect ground from "test" term.
- Disconnect TPS and check for code 21 after 15 sec. (with engine idling).

Code 21

3.
- Check voltage from harness connector term. "A" to "C" with digital voltmeter J-29125 or equivalent.
- It should be about 5 volts.

Under 4 volts

- Check for open in wire to ECM term. 21.

Over 4 volts

- It is faulty connection to TPS term. "A", TPS adj. or faulty TPS.

No code 21

4.
- Check voltage from harness conn. terminal "B" to "C" with digitl voltmeter J-29125 or equivalent.
- It should read about 5 volts.

Over 2 volts

- Check for idle set too high. If OK, it is faulty ECM

Under 2 volts

- Check for ground in wire to ECM term. "2" and short between wires to ECM term's. "2" and "22".
- If not grounded or shorted, it is faulty ECM.

- After any repair clear long term memory.

CHART C-2T-1
4.3L A/C ONLY

- IF AIR CONDITIONING (A/C) IS NOT OPERATING, REPAIR SYSTEM BEFORE CHECKING THROTTLE KICKER.
- MAKE VISUAL INSPECTION OF HOSES AND ELECTRICAL HARNESS FOR CONDITION AND MAKE CORRECTIONS AS REQUIRED.

1. WITH A/C "OFF", START ENGINE AND NOTE THROTTLE KICKER. IT SHOULD EXTEND FOR 30 SECONDS AND THEN RETRACT.

OK

2.
- TURN STEERING WHEEL TO FULL TURN. KICKER SHOULD EXTEND.
- RETURN WHEEL TO STRAIGHT AHEAD.

EXTENDS

NO TROUBLE FOUND

DOESN'T EXTEND

CHECK FOR OPEN TO KICKER RELAY TERMS. "A" AND "D". IF NOT OPEN, IT IS FAULTY RELAY CONNECTION OR RELAY.

DOES NOT EXTEND

3. TURN A/C "ON". KICKER SHOULD EXTEND.

EXTENDS

CHECK FOR OPEN IN WIRE TO ECM TERM. "E". IF NOT OPEN, CHECK CONNECTION AT ECM TERM. "E". IF OK, SEE CHART C-1.

DOESN'T EXTEND

4. CONNECT TEST LIGHT FROM KICKER SOLENOID TERMINAL "A" TO GROUND AND NOTE LIGHT.

ON

5. CHECK FOR VACUUM AT KICKER SOLENOID, IF PRESENT, CONNECT KICKER DIRECTLY TO VACUUM.

EXTENDS

IT IS KICKER SOLENOID CONNECTION OR SOLENOID.

DOESN'T EXTEND

REPLACE KICKER

OFF

REPAIR OPEN IN CIRCUIT TO KICKER SOLEMOID TERMINAL "A".

DOES NOT RETRACT

SEE CHART C-2 T-2

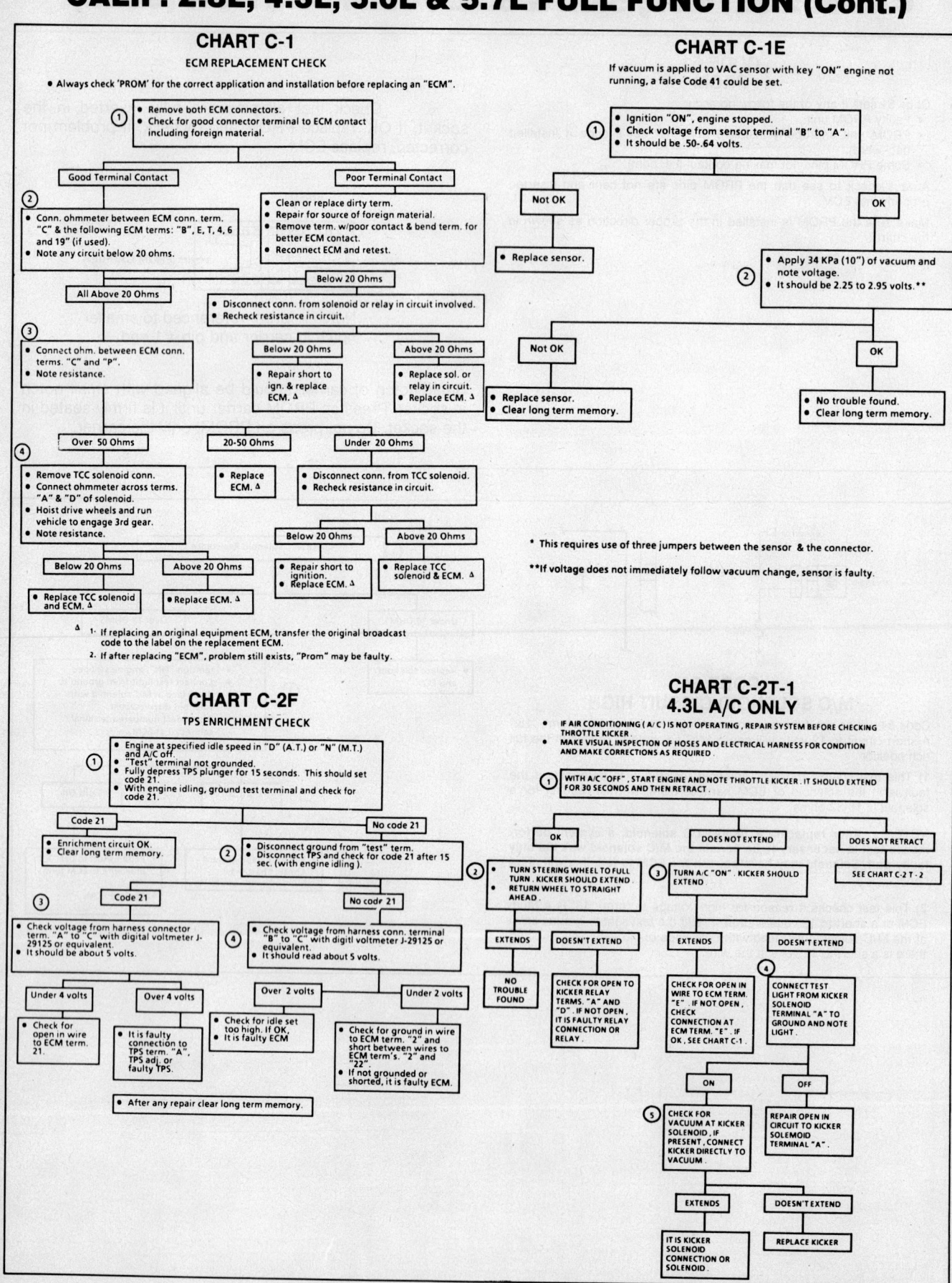

GENERAL MOTORS COMPUTER COMMAND CONTROL
CALIF. 2.8L, 4.3L, 5.0L & 5.7L FULL FUNCTION (Cont.)

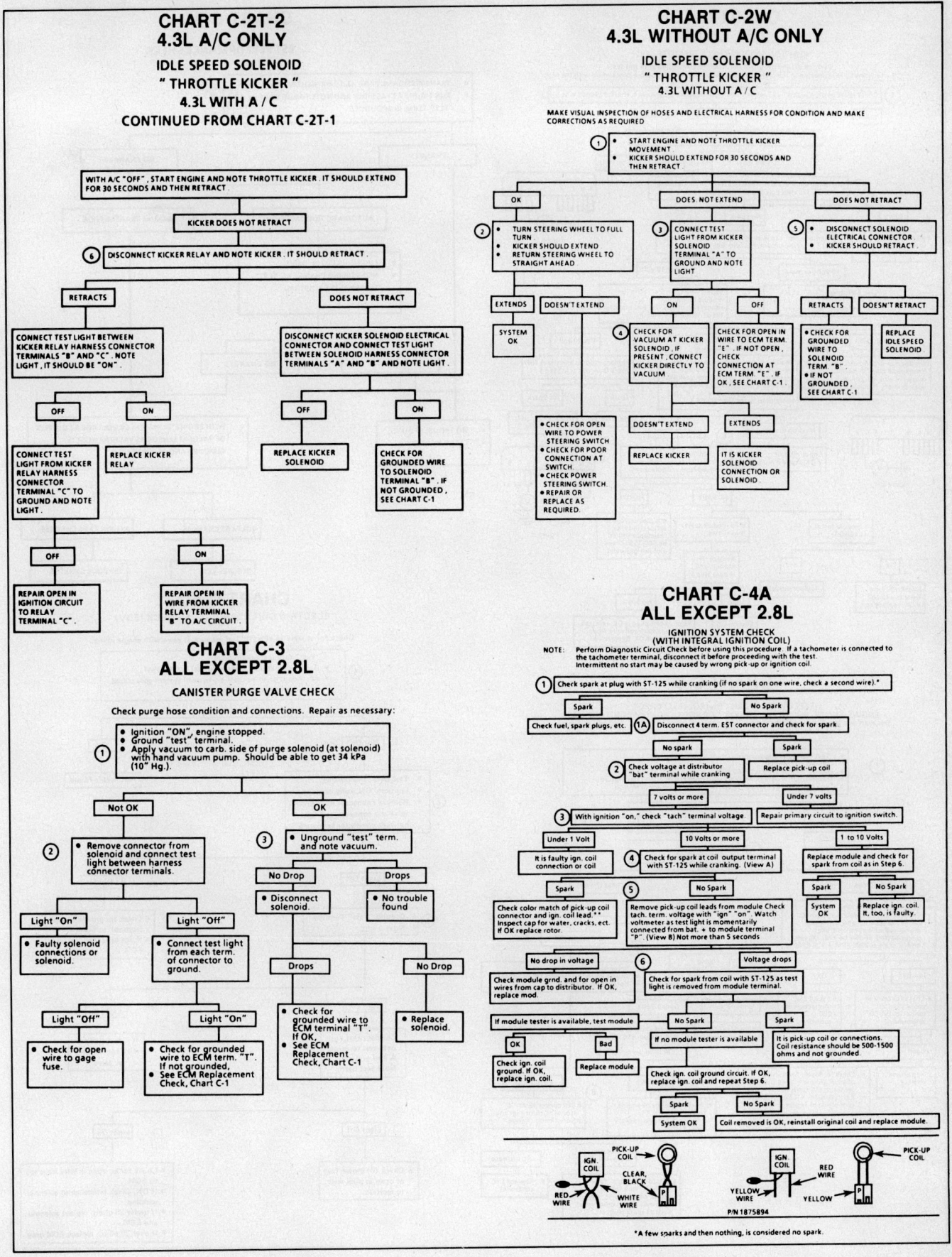

CHART C-2T-2
4.3L A/C ONLY

IDLE SPEED SOLENOID
" THROTTLE KICKER "
4.3L WITH A / C

CONTINUED FROM CHART C-2T-1

- WITH A/C "OFF", START ENGINE AND NOTE THROTTLE KICKER. IT SHOULD EXTEND FOR 30 SECONDS AND THEN RETRACT.
  - KICKER DOES NOT RETRACT
    - (6) DISCONNECT KICKER RELAY AND NOTE KICKER. IT SHOULD RETRACT.
      - RETRACTS
        - CONNECT TEST LIGHT BETWEEN KICKER RELAY HARNESS CONNECTOR TERMINALS "B" AND "C". NOTE LIGHT, IT SHOULD BE "ON".
          - OFF
            - CONNECT TEST LIGHT FROM KICKER RELAY HARNESS CONNECTOR TERMINAL "C" TO GROUND AND NOTE LIGHT.
              - OFF
                - REPAIR OPEN IN IGNITION CIRCUIT TO RELAY TERMINAL "C".
              - ON
                - REPAIR OPEN IN WIRE FROM KICKER RELAY TERMINAL "B" TO A/C CIRCUIT.
          - ON
            - REPLACE KICKER RELAY
      - DOES NOT RETRACT
        - DISCONNECT KICKER SOLENOID ELECTRICAL CONNECTOR AND CONNECT TEST LIGHT BETWEEN SOLENOID HARNESS CONNECTOR TERMINALS "A" AND "B" AND NOTE LIGHT.
          - OFF
            - REPLACE KICKER SOLENOID
          - ON
            - CHECK FOR GROUNDED WIRE TO SOLENOID TERMINAL "B". IF NOT GROUNDED, SEE CHART C-1

CHART C-2W
4.3L WITHOUT A/C ONLY

IDLE SPEED SOLENOID
" THROTTLE KICKER "
4.3L WITHOUT A / C

MAKE VISUAL INSPECTION OF HOSES AND ELECTRICAL HARNESS FOR CONDITION AND MAKE CORRECTIONS AS REQUIRED

- (1) • START ENGINE AND NOTE THROTTLE KICKER MOVEMENT. • KICKER SHOULD EXTEND FOR 30 SECONDS AND THEN RETRACT.
  - OK
    - (2) • TURN STEERING WHEEL TO FULL TURN • KICKER SHOULD EXTEND • RETURN STEERING WHEEL TO STRAIGHT AHEAD
      - EXTENDS
        - SYSTEM OK
      - DOESN'T EXTEND
        - • CHECK FOR OPEN WIRE TO POWER STEERING SWITCH • CHECK FOR POOR CONNECTION AT SWITCH. • CHECK POWER STEERING SWITCH. • REPAIR OR REPLACE AS REQUIRED.
  - DOES NOT EXTEND
    - (3) CONNECT TEST LIGHT FROM KICKER SOLENOID TERMINAL "A" TO GROUND AND NOTE LIGHT
      - ON
        - (4) CHECK FOR VACUUM AT KICKER SOLENOID, IF PRESENT, CONNECT KICKER DIRECTLY TO VACUUM
          - DOESN'T EXTEND
            - REPLACE KICKER
          - EXTENDS
            - IT IS KICKER SOLENOID CONNECTION OR SOLENOID.
      - OFF
        - CHECK FOR OPEN IN WIRE TO ECM TERM. "E". IF NOT OPEN, CHECK CONNECTION AT ECM TERM. "E". IF OK, SEE CHART C-1.
  - DOES NOT RETRACT
    - (5) • DISCONNECT SOLENOID ELECTRICAL CONNECTOR • KICKER SHOULD RETRACT.
      - RETRACTS
        - • CHECK FOR GROUNDED WIRE TO SOLENOID TERM. "B". • IF NOT GROUNDED, SEE CHART C-1
      - DOESN'T RETRACT
        - REPLACE IDLE SPEED SOLENOID

CHART C-3
ALL EXCEPT 2.8L

CANISTER PURGE VALVE CHECK

Check purge hose condition and connections. Repair as necessary:

- (1) • Ignition "ON", engine stopped. • Ground "test" terminal. • Apply vacuum to carb. side of purge solenoid (at solenoid) with hand vacuum pump. Should be able to get 34 kPa (10" Hg.).
  - Not OK
    - (2) • Remove connector from solenoid and connect test light between harness connector terminals.
      - Light "On"
        - • Faulty solenoid connections or solenoid.
      - Light "Off"
        - • Connect test light from each term. of connector to ground.
          - Light "Off"
            - • Check for open wire to gage fuse.
          - Light "On"
            - • Check for grounded wire to ECM term. "T". If not grounded, • See ECM Replacement Check, Chart C-1
  - OK
    - (3) • Unground "test" term. and note vacuum.
      - No Drop
        - • Disconnect solenoid.
          - Drops
            - • Check for grounded wire to ECM terminal "T". If OK, • See ECM Replacement Check, Chart C-1
          - No Drop
            - • Replace solenoid.
      - Drops
        - • No trouble found

CHART C-4A
ALL EXCEPT 2.8L

IGNITION SYSTEM CHECK
(WITH INTEGRAL IGNITION COIL)

NOTE: Perform Diagnostic Circuit Check before using this procedure. If a tachometer is connected to the tachometer terminal, disconnect it before proceeding with the test. Intermittent no start may be caused by wrong pick-up or ignition coil.

- (1) Check spark at plug with ST-125 while cranking (if no spark on one wire, check a second wire).*
  - Spark
    - Check fuel, spark plugs, etc.
  - No Spark
    - (1A) Disconnect 4 term. EST connector and check for spark.
      - No spark
        - (2) Check voltage at distributor "bat" terminal while cranking
          - 7 volts or more
            - (3) With ignition "on," check "tach" terminal voltage.
              - Under 1 Volt
                - It is faulty ign. coil connection or coil
              - 10 Volts or more
                - (4) Check for spark at coil output terminal with ST-125 while cranking. (View A)
                  - Spark
                    - Check color match of pick-up coil connector and ign. coil lead.** Inspect cap for water, cracks, ect. If OK replace rotor.
                  - No Spark
                    - (5) Remove pick-up coil leads from module Check tach. term. voltage with "ign" "on". Watch voltmeter as test light is momentarily connected from bat. + to module terminal "P". (View B) Not more than 5 seconds
                      - No drop in voltage
                        - Check module grnd. and for open in wires from cap to distributor. If OK, replace mod.
                      - Voltage drops
                        - (6) Check for spark from coil with ST-125 as test light is removed from module terminal.
                          - No Spark
                            - If module tester is available, test module
                              - OK
                                - Check ign. coil ground. If OK, replace ign. coil.
                              - Bad
                                - Replace module
                            - If no module tester is available
                              - Check ign. coil ground circuit. If OK, replace ign. coil and repeat Step 6.
                                - Spark
                                  - System OK
                                - No Spark
                                  - Coil removed is OK, reinstall original coil and replace module.
                          - Spark
                            - It is pick-up coil or connections. Coil resistance should be 500-1500 ohms and not grounded.
              - 1 to 10 Volts
                - Replace module and check for spark from coil as in Step 6.
                  - Spark
                    - System OK
                  - No Spark
                    - Replace ign. coil. It, too, is faulty.
          - Under 7 volts
            - Repair primary circuit to ignition switch.
      - Spark
        - Replace pick-up coil

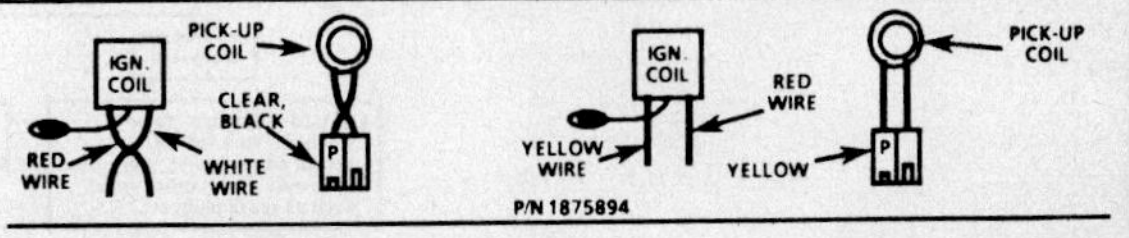

*A few sparks and then nothing, is considered no spark.

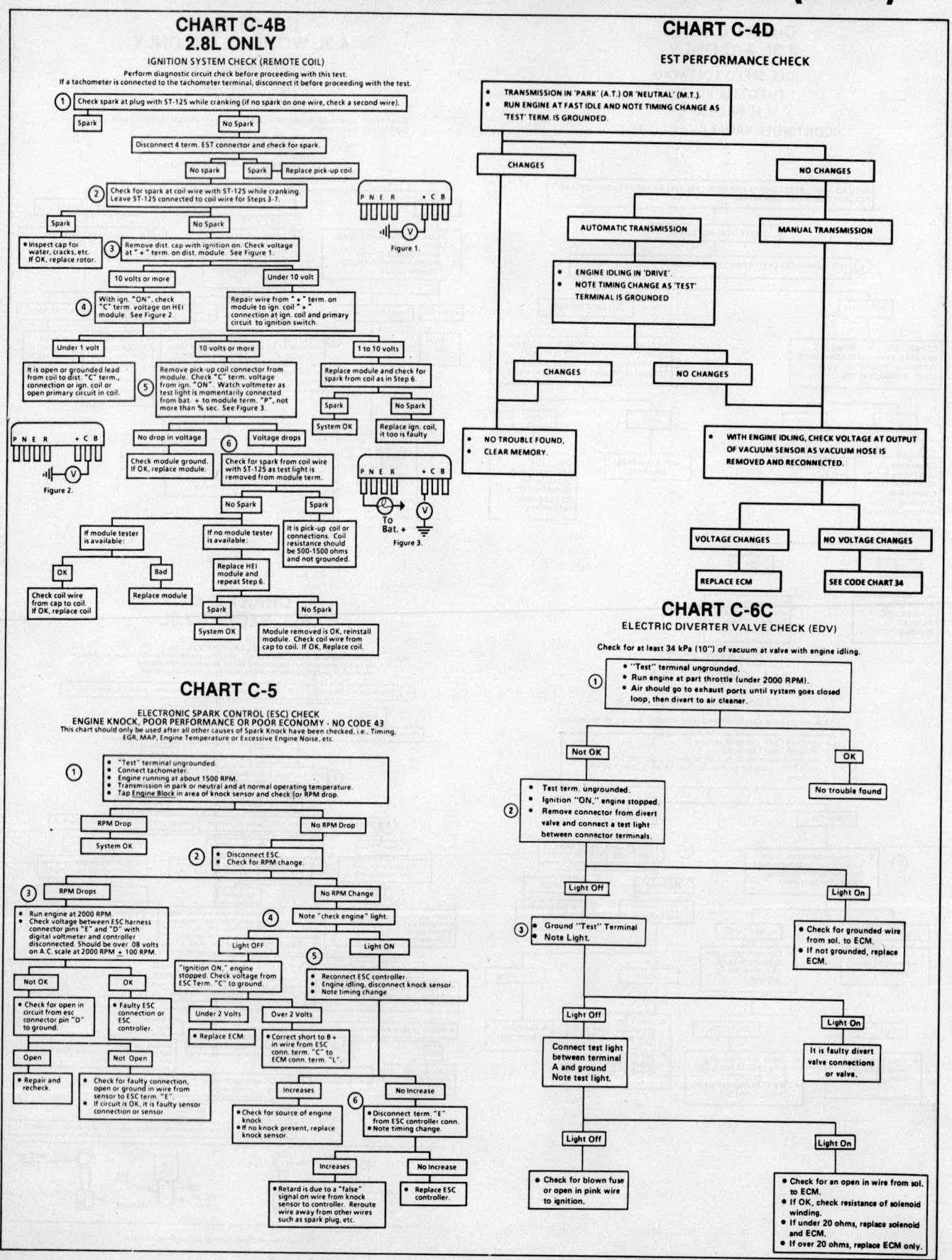

GENERAL MOTORS COMPUTER COMMAND CONTROL CALIF. 2.8L, 4.3L, 5.0L & 5.7L FULL FUNCTION (Cont.)

CHART C-4B 2.8L ONLY

IGNITION SYSTEM CHECK (REMOTE COIL)

Perform diagnostic circuit check before proceeding with this test.
If a tachometer is connected to the tachometer terminal, disconnect it before proceeding with the test.

(1) Check spark at plug with ST-125 while cranking (if no spark on one wire, check a second wire).

- Spark
- No Spark
  - Disconnect 4 term. EST connector and check for spark.
    - Spark — Replace pick-up coil.
    - No spark
      - (2) Check for spark at coil wire with ST-125 while cranking. Leave ST-125 connected to coil wire for Steps 3-7.
        - Spark — • Inspect cap for water, cracks, etc. If OK, replace rotor.
        - No Spark
          - (3) Remove dist. cap with ignition on. Check voltage at "+" term. on dist. module. See Figure 1.
            - Under 10 volt — Repair wire from "+" term. on module to ign. coil "+" connection at ign. coil and primary circuit to ignition switch.
            - 10 volts or more
              - (4) With ign. "ON", check "C" term. voltage on HEI module. See Figure 2.
                - Under 1 volt — It is open or grounded lead from coil to dist. "C" term., connection or ign. coil or open primary circuit in coil.
                - 1 to 10 volts — Replace module and check for spark from coil as in Step 6.
                  - Spark — System OK
                  - No Spark — Replace ign. coil, it too is faulty
                - 10 volts or more
                  - (5) Remove pick-up coil connector from module. Check "C" term. voltage from ign. "ON". Watch voltmeter as test light is momentarily connected from bat. + to module term. "P", not more than ⅕ sec. See Figure 3.
                    - No drop in voltage — Check module ground. If OK, replace module.
                    - Voltage drops
                      - (6) Check for spark from coil wire with ST-125 as test light is removed from module term.
                        - Spark — It is pick-up coil or connections. Coil resistance should be 500-1500 ohms and not grounded.
                        - No Spark
                          - If module tester is available:
                            - OK — Check coil wire from cap to coil. If OK, replace coil
                            - Bad — Replace module
                          - If no module tester is available:
                            - Replace HEI module and repeat Step 6.
                              - Spark — System OK
                              - No Spark — Module removed is OK, reinstall module. Check coil wire from cap to coil. If OK, Replace coil.

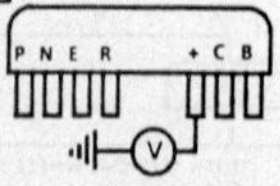

Figure 1.

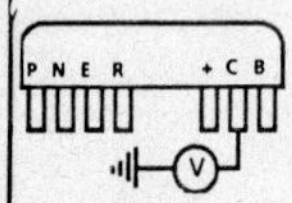

Figure 2.

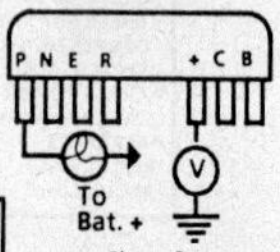

Figure 3.

CHART C-5

ELECTRONIC SPARK CONTROL (ESC) CHECK
ENGINE KNOCK, POOR PERFORMANCE OR POOR ECONOMY - NO CODE 43

This chart should only be used after all other causes of Spark Knock have been checked, i.e., Timing, EGR, MAP, Engine Temperature or Excessive Engine Noise, etc.

(1)
- "Test" terminal ungrounded.
- Connect tachometer.
- Engine running at about 1500 RPM.
- Transmission in park or neutral and at normal operating temperature.
- Tap Engine Block in area of knock sensor and check for RPM drop.

- RPM Drop — System OK
- No RPM Drop
  - (2) • Disconnect ESC. • Check for RPM change.
    - RPM Drops
      - (3) • Run engine at 2000 RPM. • Check voltage between ESC harness connector pins "E" and "D" with digital voltmeter and controller disconnected. Should be over .08 volts on A.C. scale at 2000 RPM ± 100 RPM.
        - Not OK — • Check for open in circuit from esc connector pin "D" to ground.
          - Open — • Repair and recheck.
          - Not Open — • Check for faulty connection, open or ground in wire from sensor to ESC term. "E". • If circuit is OK, it is faulty sensor connection or sensor.
        - OK — • Faulty ESC connection or ESC controller.
    - No RPM Change
      - (4) Note "check engine" light.
        - Light OFF — "Ignition ON," engine stopped. Check voltage from ESC Term. "C" to ground.
          - Under 2 Volts — • Replace ECM.
          - Over 2 Volts — • Correct short to B+ in wire from ESC conn. term. "C" to ECM conn. term. "L".
        - Light ON
          - (5) • Reconnect ESC controller. • Engine idling, disconnect knock sensor. • Note timing change
            - Increases — • Check for source of engine knock. • If no knock present, replace knock sensor.
            - No Increase
              - (6) • Disconnect term. "E" from ESC controller conn. • Note timing change.
                - Increases — • Retard is due to a "false" signal on wire from knock sensor to controller. Reroute wire away from other wires such as spark plug, etc.
                - No Increase — • Replace ESC controller.

CHART C-4D

EST PERFORMANCE CHECK

- TRANSMISSION IN 'PARK' (A.T.) OR 'NEUTRAL' (M.T.).
- RUN ENGINE AT FAST IDLE AND NOTE TIMING CHANGE AS 'TEST' TERM. IS GROUNDED.

- CHANGES — • NO TROUBLE FOUND. • CLEAR MEMORY.
- NO CHANGES
  - AUTOMATIC TRANSMISSION
    - • ENGINE IDLING IN 'DRIVE'. • NOTE TIMING CHANGE AS 'TEST' TERMINAL IS GROUNDED
      - CHANGES — • NO TROUBLE FOUND. • CLEAR MEMORY.
      - NO CHANGES — (go to voltage check below)
  - MANUAL TRANSMISSION
    - • WITH ENGINE IDLING, CHECK VOLTAGE AT OUTPUT OF VACUUM SENSOR AS VACUUM HOSE IS REMOVED AND RECONNECTED.
      - VOLTAGE CHANGES — REPLACE ECM
      - NO VOLTAGE CHANGES — SEE CODE CHART 34

CHART C-6C

ELECTRIC DIVERTER VALVE CHECK (EDV)

Check for at least 34 kPa (10") of vacuum at valve with engine idling.

(1)
- "Test" terminal ungrounded.
- Run engine at part throttle (under 2000 RPM).
- Air should go to exhaust ports until system goes closed loop, then divert to air cleaner.

- OK — No trouble found
- Not OK
  - (2) • Test term. ungrounded. • Ignition "ON," engine stopped. • Remove connector from divert valve and connect a test light between connector terminals.
    - Light On — • Check for grounded wire from sol. to ECM. • If not grounded, replace ECM.
    - Light Off
      - (3) • Ground "Test" Terminal • Note Light.
        - Light On — It is faulty divert valve connections or valve.
        - Light Off
          - Connect test light between terminal A and ground Note test light.
            - Light Off — • Check for blown fuse or open in pink wire to ignition.
            - Light On — • Check for an open in wire from sol. to ECM. • If OK, check resistance of solenoid winding. • If under 20 ohms, replace solenoid and ECM. • If over 20 ohms, replace ECM only.

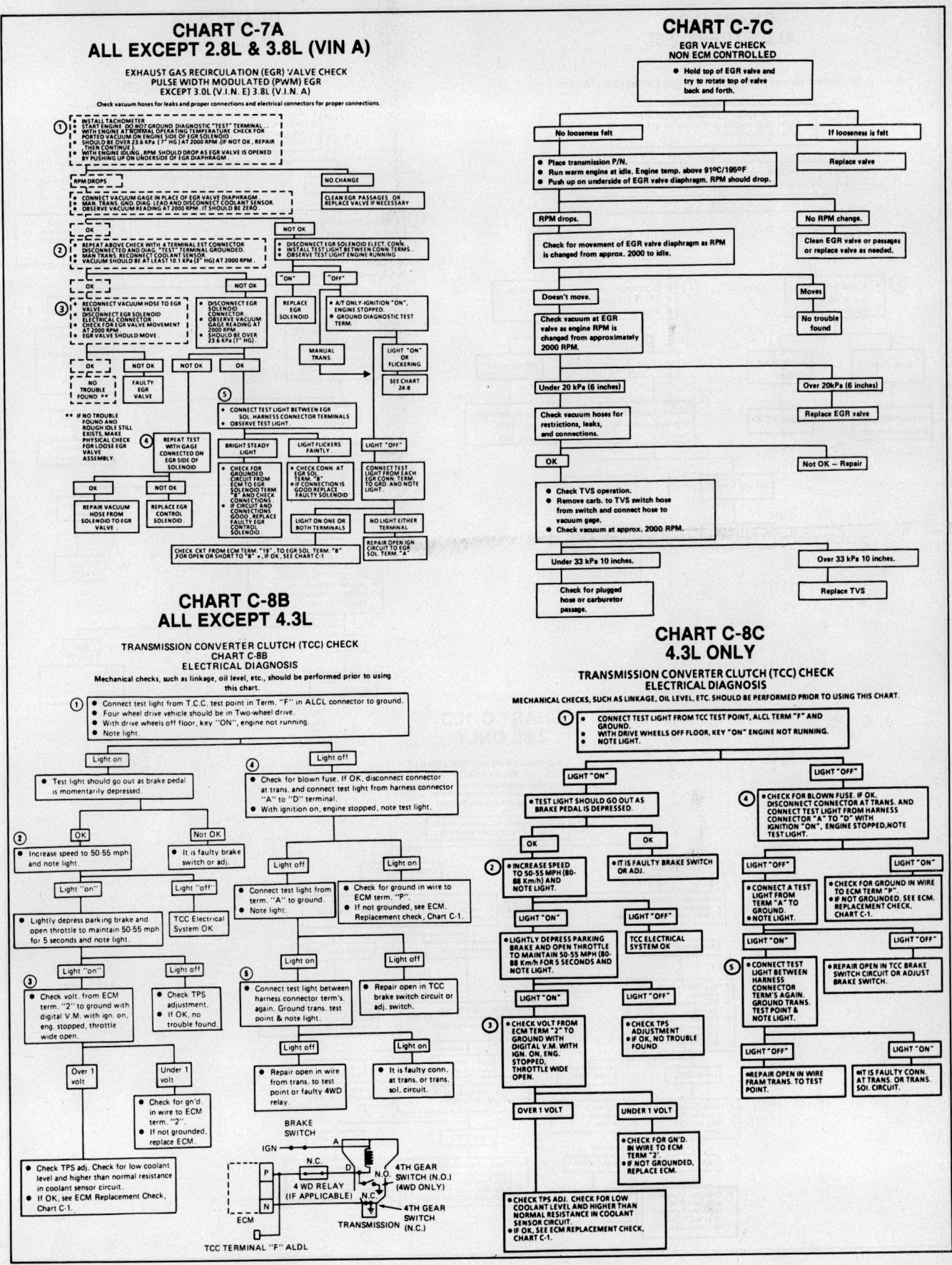

GENERAL MOTORS COMPUTER COMMAND CONTROL CALIF. 2.8L, 4.3L, 5.0L & 5.7L FULL FUNCTION (Cont.)

CHART C-7A ALL EXCEPT 2.8L & 3.8L (VIN A)

EXHAUST GAS RECIRCULATION (EGR) VALVE CHECK
PULSE WIDTH MODULATED (PWM) EGR
EXCEPT 3.0L (V.I.N. E) 3.8L (V.I.N. A)

Check vacuum hoses for leaks and proper connections and electrical connectors for proper connections.

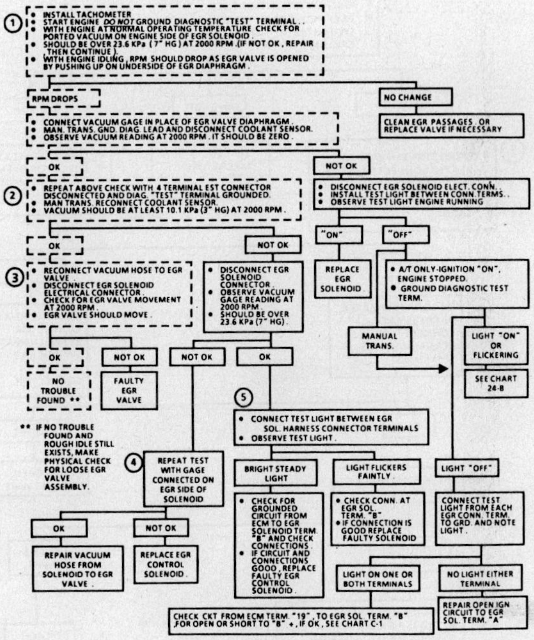

1
• INSTALL TACHOMETER
• START ENGINE DO NOT GROUND DIAGNOSTIC "TEST" TERMINAL.
• WITH ENGINE AT NORMAL OPERATING TEMPERATURE CHECK FOR PORTED VACUUM ON ENGINE SIDE OF EGR SOLENOID.
• SHOULD BE OVER 23.6 KPa (7" HG) AT 2000 RPM. (IF NOT OK, REPAIR THEN CONTINUE).
• WITH ENGINE IDLING, RPM SHOULD DROP AS EGR VALVE IS OPENED BY PUSHING UP ON UNDERSIDE OF EGR DIAPHRAGM.
RPM DROPS
NO CHANGE
CLEAN EGR PASSAGES, OR REPLACE VALVE IF NECESSARY
• CONNECT VACUUM GAGE IN PLACE OF EGR VALVE DIAPHRAGM.
• MAN. TRANS. GND. DIAG. LEAD AND DISCONNECT COOLANT SENSOR.
• OBSERVE VACUUM READING AT 2000 RPM. IT SHOULD BE ZERO.
OK
NOT OK
2
• REPEAT ABOVE CHECK WITH 4 TERMINAL EST CONNECTOR DISCONNECTED AND DIAG. "TEST" TERMINAL GROUNDED.
• MAN TRANS. RECONNECT COOLANT SENSOR.
• VACUUM SHOULD BE AT LEAST 10.1 KPa (3" HG) AT 2000 RPM.
• DISCONNECT EGR SOLENOID ELECT. CONN.
• INSTALL TEST LIGHT BETWEEN CONN. TERMS.
• OBSERVE TEST LIGHT ENGINE RUNNING
"ON"
"OFF"
REPLACE EGR SOLENOID
• A/T ONLY-IGNITION "ON", ENGINE STOPPED.
• GROUND DIAGNOSTIC TEST TERM.
OK
NOT OK
3
• RECONNECT VACUUM HOSE TO EGR VALVE.
• DISCONNECT EGR SOLENOID ELECTRICAL CONNECTOR.
• CHECK FOR EGR VALVE MOVEMENT AT 2000 RPM.
• EGR VALVE SHOULD MOVE.
• DISCONNECT EGR SOLENOID CONNECTOR.
• OBSERVE VACUUM GAGE READING AT 2000 RPM.
• SHOULD BE OVER 23.6 KPa (7" HG).
MANUAL TRANS.
LIGHT "ON" OR FLICKERING
SEE CHART 24-B
OK
NOT OK
NOT OK
OK
NO TROUBLE FOUND **
FAULTY EGR VALVE
** IF NO TROUBLE FOUND AND ROUGH IDLE STILL EXISTS, MAKE PHYSICAL CHECK FOR LOOSE EGR VALVE ASSEMBLY.
5
• CONNECT TEST LIGHT BETWEEN EGR SOL. HARNESS CONNECTOR TERMINALS
• OBSERVE TEST LIGHT.
4
REPEAT TEST WITH GAGE CONNECTED ON EGR SIDE OF SOLENOID
BRIGHT STEADY LIGHT
LIGHT FLICKERS FAINTLY.
LIGHT "OFF"
• CHECK FOR GROUNDED CIRCUIT FROM ECM TO EGR SOLENOID TERM. "B" AND CHECK CONNECTIONS.
• IF CIRCUIT AND CONNECTIONS GOOD, REPLACE FAULTY EGR CONTROL SOLENOID.
• CHECK CONN. AT EGR SOL. TERM. "B"
• IF CONNECTION IS GOOD REPLACE FAULTY SOLENOID
CONNECT TEST LIGHT FROM EACH EGR CONN. TERM. TO GRD. AND NOTE LIGHT.
OK
NOT OK
REPAIR VACUUM HOSE FROM SOLENOID TO EGR VALVE.
REPLACE EGR CONTROL SOLENOID.
LIGHT ON ONE OR BOTH TERMINALS
NO LIGHT EITHER TERMINAL
REPAIR OPEN IGN CIRCUIT TO EGR SOL. TERM. "A"
CHECK CKT FROM ECM TERM. "19", TO EGR SOL. TERM. "B" ,FOR OPEN OR SHORT TO "B" +, IF OK, SEE CHART C-1

CHART C-7C

EGR VALVE CHECK
NON ECM CONTROLLED

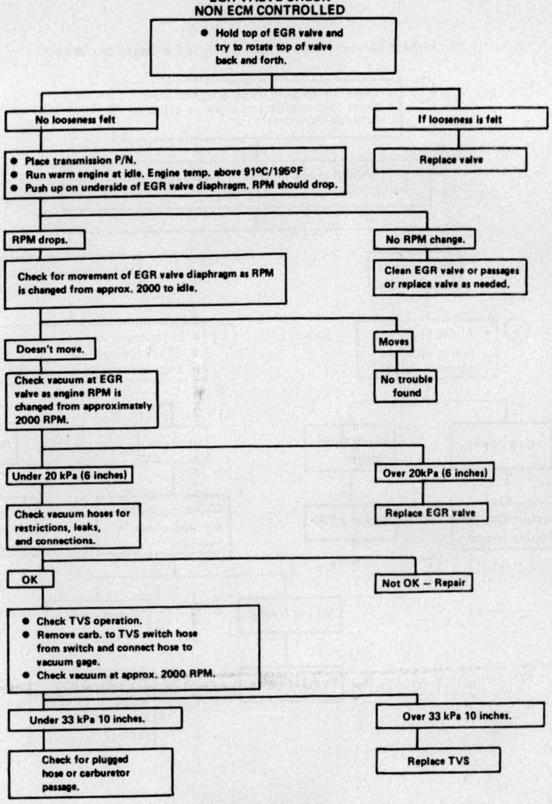

• Hold top of EGR valve and try to rotate top of valve back and forth.
No looseness felt
If looseness is felt
Replace valve
• Place transmission P/N.
• Run warm engine at idle. Engine temp. above 91°C/195°F
• Push up on underside of EGR valve diaphragm. RPM should drop.
RPM drops.
No RPM change.
Clean EGR valve or passages or replace valve as needed.
Check for movement of EGR valve diaphragm as RPM is changed from approx. 2000 to idle.
Doesn't move.
Moves
No trouble found
Check vacuum at EGR valve as engine RPM is changed from approximately 2000 RPM.
Under 20 kPa (6 inches)
Over 20kPa (6 inches)
Replace EGR valve
Check vacuum hoses for restrictions, leaks, and connections.
OK
Not OK – Repair
• Check TVS operation.
• Remove carb. to TVS switch hose from switch and connect hose to vacuum gage.
• Check vacuum at approx. 2000 RPM.
Under 33 kPa 10 inches.
Over 33 kPa 10 inches.
Check for plugged hose or carburetor passage.
Replace TVS

CHART C-8B ALL EXCEPT 4.3L

TRANSMISSION CONVERTER CLUTCH (TCC) CHECK
CHART C-8B
ELECTRICAL DIAGNOSIS

Mechanical checks, such as linkage, oil level, etc., should be performed prior to using this chart.

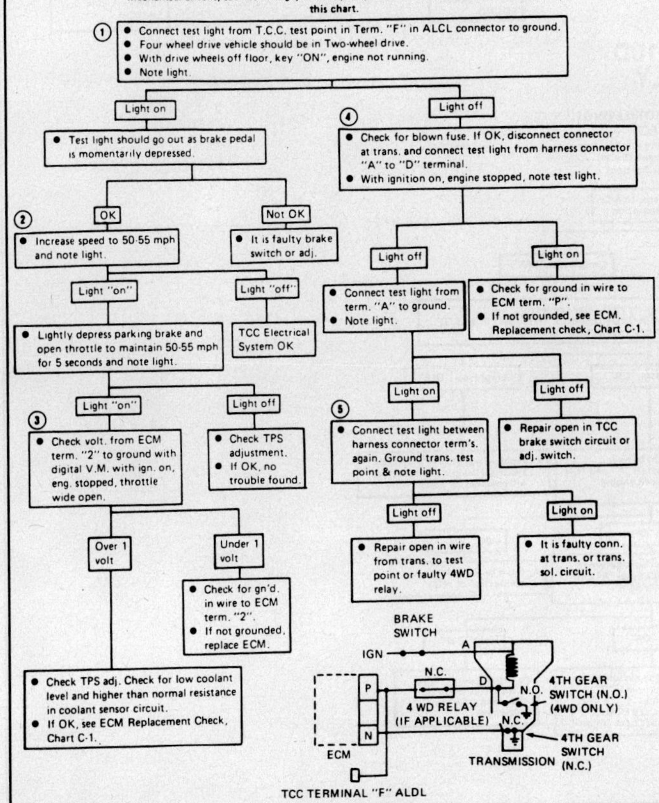

1
• Connect test light from T.C.C. test point in Term. "F" in ALCL connector to ground.
• Four wheel drive vehicle should be in Two-wheel drive.
• With drive wheels off floor, key "ON", engine not running.
• Note light.
Light on
Light off
• Test light should go out as brake pedal is momentarily depressed.
4
• Check for blown fuse. If OK, disconnect connector at trans. and connect test light from harness connector "A" to "D" terminal.
• With ignition on, engine stopped, note test light.
OK
Not OK
2
• Increase speed to 50-55 mph and note light.
• It is faulty brake switch or adj.
Light off
Light on
Light "on"
Light "off"
• Connect test light from term. "A" to ground.
• Note light.
• Check for ground in wire to ECM term. "P".
• If not grounded, see ECM. Replacement check, Chart C-1.
• Lightly depress parking brake and open throttle to maintain 50-55 mph for 5 seconds and note light.
TCC Electrical System OK
Light on
Light off
Light "on"
Light off
5
• Connect test light between harness connector term's. again. Ground trans. test point & note light.
• Repair open in TCC brake switch circuit or adj. switch.
3
• Check volt. from ECM term. "2" to ground with digital V.M. with ign. on, eng. stopped, throttle wide open.
• Check TPS adjustment.
• If OK, no trouble found.
Light off
Light on
Over 1 volt
Under 1 volt
• Repair open in wire from trans. to test point or faulty 4WD relay.
• It is faulty conn. at trans. or trans. sol. circuit.
• Check for gn'd. in wire to ECM term. "2".
• If not grounded, replace ECM.
• Check TPS adj. Check for low coolant level and higher than normal resistance in coolant sensor circuit.
• If OK, see ECM Replacement Check, Chart C-1.
BRAKE SWITCH
IGN
A
N.C.
D
P
N
4 WD RELAY (IF APPLICABLE)
4TH GEAR SWITCH (N.O.) (4WD ONLY)
N.O.
N.C.
4TH GEAR SWITCH (N.C.)
ECM
TRANSMISSION
TCC TERMINAL "F" ALDL

CHART C-8C 4.3L ONLY

TRANSMISSION CONVERTER CLUTCH (TCC) CHECK
ELECTRICAL DIAGNOSIS

MECHANICAL CHECKS, SUCH AS LINKAGE, OIL LEVEL, ETC. SHOULD BE PERFORMED PRIOR TO USING THIS CHART.

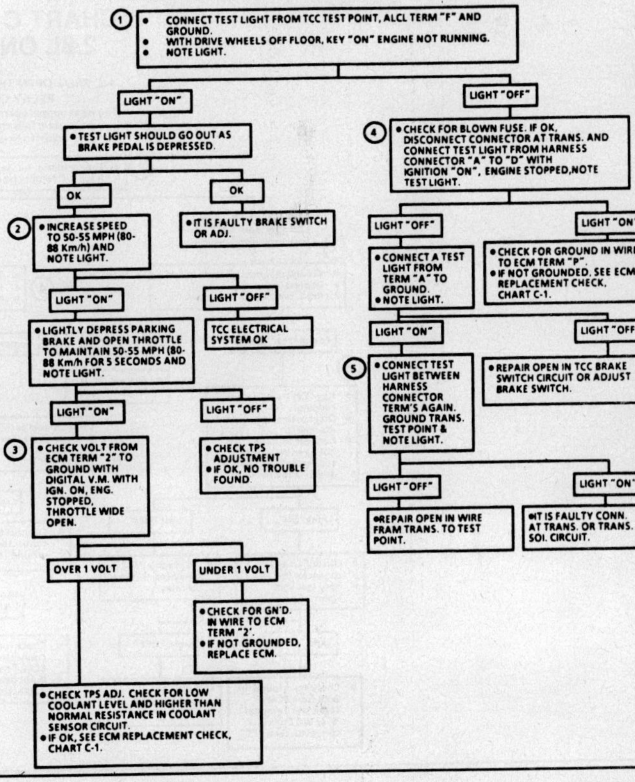

GENERAL MOTORS COMPUTER COMMAND CONTROL CALIF. 2.8L, 4.3L, 5.0L & 5.7L FULL FUNCTION (Cont.)

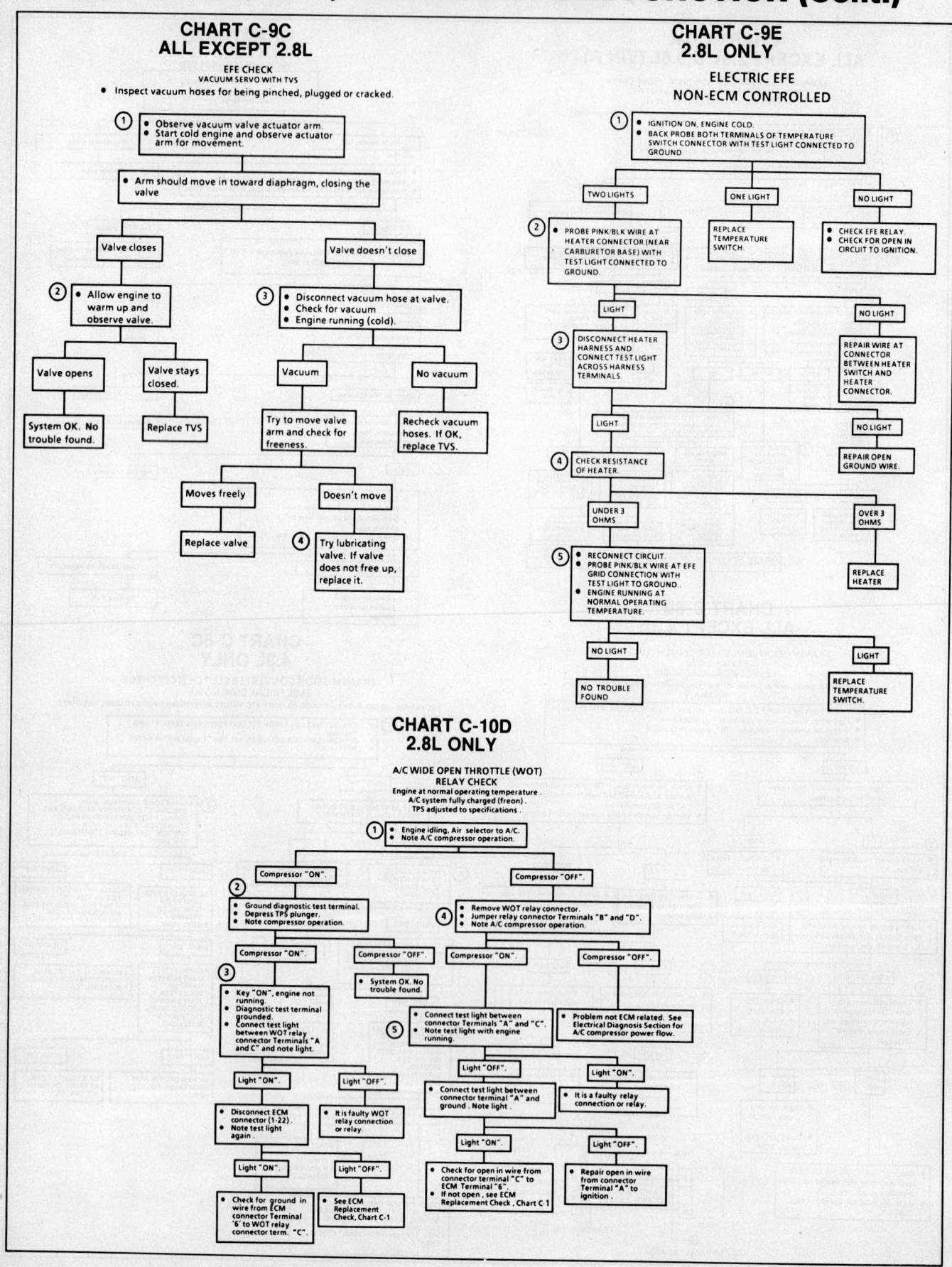

CHART C-9C
ALL EXCEPT 2.8L

EFE CHECK
VACUUM SERVO WITH TVS

- Inspect vacuum hoses for being pinched, plugged or cracked.

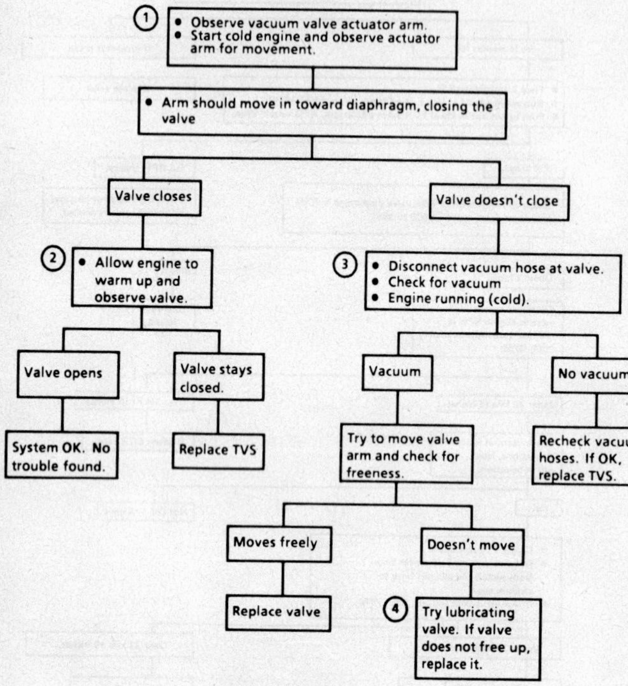

• Start cold engine and observe actuator arm for movement.
• Arm should move in toward diaphragm, closing the valve

Valve doesn't close

Try lubricating valve. If valve does not free up, replace it.

CHART C-9E
2.8L ONLY

ELECTRIC EFE
NON-ECM CONTROLLED

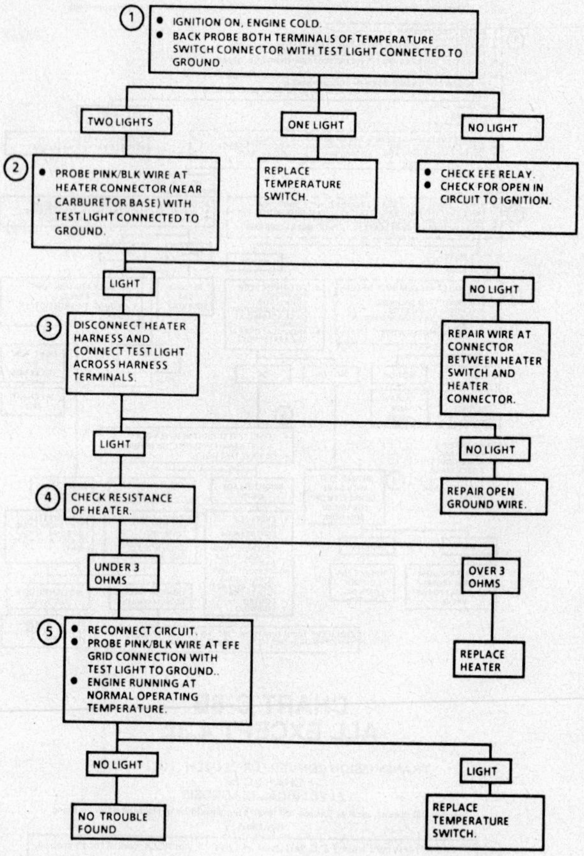

TWO LIGHTS

• PROBE PINK/BLK WIRE AT HEATER CONNECTOR (NEAR CARBURETOR BASE) WITH TEST LIGHT CONNECTED TO GROUND.

• CHECK EFE RELAY.

REPAIR WIRE AT CONNECTOR BETWEEN HEATER SWITCH AND HEATER CONNECTOR.

REPAIR OPEN GROUND WIRE.
UNDER 3 OHMS
OVER 3 OHMS

CHART C-10D
2.8L ONLY

A/C WIDE OPEN THROTTLE (WOT)
RELAY CHECK

Engine at normal operating temperature.
A/C system fully charged (freon).
TPS adjusted to specifications.

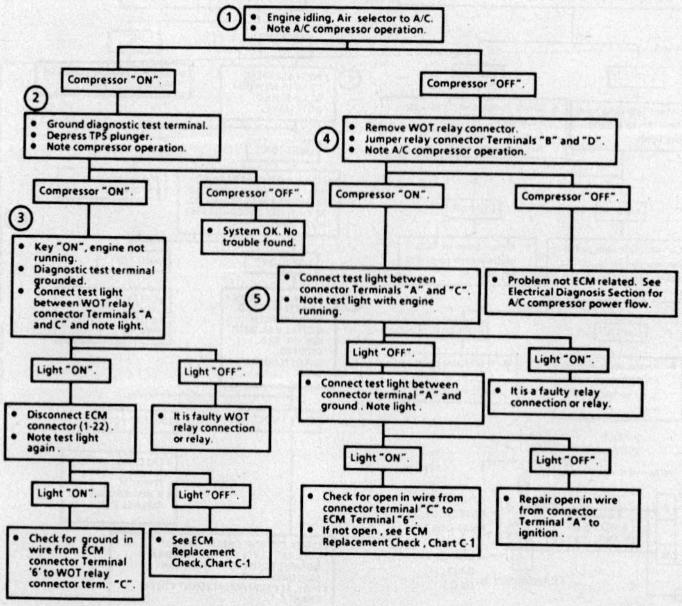

1
• Engine idling, Air selector to A/C.
• Note A/C compressor operation.
Compressor "ON".
Compressor "OFF".
2
• Ground diagnostic test terminal.
• Depress TPS plunger.
• Note compressor operation.
4
• Remove WOT relay connector.
• Jumper relay connector Terminals "B" and "D".
• Note A/C compressor operation.
Compressor "ON".
Compressor "OFF".
Compressor "ON".
Compressor "OFF".
3
• Key "ON", engine not running.
• Diagnostic test terminal grounded.
• Connect test light between WOT relay connector Terminals "A and C" and note light.
Valve stays closed.
• System OK. No trouble found.
Try to move valve arm and check for freeness.
5
• Connect test light between connector Terminals "A" and "C".
• Note test light with engine running.
• Problem not ECM related. See Electrical Diagnosis Section for A/C compressor power flow.
Light "ON".
Light "OFF".
Light "OFF".
Light "ON".
• Disconnect ECM connector (1-22).
• Note test light again.
• It is faulty WOT relay connection or relay.
• Connect test light between connector terminal "A" and ground. Note light.
• It is a faulty relay connection or relay.
Light "ON".
Light "OFF".
Light "ON".
Light "OFF".
• Check for ground in wire from ECM connector Terminal '6' to WOT relay connector term. "C".
• See ECM Replacement Check, Chart C-1
• Check for open in wire from connector terminal "C" to ECM Terminal "6".
• If not open, see ECM Replacement Check, Chart C-1
• Repair open in wire from connector Terminal "A" to ignition.

GENERAL MOTORS COMPUTER COMMAND CONTROL
CALIF. 2.8L, 4.3L, 5.0L & 5.7L FULL FUNCTION (Cont.)

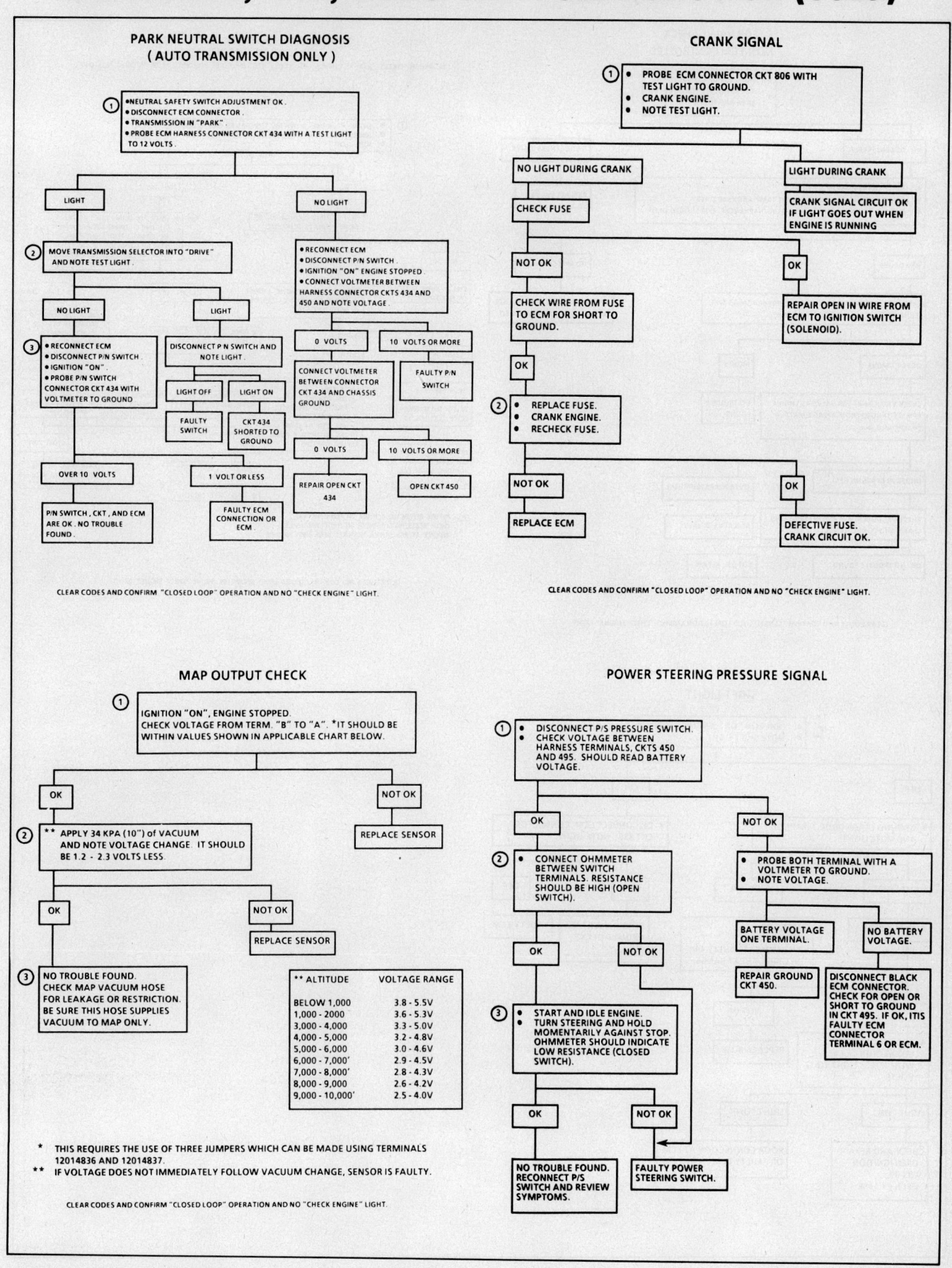

PARK NEUTRAL SWITCH DIAGNOSIS
(AUTO TRANSMISSION ONLY)

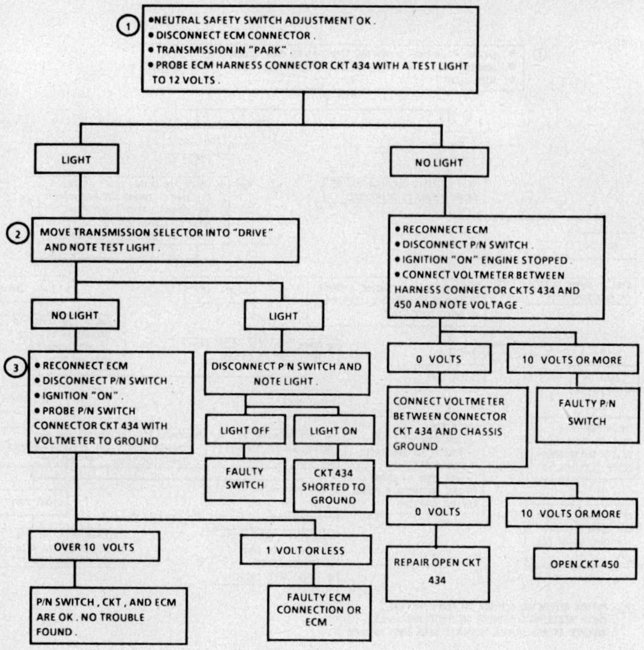

FAULTY P/N SWITCH

CKT 434 SHORTED TO GROUND

OVER 10 VOLTS

OPEN CKT 450

CLEAR CODES AND CONFIRM "CLOSED LOOP" OPERATION AND NO "CHECK ENGINE" LIGHT.

CRANK SIGNAL

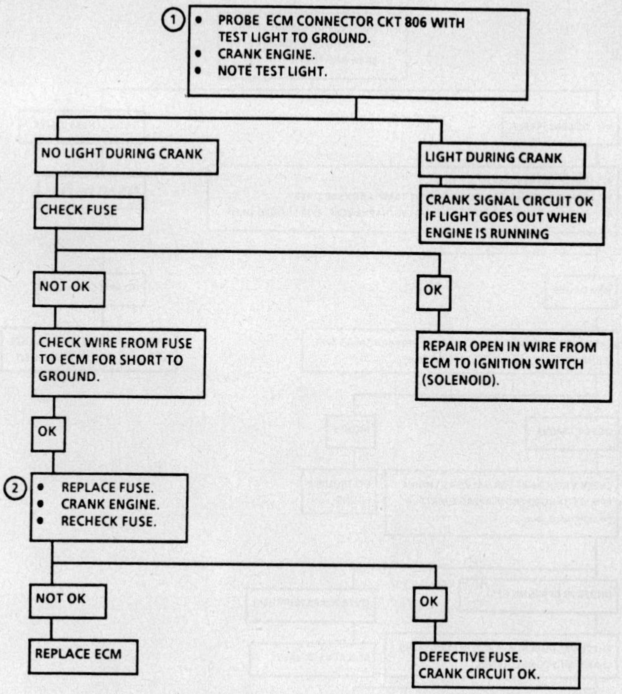

NO LIGHT DURING CRANK
LIGHT DURING CRANK

CRANK SIGNAL CIRCUIT OK IF LIGHT GOES OUT WHEN ENGINE IS RUNNING

• RECHECK FUSE.

DEFECTIVE FUSE. CRANK CIRCUIT OK.

CLEAR CODES AND CONFIRM "CLOSED LOOP" OPERATION AND NO "CHECK ENGINE" LIGHT.

MAP OUTPUT CHECK

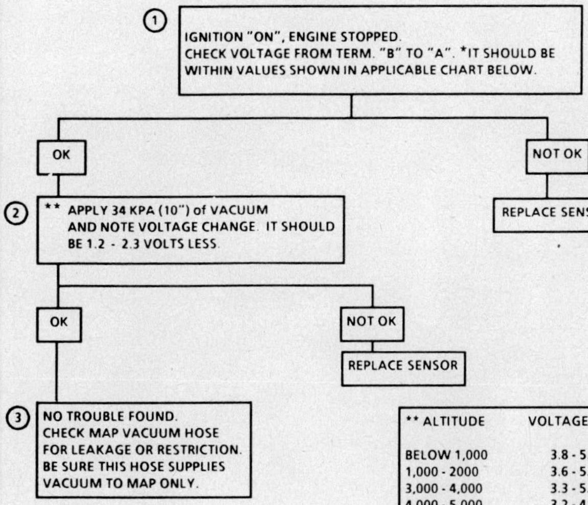

CHECK VOLTAGE FROM TERM. "B" TO "A". *IT SHOULD BE WITHIN VALUES SHOWN IN APPLICABLE CHART BELOW.

BE SURE THIS HOSE SUPPLIES VACUUM TO MAP ONLY.

** ALTITUDE	VOLTAGE RANGE
BELOW 1,000	3.8 - 5.5V
1,000 - 2000	3.6 - 5.3V
3,000 - 4,000	3.3 - 5.0V
4,000 - 5,000	3.2 - 4.8V
5,000 - 6,000	3.0 - 4.6V
6,000 - 7,000'	2.9 - 4.5V
7,000 - 8,000'	2.8 - 4.3V
8,000 - 9,000	2.6 - 4.2V
9,000 - 10,000'	2.5 - 4.0V

* THIS REQUIRES THE USE OF THREE JUMPERS WHICH CAN BE MADE USING TERMINALS 12014836 AND 12014837.

** IF VOLTAGE DOES NOT IMMEDIATELY FOLLOW VACUUM CHANGE, SENSOR IS FAULTY.

CLEAR CODES AND CONFIRM "CLOSED LOOP" OPERATION AND NO "CHECK ENGINE" LIGHT.

POWER STEERING PRESSURE SIGNAL

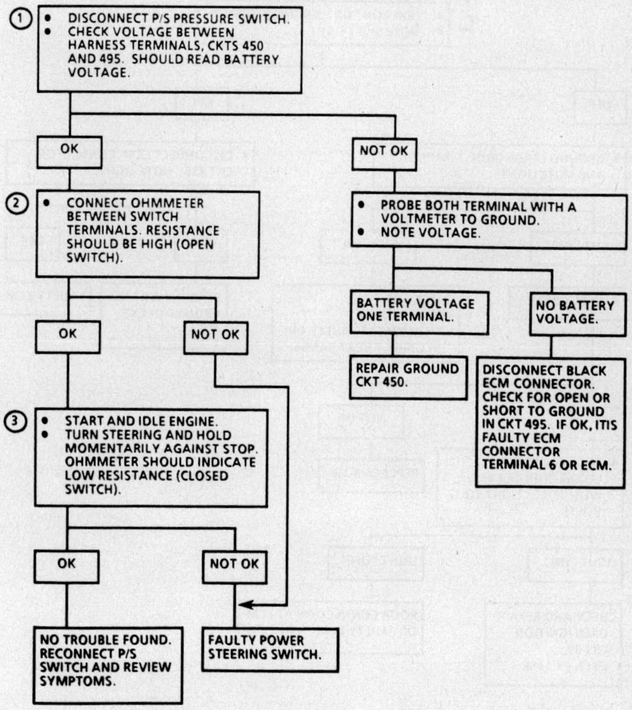

1
• DISCONNECT P/S PRESSURE SWITCH.
• CHECK VOLTAGE BETWEEN HARNESS TERMINALS, CKTS 450 AND 495. SHOULD READ BATTERY VOLTAGE.
OK
NOT OK
2
• CONNECT OHMMETER BETWEEN SWITCH TERMINALS. RESISTANCE SHOULD BE HIGH (OPEN SWITCH).
• PROBE BOTH TERMINAL WITH A VOLTMETER TO GROUND.
• NOTE VOLTAGE.
BATTERY VOLTAGE ONE TERMINAL.
NO BATTERY VOLTAGE.
OK
NOT OK
REPAIR GROUND CKT 450.
DISCONNECT BLACK ECM CONNECTOR. CHECK FOR OPEN OR SHORT TO GROUND IN CKT 495. IF OK, ITIS FAULTY ECM CONNECTOR TERMINAL 6 OR ECM.
3
• START AND IDLE ENGINE.
• TURN STEERING AND HOLD MOMENTARILY AGAINST STOP. OHMMETER SHOULD INDICATE LOW RESISTANCE (CLOSED SWITCH).
OK
NOT OK
NO TROUBLE FOUND. RECONNECT P/S SWITCH AND REVIEW SYMPTOMS.
FAULTY POWER STEERING SWITCH.

GENERAL MOTORS COMPUTER COMMAND CONTROL CALIF. 2.8L, 4.3L, 5.0L & 5.7L FULL FUNCTION (Cont.)

EGR VALVE CHECK NON-ECM CONTROLLED

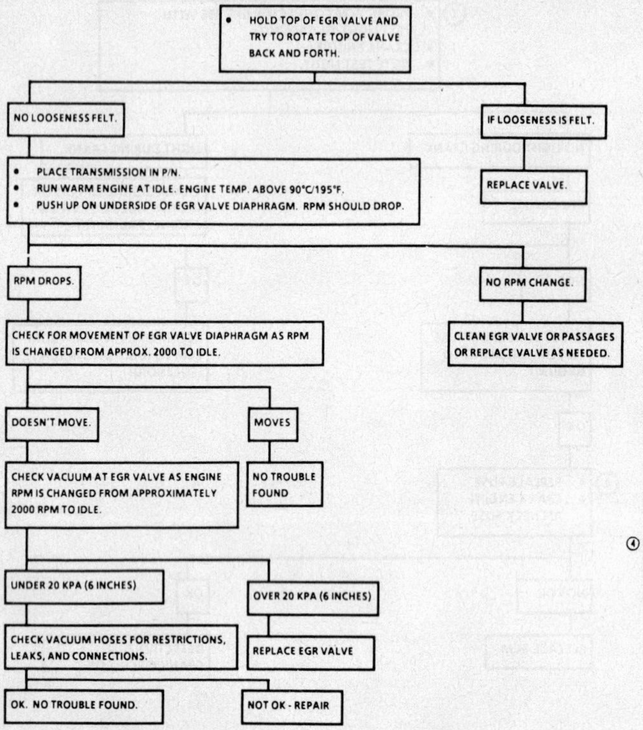

• HOLD TOP OF EGR VALVE AND TRY TO ROTATE TOP OF VALVE BACK AND FORTH.
NO LOOSENESS FELT.
IF LOOSENESS IS FELT.
• PLACE TRANSMISSION IN P/N.
• RUN WARM ENGINE AT IDLE. ENGINE TEMP. ABOVE 90°C/195°F.
• PUSH UP ON UNDERSIDE OF EGR VALVE DIAPHRAGM. RPM SHOULD DROP.
REPLACE VALVE.
RPM DROPS.
NO RPM CHANGE.
CHECK FOR MOVEMENT OF EGR VALVE DIAPHRAGM AS RPM IS CHANGED FROM APPROX. 2000 TO IDLE.
CLEAN EGR VALVE OR PASSAGES OR REPLACE VALVE AS NEEDED.
DOESN'T MOVE.
MOVES
CHECK VACUUM AT EGR VALVE AS ENGINE RPM IS CHANGED FROM APPROXIMATELY 2000 RPM TO IDLE.
NO TROUBLE FOUND
UNDER 20 KPA (6 INCHES)
OVER 20 KPA (6 INCHES)
CHECK VACUUM HOSES FOR RESTRICTIONS, LEAKS, AND CONNECTIONS.
REPLACE EGR VALVE
OK. NO TROUBLE FOUND.
NOT OK - REPAIR

CLEAR CODES AND CONFIRM "CLOSED LOOP" OPERATION AND NO "CHECK ENGINE" LIGHT.

TRANSMISSION CONVERTER CLUTCH (TCC) ELECTRICAL DIAGNOSIS

MECHANICAL CHECKS, SUCH AS LINKAGE, OIL LEVEL, ETC. SHOULD BE PERFORMED PRIOR TO USING THIS CHART.

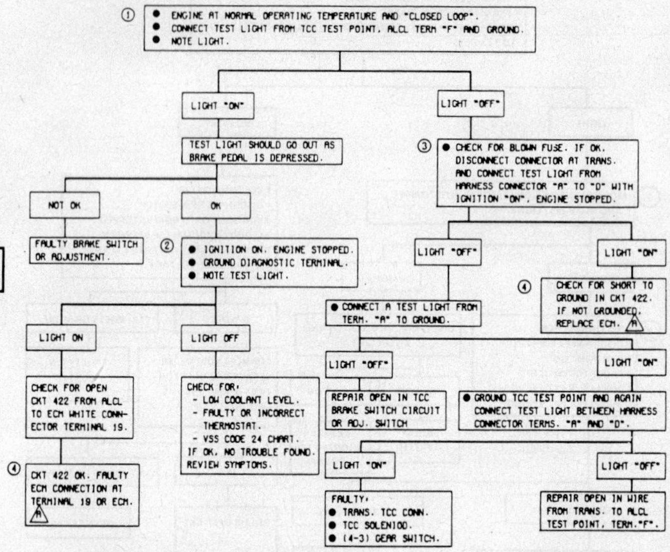

① • ENGINE AT NORMAL OPERATING TEMPERATURE AND "CLOSED LOOP".
• CONNECT TEST LIGHT FROM TCC TEST POINT, ALCL TERM "F" AND GROUND.
• NOTE LIGHT.
LIGHT "ON"
LIGHT "OFF"
TEST LIGHT SHOULD GO OUT AS BRAKE PEDAL IS DEPRESSED.
③ • CHECK FOR BLOWN FUSE. IF OK, DISCONNECT CONNECTOR AT TRANS. AND CONNECT TEST LIGHT FROM HARNESS CONNECTOR "A" TO "D" WITH IGNITION "ON", ENGINE STOPPED.
NOT OK
OK
FAULTY BRAKE SWITCH OR ADJUSTMENT.
② • IGNITION ON, ENGINE STOPPED.
• GROUND DIAGNOSTIC TERMINAL.
• NOTE TEST LIGHT.
LIGHT "OFF"
LIGHT "ON"
④ CHECK FOR SHORT TO GROUND IN CKT 422. IF NOT GROUNDED, REPLACE ECM. A
• CONNECT A TEST LIGHT FROM TERM. "A" TO GROUND.
LIGHT ON
LIGHT OFF
LIGHT "OFF"
LIGHT "ON"
CHECK FOR OPEN CKT 422 FROM ALCL TO ECM WHITE CONNECTOR TERMINAL 19.
CHECK FOR:
- LOW COOLANT LEVEL.
- FAULTY OR INCORRECT THERMOSTAT.
- VSS CODE 24 CHART.
IF OK, NO TROUBLE FOUND. REVIEW SYMPTOMS.
REPAIR OPEN IN TCC BRAKE SWITCH CIRCUIT OR ADJ. SWITCH
• GROUND TCC TEST POINT AND AGAIN CONNECT TEST LIGHT BETWEEN HARNESS CONNECTOR TERMS. "A" AND "D".
④ CKT 422 OK. FAULTY ECM CONNECTION AT TERMINAL 19 OR ECM. A
LIGHT "ON"
LIGHT "OFF"
FAULTY:
• TRANS. TCC CONN.
• TCC SOLENIOD.
• (4-3) GEAR SWITCH.
REPAIR OPEN IN WIRE FROM TRANS. TO ALCL TEST POINT, TERM."F".

A BEFORE REPLACING ECM USE AN OHMMETER AND CHECK RESISTANCE BETWEEN SOLENOID TERMINALS. REPLACE IF RESISTANCE MEASURES LESS THAN 20 OHMS.

CLEAR CODES AND CONFIRM "CLOSED LOOP" OPERATION AND NO "CHECK ENGINE" LIGHT.

SHIFT LIGHT

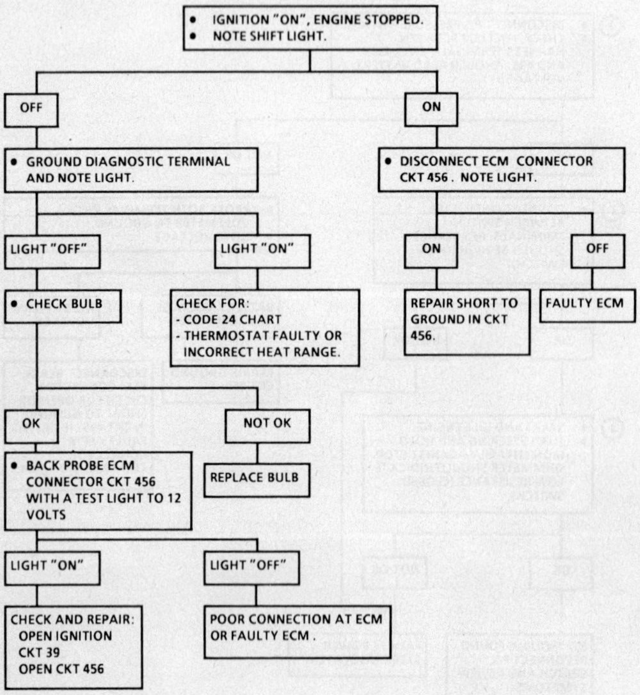

• IGNITION "ON", ENGINE STOPPED.
• NOTE SHIFT LIGHT.
OFF
ON
• GROUND DIAGNOSTIC TERMINAL AND NOTE LIGHT.
• DISCONNECT ECM CONNECTOR CKT 456. NOTE LIGHT.
LIGHT "OFF"
LIGHT "ON"
ON
OFF
• CHECK BULB
CHECK FOR:
- CODE 24 CHART
- THERMOSTAT FAULTY OR INCORRECT HEAT RANGE.
REPAIR SHORT TO GROUND IN CKT 456.
FAULTY ECM
OK
NOT OK
• BACK PROBE ECM CONNECTOR CKT 456 WITH A TEST LIGHT TO 12 VOLTS
REPLACE BULB
LIGHT "ON"
LIGHT "OFF"
CHECK AND REPAIR: OPEN IGNITION CKT 39 OPEN CKT 456
POOR CONNECTION AT ECM OR FAULTY ECM.

GENERAL MOTORS COMPUTER COMMAND CONTROL CALIF. 2.8L, 4.3L, 5.0L & 5.7L FULL FUNCTION (Cont.)

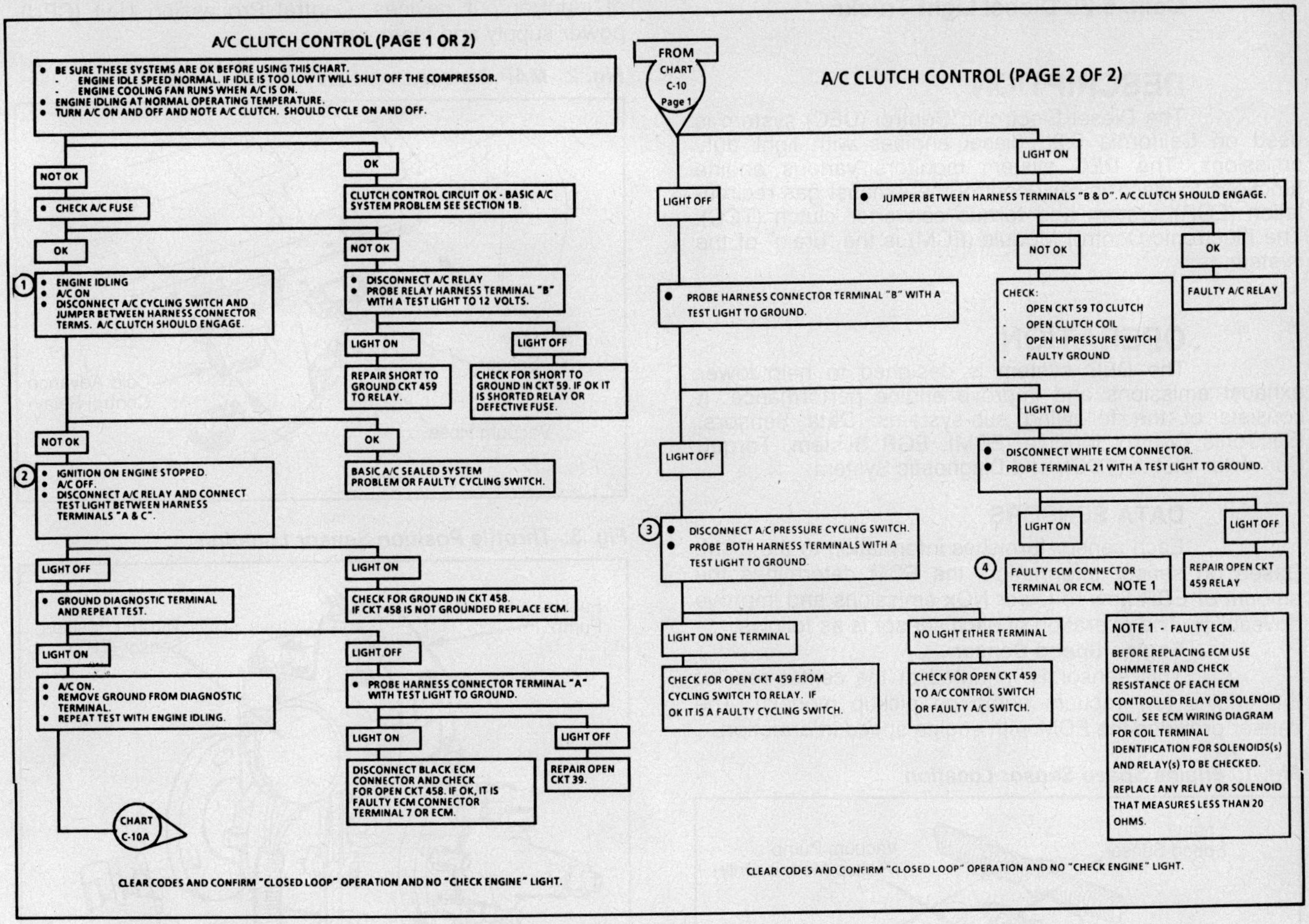

GENERAL MOTORS DIESEL ELECTRONIC CONTROL SYSTEM

Calif. 6.2L Diesel Light Trucks

DESCRIPTION

The Diesel Electronic Control (DEC) system is used on California 6.2L diesel engines with light duty emissions. The DEC system monitors various engine functions to electronically control the exhaust gas recirculation (EGR) system and torque converter clutch (TCC). The Electronic Control Module (ECM) is the "brain" of the system.

OPERATION

The DEC system is designed to help lower exhaust emissions and improve engine performance. It consists of the following sub-systems: Data Sensors, Electronic Control Module (ECM), EGR System, Torque Converter Clutch (TCC), and Diagnostic System.

DATA SENSORS

Each sensor furnishes information to the ECM. Based on sensor information, the ECM determines the amount of EGR flow to lower NOx emissions and improve driveability. The operation of each sensor is as follows:

Engine Speed Sensor

This sensor is mounted at the center rear of the engine (on vacuum pump on pickup models). The sensor provides the ECM with engine speed information.

Fig. 1: Engine Speed Sensor Location

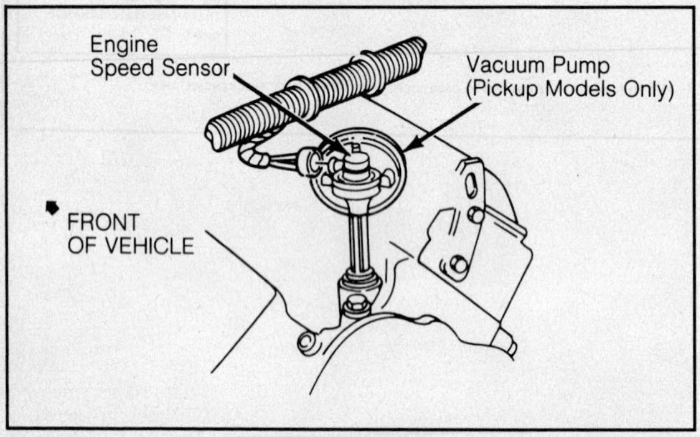

This applies to pickup models only.

Manifold Absolute Pressure (MAP) Sensor

The MAP sensor signal is used by the ECM to determine the amount of vacuum in the EGR vacuum line. This signal is derived by comparing the calculated amount of EGR vacuum and the actual amount of EGR vacuum present. The sensor is mounted on right side of firewall.

Throttle Position Sensor (TPS)

The TPS is mounted on the fuel injection pump throttle valve. The TPS provides the ECM with throttle angle information.

Vehicle Speed Sensor (VSS)

The VSS is mounted behind the speedometer in the instrument panel. The ECM uses a series of pulses provided by the VSS to determine vehicle speed.

ELECTRONIC CONTROL MODULE (ECM)

The ECM is located in the passenger compartment under right side of dash on all pickup models and under driver's seat on all van models. The ECM consists of input/output devices, Central Processing Unit (CPU), power supply and memories.

Fig. 2: MAP Sensor Location

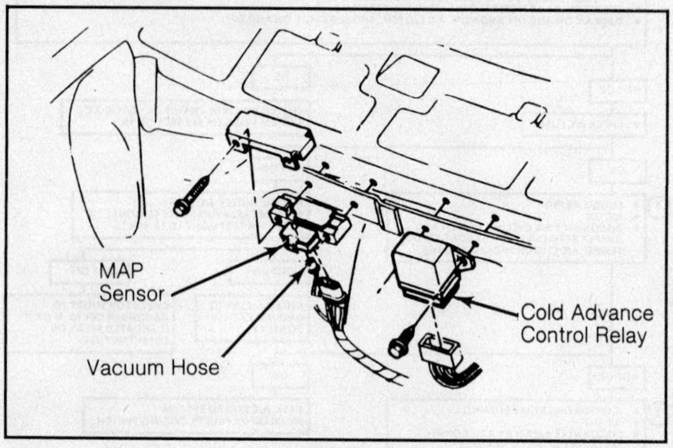

Fig. 3: Throttle Position Sensor Location

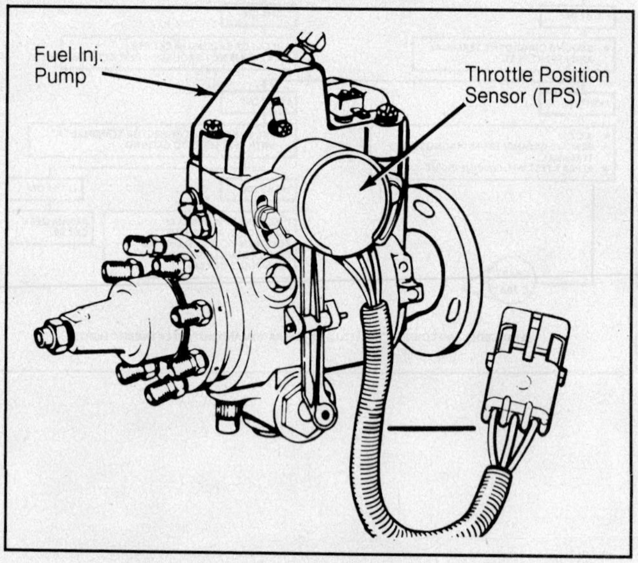

Input/Output Devices

These devices are an integral part of the ECM. They convert electrical signals, received by the ECM from the various engine sensors, into digital signals for use by the CPU.

Central Processing Unit

Digital signals received by the CPU are used to perform all mathematical computations and logic functions necessary to deliver proper EGR flow. The CPU commands operation of EGR system, torque converter clutch, and the diagnostic system.

Power Supply

The main source of power for the ECM is from the battery, through the ignition circuit.

Memories

Three types of memory are used by the ECM. These are: Read Only Memory, Random Access Memory, and Programmable Read Only Memory.

- **Read Only Memory (ROM)** – The ROM is programmed information that can only be read by the ECM. The ROM program cannot be changed. If battery voltage is removed, ROM information will be retained.

GENERAL MOTORS DIESEL ELECTRONIC CONTROL SYSTEM (Cont.)

- **Random Access Memory (RAM)** – This memory is the decision making center for the CPU. It works like a calculator. Data sensor input and results of calculations are temporarily stored in the RAM memory. If battery voltage is removed from the ECM, all information stored in the memory is lost.
- **Programmable Read Only Memory (PROM)** – This memory contains factory programmed information including engine calibration data, transmission type, vehicle weight and rear axle ratio. The PROM can be removed from the ECM. If battery voltage is removed, PROM information will be retained.

EGR SYSTEM

The EGR system is electronically controlled by the ECM and consists of an EGR solenoid, EGR valve, exhaust pressure regulator (EPR) solenoid, EPR valve, EGR vent solenoid valve, and vacuum pump.

The vacuum pump provides vacuum for EPR and EGR valve operation. The EGR and EPR solenoids are mounted at top rear of engine as an assembly.

The ECM controls the EGR solenoid to regulate the amount of vacuum at the EGR valve. The ECM controls on-off time (duty cycle) of the EGR solenoid to regulate EGR flow.

The ECM calculates the amount of EGR flow required based on information supplied by the engine speed and throttle position sensors. When EGR flow should not be recirculated back into the engine, the ECM activates the EGR vent solenoid to rapidly vent vacuum from the EGR system.

During idle situations, the ECM energizes (closes) the EPR solenoid to increase exhaust backpressure. Increasing backpressure increases EGR flow to help reduce emissions during idle.

Fig. 4: EGR System Components and Locations

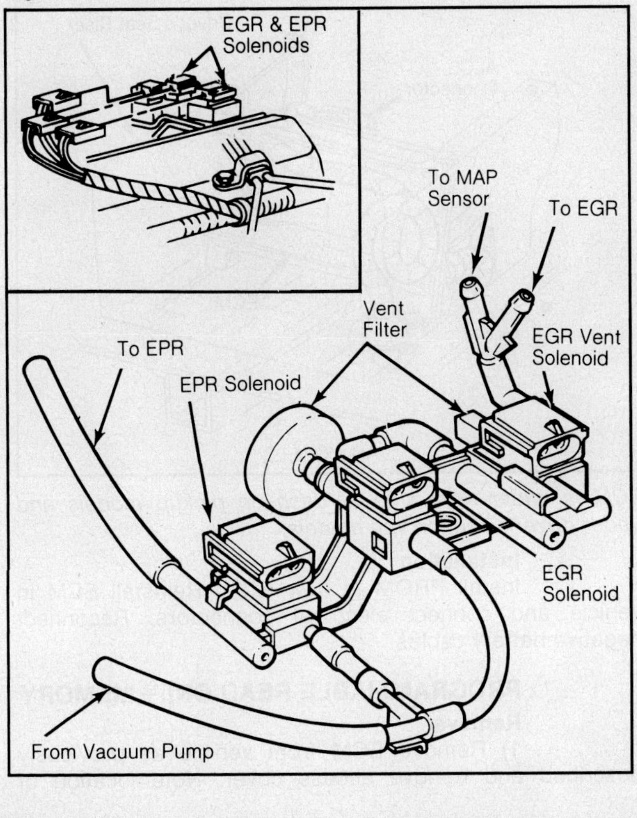

TORQUE CONVERTER CLUTCH (TCC)

Under proper operating conditions (sufficient vehicle speed), a solenoid valve in the transmission is activated by the ECM. This results in direct coupling of the flywheel to the transmission output shaft through the torque converter, reducing slippage and increasing fuel economy.

When operating conditions indicate that the transmission should function in non-lockup mode, the TCC solenoid is de-energized. This allows the transmission to return to normal automatic operation. Pressing the brake pedal immediately de-energizes the solenoid through the TCC brake switch.

DIAGNOSTIC SYSTEM

The ECM of the DEC system is equipped with self-diagnostic capabilities which detect faults in the system (EGR system or Vehicle Speed Sensor). The system does not include a "CHECK ENGINE" light in the dash. Instead, trouble codes are indicated by using the Diesel Diagnostic Check (DDC) tester (J-34750).

Fig. 5: Diesel Diagnostic Check Tester

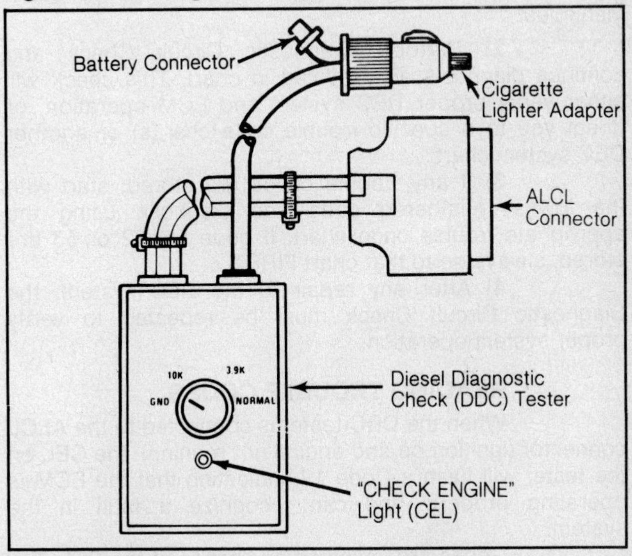

This tester must be used to determine system failures.

Fig. 6: ALCL Connector Identification

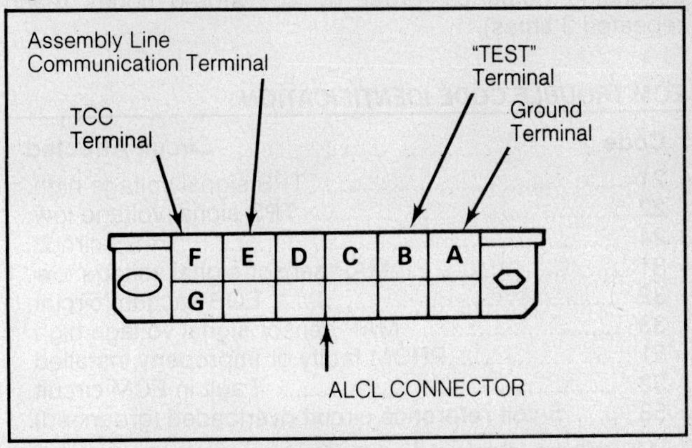

Located under left side of dash on pickup models and under driver's seat on van models.

GENERAL MOTORS DIESEL ELECTRONIC CONTROL SYSTEM (Cont.)

An Assembly Line Communication Link (ALCL) connecter is used at the factory to check the system prior to shipment. The DDC tester is connected to the ALCL connector and the cigar lighter (or BAT terminal in fuse panel) to diagnosis the DEC system. *See Fig. 5.* Trouble codes are indicated by a "Check Engine" light (CEL) on the DDC tester.

The DDC tester also has selectable diagnostic modes to evaluate a driveability problem. It is the only special tool required to diagnose the DEC system.

DIAGNOSIS & TESTING

DIAGNOSTIC PROCEDURE

Any diagnosis of the DEC system should be performed in the following order:

1) Ensure that all engine systems not related to the DEC system are operating properly. This should include a careful visual underhood inspection including: all vacuum hoses for correct routing, pinches, cuts, or disconnects; all wires in engine compartment for correct and good connections, burned or chaffed spots, pinched wires, or contact with sharp edges or hot exhaust manifolds.

2) Perform Diagnostic Circuit Check and continue diagnosis as indicated in chart. This check will either verify proper DEC system and ECM operation, or direct you to a specific trouble code chart(s) or another DEC system chart.

3) If any trouble codes are stored, start with the lowest numbered code and diagnose using the appropriate trouble code chart. If code 51, 52 or 53 are stored, always go to that chart FIRST.

4) After any repair to the DEC system, the Diagnostic Circuit Check must be repeated to verify proper system operation.

READING TROUBLE CODES

When the DDC tester is connected to the ALCL connector (ignition on and engine not running), the CEL on the tester will flash a Code 12, indicating that the ECM is operating properly and can recognize a fault in the system.

Codes are indicated by flashes of the CEL. For example, FLASH, pause, FLASH, FLASH, longer pause, identifies Code 12. This will repeat three times, followed in ascending numerical order by any stored codes (each repeated 3 times).

ECM TROUBLE CODE IDENTIFICATION

Code	Circuit Affected
21	TPS signal voltage high.
22	TPS signal voltage low.
24	VSS circuit.
31	MAP sensor signal voltage low.
32	EGR vacuum circuit.
33	MAP sensor signal voltage high.
51	PROM faulty or improperly installed.
52	Fault in ECM circuit.
53	5-volt reference circuit overloaded (grounded).

"12" will be displayed only if no reference pulses are received by the ECM from the engine speed sensor. Never stored as a malfunction.

If no other codes are stored, the light will continue to flash Code 12. Within about 5 seconds of engine start the light should go out, indicating that the ECM has not detected a fault.

CLEARING TROUBLE CODES

Trouble codes should be cleared when indicated in Diagnostic Circuit Check chart, and after the repair of a circuit. To clear trouble codes, the fused 12-volt source to the ECM must be disconnected for 10 seconds by disconnecting the positive battery terminal or removing the "ECM B" fuse at the fuse panel.

REMOVAL & INSTALLATION

ELECTRONIC CONTROL MODULE (ECM)

Removal

Turn ignition switch off. Disconnect negative battery cables. Locate ECM and remove mounting hardware. Remove electrical connector from ECM and remove ECM. Remove PROM from ECM.

Fig. 7: ECM Location

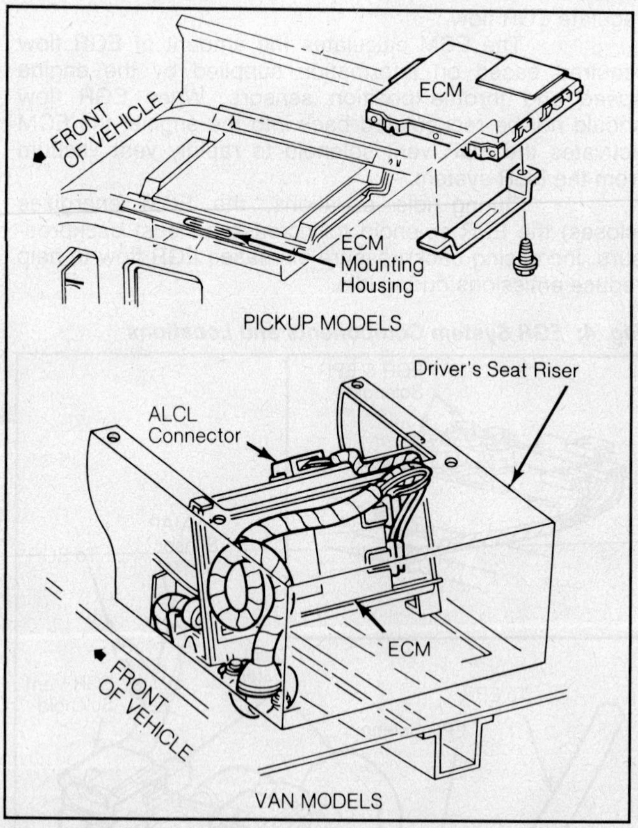

ECM is under right side of dash on pickup models and under driver's seat on van models.

Installation

Install PROM in new ECM. Reinstall ECM in vehicle and connect electrical connectors. Reconnect negative battery cables.

PROGRAMMABLE READ ONLY MEMORY

Removal

1) Remove ECM from vehicle as previously described and remove access cover. Note location of

GENERAL MOTORS DIESEL ELECTRONIC CONTROL SYSTEM (Cont.)

Fig. 8: Replacing PROM in Electronic Control Module

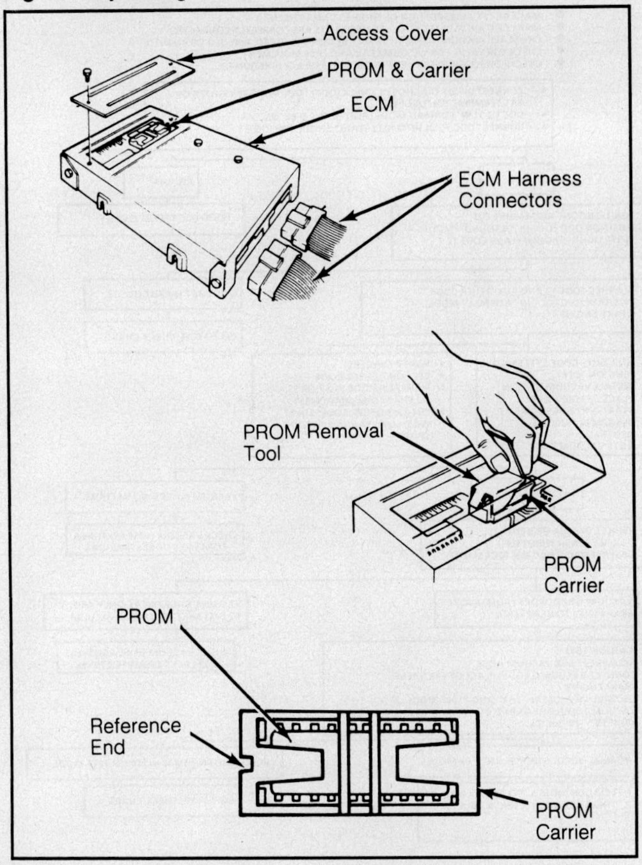

Always use PROM removal tool when replacing PROM.

reference notches in PROM and ECM for reassembly reference.

2) Engage one end of PROM carrier with hook end of rocker-type PROM removal tool. Press on vertical bar end of tool and rock engaged end of PROM carrier up as far as possible.

3) Engage opposite end of PROM carrier in the same manner and rock this end up as far as possible. Repeat process until PROM carrier and PROM are free of PROM socket.

NOTE: **PROM carrier should ONLY be removed with special PROM removal tool. Use of any other method may damage PROM or PROM socket.**

4) PROM carrier and PROM should lift off of PROM socket easily.

Installation

1) Check that new PROM has same service number as replaced PROM. Place new PROM and carrier in ECM. Press on PROM carrier until PROM is firmly seated in ECM. Make sure that reference notches in ECM and PROM are properly aligned.

2) Reinstall PROM access cover and screws. Reinstall ECM in vehicle as previously described.

Fig. 9: DEC System Component Locations for Trucks and Vans

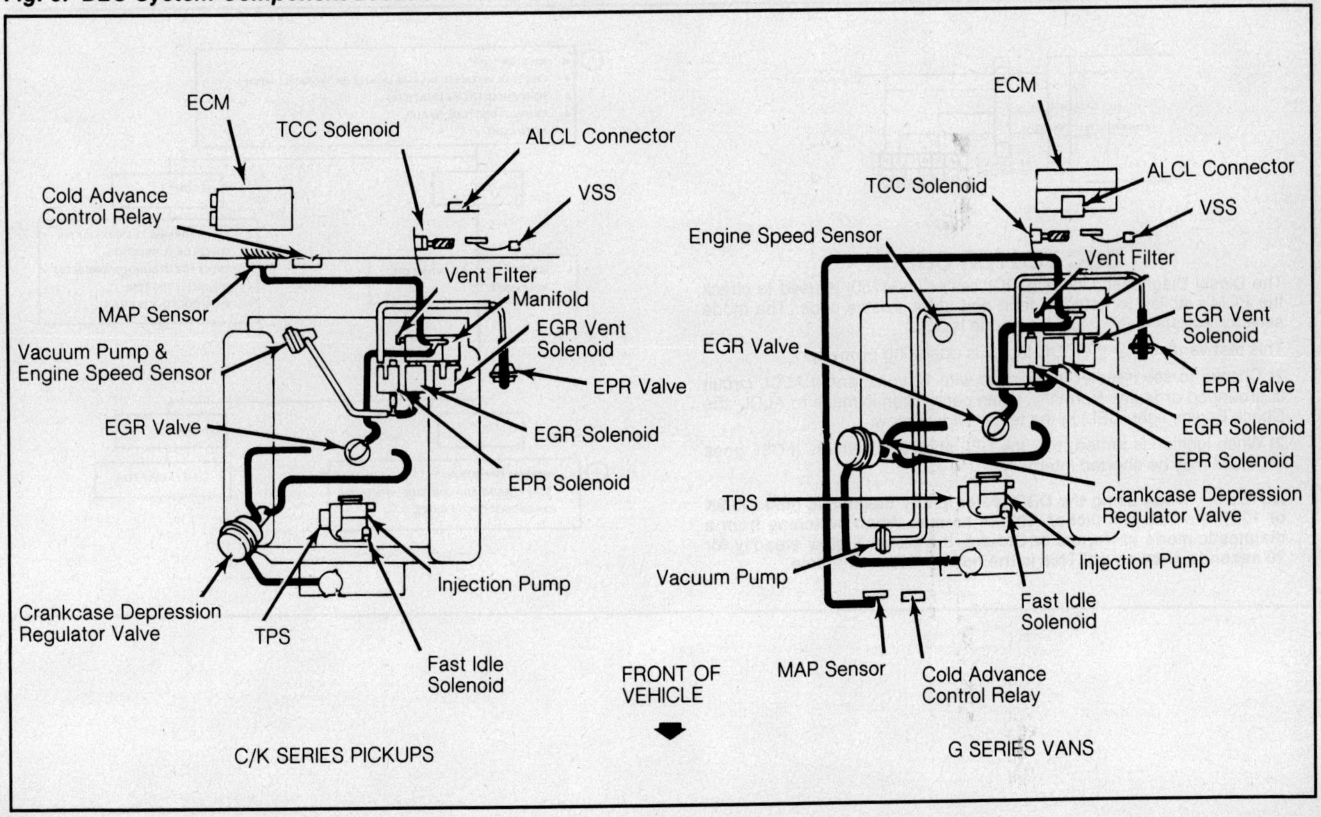

GENERAL MOTORS DIESEL ELECTRONIC CONTROL SYSTEM (Cont.)

DIAGNOSTIC CIRCUIT CHECK

Diagnostic Circuit Check determines if: 1) the ECM is operating and can recognize a fault, and 2) if any faults exist. This is the starting point for any diagnosis. If no faults are indicated, go to the Diesel Diagnostic Check (DDC) Tester Check.

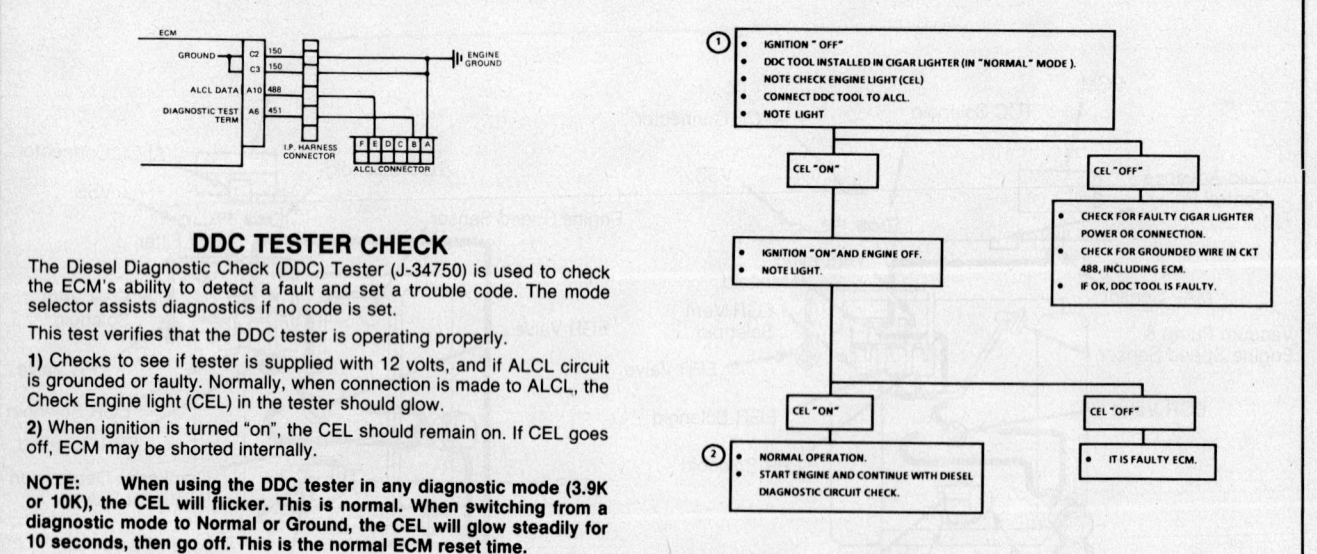

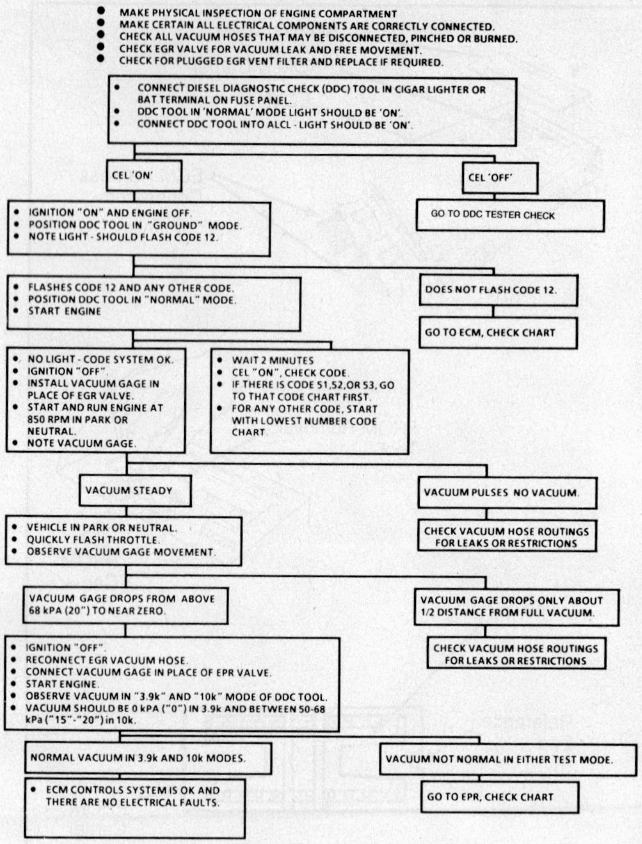

MAKE PHYSICAL INSPECTION OF ENGINE COMPARTMENT
MAKE CERTAIN ALL ELECTRICAL COMPONENTS ARE CORRECTLY CONNECTED.
CHECK ALL VACUUM HOSES THAT MAY BE DISCONNECTED, PINCHED OR BURNED.
CHECK EGR VALVE FOR VACUUM LEAK AND FREE MOVEMENT.
CHECK FOR PLUGGED EGR VENT FILTER AND REPLACE IF REQUIRED.
CONNECT DIESEL DIAGNOSTIC CHECK (DDC) TOOL IN CIGAR LIGHTER OR BAT TERMINAL ON FUSE PANEL.
DDC TOOL IN 'NORMAL' MODE LIGHT SHOULD BE 'ON'.
CONNECT DDC TOOL INTO ALCL - LIGHT SHOULD BE 'ON'.
CEL 'ON'
CEL 'OFF'
IGNITION "ON" AND ENGINE OFF.
POSITION DDC TOOL IN "GROUND" MODE.
NOTE LIGHT - SHOULD FLASH CODE 12.
GO TO DDC TESTER CHECK
FLASHES CODE 12 AND ANY OTHER CODE.
POSITION DDC TOOL IN "NORMAL" MODE.
START ENGINE
DOES NOT FLASH CODE 12.
GO TO ECM, CHECK CHART
NO LIGHT - CODE SYSTEM OK.
IGNITION "OFF".
INSTALL VACUUM GAGE IN PLACE OF EGR VALVE.
START AND RUN ENGINE AT 850 RPM IN PARK OR NEUTRAL.
NOTE VACUUM GAGE.
WAIT 2 MINUTES
CEL "ON", CHECK CODE.
IF THERE IS CODE 51, 52, OR 53, GO TO THAT CODE CHART FIRST.
FOR ANY OTHER CODE, START WITH LOWEST NUMBER CODE CHART.
VACUUM STEADY
VACUUM PULSES NO VACUUM.
VEHICLE IN PARK OR NEUTRAL.
QUICKLY FLASH THROTTLE.
OBSERVE VACUUM GAGE MOVEMENT.
CHECK VACUUM HOSE ROUTINGS FOR LEAKS OR RESTRICTIONS
VACUUM GAGE DROPS FROM ABOVE 68 kPA (20") TO NEAR ZERO.
VACUUM GAGE DROPS ONLY ABOUT 1/2 DISTANCE FROM FULL VACUUM.
IGNITION "OFF".
RECONNECT EGR VACUUM HOSE.
CONNECT VACUUM GAGE IN PLACE OF EPR VALVE.
START ENGINE.
OBSERVE VACUUM IN "3.9k" AND "10k" MODE OF DDC TOOL.
VACUUM SHOULD BE 0 kPA ("0") IN 3.9k AND BETWEEN 50-68 kPa ("15"-"20") in 10k.
CHECK VACUUM HOSE ROUTINGS FOR LEAKS OR RESTRICTIONS
NORMAL VACUUM IN 3.9k AND 10k MODES.
VACUUM NOT NORMAL IN EITHER TEST MODE.
ECM CONTROLS SYSTEM IS OK AND THERE ARE NO ELECTRICAL FAULTS.
GO TO EPR, CHECK CHART

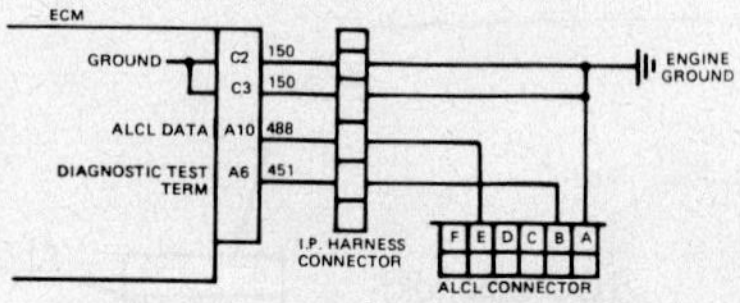

DDC TESTER CHECK

The Diesel Diagnostic Check (DDC) Tester (J-34750) is used to check the ECM's ability to detect a fault and set a trouble code. The mode selector assists diagnostics if no code is set.

This test verifies that the DDC tester is operating properly.

1) Checks to see if tester is supplied with 12 volts, and if ALCL circuit is grounded or faulty. Normally, when connection is made to ALCL, the Check Engine light (CEL) in the tester should glow.

2) When ignition is turned "on", the CEL should remain on. If CEL goes off, ECM may be shorted internally.

NOTE: When using the DDC tester in any diagnostic mode (3.9K or 10K), the CEL will flicker. This is normal. When switching from a diagnostic mode to Normal or Ground, the CEL will glow steadily for 10 seconds, then go off. This is the normal ECM reset time.

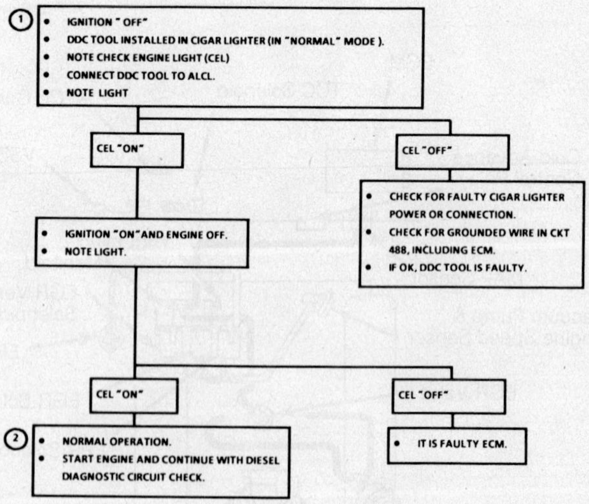

1
IGNITION "OFF"
DDC TOOL INSTALLED IN CIGAR LIGHTER (IN "NORMAL" MODE).
NOTE CHECK ENGINE LIGHT (CEL)
CONNECT DDC TOOL TO ALCL.
NOTE LIGHT
CEL "ON"
CEL "OFF"
CHECK FOR FAULTY CIGAR LIGHTER POWER OR CONNECTION.
CHECK FOR GROUNDED WIRE IN CKT 488, INCLUDING ECM.
IF OK, DDC TOOL IS FAULTY.
IGNITION "ON" AND ENGINE OFF.
NOTE LIGHT.
CEL "ON"
CEL "OFF"
2
NORMAL OPERATION.
START ENGINE AND CONTINUE WITH DIESEL DIAGNOSTIC CIRCUIT CHECK.
IT IS FAULTY ECM.

GENERAL MOTORS DIESEL ELECTRONIC CONTROL SYSTEM (Cont.)

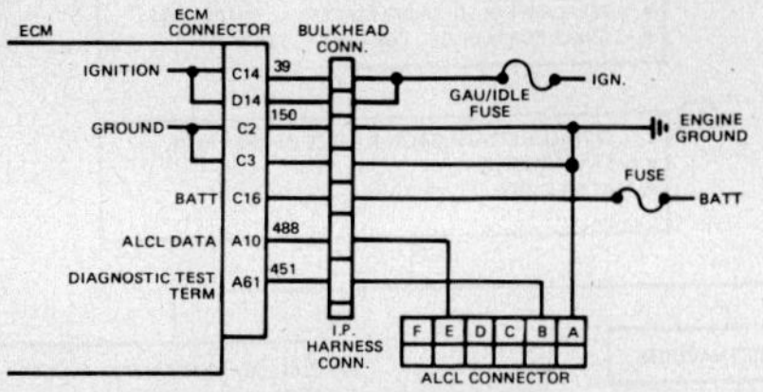

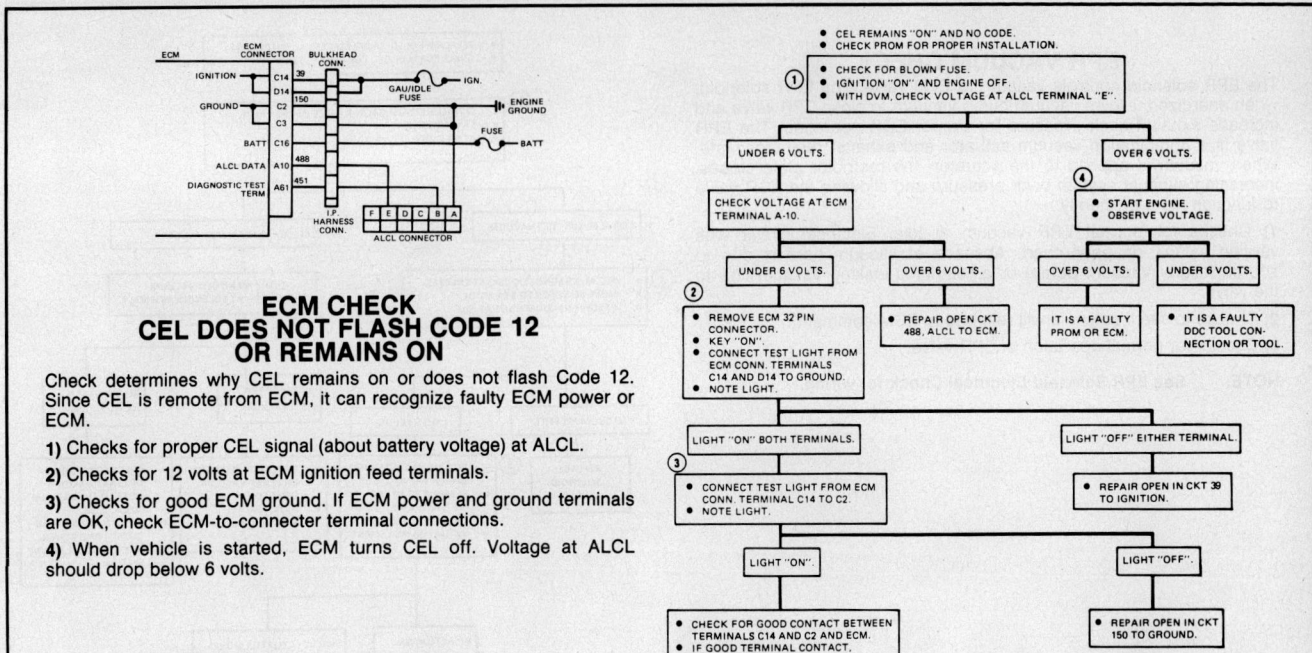

ECM CHECK CEL DOES NOT FLASH CODE 12 OR REMAINS ON

Check determines why CEL remains on or does not flash Code 12. Since CEL is remote from ECM, it can recognize faulty ECM power or ECM.

1) Checks for proper CEL signal (about battery voltage) at ALCL.

2) Checks for 12 volts at ECM ignition feed terminals.

3) Checks for good ECM ground. If ECM power and ground terminals are OK, check ECM-to-connecter terminal connections.

4) When vehicle is started, ECM turns CEL off. Voltage at ALCL should drop below 6 volts.

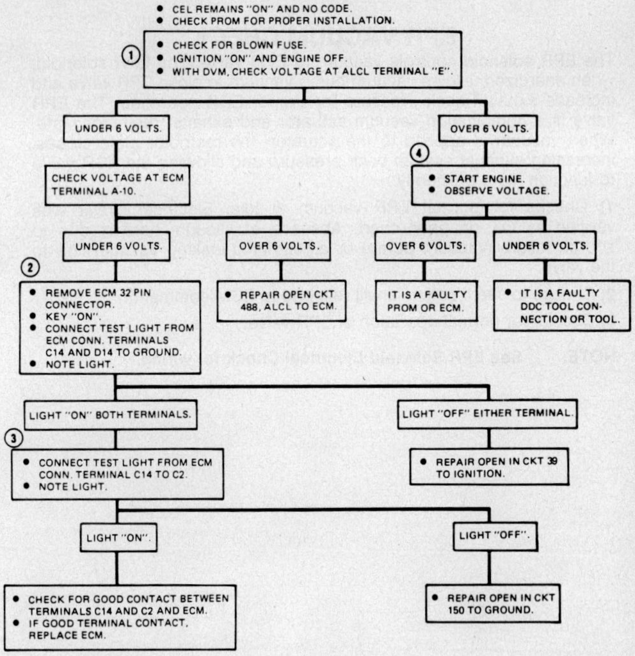

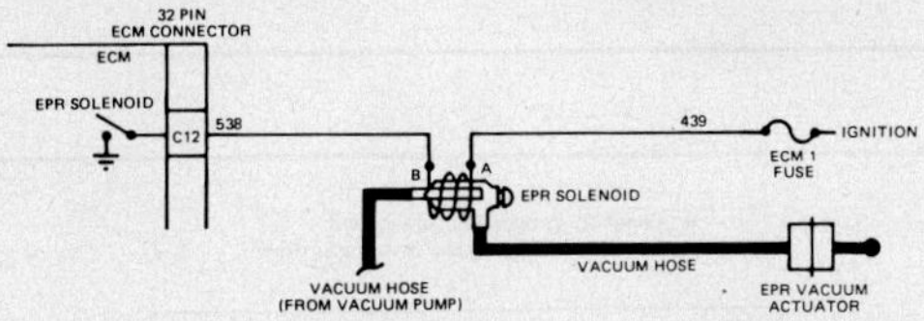

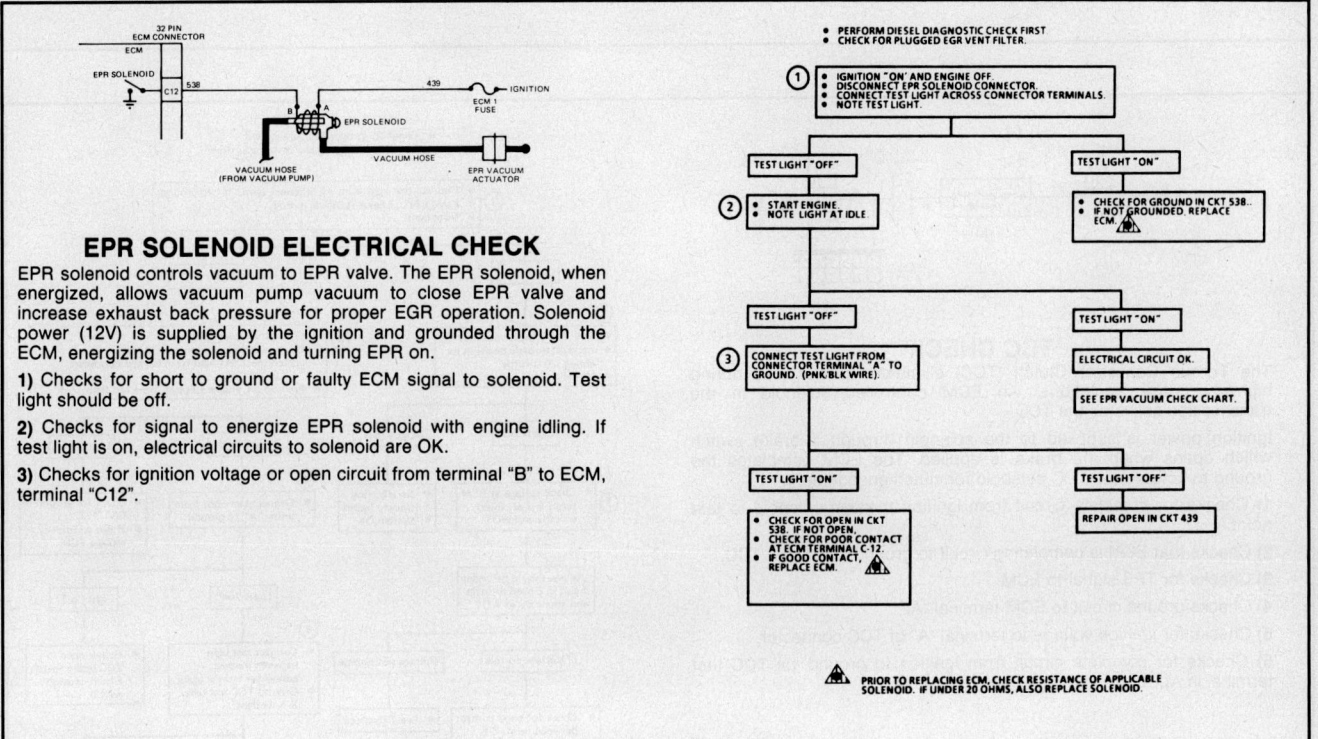

EPR SOLENOID ELECTRICAL CHECK

EPR solenoid controls vacuum to EPR valve. The EPR solenoid, when energized, allows vacuum pump vacuum to close EPR valve and increase exhaust back pressure for proper EGR operation. Solenoid power (12V) is supplied by the ignition and grounded through the ECM, energizing the solenoid and turning EPR on.

1) Checks for short to ground or faulty ECM signal to solenoid. Test light should be off.

2) Checks for signal to energize EPR solenoid with engine idling. If test light is on, electrical circuits to solenoid are OK.

3) Checks for ignition voltage or open circuit from terminal "B" to ECM, terminal "C12".

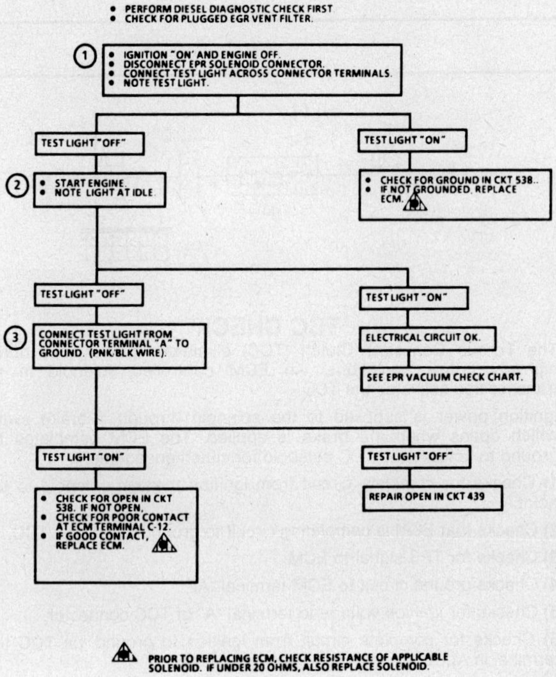

GENERAL MOTORS DIESEL ELECTRONIC CONTROL SYSTEM (Cont.)

EPR VACUUM CHECK

The EPR solenoid controls vacuum to EPR valve. The EPR solenoid, when energized, allows vacuum pump vacuum to close EPR valve and increase exhaust back pressure for proper EGR operation. The EPR valve is a combination vacuum actuator and exhaust restrictor plate. When vacuum is applied to the actuator, the restrictor plate closes, increasing exhaust system back pressure and allowing the EGR valve to function more efficiently.

1) Checks for normal EPR vacuum at idle. Electrical circuit was verified as OK on prior chart. Absence of vacuum here is due to source failure (vacuum pump) or a restricted/leaking vacuum line to the valve.

2) Checks to see if solenoid will respond to ECM command.

3) Checks for normal operation of EPR valve.

NOTE: See EPR Solenoid Electrical Check for wiring.

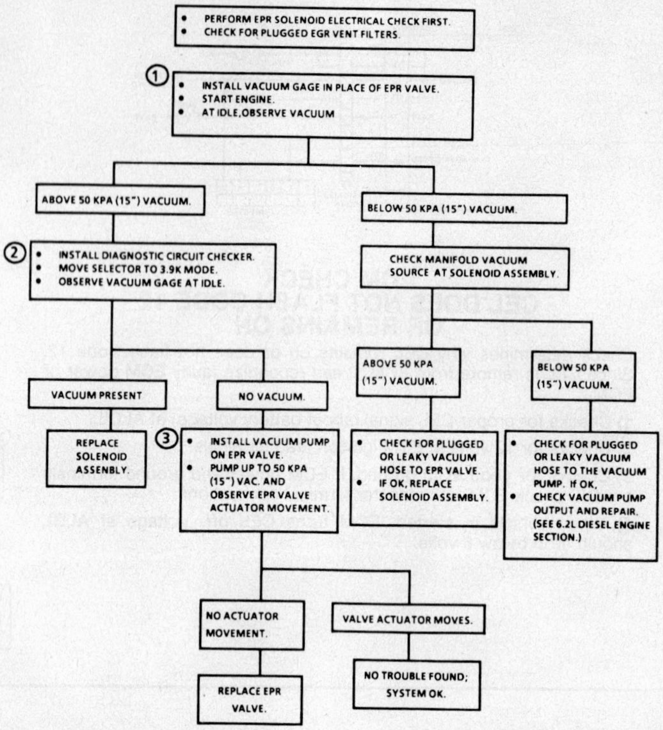

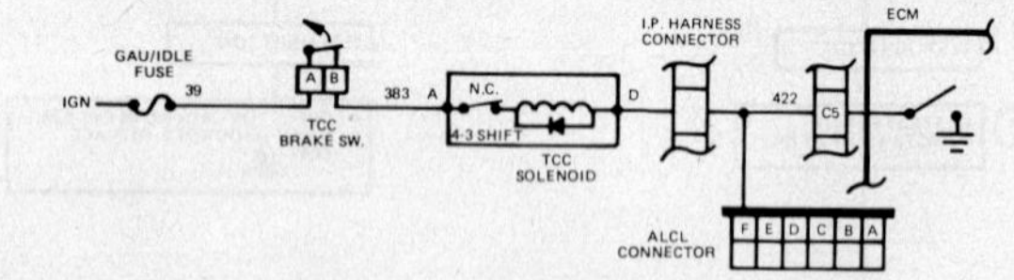

TCC CHECK

The Torque Converter Clutch (TCC) eliminates power loss during highway cruise conditions. An ECM controlled solenoid in the transmission activates the TCC.

Ignition power is supplied to the solenoid through a brake switch which opens when the brake is applied. The ECM completes the ground to activate the TCC solenoid for clutch engagement.

1) Checks for complete circuit from ignition through solenoid to test point.

2) Checks that ECM is completing circuit to ground to engage TCC.

3) Checks for TPS signal to ECM.

4) Checks ground circuit to ECM terminal "A2".

5) Checks for ignition voltage to terminal "A" of TCC connector.

6) Checks for complete circuit from ignition to ground via TCC test terminal in ALCL.

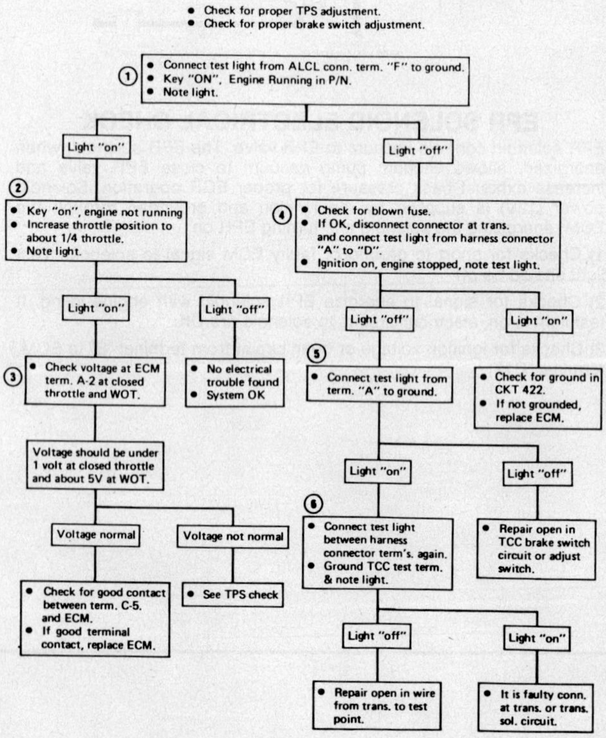

GENERAL MOTORS DIESEL ELECTRONIC CONTROL SYSTEM (Cont.)

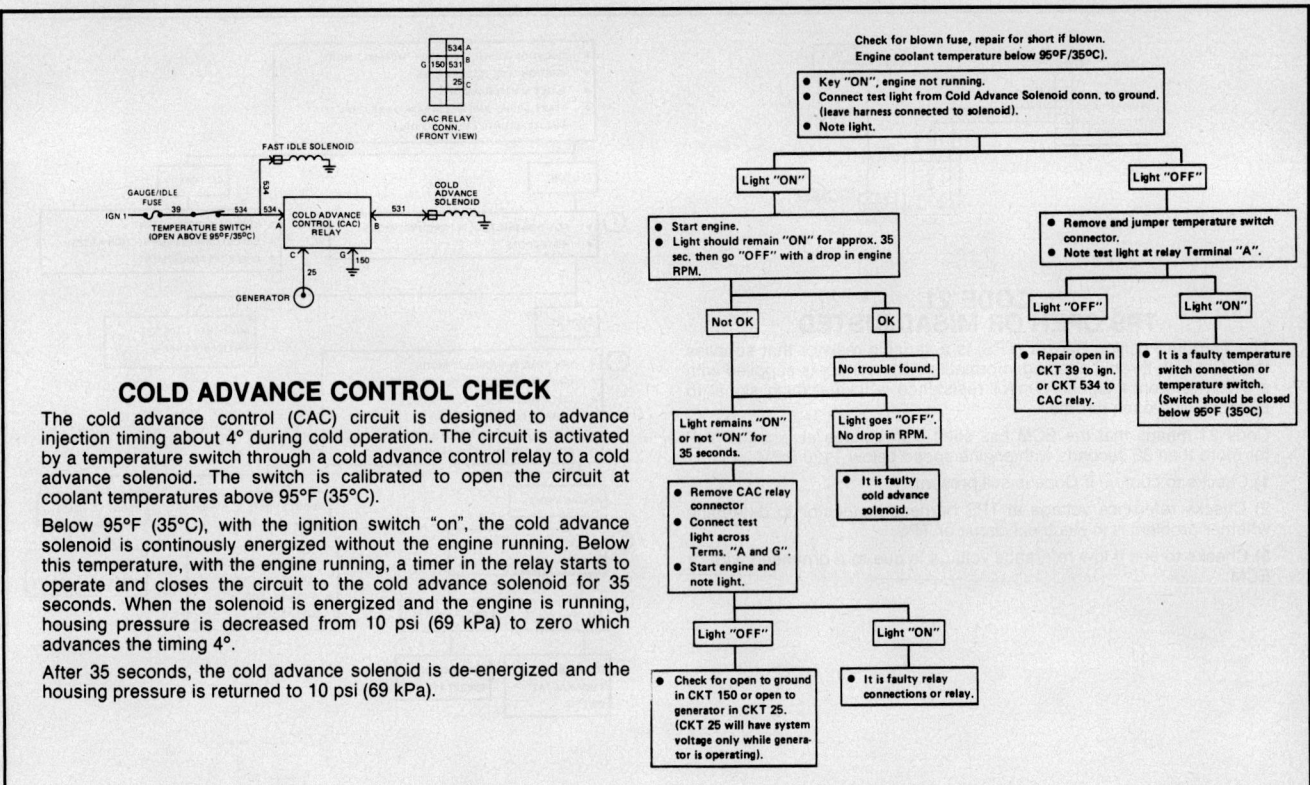

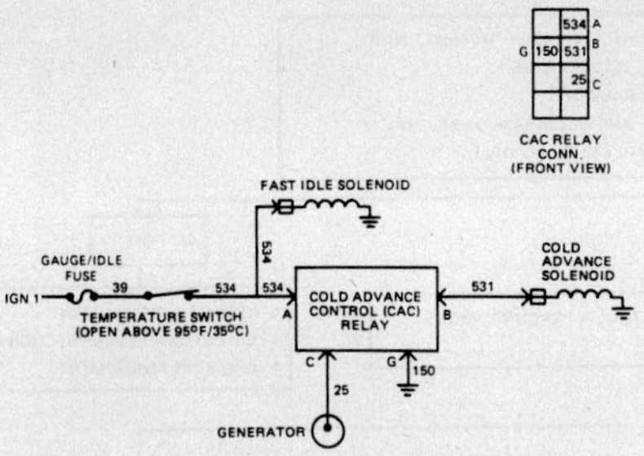

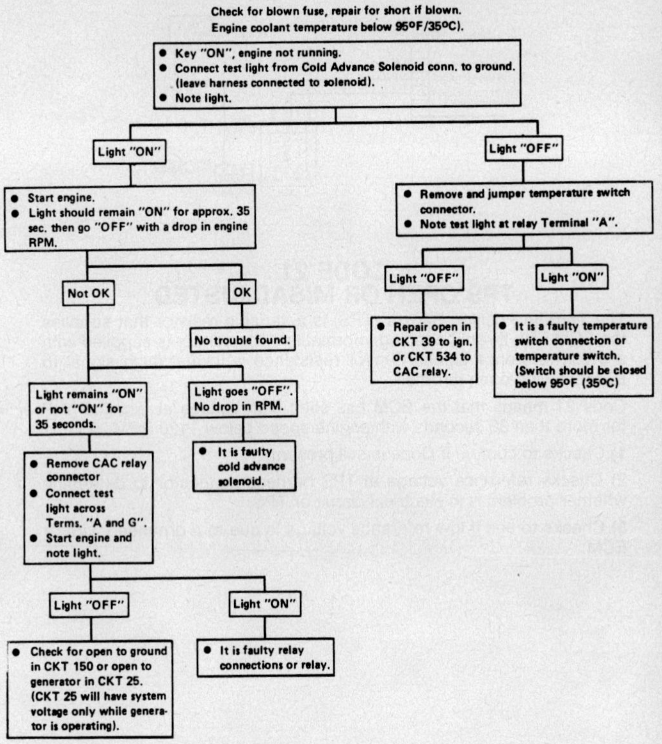

COLD ADVANCE CONTROL CHECK

The cold advance control (CAC) circuit is designed to advance injection timing about 4° during cold operation. The circuit is activated by a temperature switch through a cold advance control relay to a cold advance solenoid. The switch is calibrated to open the circuit at coolant temperatures above 95°F (35°C).

Below 95°F (35°C), with the ignition switch "on", the cold advance solenoid is continously energized without the engine running. Below this temperature, with the engine running, a timer in the relay starts to operate and closes the circuit to the cold advance solenoid for 35 seconds. When the solenoid is energized and the engine is running, housing pressure is decreased from 10 psi (69 kPa) to zero which advances the timing 4°.

After 35 seconds, the cold advance solenoid is de-energized and the housing pressure is returned to 10 psi (69 kPa).

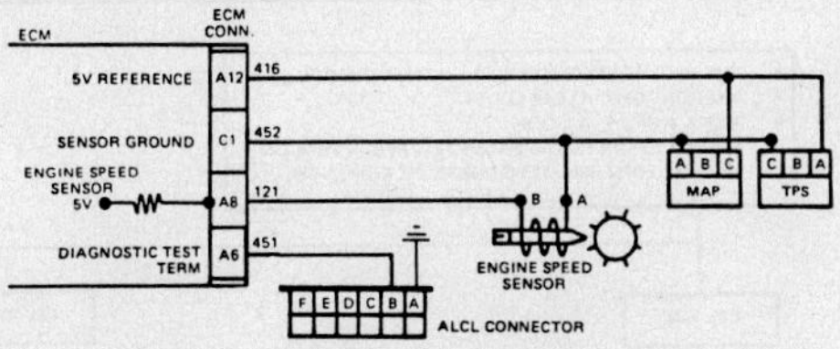

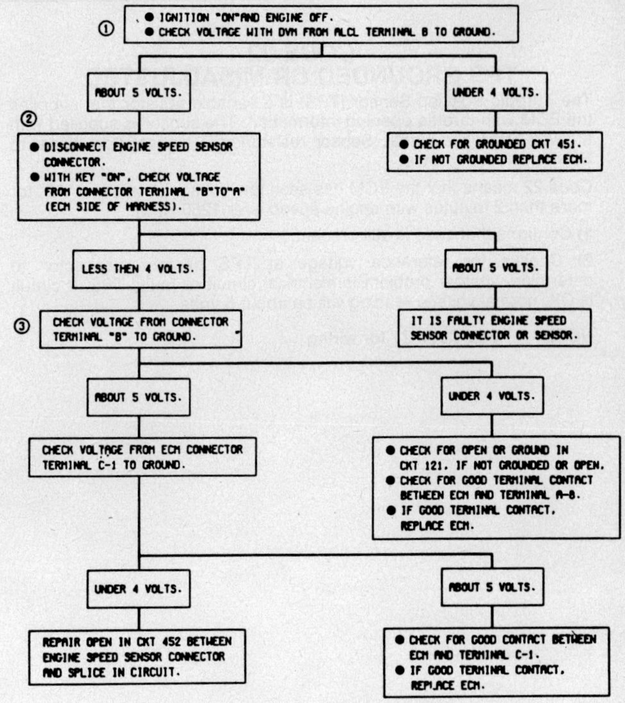

CODE 12
NO REFERENCE PULSE

Code 12 means ECM is on, but sees no reference pulse from Engine Speed Sensor (normal condition with ignition on and engine not running). Code 12 does not store, and will only flash when fault is present. With engine running, Code 12 could mean an open or ground in sensor reference circuit.

The sensor receives a 5-volt reference signal and pulses this signal back to the ECM 4 times per revolution. The ECM measures engine RPM by counting these pulses.

1) Checks for a good 5-volt reference signal.

2) Checks for proper ECM voltage to Engine Speed Sensor. If circuit to ECM is complete, normal voltage will be about 5 volts with harness disconnected from sensor.

3) Checks for good sensor ground circuit (452) to ECM. Indicates whether open indicated in step **2)** is in wire or at ECM.

GENERAL MOTORS DIESEL ELECTRONIC CONTROL SYSTEM (Cont.)

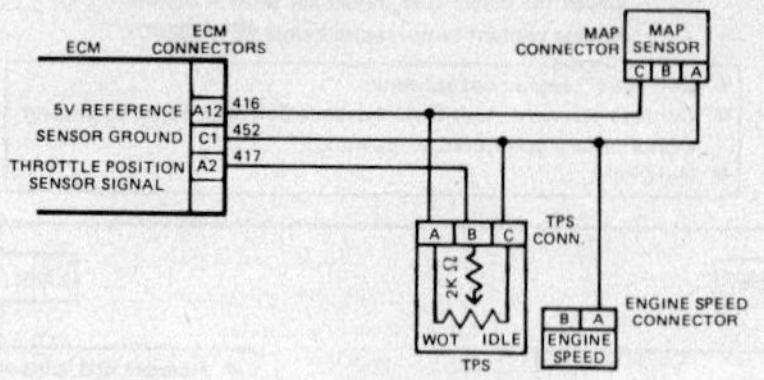

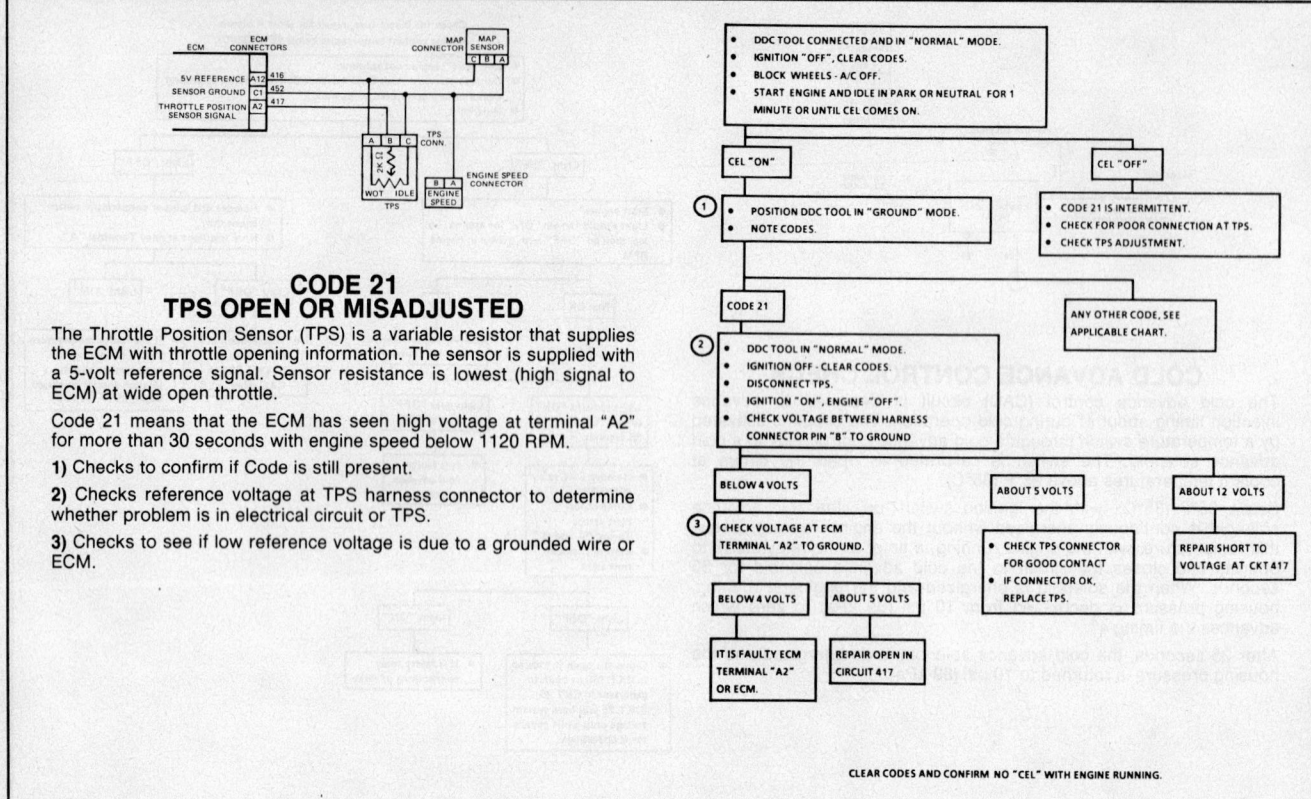

CODE 21
TPS OPEN OR MISADJUSTED

The Throttle Position Sensor (TPS) is a variable resistor that supplies the ECM with throttle opening information. The sensor is supplied with a 5-volt reference signal. Sensor resistance is lowest (high signal to ECM) at wide open throttle.

Code 21 means that the ECM has seen high voltage at terminal "A2" for more than 30 seconds with engine speed below 1120 RPM.

1) Checks to confirm if Code is still present.

2) Checks reference voltage at TPS harness connector to determine whether problem is in electrical circuit or TPS.

3) Checks to see if low reference voltage is due to a grounded wire or ECM.

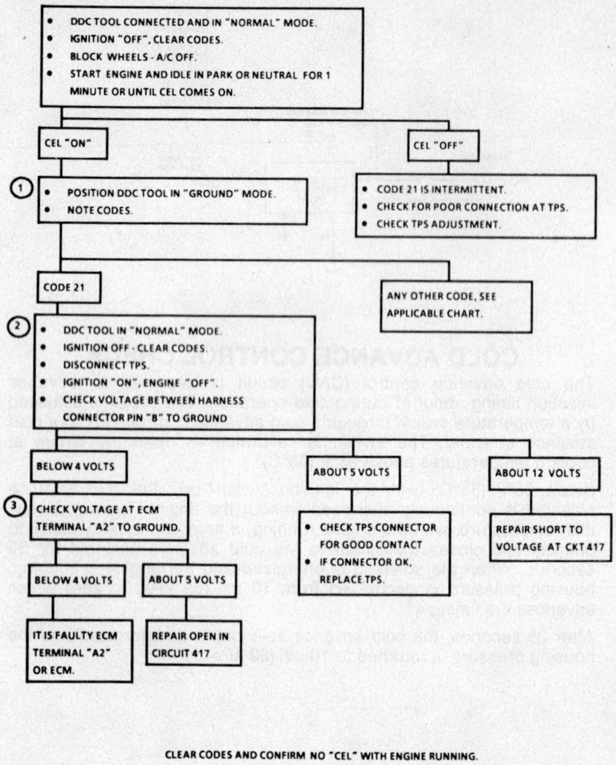

CODE 22
TPS GROUNDED OR MISADJUSTED

The Throttle Position Sensor (TPS) is a variable resistor that supplies the ECM with throttle opening information. The sensor is supplied with a 5-volt reference signal. Sensor resistance is highest (low signal to ECM) at closed throttle.

Code 22 means that the ECM has seen low voltage at terminal "A2" for more than 2 minutes with engine speed over 1250 RPM.

1) Confirms that code is still present.

2) Checks for reference voltage at TPS harness connector to determine whether problem is electrical circuit or faulty TPS. If circuit is OK, normal voltage reading will be about 5 volts.

NOTE: **See Code 21 for wiring.**

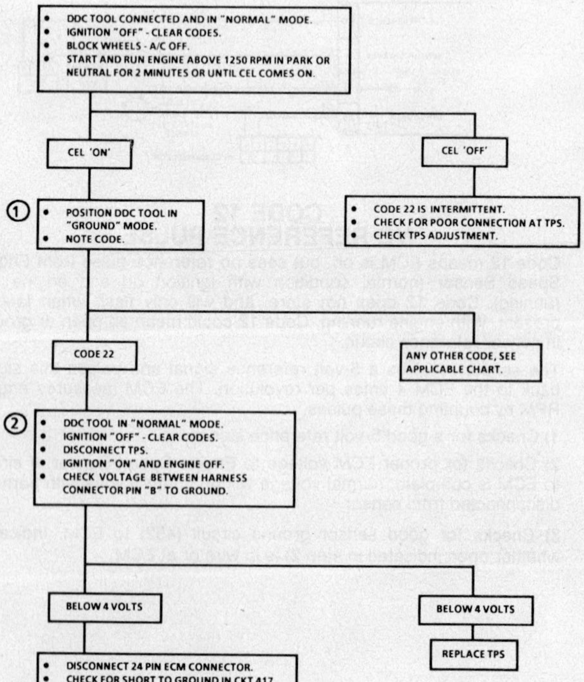

GENERAL MOTORS DIESEL ELECTRONIC CONTROL SYSTEM (Cont.)

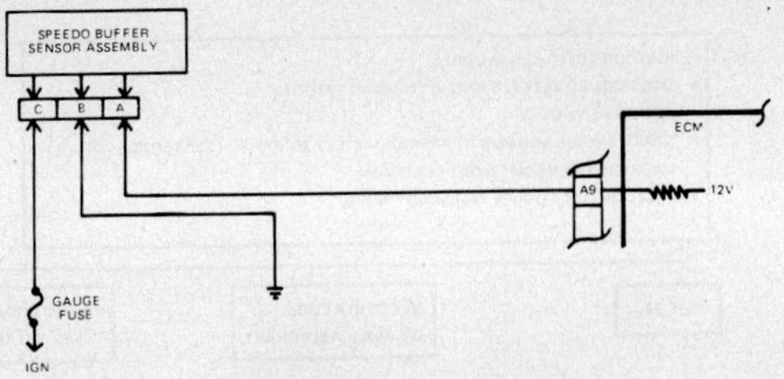

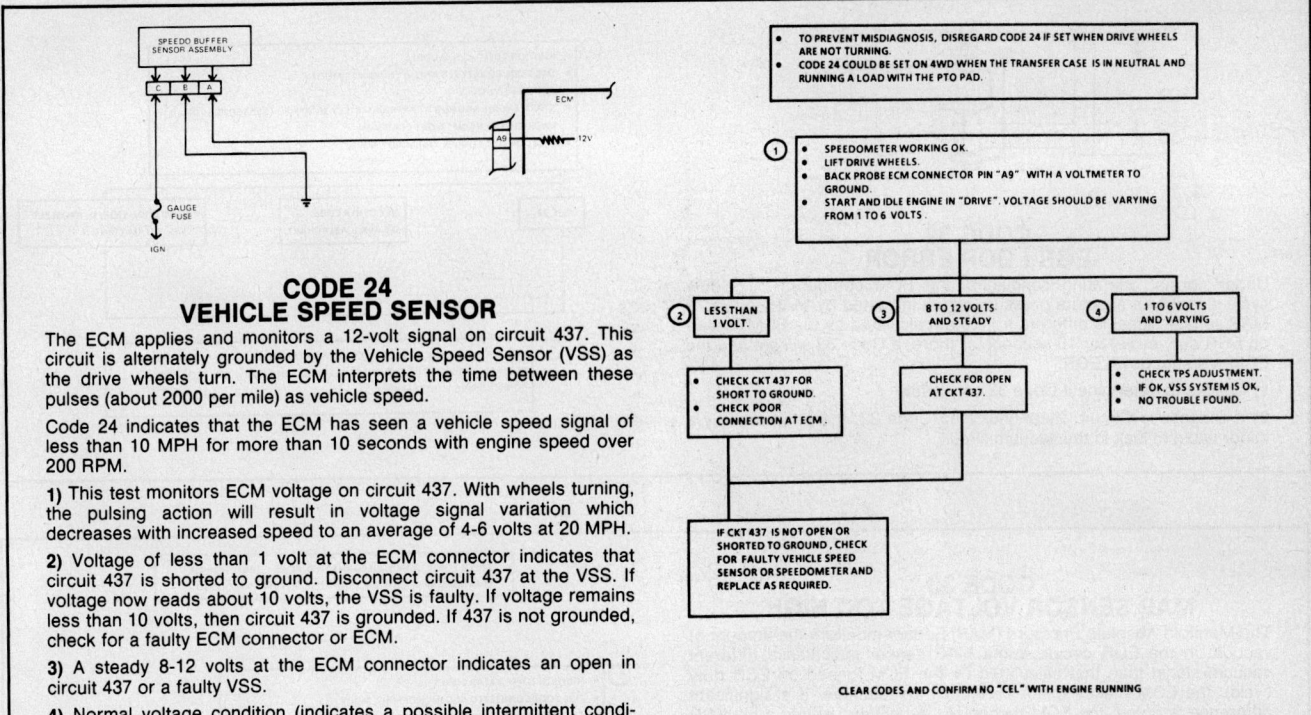

CODE 24
VEHICLE SPEED SENSOR

The ECM applies and monitors a 12-volt signal on circuit 437. This circuit is alternately grounded by the Vehicle Speed Sensor (VSS) as the drive wheels turn. The ECM interprets the time between these pulses (about 2000 per mile) as vehicle speed.

Code 24 indicates that the ECM has seen a vehicle speed signal of less than 10 MPH for more than 10 seconds with engine speed over 200 RPM.

1) This test monitors ECM voltage on circuit 437. With wheels turning, the pulsing action will result in voltage signal variation which decreases with increased speed to an average of 4-6 volts at 20 MPH.

2) Voltage of less than 1 volt at the ECM connector indicates that circuit 437 is shorted to ground. Disconnect circuit 437 at the VSS. If voltage now reads about 10 volts, the VSS is faulty. If voltage remains less than 10 volts, then circuit 437 is grounded. If 437 is not grounded, check for a faulty ECM connector or ECM.

3) A steady 8-12 volts at the ECM connector indicates an open in circuit 437 or a faulty VSS.

4) Normal voltage condition (indicates a possible intermittent condition).

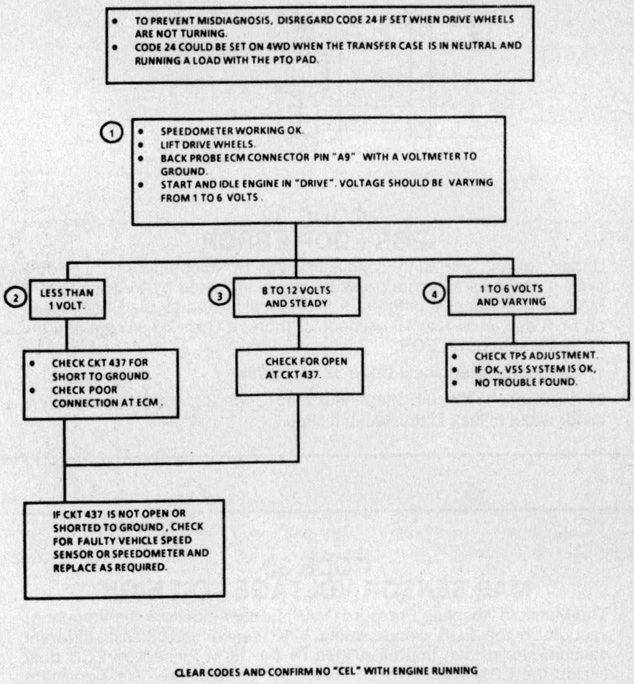

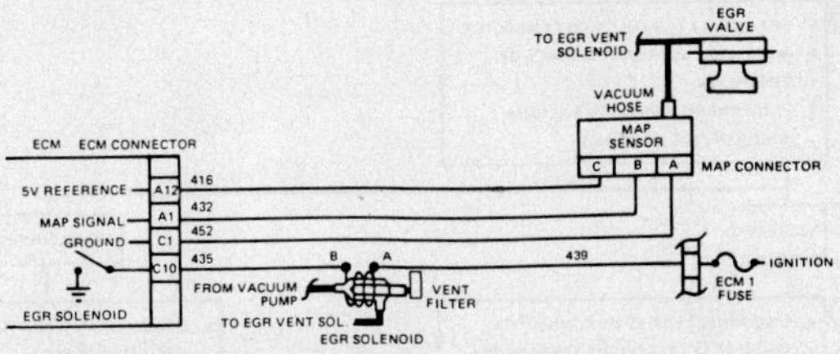

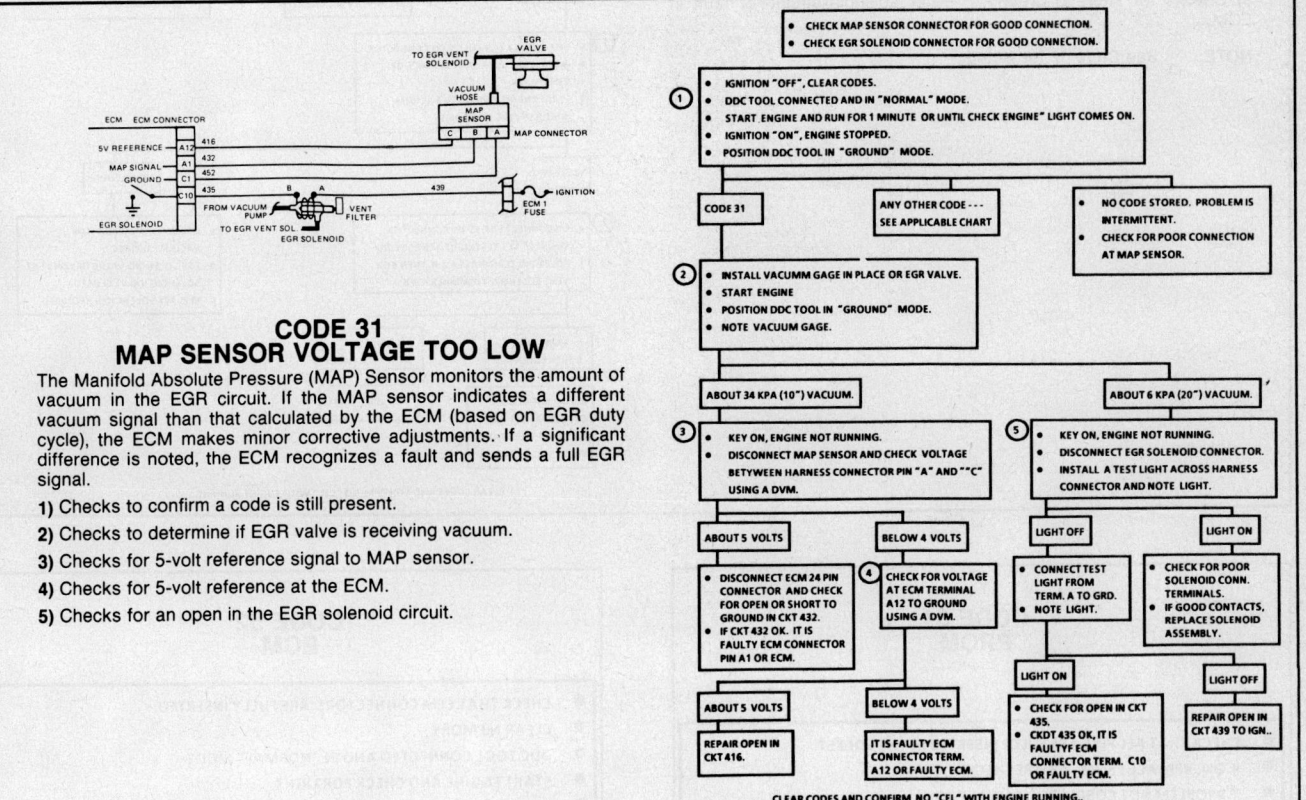

CODE 31
MAP SENSOR VOLTAGE TOO LOW

The Manifold Absolute Pressure (MAP) Sensor monitors the amount of vacuum in the EGR circuit. If the MAP sensor indicates a different vacuum signal than that calculated by the ECM (based on EGR duty cycle), the ECM makes minor corrective adjustments. If a significant difference is noted, the ECM recognizes a fault and sends a full EGR signal.

1) Checks to confirm a code is still present.

2) Checks to determine if EGR valve is receiving vacuum.

3) Checks for 5-volt reference signal to MAP sensor.

4) Checks for 5-volt reference at the ECM.

5) Checks for an open in the EGR solenoid circuit.

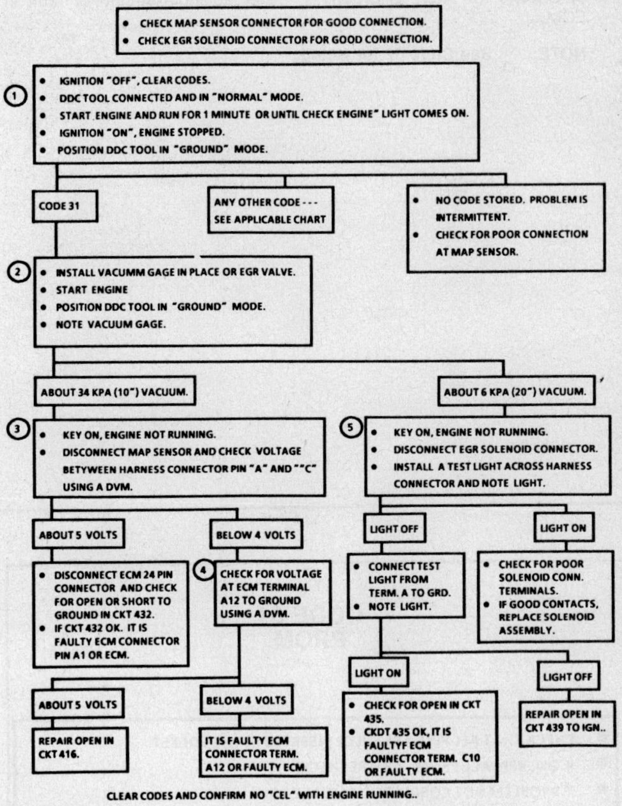

GENERAL MOTORS DIESEL ELECTRONIC CONTROL SYSTEM (Cont.)

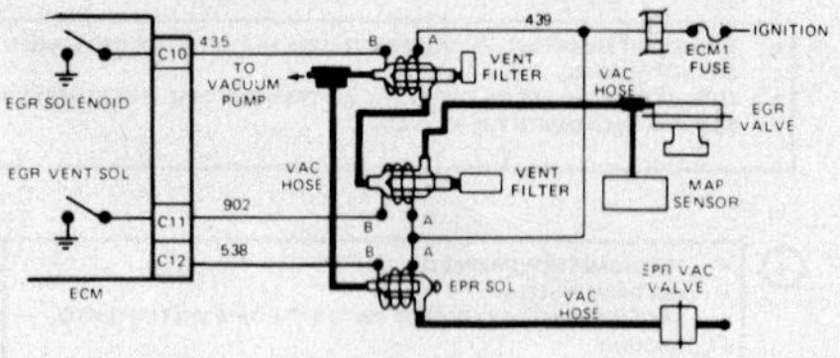

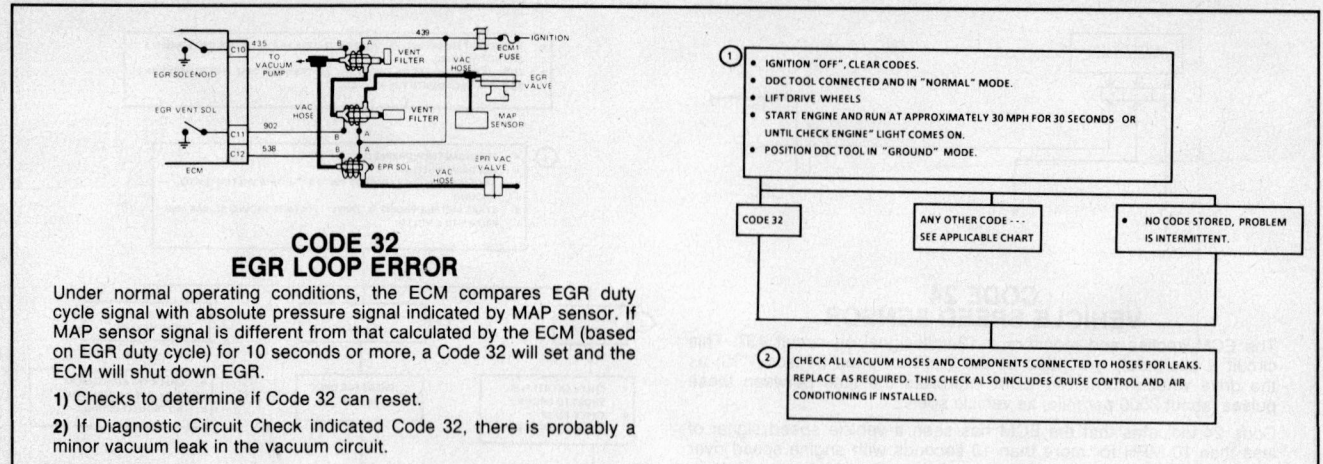

CODE 32
EGR LOOP ERROR

Under normal operating conditions, the ECM compares EGR duty cycle signal with absolute pressure signal indicated by MAP sensor. If MAP sensor signal is different from that calculated by the ECM (based on EGR duty cycle) for 10 seconds or more, a Code 32 will set and the ECM will shut down EGR.

1) Checks to determine if Code 32 can reset.

2) If Diagnostic Circuit Check indicated Code 32, there is probably a minor vacuum leak in the vacuum circuit.

(1)
- IGNITION "OFF", CLEAR CODES.
- DDC TOOL CONNECTED AND IN "NORMAL" MODE.
- LIFT DRIVE WHEELS
- START ENGINE AND RUN AT APPROXIMATELY 30 MPH FOR 30 SECONDS OR UNTIL CHECK ENGINE" LIGHT COMES ON.
- POSITION DDC TOOL IN "GROUND" MODE.

CODE 32

ANY OTHER CODE - - - SEE APPLICABLE CHART

- NO CODE STORED, PROBLEM IS INTERMITTENT.

(2) CHECK ALL VACUUM HOSES AND COMPONENTS CONNECTED TO HOSES FOR LEAKS. REPLACE AS REQUIRED. THIS CHECK ALSO INCLUDES CRUISE CONTROL AND AIR CONDITIONING IF INSTALLED.

CODE 33
MAP SENSOR VOLTAGE TOO HIGH

The Manifold Absolute Pressure (MAP) Sensor monitors the amount of vacuum in the EGR circuit. If the MAP sensor indicates a different vacuum signal than that calculated by the ECM (based on EGR duty cycle), the ECM makes minor corrective adjustments. If a significant difference is noted, the ECM recognizes a fault and sends a full EGR signal.

1) Checks to confirm a code is still present.

2) Checks to determine if solenoid is stuck closed.

3) Checks for short to ground in either solenoid circuit, or fault in ECM.

NOTE: See Code 32 for wiring.

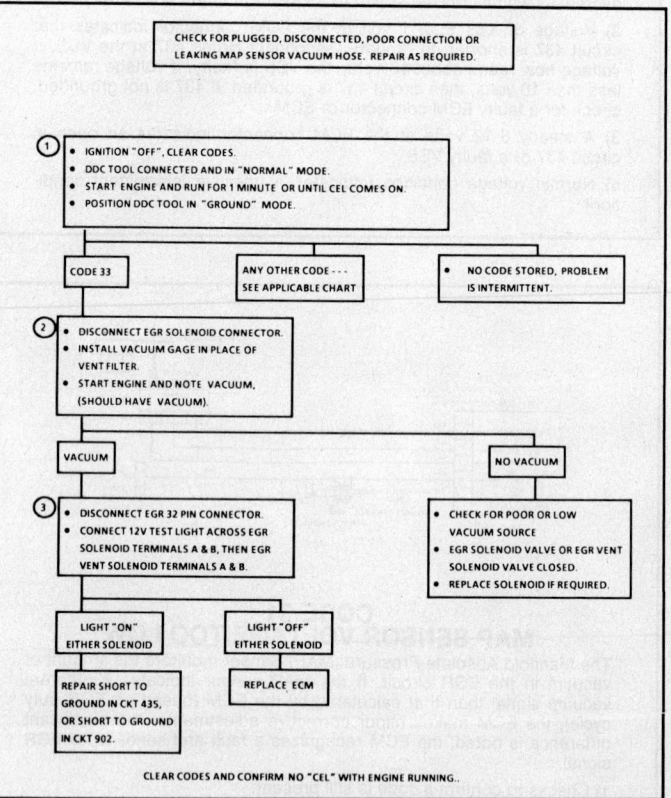

CHECK FOR PLUGGED, DISCONNECTED, POOR CONNECTION OR LEAKING MAP SENSOR VACUUM HOSE. REPAIR AS REQUIRED.

(1)
- IGNITION "OFF", CLEAR CODES.
- DDC TOOL CONNECTED AND IN "NORMAL" MODE.
- START ENGINE AND RUN FOR 1 MINUTE OR UNTIL CEL COMES ON.
- POSITION DDC TOOL IN "GROUND" MODE.

CODE 33

ANY OTHER CODE - - - SEE APPLICABLE CHART

- NO CODE STORED, PROBLEM IS INTERMITTENT.

(2)
- DISCONNECT EGR SOLENOID CONNECTOR.
- INSTALL VACUUM GAGE IN PLACE OF VENT FILTER.
- START ENGINE AND NOTE VACUUM, (SHOULD HAVE VACUUM).

VACUUM

NO VACUUM

- CHECK FOR POOR OR LOW VACUUM SOURCE
- EGR SOLENOID VALVE OR EGR VENT SOLENOID VALVE CLOSED.
- REPLACE SOLENOID IF REQUIRED.

(3)
- DISCONNECT EGR 32 PIN CONNECTOR.
- CONNECT 12V TEST LIGHT ACROSS EGR SOLENOID TERMINALS A & B, THEN EGR VENT SOLENOID TERMINALS A & B.

LIGHT "ON" EITHER SOLENOID

REPAIR SHORT TO GROUND IN CKT 435, OR SHORT TO GROUND IN CKT 902.

LIGHT "OFF" EITHER SOLENOID

REPLACE ECM

CLEAR CODES AND CONFIRM NO "CEL" WITH ENGINE RUNNING.

CODE 51
PROM

- CHECK THAT ALL PINS ARE FULLY INSERTED IN THE SOCKET.
- IF OK, REPLACE PROM, AND RECHECK.
- IF PROBLEM NOT CORRECTED, REPLACE ECM.

CODE 52
ECM

- CHECK THAT ECM CONNECTORS ARE FULLY INSERTED.
- CLEAR MEMORY
- DDC TOOL CONNECTED AND IN "NORMAL" MODE.
- START ENGINE AND CHECK FOR LIGHT.
- IF LIGHT REAPPEARS AND DDC TOOL INDICATES CODE 52, REPLACE ECM.
- CLEAR MEMORY AFTER REPAIR TO CONFIRM NO "CEL".

GENERAL MOTORS DIESEL ELECTRONIC CONTROL SYSTEM (Cont.)

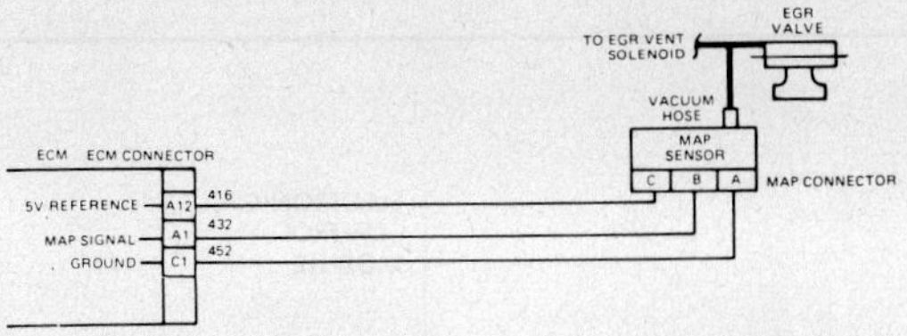

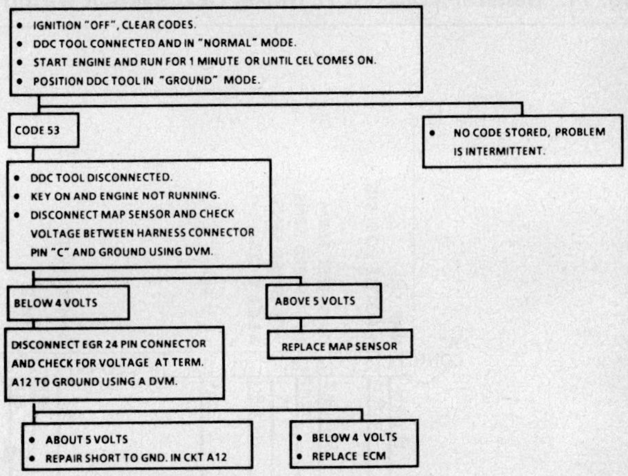

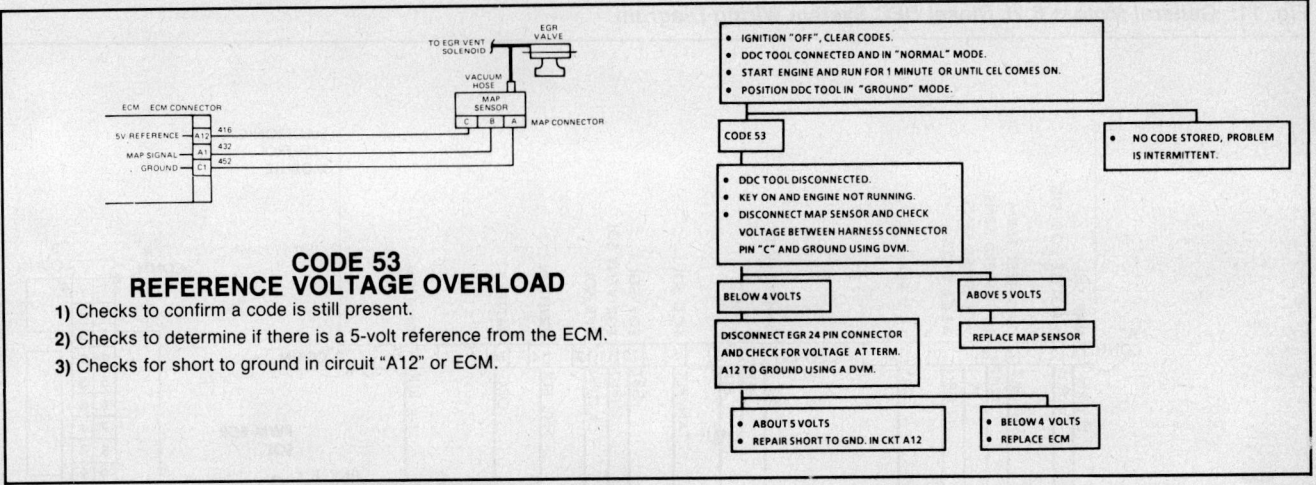

CODE 53
REFERENCE VOLTAGE OVERLOAD

1) Checks to confirm a code is still present.
2) Checks to determine if there is a 5-volt reference from the ECM.
3) Checks for short to ground in circuit "A12" or ECM.

Fig. 10: General Motors 6.2L Diesel ECM Terminal Identification

NOTE:
This ECM voltage chart is for use with a digital voltmeter to further aid in diagnosis. The voltages you get may vary due to low battery charge or other reasons, but they should be very close.

- Engine at operating temperature.
- Batteries fully charged and glow plugs not cycling.
- Test Terminal NOT grounded.
- ALCL Tool not installed.

* If less than 1 volt, rotate drive wheels to verify.

VOLTAGE KEY "ON"	VOLTAGE ENG. RUN	CRT. NO.	CIRCUIT	PIN	WIRE COLOR
4.76	1.0	432	MAP SIGNAL	A1	LT GRN
.85	.85	417	TPS SIGNAL	A2	DK BLU
			NOT USED	A3	
			NOT USED	A4	
			NOT USED	A5	
5.0	5.0	451	DIAGNOSTIC TEST TERMINAL	A6	WHT/BLK
			NOT USED	A7	
.01	.02	121	ENGINE SPEED SENSOR	A8	WHT
10.72*	12.32*	437	VEHICLE SPEED SENSOR	A9	BRN
5.73	.03	488	ALCL DATA	A10	LT GRN
			NOT USED	A11	
5.0	5.0	416	5V REFERENCE	A12	GRAY

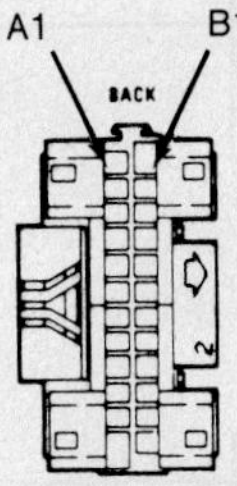

24 Pin A-B Connector

WIRE COLOR	PIN	CIRCUIT	VOLTAGE KEY "ON"	VOLTAGE ENG. RUN	CRT. NO.
	B1	NOT USED			
	B2	NOT USED			
	B3	NOT USED			
	B4	NOT USED			
	B5	NOT USED			
	B6	NOT USED			
	B7	NOT USED			
	B8	NOT USED			
	B9	NOT USED			
	B10	NOT USED			
	B11	NOT USED			
	B12	NOT USED			

0	0	452	SENSOR GROUND	C1	BLK/WHT
0	0	150	GROUND	C2	BLK
0	0	150	GROUND	C3	BLK
			NOT USED	C4	
12	14	422	TCC SOLENOID	C5	TAN/BLK
			NOT USED	C6	
			NOT USED	C7	
			NOT USED	C8	
			NOT USED	C9	
.94	14.47	435	EGR SOLENOID	C10	GRAY
.84	14.47	902	EGR VENT SOLENOID	C11	DK GRN
12.40	.87	538	EPR SOLENOID	C12	BRN
			NOT USED	C13	
12.40	14.52	439	IGN.–ECM FUSE	C14	PNK/BLK
			NOT USED	C15	
12.35	14.32	440	BATT. 12 VOLTS	C16	ORG

Back View Back of Connector

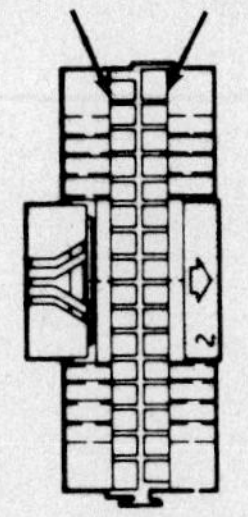

32 Pin A-B Connector

	D1	NOT USED			
	D2	NOT USED			
	D3	NOT USED			
	D4	NOT USED			
	D5	NOT USED			
	D6	NOT USED			
	D7	NOT USED			
	D8	NOT USED			
	D9	NOT USED			
	D10	NOT USED			
	D11	NOT USED			
	D12	NOT USED			
	D13	NOT USED			
PNK/BLK	D14	IGN.–ECM FUSE	12.40	14.32	439
	D15	NOT USED			
	D16	NOT USED			

GENERAL MOTORS DIESEL ELECTRONIC CONTROL SYSTEM (Cont.)

Fig. 11: General Motors 6.2L Diesel DEC System Wiring Diagram

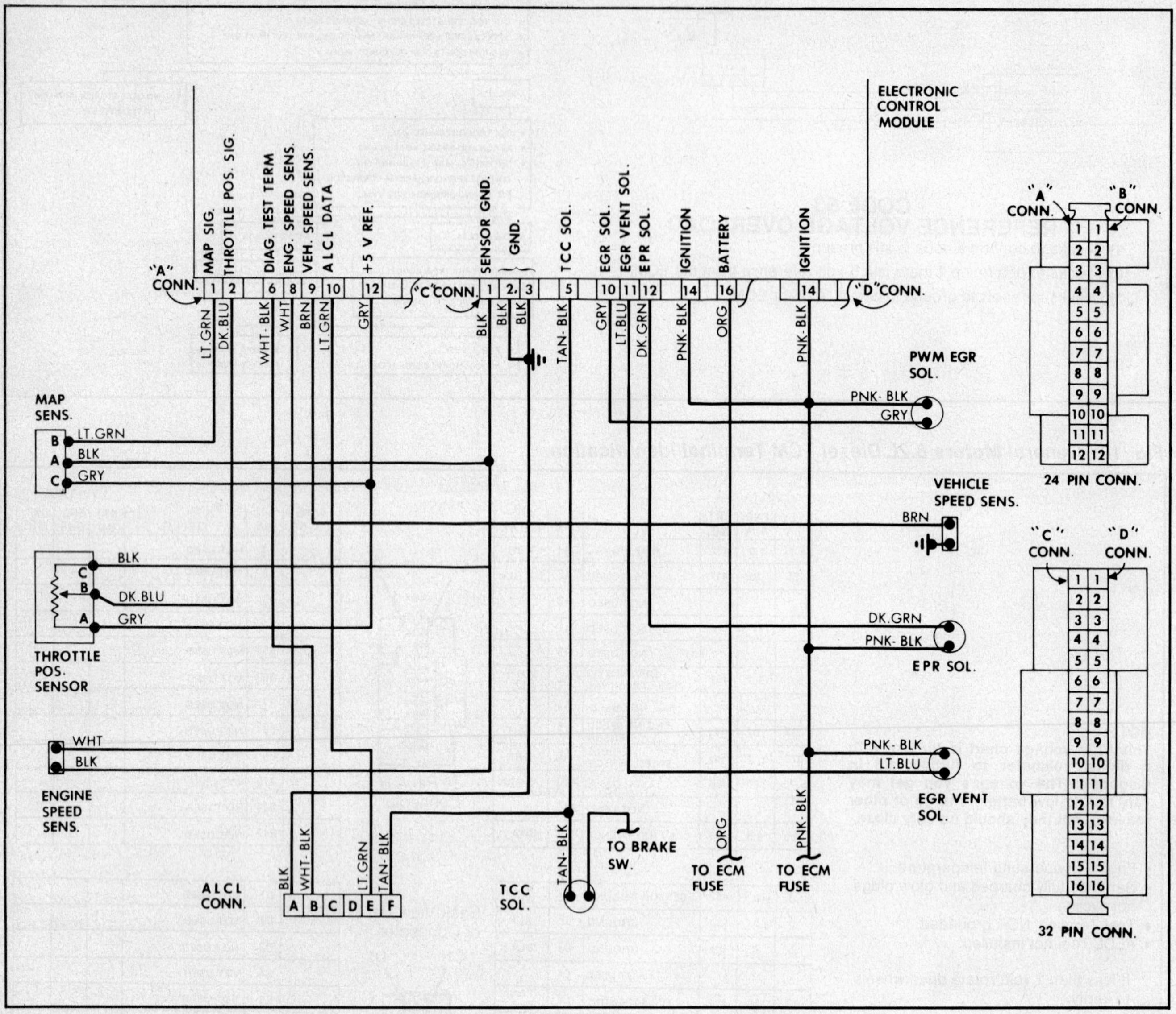

JEEP COMPUTERIZED EMISSION CONTROL 4-CYLINDER & 6-CYLINDER

Cherokee, CJ7, Calif. Grand Wagoneer, Calif. J10 & J20, Scrambler & Wagoneer

DESCRIPTION

The Computerized Emission Control (CEC) system is used on all 4 & 6-cylinder engines. It is an electronically controlled system that manages the air/fuel ratio and controls ignition timing, idle speed, and the pulse air injection system.

The primary objective of the CEC system is to maintain an ideal air/fuel ratio of 14.7:1 under all operating conditions. When the ideal air/fuel ratio is maintained, the catalytic converter can effectively control CO, HC and NOx emissions.

OPERATION

The CEC system consists of several sub-systems: fuel control, Microcomputer Control Unit (MCU), data sensors, catalytic converter, idle speed control, and pulse air injection.

FUEL CONTROL

All models are equipped with a feedback carburetor which contains an electro-mechanically operated mixture control (M/C) solenoid (4-cyl.), or a stepper motor (6-cyl.).

The M/C solenoid (4-cyl.) provides the proper air/fuel ratio by controlling the amount of air allowed to mix with the fuel. During open loop operation, air supplied by M/C solenoid is preprogrammed by MCU. During closed loop operation, M/C solenoid depends on MCU data sensor operating conditions.

The stepper motor (6-cyl.) controls metering pins which vary the size of idle and main air bleed orifices in carburetor body. The stepper motor moves the pins in and out of the orifices in steps, in response to signals received from MCU. The motor has a range of 100 steps, but normally operates in the middle of its range.

When the metering pins are stepped into the orifices, the air/fuel mixture becomes richer. When the pins are stepped out of the orifices, the mixture becomes leaner.

MICROCOMPUTER CONTROL UNIT

The MCU is located in passenger compartment, behind right kick panel. The MCU monitors the CEC system data sensors and, based upon the mode of engine operation, generates an output control signal for the M/C solenoid (4-cyl.) or stepper motor (6-cyl.) mounted in carburetor. The MCU controls the following 2 modes of operation:

Open Loop

In this mode, the MCU determines the air/fuel ratio based upon engine operation, rather than oxygen sensor input signals. The mixture control solenoid (4-cyl.) or stepper motor (6-cyl.) is controlled by MCU to provide preprogrammed amount of air for correct air/fuel mixture.

Closed Loop

When all input data and engine operation meet programmed criteria, the CEC system goes into closed loop operation. In this mode, oxygen sensor input signals are accepted by MCU to determine proper air/fuel mixture based upon oxygen content of exhaust gases.

The MCU may also receive signals from knock sensor and adjust ignition timing accordingly. Air injection is routed "downstream" or both "upstream" and "downstream" for various throttle positions.

Closed loop operation is characterized by constant movement of the M/C solenoid plunger (4-cyl.) or metering pins (6-cyl.). The MCU is constantly making small corrections in air/fuel ratio in an attempt to create the ideal air/fuel ratio.

DATA SENSORS

Oxygen Sensor

The oxygen sensor is located in the exhaust manifold to measure oxygen content of exhaust gases. As more oxygen is detected (lean mixture indication), the electrical signal generated by the sensor drops in voltage. A lower oxygen content (rich mixture indication) causes an increase in voltage signal output.

Thermal Electric Switch (TES)

This switch is attached inside the air cleaner. It provides either a ground circuit for the MCU to indicate cold weather engine start-up (below 50°F/10°C), or an open circuit to indicate normal start-up air temperature (above 65°F/18°C).

Coolant Temperature Switch

This switch is located at rear of intake manifold. This switch is controlled by coolant temperature, and is normally open in a cold engine. When closed, the switch indicates engine temperature is greater than 135°F (57°C).

4 in. Hg Vacuum Switch

This switch is mounted on a bracket attached to center of firewall (Natural color). The switch is controlled by carburetor ported vacuum and has a normally open electrical switch when vacuum level is below 4 in. Hg. When vacuum level exceeds 4 in. Hg, the electrical switch closes. This indicates to MCU that either a closed or wide open throttle condition exists.

10 in. Hg Vacuum Switch

This switch is mounted on same bracket as the 4 in. Hg switch and is Green in color. The 10 in. Hg switch is a manifold vacuum operated switch that, when open, signals the MCU that a partial throttle (below wide open) condition exists. This switch is normally closed.

Wide Open Throttle (WOT) Switch

This mechanically operated electrical switch is located on carburetor and is controlled by throttle position. This switch is normally open and, when closed, indicates a wide open throttle condition.

Closed Throttle Switch (4-Cyl. Only)

This is an electrical switch attached to the vacuum actuator portion of the sole-vac throttle positioner. When the throttle is closed, the switch indicates this closed position to the MCU.

Knock Sensor

This sensor is a tuned piezoelectric crystal transducer located in the cylinder head. Vibrations from engine knock cause the crystal inside the sensor to vibrate and produce an electrical signal. The MCU can retard the ignition timing of one cylinder or multiple cylinders to eliminate the knock condition.

Distributor Voltage

This voltage signal is supplied to the MCU from the tach terminal on the distributor. The MCU advances or retards ignition timing as required for

JEEP COMPUTERIZED EMISSION CONTROL 4-CYLINDER & 6-CYLINDER (Cont.)

optimum engine operation. This information is sent to the control unit of the ignition system to create a spark.

Altitude Jumper Wire

NOTE: Any Jeep model with altitude modification performed "Must" have an Emission Control Information Update label installed. Contact dealer for more information pertaining to the emission laws for your area.

For vehicles operated above 4000 feet, this wire must be grounded. On 4-cylinder models, the wire connector is located next to the MCU. To ground the connector, a jumper wire must be installed. *See Fig. 1.*

On 6-cylinder models, the altitude jumper wire is taped to the CEC system wiring harness in the engine compartment. To ground the jumper wire, remove the tape and extend the wire to the engine ground screw located next to the ignition coil. Remove the screw and connect wire terminal.

Fig. 1: Altitude Jumper Wire (4-Cyl.)

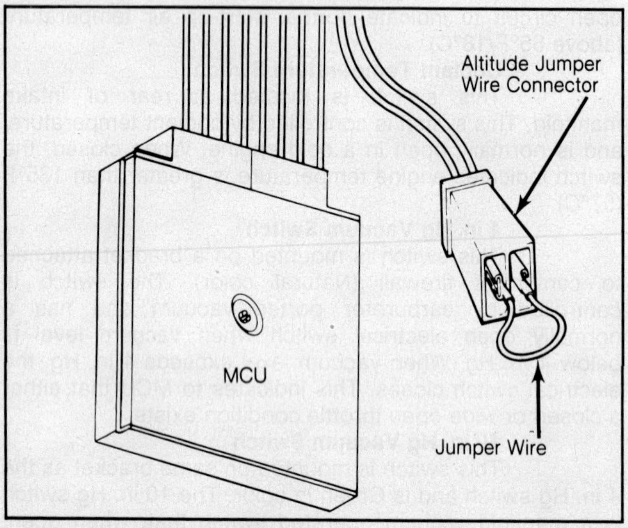

Jumper wire must be installed as shown for vehicles operated above 4000 feet.

Positive Crankcase Ventilation (PCV) Valve Shut-Off Solenoid

The PCV valve solenoid is installed in the PCV hose. The MCU turns off crankcase ventilation when engine is idling. The solenoid is also closed momentarily when the igntion key is turned off to prevent air from entering below the throttle plates. This prevents engine dieseling.

An anti-diesel relay system is also used to help prevent engine dieseling on 4-cylinder models only. The system consists of an anti-diesel relay and anti-diesel delay relay.

CATALYTIC CONVERTER

All models use a dual bed monolithic-type converter with "downstream" air injection. The injection of air between the 2 beds allows more complete oxidation of HC and CO in the closed loop mode. In order for this converter to be effective, precise control of the oxygen content of exhaust gases entering the converter is necessary; thus, the need for the oxygen sensor, MCU and feedback carburetor.

IDLE SPEED CONTROL

The idle speed control system is operated by vacuum signals and the MCU. The idle speed system raises and/or maintains the engine idle whenever high loads are present. The idle speed control system consists of an idle relay, idle solenoid and sole-vac throttle positioner. The throttle positioner consists of throttle switch (4-cyl.), holding solenoid (maintains throttle position), and vacuum actuator (increases idle speed).

When accessories (A/C, rear window defogger, etc.) are activated, the MCU energizes the idle relay by providing a ground circuit. The idle relay activates the idle solenoid (Red wires), located on same bracket as air injection solenoids. When the idle solenoid is activated, vacuum is applied to vacuum actuator to increase engine speed.

PULSE AIR INJECTION

The pulse air injection system is switched from "upstream" to "downstream" injection (or both) by the MCU. Two electrically operated vacuum solenoid valves, 1 for "upstream" and 1 for "downstream", supply operating vacuum to the air injection valves. The solenoid valves are located on a bracket on the left fender panel (4-cyl.) or on top of cylinder head cover (6-cyl.).

TESTING

TESTING PROCEDURE

1) An electronic fuel feedback tester (ET 501) is available to aid in system diagnosis. If tester is not available, test No. 1 should be performed first, then tests No. 3, 4, 6, 8A, 8B and 9. These series of tests will provide a thorough system diagnosis.

Fig. 2: Diagnostic Connector Pin Locations

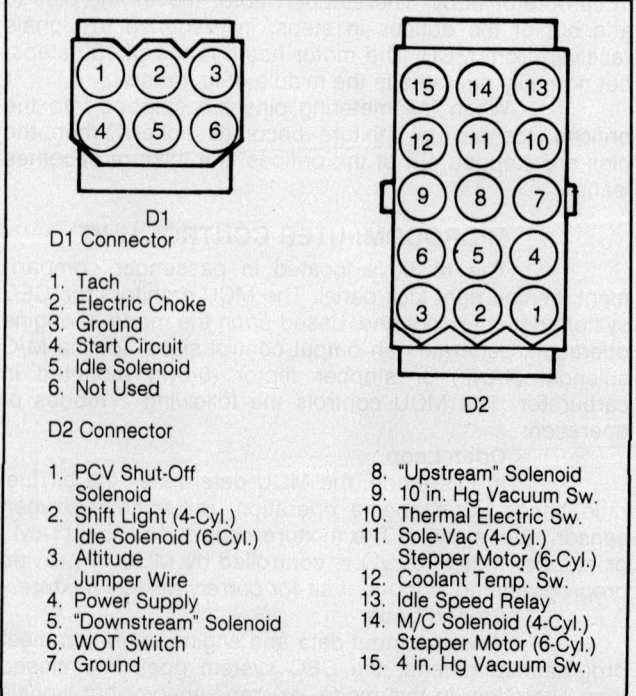

D1 Connector

1. Tach
2. Electric Choke
3. Ground
4. Start Circuit
5. Idle Solenoid
6. Not Used

D2 Connector

1. PCV Shut-Off Solenoid
2. Shift Light (4-Cyl.) Idle Solenoid (6-Cyl.)
3. Altitude Jumper Wire
4. Power Supply
5. "Downstream" Solenoid
6. WOT Switch
7. Ground
8. "Upstream" Solenoid
9. 10 in. Hg Vacuum Sw.
10. Thermal Electric Sw.
11. Sole-Vac (4-Cyl.) Stepper Motor (6-Cyl.)
12. Coolant Temp. Sw.
13. Idle Speed Relay
14. M/C Solenoid (4-Cyl.) Stepper Motor (6-Cyl.)
15. 4 in. Hg Vacuum Sw.

These diagnostic connectors are used on both 4-cylinder and 6-cylinder engines.

JEEP COMPUTERIZED EMISSION CONTROL 4-CYLINDER & 6-CYLINDER (Cont.)

2) The steps listed in the charts will provide a systematic evaluation of each component that could cause a malfunction. After completing a repair, repeat the test to ensure that the malfunction has been corrected.

3) Before performing any of the tests, make sure that the following related systems are operating properly:

- Basic carburetor adjustments.
- Mechanical engine operation (plugs, valves, rings).
- Ignition system.
- Intake manifold, carburetor or base plate gaskets.
- Loose vacuum hoses or fittings.

TEST EQUIPMENT

1) The equipment required for testing includes: tachometer, hand vacuum pump, digital volt-ohmmeter (minimum 10 megohm impedance), dwell meter (4-cyl.), and jumper wires.

2) Before beginning any of the tests for the 6-cylinder model, a clear air cleaner cover must be fabricated from plastic at least .25" thick. This is secured with air cleaner wing nut after top of air cleaner has been removed to observe operation and position of metering pins. *See Fig. 3.*

NOTE: The metering pins operate in tandem. Only the upper pin is visible.

Fig. 3: Air Cleaner Cover Dimensions (6-Cyl.)

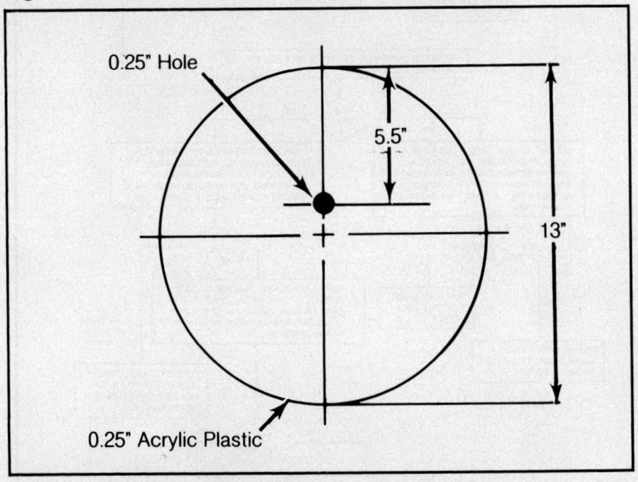

Fabricate cover to allow observation of metering pins.

SYSTEM TEST CHARTS (4-CYL.)

Chart No.	Test
No. 1	Operational Test.
No. 2	Switch Test.
No. 3	Closed Loop Test.
No. 4	Knock Test.
No. 5	Oxygen Sensor and Closed Loop Test.
No. 6	"Downstream" Solenoid Test.
No. 7	"Upstream" Solenoid Test.
No. 8A	Bowl Vent Test.
No. 8B	PCV Shut-Off Test.
No. 8C	Anti-Diesel System Test.
No. 9	Idle Speed Control System Test.
No. 10	Sole-Vac Vacuum Switching Relay Test.
No. 11	Basic Engine Test.

TEST NO. 1 OPERATIONAL TEST

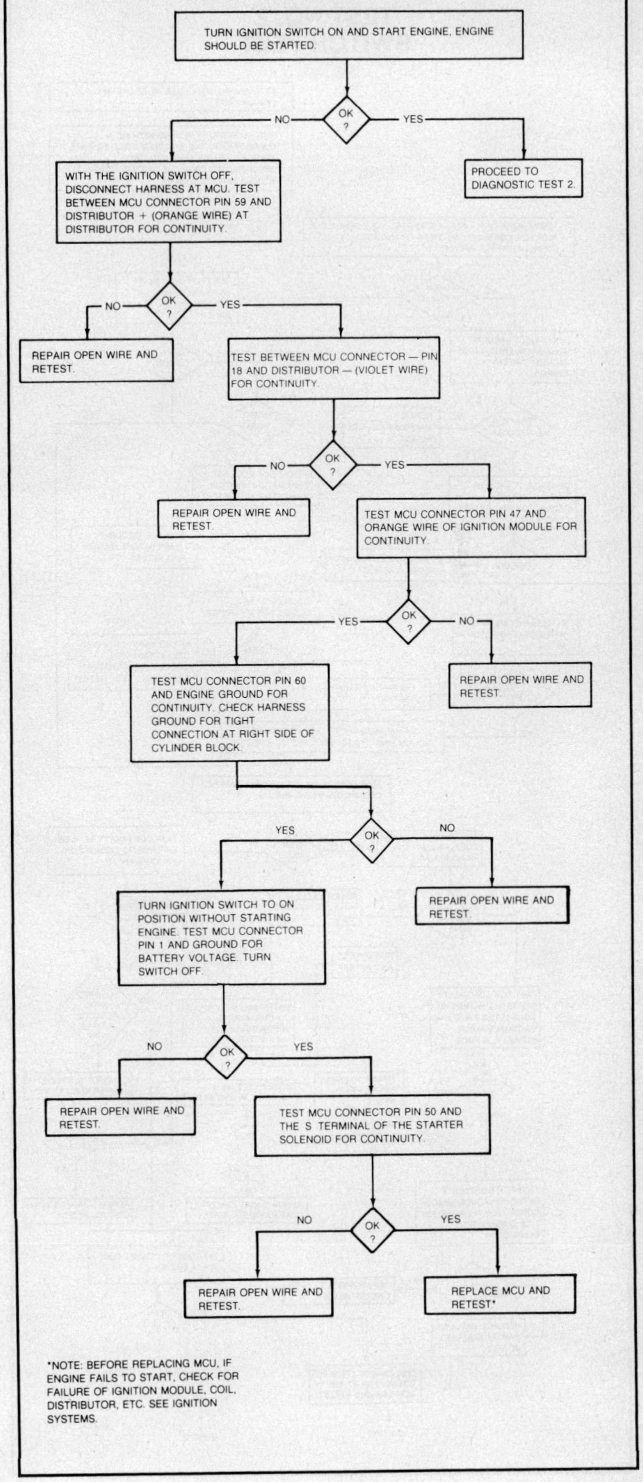

JEEP COMPUTERIZED EMISSION CONTROL 4-CYLINDER & 6-CYLINDER (Cont.)

TEST NO. 2 SWITCH TEST

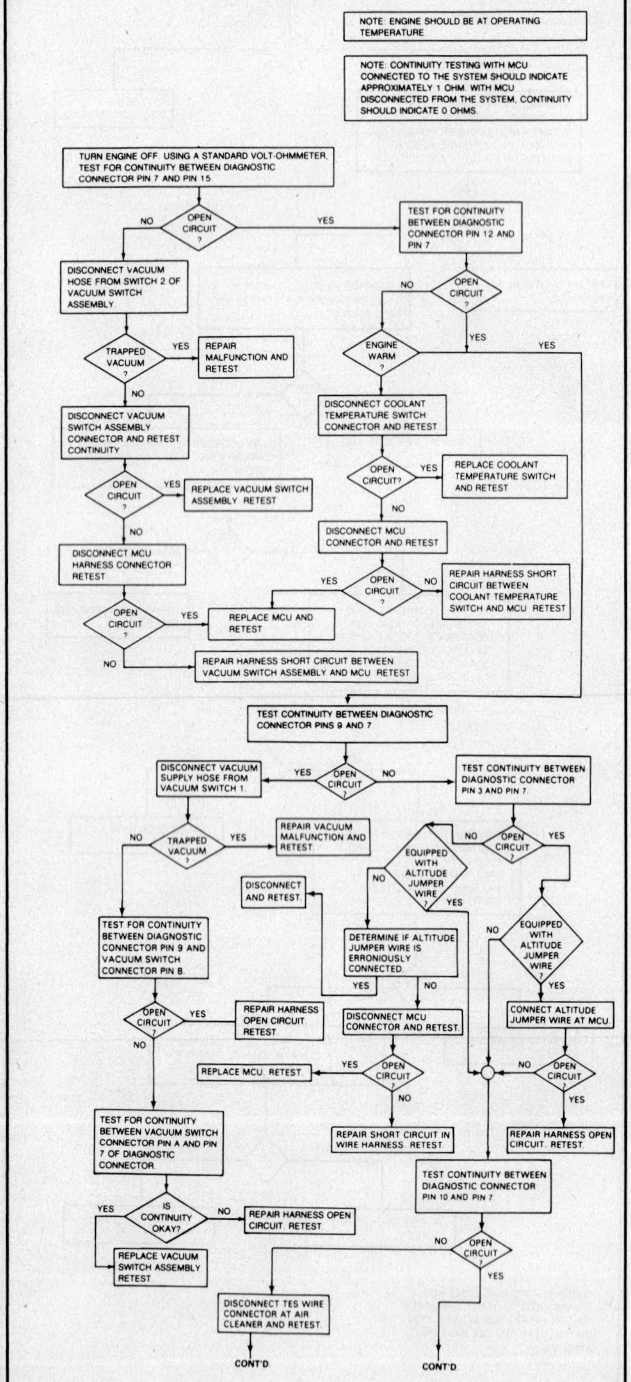
NOTE: ENGINE SHOULD BE AT OPERATING TEMPERATURE.
NOTE: CONTINUITY TESTING WITH MCU CONNECTED TO THE SYSTEM SHOULD INDICATE APPROXIMATELY 1 OHM. WITH MCU DISCONNECTED FROM THE SYSTEM, CONTINUITY SHOULD INDICATE 0 OHMS.
TURN ENGINE OFF. USING A STANDARD VOLT-OHMMETER, TEST FOR CONTINUITY BETWEEN DIAGNOSTIC CONNECTOR PIN 7 AND PIN 15
OPEN CIRCUIT ?
NO
YES
TEST FOR CONTINUITY BETWEEN DIAGNOSTIC CONNECTOR PIN 12 AND PIN 7
DISCONNECT VACUUM HOSE FROM SWITCH 2 OF VACUUM SWITCH ASSEMBLY
TRAPPED VACUUM ?
REPAIR MALFUNCTION AND RETEST
ENGINE WARM
DISCONNECT VACUUM SWITCH ASSEMBLY CONNECTOR AND RETEST CONTINUITY
DISCONNECT COOLANT TEMPERATURE SWITCH CONNECTOR AND RETEST
OPEN CIRCUIT?
REPLACE COOLANT TEMPERATURE SWITCH AND RETEST
REPLACE VACUUM SWITCH ASSEMBLY. RETEST.
DISCONNECT MCU CONNECTOR AND RETEST
DISCONNECT MCU HARNESS CONNECTOR RETEST
REPAIR HARNESS SHORT CIRCUIT BETWEEN COOLANT TEMPERATURE SWITCH AND MCU. RETEST
REPLACE MCU AND RETEST
REPAIR HARNESS SHORT CIRCUIT BETWEEN VACUUM SWITCH ASSEMBLY AND MCU. RETEST
TEST CONTINUITY BETWEEN DIAGNOSTIC CONNECTOR PINS 9 AND 7
DISCONNECT VACUUM SUPPLY HOSE FROM VACUUM SWITCH 1.
TEST CONTINUITY BETWEEN DIAGNOSTIC CONNECTOR PIN 3 AND PIN 7.
REPAIR VACUUM MALFUNCTION AND RETEST.
EQUIPPED WITH ALTITUDE JUMPER WIRE
DISCONNECT AND RETEST.
TEST FOR CONTINUITY BETWEEN DIAGNOSTIC CONNECTOR PIN 9 AND VACUUM SWITCH CONNECTOR PIN B.
DETERMINE IF ALTITUDE JUMPER WIRE IS ERRONIOUSLY CONNECTED.
EQUIPPED WITH ALTITUDE JUMPER WIRE
REPAIR HARNESS OPEN CIRCUIT. RETEST.
DISCONNECT MCU CONNECTOR AND RETEST.
CONNECT ALTITUDE JUMPER WIRE AT MCU.
REPLACE MCU. RETEST.
REPAIR SHORT CIRCUIT IN WIRE HARNESS. RETEST.
REPAIR HARNESS OPEN CIRCUIT. RETEST.
TEST FOR CONTINUITY BETWEEN VACUUM SWITCH CONNECTOR PIN A AND PIN 7 OF DIAGNOSTIC CONNECTOR
TEST CONTINUITY BETWEEN DIAGNOSTIC CONNECTOR PIN 10 AND PIN 7
IS CONTINUITY OKAY?
REPAIR HARNESS OPEN CIRCUIT. RETEST
REPLACE VACUUM SWITCH ASSEMBLY RETEST
DISCONNECT TES WIRE CONNECTOR AT AIR CLEANER AND RETEST.
CONT'D.
CONT'D

TEST NO. 2 (Cont.)

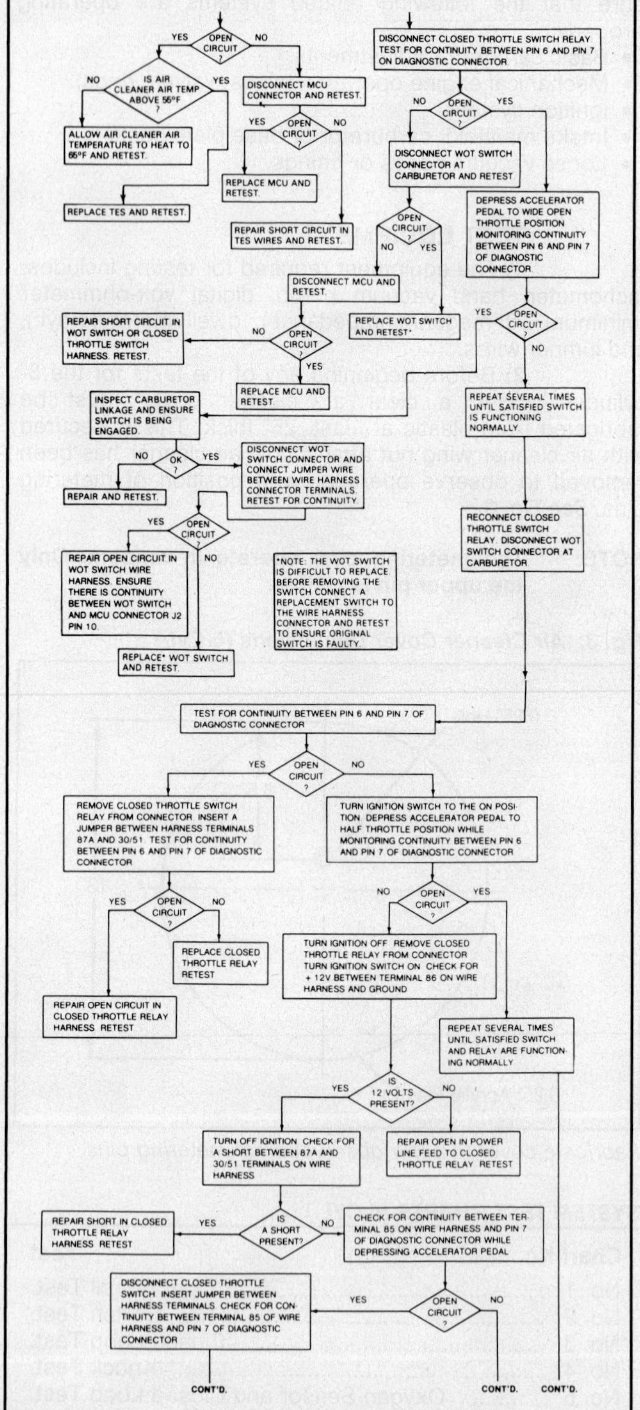
OPEN CIRCUIT ?
IS AIR CLEANER AIR TEMP ABOVE 55°F ?
DISCONNECT MCU CONNECTOR AND RETEST.
ALLOW AIR CLEANER AIR TEMPERATURE TO HEAT TO 66°F AND RETEST.
REPLACE MCU AND RETEST.
REPLACE TES AND RETEST.
REPAIR SHORT CIRCUIT IN TES WIRES AND RETEST.
DISCONNECT CLOSED THROTTLE SWITCH RELAY TEST FOR CONTINUITY BETWEEN PIN 6 AND PIN 7 ON DIAGNOSTIC CONNECTOR.
DISCONNECT WOT SWITCH CONNECTOR AT CARBURETOR AND RETEST
DEPRESS ACCELERATOR PEDAL TO WIDE OPEN THROTTLE POSITION MONITORING CONTINUITY BETWEEN PIN 6 AND PIN 7 OF DIAGNOSTIC CONNECTOR.
DISCONNECT MCU AND RETEST.
REPLACE WOT SWITCH AND RETEST*
REPAIR SHORT CIRCUIT IN WOT SWITCH OR CLOSED THROTTLE SWITCH HARNESS. RETEST.
REPLACE MCU AND RETEST.
REPEAT SEVERAL TIMES UNTIL SATISFIED SWITCH IS FUNCTIONING NORMALLY.
INSPECT CARBURETOR LINKAGE AND ENSURE SWITCH IS BEING ENGAGED.
OK ?
DISCONNECT WOT SWITCH CONNECTOR AND CONNECT JUMPER WIRE BETWEEN WIRE HARNESS CONNECTOR TERMINALS. RETEST FOR CONTINUITY.
REPAIR AND RETEST.
RECONNECT CLOSED THROTTLE SWITCH RELAY. DISCONNECT WOT SWITCH CONNECTOR AT CARBURETOR.
REPAIR OPEN CIRCUIT IN WOT SWITCH WIRE HARNESS. ENSURE THERE IS CONTINUITY BETWEEN WOT SWITCH AND MCU CONNECTOR J2 PIN 10.
*NOTE: THE WOT SWITCH IS DIFFICULT TO REPLACE. BEFORE REMOVING THE SWITCH CONNECT A REPLACEMENT SWITCH TO THE WIRE HARNESS CONNECTOR AND RETEST TO ENSURE ORIGINAL SWITCH IS FAULTY.
REPLACE* WOT SWITCH AND RETEST.
TEST FOR CONTINUITY BETWEEN PIN 6 AND PIN 7 OF DIAGNOSTIC CONNECTOR
REMOVE CLOSED THROTTLE SWITCH RELAY FROM CONNECTOR. INSERT A JUMPER BETWEEN HARNESS TERMINALS 87A AND 30/51. TEST FOR CONTINUITY BETWEEN PIN 6 AND PIN 7 OF DIAGNOSTIC CONNECTOR
TURN IGNITION SWITCH TO THE ON POSITION. DEPRESS ACCELERATOR PEDAL TO HALF THROTTLE POSITION WHILE MONITORING CONTINUITY BETWEEN PIN 6 AND PIN 7 OF DIAGNOSTIC CONNECTOR
REPLACE CLOSED THROTTLE RELAY RETEST
TURN IGNITION OFF. REMOVE CLOSED THROTTLE RELAY FROM CONNECTOR. TURN IGNITION SWITCH ON. CHECK FOR + 12V BETWEEN TERMINAL 86 ON WIRE HARNESS AND GROUND
REPAIR OPEN CIRCUIT IN CLOSED THROTTLE RELAY HARNESS. RETEST
REPEAT SEVERAL TIMES UNTIL SATISFIED SWITCH AND RELAY ARE FUNCTIONING NORMALLY
IS 12 VOLTS PRESENT?
TURN OFF IGNITION. CHECK FOR A SHORT BETWEEN 87A AND 30/51 TERMINALS ON WIRE HARNESS
REPAIR OPEN IN POWER LINE FEED TO CLOSED THROTTLE RELAY. RETEST
REPAIR SHORT IN CLOSED THROTTLE RELAY HARNESS. RETEST
IS A SHORT PRESENT?
CHECK FOR CONTINUITY BETWEEN TERMINAL 85 ON WIRE HARNESS AND PIN 7 OF DIAGNOSTIC CONNECTOR WHILE DEPRESSING ACCELERATOR PEDAL
DISCONNECT CLOSED THROTTLE SWITCH. INSERT JUMPER BETWEEN HARNESS TERMINALS. CHECK FOR CONTINUITY BETWEEN TERMINAL 85 OF WIRE HARNESS AND PIN 7 OF DIAGNOSTIC CONNECTOR
CONT'D.
CONT'D.
CONT'D.

JEEP COMPUTERIZED EMISSION CONTROL 4-CYLINDER & 6-CYLINDER (Cont.)

TEST NO. 2 (Cont.)

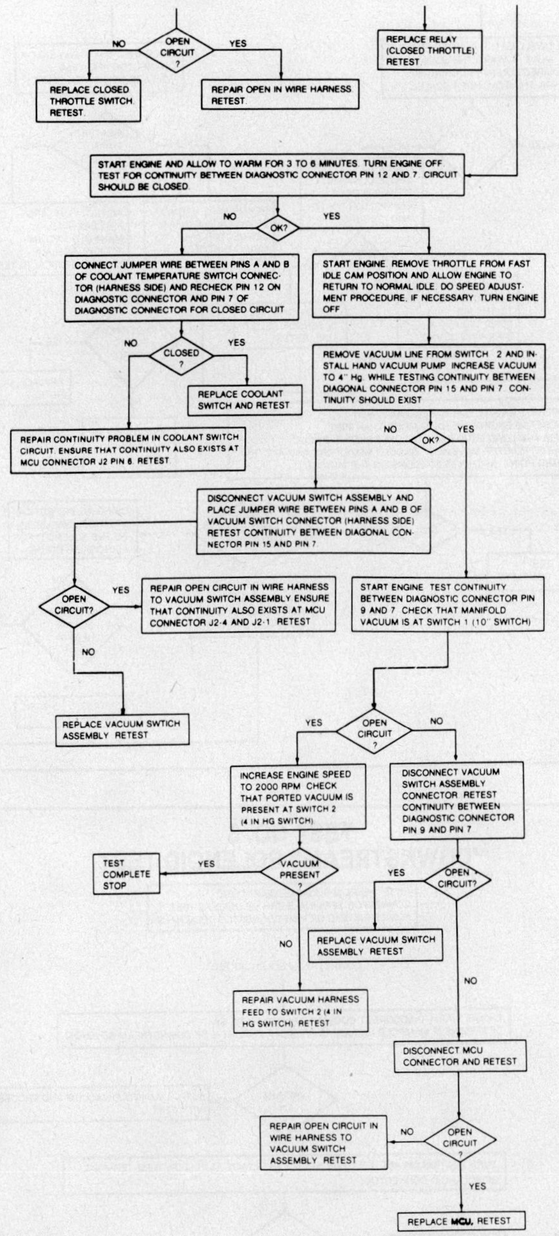
OPEN CIRCUIT ?
NO
YES
REPLACE CLOSED THROTTLE SWITCH. RETEST.
REPAIR OPEN IN WIRE HARNESS. RETEST.
REPLACE RELAY (CLOSED THROTTLE). RETEST.
START ENGINE AND ALLOW TO WARM FOR 3 TO 6 MINUTES. TURN ENGINE OFF. TEST FOR CONTINUITY BETWEEN DIAGNOSTIC CONNECTOR PIN 12 AND 7. CIRCUIT SHOULD BE CLOSED.
OK?
NO
YES
CONNECT JUMPER WIRE BETWEEN PINS A AND B OF COOLANT TEMPERATURE SWITCH CONNECTOR (HARNESS SIDE) AND RECHECK PIN 12 ON DIAGNOSTIC CONNECTOR AND PIN 7 OF DIAGNOSTIC CONNECTOR FOR CLOSED CIRCUIT
START ENGINE. REMOVE THROTTLE FROM FAST IDLE CAM POSITION AND ALLOW ENGINE TO RETURN TO NORMAL IDLE. DO SPEED ADJUSTMENT PROCEDURE, IF NECESSARY. TURN ENGINE OFF
CLOSED ?
NO
YES
REPLACE COOLANT SWITCH AND RETEST
REMOVE VACUUM LINE FROM SWITCH 2 AND INSTALL HAND VACUUM PUMP. INCREASE VACUUM TO 4" Hg. WHILE TESTING CONTINUITY BETWEEN DIAGONAL CONNECTOR PIN 15 AND PIN 7. CONTINUITY SHOULD EXIST
REPAIR CONTINUITY PROBLEM IN COOLANT SWITCH CIRCUIT. ENSURE THAT CONTINUITY ALSO EXISTS AT MCU CONNECTOR J2 PIN 6. RETEST.
OK?
NO
YES
DISCONNECT VACUUM SWITCH ASSEMBLY AND PLACE JUMPER WIRE BETWEEN PINS A AND B OF VACUUM SWITCH CONNECTOR (HARNESS SIDE) RETEST CONTINUITY BETWEEN DIAGONAL CONNECTOR PIN 15 AND PIN 7.
OPEN CIRCUIT?
YES
NO
REPAIR OPEN CIRCUIT IN WIRE HARNESS TO VACUUM SWITCH ASSEMBLY ENSURE THAT CONTINUITY ALSO EXISTS AT MCU CONNECTOR J2-4 AND J2-1. RETEST
START ENGINE. TEST CONTINUITY BETWEEN DIAGNOSTIC CONNECTOR PIN 9 AND 7. CHECK THAT MANIFOLD VACUUM IS AT SWITCH 1 (10" SWITCH)
REPLACE VACUUM SWTICH ASSEMBLY. RETEST
OPEN CIRCUIT ?
YES
NO
INCREASE ENGINE SPEED TO 2000 RPM. CHECK THAT PORTED VACUUM IS PRESENT AT SWITCH 2 (4 IN HG SWITCH).
DISCONNECT VACUUM SWITCH ASSEMBLY CONNECTOR. RETEST CONTINUITY BETWEEN DIAGNOSTIC CONNECTOR PIN 9 AND PIN 7
TEST COMPLETE STOP
YES
VACUUM PRESENT ?
NO
YES
OPEN CIRCUIT?
NO
REPLACE VACUUM SWITCH ASSEMBLY. RETEST
REPAIR VACUUM HARNESS FEED TO SWITCH 2 (4 IN HG SWITCH). RETEST
DISCONNECT MCU CONNECTOR AND RETEST
REPAIR OPEN CIRCUIT IN WIRE HARNESS TO VACUUM SWITCH ASSEMBLY. RETEST
NO
OPEN CIRCUIT ?
YES
REPLACE MCU, RETEST

TEST NO. 3
CLOSED LOOP TEST

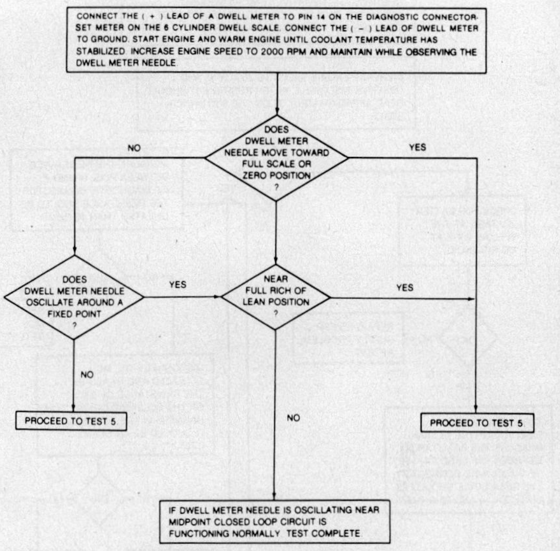
CONNECT THE (+) LEAD OF A DWELL METER TO PIN 14 ON THE DIAGNOSTIC CONNECTOR. SET METER ON THE 6 CYLINDER DWELL SCALE. CONNECT THE (–) LEAD OF DWELL METER TO GROUND. START ENGINE AND WARM ENGINE UNTIL COOLANT TEMPERATURE HAS STABILIZED. INCREASE ENGINE SPEED TO 2000 RPM AND MAINTAIN WHILE OBSERVING THE DWELL METER NEEDLE.
DOES DWELL METER NEEDLE MOVE TOWARD FULL SCALE OR ZERO POSITION ?
NO
YES
DOES DWELL METER NEEDLE OSCILLATE AROUND A FIXED POINT ?
YES
NEAR FULL RICH OF LEAN POSITION ?
YES
NO
PROCEED TO TEST 5.
NO
PROCEED TO TEST 5.
IF DWELL METER NEEDLE IS OSCILLATING NEAR MIDPOINT CLOSED LOOP CIRCUIT IS FUNCTIONING NORMALLY. TEST COMPLETE.

TEST NO. 4
KNOCK TEST

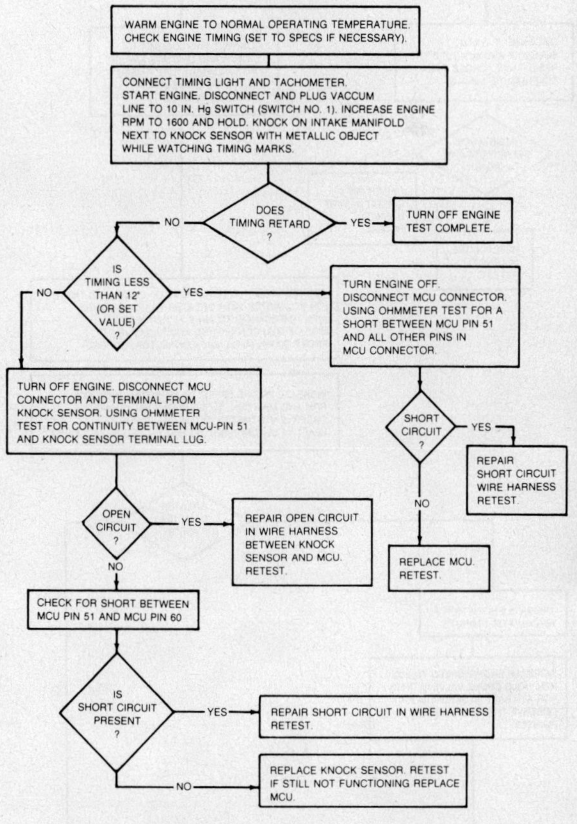
WARM ENGINE TO NORMAL OPERATING TEMPERATURE. CHECK ENGINE TIMING (SET TO SPECS IF NECESSARY).
CONNECT TIMING LIGHT AND TACHOMETER. START ENGINE. DISCONNECT AND PLUG VACCUM LINE TO 10 IN. Hg SWITCH (SWITCH NO. 1). INCREASE ENGINE RPM TO 1600 AND HOLD. KNOCK ON INTAKE MANIFOLD NEXT TO KNOCK SENSOR WITH METALLIC OBJECT WHILE WATCHING TIMING MARKS.
NO
DOES TIMING RETARD ?
YES
TURN OFF ENGINE TEST COMPLETE.
IS TIMING LESS THAN 12° (OR SET VALUE) ?
NO
YES
TURN ENGINE OFF. DISCONNECT MCU CONNECTOR. USING OHMMETER TEST FOR A SHORT BETWEEN MCU PIN 51 AND ALL OTHER PINS IN MCU CONNECTOR.
TURN OFF ENGINE. DISCONNECT MCU CONNECTOR AND TERMINAL FROM KNOCK SENSOR. USING OHMMETER TEST FOR CONTINUITY BETWEEN MCU-PIN 51 AND KNOCK SENSOR TERMINAL LUG.
SHORT CIRCUIT ?
YES
REPAIR SHORT CIRCUIT WIRE HARNESS RETEST.
NO
OPEN CIRCUIT ?
YES
REPAIR OPEN CIRCUIT IN WIRE HARNESS BETWEEN KNOCK SENSOR AND MCU. RETEST.
REPLACE MCU. RETEST.
NO
CHECK FOR SHORT BETWEEN MCU PIN 51 AND MCU PIN 60
IS SHORT CIRCUIT PRESENT ?
YES
REPAIR SHORT CIRCUIT IN WIRE HARNESS RETEST.
NO
REPLACE KNOCK SENSOR. RETEST IF STILL NOT FUNCTIONING REPLACE MCU.

JEEP COMPUTERIZED EMISSION CONTROL 4-CYLINDER & 6-CYLINDER (Cont.)

TEST NO. 5
OXYGEN SENSOR & CLOSED LOOP TEST

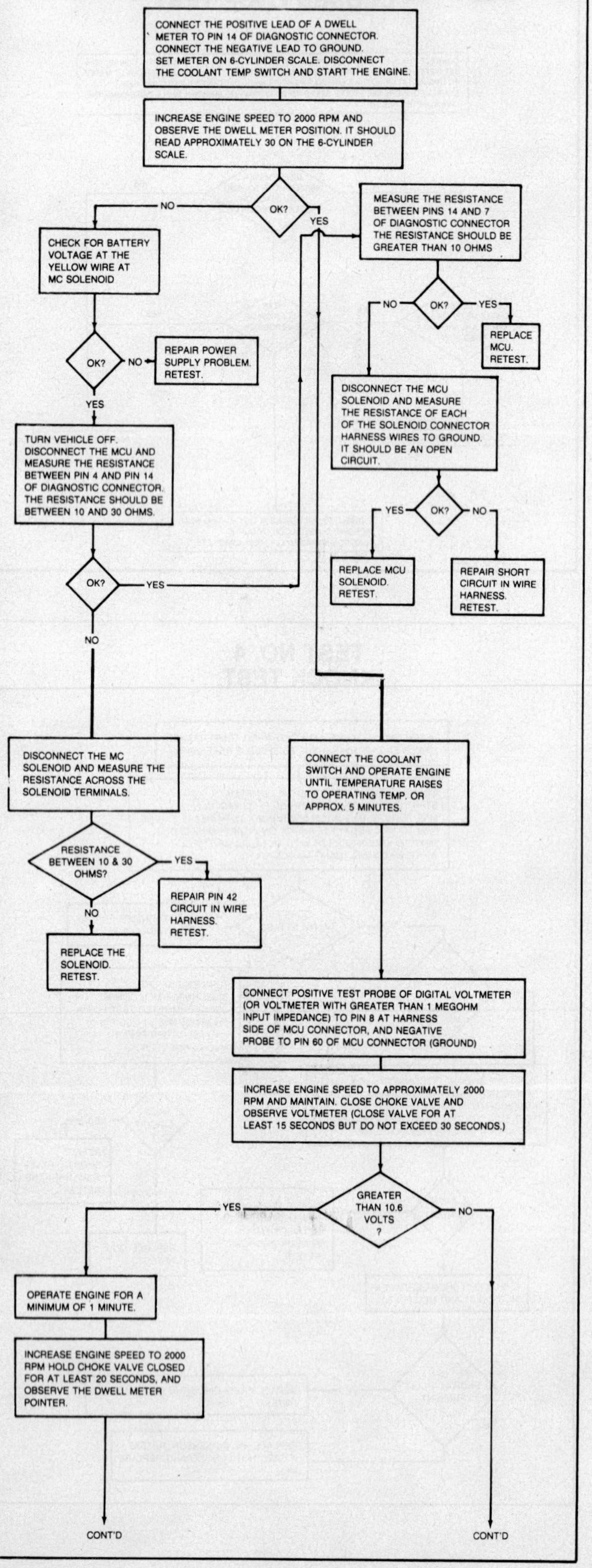

CONNECT THE POSITIVE LEAD OF A DWELL METER TO PIN 14 OF DIAGNOSTIC CONNECTOR. CONNECT THE NEGATIVE LEAD TO GROUND. SET METER ON 6-CYLINDER SCALE. DISCONNECT THE COOLANT TEMP SWITCH AND START THE ENGINE.
INCREASE ENGINE SPEED TO 2000 RPM AND OBSERVE THE DWELL METER POSITION. IT SHOULD READ APPROXIMATELY 30 ON THE 6-CYLINDER SCALE.
OK?
NO
YES
CHECK FOR BATTERY VOLTAGE AT THE YELLOW WIRE AT MC SOLENOID
OK?
NO
REPAIR POWER SUPPLY PROBLEM. RETEST.
YES
TURN VEHICLE OFF. DISCONNECT THE MCU AND MEASURE THE RESISTANCE BETWEEN PIN 4 AND PIN 14 OF DIAGNOSTIC CONNECTOR. THE RESISTANCE SHOULD BE BETWEEN 10 AND 30 OHMS.
OK?
YES
NO
MEASURE THE RESISTANCE BETWEEN PINS 14 AND 7 OF DIAGNOSTIC CONNECTOR THE RESISTANCE SHOULD BE GREATER THAN 10 OHMS
OK?
NO
YES
REPLACE MCU. RETEST.
DISCONNECT THE MCU SOLENOID AND MEASURE THE RESISTANCE OF EACH OF THE SOLENOID CONNECTOR HARNESS WIRES TO GROUND. IT SHOULD BE AN OPEN CIRCUIT.
OK?
YES
NO
REPLACE MCU SOLENOID. RETEST.
REPAIR SHORT CIRCUIT IN WIRE HARNESS. RETEST.
DISCONNECT THE MC SOLENOID AND MEASURE THE RESISTANCE ACROSS THE SOLENOID TERMINALS.
RESISTANCE BETWEEN 10 & 30 OHMS?
YES
NO
REPAIR PIN 42 CIRCUIT IN WIRE HARNESS. RETEST.
REPLACE THE SOLENOID. RETEST.
CONNECT THE COOLANT SWITCH AND OPERATE ENGINE UNTIL TEMPERATURE RAISES TO OPERATING TEMP. OR APPROX. 5 MINUTES.
CONNECT POSITIVE TEST PROBE OF DIGITAL VOLTMETER (OR VOLTMETER WITH GREATER THAN 1 MEGOHM INPUT IMPEDANCE) TO PIN 8 AT HARNESS SIDE OF MCU CONNECTOR, AND NEGATIVE PROBE TO PIN 60 OF MCU CONNECTOR (GROUND)
INCREASE ENGINE SPEED TO APPROXIMATELY 2000 RPM AND MAINTAIN. CLOSE CHOKE VALVE AND OBSERVE VOLTMETER (CLOSE VALVE FOR AT LEAST 15 SECONDS BUT DO NOT EXCEED 30 SECONDS.)
GREATER THAN 10.6 VOLTS ?
YES
NO
OPERATE ENGINE FOR A MINIMUM OF 1 MINUTE.
INCREASE ENGINE SPEED TO 2000 RPM HOLD CHOKE VALVE CLOSED FOR AT LEAST 20 SECONDS, AND OBSERVE THE DWELL METER POINTER.
CONT'D
CONT'D

TEST NO. 5 (Cont.)

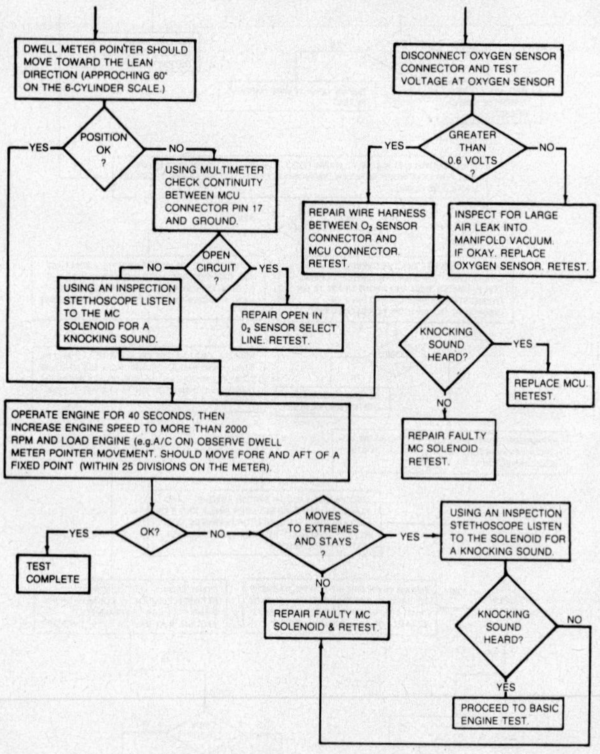

TEST NO. 6
"DOWNSTREAM" SOLENOID TEST

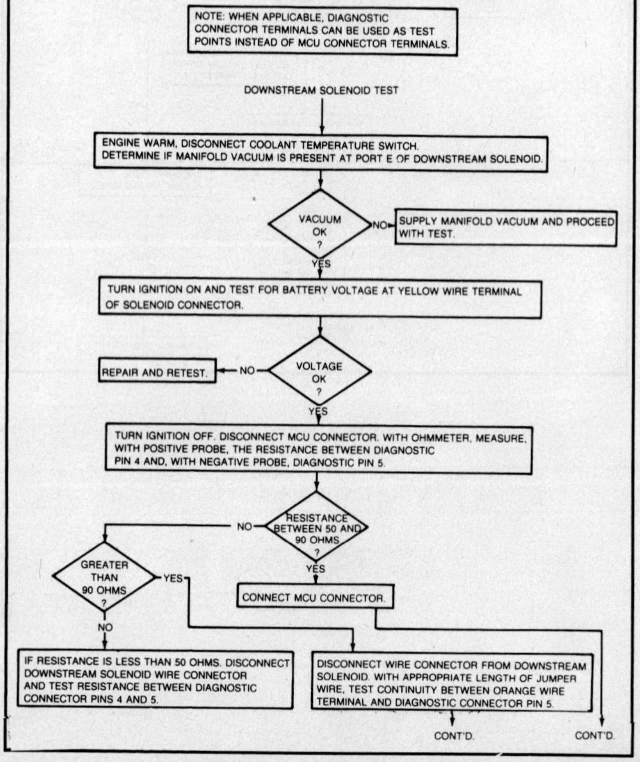

JEEP COMPUTERIZED EMISSION CONTROL 4-CYLINDER & 6-CYLINDER (Cont.)

TEST NO. 6 (Cont.)

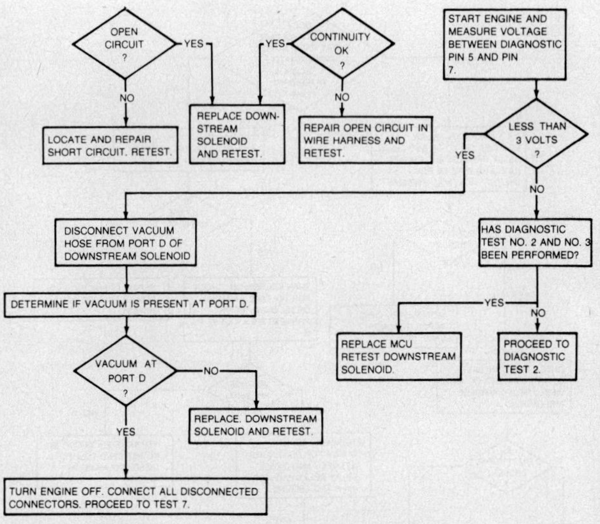

TEST NO. 7 "UPSTREAM" SOLENOID TEST

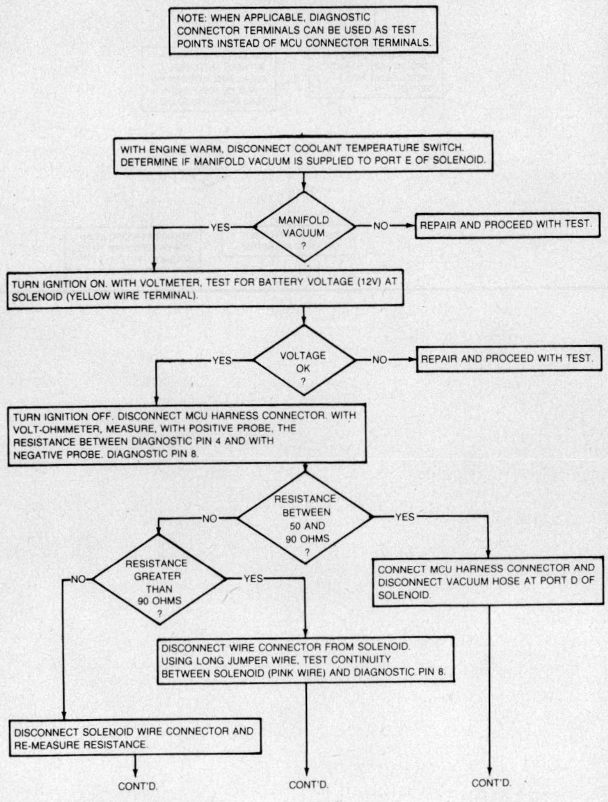

NOTE: WHEN APPLICABLE, DIAGNOSTIC CONNECTOR TERMINALS CAN BE USED AS TEST POINTS INSTEAD OF MCU CONNECTOR TERMINALS.
WITH ENGINE WARM, DISCONNECT COOLANT TEMPERATURE SWITCH. DETERMINE IF MANIFOLD VACUUM IS SUPPLIED TO PORT E OF SOLENOID.
MANIFOLD VACUUM ?
YES
NO
REPAIR AND PROCEED WITH TEST.
TURN IGNITION ON. WITH VOLTMETER, TEST FOR BATTERY VOLTAGE (12V) AT SOLENOID (YELLOW WIRE TERMINAL).
VOLTAGE OK ?
REPAIR AND PROCEED WITH TEST.
TURN IGNITION OFF. DISCONNECT MCU HARNESS CONNECTOR. WITH VOLT-OHMMETER, MEASURE, WITH POSITIVE PROBE, THE RESISTANCE BETWEEN DIAGNOSTIC PIN 4 AND WITH NEGATIVE PROBE. DIAGNOSTIC PIN 8.
RESISTANCE BETWEEN 50 AND 90 OHMS ?
RESISTANCE GREATER THAN 90 OHMS ?
CONNECT MCU HARNESS CONNECTOR AND DISCONNECT VACUUM HOSE AT PORT D OF SOLENOID.
DISCONNECT WIRE CONNECTOR FROM SOLENOID. USING LONG JUMPER WIRE, TEST CONTINUITY BETWEEN SOLENOID (PINK WIRE) AND DIAGNOSTIC PIN 8.
DISCONNECT SOLENOID WIRE CONNECTOR AND RE-MEASURE RESISTANCE.
CONT'D.
CONT'D.
CONT'D.

TEST NO. 7 (Cont.)

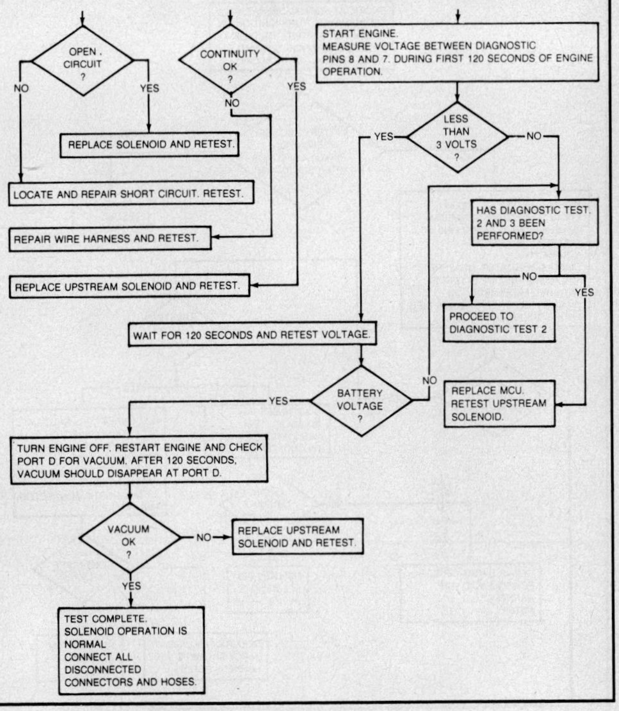

TEST NO. 8A BOWL VENT TEST

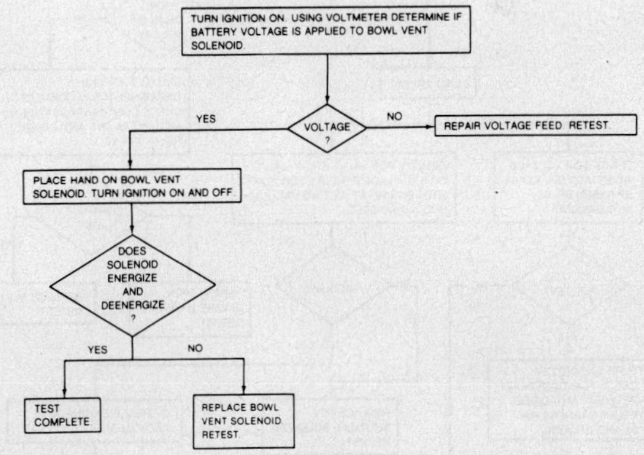

JEEP COMPUTERIZED EMISSION CONTROL
4-CYLINDER & 6-CYLINDER (Cont.)

TEST NO. 8B
PCV SHUT-OFF TEST

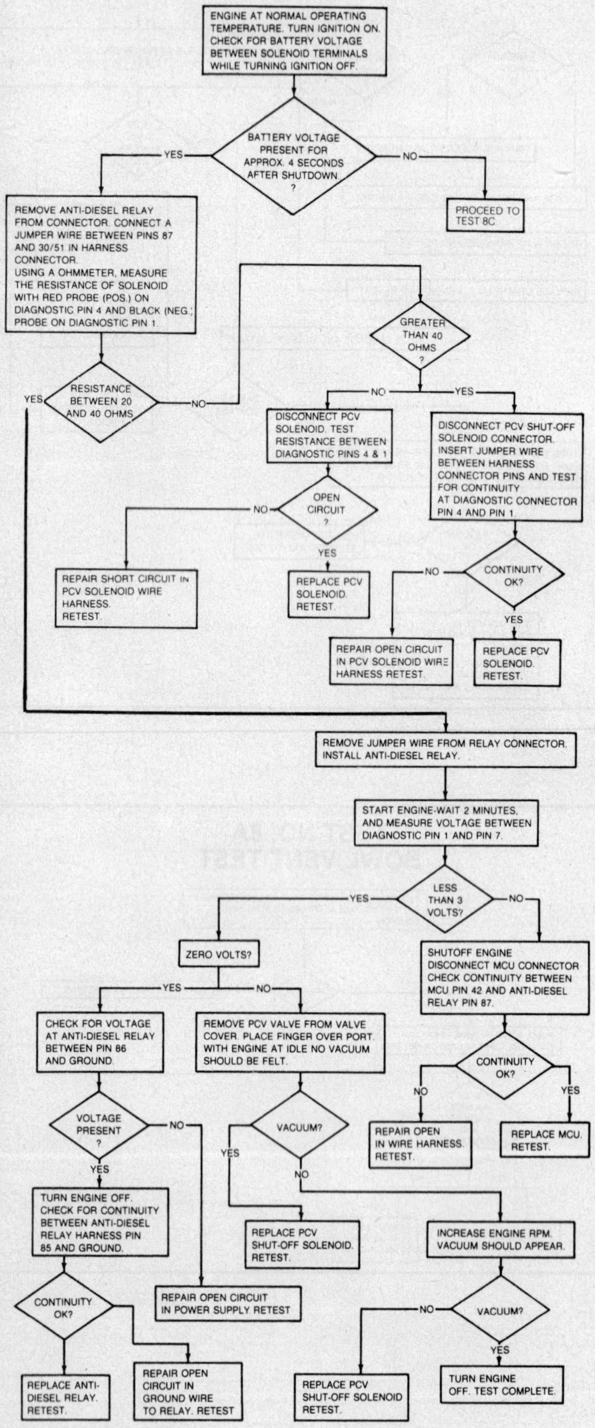

TEST NO. 8C
ANTI-DIESEL SYSTEM TEST

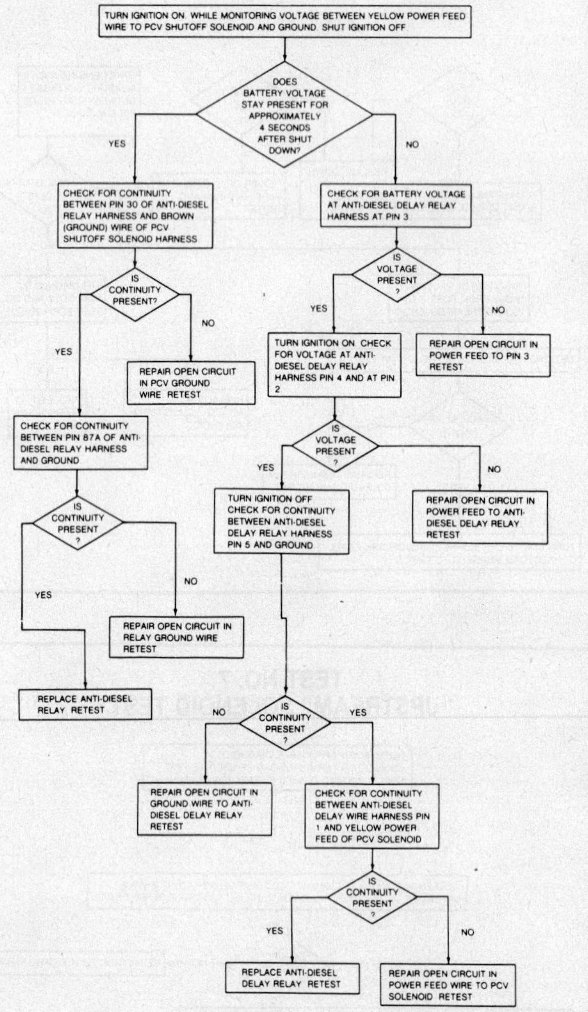

JEEP COMPUTERIZED EMISSION CONTROL 4-CYLINDER & 6-CYLINDER (Cont.)

TEST NO. 9
IDLE SPEED CONTROL SYSTEM TEST

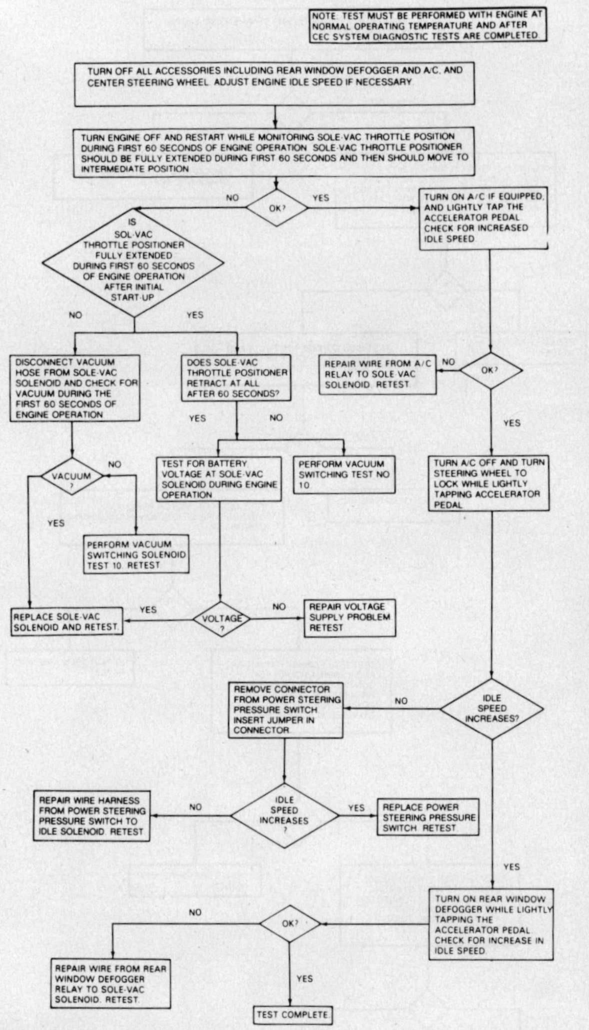

TEST NO. 10
SOLE-VAC VACUUM SWITCHING TEST

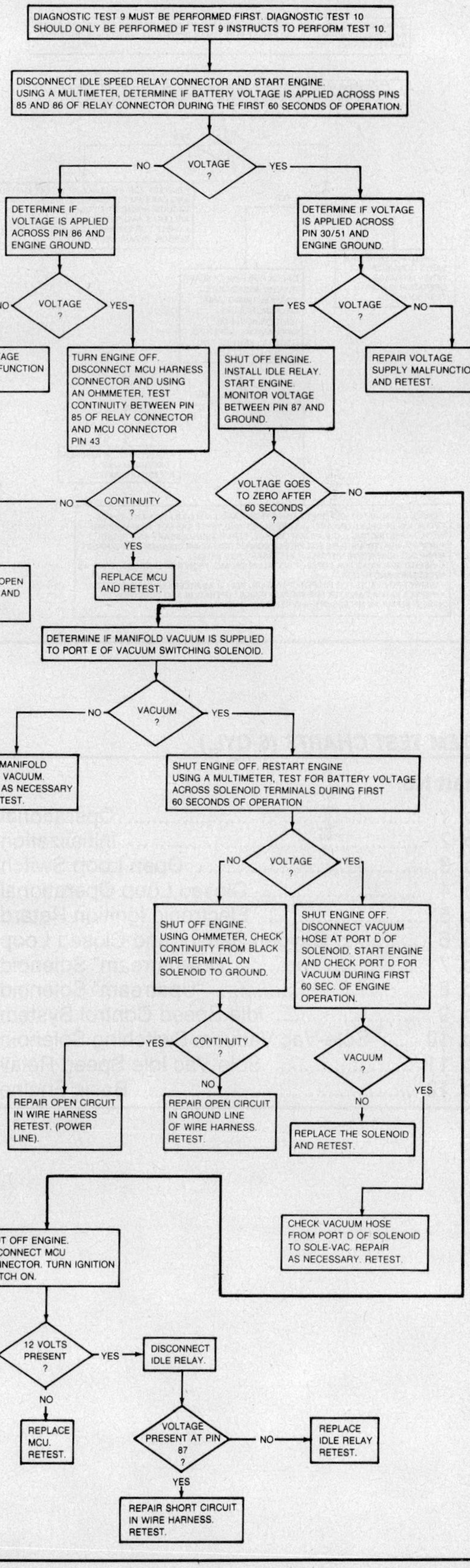

DIAGNOSTIC TEST 9 MUST BE PERFORMED FIRST. DIAGNOSTIC TEST 10 SHOULD ONLY BE PERFORMED IF TEST 9 INSTRUCTS TO PERFORM TEST 10.
DISCONNECT IDLE SPEED RELAY CONNECTOR AND START ENGINE. USING A MULTIMETER, DETERMINE IF BATTERY VOLTAGE IS APPLIED ACROSS PINS 85 AND 86 OF RELAY CONNECTOR DURING THE FIRST 60 SECONDS OF OPERATION.
NO
VOLTAGE ?
YES
DETERMINE IF VOLTAGE IS APPLIED ACROSS PIN 86 AND ENGINE GROUND.
DETERMINE IF VOLTAGE IS APPLIED ACROSS PIN 30/51 AND ENGINE GROUND.
NO
VOLTAGE ?
YES
YES
VOLTAGE ?
NO
REPAIR VOLTAGE SUPPLY MALFUNCTION AND RETEST.
TURN ENGINE OFF. DISCONNECT MCU HARNESS CONNECTOR AND USING AN OHMMETER, TEST CONTINUITY BETWEEN PIN 85 OF RELAY CONNECTOR AND MCU CONNECTOR PIN 43
SHUT OFF ENGINE. INSTALL IDLE RELAY. START ENGINE. MONITOR VOLTAGE BETWEEN PIN 87 AND GROUND.
REPAIR VOLTAGE SUPPLY MALFUNCTION AND RETEST.
NO
CONTINUITY ?
YES
VOLTAGE GOES TO ZERO AFTER 60 SECONDS ?
NO
REPAIR OPEN CIRCUIT AND RETEST.
REPLACE MCU AND RETEST.
DETERMINE IF MANIFOLD VACUUM IS SUPPLIED TO PORT E OF VACUUM SWITCHING SOLENOID.
NO
VACUUM ?
YES
CHECK MANIFOLD SUPPLY VACUUM. REPAIR AS NECESSARY AND RETEST.
SHUT ENGINE OFF, RESTART ENGINE USING A MULTIMETER, TEST FOR BATTERY VOLTAGE ACROSS SOLENOID TERMINALS DURING FIRST 60 SECONDS OF OPERATION
NO
VOLTAGE ?
YES
SHUT OFF ENGINE. USING OHMMETER, CHECK CONTINUITY FROM BLACK WIRE TERMINAL ON SOLENOID TO GROUND.
SHUT ENGINE OFF. DISCONNECT VACUUM HOSE AT PORT D OF SOLENOID. START ENGINE AND CHECK PORT D FOR VACUUM DURING FIRST 60 SEC. OF ENGINE OPERATION.
YES
CONTINUITY ?
NO
VACUUM ?
NO
YES
REPAIR OPEN CIRCUIT IN WIRE HARNESS RETEST. (POWER LINE).
REPAIR OPEN CIRCUIT IN GROUND LINE OF WIRE HARNESS. RETEST.
REPLACE THE SOLENOID AND RETEST.
CHECK VACUUM HOSE FROM PORT D OF SOLENOID TO SOLE-VAC. REPAIR AS NECESSARY. RETEST.
SHUT OFF ENGINE. DISCONNECT MCU CONNECTOR. TURN IGNITION SWITCH ON.
12 VOLTS PRESENT ?
YES
DISCONNECT IDLE RELAY.
NO
REPLACE MCU. RETEST.
VOLTAGE PRESENT AT PIN 87 ?
NO
REPLACE IDLE RELAY RETEST.
YES
REPAIR SHORT CIRCUIT IN WIRE HARNESS. RETEST.

JEEP COMPUTERIZED EMISSION CONTROL 4-CYLINDER & 6-CYLINDER (Cont.)

TEST NO. 11 BASIC ENGINE TEST

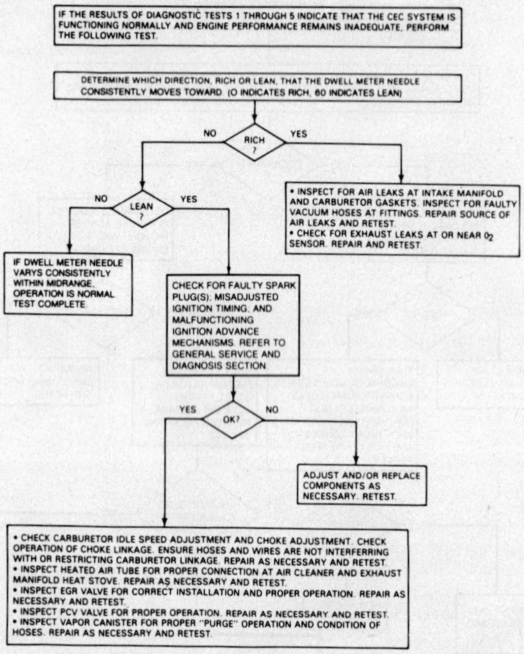

TEST NO. 1 OPERATIONAL TEST

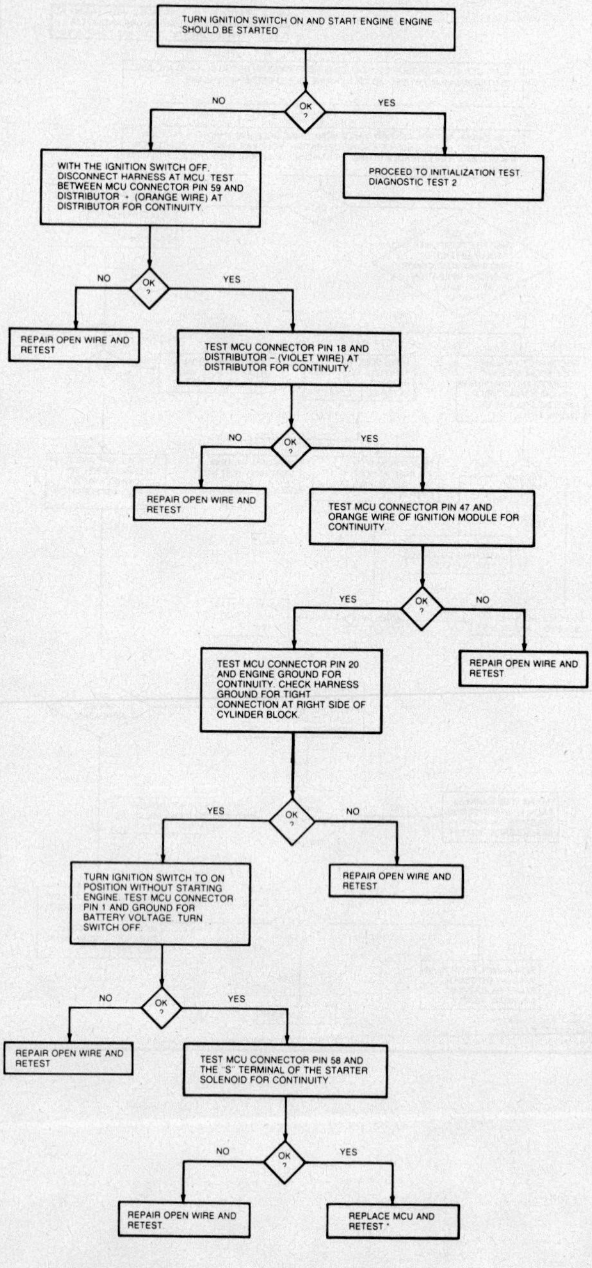

*NOTE: BEFORE REPLACING MCU, IF ENGINE FAILS TO START, CHECK FOR FAILURE OF IGNITION MODULE, COIL, DISTRIBUTOR, ETC.

SYSTEM TEST CHARTS (6-CYL.)

Chart No.	Test
No. 1	Operational Test.
No. 2	Initialization Test.
No. 3	Open Loop Switch Test.
No. 4	Closed Loop Operational Test.
No. 5	Electronic Ignition Retard Test.
No. 6	Oxygen Sensor and Closed Loop Test.
No. 7	"Downstream" Solenoid Test.
No. 8	"Upstream" Solenoid Test.
No. 9	Idle Speed Control System Test.
No. 10	Sole-Vac Vacuum Switching Solenoid Test.
No. 11	Sole-Vac Idle Speed Relay Test.
No. 12	Basic Engine Test.

JEEP COMPUTERIZED EMISSION CONTROL 4-CYLINDER & 6-CYLINDER (Cont.)

TEST NO. 2 INITIALIZATION TEST

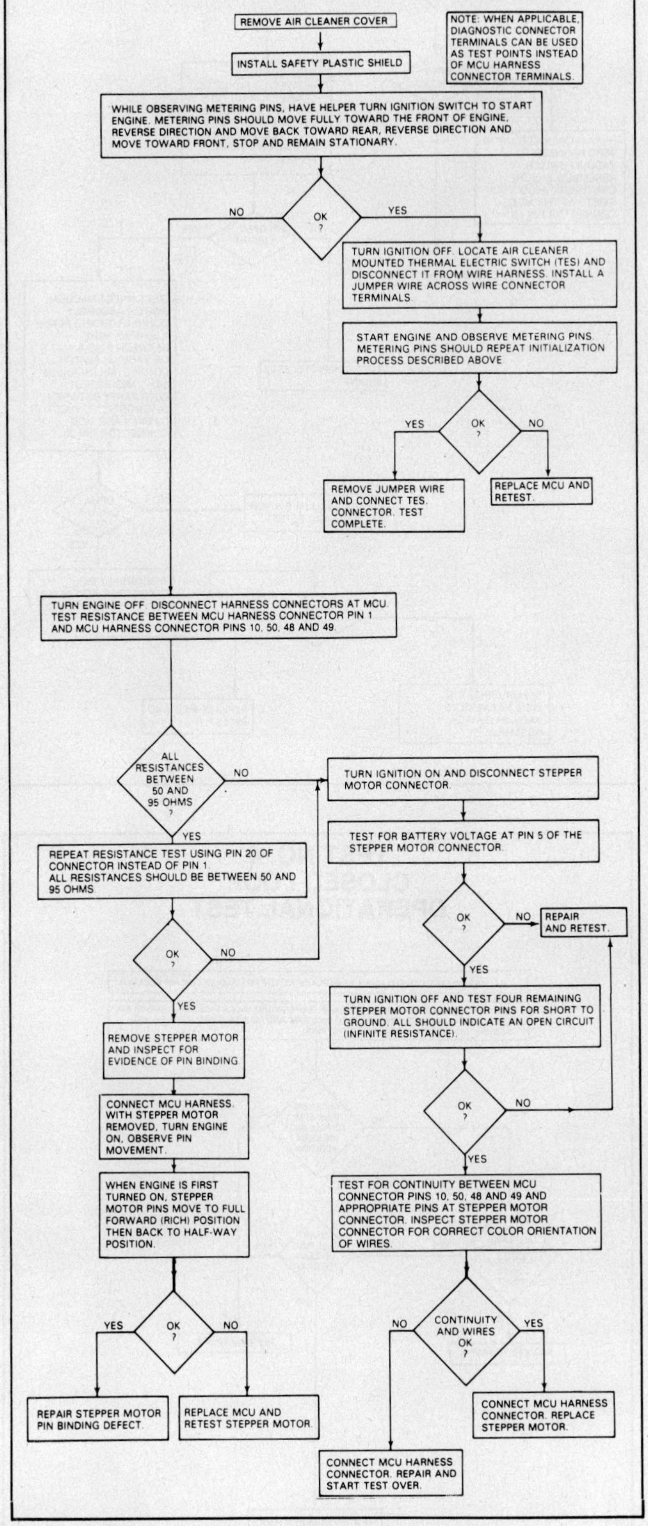

REMOVE AIR CLEANER COVER
NOTE: WHEN APPLICABLE, DIAGNOSTIC CONNECTOR TERMINALS CAN BE USED AS TEST POINTS INSTEAD OF MCU HARNESS CONNECTOR TERMINALS.
INSTALL SAFETY PLASTIC SHIELD
WHILE OBSERVING METERING PINS, HAVE HELPER TURN IGNITION SWITCH TO START ENGINE. METERING PINS SHOULD MOVE FULLY TOWARD THE FRONT OF ENGINE, REVERSE DIRECTION AND MOVE BACK TOWARD REAR, REVERSE DIRECTION AND MOVE TOWARD FRONT, STOP AND REMAIN STATIONARY.
OK ?
NO
YES
TURN IGNITION OFF. LOCATE AIR CLEANER MOUNTED THERMAL ELECTRIC SWITCH (TES) AND DISCONNECT IT FROM WIRE HARNESS. INSTALL A JUMPER WIRE ACROSS WIRE CONNECTOR TERMINALS.
START ENGINE AND OBSERVE METERING PINS. METERING PINS SHOULD REPEAT INITIALIZATION PROCESS DESCRIBED ABOVE.
OK ?
YES
NO
REMOVE JUMPER WIRE AND CONNECT TES. CONNECTOR. TEST COMPLETE.
REPLACE MCU AND RETEST.
TURN ENGINE OFF. DISCONNECT HARNESS CONNECTORS AT MCU. TEST RESISTANCE BETWEEN MCU HARNESS CONNECTOR PIN 1 AND MCU HARNESS CONNECTOR PINS 10, 50, 48 AND 49.
ALL RESISTANCES BETWEEN 50 AND 95 OHMS ?
NO
YES
TURN IGNITION ON AND DISCONNECT STEPPER MOTOR CONNECTOR.
TEST FOR BATTERY VOLTAGE AT PIN 5 OF THE STEPPER MOTOR CONNECTOR.
REPEAT RESISTANCE TEST USING PIN 20 OF CONNECTOR INSTEAD OF PIN 1. ALL RESISTANCES SHOULD BE BETWEEN 50 AND 95 OHMS.
OK ?
NO
REPAIR AND RETEST.
YES
OK ?
NO
YES
TURN IGNITION OFF AND TEST FOUR REMAINING STEPPER MOTOR CONNECTOR PINS FOR SHORT TO GROUND. ALL SHOULD INDICATE AN OPEN CIRCUIT (INFINITE RESISTANCE).
REMOVE STEPPER MOTOR AND INSPECT FOR EVIDENCE OF PIN BINDING
OK ?
NO
YES
CONNECT MCU HARNESS. WITH STEPPER MOTOR REMOVED, TURN ENGINE ON, OBSERVE PIN MOVEMENT.
TEST FOR CONTINUITY BETWEEN MCU CONNECTOR PINS 10, 50, 48 AND 49 AND APPROPRIATE PINS AT STEPPER MOTOR CONNECTOR. INSPECT STEPPER MOTOR CONNECTOR FOR CORRECT COLOR ORIENTATION OF WIRES.
WHEN ENGINE IS FIRST TURNED ON, STEPPER MOTOR PINS MOVE TO FULL FORWARD (RICH) POSITION THEN BACK TO HALF-WAY POSITION.
OK ?
YES
NO
CONTINUITY AND WIRES OK ?
NO
YES
REPAIR STEPPER MOTOR PIN BINDING DEFECT.
REPLACE MCU AND RETEST STEPPER MOTOR.
CONNECT MCU HARNESS CONNECTOR. REPLACE STEPPER MOTOR.
CONNECT MCU HARNESS CONNECTOR. REPAIR AND START TEST OVER.

TEST NO. 3 OPEN LOOP SWITCH TEST

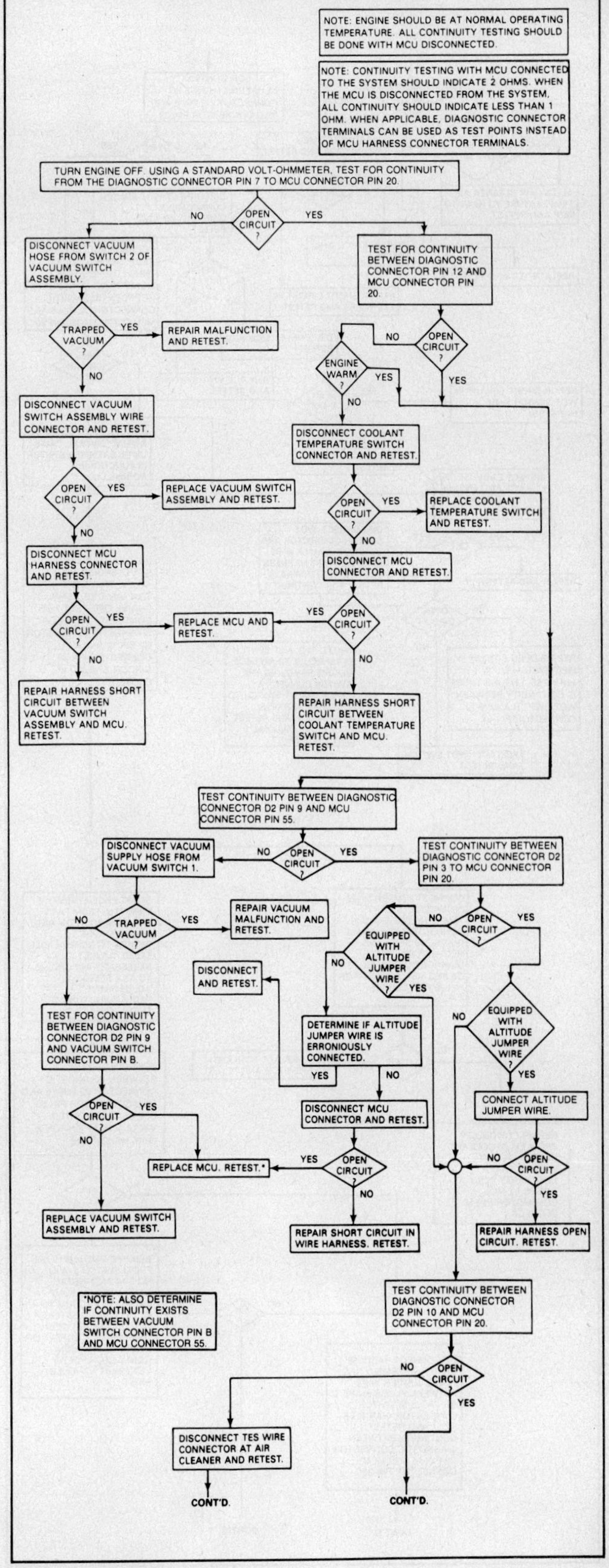

JEEP COMPUTERIZED EMISSION CONTROL 4-CYLINDER & 6-CYLINDER (Cont.)

TEST NO. 3 (Cont.)

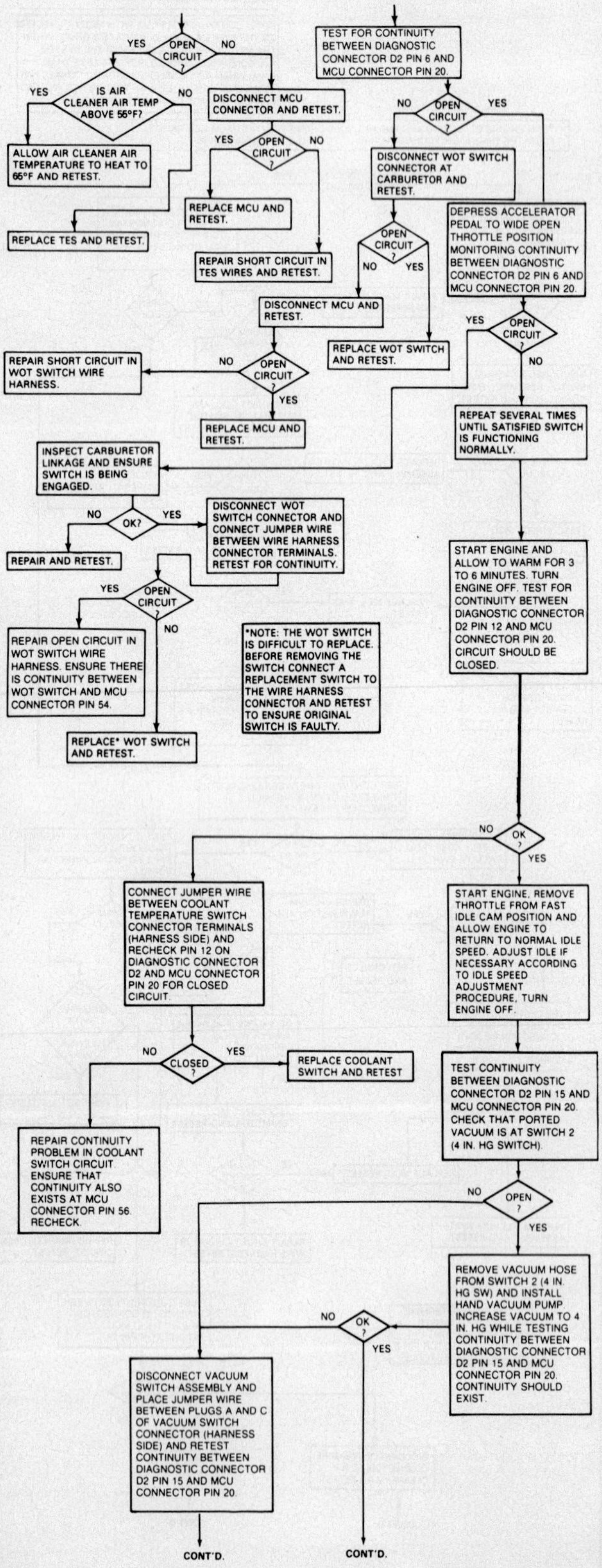

TEST NO. 3 (Cont.)

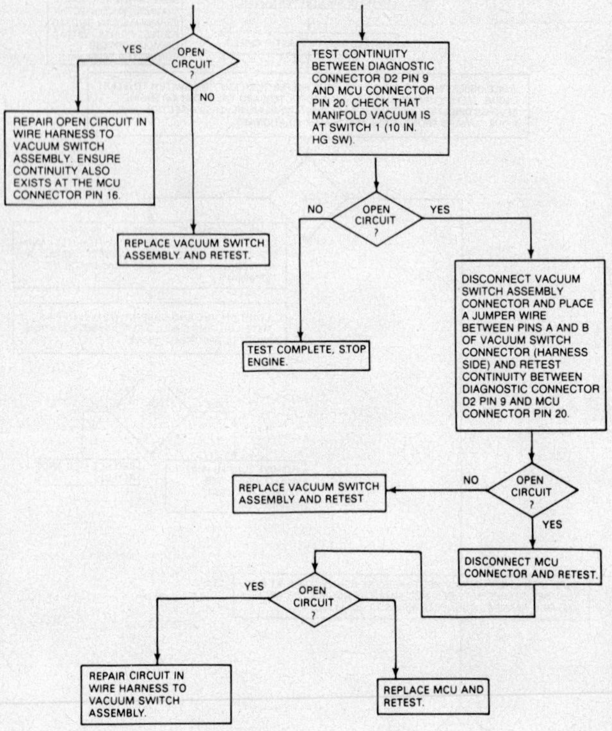

TEST NO. 4 CLOSED LOOP OPERATIONAL TEST

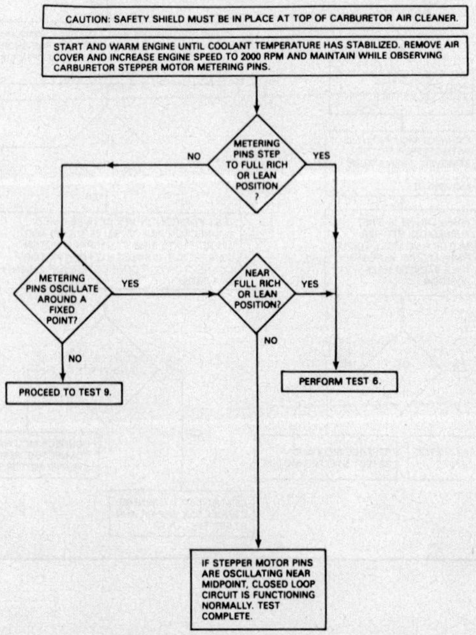

CAUTION: SAFETY SHIELD MUST BE IN PLACE AT TOP OF CARBURETOR AIR CLEANER.
START AND WARM ENGINE UNTIL COOLANT TEMPERATURE HAS STABILIZED. REMOVE AIR COVER AND INCREASE ENGINE SPEED TO 2000 RPM AND MAINTAIN WHILE OBSERVING CARBURETOR STEPPER MOTOR METERING PINS.
METERING PINS STEP TO FULL RICH OR LEAN POSITION ?
NO
YES
METERING PINS OSCILLATE AROUND A FIXED POINT?
YES
NO
NEAR FULL RICH OR LEAN POSITION?
YES
NO
PROCEED TO TEST 9.
PERFORM TEST 6.
IF STEPPER MOTOR PINS ARE OSCILLATING NEAR MIDPOINT, CLOSED LOOP CIRCUIT IS FUNCTIONING NORMALLY. TEST COMPLETE.

1985 Computerized Engine Controls

JEEP COMPUTERIZED EMISSION CONTROL 4-CYLINDER & 6-CYLINDER (Cont.)

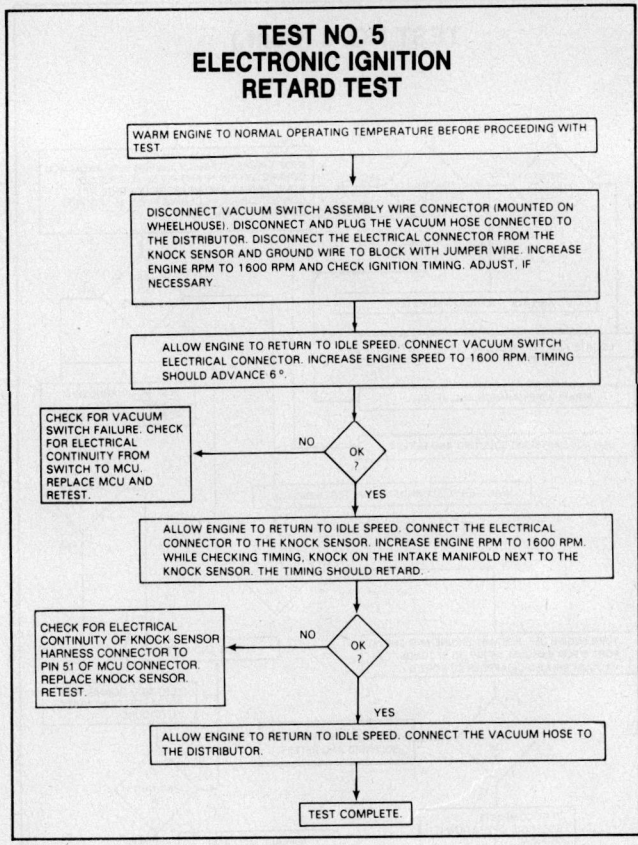

TEST NO. 5 ELECTRONIC IGNITION RETARD TEST

WARM ENGINE TO NORMAL OPERATING TEMPERATURE BEFORE PROCEEDING WITH TEST.

DISCONNECT VACUUM SWITCH ASSEMBLY WIRE CONNECTOR (MOUNTED ON WHEELHOUSE). DISCONNECT AND PLUG THE VACUUM HOSE CONNECTED TO THE DISTRIBUTOR. DISCONNECT THE ELECTRICAL CONNECTOR FROM THE KNOCK SENSOR AND GROUND WIRE TO BLOCK WITH JUMPER WIRE. INCREASE ENGINE RPM TO 1600 RPM AND CHECK IGNITION TIMING. ADJUST, IF NECESSARY.

ALLOW ENGINE TO RETURN TO IDLE SPEED. CONNECT VACUUM SWITCH ELECTRICAL CONNECTOR. INCREASE ENGINE SPEED TO 1600 RPM. TIMING SHOULD ADVANCE 6°.

OK?
- NO: CHECK FOR VACUUM SWITCH FAILURE. CHECK FOR ELECTRICAL CONTINUITY FROM SWITCH TO MCU. REPLACE MCU AND RETEST.
- YES: ALLOW ENGINE TO RETURN TO IDLE SPEED. CONNECT THE ELECTRICAL CONNECTOR TO THE KNOCK SENSOR. INCREASE ENGINE RPM TO 1600 RPM. WHILE CHECKING TIMING, KNOCK ON THE INTAKE MANIFOLD NEXT TO THE KNOCK SENSOR. THE TIMING SHOULD RETARD.

OK?
- NO: CHECK FOR ELECTRICAL CONTINUITY OF KNOCK SENSOR HARNESS CONNECTOR TO PIN 51 OF MCU CONNECTOR. REPLACE KNOCK SENSOR. RETEST.
- YES: ALLOW ENGINE TO RETURN TO IDLE SPEED. CONNECT THE VACUUM HOSE TO THE DISTRIBUTOR.

TEST COMPLETE.

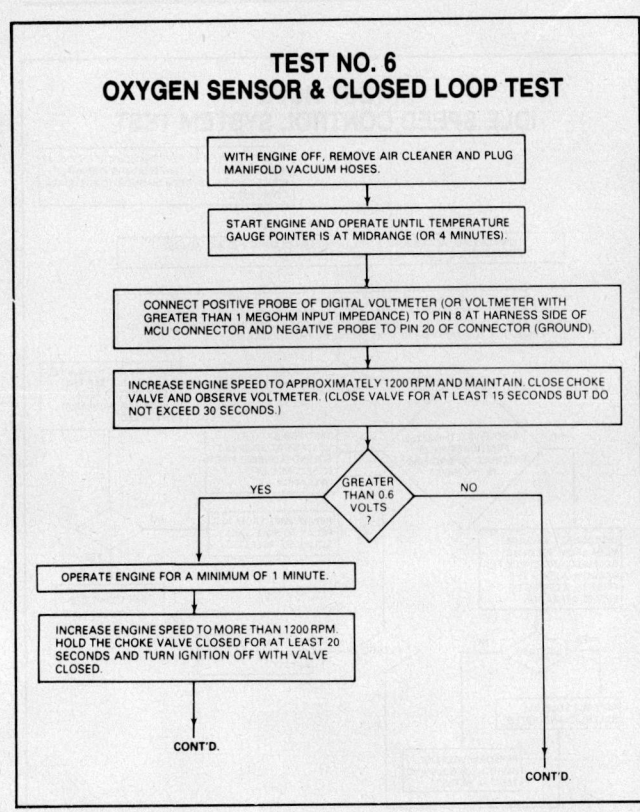

TEST NO. 6 OXYGEN SENSOR & CLOSED LOOP TEST

WITH ENGINE OFF, REMOVE AIR CLEANER AND PLUG MANIFOLD VACUUM HOSES.

START ENGINE AND OPERATE UNTIL TEMPERATURE GAUGE POINTER IS AT MIDRANGE (OR 4 MINUTES).

CONNECT POSITIVE PROBE OF DIGITAL VOLTMETER (OR VOLTMETER WITH GREATER THAN 1 MEGOHM INPUT IMPEDANCE) TO PIN 8 AT HARNESS SIDE OF MCU CONNECTOR AND NEGATIVE PROBE TO PIN 20 OF CONNECTOR (GROUND).

INCREASE ENGINE SPEED TO APPROXIMATELY 1200 RPM AND MAINTAIN. CLOSE CHOKE VALVE AND OBSERVE VOLTMETER. (CLOSE VALVE FOR AT LEAST 15 SECONDS BUT DO NOT EXCEED 30 SECONDS.)

GREATER THAN 0.6 VOLTS?
- YES: OPERATE ENGINE FOR A MINIMUM OF 1 MINUTE. → INCREASE ENGINE SPEED TO MORE THAN 1200 RPM. HOLD THE CHOKE VALVE CLOSED FOR AT LEAST 20 SECONDS AND TURN IGNITION OFF WITH VALVE CLOSED. → CONT'D.
- NO: CONT'D.

TEST NO. 6 (Cont.)

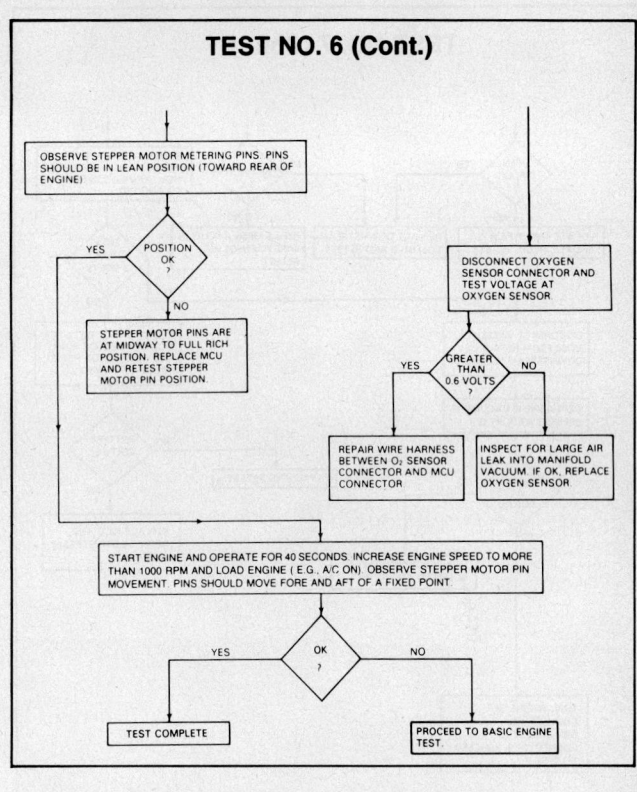

OBSERVE STEPPER MOTOR METERING PINS. PINS SHOULD BE IN LEAN POSITION (TOWARD REAR OF ENGINE).

POSITION OK?
- YES: (to START ENGINE AND OPERATE FOR 40 SECONDS...)
- NO: STEPPER MOTOR PINS ARE AT MIDWAY TO FULL RICH POSITION. REPLACE MCU AND RETEST STEPPER MOTOR PIN POSITION.

DISCONNECT OXYGEN SENSOR CONNECTOR AND TEST VOLTAGE AT OXYGEN SENSOR.

GREATER THAN 0.6 VOLTS?
- YES: REPAIR WIRE HARNESS BETWEEN O_2 SENSOR CONNECTOR AND MCU CONNECTOR.
- NO: INSPECT FOR LARGE AIR LEAK INTO MANIFOLD VACUUM. IF OK, REPLACE OXYGEN SENSOR.

START ENGINE AND OPERATE FOR 40 SECONDS. INCREASE ENGINE SPEED TO MORE THAN 1000 RPM AND LOAD ENGINE (E.G., A/C ON). OBSERVE STEPPER MOTOR PIN MOVEMENT. PINS SHOULD MOVE FORE AND AFT OF A FIXED POINT.

OK?
- YES: TEST COMPLETE
- NO: PROCEED TO BASIC ENGINE TEST.

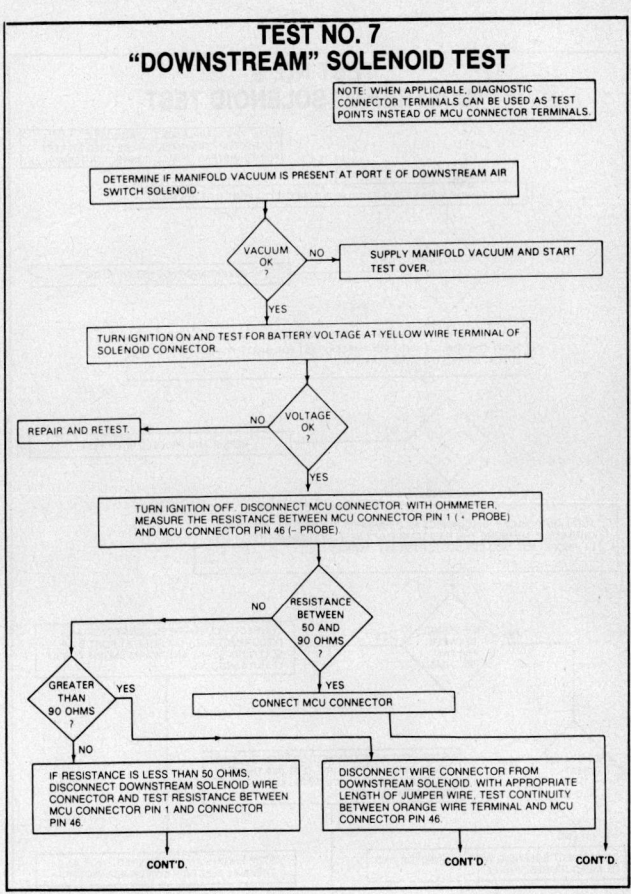

TEST NO. 7 "DOWNSTREAM" SOLENOID TEST

NOTE: WHEN APPLICABLE, DIAGNOSTIC CONNECTOR TERMINALS CAN BE USED AS TEST POINTS INSTEAD OF MCU CONNECTOR TERMINALS.

DETERMINE IF MANIFOLD VACUUM IS PRESENT AT PORT E OF DOWNSTREAM AIR SWITCH SOLENOID.

VACUUM OK?
- NO: SUPPLY MANIFOLD VACUUM AND START TEST OVER.
- YES: TURN IGNITION ON AND TEST FOR BATTERY VOLTAGE AT YELLOW WIRE TERMINAL OF SOLENOID CONNECTOR.

VOLTAGE OK?
- NO: REPAIR AND RETEST.
- YES: TURN IGNITION OFF. DISCONNECT MCU CONNECTOR. WITH OHMMETER, MEASURE THE RESISTANCE BETWEEN MCU CONNECTOR PIN 1 (+ PROBE) AND MCU CONNECTOR PIN 46 (– PROBE).

RESISTANCE BETWEEN 50 AND 90 OHMS?
- YES: CONNECT MCU CONNECTOR. → CONT'D.
- NO: GREATER THAN 90 OHMS?
  - YES: DISCONNECT WIRE CONNECTOR FROM DOWNSTREAM SOLENOID. WITH APPROPRIATE LENGTH OF JUMPER WIRE, TEST CONTINUITY BETWEEN ORANGE WIRE TERMINAL AND MCU CONNECTOR PIN 46. → CONT'D.
  - NO: IF RESISTANCE IS LESS THAN 50 OHMS, DISCONNECT DOWNSTREAM SOLENOID WIRE CONNECTOR AND TEST RESISTANCE BETWEEN MCU CONNECTOR PIN 1 AND CONNECTOR PIN 46. → CONT'D.

JEEP COMPUTERIZED EMISSION CONTROL 4-CYLINDER & 6-CYLINDER (Cont.)

TEST NO. 7 (Cont.)

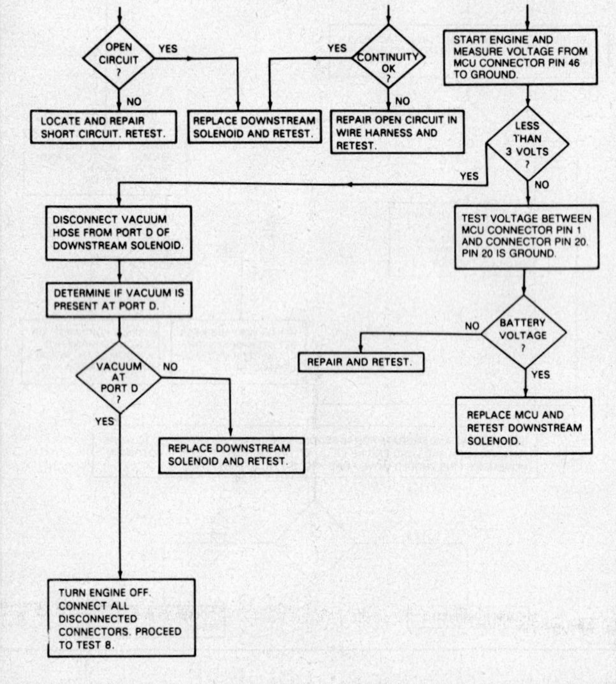

TEST NO. 8 (Cont.)

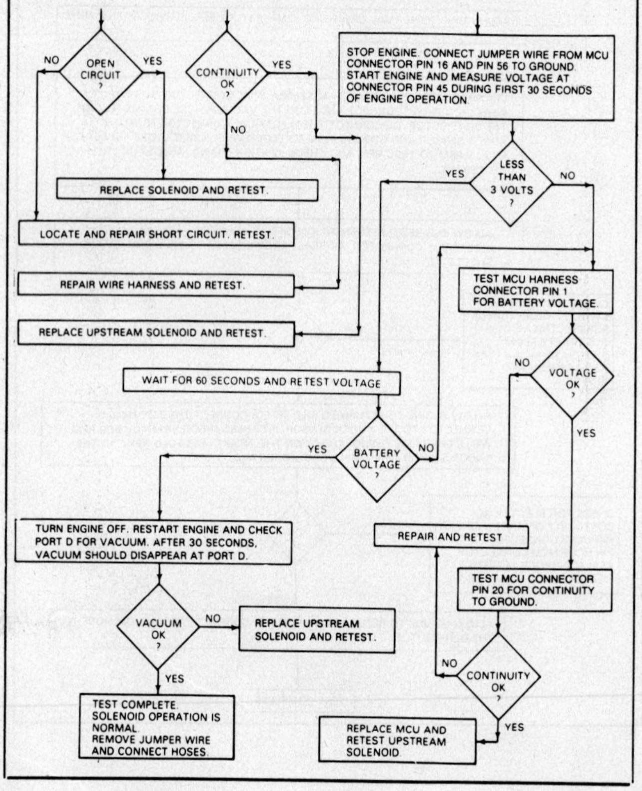

TEST NO. 8 "UPSTREAM" SOLENOID TEST

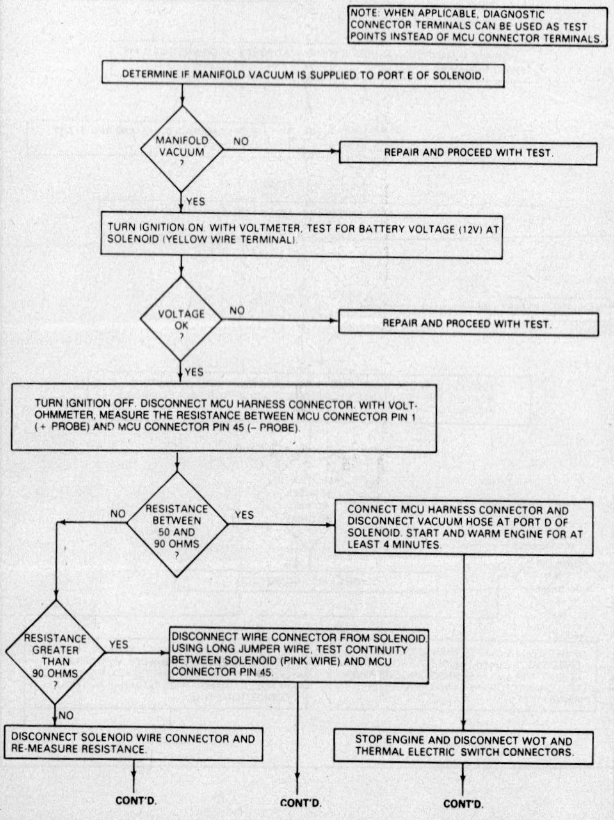

TEST NO. 9 IDLE SPEED CONTROL SYSTEM TEST

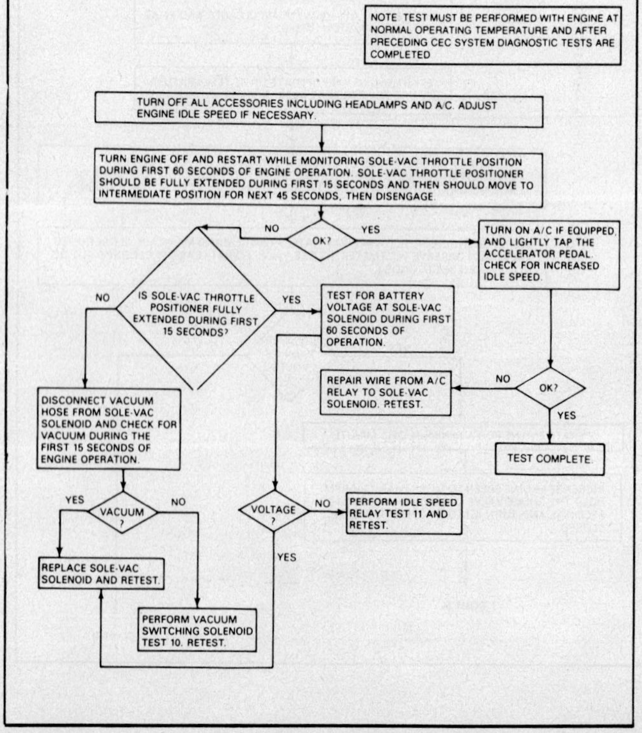

JEEP COMPUTERIZED EMISSION CONTROL
4-CYLINDER & 6-CYLINDER (Cont.)

TEST NO. 10
SOLE-VAC VACUUM SWITCHING TEST

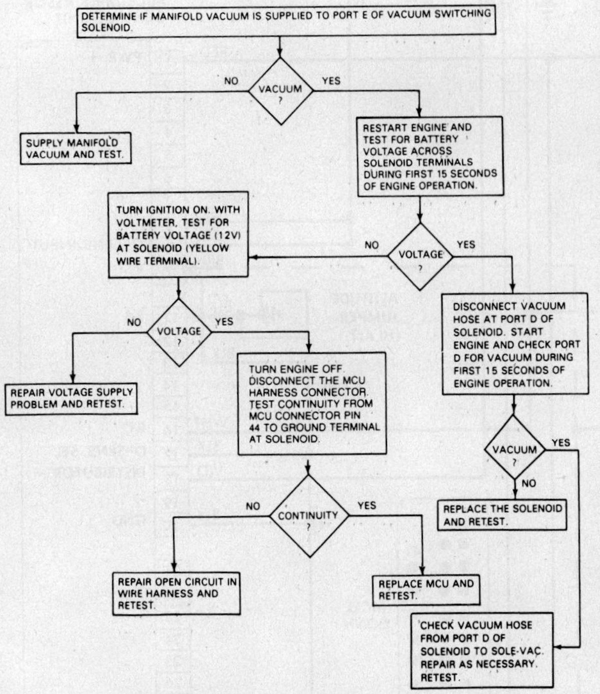

TEST NO. 11
SOLE-VAC IDLE SPEED RELAY TEST

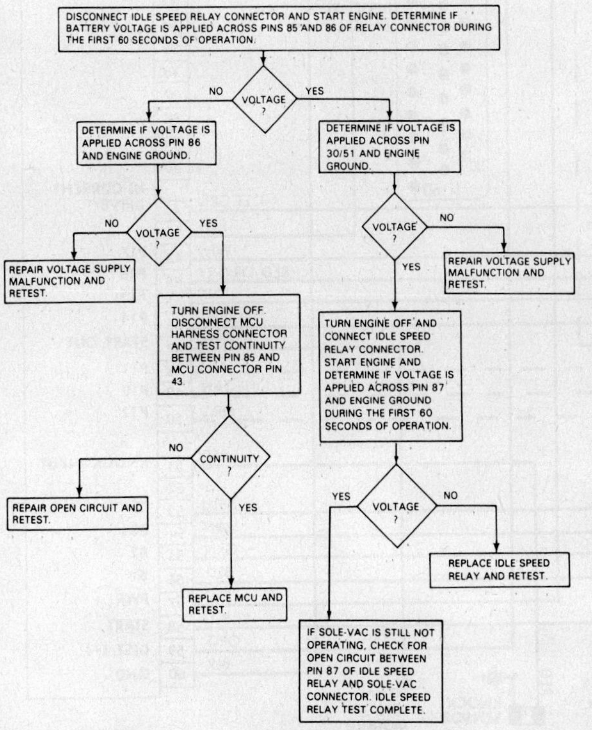

TEST NO. 12
BASIC ENGINE TEST

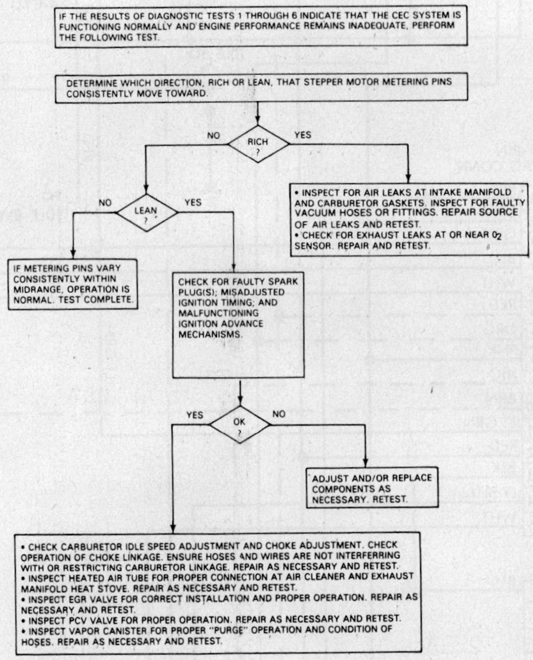

1985 Computerized Engine Controls

JEEP COMPUTERIZED EMISSION CONTROL 4-CYLINDER & 6-CYLINDER (Cont.)

Fig. 4: Jeep 4-Cylinder & 6-Cylinder CEC System Wiring Diagram

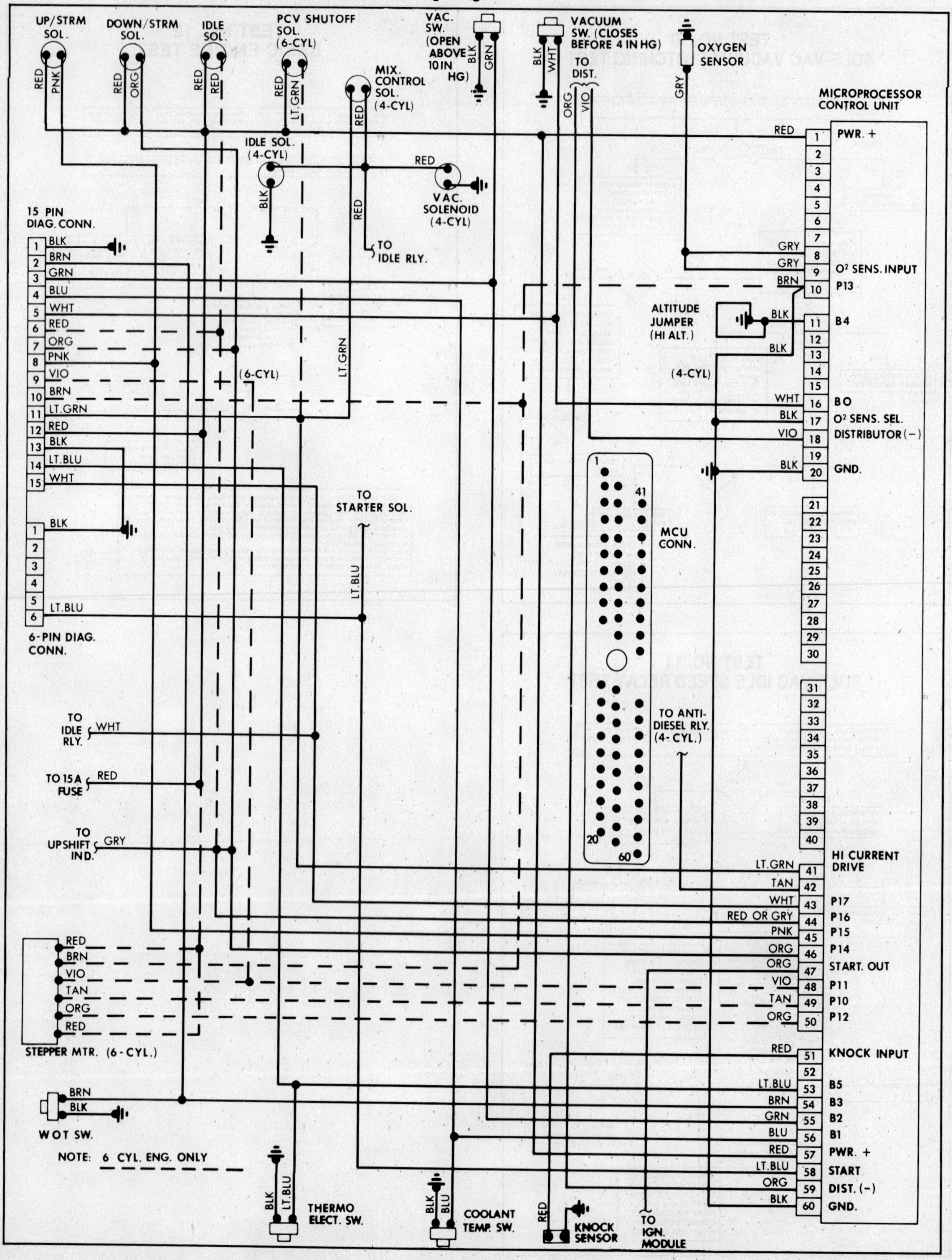

JEEP COMPUTERIZED EMISSION CONTROL 4-CYLINDER & 6-CYLINDER (Cont.)

REMOVAL & INSTALLATION

MICROCOMPUTER CONTROL UNIT

Removal & Installation

The MCU is located behind the right front kick panel. Remove MCU mounting bolts and disconnect wiring harness connector. DO NOT bend connector pins when removing. Reconnect harness to MCU and replace mounting bolts.

MIXTURE CONTROL (M/C) SOLENOID (4-CYL.)

Removal & Installation

Remove air cleaner and disconnect solenoid harness connector. Remove retaining screws and remove solenoid from carburetor. Coat rubber seal, on end of solenoid stem, with silicone grease or light engine oil prior to reinsertion. Using a new gasket, replace solenoid. Reconnect wiring harness and replace air cleaner.

Fig. 5: M/C Solenoid Location on Carburetor (4-Cyl.)

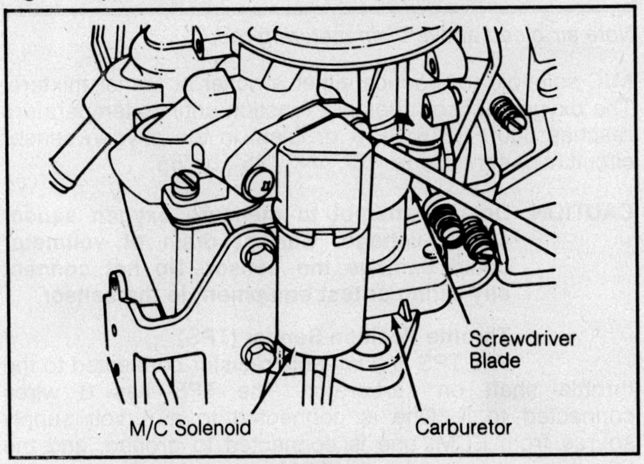

STEPPER MOTOR (6-CYL.)

Removal & Installation

Remove air cleaner and disconnect motor connector. Remove retaining screw and unit from carburetor, without dropping metering pins and spring. To install, reverse removal procedure and tighten screw to 25 INCH Lbs. (2.8 N.m).

Fig. 6: Stepper Motor Connector Terminals (6-Cyl.)

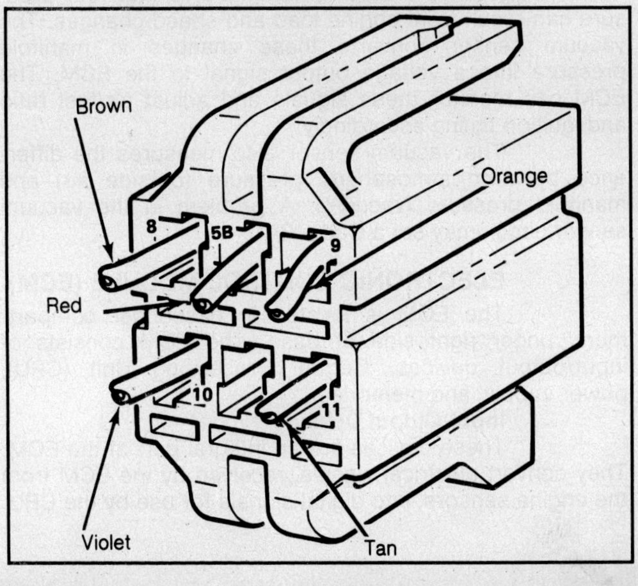

OXYGEN SENSOR

Removal & Installation

Disconnect wire connector from oxygen sensor. Remove sensor from exhaust manifold. Clean threads in manifold. Coat threads of replacement sensor with anti-seize compound. Install new sensor in exhaust manifold and tighten to 32-38 ft. lbs. (43-51 N.m). Reconnect wire connector.

JEEP V6 COMPUTERIZED EMISSION CONTROL

Calif. Cherokee & Wagoneer

DESCRIPTION

The Computerized Emission Control system (CEC) is used on California V6 models. It is an electronically controlled system that controls engine operation and lowers exhaust emissions, while maintaining good fuel economy and driveability. The Electronic Control Module (ECM) is the "brain" of the system. The ECM monitors many engine-related systems to constantly adjust engine operation.

The CEC system is primarily an emission control system, designed to maintain a 14.7:1 air/fuel ratio under all operating conditions. When the ideal air/fuel ratio is maintained, the catalytic converter can control oxides of nitrogen (NOx), hydrocarbon (HC), and carbon monoxide (CO) emissions.

OPERATION

The CEC system consists of the following sub-systems: fuel control, data sensors, Electronic Control Module (ECM), spark timing, catalytic converter, and diagnostic system. The EGR and AIR diverter solenoids are also controlled by the ECM.

FUEL CONTROL

A feedback carburetor is used which contains an electronically operated mixture control (M/C) solenoid. The M/C solenoid controls a metering rod in the float bowl. The metering rod system supplements fuel supplied by the idle and main systems in the carburetor. It varies the air/fuel ratio within a precalibrated range.

The M/C solenoid also controls air/fuel ratio through the use of an idle air bleed that operates in conjunction with the metering rod. A problem in the M/C solenoid circuit may set a Code "23" or "54".

DATA SENSORS

Each sensor furnishes electronic impulses to the ECM. The ECM computes spark timing and air/fuel mixture ratio for proper engine operation.

Coolant Temperature Sensor (CTS)

The CTS is located in coolant passage. The ECM sends a 5 volt signal to the CTS. This 5 volt signal is reduced by the resistance of the CTS and a voltage signal goes back to the ECM. When coolant temperatures are low, CTS resistance is high and a low voltage signal is sent to the ECM. When coolant temperatures are high, CTS resistance is low and a higher voltage signal is sent to the ECM. Coolant sensor problems may set a Code "14" or "15".

Distributor Reference Signal

The ECM monitors this signal to determine if the engine is running. A problem in this circuit may set a Code "12" or "41".

Oxygen Sensor

The oxygen sensor is located in the exhaust pipe to measure oxygen content of exhaust gases. The oxygen content reacts with the oxygen sensor to produce a voltage output signal. This signal is low (about .1 volt) when a lean mixture is present and high (about .9 volt) when a rich mixture is present.

When the ECM reads the voltage signal from the oxygen sensor, the ECM will alter commands to the M/C solenoid to produce either a richer or leaner mixture. The oxygen sensor does not function until its temperature reaches 600°F (316°C). A problem in the oxygen sensor circuit may set a Code "13", "44", "45", or "55".

Fig. 1: Sectional View of Mixture Control Solenoid

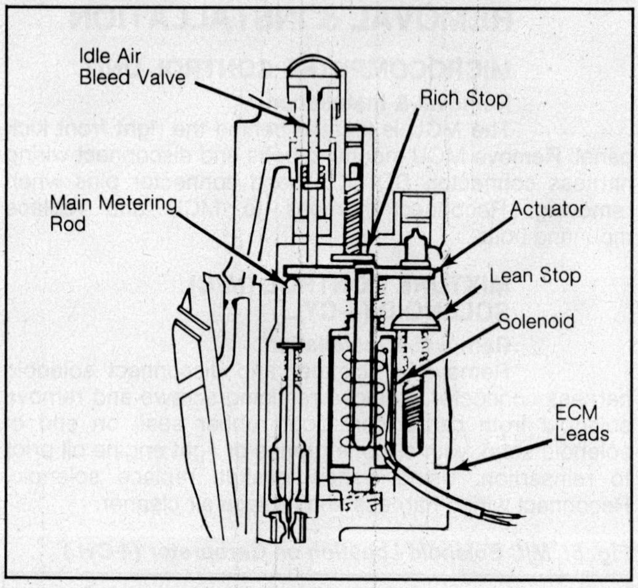

Note air bleed above main metering rod.

CAUTION: Do not attempt to measure oxygen sensor output voltage. Current drain of voltmeter could damage the sensor. Do not connect any wiring or test equipment to the sensor.

Throttle Position Sensor (TPS)

The TPS is a variable resistor connected to the throttle shaft on carburetor. The TPS has 3 wires connected to it. One is connected to a 5 volt supply source from ECM, one is connected to ground, and the other is connected to the ECM to send voltage signals according to throttle position. The voltage signal from the TPS varies from closed throttle to wide open throttle. A problem in the TPS circuit may set a Code "21".

Vacuum Sensor

The vacuum sensor measures changes in manifold pressure (vacuum). Changes in manifold pressure can result from engine load and speed changes. The vacuum sensor converts these changes in manifold pressure into a voltage output signal to the ECM. The ECM can monitor these signals and adjust air/fuel ratio and ignition timing accordingly.

The vacuum sensor also measures the difference between atmospheric pressure (outside air) and manifold pressure (vacuum). A problem in the vacuum sensor circuit may set a Code "34".

ELECTRONIC CONTROL MODULE (ECM)

The ECM is located in passenger compartment, under right side of dash. The ECM consists of input/output devices, Central Processing Unit (CPU), power supply, and memories.

Input/Output Devices

These devices are an integral part of the ECM. They convert electrical signals, received by the ECM from the engine sensors, into digital signals for use by the CPU.

JEEP V6 COMPUTERIZED EMISSION CONTROL (Cont.)

Central Processing Unit (CPU)

Digital signals received by the CPU are used to perform all mathematical computations and logic functions necessary to deliver proper air/fuel mixture. The CPU also calculates spark timing information. The CPU commands operation of closed loop fuel control and diagnostic system.

Power Supply

The main source of power for the ECM is from the battery, through the ignition circuit.

Memories

The 3 types of memories in the ECM are: Read Only Memory (ROM), Random Access Memory (RAM), and Programmable Read Only Memory (PROM).

- **Read Only Memory (ROM)** – The ROM is preprogrammed information that can only be read by the ECM. The ROM program cannot be changed. If battery voltage is removed, ROM information will be retained.
- **Random Access Memory (RAM)** – This memory is the decision making center for the CPU. It works like a calculator. Data sensor input, diagnostic codes and results of calculations are temporarily stored in the RAM memory. If battery voltage is removed from the ECM, all information stored in this memory is lost.
- **Programmable Read Only Memory (PROM)** – This memory is factory programmed information, including engine calibration data, transmission, vehicle weight, and rear axle ratio application. The PROM can be removed from the ECM. If battery voltage is removed, PROM information will be retained.

SPARK TIMING

Jeep V6 models are equipped with Delco-Remy High Energy Ignition system with Electronic Spark Timing (HEI-EST). The distributor contains a 7-terminal HEI-EST control module. The distributor is connected to the EST system by means of a 4-wire connector, leading to the external electronic control module (ECM).

When engine speed reaches 600 RPM or more (about 5-15 seconds after starting), the ECM transmits a constant 5 volt signal to the distributor HEI-EST module. This changes the position of the by-pass switch in the HEI-EST module.

When this occurs, the pickup coil's signals no longer flow directly to the ignition coil. Instead, the RPM signals are routed to the ECM.

The Programmable Read Only Memory (PROM) portion of the ECM has a basic spark advance curve based on engine speed. Spark timing is calculated by the ECM whenever an ignition pulse is present. Spark advance is controlled only when the engine is running (not during cranking). Engine sensor values are used by the ECM to modify the PROM information, increasing or decreasing spark advance to achieve maximum performance with minimum emissions.

CATALYTIC CONVERTER

Proper emission control is accomplished with the monolithic-type catalytic converter used with the CEC system. In order for the converter to be effective, precise control of the oxygen content of exhaust gases entering the converter is necessary; thus the need for the oxygen sensor, ECM and feedback carburetor.

DIAGNOSTIC SYSTEM

NOTE: **A "CHECK ENGINE" lamp driver is installed in the wiring harness from ECM to the "CHECK ENGINE" lamp. This driver amplifies the power to the "CHECK ENGINE" lamp to reduce amperage draw on the battery.**

The ECM of the CEC system is equipped with a self-diagnostic system which detects system failures or abnormalities. When a malfunction occurs, the ECM will light the "CHECK ENGINE" lamp, located on the instrument panel. When the malfunction is detected and the lamp is turned on, a corresponding trouble code will be stored in ECM memory. Malfunctions are recorded as "hard failures" or as "intermittent failures".

- "Hard failures" cause the "CHECK ENGINE" lamp to glow and remain on until the malfunction is repaired. If the "CHECK ENGINE" lamp comes on and remains on during vehicle operation, the cause of the malfunction must be determined.
- "Intermittent failures" cause the "CHECK ENGINE" lamp to flicker or go out after about 10 seconds when the fault goes away. However, the corresponding trouble code will be retained in ECM memory. "Intermittent failures" may be sensor related. If a sensor fails, the ECM will use a substitute value in its calculations to continue engine operation. In this condition, service is not mandatory; but loss of driveability may be encountered. If the related fault does not reoccur within 50 engine starts, the related trouble code will be erased from ECM memory.

As a bulb and system check, the "CHECK ENGINE" lamp will glow when the ignition switch is turned on and the engine is not running. When the engine is started, the lamp should go out. If not, a malfunction has been detected in the CEC system.

NOTE: **Trouble codes will be recorded at various operating times. Some codes require operation of that sensor or switch for 5 seconds; others require operation for 5 minutes or longer.**

DIAGNOSIS & TESTING

DIAGNOSTIC PROCEDURE

Diagnosis of the CEC system should be performed in the following order:

1) Make sure that all engine systems not related to the CEC system are operating properly. Do not proceed with testing unless all other problems have been repaired.

2) Put the system into diagnostic mode and record trouble codes flashed by "CHECK ENGINE" lamp. Exit the diagnostic mode.

3) If trouble codes were displayed, decide whether the codes are "hard" or "intermittent" trouble codes.

4) Proceed to Diagnostic Circuit Check chart. Follow all instructions given in that chart.

5) If no trouble codes were displayed, proceed to System Performance Check chart.

JEEP V6 COMPUTERIZED EMISSION CONTROL (Cont.)

6) If the lamp illuminates intermittently, but no trouble codes are stored in ECM memory, proceed to Driver Complaint chart.

7) After any repairs are made, always perform System Performance Check. Clear any trouble codes.

NOTE: **Each of the steps listed here are described later in this section. If you are unsure of the proper way to test, read through the following material.**

ENTERING OR EXITING DIAGNOSTIC MODE

1) Turn ignition switch on, but do not start engine. "CHECK ENGINE" lamp should glow. Locate diagnostic connectors in engine compartment, on left shock tower. Insert jumper wire between "TEST" terminal (6) and "GROUND" terminal (7) of diagnostic connector "D2". *See Fig. 2.*

CAUTION: **Inserting jumper wire in terminals of diagnostic connector "D2", grounds "TEST" terminal lead. Do not ground diagnostic connector until after ignition is turned on or engine is started.**

Fig. 2: Diagnostic Connector Terminals

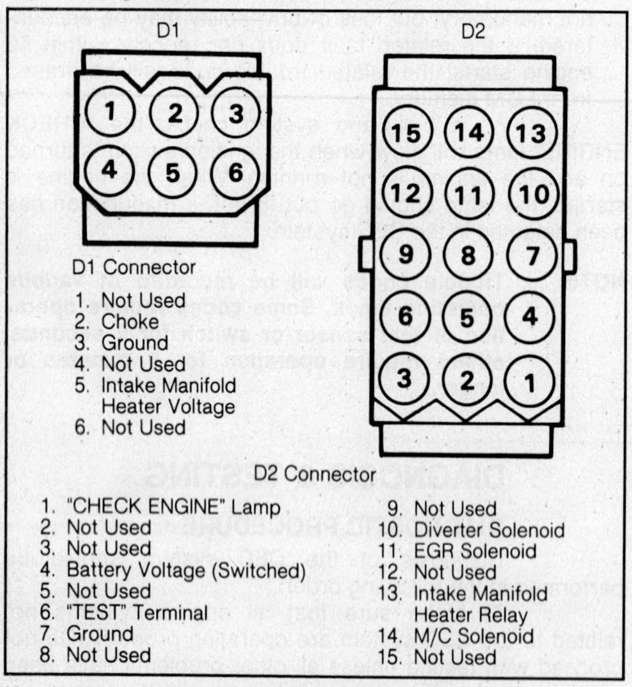

Use jumper wire to ground "TEST" terminal.

CLEARING TROUBLE CODES

To clear trouble codes from ECM memory, disconnect battery for at least 10 seconds.

READING TROUBLE CODES

The ECM stores component failure information for CEC system under a related trouble code which can be recalled for diagnosis and repair. When recalled, these codes will be displayed by flashes of the "CHECK ENGINE" lamp. Trouble codes are displayed starting with the lowest numbered code. Only codes that represent a definite malfunction will be shown.

Trouble codes are read by counting flashes of the "CHECK ENGINE" lamp. For example, "FLASH", "FLASH", pause, "FLASH", longer pause, identifies "21". The first flashes are the first digit of trouble code; second series of flashes are second digit of trouble code.

ECM TROUBLE CODE IDENTIFICATION

Code	Circuit Affected
13	Oxygen sensor circuit.
14	Shorted coolant sensor circuit.
15	Open coolant sensor circuit.
21	Open or short in TPS circuit.
23	Open or short in M/C solenoid circuit.
34	Open or short in vacuum sensor circuit.
41	No distributor reference at specified manifold vacuum level.
42	Open or short in EST system.
44	Lean exhaust indication.
45	Rich exhaust indication.
44 & 45 (At same time)	Faulty oxygen sensor circuit.
51	Faulty PROM or PROM installation.
54	Shorted M/C solenoid circuit or faulty ECM.
55	Shorted voltage reference circuit, faulty oxygen sensor or faulty ECM.

Code "12" will display only if no reference pulses are received by ECM; it will never be stored as a malfunction.

TROUBLE CODE DETERMINATION (HARD OR INTERMITTENT)

During any diagnostic procedure, you must decide between "hard failure" and "intermittent failure" codes. Diagnostic charts will not usually help analyze "intermittent failure" codes. To determine "hard failure" codes and "intermittent failure" codes, proceed as follows:

1) Enter diagnostic mode. Read and record all stored trouble codes. Exit diagnostic mode and clear trouble codes.

2) Apply parking brake and place transmission in Neutral (man. trans.) or "P" (auto. trans.). Block drive wheels and start engine. "CHECK ENGINE" lamp should go out. Run warm engine at specified curb idle for 2 minutes and note "CHECK ENGINE" lamp.

3) If "CHECK ENGINE" lamp comes on, enter diagnostic mode. Read and record trouble codes. This will reveal "hard failure" codes. Codes "13", "14", "15", "34", "44", "45" and "55" may require a road test to reset "hard failure" after trouble codes were cleared.

NOTE: **Any time codes "51", "54" or "55" are displayed with another code, start with "50-series" code first, then proceed to lowest numbered code.**

4) If "CHECK ENGINE" lamp does not come on, all stored trouble codes were "intermittent failures". Exceptions are noted under Diagnostic Procedure.

DIAGNOSTIC MATERIALS

NOTE: **The charts described in the following paragraphs are arranged later in this article.**

JEEP V6 COMPUTERIZED EMISSION CONTROL (Cont.)

Diagnostic Charts

The Diagnostic Charts are used to find and repair problems which the On-Car Diagnostics have located. These charts include:

- Charts which fix a problem when the On-Car Diagnostics don't work.
- Charts where a stored trouble code leads you to a particular problem.
- Charts which are used because the System Performance Check found a problem.
- "Engine Cranks But Won't Run" charts.

Diagnostic Circuit Check

1) If complaint is "CHECK ENGINE" lamp related, this check will lead to the most likely problem area, if a malfunction exists. Enter diagnostic mode and record trouble codes. Begin diagnosis with the lowest numbered code shown and go to the numbered trouble code chart.

2) If code "51" is displayed, see PROM removal and installation in this article. If codes "54" or "55" are displayed with another code, always refer to diagnostic chart for code "54" or 55" first, then proceed to next lowest numbered code.

Driver Complaint Chart

1) If the "CHECK ENGINE" lamp illuminates intermittently, but no trouble code is stored in ECM memory, this chart will lead to the most likely problem area. However, first make checks that would normally be made for the complaint on a vehicle without CEC system.

2) Follow instructions in chart and repair malfunction. After repair, perform System Performance Check.

System Performance Check

1) This check verifies that CEC system is functioning correctly. This check should always be made after any repair on CEC system.

2) When performing this check, always engage parking brake and block DRIVE wheels. Remove bowl vent line at carburetor and plug hose at carburetor during check and reconnect it after the check is complete.

3) The oxygen sensor may cool off after only a short period of time while engine is idling. This will cause engine to go into open loop. To restore closed loop mode, run engine at part throttle for several minutes and accelerate from part throttle several times.

NOTE: **Although there are many charts connected with CEC diagnosis, only 2 charts are needed to prove the system is operating properly. Normally, only 3 charts are necessary to find a problem, if one exists.**

DIAGNOSTIC TOOLS

The CEC system does not require special tools for diagnosis. A tachometer, a dwell meter, test light, ohmmeter, digital voltmeter with 10 megohms impedance (minimum), vacuum pump, vacuum gauge, and 6 jumper wires 6" long (1 wire with female connectors at both ends; 1 wire with male connectors at both ends; 4 wires with male and female connectors at opposite ends) are the only tools necessary for diagnosis.

A test light, rather than a voltmeter, must be used when indicated by a diagnostic chart.

The dwell meter is used to measure the time the M/C solenoid is on or off. This indicates if the M/C solenoid is working and the fuel mixture strength (rich or lean). The dwell meter is set on the 6-cylinder scale.

Dwell meter is connected to Green connector, located near the carburetor. This connector will not be connected to any circuit EXCEPT when you are testing with the dwell meter. DO NOT allow terminal wire to come in contact with any ground source, including rubber hoses.

NOTE: **If engine operation seems to change when dwell meter is connected to Green wire, remove dwell meter and use another type. A few brands are not compatible with the CEC system.**

When the engine is at operating temperature and idling, dwell meter needle should be varying between 10-50°. This indicates closed loop mode of operation. If the needle does not move, open loop operation is indicated.

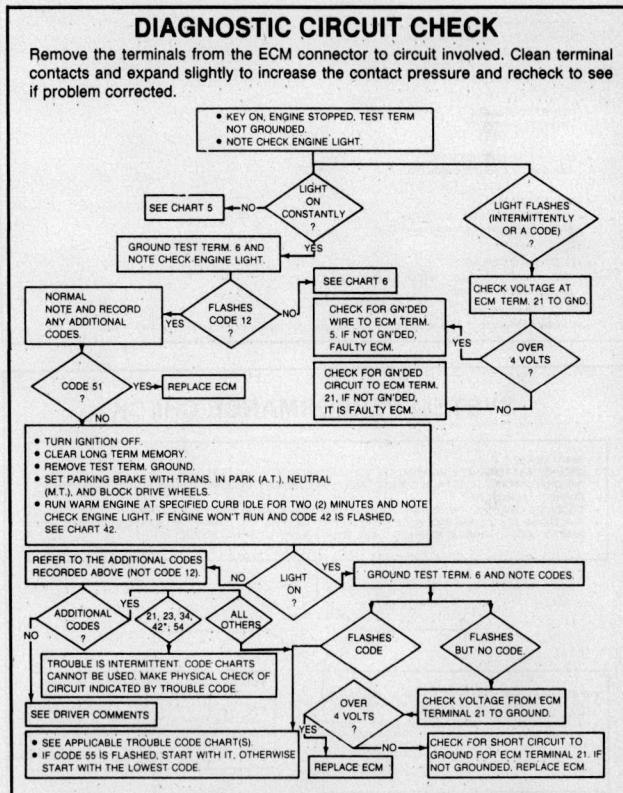

DIAGNOSTIC CIRCUIT CHECK

Remove the terminals from the ECM connector to circuit involved. Clean terminal contacts and expand slightly to increase the contact pressure and recheck to see if problem corrected.

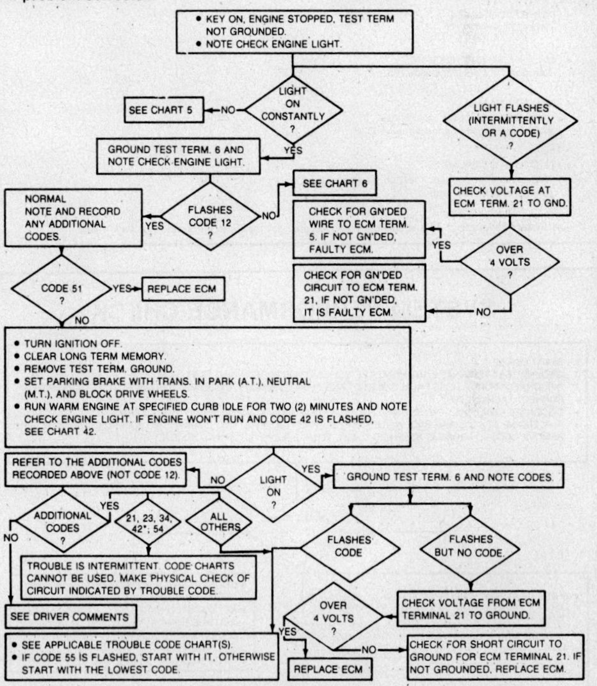

See Code Clearing Procedure. System Performance Test should be performed after any repairs to system are completed.

* It is possible to have a false code 42 on starting, but Check Engine light will not be ON. No corrective action necessary.

Before replacing ECM, remove the terminals from the ECM connector to circuit involved. Clean terminal contacts and expand slightly to increase the contact pressure and recheck to see if problem corrected. In case of repeat ECM failure, check for shorted solenoid relay or relay controlled by ECM.

JEEP V6 COMPUTERIZED EMISSION CONTROL (Cont.)

DRIVER COMPLAINT CHART

ENGINE PERFORMANCE PROBLEM (ODOR, SURGE, FUEL ECONOMY ...) EMISSION PROBLEM

IF THE CHECK ENGINE LIGHT IS NOT ON, NORMAL CHECKS THAT WOULD BE PERFORMED ON THE VEHICLE WITHOUT THE SYSTEM SHOULD BE DONE FIRST.

IF THE ALTERNATOR OR COOLANT LIGHT IS ON WITH THE CHECK ENGINE LIGHT, THEY SHOULD BE DIAGNOSED FIRST.

INSPECT FOR POOR CONNECTIONS AT COOLANT SENSOR, MC SOLENOID, ETC., AND POOR OR LOOSE VACUUM HOSES AND CONNECTIONS. REPAIR AS NECESSARY.

- Intermittent Check Engine light but no trouble code stored.
  - Check for intermittent connection in circuit from:
    - Ignition coil to ground and arcing at spark plug wires or plugs.
    - ECM Voltage Supply Terminals.
    - ECM Ground Terminals.
  - Loss of long-term memory.
    Grounding dwell lead for 10 seconds with test lead ungrounded should give Code 23, which should be retained after the engine is stopped and the ignition turned to RUN position.
    If it is not, ECM is defective.
  - EST wires should be kept away from the spark plug wires, distributor housing, coil and alternator. Wires from ECM Term. 13 to dist. and the shield around EST wires should have a good ground.
  - Open diode across A/C compressor clutch.
- Stalling, Rough Idle, Dieseling or Improper Idle Speed.
- Detonation (spark knock)
  Check: MAP or Vacuum Sensor output.
  EGR operation.
  TPS enrichment operation
  HEI operation.
- Poor Performance and/or Fuel Economy.
  Check EST system.
- Poor Full Throttle Performance
  See Chart 4 if equipped with TPS.
- Intermittent No-start
  - Incorrect pickup coil or ignition coil.
  - Intermittent ground connections on ECM.
- ALL OTHER COMPLAINTS
  Make system performance test on warm engine.
  (upper radiator hose hot).

The System Performance Test should be performed after any repairs to the system has been made.

CHART 1
DWELL FIXED UNDER 10°

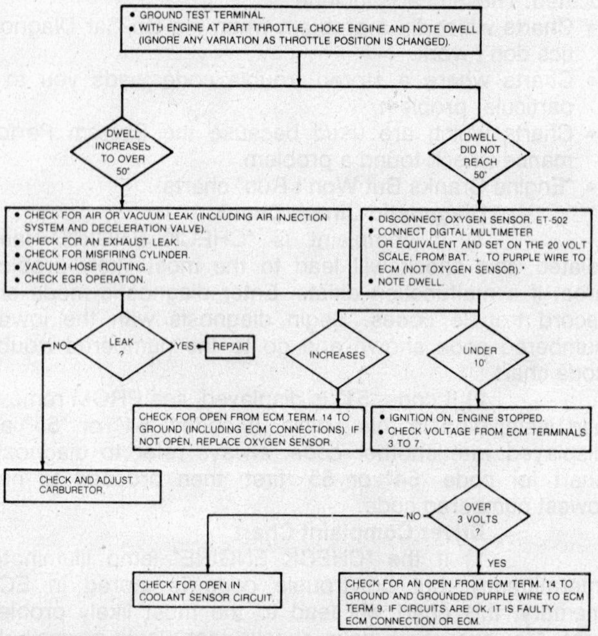

* Do not use ordinary voltmeter or jumper in place of digital voltmeter because they have too little input impedance. A voltage source of 1.0v to 1.7v (flashlight battery) can be connected with the positive terminal to the Purple wire and negative terminal to Ground as a jumper. If polarity reversed, it will not work.

SYSTEM PERFORMANCE CHECK

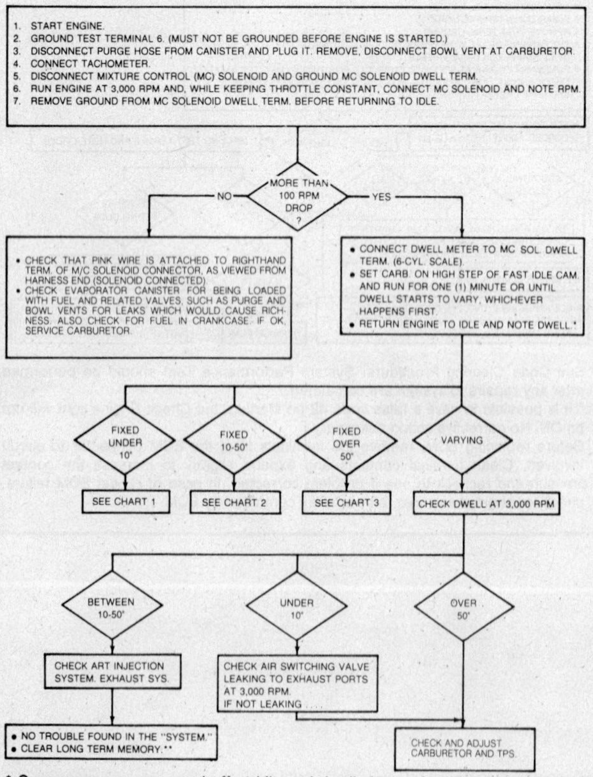

* Oxygen sensors may cool off at idle and dwell change from varying to fixed. If this happens, running engine at fast idle will warm it up again.
** See code clearing procedure.

CHART 2
DWELL FIXED BETWEEN 10°-50°

Check for sticking TPS plunger and adjustment and low coolant.

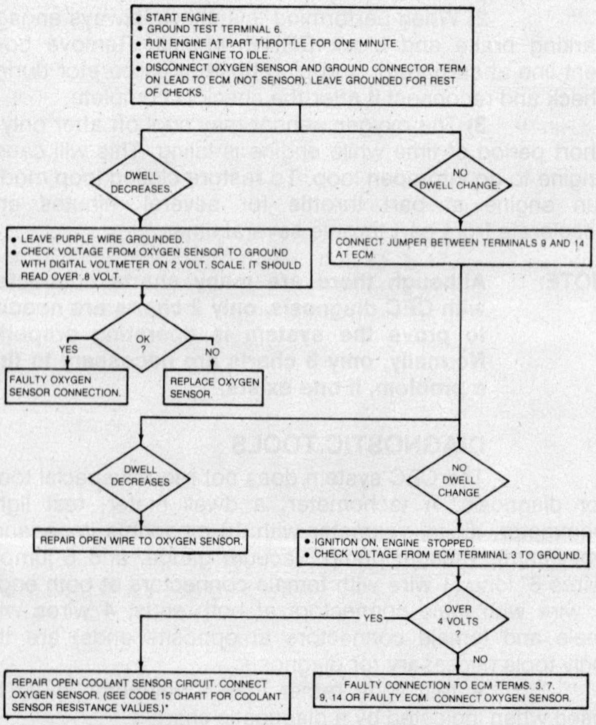

JEEP V6 COMPUTERIZED EMISSION CONTROL (Cont.)

CHART 3
DWELL FIXED OVER 50°

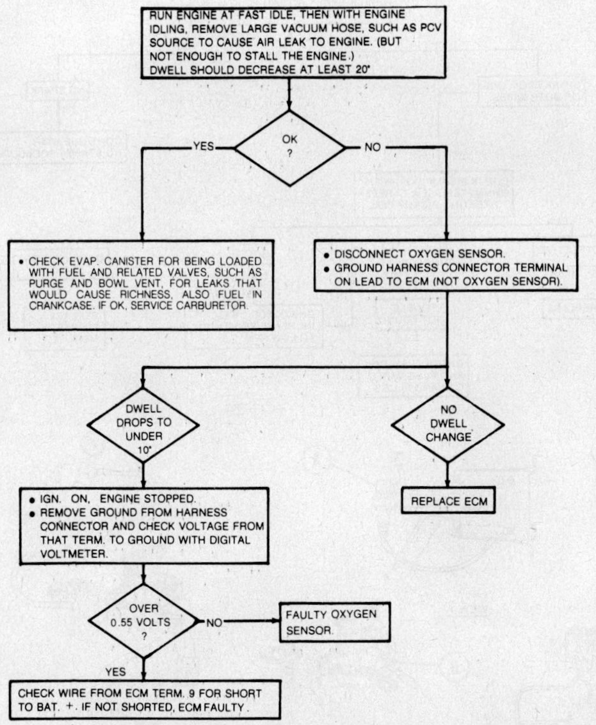

RUN ENGINE AT FAST IDLE, THEN WITH ENGINE IDLING, REMOVE LARGE VACUUM HOSE, SUCH AS PCV SOURCE TO CAUSE AIR LEAK TO ENGINE. (BUT NOT ENOUGH TO STALL THE ENGINE.) DWELL SHOULD DECREASE AT LEAST 20°
OK ?
YES
NO
• CHECK EVAP. CANISTER FOR BEING LOADED WITH FUEL AND RELATED VALVES, SUCH AS PURGE AND BOWL VENT, FOR LEAKS THAT WOULD CAUSE RICHNESS, ALSO FUEL IN CRANKCASE. IF OK, SERVICE CARBURETOR.
• DISCONNECT OXYGEN SENSOR.
• GROUND HARNESS CONNECTOR TERMINAL ON LEAD TO ECM (NOT OXYGEN SENSOR).
DWELL DROPS TO UNDER 10°
NO DWELL CHANGE
REPLACE ECM
• IGN. ON, ENGINE STOPPED.
• REMOVE GROUND FROM HARNESS CONNECTOR AND CHECK VOLTAGE FROM THAT TERM. TO GROUND WITH DIGITAL VOLTMETER.
OVER 0.55 VOLTS ?
NO
FAULTY OXYGEN SENSOR.
YES
CHECK WIRE FROM ECM TERM. 9 FOR SHORT TO BAT. +. IF NOT SHORTED, ECM FAULTY.

CHART 5
CHECK ENGINE LIGHT INOPERATIVE

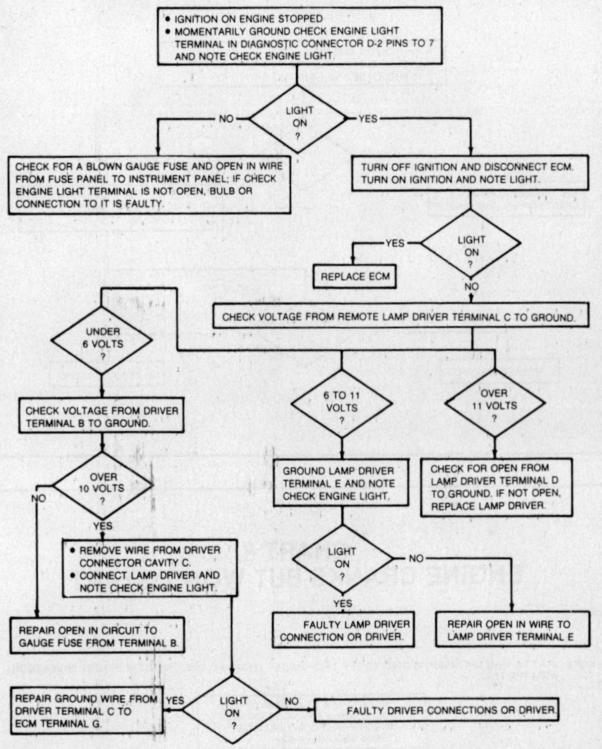

CHART 4
TPS ENRICHMENT CHECK

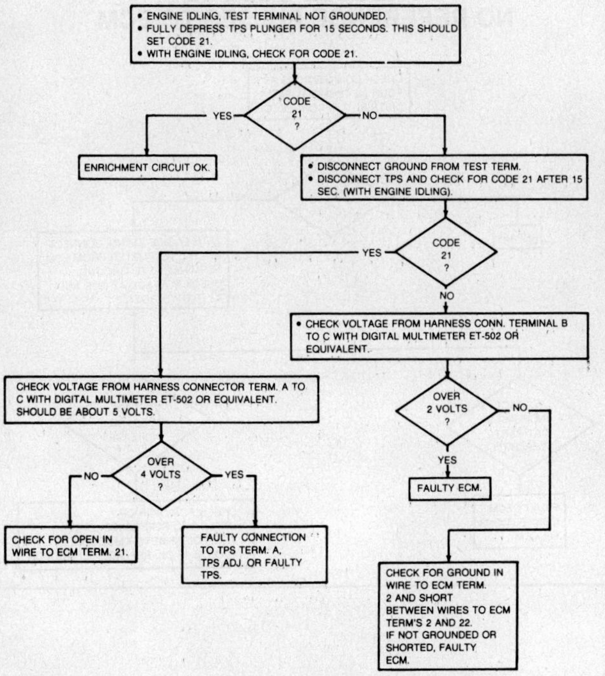

• ENGINE IDLING, TEST TERMINAL NOT GROUNDED.
• FULLY DEPRESS TPS PLUNGER FOR 15 SECONDS. THIS SHOULD SET CODE 21.
• WITH ENGINE IDLING, CHECK FOR CODE 21.
CODE 21 ?
YES
NO
ENRICHMENT CIRCUIT OK.
• DISCONNECT GROUND FROM TEST TERM.
• DISCONNECT TPS AND CHECK FOR CODE 21 AFTER 15 SEC. (WITH ENGINE IDLING).
CODE 21 ?
YES
NO
• CHECK VOLTAGE FROM HARNESS CONN. TERMINAL B TO C WITH DIGITAL MULTIMETER ET-502 OR EQUIVALENT.
CHECK VOLTAGE FROM HARNESS CONNECTOR TERM. A TO C WITH DIGITAL MULTIMETER ET-502 OR EQUIVALENT. SHOULD BE ABOUT 5 VOLTS.
OVER 2 VOLTS ?
NO
YES
FAULTY ECM.
OVER 4 VOLTS ?
NO
YES
CHECK FOR OPEN IN WIRE TO ECM TERM. 21.
FAULTY CONNECTION TO TPS TERM. A, TPS ADJ. OR FAULTY TPS.
CHECK FOR GROUND IN WIRE TO ECM TERM. 2 AND SHORT BETWEEN WIRES TO ECM TERM'S 2 AND 22. IF NOT GROUNDED OR SHORTED, FAULTY ECM.

CHART 6
CODE 12 DOES NOT FLASH
(REMOTE LAMP DRIVER IN HARNESS)

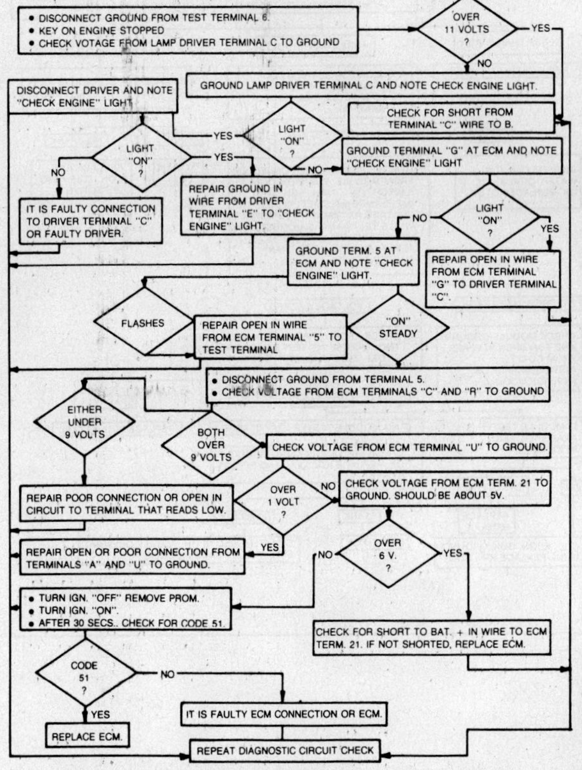

JEEP V6 COMPUTERIZED EMISSION CONTROL (Cont.)

CHART 7
VACUUM SENSOR TEST

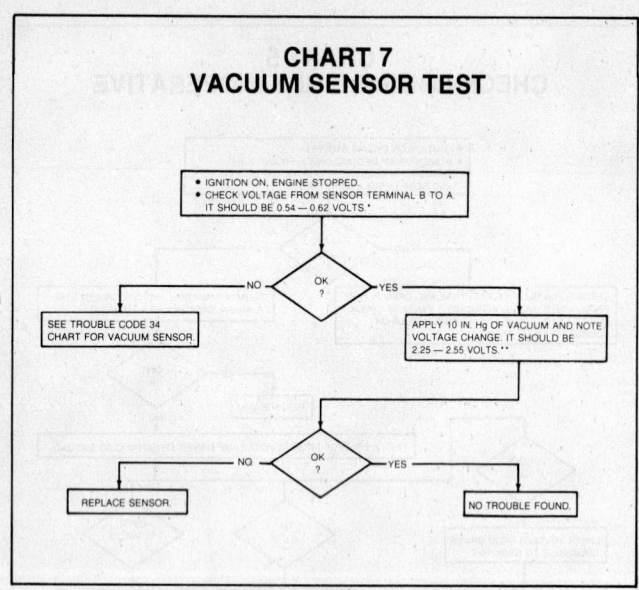

- IGNITION ON, ENGINE STOPPED.
- CHECK VOLTAGE FROM SENSOR TERMINAL B TO A. IT SHOULD BE 0.54 — 0.62 VOLTS.*

OK ?
- NO → SEE TROUBLE CODE 34 CHART FOR VACUUM SENSOR.
- YES → APPLY 10 IN. Hg OF VACUUM AND NOTE VOLTAGE CHANGE. IT SHOULD BE 2.25 — 2.55 VOLTS.**
  - OK ?
    - NO → REPLACE SENSOR.
    - YES → NO TROUBLE FOUND.

CHART 8
ENGINE CRANKS BUT WON'T START

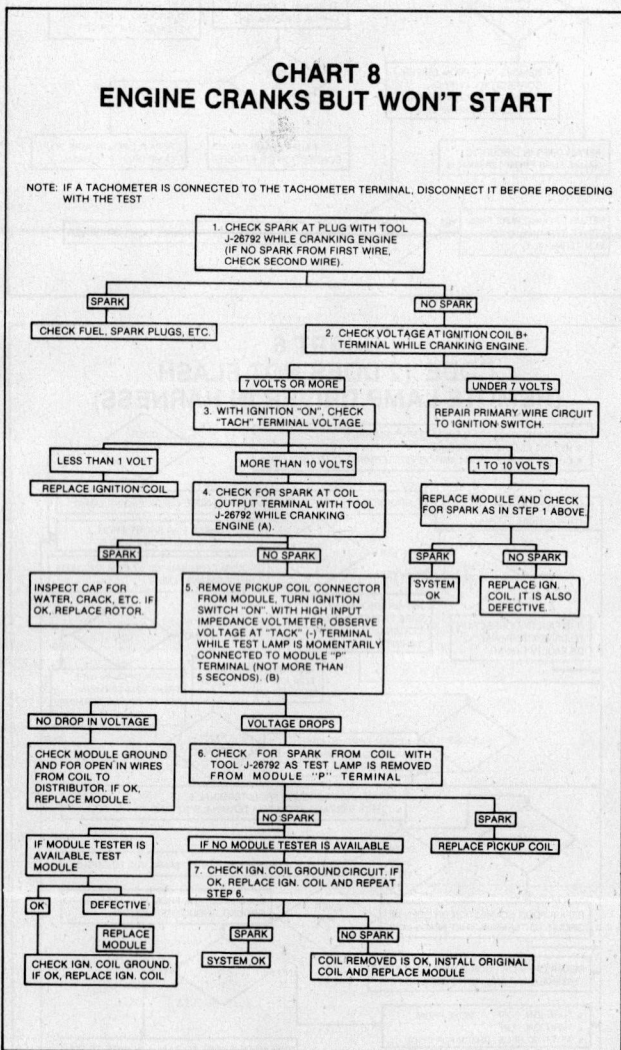

NOTE: IF A TACHOMETER IS CONNECTED TO THE TACHOMETER TERMINAL, DISCONNECT IT BEFORE PROCEEDING WITH THE TEST

1. CHECK SPARK AT PLUG WITH TOOL J-26792 WHILE CRANKING ENGINE (IF NO SPARK FROM FIRST WIRE, CHECK SECOND WIRE).
   - SPARK → CHECK FUEL, SPARK PLUGS, ETC.
   - NO SPARK → 2. CHECK VOLTAGE AT IGNITION COIL B+ TERMINAL WHILE CRANKING ENGINE.
     - UNDER 7 VOLTS → REPAIR PRIMARY WIRE CIRCUIT TO IGNITION SWITCH.
     - 7 VOLTS OR MORE → 3. WITH IGNITION "ON", CHECK "TACH" TERMINAL VOLTAGE.
       - LESS THAN 1 VOLT → REPLACE IGNITION COIL
       - 1 TO 10 VOLTS → REPLACE MODULE AND CHECK FOR SPARK AS IN STEP 1 ABOVE.
         - SPARK → SYSTEM OK
         - NO SPARK → REPLACE IGN. COIL. IT IS ALSO DEFECTIVE.
       - MORE THAN 10 VOLTS → 4. CHECK FOR SPARK AT COIL OUTPUT TERMINAL WITH TOOL J-26792 WHILE CRANKING ENGINE (A).
         - SPARK → INSPECT CAP FOR WATER, CRACK, ETC. IF OK, REPLACE ROTOR.
         - NO SPARK → 5. REMOVE PICKUP COIL CONNECTOR FROM MODULE, TURN IGNITION SWITCH "ON". WITH HIGH INPUT IMPEDANCE VOLTMETER, OBSERVE VOLTAGE AT "TACK" (-) TERMINAL WHILE TEST LAMP IS MOMENTARILY CONNECTED TO MODULE "P" TERMINAL (NOT MORE THAN 5 SECONDS). (B)
           - NO DROP IN VOLTAGE → CHECK MODULE GROUND AND FOR OPEN IN WIRES FROM COIL TO DISTRIBUTOR. IF OK, REPLACE MODULE.
           - VOLTAGE DROPS → 6. CHECK FOR SPARK FROM COIL WITH TOOL J-26792 AS TEST LAMP IS REMOVED FROM MODULE "P" TERMINAL
             - SPARK → REPLACE PICKUP COIL
             - NO SPARK →
               - IF MODULE TESTER IS AVAILABLE, TEST MODULE
                 - OK → CHECK IGN. COIL GROUND. IF OK, REPLACE IGN. COIL
                 - DEFECTIVE → REPLACE MODULE
               - IF NO MODULE TESTER IS AVAILABLE → 7. CHECK IGN. COIL GROUND CIRCUIT. IF OK, REPLACE IGN. COIL AND REPEAT STEP 6.
                 - SPARK → SYSTEM OK
                 - NO SPARK → COIL REMOVED IS OK, INSTALL ORIGINAL COIL AND REPLACE MODULE

CHART 9
INTERMITTENT ENGINE OPERATION OR ENGINE MISFIRES

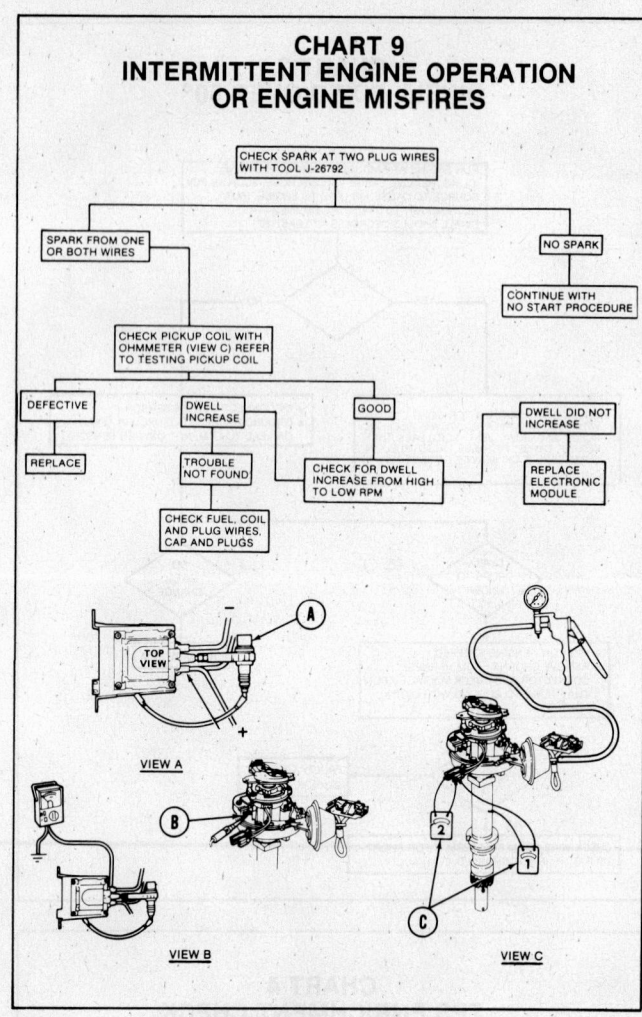

CHECK SPARK AT TWO PLUG WIRES WITH TOOL J-26792
- NO SPARK → CONTINUE WITH NO START PROCEDURE
- SPARK FROM ONE OR BOTH WIRES → CHECK PICKUP COIL WITH OHMMETER (VIEW C) REFER TO TESTING PICKUP COIL
  - DEFECTIVE → REPLACE
  - GOOD → CHECK FOR DWELL INCREASE FROM HIGH TO LOW RPM
    - DWELL INCREASE → TROUBLE NOT FOUND → CHECK FUEL, COIL AND PLUG WIRES, CAP AND PLUGS
    - DWELL DID NOT INCREASE → REPLACE ELECTRONIC MODULE

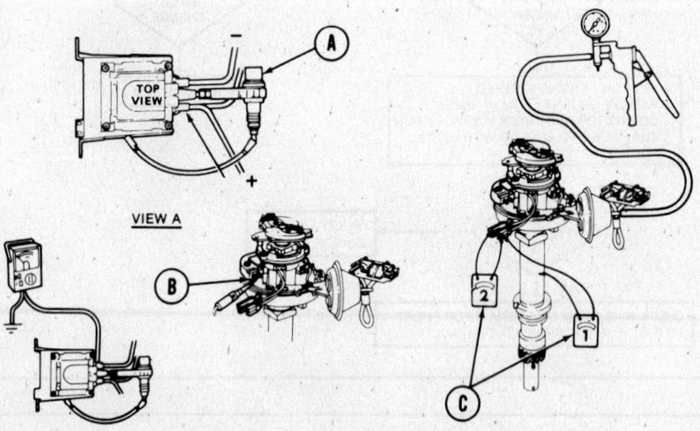

VIEW A

VIEW B

VIEW C

TROUBLE CODE 12
NO REFERENCE PULSES TO ECM

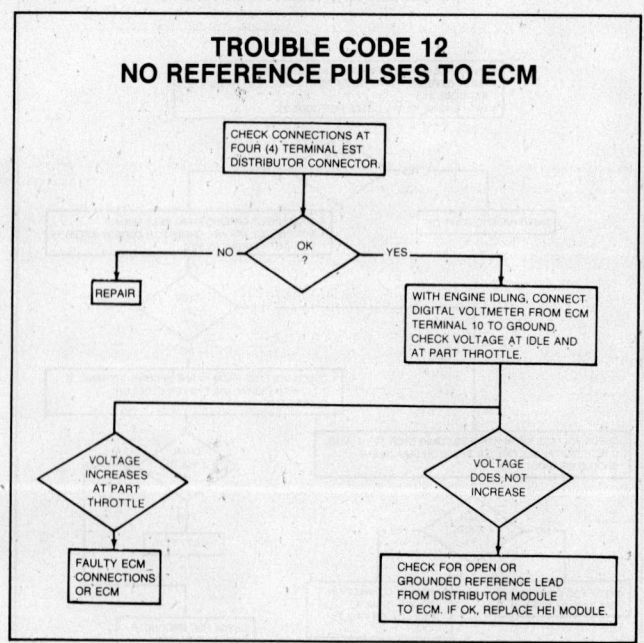

CHECK CONNECTIONS AT FOUR (4) TERMINAL EST DISTRIBUTOR CONNECTOR.

OK ?
- NO → REPAIR
- YES → WITH ENGINE IDLING, CONNECT DIGITAL VOLTMETER FROM ECM TERMINAL 10 TO GROUND. CHECK VOLTAGE AT IDLE AND AT PART THROTTLE.
  - VOLTAGE INCREASES AT PART THROTTLE → FAULTY ECM CONNECTIONS OR ECM
  - VOLTAGE DOES NOT INCREASE → CHECK FOR OPEN OR GROUNDED REFERENCE LEAD FROM DISTRIBUTOR MODULE TO ECM. IF OK, REPLACE HEI MODULE.

JEEP V6 COMPUTERIZED EMISSION CONTROL (Cont.)

TROUBLE CODE 13
OPEN OXYGEN SENSOR CIRCUIT

Check for sticking TPS plunger and adjustment. If codes 13 and 21 are displayed, go to Code 21 first.

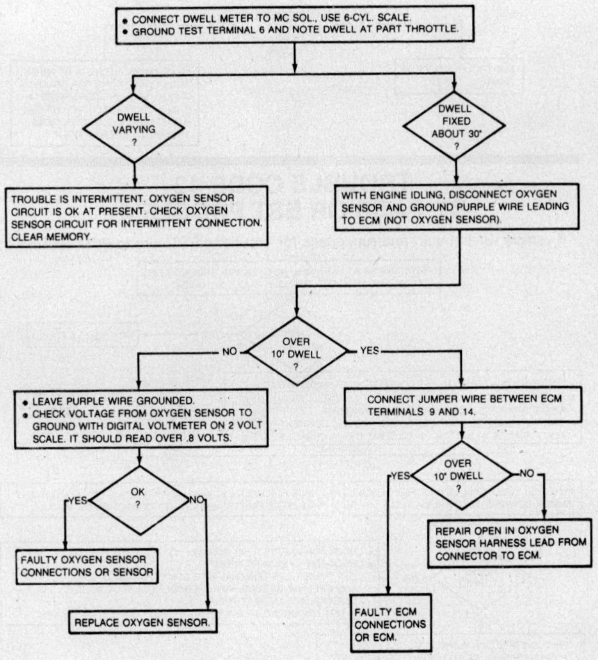

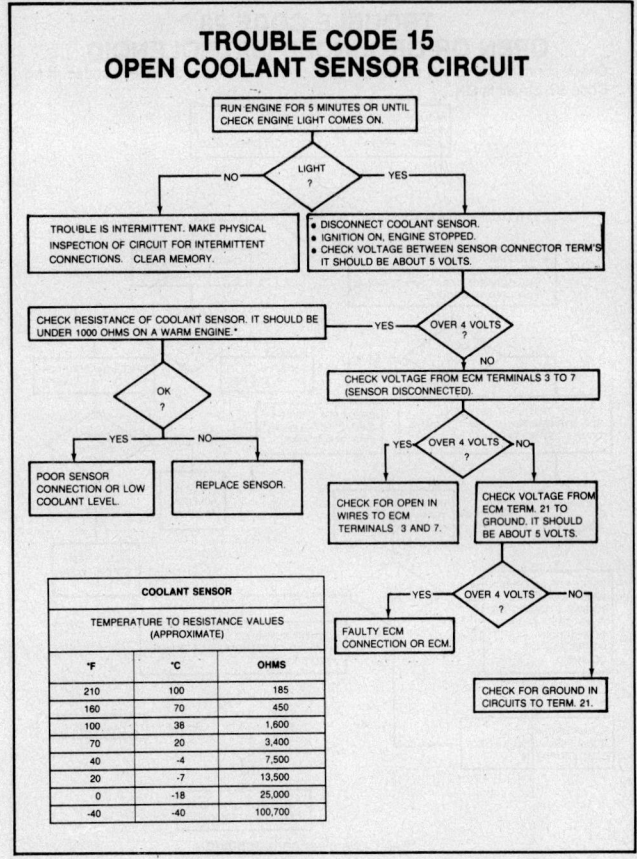

TROUBLE CODE 15
OPEN COOLANT SENSOR CIRCUIT

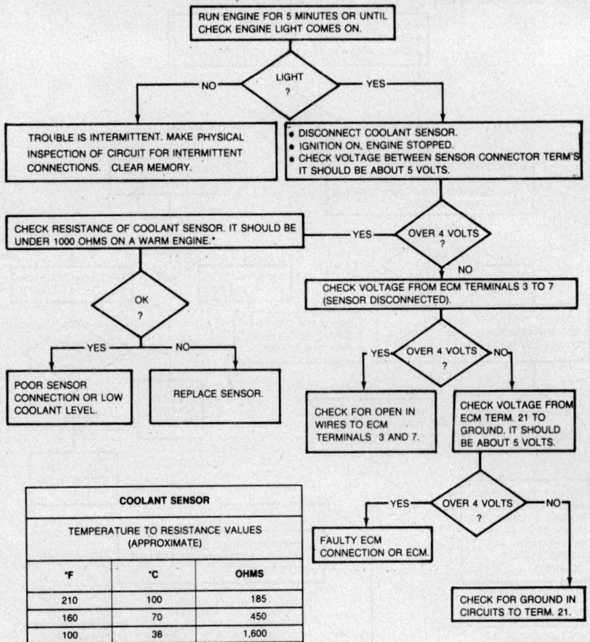

COOLANT SENSOR

TEMPERATURE TO RESISTANCE VALUES (APPROXIMATE)

°F	°C	OHMS
210	100	185
160	70	450
100	38	1,600
70	20	3,400
40	-4	7,500
20	-7	13,500
0	-18	25,000
-40	-40	100,700

TROUBLE CODE 14
SHORTED COOLANT SENSOR CIRCUIT

If engine coolant light is ON, check for overheating condition first.

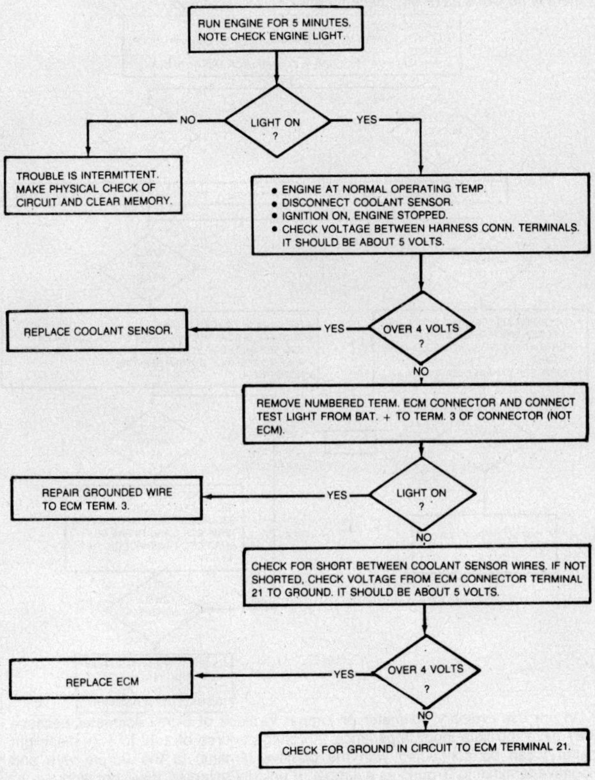

TROUBLE CODE 21
OPEN TPS CIRCUIT OR MISADJUSTED

Check for sticking TPS plunger and adjustment. Repair as necessary. If OK, proceed.

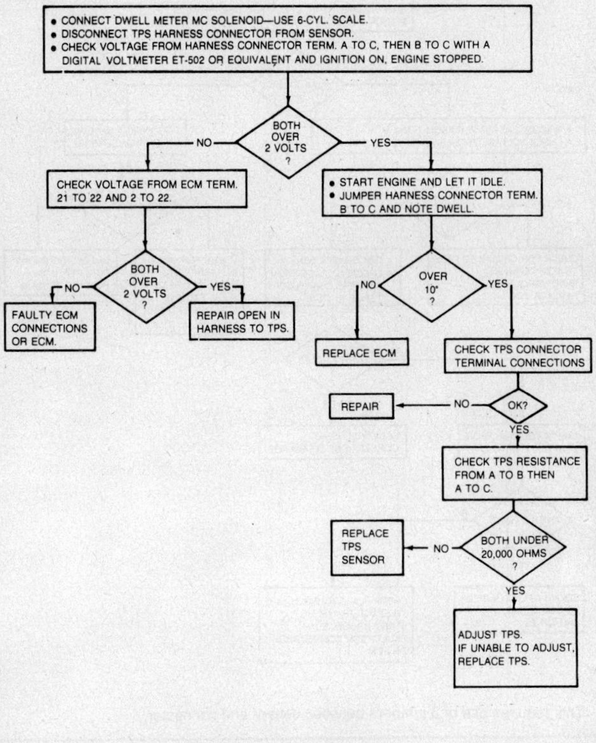

JEEP V6 COMPUTERIZED EMISSION CONTROL (Cont.)

TROUBLE CODE 23
OPEN OR GROUNDED M/C SOLENOID

Check connections at MC solenoid. If OK, clear memory* and recheck codes. If no Code 23, circuit is OK.

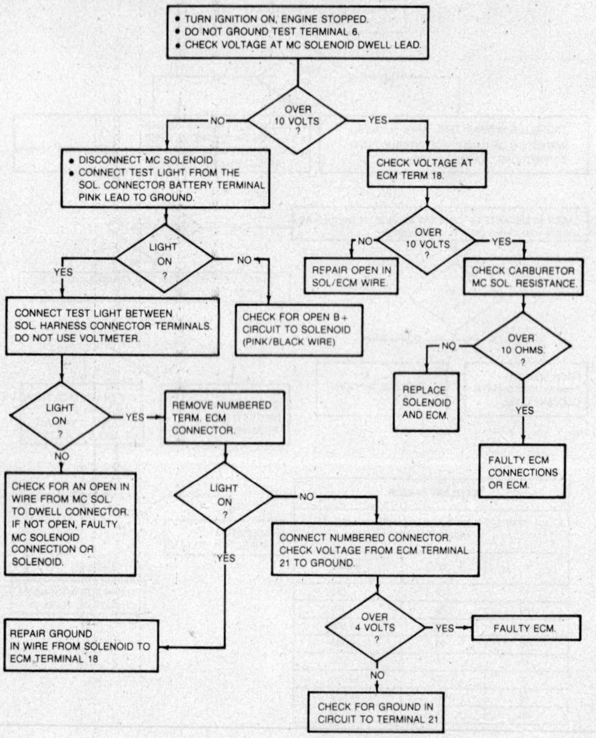

*See Code clearing procedure.

TROUBLE CODE 41
NO DISTRIBUTOR REFERENCE SIGNAL

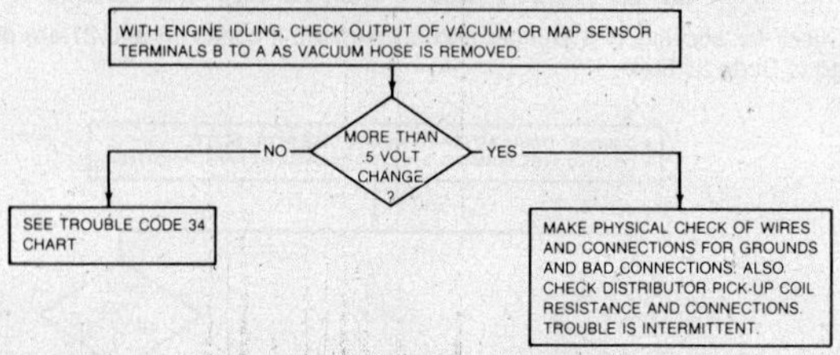

TROUBLE CODE 42
BY-PASS OR EST PROBLEM

If vehicle will not start and run, check for grounded EST wire to ECM terminal 12.

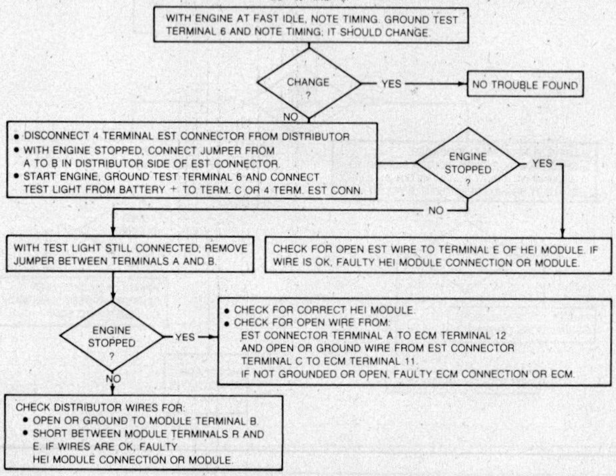

TROUBLE CODE 34
VACUUM SENSOR VOLTAGE

Check for more than 10 in. Hg vacuum at sensor with engine idling. If not OK, repair.

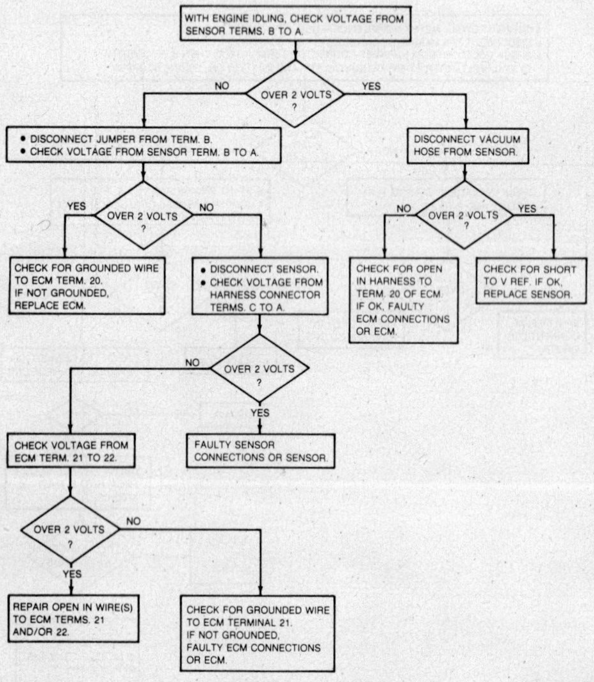

*This requires use of 3 jumpers between sensor and connector.

TROUBLE CODE 44
LEAN EXHAUST INDICATION

If MC solenoid does not click with ignition ON and test terminal 6 grounded, and there is no Code 23 or 54, check for sticking MC solenoid.

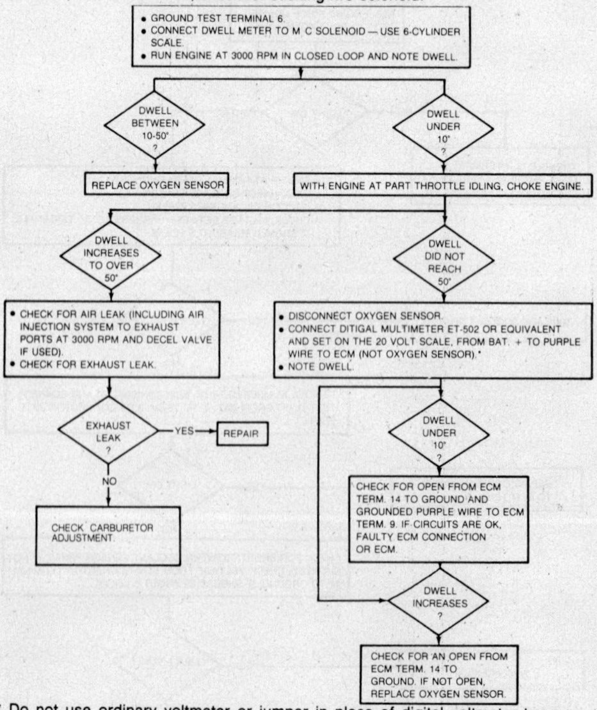

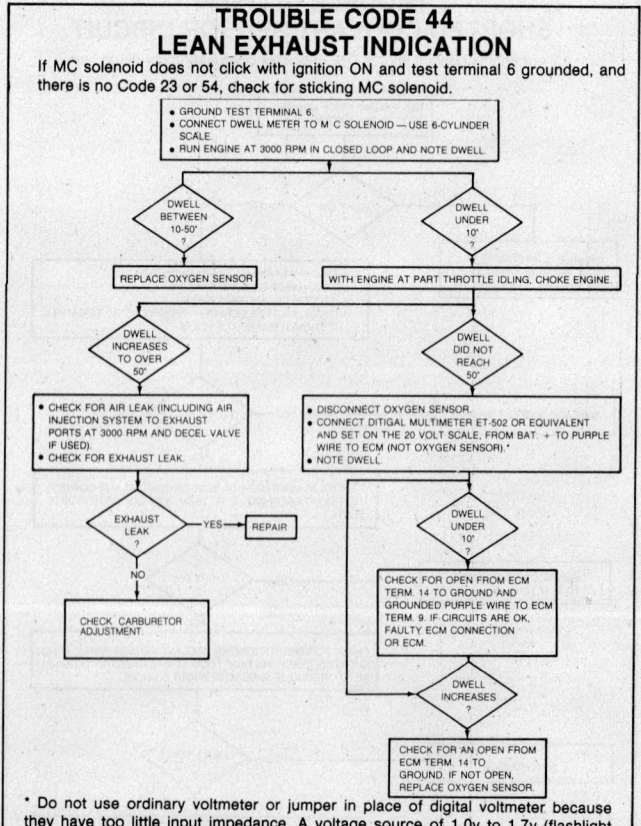

* Do not use ordinary voltmeter or jumper in place of digital voltmeter because they have too little input impedance. A voltage source of 1.0v to 1.7v (flashlight battery) can be connected with the positive terminal to the Purple wire and negative terminal to Ground as a jumper. If polarity reversed, it will not work.

JEEP V6 COMPUTERIZED EMISSION CONTROL (Cont.)

TROUBLE CODE 45
RICH EXHAUST INDICATION

If MC solenoid does not click with ignition ON and test terminal 6 grounded, and there is no Code 23 or 54, check for sticking MC solenoid.
If Code 54 is present, go to Trouble Code Chart 54 first.

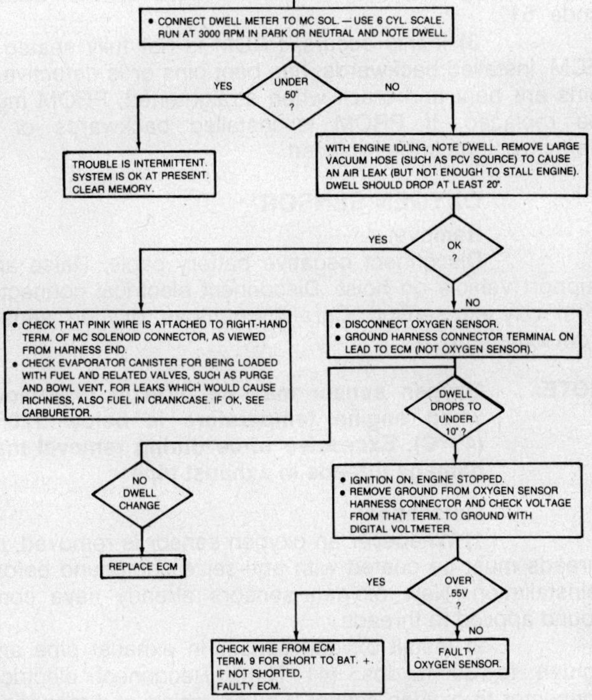

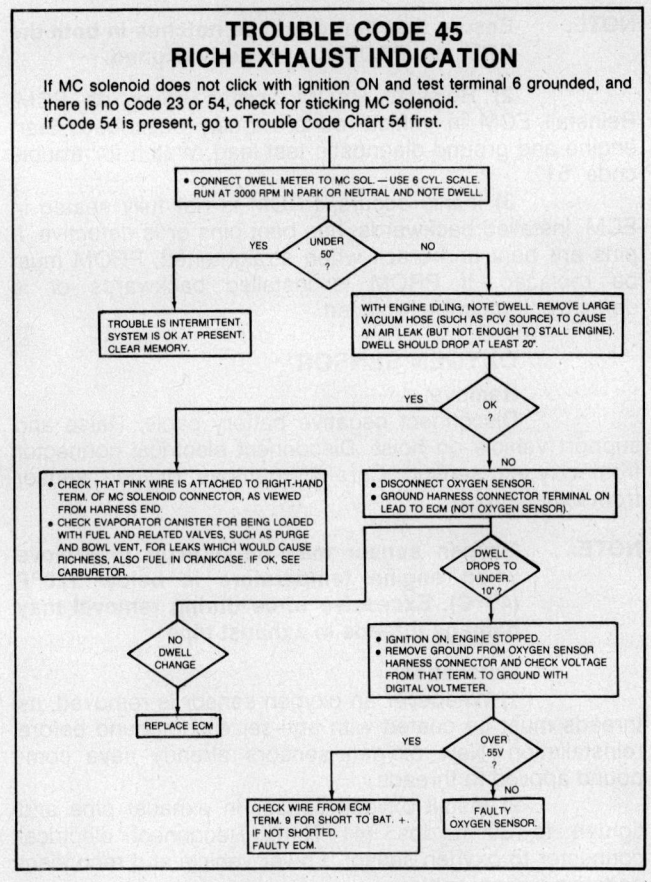

TROUBLE CODE 55
FAULTY OXYGEN SENSOR OR ECM

Check for corrosion at ECM edgeboard connectors and terminals. If present, check for coolant sensor, windshield or heater core leaks. Repair leak, clean connector terminals and replae ECM. Also check for 4 terminal EST harness being too close to electrical signals such as plug wires, distributor, generator, etc.

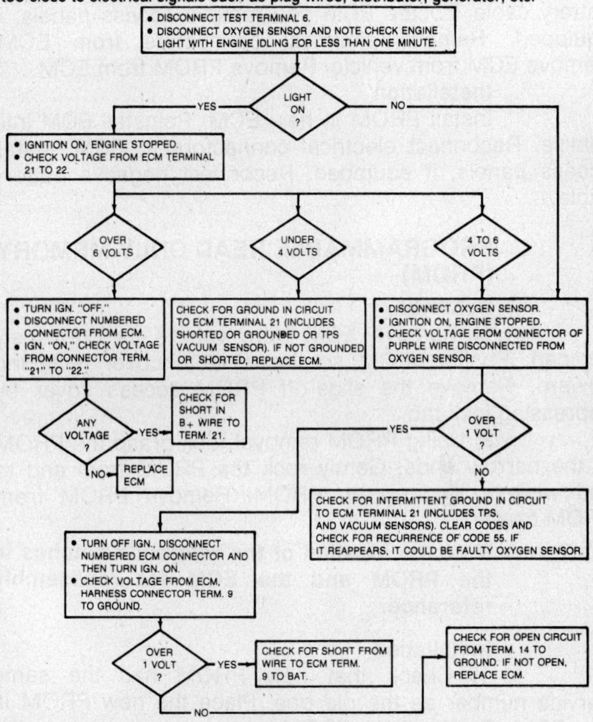

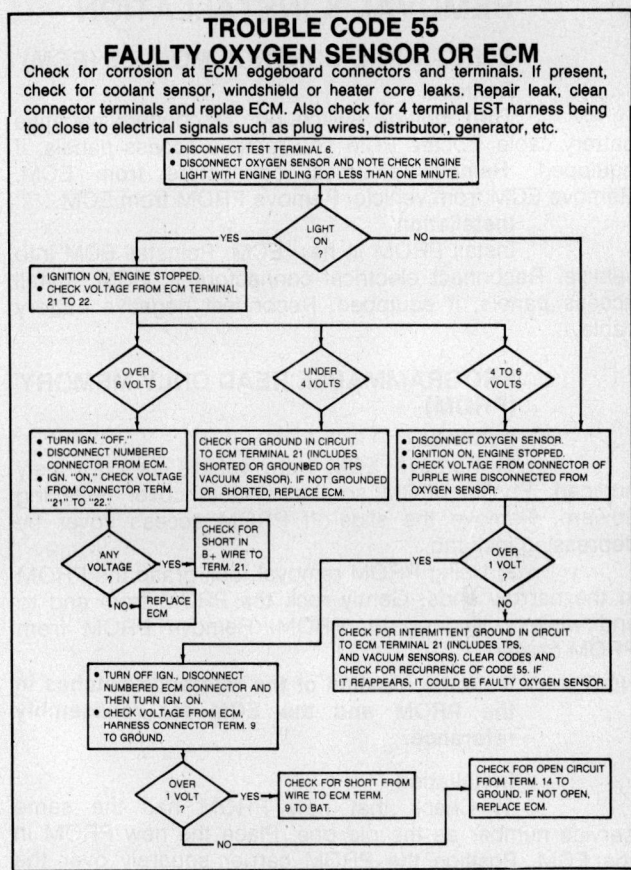

TROUBLE CODE 51
PROM PROBLEM

ENSURE THAT ALL PINS ARE FULLY INSERTED IN THE SOCKET. IF OKAY, REPLACE ECM.

TROUBLE CODE 54
HIGH VOLTAGE FROM M/C SOLENOID

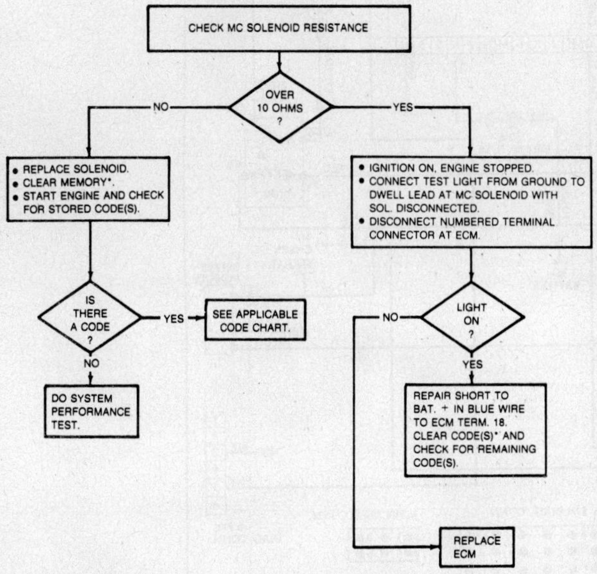

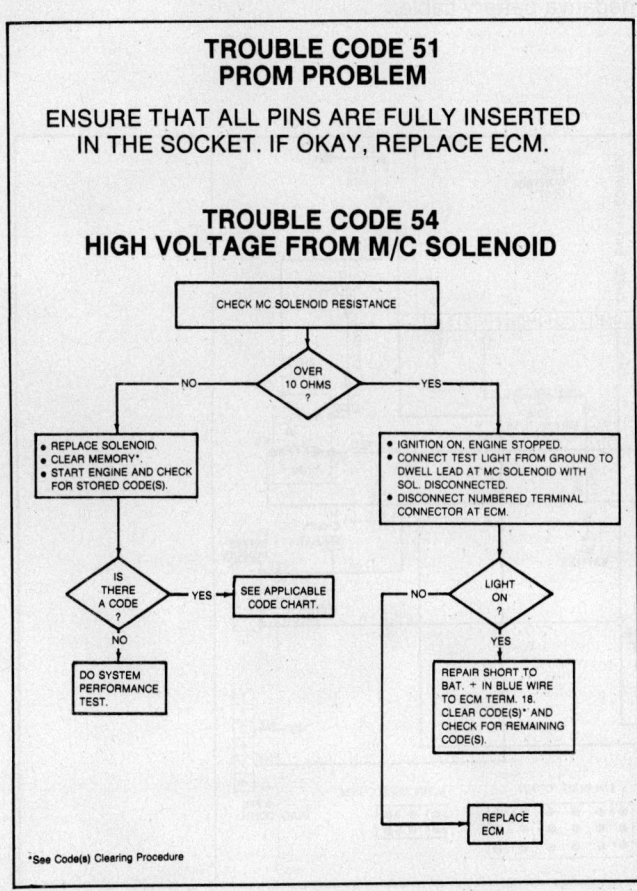

*See Code(s) Clearing Procedure

INTAKE MANIFOLD HEATER TEST

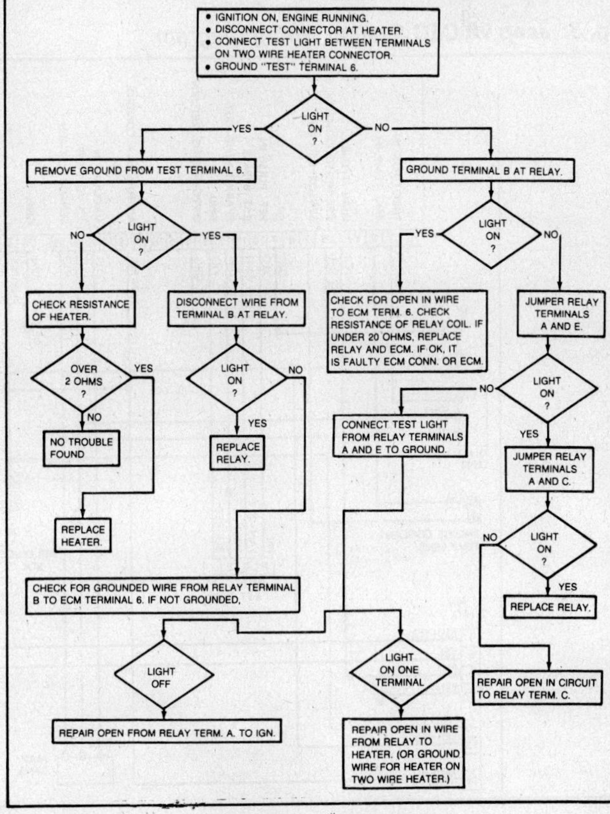

JEEP V6 COMPUTERIZED EMISSION CONTROL (Cont.)

REMOVAL & INSTALLATION

ELECTRONIC CONTROL MODULE (ECM)

Removal

Turn ignition switch off. Disconnect negative battery cable. Locate ECM and remove access panels, if equipped. Remove electrical connectors from ECM. Remove ECM from vehicle. Remove PROM from ECM.

Installation

Install PROM in new ECM. Reinstall ECM into vehicle. Reconnect electrical connectors to ECM. Install access panels, if equipped. Reconnect negative battery cable.

PROGRAMMABLE READ ONLY MEMORY (PROM)

Removal

1) Remove ECM from vehicle as previously outlined. Position ECM so that bottom cover is facing upward. Remove the slide-off PROM access cover by depressing lock tab.

2) Using PROM removal tool, grasp the PROM at the narrow ends. Gently rock the PROM from end to end while pulling up on PROM. Remove PROM from PROM carrier.

NOTE: **Note the location of the reference notches in the PROM and the ECM for reassembly reference.**

Installation

1) Check that new PROM has the same service number as the old one. Place the new PROM in the ECM. Position the PROM carrier squarely over the PROM. Press on the PROM carrier until the PROM is firmly seated in the ECM.

NOTE: **Ensure that the reference notches in both the ECM and PROM are properly aligned.**

2) Reinstall PROM access cover on ECM. Reinstall ECM in vehicle as previously described. Start engine and ground diagnostic test lead. Watch for trouble code "51".

3) If this occurs, PROM is not fully seated in ECM, installed backwards, has bent pins or is defective. If pins are bent and crack when straightened, PROM must be replaced. If PROM is installed backwards or is defective, it must be replaced.

OXYGEN SENSOR

Removal

Disconnect negative battery cable. Raise and support vehicle on hoist. Disconnect electrical connector from oxygen sensor. Carefully remove oxygen sensor from exhaust pipe.

NOTE: **Oxygen sensor may be difficult to remove when engine temperature is below 120°F (49°C). Excessive force during removal may damage threads in exhaust pipe.**

Installation

1) Whenever an oxygen sensor is removed, its threads must be coated with anti-seize compound before reinstallation. New oxygen sensors already have compound applied to threads.

2) Install oxygen sensor in exhaust pipe and tighten to 30 ft. lbs. (41 N.m). Reconnect electrical connector to oxygen sensor. Lower vehicle and reconnect negative battery cable.

Fig. 3: Jeep V6 CEC System Wiring Diagram

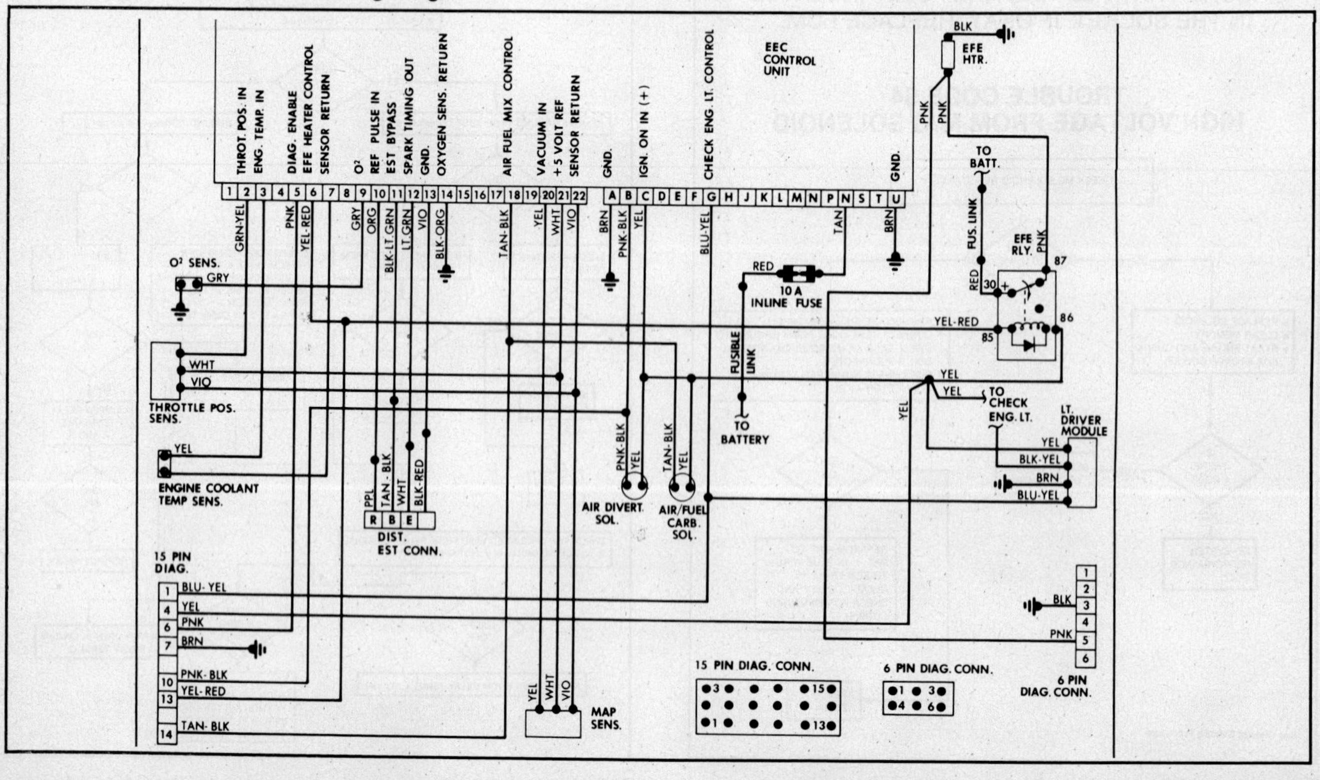

SECTION 2

FUEL SYSTEMS

CONTENTS

NOTE: **ALSO SEE GENERAL INDEX.**

IMPORTANT: Because of the many model names used by vehicle manufacturers, accurate identification of models is important. See Model Identification at the front of this publication.

1985 Fuel Systems

CARBURETOR TROUBLE SHOOTING

CONDITION	POSSIBLE CAUSE	CORRECTION
Engine Won't Start	Choke not closing Choke linkage bent	Check choke operation, see FUEL SYSTEMS Check linkage, see FUEL SYSTEMS
Engine Starts, Then Dies	Choke vacuum kick setting too wide Fast idle RPM too low Fast idle cam index incorrect Vacuum leak Low fuel pump outlet Low carburetor fuel level	Check setting and adjust, see FUEL SYSTEMS Reset RPM to specification, see TUNE-UP Reset fast idle cam index, see FUEL SYSTEMS Inspect vacuum system for leaks Repair or replace pump, see FUEL SYSTEMS Check float setting, see FUEL SYSTEMS
Engine Quits Under Load	Choke vacuum kick setting incorrect Fast idle cam index incorrect Incorrect hot fast idle speed RPM	Check setting and adjust, see FUEL SYSTEMS Reset fast idle cam index, see FUEL SYSTEMS Reset fast idle RPM, see TUNE-UP
Engine Starts, Runs Up, Then Idles Slowly With Black Smoke	Choke vacuum kick set too narrow Fast idle cam index incorrect Hot fast idle RPM too low	Reset vacuum kick, see FUEL SYSTEMS Reset fast idle cam index, see FUEL SYSTEMS Reset fast idle RPM, see TUNE-UP
	HOT STARTING SYMPTOMS	
Engine Won't Start	Engine flooded	Allow fuel to evaporate
	COLD ENGINE DRIVEABILITY SYMPTOMS	
Engine Stalls in Gear	Choke vacuum kick setting incorrect Fast idle RPM incorrect Fast idle cam index incorrect	Check setting and adjust, see FUEL SYSTEMS Reset fast idle RPM, see TUNE-UP Reset fast idle cam index, see FUEL SYSTEMS
Acceleration Sag or Stall	Defective choke control switch Choke vacuum kick setting incorrect Float level incorrect (too low) Accelerator pump defective Secondary throttles not closed	Replace choke control switch Adjust kick setting, see FUEL SYSTEMS Adjust float level, see FUEL SYSTEMS Repair or replace pump, see FUEL SYSTEMS Inspect lockout, see FUEL SYSTEMS
Sag or Stall After Warmup	Defective choke control switch Defective accelerator pump (low output) Float level incorrect (too low)	Replace control switch, see FUEL SYSTEMS Replace pump, see FUEL SYSTEMS Adjust float level, see FUEL SYSTEMS
Backfiring & Black Smoke	Plugged heat crossover system	Remove restriction
	WARM ENGINE DRIVEABILITY SYMPTOM	
Hesitation With Small Amount of Gas Pedal Movement	Vacuum leak Accelerator pump weak or inoperable Float level setting too low Metering rods sticking or binding Carburetor idle or transfer system plugged Frozen or binding heated air inlet	Inspect vacuum lines Replace pump, see FUEL SYSTEMS Reset float level, see FUEL SYSTEMS Inspect and/or replace, see FUEL SYSTEMS Inspect system and remove restrictions Inspect heated air door for binding
Hesitation With Heavy Gas Pedal Movement	Defective accelerator pump Metering rod carrier sticking or binding Large vacuum leak Float level setting too low Defective fuel pump, lines or filter Air door setting incorrect	Replace pump, see FUEL SYSTEMS Remove restriction Inspect vacuum system and repair leak Reset float level, see FUEL SYSTEMS Inspect pump, lines and filter Adjust air door setting, see FUEL SYSTEMS

NOTE: **For additional carburetor trouble shooting information, see the appropriate article in COMPUTERIZED ENGINE CONTROLS Section. Information is provided there for diagnosing fuel system problems on vehicles with feedback carburetors.**

DIESEL FUEL INJECTION TROUBLE SHOOTING

CONDITION	POSSIBLE CAUSE	CORRECTION
Engine Won't Start	No voltage-to-fuel solenoid	Check electrical connections
	Faulty glow plugs or glow plug controls	Check and/or replace glow plugs or controller
	Plugged fuel return system	Remove restrictions
	No fuel-to-nozzles	Inspect fuel delivery system
	No fuel-to-injecton pump	Inspect fuel delivery system
	Clogged fuel tank filter	Replace filter, see FUEL SYSTEMS
	Incorrect or contaminated fuel	Remove and replace fuel
	Incorrect pump timing	Reset pump timing, see FUEL SYSTEMS
Engine Stalls at Idle	Incorrect slow idle adjustment	Reset idle adjustment, see TUNE-UP
	Faulty fast idle solenoid	Replace solenoid, see FUEL SYSTEMS
	Plugged fuel return system	Remove restrictions
	Glow plugs turn off too soon	Check glow plug system, see FUEL SYSTEMS
	Incorrect pump timing	Check and reset timing, see FUEL SYSTEMS
	Limited fuel-to-injection pump	Check fuel delivery system
	Air in injection lines-to-nozzles	Check line fittings
	Incorrect or contaminated fuel	Remove and replace fuel
	Faulty injection pump	Check injection pump, see FUEL SYSTEMS
	Fuel solenoid closes in RUN position	Check solenoid operation, see FUEL SYSTEMS
Engine Starts, Idles Rough WITHOUT Unusual Noise or Smoke	Incorrect slow idle adjustment	Reset slow idle adjustment, see TUNE-UP
	Leaking injection line	Check fittings and/or replace line
	Plugged fuel return line	Remove restrictions
	Air in lines to nozzles	Check line fittings
	Air in injection pump	Check pump fittings and pump operation
	Faulty nozzle	Replace nozzle, see FUEL SYSTEMS
	Improper or contaminated fuel	Remove and replace fuel
	Uneven fuel distribution	Check fuel delivery system
Engine Starts and Idles WITH Excessive Noise and/or Smoke	Incorrect pump timing	Reset injection timing, see FUEL SYSTEMS
	Air in injection lines to nozzles	Check fittings on lines
	Faulty nozzle	Replace nozzle, see FUEL SYSTEMS
	Improperly installed high pressure lines	Remove and reinstall properly
Engine Idles Okay but Misfires Above Idle	Plugged fuel filter	Remove restrictions and/or replace filter
	Incorrect pump timing	Reset injection timing, see FUEL SYSTEMS
	Incorrect or contaminated fuel	Remove and replace fuel
Engine Will Not Idle	Linkage binding or misadjusted	Remove binding and readjust linkage
	Defective injection pump	Replace injection pump, see FUEL SYSTEMS
Fuel Leaks With No Other Engine Malfunction	Loose or broken fuel line or connection	Check all fuel line fittings and correct
	Internal seal leak in injection pump	Remove and replace injection pump
Low Engine Power	Restricted air intake	Remove restrictions
	Plugged fuel filter	Remove restriction and/or replace filter
	Restricted fuel return system	Remove restrictions
	Restricted tank-to-pump fuel supply	Check fuel delivery system
	Incorrect or contaminated fuel	Remove and replace fuel
	Restricted fuel tank filter	Replace filter
	Nozzle or glow plug compression leaks	Check fittings and replace as required
	Plugged nozzle	Remove restriction and/or replace nozzle
"Rapping" Noise From One or More Cylinders	Air in fuel system	Check fuel delivery system for leaks
	Air in high pressure lines	Check fittings for leaks
	Nozzle sticking in open position	Inspect nozzle and/or replace
	Low nozzle opening pressure	Check nozzle operation, see FUEL SYSTEMS
	Filter in nozzle broken or loose	Check nozzle filter, see FUEL SYSTEMS

DIESEL FUEL INJECTION TROUBLE SHOOTING (Cont.)

CONDITION	POSSIBLE CAUSE	CORRECTION
Excessive Combustion Noise With Black Smoke	Incorrect pump timing	Reset injection timing, see FUEL SYSTEMS
	Incorrect pump housing pressure	Check for internal leaks, FUEL SYSTEMS
	Defective injection pump	Replace injection pump, see FUEL SYSTEMS
	Incorrect firing order	Check injection lines, see TUNE-UP
Engine Will Not Shut Off With Key	Injection pump fuel solenoid does not return to off position	Check solenoid operation, see FUEL SYSTEMS

NOTE: For GASOLINE FUEL INJECTION TROUBLE SHOOTING, see the appropriate article under the individual manufacturer in this section. Also see the appropriate article in COMPUTERIZED ENGINE CONTROLS Section.

TURBOCHARGER TROUBLE SHOOTING

CONDITION	POSSIBLE CAUSE	CORRECTION
Engine Detonation	Malfunction in spark advance or retard system	Check distributor and ignition, see ELECTRICAL
	EGR system defect	Check EGR system
	Carburetor/throttle body or turbocharger air inlet restrictions	Remove restrictions
	Actuator allows too much boost	Check boost pressure and adjust
	Defect in carburetor/throttle body power system	Inspect and repair carburetor/throttle body, see FUEL SYSTEMS
	Internal turbocharger defect	Replace turbocharger, see FUEL SYSTEMS
Low Engine Power	Air inlet restriction	Remove restriction in inlet
	Exhaust system restriction	Remove restriction
	Malfunction in spark advance or retard system	Check distributor and ignition, see ELECTRICAL
	EFE system defect (GM only)	Check EFE system operation
	EGR system defect	Check EGR system
Engine Noise	EFE system defect (GM only)	Check EFE system
	Loose exhaust system or leak	Check exhaust mounting and connections
	AIR system defect	Check AIR system
	Restricted turbocharger oil supply	Check oil delivery system
Engine Surges	ESC malfunction	Check ESC system
	Defective vacuum switch	Replace defective switch
	EGR system defect	Check EGR system
	Loose turbocharger bolts on compressor side	Check mounting bolts and tighten
Excessive Oil Consumption (Blue Exhaust Smoke)	Leak at turbocharger oil inlet	Check fittings and repair
	Turbocharger oil drain hose leaks or stopped up	Check drain hose for restrictions or loose fittings
	Turbocharger seals leaking	Replace seals, see FUEL SYSTEMS

1985 Carter Carburetors

CARTER YFA & YFA FEEDBACK SINGLE BARREL

CARBURETOR APPLICATION

FORD MOTOR CO. (CARTER) CARBURETOR NO.

Application	Man. Trans.	Auto. Trans.
2.0L 4-Cyl.	E57E-DA	.....
4.9L 6-Cyl.		
Federal		
F150 (2WD)	E5TE-BA	E5TE-VA
	E5TE-FA, JA	E5TE-RA [1]
All Others	E5TE-BA	E5TE-BA, VA [3]
	[2] E5TE-HA	E5TE-MA [1 3]
	[4] E0TE-AMB	E0TE-FB [5]
California		
F150 (2WD)	E5TE-UA	E5TE-VA, RA [1]
All Others	E5TE-VA	E5TE-VA
	[3] E5TE-TA	E5TE-SA [1 3]
High Altitude		
F150 (2WD)	E5TE-DA	E5TE-BA, CA [1]
All Others	E5TE-DA	E5TE-DA, BA [6]
		E5TE-MA [1 3]

1 – With Automatic Overdrive Transmission.
2 – E150 only.
3 – E150/250 only.
4 – E350 only.
5 – E/F350 only.
6 – F150 (4WD) and Bronco only.

JEEP (CARTER) CARBURETOR NO.

Application	Man. Trans.	Auto. Trans.
2.46L 4-Cyl.		
Federal	7700/7704	7701
California	7700	7702
High Altitude	7702/7706	7703

CARBURETOR IDENTIFICATION

A carburetor identification tag is attached to carburetor. Tag contains part number prefix and suffix, design change code (if any) and assembly date code (including year, month and day). To obtain replacement parts, it is necessary to know identification number prefix, suffix and, in some instances, the design change code.

Fig. 1: Ford Motor Co. Carburetor Identification Tag

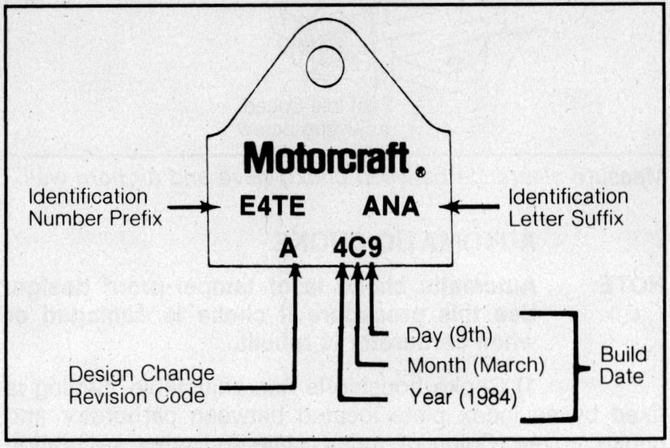

Identification tag is attached to top of carburetor.

DESCRIPTION

Carter YFA and YFA Feedback carburetors are made up of 3 main assemblies, including the air horn, main body and throttle body. An adjustment limiting vacuum diaphragm type automatic choke with an electric assist choke cap is used.

The electric choke adds a high mileage economy application to the carburetor. The main body on some models contains a temperature compensated accelerator pump which has a thermostatic disc designed to open and close within a specified range.

The YFA Feedback carburetor differs from the YFA in its addition of a feedback solenoid attached to the air horn assembly. This solenoid is used to meter air into both the idle and main circuits for improved engine performance.

A Microprocessor Control Unit (MCU) senses various engine needs and supplies feedback fuel as required by forcing air into fuel bowl, and in turn, more fuel into carburetor air stream.

ADJUSTMENT

NOTE: For all on-vehicle adjustments not covered in this article, see appropriate TUNE-UP article.

FLOAT LEVEL

1) Remove air cleaner assembly. Remove air horn and gasket from top of carburetor. Turn air horn assembly upside-down. Measure distance between top of float at free end and gasket surface of air horn.

NOTE: Do not apply pressure against needle when adjusting float.

2) Bend float arm as necessary to obtain correct clearance. DO NOT bend tab at end of float arm as this will stop float travel to bottom of fuel bowl when empty.

3) When adjustment is completed, reinstall air horn and new gasket. Start engine and check for fuel leaks. Install air cleaner.

Fig. 2: Float Level Clearance Adjustment

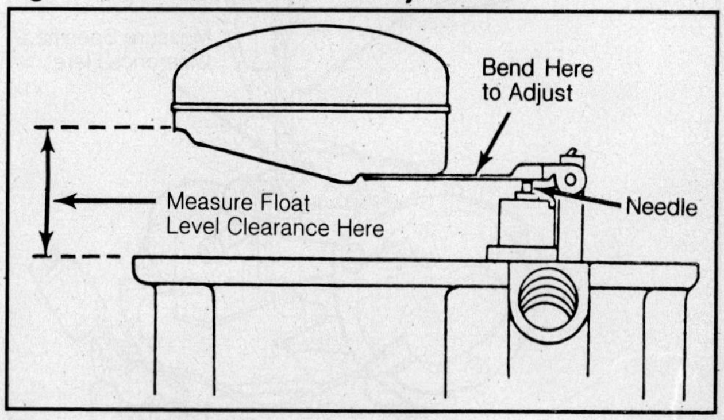

Float arm should rest gently on needle.

METERING ROD

1) Remove air cleaner, air horn and gasket from carburetor. Back out idle speed adjusting screw until throttle plate is tightly closed in throttle bore. Press down on end of pump diaphragm shaft until assembly bottoms.

2) While holding diaphragm assembly in this position, turn rod adjustment screw counterclockwise until metering rod gently bottoms in body casting. *See Fig. 3.* Turn metering rod adjustment screw clockwise exactly 1 turn for final adjustment.

3) Install air horn and new gasket on carburetor. Start engine and check for fuel leaks. Install air cleaner.

1985 Carter Carburetors

CARTER YFA & YFA FEEDBACK SINGLE BARREL (Cont.)

Fig. 3: Metering Rod Adjustment

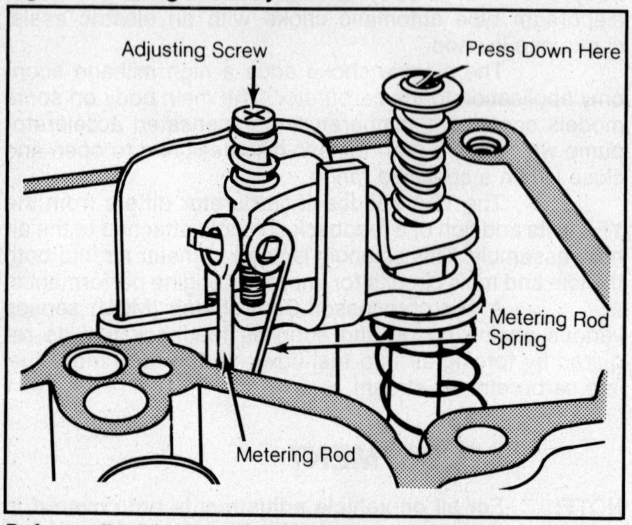

Before adjusting, press down on pump diaphragm shaft.

CHOKE UNLOADER (DECHOKE)

1) Remove air cleaner. Hold throttle valve in fully open position and press choke valve toward closed position. Measure clearance between lower edge of choke valve (upper edge on Jeep models) and air horn wall.

2) Adjust by bending arm on choke lever of throttle lever. *See Fig. 4.* Bend arm up to increase clearance or down (away from fast idle cam) to decrease clearance. Operate throttle to check for binding or clearance interference. Install air cleaner.

Fig. 4: Choke Unloader (Dechoke) Adjustment

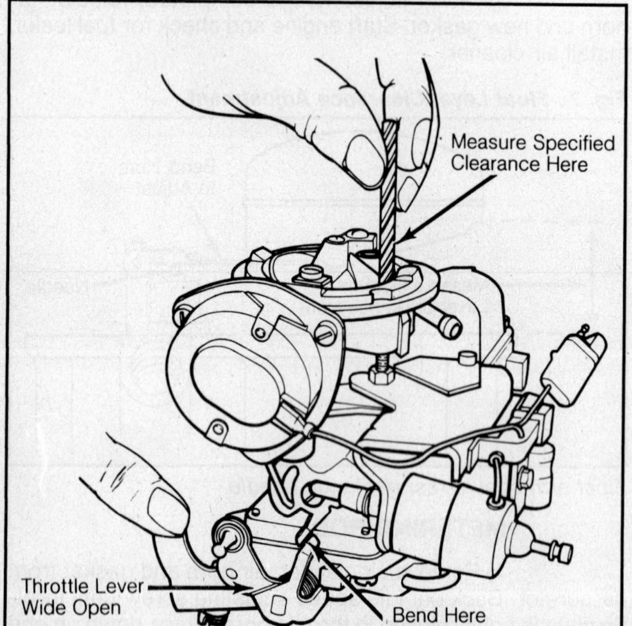

Adjust by bending choke lever arm of throttle lever.

CHOKE PLATE PULL-OFF CLEARANCE

1) Remove air cleaner. Place fast idle speed screw on highest step of fast idle cam. Cover vent hole in back of vacuum diaphragm with tape (if equipped).

2) Attach vacuum pump to pull-off diaphragm and apply enough vacuum to activate motor. Apply light closing pressure on choke valve without forcing it.

3) Check clearance between lower edge of choke valve and air horn wall. To adjust, bend choke diaphragm link. *See Fig. 5.* Remove vacuum pump and install air cleaner.

Fig. 5: Choke Plate Pull-Off Clearance Adjustment

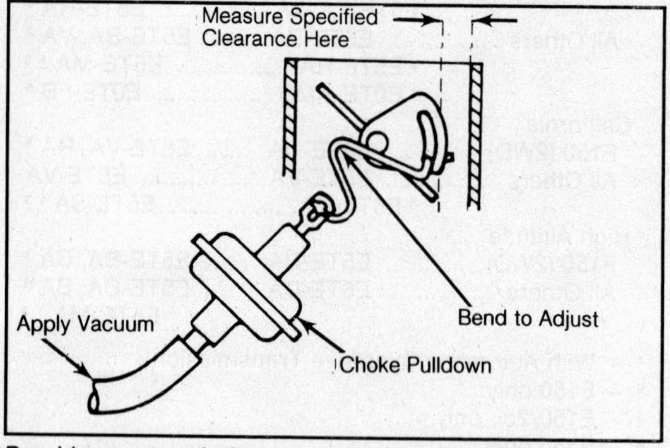

Bend lever toward piston to decrease clearance.

FAST IDLE CAM POSITION

Place fast idle speed screw on kickdown step of fast idle cam, against shoulder of highest step. *See Fig. 6.* Measure clearance between lower edge of choke valve and air horn wall. Adjust clearance as needed by bending fast idle cam link.

Fig. 6: Fast Idle Cam Position

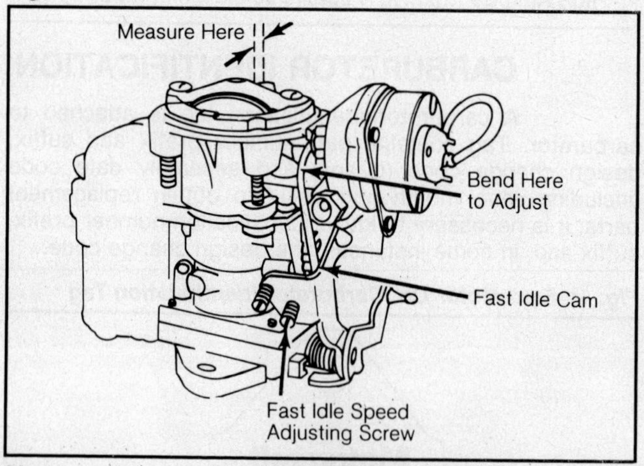

Measure clearance between choke valve and air horn wall.

AUTOMATIC CHOKE

NOTE: **Automatic choke is of tamper-proof design. Use this procedure if choke is damaged or when carburetor is rebuilt.**

1) Choke housing is non-adjustable. Setting is fixed by an index plate located between carburetor and choke cover. Color of index plate indicates calibration setting.

2) To replace index plate, loosen choke thermostat cover. Remove 2 rivets and retaining screw. Separate cover from carburetor and exchange index plates. Replace cover. Install new rivets and screw.

CARTER YFA & YFA FEEDBACK SINGLE BARREL (Cont.)

Fig. 7: Exploded View of Carter Model YFA 1-Barrel Feedback & High Altitude Carburetor (Non-Feedback YFA Similar)

1. Air Horn Assembly
2. Air Horn Retaining Screw
3. Solenoid Bracket Screw
4. Throttle Solenoid
5. Locknut
6. Index Plate Gasket
7. Index Plate Cover
8. Choke Cover Gasket
9. Choke Cover & Spring Assembly
10. Choke Cover Retainer
11. Pop Rivet
12. Choke Cover Retainer Screw
13. Feedback Solenoid Gasket
14. Feedback Solenoid
15. Needle Seat Screen
16. Needle & Seat Assembly
17. Choke Pull-Off Link
18. Choke Pull-Off Assembly
19. Air Horn Gasket
20. "E" Clip
21. Spring Clip
22. Upper Pump Spring
23. Metering Rod Arm & Adjusting Screw Assembly
24. Metering Rod
25. Adjusting Screw Plate
26. Pump Lifter Link
27. Lifter Link Spacer Washer
28. Pump Spring Retainer
29. Pump Spring
30. Pump Passage Tube
31. Pump Attaching Screw
32. Pump Housing Assembly
33. Pump Diaphragm Assembly
34. Lifter Link Seal Retainer
35. Lifter Link Seals
36. Fast Idle Rod Retainer
37. Fast Idle Rod
38. Fast Idle Rod Washer Bushing
39. Fast Idle Rod Washer
40. Fast Idle Rod Retainer
41. Weight
42. Discharge Pump Ball
43. Main Jet
44. Low Speed Jet
45. Pump Relief Valve Assembly
46. Gasket
47. Float & Lever Assembly
48. Float Pin
49. Pump Relief Screw Plug
50. Pump Relief Valve Screw
51. Main Body Assembly
52. Throttle Body Gasket
53. Throttle Position Sensor (TPS)
54. TPS Plate
55. Mixture Screw Cap
56. Mixture Adjusting Screw
57. Mixture Screw Spring
58. Mixture Screw Clip
59. Pump Connector Link
60. Pump Link Arm
61. Washer
62. Throttle Shaft Lever Screw
63. TPS Drive Coupler
64. Idle Screw Cap
65. Throttle Body Assembly
66. Throttle Body Attaching Screw

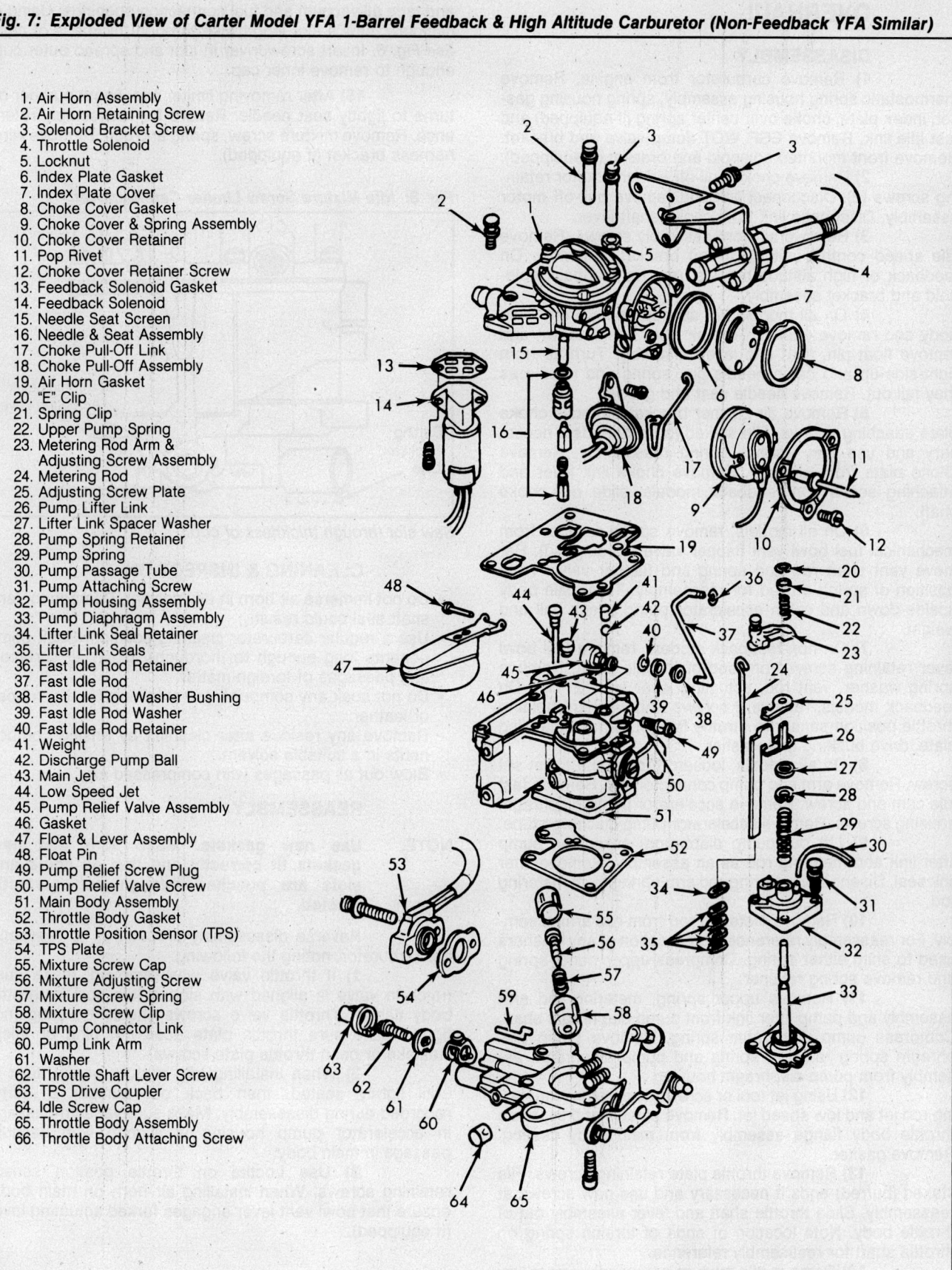

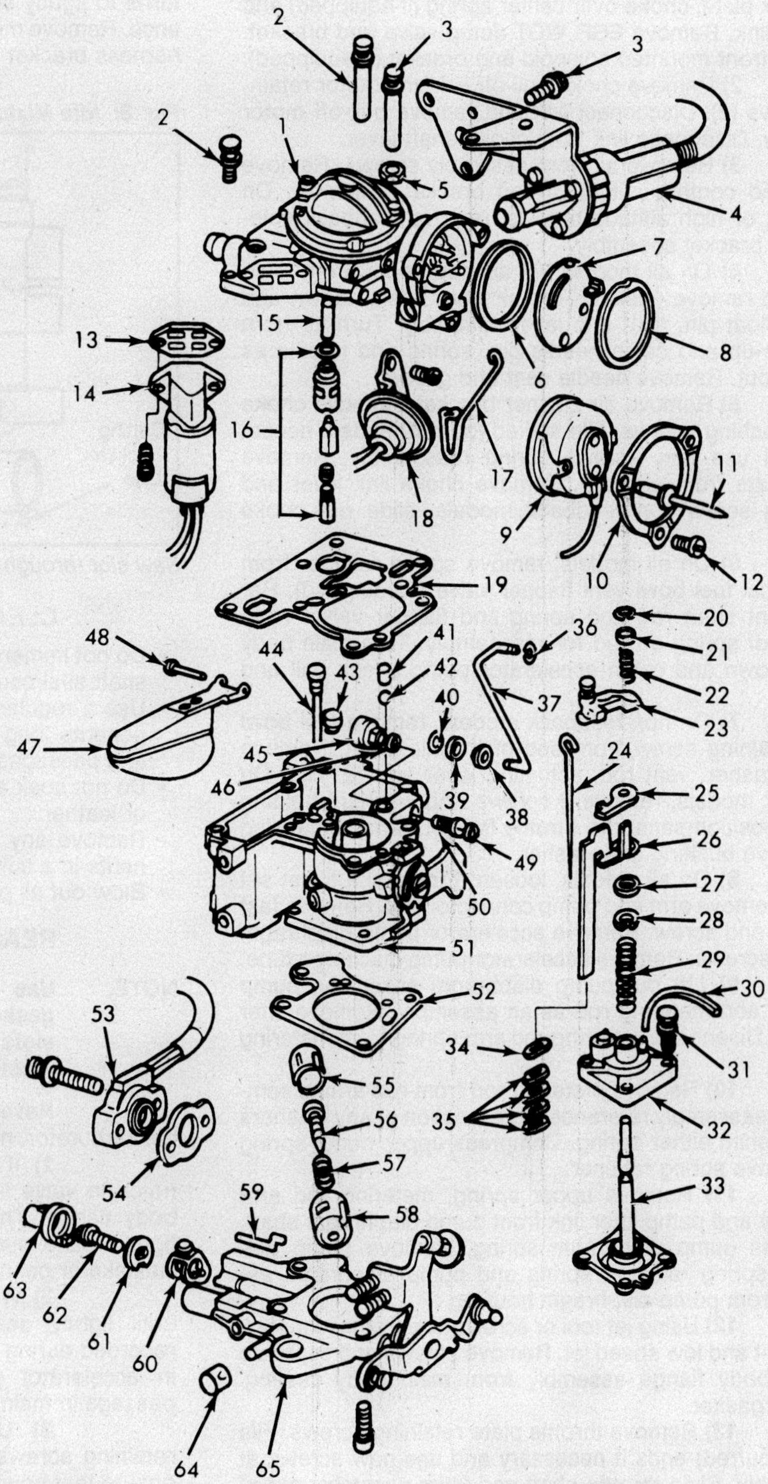

1985 Carter Carburetors

CARTER YFA & YFA FEEDBACK SINGLE BARREL (Cont.)

OVERHAUL

DISASSEMBLY

1) Remove carburetor from engine. Remove thermostatic spring housing assembly, spring housing gasket, index plate, choke over center spring (if equipped) and fast idle link. Remove EGR WOT dump valve and bracket. Remove front mounted solenoid and bracket (if equipped).

2) Remove choke pull-off link and motor retaining screws (2). Disconnect link and remove pull-off motor assembly. Disengage link from choke shaft lever.

3) Remove air horn assembly screws. Remove idle speed control unit (ISC) and bracket assembly. On feedback or high altitude models, remove feedback solenoid and bracket assembly.

4) On all models, lift air horn away from main body and remove gasket. Turn air horn upside-down and remove float pin, float and lever assembly. Turn air horn right-side-up and catch needle pin, spring and needle as they fall out. Remove needle seat and gasket.

5) Remove air cleaner bracket. Remove choke plate attaching screws. File staked (burred) ends if necessary and use new screws during reassembly. Remove choke plate from air horn. Remove choke link lever and attaching screw. On feedback models, slide out choke shaft.

6) On all models, remove spring retainer from mechanical fuel bowl vent flapper valve (if equipped). Remove vent shaft rod and spring and flapper valve. Note position of spring on rod for reassembly. Turn main body upside-down and catch accelerator pump check ball and weight.

7) On non-feedback models, remove fuel bowl lever retaining screw from end of throttle shaft. Remove spring washer, vent rod, actuating lever and "E" clip. On feedback models, remove 2 screws and washers holding throttle position sensor to throttle flange. Remove backing plate, drive bushing and washer.

8) On all models, loosen throttle shaft arm set screw. Remove arm and pump connector link. Remove fast idle cam and screw. Remove accelerator pump diaphragm housing screws. Remove accelerator pump discharge tube.

9) Lift out pump diaphragm assembly, pump lifter link and metering rod as an assembly. Remove lifter link seal. Disengage metering rod arm spring from metering rod.

10) Remove metering rod from rod arm assembly. For reassembly reference, note location of any washers used to shim either spring. Compress upper pump spring and remove spring retainer.

11) Remove upper spring, metering rod arm assembly and pump lifter link from pump diaphragm shaft. Compress pump diaphragm spring. Remove pump diaphragm spring retainer, spring and pump diaphragm assembly from pump diaphragm housing.

12) Using jet tool or screwdriver, remove metering rod jet and low speed jet. Remove screws and separate throttle body flange assembly from main body casting. Remove gasket.

13) Remove throttle plate retaining screws. File staked (burred) ends if necessary and use new screws at reassembly. Slide throttle shaft and lever assembly out of throttle body. Note location of ends of torsion spring on throttle shaft for reassembly reference.

14) Remove idle mixture screw adjustment limiting cap and cup as follows: Invert carburetor assembly and tape all vacuum and fuel connection openings. Using a hacksaw, saw a slot lengthwise through thickness of cup. *See Fig. 8.* Insert screwdriver in slot and spread outer cup enough to remove inner cap.

15) After removing limiter cap, count number of turns to lightly seat needle. Record for reassembly reference. Remove mixture screw, spring and cup. Remove wire harness bracket (if equipped).

Fig. 8: Idle Mixture Screw Limiter Cap Removal

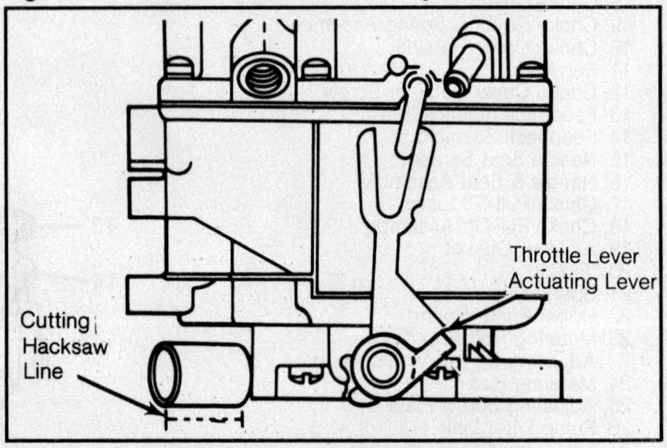

Saw slot through thickness of cup.

CLEANING & INSPECTION

- Do not immerse air horn in any solvent. Damage to vent shaft seal could result.
- Use a regular carburetor cleaning solution. Soak components long enough to thoroughly clean all surfaces and passages of foreign matter.
- Do not soak any components containing plastic, rubber or leather.
- Remove any residue after cleaning by rinsing components in a suitable solvent.
- Blow out all passages with compressed air.

REASSEMBLY

NOTE: **Use new gaskets. Make sure that new gaskets fit correctly and that all holes and slots are punched through and correctly located.**

Reverse disassembly procedures to reassemble carburetor, noting the following:

1) If throttle valve was removed, make sure notch in valve is aligned with slotted idle port in throttle body flange. Throttle valve screws should be snug (not tight). Make sure throttle plate does not bind or stick. Restake or peen throttle plate screws.

2) When installing idle mixture screw, turn in until lightly seated, then back out number of turns recorded during disassembly. Make sure vacuum passage in accelerator pump housing is aligned with vacuum passage in main body.

3) Use Loctite on throttle postion sensor retaining screws. When installing air horn on main body, ensure that bowl vent lever engages forked actuating lever (if equipped).

1985 Carter Carburetors

CARTER YFA & YFA FEEDBACK SINGLE BARREL (Cont.)

CARBURETOR ADJUSTMENT SPECIFICATIONS

Application	Float Level	Choke Unloader	Choke Pull-Down	Fast Idle Cam	Auto. Choke Index Plate
FORD					
E57E-DA	.650	.270"	.320"	.140	Gray
E0TE-AMB	.690"	.280"	.290"	Index	.....
E0TE-FB	.690"	.280"	.290"	Index	.....
E5TE-BA	.780"	.330"	.360"	.140"	Red
E5TE-CA	.780"	.330"	.360"	.140"	Red
E5TE-DA	.780"	.330"	.360"	.140"	Red
E5TE-FA	.780"	.330"	.340"	.140"	Red
E5TE-HA	.780"	.330"	.320"	.140"	Red
E5TE-JA	.780"	.330"	.360"	.140"	Red
E5TE-MA	.780"	.330"	.360"	.140"	Red
E5TE-RA	.780"	.330"	.360"	.140"	Red
E5TE-SA	.780"	.330"	.360"	.140"	Red
E5TE-TA	.780"	.330"	.360"	.140"	Red
E5TE-UA	.780"	.330"	.360"	.140"	Red
E5TE-VA	.780"	.330"	.360"	.140"	Red
JEEP					
7700	.600"	.280"	.....	.175"	TR[1]
7701	.600"	.280"	.....	.175"	TR[1]
7702	.600"	.280"	.....	.175"	TR[1]
7703	.600"	.280"	.....	.175"	TR[1]
7704	.600"	.300"	.....	.175"	TR[1]
7706	.600"	.300"	.....	.175"	TR[1]

[1] – Tamper Resistant.

1985 Carter Carburetors

CARTER BBD 2-BARREL

CARBURETOR APPLICATION

JEEP (CARTER) CARBURETOR NO.

Application	Man. Trans.	Auto.Trans.
4.2L 6-Cyl.		
50 State	8384	8383

CARBURETOR IDENTIFICATION

Carter carburetors are identified by a code number and build date. Both numbers are stamped on a tag attached to carburetor by an air horn screw. Each carburetor build month is coded alphabetically beginning with letter "A" (for January), and ending with "M" (for December). Letter "I" is not used.

Second number on tag is year in which carburetor was built. Third and fourth numbers are for build day. There may be a revision letter following build day numbers if needed.

Fig. 1: Carter Model BBD I.D. Tag

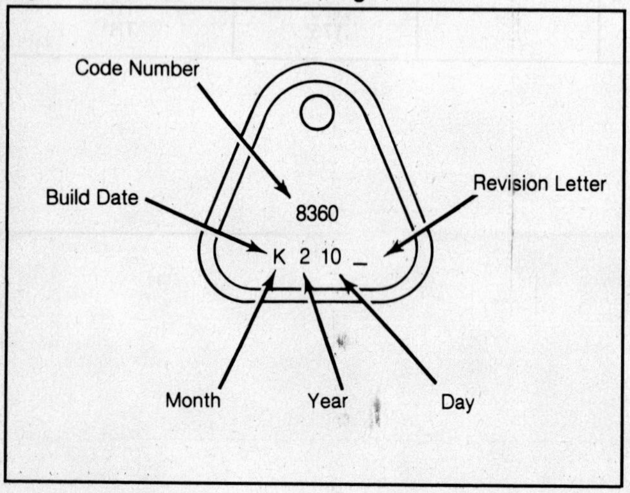

DESCRIPTION

The Carter model BBD is a 2-barrel downdraft carburetor. The BBD has 4 basic fuel metering systems: float (fuel inlet) system; idle (low speed) system; accelerator pump system; and the main (high speed) system.

The float system maintains fuel level. The idle system is used for idle and initial part-throttle operation. The main system is used for part-throttle and cruising operation. The pump system provides additional fuel for acceleration.

An electric choke with a choke diaphragm is used. The carburetor is equipped with a stepper motor to control air flow in metered air bleeds in the main fuel metering circuit. All Jeep vehicles equipped with a BBD use a vacuum solenoid called a Solevac to keep idle speed constant when load is placed on engine.

ADJUSTMENT

NOTE: **For all on-vehicle adjustments, see appropriate TUNE-UP article.**

FLOAT LEVEL (BENCH ADJUSTMENT)

1) Remove air horn. Hold float lip gently against needle. *See Fig. 2.*

2) Using a straightedge, place across float bowl to measure float level. If adjustment is needed, release float and then bend float tip to obtain correct clearance. Reinstall air horn.

NOTE: **To avoid damaging synthetic rubber tip, do not bend lip while float is resting against needle.**

Fig. 2: Adjusting Float Level

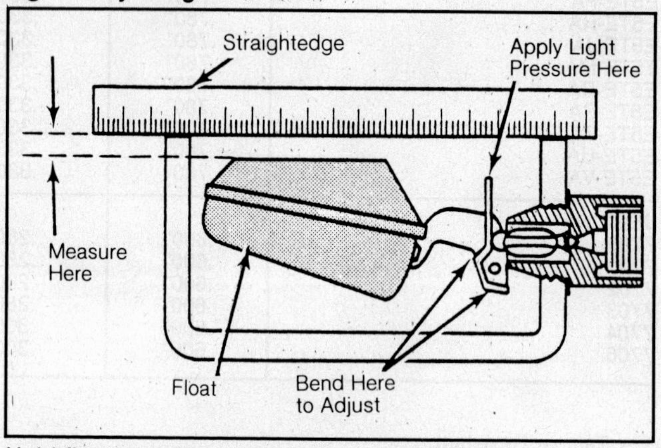

Hold finger against fulcrum pin retainer.

VACUUM STEP-UP PISTON GAP QUALIFICATION

NOTE: **This adjustment is required if step-up piston is removed or if piston lifter position is changed on actuating rod. This adjustment (qualification) places piston in a centered "mean" position.**

1) Remove step-up piston cover plate and gasket. Remove lifter lock screw and remove piston step-up assembly.

2) Measure piston gap. *See Fig. 3.* If not to specification, adjust by turning Allen head screw on top of piston.

3) Record number of turns and direction to obtain proper dimension. This must be reset to its original position after vacuum step-up piston adjustment has been made.

VACUUM STEP-UP PISTON ADJUSTMENT

NOTE: **Perform Vacuum Step-Up Piston Gap Qualification adjustment before adjusting vacuum step-up piston.**

1) With vacuum piston installed, back off idle speed screw until throttle valves are completely closed. Count number of turns so screw can be returned to its original position. *See Fig. 4.*

2) Fully depress step-up piston while holding moderate pressure on rod lifter tab. While in this position, tighten rod lifter lock screw.

3) Release piston and rod lifter. Return idle speed set screw to its original position.

4) Reset Allen head calibration screw on top of step-up piston to its original position as recorded under

1985 Carter Carburetors

CARTER BBD 2-BARREL (Cont.)

Fig. 3: Vacuum Step-Up Piston Gap Qualification

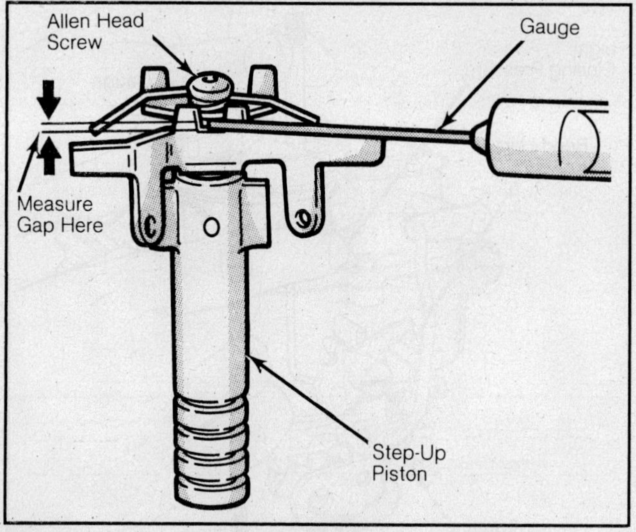

Record number of turns and direction.

Fig. 4: Adjusting Step-Up Piston

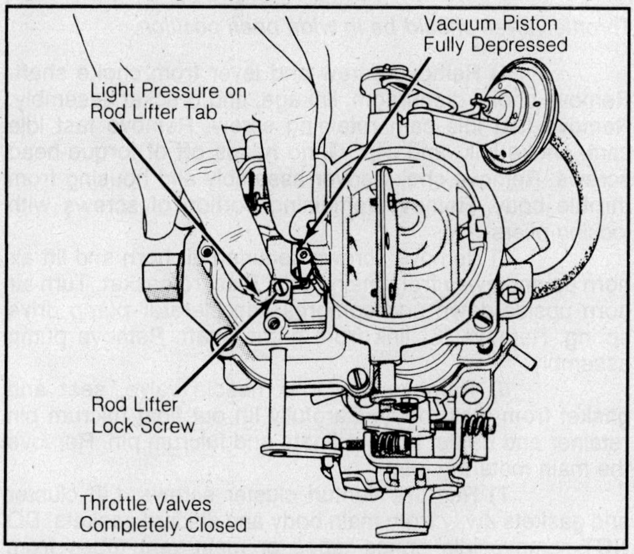

If this adjustment is changed, the step-up piston must be re-qualified.

VACUUM STEP-UP PISTON GAP QUALIFICATION. If this adjustment is changed, the step-up piston must be requalified.

ACCELERATOR PUMP STROKE ADJUSTMENT

1) Remove step-up piston cover plate and gasket. Back off curb idle screw to fully close throttle valves. Fast idle cam must be in open position. Open choke valve so that fast idle cam allows throttle valves to seat. *See Fig. 5.*

2) Turn curb idle screw until it just touches stop. Continue 2 more complete turns. Measure distance between surface of air horn and top of accelerator pump shaft.

3) If adjustment is required, loosen pump arm adjusting lock screw and turn sleeve to adjust pump travel. When correct measurement is obtained, tighten lock screw. Install step-up piston cover plate and gasket.

Fig. 5: Adjusting Accelerator Pump Stroke

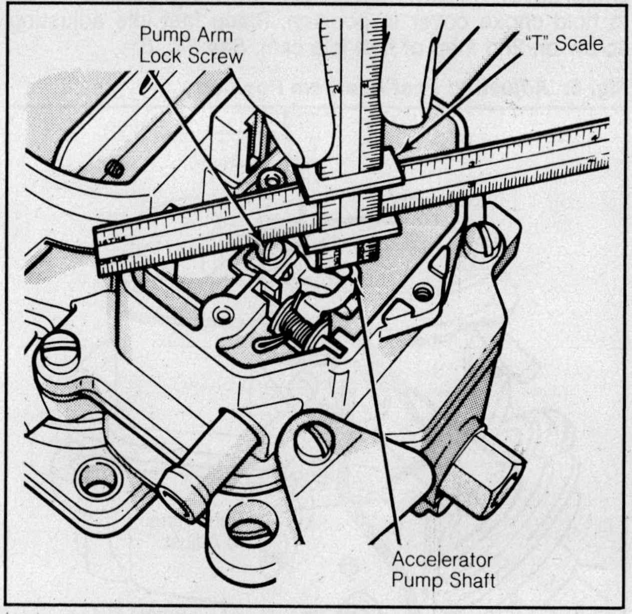

Fast idle cam must be in open position.

AUTOMATIC CHOKE

NOTE: **Normally, no readjustment is necessary from factory setting. Perform adjustment only after a major overhaul.**

Loosen choke thermostat cover retaining screws. Rotate cover in "Rich" or "Lean" direction to align reference mark on cover with specified scale graduation on choke housing. Tighten retaining screws.

VACUUM KICK (INITIAL CHOKE VALVE CLEARANCE)

NOTE: **All carburetors incorporate tamper-proof choke, choke pull-off, and idle adjusting screws. Adjustments given are for after major overhaul, or if carburetor components have been damaged.**

1) Grind off torque-head screw heads. Remove remaining portions of screws by turning counterclockwise with locking pliers. Turn choke cover 1/4 turn rich. Retain in position with 1 straight slot screw. Open throttle valve slightly to place fast idle screw on high step of cam.

2) Using a hand vacuum pump, apply at least 15 in. Hg vacuum to choke vacuum kick diaphragm. Spring in diaphragm stem should be compressed against stop without bending linkage. Measure clearance between choke plate and air horn wall.

3) Adjust clearance by bending diaphragm connecting link at "U" bend. Remove straight slot screw and adjust cover index to specified notch. Install replacement torque-head screws.

FAST IDLE CAM POSITION

NOTE: **All carburetors incorporate tamper-proof choke, choke pull-off, and idle adjusting screws. The following adjustments are for after major carburetor overhaul, or if carburetor components are damaged.**

1985 Carter Carburetors

CARTER BBD 2-BARREL (Cont.)

1) Remove torque-head screws and position choke cover 1/4 turn rich. Retain with 1 straight-slot screw to hold choke cover in position. Place fast idle adjusting screw on 2nd step of fast idle cam. *See Fig. 6.*

Fig. 6: Adjusting Fast Idle Cam Position

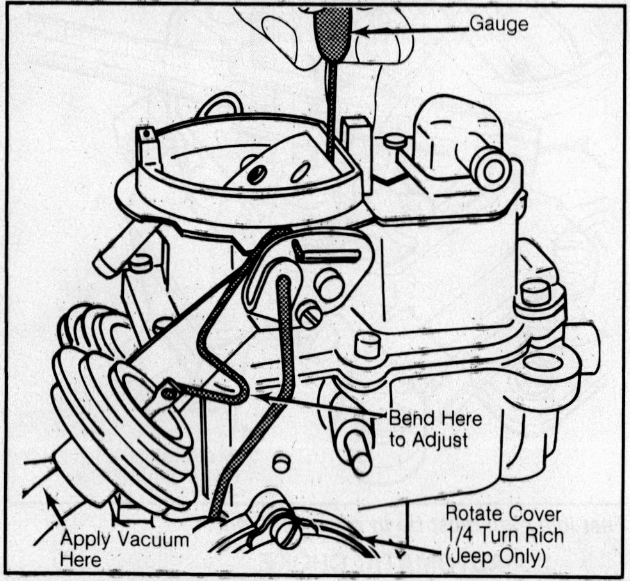

Place fast idle speed adjusting screw on 2nd step of fast idle cam.

2) With specified drill or pin gauge, measure clearance between upper edge of choke valve and air horn wall. To adjust, bend fast idle connecting rod down to increase measurement or up to decrease measurement.

3) Loosen housing cover screw and reset choke to specified index position. Install replacement torque-head screws.

CHOKE UNLOADER

1) Hold throttle valves wide open. Apply light closing pressure to choke valve lever. *See Fig. 7.*

2) Measure choke unloader specified clearance between upper edge of choke valve and air horn wall. Clearance can be checked using a specified drill or pin gauge.

3) To adjust, bend choke unloader tang. Make sure tang does not interfere with other components after it is adjusted.

Fig. 7: Adjusting Choke Unloader

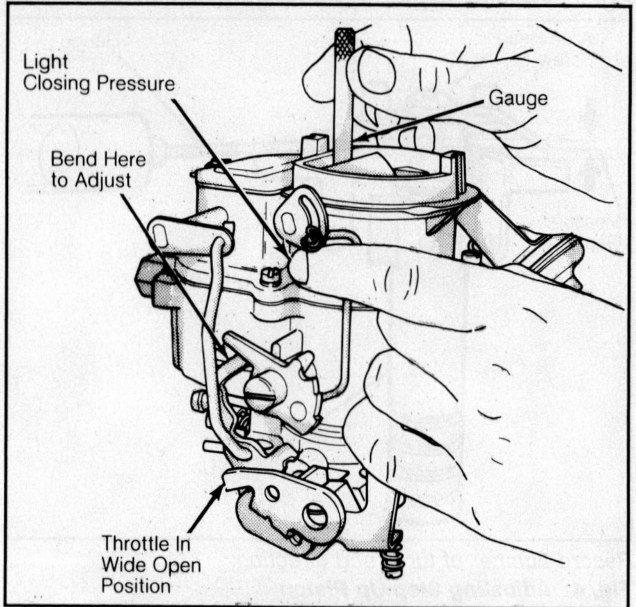

Throttle valves should be in wide open position.

OVERHAUL

DISASSEMBLY

1) Place carburetor on a repair stand, and remove stepper motor if equipped. Remove retaining clip from accelerator pump arm link and remove link.

2) Remove cover and gasket from top of air horn. Remove screws and locks from accelerator pump arm and vacuum piston rod lifter. Slide pump lever out of air horn. Remove pump arm and rod lifter.

3) Lift vacuum piston and step-up rods up and out of air horn as an assembly. Remove the vacuum piston spring. Remove choke vacuum diaphragm hose. Disconnect clips and remove link from choke housing lever and choke lever.

4) Remove screw and lever from choke shaft. Remove choke diaphragm, linkage, and bracket assembly. Remove fast idle cam retaining screw. Remove fast idle cam, choke link, and clip. Grind heads off of torque-head screws. Remove choke cover assembly and housing from throttle body. Remove remaining portion of screws with locking pliers.

5) Remove screws securing air horn and lift air horn up and away from main body. Discard gasket. Turn air horn upside-down and compress accelerator pump drive spring. Remove "S" link from pump shaft. Remove pump assembly.

6) Remove fuel inlet needle valve, seat and gasket from main body. Carefully lift out float fulcrum pin retainer and baffle. Lift out floats and fulcrum pin. Remove the main metering jets.

7) Remove venturi cluster screws. Lift cluster and gaskets away from main body and discard gaskets. DO NOT remove idle orifice tubes or main vent tubes from cluster as they can be cleaned with solvent and dried with compressed air while assembled.

8) Turn carburetor upside-down and catch accelerator pump discharge and intake check balls as they fall out.

9) Turn idle limiter caps to stop. Remove plastic caps from idle air mixture screws. Be sure to count number of turns it takes to seat screws to ease reassembly adjustment. Remove screws and springs from throttle body.

10) Remove screws and separate throttle body from main body. Discard gasket. Check choke plate in air horn for freedom of movement. If any sticking or binding is evident, clean thoroughly.

CLEANING & INSPECTION

NOTE: **Do not apply compressed air to diaphragm. Do not use wire or drill to clean jets or passageways.**

- Use a regular carburetor cleaning solution. Soak components long enough to thoroughly clean all surfaces and passages of foreign matter.

CARTER BBD 2-BARREL (Cont.)

Fig. 8: Exploded View of Carter Model BBD 2-Barrel Carburetor

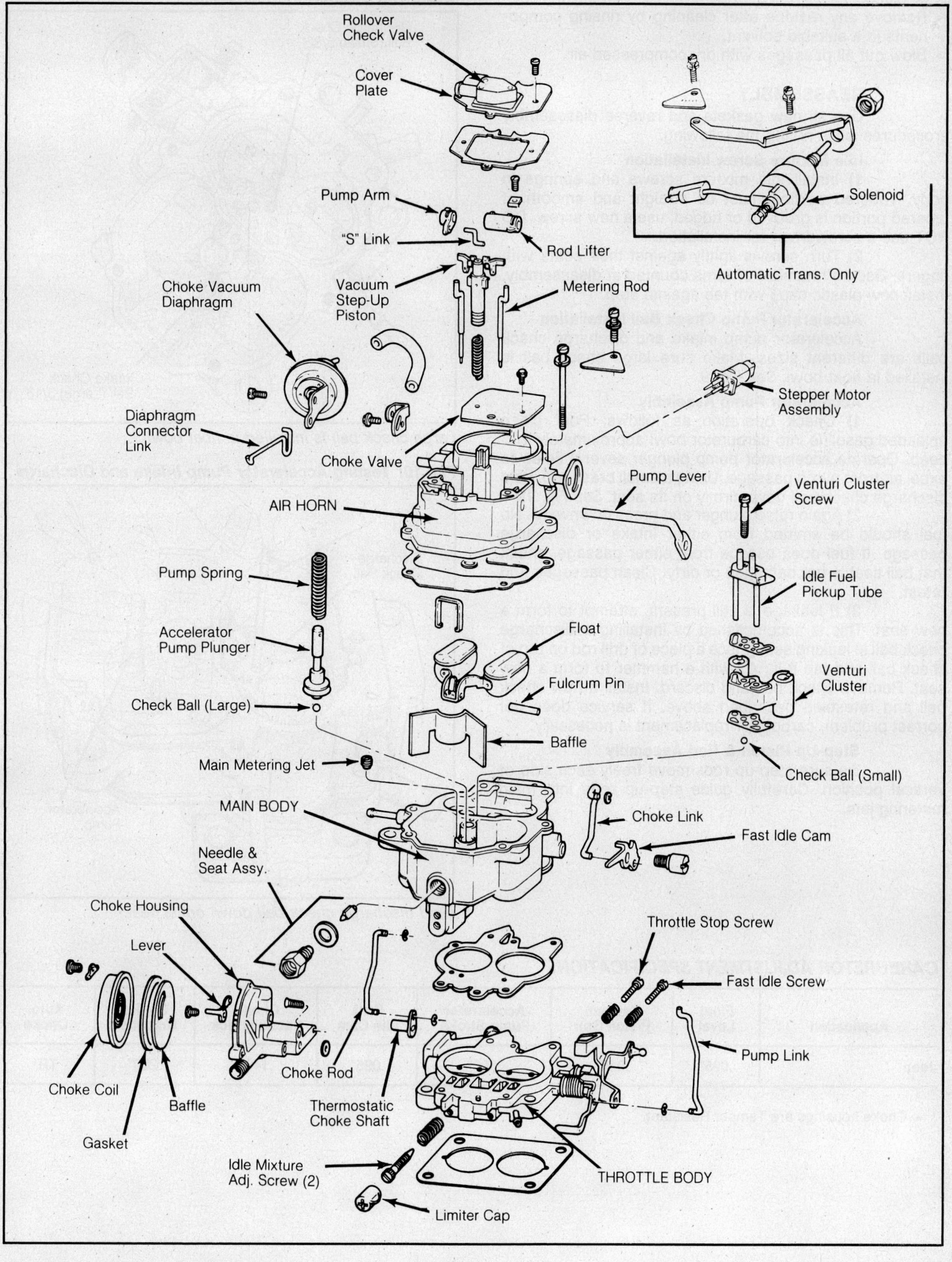

CARTER BBD 2-BARREL (Cont.)

- Do not soak any components containing rubber, leather or plastic.
- Remove any residue after cleaning by rinsing components in a suitable solvent.
- Blow out all passages with dry compressed air.

REASSEMBLY

Use all new gaskets and reverse disassembly procedures while noting the following:

Idle Mixture Screw Installation

1) Install idle mixture screws and springs in body. Tapered portion must be straight and smooth. If tapered portion is grooved or ridged, use a new screw. DO NOT use a screwdriver for installation.

2) Turn screws lightly against their seats with fingers. Back off number of turns counted at disassembly. Install new plastic caps with tab against stop.

Accelerator Pump Check Ball Installation

Accelerator pump intake and discharge check balls are different sizes. Make sure large check ball is installed in float bowl. *See Fig. 9.*

Accelerator Pump Assembly

1) Check operation as follows: Pour clean unleaded gasoline into carburetor bowl approximately 1/2" deep. Operate accelerator pump plunger several times to expel air from pump passage. Using a small brass rod, hold discharge check ball down firmly on its seat. *See Fig. 10.*

2) Again raise plunger and press downward. No fuel should be emitted from either intake or discharge passage. If fuel does escape from either passage, check that ball seat is not damaged or dirty. Clean passages and retest.

3) If leakage is still present, attempt to form a new seat. This is accomplished by installing a discharge check ball in leaking seat. Place a piece of drill rod on top of check ball and tap it lightly with a hammer to form a new seat. Remove check ball and discard. Install a new check ball and retest as described above. If service does not correct problem, carburetor replacement is necessary.

Step-Up Piston & Rod Assembly

Be sure step-up rods move freely each side of vertical position. Carefully guide step-up rods into main metering jets.

Fig. 9: Installing Accelerator Pump Intake and Discharge Check Balls

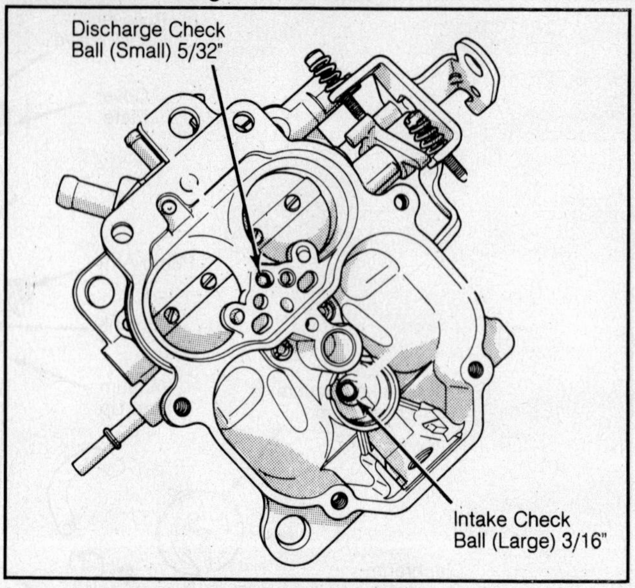

Large check ball is installed in float bowl.

Fig. 10: Testing Accelerator Pump Intake and Discharge

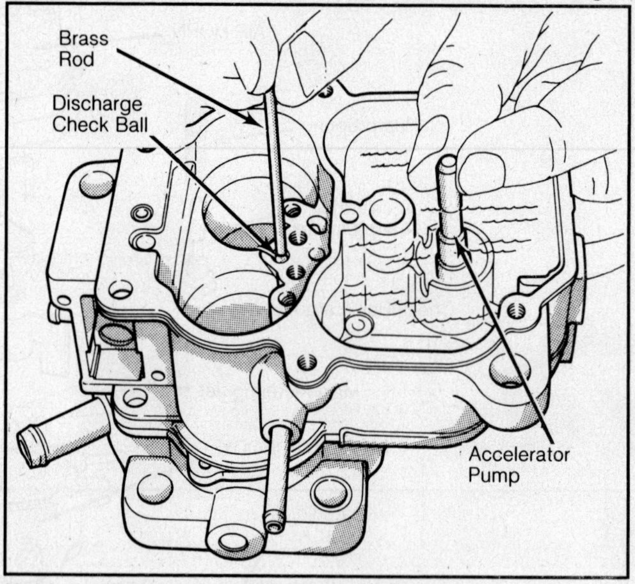

Hold discharge check ball down on its seat.

CARBURETOR ADJUSTMENT SPECIFICATIONS

Application	Float Level	Vacuum Piston Gap	Accelerator Pump Stroke	Fast Idle Cam	Choke Vacuum Kick	Choke Unloader	Auto. Choke
Jeep	.025"	.035"	.520"	.095"	.140"	.280"	TR[1]

[1] – Choke housings are Tamper Resistant.

CHRYSLER (MIKUNI) 2-BARREL

CARBURETOR APPLICATION

CHRYSLER CORP. (MIKUNI) CARBURETOR NO.

Application	Carb. No.
2.6L 4-Cyl.	
Federal	MD088138
Calif.	MD082749
High Altitude	MD083781

CARBURETOR IDENTIFICATION

Carburetor identification is located on a metal tag attached to carburetor.

DESCRIPTION

All models with 2.6L engine use a 2-bbl. carburetor of standard downdraft design. Six basic systems are used: fuel inlet, primary metering, secondary metering, automatic choke, enrichment, and fuel cut-off.

Other features include: diaphragm accelerator pump, bowl vent, fuel cut-off solenoid and air switching valve (ASV).

In addition, California and High Altitude models include a sub-EGR valve, coasting air valve (CAV), jet air control valve (JACV), and high altitude compensating system (HAC).

The main carburetor body is made of plastic resin to reduce heat transfer to the float bowl. The automatic choke is a thermo-wax pellet type controlled by engine coolant.

ADJUSTMENT

NOTE: **For all on-vehicle adjustments not covered in this article, see appropriate TUNE-UP article.**

FLOAT LEVEL

Invert air horn assembly (without gasket). Allow weight of float assembly to seat inlet valve. *See Fig. 1.* Distance from bottom edge of float to surface of air horn should be .74-.82" (19.0-21.0 mm). If not, adjust by adding or removing shims under inlet needle seat.

NOTE: **All other adjustments are factory made and should not be changed in service.**

OVERHAUL

DISASSEMBLY

1) Remove water hoses from choke assembly. Drill out staked portion or grind off heads of choke cover retaining screws. Using a small hammer and pointed punch, tap remaining choke cover screw counterclockwise to remove. Note position of scribe marks on choke pinion plate relative to punch mark. Alignment of marks MUST be the same during reassembly. *See Fig. 2.*

2) Remove "E" clip from throttle opener link, then remove screws and throttle opener. Disconnect fuel cut-off solenoid ground wire and remove solenoid. Disconnect throttle return and damper springs. Remove "E" clips and choke unloader link.

Fig. 1: Float Level Adjustment

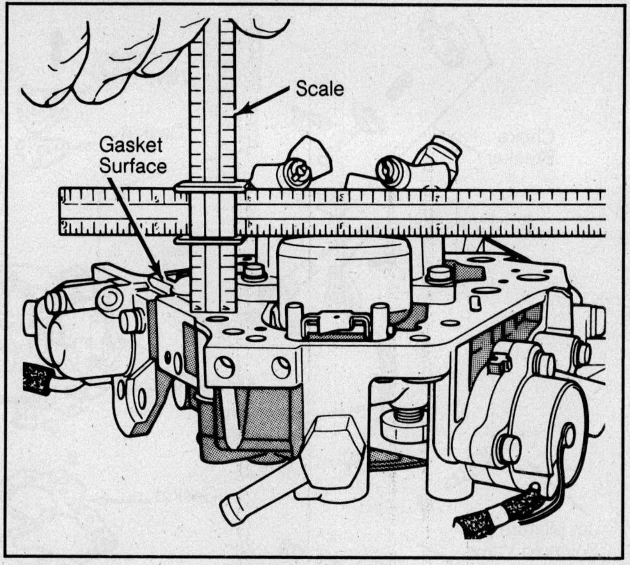

Make measurement without gasket.

Fig. 2: Pinion Plate Alignment

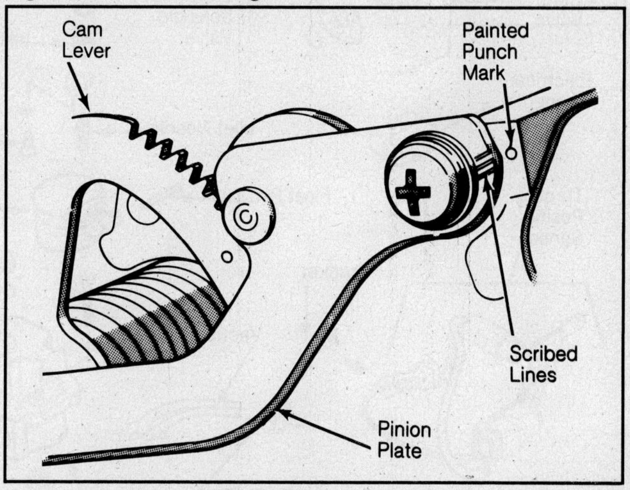

Note position of alignment marks during disassembly.

3) Disconnect vacuum hose and vacuum chamber link. Remove screws and vacuum chamber. Disconnect throttle operating rod link. Remove 6 air horn screws and lift air horn off carburetor body.

4) Remove vacuum hose connector retaining screws (2), then remove hoses and connector. Slide float pivot pin out. Remove float and inlet needle. Remove and discard air horn gasket. Remove screw and retainer, then remove needle seat and screen assembly. Be sure not to lose shim from under needle seat.

5) Remove primary and secondary venturi retainers, venturi, and "O" rings. Mark each venturi for reassembly reference. Remove primary and secondary main jets from pedestals and note jet numbers for correct reassembly. Remove screws and pedestals.

6) Remove bowl vent solenoid screws. Separate solenoid from bowl vent and remove spring. Remove bowl vent, "O" ring and seal from air horn. Discard "O" ring and seal. On California and High Altitude models, remove 3 coasting air valve (CAV) screws, CAV cover, retainer sleeve, spring, spring retainer, diaphragm and seal.

7) On all models, remove 3 enrichment valve screws, valve cover, valve, gasket, and jet. Remove 2 air

1985 Mikuni Carburetors

CHRYSLER (MIKUNI) 2-BARREL (Cont.)

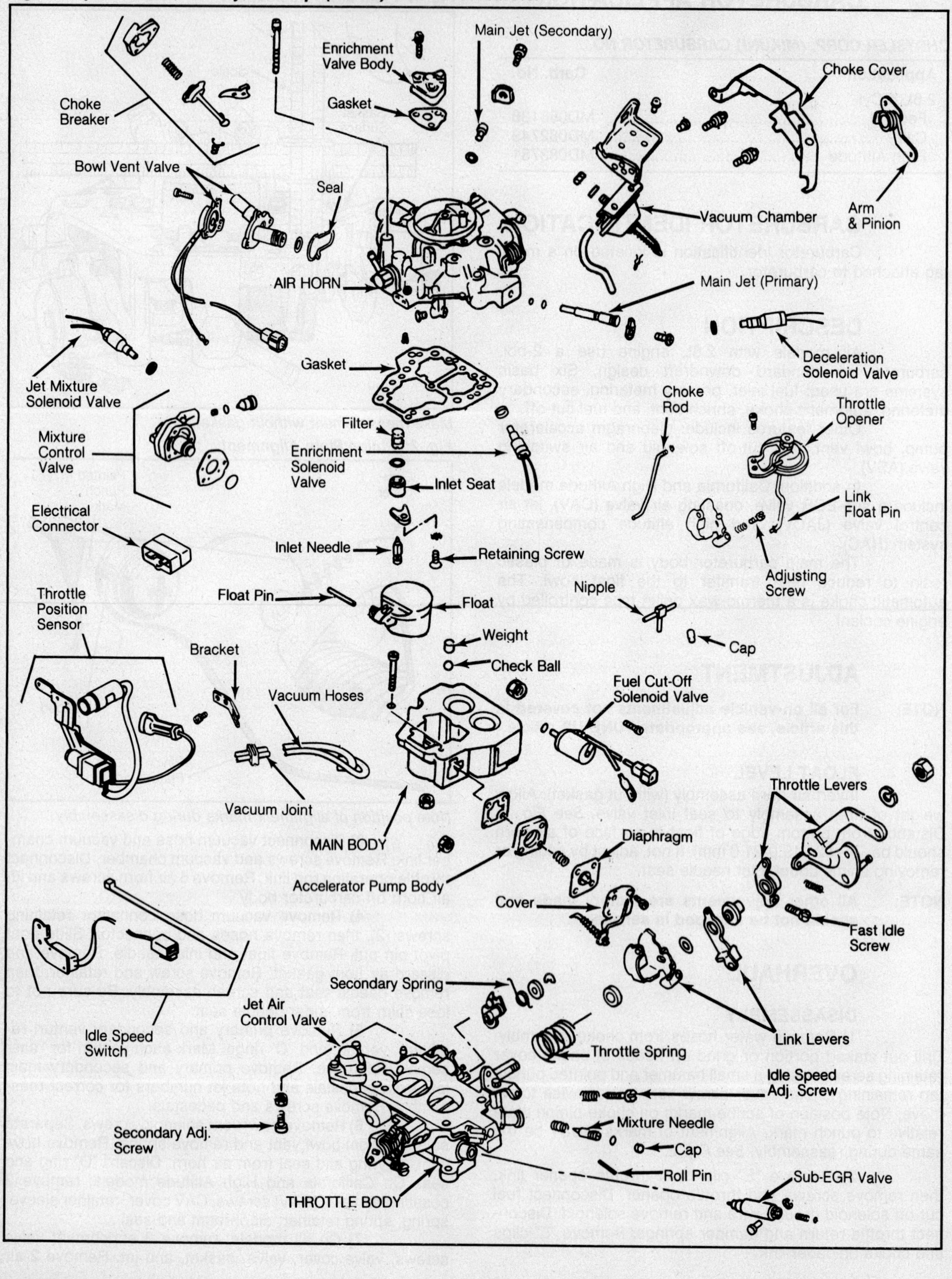

Fig. 3: Exploded View of Chrysler Corp. (Mikuni) 2-Barrel Carburetor

switching valve screws and valve assembly. Take out spring retainer sleeve, spring, retainer, and diaphagm seal. Remove screw, lock plate, and primary jet set. Repeat procedure for secondary jet set.

8) From top of air horn, remove primary and secondary air bleed jets. Note locations of jets for proper installation. Invert air horn to remove pump weight, check ball, and hex nut. Remove 4 accelerator pump screws, cover, diaphragm, spring, pump body, check ball, and gasket.

9) On California and High Altitude models, remove 3 jet air control valve screws, cover, spring, spring retainer, and diaphragm/seal. Remove "E" clip from sub-EGR valve lever. Carefully slide pin from sub-EGR valve. Spring tension on lever is caused by steel ball and spring in sub-EGR valve. Use care when removing pin so as not to lose spring and check ball. Remove valve and boot seal.

CLEANING & INSPECTION

- Do not immerse plastic or rubber parts in solvent. Do not soak solenoids or choke assembly in any liquid.
- Blow out all passages with compressed air. Do not use wire or drill bit to clean calibrated orifices or jets.
- Do not use compressed air to blow out any diaphragm fittings if diaphragm is installed.
- Inspect all parts for cracks, burrs, or pitting. Replace any damaged parts and all "O" rings, seals, and gaskets.
- If recommended by solvent manufacturer, use hot water to rinse parts after cleaning. Blow dry with compressed air.

CAUTION: NEVER "prime" carburetor with fuel to restart. Crank engine, then pump accelerator several times. This should be sufficient to start engine.

REASSEMBLY

To reassemble carburetor, reverse disassembly procedure, noting the following:

1) Install sub-EGR valve and verify proper operation. Install jet air control valve and tighten screws.

2) When installing primary and secondary air bleed jets, and primary and secondary main jets, largest numbered jet should be installed on secondary side.

3) When throttle body is completely assembled, and before installing on main body, check float level. See FLOAT LEVEL ADJUSTMENT procedure.

4) Install choke cover and stake 4 screws in position. Tighten last screw with small hammer and pointed punch. Check alignment of punch mark with scribed line of pinion plate and punch mark of cam lever with Green paint mark of pinion plate gear. *See Figs. 2 and 5.*

Fig. 5: Cam Lever Alignment

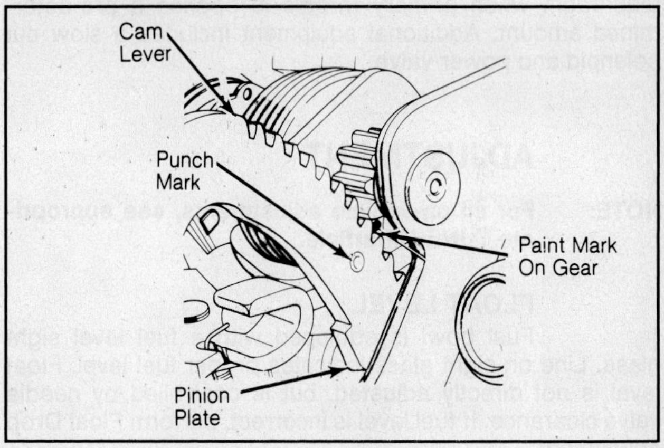

Fig. 4: Exploded View of Valve & Pump Assemblies for Chrysler (Mikuni) Carburator

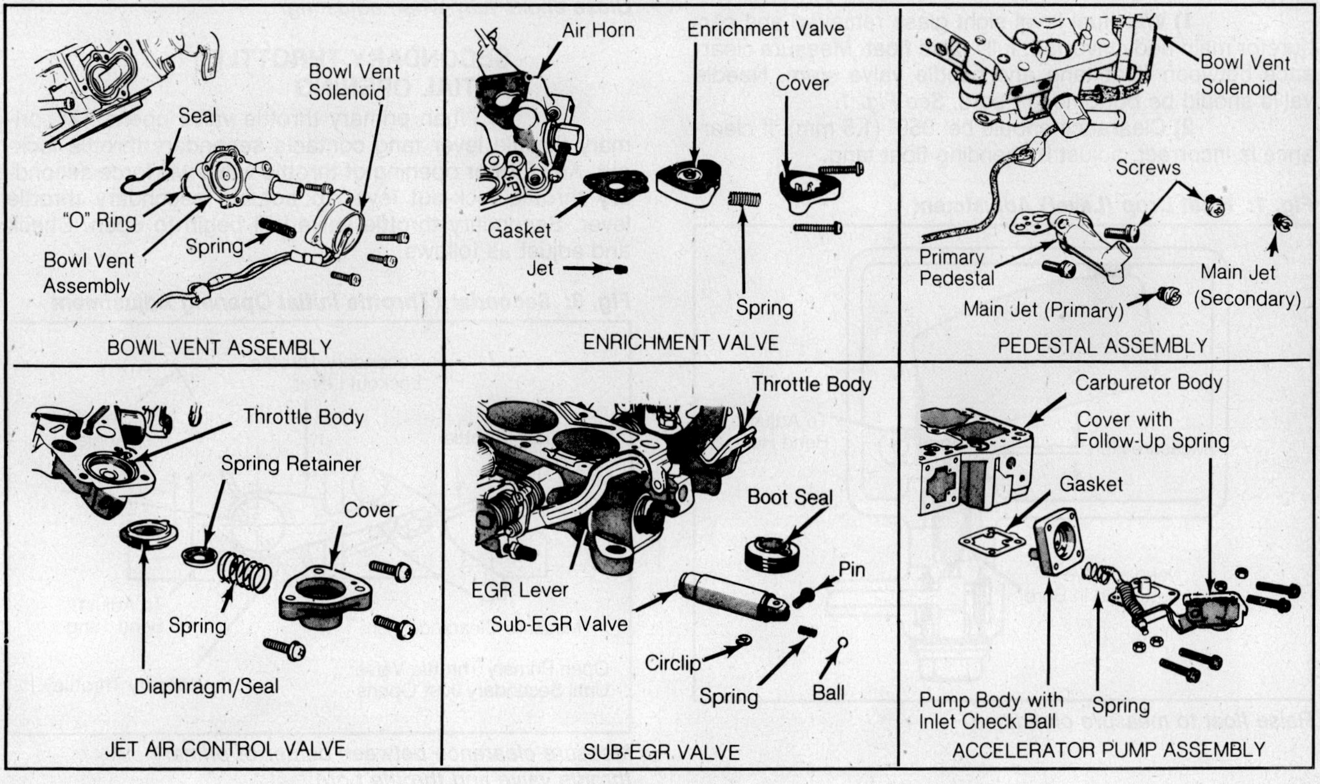

1985 Hitachi Carburetors

HITACHI DCH 340 2-BARREL

CARBURETOR APPLICATION

CHEVROLET & GMC CARBURETOR NO.

Application	Man. Trans.	Auto. Trans.
1.9L 4-Cyl. "S" Series Truck	94121895	94121895

DESCRIPTION

Carburetor is a 2-barrel downdraft type with piston type accelerator pump. Carburetor consists of low speed (primary) barrel and high speed (secondary) barrel integrated into a single unit with a common fuel bowl.

Secondary throttle is actuated by a vacuum diaphragm when primary throttle is opened a pre-determined amount. Additional equipment includes a slow cut solenoid and power valve.

ADJUSTMENT

NOTE: **For all on-vehicle adjustments, see appropriate TUNE-UP article.**

FLOAT LEVEL

Fuel bowl is equipped with a fuel level sight glass. Line on sight glass indicates proper fuel level. Float level is not directly adjusted, but is controlled by needle valve clearance. If fuel level is incorrect, perform Float Drop adjustment.

FLOAT DROP

1) With fuel level sight glass removed and carburetor main body inverted, fully raise float. Measure clearance between float tang and needle valve stem. Needle valve should be bottomed in bore. *See Fig. 1.*

2) Clearance should be .059" (1.5 mm). If clearance is incorrect, adjust by bending float tang.

Fig. 1: Float Drop (Level) Adjustment

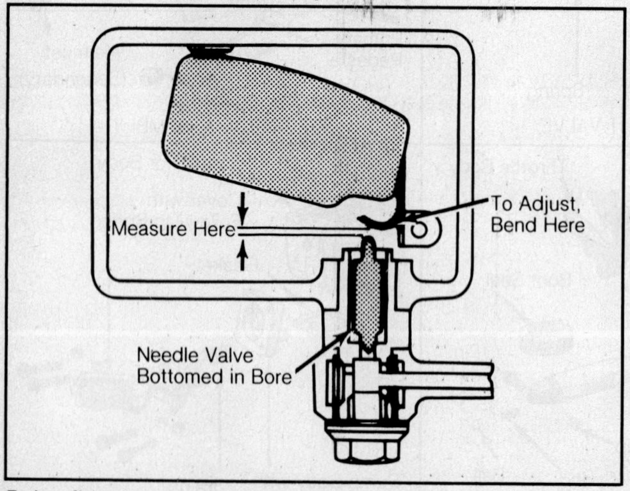

Raise float to measure clearance.

PRIMARY THROTTLE OPENING

1) Check primary throttle valve angle with choke completely closed. Adjust throttle angle by turning fast idle screw, making sure screw is all the way in before measuring clearance.

2) With choke closed, check clearance between throttle valve and throttle bore at center of throttle plate. Primary throttle valve clearance should be .050-.059" (1.28-1.51 mm) with throttle valve angle of 16°. *See Fig. 2.*

Fig. 2: Primary Throttle Valve Adjustment

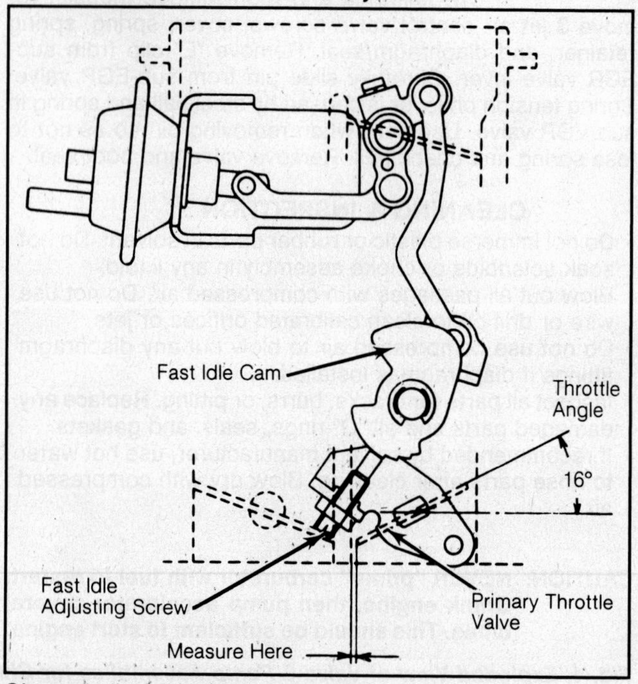

Close choke fully when adjusting.

SECONDARY THROTTLE INITIAL OPENING

1) When primary throttle valve opens 47°, primary throttle lever tang contacts secondary throttle lock-out. Any further opening of throttle valve will force secondary throttle lock-out lever to actuate secondary throttle lever. Secondary throttle valve will begin to open. Check and adjust as follows.

Fig. 3: Secondary Throttle Initial Opening Adjustment

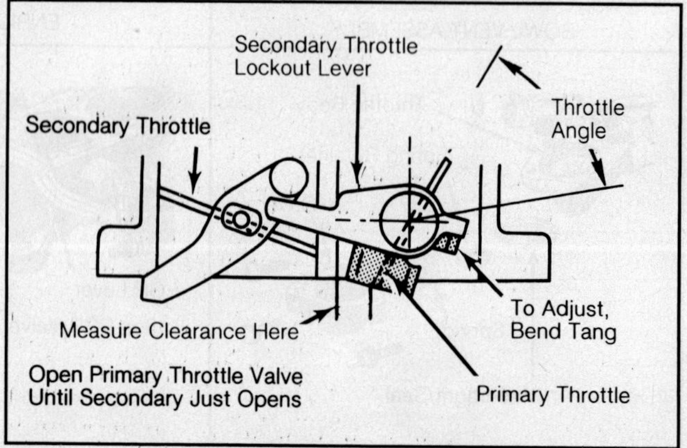

Measure clearance between center of primary throttle valve and throttle bore.

HITACHI DCH 340 2-BARREL (Cont.)

2) Open primary throttle valve until primary throttle lever tang just contacts secondary throttle lock-out. Hold throttle in this position. Clearance between center of primary throttle valve and throttle bore should be .24-.30" (6.1-7.6 mm). If not, adjust by bending primary throttle tang. *See Fig. 3.*

SECONDARY LOCK-OUT

1) Close primary throttle valve by turning throttle adjusting screw out.

2) With throttle valve completely closed, loosen lock nut on lock-out lever screw. Turn screw until it contacts return plate. Tighten lock nut. *See Fig. 4.*

Fig. 4: Secondary Lock-Out Adjustment

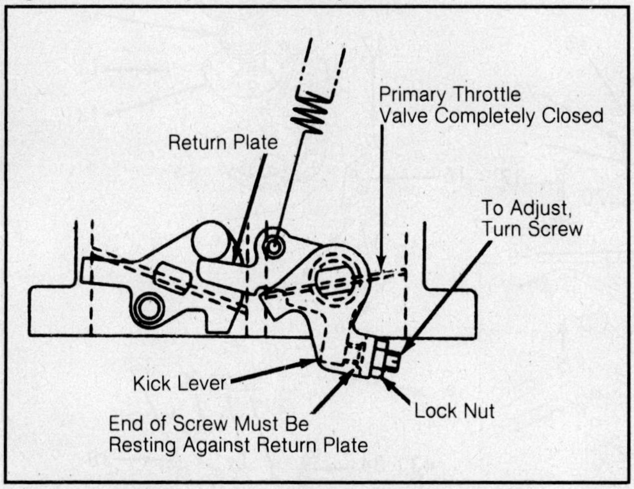

Perform adjustment with primary throttle valve completely closed.

OVERHAUL

DISASSEMBLY

1) With carburetor removed, remove main and assist throttle return springs. Disconnect accelerator pump lever.

2) Remove harness connector hanger from carburetor and disconnect automatic choke lead wire from connector. Remove fuel inlet pipe and filter.

3) Disconnect vent valve switch wire from connector. Remove circlip connecting choke rod to choke lever. Disconnect choke connecting rod.

4) Disconnect automatic choke vacuum hose. Remove 4 choke-to-air horn screws. Remove choke assembly. Remove circlip connecting vacuum break diaphragm to secondary throttle lever. Remove vacuum break diaphragm.

5) Separate main body from throttle body. Remove accelerator pump plunger assembly. Remove needle valve assembly.

6) Remove 3 float level cover screws. Remove cover, float level gauge, gasket and float assembly. Do not damage rubber seal or lose float collar.

7) Remove diaphragm cover retaining screws. Separate diaphragm cover, spring and diaphragm. Do not lose ball and spring.

8) Remove all jets from upper part of main body. Remove power valve. *See Fig. 5.* Remove pump set screw, weight and check ball.

9) Remove main jet plugs and primary and secondary main jets. Remove primary slow air bleed from air horn.

10) Further disassembly is not required. Primary and secondary throttle valves, and choke valve screws are staked in position. No attempt should be made to remove screws.

Fig. 5: Location of Jets in Main Body

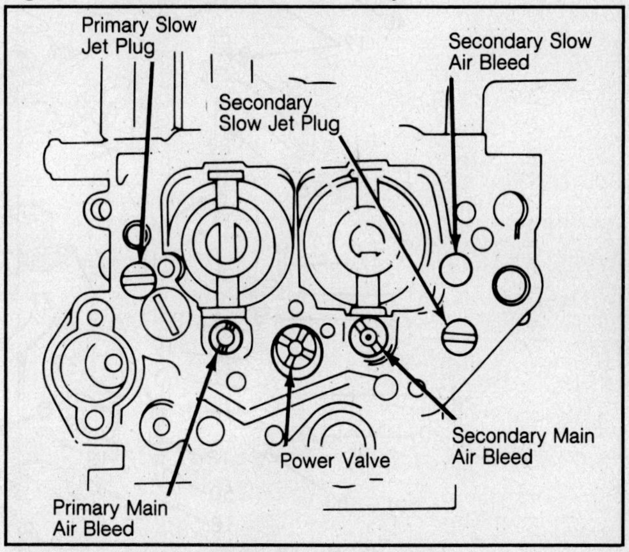

Make sure jet wrench or screwdriver fits securely in slots of jets.

INSPECTION

Air Horn

Inspect air horn for cracks and damage. Pay particular attention to mating surfaces. Check shaft holes for wear. Check choke valve and vacuum piston for smooth operation.

Main Body

1) Inspect and remove carbon deposits from inside main body. Inspect for cracks and damage, particularly on mating surfaces. Inspect threaded portion and head slots of jets for damage.

2) Check power valve for leaks. Check power valve rod for smooth operation and ensure that rod is not bent.

3) Inspect needle valve for sticking, dirt, and corrosion. Carefully check float for pin holes (leaks) and wear. Inspect filter in fuel inlet pipe for dirt, corrosion and damage.

4) Inspect accelerator pump plunger for damage and distortion. Check for smooth plunger movement within cylinder bore. Check accelerator pump boot for tears or damage.

Throttle Body

1) Check all ports for clogging. Inspect throttle valves for carbon deposits and wear. Check throttle shaft holes for wear.

2) Check mixture adjusting screw seating face for step wear. Check vacuum break diaphragm for deterioration and damage.

REASSEMBLY

To reassemble, reverse disassembly procedures and note the following:

1985 Hitachi Carburetors

HITACHI DCH 340 2-BARREL (Cont.)

Fig. 6: Exploded View of Hitachi DCH 340 2-Bbl. Carburetor

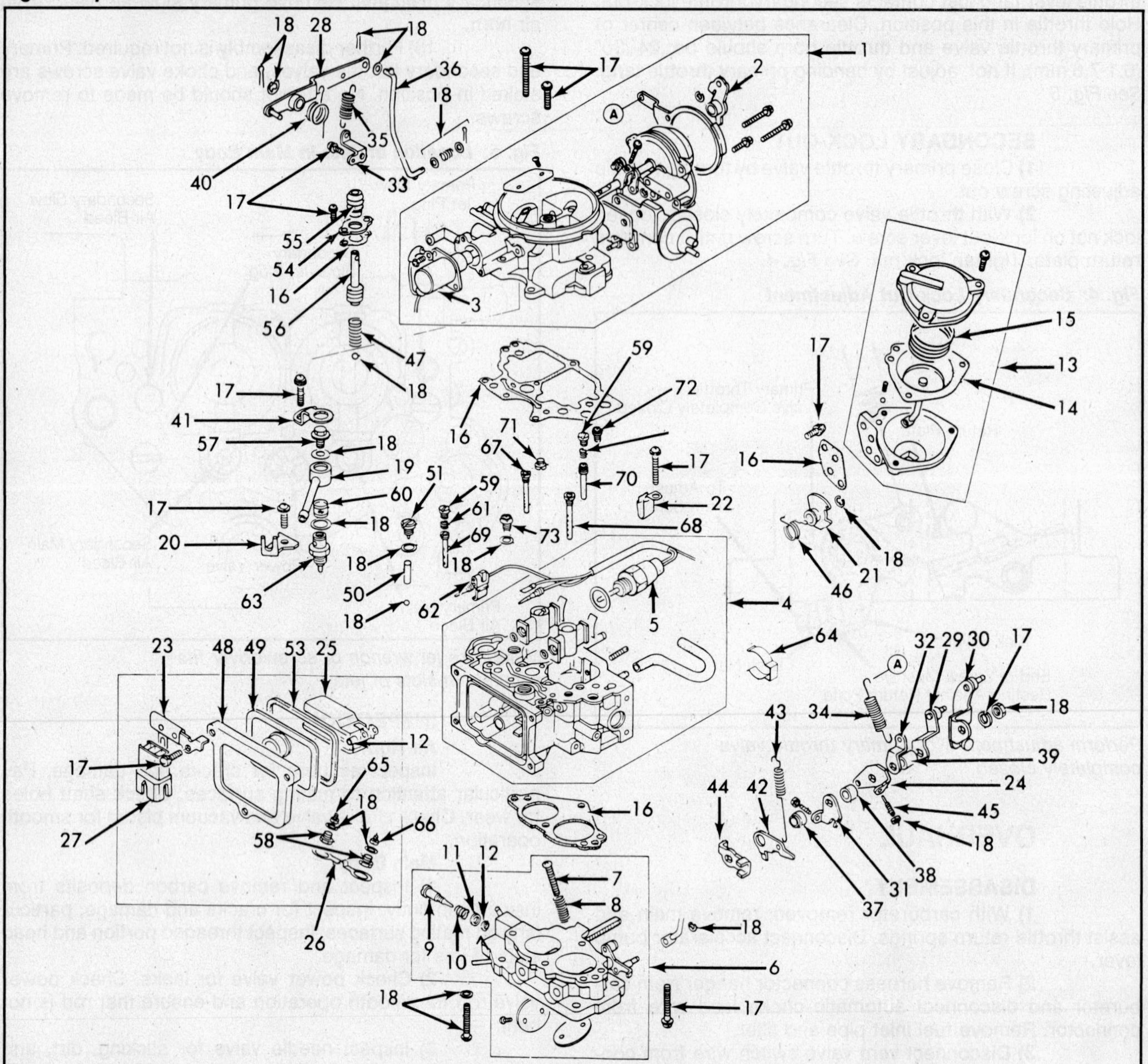

1. Air Horn Assembly
2. Choke Lever
3. Switch Vent Solenoid
4. Main Body
5. Slow Cut Solenoid
6. Throttle Body
7. Throttle Adjusting Screw
8. Throttle Adjusting Spring
9. Idle Mixture Screw
10. Idle Mixture Spring
11. Idle Mixture Washer
12. Idle Mixture Seal
13. Vacuum Break Diaphragm
14. Diaphragm
15. Diaphragm Spring
16. Gasket Kit
17. Screw & Washer Kit A
18. Screw & Washer Kit B
19. Fuel Inlet Pipe
20. Stop Plate
21. Fast Idle Cam
22. Wire Holder
23. Connector Hanger
24. Fast Idle Adjusting Lever
25. Float
26. Drain Plug Lock Plate
27. Connector
28. Pump Lever
29. Accelerator Lever
30. Cruise Lever
31. Secondary Lock-Out Lever
32. Spring Hanger
33. Spring Hanger
34. Main Spring
35. Assist Spring
36. Pump Rod
37. Sleeve
38. Collar
39. Collar
40. Pump Lever Spring
41. Lock Lever
42. Return Plate
43. Throttle Spring
44. Adjusting Lever
45. Fast Idle Screw
46. Cam Spring
47. Piston Return Spring
48. Sight Glass Cover
49. Fuel Level Sight Glass
50. Weight
51. Pump Set Screw
52. Collar
53. Seal
54. Plate
55. Dust Cover
56. Piston
57. Fuel Inlet Set Screw
58. Drain Plug
59. Taper Plug
60. Filter
61. Slow Jet Ring
62. Wire Connector
63. Needle Valve
64. Clip
65. Primary Main Jet
66. Secondary Main Jet
67. Primary Main Air Bleed
68. Secondary Main Air Bleed
69. Primary Slow Jet
70. Secondary Slow Jet
71. Primary Slow Air Bleed
72. Secondary Slow Air Bleed
73. Power Valve

1985 Hitachi Carburetors

HITACHI DCH 340 2-BARREL (Cont.)

1) Be careful not to bend rod when installing power jet valve.

2) After accelerator pump is assembled, fill cavity with fuel. Depress accelerator pump and ensure fuel is injected smoothly. Do not bend piston connecting rod during assembly.

CARBURETOR ADJUSTMENT SPECIFICATIONS

Application	Float Level	Float Drop	Primary Throttle Angle	Primary Throttle Clearance	Secondary Throttle Opening	Secondary Throttle Lockout
94121895	[1]	.059"	16°	.050-.059"	.240-.300"	[2]

[1] – Correct float drop adjustment will result in proper float level.

[2] – Adjusting screw contacting return plate with throttle closed.

1985 Holley Carburetors

HOLLEY MODEL 1945 SINGLE BARREL

CARBURETOR APPLICATION

CHRYSLER CORP. (HOLLEY) CARBURETOR NO.

Application	Man. Trans.	Auto. Trans.
3.7L 6-Cyl.		
Federal	R-40159	R-40160

CARBURETOR IDENTIFICATION

Carburetor is identified by part number stamped into main body, or by tag attached to carburetor.

DESCRIPTION

The Holley 1945 carburetor is a single venturi, concentric downdraft design with the venturi completely surrounded by a single fuel bowl. The carburetor consists of 3 main parts. These are the air horn, main body, and throttle body. Four basic fuel metering systems are used: idle and transfer, main metering system, accelerating system and power enrichment system. Fuel inlet and choke systems are also used.

ADJUSTMENTS

NOTE: **For on-vehicle adjustments not covered in this article, see appropriate TUNE-UP article.**

FLOAT LEVEL

1) With air horn removed, turn main body upside-down with gasket installed. Hold a straightedge across main body, over floats, at point farthest from fuel inlet. Floats should just contact straightedge. *See Fig. 1.*

Fig. 1: Adjusting Float Level

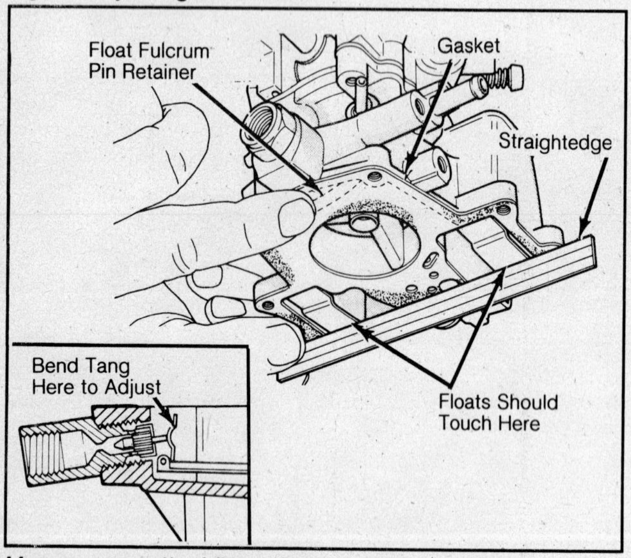

Measure at ends of floats farthest from fuel inlet.

2) To adjust, bend float tang on float arm that contacts fuel inlet needle.

CHOKE VACUUM KICK

1) Open throttle and close choke. Close throttle to trap fast idle cam in closed choke position. *See Fig. 2.*

Fig. 2: Adjusting Choke Vacuum Kick

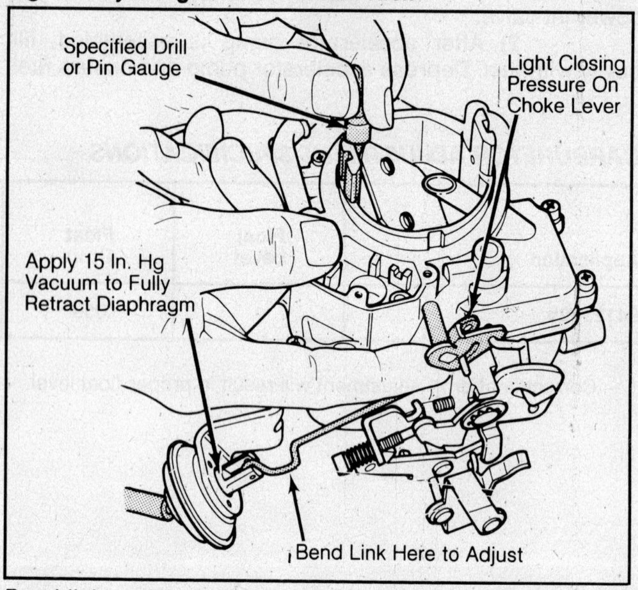

Bend link at "U" to adjust.

2) Disconnect vacuum hose from choke vacuum diaphragm. Connect hand vacuum pump to diaphragm and apply at least 15 in. Hg. Apply light finger pressure on choke shaft lever to compress spring in diaphragm stem without distorting linkage. Diaphragm stem reaches a stop as spring is compressed.

3) Measure choke vacuum kick specified clearance between upper edge of choke valve and air horn wall. Clearance can be measured using specified drill or pin gauge.

4) To adjust, bend diaphragm link at "U" bend. *See Fig. 2.* Check all linkage for freedom of movement. Remove vacuum pump and install vacuum hose on diaphragm.

FAST IDLE CAM POSITION

1) Position fast idle speed screw on 2nd step of fast idle cam. Apply light finger pressure on choke shaft lever to close choke valve. *See Fig. 3.*

Fig. 3: Adjusting Fast Idle Cam Position

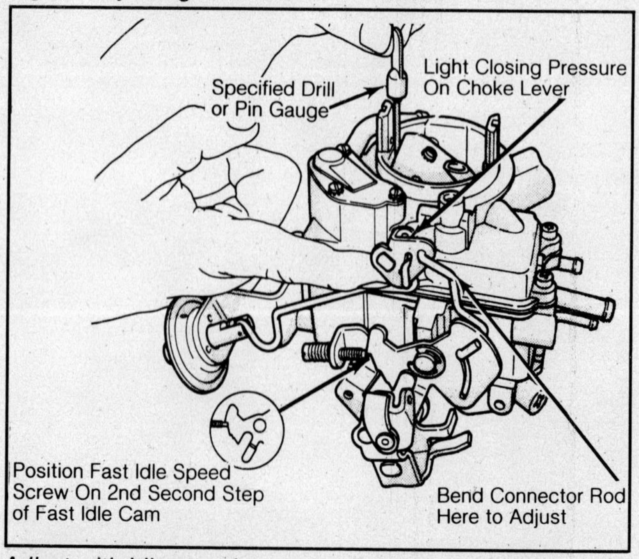

Adjust with idle speed screw on 2nd step of fast idle cam.

HOLLEY MODEL 1945 SINGLE BARREL (Cont.)

2) Using specified drill or pin gauge, measure clearance between top of choke valve and air horn wall at throttle lever side.

3) If clearance is incorrect, adjust by bending fast idle cam connector rod until correct valve opening is obtained.

CHOKE UNLOADER

1) Hold throttle valves in wide open position. Apply light finger pressure on choke shaft lever to close choke valve. *See Fig. 4.*

Fig. 4: Adjusting Choke Unloader

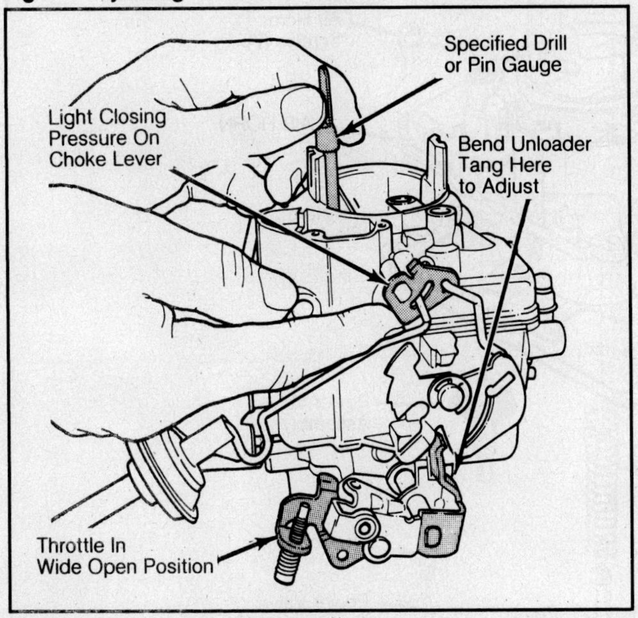

Measure with throttle valves wide open.

2) Measure choke unloader clearance between top edge of choke valve and air horn wall at throttle lever side. Check clearance with specified drill or pin gauge.

3) To adjust, bend choke unloader tang on throttle lever until correct clearance is obtained.

ACCELERATOR PUMP STROKE

1) Place throttle lever in curb idle position. Make sure accelerator pump rod link is installed in correct hole in throttle lever. *See Fig. 5.*

2) Measure length of pump operating link from center of rod in throttle lever to center of rod in accelerator pump arm. To adjust, bend accelerator pump rod at "U" bend.

Fig. 5: Adjusting Accelerator Pump Stroke

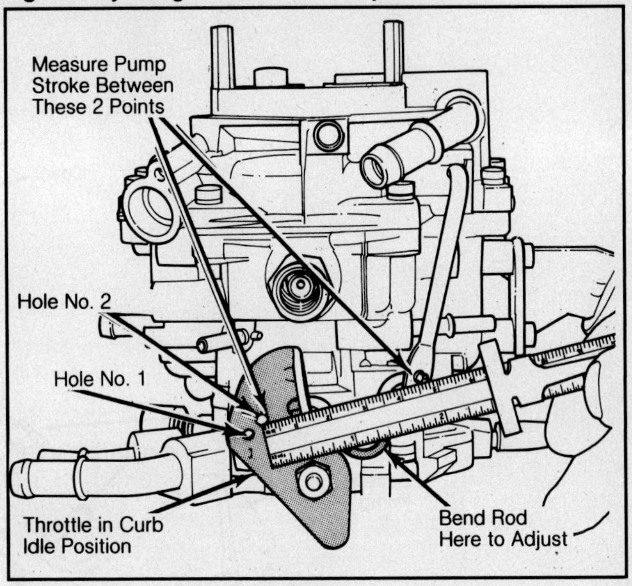

Ensure pump rod link is installed in correct hole.

OVERHAUL

DISASSEMBLY

1) Perform disassembly procedure with carburetor on stand to avoid damage to throttle valves. Remove wire retainer and bowl vent solenoid. Remove solenoid idle stop (SIS).

2) Remove fast idle cam retaining clip, fast idle cam, and connector rod. Remove rod from fast idle cam. Remove choke vacuum diaphragm, link, and bracket assembly. Disconnect diaphragm rod from slot in choke lever.

3) Remove nut and washer from throttle shaft. Note position of rod in throttle lever and record hole used for reassembly reference.

4) Remove air horn screws. Separate air horn from main body, tapping gently with plastic hammer or screwdriver handle if needed. DO NOT pry on air horn. Lift off air horn until power valve piston, accelerator pump and main well tube clear main body. Remove air horn gasket.

NOTE: **Do not use a metal gasket scraper on any carburetor surfaces. Use a nylon or hard plastic scraper as needed.**

5) Remove accelerator pump rod retainer screw and retainer. Remove accelerator pump retainer screw and accelerator pump. Rotate pump rod as needed to remove from air horn. Remove pump rod grommet from air horn.

6) Remove 3 screws and power valve diaphragm assembly. Do not attempt to remove main well tube from air horn. Main well tube must be carefully blown out with compressed air from both sides of air horn.

7) Remove fuel inlet fitting from main body and separate gaskets. Remove float pin retainer, float pin and float assembly. Turn main body upside-down and catch accelerator pump discharge check ball and weight.

8) Remove main jet using a screwdriver with a blade at least 3/8" wide. Ensure screwdriver has a good square blade.

9) Carefully depress power valve needle with 3/8" wide screwdriver until screwdriver blade seats in slot in top of valve. Remove valve assembly.

NOTE: **Power valve assembly consists of needle, seat and spring. If replacement of any part is required, replace complete assembly. Service valve includes all components.**

10) Remove 3 throttle body screws and separate throttle body from main body. Remove throttle body gasket. Remove idle speed screw from throttle body.

11) Center punch idle mixture screw housing 1/4" from end of housing. Drill through outer section of

1985 Holley Carburetors

HOLLEY MODEL 1945 SINGLE BARREL (Cont.)

Fig. 6: Exploded View of Holley Model 1945 Single Barrel Carburetor

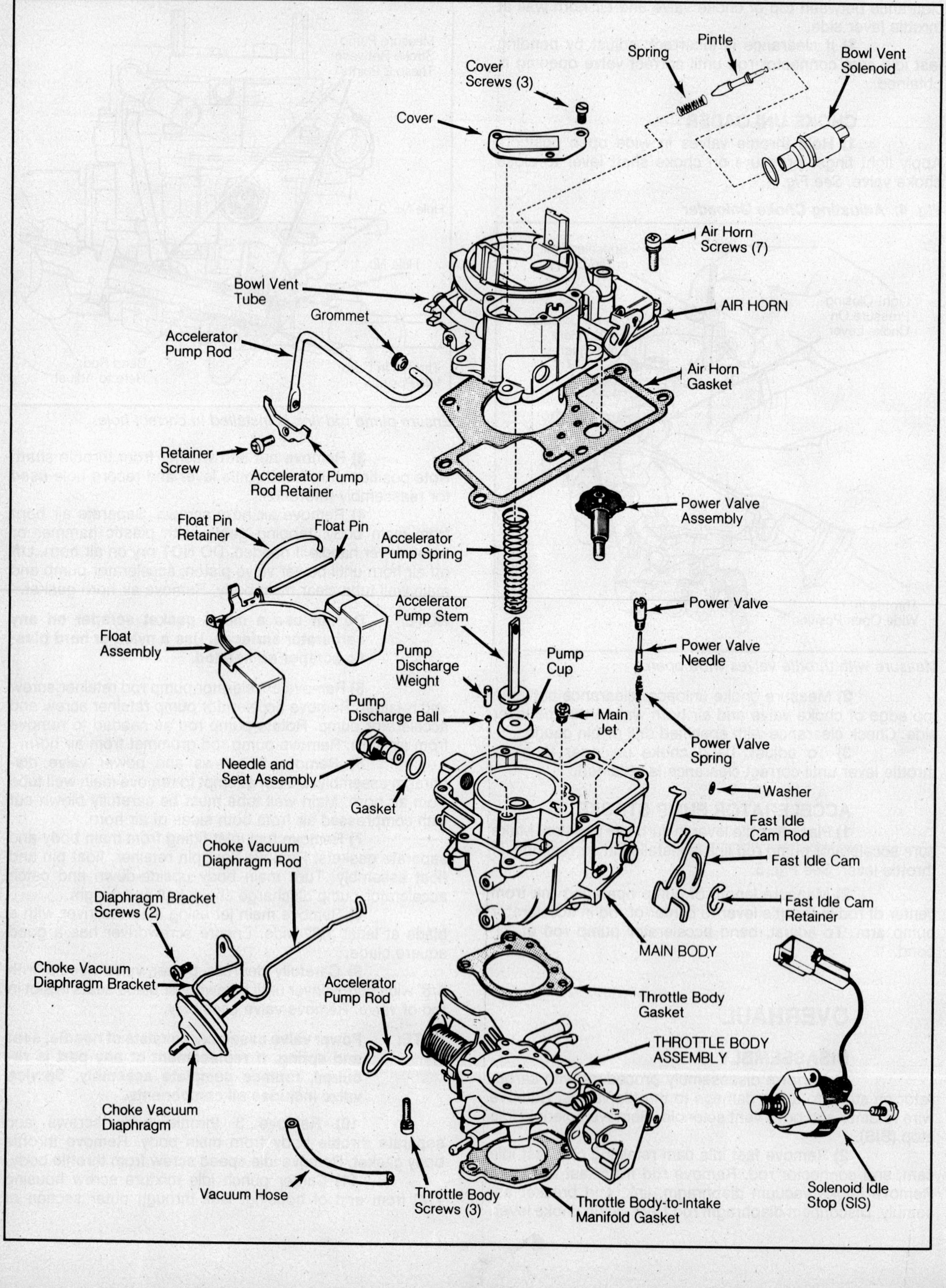

HOLLEY MODEL 1945 SINGLE BARREL (Cont.)

housing at punch mark with 3/16" drill. Pry plug out of housing and save for reassembly.

12) Turn mixture screw in until lightly seated, counting turns. Record for reassembly reference. Remove mixture screw and spring.

CLEANING & INSPECTION

- Use a regular carburetor cleaning solution. Soak components long enough to thoroughly clean all surfaces and passages of foreign matter.
- Do not soak any rubber or plastic parts in cleaner, particularly choke diaphragm and heater. These parts are best cleaned with a clean cloth and/or soft brush.
- Do not use drills or wire to clean jets or other passages.
- If cleaner manufacturer recommends rinsing with water, hot water will give best results.
- Blow out all passages with dry, compressed air.

REASSEMBLY

When reassembling carburetor, use all new gaskets and seals. Ensure that gaskets fit correctly and that all holes and slots are punched through and properly aligned. If excessive wear exists between throttle shaft and throttle body, throttle body assembly should be replaced. Manufacturer does not recommend installing a new shaft in the old throttle body.

1) Inspect idle mixture screw. Tapered portion should be straight and smooth. Replace if excessively worn. Install mixture screw and spring in throttle body. Bottom screw lightly and back out number of turns recorded during disassembly.

2) Install new throttle body gasket on main body. Place throttle body in position and tighten 3 retaining screws to 30 INCH lbs. (3 N.m).

3) Install accelerator pump discharge check ball and weight. Fill fuel bowl with clean fuel to check ball and seat operation.

4) Hold ball and weight down with brass rod. Place accelerator pump assembly in well and operate by hand. If no resistance is felt, check ball is leaking.

5) Remove weight and leave check ball in place. Using a small drift punch, lightly tap ball against seat to form a new seal. Remove old check ball and discard. Install new check ball and weight.

6) Perform fuel leak test again. If there is still no resistance felt, main body must be replaced. If resistance is felt, check ball is seating correctly. Remove check ball and weight. Install accelerator pump, pump rod and rod retainer in air horn.

7) Install power valve assembly in bottom of fuel bowl. Tighten securely. Ensure needle valve operates freely. Install main jet in main body.

8) Install float pin in main body. Place float assembly in float shaft cradle. Install float pin retainer. Check float alignment to make sure it does not bind against main body casting.

9) Install new gasket on fuel inlet fitting. Install fitting in main body. Tighten securely. Check float level and adjust as needed.

10) Insert check ball and weight into accelerator pump discharge well. Position air horn gasket on air horn. Carefully install air horn on main body. Make sure accelerator pump cup is not damaged.

11) Install 7 air horn screws and tighten alternately in steps to 30 INCH lbs. (3 N.m). Install fast idle cam and link.

12) Install choke vacuum diaphragm, solenoid idle stop (SIS), and bowl vent solenoid.

CARBURETOR ADJUSTMENT SPECIFICATIONS

Application	Float Level	Accelerator Pump		Fast Idle Cam	Choke Unloader	Choke Vacuum Kick
		Hole	Stroke			
R-40159	Flush [1]	#2	1.61"	.080"	.250"	.130"
R-40160	Flush [1]	#2	1.61"	.090"	.250"	.130"

[1] – Setting is flush with gasket installed on main body.

1985 Holley Carburetors

HOLLEY MODEL 6145 SINGLE BARREL

CARBURETOR APPLICATION

CHRYSLER CORP. (HOLLEY) CARBURETOR NO.

Application	Man. Trans.	Auto. Trans.
3.7L 6-Cyl. California	R-40161	R-40162

CARBURETOR IDENTIFICATION

Carburetor is identified by part number stamped into main body, or by tag attached to carburetor.

DESCRIPTION

The Holley model 6145 is an "Electronic Feedback" type carburetor. The carburetor is designed to maintain an air/fuel ratio within specified limits to allow the catalytic converter to operate effectively. The air/fuel ratio is controlled by the Spark Control Computer.

The carburetor includes 4 basic fuel metering systems: idle, main metering, accelerator and power enrichment. In addition, fuel inlet and choke systems are used.

ADJUSTMENTS

NOTE: **For on-vehicle adjustments not covered in this article, see appropriate TUNE-UP article.**

FLOAT LEVEL

1) With air horn removed, turn main body upside-down with gasket installed. Hold a straightedge across main body, over floats, at point farthest from fuel inlet. Floats should just contact straightedge. *See Fig. 1.*

Fig. 1: Adjusting Float Level

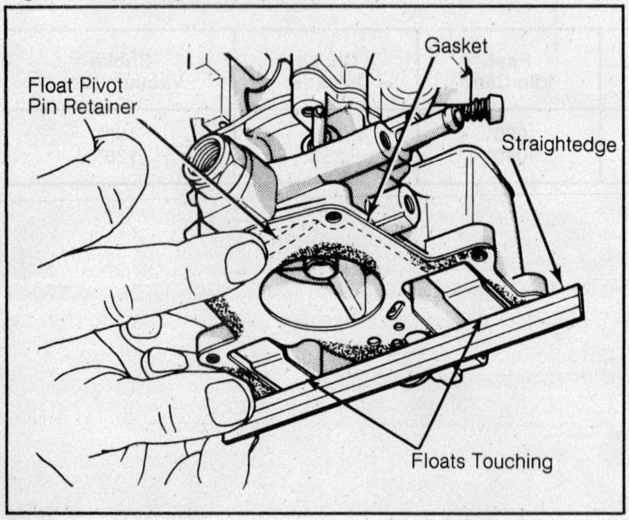

Measure at ends of floats farthest from fuel inlet.

2) To adjust, bend float tang on float arm that contacts fuel inlet needle.

CHOKE VACUUM KICK (CHOKE PULL-DOWN)

1) Open throttle and close choke. Close throttle to trap fast idle cam in closed choke position. *See Fig. 2.*

Fig. 2: Adjusting Choke Vacuum Kick (Choke Pull-Down)

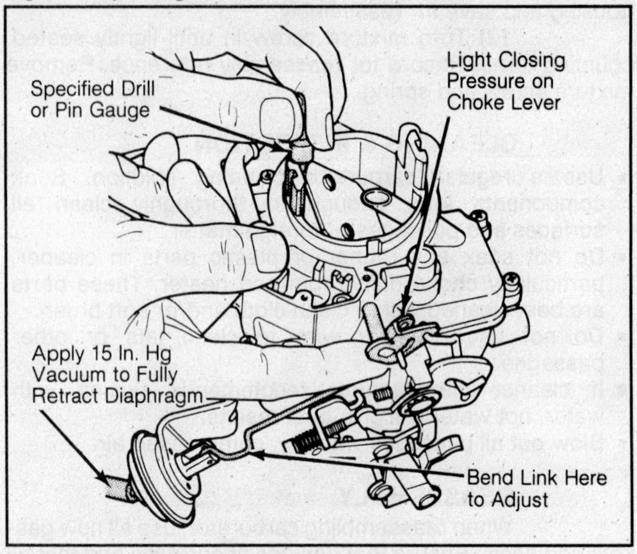

Bend link at "U" to adjust.

2) Disconnect vacuum hose from choke vacuum diaphragm. Connect hand vacuum pump to diaphragm and apply at least 15 in. Hg. Apply light finger pressure on choke shaft lever to compress spring in diaphragm stem without distorting linkage. Diaphragm stem reaches a stop as spring is compressed.

3) Measure choke vacuum kick specified clearance between upper edge of choke valve and air horn wall. Clearance can be measured using specified drill or pin gauge.

4) To adjust, bend diaphragm link at "U" bend. *See Fig. 2.* Check all linkage for freedom of movement. Remove vacuum pump and install vacuum hose on diaphragm.

FAST IDLE CAM POSITION

1) Position fast idle speed screw on 2nd step of fast idle cam. Hold choke valve toward closed position with light pressure on choke shaft lever. *See Fig. 3.*

Fig. 3: Adjusting Fast Idle Cam Position

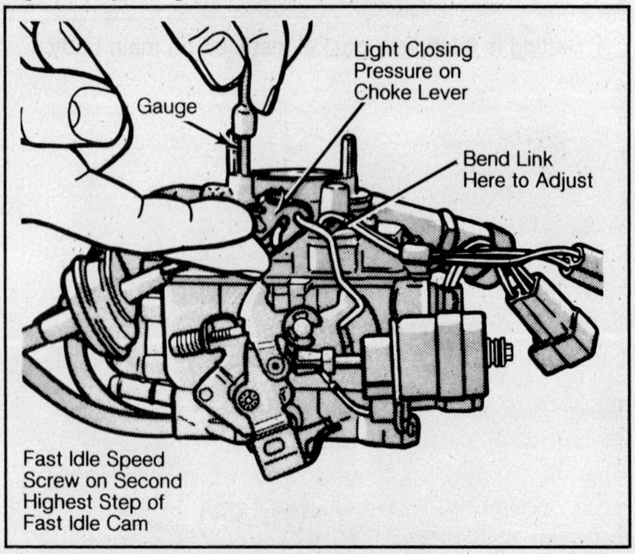

Adjust with idle speed screw on 2nd step of fast idle cam.

HOLLEY MODEL 6145 SINGLE BARREL (Cont.)

2) Using specified drill or pin gauge, measure fast idle cam specified clearance between upper edge of choke valve and air horn wall. To adjust, bend fast idle connector rod at angle.

CHOKE UNLOADER

1) Hold throttle valves in wide open position. Hold choke valve toward closed choke position by applying light closing pressure to choke lever. *See Fig. 4.*

Fig. 4: Adjusting Choke Unloader

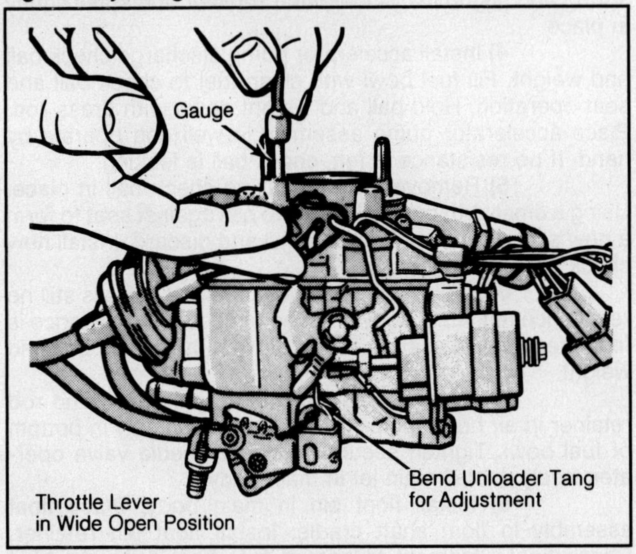

Bend choke unloader tang to adjust.

2) Using specified drill or pin gauge, measure clearance between top of choke valve and air horn wall at throttle lever side. To adjust, bend tang on throttle lever.

ACCELERATOR PUMP STROKE

1) Place throttle lever in curb idle position. Make sure accelerator pump rod link is installed in correct hole in throttle lever. *See Fig. 5.*

Fig. 5: Accelerator Pump Adjustment

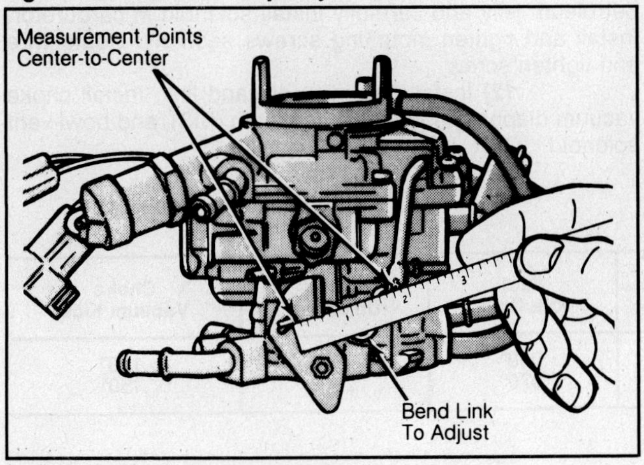

Ensure pump rod link is installed in correct hole.

2) Measure length of pump operating link from center of rod in throttle lever to center of rod in accelerator pump arm.

3) To adjust, bend accelerator pump rod at "U" bend.

OVERHAUL

DISASSEMBLY

Air Horn

1) Perform disassembly procedure with carburetor on stand to avoid damage to throttle valves. Remove wire retainer and bowl vent solenoid. Remove solenoid idle stop (SIS).

2) Remove fast idle cam retaining clip, fast idle cam, and connector rod. Remove rod from fast idle cam. Remove choke vacuum diaphragm, link, and bracket assembly. Disconnect diaphragm rod from slot in choke lever.

3) Remove nut and washer from throttle shaft. Note position of rod in throttle lever and record hole used for reassembly reference. Remove screws and duty cycle solenoid.

4) Remove air horn screws. Separate air horn from main body by tapping with a plastic hammer or screwdriver handle. DO NOT pry off. Lift air horn straight up until vacuum piston stem, accelerator pump and main well tube are clear of main body.

5) Remove air horn gasket and clean gasket surface with cleaner. DO NOT use a metal gasket scraper. Use a nylon or hard plastic scraper as needed.

6) Remove accelerator pump rod retainer screw and retainer. Remove accelerator pump assembly retainer screw and pump assembly. Rotate pump rod as needed to remove from air horn. Remove pump rod grommet from air horn.

7) Power piston assembly retaining ring is staked in position. Carefully remove staking with sharp tool. Remove vacuum piston from air horn by depressing piston and allowing it to snap up against retaining ring.

NOTE: **Do not attempt to remove main well tube from air horn. Main well tube must be carefully blown out with compressed air from both sides of air horn.**

Main Body

1) Remove fuel inlet fitting valve assembly. Remove and discard old gaskets. Remove float pivot pin retainer, pivot pin and float assembly. Turn main body upside down and catch pump discharge weight and ball as they fall out.

2) Remove main metering jet with Jet Wrench (C-3748) or 3/8" wide flat screwdriver with good square blade. Carefully depress power valve needle with 3/8" wide screwdriver until screwdriver blade seats in slot in top of valve. Remove valve assembly.

NOTE: **Power valve assembly consists of needle, seat and spring. If replacement of any part is required, replace complete assembly. Service valve includes all components.**

3) Remove 3 main body-to-throttle body screws and separate assemblies. Remove and discard gasket.

Throttle Body

1) Remove fast idle speed screw and spring. Remove idle mixture screw concealment plug. *See Fig. 6.*

2) To remove plugs, center punch idle mixture screw housing 1/4" from end of housing. Drill through outer section of housing at punch mark with 3/16" drill. Pry plug out of housing and save for reassembly.

1985 Holley Carburetors

HOLLEY MODEL 6145 SINGLE BARREL (Cont.)

3) Turn mixture screw in until lightly seated, counting turns. Record for reassembly reference. Remove mixture screw and spring.

Fig. 6: Holley Model 6145 Carburetor Assembly

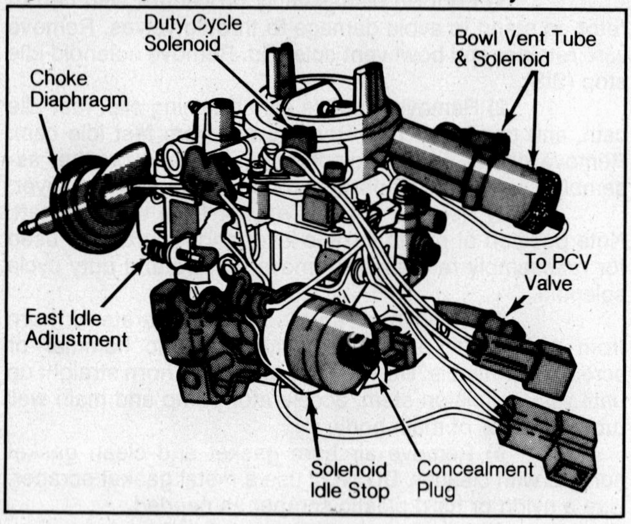

CLEANING & INSPECTION

- Use a regular carburetor cleaning solution. Soak components long enough to thoroughly clean all surfaces and passages of foreign matter.
- Do not soak any rubber or plastic parts in cleaner, particularly choke diaphragm and heater. These parts are best cleaned with a clean cloth and/or soft brush.
- Do not use drills or wire to clean jets or other passages.
- If cleaner manufacturer recommends rinsing with water, hot water will give best results.
- Blow out all passages with dry, compressed air.

REASSEMBLY

When reassembling carburetor, use all new gaskets and seals. Ensure that gaskets fit correctly and that all holes and slots are punched through and properly aligned. If excessive wear exists between throttle shaft and throttle body, throttle body assembly should be replaced. Manufacturer does not recommend installing a new shaft in the old throttle body.

1) Inspect idle mixture screw. Tapered portion should be straight and smooth. Replace if excessively worn or grooved. Install mixture screw and spring in throttle body. Bottom screw lightly and back out number of turns recorded during disassembly.

2) Install new throttle body gasket on main body. Place throttle body in position and tighten 3 retaining screws to 30 INCH lbs. (3 N.m).

3) Ensure that all staking has been removed from vacuum piston retainer cavity. Install vacuum piston spring and piston in cylinder, seat retainer and stake lightly in place.

4) Install accelerator pump discharge check ball and weight. Fill fuel bowl with clean fuel to check ball and seat operation. Hold ball and weight down with brass rod. Place accelerator pump assembly in well and operate by hand. If no resistance is felt, check ball is leaking.

5) Remove weight, leaving check ball in place. Using a small drift punch, lightly tap ball against seat to form a new seal. Remove old check ball and discard. Install new check ball and weight.

6) Perform fuel leak test again. If there is still no resistance felt, main body must be replaced. If resistance is felt, check ball is seating correctly. Remove check ball and weight.

7) Install accelerator pump, pump rod and rod retainer in air horn. Install power valve assembly in bottom of fuel bowl. Tighten securely. Ensure needle valve operates freely. Install main jet in main body.

8) Install float pin in main body. Place float assembly in float shaft cradle. Install float pin retainer. Check float alignment to ensure that float does not bind against main body casting.

9) Install new gasket on fuel inlet fitting. Install fitting in main body. Tighten securely. Check float level and adjust as needed.

10) Insert check ball and weight into accelerator pump discharge well. Position air horn gasket on air horn. Carefully install air horn on main body. Make sure accelerator pump cup is not damaged. Install 7 air horn screws and tighten alternately, in steps, to 30 INCH lbs. (3 N.m).

11) Install new duty cycle solenoid gasket on air horn. Install new "O" ring on solenoid. Lubricate lightly with petroleum jelly and carefully install solenoid in carburetor. Install and tighten mounting screws securely. Route wire and tighten screw.

12) Install fast idle cam and link. Install choke vacuum diaphragm, solenoid idle stop (SIS), and bowl vent solenoid.

CARBURETOR ADJUSTMENT SPECIFICATIONS

Application	Float Level	Accelerator Pump		Fast Idle Cam	Choke Unloader	Choke Vacuum Kick
		Hole	Stroke			
R-40161	Flush [1]	#2	1.75"	.060"	.250"	.150"
R-40162	Flush [1]	#2	1.75"	.070"	.250"	.150"

[1] – Setting is flush with gasket installed on main body.

HOLLEY 2280 & 6280 2-BARREL

CARBURETOR APPLICATION

CHRYSLER CORP. (HOLLEY) CARBURETOR NO.

Application	Man. Trans.	Auto. Trans.
5.2L V8		
Federal	[1] R-40164	[1] R-40164
	R-40132	R-40132
California	R-40133	R-40133

[1] – Model 2280. All others are 6280 models.

CARBURETOR IDENTIFICATION

Carburetor part number is stamped on main body flange. It is in front of the lever, controlled by throttle position transducer, under the choke vacuum diaphragm.

DESCRIPTION

Holley model 2280 and 6280 2-barrel carburetors use 4 basic fuel metering systems: basic idle, accelerator pump, main metering, and power enrichment. Fuel inlet and choke systems are also used. In addition, some models are equipped with a solenoid idle stop (SIS) and bowl vent solenoid.

The basic idle system provides mixture during idle and low speed engine operation. The accelerator pump system provides additional fuel for acceleration. The main metering system operates during normal cruising, and the power enrichment system provides a richer mixture when high power output is required (full throttle operation).

ADJUSTMENTS

NOTE: **For on-vehicle adjustments not covered in this article, see appropriate TUNE-UP article.**

FLOAT LEVEL

1) With air horn and gasket removed, turn main body upside-down. Catch pump intake check ball as it falls out. Hold retainer in place with finger to fully seat float pin in cradle.

2) Using a "T" scale, measure float level clearance from air horn gasket surface on main body to toe of each float. *See Fig. 1.*

3) To adjust, bend float tang. If necessary, bend either float arm to equalize float positions.

CHOKE VACUUM KICK

1) Open throttle and close choke. Now close throttle to trap fast idle cam in closed choke position. *See Fig. 2.*

2) Disconnect vacuum hose from choke vacuum diaphragm. Connect hand vacuum pump to diaphragm, and apply at least 15 in. Hg vacuum. Apply light finger pressure on choke shaft lever to compress spring in diaphragm stem without distorting linkage. Diaphragm stem reaches a stop as spring is compressed.

3) Measure choke vacuum kick clearance between upper edge of choke valve and air horn wall. Clearance can be measured using a drill or pin gauge.

Fig. 1: Adjusting Float Level

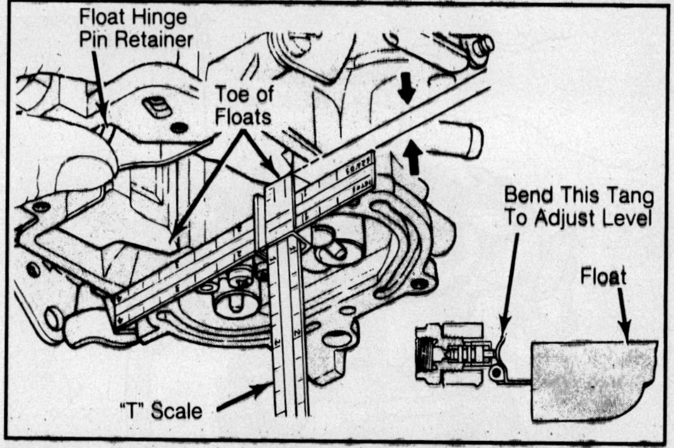

Measure from air horn gasket surface to toe of each float.

Fig. 2: Adjusting Choke Vacuum Kick

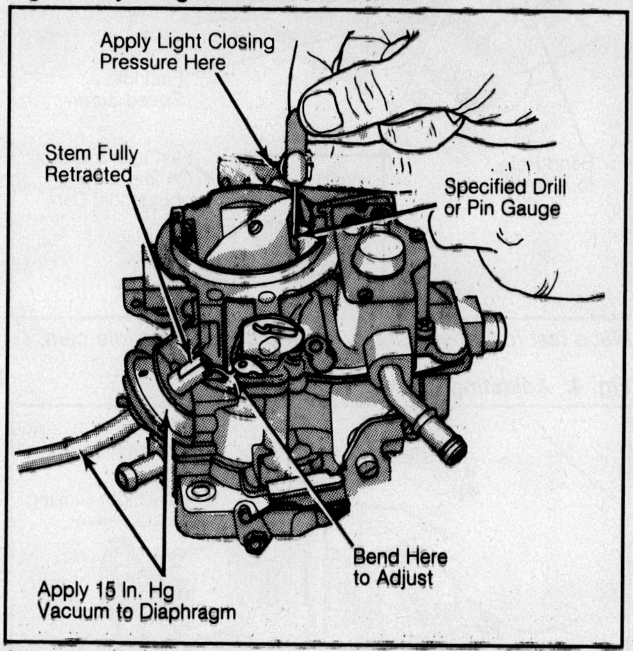

Spring in diaphragm stem must be compressed during adjustment.

4) To adjust, open or close "U" bend in vacuum diaphragm link. *See Fig. 2.* Check all linkage for freedom of movement. Remove vacuum pump, and install vacuum hose on diaphragm.

FAST IDLE CAM POSITION

1) Position fast idle speed screw on 2nd step of fast idle cam. Apply light finger pressure on choke shaft lever to close choke valve. *See Fig. 3.*

2) Measure fast idle cam clearance between center of upper edge of choke valve and air horn wall. Clearance can be measured using a drill or pin gauge.

3) To adjust, bend fast idle cam connector rod at "U" bend.

CHOKE UNLOADER

1) Hold throttle valves in wide open position. Apply light finger pressure on choke shaft lever to close choke valve. *See Fig. 4.*

1985 Holley Carburetors

HOLLEY 2280 & 6280 2-BARREL (Cont.)

Fig. 3: Adjusting Fast Idle Cam Position

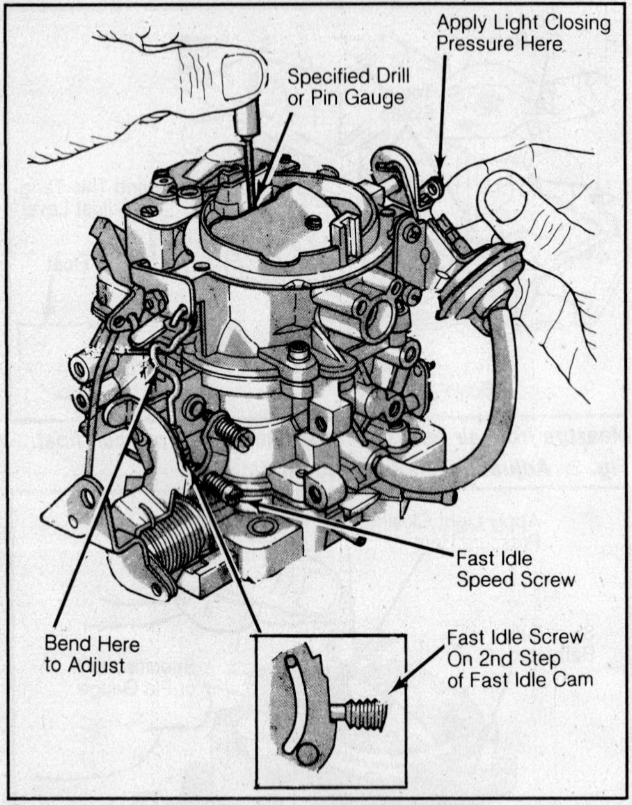

Place fast idle speed screw on 2nd step of fast idle cam.

Fig. 4: Adjusting Choke Unloader

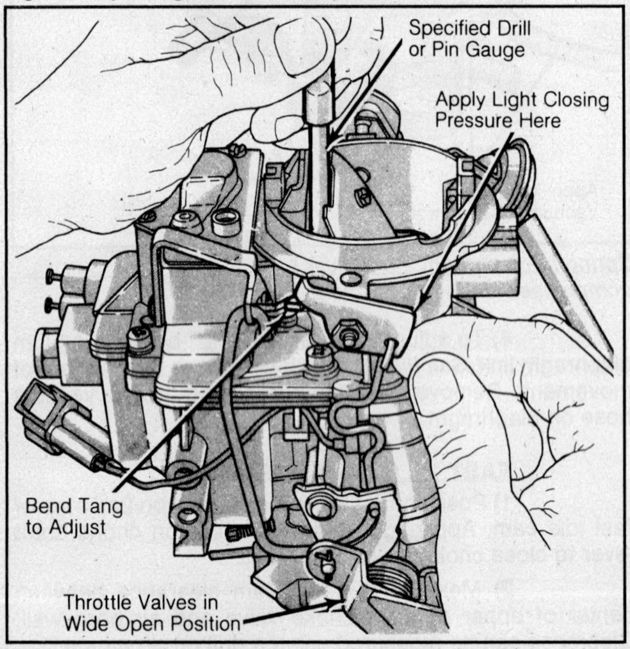

Throttle valves wide open to adjust choke unloader.

2) Check choke unloader clearance between upper edge of choke valve and air horn wall. Clearance can be checked using a drill or pin gauge.

3) To adjust, bend choke unloader tang on accelerator pump lever.

MECHANICAL POWER VALVE

1) Remove bowl vent valve cover, and hold throttle lever in wide open position. *See Fig. 5.*

Fig. 5: Adjusting Mechanical Power Valve

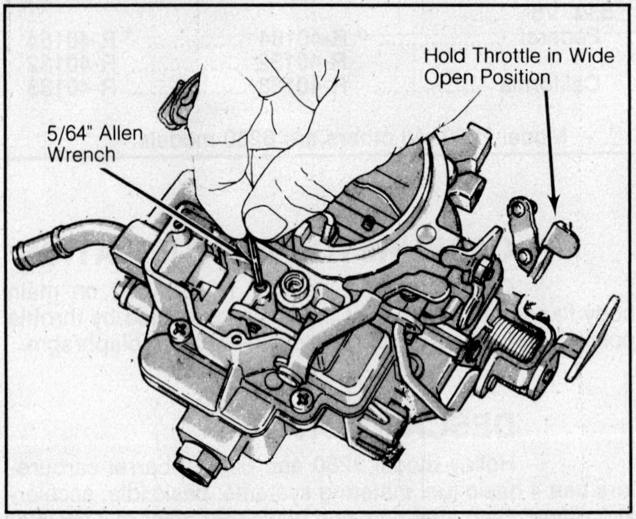

Adjust power valve clearance with 5/64" Allen wrench.

2) Insert a 5/64" Allen wrench in mechanical power valve adjustment screw. Push down on screw, then release to determine if there is any clearance. If so, turn screw clockwise until there is no clearance.

3) To adjust, turn screw counterclockwise 1 full turn from zero clearance. Install bowl vent valve cover plate and gasket.

ACCELERATOR PUMP STROKE (AT IDLE)

1) Remove bowl vent cover plate and gasket. All pump links and levers must be installed. Adjust accelerator pump cap nut for zero clearance between nut and pump lever.

Fig. 6: Adjusting Accelerator Pump Stroke

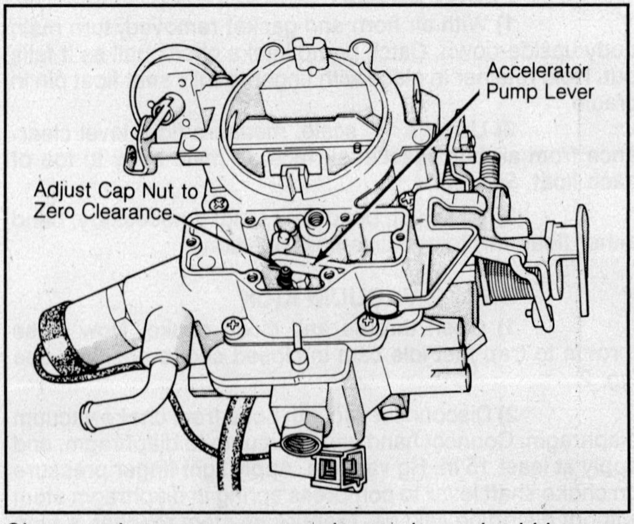

Clearance between cap nut and pump lever should be zero.

2) Check that wide open throttle can be reached without binding. Install gasket and bowl vent cover plate.

HOLLEY 2280 & 6280 2-BARREL (Cont.)

NOTE: If accelerator pump adjustment is changed, mechanical power valve and bowl vent valve (2280 models) must be re-adjusted.

BOWL VENT VALVE (MODEL 2280 ONLY)

1) Remove bowl vent valve cover and vent valve lever spring. Be careful not to dislodge or lose vent valve lever retainer.

2) With throttle at curb idle position, press firmly down on vent valve lever where spring seats.

3) Check clearance between vent valve tang and lever with drill or pin gauge. *See Fig. 7.*

Fig. 7: Adjusting Bowl Vent Valve

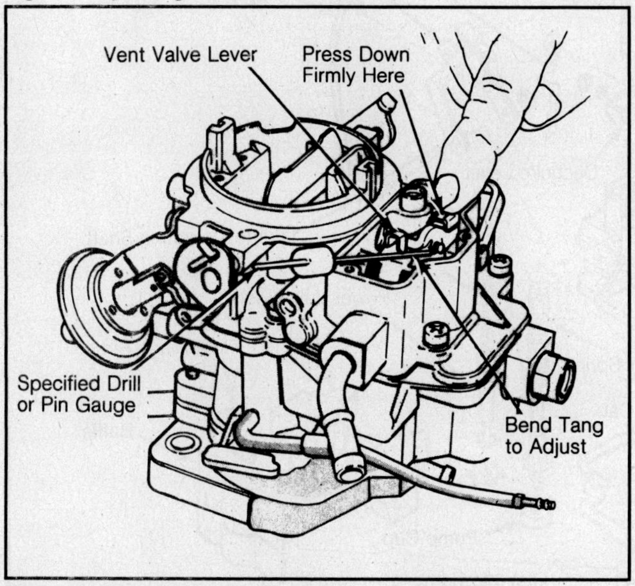

Check adjustment with throttle at curb idle position.

4) To adjust, bend end of vent valve tang up or down until gauge just fits through contact area.

OVERHAUL

DISASSEMBLY

1) Place carburetor on repair stand to prevent damage to throttle valves. Remove air cleaner bolt and retainer. Remove cotter pin from accelerator pump arm link and remove link.

2) Remove bowl vent solenoid assembly from air horn (if equipped). Remove choke vacuum diaphragm, linkage, and bracket.

3) Remove nut and washer securing fast idle cam lever to choke shaft. Disconnect fast idle cam rod from lever and fast idle cam. Disconnect and remove accelerator operating link.

4) Remove 6 air horn screws. Lift air horn straight up from main body. Remove and discard air horn gasket.

5) Remove accelerator pump operating shaft retaining clip and pull shaft straight out. Remove accelerator pump arm and internal pump lever. Using 2 wrenches, remove accelerator pump plunger cap nut while holding pump plunger steady with other wrench. Remove accelerator pump plunger.

6) Gently pry up vacuum piston retaining ring tangs. Remove vacuum power valve piston. Remove mechanical power valve push rod and spring assembly by gently prying off plastic cap and removing clip.

7) Remove fuel inlet fitting and gasket. Discard gasket. Remove float hinge pin retainer, hinge pin, float baffle and float assembly. Using a screwdriver, remove main metering jets.

8) Using Power Valve Remover (C-4231) remove vacuum power valve and mechanical power valve. Make sure blade of tool is squarely seated in slots of valves to avoid damage.

NOTE: Do not interchange the mechanical and vacuum power valve assemblies. Vacuum power valve needle is about .050" longer than mechanical power valve needle. The vacuum power valve needle has an undercut groove just above the needle stop. Mechanical power valve is located on choke side of carburetor. Do not mix up valve seats. Assemblies must be reinstalled in original locations, and must be kept with their respective needle and spring assembly.

9) Remove venturi cluster screws. Lift cluster and gasket up and away from main body. Do not remove idle well tubes. Turn main body upside-down and catch accelerator pump weight and check ball.

10) Remove 4 throttle body screws. Separate throttle body from main body and discard gasket. Remove fast idle cam retaining clip, and slide cam off stub shaft.

11) Remove idle mixture screw concealment plugs. Center punch each idle mixture screw housing about 1/4" from end of housing. Drill through outer section of housing at punch mark with 3/16" drill. Pry plug out of housing and save for reassembly. Remove idle mixture screws and springs.

CLEANING & INSPECTION

- Use a regular carburetor cleaning solution. Soak components long enough to thoroughly clean all surfaces and passages of foreign matter.
- Do not soak any rubber or plastic parts in cleaner, particularly choke diaphragm and heater. These parts are best cleaned with a clean cloth and/or soft brush.
- Do not use drills or wire to clean jets or other passages.
- If cleaner manufacturer recommends rinsing with water, hot water will give best results.
- Blow out all passages with dry, compressed air.

REASSEMBLY

Throttle Body

Install idle mixture screws and springs. Gently seat both mixture screws by hand. Now back out 1 full turn as a preliminary idle mixture adjustment.

Main Body

1) Install fast idle cam on stub shaft with steps facing fast idle speed screw. Install retaining clip.

2) Turn main body upside-down. Place throttle body gasket in position. Position throttle body on main body. Install 4 attaching screws, and tighten to 30 INCH lbs. (3 N.m).

3) Install accelerator pump discharge check ball and weight. Fill fuel bowl with clean fuel, and check ball and seat operation. Hold ball and weight down with a small

1985 Holley Carburetors

HOLLEY 2280 & 6280 2-BARREL (Cont.)

Fig. 8: Exploded View of Holley Model 2280 2-Barrel Carburetor

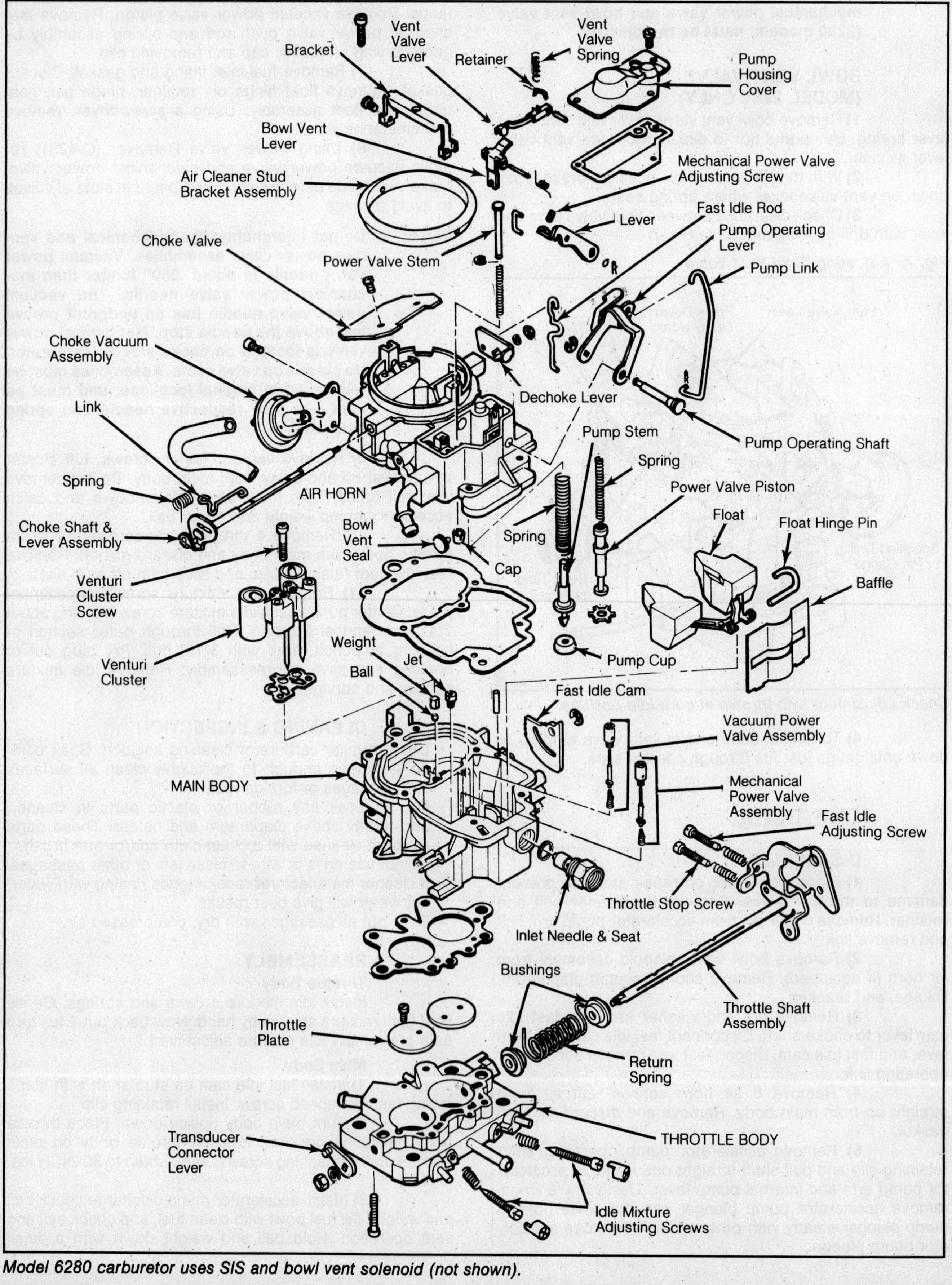

Model 6280 carburetor uses SIS and bowl vent solenoid (not shown).

HOLLEY 2280 & 6280 2-BARREL (Cont.)

brass rod. Place accelerator pump plunger in well, and operate by hand. If no resistance is felt, check ball is leaking.

4) Remove weight and leave check ball in place. Using a small drift punch, lightly tap ball against seat to form a new seal. Remove old check ball and discard. Install a new ball and weight.

5) Perform fuel leak test again. If there is still no resistance felt, main body must be replaced. If resistance is felt, check ball is seating correctly.

6) Install new venturi cluster gaskets. Install venturi cluster in position in main body. Install screws and tighten securely.

7) Install main metering jets. Using the same tool as used during disassembly, install mechanical and vacuum power valves. Use care not to damage power valve needles. Ensure valves are installed in original locations as noted during disassembly.

8) Install hinge pin in float. Insert hinge pin through slot in float baffle. Tabs on baffle should point down. Place assembly in pin cradle in main body. Install hinge pin retainer.

9) Install fuel inlet fitting with new gasket. Perform float level adjustment.

Air Horn

1) Install vacuum power piston spring and piston. Install retaining ring over piston and carefully seat in place. Check piston operation for binding or sticking. If piston binds or sticks enough to prevent smooth operation, install new piston.

2) Install mechanical power valve push rod spring, rod and retaining clip. Install plastic cap on push rod.

3) Install accelerator pump assembly through air horn and install cap nut.

4) Install new air horn gasket. Carefully lower air horn into position on main body, guiding accelerator pump plunger into its cylinder. Use care not to damage accelerator pump plunger.

5) Install air horn screws. Starting from center and working out, tighten screws to 25 INCH lbs. (2.8 N.m).

6) With pump override spring retainer contacting air horn boss, adjust cap nut for a clearance of .310" (8 mm) between housing surface and cap nut. Install accelerator pump lever, operating shaft and retaining clip.

7) Connect plain end of fast idle cam connector rod to slot in fast idle cam from inside of cam. Engage other end of rod in choke lever. Place choke valve in wide open position. Align flats, and slide choke lever onto choke shaft. Install lock washer and tighten nut. Install accelerator pump operating link.

8) Connect choke vacuum break diaphragm rod to slot in choke lever. Install diaphragm assembly and tighten screws. Install SIS assembly.

9) Install bowl vent solenoid assembly. Install bowl vent cover plate with new gasket. Install accelerator pump lever, using a new cotter pin. Install air cleaner bolt and retainer.

CARBURETOR ADJUSTMENT SPECIFICATIONS

Application	Float Level	Accel. Pump	Choke Unloader	Choke Vac. Kick	Fast Idle Cam
R-40132	9/32"	Flush [1]	.250"	.150"	.070"
R-40133	9/32"	Flush [1]	.150"	.130"	.070"
R-40164	9/32"	Flush [1]	.150"	.140"	.070"

[1] – Flush with top of bowl vent casting.

1985 Holley Carburetors

HOLLEY 5220 & 6520 2-BARREL

CARBURETOR APPLICATION

CHRYSLER CORP. (HOLLEY) CARBURETOR NO.

Application	Man. Trans.	Auto. Trans.
2.2L 4-Cyl.		
Model 5220		
Federal		
Without A/C	R-40143A R-40136A	R-40145A
With A/C	....	R-40146A
Model 6520		
Calif.	R-40140A	R-40141A
Fed. Alt.	R-40137A	....

CARBURETOR IDENTIFICATION

Carburetor identification number may be found stamped on side of float bowl or on a metal tag attached to carburetor.

DESCRIPTION

Carburetor models 5220 and 6520 are 2-stage, 2-venturi type. Primary venturi is smaller than secondary. Secondary stage is mechanically operated by linkage to primary and secondary throttle levers. Primary stage includes curb idle, accelerator pump idle transfer, main metering and power enrichment systems.

Secondary stage includes main metering and power enrichment systems. A single fuel bowl supplies fuel for both stages. Carburetor is equipped with an electric automatic choke which has a 2-stage bi-metal heating element.

On 6520 model carburetors there is also an oxygen feedback solenoid that is responsive to the oxygen sensor.

TESTING

CHOKE HEATER

1) With ignition off, connect a jumper wire between battery positive terminal and choke heater connection. Remove air cleaner and observe choke plate. Choke plate should fully open within 5 minutes when vehicle is parked inside.

2) Electrical current is supplied to the choke through the oil pressure switch. A minimum oil pressure of 4 psi is required to close the contacts in the oil pressure switch and feed current to the choke.

NOTE: **The choke housing is attached to carburetor with tamper-proof screws. Thermostat setting is not adjustable.**

ADJUSTMENT

NOTE: **For all on-vehicle adjustments, see appropriate TUNE-UP article.**

FLOAT LEVEL

1) Remove air horn and gasket. Turn air horn upside down. Allow weight of float to press down against float needle valve. *See Fig. 1.*

Fig. 1: Adjusting Float Level

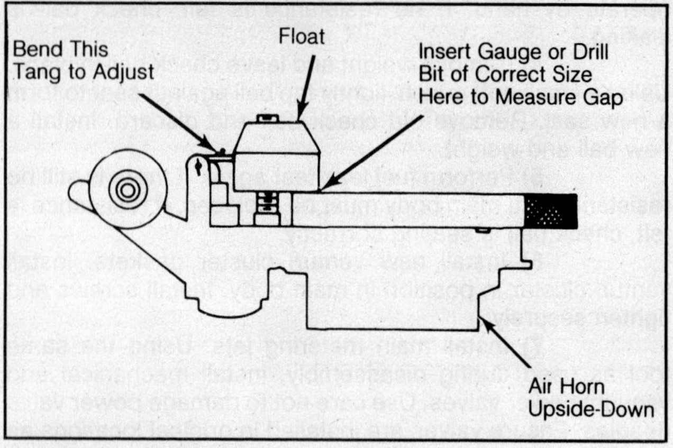

Bend tang to adjust.

2) Measure float level specified clearance between top of float and air horn gasket surface. Clearance can be checked using a drill or pin gauge.

3) Make sure float tang still rests on float needle when clearance is checked. To adjust, bend tang that contacts float needle.

NOTE: **Do not apply pressure to float needle while checking or changing adjustment.**

FLOAT DROP

1) With air horn and gasket removed, turn right side up. Using a "T" scale, measure specified float drop from air horn gasket surface to bottom of float. *See Fig. 2.*

2) To adjust, bend float tang on float arm that contacts fuel inlet needle seat boss.

Fig. 2: Adjusting Float Drop

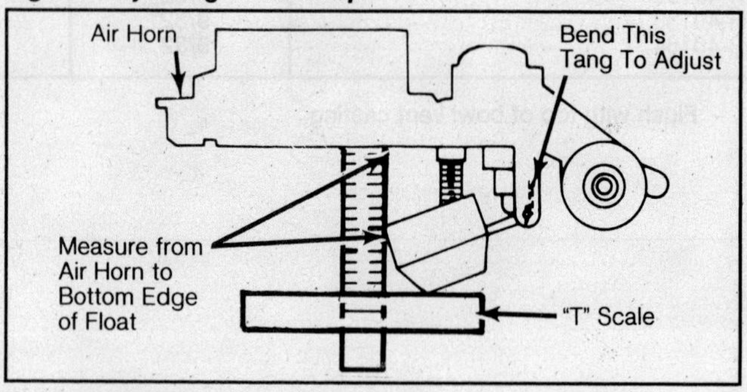

Bend tang to adjust.

CHOKE VACUUM KICK (INITIAL CHOKE VALVE CLEARANCE)

1) Open throttle and close choke. Close throttle to trap fast idle cam in closed choke position. Disconnect vacuum hose at choke vacuum diaphragm. Connect an outside vacuum source and apply 15 in. Hg (minimum) vacuum.

2) Apply slight closing pressure to choke valve without bending linkage. An internal spring within choke system will compress to stop position.

3) Using a drill or pin gauge, measure clearance between upper edge of choke valve and primary air horn wall. Adjust by rotating Allen head screw in center of diaphragm housing. *See Fig. 4.*

HOLLEY 5220 & 6520 2-BARREL (Cont.)

Fig. 3: Exploded View of Holley Model 5220 2-Barrel Carburetor

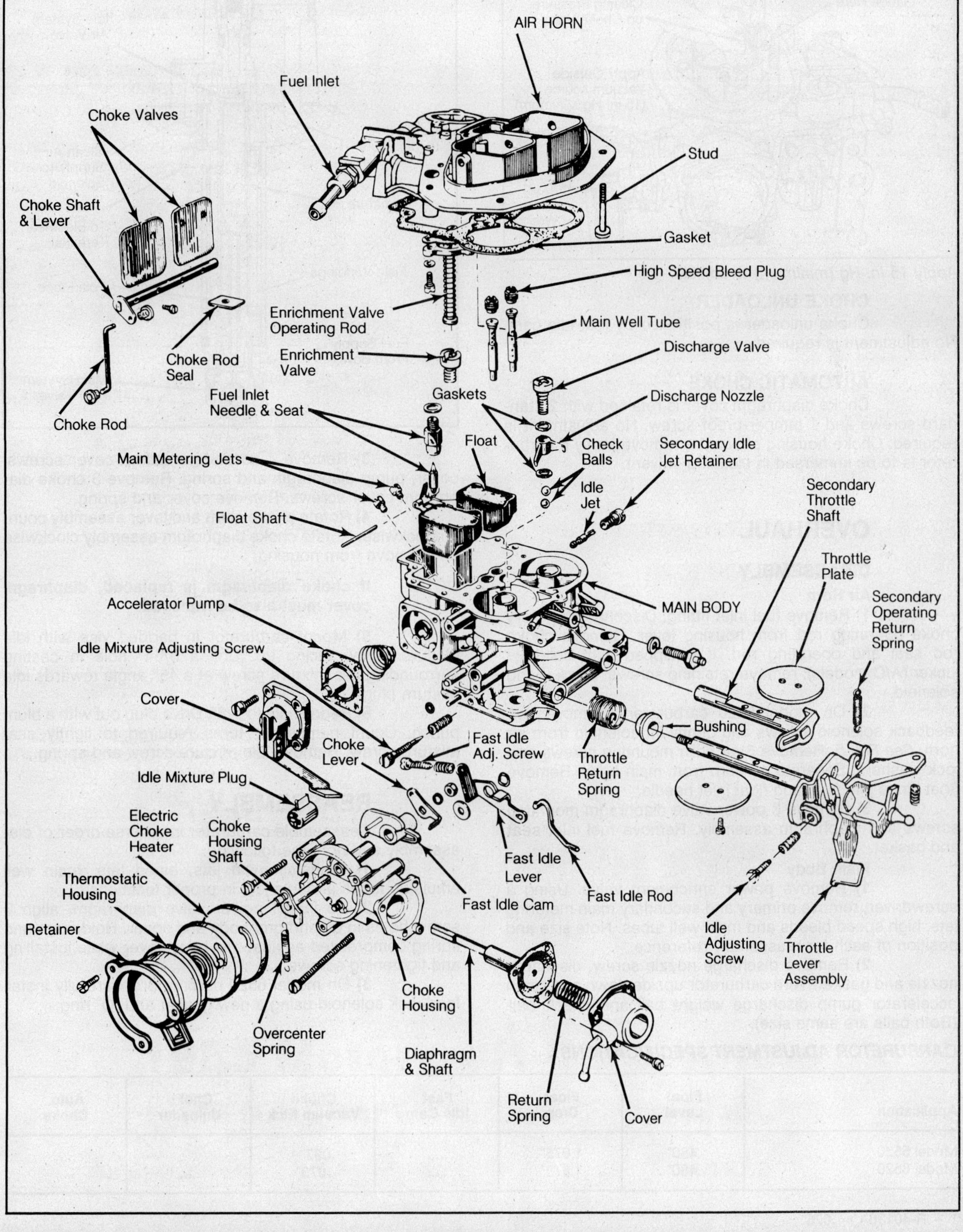

1985 Holley Carburetors

HOLLEY 5220 & 6520 2-BARREL (Cont.)

Fig. 4: Adjusting Choke Vacuum Kick (Initial Choke Valve Clearance)

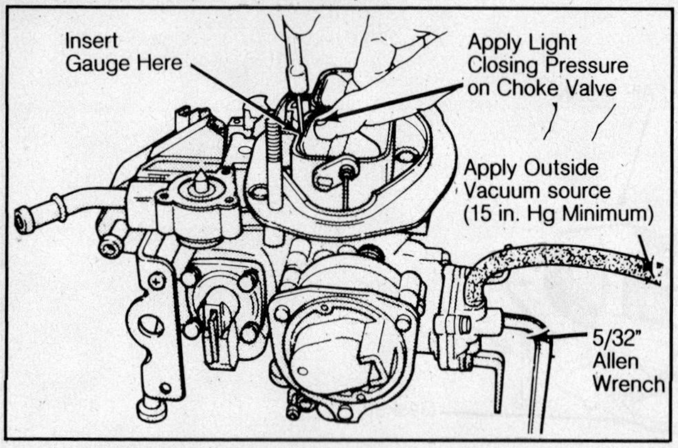

Apply 15 in. Hg (minimum) to adjust.

CHOKE UNLOADER

Choke unloader is positioned by fast idle cam. No adjustment is required.

AUTOMATIC CHOKE

Choke diaphragm cover is retained with 2 standard screws and 1 tamper-proof screw. No adjustment is required. Choke housing should be removed only if carburetor is to be immersed in cleaning solvent.

OVERHAUL

DISASSEMBLY

Air Horn

1) Remove fuel inlet fitting. Disconnect and pry choke operating rod from housing lever. Remove choke rod seal and operating rod. If equipped with solenoid kicker (A/C models), remove retaining screws, bracket and solenoid.

2) On model 6520 carburetors, remove two feedback solenoid screws and gently lift solenoid from air horn. *See Fig. 5.* Remove 5 air horn mounting screws and lock washers. Separate air horn from main body. Remove float hinge pin, float and float inlet needle.

3) Remove 3 power valve diaphragm mounting screws and diaphragm assembly. Remove fuel inlet seat and gasket.

Main Body

1) Remove power enrichment valve. Using a screwdriver, remove primary and secondary main metering jets, high speed bleeds and main well tubes. Note size and position of each for reassembly reference.

2) Remove discharge nozzle screw, discharge nozzle and gasket. Turn carburetor upside down and catch accelerator pump discharge weight ball and check ball. (Both balls are same size).

Fig. 5: Oxygen Feedback Solenoid

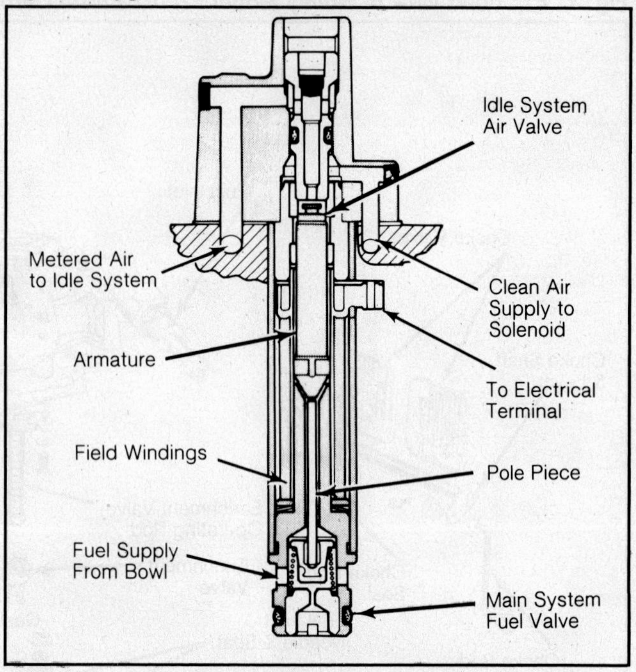

3) Remove 4 accelerator pump cover screws, cover, pump diaphragm and spring. Remove 3 choke diaphragm cover screws. Remove cover and spring.

4) Rotate choke shaft and lever assembly counterclockwise. Rotate choke diaphragm assembly clockwise and remove from housing.

NOTE: **If choke diaphragm is replaced, diaphragm cover must also be replaced.**

5) Mount carburetor in padded vise with idle mixture screw facing up. Drill a 5/64" hole in casting surrounding idle mixture screw at a 45° angle towards idle mixture plug.

6) Redrill hole to 1/8". Drive plug out with a blunt punch. Count number of turns required to lightly seat mixture screw. Remove idle mixture screw and spring.

REASSEMBLY

Reassemble carburetor in reverse order of disassembly and note the following:

1) Reinstall main jets, bleed jets, main well emulsion tubes and idle jets in proper locations.

2) To install power valve diaphragm, align 3 screw holes in diaphragm, body and cover. Hold stem and spring compressed against fuel bowl cover while installing and tightening screws.

3) On model 6520 carburetors, carefully install feedback solenoid using a new gasket and "O" ring.

CARBURETOR ADJUSTMENT SPECIFICATIONS

Application	Float Level	Float Drop	Fast Idle Cam	Choke Vacuum Kick	Choke Unloader	Auto. Choke
Model 5520	.480"	1.875"	.....	.097" [1]	.....	.....
Model 6520	.480"	1.875"	.....	.075"	.....	.....

[1] - R-40136A = .075"

1985 Holley Carburetors

HOLLEY 4180-C 4-BARREL

CARBURETOR APPLICATION

FORD CARBURETOR NO.

Application	Man. Trans.	Auto. Trans.
5.8L V8		
Federal	E4TE-ARA	E4TE-ARA
7.5L V8		
Federal	E3TE-PD	E3TE-RD
Calif.	E3TE-SC, TC	E3TE-SC, TC

CARBURETOR IDENTIFICATION

Identification tag is attached to carburetor. Tag contains part number prefix and suffix. Basic part number for all carburetors is 9510. A design change code (if any) is stamped on the tag. An assembly date code (year, month and day) is also stamped on the tag. *See Fig. 1.*

Fig. 1: Ford Motor Co. Carburetor Identification Tag

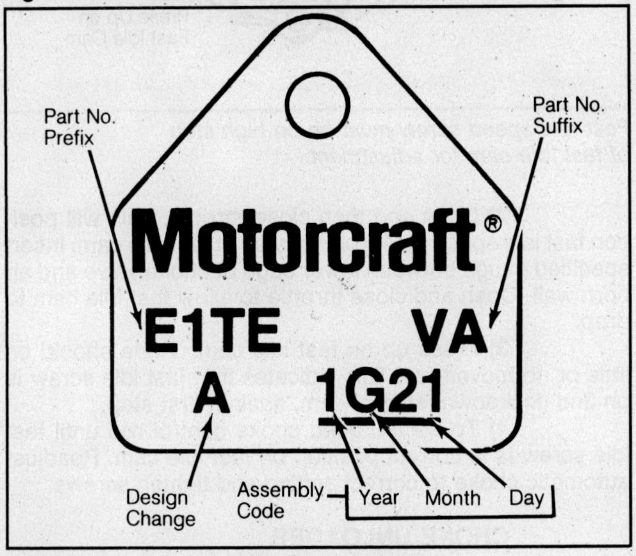

Identification tag is attached to carburetor.

DESCRIPTION

The Holley 4180-C 4-Barrel is a downdraft 2 stage carburetor. It has 2 separate stages: one supplying air/fuel mixture throughout entire range of engine operation (primary stage); the other functioning only when a greater supply of air/fuel is needed (secondary stage).

The primary stage (front section) of carburetor contains a fuel bowl, metering block, and accelerator pump assembly. The secondary (rear) section of carburetor contains a fuel bowl, metering body, and secondary throttle operating diaphragm assembly.

This model carburetor has 5 main systems: idle, main meter, secondary throttle, power enrichment and accelerating pump. In addition to these basic systems, it is also equipped with fuel inlet and automatic choke systems.

Vehicles over 8500 lbs. GVW with the 7.5L motor use a decel throttle modulator which keeps throttle plates from closing on deceleration for improved emission control. Calif. models use an external fuel bowl vent, located on top of the primary and secondary fuel bowls, connected through a purge hose to the evaporative emission canister.

ADJUSTMENT

NOTE: For all on-vehicle adjustments, see appropriate TUNE-UP article.

FLOAT LEVEL (DRY SETTING)

NOTE: Dry float setting is a preliminary adjustment only. Final adjustment (wet setting) must be made after carburetor is installed on vehicle.

1) Remove float bowl. Hold upside-down. Float is adjusted correctly if top of float is parallel with float bowl. *See Fig. 2.*

Fig. 2: Float Level Adjustment (Dry Setting)

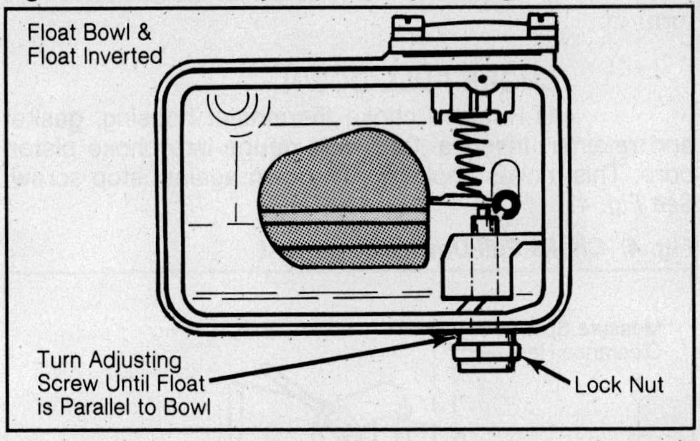

This is a preliminary setting; final adjustment must be made with carburetor installed on engine.

2) To adjust, loosen lock nut and turn adjusting screw until float is parallel.

ACCELERATOR PUMP LEVER

1) Place throttle valves in wide open position. Using a feeler gauge, measure specified clearance between the lever adjustment screw head and pump arm with the pump arm manually open. *See Fig. 3.*

Fig. 3: Accelerator Pump Lever Adjustment

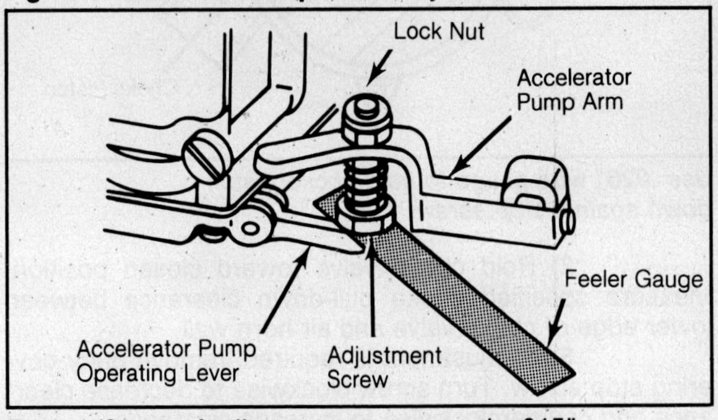

Each 1/2 turn of adjustment screw equals .015".

2) To adjust, loosen adjustment screw lock nut. Turn adjusting screw in to increase clearance and out to decrease clearance. Each 1/2 turn of adjustment screw equals .015". Tighten lock nut.

1985 Holley Carburetors

HOLLEY 4180-C 4-BARREL (Cont.)

ACCELERATOR PUMP STROKE

NOTE: Accelerator pump stroke has been preset at factory. Setting should not be changed. If original setting has been changed, adjust as follows:

1) Check that plastic accelerator pump cam is aligned with correct hole (top or bottom) in throttle lever. Plastic accelerator pump cam is located behind throttle lever.

2) If not aligned with correct hole, remove screw. Reposition in correct hole. Install and tighten screw.

SECONDARY THROTTLE VALVES

1) Hold secondary throttle valves closed. Turn secondary throttle valve stop screw out until secondary throttle valves seat in throttle bores.

2) Turn screw in until it just contacts secondary throttle valve lever. Then turn screw in an additional 1/4 turn.

CHOKE PULL-DOWN

1) Remove choke thermostat housing, gasket and retainer. Insert a .026" wire gauge into choke piston bore. This moves choke piston down against stop screw. *See Fig. 4.*

Fig. 4: Choke Pull-Down Adjustment

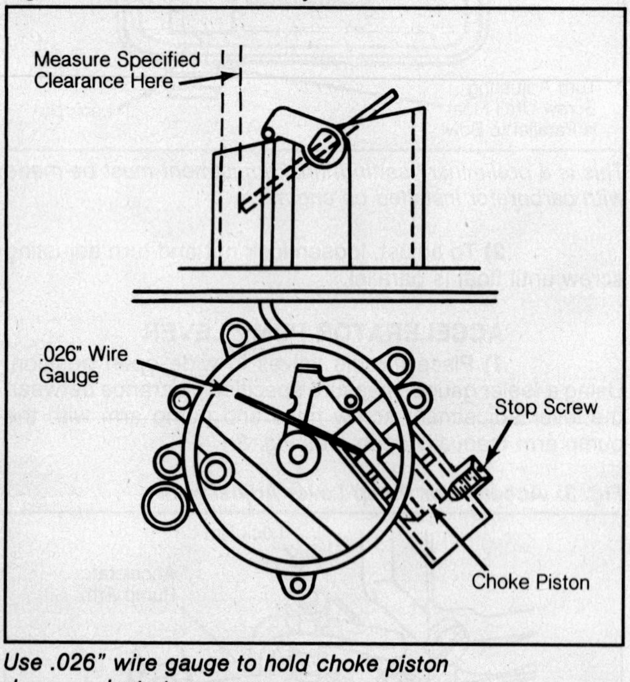

Use .026" wire gauge to hold choke piston down against stop screw.

2) Hold choke valve toward closed position. Measure specified choke pull-down clearance between lower edge of choke valve and air horn wall.

3) If adjustment is required, remove putty covering stop screw. Turn screw clockwise to decrease clearance and counterclockwise to increase clearance.

FAST IDLE CAM POSITION

1) Loosen choke thermostat housing screws. Rotate housing 45° counterclockwise (rich) to close choke valve. Tighten choke housing screws. *See Fig. 5.*

Fig. 5: Adjusting Fast Idle Cam Position

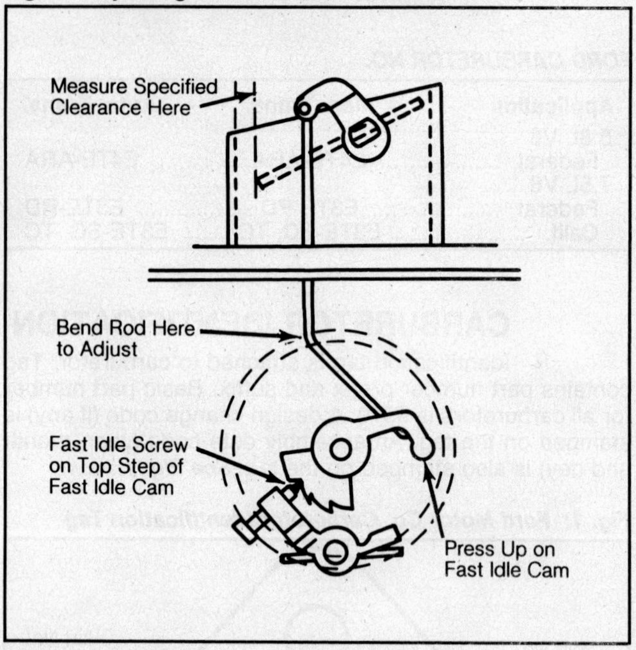

Fast idle speed screw must be on high step of fast idle cam for adjustment.

2) Open and then close throttle. This will position fast idle speed screw on top step of fast idle cam. Insert specified gauge between lower edge of choke valve and air horn wall. Open and close throttle to allow fast idle cam to drop.

3) Press up on fast idle cam. There should be little or no movement. This indicates that fast idle screw is on 2nd (kickdown) step of cam, against first step.

4) To adjust, bend choke control rod until fast idle screw is in correct position on fast idle cam. Readjust automatic choke to correct setting and tighten screws.

CHOKE UNLOADER

1) Hold throttle valves wide open. Apply light closing pressure on choke valve. *See Fig. 6.*

2) Measure specified choke unloader clearance between lower edge of choke valve and air horn wall. To adjust, bend pawl on fast idle cam lever.

AUTOMATIC CHOKE

Depress throttle lever to 1/4 open position, and rotate choke plate to closed position. Release choke plate, choke plate should rotate smoothly to open position. For adjusting choke system refer to appropriate article in TUNE-UP section.

OVERHAUL

DISASSEMBLY

Primary Fuel Bowl & Metering Block

1) Remove primary fuel bowl and gasket. Remove metering block and gasket. Discard gaskets.

2) Remove pump transfer tube and "O" rings from main body if it was not removed with metering block. Remove fuel line tube and "O" rings. Discard "O" rings.

HOLLEY 4180-C 4-BARREL (Cont.)

Fig. 6: Choke Unloader Adjustment

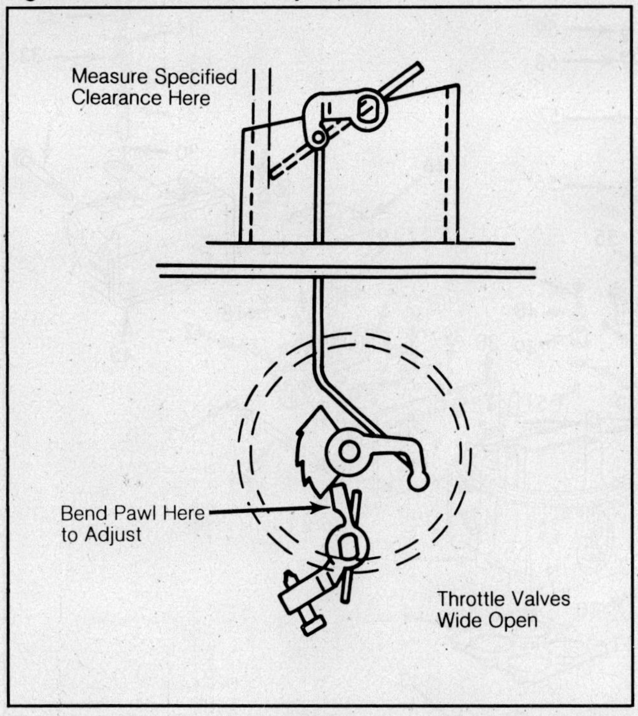

Throttle valves must be in wide open position.

3) Using a jet wrench, remove main jets from metering block. Using a socket wrench, remove power valve and gasket.

4) Remove fuel level adjustment screw and gasket. Turn lock nut counterclockwise and remove nut and gasket. Remove fuel inlet needle and seat assembly. Do not disassemble needle and seat, they are replaced as an assembly.

5) Using needle nose pliers, remove float shaft retainer clip. Slide float off shaft and remove spring from float. Remove baffle plate from fuel bowl. Remove fuel level sight plug and gasket.

6) Remove fuel inlet fitting, gasket and filter. Invert fuel bowl and remove accelerator pump cover, diaphragm and spring. Do not remove accelerator pump inlet check ball. Check ball is not serviced separately.

Secondary Fuel Bowl & Metering Block

Remove fuel bowl. Using a clutch type screwdriver, remove metering block screws. Remove metering block, plate and gaskets. Discard gaskets. Disassemble fuel bowl by following steps **4)** and **5)** in PRIMARY FUEL BOWL & METERING BLOCK in this article.

Main Body

1) Remove air cleaner stud. Remove secondary diaphragm link retainer. Invert carburetor and remove throttle body retaining screws and lock washers. Lift off throttle body and discard throttle body gasket.

2) Remove choke rod cotter pin from choke housing shaft and lever assembly. Remove choke cover, thermostatic spring and gasket. Remove choke main housing and gaskets from main body.

3) Remove choke housing shaft nut, lock washer and spacer. Remove shaft and fast idle cam. Remove choke piston and lever assembly.

4) If it is necessary to remove choke valve and shaft, tips of choke valve screws may have to be filed because they are staked into shaft. After removing screws, remove valve and slide out choke shaft.

5) Remove secondary diaphragm housing and gasket. Secondary diaphragm housing must be removed before attempting to remove cover. Remove diaphragm housing cover, spring diaphragm and vacuum check ball.

6) Remove accelerator pump discharge nozzle screw. Lift off discharge nozzle and gaskets. Invert main body and catch accelerator pump discharge needle as it falls out of bore in main body.

Throttle Body

Components of throttle body are matched to meet emission control standards. Manufacturer does not recommend disassembly of throttle body.

CLEANING & INSPECTION

- Use a regular carburetor cleaning solution. Soak components long enough to thoroughly clean all surfaces and passages of foreign matter.
- Do not soak any components containing rubber, leather or plastic.
- Do not use wire, drill or any hard parts to clean passages and orifices in carburetor.
- Remove any residue after cleaning by rinsing components in suitable solvent.
- Blow out all passages with dry compressed air.

REASSEMBLY

Use new gaskets and seals. Make sure that new gaskets fit correctly and that all holes and slots are punched through and correctly located. To reassemble carburetor, reverse disassembly procedure and note the following:

1) Apply petroleum jelly to all "O" rings before installation.

2) Make sure projection on the choke rod is positioned under the fast idle cam. This will ensure that fast idle cam will be raised up when the choke valve closes.

3) It will be necessary to install the secondary diaphragm housing cover and all 4 screws before diaphragm housing is installed onto main body.

CARBURETOR ADJUSTMENT SPECIFICATIONS

Application	Accelerator Pump		Choke Pulldown Setting	Fast Idle Cam Setting	Choke Unloader Setting	Auto. Choke Setting
	Lever (Clearance)	Stroke (Hole No.)				
E4TE-ARA	.015"	#1	.185"	.....	.300"	3 Rich
E3TE-RD	.015"	#1	.200"	.....	.315"	3 Rich
E3TE-PD, SC & TC	.015"	#1	.220"	.....	.315"	3 Rich

1985 Holley Carburetors

HOLLEY 4180-C 4-BARREL (Cont.)

Fig. 7: Exploded View of Holley Model 4180-C 4-Barrel Carburetor

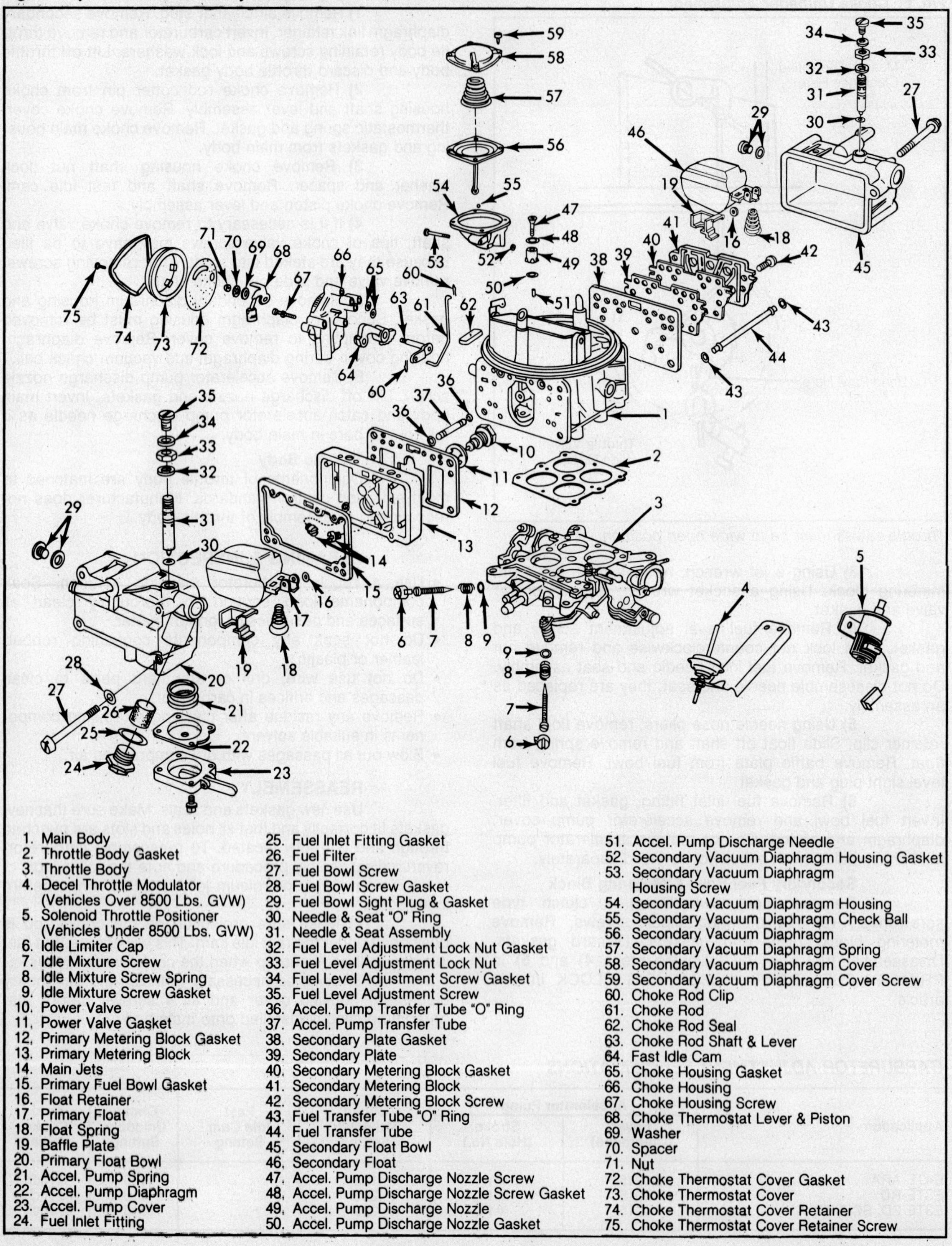

1. Main Body
2. Throttle Body Gasket
3. Throttle Body
4. Decel Throttle Modulator (Vehicles Over 8500 Lbs. GVW)
5. Solenoid Throttle Positioner (Vehicles Under 8500 Lbs. GVW)
6. Idle Limiter Cap
7. Idle Mixture Screw
8. Idle Mixture Screw Spring
9. Idle Mixture Screw Gasket
10. Power Valve
11. Power Valve Gasket
12. Primary Metering Block Gasket
13. Primary Metering Block
14. Main Jets
15. Primary Fuel Bowl Gasket
16. Float Retainer
17. Primary Float
18. Float Spring
19. Baffle Plate
20. Primary Fuel Bowl
21. Accel. Pump Spring
22. Accel. Pump Diaphragm
23. Accel. Pump Cover
24. Fuel Inlet Fitting
25. Fuel Inlet Fitting Gasket
26. Fuel Filter
27. Fuel Bowl Screw
28. Fuel Bowl Screw Gasket
29. Fuel Bowl Sight Plug & Gasket
30. Needle & Seat "O" Ring
31. Needle & Seat Assembly
32. Fuel Level Adjustment Lock Nut Gasket
33. Fuel Level Adjustment Lock Nut
34. Fuel Level Adjustment Screw Gasket
35. Fuel Level Adjustment Screw
36. Accel. Pump Transfer Tube "O" Ring
37. Accel. Pump Transfer Tube
38. Secondary Plate Gasket
39. Secondary Plate
40. Secondary Metering Block Gasket
41. Secondary Metering Block
42. Secondary Metering Block Screw
43. Fuel Transfer Tube "O" Ring
44. Fuel Transfer Tube
45. Secondary Float Bowl
46. Secondary Float
47. Accel. Pump Discharge Nozzle Screw
48. Accel. Pump Discharge Nozzle Screw Gasket
49. Accel. Pump Discharge Nozzle
50. Accel. Pump Discharge Nozzle Gasket
51. Accel. Pump Discharge Needle
52. Secondary Vacuum Diaphragm Housing Gasket
53. Secondary Vacuum Diaphragm Housing Screw
54. Secondary Vacuum Diaphragm Housing
55. Secondary Vacuum Diaphragm Check Ball
56. Secondary Vacuum Diaphragm
57. Secondary Vacuum Diaphragm Spring
58. Secondary Vacuum Diaphragm Cover
59. Secondary Vacuum Diaphragm Cover Screw
60. Choke Rod Clip
61. Choke Rod
62. Choke Rod Seal
63. Choke Rod Shaft & Lever
64. Fast Idle Cam
65. Choke Housing Gasket
66. Choke Housing
67. Choke Housing Screw
68. Choke Thermostat Lever & Piston
69. Washer
70. Spacer
71. Nut
72. Choke Thermostat Cover Gasket
73. Choke Thermostat Cover
74. Choke Thermostat Cover Retainer
75. Choke Thermostat Cover Retainer Screw

MOTORCRAFT 2150 2-BARREL

CARBURETOR APPLICATION

FORD (MOTORCRAFT) CARBURETOR NO.

Application	Man. Trans.	Auto. Trans.
2.8L V6		
50 State	E57E-CA	E57E-CA
Federal	E57E-BA	E57E-YA
California	E57E-BA	.....
5.0L V8		
Federal	.....	E5TE-ACA, YA
California	.....	E5TE-YA
5.8L V8		
50 State	E3UE-DA	E3UE-DA
	E3UE-EA	E3UE-EA
Federal	.....	E4TE-ADA
California	.....	E5TE-AAA

CARBURETOR IDENTIFICATION

JEEP CARBURETOR NO.

Application	Man. Trans.	Auto. Trans.
6.0L V8		
50 State	4RHA2	4RHA2

FORD

A carburetor identification tag is attached to carburetor. The tag contains part number prefix and suffix. Basic part number for all carburetors is 9510.

A design change code (if any) is also stamped on the tag. An assembly date code (year, month and day) is also stamped on the tag. *See Fig. 1.*

Fig. 1: Ford Carburetor Identification Tag

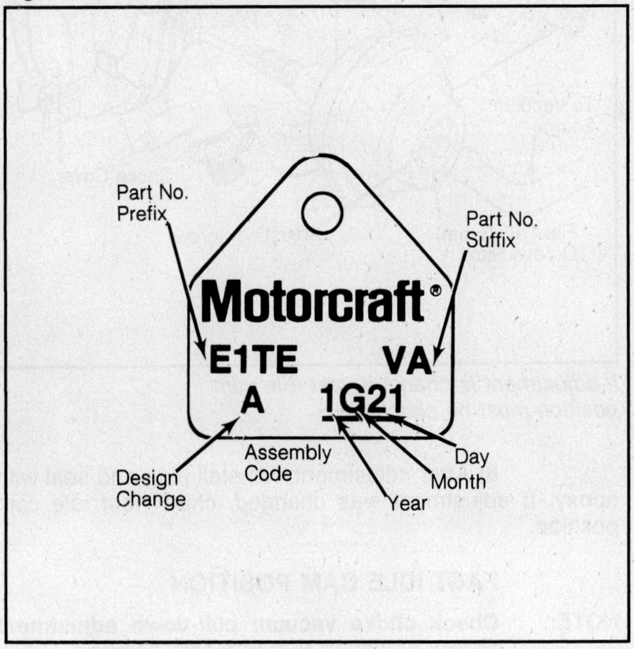

JEEP

A carburetor identification tag is attached to carburetor. The tag contains the Jeep carburetor list number. An assembly date code (year, month and day) is also stamped on the tag. *See Fig. 2.*

Fig. 2: Jeep Carburetor Identification Tag

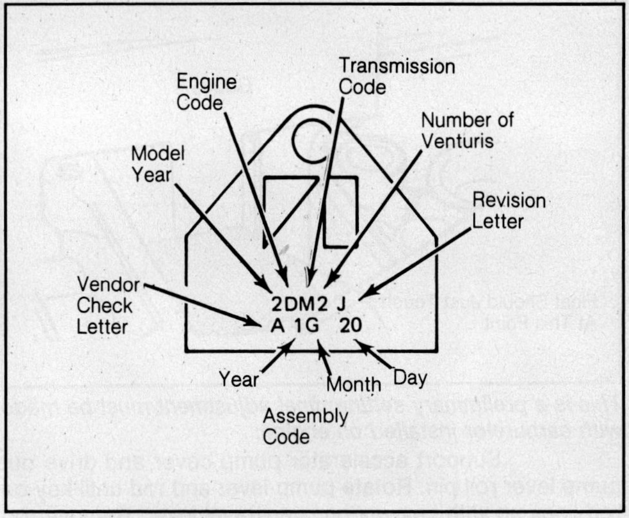

DESCRIPTION

The Motorcraft 2150 carburetor has 2 main assemblies: the air horn and main body.

The air horn contains choke plate, fuel bowl vent, and hot idle compensator. The main body houses throttle plate, accelerator pump assembly, float assembly, power valve, fuel bowl and duty cycle solenoid on feedback models.

Each bore contains main and boost venturi, main fuel discharge, accelerator pump discharge, idle fuel discharge and throttle plate.

On some applications, booster venturi contain variable high speed bleed control system. This system allows control of air/fuel mixture for improved high speed operation and low speed responses. Feedback models use a duty cycle solenoid/altitude compensator to control air/fuel mixture. The duty cycle solenoid is operated by an Electronic Control Assembly.

Vehicles sold for high altitude use (above 4000 ft. or 1219 m) contain an altitude compensator. This circuit compensates for thinner air by metering an additional amount of air into the air/fuel mixture, preventing an over-rich situation. An aneroid (automatic device) reacts to atmospheric pressure and overrides the compensation feature at lower altitudes.

ADJUSTMENT

NOTE: For all on-vehicle adjustments, see TUNE-UP SERVICE PROCEDURES.

FLOAT LEVEL (DRY SETTING)

NOTE: Dry float setting is a preliminary adjustment only. Final adjustment (wet setting) must be made after carburetor is installed on vehicle.

Remove float bowl. Hold upside-down. Float is adjusted correctly if top of float is specified distance from top of float bowl. *See Fig. 3.*

ACCELERATOR PUMP STROKE

NOTE: Accelerator pump stroke has been preset at factory. Setting should not be changed. If original setting has been changed, adjust as follows.

1985 Motorcraft Carburetors

MOTORCRAFT 2150 2-BARREL (Cont.)

Fig. 3: Float Level Adjustment (Dry Setting)

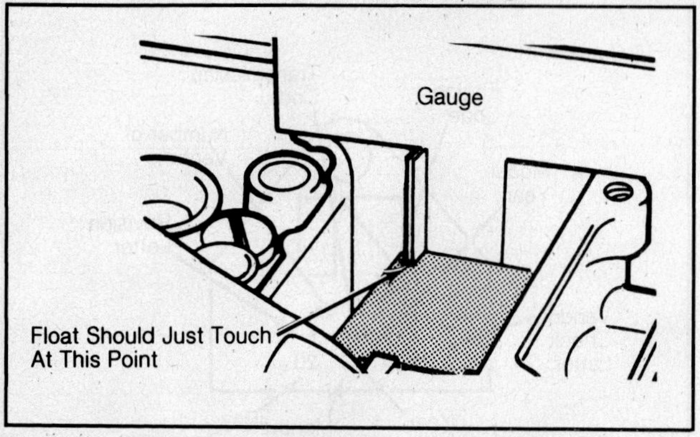

This is a preliminary setting; final adjustment must be made with carburetor installed on engine.

Support accelerator pump cover and drive out pump lever roll pin. Rotate pump lever and rod until key on rod lines up with keyway on over-travel lever. Remove rod and reposition in proper hole of over-travel lever. Reinstall pump lever and roll pin. *See Fig. 4.*

Fig. 4: Accelerator Pump Stroke Adjustment

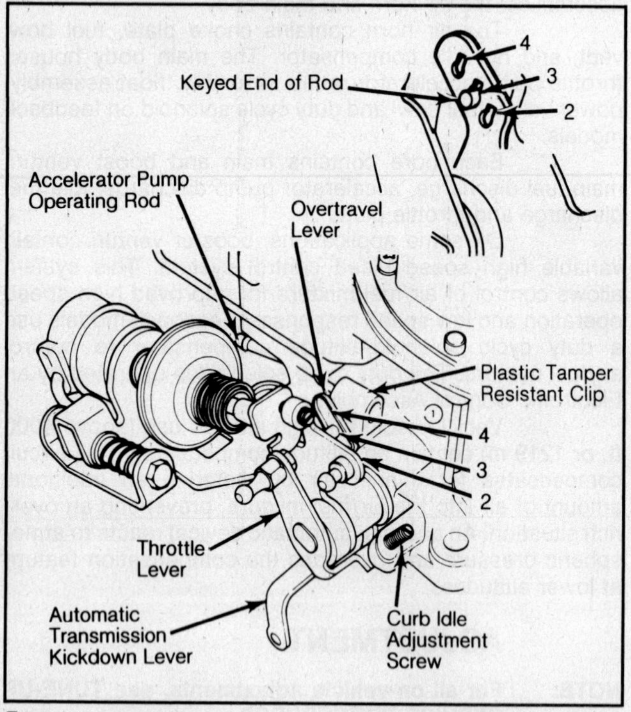

Ensure connecting rod is installed in correct hole of overtravel lever.

CHOKE PULL-DOWN

NOTE: **Most applications have a tamper-proof choke, incorporating a sealed pull-down motor and break-away choke cap screws. Adjustments given are used when a major overhaul is performed or if components are damaged.**

1) Loosen choke cover retainers. Open throttle and rotate choke cover until choke valve is held closed. Tighten choke cover.

2) Using an external vacuum source, apply vacuum to hold choke diaphragm against set screw. Do not apply pressure to linkage.

NOTE: **If vacuum is applied to choke diaphragm with a hand vacuum pump, and a air leak is detected, replace vacuum pulldown unit.**

3) Using a specified drill or pin gauge, measure clearance between lower edge of choke valve and air horn.

4) If adjustment is required, file a 1/8" (3 mm) deep recessed groove 1/4" (6 mm) behind edge of adjusting screw end of diaphragm.

5) Using an awl angled toward plug, drive plug out. Turn adjusting screw until specified clearance is obtained. *See Fig. 5.*

Fig. 5: Adjusting Choke Pull-Down Clearance

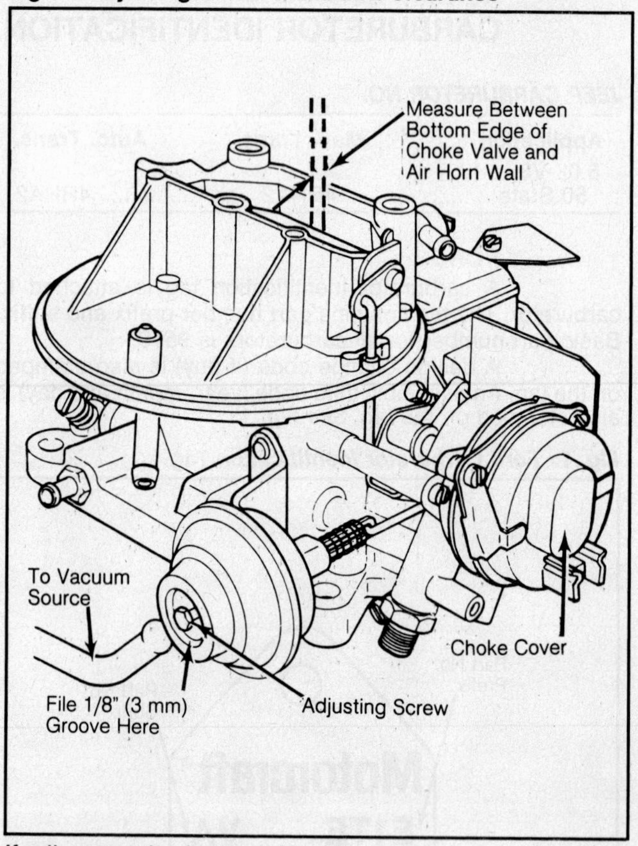

If adjustment is changed, fast idle cam position must be checked.

6) After adjustment, reinstall plug and seal with epoxy. If adjustment was changed, check fast idle cam position.

FAST IDLE CAM POSITION

NOTE: **Check choke vacuum pull-down adjustment before adjusting fast idle cam position.**

MOTORCRAFT 2150 2-BARREL (Cont.)

1) Perform steps **1)** and **2)** of Choke Pull-Down adjustment.

2) Open and close throttle. Fast idle cam should drop to 2nd (kickdown) step. Fast idle screw should be opposite "V" notch on cam. *See Fig. 6.*

NOTE: **On models equipped with an idle speed control motor, the fast idle screw does not actually touch fast idle cam. However, the screw should still line up with the "V" notch on the cam.**

Fig. 6: Ford Fast Idle Cam Position Adjustment

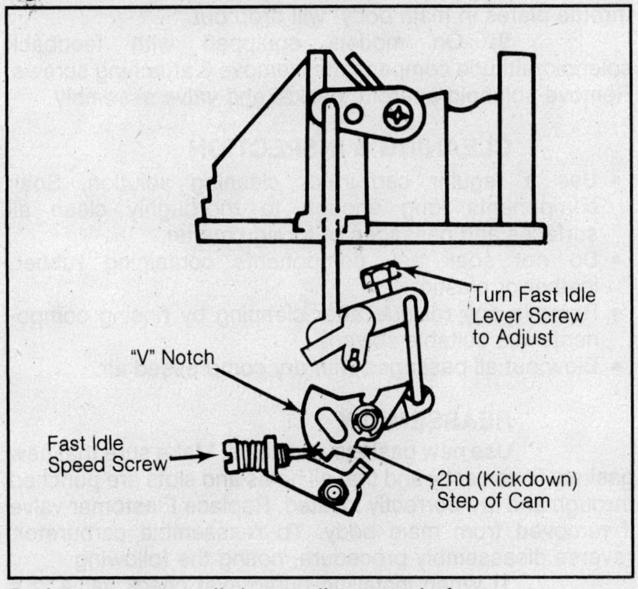

Perform vacuum pull-down adjustment before adjusting fast idle cam position.

3) To adjust, turn fast idle lever screw to align fast idle speed screw with "V" notch. Screw is located in plastic fast idle cam lever. Reset choke.

4) On Jeep models, push down on fast idle cam lever until fast idle speed screw is in contact with 2nd step and against shoulder of high step. *See Fig. 7.*

Fig. 7: Jeep Fast Idle Cam Position Adjustment

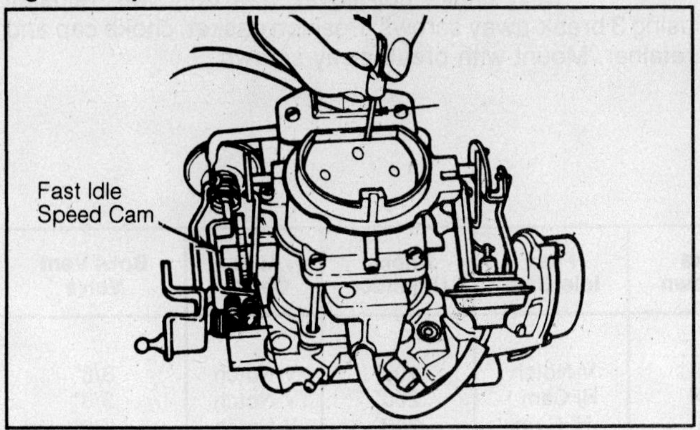

Perform vacuum pull-down adjustment before adjusting fast idle cam position.

5) To adjust, turn fast idle lever screw. Reset choke to proper adjustment notch.

CHOKE UNLOADER

1) Hold throttle fully open, and lightly press choke valve toward closed position. Using a specified drill or pin gauge, measure specified choke unloader clearance between lower edge of choke valve and air horn wall.

2) To adjust, bend choke unloader tang that contacts fast idle cam. Bend tang toward cam to increase clearance and away from cam to decrease clearance. Do not bend unloader tang downward from a horizontal plane. *See Fig. 8.*

Fig. 8: Choke Unloader Adjustment

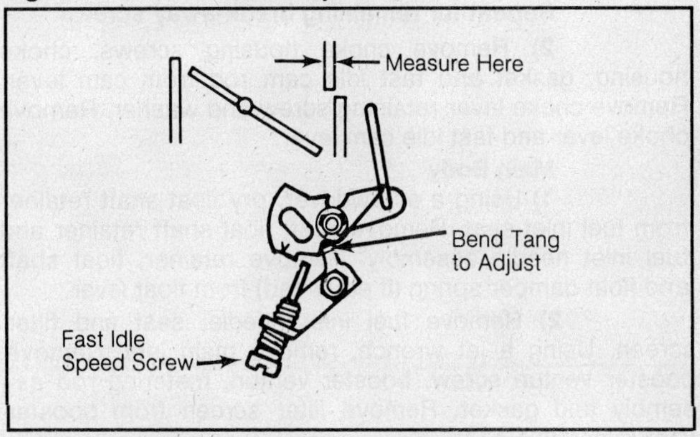

Do not bend unloader tang downward from a horizontal plane.

3) After correct adjustment is obtained on Jeep models, open throttle until unloader tang is directly under fast idle cam pivot. Make sure there is .070" (1.78 mm) clearance, between unloader tang and fast idle cam.

4) Operate throttle after adjustment. Make sure that tang does not stick or bind against any portion of the linkage or carburetor casting.

AUTOMATIC CHOKE

Loosen choke thermostat cover retaining screws. Rotate cover assembly in "Rich" or "Lean" direction to align reference marks. Tighten cover screws.

OVERHAUL

DISASSEMBLY

Air Horn

1) Remove air cleaner anchor screw and automatic choke control rod retainer. Remove air horn attaching screws, lock washers, carburetor identification tag and air horn. Remove screw securing choke lever to choke shaft. Remove choke rod and seal from air horn.

2) Remove choke diaphragm assembly. If necessary to remove choke valve, file staking from retaining screws. Remove screws. Slide choke valve out from top of air horn. Remove choke shaft.

3) On models equipped with altitude compensator, remove by-pass choke plate in same way as main choke plate. To remove shaft, remove link retainer and slide shaft out of air horn.

1985 Motorcraft Carburetors

MOTORCRAFT 2150 2-BARREL (Cont.)

Automatic Choke

1) Remove fast idle cam retainer and thermostatic choke coil housing screws. Remove clamp and gasket.

NOTE: **Some models are equipped with break-away screws retaining coil cover to prevent tampering with factory adjustment. To remove break-away screws, align a 1/4" (6 mm) drill on head, and drill only enough to remove head. Using an 1/8" (3 mm) punch, drive remaining portion of screw from housing. Repeat for remaining break-away screws.**

2) Remove choke housing screws, choke housing, gasket and fast idle cam rod from cam lever. Remove choke lever retaining screw and washer. Remove choke lever and fast idle cam lever.

Main Body

1) Using a screwdriver, pry float shaft retainer from fuel inlet seat. Remove float, float shaft retainer and fuel inlet needle assembly. Remove retainer, float shaft and float damper spring (if equipped) from float lever.

2) Remove fuel inlet needle, seat and filter screen. Using a jet wrench, remove main jets. Remove booster venturi screw, booster venturi, metering rod assembly and gasket. Remove filter screen from booster venturi screw.

3) Invert main body and catch accelerator pump discharge weight and check ball. To disassemble lift rod from booster, remove lift spring retaining clip and spring. Separate lift rod assembly from booster. Do not disassemble metering rod hanger from lift rod.

4) Remove accelerator pump operating rod from overtravel lever and retainer, by pressing ends of retainer together. At the same time, press rod away from retainer until it is free.

5) Remove accelerator pump cover screws. Remove bowl vent rod and bracket, accelerator pump cover diaphragm, and spring. If necessary to remove pump inlet check valve, grasp firmly from outside main body and pull out.

NOTE: **If tip of check valve breaks off during removal, make sure it is removed from fuel bowl. Pump inlet check valve must be replaced, whenever it is removed.**

6) Invert main body and remove enrichment valve cover and gasket. Using a box wrench, remove enrichment valve. Remove and discard enrichment valve gasket.

7) Remove mixture needle limiter caps, mixture needles and springs. If necessary, remove nut and washer securing fast idle adjusting lever, and remove lever. Remove throttle positioner solenoid (if equipped).

NOTE: **To remove tamper-resistant mixture needle limiter caps, support area under limiter plug and tap cap forward.**

8) If necessary to remove throttle plates, mark each plate for reassembly reference. Remove throttle position sensor if equipped. Slide throttle shaft from main body. Mechanical high speed bleed actuator (located between throttle plates in main body) will drop out.

9) On models equipped with feedback solenoid/altitude compensator, remove 3 attaching screws. Remove solenoid/aneroid, gasket and valve assembly.

CLEANING & INSPECTION

- Use a regular carburetor cleaning solution. Soak components long enough to thoroughly clean all surfaces and passages of foreign matter.
- Do not soak any components containing rubber, leather or plastic.
- Remove any residue after cleaning by rinsing components in a suitable solvent.
- Blow out all passages with dry compressed air.

REASSEMBLY

Use new gaskets and seals. Make sure that new gaskets fit correctly and that all holes and slots are punched through and are correctly located. Replace Elastomer valve if removed from main body. To reassemble carburetor, reverse disassembly procedure, noting the following:

1) When installing pump inlet check valve (if it was removed), lubricate tip of new valve, and insert tip into center hole of accelerator pump cavity. Insert needle nose pliers in fuel bowl, and pull valve in, until fully seated. Cut off excess valve tip at retaining shoulder, and remove tip from fuel bowl.

2) When installing idle mixture needles and springs, turn screws in with fingers until lightly seated. Back screws off seated position 1 1/2 turns for an initial adjustment. Do not install idle screw limiter caps, until final adjustments have been made.

3) If choke coil cover was removed, reinstall using 3 break-away screws. Position gasket, choke cap and retainer. Mount with break-away screws.

CARBURETOR ADJUSTMENT SPECIFICATIONS

Application	Float Level (Dry Setting)	Accel. Pump	Choke Pull-Down	Fast Idle Cam	Choke Unloader	Auto. Choke	Bowl Vent Valve
Ford							
E5TE-AAA	1/4"	#4	.155"	V-Notch	.200"	V-Notch	3/8"
E5TE-ACA, YA	31/64"	#4	.150"	Hi Cam [1]	.200"	V-Notch	3/8"
E57E-BA, CA	1/4"	#4	.136"	Hi Cam	.250"	V-Notch	3/8"
E5TE-PA	1/4"	#4	.152"	Hi Cam	.200"	V-Notch	3/8"
E3UE-DA, EA	31/64"	#3	.180"	V-Notch	.250"	V-Notch	3/8"
Jeep							
4RHA2	21/64"	#3	.113"	.086"	.350"	2 Rich	.120"

[1] - Calibration 4-54R-R12 = V-Notch.

MOTORCRAFT 2150 2-BARREL (Cont.)

Fig. 9: Exploded View of Motorcraft Model 2150 2-Barrel Carburetor

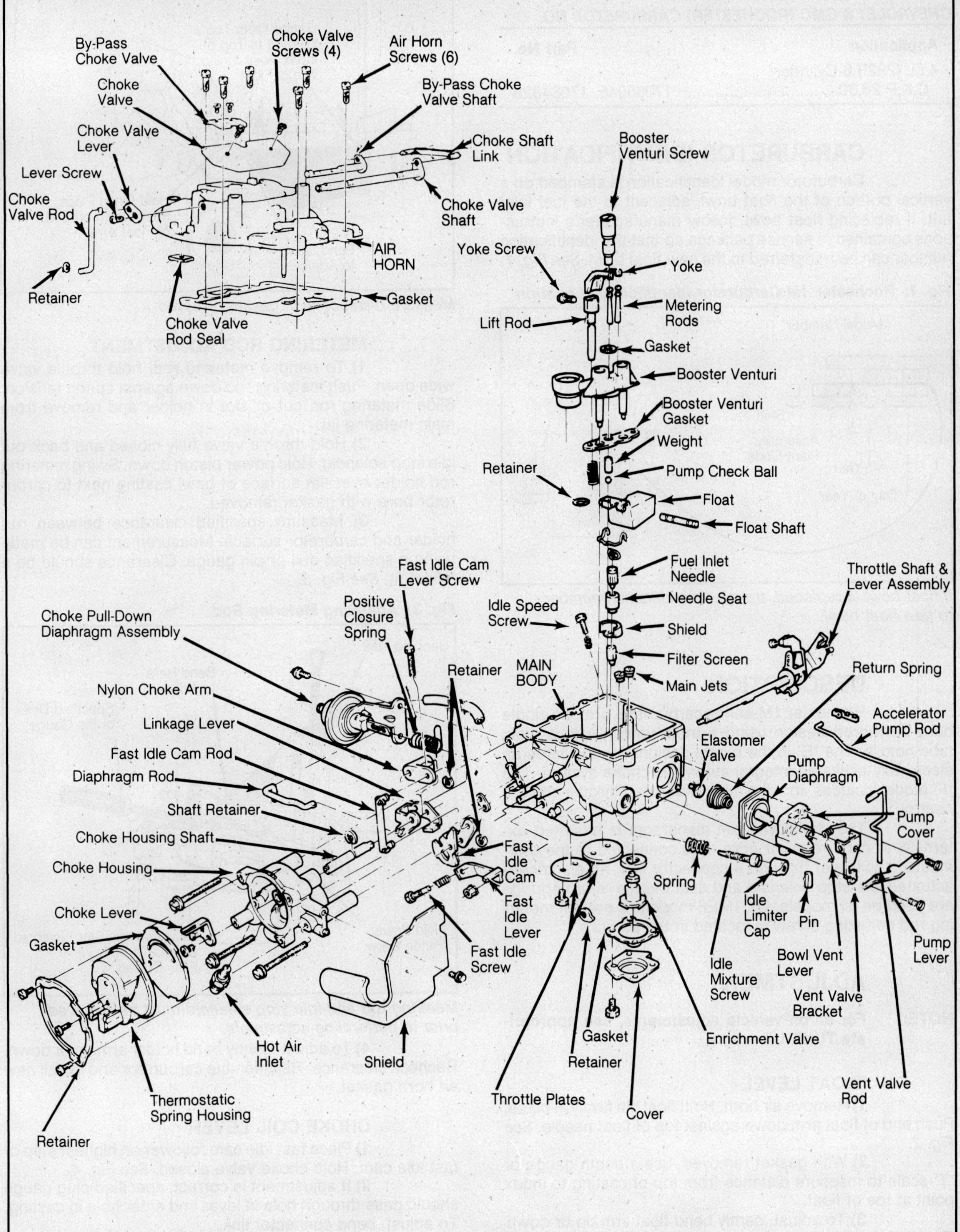

Duty cycle solenoid is used in place of altitude compensator on feedback models.

1985 Rochester Carburetors

ROCHESTER 1ME & 1MEF SINGLE BARREL

CARBURETOR APPLICATION

CHEVROLET & GMC (ROCHESTER) CARBURETOR NO.

Application	Part No.
4.8L (292") 6-Cylinder	
C,K,P 20,30	17085045, 17084329

CARBURETOR IDENTIFICATION

Carburetor model identification is stamped on a vertical portion of the float bowl, adjacent to the fuel inlet nut. If replacing float bowl, follow manufacturer's instructions contained in service package so that the identification number can be transferred to the new float bowl. *See Fig. 1.*

Fig. 1: Rochester 1M Carburetor Identification Location

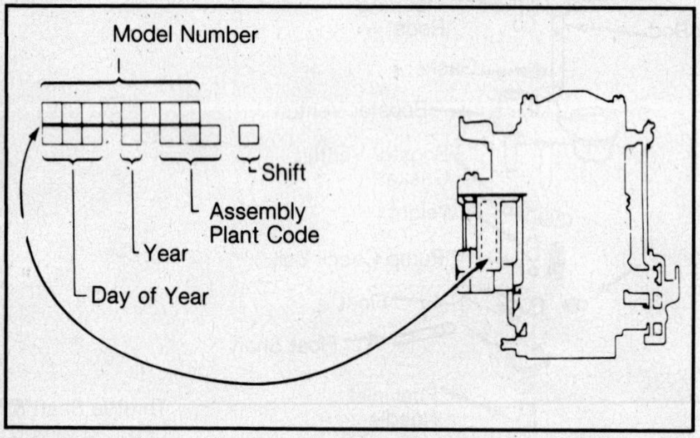

If float bowl is replaced, transfer identification number to new float bowl.

DESCRIPTION

Rochester 1M-series carburetors are of a single bore downdraft design using a triple venturi with a plain tube nozzle. The "E" in the model designation indicates an electrically-activated integral automatic choke system. The "F" model includes an adjustable wide open throttle mixture control.

The choke vacuum diaphragm is mounted externally to carburetor air horn. It is connected to the thermostatic coil lever through a connector link. An electrically actuated idle stop solenoid and dual throttle return springs are used on all models. On 1MEF models, a pre-set metering rod adjusting screw is located in the air horn.

ADJUSTMENT

NOTE: **For all on-vehicle adjustments, see appropriate TUNE-UP article.**

FLOAT LEVEL

1) Remove air horn. Hold float pin firmly in place. Push end of float arm down against top of float needle. *See Fig. 2.*

2) With gasket removed, use a depth gauge or "T" scale to measure distance from top of casting to index point at toe of float.

3) To adjust, gently bend float arm up or down. To avoid damage, do not force needle against needle seat.

Fig. 2: Adjusting Float Level

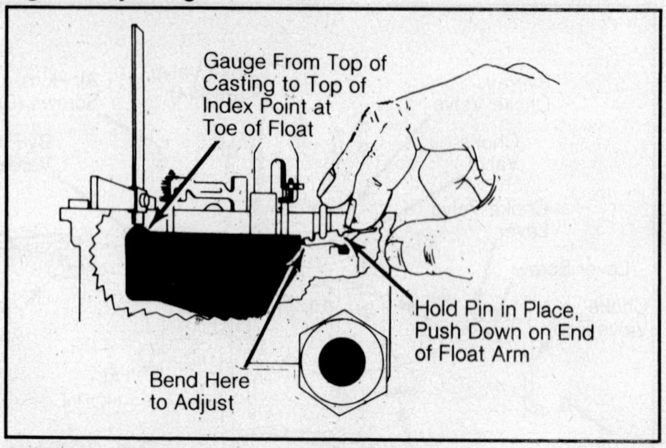

Measure distance with gasket removed.

METERING ROD ADJUSTMENT

1) To remove metering rod, hold throttle valve wide open. Push metering rod down against spring tension. Slide metering rod out of slot in holder and remove from main metering jet.

2) Hold throttle valve fully closed and back out idle stop solenoid. Hold power piston down. Swing metering rod holder over flat surface of bowl casting next to carburetor bore with gasket removed.

3) Measure specified clearance between rod holder and carburetor surface. Measurement can be made using a specified drill or pin gauge. Clearance should be a "slide" fit. *See Fig. 3.*

Fig. 3: Adjusting Metering Rod

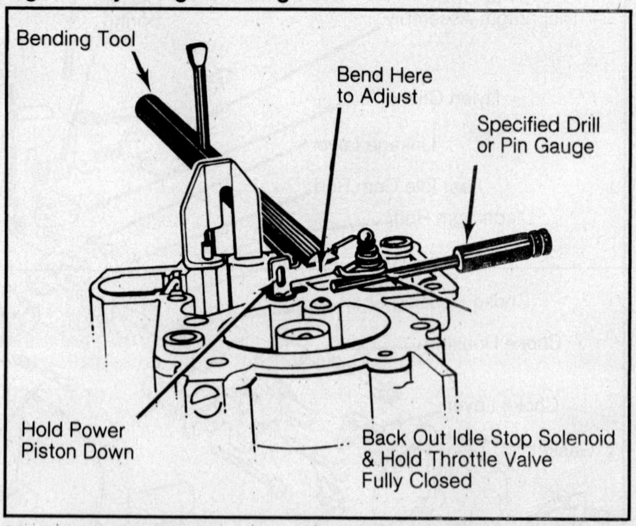

Metering rod and idle stop solenoid must be removed prior to performing adjustment.

4) To adjust, gently bend holder arm up or down. Recheck clearance. Reassemble carburetor and install new air horn gasket.

CHOKE COIL LEVER

1) Place fast idle cam follower on highest step of fast idle cam. Hold choke valve closed. *See Fig. 4.*

2) If adjustment is correct, specified plug gauge should pass through hole in lever and enter hole in casting. To adjust, bend connector link.

ROCHESTER 1ME & 1MEF SINGLE BARREL (Cont.)

Fig. 4: Adjusting Choke Coil Lever

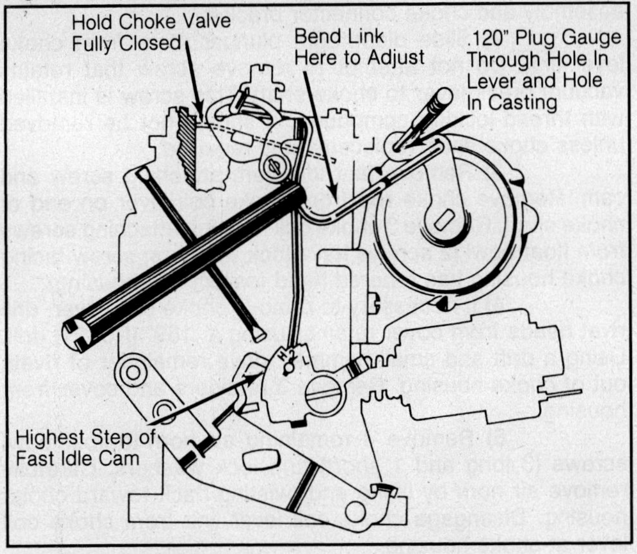

Fast idle cam follower must be on highest step of fast idle cam.

FAST IDLE CAM POSITION (CHOKE ROD)

1) Make sure fast idle speed is correctly set. Hold fast idle cam follower on 2nd step of fast idle cam, against highest step. *See Fig. 5.*

Fig. 5: Adjusting Fast Idle Cam Position (Choke Rod)

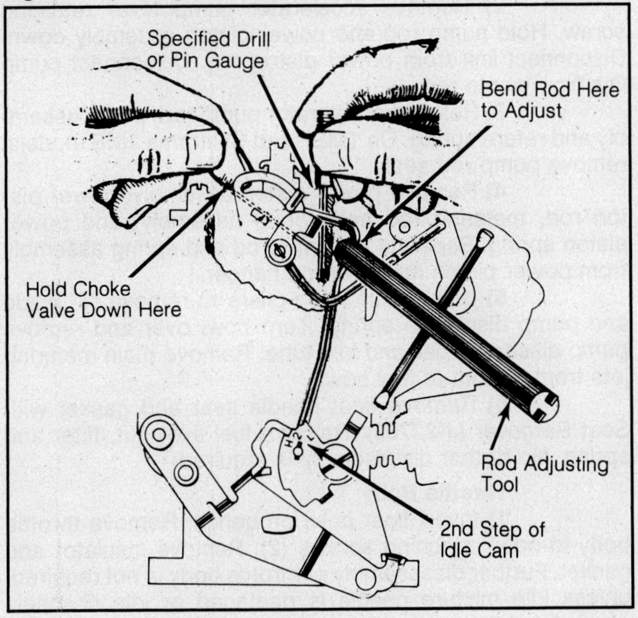

Hold fast idle cam follower on 2nd step of fast idle cam, against highest step.

2) Apply light closing pressure to choke valve. Measure specified clearance between lower edge of choke valve (center) and air horn wall. Measurement can be made with a specified drill or pin gauge. To adjust, bend fast idle cam rod.

AUTOMATIC CHOKE

NOTE: **Choke coil cover uses rivets in place of retaining screws. If necessary to remove choke coil cover, refer to AIR HORN DISASSEMBLY in OVERHAUL section.**

VACUUM BREAK

1) Place fast idle cam follower on highest step of fast idle cam. Using an outside vacuum source, apply enough vacuum to seat diaphragm. Push down on choke valve. Diaphragm plunger should be seated and bucking spring compressed (if used). *See Fig. 6.*

Fig. 6: Adjusting Vacuum Break

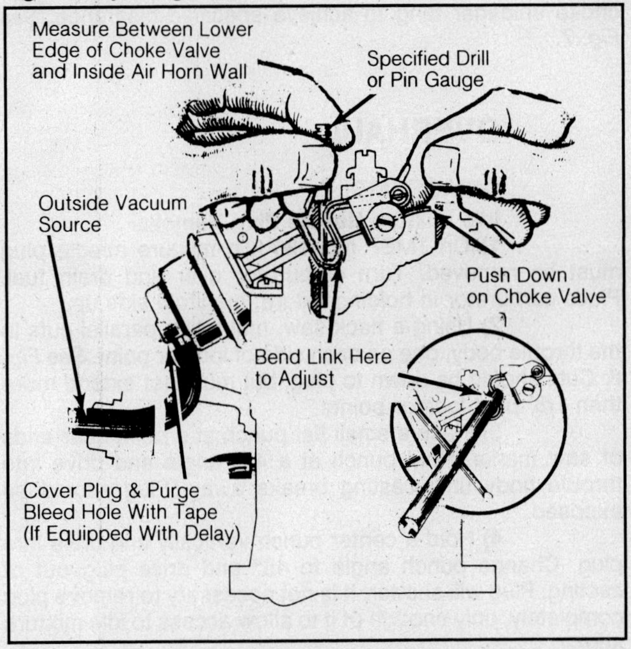

Place fast idle cam follower on highest step of cam.

2) Measure clearance, between lower edge of choke valve and inside air horn wall, using specified drill or pin gauge. On models equipped with delay feature, cover plug and purge bleed hole in vacuum break end cover with masking tape.

Fig. 7: Adjusting Choke Unloader

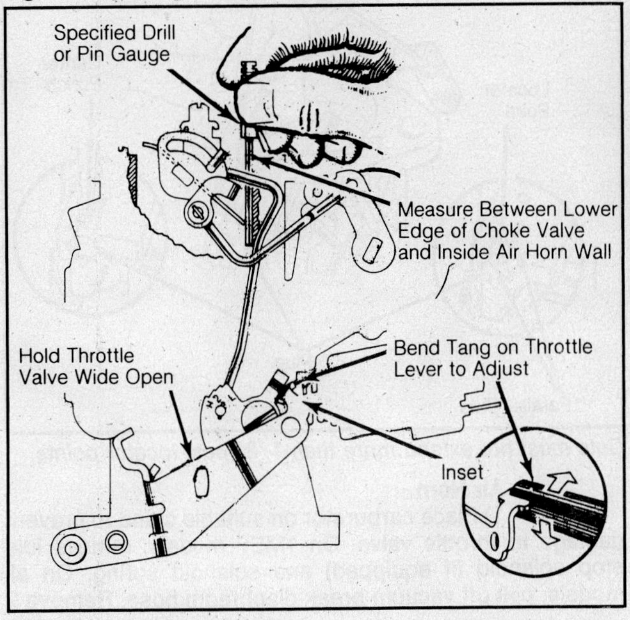

Hold throttle valve wide open.

ROCHESTER 1ME & 1MEF SINGLE BARREL (Cont.)

3) To adjust, bend "U" shaped portion of vacuum diaphragm connector link. Remove masking tape. Check linkage for binding and freedom of movement.

CHOKE UNLOADER

1) Install choke coil in housing and index properly. If choke is warm, cool down to point where choke valve will fully close.

2) Hold throttle valve wide open. Measure clearance, between lower edge of choke valve and inside air horn wall, using specified drill or pin gauge. To adjust, bend choke unloader tang to achieve specified clearance. *See Fig. 7.*

OVERHAUL

DISASSEMBLY

Idle Mixture Needle Plug Removal

1) On 1MEF models, idle mixture needle plug must be removed. Turn carburetor over and drain fuel. Place carburetor in holding fixture, manifold side up.

2) Using a hack saw, make two parallel cuts in the throttle body, one on each side of locator point. *See Fig. 8.* Cuts should be down to plug, but must not extend more than 1/8" past locator points.

3) Place a small flat punch at a point near ends of saw marks. Hold punch at a 45° angle and drive into throttle body until casting breaks away. Plug should be exposed.

4) Hold a center punch vertically and drive into plug. Change punch angle to 45° and drive plug out of casting. Plug will shatter. It is not necessary to remove plug completely, only enough of it to allow access to idle mixture screw.

Fig. 8: Removing Idle Mixture Needle Plug

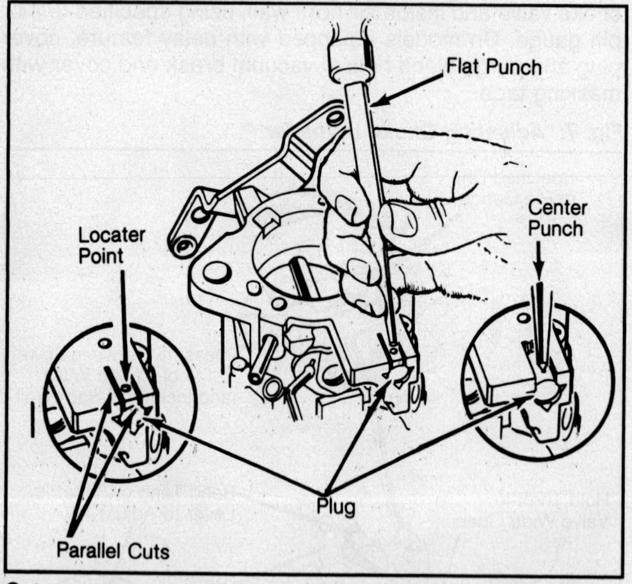

Cuts must not extend more than 1/8" past locator points.

Air Horn

1) Place carburetor on suitable stand to prevent damage to throttle valve. On 1MEF models, remove idle stop solenoid (if equipped) and solenoid spring. On all models, pull off vacuum break diaphragm hose. Remove 2 diaphragm assembly attaching screws. Remove diaphragm assembly and choke connector bracket.

2) Slide diaphragm plunger stem from choke lever link. Do not attempt to remove screw that retains vacuum break lever to choke shaft. This screw is installed with thread-locking compound. It should not be removed unless choke shaft replacement is required.

3) Remove fast idle cam attaching screw and cam. Remove choke rod from choke coil lever on end of choke shaft. Remove 3 choke coil housing attaching screws from float bowl (2 screws have lock washers; screw facing choke housing has tapered head for locating housing).

4) If necessary to remove choke coil cover, drill rivet heads from cover retainer using a .159" (No. 21) drill. Using a drift and small hammer, drive remainder of rivets out of choke housing. Remove 3 retainers and cover from housing.

5) Remove 4 remaining air horn-to-float bowl screws (3 long and 1 short) and lock washers. Carefully remove air horn by lifting and twisting back toward choke housing. Disengage choke coil lever link from choke coil lever at choke housing.

6) Choke valve retaining screws are staked into place. Choke valve should not be removed. On 1MEF models, DO NOT turn or remove metering rod adjusting screw as improper adjustment could cause engine damage and/or increased emissions.

Float Bowl

1) Remove air horn gasket. Lift up on float hinge pin to remove float assembly from bowl. Remove hinge pin from float arm. Withdraw float needle from seat.

2) Remove accelerator pump lever retaining screw. Hold pump rod and power piston assembly down. Disconnect link from power piston rod. Disconnect pump link from pump rod.

3) Remove accelerator pump rod, pump assembly and return spring. On 1MEF and California 1ME models, remove pump rod seal.

4) Remove power piston assembly, power piston rod, metering rod and spring assembly, and power piston spring. Separate metering rod and spring assembly from power piston metering rod hanger.

5) Use needle nose pliers to remove "T" guide and pump discharge spring. Turn bowl over and remove pump discharge ball and idle tube. Remove main metering jets from bottom of fuel bowl.

6) Remove float needle seat and gasket with Seat Remover (J-22769). Remove fuel inlet nut, filter and spring. No further disassembly is required.

Throttle Body

1) Invert float bowl on bench. Remove throttle body-to-bowl attaching screws (2). Remove insulator and gasket. Further disassembly of throttle body is not required, unless idle mixture needle is damaged or idle channels need cleaning.

2) If idle mixture needle must be removed, cut tang from plastic limiter cap (1ME models). Do not replace cap. Turn mixture screw in until needle is lightly seated, counting number of turns. Record for reassembly reference. Remove needle.

NOTE: **Due to close tolerance fit of throttle valve in bore of throttle body, throttle valve or shaft must NOT be removed.**

1985 Rochester Carburetors

ROCHESTER 1ME & 1MEF SINGLE BARREL (Cont.)

Fig. 9: Exploded View of Rochester 1M-Series Single Barrel Carburetor

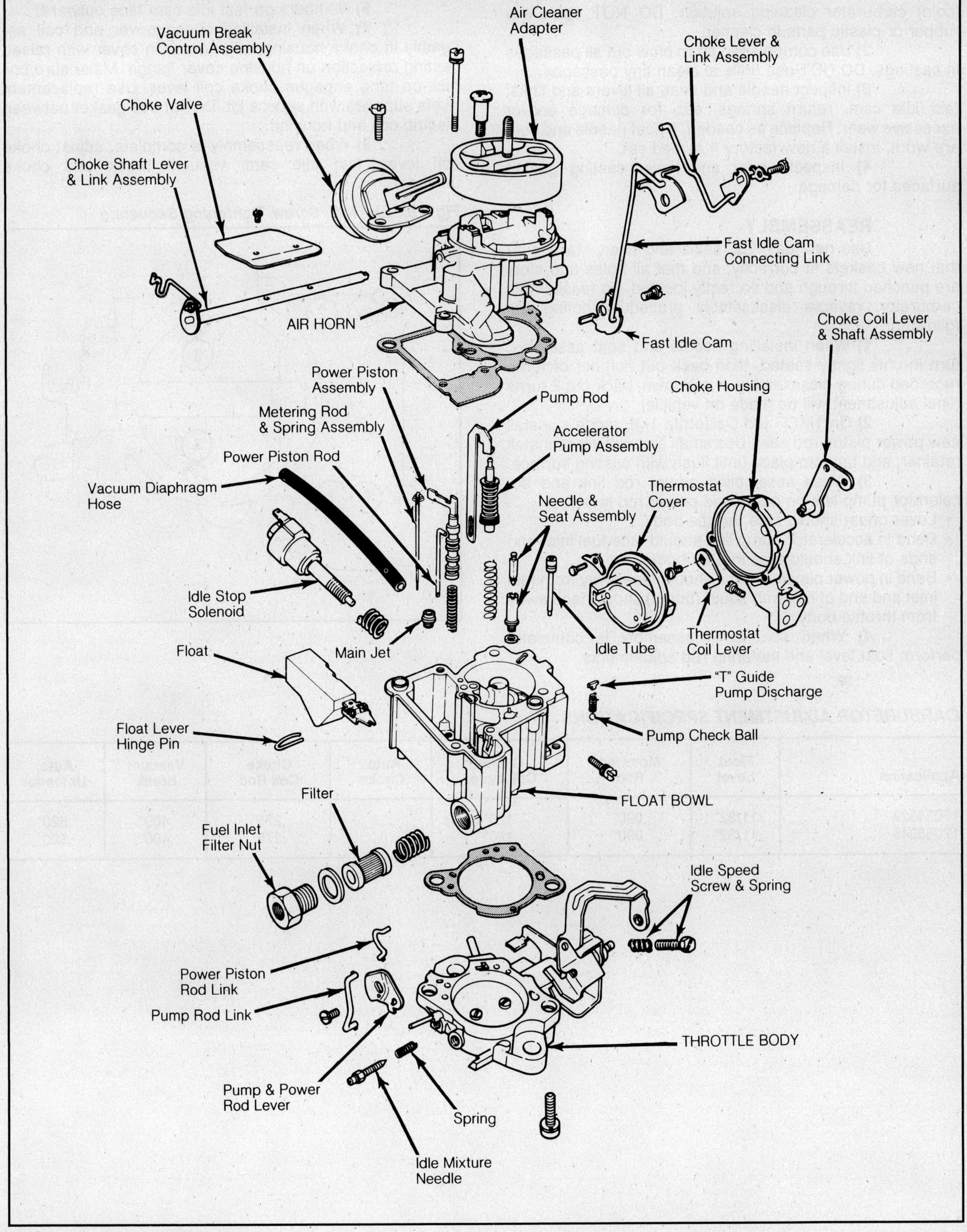

Model 1ME shown, 1MEF similar.

ROCHESTER 1ME & 1MEF SINGLE BARREL (Cont.)

CLEANING & INSPECTION

1) Clean all metal carburetor parts in regular (cold) carburetor cleaning solution. DO NOT soak any rubber or plastic parts in cleaner.

2) Use compressed air to blow out all passages in castings. DO NOT use drills to clean any passages.

3) Inspect needle and seat, all levers and links, fast idle cam, return springs, etc. for damage and/or excessive wear. Replace as needed. If float needle and seat are worn, install a new factory matched set.

4) Inspect upper and lower casting gasket surfaces for damage.

REASSEMBLY

Use new gaskets, seals and filter. Make sure that new gaskets fit correctly, and that all holes and slots are punched through and correctly located. To reassemble carburetor, reverse disassembly procedure noting the following:

1) When installing needle and seat assembly, turn in until lightly seated, then back out number of turns recorded during disassembly. If unknown, back out 2 turns (final adjustment will be made on vehicle).

2) On 1MEF and California 1ME models, install new power piston rod seal. Use small screwdriver to install retainer, and tap into place until flush with casting surface.

3) When assembling power rod link and accelerator pump link on pump and power rod lever:
- Lever offset should face throttle body.
- Bend in accelerator pump link should face fuel inlet and ends of link should face throttle body.
- Bend in power piston rod link should face away from fuel inlet and end of link with squirt (bump) should face away from throttle body.

4) When float bowl assembly is complete, perform float level and metering rod adjustments.

5) When attaching air horn to float bowl, tighten screws in order indicated in *Fig. 10.*

6) Numbers on fast idle cam face outward.

7) When installing choke cover and coil assembly in choke housing, align notch in cover with raised casting projection on housing cover flange. Make sure coil pick-up tang engages choke coil lever. Use replacement rivets supplied with service kit. Do not use gasket between electric coil and housing.

8) When reassembly is complete, adjust choke coil lever, fast idle cam, vacuum break and choke unloader.

Fig. 10: Air Horn Screw Tightening Sequence

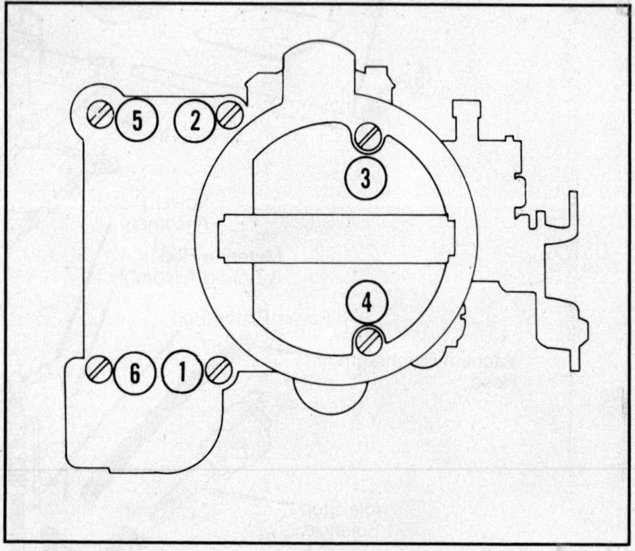

CARBURETOR ADJUSTMENT SPECIFICATIONS

Application	Float Level	Metering Rod	Choke Coil Lever	Auto. Choke	Choke Coil Rod	Vacuum Break	Auto. Unloader
17084329	11/32"	.090"	.120"	.....	.275"	.400"	.520"
17085045	11/32"	.090"	.120"	.....	.275"	.400"	.520"

ROCHESTER 2SE & E2SE 2-BARREL

NOTE: SERIES IDENTIFICATION: The vehicle numbers used in this article have been abbreviated for common reference to both Chevrolet and GMC models. References to the Chrevrolet S10 also apply to the GMC S15.

CARBURETOR APPLICATION

CHEVROLET & GMC (ROCHESTER) CARBURETOR NO.

Application	Man. Trans.	Auto. Trans.
2.8L V6		
Federal		
Without A/C	17085351	17085348
	17085363	17085360
		17085374
With A/C		17084350
		17085362
		17085372
Calif.		
Without A/C	17085357	17085356
	17085396	17085368
With A/C	17085359	17085358
	17085371	17085368
High Alt.		
Without A/C	17085355	17085352
	17085367	17084364
With A/C		17085354
		17084366

JEEP (ROCHESTER) CARBURETOR NO.

Application	Man. Trans.	Auto. Trans.
2.8L V6		
Federal (2SE)	17085381	17085380
Altitude(2SE)	17085383	17085382
Calif. (E2SE)	17085384	17085384

CARBURETOR IDENTIFICATION

The Rochester 2SE and E2SE carburetor numbers are stamped vertically on the float bowl, next to the vacuum tube. If float bowl is replaced, follow manufacturer's instructions contained in service package to transfer part number to new float bowl. *See Fig. 1.*

Fig. 1: Carburetor Part Number Location

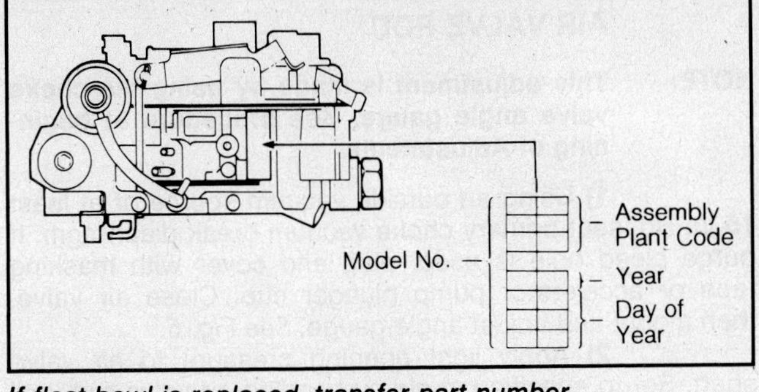

If float bowl is replaced, transfer part number to new float bowl.

DESCRIPTION

The Rochester 2SE and E2SE are 2-stage, 2-barrel downdraft carburetors. The primary stage consists of a triple venturi with a 35 mm bore.

The secondary stage has a 46 mm bore and is equipped with an air valve with a single tapered metering rod. Both are equipped with integral electronically-activated chokes, a choke vacuum break diaphragm, and an idle speed solenoid.

The E2SE model is used with the Jeep Computerized Emission Control (CEC) system and the Chevrolet/GMC Computer Command Control (CCC) system.

The E2SE model is equipped with an electrically-actuated mixture control solenoid mounted in the air horn. Fuel metering is controlled by the mixture control solenoid plunger, which opens and closes in response to signals from the on-board computer.

This opening and closing action causes a variable restriction of fuel to the main metering circuit, changing air/fuel ratio. Also, air metered to the idle system is controlled by the movement of the mixture control solenoid plunger.

The solenoid is activated by an electronic signal from the Electronic Control Module (ECM). The ECM responds to a signal from the oxygen sensor in the exhaust. When energized, the solenoid moves the plunger down to a lean position. When de-energized, the solenoid moves the plunger up to a rich position.

Air metered (by the solenoid plunger) to the idle system is controlled by an idle air bleed valve located in the air horn. This valve follows movement of the mixture control solenoid.

On E2SE models, a Throttle Position Sensor (TPS) is used to signal the ECM of throttle position changes as they occur. When throttle position is changed, a tang on the pump lever moves the TPS plunger. This signals the ECM to hold the last known air/fuel ratio to aid in throttle response.

ADJUSTMENT

NOTE: For all on-vehicle adjustments, see TUNE-UP SERVICE PROCEDURES.

ANGLE GAUGE ADJUSTMENT TOOL

Manufacturer recommends that some carburetor adjustments be performed using a choke valve angle gauge (Kent-Moore tool no. J-26701). While preparations and actual adjustments may vary with each individual adjustment, the procedure for using the angle gauge to check the choke valve angle remains the same. Use the following procedure to perform adjustments requiring the use of the choke angle gauge.

1) Rotate degree scale on angle gauge so that 0° mark is opposite pointer.

2) With choke valve closed, place angle gauge magnet squarely on choke valve. Rotate leveling bubble on angle gauge until it is centered. Rotate degree scale until specified degree mark is opposite pointer

3) Perform individual adjustment preparations as outlined in the following carburetor adjustments requiring angle gauge. If bubble is centered, adjustment is correct. If not, adjust carburetor as outlined.

ROCHESTER 2SE & E2SE 2-BARREL (Cont.)

FLOAT LEVEL

1) Remove air horn, gasket from float bowl and upper float bowl insert. Attach Adapter (J-34817-1 or BT-8227A-1) to float bowl. *See Fig. 2.*

2) Place Float Positioner (J-34817-3 or BT-8227A) in base, with contact pin resting on outer edge of float lever. Measure distance from top of casting to top of float, at point farthest from float hinge. Use "T" scale.

3) If more than 2/32" (1.59 mm) from specification, use Bender (J-34817-20 ro BT-8045A) to bent lever up or down. Remove bending tool and measure float. Repeat if necessary.

Fig. 2: Float Level Adjustment

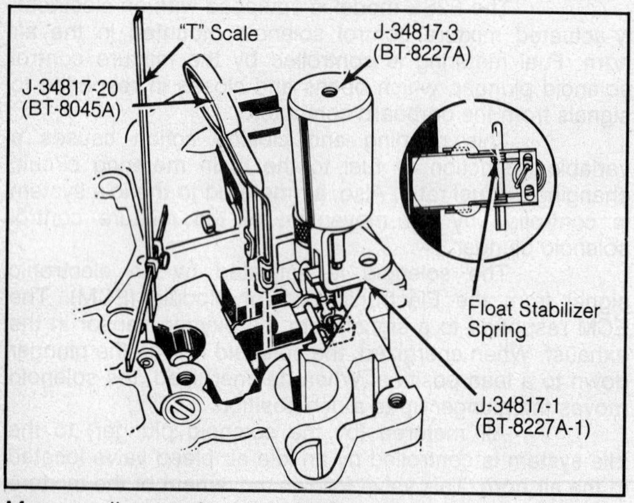

Measure distance from float bowl casting to float.

CHOKE COIL LEVER

NOTE: Choke coil cover is retained on housing with rivets to prevent tampering with adjustment. If necessary to remove cover, refer to Overhaul procedures in this article. If rivets and cover are removed, a choke cover retainer kit is required for reassembly.

Fig. 3: Choke Coil Lever Adjustment

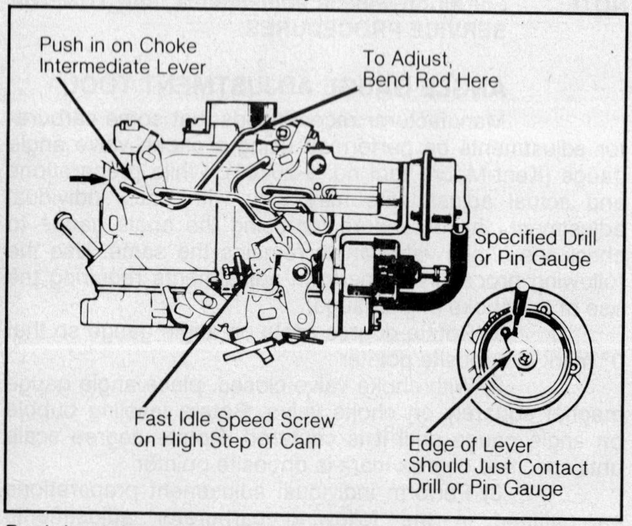

Push in on intermediate choke lever until choke valve is fully closed.

1) Remove choke thermostatic cover from choke housing. Place fast idle speed screw on high step of fast idle cam. Push on intermediate choke lever until choke valve is fully closed.

2) Insert specified drill or pin gauge in hole provided in choke housing. Edge of choke lever (inside housing) should just touch drill or pin gauge. *See Fig. 3.*

3) To adjust, bend intermediate choke rod at point shown in *Fig. 3.* Reinstall choke cover, and adjust.

CHOKE ROD (FAST IDLE CAM)

NOTE: Before adjusting choke rod, choke coil lever adjustment must be correct and fast idle adjustment must be made. Use angle gauge adjustment tool to perform adjustments. See Angle Gauge Adjustment Tool at beginning of Adjustments.

1) Place fast idle speed screw on 2nd step of fast idle cam, against shoulder of highest step.

2) Close choke valve by lightly pushing on intermediate choke lever. Hold in place with rubber band. Push vacuum break lever toward open choke position, until lever is against rear tang on choke lever. *See Fig. 4.*

Fig. 4: Choke Rod (Fast Idle Cam) Adjustment

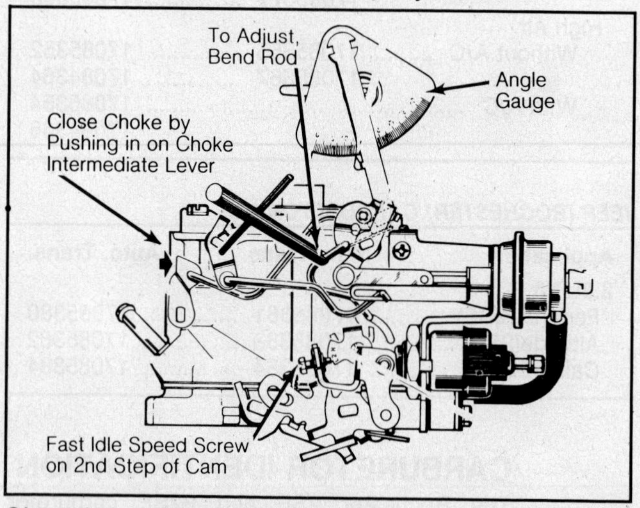

Close choke valve by lightly pushing on intermediate choke lever.

3) Bubble on choke angle gauge should be centered, with specified degree mark opposite pointer.

4) To adjust, bend fast idle cam rod at point shown in *Fig. 4* until bubble is centered in angle gauge.

AIR VALVE ROD

NOTE: This adjustment is made by using the choke valve angle gauge. See procedure at beginning of Adjustments.

1) Using an outside vacuum source of at least 15 in. Hg, seat primary choke vacuum break diaphragm. If purge bleed hole is used, plug end cover with masking tape or accelerator pump plunger cup. Close air valve, then mount and adjust angle gauge. *See Fig. 5.*

2) Apply light opening pressure to air valve shaft. Set to specified angle by bending air valve rod until angle gauge bubble is centered. Remove masking tape, if used.

ROCHESTER 2SE & E2SE 2-BARREL (Cont.)

Fig. 5: Air Valve Rod Adjustment

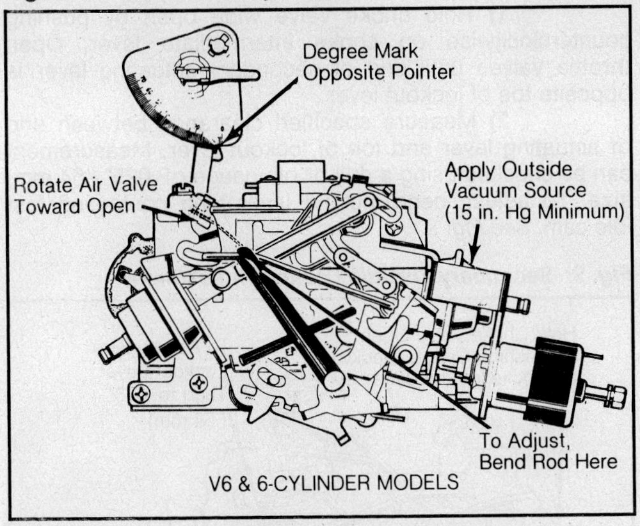

If equipped with purge bleed hole, cover hole with masking tape or accelerator pump plunger cup.

AIR VALVE SPRING

1) Using an Allen wrench, loosen lock screw. Turn tension adjusting screw clockwise until air valve partially opens.

2) Turn tension adjusting screw counterclockwise, until air valve just closes. Turn screw counterclockwise, specified additional turns. Tighten lock screw.

3) Lubricate contact area of air valve shaft pin and closing spring with lithium base grease.

PRIMARY VACUUM BREAK

NOTE: This adjustment is performed using the choke valve angle gauge. See procedure at beginning of Adjustments.

1) Attach a rubber band to intermediate choke lever. Open throttle to allow choke valve to close. Set up angle gauge and set to specification. Using an outside vacuum source of at least 18 in. Hg, seat primary choke vacuum break diaphragm. On models with air bleed, plug air bleed hole to maintain vacuum.

2) Air valve rod must not restrict plunger from retracting fully. If necessary, bend air valve rod to permit full plunger travel. If equipped with bucking spring, plunger stem must be at full extent of travel to compress spring. Bubble on choke valve angle gauge should be centered with specified degree mark opposite pointer. *See Fig. 6.*

3) To adjust, bend rod at location shown in *Fig. 6* until bubble of angle gauge is centered or use a 1/8" Allen wrench to turn diaphragm screw in or out until bubble of angle gauge is centered. Perform either adjustment with vacuum still applied. Apply a bead of sealer over screw to seal adjustment.

SECONDARY VACUUM BREAK

NOTE: This adjustment is made using the choke valve angle gauge. See procedure at beginning of Adjustments.

1) Attach a rubber band to intermediate choke lever. Open throttle to allow choke valve to close. Set up angle gauge and set to specification. Using an outside vacuum source of at least 18 in. Hg, seat primary choke vacuum break diaphragm. On models with air bleed, plug air bleed hole to maintain vacuum.

Fig. 6: Primary Vacuum Break Adjustment

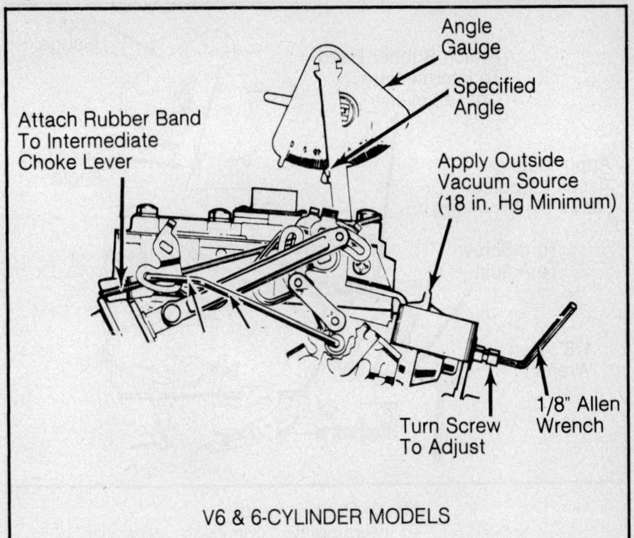

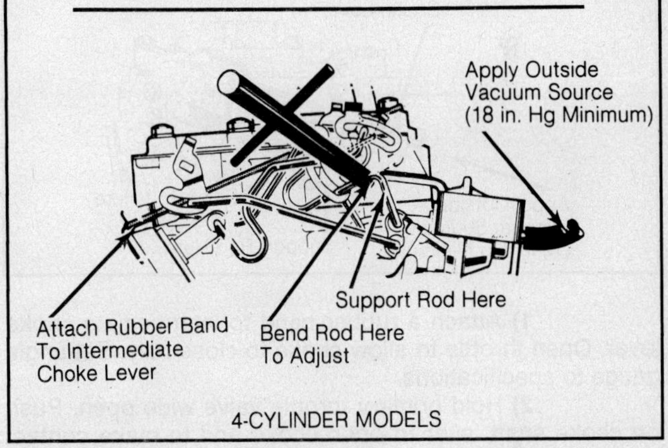

2) If equipped with bucking spring, plunger stem must be at full extent of travel to compress spring. Bubble on choke valve angle gauge should be centered with specified degree mark opposite pointer. *See Fig. 7.*

3) To adjust, bend rod at location shown in *Fig. 7* until bubble of angle gauge is centered or use a 1/8" Allen wrench to turn diaphragm screw in or out until bubble of angle gauge is centered. Perform either adjustment with vacuum still applied. Apply a bead of sealer over screw to seal adjustment.

AUTOMATIC CHOKE

NOTE: Choke coil cover is retained on housing with rivets to prevent tampering with factory adjustment. If necessary to remove cover, refer to Disassembly and reassembly procedures in this Section.

CHOKE UNLOADER

NOTE: This adjustment is performed using the choke valve angle gauge. See procedure at beginning of Adjustments.

ROCHESTER 2SE & E2SE 2-BARREL (Cont.)

Fig. 7: Secondary Vacuum Break Adjustment

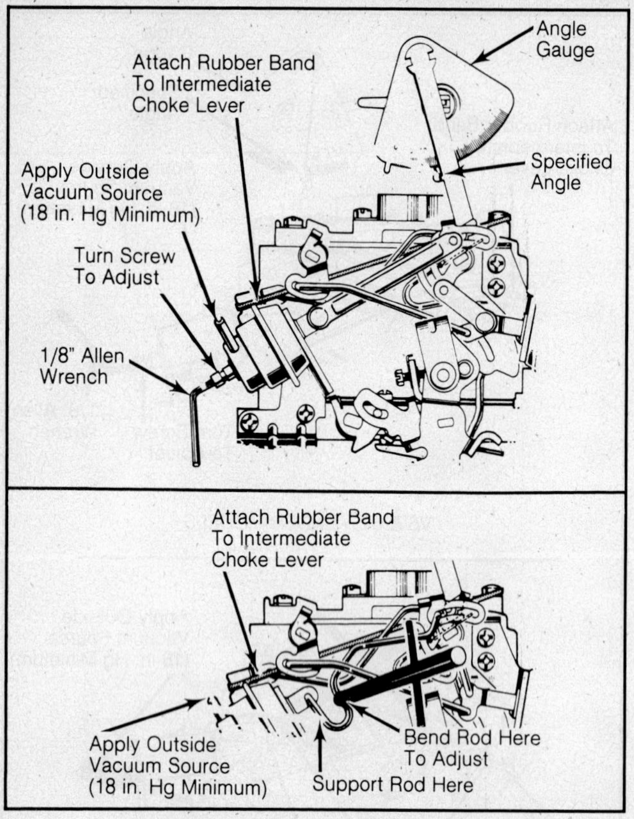

1) Attach a rubber band to intermediate choke lever. Open throttle to allow choke to close fully. Set angle gauge to specifications.

2) Hold primary throttle valve wide open. Push on choke shaft lever to open choke and to make contact with Black closing tang. To adjust, bend tang on throttle lever until bubble in angle gauge is centered. *See Fig. 8.*

Fig. 8: Choke Unloader Adjustment

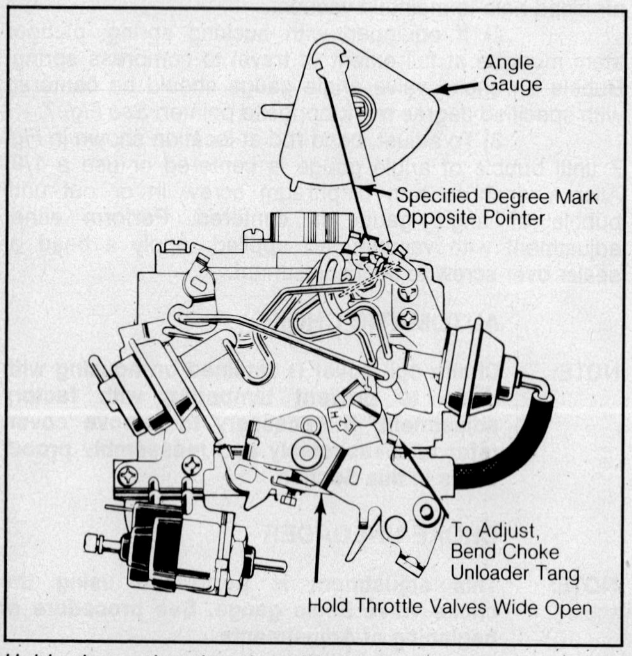

Hold primary throttle valve wide open.

SECONDARY LOCKOUT

1) Hold choke valve wide open by pushing counterclockwise on choke intermediate lever. Open throttle valves until end of secondary actuating lever is opposite toe of lockout lever.

2) Measure specified clearance between end of actuating lever and toe of lockout lever. Measurement can be checked using a drill or pin gauge of .025" (.64 mm) size. To adjust, bend lockout lever tang contacting fast idle cam. *See Fig. 9.*

Fig. 9: Secondary Throttle Lockout Adjustment

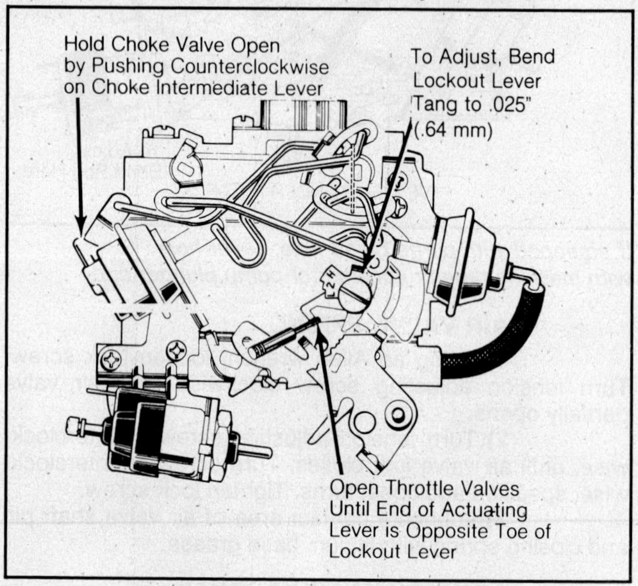

Measure clearance between end of actuating lever and toe of lockout lever.

OVERHAUL

DISASSEMBLY

NOTE: Before disassembling carburetor, mount unit in a suitable holding fixture to prevent damage to throttle valves or linkage.

Air Horn

1) Remove hose from vacuum break assembly or assemblies. Remove vacuum break and idle speed solenoid bracket attaching screws from air horn. Rotate vacuum break and bracket assembly to disengage vacuum break link (T-pin) from slot in vacuum break lever, and air valve rod from slot in air valve lever.

2) Remove secondary vacuum break bracket assembly attaching screws from throttle body (if equipped). Rotate bracket to remove vacuum break link from vacuum break lever slot. Remove clip from hole in accelerator pump rod.

NOTE: Do not remove pump lever retaining screw. Pump lever and washer must not be removed from air horn assembly.

3) If necessary to remove air valve rod from vacuum break, remove and discard retaining clip from end of air valve. New retaining clip must be used on reassembly. Plastic bushing used on rod may be reused.

ROCHESTER 2SE & E2SE 2-BARREL (Cont.)

4) Remove and discard retaining clip from intermediate choke rod at choke lever. Use a new retaining clip at reassembly. Remove plastic choke rod and bushing from choke lever. Bushing may be reused.

5) If equipped, remove hot idle compensator valve screws. Remove valve and seal from air horn, discard seal. Valve removal is necessary to gain access to short air horn-to-bowl attaching screw.

6) On E2SE models, remove 3 mixture control solenoid screws, and remove mixture control solenoid using a light twisting motion. Remove and discard solenoid gasket, plunger seal and plunger seal retainer. Retain spacer for use during reassembly.

7) Remove air horn-to-float bowl screws and lock washers. Remove vent and screen assembly. Rotate fast idle cam to full "UP" (12 o'clock) position. Remove air horn assembly by tilting to disengage fast idle cam rod from slot in fast idle cam and pump rod from hole in pump lever.

8) Disconnect fast idle cam rod from choke lever by aligning tang on rod with slot in lever. Remove from air horn assembly.

9) On E2SE models, remove throttle position sensor plunger by pushing through seal in air horn. Remove seal retainer and seal. Remove accelerator pump plunger seal from air horn.

NOTE: **To prevent damage to sealing surface, use fingers only (no tools) when removing plunger. To prevent damage to air horn, use care in removing plunger seal retainer and plunger stem seal retainer. Discard seals and retainers.**

10) It is not necessary to remove choke valve and shaft unless they are bent or damaged. Choke valve screws are staked in place. Staking must be removed before screws are removed.

NOTE: **Do not remove plugs covering idle air bleed screw during routine service. This adjustment is factory-set, and no attempt should be made to change the adjustment, unless air horn or float bowl is replaced.**
Do not turn secondary metering rod adjusting screw. Rod could come out of jet and cause damage.

Float Bowl

1) Remove air horn gasket. Remove pump plunger and pump spring from pump well. Remove plastic filler block from float valve. Remove float assembly and float valve by pulling up on retaining pin.

2) Remove float needle seat, gasket and extended metering jet from float bowl. Use a jet tool (J 22769) or screwdriver that fully fits slot in top of jet. Do not remove or change adjustment of screw located deep inside the metering jet (if equipped).

3) On E2SE models, push up from bottom on electrical connector and remove throttle position sensor and connector from float bowl. Remove spring from bottom of throttle position sensor well in bowl.

4) On 2SE models, press down on power piston stem and allow it to snap up. Repeat this until plastic retainer is dislodged. Remove power piston and metering rod assembly. Do not remove power piston by using pliers on metering rod holder.

5) Remove spring from power piston bore. If necessary to remove metering rod from hanger, compress spring on metering rod and align groove on rod with slot in holder. Care must be taken not to damage tip of metering rod.

6) Remove main metering jet using a screwdriver that fits tight in groove. On all models, use a small slide hammer to remove plastic retainer holding pump discharge spring and check ball in place in float bowl. Discard retainer. Turn float bowl upside-down and catch pump discharge spring and check ball.

NOTE: **Do not attempt to remove retainer by prying out with a screwdriver or punch. Any damage to sealing beads on bowl casting surface requires replacement of float bowl assembly.**

7) If necessary to remove tamper-resistant choke cover and coil assembly, align a .159" (No. 21) drill on choke cover retaining rivets. Drill only enough to remove rivet heads. Remove rivets, choke cover and coil assembly.

8) Remove screw from end of intermediate choke shaft in choke housing. Remove choke coil lever from shaft. Slide intermediate choke shaft out of float bowl. Remove choke housing screws and remove choke housing.

9) Remove fuel inlet nut with gasket. Remove check valve/filter and spring. Discard gasket and filter. Remove 4 screws securing throttle body to float bowl. Remove throttle body. Remove throttle body insulator gasket.

Throttle Body

1) Hold throttle valves wide open. Disengage pump rod from throttle lever by rotating rod until tang on rod aligns with slot in lever.

2) Do not remove plug covering idle mixture screw unless it is necessary to replace mixture screw or normal soaking and air pressure fails to clean idle mixture passages. Remove curb idle and fast idle speed screws and springs if necessary.

NOTE: **Further disassembly of throttle body is not required. Throttle valve screws are permanently staked. Do not remove idle mixture screw plug unless necessary to replace mixture screw or cleaning and air pressure fails to clean idle mixture passage. If necessary to remove, proceed as follows:**

3) Invert throttle body and position on a holding fixture with manifold side up. Using a small hacksaw, make 2 small cuts, one on either side of mixture screw plug location. Position a small flat punch on throttle body between cuts.

4) Drive punch down and break out portion of throttle body between the 2 cuts. Hold punch at a 45° angle and drive out hardened steel plug. Plug should shatter when struck. Remove loose pieces to allow the use of adjusting tool (J 29030 or equivalent) to remove adjusting screw and spring.

5) Turn mixture screw in carefully, counting turns needed to seat screw. Record number of turns for reassembly reference. Remove mixture screw.

ROCHESTER 2SE & E2SE 2-BARREL (Cont.)

CLEANING & INSPECTION

- Use a regular carburetor cleaning solution. Soak components long enough to thoroughly clean all surfaces and passages of foreign matter.
- Do not soak any components containing rubber, leather or plastic. Definitely do not soak idle speed solenoid or control mixture control solenoid, throttle position sensor, electric choke, diaphragms, pump plunger and plastic filler block. Plastic bushings in end of vacuum break link and air valve rod will withstand normal cleaning.
- Remove any residue after cleaning by rinsing components in a suitable solvent.
- Blow out all passages with dry compressed air.

REASSEMBLY

Use new gaskets and seals. Make sure new gaskets fit correctly and all holes are punched through and properly located. To reassemble carburetor, reverse disassembly procedure, noting the following:

1) Install fuel inlet needle pull clip over edge of flat on float arm facing float. Do not hook clip in holes in float arm.

2) After throttle body is installed on float bowl, make sure secondary lockout tang is in correct position to engage secondary lockout lever.

3) Install new accelerator pump discharge check ball, spring and plastic retainer. Insert end of retainer in spring and place in position in float bowl. Lightly tap retainer into position until it is flush in float bowl.

4) Make sure holes in fuel filter face toward fuel inlet fitting when filter is installed. This will ensure that check valve end of filter is installed properly.

5) Some linkage retaining clips are dished. Make sure portion of clip that bends outward is toward end of rod. Make sure clip makes full contact with rod.

6) Place fast idle screw on high step of fast idle cam. Install choke coil cover, aligning notch in cover with raised boss on housing cover flange. If choke cover and coil assembly was removed from housing, a service rivet kit must be used to restore tamper-resistant feature.

7) On E2SE models, be sure coil pick-up lever is located inside choke coil tang. On electric chokes, the ground contact is provided by a metal plate at rear of choke cover assembly. Do not install a choke cover gasket between electric choke assembly and choke housing.

8) Install air horn screws, noting location and type of screw for correct installation. Tighten all screws evenly, securely and in sequence. *See Fig. 10.*

9) On E2SE models, install mixture control solenoid seal on solenoid stem. Using a 3/16" socket and hammer, lightly tap retainer in place on stem. Leave a slight clearance between retainer and seal. Apply silicone grease to seal before installation of solenoid.

Fig. 10: Air Horn Screw Location and Tightening Sequence

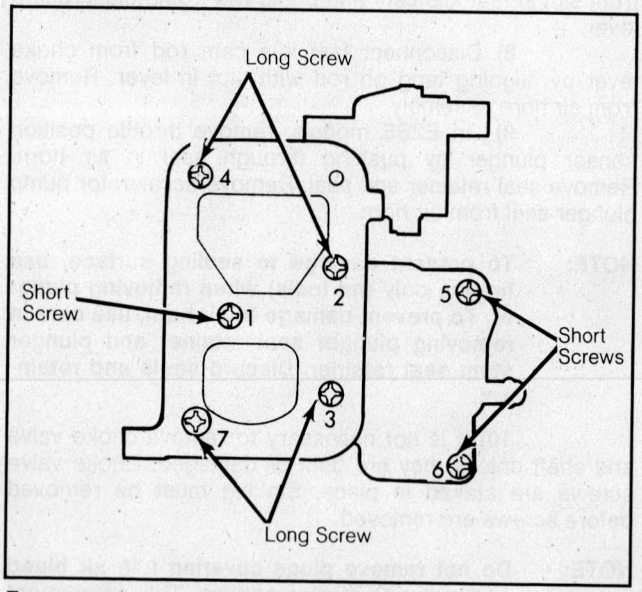

Ensure screws are properly located.

ROCHESTER 2SE & E2SE 2-BARREL (Cont.)

Fig. 11: Exploded View of Rochester Model 2SE Carburetor

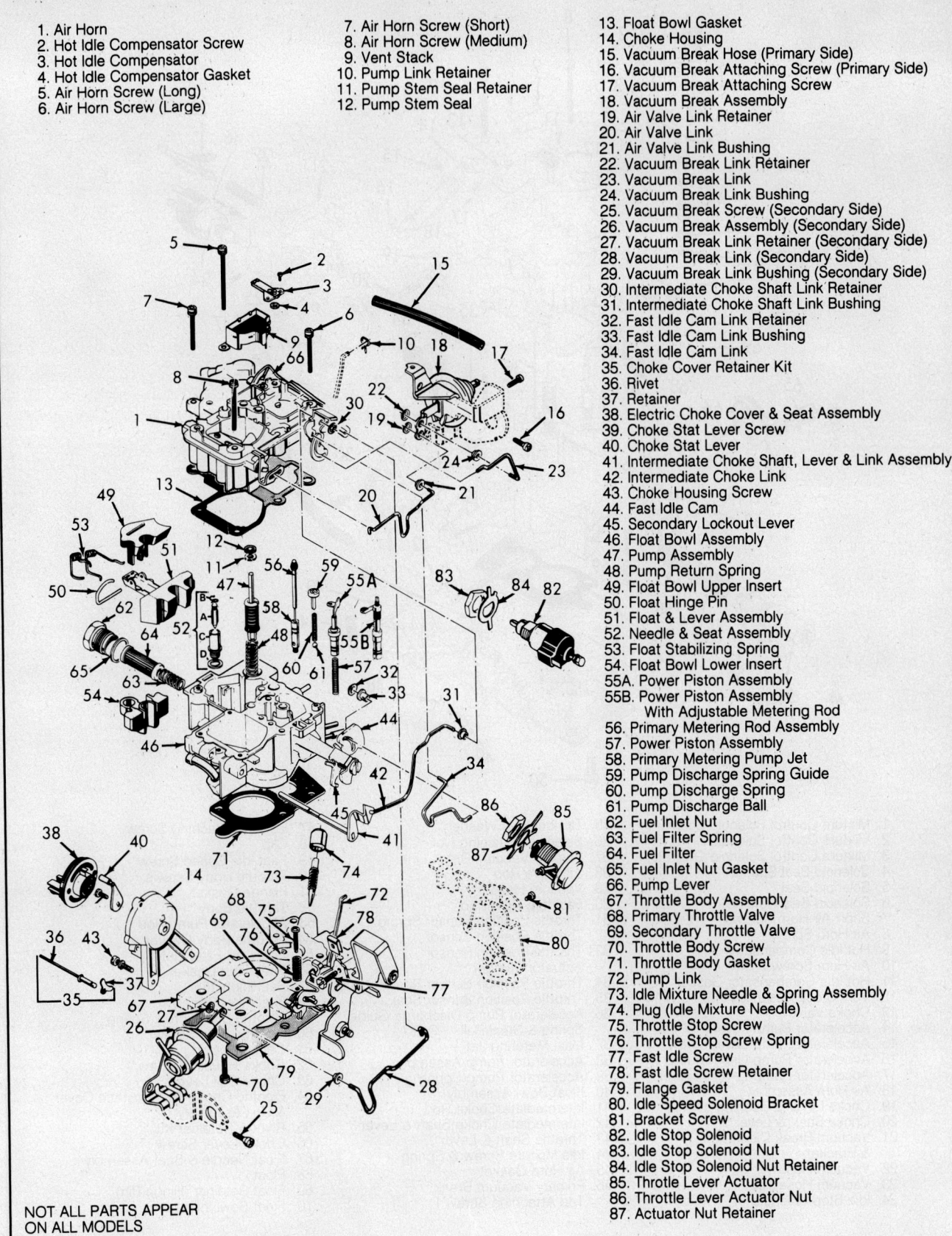

1. Air Horn
2. Hot Idle Compensator Screw
3. Hot Idle Compensator
4. Hot Idle Compensator Gasket
5. Air Horn Screw (Long)
6. Air Horn Screw (Large)
7. Air Horn Screw (Short)
8. Air Horn Screw (Medium)
9. Vent Stack
10. Pump Link Retainer
11. Pump Stem Seal Retainer
12. Pump Stem Seal
13. Float Bowl Gasket
14. Choke Housing
15. Vacuum Break Hose (Primary Side)
16. Vacuum Break Attaching Screw (Primary Side)
17. Vacuum Break Attaching Screw
18. Vacuum Break Assembly
19. Air Valve Link Retainer
20. Air Valve Link
21. Air Valve Link Bushing
22. Vacuum Break Link Retainer
23. Vacuum Break Link
24. Vacuum Break Link Bushing
25. Vacuum Break Screw (Secondary Side)
26. Vacuum Break Assembly (Secondary Side)
27. Vacuum Break Link Retainer (Secondary Side)
28. Vacuum Break Link (Secondary Side)
29. Vacuum Break Link Bushing (Secondary Side)
30. Intermediate Choke Shaft Link Retainer
31. Intermediate Choke Shaft Link Bushing
32. Fast Idle Cam Link Retainer
33. Fast Idle Cam Link Bushing
34. Fast Idle Cam Link
35. Choke Cover Retainer Kit
36. Rivet
37. Retainer
38. Electric Choke Cover & Seat Assembly
39. Choke Stat Lever Screw
40. Choke Stat Lever
41. Intermediate Choke Shaft, Lever & Link Assembly
42. Intermediate Choke Link
43. Choke Housing Screw
44. Fast Idle Cam
45. Secondary Lockout Lever
46. Float Bowl Assembly
47. Pump Assembly
48. Pump Return Spring
49. Float Bowl Upper Insert
50. Float Hinge Pin
51. Float & Lever Assembly
52. Needle & Seat Assembly
53. Float Stabilizing Spring
54. Float Bowl Lower Insert
55A. Power Piston Assembly
55B. Power Piston Assembly With Adjustable Metering Rod
56. Primary Metering Rod Assembly
57. Power Piston Assembly
58. Primary Metering Pump Jet
59. Pump Discharge Spring Guide
60. Pump Discharge Spring
61. Pump Discharge Ball
62. Fuel Inlet Nut
63. Fuel Filter Spring
64. Fuel Filter
65. Fuel Inlet Nut Gasket
66. Pump Lever
67. Throttle Body Assembly
68. Primary Throttle Valve
69. Secondary Throttle Valve
70. Throttle Body Screw
71. Throttle Body Gasket
72. Pump Link
73. Idle Mixture Needle & Spring Assembly
74. Plug (Idle Mixture Needle)
75. Throttle Stop Screw
76. Throttle Stop Screw Spring
77. Fast Idle Screw
78. Fast Idle Screw Retainer
79. Flange Gasket
80. Idle Speed Solenoid Bracket
81. Bracket Screw
82. Idle Stop Solenoid
83. Idle Stop Solenoid Nut
84. Idle Stop Solenoid Nut Retainer
85. Throtle Lever Actuator
86. Throttle Lever Actuator Nut
87. Actuator Nut Retainer

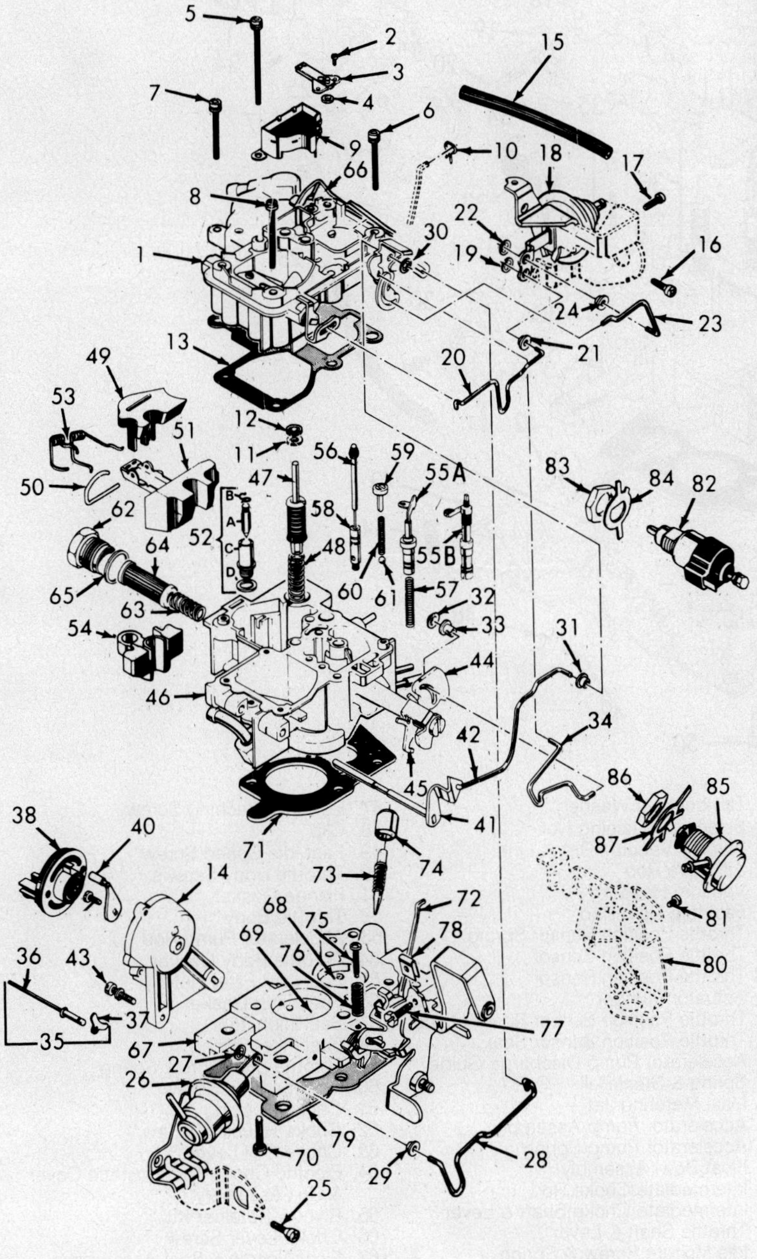

NOT ALL PARTS APPEAR ON ALL MODELS

ROCHESTER 2SE & E2SE 2-BARREL

Fig. 12: Exploded View of Rochester Model E2SE Carburetor

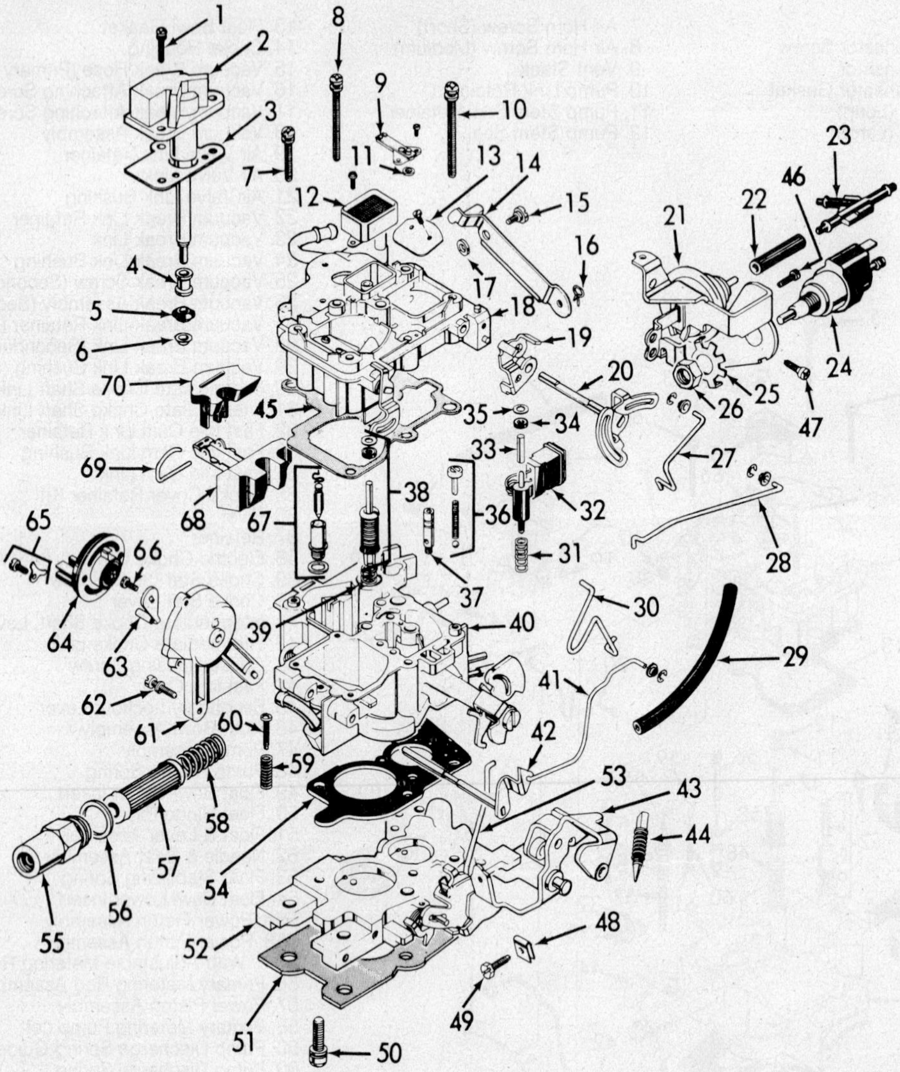

1. Mixture Control Solenoid Screw
2. Mixture Control Solenoid
3. Mixture Control Solenoid Gasket
4. Solenoid Seal Spacer
5. Solenoid Seal
6. Solenoid Seal Retainer
7. Short Air Horn Screws
8. Air Horn Screw
9. Hot Idle Compensator
10. Air Horn Screw
11. Hot Idle Compensator Gasket
12. Vent Stock Assembly
13. Choke Valve
14. Accelerator Pump Lever
15. Accelerator Pump Lever Screw
16. Accelerator Pump Link Retainer
17. Accelerator Pump Lever Washer
18. Air Horn Assembly
19. Choke Lever & Bushing
20. Choke Shaft & Lever
21. Vacuum Break Diaphragm & Bracket
22. Vacuum Hose
23. Vacuum Hose Tee
24. Idle Stop Solenoid
25. Tab Locking Washer
26. Solenoid Retaining Nut
27. Primary Vacuum Break Link
28. Air Valve Rod
29. Vacuum Hose
30. Fast Idle Cam Rod
31. Throttle Position Sensor Spring
32. Throttle Position Sensor
33. Throttle Position Sensor Actuator Plunger
34. Throttle Position Sensor Seal Retainer
35. Throttle Position Sensor Seal
36. Accelerator Pump Discharge Guide, Spring & Steel Ball
37. Main Metering Jet
38. Accelerator Pump Assembly
39. Accelerator Pump Spring
40. Float Bowl Assembly
41. Intermediate Choke Rod
42. Intermediate Choke Shaft & Lever
43. Throttle Shaft & Lever
44. Idle Mixture Screw & Spring
45. Air Horn Gasket
46. Primary Vacuum Break Top Attaching Screw
47. Bottom Attaching Screw
48. Clip
49. Fast Idle Speed Screw
50. Throttle Body Screws
51. Flange Gasket
52. Throttle Body
53. Accelerator Pump Rod
54. Throttle Body Gasket
55. Fuel Inlet Filter Nut
56. Fuel Filter Gasket
57. Fuel Inlet Filter
58. Fuel Filter Spring
59. Throttle Stop Screw Spring
60. Throttle Stop Screw
61. Choke Housing
62. Choke Housing Screw
63. Choke Coil Lever
64. Electric Choke Thermostatic Cover & Coil Assembly
65. Rivet & Retainer Kit
66. Choke Lever Screw
67. Float Needle & Seat Assembly
68. Float
69. Float Retainer (Hinge Pin)
70. Float Bowl Insert

ROCHESTER 2SE & E2SE 2-BARREL (Cont.)

CARBURETOR ADJUSTMENT SPECIFICATIONS

Application	Float Level	Accel. Pump	Choke Coil Lever	Choke Rod	Air Valve Rod	Vacuum Break		Auto. Choke	Choke Unloader	Air Valve Spring [1]
						Primary	Secondary			
GM (2SE)										
17085348	5/32"	TR	.085"	22°	1°	32°	36°	TR	40°	1
17085350	5/32"	TR	.085"	22°	1°	32°	36°	TR	40°	1
17085351	11/32"	TR	.085"	22°	1°	32°	36°	TR	40°	1
17085352	5/32"	TR	.085"	22°	1°	30°	34°	TR	40°	1
17085354	5/32"	TR	.085"	22°	1°	30°	34°	TR	40°	1
17085355	11/32"	TR	.085"	22°	1°	30°	34°	TR	40°	1
17085360	5/32"	TR	.085"	22°	1°	32°	36°	TR	40°	1
17085362	5/32"	TR	.085"	22°	1°	32°	36°	TR	40°	1
17085363	11/32"	TR	.085"	22°	1°	32°	36°	TR	40°	1
17085364	5/32"	TR	.085"	22°	1°	30°	34°	TR	40°	1
17085366	5/32"	TR	.085"	22°	1°	30°	34°	TR	40°	1
17085367	11/32"	TR	.085"	22°	1°	30°	34°	TR	40°	1
17085372	5/32"	TR	.085"	22°	1°	32°	36°	TR	40°	3/4
17085374	5/32"	TR	.085"	28°	1°	32°	36°	TR	40°	3/4
GM (E2SE)										
17085356	1/8"	TR	.085"	22°	1°	25°	30°	TR	30°	1
17085357	9/32"	TR	.085"	22°	1°	25°	30°	TR	30°	1
17085358	1/8"	TR	.085"	22°	1°	25°	30°	TR	30°	1
17085359	9/32"	TR	.085"	22°	1°	25°	30°	TR	30°	1
17085368	1/8"	TR	.085"	22°	1°	25°	30°	TR	30°	1
17085369	9/32"	TR	.085"	22°	1°	25°	30°	TR	30°	1
17085370	1/8"	TR	.085"	22°	1°	25°	30°	TR	30°	1
17085371	9/32"	TR	.085"	22°	1°	25°	30°	TR	30°	1
JEEP (2SE)										
17085380	5/32"	TR	.085"	22°	1°	26°	32°	TR	40°	1
17085381	5/32"	TR	.085"	22°	1°	26°	32°	TR	40°	1
17085382	5/32"	TR	.085"	22°	1°	26°	32°	TR	40°	1
17085383	5/32"	TR	.085"	22°	1°	25°	32°	TR	40°	1
JEEP (E2SE)										
17085384	1/8"	TR	.085"	22°	1°	25°	30°	TR	40°	1

1 – Number of turns.

ROCHESTER E4ME & E4MED 4-BARREL

CARBURETOR APPLICATION

GENERAL MOTORS (ROCHESTER) CARBURETOR NO.

Application	Man. Trans.	Auto. Trans.
4.3L		
C10, G10/20, Astro/Safari & K10	17085503	17085502
5.0L		
C10, G10/20		
Exc. A/C	17085524	17085524
With A/C	17085526	17085526
5.7L		
C & K10/20, G20/30		
Exc. A/C	17085506	17085506
With A/C	17085508	17085508

CARBURETOR IDENTIFICATION

The Rochester E4ME or E4MED carburetor number is stamped vertically on the float bowl, near secondary throttle. If float bowl is replaced, follow manufacturer's instructions contained in service package to transfer part number to new float bowl. Some models have machined pump wells to reduce the pump well taper.

The E4ME and E4MED Quadrajet carburetors are used on California Light Duty truck with the Computer Command Control (CCC) system. The first letter "E" indicates the carburetor is a part of the CCC system. The third letter, if "E", indicates the carburetor is equipped with an electric choke.

Fig. 1: Carburetor Identification Label

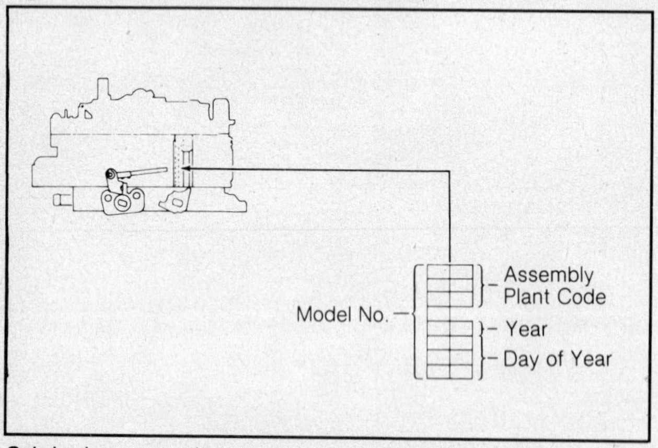

Original part number must be transfered from old float bowl if new float bowl is installed.

DESCRIPTION

The E4ME and E4MED carburetors are of a 2-stage, downdraft design. Each bore has a triple venturi system. The secondary side is composed of 2 large throttle bores, using the air valve principle, in which fuel is metered in direct proportion to the amount of air passing through the secondary throttle bores. A baffle is attached to the secondary side of the air horn, above the main well bleed tubes. This deflects incoming air to improve secondary nozzle operation on heavy acceleration.

The E4ME and E4MED carburetors use an electrically-actuated choke assembly, and 2 vacuum break diaphragm assemblies, the front and rear. Both models are used in conjunction with the Computer Command Control (CCC) System. The carburetors are equipped with an electrically-actuated mixture control solenoid mounted in the float bowl. Fuel metering is controlled by stepped metering rods that operate in removable jets.

The E4MED model carburetor incorporates a float bowl mounted dual capacity fuel pump and a combined mixture control/dual capacity pump solenoid assembly. When the engine is cold, more fuel is necessary to ensure a smotth transition from idle to part throttle. When the engine is warm, less fuel is required. The dual capacity pump is controllled by the coolant temperature sensor. When coolant temperature is approximately 170°F (77°C), a solenoid within the carburetor is energized, opening a by-pass valve. This lowers the capacity of the pump by about one-half.

All models include tamper-resistant factory settings of the mixture control solenoid rich mixture stop screw and lean mixture screw, idle air bleed valve, TPS, ISC, ISS and idle mixture screws. No attempt should be made to adjust these except during major overhaul or replacement of air horn, float bowl or throttle body. Both electric and hot air chokes have riveted covers which must not be removed except for major overhaul.

These carburetors may be equipped with an Idle Speed Control (ISC) on the fuel bowl. Controlled by the ECM, the ISC controls the normal curb idle speed and acts as a dashpot on deceleration and throttle closing. On vehicles without an ISC, but with air conditioning, an Idle Speed Solenoid (ISS) maintains a specific idle speed during A/C operation.

TESTING

ELECTRIC CHOKE

NOTE: This test should be performed when air temperature is 60-80°F (15-27°C).

1) Allow choke to cool to permit full closing of choke blade when throttle is opened slightly. Start engine and time the interval required for choke blade to reach full open position. (Start timing when engine starts). If choke blade does not fully open within 3 1/2 minutes, proceed with test.

2) With engine running, check voltage at choke heater connection. If voltage is about 12-15 volts, replace electric choke unit. If voltage is low or zero, check all wires and connections and repair as required. Power for choke unit is through the oil pressure switch. Ensure switch circuitry is good.

3) If procedure in step **2)** does not correct the problem, replace oil pressure switch.

MIXTURE CONTROL SOLENOID PLUNGER TRAVEL

NOTE: Mixture control solenoid plunger travel should be checked before proceeding with any carburetor adjustments or disassembly.

1) Remove air cleaner and gasket. Insert Float Gauge (J-34935-1) down "D" shaped vent hole. Lightly press down on float gauge and release. Ensure that gauge moves freely and does not bind.

ROCHESTER E4ME & E4MED 4-BARREL (Cont.)

2) With float gauge released, read gauge at eye level and record reading of gauge mark that lines up with top upper edge of air horn casting. Lightly press down on gauge until plunger is bottomed out. Read and record reading of gauge mark that lines up with top upper edge of air horn casting.

3) Subtract float gauge "UP" position from float gauge "DOWN" position and record difference of total plunger travel. If reading is within specification, adjust idle air bleed valve. See appropriate TUNE-UP article.

4) If plunger total travel is not between 2/32" and 6/32", adjust mixture control solenoid plunger travel. See ADJUSTMENTS in this article.

ADJUSTMENTS

NOTE: **For all on-vehicle adjustments not covered in this article, see appropriate TUNE-UP article.**

CHOKE VALVE ANGLE GAUGE

Manufacturer recommends that some carburetor adjustments be performed using a Choke Valve Angle Gauge (J-26701). While preparations and actual adjustment may vary with each individual adjustment, the procedure for using the angle gauge to check the choke valve angle remains the same. Use the following procedure to perform adjustments requiring the use of the choke valve angle gauge.

Fig. 2: Choke Valve Angle Gauge

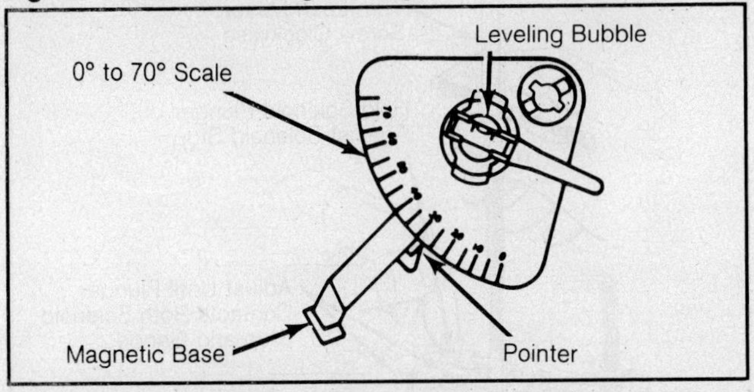

This gauge must be used to perform some adjustments.

1) With choke valve closed, place angle gauge magnet squarely on choke valve.

2) Rotate degree scale on angle gauge so that 0° mark is opposite pointer.

3) Rotate leveling bubble on angle gauge until it is centered.

4) Rotate degree scale until specified degree mark is opposite pointer.

5) Now perform individual adjustment preparation as outlined in the following carburetor adjustments requiring an angle gauge.

6) If bubble is centered, adjustment is correct. If not, adjust carburetor as outlined in appropriate adjustment procedure.

FLOAT LEVEL (WET SETTING)

NOTE: **This is an on-vehicle adjustment.**

1) With engine running at idle and choke wide open, carefully insert Float Gauge (J-34935-1) into vent slot or vent hole (next to air cleaner mounting stud) in air horn. Allow gauge to float freely. *See Fig. 3.*

NOTE: **Pressing down on float gauge could result in float damage or carburetor flooding.**

Fig. 3: Wet Float Level Adjustment

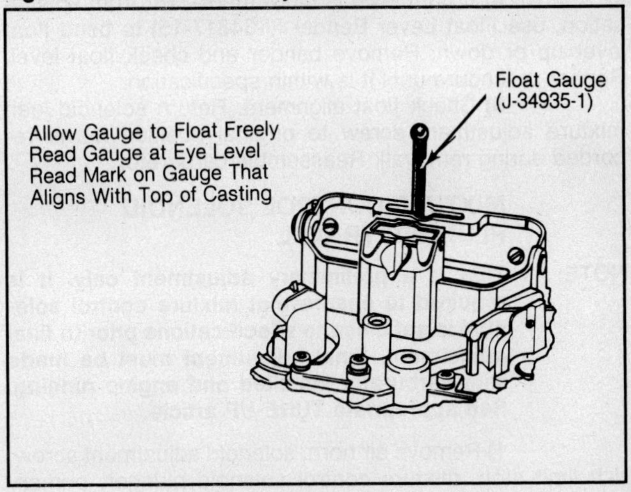

Allow float gauge to float freely.

2) With gauge floating freely, observe mark on gauge which aligns with top of casting (at eye level). Reading should be within 1/16" of specified float level. Incorrect fuel pressure will affect fuel level.

3) If reading is not within 1/16" of specified float level, remove carburetor. Remove air horn and perform Float Level (Dry Setting) adjustment.

FLOAT LEVEL (DRY SETTING)

1) Remove air horn and gasket. Remove solenoid plunger, metering rod, and float bowl insert.

2) If it is necessary to remove lean mixture solenoid adjustment screw, count and record the number of turns it takes to slightly bottom screw using Wrench (J-28696-10).

3) Attach Adjustment Base (J-34817-1) to float bowl. Place Float Weight (J-34817-3) in base with contact pin resting on outer edge of float lever. Using Float Adjust-

Fig. 4: Dry Float Level Adjustment

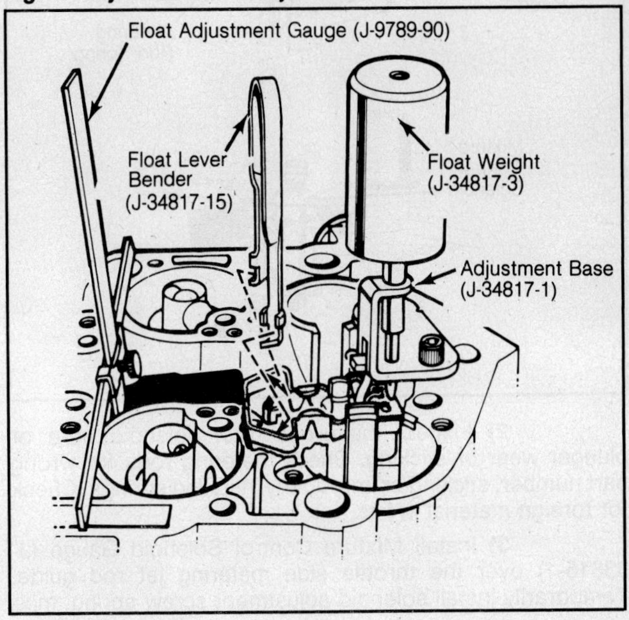

ROCHESTER E4ME & E4MED 4-BARREL (Cont.)

ment Gauge (J-9789-90), measure distance from top of casting to top of float at at point 3/16" from large end of float.

4) If float level is more than 1/16" from specification, use Float Lever Bender (J-34817-15) to bend float lever up or down. Remove bender and check float level. Repeat procedure until it is within specification.

5) Check float alignment. Return solenoid lean mixture adjustment screw to original position (turns recorded during removal). Reassemble carburetor.

MIXTURE CONTROL SOLENOID PLUNGER TRAVEL

NOTE: **This is a preliminary adjustment only. It is required to ensure that mixture control solenoid is set close to specifications prior to final adjustment. Final adjustment must be made with carburetor installed and engine running. See appropriate TUNE-UP article.**

1) Remove air horn, solenoid adjustment screw, rich limit stop, mixture control solenoid plunger, primary metering rods with springs. plastic filler block and mixture control solenoid. *See Fig. 5.*

Fig. 5: Removing Mixture Control Solenoid

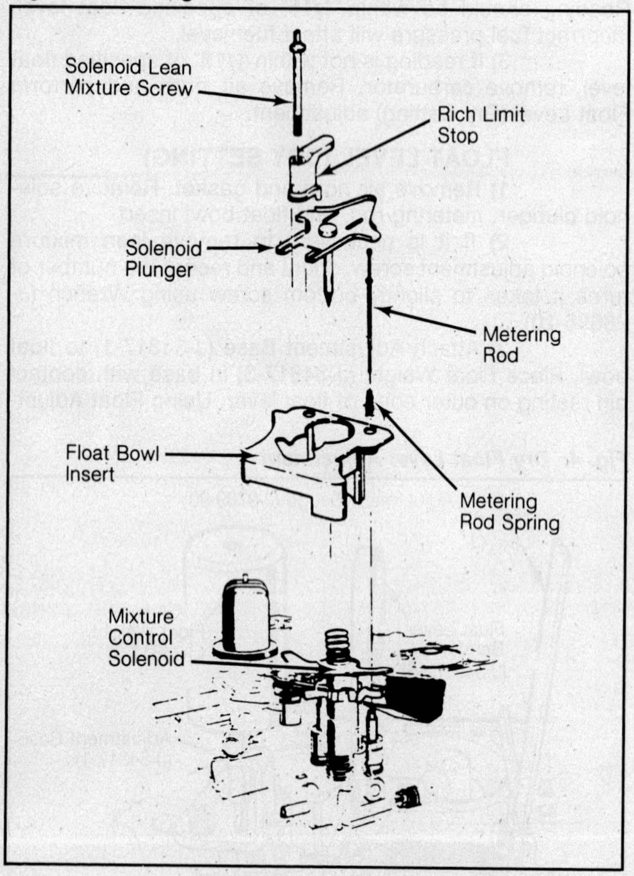

2) Inspect mixture control solenoid bore or plunger wear or sticking. Check metering rods for wrong part number, sticking or improperly installed springs. Check for foreign material in jets.

3) Install Mixture Control Solenoid Gauge (J-33815-1) over the throttle side metering jet rod guide. Temporarily install solenoid adjustment screw spring, mixture control solenoid, plunger, rich limit stop, and solenoid adjustment screw. *See Fig. 6.*

Fig. 6: Installing Mixture Control Solenoid Gauge

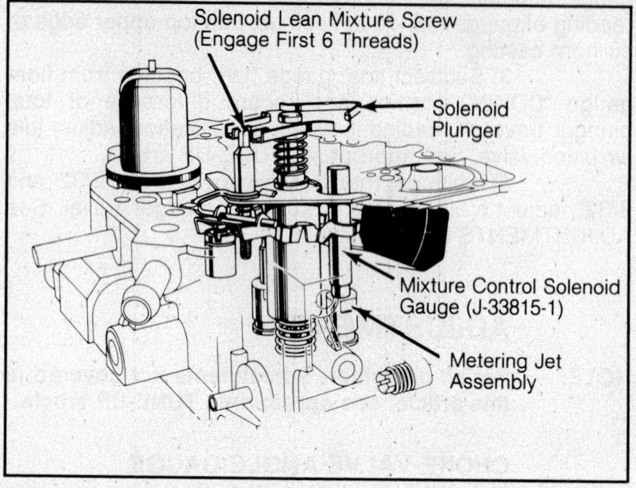

4) Hold solenoid plunger "DOWN" with light finger pressure and as close to plunger shaft as possible. Using Wrench (J-28696-10), slowly turn solenoid adjustment screw clockwise until plunger contacts gauge. *See Fig. 7.*

Fig. 7: Adjusting Mixture Control Solenoid

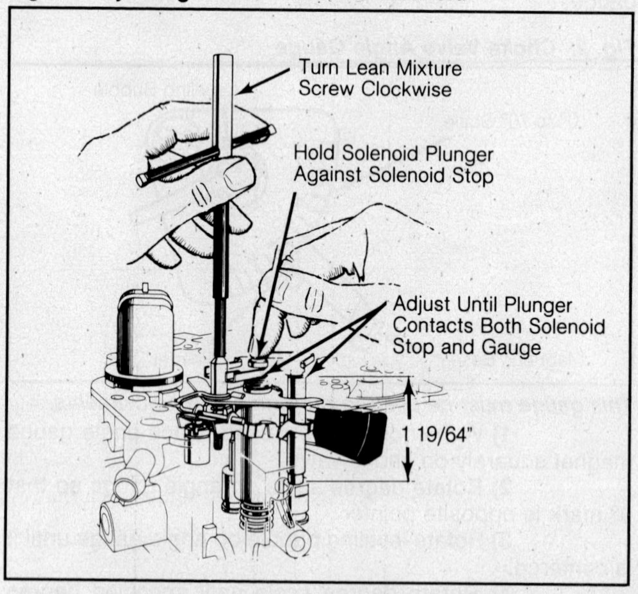

5) Slowly turn solenoid adjustment screw counterclockwise until the plunger breaks contact with gauge. The adjustment is correct when solenoid plunger is contacting both the solenoid stop and gauge.

6) Note position of "T" handle on wrench. Count and record the number of turns required to turn the solenoid adjustment screw clockwise until the solenoid bottoms out against float bowl.

7) Remove solenoid adjustment screw, rich limit stop, mixture control solenoid, plunger, solenoid adjustment screw spring, and gauge. Install solenoid adjustment screw spring, mixture control solenoid, and plastic filler block. Install primary metering rods and springs.

8) Install mixture control solenoid plunger, rich limit stop, and solenoid adjustment screw. Using wrench,

ROCHESTER E4ME & E4MED 4-BARREL (Cont.)

turn solenoid adjustment screw clockwise until mixture control solenoid bottoms out against float bowl.

9) Turn wrench couterclockwise the exact number of turns recorded in step **6)**. Install new air horn gasket and install air horn on carburetor. Tighten carburetor screws using tightening sequence. *See Fig. 22.*

SOLENOID RICH MIXTURE STOP SCREW (BENCH ADJUSTMENT)

NOTE: This is a preliminary adjustment only. It is required to ensure that solenoid rich mixture stop screw is set close to specifications prior to final adjustment. Final adjustment must be made with carburetor installed and engine running. See appropriate TUNE-UP article.

Fig. 8: Solenoid Rich Mixture Stop Screw Bench Adjustment

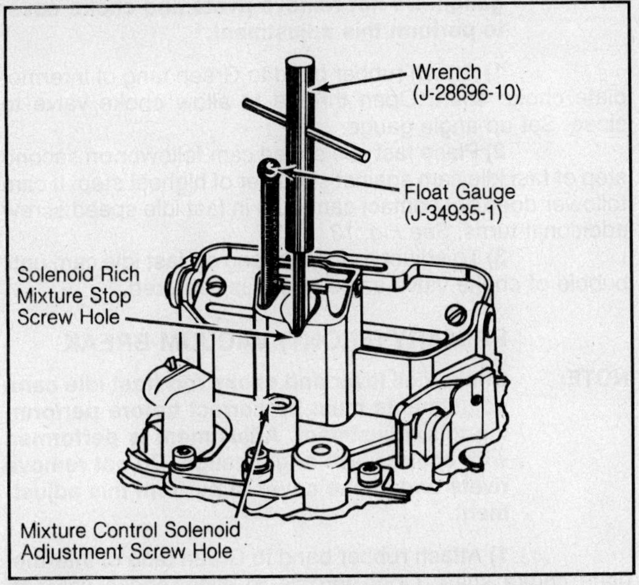

Air horn must be properly installed prior to adjustment.

Fig. 9: Installing Lean Mixture & Solenoid Rich Mixture Stop Screw Plugs

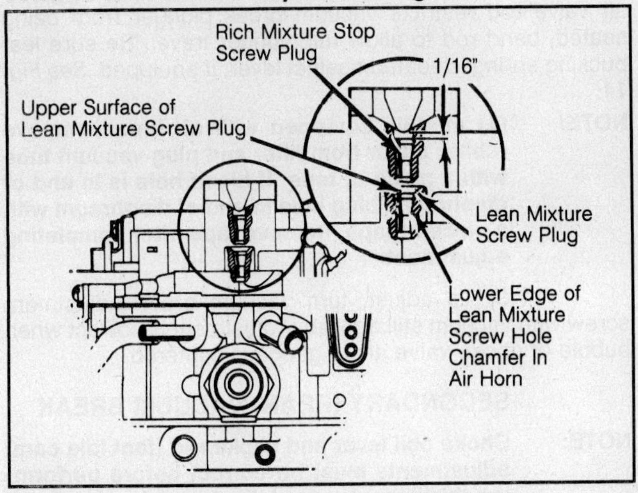

Plugs seal settings and prevent loss of fuel vapor.

1) With mixture control solenoid plunger travel properly set and air horn installed, insert Float Gauge (J-34935-1) in vertical "D" shaped vent hole in air horn casting.

2) With gauge installed, read mark (in inches) on gauge that lines up with top of air horn casting at eye level. Record reading. Lightly depress float gauge and again read mark on gauge that lines up with top of casting. Record reading.

3) Subtract the 2 readings taken in step **2)**. This difference is the total solenoid travel. Using Wrench (J-28696-10), turn rich mixture stop screw until total solenoid travel (difference between readings) is 4/32". *See Fig. 8.*

4) After adjustment, install lean mixture screw and solenoid rich mixture stop screw plugs. Plugs must be installed to seal settings and to prevent fuel vapor loss. *See Fig. 9.*

IDLE MIXTURE NEEDLES & AIR BLEED VALVE (BENCH ADJUSTMENTS)

NOTE: This is a preliminary adjustment only. It is required to ensure that mixture screws and idle air bleed valve are set close to specifications prior to final adjustment. Final adjustment must be made with carburetor installed and engine running. See appropriate TUNE-UP article.

1) Before adjusting idle mixture needles ensure that air horn properly installed. Lightly seat idle mixture needles, then back out 3 turns.

2) The idle air bleed valve is sealed with a riveted cover. This cover should not be removed unless required for cleaning, part replacement, improper dwell readings, or if Computer Command Control System Performance Check indicates that carburetor requires adjustment.

3) If idle air bleed cover was previously removed, or if conditions described in step **2)** are met, check idle air bleed valve for a letter inscribed on top of valve. This will determine the correct on-vehicle adjustment procedure.

4) To adjust air bleed valve, insert idle Air Bleed Valve Gauge (J-33815-2) in throttle side "D" shaped vent hole of air horn casting. Upper end of tool should be positioned over cavity next to valve. *See Fig. 10.*

5) Lightly push down on gauge so that solenoid plunger is against solenoid stop. Adjust idle air bleed valve so that gauge will pivot over and just contact top of air bleed valve. *See Fig. 10*. Install, adjust and plug all screws to restore tamper-resistant design.

AIR VALVE SPRING

1) Use a 3/32" hex wrench to loosen lock screw. Turn tension adjusting screw counterclockwise until air valve opens part way.

2) Turn tension adjusting screw clockwise until air valve just closes. Then turn adjusting screw clockwise specified number of turns. *See Fig. 11.*. Tighten lock screw. Apply lithium base grease to lubricate contact area.

CHOKE COIL LEVER

NOTE: Choke coil cover uses rivets in place of retaining screws. If necessary to remove choke coil cover, refer to Disassembly and Reassembly procedures in this article.

1) Remove retaining rivets. Remove choke cover and coil assembly. Position fast idle speed cam

ROCHESTER E4ME & E4MED 4-BARREL (Cont.)

Fig. 10: Idle Mixture Needles & Air Bleed Valve Bench Adjustments

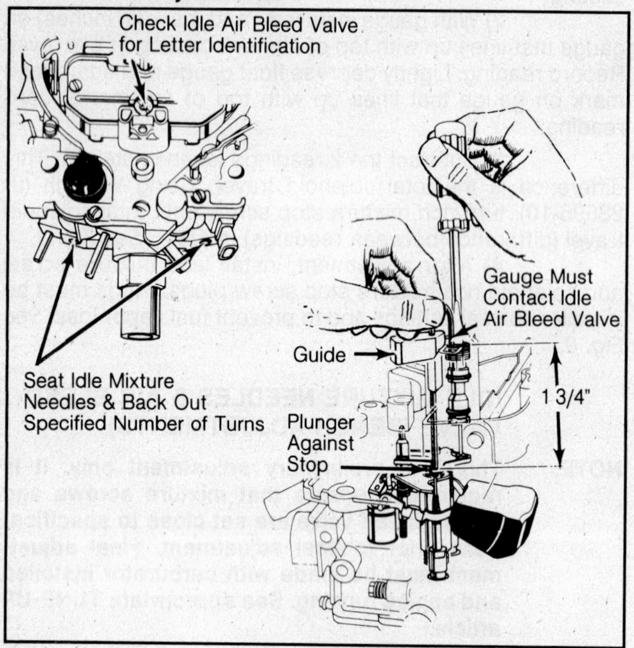

Final adjustments must be performed with carburetor installed and engine running.

Fig. 11: Air Valve Spring Adjustment

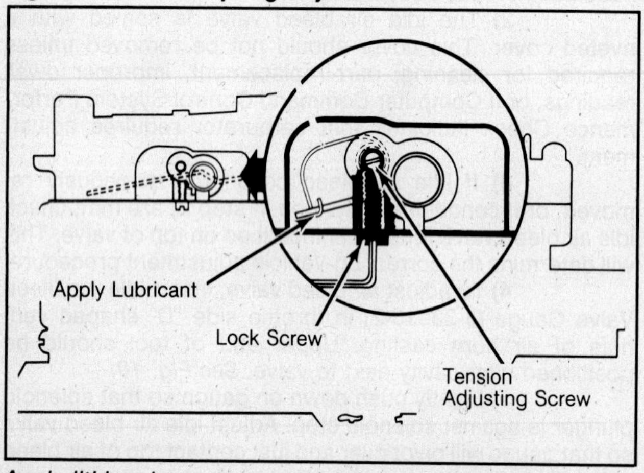

Apply lithium base grease to lubricate contact area.

follower on high step of fast idle cam. Push up (counterclockwise) on choke coil tang to close choke valve. *See Fig. 12.*

2) Insert a .120" drill or pin gauge in hole provided in choke housing. Lower edge of choke lever inside housing should just touch drill or pin gauge. To adjust lever, bend choke rod. *See Fig. 12.*

NOTE: **Ground contact for electric choke is provided by metal plate located at rear of choke cover assembly. Do not install choke cover gasket between electric choke and housing.**

CHOKE ROD (FAST IDLE CAM)

NOTE: **Choke coil lever adjustment must be correct before performing this adjustment. Fast idle speed adjustment must be performed using the Emission Control Tune-Up Decal with carburetor installed and vehicle running. Adjustment is performed with choke valve angle gauge. Do not remove rivets and choke cover to perform this adjustment.**

Fig. 12: Choke Coil Lever Adjustment

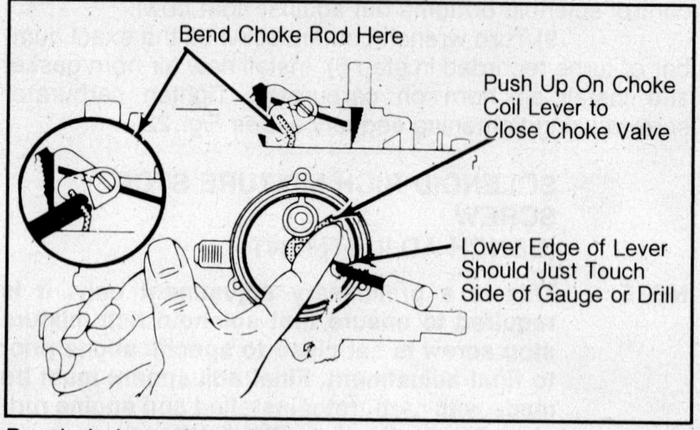

Bend choke rod to adjust.

1) Attach rubber band to Green tang of intermediate choke shaft. Open throttle to allow choke valve to close. Set up angle gauge.

2) Place fast idle speed cam follower on second step of fast idle cam against shoulder of highest step. If cam follower does not contact cam, turn in fast idle speed screw additional turns. *See Fig. 13.*

3) To adjust rod, bend tang on fast idle cam until bubble of choke valve angle gauge is centered.

PRIMARY (FRONT) VACUUM BREAK

NOTE: **Choke coil lever and choke rod (fast idle cam) adjustments must be correct before performing this adjustment. Adjustment is performed with choke valve angle gauge. Do not remove rivets and choke cover to perform this adjustment.**

1) Attach rubber band to Green tang of intermediate choke shaft. Open throttle to allow choke valve to close. Set up angle gauge.

2) Using an outside vacuum source of at least 18 in. Hg, seat primary (front) vacuum break diaphragm. If air valve rod restricts vacuum break plunger from being seated, bend rod to allow full plunger travel. Be sure leaf bucking spring is seated against lever, if equipped. *See Fig. 14.*

NOTE: **On models equipped with air bleed, remove rubber cover from filter and plug vacuum tube with a piece of tape. If bleed hole is in end of diaphragm, plug hole in end of diaphragm with a piece of tape. Remove tape after completing adjustment.**

3) To adjust, turn vacuum break adjustment screw with vacuum still applied. Adjustment is correct when bubble of choke valve angle gauge is centered.

SECONDARY (REAR) VACUUM BREAK

NOTE: **Choke coil lever and choke rod (fast idle cam) adjustments must be correct before performing this adjustment. Adjustment is performed with choke valve angle gauge. Do not remove rivets and choke cover to perform this adjustment.**

ROCHESTER E4ME & E4MED 4-BARREL (Cont.)

Fig. 13: Choke Rod (Fast Idle Cam) Adjustment

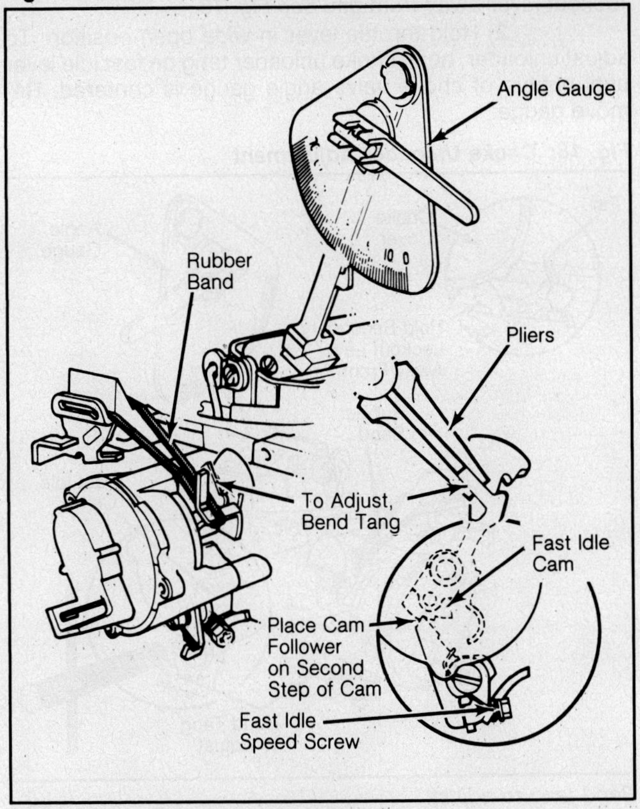

Bend tang on fast idle cam to adjust.

1) Attach rubber band to Green tang of intermediate choke shaft. Open throttle to allow choke valve to close. Set up angle gauge.

Fig. 14: Primary (Front) Vacuum Break Adjustment

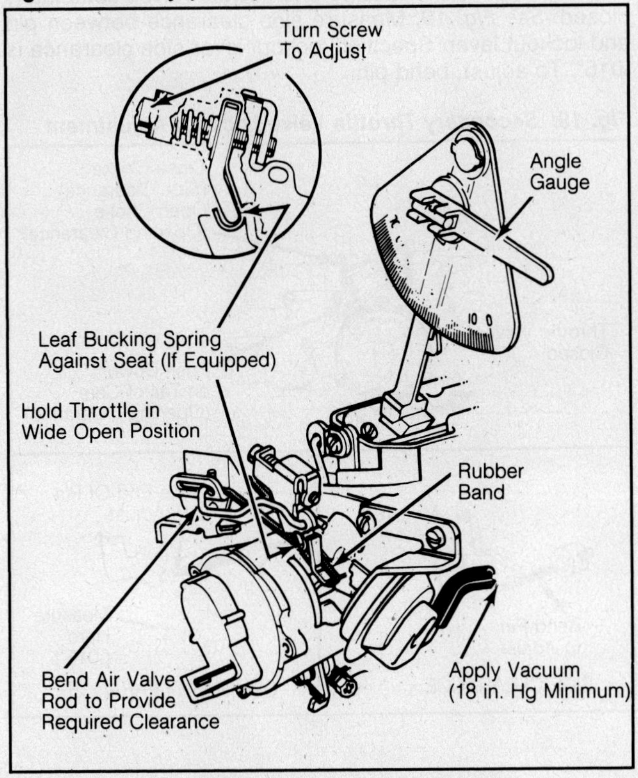

Turn vacuum break adjustment screw to adjust.

Fig. 15: Secondary (Rear) Vacuum Break Adjustment

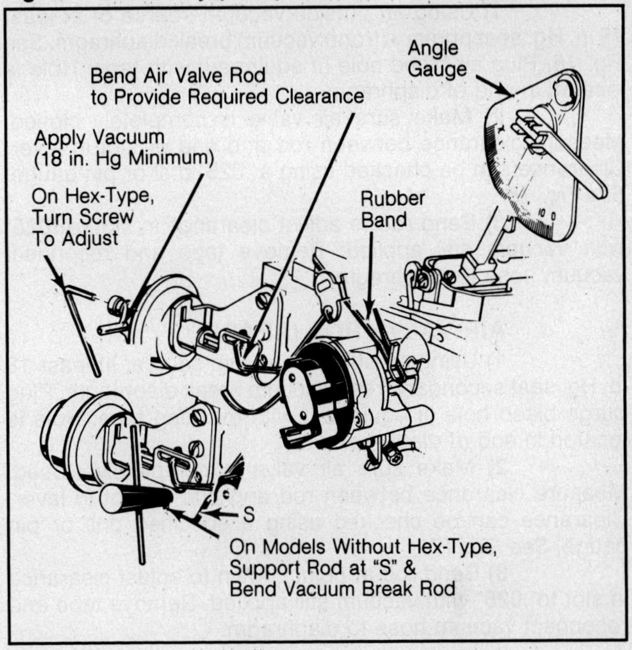

Turn screw or bend vacuum break rod to adjust.

Fig. 16: Air Valve Rod Adjustment (Front)

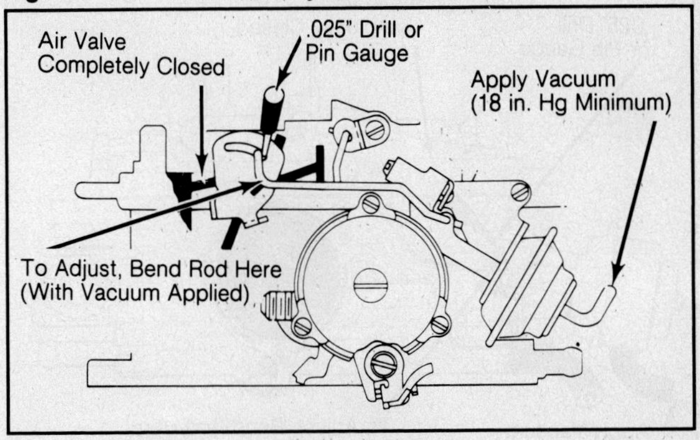

Air valve must be completely closed.

2) Using an outside vacuum source of at least 18 in. Hg, seat secondary (rear) vacuum break diaphragm. If air valve rod restricts vacuum break plunger from being seated, bend rod to allow full plunger travel. Be sure leaf bucking spring is compressed, if equipped. *See Fig. 15.*

NOTE: On models equipped with air bleed, remove rubber cover from filter and plug vacuum tube with a piece of tape. If bleed hole is in end of diaphragm, plug hole in end of diaphragm with tape. On delay models with air bleed, plug end cover with an accelerator pump plunger cup. Remove tape or cup after completion of adjustment.

3) On models equipped with hex adjustment, use a 1/8" hex wrench to turn adjustment screw in rear cover of vacuum break with vacuum still applied. Adjustment is correct when bubble of choke valve angle gauge is centered.

4) On models without hex adjustment, support rod at "S" and bend vacuum break rod with vacuum still applied. Adjustment is correct when bubble of choke valve angle gauge is centered.

ROCHESTER E4ME & E4MED 4-BARREL (Cont.)

AIR VALVE ROD (FRONT)

1) Using an outside vacuum source of at least 18 in. Hg, seat primary (front) vacuum break diaphragm. *See Fig. 16.* Plug air bleed hole (if equipped) with tape. Hole is located in end of diaphragm.

2) Make sure air valve is completely closed. Measure clearance between rod and end of slot in lever. Clearance can be checked using a .025" drill or pin gauge. *See Fig. 16.*

3) Bend rod to adjust clearance in slot to .025" with vacuum still applied. Remove tape and reconnect vacuum hose to diaphragm.

AIR VALVE ROD (REAR)

1) Using an outside vacuum source, at least 18 in. Hg, seat secondary (rear) vacuum break diaphragm. Plug purge bleed hole (if equipped) with masking tape. Hole is located in end of diaphragm.

2) Make sure air valve is completely closed. Measure clearance between rod and end of slot in lever. Clearance can be checked using a specified drill or pin gauge. *See Fig. 17.*

3) Bend rod at point shown to adjust clearance in slot to .025" with vacuum still applied. Remove tape and reconnect vacuum hose to diaphragm.

Fig. 17: Air Valve Rod Adjustment (Rear)

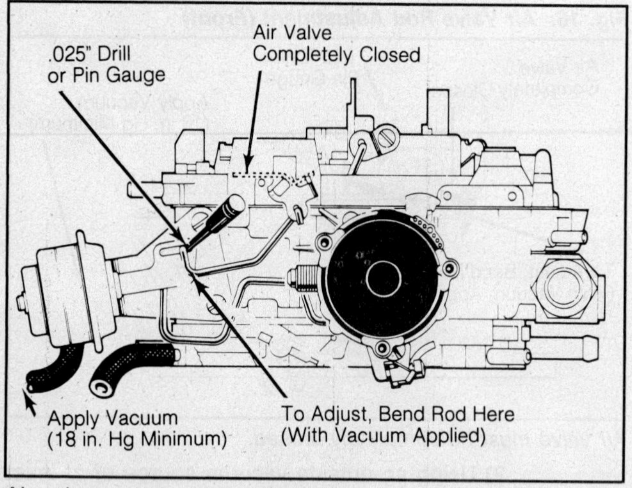

Air valve must be completely closed.

AUTOMATIC CHOKE

NOTE: **Choke coil cover is retained in place with rivets. No adjustment is required. If necessary to remove choke coil cover, refer to Disassembly and Reassembly procedures in this article. Only remove choke cover if major overhaul is required or if choke cover requires replacement.**

CHOKE UNLOADER

NOTE: **Choke coil lever and choke rod (fast idle cam) adjustments must be correct before performing this adjustment. Adjustment is performed with choke valve angle gauge. Do not remove rivets and choke cover to perform this adjustment.**

1) Attach rubber band to Green tang of intermediate choke shaft. Open throttle to allow choke valve to close. Set up angle gauge. Hold secondary lockout lever away from pin. *See Fig. 18.*

2) Hold throttle lever in wide open position. To adjust unloader, bend choke unloader tang on fast idle lever until bubble of choke valve angle gauge is centered. Remove gauge.

Fig. 18: Choke Unloader Adjustment

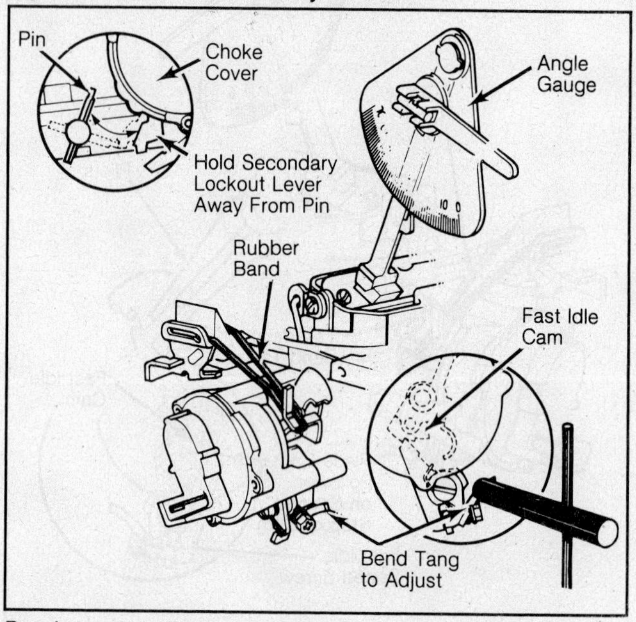

Bend tang to adjust.

SECONDARY THROTTLE VALVE LOCKOUT

Lockout Lever Side Clearance

Hold choke valve and throttle valves completely closed. *See Fig. 19.* Measure side clearance between pin and lockout lever. Specified lockout lever side clearance is .015". To adjust, bend pin.

Fig. 19: Secondary Throttle Valve Lockout Adjustment

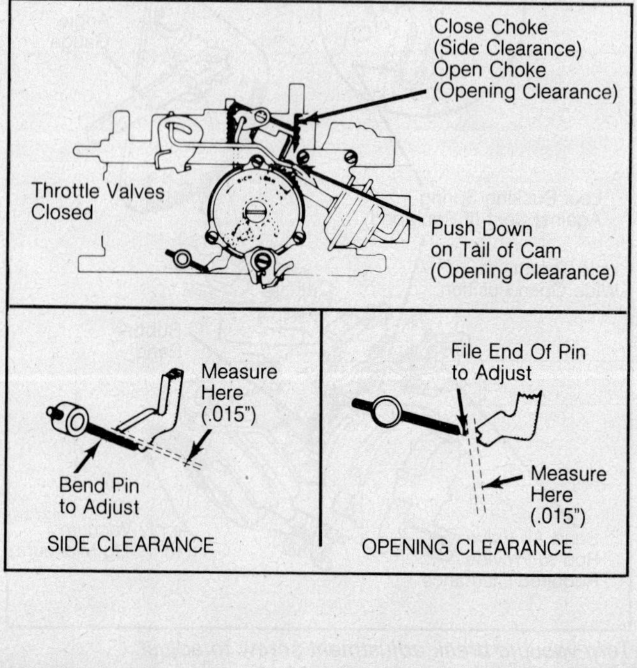

ROCHESTER E4ME & E4MED 4-BARREL (Cont.)

Lockout Lever Opening Clearance

Push down on tail of fast idle cam and open choke valve completely. Measure opening clearance between end of pin and toe of lockout lever. Specified clearance is .015". To adjust, file end of lock out pin. Make sure all burrs are removed.

OVERHAUL

DISASSEMBLY

NOTE: **Before performing any service on carburetor, it is essential that carburetor be placed on Holding Fixture (J-9789-118) to prevent damage to throttle valves.**

Air Horn

1) Remove ISC or ISS attaching screws, bracket and assembly. Remove upper choke lever from end of choke shaft by removing retaining screw. Rotate upper choke lever to remove choke rod from slot in lever.

2) Remove choke link from lower lever inside float bowl casting. Remove link by holding lower lever outward with small screwdriver and twisting link counterclockwise.

3) Remove secondary metering rods by removing small screw in top of metering rod hanger. Lift up on metering rod hanger until secondary metering rods clear air horn. Metering rods may be removed from hanger by rotating ends out of holes in end of hanger.

4) Remove pump link retainer, then remove link from pump lever. Remove vacuum hose from front vacuum break unit and note location for reassembly reference. Remove 11 air horn-to-float bowl screws. Remove 2 countersunk screws located near venturi.

NOTE: **Do not attemp to remove pump lever from air horn as damage to air horn could result.**

5) Remove secondary air baffle deflector (if equipped) from beneath 2 center air horn screws. Remove air horn from float bowl by lifting straight up. Air horn gasket should remain on float bowl.

NOTE: **Use care not to damage mixture control solenoid connector, TPS adjustment lever, and small tubes protruding from air horn. Do not attempt to remove tubes.**

6) Remove primary (front) vacuum break diaphragm. Remove air valve rod from vacuum break and air valve lever. Using fingers only, remove TPS plunger by pushing plunger up through air horn seal.

8) Invert air horn. Using a small screwdriver, remove staking that holds TPS seal and pump plunger stem seal retainers. Use care when removing retainers and seals to prevent damage to air horn casting. Discard retainers and seals.

9) Using a small punch, drive the solenoid adjutment screw plug out of air horn. Discard plug. Further disasssembly of air horn is not required for cleaning purposes.

10) Choke valve and choke valve screws, air valve and air valve shaft should not be removed. Instructions for replacing the air valve closing spring and plastic cam are included in service kit.

11) The air horn has an idle air bleed valve which is preset and sealed at the factory. The idle air bleed valve should not be removed unless "System Performance Check" of Computer Command Control system indicates need for adjustment or repair.

NOTE: **Air horn assembly, with idle air bleed valve installed, should be cleaned only in low volatile cleaning solvent. Do not place air horn (with idle air bleed valve) in carburetor cleaner. No tamper-resistant plug should be removed during normal carburetor cleaning and servicing unless carburetor or mixture control solenoid has been diagnosed as cause of poor engine performance.**

Air Bleed Valve

1) If necessary to replace idle air bleed valve or disassemble air horn for immersion in carburetor cleaner, cover internal bowl vents and air inlets to bleed valve with tape.

2) Drill off rivet heads of bleed valve cover with a 7/64" drill. Drive remainder of rivet out of tower with drift and small hammer. Lift out cover over valve and remove remaining rivet pieces from inside tower.

3) After removing cover, check for letter identification on top of idle air bleed valve. This will determine the necessary adjustment procedure after reassembly.

4) Turn valve counterclockwise and remove from air horn. Remove and discard "O" ring seals from air bleed valve. Air bleed valve is serviced as a complete assembly only.

NOTE: **A missing air valve cover indicates that idle air bleed valve setting has been changed from original factory setting.**

Float Bowl

1) Remove air horn gasket by lifting off of dowel locating pins, and from under and around solenoid plunger. Discard gasket. Remove pump plunger and return spring from pump well.

2) Remove mixture control/dual capacity pump solenoid assembly as follows: Remove solenoid attaching screw. Do not remove solenoid connector from float bowl at this time.

3) Using Wrench (J-28696-10), remove mixture control solenoid adjustment screw, solenoid plunger, and solenoid plunger rich limit stop as an assembly. Do not remove plunger return spring or connector wires from solenoid bodies. The mixture control solenoid, plunger and connectors, are serviced as an assembly.

4) Remove plastic insert from top of mixture control assembly. Carefully lift each metering rod out of its metering jet guide. Ensure that return spring is removed with each rod.

5) Remove rubber gasket from top of solenoid connector. Discard gasket. Remove solenoid adjusting screw tension spring from float bowl, next to float hanger pin.

6) Remove float assembly and float needle by pulling up on retaining pin. Using Seat Remover (J-22769), remove needle, seat and gasket. Remove large mixture control solenoid tension spring from boss on bottom of float bowl, located between metering jets.

7) Remove staking holding TPS in bowl as follows: Protect gasket surface by laying a flat piece of metal across casting. Using a small screwdriver, lightly depress and hold TPS down against spring tension.

ROCHESTER E4ME & E4MED 4-BARREL (Cont.)

8) Carefully remove staking from around TPS by prying upward with a small chisel against the metal piece (not bowl casting). Push up from bottom on electrical connector and remove TPS and connector assembly from bowl. Use care not to damage sensor.

9) Remove spring from bottom of TPS well in float bowl. If necessary, remove primary main metering jets using Metering Jet Remover (J-28696-4). Use care not to damage metering rod guide upper areas.

NOTE: **Do not attempt to remove secondary metering jets. Secondary jets are permanent and if damaged, float bowl must be replaced.**

10) On E4MED carburetor, use Accelerator Bypass Valve Wrench (J-34928) to remove accelerator bypass valve and gasket. Remove pump discharge ball retainer.

11) Invert bowl and catch discharge ball as it falls. Remove secondary air baffle, if replacement is required. If necessary, remove pump well fill slot baffle.

12) Remove hose from rear vacuum break assembly. Remove 2 attaching screws from float bowl. Remove rear vacuum break and bracket assembly. Rotate assembly to remove vacuum break link from slot in plunger.

13) Remove fuel inlet nut, gasket, filter assembly, and spring. Discard filater assembly and gasket. Remove 3 throttle body-to-bowl attaching screws and lock washers. Remove throttle body assembly. Remove throttle body-to-bowl insulator gasket.

Choke Cover

1) Align a 5/32" drill on choke cover retaining rivets and drill only enough to remove rivet head. Using a drift and hammer, drive remainder of rivets out of choke housing. Remove 3 retainers and choke cover from choke housing.

2) Remove retaining screw and washer from inside choke housing. Slide choke housing away from float bowl. Remove secondary throttle valve lockout lever from float bowl. Invert bowl and remove lower choke lever from inside bowl cavity.

3) To disassemble intermediate choke shaft from from choke housing, remove coil lever retaining screw from end of choke shaft. Remove thermostatic coil lever from flats on choke shaft.

4) Slide intermediate choke shaft out of choke housing. Remove fast idle cam from choke shaft. Remove cup seal from float bowl insert. Do not remove insert.

Throttle Body

Remove accelerator pump link from throttle lever by rotating link until tang on link aligns with slot in lever.

NOTE: **Further disassembly of throttle body is not required for normal cleaning. Throttle valve screws are permanently staked in position. Throttle body is serviced as complete assembly. Do not remove mixture screw plugs unless diagnosis indicates the carburetor is cause of poor engine performance or idle mixture needles or throttle body must be replaced. If necessary to remove plugs, proceed as follows:**

Idle Mixture Needle Plugs

1) Turn throttle body over, and make 2 parallel cuts in throttle body using a small hacksaw, cutting on each side of idle mixture needle plugs. Cuts should reach down to steel plug, but no more than 1/8" beyond locator points. Distance between saw marks will depend upon size of punch used.

2) Place a flat punch at a point near ends of saw marks. Hold punch at 45° angle and drive it into throttle body until casting breaks away, exposing steel plug. *See Fig. 21.*

3) Hold punch vertically and drive it into steel plug. Then hold punch at 45° angle and drive plug out of casting. Repeat process for remaining mixture needle plug. When removing or installing needles, refer to appropriate TUNE-UP article.

CLEANING & INSPECTION

- Use a regular carburetor cleaning solution. Soak components long enough to thoroughly clean all surfaces and passages of foreign matter.
- Do not soak any components containing rubber, leather or plastic. Particularly do not soak air horn with idle air bleed valve installed, electric choke, ISS, ISC, TPS, thermostatic choke cover and coil, vacuum break diaphragms, pump plunger and other such parts.
- Remove any residue after cleaning by rinsing components in a suitable solvent.
- Blow out all passages with dry compressed air.
- If float bowl needs replacement, inspect for letters "MW" (next to fuel inlet) on casting. These letters indicate a machined pump well, and determine type of pump needed. Replacement float bowl also must have "MW" letters.

REASSEMBLY

NOTE: **Use new gaskets and seals. Make sure that new gaskets fit correctly and that all holes and slots are punched through and correctly located.**

Reassemble carburetor in reverse order of disassembly, noting the following:

1) The intermediate choke shaft lever and fast idle cam are assembled correctly when tang on lever is beneath fast idle cam.

2) When installing float and retaining pin, make sure open end of float retaining pin faces accelerator pump well.

3) When installing fuel inlet valve, hook pull clip over edge of flat on float arm. Do not hook clip in holes in float arm.

4) When installing mixture control solenoid, make sure pin on end of solenoid aligns with hole in raised boss at bottom of float bowl. After assembly perform mixture control solenoid travel adjustment. See ADJUSTMENTS in this article.

5) When installing idle air bleed valve, lighty coat 2 new "O" ring seals with automatic transmission fluid. Thick seal goes in upper groove and thin seal goes on lower groove. Adjust air bleed valve. See ADJUSTMENTS in this article.

NOTE: **If choke coil cover was removed, it will be necessary to install service rivet retaining kit. Before installing cover, place fast idle screw on high step of fast idle cam. Align notch in cover with raised boss on housing cover flange and install rivets.**

ROCHESTER E4ME & E4MED 4-BARREL (Cont.)

Fig. 20: Exploded View of Rochester Model E4ME & E4MED 4-Barrel Carburetor

1. Air Horn Assembly
2. Air Horn Gasket
3. Pump Actuating Lever
4. Pump Lever Hinge Pin
5. Long Air Horn Screws (2)
6. Short Air Horn Screws
7. Air Horn Countersunk Screws (2)
8. Solenoid Connector-to-Air Horn Gasket
9. Secondary Metering Rods (2)
10. Secondary Metering Rod Holder and Screw
11. Secondary Air Baffle
12. Idle Air Bleed Valve
13. Thick "O" Ring
14. Thin "O" Ring
15. TPS Actuator Plunger
16. TPS Plunger Seal
17. TPS Seal Retainer
18. TPS Adjusting Screw
19. TPS Screw Plug
20. Pump Plunger Seal
21. Pump Seal Retainer
22. Solenoid Rich Mixture Stop Screw
23. Solenoid Rich Mixture Stop Screw Plug
24. Solenoid Lean Mixture Screw Plug
25. Front (Primary) Vacuum Break
26. Vacuum Break Attaching Screws
27. Vacuum Hose
28. Air Valve Rod
29. Upper Choke Rod Lever
30. Choke Lever Screw
31. Choke Rod
32. Lower Choke Rod Lever
33. Intermediate Choke Shaft Seal
34. Secondary Lockout Lever
35. Rear (Secondary) Vacuum Break Link
36. Intermediate Choke Shaft and Lever
37. Fast Idle Cam
38. Vacuum Hose
39. Choke Housing
40. Choke Housing-to-Bowl Screw
41. Choke Cover Retainer
42. Choke Coil Lever
43. Choke Coil Lever Screw
44. Choke Cover Rivet
45. Vacuum Hose
46. Electric Choke Cover and Coil Assembly
47. Rivet Service Kit
48. Rear Vacuum Break
49. Rear Vacuum Break Screws
50. Float Bowl Assembly
51. Primary Metering Jets (2)
52. Pump Discharge Ball
53. Pump Discharge Ball Retainer
54. Pump Well Baffle
55. Needle & Seat Assembly
56. Float Assembly
57. Float Assembly Hinge Pin
58. Primary Metering Rod (2)
59. Primary Metering Rod Springs
60. Float Bowl Insert
61. Bowl Cavity Insert
62. Connector Attaching Screw
63. Mixture Control Solenoid & Plunger Assembly
64. Solenoid Tension Spring
65. Solenoid Lean Mixture Screw
66. Solenoid Adj. Screw Spring
67. Pump Return Spring
68. Pump Assembly
69. Pump Link
70. Secondary Bore Baffle
71. Throttle Position Sensor (TPS)
72. TPS Tension Spring
73. Fuel Inlet Filter Nut
74. Filter Nut Gasket
75. Fuel Inlet Filter
76. Fuel Filter Spring
77. Idle Stop Screw
78. Idle Stop Screw Spring
79. Idle Speed Solenoid (If Equipped)
80. Throttle Return Spring Bracket
81. Idle Load Compensator (ILC) (If Equipped)
82. Idle Speed Control (ISC) (If Equipped)
83. Attaching Screws
84. Throttle Body Assembly
85. Throttle Body Gasket
86. Throttle Body Screw
87. Idle Needle & Springs (2)
88. Fast Idle Adjusting Screw
89. Fast Idle Screw Spring
90. Vaccum Hose "T"
91. Flange Gasket
92. Mixture Control/Dual Capacity Pump Solenoid Assembly

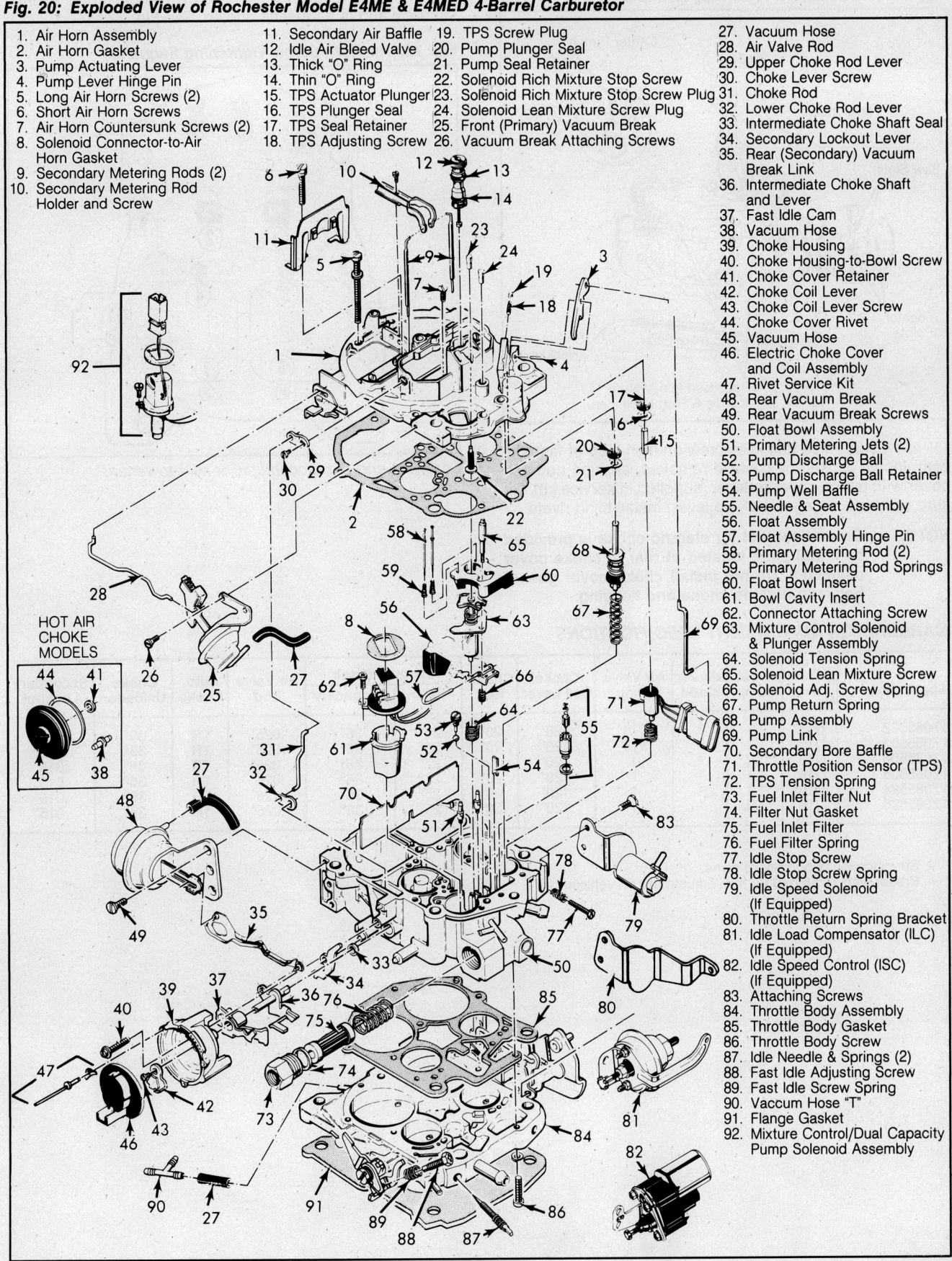

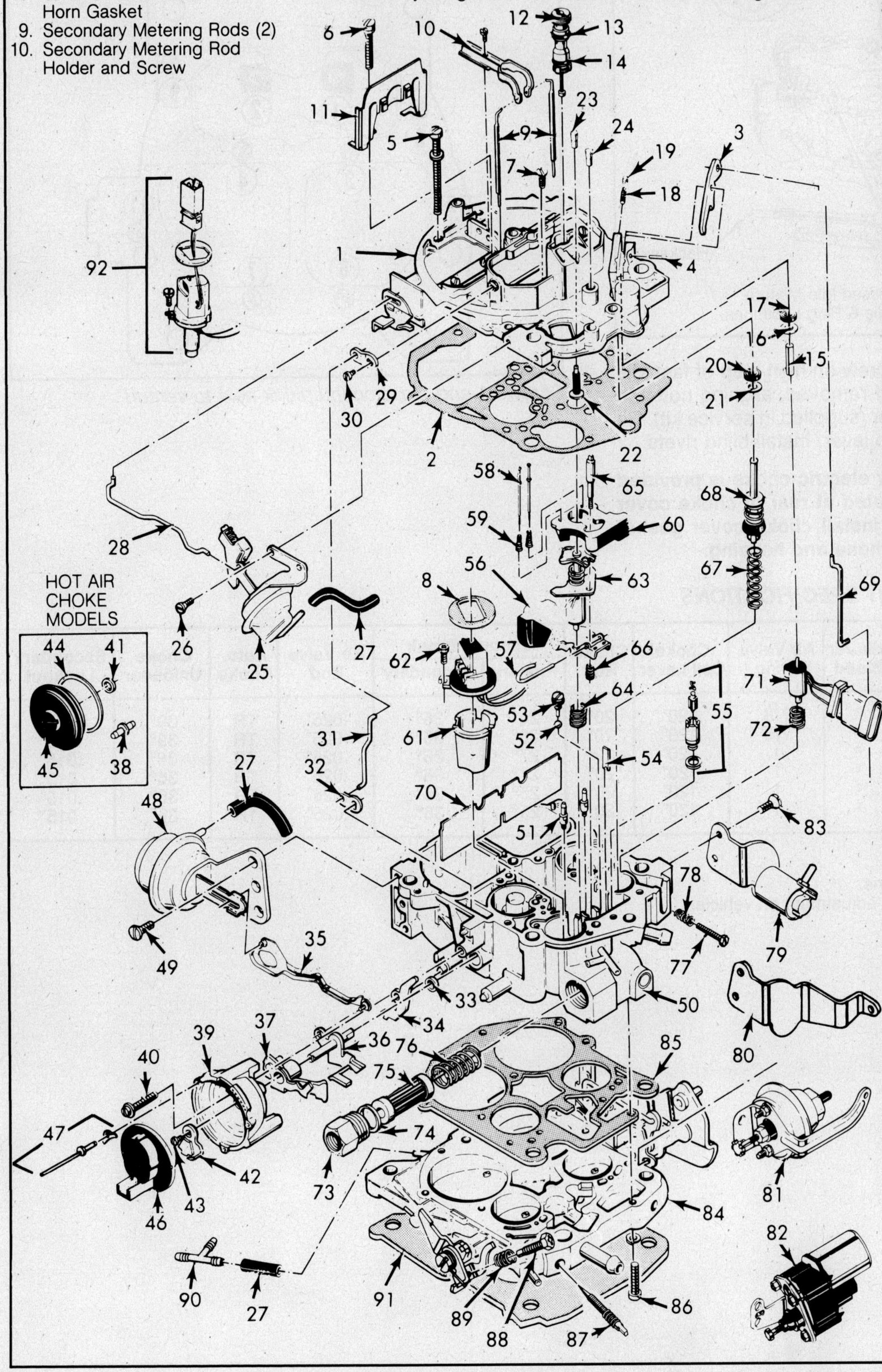

ROCHESTER E4ME & E4MED 4-BARREL (Cont.)

Fig. 21: Idle Mixture Needle Plug Removal

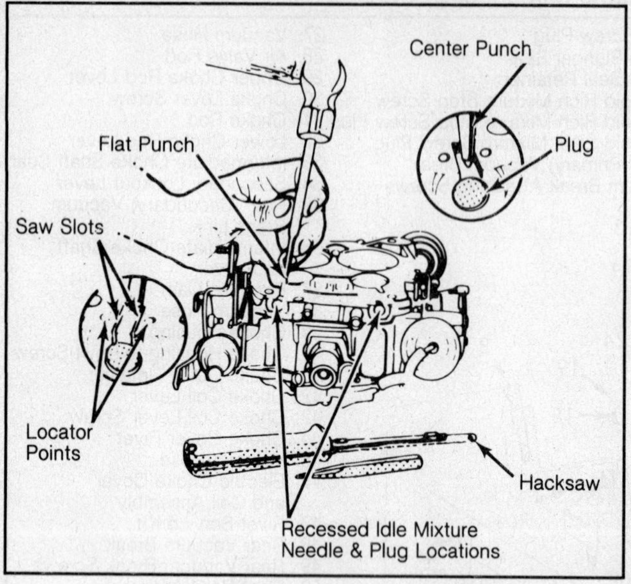

6) Place fast idle screw on high step of fast idle cam. Install choke coil cover if removed, aligning notch in cover with tab on cover retainer (supplied in service kit). Be sure coil tang engages pick-up lever. Install blind rivets.

NOTE: Ground contact for electric choke is provided by metal plate located at rear of choke cover assembly. Do not install choke cover gasket between electric choke and housing.

7) Install air horn screws and tighten evenly, securely and in sequence shown. *See Fig. 22.*

Fig. 22: Air Horn Screw Tightening Sequence

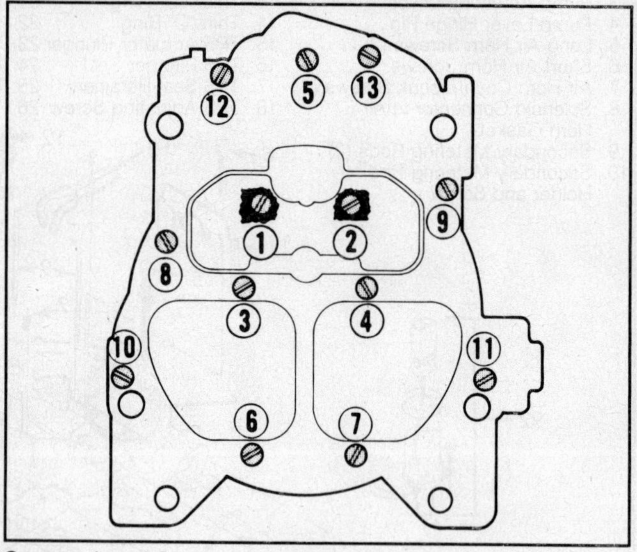

Screws 1 and 2 are countersunk next to venturi.

CARBURETOR ADJUSTMENT SPECIFICATIONS

Application	Float Level	Accel. Pump	Idle Air Bleed	Air Valve Spring [1]	Choke Coil Lever	Choke Rod	Vacuum Break Primary	Vacuum Break Secondary	Air Valve Rod	Auto. Choke	Choke Unloader	Secondary Lockout
17085502	7/16"	TR	[2]	7/8	.120"	20°	26°	36°	.025"	TR	39°	.015"
17085503	7/16"	TR	[2]	7/8	.120"	20°	26°	36°	.025"	TR	39°	.015"
17085506	7/16"	TR	[2]	1	.120"	20°	27°	36°	.025"	TR	36°	.015"
17085508	7/16"	TR	[2]	1	.120"	20°	27°	36°	.025"	TR	36°	.015"
17085524	7/16"	TR	[2]	1	.120"	20°	25°	36°	.025"	TR	36°	.015"
17085526	7/16"	TR	[2]	1	.120"	20°	25°	36°	.025"	TR	36°	.015"

[1] – Specification is number of turns.
[2] – Preset with 1.756 gauge, final adjustment on vehicle.

ROCHESTER M4MC, M4ME, M4MED, M4MEF 4-BBL.

NOTE: Vehicle numbers used in Chevrolet/GMC table are abbreviated. Chevrolet models use numerical designations listed; GMC models are identified as follows: 10 = 1500; 20 = 2500; 30 = 3500.

CARBURETOR APPLICATION

CHEVROLET & GMC (ROCHESTER) CARBURETOR NO.

Application	Man. Trans.	Auto. Trans.
4.3L		
Federal		
C10,20, G10, & Astro/Safari		
Exc. A/C or P/S	17085209	17085208
With A/C or P/S	17085211	17085210
G20,30, K10	17085211	17085210
High Alt.		
C10,20, G10, & Astro/Safari		
Exc. A/C or P/S	17085223	17085222
With A/C or P/S	17085225	17085224
G20,30	17085225	17085224
K10	17085225	17085224
5.0L		
Federal		
Exc. A/C		
C10	17085220	17085227
C20	17085239	17085227
G10,20, K10	17085239	17085227
With A/C		
C10	17085221	17085226
C20, G10,20, K10	17085238	17085226
High Alt.		
C10,20, K10	17085231	17085230
G10,20	17085231	17085215
5.7L		
Federal		
Exc. A/C		
C10		17085290
G10,20		17085229
G30	17085294	17085294
K10,20	17085291	17085290
With A/C		
C10		17085292
G10,20		17085228
G30	17085298	17085298
K10,20	17085293	17085292
P30		17085213
High Alt.		
C10,20		17085206
G10,20,30	17085206	17085206
K10,20	17085235	17085206
California		
P20,30	17084500	17084500
7.4L		
California		
P20,30	17084502	17084502

CARBURETOR IDENTIFICATION

Rochester M4M-series carburetor numbers are stamped vertically on the float bowl, near the secondary throttle. If float bowl is replaced, follow manufacturer's instructions contained in service package to transfer part number to new float bowl. *See Fig. 1.*

CHRYSLER (ROCHESTER) CARBURETOR NO.

Application	Man. Trans.	Auto. Trans.
5.9L		
Federal	17085417 [1]	17085408 [2]
High Alt.	17085417 [1]	17085409 [3]
California	17085415 [4]	17085415 [4]

[1] – Chrysler part number 4306417.
[2] – Chrysler part number 4306408.
[3] – Chrysler part number 4306409.
[4] – Chrysler part number 4306415.

Fig. 1: Carburetor Part Number Location

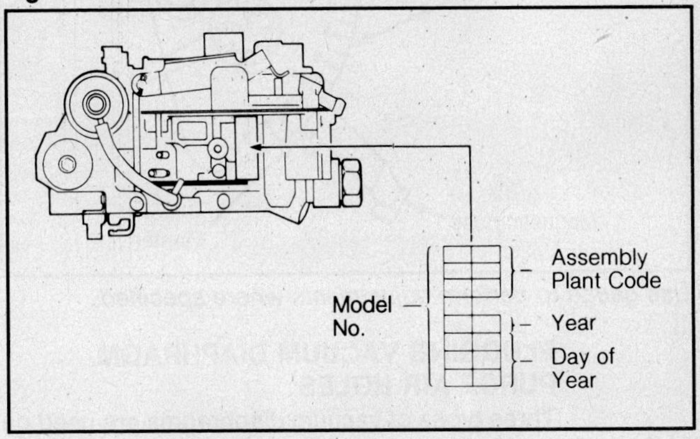

If float bowl is replaced, transfer part number.

DESCRIPTION

The M4M-series carburetors are all 4-barrel, two-stage designs. The primary side has a triple venturi system. The secondary side is composed of 2 large bores using the air valve principle (fuel is metered in direct proportion to amount of air passing through secondary bores). M4MC models use a hot air choke; all others use an electric choke.

M4MEF models (GM only) have adjustable wide open throttle mixture control. During wide open throttle conditions a factory-set secondary air bleed adjusting screw provides more precise control of the air/fuel mixture.

A dual capacity accelerator pump valve assembly, mounted in the float bowl, is used on M4MED models (GM only). A dual capacity pump solenoid is used. When the engine is cold, more fuel is necessary to ensure a smooth transition from idle to part throttle. When the engine is warm, less fuel is needed. A coolant temperature sensor energizes a pump solenoid when coolant temperature exceeds 170°F (77°C). This solenoid opens the dual capacity pump valve, reducing pump capacity by about one-half.

ADJUSTMENT

NOTE: For all on-vehicle adjustments, see appropriate TUNE-UP article.

ANGLE GAUGE ADJUSTMENT TOOL

Several adjustments are made using a Choke Valve Angle Gauge (Kent-Moore tool no. J-26701). While preparations and actual adjustments may vary with each individual adjustment, the procedure for using the angle gauge to check choke valve angle remains the same. Use

ROCHESTER M4MC, M4ME, M4MED, M4MEF 4-BBL. (Cont.)

the following procedure to perform adjustments requiring the use of the choke angle gauge.

1) Rotate degree scale on angle gauge so that 0° mark is opposite pointer.

2) With choke valve closed, place angle gauge magnet squarely on choke valve. Rotate leveling bubble on angle gauge until it is centered. Rotate degree scale until specified degree mark is opposite pointer. *See Fig. 2.*

3) Perform individual adjustments as described in carburetor adjustment procedures. Adjustments are correct when bubble is centered.

Fig. 2: Choke Valve Angle Gauge

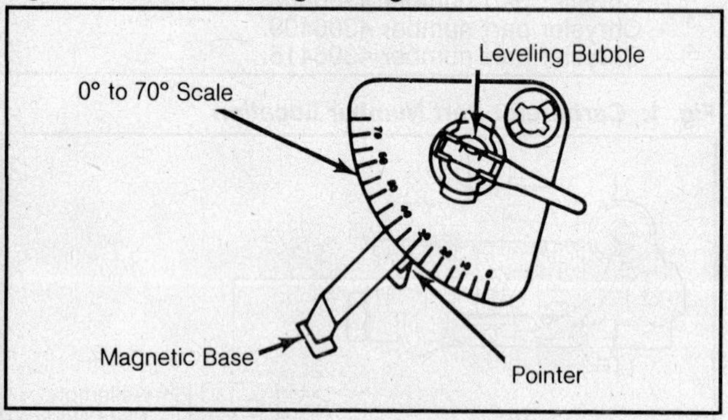

Use gauge to perform adjustments where specified.

PLUGGING VACUUM DIAPHRAGM PURGE AIR HOLES

Three types of vacuum diaphragms are used on M4M-series carburetors. When performing adjustment procedures with vacuum applied to diaphragms, purge holes must be plugged. *Fig. 3* shows the 3 types of vacuum diaphragms and the proper method to use for plugging purge holes.

Fig. 3: Plugging Vacuum Diaphragm Purge Bleed Holes

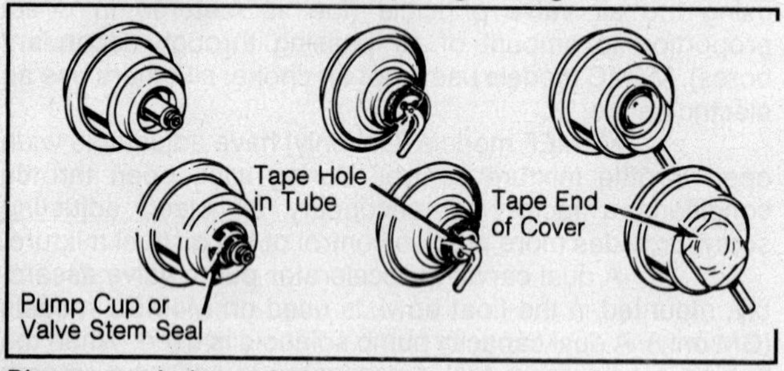

Plug purge holes to hold vacuum during adjustment procedures.

FLOAT LEVEL

1) Remove air horn and gasket. Remove power piston, metering rod assembly and float bowl insert.

2) On GM models, attach Float Measuring Gauge (J-34817-1) to float bowl. Place Float Weight (J-34817-3) in base with contact pin against outer edge of float lever. On Chrysler models, hold float down lightly against needle.

3) On all models, measure float level from top of casting to a point 3/16" from large end of float. *See Fig. 4.* Adjust float level if more than 1/16" from specification.

4) On GM models, adjust level by bending float lever with Bender (J-34817-25). Remove tool. On Chrysler models, hold float retainer in place and push down on center of float if level is too high, or bend float up if level is too low.

5) On all models, check float level. Repeat procedure as needed until correct level is obtained.

Fig. 4: Float Level Adjustment

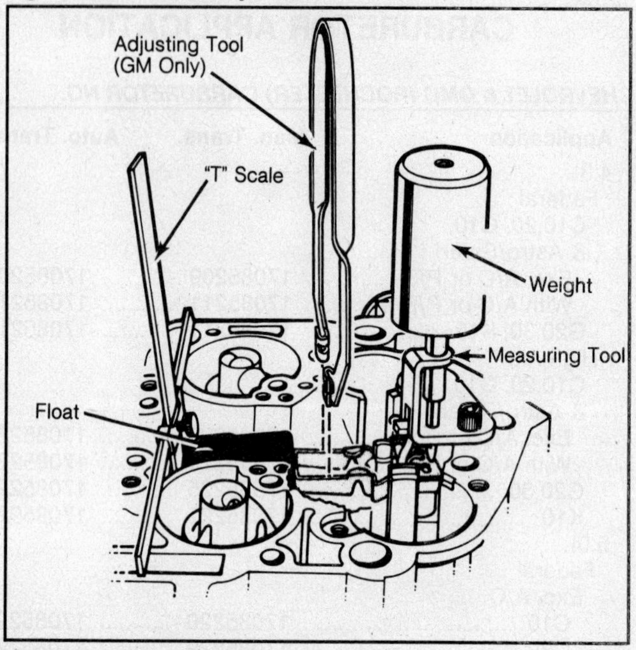

Use special tools on GM models, only.

Fig. 5: Accelerator Pump Adjustment

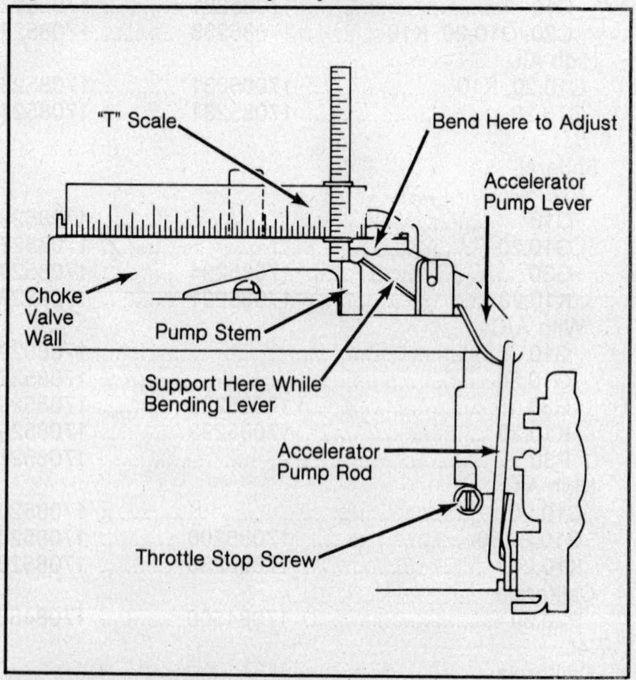

Adjustment procedure applies to GM models, only.

ACCELERATOR PUMP

NOTE: Adjustment procedure for Chrysler products not provided. Pump rod position in pump lever is factory pre-set. Record at disassembly and reinstall in same hole.

ROCHESTER M4MC, M4ME, M4MED, M4MEF 4-BBL. (Cont.)

1) With accelerator pump rod in specified hole (inner or outer) of accelerator pump lever, make sure fast idle cam follower is off fast idle cam steps. Turn throttle stop screw out until it no longer contacts throttle lever.

2) Using a "T" scale, measure specified distance from top of choke valve wall (next to vent stack) to top of pump stem.

3) To adjust, support accelerator pump lever with screwdriver and bend at notch. *See Fig. 5.*

CHOKE COIL LEVER

NOTE: **On some models, choke coil cover is riveted in place. To remove cover, refer to DISASSEMBLY and REASSEMBLY procedures in this article. A choke thermostat cover retainer kit is required for reassembly.**

1) Remove choke thermostatic cover from choke housing. Place fast idle speed screw on high step of fast idle cam. Push up on thermostatic coil tang (counterclockwise) until choke valve is fully closed.

2) Insert specified drill or pin gauge in hole provided in choke housing. Lower edge of choke lever (inside housing) should just touch drill or gauge. *See Fig. 6.*

Fig. 6: Choke Coil Lever Adjustment

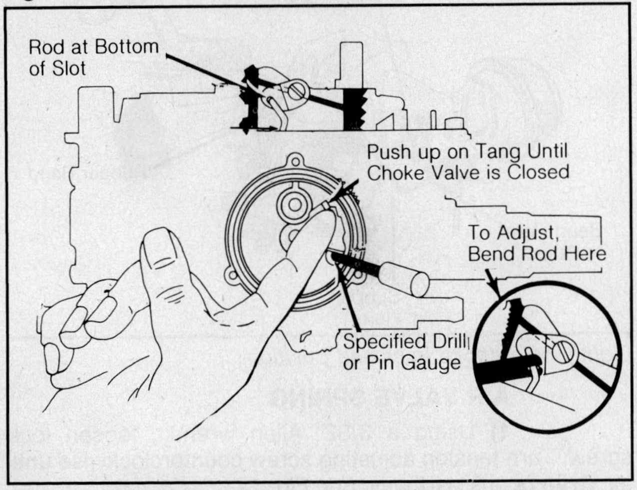

Place fast idle speed screw on high step of fast idle cam.

3) To adjust, bend choke rod at point shown in *Fig. 6.* Reinstall choke cover and adjust.

CHOKE ROD (FAST IDLE CAM)

NOTE: **Adjustment is performed using choke valve angle gauge. See procedure at beginning of ADJUSTMENT section of this article.**

1) Attach a rubber band to Green tang of intermediate choke shaft. *See Fig. 7.* Open throttle and allow choke valve to close.

2) Place fast idle cam follower on 2nd step of fast idle cam against shoulder of highest step. With angle gauge in position and set to specification, bubble should be centered. If not, bend tang on fast idle cam to center bubble.

FRONT AIR VALVE ROD (GM MODELS ONLY)

1) Using an outside vacuum source, seat front (primary) choke vacuum break diaphragm. Plug purge bleed hole.

Fig. 7: Choke Rod (Fast Idle Cam) Adjustment

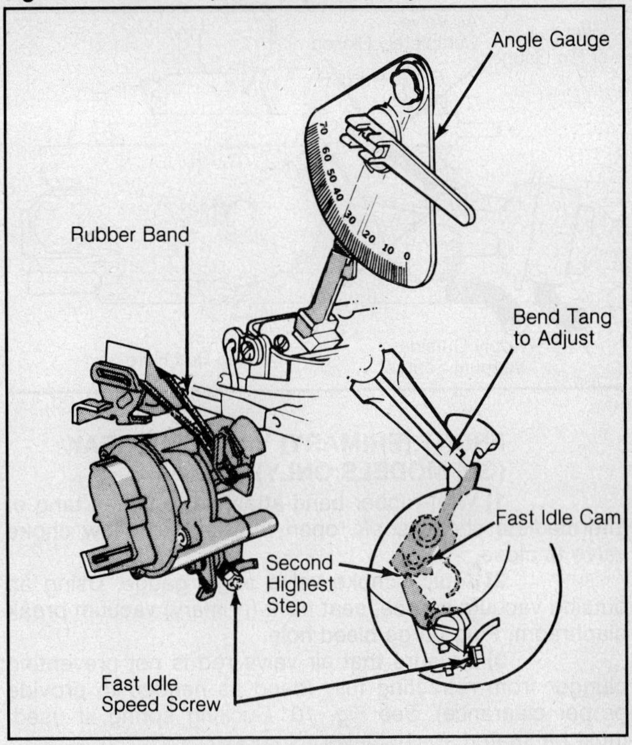

Hold choke closed with a rubber band.

2) Make sure air valve is completely closed. Insert a .025" drill or pin gauge between rod and end of slot in lever. *See Fig. 8.*

3) Bend rod at point shown in *Fig. 8* to adjust clearance in slot. Remove tape and reconnect vacuum hose to diaphragm.

Fig. 8: Front Air Valve Rod Adjustment

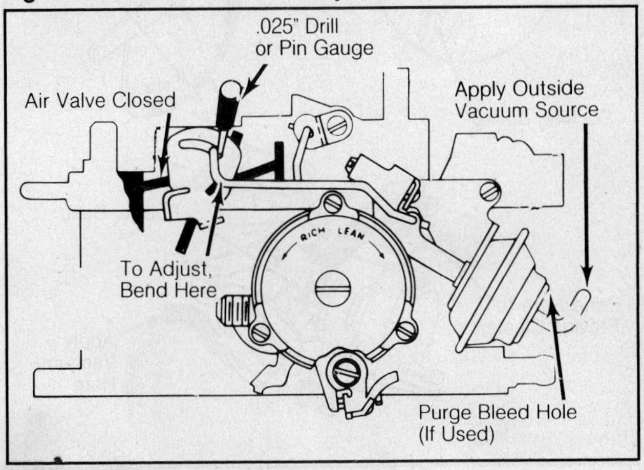

Place drill or pin gauge between rod and end of slot in lever.

REAR AIR VALVE ROD

1) Using an outside vacuum source, seat rear (secondary) choke vacuum break diaphragm. Make sure air valve is completely closed.

2) Insert a .025" drill or pin gauge between rod and end of slot in lever. *See Fig. 9.*

3) Bend rod at point shown in *Fig. 9* to adjust clearance in slot. Reconnect vacuum hose to diaphragm.

ROCHESTER M4MC, M4ME, M4MED, M4MEF 4-BBL. (Cont.)

Fig. 9: Rear Air Valve Rod Adjustment

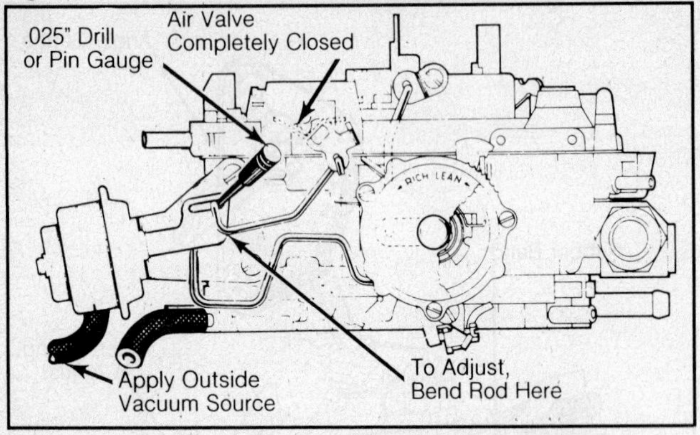

FRONT (PRIMARY) VACUUM BREAK (GM MODELS ONLY)

1) With rubber band attached to Green tang of intermediate choke shaft, open throttle and allow choke valve to close.

2) Attach choke valve angle gauge. Using an outside vacuum source, seat front (primary) vacuum break diaphragm. Plug purge bleed hole.

3) Be sure that air valve rod is not preventing plunger from retracting fully (bend as needed to provide proper clearance). *See Fig. 10.* Bucking spring, if used, must be seated against lever as shown.

Fig. 10: Front Vacuum Break Adjustment

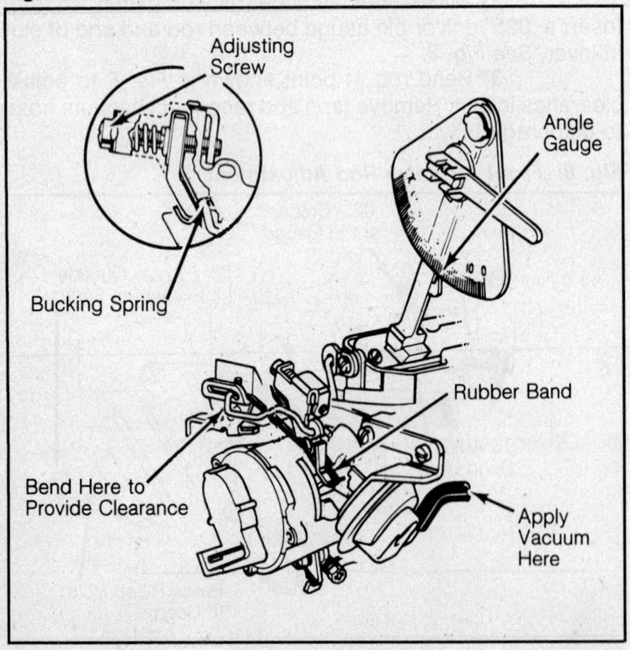

Use angle gauge to check for proper vacuum break adjustment.

4) To adjust, turn vacuum break adjustment screw in until bubble of choke valve angle gauge is centered. Remove gauge.

NOTE: **Some models will have tamper-proof plugs over the adjustment screw. To gain access to adjustment screw, remove vacuum break bracket from carburetor. Carefully grind off plugs over adjustment screw and replace vacuum break diaphragm.**

REAR (SECONDARY) VACUUM BREAK

1) Attach rubber band to Green tang of intermediate choke shaft. Open throttle to allow choke valve to close.

2) Attach angle gauge and set angle to specification. Using outside vacuum source, apply at least 18 in. Hg to retract vacuum break plunger. Plug purge bleed hole.

3) If air valve rod prevents plunger from retracting fully, bend rod to permit full plunger travel. *See Fig. 11.* Adjust final rod clearance after rear vacuum break adjustment has been made. On models so equipped, plunger stem must be extended fully to compress plunger bucking spring.

4) Check angle with vacuum applied. On models so equipped, adjust by turning screw in end of vacuum break with 1/8" Allen wrench. On all other models, support vacuum break rod and bend at point indicated in *Fig. 11.*

Fig. 11: Rear Vacuum Break Adjustment

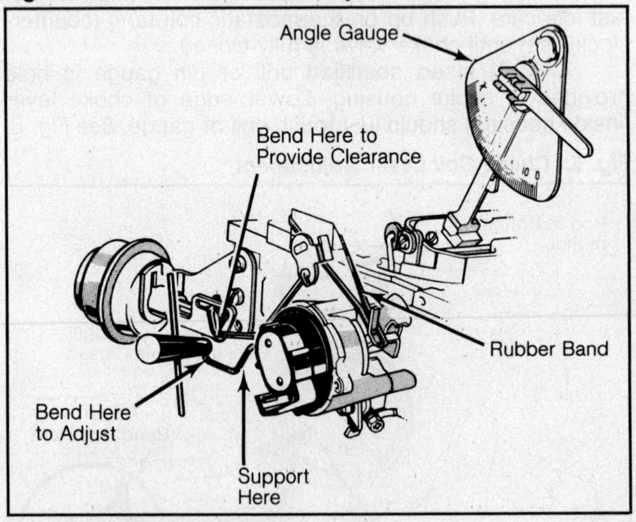

Lightly hold choke in closed position.

AIR VALVE SPRING

1) Using a 3/32" Allen wrench, loosen lock screw. Turn tension adjusting screw counterclockwise until air valve opens part way. *See Fig. 12.*

Fig. 12: Air Valve Spring Adjustment

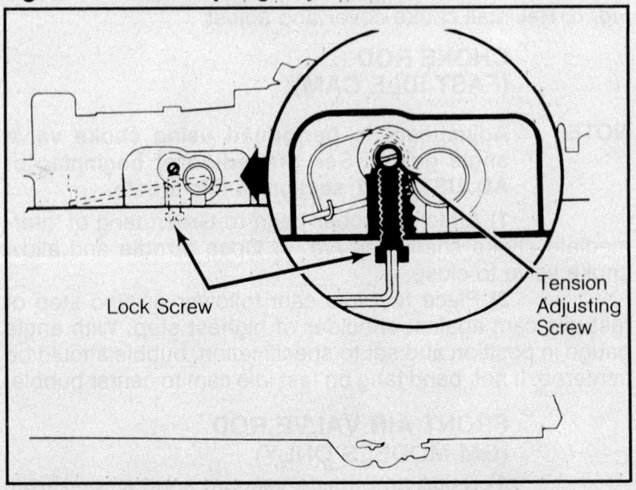

Tighten adjusting screw specified number of turns.

ROCHESTER M4MC, M4ME, M4MED, M4MEF 4-BBL. (Cont.)

2) Turn tension adjusting screw clockwise until air valve just closes. Then turn adjusting screw clockwise specified number of turns. Hold adjusting screw and tighten lock screw.

AUTOMATIC CHOKE

NOTE: **Choke coil cover is retained on housing by rivets to prevent tampering with factory adjustment. If necessary to remove cover, refer to DISASSEMBLY and REASSEMBLY procedures in this article.**

CHOKE UNLOADER

NOTE: **Adjustment is performed using choke valve angle gauge. See procedure at beginning of ADJUSTMENTS in this article.**

1) Attach rubber band to Green tang of intermediate choke shaft. Open throttle to allow choke valve to close. Attach angle gauge and set angle to specification.

2) Hold secondary lock-out lever away from pin. Hold throttle lever in wide open position. *See Fig. 13.*

3) To adjust, bend fast idle lever tang until bubble of angle gauge is centered.

Fig. 13: Choke Unloader Adjustment

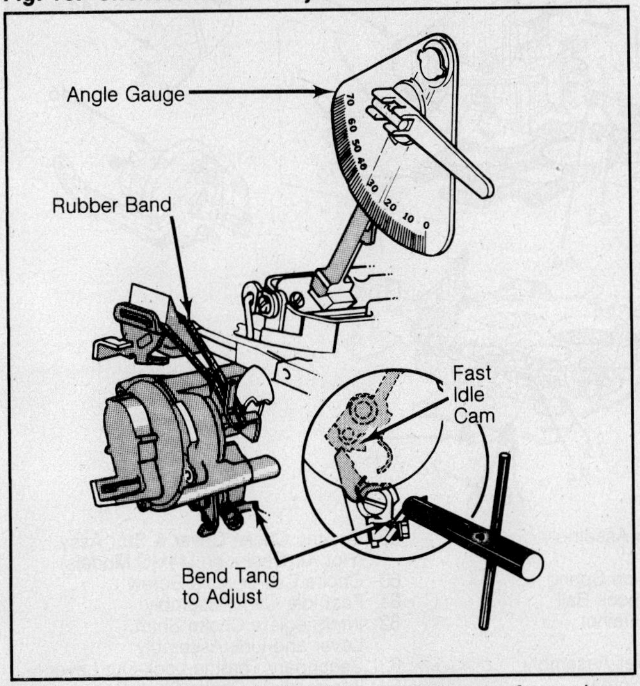

Adjust with secondary lock-out lever held away from pin.

SECONDARY THROTTLE VALVE LOCK-OUT

Lock-Out Lever Side Clearance

1) Hold choke valve and throttle valves closed.

2) Measure secondary throttle valve lock-out lever side clearance between pin and lock-out lever. Bend pin to obtain clearance of .015". *See Fig. 14.*

Lock-Out Lever Opening Clearance

1) Push down on tail of fast idle cam to completely open choke valve.

2) Measure secondary throttle valve lock-out lever opening clearance between end of pin and toe of lock-out lever. *See Fig. 14.*

3) File end of lock-out pin to obtain clearance of .015". Make sure all burrs are removed.

Fig. 14: Secondary Throttle Valve Lock-Out Adjustments

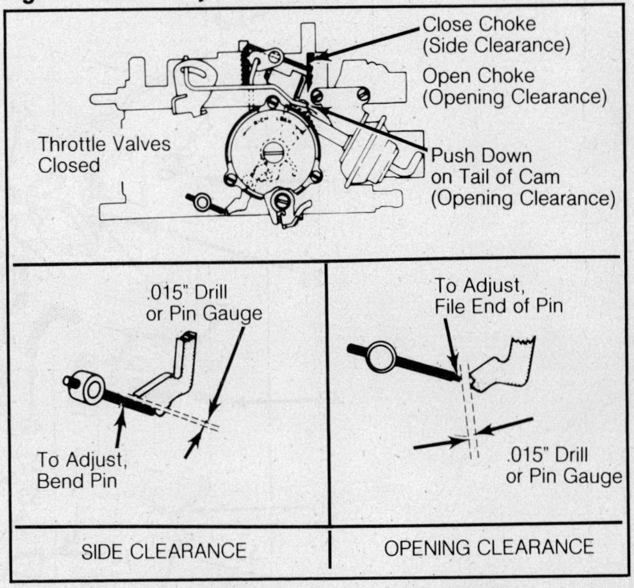

Both steps must be done to perform adjustment.

Fig. 15: Removing Idle Mixture Needle Plugs

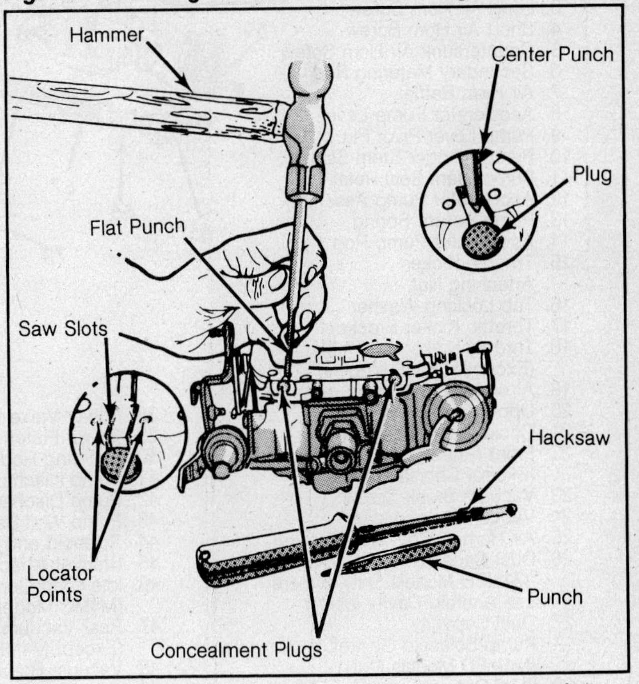

Cuts must not extend more than 1/8" past locator points.

OVERHAUL

DISASSEMBLY

NOTE: **All carburetor servicing should be performed with carburetor in holding fixture to prevent damage to throttle valves.**

ROCHESTER M4MC, M4ME, M4MED, M4MEF 4-BBL. (Cont.)

Fig. 16: Exploded View of Rochester M4M-Series 4-Barrel Carburetor

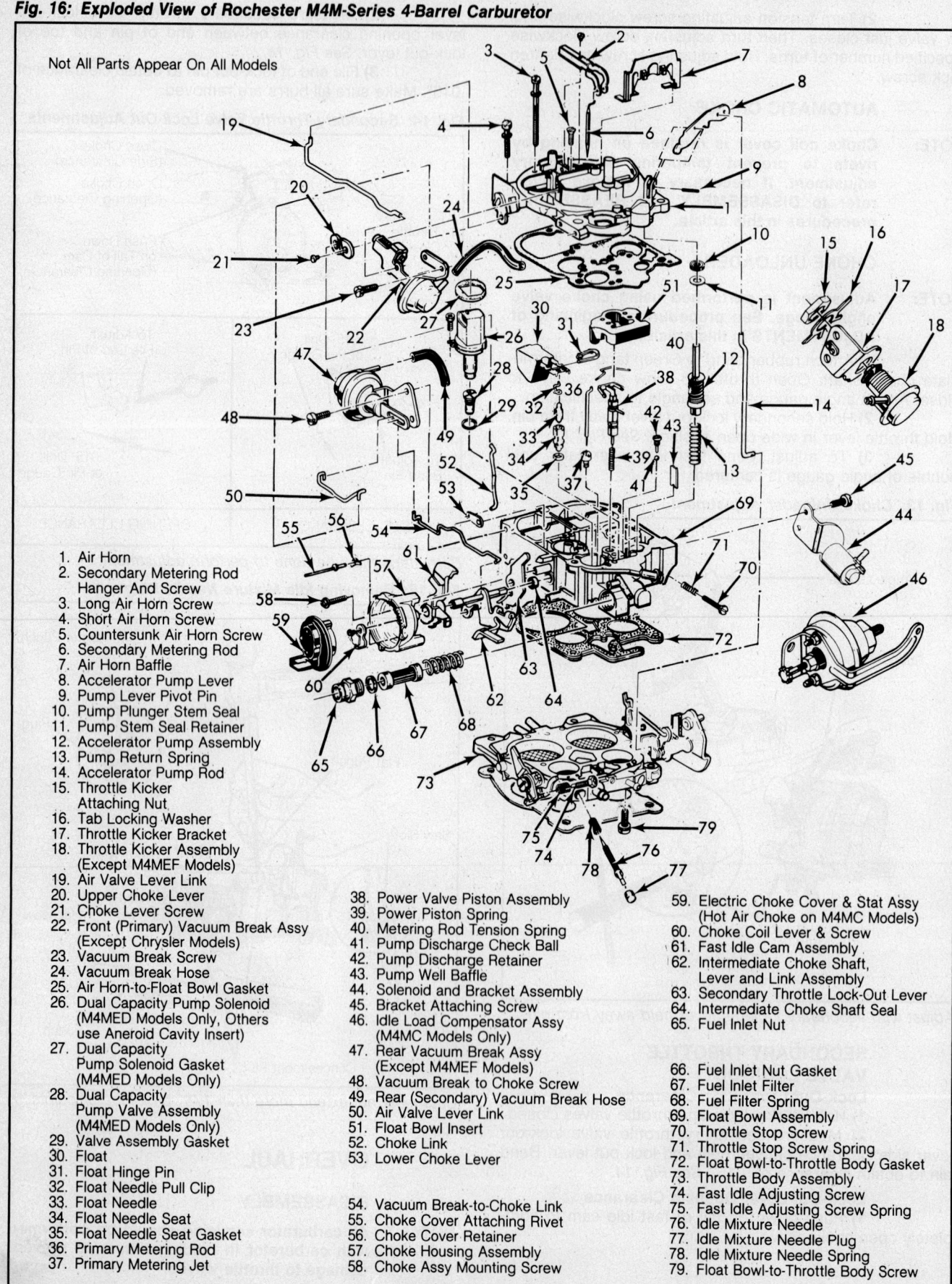

Not All Parts Appear On All Models

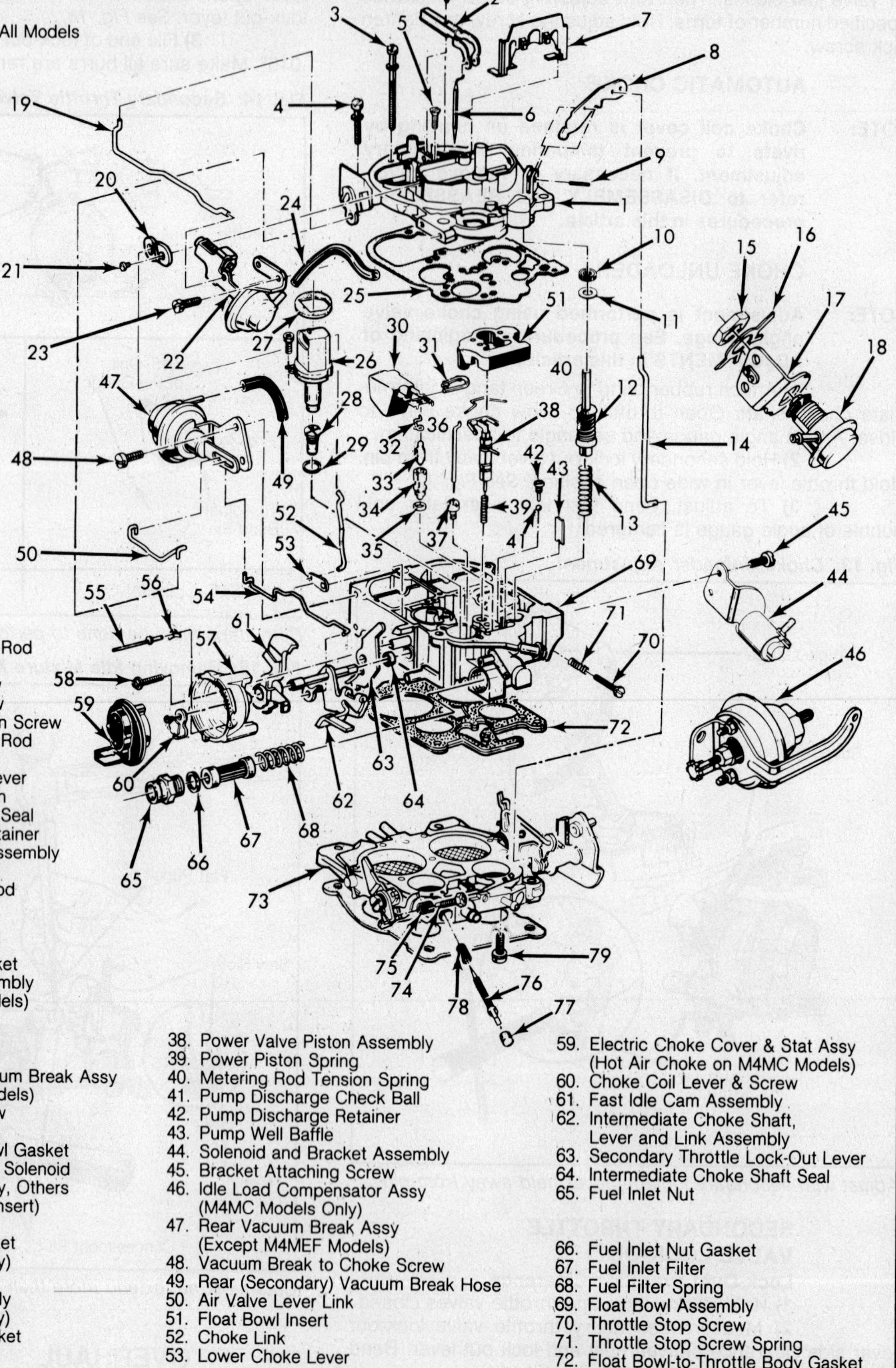

1. Air Horn
2. Secondary Metering Rod Hanger And Screw
3. Long Air Horn Screw
4. Short Air Horn Screw
5. Countersunk Air Horn Screw
6. Secondary Metering Rod
7. Air Horn Baffle
8. Accelerator Pump Lever
9. Pump Lever Pivot Pin
10. Pump Plunger Stem Seal
11. Pump Stem Seal Retainer
12. Accelerator Pump Assembly
13. Pump Return Spring
14. Accelerator Pump Rod
15. Throttle Kicker Attaching Nut
16. Tab Locking Washer
17. Throttle Kicker Bracket
18. Throttle Kicker Assembly (Except M4MEF Models)
19. Air Valve Lever Link
20. Upper Choke Lever
21. Choke Lever Screw
22. Front (Primary) Vacuum Break Assy (Except Chrysler Models)
23. Vacuum Break Screw
24. Vacuum Break Hose
25. Air Horn-to-Float Bowl Gasket
26. Dual Capacity Pump Solenoid (M4MED Models Only, Others use Aneroid Cavity Insert)
27. Dual Capacity Pump Solenoid Gasket (M4MED Models Only)
28. Dual Capacity Pump Valve Assembly (M4MED Models Only)
29. Valve Assembly Gasket
30. Float
31. Float Hinge Pin
32. Float Needle Pull Clip
33. Float Needle
34. Float Needle Seat
35. Float Needle Seat Gasket
36. Primary Metering Rod
37. Primary Metering Jet
38. Power Valve Piston Assembly
39. Power Piston Spring
40. Metering Rod Tension Spring
41. Pump Discharge Check Ball
42. Pump Discharge Retainer
43. Pump Well Baffle
44. Solenoid and Bracket Assembly
45. Bracket Attaching Screw
46. Idle Load Compensator Assy (M4MC Models Only)
47. Rear Vacuum Break Assy (Except M4MEF Models)
48. Vacuum Break to Choke Screw
49. Rear (Secondary) Vacuum Break Hose
50. Air Valve Lever Link
51. Float Bowl Insert
52. Choke Link
53. Lower Choke Lever
54. Vacuum Break-to-Choke Link
55. Choke Cover Attaching Rivet
56. Choke Cover Retainer
57. Choke Housing Assembly
58. Choke Assy Mounting Screw
59. Electric Choke Cover & Stat Assy (Hot Air Choke on M4MC Models)
60. Choke Coil Lever & Screw
61. Fast Idle Cam Assembly
62. Intermediate Choke Shaft, Lever and Link Assembly
63. Secondary Throttle Lock-Out Lever
64. Intermediate Choke Shaft Seal
65. Fuel Inlet Nut
66. Fuel Inlet Nut Gasket
67. Fuel Inlet Filter
68. Fuel Filter Spring
69. Float Bowl Assembly
70. Throttle Stop Screw
71. Throttle Stop Screw Spring
72. Float Bowl-to-Throttle Body Gasket
73. Throttle Body Assembly
74. Fast Idle Adjusting Screw
75. Fast Idle Adjusting Screw Spring
76. Idle Mixture Needle
77. Idle Mixture Needle Plug
78. Idle Mixture Needle Spring
79. Float Bowl-to-Throttle Body Screw

ROCHESTER M4MC, M4ME, M4MED, M4MEF 4-BBL. (Cont.)

Removing Idle Mixture Screw Plugs

1) For complete overhaul, idle mixture needle plugs must be removed. Turn carburetor over and drain out fuel. Place carburetor in holding fixture, manifold side up.

2) Using a hacksaw, make 2 parallel cuts in the throttle body, one on each side of locator point. *See Fig. 15.* Cuts should be down to plug, but must not extend more than 1/8" past locator points.

3) Place a small flat punch at a point near ends of saw marks. Hold punch at a 45° angle and drive into throttle body until casting breaks away. Plug should be exposed.

4) Hold a center punch vertically and drive into plug. Change punch angle to 45° and drive plug out of casting. Plug will shatter. It is not necessary to remove plug completely, only enough to allow access to idle mixture screw. Repeat procedure for other plug.

Vacuum Break Assemblies

1) Remove vacuum break hoses and attaching screws. Remove front (primary) vacuum break assembly and air valve lever link.

2) Rotate rear (secondary) vacuum break assembly to remove link from slot. Remove rear vacuum break assembly, air valve lever link and vacuum break-to-choke link.

Air Horn

1) Remove upper choke lever retaining screw and choke lever. Disconnect choke rod from lower lever inside float bowl casting by holding lower lever outward with small screwdriver and twisting rod counterclockwise.

2) Remove retaining screw from secondary metering rod hanger. Lift out hanger and secondary metering rods as an assembly.

3) Drive pump lever pivot pin inward until pump lever can be removed. Disconnect pump rod from pump lever, noting location of rod in lever for reassembly reference.

4) Remove air horn-to-float bowl attaching screws. Countersunk screws (2) are located next to venturi. Remove secondary air baffle deflector (if equipped) from beneath 2 center attaching screws. Remove air horn from float bowl by lifting straight up. Gasket should remain on float bowl for later removal.

5) Invert air horn to remove pump plunger stem seal (if used). Using a small screwdriver, remove staking holding seal retainer in position. Remove and discard retainer and seal. Use care when removing stem seal to prevent damage to air horn casting.

6) Further disassembly of air horn is not required. If air valve closing spring and/or plastic cam need replacing, a repair kit is available.

CAUTION: On M4MEF models, DO NOT turn or remove Rich Stop Adjusting Bushing. Unnecessary adjustment of this bushing could result in engine damage or increased exhaust emissions.

Choke Cover

The choke assembly is attached with rivets to discourage tampering. For complete carburetor overhaul, cover must be removed.

1) Support float bowl and throttle body, as an assembly, on holding fixture. Align a 5/32" (No. 21) drill on rivet head and drill just enough to remove head. Repeat for all 3 rivets.

2) Use a drift and small hammer to drive the remainder of the rivets out of the choke housing. Remove choke retainers (3), and choke cover gasket (M4MC only, if used). Remove choke cover.

Float Bowl

1) Remove and discard air horn-to-float bowl gasket. Remove gasket by lifting out of dowel locating pins. Lift tab of gasket from beneath power piston hanger, being careful not to distort springs holding main metering rods.

2) On M4MED models, remove dual capacity pump solenoid gasket and discard.

3) On all models, remove accelerator pump plunger and return spring from pump well. Remove power piston and metering rods by depressing piston stem and allowing it to snap free. Repeat until piston force dislodges retainer. Do not use pliers on metering rod hanger to remove power piston. Remove power piston spring from well.

NOTE: The adjustable part throttle (APT) metering rod adjustment screw is located in a well next to power piston well. The APT is preset at the factory and no attempt should be made to alter its setting. If a new float bowl is required, it will contain a preset APT screw.

4) Remove metering rods from power piston by disconnecting tension spring from top of each rod. Note position of spring for reassembly reference. Rotate rods out of hanger.

5) Remove plastic filler block located over float valve. Remove float assembly and fuel inlet needle by pulling up on retaining pin. Remove inlet seat and gasket.

6) On M4MED models, remove dual capacity pump solenoid. Remove dual capacity pump valve assembly. On all other models, remove aneroid cavity insert.

7) On all models, remove primary (main) metering jets. Do not remove secondary jets as they are a permanent part of the float bowl. If secondary jets are damaged, complete float bowl must be replaced.

8) Remove pump discharge check ball retainer. Invert bowl and catch check ball. On Chrysler models, remove secondary air baffle (if replacement is required). On all models, remove pump well baffle.

9) Remove choke coil cover as previously described. Remove choke mounting screw and washer from inside choke housing and slide choke assembly out of float bowl.

10) On M4MC models, remove choke housing-to-float bowl seal. On all models, remove secondary lockout lever from float bowl. Disconnect vacuum link from lever.

11) Remove choke coil lever attaching screw and choke coil lever. Remove intermediate choke shaft, lever and link assembly. Remove fast idle cam assembly.

12) On M4MC models, remove intermediate choke shaft seal. On all models, remove intermediate choke shaft seal from float bowl insert for bowl cleaning. Do not attempt to remove plastic insert.

13) Remove fuel inlet nut, gasket, filter and spring. Remove throttle body-to-float bowl attaching screws (3). Remove throttle body. Remove throttle body-to-float bowl insulator gasket.

Throttle Body

1) Remove accelerator pump rod from throttle lever by rotating rod until tang on rod aligns with slot in lever.

ROCHESTER M4MC, M4ME, M4MED, M4MEF 4-BBL. (Cont.)

2) If not already removed, remove idle mixture needle plugs as described earlier. Count number of turns required to lightly seat mixture needles and record for reassembly reference. Remove mixture needles.

3) Further disassembly of throttle body is not required. Throttle valve screws are staked in place and should not be removed. The throttle body is serviced as a complete assembly.

CLEANING & INSPECTION

1) Clean all metal carburetor parts in standard carburetor cleaning solution. Do not soak any rubber or plastic parts, solenoids, pump plunger, pump stem seal, etc., in cleaning solution as they will swell, harden or distort.

2) The plastic cam on the air valve shaft and the bushing in the fuel bowl MAY be cleaned in carburetor cleaner. Rinse thoroughly after cleaning.

3) Thoroughly clean all metal parts and blow dry with shop air. Make sure all passages and metering parts are free of burrs and dirt. Do not pass drills or wire through jets.

4) The power valve piston bore in the float bowl may be cleaned with a .375" soft-wire brush. Turn brush clockwise through full length of bore, plus several more turns to remove dirt and varnish.

5) Inspect upper and lower surfaces of carburetor castings for damage.

NOTE: **The letters "MW" on the float bowl, if present, indicate a Machined Pump Well. If replacement of the float bowl is required, the new float bowl must also display these letters.**

6) Inspect holes in levers for excessive wear or out-of-round condition. Replace levers if worn.

7) Inspect plastic parts for cracks, damage, etc. Replace, if necessary.

REASSEMBLY

1) Use new gaskets and seals. Make sure that new gaskets fit correctly. Make sure that all holes and slots are punched through and correctly located. To reassemble carburetor, reverse disassembly procedure, noting the following:

2) Turn idle mixture adjusting screws in until lightly seated, then back out number of turns recorded during disassembly. If number unknown, back out 3 turns as a preliminary adjustment.

3) Install fuel inlet needle pull clip over edge of flat on float arm facing float. Do not hook clip in holes in float arm.

4) Install plastic float bowl filler block after float level adjustment and before metering rod installation.

5) Lubricate air valve shaft pin with lithium-based grease where contacted by spring.

6) When installing new pump plunger stem seal and retainer in air horn, lip on seal faces out. Lightly stake seal retainer in place at 3 locations, different from original stakings.

7) When installing air horn screws, countersunk screws (2) are installed next to venturi area. Install secondary air baffle under screws No. 2 and 4. Tighten air horn screws evenly and in sequence. *See Fig. 16.*

8) Install accelerator pump rod link in hole of pump lever as noted during disassembly.

9) The intermediate choke shaft lever and fast idle cam are installed correctly when the tang on lever is beneath the fast idle cam.

10) Make all choke coil lever adjustments before installing choke cover assembly. A gasket is used between choke housing and choke coil cover on M4MC models, only. Surface contact is needed to provide a ground for electric choke on all other models.

11) When installing choke cover, place fast idle screw on high step of fast idle cam and be sure that coil tang engages the inside coil pick-up lever. Install choke cover with rivets supplied in service kit.

Fig. 17: Air Horn Screw Tightening Sequence

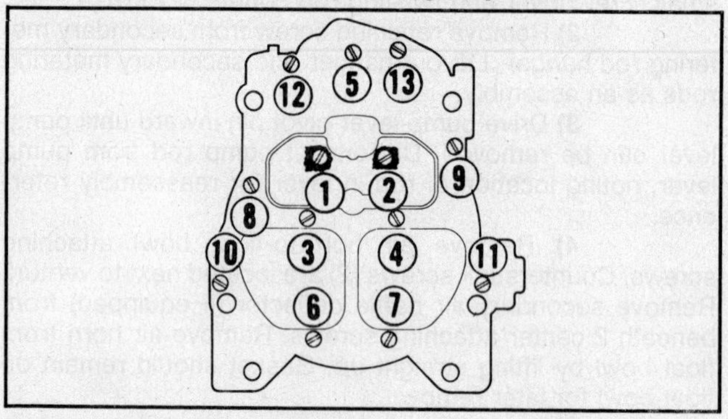

Some models do not include screws 8, 9, 12 and 13.

ROCHESTER M4MC, M4ME, M4MED, M4MEF 4-BBL. (Cont.)

CARBURETOR ADJUSTMENT SPECIFICATIONS

Application	Float Level	Accelerator Pump		Choke Coil Lever	Choke Rod	Vacuum Break		Air Valve Spring [1]	Auto. Choke	Choke Unloader
		Stem	Hole			Primary	Secondary			
17084500	12/32"	9/32"	Inner	.120"	37°	23°	30°	1	TR	40°
17084502	12/32"	9/32"	Inner	.120"	46°	24°	30°	7/8	TR	40°
17085206	13/32"	9/32"	Inner	.120"	46°	.....	26°	7/8	TR	39°
17085208	13/32"	9/32"	Inner	.120"	20°	26°	38°	7/8	TR	39°
17085209	13/32"	3/8"	Outer	.120"	20°	26°	36°	7/8	TR	39°
17085210	13/32"	9/32"	Inner	.120"	20°	26°	38°	7/8	TR	39°
17085211	13/32"	3/8"	Outer	.120"	20°	26°	36°	7/8	TR	39°
17085213	13/32"	9/32"	Inner	.120"	46°	23°	.....	7/8	TR	35°
17085215	13/32"	9/32"	Inner	.120"	46°	.....	26°	7/8	TR	32°
17085220	13/32"	3/8"	Outer	.120"	20°	.....	26°	7/8	TR	32°
17085221	13/32"	3/8"	Outer	.120"	20°	.....	26°	7/8	TR	32°
17085222	13/32"	9/32"	Inner	.120"	20°	26°	36°	1/2	TR	39°
17085223	13/32"	3/8"	Outer	.120"	20°	26°	36°	1/2	TR	39°
17085224	13/32"	9/32"	Inner	.120"	20°	26°	36°	1/2	TR	39°
17085225	13/32"	3/8"	Outer	.120"	20°	26°	36°	1/2	TR	39°
17085226	13/32"	9/32"	Inner	.120"	20°	.....	24°	7/8	TR	32°
17085227	13/32"	9/32"	Inner	.120"	20°	.....	24°	7/8	TR	32°
17085228	13/32"	9/32"	Inner	.120"	46°	.....	24°	7/8	TR	39°
17085229	13/32"	9/32"	Inner	.120"	46°	.....	24°	7/8	TR	39°
17085230	13/32"	9/32"	Inner	.120"	20°	.....	26°	7/8	TR	32°
17085231	13/32"	9/32"	Inner	.120"	20°	.....	26°	7/8	TR	32°
17085235	13/32"	9/32"	Inner	.120"	46°	.....	26°	7/8	TR	39°
17085238	13/32"	3/8"	Outer	.120"	20°	.....	26°	7/8	TR	32°
17085239	13/32"	3/8"	Outer	.120"	20°	.....	26°	7/8	TR	32°
17085290	13/32"	9/32"	Inner	.120"	46°	.....	24°	7/8	TR	39°
17085291	13/32"	3/8"	Outer	.120"	46°	.....	26°	7/8	TR	39°
17085292	13/32"	9/32"	Inner	.120"	46°	.....	24°	7/8	TR	39°
17085293	13/32"	3/8"	Outer	.120"	46°	.....	26°	7/8	TR	39°
17085294	13/32"	9/32"	Inner	.120"	46°	.....	26°	7/8	TR	39°
17085298	13/32"	9/32"	Inner	.120"	46°	.....	26°	7/8	TR	39°
17085408 [2]	13/32"	.....	[6]	.120"	20°	.....	27°	1/2	TR	38°
17085409 [3]	13/32"	.....	[6]	.120"	20°	.....	27°	5/8	TR	38°
17085415 [4]	13/32"	.....	[6]	.120"	20°	.....	27°	1/2	TR	38°
17085417 [5]	13/32"	.....	[6]	.120"	20°	.....	27°	3/4	TR	38°

[1] – Specification is amount of turns.
[2] – Chrysler Number: 4306408
[3] – Chrysler Number: 4306409
[4] – Chrysler Number: 4306415
[5] – Chrysler Number: 4306417
[6] – Factory set. Record at disassembly and reinstall in same hole.
TR – Tamper Resistant

1985 Fuel Injection

FORD ELECTRONIC – MULTI-POINT

2.3L & 5.0L Engines

DESCRIPTION

The Electronic Fuel Injection (EFI) system is a multi-point, pulse time fuel injection system, with a mass air flow sensor. Fuel is metered into intake air stream, according to engine demand, through injectors mounted on a tuned intake manifold.

An on-board electronic engine control (EEC-IV) module accepts inputs from various engine sensors to compute required fuel flow rate necessary to maintain correct air/fuel ratio throughout RPM range.

The EEC-IV computer sends a command to injectors to meter approximate quantity of fuel. System will automatically sense and compensate for changes in altitude. It will also permit push-starting of vehicle if necessary (M/T only).

Fig. 1: 5.0L Multi-Point Fuel Injection System

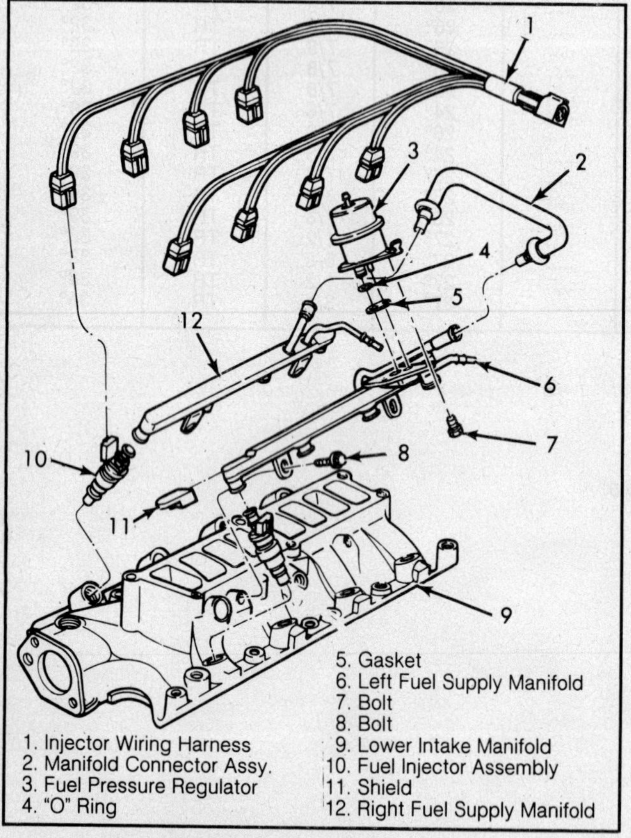

OPERATION

FUEL DELIVERY

The fuel delivery sub-system consists of a low pressure fuel pump mounted in fuel tank, a fuel filter-/reservoir and a high pressure electric fuel pump. Pump delivers fuel from fuel tank through a 20 micron fuel filter to a fuel charging manifold assembly. The fuel charging manifold assembly incorporates electrically actuated injectors directly above each engine intake port.

When energized, injectors spray a metered quantity of fuel into intake air stream. On 5.0L engines, a bank of four injectors is energized once every crankshaft revolution, followed by second bank of injectors during next crankshaft revolution. On 2.3L engines, all injectors are energized simultaneously, once per crankshaft revolution.

The length of time that injectors are energized (injector "on time" or "pulse width") is controlled by EEC module. A constant fuel pressure drop is maintained across injector nozzles by a pressure regulator.

Fig. 2: 2.3L Multi-Point Fuel Injection System

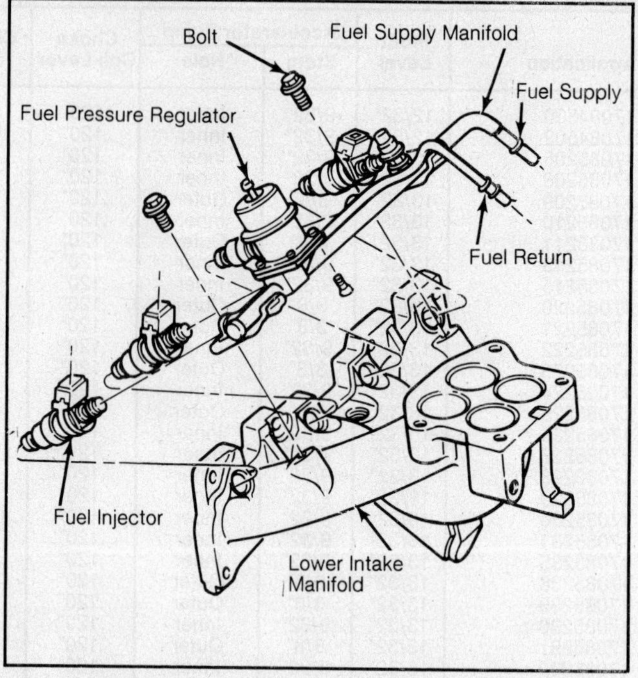

FUEL PRESSURE REGULATOR

The regulator is positioned downstream from injectors. Excess fuel not required by engine, passes through regulator and returns to fuel tank through a fuel return line.

The regulator is a diaphragm operated relief valve. One side of diaphragm senses fuel pressure and other side senses intake manifold vacuum. Nominal fuel pressure is established by an applied spring preload on diaphragm. Balancing one side of diaphragm with manifold pressure maintains a constant fuel pressure drop across injectors.

FUEL PUMP CONTROL

The electrical system has a fuel pump relay, controlled by EEC module, which provides power to fuel pump under various operating conditions. When ignition is in "OFF" position, EEC power and fuel pump relay contacts are open.

After engine starts, and ignition is returned to "ON" position, power to fuel pump is again supplied through fuel pump relay. EEC module senses engine speed and shuts off fuel pump relay when engine stops (or when engine speed falls below 120 RPM).

AIR THROTTLE BODY ASSEMBLY

The throttle body assembly controls air flow to engine through a double (5.0L) or a single (2.3L) butterfly valve. Throttle position is controlled by multiple-link, progressive opening, throttle linkage. Throttle body is a single piece die casting made of aluminum. It has a dual (5.0L) or a single (2.3L) bore with an air by-pass channel around throttle plate.

This by-pass channel controls both cold and warm engine idle air flow control as regulated by an air by-pass valve assembly mounted to throttle body (5.0L) or air cleaner (2.3L). Valve assembly is an electro-mechanical device controlled by EEC module.

It incorporates a linear actuator which positions a variable area metering valve. It also features a preset stop to locate W.O.T. position, a throttle body mounted throttle position sensor, canister purge ports for evaporative emission control (5.0L), and an adjustment screw to set throttle plate at minimum idle air flow position (2.3L).

FUEL SUPPLY MANIFOLD ASSEMBLY

The fuel supply manifold assembly delivers fuel at high pressure from vehicle fuel supply line to injectors. Assembly consists of 2 banks of stamped fuel rails connected by a crossover connection (5.0L), or 2 preformed tubes or stampings, one for fuel supply and one for fuel return (2.3L).

Fuel pressure manifold assembly has injector connectors and a mounting flange to fuel pressure regulator. It also has mounting attachments which locate fuel manifold assembly and provide injector retention. On models with 2.3L, manifold is also equipped with a fuel pressure relief valve on fuel supply tube.

FUEL INJECTORS

The injector nozzles meter and atomize fuel delivered to engine. Injectors are mounted in lower intake manifold and direct fuel just ahead of engine intake valves.

Injector bodies consist of a solenoid actuated pintle and needle valve assembly. An electrical control signal from EEC module activates injector solenoid, causing pintle to move upward off seat, allowing fuel to flow.

Since injector flow orifice diameter is fixed and fuel pressure drop across injector tip is constant, fuel flow to engine is regulated by length of time solenoid remains energized. Atomization is obtained by contouring pintle at point where fuel separates.

AIR INTAKE MANIFOLD

The air intake manifold is a 2-piece (upper and lower) aluminum casting. Runner lengths are tuned to optimize engine torque and power output. Manifold provides mounting flanges for air throttle body assembly, fuel supply manifold, accelerator control brackets, EGR valve and supply tube.

Vacuum taps are provided to support various engine accessories. Pockets for injectors are machined to prevent air and fuel leakage. Pockets in which injectors are mounted, are placed to direct injector fuel spray immediately in front of each engine intake valve.

TROUBLE SHOOTING

PRELIMINARY CHECKS

The following systems and components must be in good conditon and operating properly before beginning diagnosis of injection system:

- All support systems and wiring.
- Battery connections and specific gravity.
- Ignition system.
- Compression pressure.
- Fuel supply system pressure and flow.
- All electrical connections and terminals.
- Vacuum line, fuel hose and pipe connections.
- Air cleaner and air ducts.
- Engine coolant level.

TROUBLE SHOOTING

NOTE: **Some vehicles may not include all components listed in this article.**

Engine Does Not Crank

Check starting and charging systems.

Engine Cranks But Does Not Start

1) Ensure fuel tank is not empty, do not assume that fuel gauge is correct. Check ignition system for strong secondary current at spark plugs. If none exists or current is weak, repair ignition system problem before continuing with injection diagnosis.

2) Check fuel lines and fittings for leaks. If no leaks are found, check fuel delivery system for proper operation, pressure and volume. Reset inertia switch if necessary.

Hard to Start (Engine Cold)

1) Choke system may not be functioning correctly. Check linkage for proper operation and adjustment. Clean, service or replace as required.

2) Choke thermostat housing may be incorrectly adjusted. Adjust if needed. If it is tamper proof-type, check for incorrect assembly.

3) Intake manifold or fuel charging assembly gaskets may be leaking. Replace leaking gaskets as needed.

Rough Idle (Engine Cold)

1) Choke system may not be functioning correctly. Check linkage for proper operation and adjustment. Clean, service, or replace as required. Check pull-down adjustment.

2) Fast idle adjustments may be incorrect, or air cleaner duct vacuum motor may be damaged or stuck open. Replace or service as required.

Stall, Stumble, Hesitation (Engine Hot or Cold)

1) Choke system may not be functioning correctly. Check linkage for proper operation and adjustment. Clean, service, or replace as required. Check choke pull-down.

2) Fuel pump output may be low or fuel filter may be clogged. Service or replace as required. Air cleaner vacuum motor may be damaged. Service or replace as required.

Hard Start (Engine Hot)

1) Choke system may not be functioning correctly. Check linkage for proper operation and adjustment. Clean, service, or replace as required.

2) Choke thermostat housing may be incorrectly adjusted. Adjust choke thermostat setting if needed. If it is tamper proof-type, check for incorrect assembly.

3) Intake manifold or fuel charging assembly gaskets may be leaking. Replace leaking gaskets as needed.

FORD ELECTRONIC – MULTI-POINT (Cont.)

Rough Idle (Engine Hot)

Choke system may not be functioning correctly. Check linkage for proper operation and adjustment. Clean, service, or replace as required.

Stalls on Deceleration or Quick Stop

Throttle positioner may be functioning improperly. Service as required. Intake manifold or fuel charging assembly gaskets may be leaking. Replace leaking gaskets as needed.

Lack of Power

Fuel filter may be clogged. Check fuel delivery and repair as needed.

Reduced Top Speed/Power

1) Throttle linkage may be binding. Clean and service as required. Fuel pump volume may be low. Test fuel delivery system. Fuel filter may be clogged. Locate cause, and replace as required.

2) Injectors may be plugged or pressure regulator may be damaged. Repair or replace as needed.

Surge at Cruise

Fuel filter may be clogged. Locate cuase and replace filter. Fuel pump pressure or volume may be low. Test fuel delivery system. Fuel may be contaminated. Drain fuel and clean out system as necessary.

TESTING & DIAGNOSIS

FUEL PUMP CONTROL

When ignition is turned on, EEC power relay is energized, closing its contacts. Power is provided to both fuel pump relay and a timing device in EEC module. Fuel pump runs through contacts of fuel pump relay. If ignition is not turned on within 1 second, timing device in EEC module will create an open ground circuit.

Opening ground circuit de-energizes fuel pump relay (opening its contacts), which in turn de-energizes fuel pump. This circuitry provides for pre-pressurization of fuel system. When ignition switch is turned to "START" position, EEC module operates fuel pump relay to provide fuel for starting engine while cranking.

INERTIA SWITCH

CAUTION: Do not reset the inertia switch until the complete fuel system has been inspected for leaks.

In event of a collision, electrical contacts in inertia switch open and fuel pump automatically shuts off. Fuel pump will shut off even if engine does not stop running. The engine, however, will stop a few seconds after fuel pump stops. It is not possible to restart engine until inertia

Fig. 3: Fuel Pump Circuit Wiring Diagram

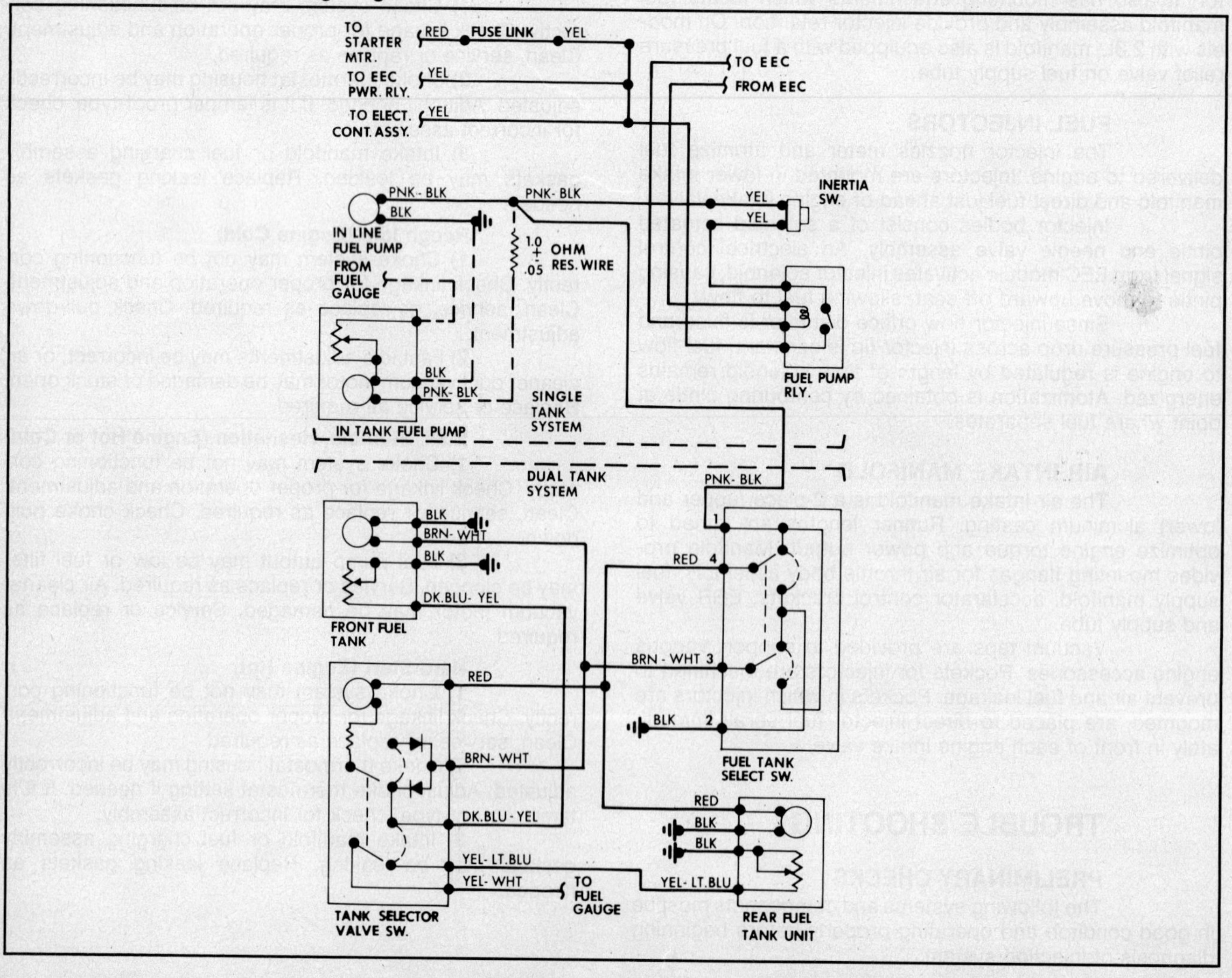

switch is manually reset. Inertia switch is located behind instrument panel. To reset inertia switch, depress button on top of switch.

HIGH PRESSURE FUEL PUMP

1) Check fuel tank(s) for adequate fuel supply, do not assume fuel gauge is correct. Check for fuel leakage at all fittings and lines. To check for electrical continuity to fuel pump, locate fuel pump connector at rail mounted (high pressure) fuel pump. Disconnect connector from body wiring harness and connect a volt/ohmmeter (VOM) across body connector.

2) With ignition off, measure resistance. If resistance is 5 ohms or less, go to step **4)**. If resistance is 5 ohms or more, connect lead of VOM to ground lead of body wiring harness and check for continuity to ground. If there is no continuity, repair wiring or body ground and repeat step **2)**.

3) If there is continuity, attach VOM to Pink/Black H wire of body connector and check continuity to ground. If not okay, it will be necessary to check wiring at pump-sender. If wiring checks okay, check continuity across pump terminals. If not okay, replace pump-sender assembly. Check for a good connection at pump-sender connector.

4) Set meter to read voltage and turn ignition on. Voltage should rise to 12 volts for one second and then return to zero. If voltage is not within specification, check electrical circuit and repair as required.

5) Attach VOM to pump harness leads and check continuity across leads. If okay, go to step **6)**. If not, check at pump terminals. If not okay at pump terminals, replace pump.

6) Check fuel pump pressure and flow as follows: with an assistant in vehicle, raise vehicle on a hoist and attach pressure gauge to fuel diagnostic valve. As a preliminary check, turn ignition on, and check pressure gauge reading. Gauge should read 30-40 psi if pump is operating properly and other system components are okay. Go to next step.

7) Disconnect fuel return line at fuel rail. Use care to avoid fuel spillage. Connect hose from fuel rail fitting to a calibrated container of at least one quart capacity. Replace fuel pump relay with modified relay. See MODIFYING FUEL CUT-OFF RELAY in this article. Take ground lead to a convenient location on vehicle and ground it. This procedure should run fuel pump. Energize fuel pump for 10 seconds.

8) Allow fuel to drain from return hose into container and observe volume. Fuel pump is operating properly if fuel pressure reaches 35-45 psi, fuel flow is a minimum of 5.6 oz. in 10 seconds and fuel pressure remains a minimim of 30 psi immediately after de-energization.

9) If all 3 conditions are met, fuel pump is operating normally. If conditions are not met, check for engine and electrical problems. If okay, go to next step.

10) Check for engine and electrical problems. If fuel pressure meets specification but fuel flow does not, check for blocked filter(s), fuel supply lines, and/or tank selector valve. After correcting any blockages, repeat above tests. If fuel flow still does not meet specification, replace pump.

11) If both fuel pressure and fuel flow meet specification but system will not stay pressurized after pumps are turned off, check for leaking injectors or regulator. If they are both okay, replace fuel pump. If no fuel flow or fuel pressure is observed, fuel system should be checked as in step **10)**. If system is okay, replace fuel pump.

MODIFYING FUEL CUT-OFF RELAY

1) Using relay (E3EB-9345-BA, CA, DA or E3TF-9345-AA), drill a 1/8" hole in-line with pins, and as close to relay base as possible.

NOTE: Part of relay skirt may be cut away to provide easier access to pins.

2) Solder a 16-18 gauge jumper wire between pins 2 and 4. Feed one end of an 8-10 ft. flexible wire through hole drilled in relay skirt and solder to pin No. 1. *See Fig. 4.*

NOTE: Leads should be soldered as close to relay base as possible to permit insertion of relay into socket with minimum interference.

3) Solder an alligator clip to other end of 8-10 ft. flexible wire.

Fig. 4: Modifying Fuel Pump Cut-Off Relay

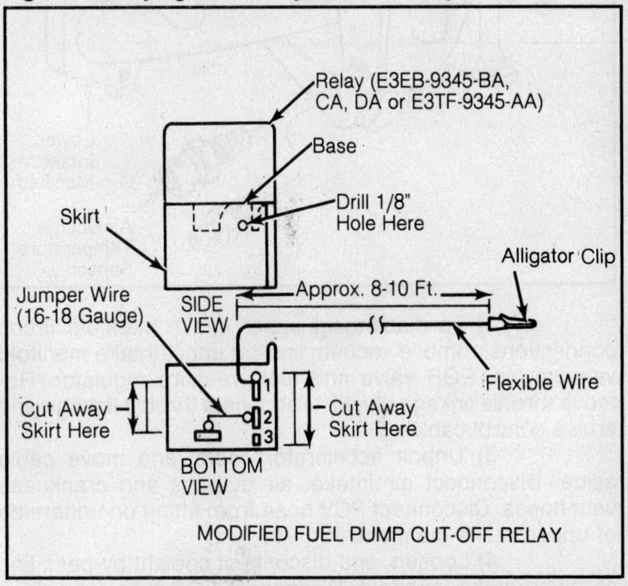

LOW PRESSURE FUEL PUMP

1) Open fuel line at high pressure pump inlet. Connect hose to line from fuel tank. Route hose to a 1 quart, calibrated container. Disconnect high pressure fuel pump electrical connector from body wiring harness.

2) Replace fuel pump relay with modified relay. See MODIFYING FUEL CUT-OFF RELAY in this article. Ground wire coming from relay to a convenient ground point to energize fuel pump and measure flow for 10 seconds.

NOTE: It may be necessary to momentarily block fuel hose to prime low pressure pump with outlet open and no back pressure on outlet; this is normal.

3) If fuel pump produces a minimum flow of 16 oz. of fuel in 10 seconds, pump is operating correctly. If there is no flow from pump, check electrical circuit, and check for inlet restriction. Replace pump if required.

1985 Fuel Injection

FORD ELECTRONIC – MULTI-POINT (Cont.)

REMOVAL & INSTALLATION

FUEL SUPPLY MANIFOLD & LOWER INTAKE MANIFOLD

Removal (2.3L Engine)

1) Drain engine coolant. Disconnect electrical connections at throttle position sensor, injector wiring harness, knock sensor, air charge temperature sensor and engine coolant temperature sensor. *See Fig. 5.*

Fig. 5: 2.3L Engine Temperature Sensor Locations

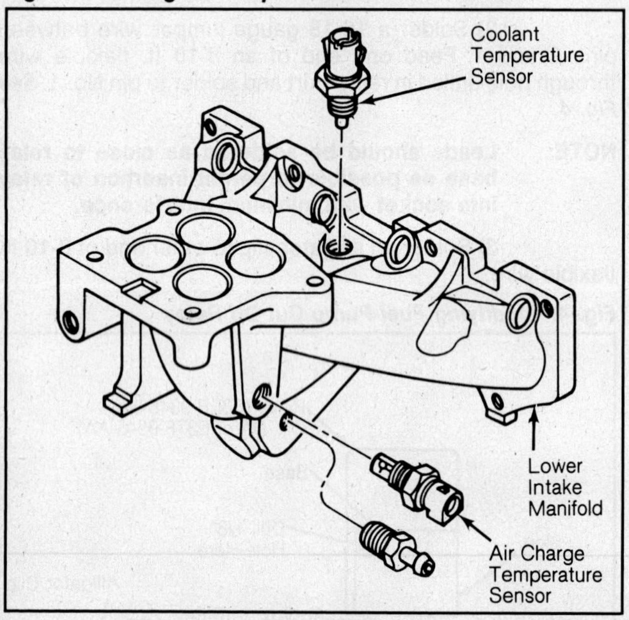

2) To disconnect upper intake manifold fitting connections, remove vacuum lines at upper intake manifold vacuum tee, EGR valve and fuel pressure regulator. Remove throttle linkage shield. Disconnect throttle linkage and cruise control cables.

3) Unbolt accelerator cable, and move cable aside. Disconnect air intake, air by-pass and crankcase vent hoses. Disconnect PCV hose from fitting on underside of upper intake manifold.

4) Loosen, and disconnect coolant by-pass line at lower intake manifold. Disconnect EGR tube from EGR valve by removing flange nut. Remove 4 upper intake manifold retaining nuts. Remove upper intake manifold and air throttle body assembly.

5) Disconnect "push-connect" fittings from fuel supply manifold and fuel return lines. See PUSH-CONNECT FITTINGS in this article for proper removal. Remove oil dipstick bracket retaining bolt.

6) Disconnect electrical connectors from all fuel injectors, and set wiring harness aside. Remove 2 fuel supply manifold retaining bolts. Carefully remove fuel supply manifold and injectors.

7) Remove injectors from fuel supply manifold by using a slight twisting/pulling motion. Remove 4 bottom retaining bolts from lower manifold. Remove 4 upper retaining bolts from lower manifold. Remove lower intake manifold.

Installation

Clean and oil manifold bolt threads. To install, reverse removal procedure, using new manifold gaskets. When installing injectors, see FUEL INJECTORS in this article. Tighten manifold bolts in correct order. *See Fig. 6.*

Fig. 6: Tightening Sequence For Lower Intake Manifold Bolts

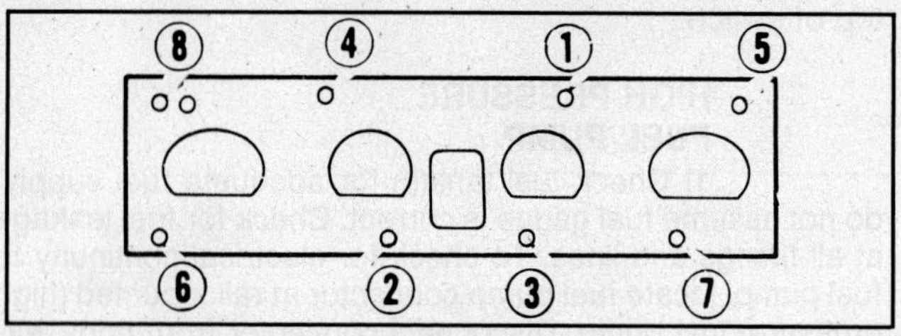

Always use new gasket during installation.

Removal (5.0L Engine)

1) Disconnect battery negative cable. Remove fuel tank and pressure relief valve caps. Install EFI Pressure Gauge (T80L-9974-A) at pressure relief valve and depressurize fuel system. Remove upper intake manifold and throttle body assembly.

2) Disconnect crossover fuel hose using Spring Lock Coupler (T81P-19623-G; T83P-19623-C for 5/8" line). Install coupler over coupling. *See Fig. 11.* Push coupler along tube, and into coupling, to release female fitting from garter spring. Pull spring lock coupling apart. Remove coupler from disconnected spring lock coupling.

3) Disconnect fuel supply and return line connections at fuel supply manifold. See PUSH-CONNECT FITTINGS in this article for proper removal. Remove 2 fuel supply manifold retaining bolts. Carefully disengage fuel supply manifold from lower intake manifold.

4) Drain cooling system. Index mark position of distributor. Remove distributor, cap and wires. Disconnect electrical connections at throttle position sensor, injector wiring harness, knock sensor, air charge temperature sensor and engine coolant temperature sensor. *See Fig. 7.*

5) Disconnect injector wiring harness from main engine harness assembly. *See Fig. 7.* Remove intake manifold ground wire. Disconnect "push-connect" fittings from fuel supply mainfold and fuel return lines. See PUSH-CONNECT FITTINGS in this article for proper removal.

6) Remove upper radiator hose from thermostat housing. Remove coolant by-pass hose. Remove heater outlet hose at intake manifold. Remove 3 air cleaner bracket attaching nuts. Remove coil bracket nut and move bracket aside.

Fig. 7: 5.0L Engine Temperature Sensor Locations

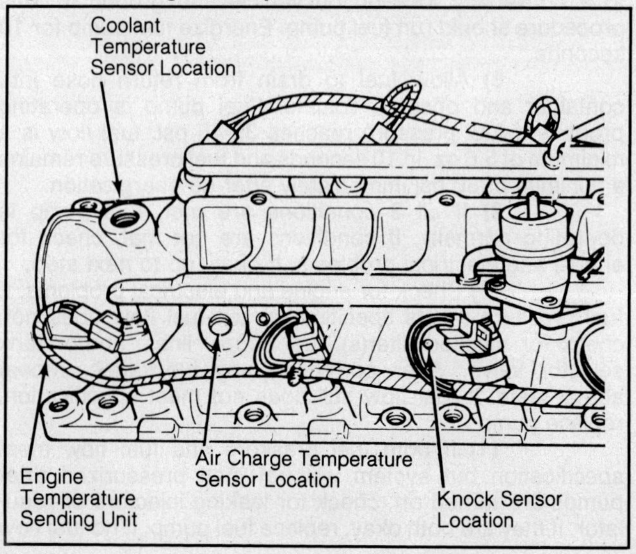

FORD ELECTRONIC – MULTI-POINT (Cont.)

7) Remove lower intake manifold studs and bolts. To ease installation, note position of studs and bolts as they are removed. Remove lower intake manifold assembly.

Installation

1) Clean and inspect manifold mounting surfaces. Apply RTV sealer to end seal joints. *See Fig. 8.* Position new gaskets, and install 2 locater pins in opposite corners of manifold. Lower manifold into position.

Fig. 8: 5.0L Engine Gasket Sealant Application

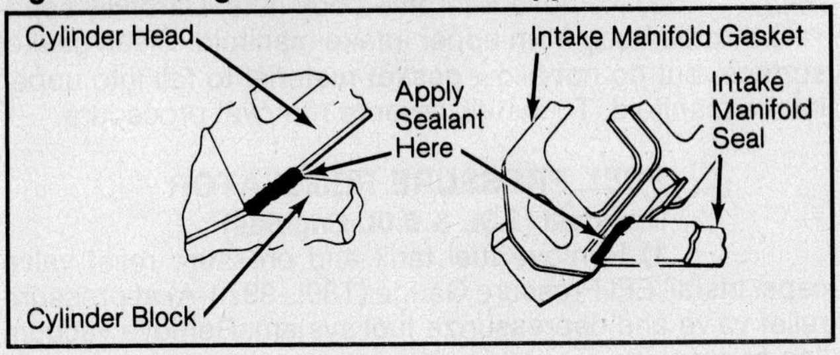

2) Tighten intake manifold studs and bolts, in proper sequence, to 25-25 ft. lbs. (32-33 N.m). *See Fig. 9.* After 10 minutes, retighten bolts and studs.

Fig. 9: 5.0L Intake Manifold Bolt Tightening Sequence

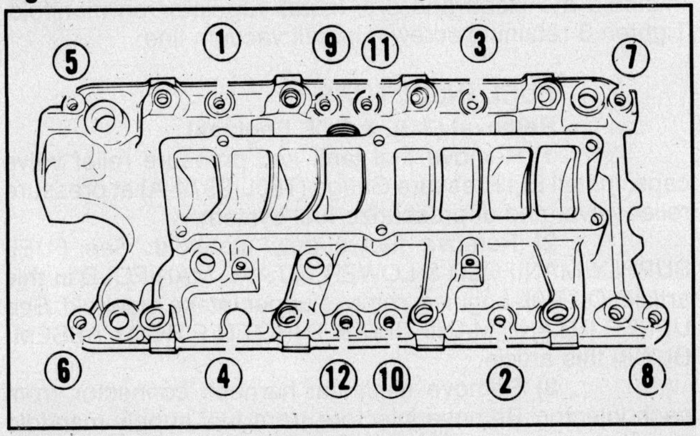

Retighten after 10 minutes.

3) Check for damaged crossover fuel hose garter spring and "O" rings. Replacement garter spring and "O" rings are available in coupler rebuild kit (E35Y-1D690-A). Wipe end of crossover lines with clean cloth. Install new "O" rings onto tube.

4) Lubricate ends of lines with clean refrigerant oil. To complete assembly, push fitting together with a slight twisting motion. Ensure garter spring is over flared end of female fitting. To complete installation, reverse removal procedure.

UPPER INTAKE MANIFOLD & THROTTLE BODY ASSEMBLY

Removal (2.3L Engine)

1) Drain engine coolant. Disconnect electrical connections at throttle position sensor, injector wiring harness, knock sensor, air charge temperature sensor and engine coolant temperature sensor. *See Fig. 5.*

2) To disconnect upper intake manifold fitting connections, remove vacuum lines at upper intake manifold vacuum tee, EGR valve and fuel pressure regulator. Remove throttle linkage shield, and disconnect throttle linkage and cruise control cables.

3) Unbolt accelerator cable, and move cable aside. Disconnect air intake, air by-pass and crankcase vent hoses. Disconnect PCV hose from fitting on underside of uppper intake manifold.

4) Loosen, and disconnect coolant by-pass line at lower intake manifold. Disconnect EGR tube from EGR valve by removing flange nut. Remove 4 upper intake manifold retaining nuts. Remove upper intake manifold and air throttle body assembly.

Installation

Remove old manifold separation gasket. DO NOT allow gasket particles to fall into lower manifold. To install, reverse removal procedure, using new manifold gasket. Tighten manifold retaining bolts alternatly.

Removal (5.0L Engine)

1) Disconnect electrical connections at throttle position sensor, EGR position sensor and air by-pass sensor. Disconnect throttle linkage at pivot ball, and transmission linkage at throttle body.

2) Remove vacuum lines at upper intake manifold vacuum tee, EGR valve and fuel pressure regulator. Disconnect PCV system by removing hose from fitting on rear of upper intake manifold.

3) Remove 2 canister purge lines from fitting on throttle body. Remove upper intake manifold support bracket bolt. Remove 6 manifold retaining bolts. Remove upper intake manifold and throttle body as an assembly.

Installation

To install, reverse removal procedure. Use new gasket between upper and lower intake manifolds.

PUSH-CONNECT FITTINGS

5.0L & 2.3L Except Aerostar
Removal & Installation
(3/8 Straight & 5/16" Elbow Fittings)

1) Inspect visible internal portion of fitting for dirt accumulation. If dirty, fitting must be cleaned prior to removal. Slowly twist fitting on tube, then push and pull the fitting until it moves freely on tube.

2) To remove hairpin clip from fitting, bend shipping tab downward until it clears the body. Next, separate 2 clip legs (about 1/8" each) to disengage body, and then push legs into fitting. *See Fig. 10.*

3) Lightly pull clip from triangle end, and work clip free of tube and fitting. Grasp fitting and hose assembly, and pull straight apart. Inspect fitting and tube for parts that may have been disloged from fitting during removal.

NOTE: Always use new clip when installing fittings.

4) To install, insert new clip into any 2 adjacent openings, with triangular portion pointing away from fitting opening. Install clip fully. Legs of clip must be locked on outside of body.

5) Wipe tube end with clean cloth. Ensure fitting is clear of dirt and obstructions. Push fitting straight onto tube end. When fitting is properly engaged, a "click" will be heard. Pull on tube to ensure that fitting is fully engaged.

Removal & Installation
(1/4" Straight Fittings)

1) Inspect visible internal portion of fitting for dirt accumulation. If dirty, fitting must be cleaned prior to removal. slowly twist the fitting on the tube, then push and pull the fitting until it moves freely on tube.

2) Align jaws of narrow pliers (less than .2 in. (5 mm) wide) with openings in side of fitting case, and com-

1985 Fuel Injection

FORD ELECTRONIC – MULTI-POINT (Cont.)

Fig. 10: Exploded View of "Push-Connect" Fittings

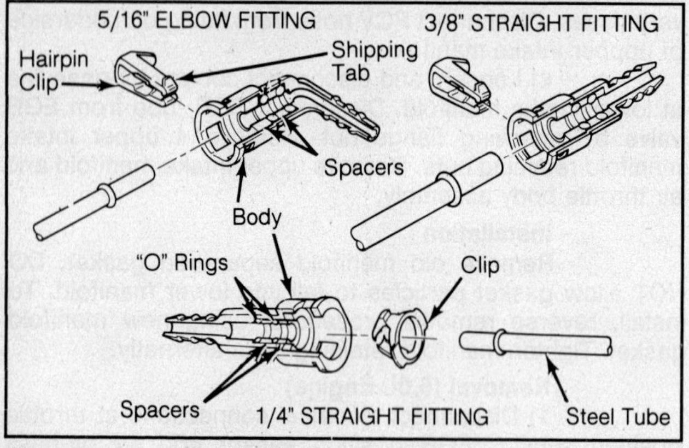

Always use a new clip during installation.

press portion of clip that retains fitting in case. *See Fig. 10.* Pull fitting from tube. If clip has been properly disengaged, fitting can be pulled from tube with little effort.

NOTE: Always use new clip when installing fittings.

3) Inspect fitting and tube for parts that may have been disloged from fitting during removal. Install new replacement clip into fitting body by inserting one serrated edge in first, then push other edges inward, into place. A "click" will be heard when clip is properly installed.

4) Wipe end of tube with clean cloth. Push fitting straight onto tube end. When fitting is properly engaged, a "click" will be heard. Pull on tube to ensure that fitting is fully engaged.

2.3L Aerostar
(3/8", 1/2" & 5/8" Straight Fittings)

1) To disconnect spring lock-type "push-connect" fittings, place Spring Lock Coupler (T81P-19623-G; T83P-19623-C for 5/8" line) over coupling. *See Fig. 11.*

2) Push coupler along tube, and into coupling, to release female fitting from garter spring. Pull spring lock coupling apart. Remove coupler from disconnected spring lock coupling.

3) Check for damaged garter spring and "O" rings. Replacement garter spring and "O" rings are available in coupler rebuild kit (E35Y-1D690-A). Wipe end of lines with clean cloth. Install new "O" rings onto tube.

4) Lubricate ends of lines with clean refrigerant oil. To complete assembly, push fitting together with a slight

Fig. 11: Installing Lock Spring-Type Coupler

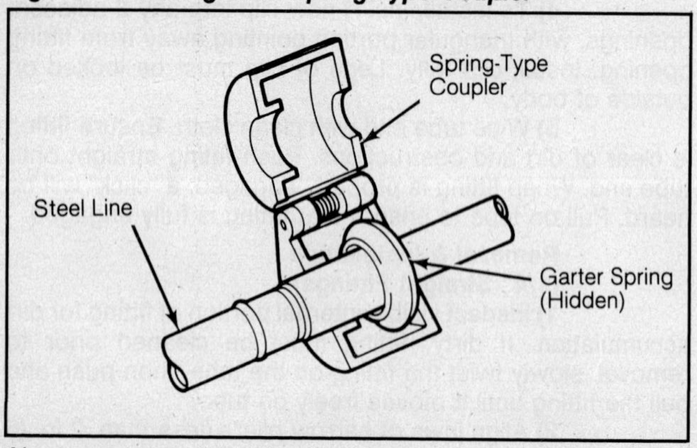

Always use new "O" rings during coupling installation.

twisting motion. Ensure garter spring is over flared end of female fitting.

AIR INTAKE THROTTLE BODY

Removal & Installation
(2.3L & 5.0L Engines)

1) On 2.3L engines, remove throttle linkage shield, throttle cable, cruise control cable and crankcase vent. On all engines, remove throttle position sensor wiring. Remove air by-pass and air intake hoses.

2) Remove 4 throttle body nuts. Carefully separate throttle body from upper intake manifold. Clean gasket surface, but do not allow gasket material to fall into upper intake manifold. To install, reverse removal procedure.

FUEL PRESSURE REGULATOR

Removal (2.3L & 5.0L Engines)

1) Remove fuel tank and pressure relief valve caps. Install EFI Pressure Gauge (T80L-9974-A) at pressure relief valve and depressurize fuel system. Remove vacuum line at pressure regulator.

2) Remove 3 allen screw from regulator housing. Remove pressure regulator, gasket and "O" ring.

Installation

Lubricate "O" ring with a light oil. DO NOT use silicone grease. Ensure gasket surfaces of regulator and manifold are clean and dry. Install regulator on manifold. Tighten 3 retaining screws. Install vacuum line.

FUEL INJECTORS

Removal (2.3L & 5.0L Engines)

1) Remove fuel tank and pressure relief valve caps. Install EFI Pressure Gauge (T80L-9974-A) at pressure relief valve, and depressurize fuel system.

2) Remove fuel supply manifold. See FUEL SUPPLY MANIFOLD & LOWER INTAKE MANIFOLD in this article. On 5.0L engines, remove upper intake manifold. See UPPER INTAKE MANIFOLD & THROTTLE BODY ASSEMBLY in this article.

3) Remove electrical harness connector from each injector. Remove injectors from fuel supply manifold by using a slight twisting/pulling motion.

Installation

Lubricate new injector "O" rings with a light oil. DO NOT use silicone grease. To complete installation, reverse removal procedure.

TIGHTENING SPECIFICATIONS

Application	Ft. Lbs. (N.m)
ACT Sensor	12-18 (16-24)
Upper Intake Manifold Bolts	
2.3L	15-22.5 (20-30)
5.0L	12-18 (17-24)
Coolant Temperature Sensor	23-33 (31-45)
Fuel Supply Manifold Bolts	15-22 (20-30)
Lower Intake Manifold Bolts	
2.3L	12-15 (16-20)
5.0L	23-25 (32-33)
EGR Tube-To-EGR Valve	6-8.5 (8-11.5)
Throttle Body Retaining Bolts	12-25 (16-20)
Pressure Relief Valve	4-7 (6.0-9.0)
	INCH Lbs. (N.m)
Pressure Regulator Screws	26-40 (3.0-4.0)
Throttle Position Sensor	14-16 (1.6-1.8)
Pressure Relief Valve Cap	4-6 (.5-.7)

GENERAL MOTORS ELECTRONIC – SINGLE UNIT

Astro, Safari & "S" Series

APPLICATION

ROCHESTER THROTTLE BODY NO.

Application	Part No.
Astro & Safari 2.5L	17085062
"S" Series 2.5L	17085065

THROTTLE BODY IDENTIFICATION

The throttle body injection (TBI) identification number is stamped on TBI mounting flange (throttle lever side). *See Fig. 1.* Alphabetical code letters are stamped on the throttle body at external tube locations to identify vacuum hose connections.

Fig. 1: Throttle Body Identification Location

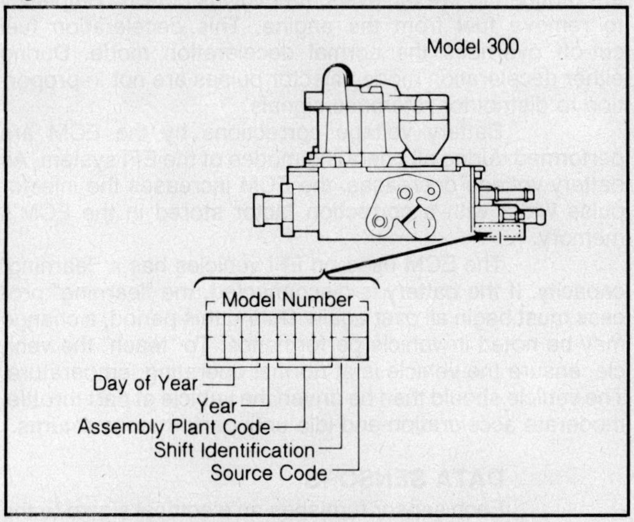

DESCRIPTION

The single unit electronic fuel injection (EFI) system consists of 7 major sub-assemblies: Fuel supply system, throttle body injector (TBI) assembly, Idle Air Control System (IAC), Electronic Control Module (ECM), Electronic Spark Timing (EST), data sensors and emission controls. Fuel is supplied to the engine through an electronically pulsed (timed) injector valve located in the throttle body unit on top of the intake manifold. The ECM controls the amount of fuel metered through the injector valve based upon engine demand and efficiency information. The ECM is a digital electronic computer which receives and computes signals from various data sensors.

NOTE: Primary sub-systems which affect fuel system operation will be covered in this article: Fuel supply system, TBI assembly, IAC system, ECM and data sensors.

OPERATION

FUEL SUPPLY SYSTEM

An electric fuel pump (located inside fuel tank as an integral part of the fuel gauge sending unit) supplies fuel under pressure to the throttle body assembly. A fuel pump relay controls fuel pump operation. When the ignition switch is turned on, the fuel pump relay activates the fuel pump for 1 seconds to prime the injector. If the ECM does not receive reference pulses (engine cranking) from the distributor after this period, the ECM deactivates the fuel pump relay. The fuel pump relay will be activated again when the ECM receives distributor reference pulses.

As a back-up system to the fuel pump relay, the fuel pump can also be activated by oil pressure sending unit. The sending unit has 2 internal circuits. One circuit operates the oil pressure indicator in the instrument panel. The second circuit is normally an open switch which closes when the oil pressure reaches about 4 psi (.3 kg/cm^2). If fuel pump relay fails, oil pressure sending unit will close, and supply voltage to fuel pump.

THROTTLE BODY INJECTOR ASSEMBLY

The throttle body injector (TBI) assembly is composed of 2 castings: a throttle body with a valve to control air flow, and a fuel body with an integral pressure regulator and fuel injector. The throttle body casting may contain ports to generate vacuum signals for EGR valve, MAP sensor and canister purge system.

The pressure regulator is a diaphragm-operated relief valve with injector pressure acting on one side of the valve and air cleaner pressure acting on the other side of the valve. The pressure regulator maintains a constant pressure drop of about 10 psi (.7 kg/cm^2) across the injector, throughout all engine operating conditions. *See Fig. 2.*

Fig. 2: Sectional View of Throttle Body Assembly

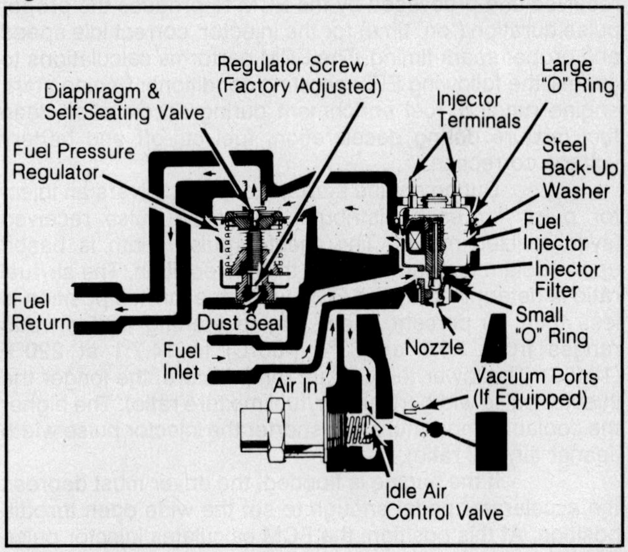

The fuel injector is a solenoid-operated device controlled by the ECM. Fuel is supplied at the lower end of the injector by the fuel supply system. The ECM activates the solenoid which lifts a normally closed ball valve off its seat. Fuel under pressure is injected in a conical spray pattern at the walls of the throttle bore, above the throttle valve. Excess fuel passes through the pressure regulator and is returned to the fuel tank.

During engine cranking, the fuel injector is activated (pulsed) once for each distributor reference pulse received by the ECM. This is referred to as the synchronized mode. In the non-synchronized mode, the injector is pulsed once every 6.25-12.5 milliseconds, depending upon engine calibration and operating conditions. In this mode, the pulse is totally independent of distributor reference pulses.

IDLE AIR CONTROL (IAC) SYSTEM

The IAC system consists of an electrically controlled motor (actuator) which positions the IAC valve in the air by-pass channel around the throttle valve. The IAC valve is a part of the throttle body casting. The ECM calculates the desired position of the IAC valve based upon battery voltage, coolant temperature, engine load and engine speed to control idle speed while preventing stalls due to engine load changes.

If engine speed is lower than desired, the ECM activates the IAC motor to retract the IAC valve. When the IAC valve is retracted, more air is diverted around the throttle valve to increase engine speed. If engine speed is higher than desired, the ECM activates the IAC motor to extend the IAC valve. When the IAC valve is extended, less air is diverted around the throttle valve, decreasing engine speed. If engine speed falls below a preset level and the throttle valve is closed, the ECM senses a near stall condition. To prevent stalling, the ECM will calculate an IAC valve position based upon barometric pressure.

ELECTRONIC CONTROL MODULE

The electronic control module (ECM) is located in the passenger compartment and is the "brain" of both the EFI and Computer Command Control systems. Locations vary, but the ECM is generally located under the instrument panel behind the glove compartment or behind the passenger footwell kick panel. Information from all data sensors is received and processed by the ECM to produce the proper pulse duration ("on" time) for the injector, correct idle speed and proper spark timing. The ECM performs calculations to control the following EFI operating conditions: Engine start, engine running, fuel enrichment during acceleration, lean fuel mixture during deceleration, fuel cut-off and battery voltage correction.

During engine starts, the ECM delivers an injector pulse for each distributor reference pulse received (synchronized mode). The injector pulse width is based upon coolant temperature and throttle position. The air/fuel ratio is determined by the ECM when the throttle position is less than 80 percent open. Engine starting air/fuel ratio ranges from 1.5:1 at -33°F (-36°C) to 14.7:1 at 220°F (104°C). The lower the coolant temperature, the longer the injector pulse width (richer air/fuel mixture ratio). The higher the coolant temperature, the shorter the injector pulse width (leaner air/fuel ratio).

If the engine is flooded, the driver must depress the accelerator pedal enough to set the wide open throttle position. At this position, the ECM calculates injector pulse width equal to an air/fuel ratio of 20:1. This air/fuel ratio will be maintained as long as the throttle remains in the wide open position and engine speed is below 600 RPM. If the throttle position becomes less than 80 percent open and/or the engine speed exceeds 600 RPM, the ECM changes the injector pulse width to that used during engine starting (based upon coolant temperature and manifold vacuum).

When the engine is running above 600 RPM, the ECM operates in the open loop mode. In open loop, the ECM calculates injector pulse width based upon coolant temperature and manifold absolute pressure (MAP). The engine will remain in open loop operation until the oxygen sensor reaches operating temperature, the coolant temperature reaches a preset temperature, and a specific period of time has elapsed after the engine starts. When all these conditions are met, the ECM operates in the closed loop mode. In closed loop, the ECM controls injector pulse width based upon oxygen sensor signals to maintain the air/fuel mixture ratio close to 14.7:1.

Fuel enrichment during acceleration is provided by the ECM. Sudden opening of the throttle valve causes a rapid increase in MAP. Pulse width is directly related to MAP, throttle position and coolant temperature. The higher the MAP and the wider the throttle angle, the wider the pulse width (richer mixture). During enrichment, the injector pulses are not in proportion to distributor reference signals (non-synchronized). Any reduction in throttle angle cancels fuel enrichment.

During normal deceleration, the air/fuel mixture must be leaner. The ECM calculates the injector pulse width in a manner similar to that used for fuel enrichment, and fuel output is reduced. This reduction in available fuel serves to remove residual fuel from intake manifold. During sudden deceleration, when MAP, throttle position and engine speed are reduced to preset levels, fuel flow is cut-off completely to remove fuel from the engine. This deceleration fuel cut-off overrides the normal deceleration mode. During either deceleration mode, injector pulses are not in proportion to distributor reference signals.

Battery voltage corrections by the ECM are performed during all operating modes of the EFI system. As battery voltage decreases, the ECM increases the injector pulse width with a correction factor stored in the ECM's memory.

The ECM used on EFI vehicles has a "learning" capacity. If the battery is disconnected, the "learning" process must begin all over again. During this period, a change may be noted in vehicle performance. To "teach" the vehicle, ensure the vehicle is at normal operating temperature. The vehicle should then be driven the vehicle at part throttle, moderate acceleration and idle until performance returns.

DATA SENSORS

Each sensor furnishes an electrical signal to the ECM, modifying injector pulse width to conform to engine operating conditions. These sensors are as follows:

Coolant Temperature Sensor (CTS)

The CTS is located in the thermostat housing. It is a variable resistor (thermister) type sensor, and transmits an electrical signal to the ECM proportionate to engine temperature. Low coolant temperature produces high resistance while high coolant temperature produces low resistance.

The ECM supplies a 5-volt signal to the CTS and measures the voltage that returns. By measuring the voltage drop between the 2 readings, the ECM is informed of engine coolant temperature. Coolant temperature is used for fuel management, idle air control, spark timing, EGR operation, canister purge operation and other engine operating functions.

Oxygen Sensor

The oxygen sensor used in the EFI system is a closed-end Zirconia sensor placed in the exhaust gas stream. The sensor is constructed in such a way that the exhaust gases pass by the bottom of the sensor and atmospheric air is admitted at the top of the sensor. The Zirconia produces an electrical voltage when exposed to oxygen, similar to a small battery. By comparing the amount of oxygen present in the exhaust gases to the amount of oxygen in the atmosphere, the sensor produces a signal which is proportional to the oxygen concentration in the exhaust gases.

As the oxygen content of the exhaust gases increases relative to the surrounding atmosphere, a lean fuel mixture is indicated by a low voltage output. As the oxygen content decreases, a rich fuel mixture is indicated by a higher voltage output. The ECM interprets the electrical signal and adjusts the injector pulse width to maintain the air/fuel ratio close to 14.7 to 1.

NOTE: No attempt should be made to measure oxygen sensor voltage output. Current drain of conventional voltmeter could permanently damage sensor, shift sensor calibration and/or render sensor unusable. Do not connect jumper wire, test leads or other electrical connectors to sensor.

Manifold Absolute Pressure (MAP) Sensor

The MAP sensor is mounted on the right side of the engine compartment. This sensor is a variable resistance type which measures the changes in the intake manifold pressure which result from engine load and speed changes.

The pressure measured by the MAP sensor is the difference between barometric pressure (atmospheric air) and manifold pressure (vacuum). A closed throttle condition (engine coast down) would produce a low MAP reading while a wide open throttle condition (engine acceleration) would produce a high MAP reading. The high value is produced because the pressure inside the intake manifold (vacuum) is the same as the pressure outside the manifold (atmospheric air).

The ECM supplies a 5-volt reference signal to the MAP sensor. As MAP changes, the electrical resistance of the sensor also changes. By monitoring the sensor output voltage (similar to the CTS), the ECM is informed of intake manifold pressure. A higher pressure (high voltage) requires more fuel, while a lower pressure (low voltage) requires less fuel.

Vehicle Speed Sensor (VSS)

This sensor is mounted behind the speedometer in the instrument cluster. It provides the ECM with pulses to determine vehicle speed. This information is used by the ECM to control the IAC motor.

NOTE: The vehicle should not be driven without the vehicle speed sensor installed.

Throttle Position Sensor (TPS)

The TPS is mounted on the side of the throttle body and is connected to the throttle shaft. As the throttle valve angle changes (accelerator pedal moved), the resistance of the sensor also changes. The ECM supplies a 5-volt reference signal to the TPS. A closed throttle condition produces high resistance at the sensor and the output signal to the ECM will be low (about .5 volts). A wide open throttle condition produces low resistance at the sensor. The output signal to the ECM will be high (about 5 volts).

By monitoring the output voltage of the TPS and comparing that value to the reference signal, the ECM can calculate fuel requirements based upon throttle valve angle (driver demand).

Engine Speed Sensor

The engine speed signal comes from the Hall Effect Unit mounted above the distributor.Pulses from the distributor are sent to the ECM where the time between these pulses is used to calculate the engine speed. The ECM adds spark advance modifications to the signal and sends the signal back to the distributor.

NOTE: For information on other sensors that are used by the ECM to control engine performance and other systems, refer to GENERAL MOTORS COMPUTER COMMAND CONTROL article in COMPUTERIZED ENGINE CONTROL section.

Fig. 3: Component Location

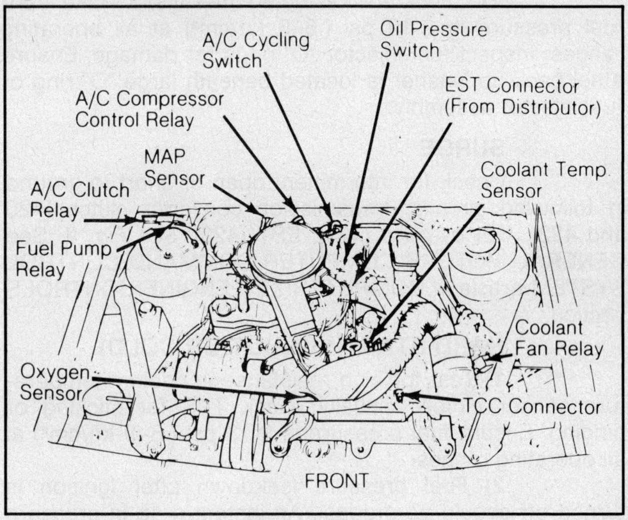

TROUBLE SHOOTING

PRELIMINARY CHECKS

The following systems and components must be in good condition and operating properly before beginning diagnosis of the fuel injection system:

- All support systems and wiring.
- Battery connections and specific gravity.
- Ignition system.
- Compression pressure.
- Fuel supply system pressure and flow.
- All electrical connections and terminals.
- Vacuum line, fuel hose and pipe connections.

NOTE: Trouble shooting and diagnosis of fuel system should begin with determining fuel system pressure. Before performing any test on the fuel system, pressure must be released from the system.

HESITATES, SLUGGISH, SAGS OR POOR MILEAGE

1) Visually check MAP sensor hose for leaks or restrictions (water in hose). Replace hose if required. Check TPS for sticking or binding and repair or replace if required. Make sure fuel pressure is a steady 9-13 psi (.6-.9 kg/cm^2) at all operating ranges. If pressure is incorrect, go to FUEL SYSTEM DIAGNOSIS chart. Ensure base engine timing is correct.

2) With fuel injector electrical connector disconnected, check for fuel leakage from injector while cranking. If leakage occurs, replace injector. Check fuel injector fuel filter for blockage and replace if necessary. Check for an open in the HEI ground circuit and repair as required.

3) Check the operation of the A/C compressor control, torque converter clutch (TCC) and cooling fan control circuit systems, and repair as required.

CUTS OUT OR STALLS

1) Check for intermittent open or short to ground in the following circuits: 5-volt reference (416), HEI reference (430), fuel pump circuit (120), injector drive circuits (467 and 468), IAC drive circuits (441, 442, 443 or 444). *See Fig. 9.*

2) Check for restricted fuel filter. Make sure fuel pressure is 9-13 psi (.6-.9 kg/cm²) at all operating ranges. Inspect fuel injector "O" rings for damage. Ensure steel back-up washer is located beneath large "O" ring of fuel injector assembly.

SURGE

Check for intermittent open or short to ground in following circuits: transmission converter clutch (420 and 422), HEI by-pass (424), EST (423). *See Fig. 9.* See GENERAL MOTORS COMPUTER COMMAND CONTROL SYSTEM article in COMPUTERIZED ENGINE CONTROLS section.

HARD STARTING (HOT OR COLD)

1) Test for high resistance in coolant temperature sensor circuit. Visually check TPS for sticking or binding. Ensure fuel pressure is 9-13 psi (.6-.9 kg/cm²) at all operating ranges.

2) Fuel pressure leakdown after ignition is turned off should be gradual. An instant drop in pressure indicates a leaking in-tank fuel pump coupling, hose or check valve.

3) Check fuel pump relay. Disconnect oil pressure switch. If engine cranks but will not start, perform fuel system diagnosis (to point where fuel pump fuse proves okay).

4) Check injector. With injector harness connector disconnected, check for fuel leakage while cranking. Check cranking circuit. See GENERAL MOTORS COMPUTER COMMAND CONTROL SYSTEM article in COMPUTERIZED ENGINE CONTROLS section.

TESTING & DIAGNOSIS

FUEL SYSTEM PRESSURE TEST

1) Remove "FUEL PUMP" fuse from fuse block in passenger compartment. Crank engine. Engine will start and run until fuel supply remaining in fuel lines is used. Engage starter again for about 3 seconds to make sure all fuel is out of lines. Turn ignition off and replace fuse.

2) Remove air cleaner and plug air cleaner (THERMAC) vacuum port on throttle body. Remove steel fuel line between throttle body and fuel filter. When removing fuel line, always use 2 wrenches to prevent damage. Install a fuel pressure gauge (J-29658) between throttle body and fuel filter.

3) Start vehicle and observe fuel pressure reading. Fuel pressure should be 9-13 psi (.6-.9 kg/cm²). If not, see FUEL SYSTEM DIAGNOSIS chart in this article. See INJECTOR SYSTEM DIAGNOSIS chart in this article if pressure is correct.

4) Depressurize fuel system as described in step **1)**. Remove fuel pressure gauge and reinstall steel line between filter and throttle body. Start vehicle and watch for leaks. Remove plug from throttle body thermal vacuum port and reinstall air cleaner.

REMOVAL & INSTALLATION

ELECTRONIC CONTROL MODULE (ECM)

NOTE: **Location of ECM varies between model application. ECM is located in passenger compartment either behind right kick panel or under instrument panel.**

Removal & Installation

Disconnect battery negative cable. Disconnect 2 electrical connectors from ECM. Remove ECM mounting hardware and ECM. To install, reverse removal procedure.

FUEL PUMP RELAY

Removal & Installation

Fuel pump relay is located on left or right side of engine compartment. On left side, relay is mounted in area of brake master cylinder and is closest relay to fender. If relay is mounted on right side, relay is nearest firewall. Remove electrical connector, mounting screws and relay. To install, reverse removal procedure.

MANIFOLD ABSOLUTE PRESSURE (MAP) SENSOR

Removal and Installation

MAP sensor is located in engine compartment. Location varies between application, but is generally mounted on firewall. Remove vacuum hose, mounting screws and MAP sensor. To install, reverse removal procedure.

VEHICLE SPEED SENSOR (VSS)

Removal & Installation

Remove instrument cluster and speedometer assembly. Disconnect VSS from speedometer. Disconnect VSS electrical connector and remove VSS. To install, reverse removal procedure.

COOLANT TEMPERATURE SENSOR (CTS)

Removal & Installation

Disconnect battery negative cable. Disconnect electrical connector and remove CTS. To install, reverse removal procedure.

NOTE: **Handle CTS with care to prevent damage to sensor calibration.**

OXYGEN SENSOR

NOTE: **Oxygen sensor may be difficult to remove when engine temperature is below 120°F (49°C). Excessive force may damage threads.**

Removal & Installation

Disconnect battery negative cable. Disconnect electrical connector. Do not attempt to remove single wire from oxygen sensor. Carefully back sensor out of exhaust manifold. Handle sensor with care and do not allow dirt or other foreign matter to contact louvered end of sensor. To install, reverse removal procedure.

NOTE: **Prior to reinstalling a serviceable sensor, coat threads with liquid graphite compound containing glass beads (special anti-seize compound).**

GENERAL MOTORS ELECTRONIC – SINGLE UNIT (Cont.)

FUEL SYSTEM DIAGNOSIS

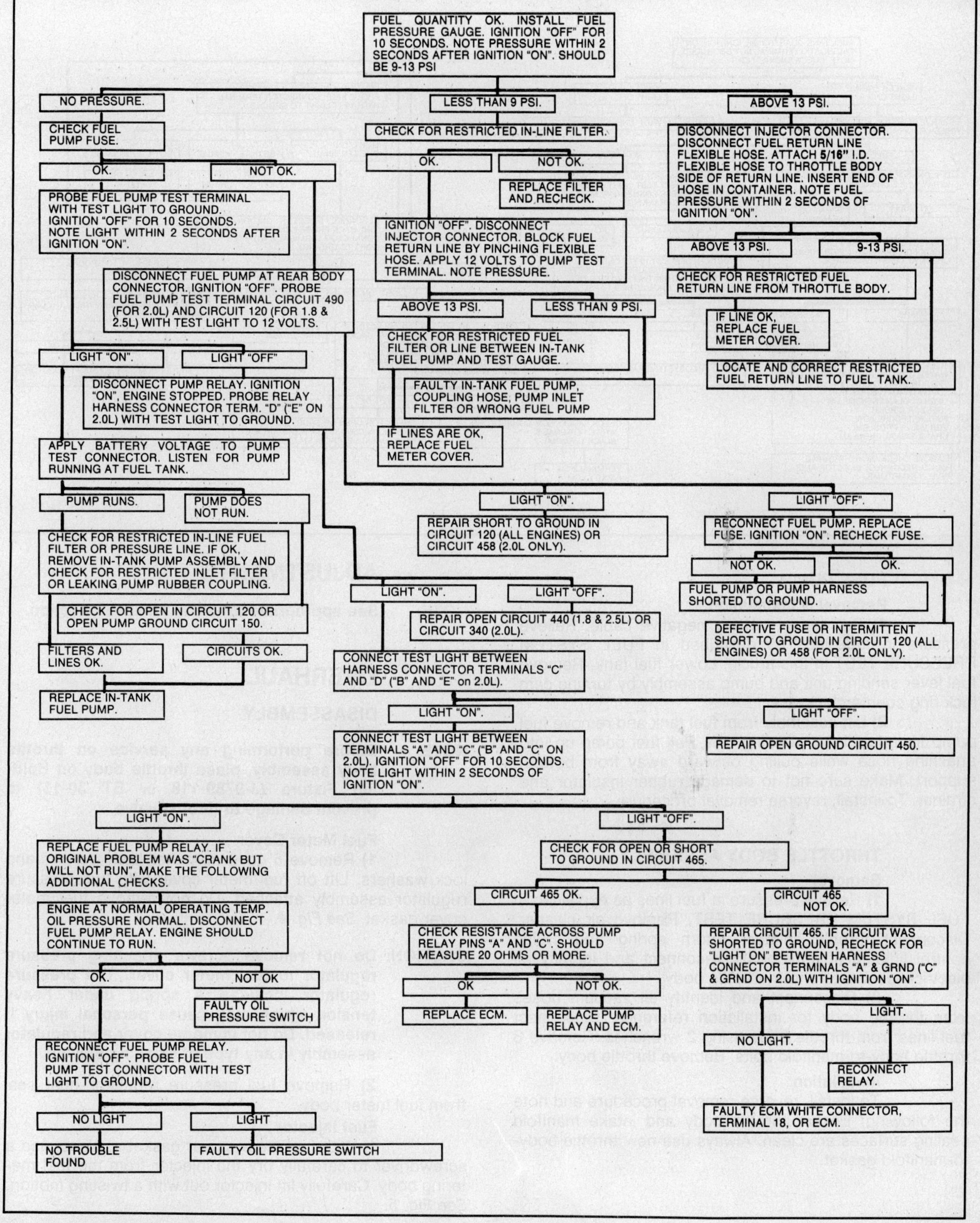
FUEL QUANTITY OK. INSTALL FUEL PRESSURE GAUGE. IGNITION "OFF" FOR 10 SECONDS. NOTE PRESSURE WITHIN 2 SECONDS AFTER IGNITION "ON". SHOULD BE 9-13 PSI
NO PRESSURE.
LESS THAN 9 PSI.
ABOVE 13 PSI.
CHECK FUEL PUMP FUSE.
CHECK FOR RESTRICTED IN-LINE FILTER.
DISCONNECT INJECTOR CONNECTOR. DISCONNECT FUEL RETURN LINE FLEXIBLE HOSE. ATTACH 5/16" I.D. FLEXIBLE HOSE TO THROTTLE BODY SIDE OF RETURN LINE. INSERT END OF HOSE IN CONTAINER. NOTE FUEL PRESSURE WITHIN 2 SECONDS OF IGNITION "ON".
OK.
NOT OK.
OK.
NOT OK.
REPLACE FILTER AND RECHECK.
PROBE FUEL PUMP TEST TERMINAL WITH TEST LIGHT TO GROUND. IGNITION "OFF" FOR 10 SECONDS. NOTE LIGHT WITHIN 2 SECONDS AFTER IGNITION "ON".
IGNITION "OFF". DISCONNECT INJECTOR CONNECTOR. BLOCK FUEL RETURN LINE BY PINCHING FLEXIBLE HOSE. APPLY 12 VOLTS TO PUMP TEST TERMINAL. NOTE PRESSURE.
ABOVE 13 PSI.
9-13 PSI.
CHECK FOR RESTRICTED FUEL RETURN LINE FROM THROTTLE BODY.
DISCONNECT FUEL PUMP AT REAR BODY CONNECTOR. IGNITION "OFF". PROBE FUEL PUMP TEST TERMINAL CIRCUIT 490 (FOR 2.0L) AND CIRCUIT 120 (FOR 1.8 & 2.5L) WITH TEST LIGHT TO 12 VOLTS.
ABOVE 13 PSI.
LESS THAN 9 PSI.
IF LINE OK, REPLACE FUEL METER COVER.
CHECK FOR RESTRICTED FUEL FILTER OR LINE BETWEEN IN-TANK FUEL PUMP AND TEST GAUGE.
LIGHT "ON".
LIGHT "OFF"
LOCATE AND CORRECT RESTRICTED FUEL RETURN LINE TO FUEL TANK.
DISCONNECT PUMP RELAY. IGNITION "ON", ENGINE STOPPED. PROBE RELAY HARNESS CONNECTOR TERM. "D" ("E" ON 2.0L) WITH TEST LIGHT TO GROUND.
FAULTY IN-TANK FUEL PUMP, COUPLING HOSE, PUMP INLET FILTER OR WRONG FUEL PUMP
APPLY BATTERY VOLTAGE TO PUMP TEST CONNECTOR. LISTEN FOR PUMP RUNNING AT FUEL TANK.
IF LINES ARE OK, REPLACE FUEL METER COVER.
PUMP RUNS.
PUMP DOES NOT RUN.
LIGHT "ON".
LIGHT "OFF".
REPAIR SHORT TO GROUND IN CIRCUIT 120 (ALL ENGINES) OR CIRCUIT 458 (2.0L ONLY).
RECONNECT FUEL PUMP. REPLACE FUSE. IGNITION "ON". RECHECK FUSE.
CHECK FOR RESTRICTED IN-LINE FUEL FILTER OR PRESSURE LINE. IF OK, REMOVE IN-TANK PUMP ASSEMBLY AND CHECK FOR RESTRICTED INLET FILTER OR LEAKING PUMP RUBBER COUPLING.
NOT OK.
OK.
LIGHT "ON".
LIGHT "OFF".
FUEL PUMP OR PUMP HARNESS SHORTED TO GROUND.
CHECK FOR OPEN IN CIRCUIT 120 OR OPEN PUMP GROUND CIRCUIT 150.
REPAIR OPEN CIRCUIT 440 (1.8 & 2.5L) OR CIRCUIT 340 (2.0L).
DEFECTIVE FUSE OR INTERMITTENT SHORT TO GROUND IN CIRCUIT 120 (ALL ENGINES) OR 458 (FOR 2.0L ONLY).
FILTERS AND LINES OK.
CIRCUITS OK.
CONNECT TEST LIGHT BETWEEN HARNESS CONNECTOR TERMINALS "C" AND "D" ("B" AND "E" on 2.0L).
REPLACE IN-TANK FUEL PUMP.
LIGHT "ON".
LIGHT "OFF".
CONNECT TEST LIGHT BETWEEN TERMINALS "A" AND "C" ("B" AND "C" ON 2.0L). IGNITION "OFF" FOR 10 SECONDS. NOTE LIGHT WITHIN 2 SECONDS OF IGNITION "ON".
REPAIR OPEN GROUND CIRCUIT 450.
LIGHT "ON".
LIGHT "OFF".
REPLACE FUEL PUMP RELAY. IF ORIGINAL PROBLEM WAS "CRANK BUT WILL NOT RUN", MAKE THE FOLLOWING ADDITIONAL CHECKS.
CHECK FOR OPEN OR SHORT TO GROUND IN CIRCUIT 465.
CIRCUIT 465 OK.
CIRCUIT 465 NOT OK.
ENGINE AT NORMAL OPERATING TEMP. OIL PRESSURE NORMAL. DISCONNECT FUEL PUMP RELAY. ENGINE SHOULD CONTINUE TO RUN.
CHECK RESISTANCE ACROSS PUMP RELAY PINS "A" AND "C". SHOULD MEASURE 20 OHMS OR MORE.
REPAIR CIRCUIT 465. IF CIRCUIT WAS SHORTED TO GROUND, RECHECK FOR "LIGHT ON" BETWEEN HARNESS CONNECTOR TERMINALS "A" & GRND ("C" & GRND ON 2.0L) WITH IGNITION "ON".
OK.
NOT OK
OK
NOT OK.
FAULTY OIL PRESSURE SWITCH
REPLACE ECM.
REPLACE PUMP RELAY AND ECM.
LIGHT.
NO LIGHT.
RECONNECT FUEL PUMP RELAY. IGNITION "OFF". PROBE FUEL PUMP TEST CONNECTOR WITH TEST LIGHT TO GROUND.
RECONNECT RELAY.
FAULTY ECM WHITE CONNECTOR, TERMINAL 18, OR ECM.
NO LIGHT
LIGHT
NO TROUBLE FOUND
FAULTY OIL PRESSURE SWITCH

1985 Fuel Injection

GENERAL MOTORS ELECTRONIC – SINGLE UNIT (Cont.)

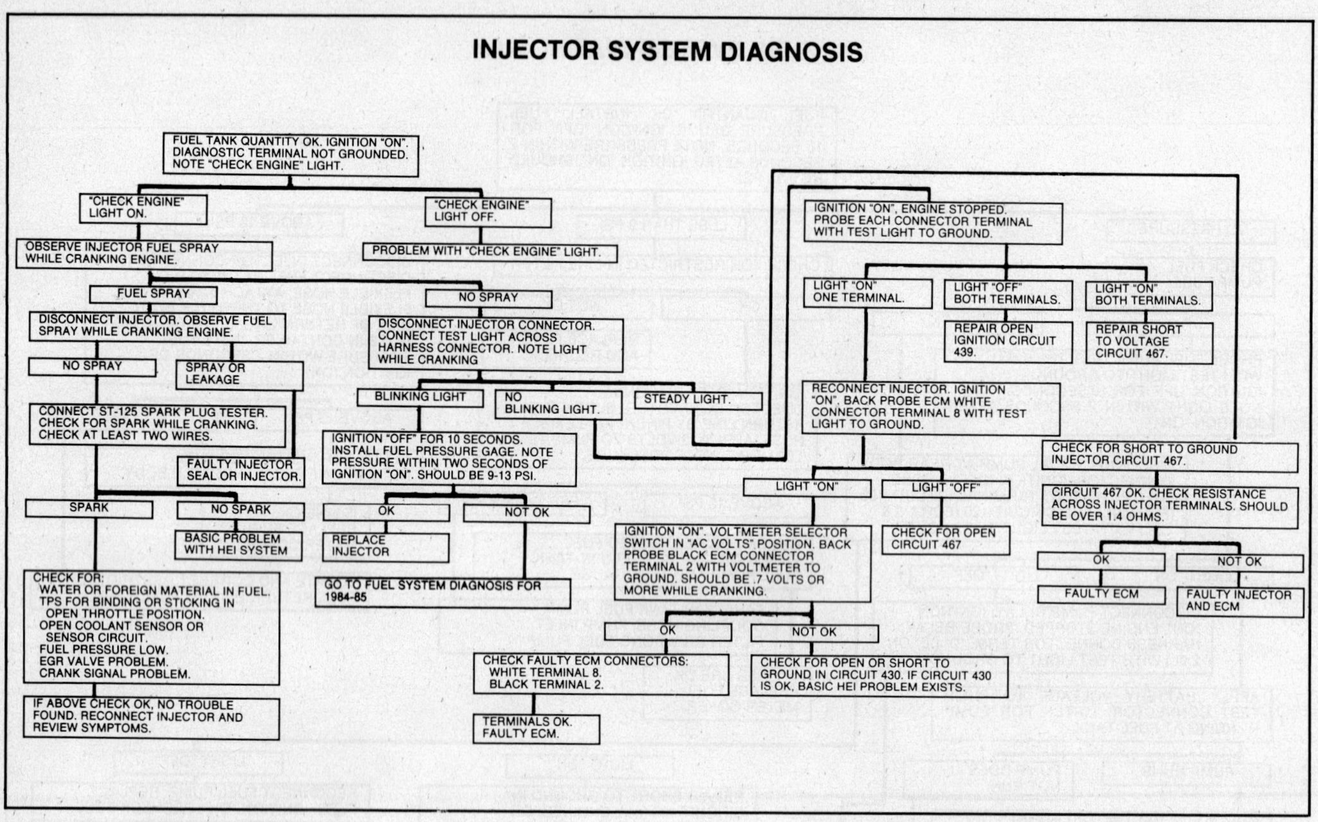

FUEL PUMP

Removal & Installation

1) Disconnect battery negative cable. Relieve pressure in fuel lines as described in FUEL SYSTEM PRESSURE TEST in this article. Lower fuel tank. Remove fuel lever sending unit and pump assembly by turning cam lock ring counterclockwise.

2) Lift assembly from fuel tank and remove fuel pump from fuel lever sending unit. Pull fuel pump up into attaching hose while pulling outward away from bottom support. Make sure not to damage rubber insulator and strainer. To install, reverse removal procedure.

THROTTLE BODY ASSEMBLY

Removal

1) Relieve pressure in fuel lines as explained in FUEL SYSTEM PRESSURE TEST. Remove air cleaner. Disconnect throttle linkage, return spring and cruise control linkage (if equipped). Disconnect and identify all electrical connectors from throttle body.

2) Disconnect and identify all vacuum hoses from throttle body for installation reference. Disconnect fuel lines from throttle body using 2 wrenches. Remove 3 throttle body-to-manifold bolts. Remove throttle body.

Installation

To install, reverse removal procedure and note the following: Ensure throttle body and intake manifold sealing surfaces are clean. Always use new throttle body-to-manifold gasket.

ADJUSTMENTS

NOTE: **See appropriate article in TUNE-UP section.**

OVERHAUL

DISASSEMBLY

NOTE: **Before performing any service on throttle body assembly, place throttle body on Holding Fixture (J-9789-118 or BT 30-15) to prevent damage to throttle valve.**

Fuel Meter Cover

1) Remove 5 cover-to-meter body screws and lock washers. Lift off fuel meter cover with fuel pressure regulator assembly attached. Do not remove fuel meter cover gasket. *See Fig. 4.*

CAUTION: **Do not remove screws attaching pressure regulator to fuel meter cover. The pressure regulator includes a spring under heavy tension which may cause personal injury if released. Do not immerse cover and regulator assembly in any type of cleaning solvent.**

2) Remove fuel pressure regulator dust seal from fuel meter body.

Fuel Injector

1) With fuel meter cover gasket in place, use a screwdriver to carefully pry the injector from the fuel metering body. Carefully lift injector out with a twisting motion. *See Fig. 5.*

GENERAL MOTORS ELECTRONIC – SINGLE UNIT (Cont.)

Fig. 4: Removing Fuel Meter Cover Assembly

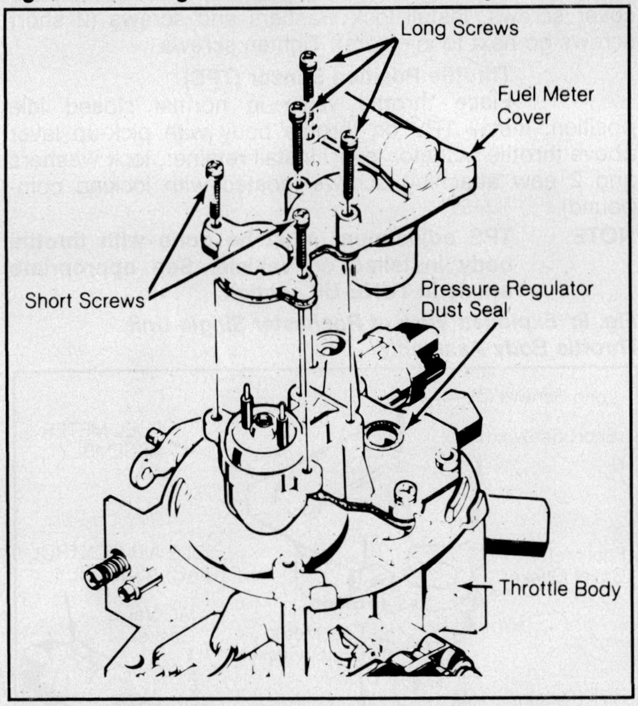

Do not remove fuel meter cover gasket at this time.

NOTE: Use care in removing injector to prevent damage to electrical connectors, fuel filter and nozzle. Injector is serviced as complete assembly only.

Fig. 5: Fuel Injector Assembly Removal

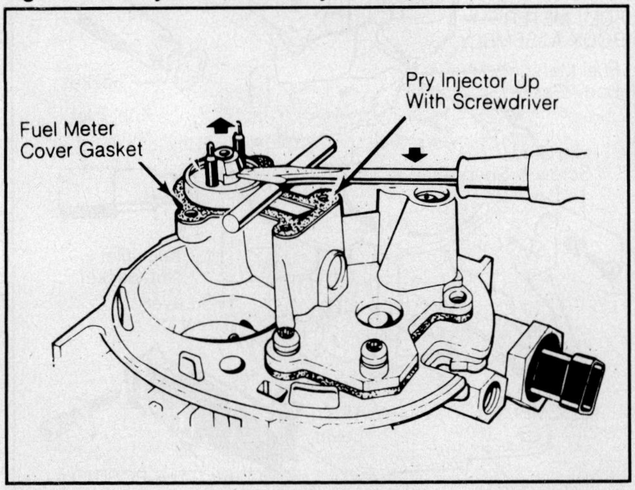

Keep fuel meter cover gasket in place until injector is removed to prevent damage to casting.

2) Remove small "O" ring from the nozzle end of injector. Carefully rotate injector filter back and forth to remove from base of injector. Remove large "O" ring and steel back-up washer at top of injector cavity in fuel meter body.

Fuel Meter Body

Remove fuel inlet and outlet nuts and gaskets from fuel meter body. Remove air cleaner stud. Remove 3 fuel meter body-to-throttle body screws and lock washers. Remove fuel meter body and gasket. Remove insulator gasket.

Throttle Body

1) Disassembly of throttle body unit for immersion in cleaning solvent requires removal of TPS and IAC assembly. Throttle valve screws are staked in position and should not be removed. If necessary to remove TPS, continue as follows:

2) Invert throttle body assembly and place on clean, flat surface. Remove and discard 2 TPS attaching screws, lock washers and retainers. Remove TPS from throttle body. *See Fig. 6.*

3) If necessary, remove TPS actuator lever-to-throttle shaft screw. Remove IAC assembly from throttle body. Remove and discard IAC gasket.

Fig. 6: Removing TPS Assembly

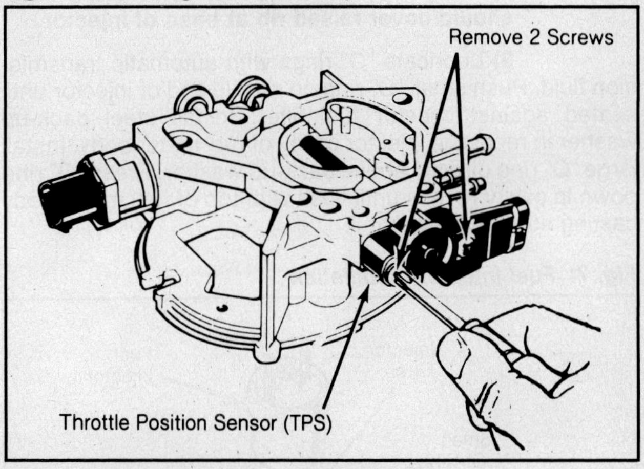

Invert throttle body unit to remove TPS.

CLEANING & INSPECTION

1) Clean all metal parts in a cold immersion-type cleaner and blow dry with compressed air.

2) Do not immerse TPS, IAC, fuel meter cover and pressure regulator assembly, fuel injector, fuel filter, rubber parts and diaphragms in cleaner.

3) Inspect mating surfaces for damage that may prevent gasket sealing. Repair or replace components which may be cause of problems listed under TROUBLE SHOOTING and TESTING & DIAGNOSIS in this article.

REASSEMBLY

Throttle Body

Place throttle body on holding fixture. Install IAC assembly with new gasket. Tighten securely. Install TPS actuator lever by aligning flats on lever with flats on end of shaft. Do not install TPS until assembly of throttle body is complete.

NOTE: Before installing IAC assembly, measure distance that valve extends from motor housing. Measuring from gasket mounting surface of housing to end of pintle, distance should not exceed 1 1/8" (28 mm). If not to specification, push pintle inward (IAC valve with collar on electrical connector) or compress pintle retaining spring toward IAC body while turning pintle inward with a clockwise motion (IAC valve without collar on connector). On IAC valves without collar, return spring to original position with straight portion of spring end aligned with flat surface under pintle head.

GENERAL MOTORS ELECTRONIC – SINGLE UNIT (Cont.)

Fuel Meter Body

1) Install fuel meter body insulator gasket on throttle body. Cut-out portions of gasket must match cut-outs on throttle body. Install fuel meter body on gasket.

2) Apply thread locking compound (supplied in service kit) on 3 attaching screws. Install lock washers and screws. Tighten screws. Install fuel inlet and outlet nuts with new gaskets.

Fuel Injector

1) Using a slight twisting motion, install fuel injector filter on nozzle end of injector until seated against injector base.

NOTE: Filter is cone-shaped. Large end of filter points up toward injector electrical connectors. Filter should cover raised rib at base of injector.

2) Lubricate "O" rings with automatic transmission fluid. Push small "O" ring on nozzle end of injector until seated against injector fuel filter. Install steel back-up washer in recess in injector cavity of fuel meter body. Install large "O" ring directly above back-up washer. Press "O" ring down in cavity recess until flush with top of fuel meter body casting surface. *See Fig. 7.*

Fig. 7: Fuel Injector Installation

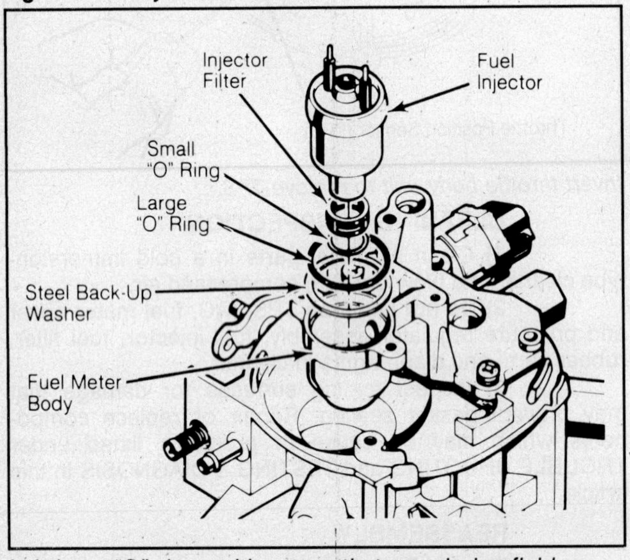

Lubricate "O" rings with automatic transmission fluid.

NOTE: "O" rings and back-up washer must be installed in this manner. Do not attempt to seat "O" rings and washer after injector is placed in cavity.

3) Using a pushing/twisting motion, install injector in cavity. Align raised lug on injector base with notch in fuel meter body. Push down on injector to center "O" ring in bottom of cavity and to seat injector. Injector is correctly installed when lug on injector is seated in fuel meter body notch and electrical connections are parallel to throttle shaft in throttle body.

Fuel Meter Cover

1) Install new fuel pressure regulator dust seal in fuel meter body recess. Install new fuel return passage gasket. Install new fuel meter cover gasket on fuel meter body.

2) Install fuel meter cover. Ensure pressure regulator dust seal and gaskets are properly positioned. Apply thread locking compound (supplied in service kit) to 5 cover screws. Install lock washers and screws (2 short screws go next to injectors). Tighten screws.

Throttle Position Sensor (TPS)

Place throttle valve in normal closed idle position. Install TPS on throttle body with pick-up lever above throttle actuator lever. Install retainer, lock washers and 2 new attaching screws (coated with locking compound).

NOTE: TPS adjustment must be done with throttle body installed on vehicle. See appropriate article in TUNE-UP section.

Fig. 8: Exploded View of Rochester Single Unit Throttle Body Assembly

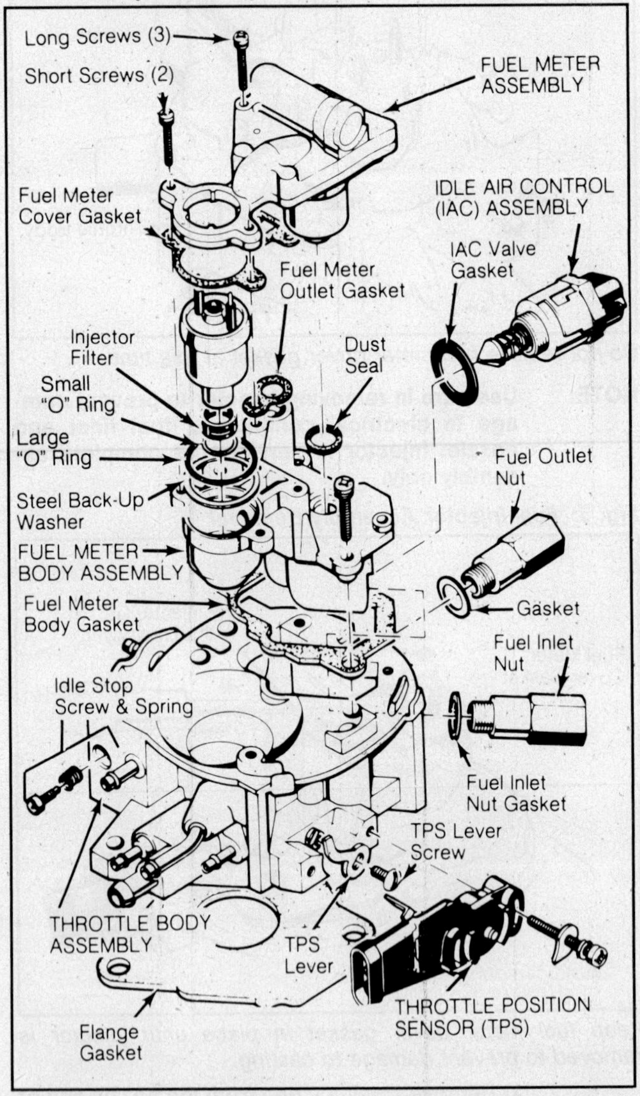

TIGHTENING SPECIFICATIONS

Application	Ft. Lbs. (N.m)
Oxygen Sensor	30 (41)
Throttle Body-to-Manifold Bolts	17 (23)
Idle Air Control (IAC) Assembly	13 (18)
Fuel Inlet and Outlet Nuts	22 (30)
	INCH Lbs. (N.m)
Fuel Meter Cover Screws	28 (3.0)

GENERAL MOTORS ELECTRONIC – SINGLE UNIT (Cont.)

Fig. 9: Fuel Injection Wiring Diagram

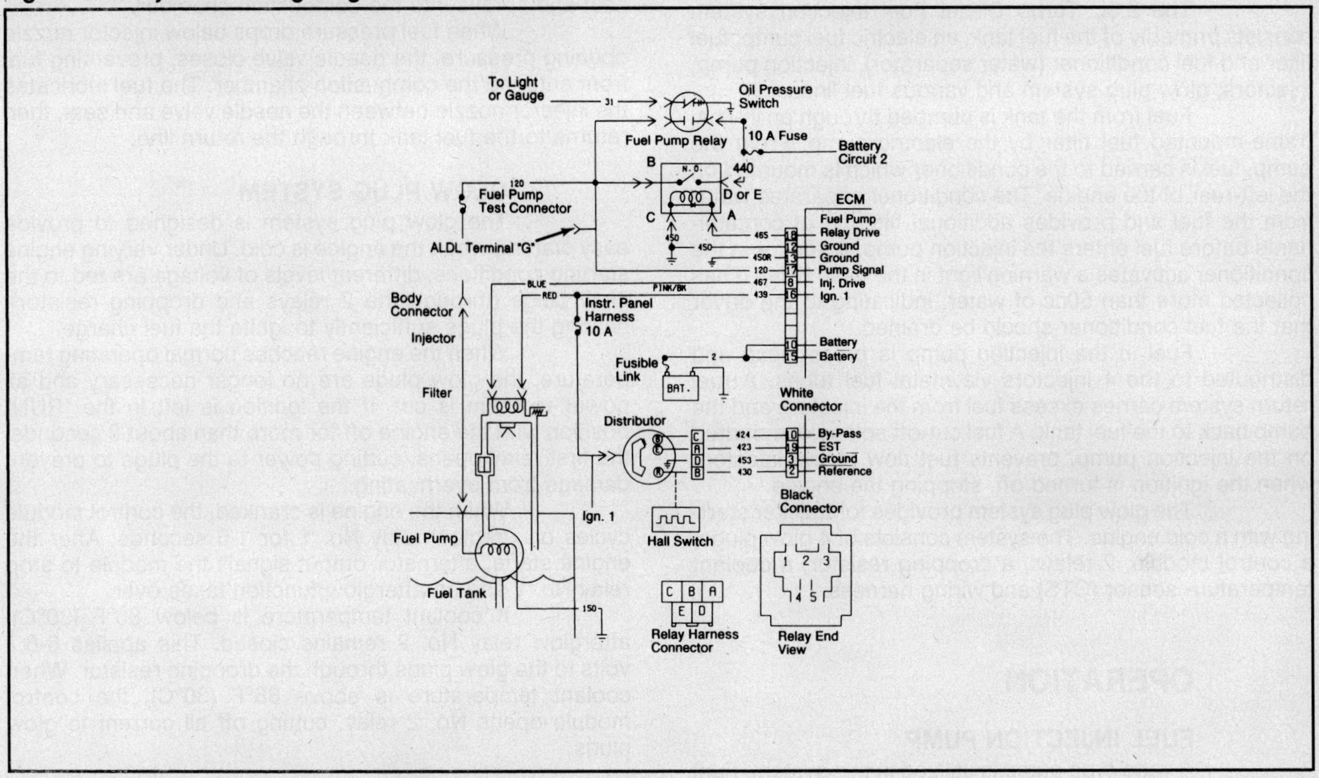

Also see chassis wiring diagram in WIRING DIAGRAM section.

1985 Diesel Fuel Injection

FORD 2.3L TURBO DIESEL

DESCRIPTION

The 2.3L Turbo Diesel Fuel Injection system consists primarily of the fuel tank, an electric fuel pump, fuel filter and fuel conditioner (water separator), injection pump, injectors, glow plug system and various fuel lines.

Fuel from the tank is pumped through an in-line, frame-mounted fuel filter by the electric pump. From the pump, fuel is carried to the conditioner which is mounted on the left-rear of the engine. The conditioner separates water from the fuel and provides additional filtering of contaminants before fuel enters the injection pump. A sensor in the conditioner activates a warning light in the dash when it has collected more than 50cc of water, indicating to the driver that the fuel conditioner should be drained.

Fuel in the injection pump is pressurized and distributed to the 4 injectors via metal fuel tubes. A fuel return system carries excess fuel from the injectors and the pump back to the fuel tank. A fuel cut-off solenoid, mounted on the injection pump, prevents fuel flow to the injectors when the ignition is turned off, stopping the engine.

The glow plug system provides for quicker starting with a cold engine. The system consists of 4 glow plugs, a control module, 2 relays, a dropping resistor, a coolant temperature sensor (CTS) and wiring harness.

OPERATION

FUEL INJECTION PUMP

A vane-type pump is utilized in this system. Fuel supplied to the pump is pressurized and fed into the pump body, where it is held in a high pressure chamber at the upper part of the pump plunger. Fuel injection is controlled by a sliding sleeve, operated by the throttle linkage, which governs the amount of fuel supplied to the injectors. Injection pressure varies with engine speed.

Surplus fuel in the injection pump is returned to the fuel tank through the overflow line after circulating through the pump to provide cooling and lubrication.

Fig. 1: 2.3L Turbo Diesel Fuel Injection Pump

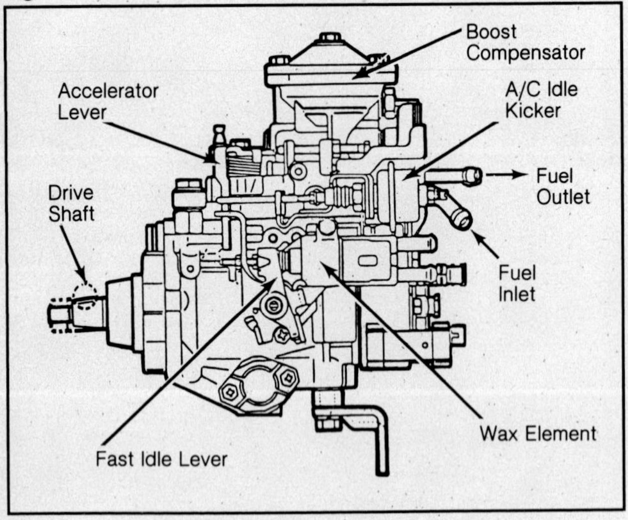

INJECTORS

The fuel injector nozzles inject fuel directly into the swirl combustion chamber. When high pressure fuel reaches 1707 psi (120 kg/cm^2) or more, it overcomes the injector needle pressure spring, lifts the needle valve off its seat and sprays into the combustion chamber.

When fuel pressure drops below injector nozzle opening pressure, the needle valve closes, preventing fuel from entering the combustion chamber. The fuel lubricates the injector nozzle between the needle valve and seat, then returns to the fuel tank through the return line.

GLOW PLUG SYSTEM

The glow plug system is designed to provide easy starting when the engine is cold. Under varying engine starting conditions, different levels of voltage are fed to the glow plugs (through the 2 relays and dropping resistor), heating the plugs sufficiently to ignite the fuel charge.

When the engine reaches normal operating temperature, the glow plugs are no longer necessary and all power to them is cut. If the ignition is left in the "RUN" position with the engine off for more than about 3 seconds, the first relay opens, cutting power to the plugs to prevent damage from overheating.

When the engine is cranked, the control module cycles on preglow relay No. 1 for 1-6 seconds. After the engine starts, alternator output signals the module to stop relay No. 1 and an afterglow function takes over.

If coolant temperature is below 86°F (30°C), afterglow relay No. 2 remains closed. This applies 6-6.7 volts to the glow plugs through the dropping resistor. When coolant temperature is above 86°F (30°C), the control module opens No. 2 relay, cutting off all current to glow plugs.

TESTING

INJECTORS

CAUTION: When testing injector nozzles, keep spray contained to avoid serious injury. DO NOT allow injector to release line pressure on hands, arms or any part of body, as pressure is high enough to penetrate skin.

Test Preparation

1) Always use CLEAN calibration fluid in injector test stand. Open test stand valve slightly and operate handle to bleed air from stand and pipe. Pump handle until clear, bubble-free fluid flows from pipe. Close valve.

2) Attach injector to stand and tighten securely. Bleed air from injector by opening stand valve and quickly operating tester handle through several strokes, until clear fluid is emitted from injector. Close valve.

Opening Pressure Test

Slowly lower tester handle and note pressure shown on gauge as injector nozzle opens. Repeat several times to obtain accurate reading. Injection starting pressure should be 1705-1850 psi (120-130 kg/cm^2). If starting pressure is not as indicated, replace injector.

Leakage Test

1) Wipe injector tips dry (do not use fingers). Using injector tester, maintain pressure at 1420-1565 psi (100-110 kg/cm^2). No fuel leakage should occur. A slight wetting of injector tip after 5 seconds is OK, but if droplets form or fall from injector, it must be replaced.

2) Operate tester using quick strokes while observing flow from injector return ports. A slight leak-off of 1 or 2 drops per stroke is normal. If fuel squirts from return port, injector must be replaced.

FORD 2.3L TURBO DIESEL (Cont.)

Fig. 2: Injector Spray Patterns

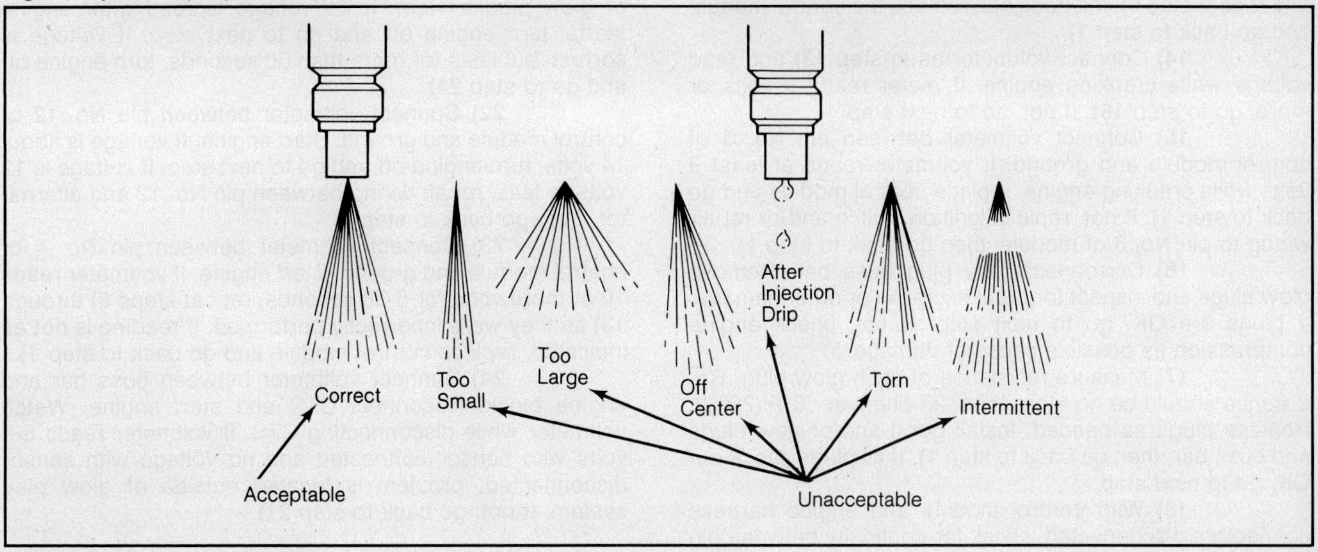

Injector must not drip when needle valve is closed.

Spray Pattern Test

Operate injector tester with smooth, even strokes and observe fuel spray pattern. Fuel should be uniformly atomized in an even, straight pattern. An uneven spray, fuel droplets or a solid stream of fuel indicates a faulty nozzle. *See Fig. 2.* Clean nozzle and repeat test. If injector still fails test it should be replaced.

Cleaning Injectors

1) If injectors pass tests, they should be cleaned and installed. Injectors may be cleaned by soaking in cold cleaning solution for 1 hour, or with a sonic cleaner and cleaning fluid (follow manufacturer's directions).

2) Remove injectors from cleaning solution and remove any remaining carbon from end of injector with brass wire brush. Wash off outside of injector, dry with compressed air. Make sure protective caps are clean. Install caps on injectors until injectors are ready to install.

GLOW PLUG SYSTEM

NOTE: If engine coolant temperature is above 86°F (30°C), disconnect wire from coolant temperature sensor (CTS) for all tests. Unless otherwise noted, peform all tests with engine off.

1) Turn on ignition. Check voltage between glow plug buss bar and engine block. If voltage is at least 10 volts for 1-6 seconds after ignition is turned on, go to step **9)**. If not, go to step **2)**.

2) Check for battery voltage on battery side of glow plug relay No. 1. If voltage exists, go to step **3)**. If not, repair or replace circuit between battery and relay No. 1, then go back to step **1)**.

3) Connect voltmeter between pin No. 1 of control module and ground. Turn on ignition and read voltage. If voltage is at least 10 volts, go to step **4)**. If not, replace ignition switch or repair circuit to control module pin No. 1, then go back to step **1)**.

4) Turn off ignition. Check for continuity between No. 1 glow plug relay and buss bar. If continuity exists, go to step **5)**. If not, repair or replace circuit as needed, then go back to step **1)**.

5) With voltmeter connected between pin No. 2 of control module and ground, turn on ignition. If voltmeter reads at least 10 volts for 1-6 seconds after ignition is turned on, replace glow plug relay No. 1, then go back to step **1)**. If not, go to next step.

6) Disconnect CTS and control module connector. Check for continuity between pin No. 13 of control module and ground. If continuity is indicated, repair short to ground in pin No. 13 circuit. If no continuity exists, go to next step.

7) Reconnect control module connector (leave CTS disconnected). Connect voltmeter between pin No. 2 of control module and ground. Turn on ignition. Voltmeter should read at least 10 volts for 1-6 seconds after ignition is turned on. If not, replace control module and go back to step **1)**. If voltage is correct, go to next step.

8) Remove CTS. Place sensor in water at 68°F (20°C). Check resistance of sensor. If resistance is between 2800 and 3800 ohms, repair circuit between pin No. 13 of control module and CTS. If not, replace CTS. After repairing circuit or replacing CTS, go back to step **1)**.

9) Connect voltmeter between buss bar and ground. Turn ignition on. Voltage should be 5-8 volts for 6 seconds after glow plug relay No. 1 turns off. If voltage reading is correct, go to step **14)**. If not, go to next step.

10) Check for battery voltage at glow plug relay No. 2. If voltage exists, go to next step. If not, repair circuit between battery and relay No. 2, then go back to step **1)**.

11) Turn off ignition and check for continuity between buss bar and glow plug relay No. 2. If continuity exists, go to step **13)**. If not, go to next step.

12) Disconnect glow plug system dropping resistor from wiring harness. With ohmmeter multiply knob on "X1" setting, check continuity of resistor. If continuity exists, repair circuit as needed. If not, replace resistor and go back to step **1)**.

CAUTION: Use care when handling resistor as it becomes very hot during glow plug system testing.

13) Connect voltmeter between pin No. 4 of control module and ground. Read voltage while cranking engine. If voltmeter indicates 10 volts or more for at least 7

FORD 2.3L TURBO DIESEL (Cont.)

seconds after cranking starts, replace glow plug relay No. 2 and repeat step **9)**. If it does not, replace the control module and go back to step **1)**.

14) Connect voltmeter as in step **13)** and read voltage while cranking engine. If meter reads 9 volts or more, go to step **16)**. If not, go to next step.

15) Connect voltmeter between pin No. 3 of control module and ground. If voltmeter reads at least 9 volts while cranking engine, replace control module and go back to step **1)**. If not, replace ignition switch and/or repair wiring to pin No. 3 of module, then go back to step **1)**.

16) Disconnect glow plug buss bar. Remove glow plugs and inspect for breaks, cracks or other damage. If plugs are OK, go to next step. If not, check engine compression as possible cause of damage.

17) Measure resistance of each glow plug. Resistance should be no more than .23 ohms at 68°F (20°C). Replace plugs as needed. Install good and/or new plugs and buss bar, then go back to step **1)**. If all plugs check out OK, go to next step.

18) With control module and engine harness connectors disconnected, check for continuity between pin No. 7 and pin No. 9 of control module and pin No. 4 of engine harness connector (from harness side). If continuity exists in both circuits, leave engine harness disconnected and go to next step. If not, repair defective circuit and go back to step **1)**.

19) Check for continuity between pin No. 4 of engine harness connector (engine side) and ground. If continuity exists, reconnect engine harness and go to next step. If not, repair circuit and go back to step **1)**.

20) If engine will start, go to next step. If not, the glow plug system is OK. Problem is engine related.

21) Connect voltmeter connected between buss bar and ground and start engine. Voltmeter should indicate 5-8 volts for 6-30 seconds. If so, problem is located outside of glow plug system. If no voltage is read after engine starts, turn engine off and go to next step. If voltage is correct, but lasts for more than 30 seconds, turn engine off and go to step **24)**.

22) Connect voltmeter between pin No. 12 of control module and ground. Start engine. If voltage is about 14 volts, turn engine off and go to next step. If voltage is 12 volts or less, repair wiring between pin No. 12 and alternator, then go back to step **1)**.

23) Connect voltmeter between pin No. 4 of control module and ground. Start engine. If voltmeter reads 10 or more volts for 6-30 seconds, repeat steps **9)** through **13)** as they were incorrectly performed. If reading is not as indicated, replace control module and go back to step **1)**.

24) Connect voltmeter between buss bar and engine block. Reconnect CTS and start engine. Watch voltmeter while disconnecting CTS. If voltmeter reads 5-8 volts with sensor connected and no voltage with sensor disconnected, problem is located outside of glow plug system. If not, go back to step **21)**.

Fig. 3: Glow Plug System Wiring Diagram

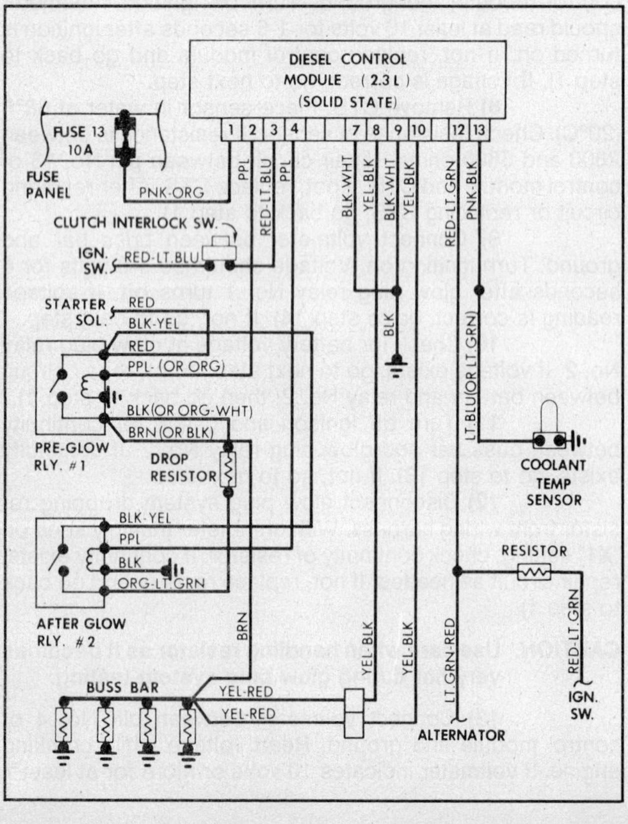

REMOVAL & INSTALLATION

FUEL INJECTION PUMP

Removal

1) Disconnect negative cables from both batteries. Remove radiator fan, shroud and all belts. Turn crankshaft in direction of normal engine rotation to bring No. 1 piston to TDC on compression stroke.

2) Remove timing belt covers. Loosen timing belt tensioner. Loosen and remove timing belt from injection pump sprocket. *See Fig. 4.*

3) Remove nut attaching sprocket to injection pump. Using puller, remove sprocket. Disconnect throttle cable and speed control cable, if equipped. Disconnect coolant hoses from injection pump wax element.

4) Disconnect hoses from boost compensator and A/C throttle kicker. Disconnect fuel return line at injection pump from injection return pipe.

5) Disconnect and plug chassis fuel return line from injection pump. Disconnect and cap fuel supply line from fuel conditioner. Disconnect and remove fuel lines at injection pump and injectors. Cap all lines and fittings. Remove injection pump-to-front cover nuts (2), injection pump bracket-to-engine bracket bolts (2) and engine bracket-to-engine block bolts (2). Remove pump.

Installation

1) Position injection pump on engine and install 2 injection pump-to-front cover nuts. Install mounting brackets and and tighten bolts.

2) Install pump sprocket. To ease timing belt installation, fabricate a tensioner spring tool. *See Fig. 5.* Using tensioner spring tool, release belt tension, then rotate tensioner toward water pump and tighten tensioner top bolt. Install belt in original direction of rotation.

NOTE: **Maintain tension on belt to prevent it from slipping on crankshaft, camshaft and injection pump sprockets. After belt is positioned, loosen tensioner top bolt to tension belt.**

3) Ensure all timing marks are properly aligned. *See Fig. 4.* Adjust injection pump timing. Tighten 2 injection pump retaining nuts and 4 bolts.

FORD 2.3L TURBO DIESEL (Cont.)

Fig. 4: Installing Timing Belt

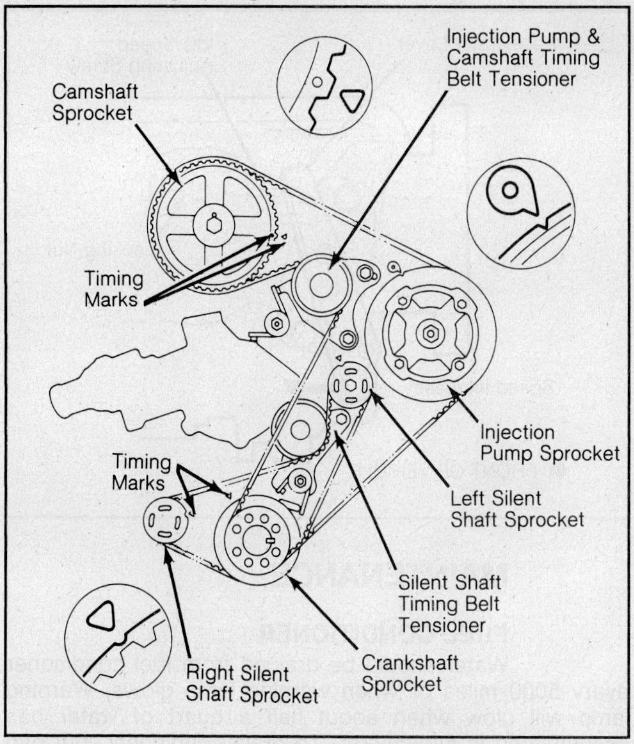

Ensure all timing marks are properly aligned.

4) Install and tighten injection lines on injection pump and injectors. Install all remaining fuel lines. Connect hoses to boost compensator and A/C throttle kicker.

5) Connect throttle cable and speed control cable, if equipped. Install timing covers. Install drive belts, radiator fan and shroud. Connect battery ground cables. Start engine and check for leaks.

Fig. 5: Using Tensioner Spring Tool To Install Timing Belt

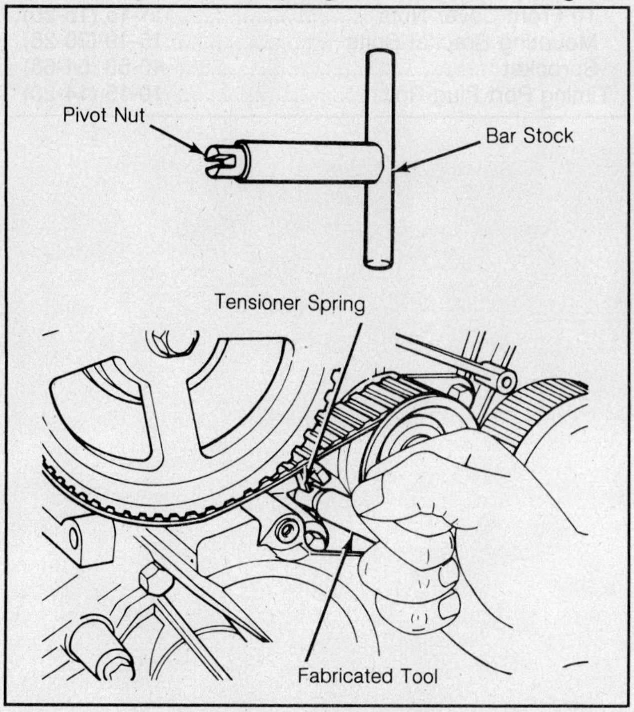

GLOW PLUGS

Removal & Installation

Disconnect negative cable from both batteries. Remove buss bar retaining nuts, disconnect electrical connectors from No. 3 and 4 glow plugs and remove buss bar. Remove glow plugs with a 12 mm deep socket. Reverse removal procedure to install.

INJECTORS

Removal

1) Disconnect battery negative cable from both batteries. Disconnect and remove injection lines from injectors and injection pump. Cap all lines and fittings.

2) Remove fuel return pipe and gaskets. Discard gaskets. Remove injectors using a 21 mm deep socket. Remove holder gasket and injector gasket with "O" Ring Remover (T71P-19703-C).

Installation

Clean outside of injectors with a brass brush and clean solvent. Dry thoroughly. Install new injector gasket and holder gasket. Install injectors. Reverse removal procedure to complete installation. Start engine and check for leaks.

ADJUSTMENTS

INJECTION PUMP TIMING

1) Remove upper timing belt cover. Turn crankshaft in normal direction of rotation to bring No. 1 piston to TDC on compression stroke. Verify piston position by checking timing marks. *See Fig. 4.*

2) If coolant temperature is above 122°F (50°C), go to step **3)**. If temperature is below 122°F (50°C), by-pass cold start mechanism by rotating fast idle lever and inserting a spacer or wrench at least .27" (7 mm) thick between cold start advance lever and cold start device. *See Fig. 6.*

3) Loosen injection pump-to-front cover and injection pump-to-mounting bracket nuts. Using back-up wrench, loosen fuel injection line nuts at pump. Remove plug bolt from timing port at center of pump hydraulic head.

Fig. 6: By-Passing Injection Pump Cold Start Device

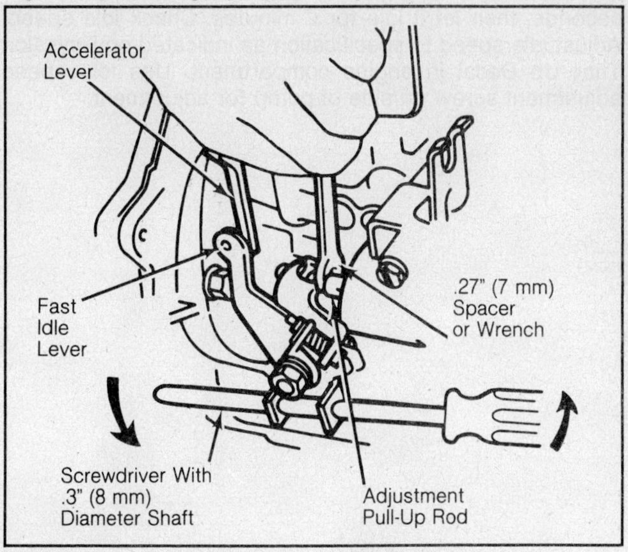

By-pass cold start device if coolant temperature is below 122F (50C).

FORD 2.3L TURBO DIESEL (Cont.)

4) Install Timing Adapter (014-00303) in timing port and mount dial indicator in adapter. *See Fig. 7.* Preload dial indicator to at least .10" (.25 mm). Rotate crankshaft about 30° counterclockwise and zero indicator dial.

Fig. 7: Timing Adapter & Dial Indicator Installed

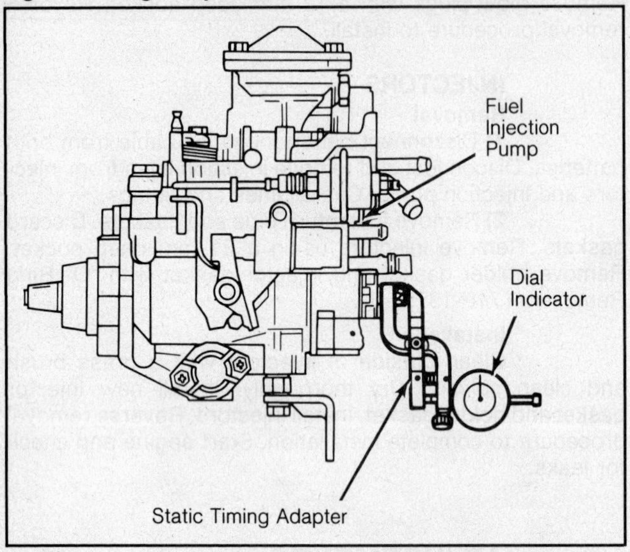

5) Rotate crankshaft clockwise to 5° ATDC. Dial indicator should read .0383-.0405" (.97-1.03 mm). Rotate injection pump body as needed to obtain correct reading. Rotate pump clockwise to decrease value, counterclockwise to increase value.

6) Tighten injection pump mounting nuts and repeat steps **4)** and **5)** to ensure timing is correct. Tighten fuel injection line nuts. Install timing port plug bolt with new copper gasket. Remove spacer and screwdriver (if used). Install timing belt cover, start engine and check for leaks.

IDLE SPEED

1) With transmission in Neutral and all lights and accessories off, bring engine to normal operating temperature. Connect tachometer to engine. Ensure idle speed adjusting screw is against its stop.

2) Run engine at 2000-3000 RPM for about 5 seconds, then let it idle for 2 minutes. Check idle speed. Adjust idle speed to specification as indicated on Emission Tune-Up Decal in engine compartment. Use idle speed adjustment screw on side of pump for adjustment.

Fig. 8: Adjusting Idle Speed

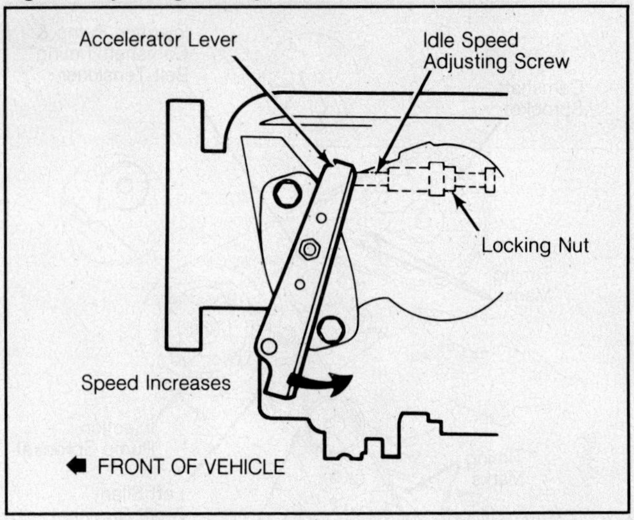

MAINTENANCE

FUEL CONDITIONER

Water should be drained from fuel conditioner every 5000 miles or when warning lamp glows. Warning lamp will glow when about half a quart of water has accumulated in sedimenter. To drain conditioner, put pan under conditioner, located under left rear side of engine. Pull conditioner ring until outflowing fuel is free of water. Release pull ring and ensure draining has stopped.

TIGHTENING SPECIFICATIONS

Application	Ft. Lbs. (N.m)
Glow Plugs	11-14 (15-19)
Injection Pump	
Fuel Line Nuts	17-26 (23-36)
To Front Cover Nuts	11-15 (15-20)
Mounting Bracket Bolts	15-19 (20-26)
Sprocket	40-50 (54-68)
Timing Port Plug Bolt	10-15 (14-20)

1985 Diesel Fuel Injection

FORD 6.9 LITER

DESCRIPTION

In this diesel system, a mechanical high pressure rotary pump is gear driven at camshaft speed. Through this method the pump injects a precisely metered amount of fuel into each cylinder at the proper time. The pump is mounted on top of the engine and provides necessary timing advance under all operating conditions.

Eight high pressure fuel pipes carry fuel from pump to an injection nozzle in each cylinder. All 8 pipes are the same length to ensure that there is no variance in timing. Engine RPM is controlled by a rotary fuel metering valve. As the accelerator pedal is pushed down, a throttle cable opens the metering valve and allows increased fuel delivery. A mechanical fuel pump located on the right side of the engine, draws fuel from the fuel tank and delivers it to the injection pump via a fuel filter.

The fuel filter is located between the mechanical pump and injection pump (mounted on side of engine block). Any excess fuel in the supply system is returned to the tank by a fuel return system. A water separator is located in the fuel line between the tank and the mechanical fuel pump. The separator collects water out of the fuel system. When the separator becomes about 1/3 full, a warning lamp on the dash will light up. When the warning lamp lights up, water should be drained from the separator. The warning lamp will also light when the key is in the "START" position to serve as a lamp test.

An electrical glow plug system is used to assist in engine starting and cold operation. A glow plug is located in the pre-chamber for each cylinder. Glow plug current is controlled by a temperature switch, a power relay and an after glow relay.

OPERATION

FUEL INJECTION PUMP

The Stanadyne DB-2 twin plunger mechanical injection pump contains a low pressure vane-type transfer pump, a high pressure distributor-type injection pump, a centrifugal governor and an injection timing advance mechanism.

The transfer pump output pressure (sometimes referred to as injection pump housing pressure) averages 50-100 psi (3.5-7.0 kg/cm^2) depending upon engine speed and application. The plunger injection pump boosts fuel pressure to about 2000 psi (140 kg/cm^2). The pump assembly is also equipped with an electric fuel shut-off valve.

INJECTORS

The injection nozzles spray fuel into a prechamber as each compression stroke occurs. Injector opening pressure is adjusted with a shim on top of the needle valve return spring. *See Fig. 3.* The injector receives a high pressure pulse of fuel which forces open the needle valve allowing the fuel to pass into the prechamber.

FUEL SUPPLY SYSTEM

Diesel fuel is drawn through a water separator from the fuel tank by an engine mounted mechanical fuel pump. This pump is driven by an eccentric cam mounted on the crankshaft and puts out about 3 psi to the injection pump. A small screen type filter is located in the fuel tank at the pickup. Diesel fuel arrives at the center inlet fitting on the injection pump after leaving the filter. A fuel return line is provided to return any excess fuel to the tank.

Fig. 1: Stanadyne DB-2 Diesel Fuel Injection Pump

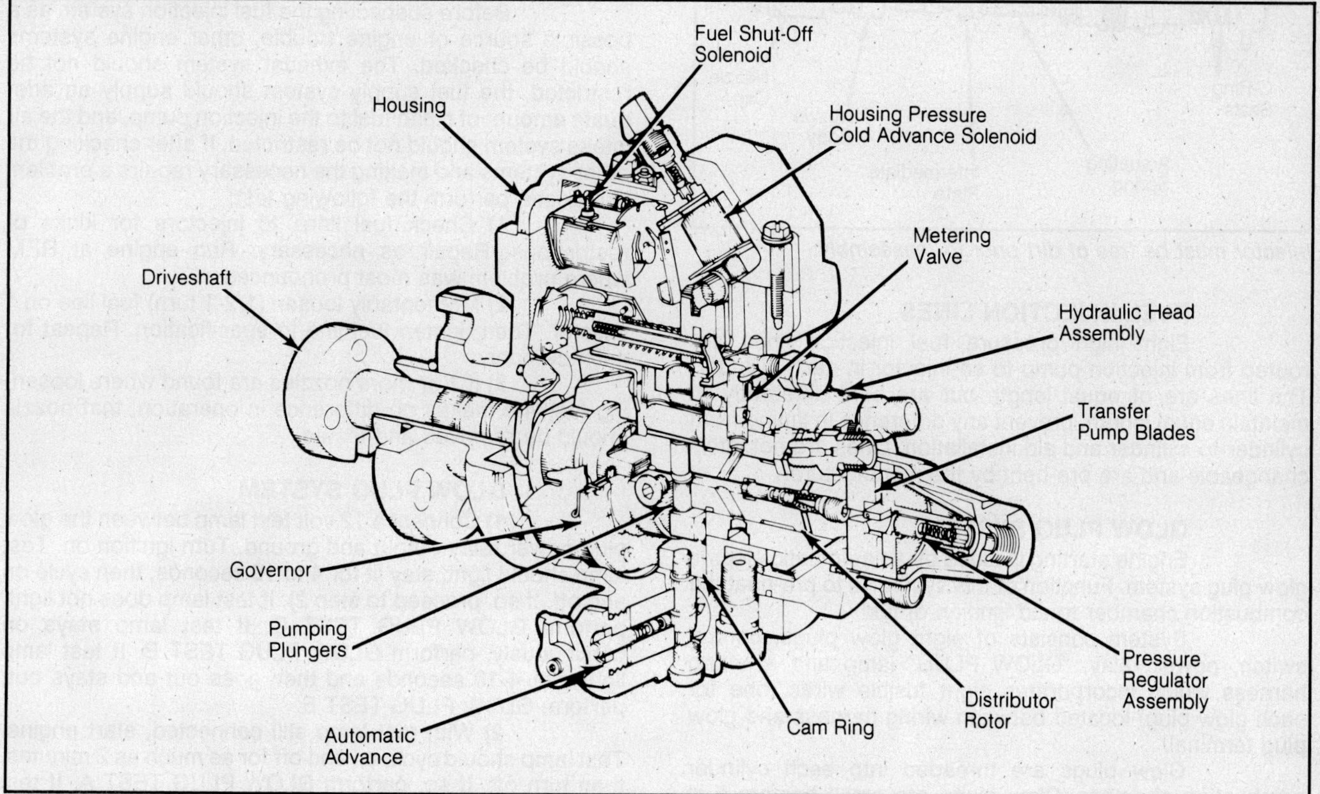

Disassembly of pump should only be performed by an authorized calibration shop.

FORD 6.9 LITER (Cont.)

Fig. 2: Ford Diesel Fuel System

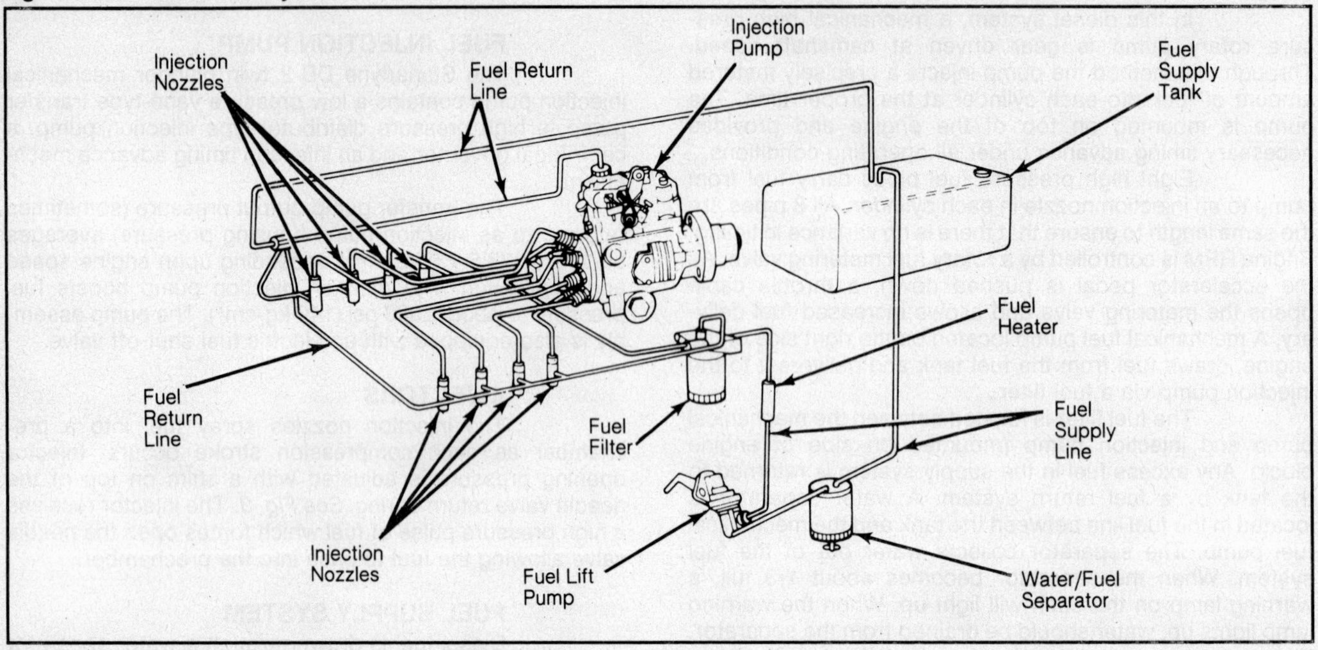

Bleed air from system whenever fuel lines are opened.

Fig. 3: Ford Diesel Injector

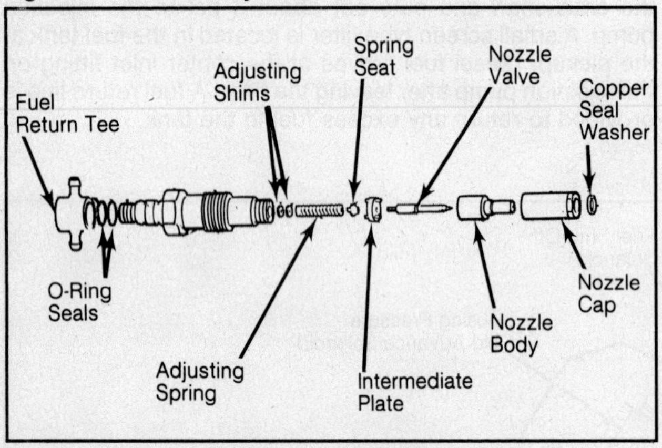

Injector must be free of dirt prior to reassembly.

FUEL INJECTION LINES

Eight high pressure fuel injection lines are routed from injection pump to an injector in each cylinder. The lines are of equal length but are bent differently to maintain equal length, prevent any difference in timing from cylinder-to-cylinder and aid installation. Lines are not interchangeable and are pre-bent by the manufacturer.

GLOW PLUG SYSTEM

Engine starting is aided by an automatic electric glow plug system. Function of this system is to pre-heat the combustion chamber to aid ignition of fuel.

System consists of eight glow plugs, control switch, power relay, "GLOW PLUG" lamp and a wiring harness which incorporates eight fusible wires (one for each glow plug) located between wiring harness and glow plug terminal.

Glow plugs are threaded into each cylinder combustion chamber. Glow plugs are small heaters that assist in cold starting. The glow plug controller and relay cycle 12 volts to these 6 volt heaters, which causes them to heat rapidly. After the engine starts, the glow plugs remain on between 4 and 10 seconds during initial starting cycle.

TROUBLE SHOOTING

FUEL INJECTION SYSTEM

Before suspecting the fuel injection system as a possible source of engine trouble, other engine systems should be checked. The exhaust system should not be restricted, the fuel supply system should supply an adequate amount of clean fuel to the injection pump, and the air intake system should not be restricted. If after checking the other systems and making the necessary repairs a problem still exists, perform the following test:

1) Check fuel lines to injectors for kinks or restrictions. Repair as necessary. Run engine at RPM where problem was most pronounced.

2) Momentarily loosen (1/2-1 turn) fuel line on 1 injector. Then tighten fuel line to specification. Repeat for each cylinder.

3) If 1 or more nozzles are found where loosening fuel line makes no difference in operation, that nozzle should be removed and tested.

GLOW PLUG SYSTEM

1) Connect a 12 volt test lamp between the glow plug power relay output and ground. Turn ignition on. Test lamp should light, stay lit for 4 to 10 seconds, then cycle on and off. If so, proceed to step **2)**. If test lamp does not light, perform GLOW PLUG TEST C. If test lamp stays on continuously, perform GLOW PLUG TEST B. If test lamp lights for 4-10 seconds and then goes out and stays out, perform GLOW PLUG TEST E.

2) With test lamp still connected, start engine. Test lamp should cycle on and off for as much as 2 minutes, then turn off. If so, perform GLOW PLUG TEST A. If test lamp continues to cycle on and off after 2 minutes, perform

Fig. 4: Engine Wiring System Diagram

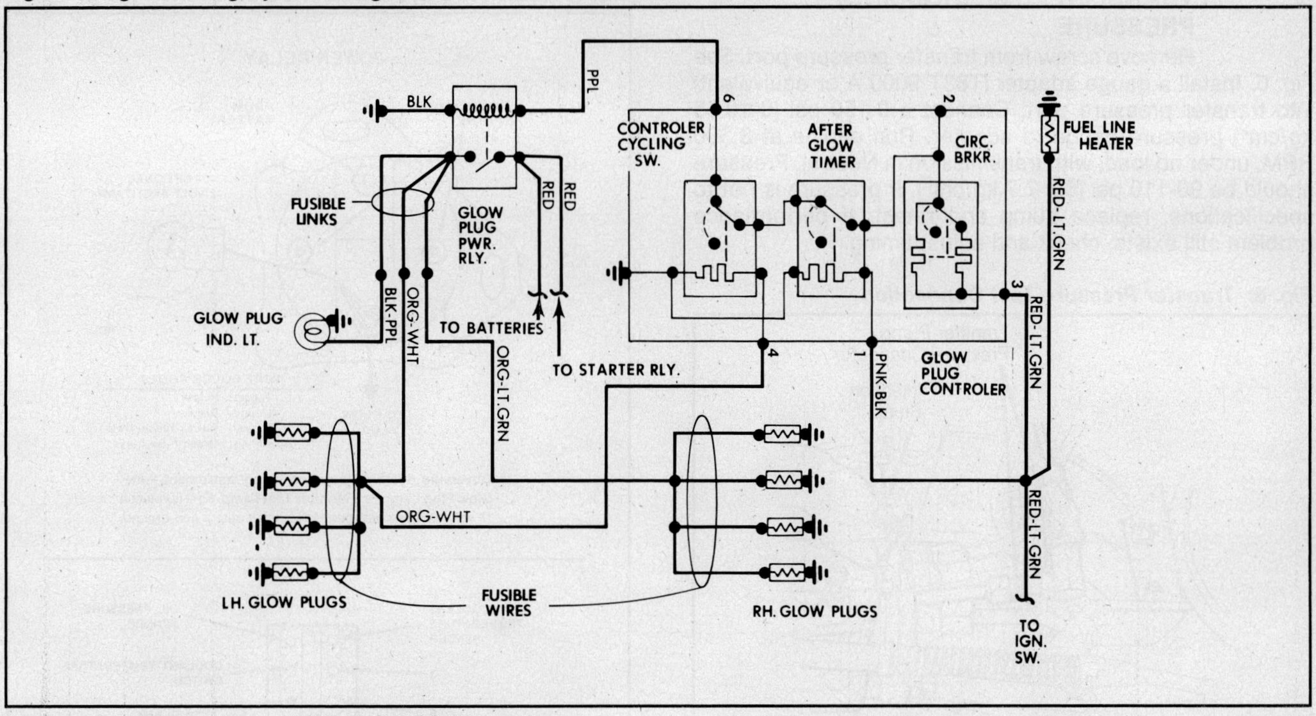

Also see chassis wiring in WIRING DIAGRAM section.

GLOW PLUG TEST D. If test lamp does not light, perform GLOW PLUG TEST E.

GLOW PLUG LAMP

1) Turn ignition on. Glow plug lamp should light for 4-10 seconds, depending on engine temperature, and then go out. If lamp lights for 4-10 seconds, glow plug lamp system is okay. Perform GLOW PLUG SYSTEM TROUBLE SHOOTING. If lamp does not light and engine is at or near operating temperature, allow engine to cool down and retest. If lamp still does not light, proceed to step **2)**.

2) Perform GLOW PLUG TEST C. If test lamp functions as required and glow plug lamp did not light in step **1)**, proceed to step **3)**. If test lamp does not function properly, fault is within glow plug system. Repeat GLOW PLUG SYSTEM TROUBLE SHOOTING procedure.

3) Remove bulb from "GLOW PLUG" indicator and check bulb. Replace as needed. If bulb is good, repair or replace chassis wiring as needed. Repeat GLOW PLUG LAMP TROUBLE SHOOTING.

TESTING

INJECTORS

1) Remove injection nozzles from engine. Test injectors using calibration fluid at room temperature. Bleed air out of tester by opening tester valve slightly and pumping handle several times. Close valve.

2) Install injection nozzle on tester. Open tester valve and pump tester handle quickly 8-10 times to bleed air from nozzle. Slowly lower tester handle and note pressure shown on gauge as injector nozzle opens. Repeat several times to obtain accurate reading.

3) Normal injection starting pressure should be 1800-1950 psi (126-137 kg/cm^2). If injection starting pressure is below 1425 psi (100 kg/cm^2), replace injector.

4) Using injector tester, maintain pressure at about 200 psi (14 kg/cm^2) below nozzle opening pressure. No fuel leakage should occur. Slight wetting of tip after 5 seconds is OK. Do not wipe tip of nozzle with fingers. If leakage does occur, injector must be replaced.

5) Operate tester using quick strokes while observing flow from injector return ports. A slight leak-off of 1 or 2 drops per stroke is normal. If a solid stream is expelled from return port, injector must be replaced.

6) Build up pressure in the injector tester to just below injection starting pressure. Quickly lower handle on tester and observe fuel spray pattern. Fuel should be uniformly atomized. Droplets or a solid stream of fuel indicates a faulty nozzle. *See Fig. 5.*

Fig. 5: Injector Spray Patterns

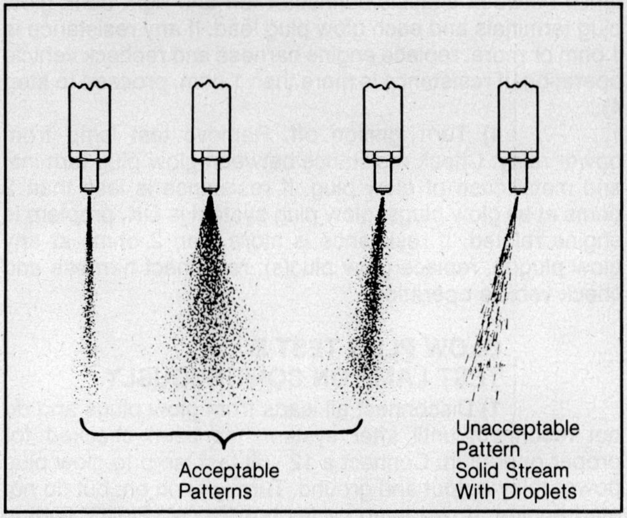

Injector must not drip when needle valve is closed.

FORD 6.9 LITER (Cont.)

TRANSFER PUMP (HOUSING) PRESSURE

Remove screw from transfer pressure port. *See Fig. 6.* Install a gauge adapter (T83T 9000 A or equivalent) into transfer pressure port. Connect a 0-150 psi (0-10.55 kg/cm²) pressure gauge to adapter. Run engine at 3,300 RPM, under no load, with transmission in Neutral. Pressure should be 90-110 psi (6.3-7.7 kg/cm²). If pressure is not to specifications, replace pump and retest. If performance problem still exists, check and adjust timing.

Fig. 6: Transfer Pressure Test Connection

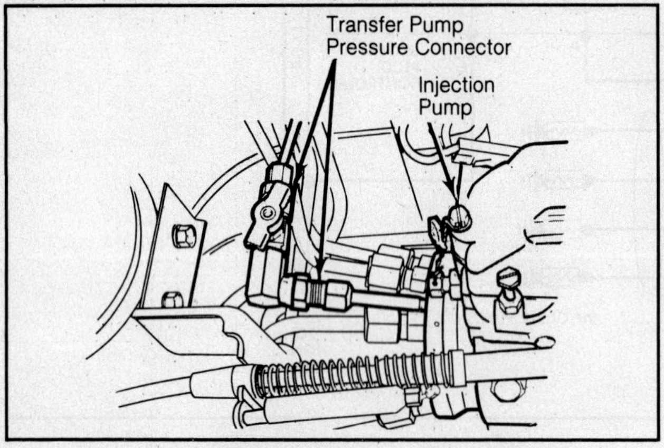

GLOW PLUG TEST A
TEST LAMP SIGNAL CORRECT

1) Remove all leads from glow plugs. Connect a test lamp between glow plug power relay output and ground. Turn ignition on. Measure voltage at each glow plug lead whenever test lamp is lit. Voltage should be at least 11 volts. If voltage is ok at all leads, proceed to step **4)**. If voltage is not ok at 1 or more leads, proceed to step **2)**.

2) Turn ignition off. Disconnect fusible links from chassis harness and engine glow plug harness. Check continuity of fusible links with an ohmmeter. If 1 or both fusible links are open, replace fusible link and repeat step **1)**. If both fusible links are ok, proceed to step **3)**.

3) Turn ignition off. Disconnect engine harness from chassis connector and all glow plugs. Check resistance between chassis connector left and right bank glow plug terminals and each glow plug lead. If any resistance is 1 ohm or more, replace engine harness and recheck vehicle operation. If resistance is more than 1 ohm, proceed to step **4)**.

4) Turn ignition off. Remove test lamp from power relay. Check resistance between glow plug terminal and metal case of glow plug. If resistance is less than 2 ohms at all glow plugs, glow plug system is OK, problem is engine related. If resistance is more than 2 ohms at any glow plug(s), replace glow plug(s), reconnect harness and check vehicle operation.

GLOW PLUG TEST B
TEST LAMP ON CONTINUOUSLY

1) Disconnect all leads from glow plugs and do not reconnect until after system has been checked for proper operation. Connect a 12 volt test lamp to glow plug power relay output and ground. Turn ignition on, but do not start engine. If test lamp cycles but "GLOW PLUG" light in

Fig. 7: Glow Plug System Test Connections

POWER RELAY

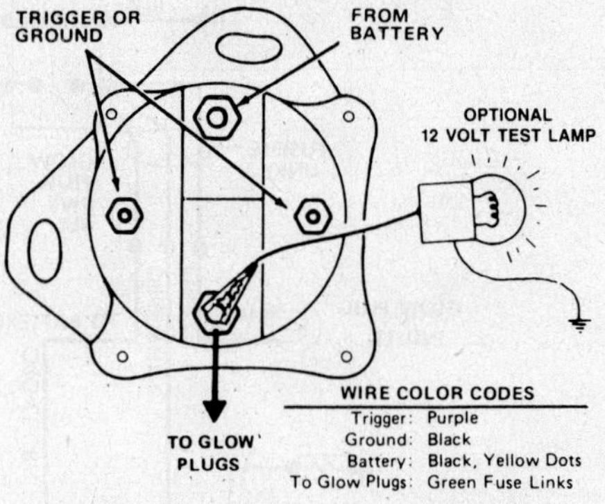

Observing System Operation Using Instrument Panel Glow Plug Lamp or a Monitor Test Lamp. First connect a 12 volt test lamp between power relay output and ground.

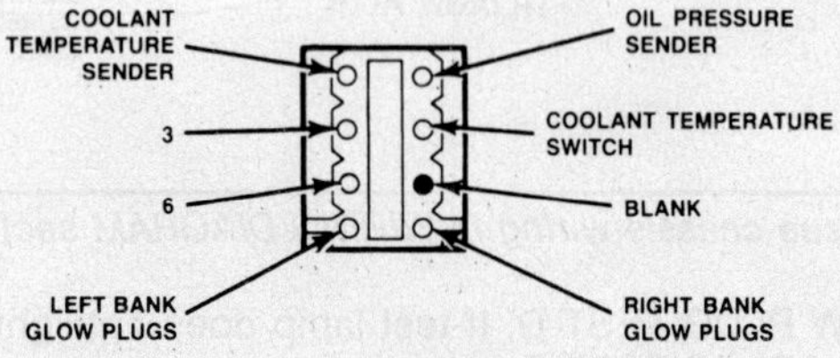

Electrical Connector, Glow Plug Harness To Chassis Harness Chassis Side View

TERMINAL #	WIRE COLOR CODES
3	RED W LIGHT GREEN STRIPE
6	PURPLE
LEFT BANK GLOW PLUGS	ORANGE W WHITE STRIPE
RIGHT BANK GLOW PLUGS	ORANGE W GREEN DOTS
OIL PRESSURE SENDER	WHITE W RED STRIPE
COOLANT TEMPERATURE SENDER	RED W WHITE STRIPE
COOLANT TEMPERATURE SWITCH	RED W BLACK DOTS

WIRING HARNESS PLUG FOR CONTROL SWITCH

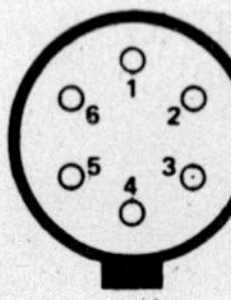

Viewing Connector Face

TERMINAL #	WIRE COLOR CODES
1	①, ②
3	RED W/GREEN STRIPE
4	ORANGE W/WHITE
5	BLACK
6	PURPLE

①E-SERIES — PINK WITH BLACK DOTS
②F-SERIES — RED WITH GREEN STRIPE

FORD 6.9 LITER (Cont.)

dash does not, repair or replace circuit wiring to light, or replace bulb, as needed. Repeat GLOW PLUG SYSTEM TROUBLE SHOOTING. If test lamp does not turn off, proceed to step **2)**.

2) With test lamp still connected, turn ignition on. Disconnect wiring harness from control switch. If test lamp goes out, replace control switch and repeat GLOW PLUG SYSTEM TROUBLE SHOOTING. If test lamp does not go out, proceed to step **3)**.

3) With test lamp still connected, turn ignition on. Disconnect engine harness from chassis harness. If test lamp goes out, replace engine harness and go to step **7)**. If lamp stays on, go to step **4)**.

4) Turn ignition off. Disconnect signal lead from power relay. Turn ignition on. If test lamp goes out, repair or replace chassis harness as needed and go to step **5)**. If lamp stays on, go to step **5)**.

5) Turn ignition off, remove test lamp and disconnect battery lead from power relay. Reconnect test lamp. With power relay output lead still connected, turn ignition on. If test lamp remains on, repair or replace chassis wiring harness to glow plugs. If lamp goes out, replace power relay.

6) With ignition off, remove test lamp from power relay and reconnect all leads (EXCEPT glow plugs). Check continuity from each glow plug lead to power relay output. If resistance is less than 1 ohm for all glow plugs, go to step **8)**. If resistance is 1 ohm or greater for 1 or more glow plugs, go to step **7)**.

7) With ignition off, disconnect engine harness and chassis harness fusible links from chassis harness. Check resistance of all fusible links. If resistance of all links is less than 1 ohm, replace engine harness. If resistance of one or more fusible link is 1 ohm or greater, replace link and repeat step **6)**.

8) With ignition off and engine harness disconnected at glow plugs, check resistance between each glow plug terminal and metal shell of glow plug. If resistance is less than 2 ohms for all plugs, glow plug system is OK. Reconnect engine harness to glow plugs and repeat GLOW PLUG SYSTEM TROUBLE SHOOTING. If resistance for any plug is 2 ohms or greater, replace glow plug(s). Reconnect engine harness to glow plugs and repeat GLOW PLUG SYSTEM TROUBLE SHOOTING.

GLOW PLUG TEST C
TEST LAMP DOES NOT LIGHT

1) Ensure that ignition has been off for at least 1 minute, then turn ignition on. If "GLOW PLUG" dash light comes on, perform GLOW PLUG TEST E. If not, for engine at normal operating temperature, condition is normal. For coolant temperatures below normal, turn ignition off, wait 2 minutes, and turn ignition back on. If light comes on, perform GLOW PLUG TEST E. If light does not come on, proceed to step **2)**.

2) Check batteries for sufficient charge. Batteries should be able to crank engine. If charge is ok, proceed to step **3)**. If charge is low, charge or replace batteries as necessary and repeat GLOW PLUG SYSTEM TROUBLE SHOOTING.

3) Turn ignition off. Wait at least 1 minute, then connect test lamp between power relay output and ground. Turn ignition on. If test lamp comes on but dash light does not, repeat GLOW PLUG LAMP TROUBLE SHOOTING, step **3)**. If test lamp does not light, proceed to step **4)**.

4) Check fusible link from ignition switch to control switch. If fusible link is ok, go to step **8)**. If fusible link is not ok, proceed to step **5)**.

5) Replace fusible link and repeat GLOW PLUG SYSTEM TROUBLE SHOOTING. If fuse blows, proceed to step **6)**. If fuse does not blow and system operates correctly, testing is complete. If fuse does not blow and system still does not operate correctly, go to step **8)**.

6) Remove signal lead from power relay. Replace fusible link. Turn ignition on and then off. If fuse blows, proceed to step **7)**. If fuse does not blow, replace power relay and repeat GLOW PLUG SYSTEM TROUBLE SHOOTING.

7) Disconnect chassis harness from engine harness. Replace fusible link. Turn ignition on and then off. If fuse blows, repair chassis wiring harness and repeat GLOW PLUG SYSTEM TROUBLE SHOOTING. If fuse does not blow, proceed to step **8)**.

8) Turn ignition off. Reconnect all leads (including power relay signal lead). Wait at least 1 minute and turn ignition back on. Check voltage between power relay signal lead and ground. If voltage is at least 11 volts, proceed to step **9)**. If less than 11 volts, go to step **10)**.

9) With ignition off, check voltage between power relay input terminal and ground. If voltage is at least 11 volts, check power relay ground connection or replace relay. If voltage is below 11 volts, charge or replace batteries and/or repair wiring from batteries to power relay. Repeat GLOW PLUG SYSTEM TROUBLE SHOOTING.

10) With ignition off, disconnect power relay signal lead and engine harness at control switch. Check resistance between control switch connector Pin No. 6 and power relay signal lead. If resistance is less than 1 ohm, go to step **12)**. If not, proceed to step **11)**.

11) With ignition off, disconnect chassis harness from engine harness. Disconnect power relay signal lead. Check resistance between chassis side wiring connector terminal No. 6 and power signal lead. If resistance is less than 1 ohm, replace engine harness. If not, repair or replace chassis wiring. Repeat GLOW PLUG SYSTEM TROUBLE SHOOTING.

12) Remove engine harness connector to control switch and turn ignition on. Check voltage between control switch connector Pin No. 3 and ground. If voltage is 11 volts or greater, replace glow plug control switch and repeat GLOW PLUG SYSTEM TROUBLE SHOOTING. If voltage is less than 11 volts, proceed to step **13)**.

13) Turn ignition off. Disconnect chassis harness from engine harness, Turn ignition back on. Check voltage at Pin No. 3 on chassis side of connector. If voltage is 11 volts or greater, replace engine harness. If not, repair or replace chassis wiring. Repeat GLOW PLUG SYSTEM TROUBLE SHOOTING.

GLOW PLUG TEST D
TEST LAMP CYCLES CONTINUOUSLY

Disconnect engine harness connector at control switch. Turn ignition on. Check voltage between control switch connector Pin No. 1 and ground. If voltage is 11 volts or more, turn ignition off and replace control switch. If not, turn ignition off and replace engine harness. Repeat GLOW PLUG SYSTEM TROUBLE SHOOTING and step **4)** of GLOW PLUG TEST A.

FORD 6.9 LITER (Cont.)

GLOW PLUG TEST E
TEST LAMP DOES NOT CYCLE

1) Connect a test lamp between glow plug power relay output and ground. Turn ignition on, but do not start engine. If test lamp lights, proceed to step **2)**. If test lamp does not light, for coolant temperatures of 140° F (60° C) or above, condition is normal. For coolant temperatures below 140° F (60°C), turn ignition off, wait 5 minutes, and turn ignition back on. If lamp lights, proceed to step **2)**. If lamp does not light, perform GLOW PLUG TEST C.

2) Turn ignition off. Disconnect chassis harness from glow plug power relay. Disconnect engine harness from control switch and all glow plugs. Check resistance between control switch connector Pin 4 and glow plug relay power output. If resistance is less than 1 ohm, go to step **4)**. If resistance is 1 ohm or more, proceed to step **3)**.

3) Turn ignition off. Disconnect chassis harness from engine harness. Check resistance between chassis harness and glow plug power relay output. If resistance is less than 1 ohm, replace engine harness. If more than 1 ohm, replace fusible link(s) or repair chassis harness. Repeat GLOW PLUG SYSTEM TROUBLE SHOOTING.

4) With ignition off, check resistance between control switch connector Pin 5 and ground. If resistance is less than 1 ohm, proceed to step **5)**. If not, repair engine harness ground connection or replace harness. Repeat GLOW PLUG SYSTEM TROUBLE SHOOTING.

5) With ignition off, disconnect engine harness at control switch. Connect all other leads. Check resistance between control switch Pin 6 and ground. If resistance is 2.5 ohms or more, replace control switch. If not, replace power relay. Repeat GLOW PLUG SYSTEM TROUBLE SHOOTING and step **4)** of GLOW PLUG TEST A.

REMOVAL & INSTALLATION

INJECTION PUMP

Removal

1) Open hood. Disconnect battery ground cables from both batteries. Remove engine oil filler neck. Remove bolts attaching injection pump to drive gear. Disconnect electrical connectors from injection pump. Disconnect accelerator cable and cruise control cable (if equipped) from throttle lever.

2) Remove air cleaner and cover air intake. Remove accelerator cable bracket, with cables attached, and position out of the way. On van models, remove fuel inlet and return lines from fuel filter. Remove filter bracket and filter as an assembly.

3) On all models, remove fuel line from injection pump inlet and cap fittings. Remove and cap injection pump inlet elbow and fitting adapter.

4) Remove fuel return line from injection pump, rotate out of the way and cap both fittings. If injector lines are to be removed, loosen line fittings at pump. Disconnect fuel lines from injection nozzles and cap line fittings and nozzles.

5) Remove 3 injection pump retaining nuts. If injection pump or fuel lines are to be replaced, remove injector lines from pump and cap all fittings. Injector lines must be removed in the following order: 5-6-4-8-3-1-7-2. *See Fig. 8.* Remove injection pump from engine compartment (through passenger compartment on van models).

Installation

To install, reverse removal procedure, noting the following:

- Use a new "O" ring on drive gear end of injection pump.
- Install injector lines AFTER pump is installed. Lines must be installed in the following order: 2-7-1-3-8-4-6-5.
- Use new "O" ring on injection pump fitting adapter.
- Purge injector lines by loosening connector 1/2 to 1 turn and cranking engine until a solid stream of fuel flows from connector.
- Check and adjust injection pump timing as necessary.

INJECTOR NOZZLES

Fig. 8: Injection Pump Line Sequence

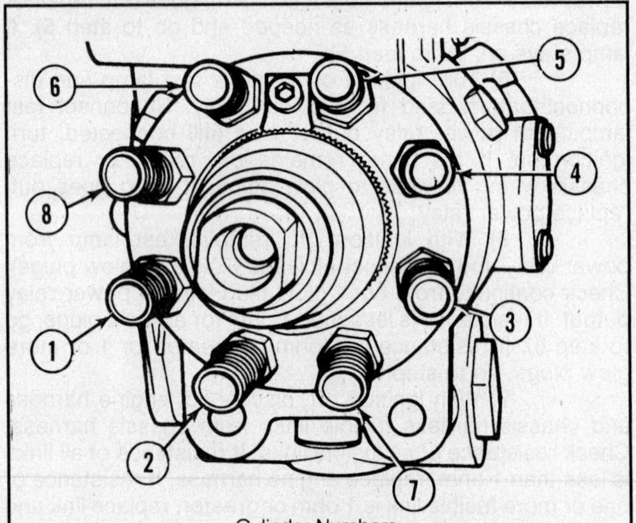

Remove and install injector lines in proper sequence.

Removal

1) Before removing nozzles, clean nozzle, surrounding area and piping connections with clean fuel or solvent to prevent contamination. Blow area dry with compressed air. Remove fuel line retaining clamps from lines being removed.

2) Disconnect nozzle fuel inlet and fuel return "T" fittings from each nozzle and position out of way. Cap all open connections. Unscrew nozzle and remove nozzle and copper washer from engine.

3) Do not strike nozzle tip against any hard surface during removal. Cap both ends of nozzle and store in a rack such that nozzles may be reinstalled in their original cylinders.

Installation

1) Clean nozzle bore in cylinder head thoroughly before reinstalling nozzle. Remove protective cap from nozzle tip. Coat nozzle threads with anti-seize compound. Install a new copper gasket on nozzle using a small amount of grease to retain gasket on nozzle.

2) Install nozzle into cylinder head bore and tighten. Remove caps from fuel lines and nozzle fittings. Install fuel inlet and return "T" fittings on nozzle. Install 2 new "O" rings on each "T" fitting. Connect fuel line to nozzle.

3) Install fuel line retainer clamps and tighten. Purge injector lines if needed by loosening connector 1/2 to 1 turn and cranking engine until a solid stream of fuel flows from connector. Run engine and check for fuel line leakage.

FORD 6.9 LITER (Cont.)

ADJUSTMENTS

INJECTION PUMP TIMING

Static Timing (Engine Stopped)

1) Remove fast idle bracket and solenoid from injection pump. Loosen (keep snug) 3 nuts attaching fuel injection pump to pump mounting adapter with Injector Pump Wrench (T83T-9000-B).

2) Install Injection Pump Rotater (T83T-9000-C) on front of pump. Rotate pump to align injection pump mounting flange timing mark with pump mounting adapter timing mark. *See Fig. 9.*

Fig. 9: Static Timing Mark Alignment

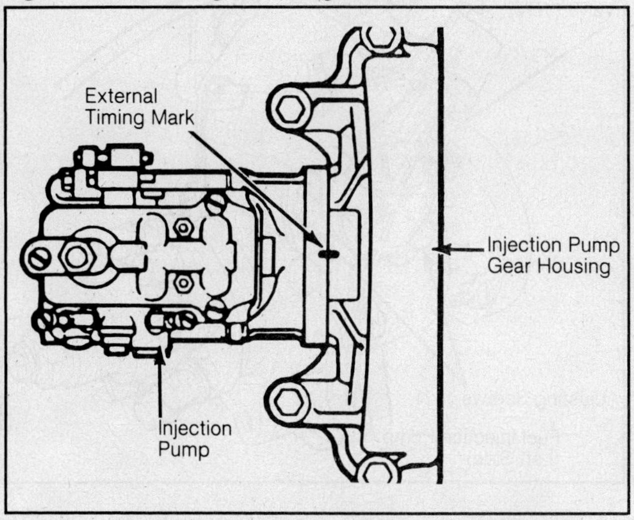

Keep mounting nuts snug during static timing check.

3) Remove tools and tighten mounting nuts. Visually recheck timing to ensure that marks are still aligned after tightening nuts.

Dynamic Timing (Engine Running)

Correct timing specifications vary with cetane value of engine fuel. Before performing timing test, determine cetane value as follows:

1) Obtain a small fuel sample from injection system. Temperature of fuel must be 75-95°F (24-35°C) to obtain accurate results.

2) Fill hydrometer container included with Dynamic Timing Meter (078-00100) with fuel until hydrometer floats. Spin container gently to break surface tension of fuel.

3) Read number at lowest point of fuel level in hydrometer. Compare reading to DIESEL FUEL CETANE VALUES chart to determine Cetane value.

DIESEL FUEL CETANE VALUES

Hydrometer Reading	Cetane Value
.837	50
.846	47
.849	46
.858	43
.862	42
.876	38

4) Start and warm engine to normal operating temperature. Coolant temperature MUST be 192-212°F (89-100°C) when performing dynamic timing procedure. Stop engine and install magnetic pick-up probe of Dynamic Timing Meter (78-0100) into timing pointer probe hole. *See Fig. 10.*

Fig. 10: Magnetic Pick-Up Probe Installation

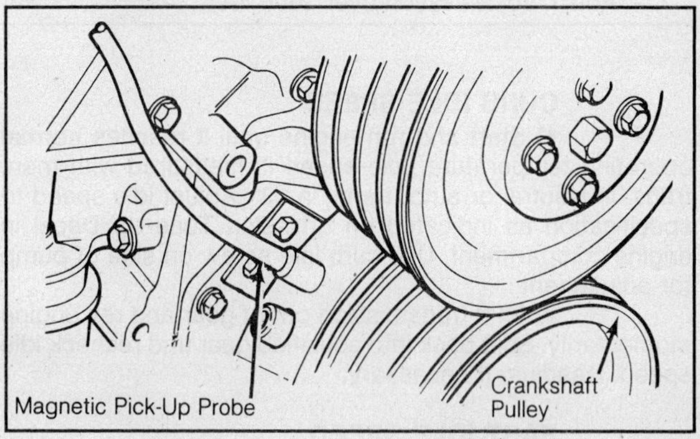

5) Remove No. 1 cylinder glow plug. Install luminosity probe in place of glow plug and tighten to 12 ft. lbs. (16 N.m). *See Fig. 11.* Connect photocell over luminosity probe and connect to timing meter. Connect meter to battery and adjust offset on meter.

Fig. 11: Luminosity Probe Installation

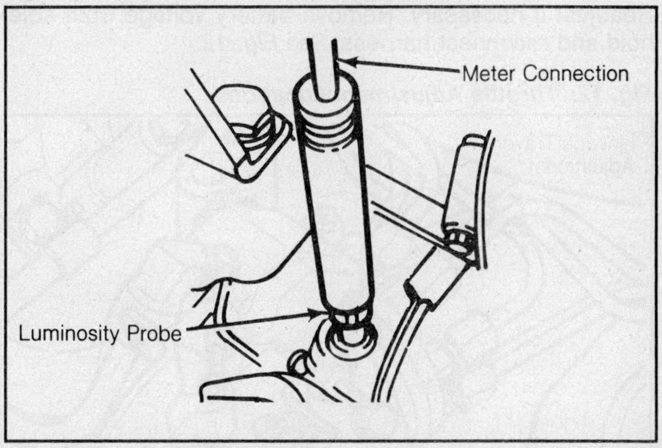

6) Raise and support rear wheels. Place transmission in Neutral and start engine. Using Throttle Controller (014-00302), set engine speed at 1400 RPM with no accessory load. Read injection timing on meter.

7) If injection timing is not within 2° of value indicated in DYNAMIC INJECTION TIMING SPECIFICATIONS chart, timing must be adjusted. If timing is not within specifications, stop engine and loosen pump retaining nuts (keeping nuts snug).

8) Using pump rotator, rotate pump clockwise to retard timing or counterclockwise to advance timing (as viewed from front of engine). Tap rotator with rubber mallet as needed to rotate pump.

9) Moving timing mark .030" (.75 mm) is equal to 2° of timing. Retighten nuts. Recheck timing using meter. Repeat step **8)** as needed to obtain correct timing. Remove timing meter and other test equipment. Reinstall glow plug using anti-seize compound on threads.

FORD 6.9 LITER (Cont.)

DYNAMIC INJECTION TIMING SPECIFICATIONS

Fuel Cetane Value	°ATDC [1]
38-42	3.5
43-46	2.5
More than 46	1.5

1 - Add 1° for elevation over 3000 feet.

CURB IDLE SPEED

1) Start and run engine until it reaches normal operating temperature. Idle speed is measured with man. trans. in Neutral or auto. trans. in "D". Adjust idle speed to specification as indicated on Emission Tune-Up Decal in engine compartment. Use curb idle screw on side of pump for adjustment.

2) Shift transmission out of gear and rev engine momentarily. Shift back into specified gear and recheck idle speed. Readjust if necessary.

FAST IDLE SPEED

1) Start and run engine until it reaches normal operating temperature. Disconnect wiring harness from fast idle solenoid. Apply battery voltage to solenoid to activate it. Rev engine momentarily to set solenoid plunger. Fast idle speed should be 850-900 RPM.

2) Adjust fast idle speed if necessary by turning solenoid plunger. Rev engine and recheck fast idle speed. Readjust if necessary. Remove battery voltage from solenoid and reconnect harness. *See Fig. 12.*

Fig. 12: Throttle Adjustment Locations

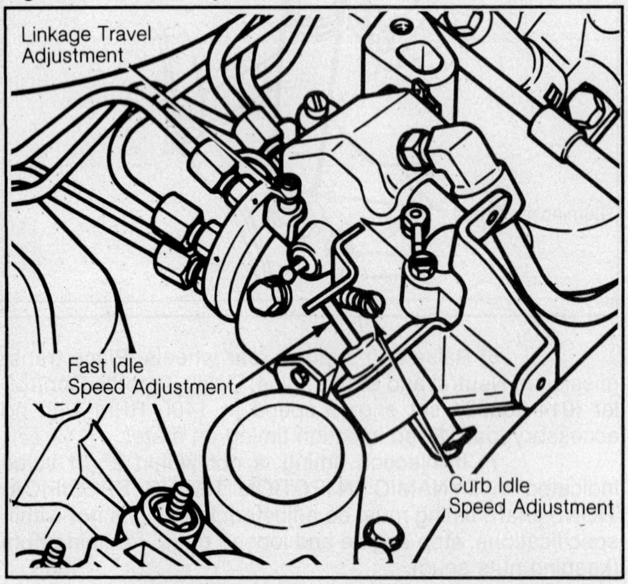

ACCELERATOR LINKAGE ADJUSTMENT

With engine off, check that throttle lever contacts injection pump stop at full accelerator depression. Adjust stop screw on throttle lever if necessary.

VACUUM REGULATOR VALVE (AUTO. TRANS. ONLY)

1) The vacuum regulator valve provides vacuum signals to control transmission shift points. Vacuum setting of valve should be checked periodically, using the following procedure. Engine MUST NOT be running during this procedure.

2) Disconnect 2-port vacuum connector from vacuum regulator valve, located on left side of pump. *See Fig. 13.* Remove throttle cable from pump throttle lever, located on right side of pump.

Fig. 13: Location of Vacuum Regulator Valve

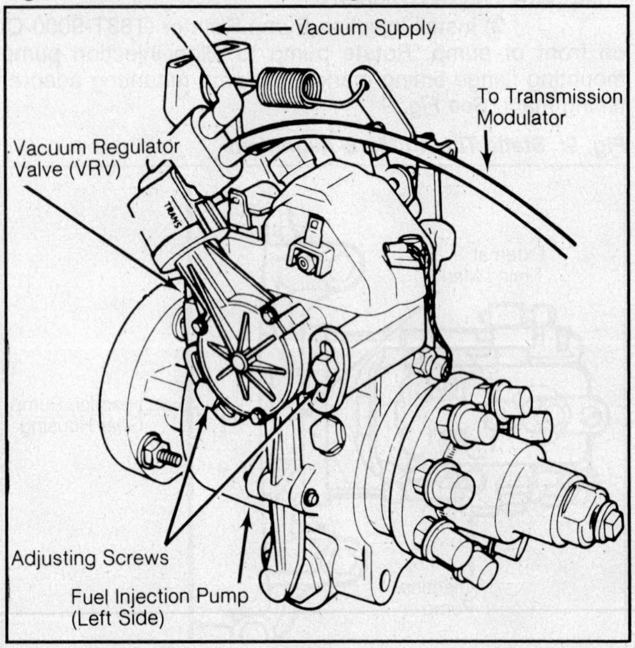

3) Remove throttle return spring and reposition. Place end of spring over throttle lever ball stud and other end over throttle cable support bracket. Insert Gauging Block (T83T 7B200 AH) between pump boss and wide open throttle stop screw. *See Fig. 14.*

Fig. 14: Repositioning Throttle Return Spring

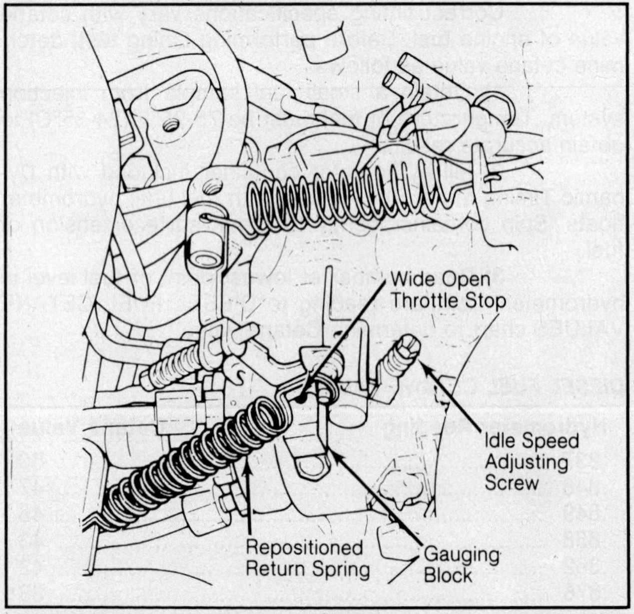

Insert gauging block between pump boss and wide open throttle stop screw.

FORD 6.9 LITER (Cont.)

4) Attach a vacuum pump to upper port (labeled "VAC") of vacuum regulator valve. Attach vacuum gauge to lower port (labeled "TRANS") of regulator valve.

5) Apply and maintain 20 in. Hg to vacuum regulator valve. Vacuum gauge attached to regulator valve should indicate 6 1/2-7 1/2 in. Hg. If not, adjust regulator valve.

6) To adjust valve, loosen 2 vacuum regulator valve-to-injection pump mounting screws and rotate valve until vacuum gauge reads 6 1/2-7 1/2 in. Hg. Tighten screws. If valve cannot be adjusted to obtain vacuum reading, replace regulator valve.

7) Release vacuum and remove gauging block. Reconnect throttle return spring in original position and make sure fuel injection pump lever returns and stays at idle position.

8) Apply and maintain 20 in. Hg to vacuum regulator valve again. Vacuum gauge MUST indicate at least 13 in. Hg. If vacuum reading is less than 13 in. Hg, replace vacuum regulator valve and adjust new valve using above procedure.

9) Remove vacuum pump and gauge. Reconnect all disconnected components in their original positions.

MAINTENANCE

WATER SEPARATOR

1) When water level in water separator reaches maximum level, a warning lamp on the dash will light up. When warning lamp is lit, it is necessary to drain water from the separator.

2) Stop vehicle and shut off engine. On pickup models, unscrew vent (located on top of separator) 2 1/2-3 turns. Unscrew drain (located on bottom of separator) 1-1 1/2 turns. Drain water into a container. Close vent and drain.

3) On van models, locate water separator drain knob on left side of firewall under hood. Place a container under separator, located behind left front wheel. Pull knob out and hold for 45 seconds. Release knob and remove container.

4) On all models, restart engine and check warning lamp. If warning lamp is still lit, fuel system needs to be checked or repaired. The only servicable item on the separator is the water level sensor.

TIGHTENING SPECIFICATIONS

Application	Ft. Lbs. (N.m)
Glow Plug	12 (16)
Injection Pump Adapter	14 (19)
Injection Pump Gear Mounting Bolts	25m(34)
Injection Pump Outlet Fitting Nut	22 (30)
Nozzle Assembly	35 (47)
Nozzle Connector Nut	22 (30)

1985 Diesel Fuel Injection

DIESEL KIKI – GENERAL MOTORS

"S" Series Truck

DESCRIPTION

The fuel injection system consists of a combination injection pump and fuel distributor, four injection nozzles, a fuel tank, lines and hoses, and fuel filter assembly. The filter assembly contains a fuel filter, integral priming pump, and a water separator. The injectors use a needle type valve at the end of each nozzle.

The glow plug system uses 4 glow plugs to assist in cold starting. The thermal glow plug system has a controller, relays, thermo switch, dropping resistor, sensing resistor, and glow plugs. Warning lights in the instrument cluster indicate when the glow plugs are operating or the fuel filter is filled with water.

OPERATION

FUEL INJECTION PUMP

The injection pump is located on the lower right side of the engine and is driven by a toothed belt. It draws fuel from the tank, pressurizes it and sends a specific quantity to each cylinder at the proper time. Excess fuel from the injectors is returned to the fuel tank.

A fast idle system is used when coolant is below a specific temperature. A vacuum unit actuates the throttle to increase idle speed.

A fuel cut solenoid is actuated by the ignition switch, stopping fuel flow at the pump to shut down the engine. The injection pump is also equipped with an altitude compensator for proper fuel delivery at high altitudes.

INJECTION NOZZLES

Injection nozzles spray fuel into a prechamber as each compression stroke occurs. A fuel return line connects all injectors and returns excess fuel to the pump. Injectors are opened by high pressure in the fuel lines. Injector opening pressures are adjustable, using an adjustment screw in the injector nozzle. If spray patterns are incorrect, nozzles can be overhauled.

FUEL FILTER & WATER WARNING SYSTEM

The diesel injection system uses an integral fuel filter and water separator. A water sensor is fitted into the bottom of a fuel filter cartridge and lights a warning lamp when water accumulates in the filter. A hand pump is also incorporated into the filter housing to prime the pump after filter replacement.

GLOW PLUGS

The glow plug system uses 4 glow plugs to assist in cold starting. When engine coolant is below 122°F (50°C), the No. 1 relay supplies battery voltage to heat the glow plugs quickly.

When the glow plugs reach maximum temperature, relay No. 1 is turned off and relay No. 2 provides a lower voltage to maintain glow plug temperature. When the engine starts, the glow plug system is turned off. At coolant temperatures above 122°F (50°C), only relay No. 2 is operated. This operation provides easy starting but does not drain the battery or overheat glow plugs.

TROUBLE SHOOTING

HARD STARTING

Check fuel delivery, injection pump timing and nozzle opening pressures. Check fuel cut solenoid and fuel restrictions. Air leaks.

ROUGH IDLE

Adjust idle speed. Contaminated fuel, injection timing, nozzle opening pressure or sticking delivery valve in pump.

LACK OF POWER

Air cleaner restriction. Accelerator linkage. Exhaust restriction. Fuel contamination or restriction in lines. Injection timing.

EXHAUST SMOKE

Check for air cleaner restrictions or contaminated fuel. Injection timing or nozzle opening pressure.

GLOW PLUG INDICATOR INOPERATIVE

Check for burned out bulb, blown fuse or fusible link. Bad connections at controller. Controller or ignition switch defective.

IMPROPER OPERATION OF GLOW PLUGS

Thermal sensor or glow plugs defective. Controller inoperative. Ignition switch "R" circuit intermittent or open.

TESTING

INJECTION NOZZLES

Spray Pattern

Remove nozzles and mount on injection nozzle tester. Pump tester lever about 1 stroke every 2 seconds to observe spray pattern. *See Fig. 1*. If spray is faulty, injector must be cleaned or replaced.

Opening Pressure

1) Pump pressure up slowly to note opening pressure. If opening pressure is less than 1493 psi (105 kg/cm^2) injector must be cleaned or replaced.

2) Check injector nozzles for leakage by installing in tester and maintaining a pressure of 285 psi (20 kg/cm^2). If leakage is evident, injector must be cleaned or replaced (slight wetting around tip after 10 seconds is OK).

Nozzle Cleaning

1) Disassemble injector nozzle. If nozzle needle is damaged, fused, seized or discolored, replace entire nozzle assembly. Check all other parts for excessive wear or damage. Replace as needed. *See Fig. 2.*

2) Scrape off carbon deposits with a piece of wood and clean each part in clean solvent. After cleaning, keep parts immersed in light oil. Be sure to remove all deposits from components. Nozzle must be replaced if needle seats are worn or damaged.

3) Hold nozzle vertically and insert needle. Lift needle about 1/3 way out of nozzle and release. Needle should slide smoothly back into place. Repeat procedure several times, rotating needle slightly each time. If needle does not slide smoothly, replace nozzle body and needle.

Fig. 1: Injection Nozzle Spray Patterns

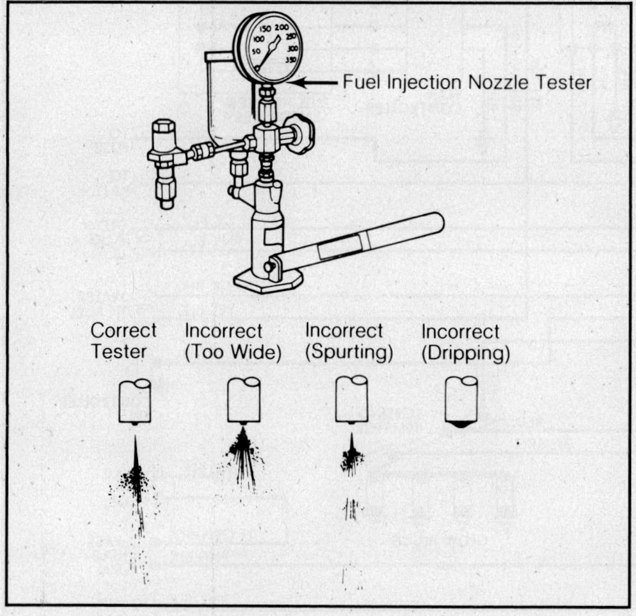

Fig. 2: Injection Nozzle

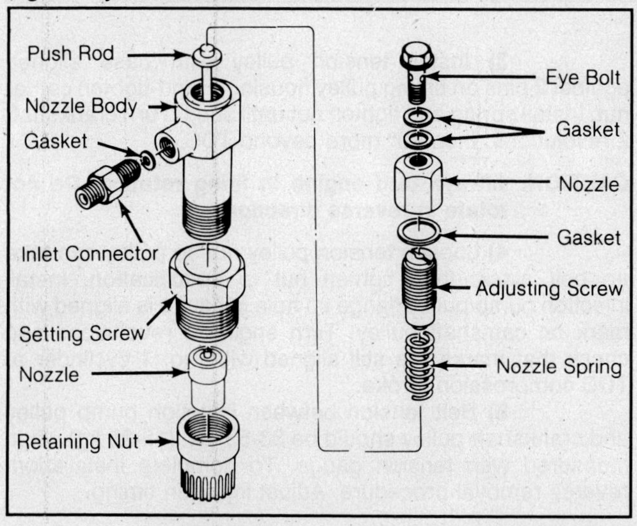

4) When assembling injectors, use Centering Gauge (J-33178) to install nozzle in center of nozzle body holder. *See Fig. 3.* Tighten retaining nut to 65 ft. lbs. (88 N.m).

5) After tightening retaining nut, draw out centering tool. If it can't be drawn out easily, nozzle body has not been fitted properly. Loosen retaining nut and tighten properly. Adjust nozzle opening pressure after assembly.

GLOW PLUG SYSTEM

Glow Plug Relays

No continuity should be present across terminals "C" and "D". With battery voltage applied to terminals "A" and "B", continuity should be present across "C" and "D". If not, replace relay. *See Fig. 4.*

Fig. 3: Centering Injector Nozzle

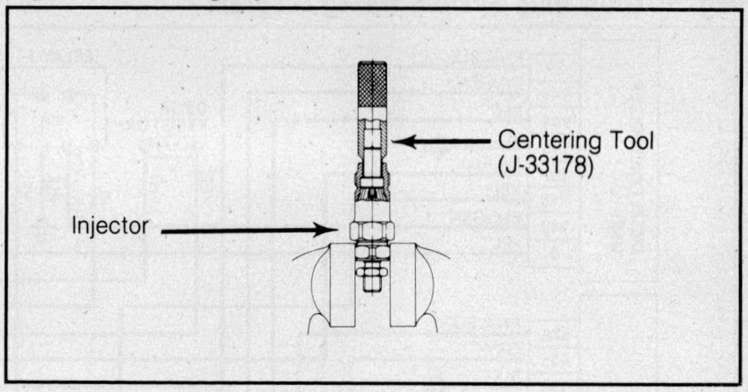

Fig. 4: Glow Plug Relay Testing

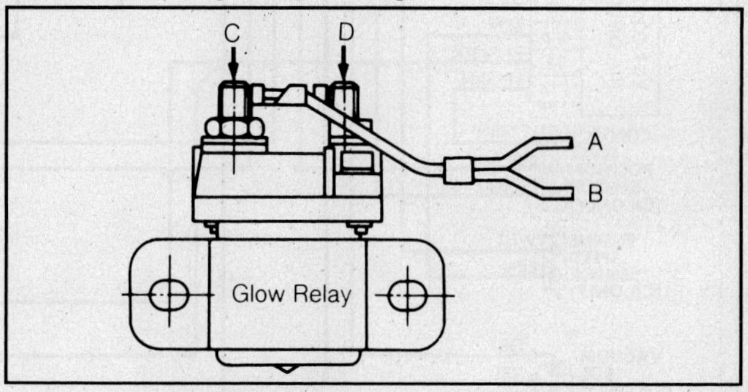

Dropping Resistor

Check for continuity across terminals of resistor. If no continuity, replace resistor. Resistor is located on right front fender near battery.

Glow Plugs

Continuity should exist between plug end terminal and body. If not, replace plug.

Thermo Switch

Continuity should exist when switch temperature is lower than 117-127°F (47-53°C). No continuity should exist when above 127°F (53°C). If switch does not operate properly, replace it.

REMOVAL & INSTALLATION

INJECTION PUMP & TIMING BELT

NOTE: **When timing belt is loosened or removed, it must be replaced. Do not re-tension or install a used timing belt.**

Removal

1) Disconnect negative battery cable. Align crank pulley with timing pointer, loosen belts and remove pulley. Remove power steering reservoir and upper fan shroud. Remove fan and fan drive pulley. Remove upper timing belt cover.

2) Remove alternator belt and lower timing belt cover. Remove injection pump timing pulley flange bolts. Remove tension spring using care not to distort spring. Remove tension pulley center nut, then remove pulley and center. Remove timing belt.

3) Remove injection pump gear. Remove fuel feed and return lines from pump. Disconnect electrical wiring, throttle cable and injection lines. Remove throttle

1985 Diesel Fuel Injection

DIESEL KIKI – GENERAL MOTORS (Cont.)

Fig. 5: Glow Plug System Wiring Diagram

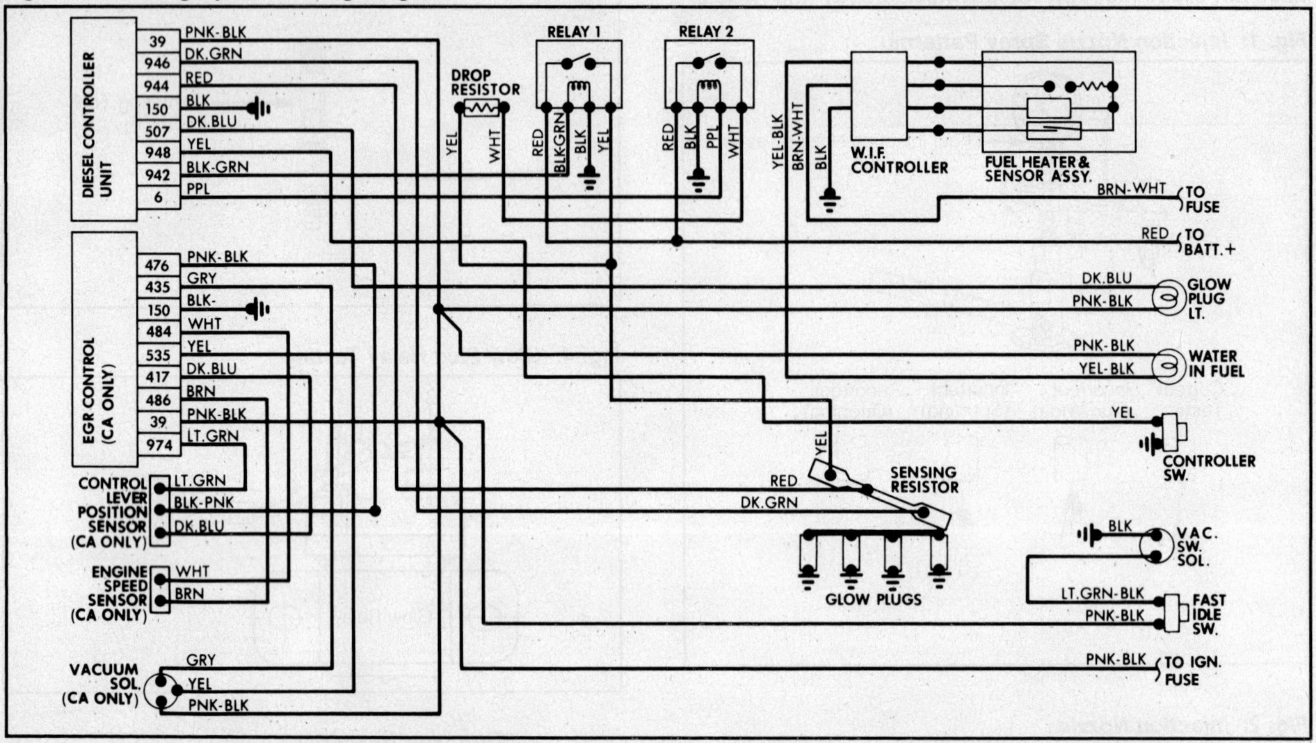

Also see chassis wiring in WIRING DIAGRAM section.

return spring. Raise vehicle and remove injection pump-to-bracket bolts. Lower vehicle and remove pump.

NOTE: If injection pump bracket is removed, refer to INJECTION PUMP TIMING procedure.

Installation

1) Install injection pump, aligning marks on flange and front bracket. Install injection pump pulley, using holding bolt to keep pulley from turning. Set No. 1 cylinder at TDC compression stroke.

2) Align pulleys so marks are together. *See Fig. 6.* Install timing belt on crankshaft pulley, camshaft pulley and injection pump pulley in order. Position belt so slack is in area of idler pulley.

Fig. 6: Timing Belt Pulley Alignment

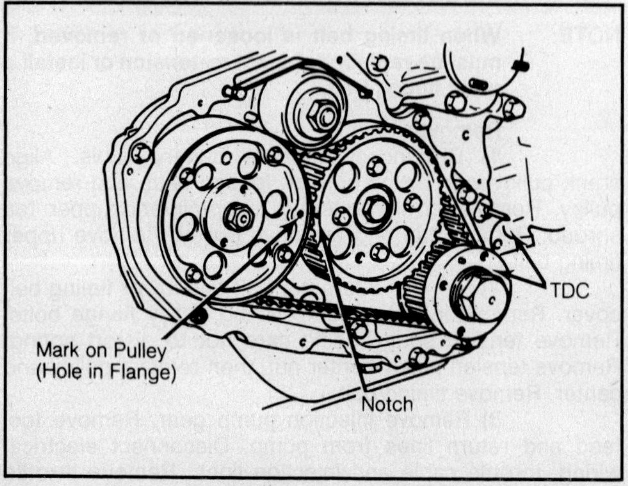

3) Install tension pulley with base aligned against 2 pins on timing pulley housing. Hand-tighten center nut. Install spring and tighten nut until snug. Turn crankshaft 2 revolutions, then 90° more beyond TDC.

CAUTION: Always turn engine in firing rotation. Do not rotate in reverse direction.

4) Loosen tension pulley nut so pulley can take up belt slack, then tighten nut to specification. Install injection pump pulley flange so hole in flange is aligned with mark on camshaft pulley. Turn engine 2 revolutions and check that marks are still aligned with No. 1 cylinder at TDC compression stroke.

5) Belt tension between injection pump pulley and crankshaft pulley should be 33-55 lbs. (15-25 kg) when measured with tension gauge. To complete installation, reverse removal procedure. Adjust injection timing.

FUEL FILTER

Removal & Installation

1) Disconnect negative battery cable. Disconnect water sensor wiring at connector. Disconnect water sensor-to-main body hose. Remove filter cartridge and pour out fuel. Remove water sensor.

2) Lubricate sensor "O" ring with diesel fuel and install sensor on new filter cartridge. Lubricate gasket with fuel, then install filter cartridge. Tighten 2/3 turn after filter contacts base.

3) Reconnect water sensor wiring and hose. Disconnect filter-to-injection pump fuel line at pump and place open end in container. Pump hand pump until fuel flows from fuel line. Reconnect fuel line to injection pump. Start engine and check for leaks.

Draining Water

1) Place 2-quart container under drain hose. Open drain plug about 4 turns and operate hand pump until all water is removed from filter. Tighten drain plug.

2) Operate pump several times until pressure builds up. Start engine and check for leaks. "WATER IN FUEL" lamp on dashboard should be off. If light remains on, fuel tank must be drained.

Fig. 7: Fuel Filter and Water Separator

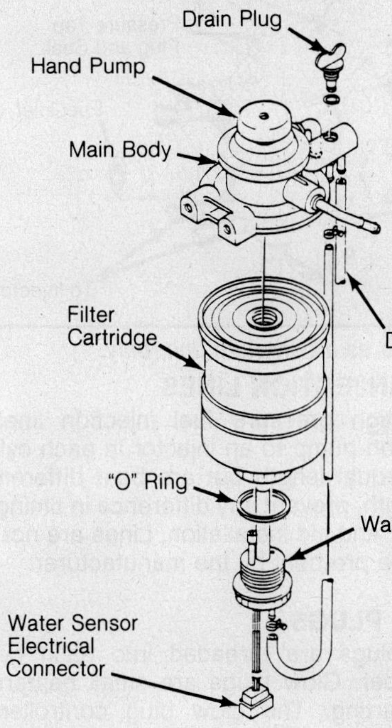

ADJUSTMENT

INJECTION PUMP TIMING

1) Check that notch in pump flange is in line with notch in front bracket. Set No. 1 cylinder at TDC compression stroke. Remove injection pump pulley cover (right half of timing belt cover) to ensure timing marks are aligned. *See Fig. 6.*

2) Disconnect injection pipe from pump (using back-up wrench) and remove distributor head screw. Install Timing Gauge (J-29763) and set lift approximately .04" (1 mm) from plunger.

3) Turn engine until No. 1 cylinder is 45-60° BTDC. Set dial indicator to zero. Turn crankshaft pulley slightly in both directions to check that zero reading does not change.

4) Turn crankshaft in normal direction of rotation until timing mark (15° BTDC or 13°BTDC for California models) on crankshaft pulley is in line with indicator. *See Fig. 8*. Dial indicator should show .020" (0.5 mm). If not, loosen pump bolts and rotate pump slightly to obtain proper timing.

Fig. 8: Timing Mark Identification

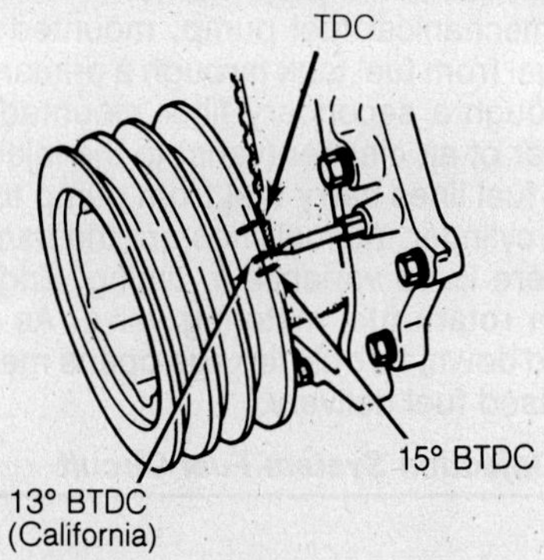

IDLE & FAST IDLE SPEED

NOTE: For all on-vehicle adjustments, see appropriate TUNE-UP article.

VACUUM PUMP

Description

An auxiliary vacuum pump is used on diesel engines. The pump is belt-driven off the crankshaft pulley and supplies vacuum for the power brake booster and any vacuum-operated accesories.

Testing

1) Disconnect vacuum pump-to-brake booster hose at pump and attach vacuum gauge to fitting. Disconnect vacuum outlet hose. Plug hose (DO NOT plug pump fitting). With engine at idle speed (800 RPM), vacuum should be at least 21 in. Hg within 30 seconds.

2) If vacuum is low, check gauge and connections for leaks. Check belt tension and idle speed. If reading is still low, replace pump.

3) Install a "T" fitting in vacuum hose between pump and brake booster. Attach vacuum gauge at "T". Run engine at idle for about 1 minute. Vacuum should be no more than 3 in. Hg lower than in step **1)**.

4) If vacuum is too low, check gauge and connections for leaks. If reading is still low, check power booster and any vacuum operated accessories for leaks. Repair or replace as needed.

TIGHTENING SPECIFICATIONS

Application	Ft. Lbs. (N.m)
Injection Pump Pulley Nut	42-52 (57-71)
Injection Nozzles	51-58 (69-79)
Timing Belt Tension Pulley Center Bolt	79-84 (108-127)

1985 Diesel Fuel Injection

GENERAL MOTORS 6.2 LITER

DESCRIPTION

General Motors 6.2L engine uses a mechanical high pressure rotary pump, gear driven by camshaft at camshaft speed. It injects a precisely metered amount of fuel to each cylinder at the proper time.

A mechanical fuel pump, mounted on right of engine, pulls fuel from fuel tank through a primary filter. Fuel is pumped through a secondary filter mounted on firewall (pickups) or rear of air cleaner (vans) to the injection pump. High pressure fuel lines carry fuel from pump to 1 injection nozzle in each cylinder. All fuel lines are the same length to ensure that there is no variance in timing. Engine RPM is controlled by a rotary fuel metering valve. As accelerator pedal is pushed down, throttle linkage opens metering valve to allow increased fuel delivery.

Fig. 1: Diesel Injection System Fuel Circuit

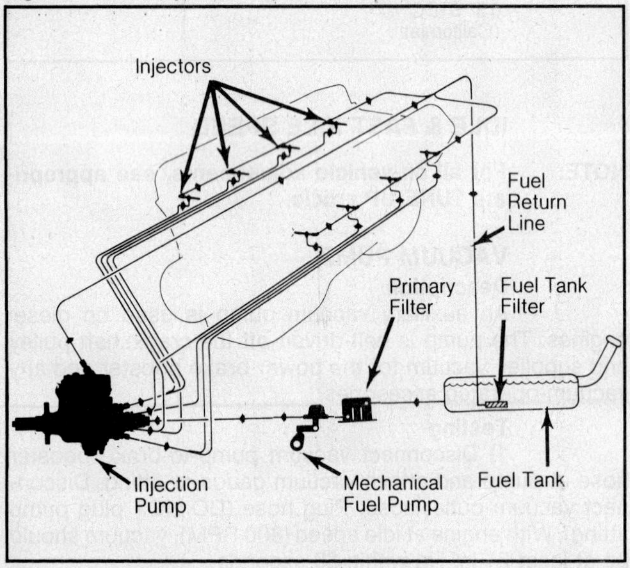

Secondary fuel filter is mounted on firewall (pickups) or rear of air cleaner (vans).

OPERATION

AIR INDUCTION SYSTEM

Intake manifold is always open to atmospheric pressure. Intake manifold has a single inlet for drawing air through an air filter assembly mounted above. Manifold consists of 8 branches, one leading to each cylinder.

DIESEL INJECTION PUMP

The high pressure diesel injection pump is mounted at top of engine below intake manifold. The pump is gear driven by camshaft at camshaft speed. Pump precisely governs time and amount of fuel injection.

A built-in fuel pressure regulator and transfer pump picks up fuel at pump inlet, pushing it through a passage to the pump head. The pump head distributes fuel at transfer pump pressure (8-12 psi) to metering valve, governor and automatic advance mechanisms. Fuel then passes to rotary fuel metering valve and into a charging passage. As pump shaft rotates, fuel is directed at high pressure through each delivery pipe to an injector. Pump is not serviceable and must be exchanged in the event of a malfunction.

Fig. 2: Diesel Injection Pump

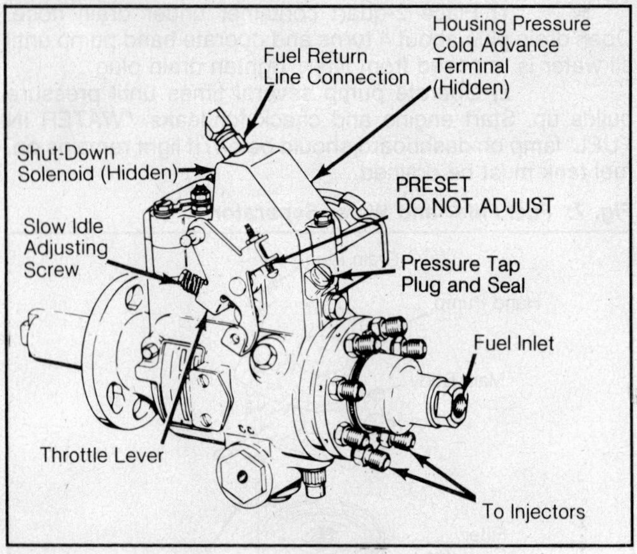

Pump is serviceable as a complete unit, only.

FUEL INJECTION LINES

Eight high pressure fuel injection lines are routed from injection pump to an injector in each cylinder. The lines are of equal length but are bent differently to maintain equal length, prevent any difference in timing from cylinder-to-cylinder and aid installation. Lines are not interchangeable and are pre-bent by the manufacturer.

GLOW PLUGS

Glow plugs are threaded into each cylinder combustion chamber. Glow plugs are small heaters that assist in cold starting. The glow plug controller/relay (mounted on top-rear of engine) cycles 12 volts to these 6 volt heaters, which causes them to heat rapidly. After the engine starts, glow plugs continue to cycle on and off for about 25 seconds, depending on coolant temperature.

NOTE: Any attempt to by-pass relay with jumper wire may result in glow plug failure.

INJECTION NOZZLES

Each engine cylinder combustion chamber is equipped with 1 injection nozzle. The injection nozzle has a single fuel inlet fitting and 2 fuel return fittings (1 on each side of fuel inlet fitting). The nozzle is threaded into the cylinder head. Injection nozzles are spring loaded and calibrated to open at a specified fuel line pressure. The combustion chamber end of the nozzle has a replaceable compression seal and carbon stop seal.

Fig. 3: Injection Nozzle Installation

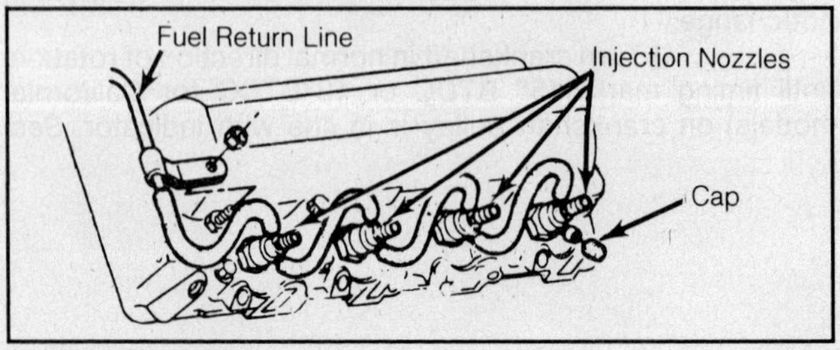

Last nozzle on cylinder bank has 1 fuel return fitting plugged.

GENERAL MOTORS 6.2 LITER (Cont.)

VACUUM PUMP

Vacuum to operate accessory systems on diesel vehicles is provided by a vacuum pump which is located at the rear of the block and driven by the cam. The engine should never be operated without the vacuum pump in place as it is also the oil pump drive.

HOUSING PRESSURE COLD ADVANCE (HPCA)

The HPCA circuit is used to improve cold starting and aid emission control. The circuit is controlled by a temperature switch located on rear of right-hand cylinder head. The circuit advances injection timing about 4° when the engine is cold.

When engine temperature is below 95°F (35°C), the circuit decreases housing pressure from 10 psi to zero. At the same time, the fast idle solenoid is activated. When the temperature switch opens, the HPCA circuit is de-energized and housing pressure rises, retarding pump timing. The temperature switch will close again when engine temperature falls below 85°F (30°C).

DIESEL FUEL HEATER

This option is used to heat the fuel during low temperature operation, below 20°F (B 5°C). This prevents wax crystals from building up and blocking the fuel filters. The heater is located along the right side of the intake manifold and uses a resistance wire spiralled around the fuel line.

ADJUSTMENT

NOTE: For all on-vehicle adjustments, see appropriate TUNE-UP article.

VACUUM REGULATOR VALVE (AUTO. TRANS. ONLY)

1) The vacuum regulator valve provides vacuum signals to control transmission shift points. Vacuum setting of valve should be checked periodically, using the following procedure. Engine MUST NOT be running during this procedure.

2) Attach vacuum regulator valve snugly to fuel injection pump. Switch body must be free to rotate on pump.

Fig. 4: Vacuum Regulator Valve Adjustment

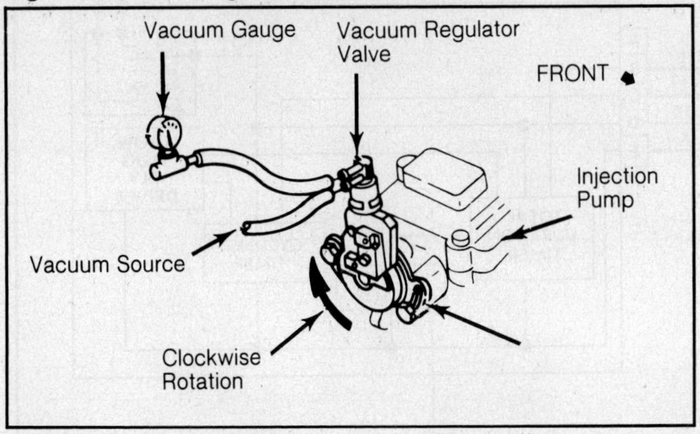

Valve must be set while rotating valve body in clockwise direction only.

3) Attach vacuum source of 20 in. Hg. to bottom vacuum nipple. Insert vacuum regulator valve Gauge Block (J-33043-2) between gauge boss on injection pump and wide open stop screw on throttle lever (switch on position).

Fig. 5: Vacuum Regulator Gauge Block

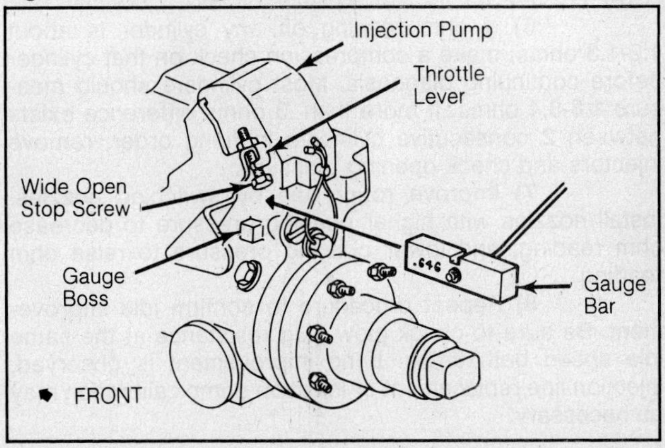

4) Rotate and hold throttle shaft against gauge. Slowly rotate vacuum regulator valve body clockwise (facing valve) until vacuum gauge reads 8 ±.6 in. Hg. Hold valve body at this position and tighten mounting screws.

5) Check by releasing throttle shaft allowing it to return to idle stop position. Then rotate throttle shaft back aganist gauge block to determine if vacuum gauge reads within 8 ±.6 in. Hg. If vacuum is outside limits, reset valve.

TESTING

GLOW PLUG ELECTRICAL SYSTEM

Glow plug system charts should be used only after ensuring that glow plug system is properly installed. Check that all connectors are correctly installed and that all connections are clean and tight.

The PRELIMINARY DIAGNOSIS chart provides a quick procedure for determining if a problem exists in the glow plug system itself, or elsewhere in the electrical system. This test should always be completed before proceeding with the ELECTRICAL SYSTEM DIAGNOSIS chart.

GLOW PLUG RESISTANCE TEST

CAUTION: The following test requires a high impedance ohmmeter. Select scale values as follows: Left-hand switch – "OHMS" position; Right-hand switch – fully counterclockwise (200 ohms); Slide center switch – left position ("DC-LOW")

1) Start engine, turn on heater and allow engine to warm up. Remove all electrical feed wires at glow plugs.

2) Use a magnetic pickup tachometer to adjust engine speed. Turn idle speed screw on side of injection pump until engine idle is roughest. About 860 RPM is desirable, but do not exceed 900 RPM.

3) Allow engine to run for 1 minute at roughest idle. Thermostat must be open and upper radiator hose hot.

4) Attach jumper wire between voltmeter ground lead and engine lift point on left side of intake manifold. DO NOT use any other point for ground connection. Ground

1985 Diesel Fuel Injection

GENERAL MOTORS 6.2 LITER (Cont.)

wire must remain in position until all tests have been completed.

5) Check resistance by touching positive lead of voltmeter to glow plug terminal (with engine running). Record value obtained in firing order sequence (1-8-7-2-6-5-4-3).

6) If ohm reading on any cylinder is about 1.2-1.3 ohms, make a compression check on that cylinder before continuing diagnosis. Most cylinders should measure 1.8-3.4 ohms. If more than .3 ohms difference exists between 2 consecutive cylinders in firing order, remove injectors and check opening pressure.

7) Improve rough idle by switching nozzles. Install nozzles with higher opening pressure to decrease ohm reading, and lower opening pressure to raise ohm reading.

8) Repeat procedure to confirm idle improvement. Be sure to check glow plug resistance at the same idle speed both times. If no improvement is observed, injection line replacement or injection pump calibration may be necessary.

GLOW PLUG CONTROLLER

A faulty controller/relay assembly may result in excessive white smoke in exhaust and/or poor idle immediately after starting. The following procedure checks for proper operation of controller circuit.

NOTE: Engine coolant temperature must be below 80°F (27°C) before beginning test.

1) Turn ignition to "RUN" and allow glow plugs to cycle. Wait 2 minutes, then turn ignition to "CRANK" for 1 second and back to "RUN". Glow plugs should cycle on at least once. If glow plugs do not cycle as described, proceed to step **2)**.

2) Disconnect controller connector. Connect 12-volt test light between harness connector terminal "B" (Purple wire) and ground. With ignition in "RUN" position, test light should be off. With ignition in "CRANK" position, light should be on.

3) If test light does not operate as described, repair short or open in engine harness Purple wire. If light operates properly but glow plugs did not cycle in step **1)**, replace controller.

INJECTION PUMP HOUSING FUEL PRESSURE

1) Remove injection pump and drain all fuel. Connect an air supply line to fuel inlet fitting. Be sure air supply is clean and dry.

2) Seal the return line fitting. Completely immerse pump assembly in a container of clean test oil.

3) Apply 20 psi (1.4 kg/cm^2) to pump. Leave pump immersed for 10 minutes to allow any trapped air to escape. Watch for leaks after 10 minutes.

4) If no leaks are noticed after 10 minutes, reduce air pressure to 2 psi (.14 kg/cm^2) for 30 seconds. If there are still no leaks, increase pressure to 20 psi (1.4 kg/cm^2) again.

5) If no leaks are observed, pump must be exchanged for replacement unit.

Fig. 6: Engine Wiring System Diagram

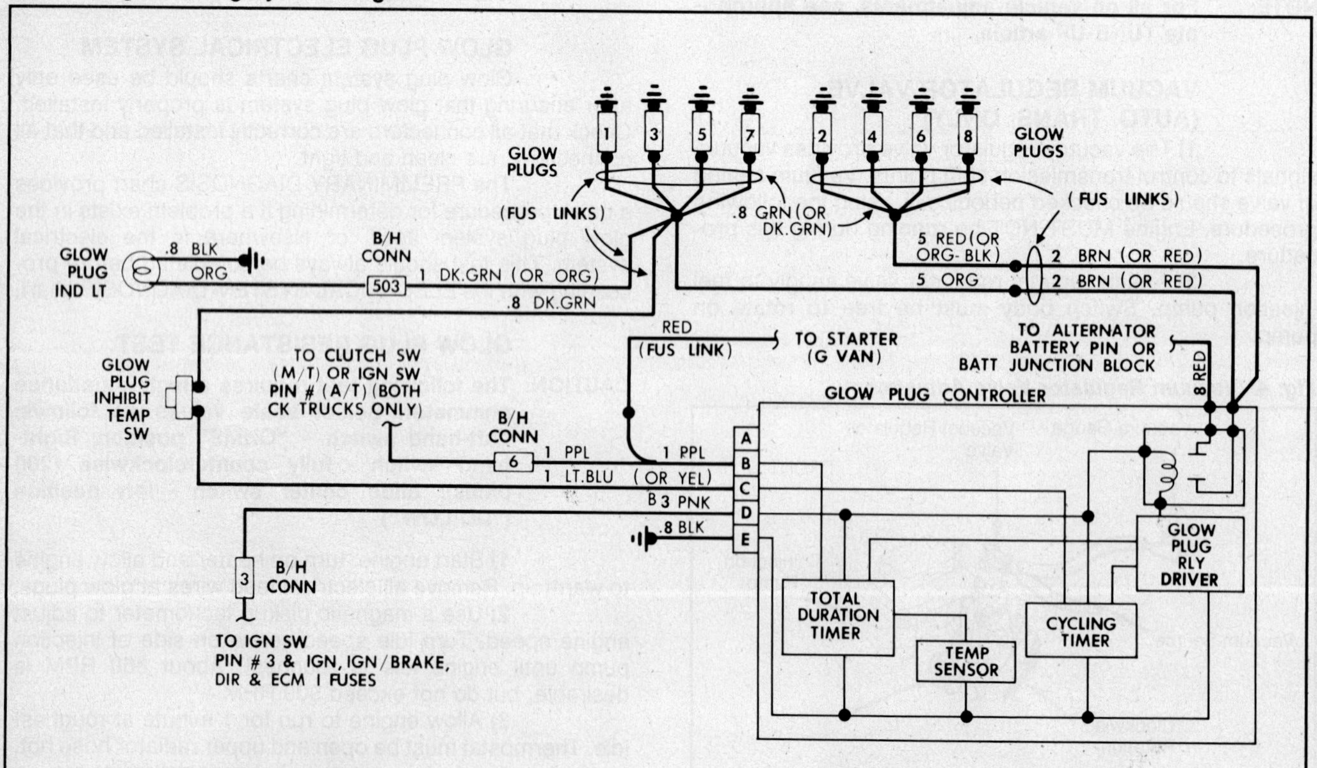

Also see chassis wiring in WIRING DIAGRAM Section.

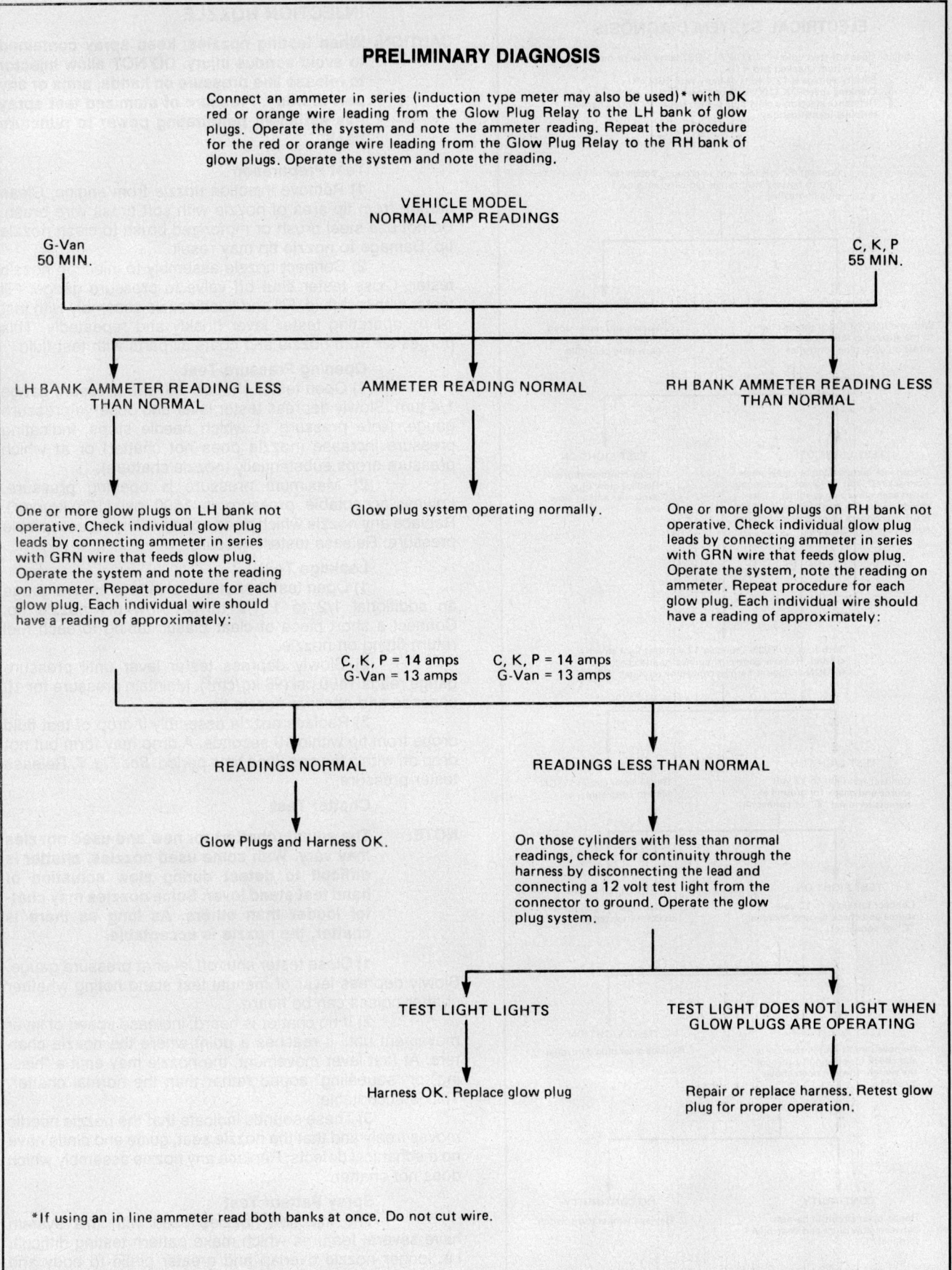

PRELIMINARY DIAGNOSIS

Connect an ammeter in series (induction type meter may also be used)* with DK red or orange wire leading from the Glow Plug Relay to the LH bank of glow plugs. Operate the system and note the ammeter reading. Repeat the procedure for the red or orange wire leading from the Glow Plug Relay to the RH bank of glow plugs. Operate the system and note the reading.

VEHICLE MODEL
NORMAL AMP READINGS

G-Van
50 MIN.

C, K, P
55 MIN.

LH BANK AMMETER READING LESS THAN NORMAL

One or more glow plugs on LH bank not operative. Check individual glow plug leads by connecting ammeter in series with GRN wire that feeds glow plug. Operate the system and note the reading on ammeter. Repeat procedure for each glow plug. Each individual wire should have a reading of approximately:

C, K, P = 14 amps
G-Van = 13 amps

AMMETER READING NORMAL

Glow plug system operating normally.

RH BANK AMMETER READING LESS THAN NORMAL

One or more glow plugs on RH bank not operative. Check individual glow plug leads by connecting ammeter in series with GRN wire that feeds glow plug. Operate the system, note the reading on ammeter. Repeat procedure for each glow plug. Each individual wire should have a reading of approximately:

C, K, P = 14 amps
G-Van = 13 amps

READINGS NORMAL

Glow Plugs and Harness OK.

READINGS LESS THAN NORMAL

On those cylinders with less than normal readings, check for continuity through the harness by disconnecting the lead and connecting a 12 volt test light from the connector to ground. Operate the glow plug system.

TEST LIGHT LIGHTS

Harness OK. Replace glow plug

TEST LIGHT DOES NOT LIGHT WHEN GLOW PLUGS ARE OPERATING

Repair or replace harness. Retest glow plug for proper operation.

*If using an in line ammeter read both banks at once. Do not cut wire.

1985 Diesel Fuel Injection

GENERAL MOTORS 6.2 LITER (Cont.)

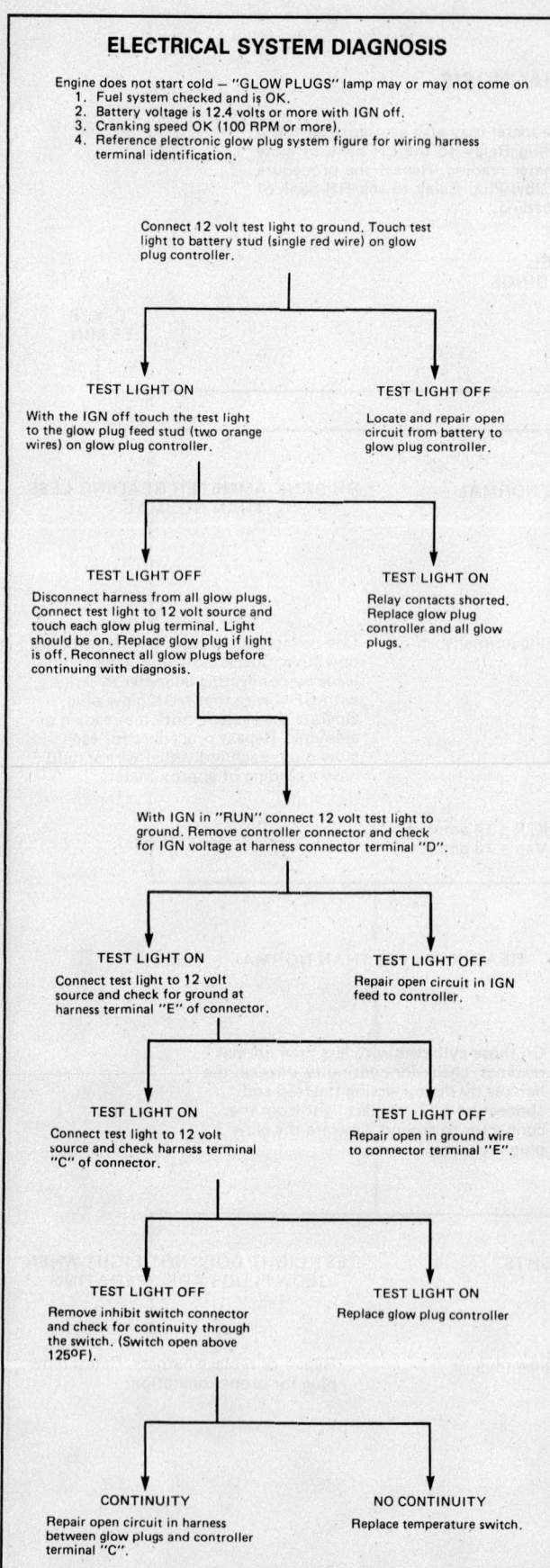

ELECTRICAL SYSTEM DIAGNOSIS

Engine does not start cold – "GLOW PLUGS" lamp may or may not come on

1. Fuel system checked and is OK.
2. Battery voltage is 12.4 volts or more with IGN off.
3. Cranking speed OK (100 RPM or more).
4. Reference electronic glow plug system figure for wiring harness terminal identification.

Connect 12 volt test light to ground. Touch test light to battery stud (single red wire) on glow plug controller.

TEST LIGHT ON
With the IGN off touch the test light to the glow plug feed stud (two orange wires) on glow plug controller.

TEST LIGHT OFF
Locate and repair open circuit from battery to glow plug controller.

TEST LIGHT OFF
Disconnect harness from all glow plugs. Connect test light to 12 volt source and touch each glow plug terminal. Light should be on. Replace glow plug if light is off. Reconnect all glow plugs before continuing with diagnosis.

TEST LIGHT ON
Relay contacts shorted. Replace glow plug controller and all glow plugs.

With IGN in "RUN" connect 12 volt test light to ground. Remove controller connector and check for IGN voltage at harness connector terminal "D".

TEST LIGHT ON
Connect test light to 12 volt source and check for ground at harness terminal "E" of connector.

TEST LIGHT OFF
Repair open circuit in IGN feed to controller.

TEST LIGHT ON
Connect test light to 12 volt source and check harness terminal "C" of connector.

TEST LIGHT OFF
Repair open in ground wire to connector terminal "E".

TEST LIGHT OFF
Remove inhibit switch connector and check for continuity through the switch. (Switch open above 125°F).

TEST LIGHT ON
Replace glow plug controller

CONTINUITY
Repair open circuit in harness between glow plugs and controller terminal "C".

NO CONTINUITY
Replace temperature switch.

INJECTION NOZZLE

CAUTION: When testing nozzles, keep spray contained to avoid serious injury. DO NOT allow injector to release line pressure on hands, arms or any part of body. Pressure of atomized test spray has sufficient penetrating power to puncture flesh.

Test Preparation

1) Remove injection nozzle from engine. Clean carbon from tip area of nozzle with soft brass wire brush. Do not use steel brush or motorized brush to clean nozzle tip. Damage to nozzle tip may result.

2) Connect nozzle assembly to injection nozzle tester. Close tester shut off valve to pressure gauge. Fill tester with test fluid. Fill and flush nozzle assembly with test oil by operating tester lever briskly and repeatedly. This purges air from nozzle and coats all parts with test fluid.

Opening Pressure Test

1) Open tester shut off valve to pressure gauge 1/4 turn. Slowly depress tester lever and observe pressure gauge. Note pressure at which needle stops, indicating pressure increase (nozzle does not chatter) or at which pressure drops substantially (nozzle chatters).

2) Maximum pressure is opening pressure. Lowest acceptable pressure is 1500 psi (105 kg/cm^2). Replace any nozzle which does not meet lowest acceptable pressure. Release tester pressure.

Leakage Test

1) Open tester shut off valve to pressure gauge an additional 1/2 to 1 1/2 turns. Blow dry nozzle tip. Connect a short piece of clear plastic tubing to each fuel return fitting on nozzle.

2) Slowly depress tester lever until pressure gauge reads 1400 psi (98 kg/cm^2). Maintain pressure for 10 seconds and observe nozzle tip.

3) Replace nozzle assembly if drop of test fluid drops from tip within 10 seconds. A drop may form but not drop off within the specified time period. *See Fig. 7.* Release tester pressure.

Chatter Test

NOTE: The sound (chatter) for new and used nozzles may vary. With some used nozzles, chatter is difficult to detect during slow actuation of hand test stand lever. Some nozzles may chatter louder than others. As long as there is chatter, the nozzle is acceptable.

1) Close tester shut off lever at pressure gauge. Slowly depress lever of manual test stand noting whether chatter noises can be heard.

2) If no chatter is heard, increase speed of lever movement until it reaches a point where the nozzle chatters. At fast lever movement, the nozzle may emit a "hissing" or "squealing" sound rather than the normal chatter. This is acceptable.

3) These sounds indicate that the nozzle needle moves freely and that the nozzle seat, guide and pintle have no mechanical defects. Replace any nozzle assembly which does not chatter.

Spray Pattern Test

The injection nozzles used with this system have several features which make pattern testing difficult, i.e. longer nozzle overlap and greater pintle to body and needle to body clearances than other nozzle types, and an internal wave washer between the nozzle nut and nozzle. Typical injector testers cannot deliver fuel with sufficient velocity to obtain proper spray patterns. Therefore, this type nozzle should not be rejected due to spray pattern.

Fig. 7: Nozzle Leakage Test

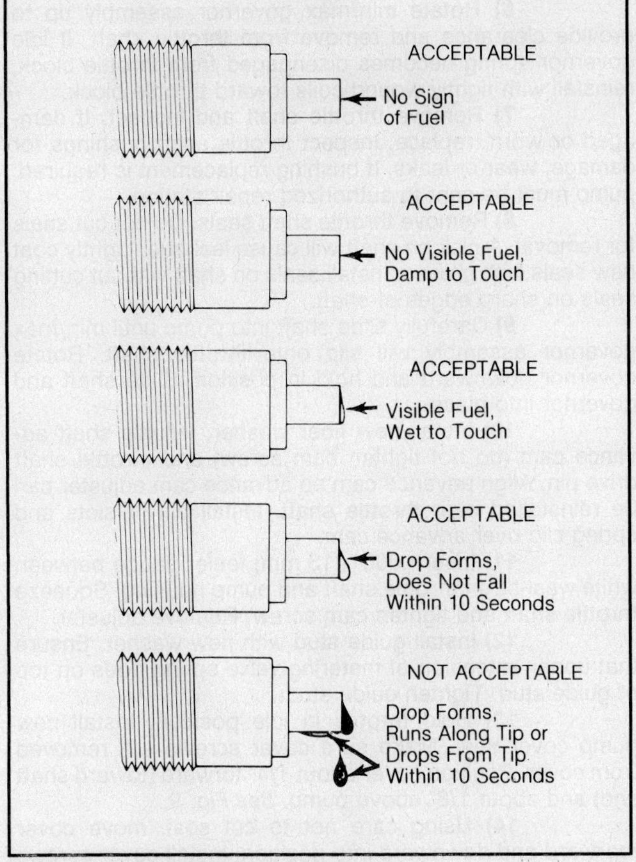

A drop of test fluid may form but not drop off within 10 seconds.

REMOVAL & INSTALLATION

NOTE: Manufacturer does not recommend disassembly of pump. However, the following seals can be replaced with the injection pump installed on the engine. For problems not covered in this article, pump must be removed and taken to an authorized repair station.

INJECTION PUMP SEAL REPLACEMENT

Pump Cover Seal & Guide Stud Seal

1) Disconnect ground cables from both batteries. Remove air cleaner and air cleaner intake. Install Screens (J-29664) in cylinder heads to prevent entrance of dirt. Disconnect fuel return line and wiring from injection pump.

2) Remove throttle cable and return springs. Remove top fast idle solenoid attaching bolt. Loosen lower bolt and move solenoid aside. Clean injection pump cover and area around throttle rod and guide stud. Place rags in engine valley to catch fuel. Remove injection pump cover and remove screws from cover.

NOTE: After removing injection pump cover, use extreme care to prevent dirt or other foreign matter from entering pump.

3) Note position of metering valve spring over top of guide stud. This position must be exactly duplicated during reassembly. Remove guide stud and washer. *See Fig. 8.*

Fig. 8: Guide Stud Seal Replacement

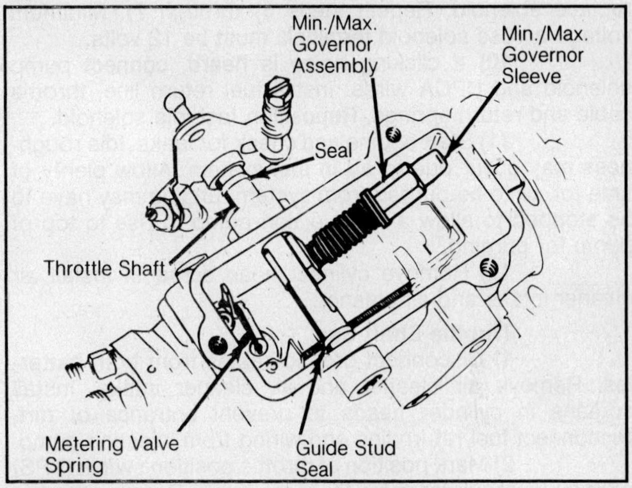

Metering valve spring must be installed in original position over guide stud.

4) Install guide stud with new washer. Ensure that upper extension of metering valve spring rides on top of guide stud. Carefully tighten guide stud.

5) Hold throttle in idle position. Install new pump cover seal. Make sure cover screws are removed from cover. Position cover about 1/4" forward (toward shaft end) and about 1/8" above pump. *See Fig. 9.*

Fig. 9: Injection Pump Cover Installation

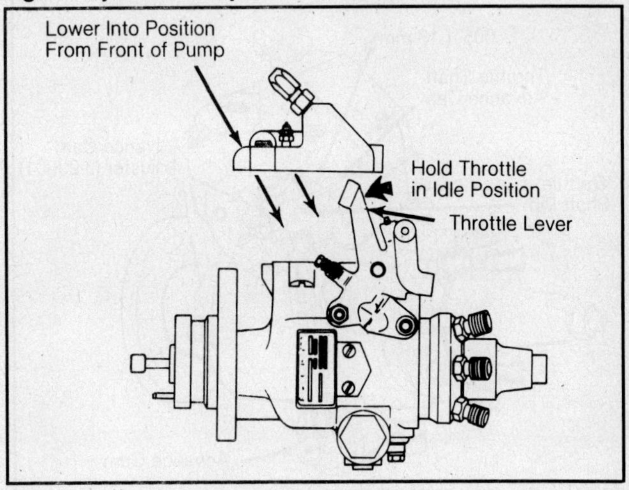

Screws must be removed from cover before installing cover to prevent screws from falling into pump.

6) Using care not to cut seal, move cover rearward and downward into position. Install cover screws with flat washer against cover. Use care not to drop lock washers or flat washers into pump. Tighten screws.

7) Reconnect negative battery cables to both batteries. Turn ignition switch to "RUN" position. Momentarily touch Pink solenoid wire to solenoid. A clicking noise

1985 Diesel Fuel Injection

GENERAL MOTORS 6.2 LITER (Cont.)

should be heard as wire is connected and disconnected at solenoid. If clicking noise is heard, go to step **10)**. If not, go to step **8)**.

8) If clicking noise is not heard, linkage may be jammed in wide open throttle position. Engine MUST NOT be started. Remove cover.

9) Ground solenoid lead (opposite "hot" lead) and connect Pink wire. With ignition switch in "RUN" position, solenoid in cover should move the linkage. If not, replace solenoid. Repeat steps **5)** through **7)**. Minimum voltage across solenoid terminals must be 12 volts.

10) If clicking noise is heard, connect pump solenoid and HPCA wires. Install fuel return line, throttle cable and return springs. Reposition fast idle solenoid.

11) Start engine and check for leaks. Idle roughness may occur due to air in fuel system. Allow plenty of time for air to be purged from system. Engine may have to be stopped to allow air in injection pump to rise to top of pump for purging.

12) Remove cylinder head screens. Install air cleaner intake and air cleaner.

Throttle Shaft Seal

1) Disconnect ground cables from both batteries. Remove air cleaner and air cleaner intake. Install screens in cylinder heads to prevent entrance of dirt. Disconnect fuel return line and wiring from injection pump.

2) Mark position of throttle position switch (TPS) or vacuum regulator valve for reassembly. Remove throttle rod and return springs. Loosen fast idle solenoid and move aside. Remove throttle cable bracket.

3) Install Advance Cam Adjuster (J-29601) over throttle shaft with slots of adjuster engaging pin. Place spring clip over throttle shaft advance cam and tighten wing nut. Without loosening wing nut, pull adjuster off throttle shaft to provide alignment for reassembly. *See Fig. 10.*

Fig. 10: Advance Cam Adjuster Installed On Injection Pump

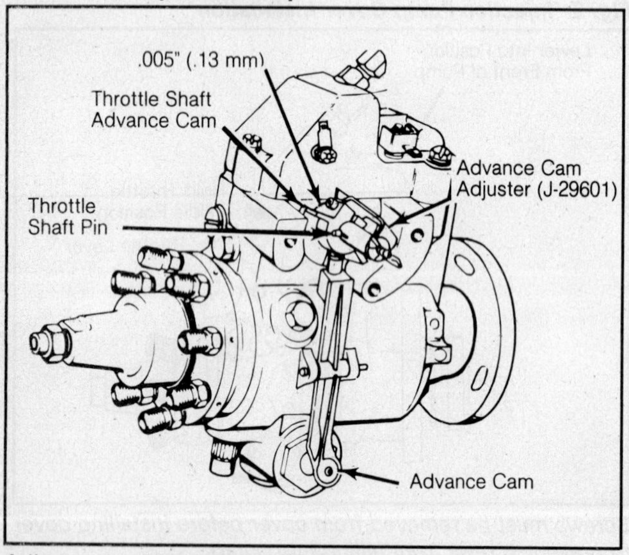

Adjuster provides proper alignment of throttle shaft advance cam for reassembly.

4) Drive pin from throttle shaft. Remove throttle shaft advance cam and fiber washer. Remove any burrs from throttle shaft after removing cam. Clean injection pump cover, upper portion of pump, throttle shaft and guide stud area. Place rags in engine valley to catch fuel. Remove injection pump cover and remove screws from cover.

NOTE: Do not allow any dirt or foreign objects to drop into injection pump after cover is removed. Pump damage may result.

5) Note position of metering valve spring over top of guide stud for reassembly reference. Note position of guide stud and washer. Remove guide stud and washer. *See Fig. 11.*

6) Rotate min/max governor assembly up to provide clearance and remove from throttle shaft. If idle governor spring becomes disengaged from throttle block, reinstall with tightly wound coils toward throttle block.

7) Remove throttle shaft and inspect. If damaged or worn, replace. Inspect throttle shaft bushings for damage, wear or leaks. If bushing replacement is required, pump must be sent to authorized repair station.

8) Remove throttle shaft seals. Do not cut seals for removal. A nick on shaft will cause leakage. Lightly coat new seals with grease. Install seals on shaft without cutting seals on sharp edges of shaft.

9) Carefully slide shaft into pump until min/max governor assembly will slip onto throttle shaft. Rotate governor downward and hold in position. Slide shaft and governor into place.

10) Install new fiber washer, throttle shaft advance cam (do not tighten cam screw) and throttle shaft drive pin. Align advance cam so advance cam adjuster can be reinstalled over throttle shaft. Install pin in slots and spring clip over advance cam.

11) Insert .005" (.13 mm) feeler gauge between white washer on throttle shaft and pump housing. Squeeze throttle shaft and tighten cam screw. Remove adjuster.

12) Install guide stud with new washer. Ensure that upper extension of metering valve spring rides on top of guide stud. Tighten guide stud.

13) Hold throttle in idle position. Install new pump cover seal. Make sure cover screws are removed from cover. Position cover about 1/4" forward (toward shaft end) and about 1/8" above pump. *See Fig. 9.*

14) Using care not to cut seal, move cover rearward and downward into position. Install cover screws with flat washer against cover. Use care not to drop lock washers or flat washers into pump. Tighten screws. Install vacuum regulator or TPS.

15) Reconnect negative battery cables to both batteries. Turn ignition switch to "RUN" position. Momentarily touch Pink solenoid wire to solenoid. A clicking noise should be heard as wire is connected and disconnected at solenoid. If clicking noise is heard, go to step **18)**. If not, go to step **16)**.

16) If clicking noise is not heard, linkage may be jammed in wide open throttle position. Engine MUST NOT be started. Remove cover.

17) Ground solenoid lead (opposite "hot" lead) and connect Pink wire. With ignition switch in "RUN" position, solenoid in cover should move linkage. If not, replace solenoid and repeat step **15)**. Minimum voltage across solenoid terminals must be 12 volts.

18) If clicking noise is heard, connect pump solenoid and HPCA wires. Install fuel return line, throttle cable, throttle cable bracket and return springs. Reposition fast idle solenoid.

19) Start engine and check for leaks. Idle roughness may occur due to air in fuel system. Allow plenty of time for air to be purged from system. Engine may have to be stopped to allow air in injection pump to rise to top of pump for purging.

GENERAL MOTORS 6.2 LITER (Cont.)

20) Remove cylinder head screens. Install air cleaner intake and air cleaner.

NOTE: The following seals must be replaced with the injection pump removed from the engine. For problems not covered in this article, pump must be removed and taken to an authorized repair station.

Advance Pin Hole Plug Seal

1) Tap advance pin hole plug lightly with a hammer to loosen. Remove plug. Remove and discard seal. *See Fig. 11.*

2) Lubricate and install new seal. Install and tighten plug.

Fig. 11: Exploded View of Automatic Advance Assembly

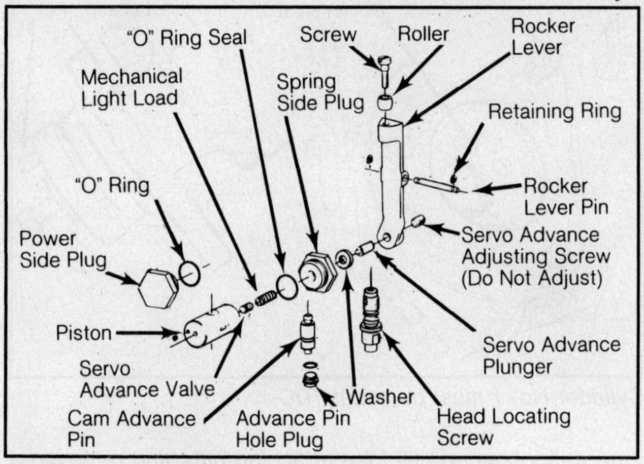

Seals must be replaced with injection pump removed from engine.

Automatic Advance Seals

1) Remove advance pin hole plug as previously described. Remove spring side advance piston hole plug. Remove plug, piston, spring and washer.

2) Remove power side advance piston hole plug. Remove plug, piston and washer. Disassemble plugs and pistons. Discard seals.

3) Lubricate and install new seals. Reverse removal procedure and tighten plugs. *See Fig. 11.*

Hydraulic Head Seal

1) Remove throttle shaft and seals as previously described. Remove metering valve. Remove housing vent screw assembly. Remove advance pin hole plug and advance pin.

2) Install pump in holding fixture so that rear of pump is tilted downward. Remove hydraulic head locating screw. Remove 2 hydraulic head locking screws and discard seals.

3) Using a twisting motion, remove hydraulic head from pump assembly. Remove and discard "O" ring seal.

4) Lubricate and install new seal. Install hydraulic head into pump assembly. Lubricate and install 2 locking screw seals. Install locating screw. Install and tighten locking screws.

5) Install advance pin, advance pin seal and advance pin hole plug. Position pump so cover opening is up, and install metering valve. Install throttle shaft, seals and pump cover.

Fig. 12: Injection Pump Fuel Line Routing.

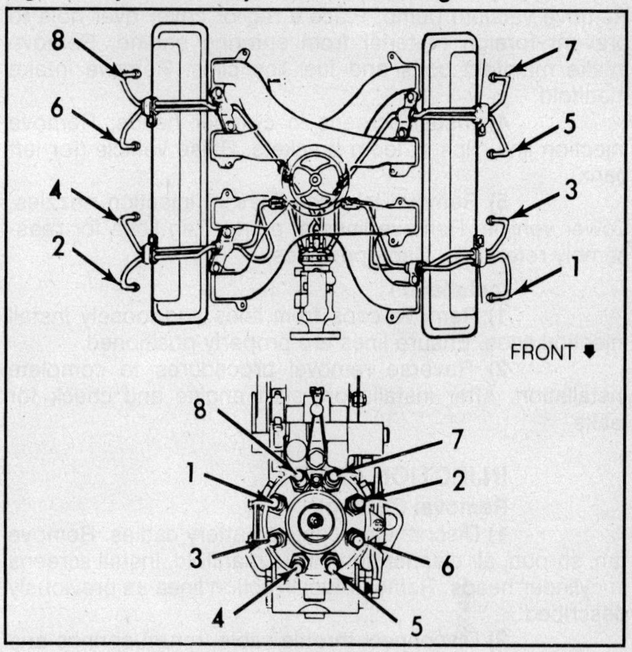

Drive Shaft Seal

1) Mount pump in Holding Fixture (J-29692-B) and tilt pump slightly towards you. Remove fast idle solenoid bracket.

2) Remove drive shaft from pump with a rotating motion while pulling on shaft (shaft is retained by "O" ring clip). Remove and discard drive shaft seals.

3) Install new seals with Seal Installer (J-29745-A). Lubricate installer with light grease and install 1 Black seal. Lubricate installer again and install Red seal. Lubricate installer once more and install remaining Black seal.

4) Install a new "O" ring retining clip on drive shaft. Install drive shaft, ensuring that drill points on shaft end and rotor are matched. Install fast idle solenoid bracket.

FUEL INJECTION LINES

Removal (Pickup)

1) Disconnect negative battery cables. Disconnect air cleaner bracket from valve cover. Remove crankcase vent bracket and move aside.

2) Loosen vacuum pump hold-down clamp. Rotate pump to gain access to intake manifold bolt. Remove intake manifold. Install screens in cylinder heads.

3) Remove injection line clips at loom brackets. Remove injection lines at injection nozzles. Remove lines at pump. Tag lines for reassembly reference. Cap open lines.

Installation

1) Remove caps from lines and install injection lines. Ensure lines are properly positioned. *See Fig. 12.*

2) Reverse removal procedures to complete installation. After installation, start engine and check for leaks.

Removal (Van)

1) Disconnect negative battery cables. Remove engine cover and air cleaner. Disconnect necessary wires and hoses. Remove EGR/EPR switches.

2) Remove crankcase depression regulator valve hoses from intake manifold. Remove rear A/C compressor bracket (if equipped).

3) Remove fuel filter to intake manifold bracket. Remove vacuum pump. Place a rag or cover over hole to prevent foreign material from entering engine. Remove intake mainfold bolts and fuel line clips. Remove intake manifold.

4) Install screens in cylinder heads. Remove injection line clips at loom brackets. Raise vehicle (for left bank).

5) Remove injection lines at injection nozzles. Lower vehicle. Remove lines at pump. Tag lines for reassembly reference. Cap open lines.

Installation

1) Remove caps from lines and loosely install injection lines. Ensure lines are properly positioned.

2) Reverse removal procedures to complete installation. After installation, start engine and check for leaks.

INJECTION PUMP

Removal (Pickup)

1) Disconnect negative battery cables. Remove fan, shroud, air cleaner and intake manifold. Install screens in cylinder heads. Remove fuel injection lines as previously described.

2) Disconnect throttle cable, return springs and detent cable (if equipped). Disconnect wires, fuel return line, fuel supply line and fuel injection lines at pump. Cap all fuel lines.

3) Remove A/C hose retainer bracket, if equipped. Remove oil filler tube and PCV vent hose assembly. Remove grommet. Scribe or paint an alignment mark on front cover and injection pump.

4) Rotate engine to remove injection pump retaining bolts that are accessible through oil filler neck hole. Remove injection pump-to-front cover nuts. Remove injection pump and gasket.

Installation

1) Install new injection pump gasket. Position cylinder No. 1 at TDC by lining up crankshaft pulley mark with indicator. Align locating pin on injection pump hub with slot in injection pump driven gear. At the same time, align injection pump timing marks. *See Fig. 13.*

2) Attach injection pump to front cover. Alignment marks made during removal must be aligned. Tighten nuts. Attach pump to drive gear and tighten bolts.

3) To complete installation, reverse removal procedure. Check timing and perform on-vehicle adjustments, if required.

Removal (Van)

1) Disconnect negative battery cables. Remove engine cover and air cleaner. Disconnect necessary wires and hoses. Remove EGR/EPR switches.

2) Remove crankcase depression regulator valve hoses from intake manifold. Remove rear A/C compressor bracket (if equipped).

3) Remove fuel filter to intake manifold bracket. Remove vacuum pump. Place a rag or cover over hole to prevent foreign material from entering engine. Remove intake mainfold bolts and fuel line clips. Remove intake manifold.

4) Rotate snorkel of air cleaner inlet hose up. Remove hood latch, disconnect cable and move aside.

5) Remove windshield washer bottle, fan shroud bolts and upper shroud. Disconnect rubber hose from oil fill tube. Disconnect oil fill tube attaching nuts and remove oil fill tube.

Fig. 13: Injection Pump Timing Mark Locations

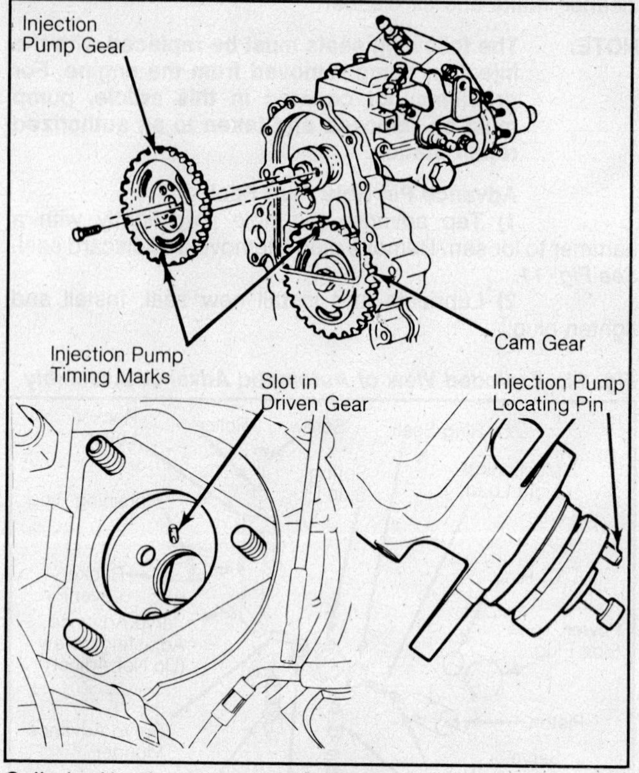

Cylinder No. 1 must be set at TDC.

6) Remove oil fill tube grommet. Rotate engine as necessary and remove drive gear to pump bolts. Remove fuel filter and bracket including line to injection pump.

7) Disconnect wire looms from injection lines and injection lines at brackets. Disconnect oil pan dipstick tube at left cylinder head.

8) Disconnect electrical connections at injection pump. If equipped with automatic transmission, disconnect TV cable. Disconnect accelerator cable.

9) Disconnect injection lines at nozzles 2, 4, 5, 6, 7 and 8. Raise vehicle and disconnect remaining lines. Cover nozzles 1, 3, 5 and 7.

10) Lower vehicle. Cover nozzles 2, 4, 6 and 8. Disconnect injection lines at pump and remove lines. Tag lines for reassembly reference. Cap all fuel lines.

11) Disconnect fuel return line. Scribe or paint a mark on front cover and pump flange. Remove pump to front cover attaching nuts. Remove injection pump. Cap all open discharge fittings.

Installation

1) Install new injection pump gasket. Align locating pin on injection pump hub with slot in injection pump driven gear. At the same time, align injection pump timing marks. *See Fig. 13.*

2) Attach injection pump to front cover. Alignment marks made during removal must be aligned. Tighten nuts. Attach pump to drive gear and tighten bolts.

3) To complete installation, reverse removal procedure. Check timing and perform on-vehicle adjustments, if required.

1985 Diesel Fuel Injection

GENERAL MOTORS 6.2 LITER (Cont.)

INJECTION NOZZLES

Removal

1) Disconnect negative battery cables. Disconnect fuel line clip. Remove fuel return line from nozzle without bending line. Remove fuel injection line.

2) Using Injector Remover/Installer (J-29873), remove injection nozzle. Always remove injector by placing remover on 30 mm hex flats of injector body to prevent damage to injector body. Cap injector and lines.

Installation

1) Remove caps from injector and fuel lines. Install injector nozzle with installer. Connect fuel line.

2) Install fuel return hose and fuel line clip. Connect battery cables. Start engine and check for leaks.

TIGHTENING SPECIFICATIONS

Application	Ft. Lbs. (N.m)
Fuel Line to	
Fuel Filter	15-20 (20-27)
Injection Pump	18 (25)
Injector Nozzle	18 (27)
Fuel Injector Nozzles	52 (70)
Injection Pump-to-Front	
Cover Nuts	33 (45)
Injection Pump Gear	
Attaching Bolts	18 (25)
Inj. Pump Hydraulic	
Head Bolts	15-18 (20-25)
	INCH Lbs. (N.m)
Glow Plugs	97-142 (11-16)
Injection Pump Guide Stud	84 (9.5)
Injection Pump Cover Bolts	31 (3.5)

JEEP 2.1L TURBO DIESEL

DESCRIPTION

A Bosch VE4, single piston, high pressure rotary pump is used to inject a precisely metered amount of fuel into each cylinder at precise intervals. The pump is mounted on left side of engine, and provides correct amount of timing advance for various operating conditions.

High pressure fuel lines carry fuel from pump to an injection nozzle at each precombustion chamber. All lines are of equal length to ensure that there is no variance in timing. Any excess fuel in supply system is returned to tank by a fuel return system.

A reference pressure regulator is attached to firewall (above engine). This regulator automatically compensates for altitude changes.

An electrical glow plug system is used to assist in engine starting and cold operation. A glow plug is located in precombustion chamber for each cylinder. Glow plug current is controlled by a timer.

Fig. 1: Cut-Away View of Bosch VE4 Fuel Injection Pump

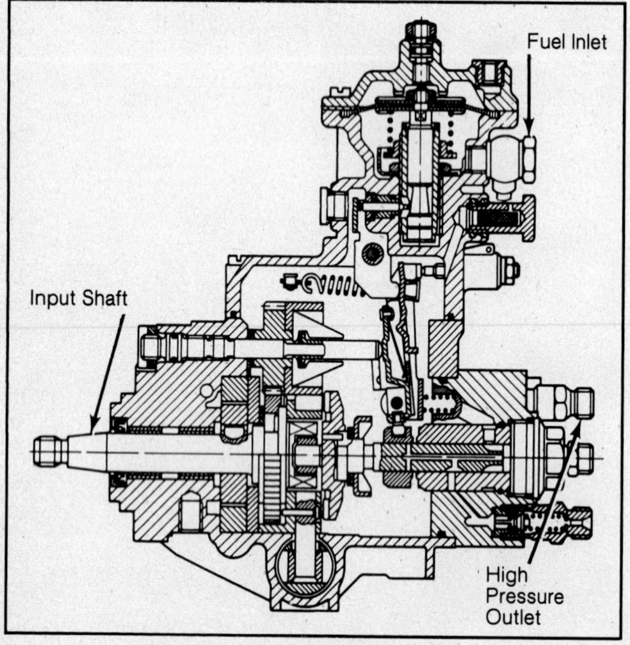

OPERATION

COLD START SYSTEM

The cold start system consists of a capsule (spring housing), linkage, thermostat and a bi-metallic spring. When engine is cold, thermostat inside capsule releases bi-metallic spring. The spring pulls timing control lever toward "ADVANCE" position, and throttle lever is pulled toward fast idle.

As engine temperature increases, thermostat slowly expands, compressing spring. When spring is compressed, control cable is released, and throttle lever returns to original position.

FUEL INJECTION PUMP

The Bosch VE4 mechanical injection pump contains a low pressure vane-type transfer pump and a high pressure distributor-type injection pump. Transfer pump output pressure (injection pump housing pressure) averages 50-100 psi (3.5-7.0 kg/cm²) depending upon engine speed. The plunger injection pump boosts fuel pressure to about 2000 psi (140 kg/cm²). Pump assembly is also equipped with an electric fuel shut-off solenoid.

INJECTORS

The injection nozzles spray fuel into a prechamber as each compression stroke occurs. Each injector receives a high pressure pulse of fuel which forces open needle valve allowing fuel to pass into precombustion chamber.

FUEL HEATER/WATER SEPARATOR

An in-line fuel filter/water separator is attached to dash panel near power brake unit. This assembly removes water and contaminants from incoming fuel supply. This filter/water separator also heats fuel when ambient temperature falls below 46°F (8°C).

FUEL SUPPLY SYSTEM

Diesel fuel is drawn through a water separator from fuel tank by an engine mounted mechanical fuel pump. This pump is driven by an eccentric cam mounted on crankshaft and puts out about 3 psi to injection pump. A small screen type filter is located in fuel tank at pick-up. After leaving filter, diesel fuel enters pump through center inlet fitting. A fuel return line is provided to return excess fuel to tank.

FUEL INJECTION LINES

A high pressure fuel injection lines is routed from injection pump to each injector. Injection lines are of equal length but are formed differently, to prevent timing difference from cylinder-to-cylinder, and ease installation. Lines are pre-formed by manufacturer, and are not interchangeable.

GLOW PLUG SYSTEM

Engine starting is aided by an electric glow plug system. Glow plugs are small heaters that assist in cold starting. A glow plug is threaded into each cylinder combustion chamber. This system pre-heats each combustion chamber to aid ignition of fuel.

System consists of 4 glow plugs, control switch, timer and a wiring harness which incorporates 4 fused wires (one for each glow plug) located between wiring harness and glow plug terminal.

The glow plug controller and relay cycle 12 volts to these 6 volt heaters, which causes them to heat rapidly. After engine starts, glow plugs remain on between 4 and 10 seconds during initial starting cycle.

TROUBLE SHOOTING

FUEL INJECTION SYSTEM

Before suspecting fuel injection system as source of engine trouble, other engine systems should be checked. Ensure that air intake and exhaust systems are not restricted, and that fuel supply system provides an adequate amount of clean fuel to injection pump. If a problem still exists after checking these systems, go to step **1)**.

1) Check fuel lines to injectors for kinks or restrictions. Replace as necessary. Run engine at RPM where problem was most pronounced.

JEEP 2.1L TURBO DIESEL (Cont.)

2) Momentarily loosen (1/2-1 turn) fuel line on 1 injector. Then tighten fuel line. Repeat for each cylinder.

3) If there is no difference in engine operation when a fuel line is loosened, that nozzle should be removed and tested. See FUEL INJECTOR TESTING.

GLOW PLUG SYSTEM

Fig. 2: Glow Plug Wiring Diagram

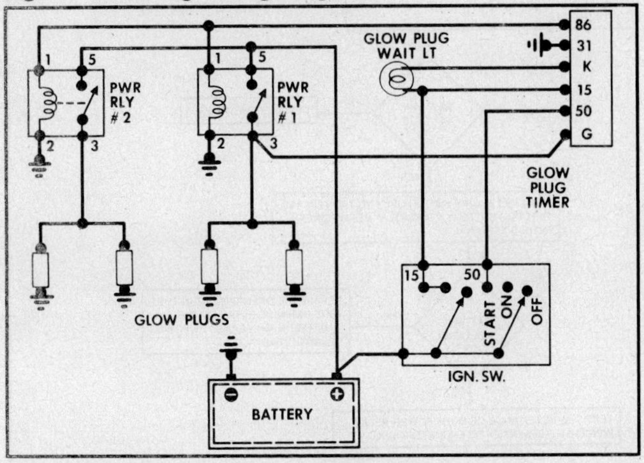

Also see chassis wiring in WIRING DIAGRAM section.

REFERENCE PRESSURE REGULATOR

Install "T" fitting at connection "A". *See Fig. 3.* Connect a vacuum gauge to "T" fitting. Start engine and run at idle. Note vacuum reading. Compare reading with specification, and replace pressure regulator if vacuum reading is incorrect. See ALTITUDE COMPENSATED VACUUM table.

Fig. 3: Testing Reference Pressure Regulator

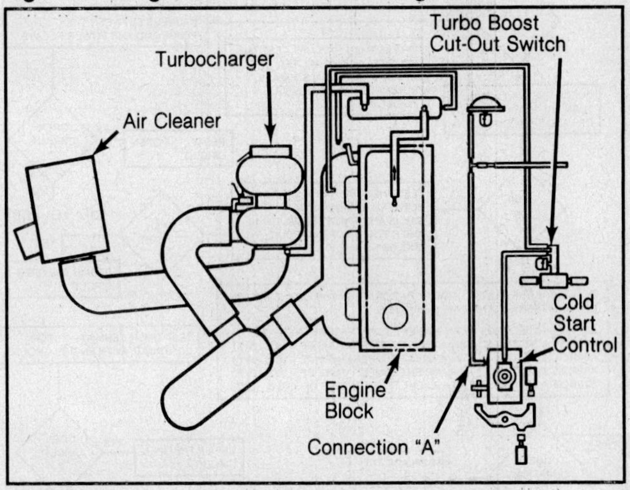

Install vacuum gauge "T" fitting at connection "A".

ALTITUDE COMPENSATED VACUUM

Altitude	Vacuum Hg
0	8-10
1000	7-9
2000	6-8
3000	4.5-6.5
4000	3-5
5000	2-4

TESTING

INJECTORS

1) Remove injection nozzles from engine. Check injectors for erosion (due to unfiltered air particles), carbon build-up, or Blue-colored tip (caused excessive engine heat). Replace any damaged injectors as necessary.

CAUTION: DO NOT allow test oil to be sprayed onto hands or fingers while testing. High pressure from nozzle spray can penetrate skin, which could cause blood poisoning.

2) Fill reservoir of Bosch Nozzle Pressure Tester (EFEP60H) with clean test oil. Connect nozzle and nozzle holder assembly to tester. Close pressure gauge valve. Quickly operate tester lever 8-10 times to bleed air from tester.

3) Open pressure gauge valve 1/4 turn. Slowly operate tester (1 pump/second), noting pressure required to open nozzle. Nozzle opening pressure should be 1885-2000 psi (132-140.6 kg/cm^2). Injectors with incorrect opening pressure should be replaced.

4) Slowly operate tester (1 pump/second), noting spray pattern of each nozzle. Spray should emerge at a 90° angle to nozzle tip, and should be in an even, finely atomized pattern. Replace any injectors that do not have correct spray pattern. A "whistle" sound, produced during testing, is a normal condition.

5) Slowly operate tester (1 pump/second) until pressure reading is 300 psi below normal opening pressure. Hold pressure at that point for 10 seconds. No fuel should drip from nozzle. If leakage occurs during 10 second period, replace injector.

NOTE: During this test procedure, a slight wetting of nozzle tip is normal.

Fig. 4: Testing Turbo Boost Cut-Out Switch

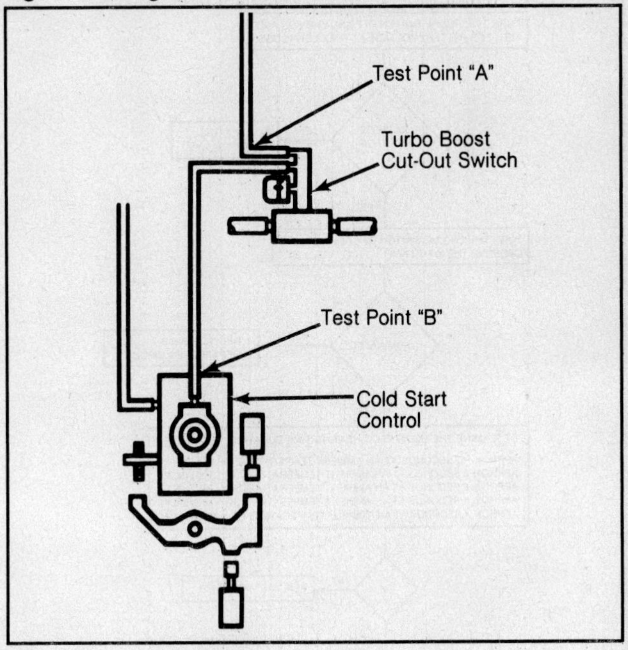

1985 Diesel Fuel Injection

JEEP 2.1L TURBO DIESEL (Cont.)

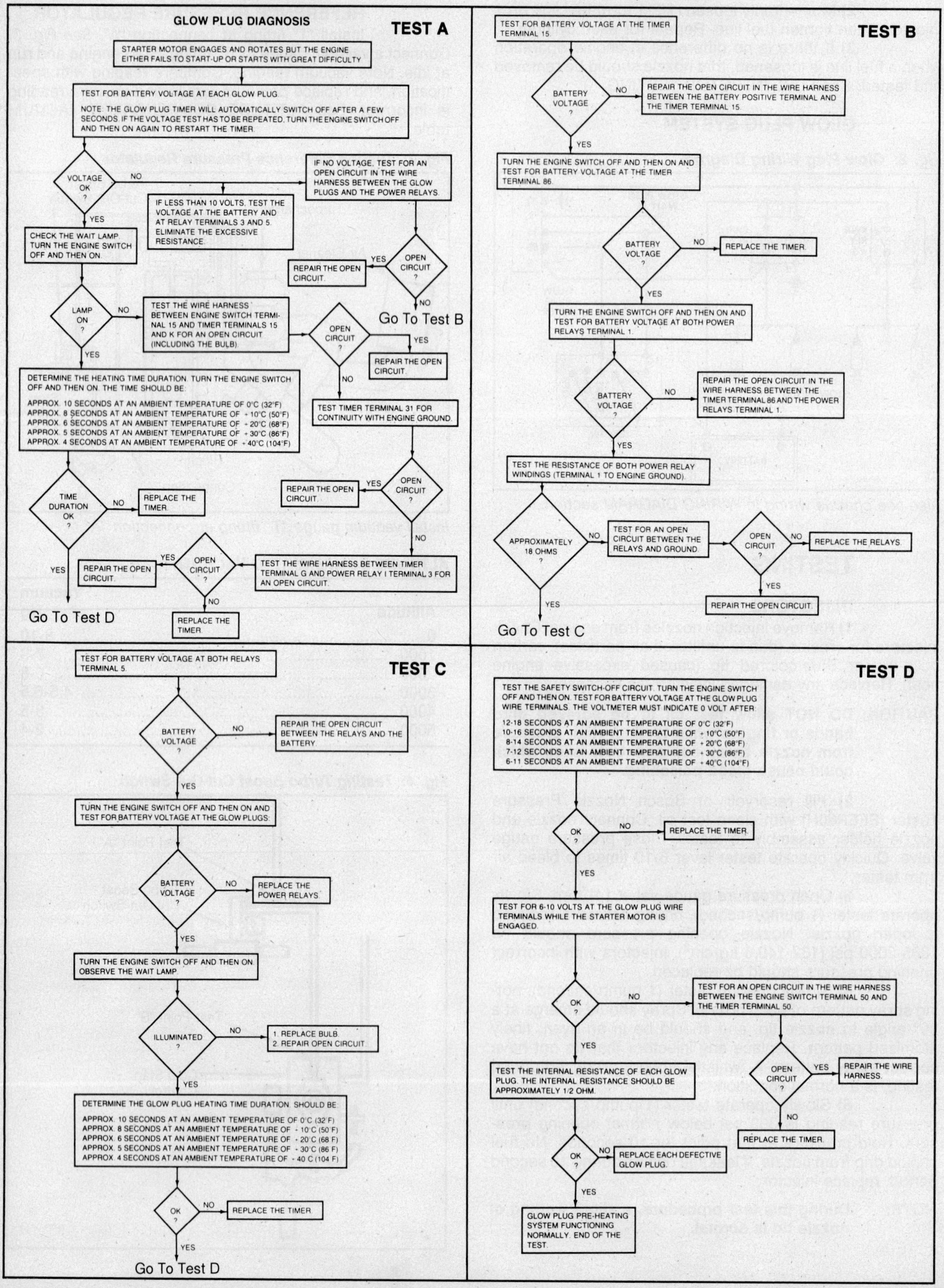

JEEP 2.1L TURBO DIESEL (Cont.)

TURBO BOOST CUT-OUT SWITCH

1) Disconnect hose from test point "A". *See Fig. 4.* Connect a pressure gauge to hose. Start engine, and run at 3000 RPM. Record pressure reading. Disconnect gauge and reconnect hose.

NOTE: **If no pressure is indicated, check turbocharger operation, and for a pinched hose between manifold and turbo boost cut-out switch.**

2) Disconnect hose from test point "B". *See Fig. 4.* Connect a pressure gauge to hose. Start engine, and run at 3000 RPM. Record pressure reading. Pressure reading should be equal to reading at test point "A", in step **1)**.

3) If pressure is okay, turbo boost cut-out switch is operating. If pressure is not okay, (and engine coolant temperature is below 239°F (115°C), replace cut-out switch. Disconnect gauge and reconnect hose.

REMOVAL & INSTALLATION

COLD START THERMOSTAT CAPSULE

Removal

CAUTION: **High spring tension was created when capsule housing was attached to bracket. The following procedures must be followed exactly. The capsule could explode and cause injury, if the correct removal procedure is not followed.**

1) Clamp, and remove, coolant lines from cold start capsule. Remove 1 capsule retaining bolt, and replace it with a threaded rod (6mm dia. X 70 mm long).

2) Install, and tighten nut onto threaded rod. Remove other capsule retaining bolt, and replace it with a duplicate threaded rod. Install, and tighten nut onto second threaded rod.

3) Alternately loosen the 2 nuts. After tension is released, remove nuts completely, and separate rear capsule housing from bracket. Remove retaining nut, thermostat capsule and "O" ring from housing.

Installation

Ensure all capsule components are in position. *See Fig. 5.* To complete installation, reverse removal procedure.

Fig. 5: Exploded View of Cold Start Capsule

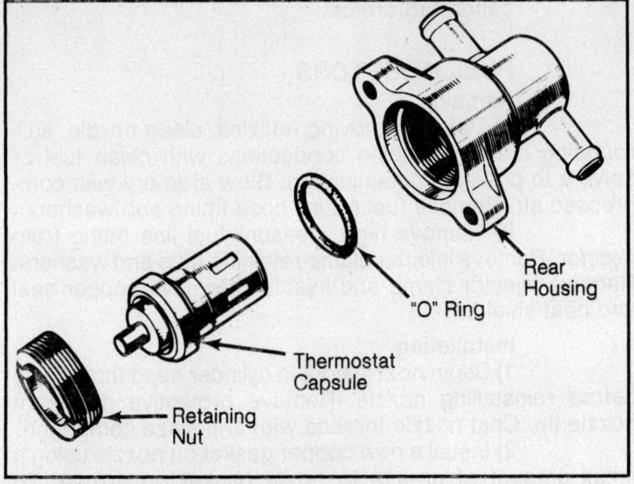

To avoid injury, follow removal procedures precisely.

INJECTION PUMP

Removal

1) Disconnect battery negative cable. Clamp cold start thermostat capsule coolant hoses. Remove capsule coolant hoses from capsule. Disconnect throttle cable and fuel shut-off solenoid wire connector.

2) Disconnect A/T throttle and cruise control cables (if equipped). Disconnect, and plug fuel delivery and return lines. Remove alternator and power steering drive belts. Remove timing belt cover.

3) Rotate crankshaft until No. 1 piston is at TDC position. Ensure that sprocket timing mark is aligned with center of boss on cylinder head cover, and that injection pump sprocket timing mark is aligned with center of injection pump boss. *See Fig. 6.*

Fig. 6: Removing Fuel Injection Pump

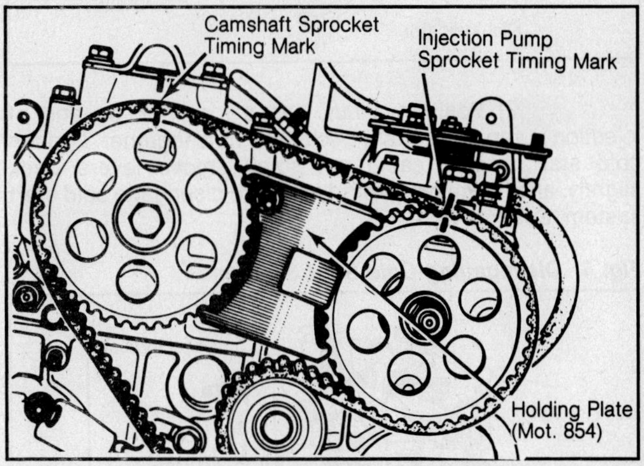

Turn crankshaft slightly, to position holding plate.

4) Position Holding Plate (Mot. 854) between camshaft and injection pump sprockets. *See Fig. 6.* It may be necessary to turn crankshaft back-and-forth slightly, to position holding plate correctly.

5) Loosen sprocket retaining nut, and turn nut out until it reaches beginning of threads. Attach Puller Sections (B.Vi 28-01, 859 and 48) to sprocket. Disconnect, and plug fuel pipe fittings from injectors.

6) Remove fuel pipes. Remove injection pump rear attaching bolts. Remove plastic shield from underneath injection pump. Remove 3 retaining nuts at front of pump.

NOTE: **It may be necessary to remove the alternator, to gain access to lower, front injection pump retaining nut.**

7) Separate injection pump from sprocket bolts using Sprocket Separator (B.Vi. 28-01). Remove separator and sprocket retaining nut. DO NOT remove sprocket. Sprocket holding plate and timing belt will hold sprocket in place to ease installation.

8) Remove injection pump from mounting bracket. Remove key from injection pump drive shaft.

Installation

1) Remove screw plug and copper washer from center of 4 high pressure outlets on rear of injection pump. *See Fig. 7.* Install Dial Indicator Support (Mot. 856) in place of screw plug. Insert stem of dial indicator into support tool. *See Fig. 7.*

JEEP 2.1L TURBO DIESEL (Cont.)

Fig. 7: Installing Dial Indicator

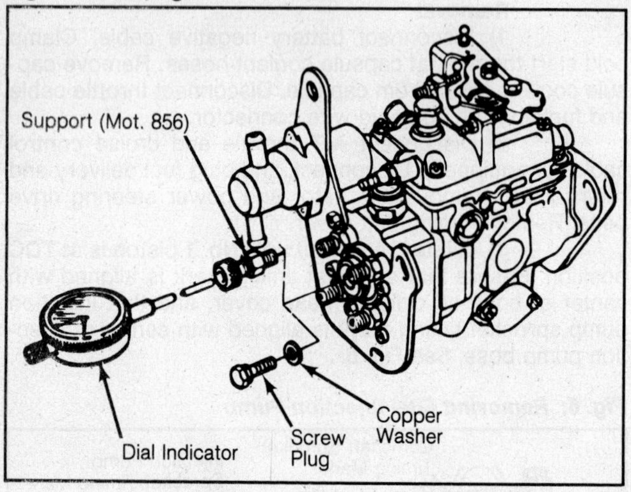

2) Position a nut, and a lock nut, on end of injection pump drive shaft. Lock the 2 nuts together. Loosen cold start throttle cable set screw, move levers back slightly, and rotate clevis pin 1/4 turn to disengage cold start system. *See Fig. 8.*

Fig. 8: Disengaging Cold Start System

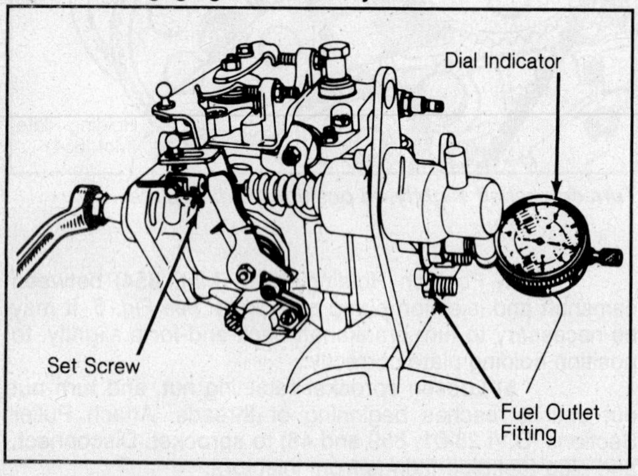

3) Rotate injection pump until piston is at BDC position (dial indicator will stop moving at this point). Zero dial indicator.

NOTE: **With injection pump piston at BDC position, the pump shaft keyway should be positioned just before centerline of No. 1 fuel outlet fitting.**

4) Remove nut and lock nut from pump drive shaft. Insert key in pump shaft keyway. Install injection pump, leaving dial indicator in place. Ensure drive shaft key is aligned with keyway in sprocket. Loosely install pump retaining nuts.

5) Install sprocket washer and retaining nut onto pump shaft. Tighten sprocket retaining nut. Remove sprocket holding plate. Rotate crankshaft 3 revolutions. Check timing belt tension, and adjust if necessary.

6) Remove screw plug from TDC access hole in cylinder block, and install TDC Rod (Mot. 861). *See Fig. 9.* Slowly rotate crankshaft clockwise, until TDC rod can be inserted into TDC hole in crankshaft counterweight.

Fig. 9: Inserting TDC Rod

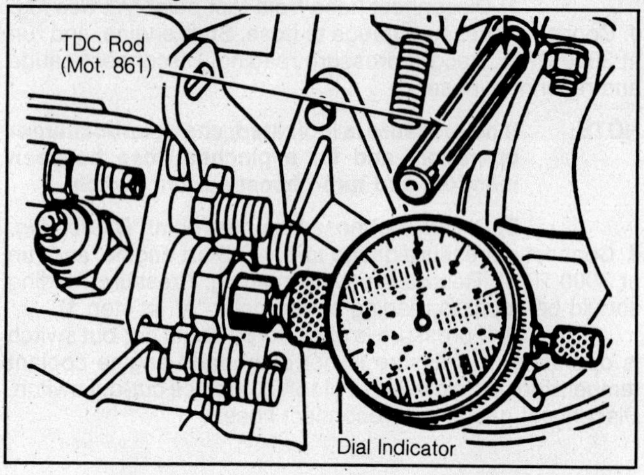

7) With TDC rod in TDC hole, dial indicator should read .031-.033 in. (.80-.84 mm). This reading represents the amount of pump piston lift. If reading is correct, go to step **10)**. If reading is incorrect, go to next step.

8) To increase piston lift, rotate pump toward engine, and then slowly rotate pump away from engine until correct reading is obtained. To decrease piston lift, slowly rotate pump away from engine until correct reading is obtained.

9) Remove TDC rod. Slowly rotate crankshaft clockwise 2 complete revolutions, and insert TDC rod in TDC hole in crankshaft counterweight. Dial indicator should read .031-.033 in. (.80-.84 mm). If reading is incorrect, repeat steps **8)** and **9)**. If reading is correct, go to next step.

10) Remove TDC rod from TDC hole, and install screw plug. Remove dial indicator and support. Install copper washer and screw plug. Reconnect fuel pipes. Compress timing control lever and install clevis pin.

11) Hold lever against clevis, and tighten set screw. Install, and tighten, injection pump rear bracket nuts. To complete installation, reverse removal procedure. The fuel return banjo nut is matched and calibrated to pump. If a new pump is installed, a new matched banjo nut must be used.

NOTE: **Do not reverse the 2 fuel line banjo nuts. The delivery line nut has two .1575 in. (4 mm) diameter holes, and the return line nut has a calibrated orifice.**

FUEL INJECTORS

Removal

1) Before removing nozzles, clean nozzle, surrounding area and piping connections with clean fuel or solvent to prevent contamination. Blow area dry with compressed air. Remove fuel return hose fitting and washer.

2) Remove high pressure fuel line fitting from injector. Remove injector clamp retaining nuts and washers. Remove injector clamp and injector. Remove copper seal and heat shield.

Installation

1) Clean nozzle bore in cylinder head thoroughly before reinstalling nozzle. Remove protective cap from nozzle tip. Coat nozzle threads with anti-seize compound.

2) Install a new copper gasket on nozzle using a small amount of grease to retain gasket on nozzle. To

JEEP 2.1L TURBO DIESEL (Cont.)

complete installation, reverse removal procedure, using a new heat shield and copper seal.

ADJUSTMENTS

INJECTION PUMP TIMING

Static Timing
(Engine Stopped)

1) Remove screw plug and copper washer from center of 4 high pressure outlets on rear of injection pump. Install Dial Indicator Support (Mot. 856) in place of screw plug. Insert stem of dial indicator into support tool. *See Fig. 7.*

2) Position nut, and lock nut, on end of injection pump drive shaft. Lock the 2 nuts together. Loosen cold start throttle cable set screw, move levers back slightly, and rotate clevis pin 1/4 turn to disengage cold start system. *See Fig. 8.*

3) Rotate injection pump until piston is at BDC position (dial indicator will stop moving at this point). Zero dial indicator.

NOTE: **With injection pump piston at BDC position, the pump shaft keyway should be positioned just before centerline of No. 1 fuel outlet fitting.**

4) Remove screw plug from TDC access hole in cylinder block, and install TDC Rod (Mot. 861). *See Fig. 9.* Slowly rotate crankshaft clockwise, until TDC rod can be inserted into TDC hole in crankshaft counterweight.

5) With TDC rod in TDC hole, dial indicator should read .031-.033 in. (.80-.84 mm). This reading represents amount of piston lift. If reading is correct, go to step **8)**. If reading is incorrect, pump piston lift must be adjusted.

6) To increase piston lift, rotate pump toward engine, and then slowly rotate pump away from engine until correct reading is obtained. To decrease piston lift, slowly rotate pump away from engine until correct reading is obtained.

7) Remove TDC rod. Slowly rotate crankshaft clockwise 2 complete revolutions, until TDC rod can be reinserted into TDC hole in crankshaft counterweight. With TDC rod in TDC hole, dial indicator should read .031-.033 in. (.80-.84 mm). If reading is correct, go to step **8)**. If reading is incorrect, repeat steps **6)** and **7)**.

8) Remove TDC rod from TDC hole, and install screw plug. Remove dial indicator and support. Install copper washer and screw plug. Reconnect fuel pipes.

Dynamic Timing
(Engine Running) & Idle Speed

1) Start and warm engine to normal operating temperature. Stop engine and connect Injection Pulse Sensor Clamp (part of Dynamic Timing Meter J-33300-200) to No. 1 cylinder injection pipe. Install magnetic pick-up probe into TDC access slot. *See Fig. 10.*

NOTE: **To ease placement of probe in TDC access slot, it may be necessary to cut away a small portion of plastic shield underneath pump.**

2) Ensure that probe insertion limiting device is placed at a depth of 1.4567 in. (37 mm). Connect battery voltage to timing meter. Place rocker timing meter rocker switches to "MAGNETIC PICK-UP" and "CLAMP-ON/PICK-UP" positions.

3) Start engine. Set magnetic offset control for 0°. Observe test display. Injection pump timing should be about 8°. If timing is incorrect, perform STATIC TIMING (ENGINE STOPPED) adjustment procedure. If timing is correct, set idle speed to 800 RPM using idle set screw. *See Fig. 11.*

Fig. 10: Magnetic Pick-Up Probe Installation

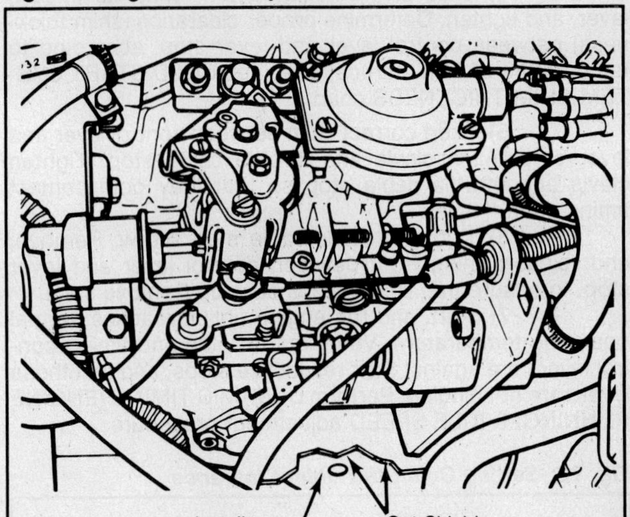

If necessary, cut plastic shield as shown.

Fig. 11: Adjusting Cold Start System

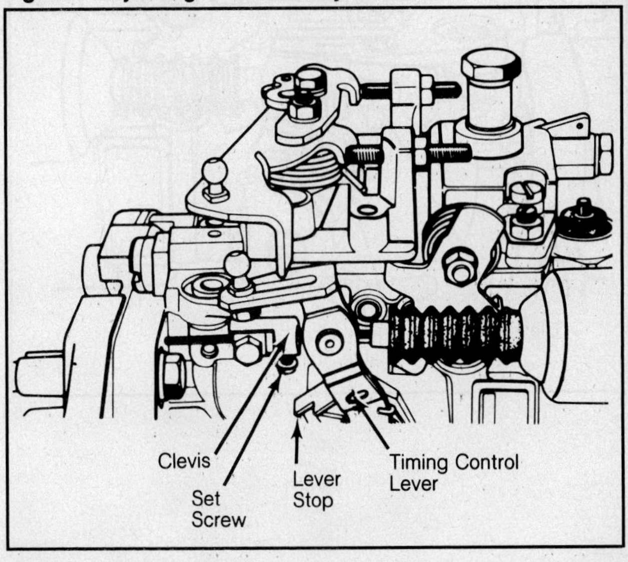

COLD START SYSTEM

1) With engine cold (not started for at least 3 hours), verify that idle control lever is resting on lever stop. If lever is okay, go to step **2)**. If lever is not resting on stop, loosen set screw and turn clevis 1/4 turn. *See Fig. 11.*

2) Rotate crankshaft clockwise 2 revolutions, remove screw plug from TDC access hole in cylinder block, and install TDC Rod. *See Fig. 9.* Move timing control lever to detent position. Ensure clearance between timing control lever and lever stop is .0020 in. (.5mm).

3) If necessary, adjust clearance by turning stop lever screw. Insert a .2561 in. (6.5 mm) shim between control lever and lever stop. Insert a .1181 in. (3.0 mm) shim between throttle lever and idle stop screw. Loosen ball joint nut. *See Fig. 12.*

JEEP 2.1L TURBO DIESEL (Cont.)

4) Slide ball joint nut until it contacts throttle lever, and tighten. Determine proper clearance (shim thickness) between control lever and lever stop, according to temperature of cold start capsule. See COLD START SYSTEM SHIM THICKNESS chart.

5) Insert correct shim between control lever and lever stop. Align clevis and throttle cable stop. Tighten clevis and throttle cable stop so that they both contact timing control lever.

6) Tighten throttle cable stop screw. Remove, and reinsert shim, from between control lever and lever stop, to ensure that clearance is correct. Remove shim.

7) Start, and run engine until it reaches normal operating temperature. Verify that throttle and timing control levers are against their respective stops, and that these levers are not binding. Perform DYNAMIC TIMING (ENGINE RUNNING) & IDLE SPEED adjustment procedure.

Fig. 12: Setting Cold Start Shim Clearance

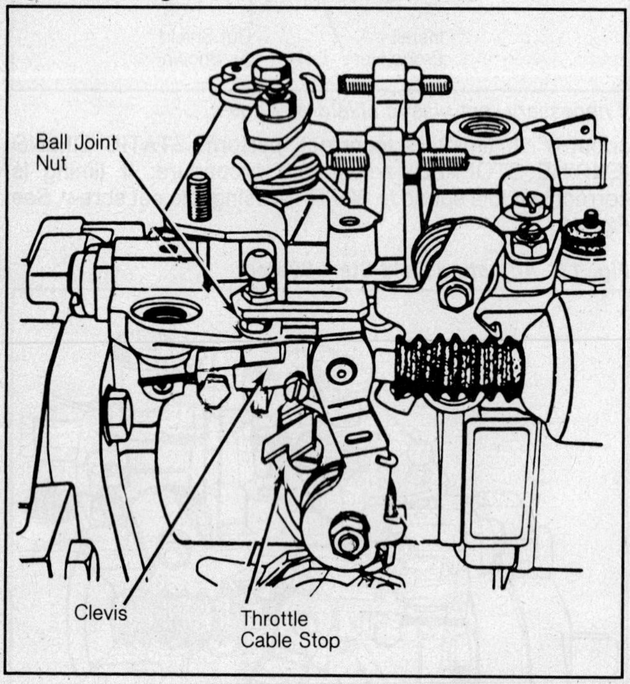

COLD START SYSTEM SHIM THICKNESS

Capsule Temp. °F (°C)	Shim Thickness In. (mm)
66 (19) Or Less	.2561 (6.5)
72 (22)	.2325 (5.9)
77 (25)	.2167 (5.5)
86 (30)	.8172 (4.75)
95 (35)	.1575 (4)
104 (40)	.1281 (3.25)

TIGHTENING SPECIFICATIONS

Application	Ft. Lbs (N.m)
Glow Plugs	15-22 (20-30)
Fuel Shut-Off Solenoid	11-18 (15-25)
Pump Shaft Sprocket Retaining Nut	37 (50)
	INCH Lbs. (N.m)
Fuel Return Hose Fitting	88 (10)

FORD & JEEP – DIESEL

VEHICLE APPLICATION

ENGINE CODE

Application	VIN Code
Ford 2.3L 4-Cyl. Turbo	E
Jeep 2.1L 4-Cyl. Turbo	J8S

DESCRIPTION

A turbocharger is used on Ford 2.3L and Jeep 2.1L diesel engines to improve fuel efficiency and performance. Turbocharger assembly is mounted on right side of engine, and consists of a turbine/compressor assembly, oil supply system and wastegate.

Fig. 1: View of Jeep 2.1L Diesel Turbocharger

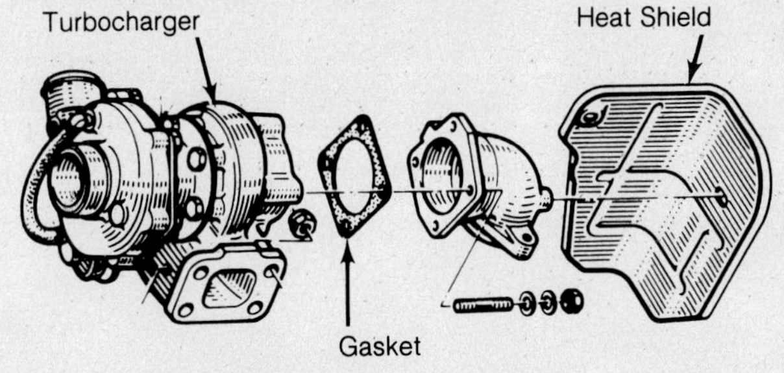

Ford 2.3L turbocharger is similar.

OPERATION

As air/fuel mixture is burned, greater volume of hot exhaust gas enters exhaust system. This gas is directed into turbine housing of turbocharger. Energy contained in exhaust gas is used to increase speed of turbine wheel, which drives compressor wheel. Compressor wheel forces incoming air through plenum chamber and into intake manifold.

The amount of boost is controlled by a wastegate and diaphragm. As boost increases, diaphragm pushes against wastegate actuator rod, opening wastegate. Exhaust gases are then diverted away from turbine.

TURBINE ASSEMBLY

Turbocharger is mounted on right side of engine. Turbine and compressor are connected by a shaft. Hot exhaust gases are fed into turbine through exhaust manifold. Gases hitting turbine blades cause blades to spin, which in turn, causes compressor wheel to spin.

WASTEGATE & PRESSURE REGULATOR

A wastegate controls amount of boost allowed into engine. Exhaust gas enters turbine continuously. Once engine demand is satisfied and proper boost level is attained, wastegate, acting on command from pressure regulator, by-passes enough exhaust gas into exhaust system to maintain required turbine speed.

The pressure regulator is a pressure-sensitive diaphram unit. It is installed so it can sense pressure differential between intake manifold and compressor. Once this differential reaches a certain level, diaphram reacts on an integral spring, to partially open wastegate.

OIL SUPPLY

Rotating assembly, consisting of turbine wheel, connecting shaft and compressor wheel, can reach speeds in excess of 50,000 RPM. Engine oil enters turbocharger housing through an inlet fitting, and returns to oil pan through an oil return line. A steady supply of clean engine oil is absolutely necessary for proper operation. Any interruption or contamination of oil may result in major turbocharger damage.

Any time center housing rotating assembly is replaced (in part or in whole), oil and filter should be changed. If oiling system has been contaminated, oil and filter must be changed, and assembly must be flushed with clean oil.

PRESSURE RELIEF VALVE

A pressure relief valve, located on intake manifold, diverts excess boost into the atmosphere. This valve will open if wastegate cannot divert enough exhaust gas away from turbine wheel, or if a malfunction occurs, preventing proper operation of wastegate system.

Pressure relief valve opens when boost pressure exceeds a predetermined amount (8.7 psi for Jeep 2.1L). On Ford vehicles, "CHECK ENGINE" light will come on while valve is open. The lamp will go out when boost drops (and valve closes).

TURBO BOOST CUT-OUT SWITCH

Jeep Models Only

A turbo boost cut-out switch is used to prevent turbocharger boost pressure from contacting the fuel injection pump diaphragm when engine temperature is above 239° F (115° C).

This switch is operated by coolant temperature and is located behind cold start thermostat capsule (attached to the injection unit), and is mounted in a coolant line fitting.

TESTING

NOTE: **Turbochargers for both Ford and Jeep are serviced by replacement ONLY.**

BEARING AXIAL CLEARANCE CHECK

Ford and Jeep

1) Attach a dial indicator with tip of indicator against end of shaft. Manually move shaft in one direction as far as possible and zero dial indicator.

2) Move shaft in extreme opposite direction (without rotating shaft) and observe dial indicator.

3) Rotate shaft 90° and check bearing clearance again. If bearing axial clearance is greater than .0012-.0031" (.03-.08 mm), replace turbocharger assembly.

REMOVAL & INSTALLATION

TURBOCHARGER ASSEMBLY

Ford and Jeep

Before servicing turbocharging system, ensure the following precautions have been taken:

- Clean area around turbocharger with non-caustic solution before disassembly.

Turbocharging Systems

FORD & JEEP – DIESEL (Cont.)

- Use extreme care during removal to avoid damaging turbine blades. Any damage may cause turbocharger failure when engine is started.
- Scribe reference marks on turbine and compressor housing before disassembly to ensure correct reassembly position.
- If any joints are found to be coated with sealer, clean thoroughly and recoat with sealant during assembly.

Removal

1) Remove 2 bolts connecting exhaust pipe to turbocharger. Disconnect air cleaner assembly. Remove oil supply line bolts at top of turbocharger center housing. Remove clamp from oil lines and remove oil return line.

2) Remove bolt and sealing washers (if equipped) connecting oil supply line to oil filter housing. Remove bolts connecting turbocharger to exhaust manifold.

Installation

1) Clean mating surfaces of turbocharger and exhaust manifold. Using new seals (if equipped) on oil supply line, reverse removal procedure to install. Disconnect fuel cut-off solenoid at injection pump and disconnect glow plug harness from engine wiring harness.

2) Crank engine several times (30 seconds maximum), until oil pressure light goes out. Reconnect fuel cut-off solenoid and glow plug harness, and start engine. Check for exhaust leaks.

TIGHTENING SPECIFICATIONS

Application	Ft. Lbs. (N.m)
Ford	
Oil Return From Turbo	6-7.5 (8-10)
Turbo-to-Exhaust Pipe	35-47 (47-64)

Electric Fuel Pumps

FORD & GENERAL MOTORS

Ford: 2.3L EFI, 5.0L EFI & 7.5L;
General Motors: 2.5L TBI

DESCRIPTION & OPERATION

FORD

Fuel Pump

A frame-mounted pump is used on vehicles with 2.3L and 5.0L EFI engines. This high pressure (up to 39 psi) pump is frame-mounted, and can supply up to 15.9 gallons (60 liters) of fuel per hour. A pressure relief valve, mounted internally, protects against over-pressurization of system if fuel flow is restricted.

Vehicles with 7.5L engines use a submerged, in-tank fuel pump, designed to prevent loss of fuel flow during off-road use. Vehicles with 5.0L EFI use both a frame-mounted and an in-tank pump.

Inertia Switch

If vehicle in involved in a collision or rollover, an inertia switch will stop fuel flow. Engine will run until present fuel supply is exhausted. After that point, inertia switch must be reset before vehicle can be restarted. To reset switch (located under instrument panel), depress button on switch.

Fuel Selector Valves

For information on operation and testing of fuel selector valves, see FUEL SELECTOR VALVE article in ACCESORIES & EQUIPMENT section.

GENERAL MOTORS

Fuel Pump

All 2.5L engines with throttle body injection (TBI) use a model LN8, low pressure pump with a rated output of 4-13 psi. The LN8 fuel pump is mounted to fuel sending unit in fuel tank.

A power relay is used to control fuel pump operation. When ignition is turned on, relay activates fuel pump for about 2 seconds. This activation is used to prime injectors. If electronic pulses from distributor are not received after the 2 second time period, relay shuts fuel pump off.

TESTING

ELECTRICAL

Ford (Frame-Mounted Pump)

1) Check fuel tanks for adequate fuel supply, do not assume fuel gauge is correct. Check for fuel leakage at fittings and lines. Locate fuel pump connector at end of "short harness" (wiring between pump body harness). Remove connector and check continuity between connector terminals.

2) If continuity is 5 ohms or less, go to step **5)**. If continuity is 5 ohms or more, check for continuity between ground lead of connector and ground. If continuity is not present, repair open in pump ground circuit and recheck system operation. If continuity is present, go to next step.

3) Check for continuity between Pink/Black wire of connector and ground. If continuity is present, repair short in pump power wiring circuit and recheck system operation. If continuity is not present, go to next step.

4) Check continuity across pump terminals. If continuity is present, go to step **5)**. If continuity is not present, check pump sender wiring. If wiring is okay, replace pump sender assembly and recheck system operation.

5) Check for voltage between Pink/Black wire of connector and ground, while turning ignition on. Voltage should be 12 volts momentarily, then drop to 0 volts. If voltage is not correct, check pump power circuitry and repair as required.

6) Check for continuity between leads of "short harness". If continuity is present, remove "short harness" leads at pump and check continuity across pump terminals. If continuity is not present, replace pump. If continuity is present, replace "short harness".

Ford (In-Tank Pump – 7.5L Engines)

1) Check for adequate fuel supply, do not assume fuel gauge is correct. Check for fuel leakage from lines and fittings. Replace lines and/or fitting as necessary.

2) Remove fuel pump cut-off relay connector. Check for voltage between Yellow wire at connector and ground. If 12 volts are present, go to step **3)**. If voltage is not present, check inertia switch. Reset switch if necessary.

3) Connect voltmeter between Pink/Black wire of connector and ground. Crank engine momentarily, and note voltage reading. If 10-12 volts are present while cranking, go to step **4)**. If voltage is less than 10 volts, check fuse link and resistance wiring.

4) Check for continuity between Pink/Black wire and ground. If continuity is present, reinstall relay and go to step **5)**. If continuity is not present, check tank selector relay (if equipped). If relay is okay, or is not used, check continuity across fuel pump terminals.

5) If continuity is present across both the terminals and wiring harness, go to step **6)**. If continuity is present across pump terminals, but not wiring harness, replace pump sender assembly. If continuity is present across wiring harness, but not pump terminals, replace pump and recheck system operation.

6) Attach relay connector. Connect voltmeter leads between Pink/Black wire and ground. Crank engine momentarily (until oil pressure is built up), and note voltage reading.

7) Turn ignition back to "RUN" position, and note voltage reading. If voltage (10-12 volts) remains steady, check fuel pump flow capacity. See FUEL PUMP TESTING (IN-TANK) in this article. If voltage (10-12 volts) does not remains steady, or never existed, check relay circuit and oil pressure switch.

MODIFYING FUEL CUT-OFF RELAY

1) Using new Relay (E3EB-9345-BA, CA, DA or E3TF-9345-AA), drill a 1/8" hole in-line with pins, and as close to pins as possible.

NOTE: **Part of relay skirt may be cut away to provide easier access to pins.**

2) Solder a 16-18 gauge jumper wire between pins "2" and "4". *See Fig. 1.* Feed end of a long (8-10'), insulated, flexible wire through hole drilled in relay skirt, and solder end to exposed base of pin No. "1" (as close to relay base as possible). This will permit full insertion of relay into socket. Solder an alligator clip to other end of long flexible wire.

FUEL PUMP

Ford (Frame-Mounted Pump)

1) With assistant in vehicle, raise vehicle on hoist. Locate fuel diagnostic valve. If diagnostic valve is

Electric Fuel Pumps

FORD & GENERAL MOTORS (Cont.)

Fig. 1: Modifying Fuel Pump Cut-Off Relay

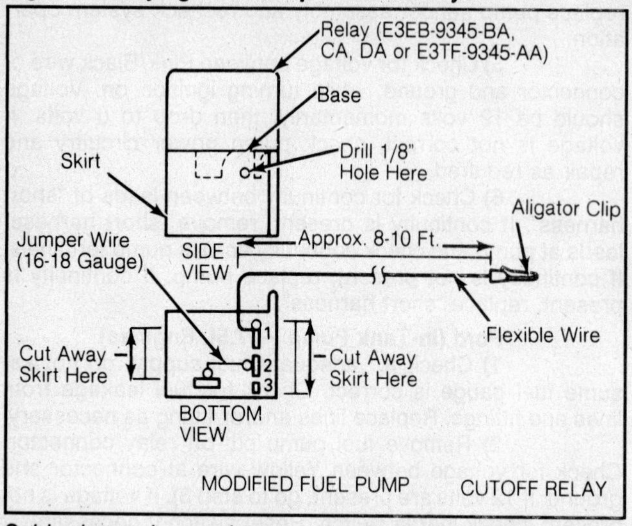

Solder long wire as close to relay base as possible.

present, go to step **2)**. If pump does not have diagnostic valve, fabricate test line and fitting assembly. *See Fig. 2.*

2) Attach gauge to diagnostic valve (or test line and fitting assembly). Turn ignition on and check pressure reading. Reading should be 30-40 psi, if pump is operating properly and other system components are okay.

3) Disconnect fuel return line at fuel rail. Use care to avoid fuel spillage. Route hose from fuel rail fitting to a calibrated container of at least 1 quart capacity.

4) Replace fuel pump relay with modified relay. See MODIFYING FUEL CUT-OFF RELAY in this article. Place end of return hose into calibrated container. Route long wire to vehicle ground. Pump should now operate. Run fuel pump for 10 seconds.

5) Observe fuel flow volume and pressure. Fuel pump is operating properly if fuel pressure is 35-45 psi, fuel flow is a minimum of 5.6 oz. in 10 seconds and fuel pressure remains at a minimim of 30 psi immediately after pump stops.

6) If all 3 conditions are met, fuel pump is operating normally. If conditions are not met, check for engine and electrical problems. If okay, go to next step.

7) If fuel pressure meets specification, but fuel flow does not, check for blocked filter(s), fuel supply lines, and/or tank selector valve. After correcting any blockages, repeat above tests. If fuel flow still does not meet specification, replace pump.

8) If both fuel pressure and fuel flow meet specification, but system will not stay pressurized after pump is turned off, check for leaking injectors or regulator. If they are both okay, replace fuel pump. If no fuel flow or fuel pressure is observed, fuel system should be checked as in step **7)**. If system is okay, replace fuel pump.

Ford
(In-Tank Pump – 2.3L & 5.0L Engines)

1) Open fuel line at high pressure pump inlet. Connect hose to line from fuel tank. Route hose to a 1 quart, calibrated container. Disconnect high pressure fuel pump electrical connector from body wiring harness.

2) Replace fuel pump relay with modified relay. See MODIFYING FUEL CUT-OFF RELAY in this article. Ground wire coming from relay to a convenient ground point to energize fuel pump and measure flow for 10 seconds.

Fig. 2: Test Line And Fitting Assembly

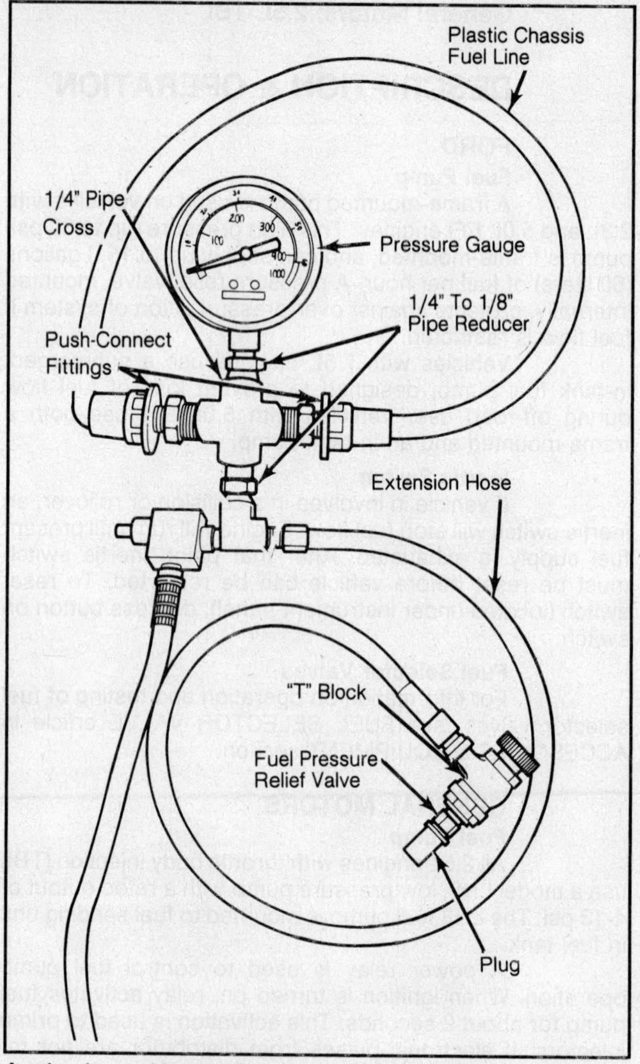

Apply pipe sealant to fittings.

NOTE: **It may be necessary to momentarily block fuel hose to prime low pressure pump with outlet open and no back pressure on outlet; this is normal.**

3) If fuel pump produces a minimum flow of 16 oz. of fuel, within 10 seconds, pump is operating correctly. If there is no flow from pump, check electrical circuit and check for inlet restriction. If electrical circuits are okay and inlet is not restricted, replace pump.

Ford (In-Tank Pump – 7.5L Engine)

1) Disconnect fuel line just before vapor separator. Route end of hose to a calibrated container of at least 1 quart capacity. Turn ignition on, but do not start engine. Create a short condition across oil switch terminals. Run fuel pump for 10 seconds.

NOTE: **To initate fuel flow, it may be necessary to momentarily block the hose to create a back pressure condition.**

2) If 16 oz. (473 ml) of fuel, or more, flows from pump during 10 second test, pump is okay. If fuel flow does not meet specification, check for the following conditions; a

Electric Fuel Pumps

FORD & GENERAL MOTORS (Cont.)

blockage or restriction in fuel lines, a blockage or restriction in fuel filter, or spare tire pinching inlet line of fuel pump. If all 3 conditions are okay, replace pump sender assembly.

General Motors
Flow Test

1) Disconnect EFI fuel feed line from throttle body. Route line to a 1 quart, calibrated container. Apply battery voltage to terminal "G" of assembly line communications link (ALCL). *See Fig. 3.* Fuel pump should supply volume of 1/2 pint or more, within 15 seconds.

Fig. 3: Assembly Line Test Link

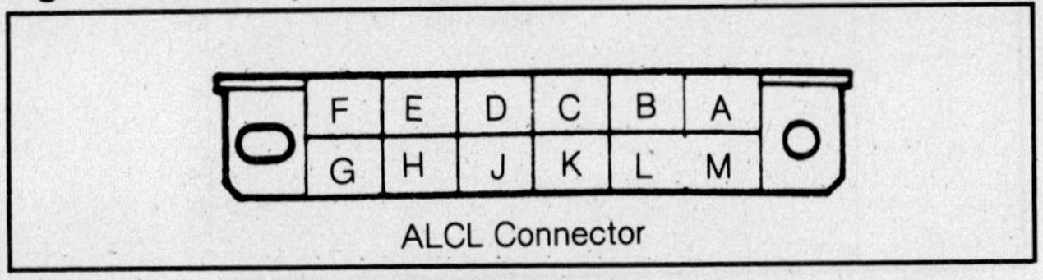

Test link is under left side of instrument panel.

2) If fuel supply is okay, pump is operating properly. If fuel supply is not okay, check for restriction in supply line. Repair or replace line if necessary. If there are no restrictions, perform PRESSURE TEST in this article.

General Motors
Pressure Test

1) Remove air cleaner, and plug thermal vacuum port on throttle body. Remove fuel pump fuse from fuse block in passenger compartment. Start engine. Engine will run until present fuel supply is exhausted. Replace fuse.

2) Remove steel fuel pipe between TBI and fuel filter. Install Pipe and Adaptor Assemblies (J-29658-02) onto Gauge Assembly (J-29658). Install gauge between TBI unit and fuel filter. Start vehicle, and note pressure reading.

3) Reinstall steel fuel line, using new "O" rings if necessary. Start vehicle, check for leaks and turn ignition off. Remove plug covering thermal vacuum porton throttle body. Install air cleaner.

4) Disconnect fuel line at TBI unit. Install low pressure gauge to line. Start engine and note pressure reading. Fuel pump pressure should be 4-6 psi.

5) If pressure reading is correct, pump is okay. If pressure reading is not okay, check for restricted fuel filter, lines and hoses. If all are okay, check power relay.

REMOVAL & INSTALLATION

FUEL PUMP

Removal & Installation
(Ford Frame-Mounted Pump)

Disconnect "short harness" wiring at pump. Disconnect fuel line fittings. Unbolt 3 bolts attaching pump to frame. To install, reverse removal procedure. Start engine and check for leaks.

Removal & Installation
(Ford In-Tank Pump)

1) Disconnect battery negative cable. Raise and support vehicle. Remove fuel tank. Turn sending unit lock ring counterclockwise and pull ring away from tank. *See Fig. 4.*

2) Lift fuel lever sending unit and pump assembly from tank. Note position of alignment tabs (if equipped).

Fig. 4: Ford Electric Fuel Pump & Sender Assembly

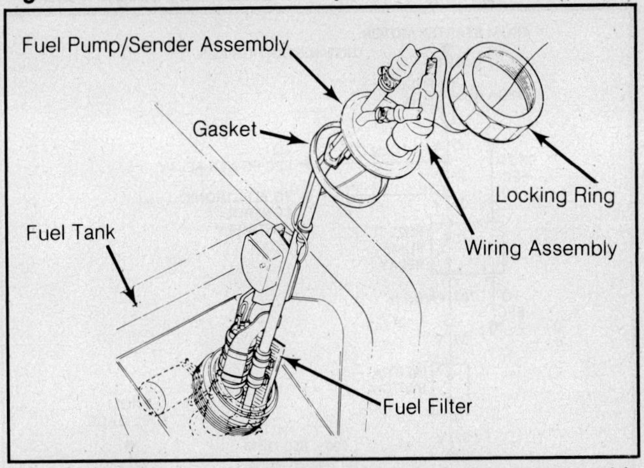

Assembly shown is for vehicles with 7.5L engines, assembly for 2.3L & 5.0L engines is similar.

Remove pump from sending unit. To install, reverse removal procedure. Start engine and check for leaks.

Removal & Installation
(General Motors)

1) Remove fuel pump fuse from fuse block in passenger compartment. Start engine. Engine will run until present fuel supply is exhausted. Replace fuse. Disconnect battery negative cable. Raise and support vehicle.

2) Remove fuel tank. Turn sending unit lock ring counterclockwise, and pull lock ring away from tank. Lift fuel lever sending unit and pump assembly from tank. Remove pump from sending unit. To install, reverse removal procedure. Start engine and check for leaks.

Fig. 5: Wiring Diagram For Ford 2.3L With Single Tank

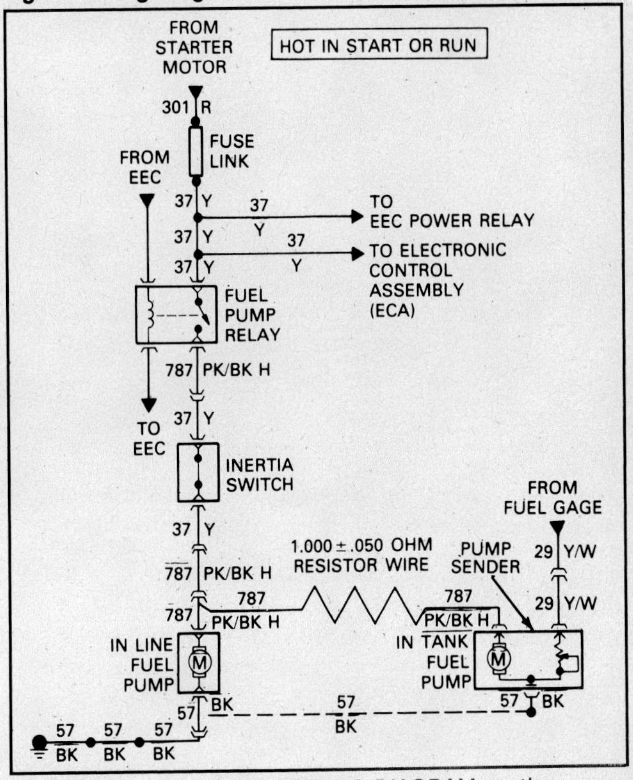

Also see chassis wiring in WIRING DIAGRAM section.

Electric Fuel Pumps

FORD & GENERAL MOTORS (Cont.)

Fig. 6: Wiring Diagram For Ford 5.0L With Single Tank

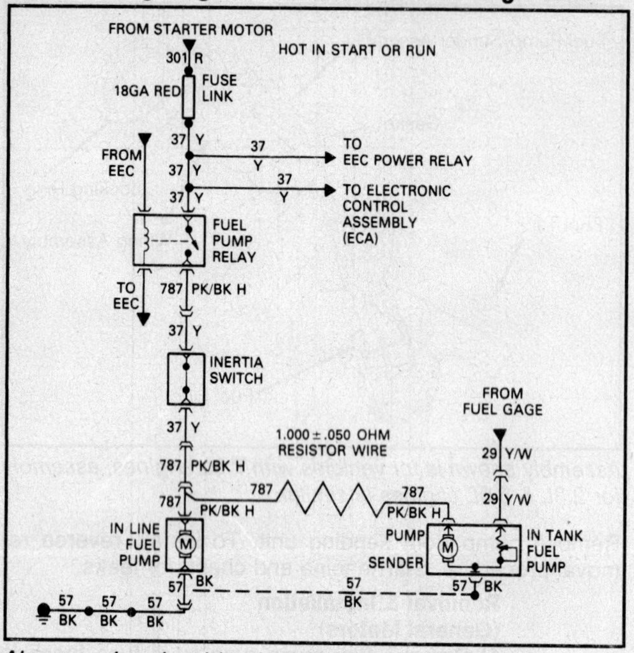

Also see chassis wiring in WIRING DIAGRAM section.

Fig. 7: Wiring Diagram For Ford 7.5L With Single Tank

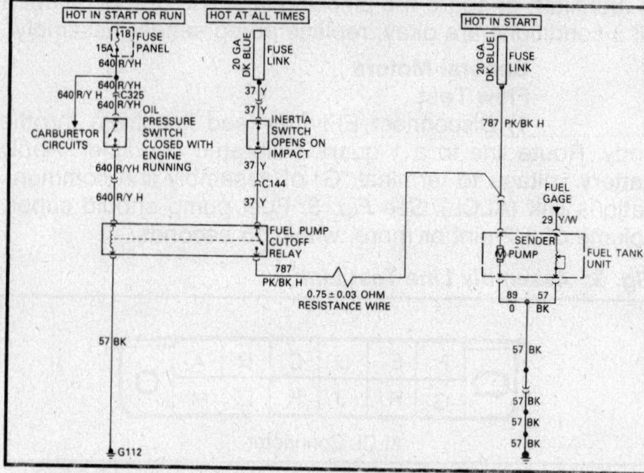

Also see chassis wiring in WIRING DIAGRAM section.

SECTION 3

EMISSION CONTROL

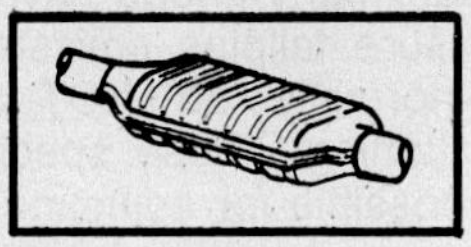

CONTENTS

NOTE: **ALSO SEE GENERAL INDEX.**

IMPORTANT: **Because of the many model names used by vehicle manufacturers, accurate identification of models is important. See Model Identification at the front of this publication.**

1985 Exhaust Emission Systems

EMISSION STANDARDS & TUNE–UPS

MANUFACTURING STANDARDS

Federal and state governments have established air quality standards during the past 20 years. Automobile manufacturers design their vehicles to conform to standards where the vehicle will be sold. These standards cover carbon monoxide (CO), hydrocarbons (HC) and oxides of nitrogen (NOx).

Federal and California standards which must be met by manufacturers are specified in units easily measured in a testing laboratory. Since 1970, these standards have been in "grams per mile". This means no vehicle, whether 2-cylinder or V8, may emit more than a set weight (in grams) of pollutants for each mile it travels. Since large engines burn more fuel per mile than smaller ones, they must be "cleaner" per gallon burned if they are to meet these standards.

When manufacturers certify vehicles, the cars are placed on a dynamometer and the exhaust gases are collected in a bag. After the vehicle runs for a specified time, the gases are analyzed and weighed. Engines and emission systems are designed so the weight of emissions will be less than the specified grams per mile.

Infra-red exhaust analyzers are commonly used in automotive test stations. They use a test probe placed in the exhaust stream, and measure the percentage of CO in the exhaust gas, or parts per million of HC. These are not the same units used by the manufacturer when the car is certified. (NOx emissions can be measured only in a laboratory.)

TUNE-UP STANDARDS

When a tune-up is performed, the mechanic must have specifications to use when adjusting the vehicle. The first few years of emission-regulated vehicles were adjusted using carbon monoxide percentage or hydrocarbon parts per million. These are the units measured by an exhaust gas analyzer.

In the past few years, manufacturers have made their vehicles much cleaner (measured in grams per mile). The CO% and HC ppm have become very low, especially when measured AFTER a catalytic converter. It has become hard to accurately measure the effect of turning the idle mixture screws.

One solution to this problem requires the use of artifically-enriched propane adjustments. The added propane boosts the emissions by a known amount, and makes the effect of turning the mixture screws easily measureable. However, CO and HC can only be accurately measured while the propane is being added.

As computer-controlled systems were developed, it became possible for the vehicle to adjust its own mixture throughout the entire engine operating range, not just at idle. These "feedback" systems use oxygen sensors to measure how much unburned oxygen is left in the exhaust. The computer can then determine when the air/fuel mixture is too rich or too lean, and correct it as necessary. Even if a mechanic incorrectly adjusts the mixture, most computers can compensate enough so the vehicle will still run clean. In fact, newer cars burn fuel so completely that changes in the pollutant levels after the catalytic converter are hard to measure accurately.

New vehicles are now adjusted by measuring the percentage of time that the computer-controlled system is adding fuel versus the time fuel is shut off. The mechanic checks this percentage with a dwell meter (normally used to measure the time a set of points is open/closed), then adjusts the fuel system until the percentage is correct.

Although many shops have exhaust gas analyzers which measure tailpipe emissions, computer-controlled engines normally do NOT have CO or HC specifications for tuning. These specifications would be neither useful or possible for adjusting new vehicles. This manual provides procedures and specifications given by the manufacturers and does not necessarily list CO or HC specifications.

STATE TEST STANDARDS

Some states have established standards for testing used vehicles to see if they are still running clean. Generally speaking, these standards are given in CO% and HC ppm. They can be checked with an exhaust gas analyzer. Typical standards for newer cars would be less than 2.0% CO (non-catalyst) or 0.5% CO (with catalyst) and less than 200 ppm of HC. If vehicle emissions are below these levels, the vehicle passes inspection. The important thing to remember is that these specifications are NOT to be used for TUNING. They are only for testing to see if the vehicle is functioning properly. If it isn't, it must be tuned using the manufacturer's procedures and specifications, then tested again.

Test standards change each year and vary from state to state, and even by county within each state. It is not possible to provide an accurate and up-to-date list in this manual. Specifications can be obtained from your local county or state government. Remember that these standards are ONLY for test purposes. The manufacturer's adjustment procedures and specifications MUST be used when actually tuning a vehicle.

1985 Emission Control Application

CHRYSLER CORP.

1985 CHRYSLER CORP.

Engine	Emission Control Systems & Devices	Remarks
Light Duty Emission		
2.2L 4-Cyl.	APREVLV [5], AICV, AIR, ASV, ATS, CAT, CBVV, CCERG, CCEVS, CTS, CVSCC, CVSCO, EGR, ESC, OS, PCV, PVCS, RVSV, TAC	[1] – Federal only. [2] – Calif. only. [3] – Some models. [4] – With A/C. [5] – Altitude models only.
2.6L 4-Cyl.	ASV, ATS, ACT, CBVV, CCEGR, CCEVS, CTS, CVSCC, EGR, EIS, OS, PAF, PCV, PVCS,	
3.7L 6-Cyl.	AIR, APDV, APREVLV [1], ASV [2], CAT, CCEGR, CCEVS [2], ChVLV, EAC, ECS, EGR, EGR-CTS, EGR-DV [3], ESA, MHCV, MCU, OSAC [3], PCV, TAC	
5.2L V8	AAS, AIR, APDV [2], APREVLV [1], CAT, CCEGR, CCEVS [2], ChVLV, EAC, ESA, EGR, EGR-CTS, EGR-DV [3], MHCV, MCU, OSAC [3], PCV, TAC	
Heavy Duty Emissions		
5.2L V8	AIR, APDV [2], APREVLV [1], CAT, CCEGR, CCEVS [2], ChVLV, ECS, EGR, EGR-DV [3], MHCV, PCV, TAC, TIDC [4]	
5.9L V8	AIR, APDV [2], APREVLV [1], CAT [2], CCEGR, CCEVS [2], ChVLV, ECS, EGR, EGR-DV [3], MHCV, MCU, OSAC, PCV, TAC, TIDC	

Light Duty Emissions: Vehicles up to 8500 GVW. **Heavy Duty Emissions:** Vehicles over 8500 GVW.

AAS – Aspirator Air System
AICV – Air Injection Check Valve
AIR – Air Injection Reactor
APDV – Air Pump Diverter Valve
APREVLV – Air Pump Relief Valve
AST – Air Temperature Sensor
ASV – Air Switching Valve
CAT – Catalytic Converter
CBVV – Carburetor Bowl Vent Valve
CCEGR – Coolant Controlled Exhaust Gas Recirculation
CCEVS – Coolant Controlled Engine Vacuum Switch
ChVLV – Check Valve
CTS – Coolant Temperature Switch
CVSCC – Coolant Vacuum Switch Cold Close
EAC – Electric Assist Choke
ECS – Emission Control System
EGR – Exhaust Gas Recirculation
EGR-CTS – Exhaust Gas Recirculation Charge Temperature Switch
EGR-DV – Exhaust Gas Recirculation Delay Valve
ESA – Electronic Spark Advance
MHCV – Manifold Heat Control Valve
MCU – Micro Computer Unit
OSAC – Orifice Spark Advance Control
OS – Oxygen Sensor
PAF – Pulse Air Feeder
PCV – Positive Crankcase Ventilation
PVCS – Ported Vacuum Control System
RVSV – Rollover/Vapor Separator Valve
SEGR – Sub-Exhaust Gas Recirculation Valve
TAC – Thermostatic Air Cleaner
TIDC – Thermostatic Ignition Distributor Control

JEEP

1985 JEEP

Engine	Emission Control Systems & Devices	Remarks
2.5L 4-Cyl.	CAT, CEC, DC-VLV [2], DLV, EGR, EGR-CTO, EGR-TVS, HDVA-CTO [3], MCU, PCV, RDV, TSD, VA-CTO, VSA [2]	[1] – Federal only. [2] – Calif. only. [3] – Heavy duty. [4] – Some models. [5] – Some Federal, all Calif.
4.2L 6-Cyl.	ACV [1], ASV [2], CAT, CEC [5], DLV, DVTRV, EGR, EGR-CTO, EGR-FDLV [4], EGR-TVS, HDSP-CTO [3], HDVA-CTO [3] MCU, NLRV [1], PAIR, PCV, RDV, SLV, VA-CTO, VSA [5]	
2.8L V6	ACV, AIR, CAT, CEC, DVTRV, EGR, EGR-TVS, MCU, PCV, SLV, TSD, VSA	
6.0L V8	ACV, AIR, CAT, CEC, DLV, DVTRV, EGR, EGR-CTO, EGR-TVS, HDVA-CTO [3], MCU [2], NLRV [1], PCV, RDV, VA-CTO, VSA [2]	

Light Duty Emissions: Vehicles up to 8500 GVW. **Heavy Duty Emissions:** Vehicles over 8500 GVW.

ACV – Air Control Valve
AIR – Air Injection System
ASV – Air Switching Valve
CAT – Catalytic Converter
CEC – Computerized Emission Control
DC-VLV – Deceleration Valve
DLV – Delay Valve
DVTRV – Diverter Valve
EGR – Exhaust Gas Recirculation
EGR-CTO – Exhaust Gas Recirculation Coolant Temperature Override
EGR-FDLV – Exhaust Gas Recirculation Forward Delay Valve
EGR-TVS – Exhaust Gas Recirculation Thermal Vacuum Switch
HDSP-CTO [3] – Heavy Duty Spark Coolant Temperature Override
HDVA-CTO [3] – Heavy Duty Vacuum Advance Coolant Temperature Override
MCU – Micro Computer Unit
NLRV – Non-Linear Valve
PAIR – Pulse-Air Injection
PCV – Positive Crankcase Ventilation
RDV – Reverse Delay Valve
SLV – Solevac
TSD – Throttle Solenoid
VA-CTO – Vacuum Advance Coolant Temperature Override
VSA – Vacuum Switch Assembly

1985 Emission Control Application

FORD MOTOR CO.

1985 FORD MOTOR CO.

Engine	Emission Control Systems & Devices	Remarks
Light Duty Emissions		
2.0L 4-Cyl.	A/CL-BMS, A/CL-TSOV, A/CL-VCD, A/CL-VCV, A/CL-VM, ACV, AIR, AIR-BPV, AIR-ChV, AIR-IVV, CAT, DMV, DRCV, DVCV, EGR, EGR-BPTV, EGR-RSR, EGR-VCV, EGR-VSOL, EVCR, FCS, FVEC, OS, PCV, TAC, V-RSR, V-RST	1 – Calif. only. 2 – High alt. only. 3 – Man. trans. only. 4 – Some models.
2.3L 4-Cyl.	A/CL-BMS, A/CL-TSOV, A/CL-VCD, A/CL-VCV, A/CL-VM, ACV, AIR, AIR-BPV, AIR-ChV, AIR-IVV, BPS, CAT, DMV, DRCV, DVCV, EGR, EGR-BPTV, EGR-RSR, EGR-VCV, EGR-VSOL, EVCR, FVEC, MCU, OS, PCV, TAC, V-RSR, V-RST,	
4.9L 6-Cyl.	A/CL-BMS, A/CL-TSOV, A/CL-VCD, A/CL-VCV, A/CL-VM, ACV [1], AIR, AIR-BPV, AIR-ChV, BPS [2], CAT, DMV [1], DRCV, DVCV, EGR, EGR-BPTV, EGR-VCV, EGR-VSOL [1], FCS [1], FVEC, ITVS, MCU [1], OS [1], PCV, TAC, V-RSR, V-RST [1]	
2.8L V6	A/CL-BMS, A/CL-VCD, A/CL-VM, ACV, AIR, AIR-BPV, AIR-ChV, BMAPS, CAT, DRCV, EEC, EGR, EGR-EPV, EGR-RSR, EGR-VSOL, FVEC, OS, PCV, TAC, V-RSR	
5.0L V8	A/CL-BMS, A/CL-TSOV [4], A/CL-VCD, A/CL-VCV, A/CL-VM, ACV [1], AIR, AIR-BPV, AIR-ChV, AIR-IVV, BMAPS [4], BPS [2 3], CAT [4], CTS [1], DVCV, DRCV, DMV, EEC [1], EGR, EGR-BPTV, EGR-CLR [1], EGR-EPV [1], EGR-VCV, EGR-VSOL [1], EVCR [4], FCS [1], FVEC, HIC, ITVS, OS [1], PCV, TAC, TP, V-RSR, V-RST	
5.8L V8	A/CL-BMS, A/CL-VCD, A/CL-VCV, A/CL-VM, ACV [4], AIR, AIR-BPV, AIR-ChV, BMAPS [1 4], CAT [4], CTS [4], DVCV, EEC [4], EGR, EGR-BPTV, EGR-CLR [4], EGR-EPV [4], EGR-VCV, EGR-VSOL [4], FCS [4], FVEC, HIC, ITVS, OS [4], PCV, TAC, TP, V-RSR, V-RST	
Heavy Duty Emissions		
4.9L 6-Cyl.	A/CL-BMS, A/CL-TSOV, A/CL-VCV, A/CL-VM, AIR, AIR-BPV, DVCV, EGR, EGR-RSR, EGR-VCV, EGR-VSOL, FVEC, PCV, TAC	
5.8L V8	A/CL-BMS, A/CL-VM, AIR, AIR-BPV, DVCV, EGR, EGR-VCV, EGR-VSOL, FVEC, PCV, TAC, TP, V-RST	
7.5L V8	A/CL-BMS, A/CL-VM, AIR, AIR-BPV, DVCV, EGR, EGR-RSR, EGR-VCV, EGR-VSOL, FVEC, HIC, PCV, TAC, TP, V-RST	

Light Duty Emissions: Vehicles up to 8500 GVW. **Heavy Duty Emissions:** Vehicles over 8500 GVW.

A/CL-BMS – Air Cleaner Bi-Metal Sensor
A/CL-TSOV – Air Cleaner Temperature Sensor Override Valve
A/CL-VCD – Air Cleaner Vacuum Control Delay
A/CL-VCV – Air Cleaner Vacuum Control Valve
A/CL-VM – Air Cleaner Vacuum Motor
ACV – Air Control Valve
AIR – Air Injection System
AIR-BPV – Air By-Pass Valve
AIR-ChV – Air Check Valve
AIR-IVV – Air Idle Vacuum Valve
BMAPS – Barometric/Manifold Absolute Pressure Sensor
BPS – Barometric Pressure Switch
CAT – Catalytic Converter
CTS – Coolant Temperature Sensor
DMV – Distributor Modulator Valve
DRCV – Distributor Retard Control Valve
DVCV – Distributor Vacuum Control Valve
EEC – Electronic Engine Control
EGR – Exhaust Gas Recirculation
EGR-BPTV – EGR Backpressure Transducer Valve
EGR-CLR – EGR Cooler
EGR-EPV – EGR External Pressure Valve
EGR-RSR – EGR Reservoir
EGR-VCV – EGR Vacuum Control Valve
EGR-VSOL – EGR Vacuum Solenoid
EVCR – Emission Vacuum Control Regulator
FCS – Fuel Control System
FVEC – Fuel Vapor Emission Conrol
HIC – Hot Idle Compensator
ITVS – Ignition Timing Vacuum Switch
MCU – Micro Computer Unit
OS – Oxygen Sensor
PCV – Positive Crankcase Ventilation
TAC – Thermostatic Air Cleaner
TP – Throttle Positioner
V-RSR – Vacuum Reservoir
V-RST – Vacuum Restrictor

GENERAL MOTORS

1985 GENERAL MOTORS

Engine	Emission Control Systems & Devices	Remarks
Light Duty Emissions		
1.9L 4-Cyl.	ABAV [1], A/CL-BMS, A/CL-VM, AIR, AIR-DVLV, CAT, DCM/C-VLV, EEC, EGR, EGR-BPTV, EGR-TVS, HIC, IS [1], MCU [1], PCV, TAC, TCVS [2], VCV [1], VSV [1], WOT-SW [1]	[1] – Calif. only. [2] – Auto. trans. only. [3] – Some models. [4] – High alt. only.
2.0L 4-Cyl.	A/CL-BMS, A/CL-VM, ACV, AIR, CP-TVS, DCM/C-VLV, EGR, EGR-BldSOL, EGR-DVLV, EGR-TVS, PCV, PVBrk, SADV-TVS, SVBrk, SVBrk-TVS, TCVS	
2.5L 4-Cyl.	ATS, CAT, ChVLV, CTS, EEC, EGR-BPTV, IAC, MAP, OXS, PCV, TAC, TCC, TPS, TVS, VSS	
4.3L 6-Cyl.	A/CL-BMS, A/CL-VM, AIR [3], AIR-DVLV [3], CAT, DC-VLV DCP-TVS, EEC, EFE, EFE-TVS, EGR, EGR-BldSOL[4], EGR-TVS, PCV, SRD-VLV, SVBrk, SVBrk-TVS TAC, TC-DVLV [2], TC-TVS [2], TCVS [2], VRV [3]	
2.8L V6	A/CL-BMS, A/CL-VM, ACV, AIR, CAT, CP-TVS, DC-VLV, DD-VLV [3], DVRV [4], DV-TVS [4], EEC, EGR, EGR/TC-TVS [2], EGR-TVS, MVS, PCV, PVBrk, SVBrk, SVBrK-TVS, TAC, TC-DVLV [2], TCVS [2]	
5.0L V8	A/CL-BMS, A/CL-VM, AIR [3], AIR-DVLV [3], CAT, ChVLV, DC-VLV [3], DD-VLV, EEC, EFE, EFE-TVS, EGR, EGR-BldSOL [3], EGR-TVS, PCV, PTVS, SVBrk [3], SVBrK-TVS [3], TAC, TC-DVLV [2], TC-TVS [2], TCVS [2]	
5.7L V8	A/CL-BMS, A/CL-VM, AIR, AIR-DVLV [3], CAT, ChVLV, DC-VLV [3], DD-VLV, EEC, EFE, EFE-TVS, EGR, EGR-BldSOL [3], EGR-TVS, PCV, SVBrk [1], SVBrk-TVS [1], TAC, TC-DVLV [2], TC-TVS [2], TCVS [2]	
Heavy Duty Emissions		
4.8L 6-Cyl.	A/CL-BMS, A/CL-VM, AIR, AIR-DVLV, DD-VLV, DV-TVS, TLA, TRC-VLV	
5.7L V8	A/CL-BMS, A/CL-VM, AIR, AIR-DVLV, ChVLV [3], EEC [3], EFE, EFE-TVS, PCV, SADV-TVS, SVBrk, SVBrK-TVS, TAC, TC-DVLV [2], TC-TVS [2], TCVS [2], TLA, TRC-SOL, VDVLV	
6.2L V8 (Diesel)	CD-REGVLV, EGR [3], EGR-SOL [3], EPR-SOL [3], EPR-VLV [3], VACP [3]	
7.4L V8	A/CL-BMS, A/CL-VM, AIR, AIR-DVLV, ChVLV, EEC [1] EFE, EFE-TVS, PCV, SADV-TVS, SVBrk, SVBrk-TVS, TAC, TLA, TRC-SOL	

Light Duty Emissions: Vehicles up to 8500 GVW. **Heavy Duty Emissions:** Vehicles over 8500 GVW.

ABAV – Air Bleed Actuator Valve
A/CL-BMS – Air Cleaner Bi-Metal Sensor
A/CL-VM – Air Cleaner Vacuum Motor
ACV – Air Control Valve
AIR – Air Injection Reactor
AIR-DVLV – AIR Diverter Valve
ATS – Air Temperature Sensor
CAT – Catalytic Converter
CD-REGVLV – Crankcase Depression Regulator Valve
ChVLV – Check Valve
CP-TVS – Canister Purge Thermal Vacuum Switch
CTS – Coolant Temperature Switch
DC-VLV – Deceleration Valve
DCM/C-VLV – Deceleration Mixture Control Valve
DCP-TVS – Distributor and Canister Purge Thermal Vacuum Switch
DD-VLV – Distributor Delay Valve
DVRV – Distributor Vacuum Regulator Valve
DV-TVS – Distributor Vacuum Thermal Vacuum Switch
EEC – Evaporative Emission Control
EFE – Early Fuel Evaporation
EFE-TVS – EFE Thermal Vacuum Switch
EGR – Exhaust Gas Recirculation
EGR-BldSOL – EGR Bleed Solenoid
EGR-BPTV – EGR Backpressure Transducer Valve
EGR-DVLV – EGR Delay Valve
EGR-RST – EGR Restrictor
EGR-SOL – EGR Solenoid
EGR/TC-TVS – EGR/Torque Converter Thermal Vacuum Switch
EGR-TVS – EGR Thermal Vacuum Switch
EPR-SOL – Exhaust Pressure Regulator Solenoid
EPR-VLV – Exhaust Pressure Regulator Valve
HIC – Hot Idle Compensator
IAC – Idle Air Control
IS – Idle Switch
MAP – Manifold Absolute Press. Sensor
MVS – Manifold Vacuum Switch
OXS – Oxygen Sensor
PAIR – Pulse Air Injection System
PCV – Positive Crankcase Ventilation
PTVS – Purge Thermal Vacuum Switch
PVBrk – Primary Vacuum Break
SADV-TVS – Spark Advance Thermal Vacuum Switch
SRD-VLV – Spark Retard Delay Valve
SVBrk – Secondary Vacuum Break
SVBrK-TVS – Secondary Vacuum Break Thermal Vacuum Switch
TAC – Thermostatic Air Cleaner
TC-DVLV – Torque Converter Delay Valve
TC-TVS – Torque Converter Thermal Vacuum Switch
TCVS – Torque Converter Vacuum Switch
TLA – Throttle Lever Actuator
TPS – Throttle Position Sensor
TRC-SOL – Throttle Return Control Solenoid
TRC-VLV – Throttle Return Control Valve
TVS – Thermo Vacuum Switch
VACP – Vacuum Pump
VCV – Vacuum Control Valve
VDVLV – Vacuum Delay Valve
VRV – Vacuum Regulator Valve
VSS – Vacuum Switch Solenoid
VSV – Vacuum Switching Valve
WOT-SW – Wide Open Throttle Switch

1985 Crankcase Ventilation

POSITIVE CRANKCASE VENTILATION SYSTEMS

All Models

DESCRIPTION

Crankcase ventilation systems are designed to prevent contaminating hydrocarbons from escaping to the atmosphere. This is accomplished by routing vapors from the crankcase through a vacuum-controlled ventilating valve (PCV Valve) into the intake manifold. In the intake manifold, the crankcase vapors mix with the air/fuel mixture and are burned in the combustion process.

OPERATION

Air is supplied to the crankcase ventilation system through a crankcase ventilating filter assembly, located in air cleaner housing or on rocker arm cover.

When engine is operating, fresh air enters crankcase ventilation system through the air cleaner and filter.

Air then flows into the rocker arm cover and valve compartment. It combines with blow-by gas and unburned air/fuel mixture and burns in combustion chamber. *See Fig. 1.*

Fig. 1: Typical Crankcase Ventilation System

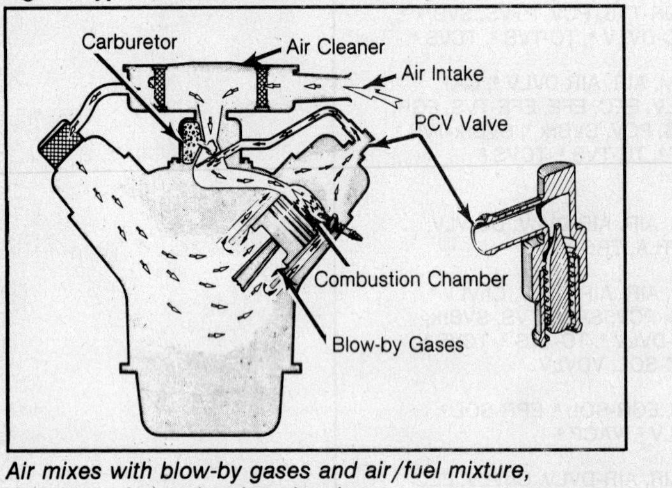

Air mixes with blow-by gases and air/fuel mixture, then burns in combustion chamber.

Ventilator valve is held closed by spring pressure when engine is not running. *See Fig. 2.* This prevents accumulation of hydrocarbon fumes from collecting in intake manifold, which could result in hard starting.

Fig. 2: Typical PCV Valve & Airflow

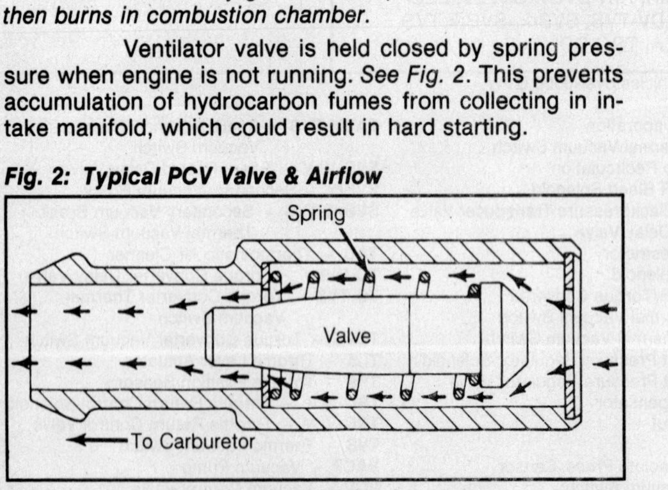

Air flows through valve when engine is running.

When engine is started, manifold vacuum pulls valve open against spring pressure. As long as there is engine vacuum, the valve floats, permitting crankcase fumes to enter intake manifold.

A baffle in rocker arm cover prevents oil from being drawn into intake manifold through ventilator valve.

If the engine backfires, the ventilator valve will close. This will prevent ignition of fumes in crankcase.

During certain engine operations, more blow-by is created than ventilator valve can handle. Excess blow-by is returned to air cleaner and carburetor through rocker arm cover and breather assembly. It is then burned in the combustion chamber.

A breather assembly acts as separator to keep oil from being drawn into air cleaner during this operation.

TESTING

ALL MODELS

To test crankcase ventilation system, start engine and allow it to reach normal operating temperature. Make sure engine is idling at normal curb idle, and perform following checks:

1) Remove PCV valve from its mounting. If valve is functioning properly, hissing noise will be heard as air passes through it. Strong vacuum should be felt when your finger is placed over valve inlet. While finger is over inlet, check for presence of vacuum leaks in hose line and at all connections.

2) Reinstall PCV valve, then remove crankcase air inlet hose at air cleaner.

3) Loosely hold piece of stiff paper over opening at end of inlet hose. Paper should be sucked against hose opening with noticeable force after sufficient time has elapsed for crankcase pressure to lower (usually about a minute). For final check, stop engine, remove PCV valve and shake it. Metallic clicking noise should be heard, indicating valve is free.

4) If system passes both engine running and stopped tests, it is functioning properly. No further tests are required. If it has failed either test, replace appropriate components and retest. If it does not pass on second try, clean system.

MAINTENANCE

Engine may idle slow or rough due to clogged ventilator valve or system. Therefore, never adjust carburetor idle without first checking valve and system.

If ventilator valve or system becomes clogged, all crankcase ventilation will stop, and serious engine damage could result.

Although following manufacturers' service procedures give specific intervals, it is recommended the crankcase ventilation system be checked more frequently if vehicle is operated under severe conditions (extreme dust, prolonged idling, trailer hauling or short trips in cold weather).

CHRYSLER CORP.

PCV Valve

On Light Duty Emission models (up to 8500 lbs. GVW), check PCV valve every 15,000 miles and replace every 30,000 miles. On Heavy Duty Emission models (over 8500 lbs. GVW), check PCV valve every 12,000 miles and replace it every 24,000 miles. Valve is located on rocker arm cover.

POSITIVE CRANKCASE VENTILATION SYSTEMS (Cont.)

Filter Element

On Light Duty Emission models, clean crankcase inlet air filter every 30,000 miles. On Heavy Duty Emission models, clean filter every 12,000 miles. Filter is located on rocker arm cover.

FORD

PCV Valve

On all models replace PCV valve every 30,000 miles. Valve is located on rocker arm cover.

Filter Element

Replace crankcase filter every 30,000 miles. Filter is located in air cleaner housing.

GENERAL MOTORS

PCV Valve

Check PCV valve every 15,000 miles and replace it every 30,000 miles on Light Duty Emission models (up to 8500 lbs. GVW). Check PCV valve every 12,000 miles and replace it every 24,000 miles on Heavy Duty Emission models (over 8500 lbs. GVW). Valve is located on rocker arm cover.

Filter Element

Replace filter element every 30,000 miles on Light Duty Emission models; every 24,000 miles on Heavy Duty Emission models. Filter is located in air cleaner housing.

JEEP

PCV Valve

Replace PCV valve every 30,000 miles. Valve is located on rocker arm cover of 4-cylinder, 6-cylinder and V6 models and on intake manifold of V8 models.

Filter Element

Clean filter element every 30,000 miles. Filter is located inside air cleaner of 4-cylinder, 6-cylinder and V6 models and in oil filler cap of V8 models.

1985 Fuel Evaporation Systems

CHRYSLER CORP.

DESCRIPTION

Evaporation control system prevents fuel tank and carburetor gasoline vapors from escaping into the atmosphere. The systems are dual canister types.

Fig. 1: Typical Dual Canister Mounting on Chrysler "D" & "W" Models

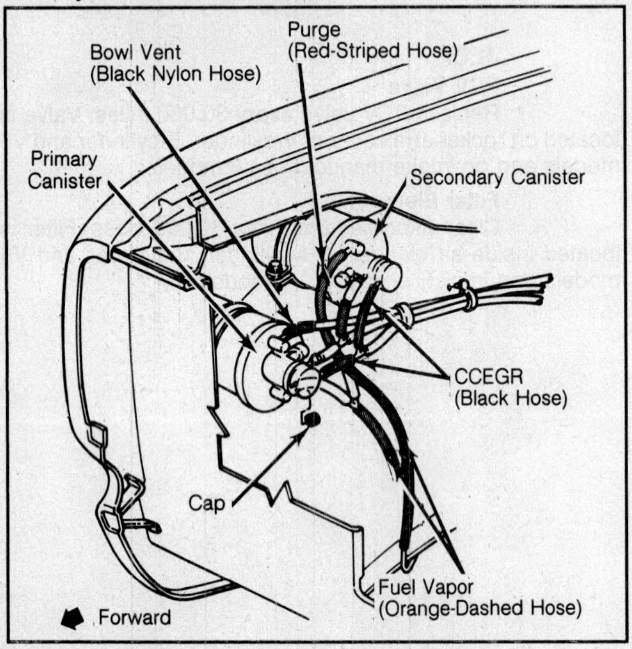

Canisters are mounted on right front fender.

OPERATION

When fuel evaporates in carburetor float chamber or fuel tank, vapors pass through vent hoses or tubes to the charcoal canister.

Fuel vapors are held on the activated charcoal surface until they are drawn into the intake manifold (when the engine is running). Vacuum port in carburetor base controls vapor flow to engine.

Fuel vapors from primary canister are purged through carburetor port. When distributor vacuum signal activates purge switch, vapors from secondary canister are purged through PCV hose to carburetor.

Damping canister is used on "H" and "K" models with 2-canister system. It cushions sudden releases of fuel vapors when purge control valve opens. Fuel vapors are held in canister and gradually released into intake manifold.

MAINTENANCE

There is no service required on the fuel evaporation control system, except replacement of the filter element in the charcoal canister. Replace filters every 18,000 miles on Heavy Duty Emission models (over 8500 lbs. GVW). On all other models replace filter every 30,000 miles.

Fig. 3: Typical Vapor Hose Routing for Dual Canister Chrysler "B" Models

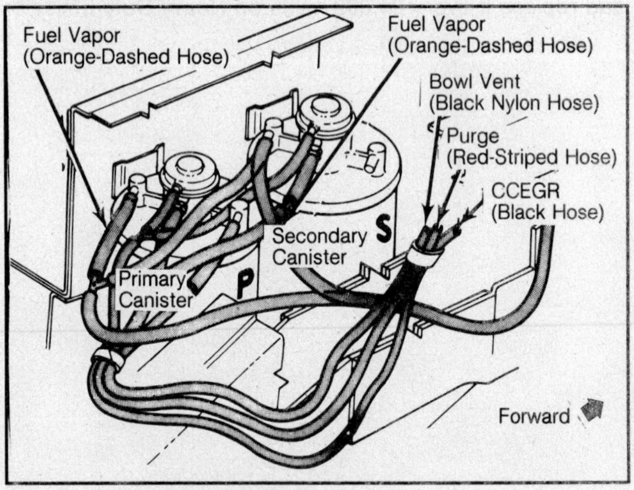

"H" & "K" models are similar.

Fig. 2: Typical Evaporation Control System Hose Routing for Chrysler "D" & "W" Models

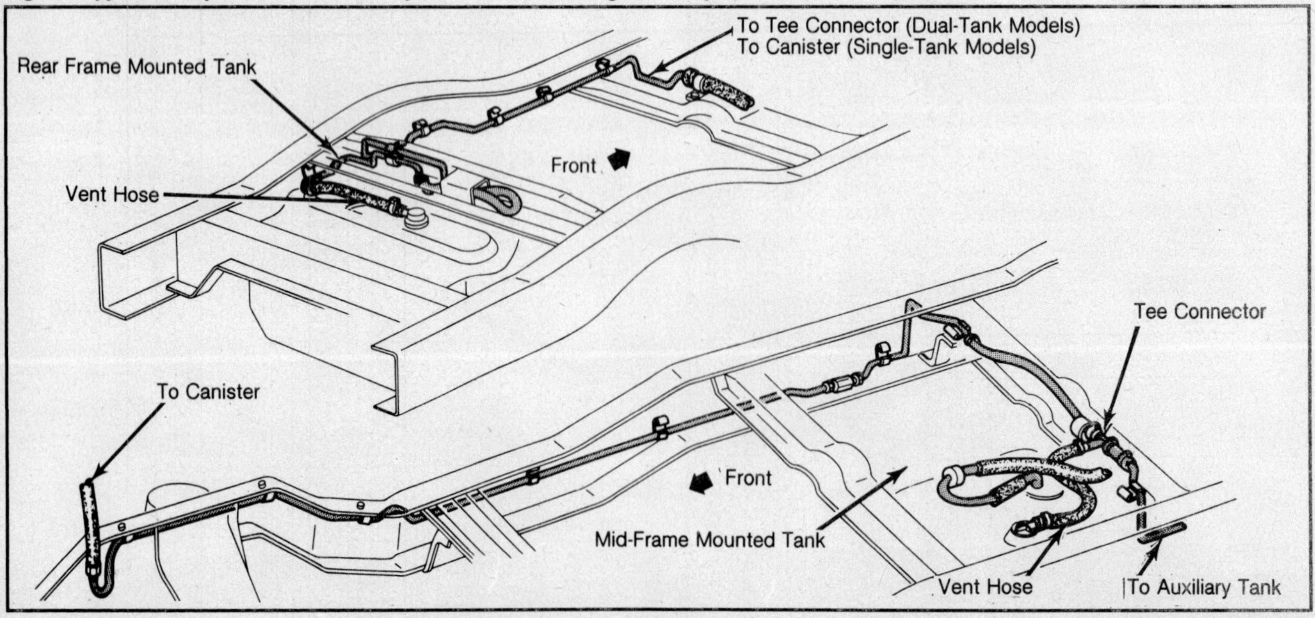

1985 Fuel Evaporation Systems

FORD

DESCRIPTION

All models are equipped with fuel evaporation emission control systems. This closed system is designed to limit amount of fuel vapor released to the atmosphere. The system consists of a special fuel filler cap, specially designed fuel tank, carbon-filled canister, orifice valve and necessary fuel vent vapor lines. All 6-cylinder models with dual fuel tanks and some V8 models use 2 carbon canisters.

FUEL FILLER CAP

Fuel filler cap has one-way vent. This prevents tank collapse, by allowing air to enter tank as fuel is consumed.

FUEL TANK

In most installations, fuel tank is constructed with dome in top. Fuel vapors rise and gather in this dome.

ORIFICE VALVE

On all vehicles, liquid fuel is prevented from entering vapor lines by restricted orifices. Orifices usually are a .050" (1.27 mm) orifice valve, located in emission control valve in fuel tank dome.

CARBON CANISTER

Carbon-filled canister acts as storage system for fuel vapors vented from fuel tank and carburetor. Outlet of canister is connected to carburetor bowl vent.

OPERATION

Fuel vapors, trapped in sealed fuel tank, are vented through orifice vapor separator assembly in top of tank.

Vapors then leave separator through a single vapor line, and continue to the carbon canister in engine compartment.

There, they are absorbed by carbon granules, until they are purged from canister by carburetor vacuum once engine is started.

MAINTENANCE

No regular replacement of components is required with this system. Periodically inspect components for proper functioning.

Fig. 1: Ford Evaporation Emission Control System (F150/250 Reg. Cab Shown, Others Similar)

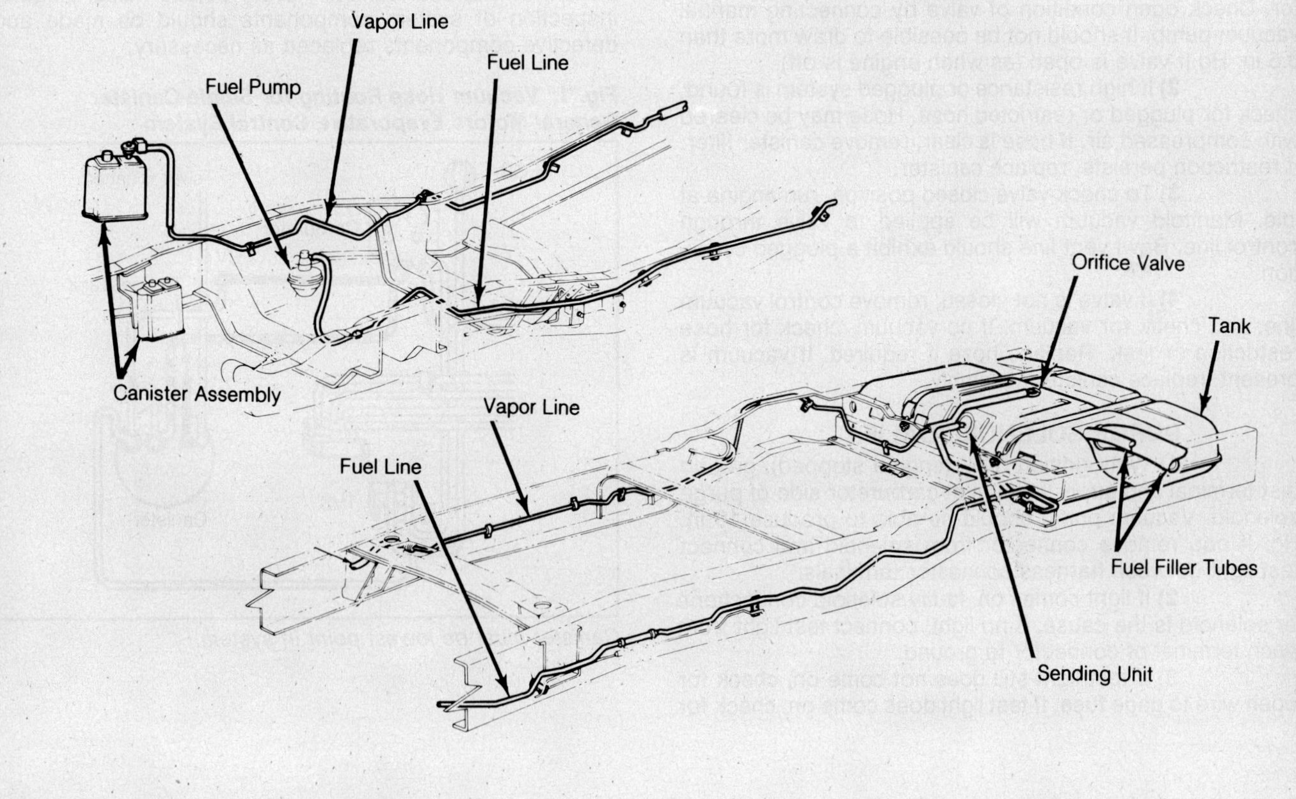

Canister must be at lowest point in system.

1985 Fuel Evaporation Systems

GENERAL MOTORS

DESCRIPTION

All Light and some Heavy Duty emissions models are equipped with an Evaporative Emission Control System (EECS), designed to prevent raw fuel vapors from escaping to the atmosphere. System consists of special fuel tank with expansion section; venting system which allows only vaporous fuel to be drawn into the system; pressure-vacuum relief valve in gas cap to control tank pressure; and vapor-storing charcoal canister.

OPERATION

During periods of engine operation, vapors are drawn through system vent lines and into intake manifold. When engine is off, fuel vapors are stored in charcoal of the vapor storage canister. Vapors are then drawn into intake manifold when engine is running again.

Canister purge solenoid is used on California models. It is controlled by the Electronic Control Module (ECM).

TESTING

BOWL VENT VALVE

1) Remove bowl vent vapor hose from carburetor. Check open condition of valve by connecting manual vacuum pump. It should not be possible to draw more than 0.5 in. Hg if valve is open (as when engine is off).

2) If high resistance or plugged system is found, check for plugged or restricted hose. Hose may be cleared with compressed air. If hose is clear, remove canister filter. If restriction persists, replace canister.

3) To check valve closed position, run engine at idle. Manifold vacuum will be applied to valve through control line. Bowl vent line should exhibit a plugged condition.

4) If valve is not closed, remove control vacuum line, and check for vacuum. If no vacuum, check for hose restriction or leak. Replace hose if required. If vacuum is present, replace canister assembly.

PURGE SOLENOID (CALIF.)

1) With ignition "ON" (engine stopped), ground test terminal and apply vacuum at carburetor side of purge solenoid. Vacuum pump should be able to produce 10 in. Hg. If not, remove connector from solenoid and connect test light between harness connector terminals.

2) If light comes on, faulty solenoid connections or solenoid is the cause. If no light, connect test light from each terminal of connector to ground.

3) If test light still does not come on, check for open wire to gage fuse. If test light does come on, check for grounded wire at ECM terminal "E" ("T" on Astro/Safari). If not grounded, check and/or replace ECM.

4) If requirements from step **1)** are met, check to see if solenoid passes vacuum when test terminal is ungrounded (solenoid de-energized). It should open and keep pump from building up vacuum. If there is no vacuum drop, disconnect solenoid.

5) If there is still no drop after disconnecting solenoid, replace solenoid. If vacuum does drop after disconnecting solenoid, check for open wire to ECM terminal "E" ("T" on Astro/Safari). If OK, check and/or replace ECM.

PURGE VALVE (ON CANISTER)

1) Remove purge valve control vacuum line. Check for vacuum at line with engine running at approximately 1500 RPM. If there is no vacuum present, check EGR system.

2) Apply external vacuum to valve. Vacuum should hold. If not, replace canister assembly. If vacuum holds, remove purge line, and check for vacuum. If no vacuum, check PCV system.

MAINTENANCE

No adjustments are required with this system. Check system and replace air inlet filter (if equipped) in bottom of charcoal canister, every 30,000 miles. Regular inspection of system components should be made and defective components replaced as necessary.

Fig. 1: Vacuum Hose Routing for Single-Canister General Motors Evaporative Control System

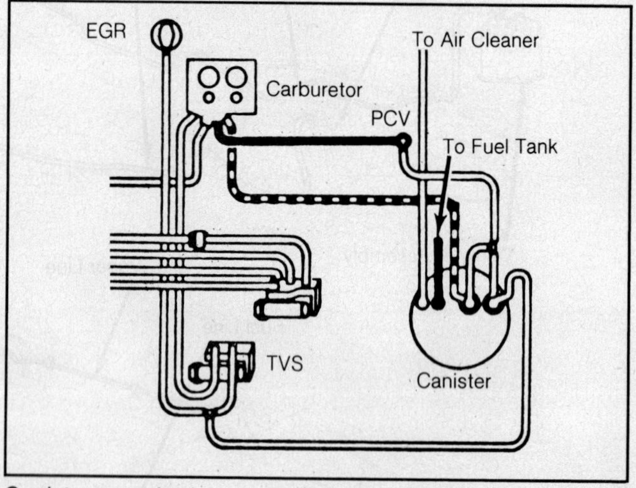

Canister must be lowest point in system.

1985 Fuel Evaporation Systems

JEEP

DESCRIPTION

Fuel evaporation control system is used on all models. It is designed to retain raw fuel vapors, which would normally escape to the atmosphere, transferring them to the intake manifold for burning. System consists of, special fuel tank, sealed gas cap, rollover check valve, charcoal canister, connecting lines and hoses.

OPERATION

During periods of non-operation, raw vapors from fuel tank and carburetor are channeled to charcoal canister, where they are stored. When engine is running, canister is purged of these vapors, which are then taken into intake manifold and burned.

Rollover valve prevents fuel flow from tank in the event of vehicle rollover.

ROLLOVER VALVE

Valve consists of a plunger and stainless steel ball. When valve is inverted, stainless steel ball pushes the plunger against its seat, blocking fuel flow through valve.

Fig. 1: Typical Charcoal Canister Connections

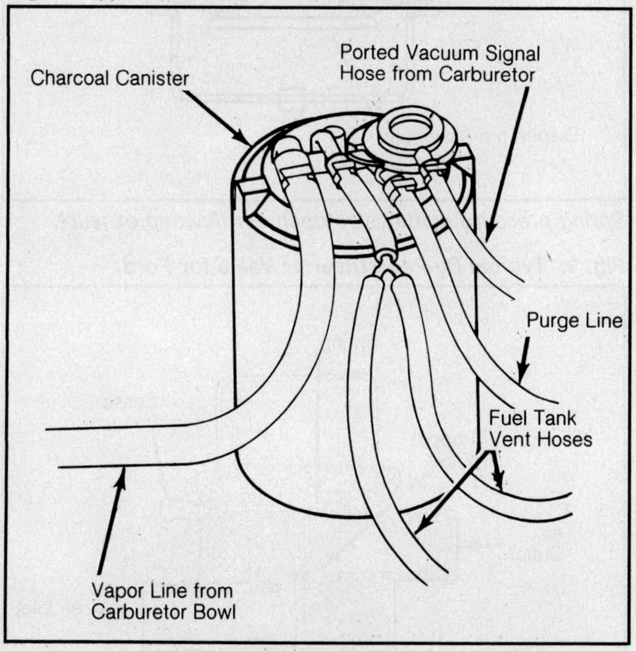

Vapors are stored in canister until engine is started.

CHARCOAL CANISTER

All models are equipped with a dual-purge type canister. Two inlets are provided: one for carburetor fuel bowl vapors and one for fuel tank vapors. The outlet is connected to intake manifold vacuum. 4th nipple (secondary purge) connects to the carburetor spark port.

When engine is running, manifold vacuum draws fresh air through inlet filter in bottom of canister and purges stored vapors. When ported vacuum reaches 12 in. Hg, secondary purge circuit is opened, and canister is purged at a much higher rate.

CARBURETOR BOWL VENT

Carburetor bowl vent used on all models provides an outlet for fuel vapors when engine is not running. When engine is running, fuel bowl is vented to inside of air cleaner. Bowl is automatically closed by mechanical link to throttle when engine is started.

MAINTENANCE

No adjustments are required with this system. Air inlet filter in bottom of charcoal canister should be replaced every 30,000 miles. Regular inspection of system components should be made and defective components replaced as necessary.

Fig. 2: Typical Jeep Evaporation Control System

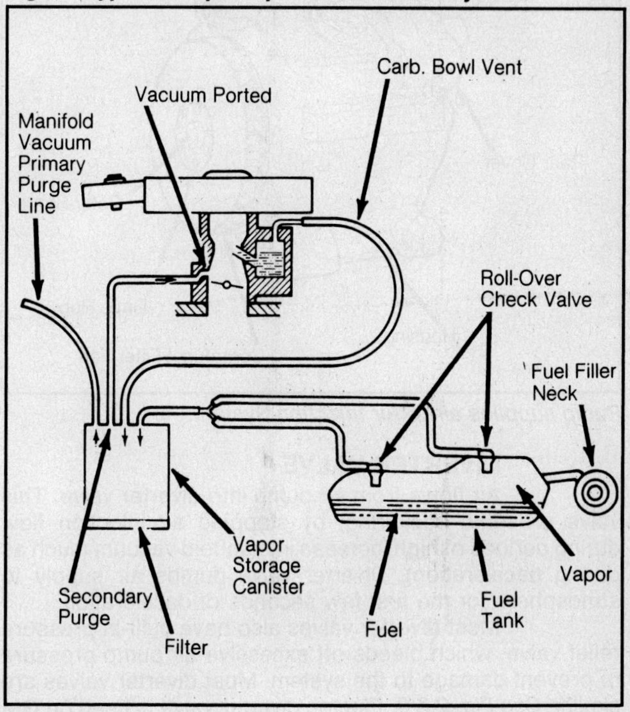

AIR INJECTION SYSTEMS – AIR PUMP TYPE

DESCRIPTION

Air injection systems, used in many applications (may vary according to engine and equipment), are designed to reduce carbon monoxide and hydrocarbon emissions. This is done by injecting fresh air at critical points in the exhaust manifold to burn those gases which passed through the combustion cycle.

System consists of an air pump with integral filter, diverter/by-pass valve, check valve(s), external or internal injection tubing and connecting hoses. Some Ford and all Chrysler models use additional valves, depending on applications. These valves are explained below.

OPERATION

AIR PUMP

The air pump uses an eccentric (off-center) vane to draw in fresh air, compress it, and force it on through the system. The pump is belt-driven. *See Fig. 1.*

Fig. 1: Typical Eccentric Vaned Air Injection Pump

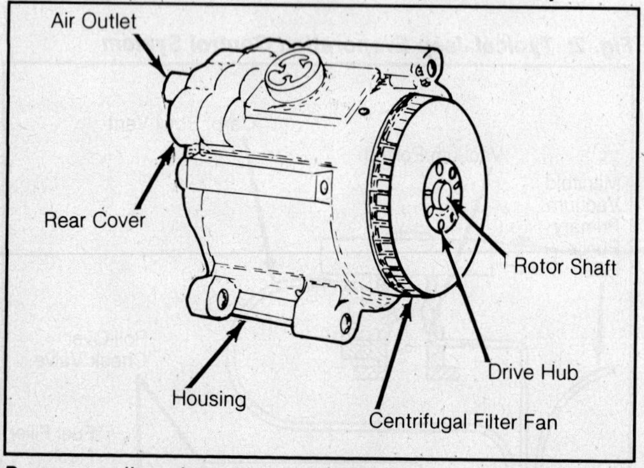

Pump supplies air to Air Injection System.

DIVERTER VALVE

Air flows from air pump into diverter valve. This valve prevents backfiring, by stopping air injection flow during periods of high increase in manifold vacuum (such as during deceleration). Diverter valve dumps air supply to atmosphere for the first few seconds of deceleration.

Most diverter valves also have built-in pressure relief valve, which bleeds off excessive air pump pressure to prevent damage to the system. Most diverter valves are similar. *See Fig. 2 & 3.* Electric diverter valve is used on GM and Jeep V6 California models and is controlled by the Electronic Control Module (ECM).

Ford Timed By-Pass Valve

This is a normally-open valve. During normal operation, vacuum is equalized on both sides of diaphragm. Spring pressure holds valve open, allowing fresh air to the exhaust.

On deceleration, manifold vacuum pulls diaphragm, and air is directed to the atmosphere. Small orifice in diaphragm will allow pressure to quickly equalize again. *See Fig. 3.*

Ford Normally-Closed By-Pass Valve

When no vacuum is applied, all air pump air is diverted to the atmosphere to protect the catalytic converter. When vacuum is received, air then passes to exhaust ports.

Fig. 2: Typical Diverter Valve for Chevrolet, Chrysler Corp. & GMC

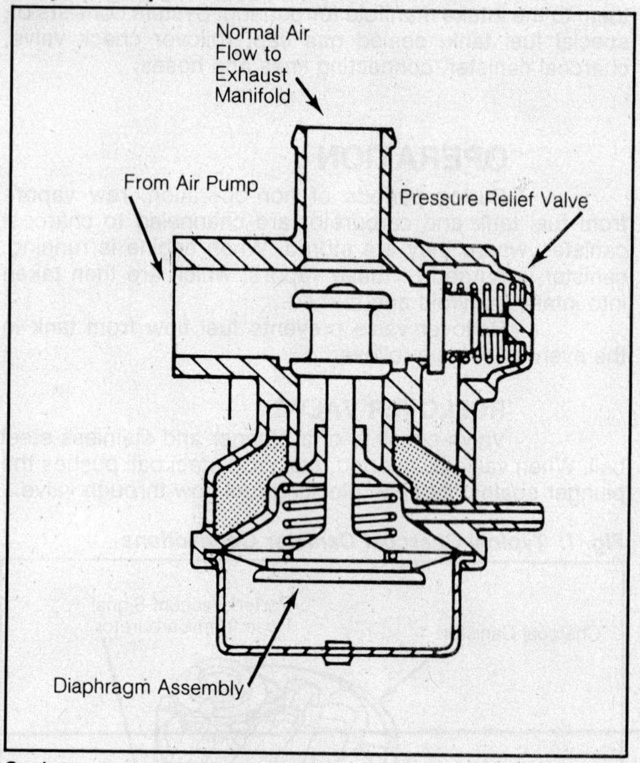

Spring pressure holds valve open; air flows to exhaust.

Fig. 3: Typical By-Pass Diverter Valve for Ford

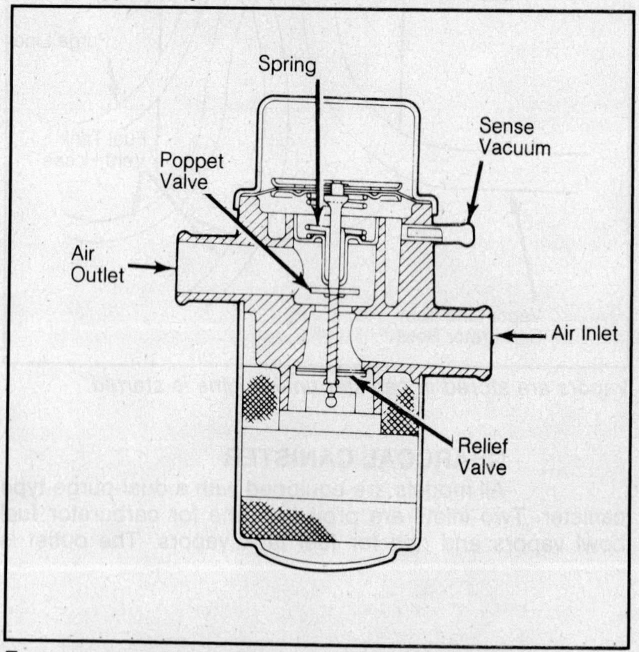

Zero vacuum pressure diverts air to atmosphere.

Ford Timed & Vented By-Pass Valve

Valve operation is similar to that of timed valve described earlier. When vacuum signal is 3 in. Hg or more, valve will continuously vent air pump air to the atmosphere. *See Fig. 5.*

AIR INJECTION SYSTEMS – AIR PUMP TYPE (Cont.)

Fig. 4: Three Different Types of Air Injection Systems Used on V8 Engines

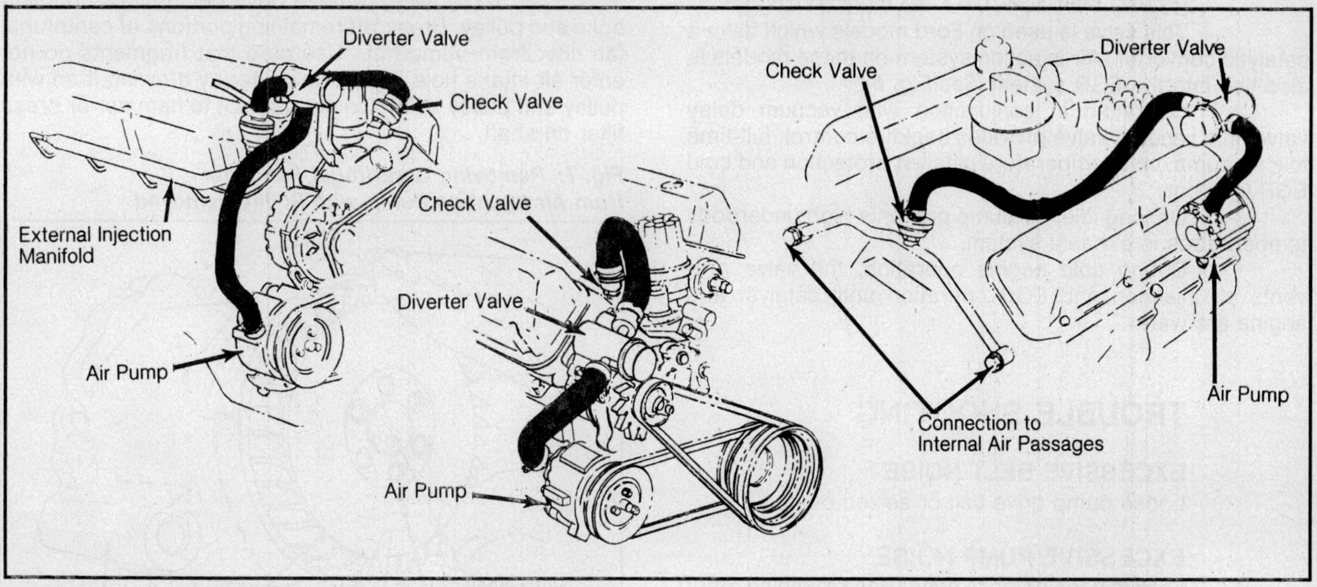

Air injection systems may vary according to equipment.

Fig. 5: Ford Timed & Vented By-Pass Valve

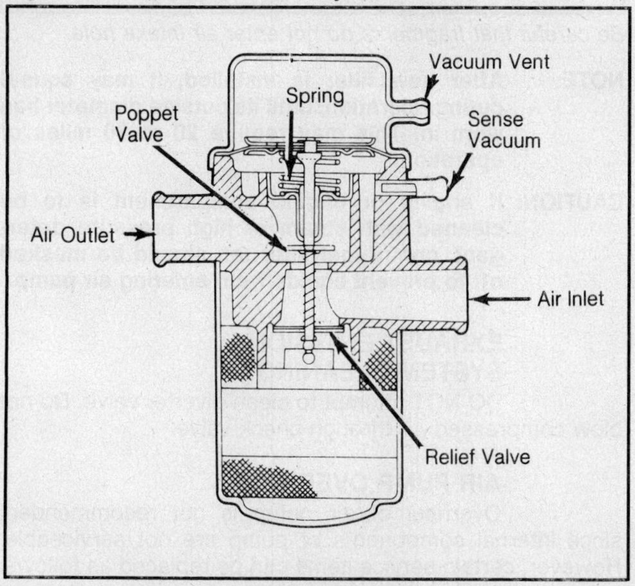

Apply 3 in. Hg or more to operate valve.

AIR SWITCHING VALVE (CHRYSLER CORP. ONLY)

This valve is used to switch injection air from exhaust ports to a point downstream after engine warm-up. Bleed hole in switching valve allows small portion of air to be injected at exhaust ports at all times to assist in reducing emissions.

POWER HEAT CONTROL VALVE (CHRYSLER CORP. ONLY)

This vacuum-operated valve is located between right exhaust manifold and exhaust pipe. It directs majority of exhaust gas flow through left side exhaust manifold, until engine temperature reaches pre-determined point. After that temperature is reached, gas flows through both manifolds.

INJECTION MANIFOLD

Injection manifold in many applications is an external tubing system, mounted to exhaust manifold with air delivery ports for each exhaust port. It is through this manifold that air pump air reaches the exhaust system. Some applications have internal air injection system, consisting of specially drilled passages in intake manifold, which carry air pump air to exhaust ports. External tubing is eliminated.

CHECK VALVE

Check valve is a 1-way flow valve. It prevents exhaust manifold air from backing up through the system and reaching air pump. Check valve will be found either in tubing, leading to injection manifold or as an integral part of manifold.

Fig. 6: Schematic of Typical Ford Air Injection System

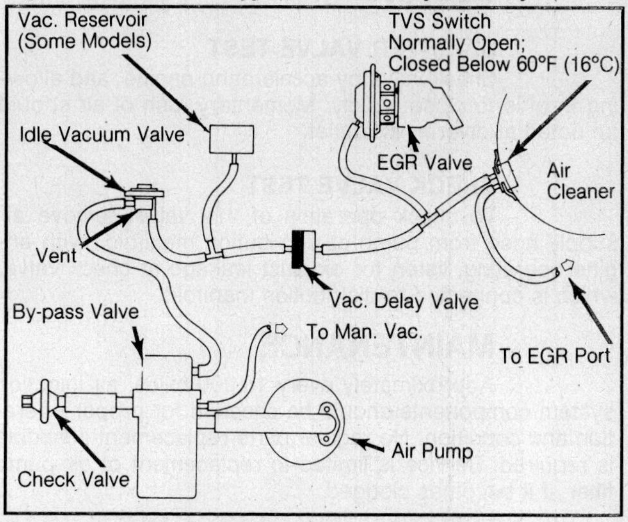

Notice system includes idle vaccum valve.

AIR INJECTION SYSTEMS – AIR PUMP TYPE (Cont.)

IDLE VACUUM VALVE (FORD ONLY W/CAT. CONVERTER)

This valve is used on Ford models which have a catalytic converter. Air injection system on these models is also tied into the EGR system. *See Fig. 6*.

Operating in conjunction with vacuum delay valve, idle vacuum valve provides backfire control, full-time idle air dump, cold temperature catalyst protection and cold EGR lock-out.

On long idle, air dump prevents high underbody temperatures in exhaust system.

During cold engine operation, the valve prevents air injection and EGR operation until catalyst and engine are warm.

TROUBLE SHOOTING

EXCESSIVE BELT NOISE

Loose pump drive belt or seized pump.

EXCESSIVE PUMP NOISE

Leak in hose or loose hose. Hose touching other engine parts. Diverter valve or by-pass valve failure. Check for valve failure, pump mounting loose, pump or impeller damaged.

NO AIR SUPPLY

Loose drive belt, leak in hose or hose fitting. Diverter valve or by-pass valve failure. Check for valve failure or pump failure.

EXHAUST BACKFIRE

Incorrect engine tune-up, engine vacuum leaks, faulty diverter valve or check valve.

NOTE: Proper operation of Air Injection System is dependent upon proper engine tune-up. See individual vehicle models for specifications and procedures.

TESTING

DIVERTER VALVE TEST

Check valve by accelerating engine, and allowing throttle to close rapidly. Momentary rush of air should be noted at diverter air outlet.

CHECK VALVE TEST

To check operation of this valve, remove air supply hose from pump at distribution manifold. With engine operating, listen for exhaust leakage at check valve, which is connected to distribution manifold.

MAINTENANCE

Approximately every 15,000 miles, air injection system components should be checked for proper operation and condition. No regular parts replacement schedule is required. Service is limited to replacement of air pump filter, if it becomes clogged.

CENTRIFUGAL FAN FILTER

To replace, remove drive belt, pulley mounting bolts and pulley. Break off remaining portions of centrifugal fan filter from pump hub. Use care that fragments do not enter air intake hole. Install new filter by drawing it on with pulley and pulley bolts. Do not attempt to hammer or press filter on shaft.

Fig. 7: Removing Centrifugal Fan Filter from Air Injection Pump with Pulley Removed

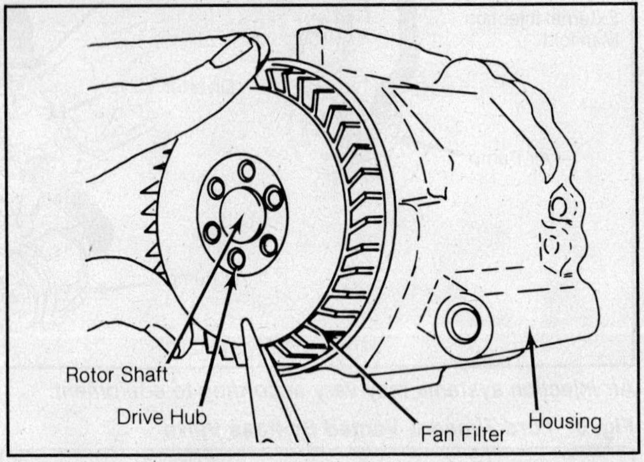

Be careful that fragments do not enter air intake hole.

NOTE: After new filter is installed, it may squeal during operation, until its outside diameter has worn in. This may require 20 to 30 miles of operation.

CAUTION: If engine or engine compartment is to be cleaned with steam or high pressure detergent, centrifugal filter fan should be masked off to prevent liquids from entering air pump.

EXHAUST EMISSION SYSTEM CLEANING

DO NOT attempt to clean diverter valve. Do not blow compressed air through check valve.

AIR PUMP OVERHAUL

Overhaul of air pump is not recommended, since internal components of pump are not serviceable. However, certain service items can be replaced as follows:

Pump Exhaust Tube Replacement

Remove by placing tube in vise, or use pliers to pull tube with twisting motion. Insert new tube into hole, and tap in using block of wood to protect tube. Approximately 7/8" (22 mm) of tube should extend above cover.

1985 Exhaust Emission Systems

CATALYTIC CONVERTERS

All Light Duty Emission Models

NOTE: Light Duty Emission vehicles are those vehicles whose Gross Vehicle Weight (GVW) does not exceed 8500 lbs.

DESCRIPTION & OPERATION

Catalytic converter(s) is located in exhaust system in front of muffler. It is a stainless steel, muffler shaped, device that reduces exhaust emissions by changing toxic gases into less harmful ones.

There are three types of catalytic converters: Conventional Oxidation Converter (COC), Three-Way Converter (TWC) and Light Off Converter (LOC). Catalytic converters may be one of 2 designs: honeycomb-type block or small alumina beads.

Even though converters contain base material of alumina, COC is impregnated with platinum/palladium and TWC contains material coated with platinum/rhodium. While converters reduce hyrocarbons (HC) and carbon monoxide (CO), TWC also reduces oxides of nitrogen (NOx).

NOTE: Use ONLY unleaded fuel in vehicles using catalytic converters. If leaded fuel is used, the Tetra Eythel Lead will coat the palladium, platinum and rhodium, rendering these catalysts inoperative. If this happens, the converter must be replaced.

On some models, TWC is used in conjunction with COC (fresh air is introduced between converters to aid in oxidation of gases), this is called a dual-bed converter. *See Fig. 1.*

Fig. 1: Cross Section of Dual-Bed Catalytic Converter

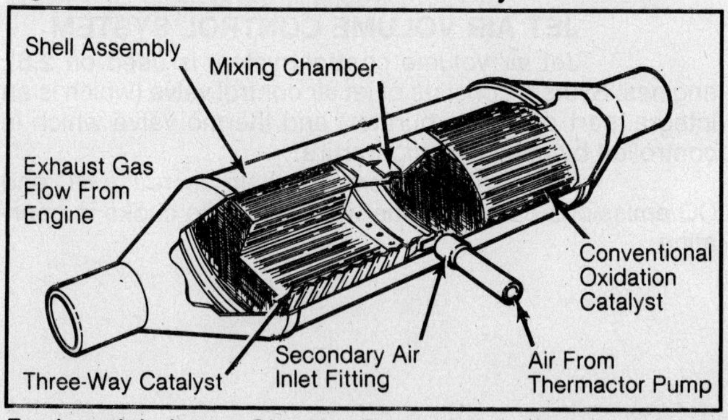

Ford model shown; Chrysler Corp., GM & Jeep models are similar.

On some models, first converter in exhaust system is a LOC. This is a single-bed converter designed to control exhaust emissions during engine warm-up.

HEAT SHIELDS

Combustion reaction, which is furthered by converter, releases additional heat. Temperature in catalytic converter can reach 1600°F (871°C) under normal conditions. Special heat shields are used to protect underbody and components from this extreme heat.

Fig. 2: Cutaway View of Bead-Type Catalytic Converter

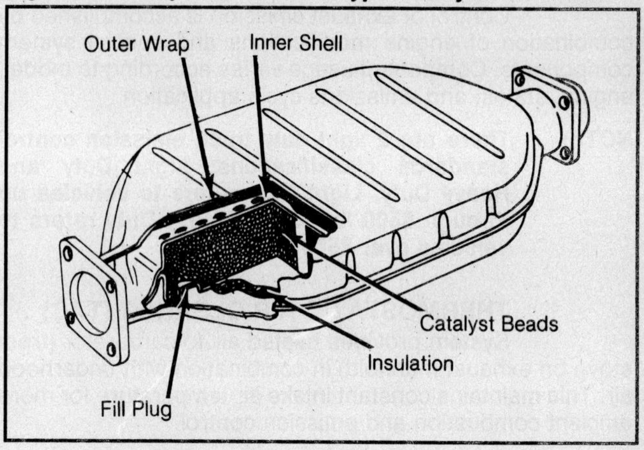

SERVICE

MAINTENANCE

There is no scheduled maintenance required for catalytic converters. If vehicle is raised for other service, it is advisable to check the general condition of the catalytic converter(s).

BOTTOM COVER REPLACEMENT (GENERAL MOTORS ONLY)

1) Using hand or power tool, remove bottom cover by making shallow, close cut to bottom outside edge.

Fig. 3: Removal of Converter Bottom Cover (General Motors Vehicles Only)

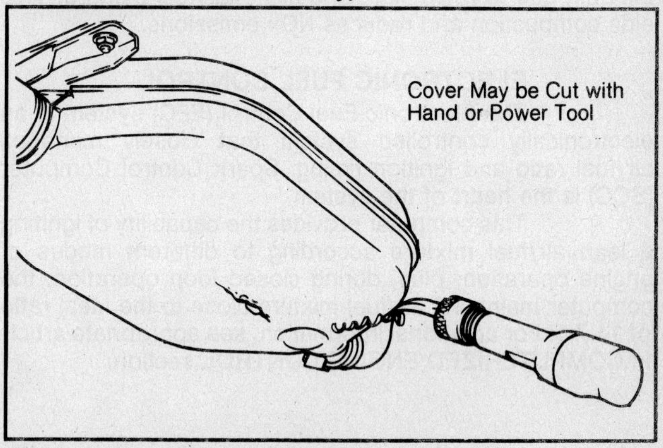

Make shallow cut; avoid damage to inner shell.

2) Remove insulation and check inner shell for damage. If damage is found, entire converter must be replaced.

3) If no damage is found, position new insulation into replacement cover. Apply Sealer (8998245) around edge of cover, using extra sealer at front and rear pipe openings.

4) Install replacement cover on converter, and position retaining channel along edges. Complete the installation by attaching clamps (provided with replacement cover) to both ends of converter.

1985 Exhaust Emission Systems

CHRYSLER CORP. SYSTEMS

DESCRIPTION

Control of exhaust emission is accomplished by combination of engine modifications and special system components. Component usage varies according to model, engine, states, and emissions cycle application.

NOTE: There are 2 light duty truck emission control standards classifications: Light Duty and Heavy Duty. Light Duty refers to vehicles up through 8500 lbs. GVW; Heavy Duty refers to vehicles over 8500 lbs. GVW.

THERMOSTATIC AIR CLEANER (TAC)

System provides heated air to carburetor (from stove on exhaust manifold) in combination with underhood air. This maintains constant intake air temperature for more efficient combustion and emission control.

AIR INJECTION

System consists of air pump, diverter valve, check valves and various air distribution lines. Injection of fresh air adjacent to exhaust valves creates an afterburn effect, which results in lower emission levels.

ASPIRATOR AIR SYSTEM

System is used to reduce carbon monoxide and hydrocarbon emissions by drawing fresh air from air cleaner, and allowing it to mix with exhaust gases. System consists of aspirator air valve and connecting tubes to air cleaner and exhaust manifold.

EXHAUST GAS RECIRCULATION (EGR)

System allows a predetermined amount of hot exhaust gas to recirculate and dilute air/fuel mixture. This aids combustion and reduces NOx emissions.

ELECTRONIC FUEL CONTROL

The Electronic Fuel Control (EFC) system is an electronically controlled system that closely manages air/fuel ratio and ignition timing. Spark Control Computer (SCC) is the heart of the system.

This computer provides the capability of igniting a lean air/fuel mixture according to different modes of engine operation; plus, during closed loop operation, the computer maintains air/fuel mixture close to the ideal ratio of 14.7:1. For additional information, see appropriate article in COMPUTERIZED ENGINE CONTROL section.

ELECTRIC ASSIST CHOKE

System is designed to give faster choke openings at temperatures above 60°F (16°C) and slower choke openings below 60°F (16°C).

CATALYTIC CONVERTER

Converter brings about combustion-type reaction to further consume unburned elements in engine exhaust. Converter is located in exhaust system ahead of muffler. Vehicles equipped with catalytic converters must use unleaded fuel only.

POSITIVE CRANKCASE VENTILATION (PCV)

System is used on all vehicles to eliminate fumes and vapors from crankcase. It does so by directing them back through combustion chamber to be burned.

EVAPORATION CONTROL SYSTEM

Dual canister evaporation control system is used on all vehicles. System routes fuel vapors from fuel tank through filter canisters to engine for burning. This closed system prevents vapors from venting to the atmosphere.

PULSE AIR FEEDER SYSTEM (2.6L)

Pulse air feeder system supplies secondary air into exhaust system between front and rear catalytic converters. This promotes oxidation of exhaust emissions in the rear catalytic comverter.

This system consists of main reed valve and sub reed valve. Main reed valve is controlled by diaphragm which is activated by pressure pulses from within the crankcase. Sub reed valve is activated by pulsation in exhaust system between front and rear converters.

JET AIR VOLUME CONTROL SYSTEM

Jet air volume control system is used on 2.6L engines. System consists of jet air control valve (which is an integral part of the carburetor) and thermo valve which is controlled by coolant temperarure.

Purpose of system is to help decrease HC and CO emissions during engine warm-up while choke is operating.

CHRYSLER CORP. EXHAUST GAS RECIRCULATION

DESCRIPTION

Exhaust Gas Recirculation (EGR) allows a predetermined amount of hot exhaust gas to recirculate in intake manifold. This dilutes incoming air/fuel mixture.

This diluting of air/fuel mixture reduces peak flame temperature during combustion, thereby reducing emissions of oxides of nitrogen (NOx).

OPERATION

Ported vacuum control provides signals for EGR operation on 2.2L engine. The 2.6L engine utilizes carburetor vacuum controlled dual EGR control valve in addition to mechanically-linked sub-EGR control valve. Ventrui vacuum control is used for EGR operation on 6-cylinder and V8 engines.

PORTED VACUUM CONTROL SYSTEM

2.2L Engine

As throttle blade opens, slot type port in carburetor throttle body is exposed to an increasing percentage of manifold vacuum. This port is connected through an external nipple directly to EGR.

Flow rate is dependent on manifold vacuum, throttle position and exhaust gas back-pressure.

Fig. 1: 2.2L Ported Vacuum Control EGR System

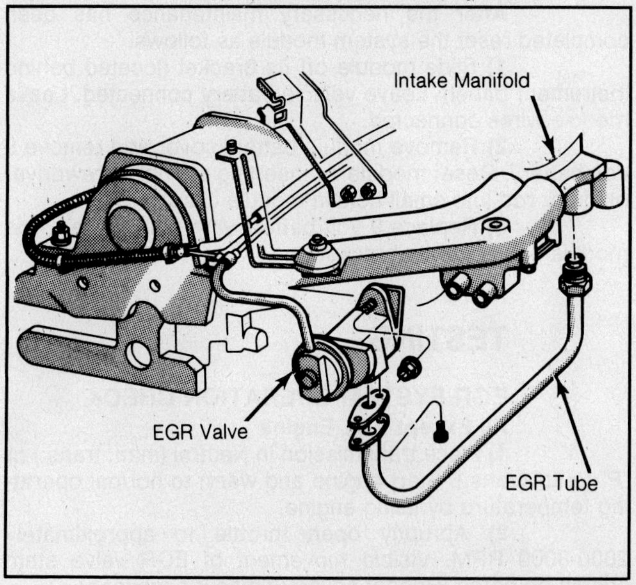

DUAL EGR SYSTEM CONTROL VALVE

2.6L Engine

Dual EGR system has primary and secondary valves which respond to different carburetor vacuums in response to throttle openings. EGR operation is suspended at idle and wide open throttle.

Primary valve controls EGR flow at relatively small throttle opening angles. Secondary control valve allows recirculation of exhaust gas into intake mixture at larger throttle opening angles.

Vacuum applied to dual EGR control valve is controlled by thermo valve. Sub-EGR valve is directly opened and closed with motion of throttle valve through mechanical linkage.

Fig. 2: Sectional View of Dual EGR Control Valve

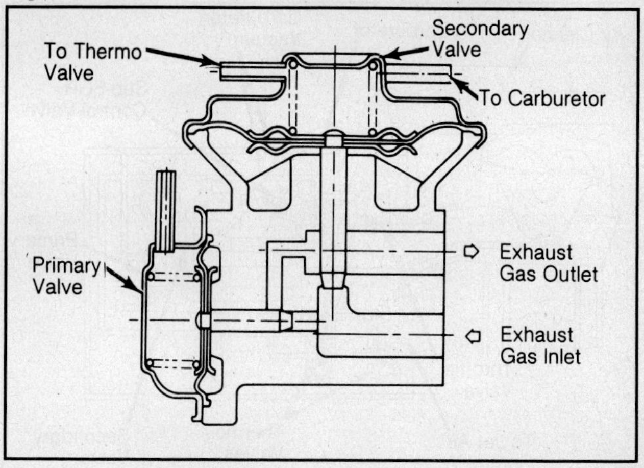

Two thermo valves sense coolant temperature at intake manifold and prevent operation of dual EGR valve below preset temperature of thermo valve.

Fig. 3: Sectional View of Sub-EGR Control Valve

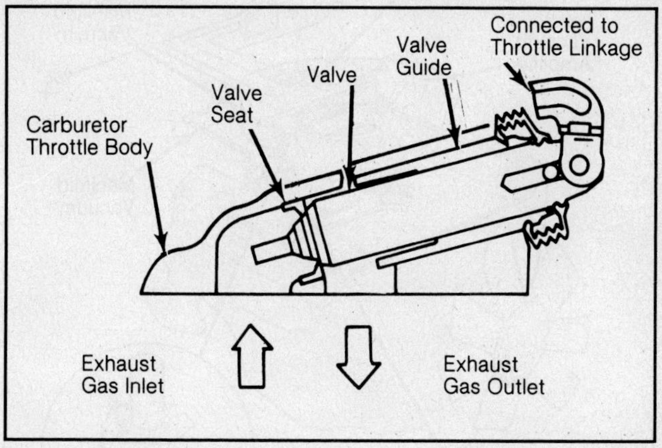

VENTURI VACUUM CONTROL SYSTEM

6-Cyl. and V8 Engines

Vacuum is tapped at throat of carburetor venturi or air flow sensor to provide control vacuum to vacuum amplifier. This low amplitude vacuum signal is increased in amplifier to a level which will operate EGR valve.

Dump diaphragm compares venturi and manifold vacuum to prevent EGR operation at wide open throttle. EGR operation is determined primarily by venturi signal, but is also effected by intake manifold vacuum and exhaust gas pressure.

COOLANT VACUUM SWITCH COLD CLOSED VALVE (CVSCC)

CVSCC valve is used with EGR system to delay EGR operation until engine warm-up is achieved. Valve location and opening temperature varies according to vehicle model and engine type.

On models with CVSCC valve in radiator tank, opening temperature is 59°F (15°C). On models with valve in thermostat housing, opening temperature is 108-115°F (42-52°C).

CHRYSLER CORP. EXHAUST GAS RECIRCULATION (Cont.)

Fig. 4: 2.6L EGR System

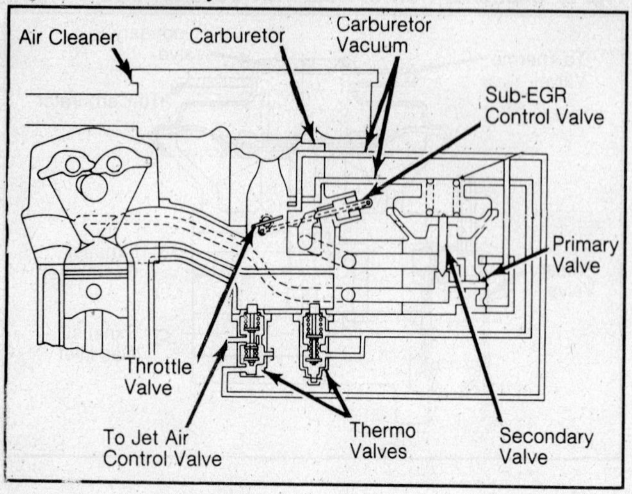

Fig. 5: V8 EGR System

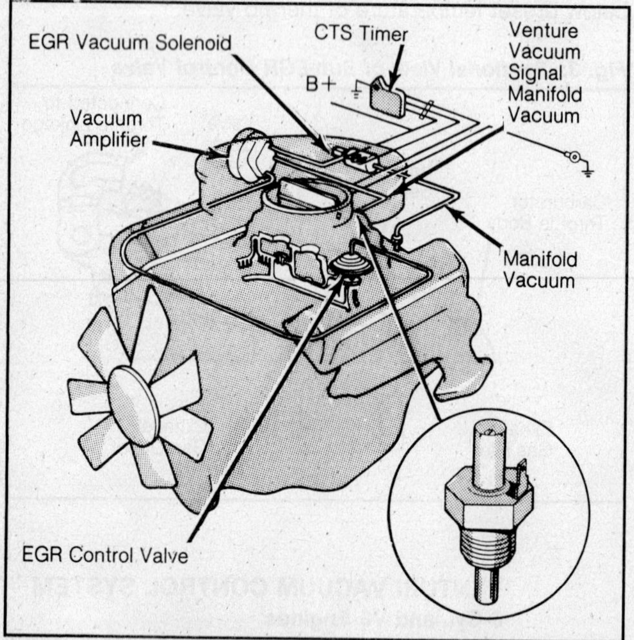

CTS is circled in illustration.

CHARGE TEMPERATURE SWITCH (CTS)

Charge Temperature Switch (CTS) is installed in intake manifold No. 6 branch runner on six-cylinder engines and No. 8 runner on V8 engines.

When air/fuel mixture temperature is below 60°F (16°C), switch closes. This prevents EGR timer and EGR valve operation. When air/fuel temperature is above 60°F (16°C), switch opens. This again allows EGR timer and EGR valve to operate.

EGR MAINTENANCE REMINDER SYSTEM

The purpose of this system is a reminder that the emission maintenance must be performed as soon as possible. It is not intended to indicate a warning.

CAUTION: There is no test procedure for this system, any attempt to test it will result in damage to the system components.

Fig. 6: Typical CVSCC Valve & Charge Temperature Switch

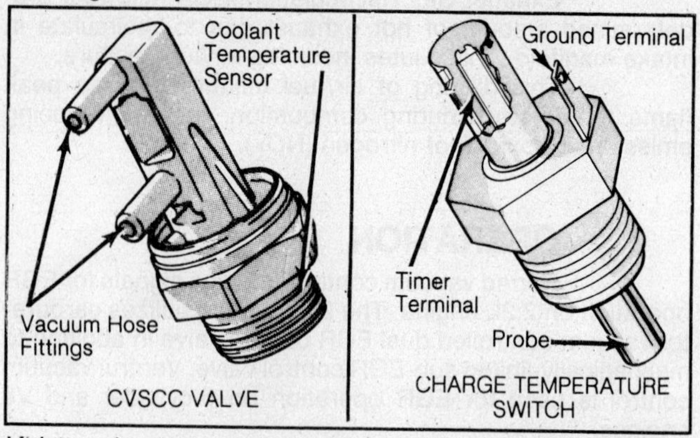

Valve and switch are both activated by engine temperature.

Heavy Duty Vehicles

Instrument panel lamp will come on when the first 12,000 miles (19,000 km) has been reached, and every subsequent 12,000 miles (19,000 km) thereafter.

Light Duty Vehicles

Instrument panel lamp will come on when the first 52,224 miles (84,046 km) has been reached, and every subsequent 52,224 miles (84,046 km) thereafter.

Reset Procedure

After the necessary maintenance has been completed reset the system module as follows.

1) Slide module off its bracket (located behind instrument panel). Leave vehicle battery connected. Leave module wires connected.

2) Remove module battery cover and remove 9 volt battery. Reset module by inserting a small screwdriver blade or rod into small hole in module case.

3) Replace 9 volt battery with a new one. Slide module back onto its bracket.

TESTING

EGR SYSTEM OPERATION CHECK

All Except 2.6L Engine

1) Place transmission in Neutral (man. trans.) or "P" (auto. trans.). Start engine and warm to normal operating temperature by idling engine.

2) Abruptly open throttle to approximately 2000-3000 RPM. Visible movement of EGR valve stem should be noted. Repeat several times if necessary.

3) Attach hand vacuum pump to EGR valve with engine at idle. Apply at least 5 in. Hg of vacuum and engine should run rough or stall.

4) Attach vacuum gauge to EGR hose and open throttle quickly several times. Fluctuation of several in. Hg should be noted.

2.6L Engine

1) Check vacuum hose condition, routing and installation. Start cold engine and run at idle. Increase engine speed to 2500 RPM. Secondary EGR valve should not operate. If secondary EGR valve operates, replace thermo valve.

2) Warm engine to at least 150°F (66°C). Accelerate engine to 2500 RPM. Secondary EGR valve should operate. If it does not, inspect EGR valve or thermo valve and replace as necessary.

CHRYSLER CORP. EXHAUST GAS RECIRCULATION (Cont.)

3) Disconnect Green striped hose from nipple on carburetor. Connect vacuum pump to hose. Pull sub-EGR valve by hand and apply 6 in. Hg vacuum.

4) If engine idling speed becomes unstable, secondary valve is operating properly. If no change, EGR valve or thermo valve is not operating properly.

5) Disconnect vacuum pump. Reconnect Green striped hose to carburetor. Disconnect Yellow striped hose. Apply 6 in. Hg vacuum with hand pump.

6) If engine idling speed becomes unstable, primary valve is operating properly. If on change, EGR valve or thermo valve is not operating properly.

CVSCC TEST

1) Remove CVSCC valve from vehicle. Place it in ice bath to bring temperature of coolant sensing portion to below 40°F (4°C).

2) Attach hand vacuum pump with gauge to CVSCC nipple corresponding to Blue stripe hose on V8 engines or Yellow stripe hose on 4-cylinder engines.

3) Apply vacuum of 10 in. Hg. Observe gauge for 1 minute. There should be no more than 1 in. Hg drop in vacuum within this time. If so, replace CVSCC valve.

EGR DELAY SYSTEM TEST

1) If equipped with Delay System, stop engine, then restart. Immediately open throttle to approximately 1000 RPM, and watch EGR valve stem for movement. *See Fig. 7.*

2) If it moves during first 30 seconds after starting, EGR time delay system is defective.

3) Check hose connections to time delay solenoid valve. If okay, detach electrical plug from solenoid valve. Energize valve by grounding either terminal and connecting other terminal to positive battery post.

4) If EGR valve stem moves on this test, solenoid valve is defective and must be replaced.

5) If EGR valve stem did not move, EGR timer control should be replaced. If this does not correct the problem, check wiring for proper connections.

TROUBLE SHOOTING

EGR VALVE STEM DOES NOT MOVE ON SYSTEM TEST

1) Check for correct hose connections. Leak check to confirm all hoses are in good condition.

2) Check EGR valve for ruptured diaphragm or frozen valve stem. Connect external vacuum source of 10 in. Hg or greater to valve diaphragm. If no valve movement occurs, replace valve.

3) If valve opens 1/8" (3 mm), pinch off supply hose to check for diaphragm leakage. Valve should remain open 30 seconds or longer. If leakage occurs, replace valve.

EGR VALVE STEM DOES NOT MOVE ON TEST; OPERATES NORMALLY WITH EXTERNAL VACUUM APPLIED

1) Follow this procedure to check system for defective CVSCC valve or CTS:

- On CVSCC systems, by-pass CVSCC valve and connect vacuum amplifier directly to EGR valve. If EGR valve operates normally, replace CVSCC valve.
- On CTS systems, by-pass EGR solenoid and connect vacuum amplifier directly to EGR valve. If EGR valve operates normally, reconnect EGR solenoid hoses, and remove wire from timer terminal of CTS. If EGR valve operates within 90 seconds, replace CTS.

2) In Venturi Vacuum Control System, remove venturi vacuum hose from carburetor nipple. With engine at idle, apply 2 in. Hg vacuum to hose. Engine speed should drop 150 RPM or more, and EGR valve stem should move 1/8" (3 mm) or more. If this does not occur, replace vacuum control valve.

3) If vacuum control amplifier operated normally in previous test, plugged vacuum tap to carburetor is indicated. Use carburetor solvent to remove deposits from passage, and clear with light air pressure.

NOTE: **Do not use drills or wires to clear carburetor control passages for either control system. Calibration of precision orifices could be altered, resulting in unsatisfactory vehicle operation.**

ROUGH IDLE, SLOW IDLE, OR STALL ON RETURN TO IDLE

1) Disconnect hose from EGR valve and plug hose. Recheck idle. If satisfactory, replace vacuum control amplifier.

2) If vacuum hose removal does not correct problem, remove EGR valve and inspect to ensure poppet is seated. Clean poppet seat, or replace if poppet does not seat correctly.

POOR COLD DRIVEABILITY, ROUGH IDLE OR STALLS ON RETURN TO IDLE

CVSCC valve or EGR control valve could be leaking. Check by performing leak test, and replace valves as necessary.

WEAK PERFORMANCE AT WIDE OPEN THROTTLE

Disconnect hose from EGR valve and plug hose. Road test vehicle, if performance is restored, replace vacuum control amplifier.

Fig. 7: Vacuum-Actuated EGR Valve

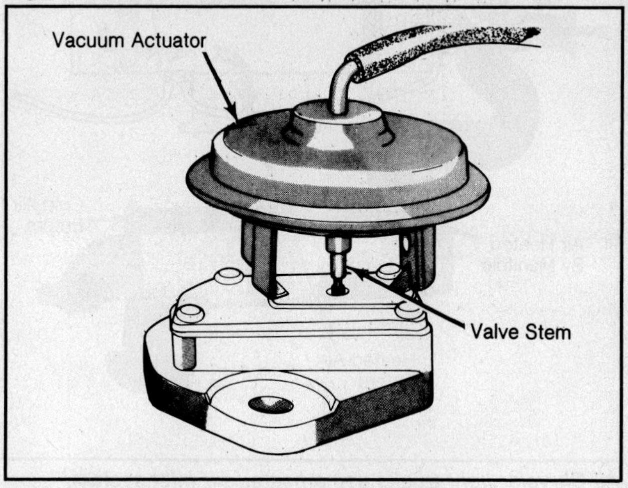

Watch for EGR valve stem movement during tests.

CHRYSLER CORP. THERMOSTATIC AIR CLEANER

DESCRIPTION

All Chrysler Light Duty Truck models use a heated air inlet system, as part of the air cleaner. System controls temperature, permitting carburetor to be calibrated leaner to control hydrocarbon (HC) emissions and improve warm-up characteristics.

System consists of an air cleaner assembly, temperature sensor, air control valve, vacuum diaphragm, duct system and shroud on exhaust manifold.

OPERATION

When ambient air temperature is less than 50°F (10°C), carburetor intake air flows through shroud, into flexible connector, through vacuum diaphragm and into carburetor.

When temperature rises to operating temperature, vacuum diaphragm shuts off air coming from shroud, and allows fresh air to enter carburetor. When temperature is between minimum and maximum, air will flow through both circuits.

TESTING

1) Ensure that all vacuum hoses, flexible duct hose and air cleaner duct are in good condition. With engine cold, heat control door in air cleaner snorkel should be up, in heat "ON" position.

2) With engine running at normal operating temperature, door should be in down, or heat "OFF" position.

3) Turn off engine and allow it to cool to 50°F (10°C). Remove air cleaner. Using external vacuum source, apply 20 in. Hg (15 in. Hg on 2.6L) vacuum to temperature sensor. Door should be in up position. If not, check vacuum diaphragm for proper operation.

Fig. 1: Chrysler Corp. Thermostatic Air Cleaner

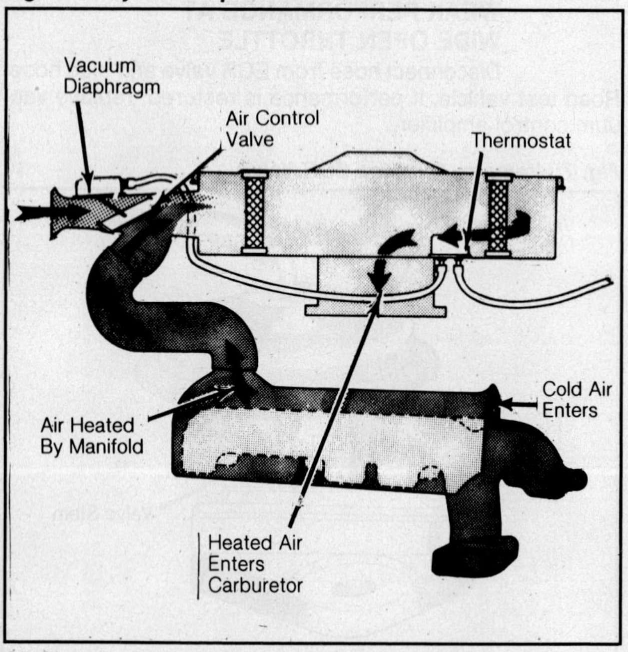

All Chrysler light trucks use a heated air inlet system.

4) Apply 20 in. Hg vacuum to diaphragm. Diaphragm should not bleed down more than 10 in. Hg, in 5 minutes. Door should not lift off bottom at less than 5 in. Hg, and should be in full up position at no more than 8.5 in. Hg. On 2.6L engine, test vacuum motor by applying 10 in. Hg. Air control valve should be in up position. If not, replace air cleaner body assembly.

5) If vacuum diaphragm does not operate properly, replace it and repeat steps **1)** and **2)**. If diaphragm works correctly, but proper temperature is not maintained, replace temperature sensor and repeat temperature checks.

Fig. 2: Heated Air System for 2.2L & 2.6L

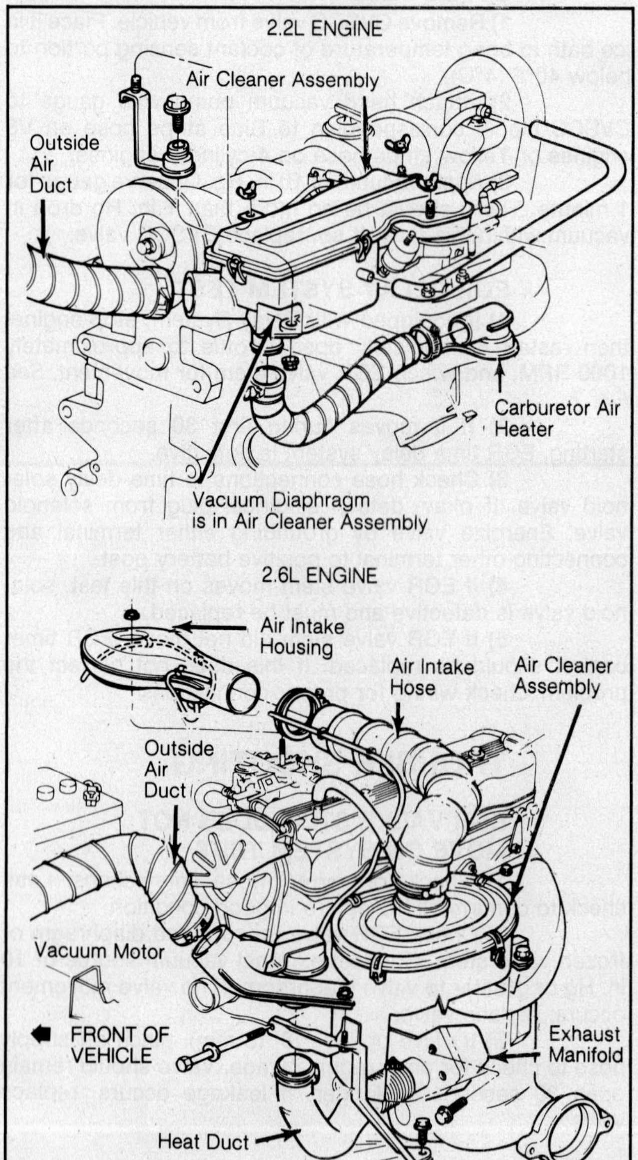

1985 Exhaust Emission Systems

CHRYSLER CORP. ASPIRATOR AIR SYSTEM

DESCRIPTION

Aspirator air system consists of an aspirator valve and an aspirator tube assembly. Aspirator valve uses exhaust pressure pulsation to draw air into exhaust system, reducing carbon monoxide (CO) and hydrocarbon (HC) emissions.

Tube assembly connects aspirator valve to air cleaner at one end, and exhaust manifold at the other end.

Fig. 1: Chrysler Corp. Aspirator Valve Air Flow

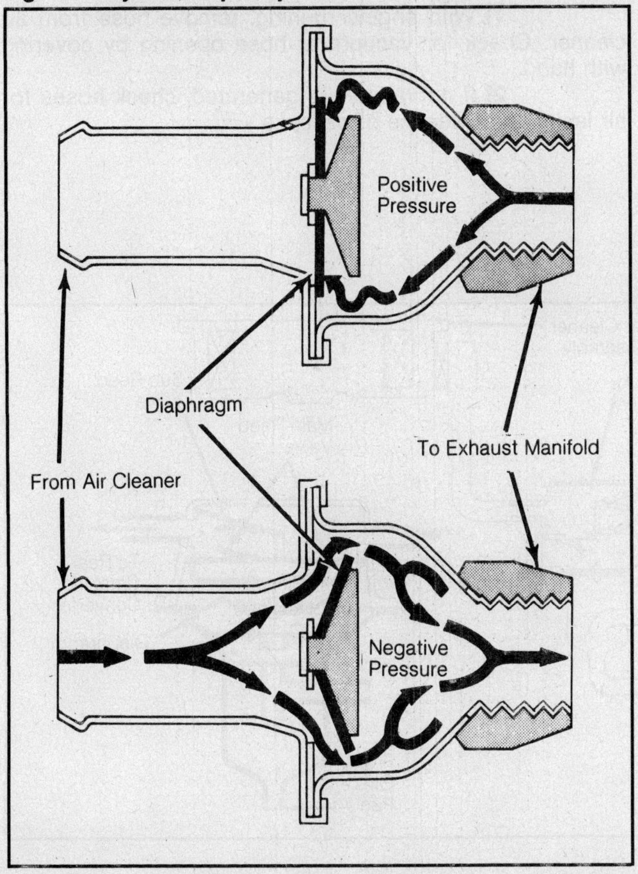

Aspirator is used when air injection pump is not necessary.

OPERATION

Aspirator valve draws fresh air from "clean" side of air cleaner, past a 1-way, spring-loaded rubber diaphragm. Diaphragm opens to allow fresh air to mix with exhaust gases during negative pressure (vacuum) pulses, which occur at exhaust ports and manifold passages.

If pressure is positive, diaphragm closes and no exhaust gas is allowed to flow past valve into "clean" side of air cleaner.

Aspirator valve works best at idle and slightly off-idle, when negative pulses are at maximum. At higher engine speeds, valve remains closed.

TESTING

Aspirator valve is not repairable. If valve fails, it must be replaced. Check all connections for proper assembly. If leakage is noted at any joints, repair before testing valve.

To test aspirator valve, disconnect hose from aspirator inlet. With engine idling in Neutral, vacuum exhaust pulses should be felt at aspirator inlet. If hot exhaust gas is escaping from inlet, valve is defective and must be replaced.

Fig. 2: Chrysler Corp. Aspirator Air System Assembly

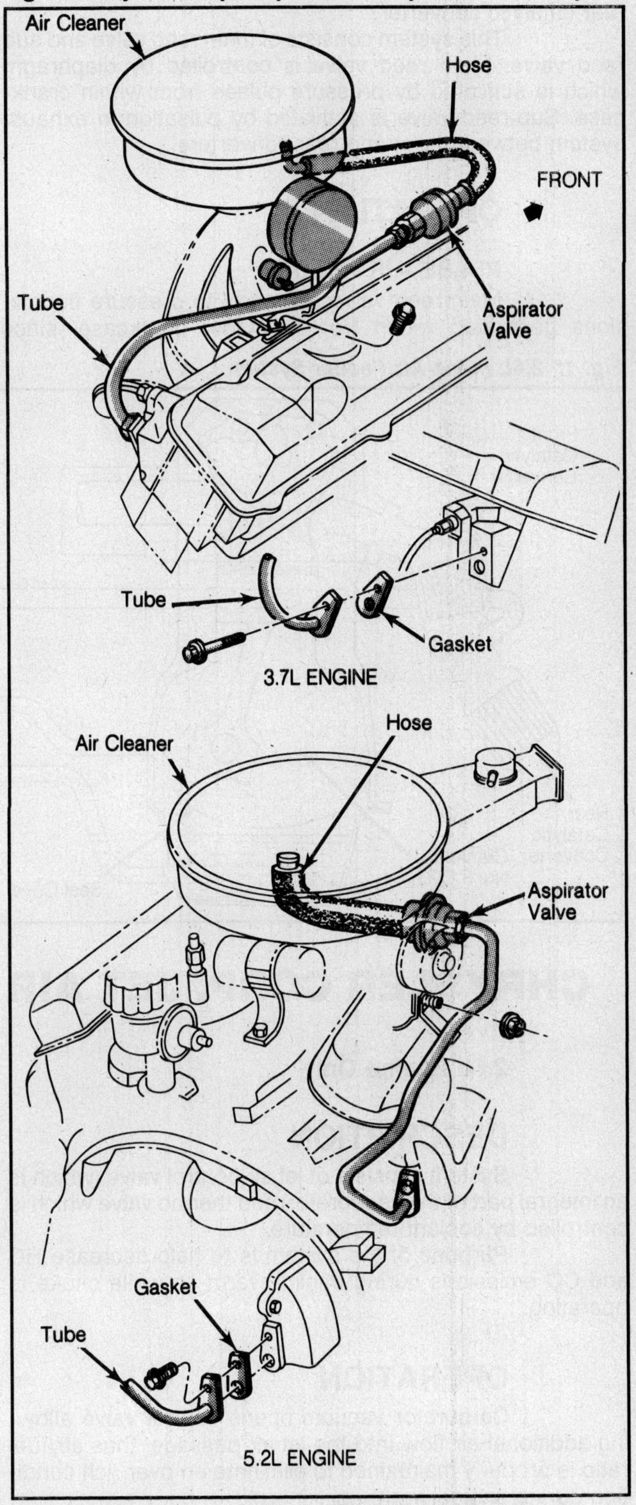

Valve draws fresh air from "clean" side of air cleaner.

CHRYSLER CORP. PULSE AIR FEEDER SYSTEM

2.6L Engine Only

DESCRIPTION

Pulse air feeder system supplies secondary air into exhaust system between front and rear catalytic converters. This promotes oxidation of exhaust emissions in rear catalytic converter.

This system consists of main reed valve and sub reed valve. Main reed valve is controlled by diaphragm which is activated by pressure pulses from within crankcase. Sub-reed valve is activated by pulsation in exhaust system between front and rear converters.

OPERATION

PULSE AIR FEEDER

Main-reed valve responds to pressure fluctuations generated within No. 3 cylinder crankcase, since crankcase is sealed by seal cover. This cover has a small hole for discharging oil and any blow-by gases.

Sub-reed valve is actuated by exhaust vacuum generated from pulsation in exhaust system between front and rear catalytic converters.

TESTING

PULSE AIR FEEDER

1) With engine running, remove hose from air cleaner. Check for vacuum at hose opening by covering with hand.

2) If no vacuum is generated, check hoses for air leaks and evidence of oil leaks.

Fig. 1: 2.6L Pulse Air Feeder System

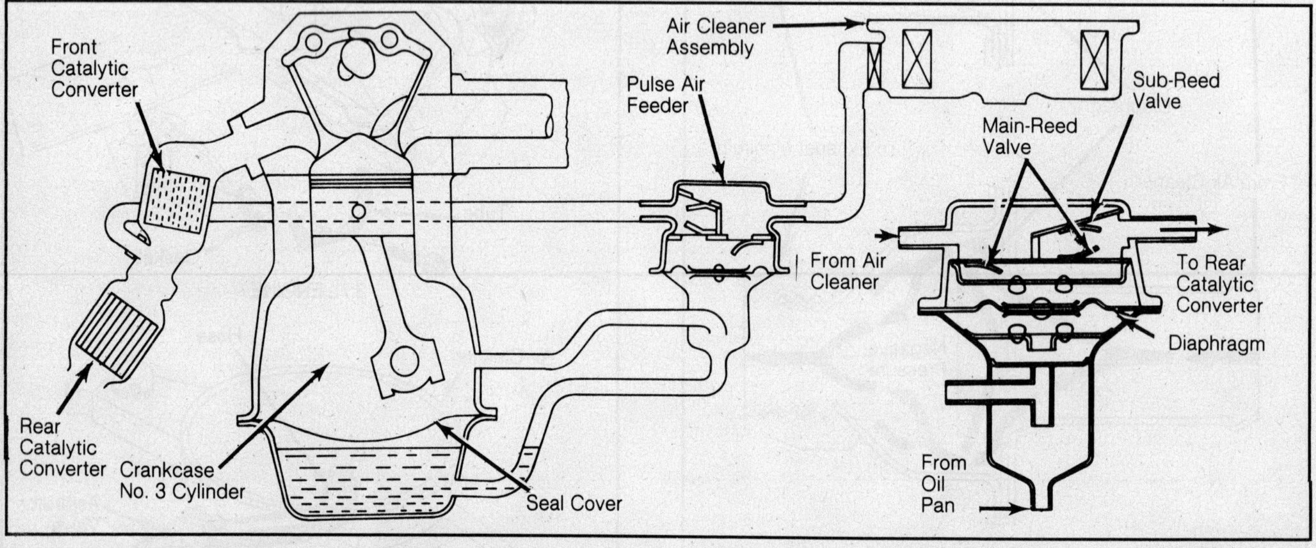

CHRYSLER CORP. JET AIR VOLUME CONTROL SYSTEM

2.6L Engine Only

DESCRIPTION

System consists of jet air control valve (which is an integral part of the cagburetor) and thermo valve which is controlled by coolant temperature.

Purpose of the system is to help decrease HC and CO emissions during engine warm-up while choke is operating.

OPERATION

Carburetor vacuum opens control valve allowing additional air flow into the jet air passage, thus air/fuel ratio is properly maintained to eliminate an over rich condition during engine warm-up.

Function of thermo valve is to stop operation of the jet air control valve when coolant temperture is below or above pre-set value. Thermo valve also works in conjunction with and as part of the EGR system.

Fig. 1: Jet Air Volume Control System

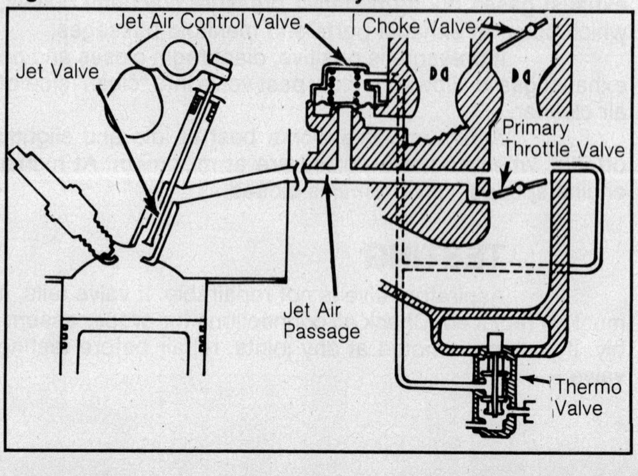

CHRYSLER CORP. ELECTRIC ASSIST CHOKE

DESCRIPTION

All Light Duty Emission models are equipped with an electric assist choke system (except 2.6L). This system helps to control hydrocarbon (HC) and carbon monoxide (CO) emissions and to shorten warm-up time.

Electric assist choke system consists of an electric heating element, bimetal spring, thermostatic choke coil and connecting linkage.

OPERATION

Choke thermostatic coil spring reacts to engine temperature. However, electric heating element (located next to bi-metal spring inside choke well) assists engine heat during both summer and winter operations to shorten choke "on-time."

This single-stage electric assist choke is designed to give rapid choke opening at temperatures above 60°F (16°C), and slower choke opening below this temperature.

Wire from choke heater is connected to electrical control switch. Above 60°F (16°C), control switch energizes choke heater.

Since heater control switch is mounted on engine, some cold weather operation may energize choke heater. This could occur after choke has opened without benefit of electric heat. No adverse reaction will occur.

TESTING

CONTROL SWITCH TEST

1) Before starting test, check test light by connecting it to battery terminals. Note light intensity.

2) Before starting engine, detach ignition harness electrical connector from heater control switch.

3) Connect test light to load (choke) terminal of control switch and to ground.

4) Start engine and allow it to reach normal operating temperature.

5) Apply 12 volts to ignition harness terminal of control switch. If test light does not light or have original intensity, replace defective control switch.

CHOKE HEATING ELEMENT TEST

1) Disconnect only "B+" wire at control switch. Connect ohmmeter lead to choke housing or choke retainer screw.

2) Touch other meter lead to bare portion of choke wire connector at switch (not "B+" terminal). Meter reading of 4 to 12 ohms indicates heater is electrically functional. If circuit is open or shorted, install new choke assembly.

NOTE: **Never immerse heater element in any fluid. Electrical short to choke heater will also short circuit ignition system.**

Fig. 1: Typical Electric Assist Choke System

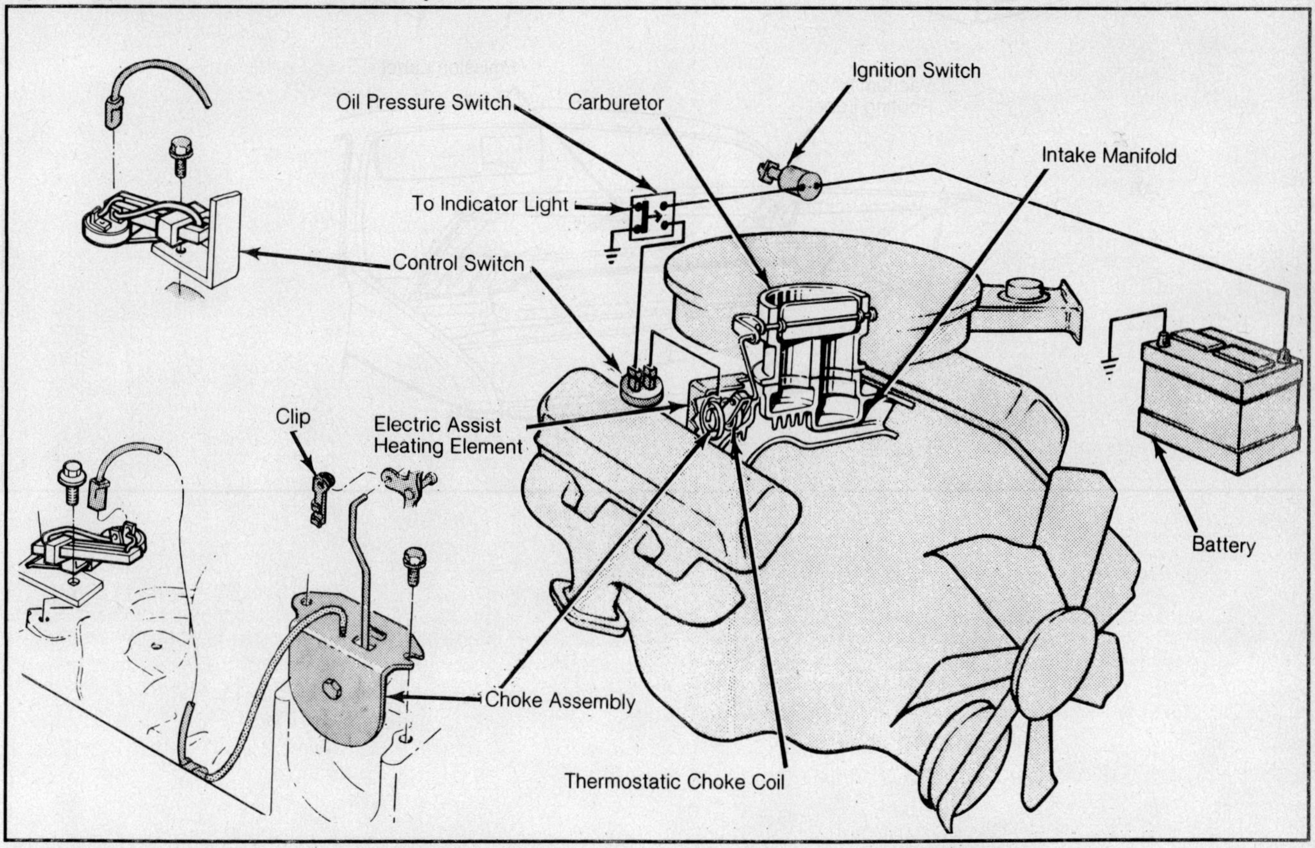

All Light Duty Emission models are equipped with an electric assist choke system (except 2.6L).

CHRYSLER CORP. VACUUM DIAGRAMS

LABEL LOCATION

All vehicles are equipped with vacuum hose routing label and emission label which are located in engine compartment. These labels are permantly attached and connot be removed without destroying them. All hoses must be connected and routed as shown on label.

Label Locations

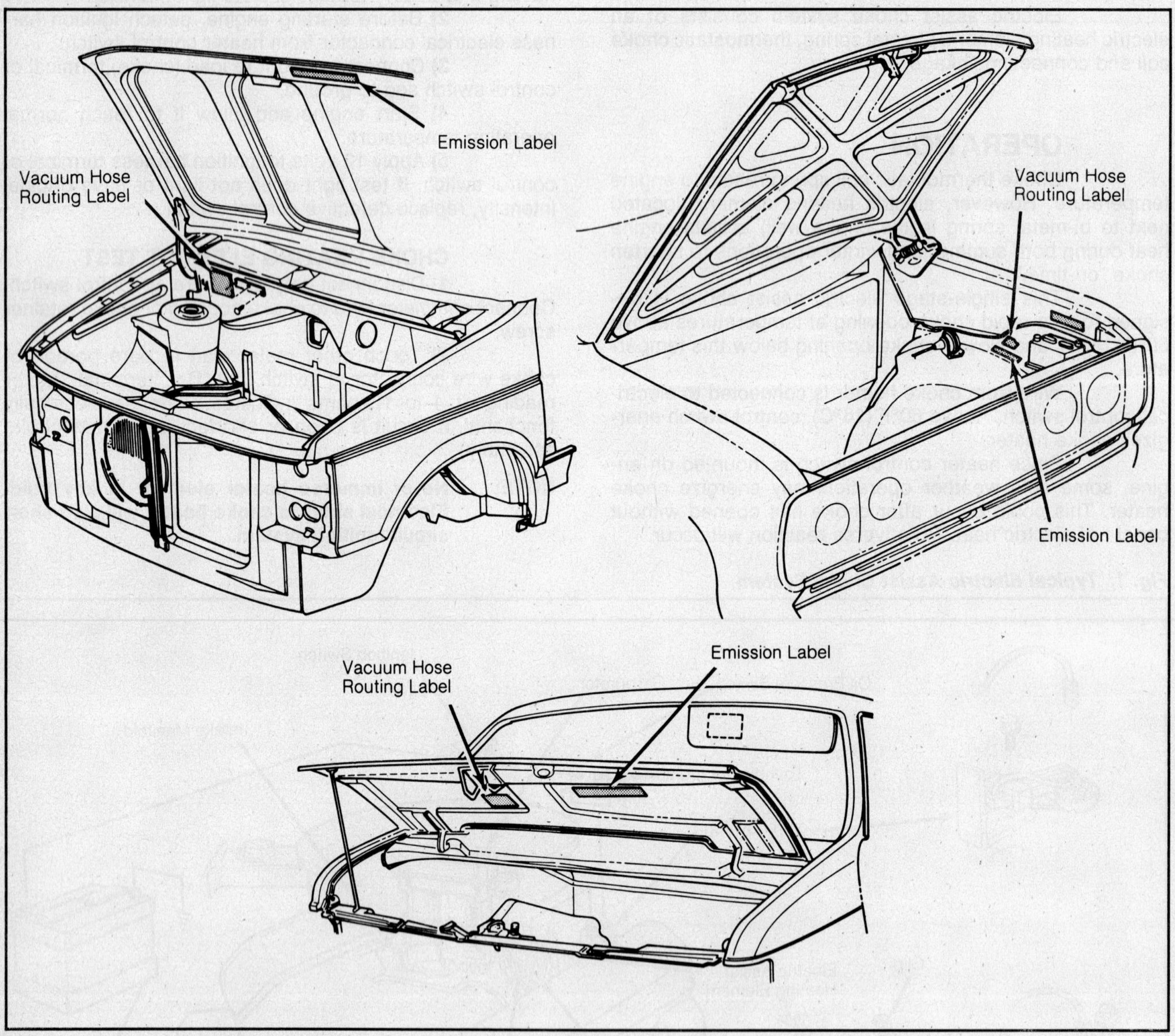

CHRYSLER CORP. VACUUM DIAGRAMS (Cont.)

Fig. 1: 2.2L Federal

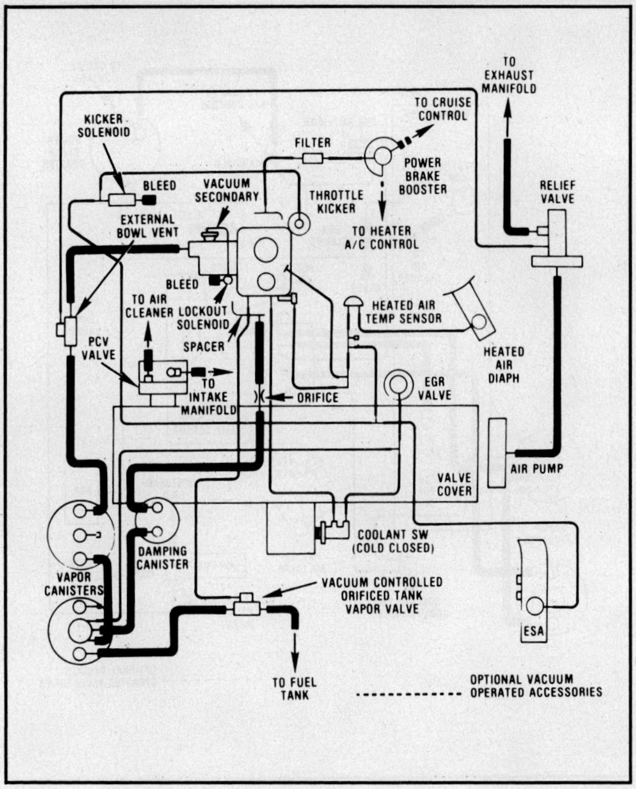

Fig. 2: 2.2L California

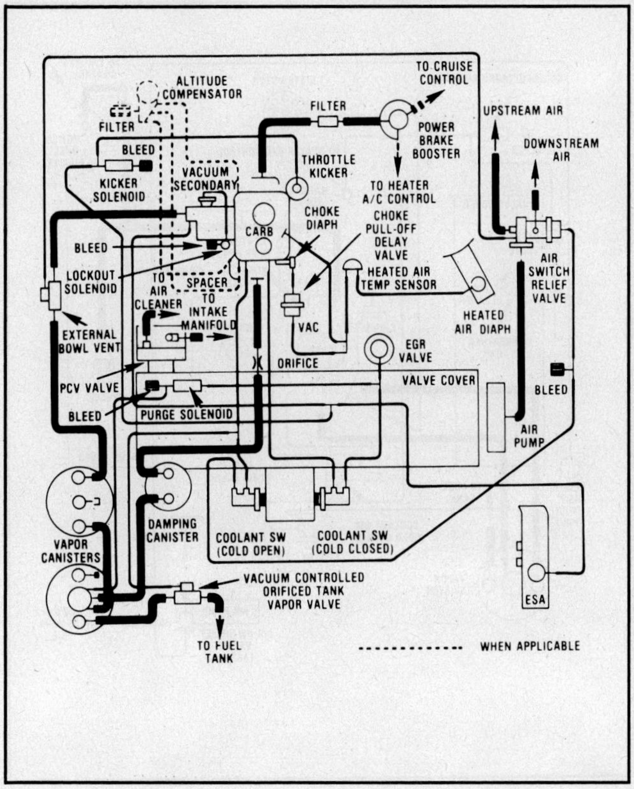

Fig. 3: 2.6L Federal

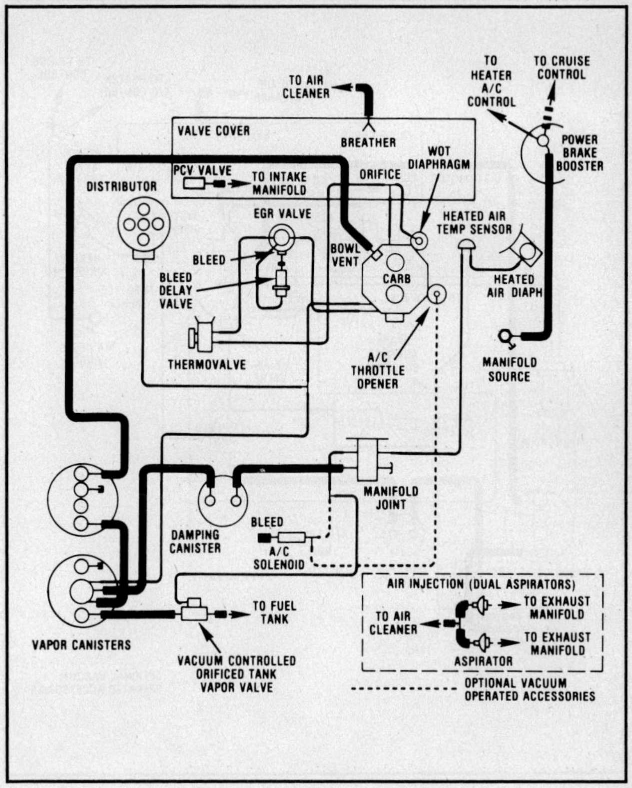

Fig. 4: 2.6L California

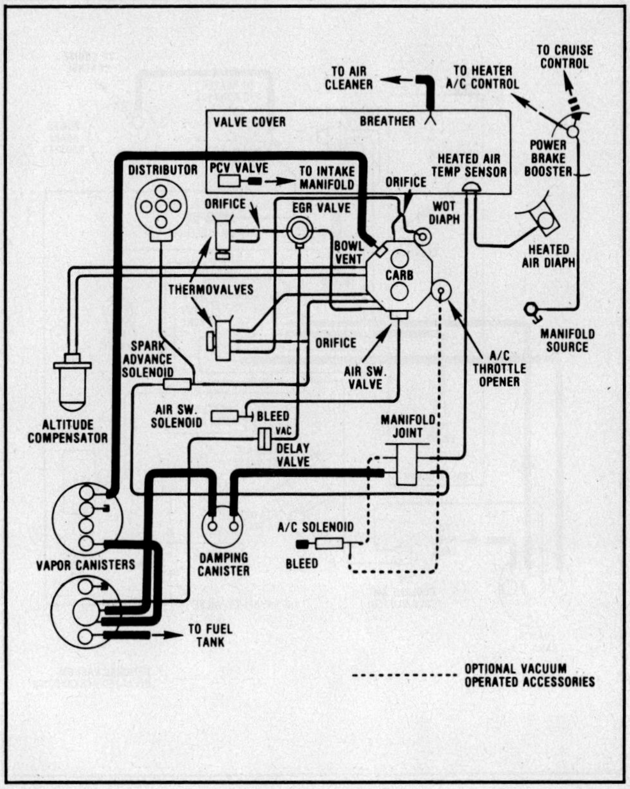

CHRYSLER CORP. VACUUM DIAGRAMS (Cont.)

Fig. 5: 2.6L Federal, High Altitude

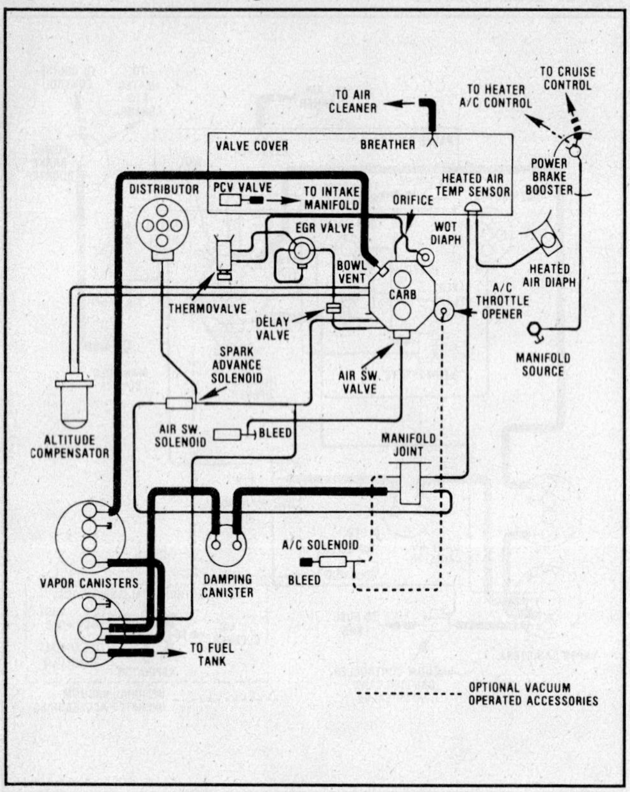

Fig. 6: 3.7L Federal

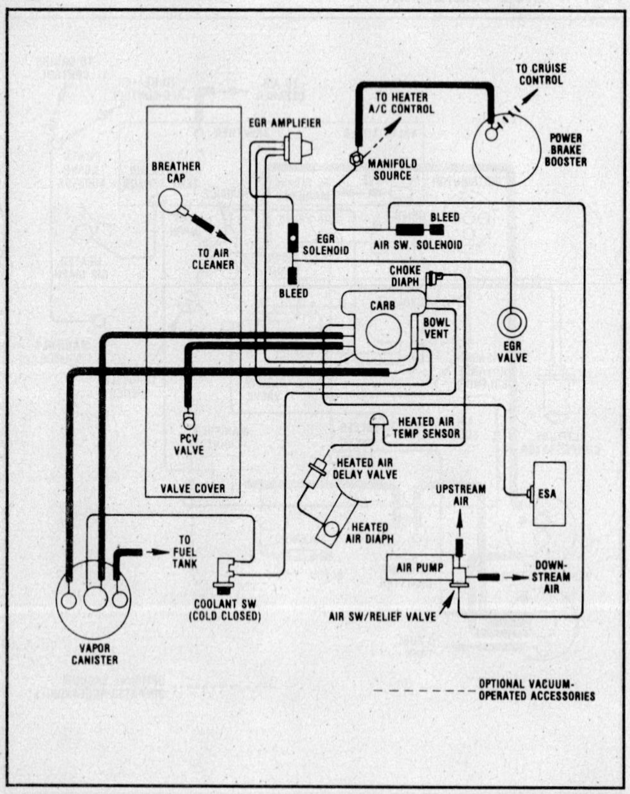

Fig. 7: 3.7L California

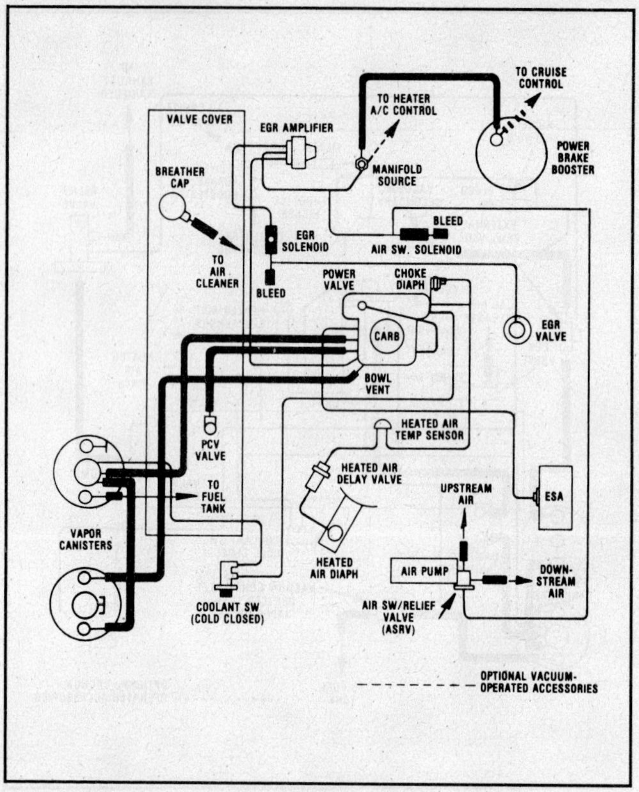

Fig. 8: 5.2L Federal Without ESA

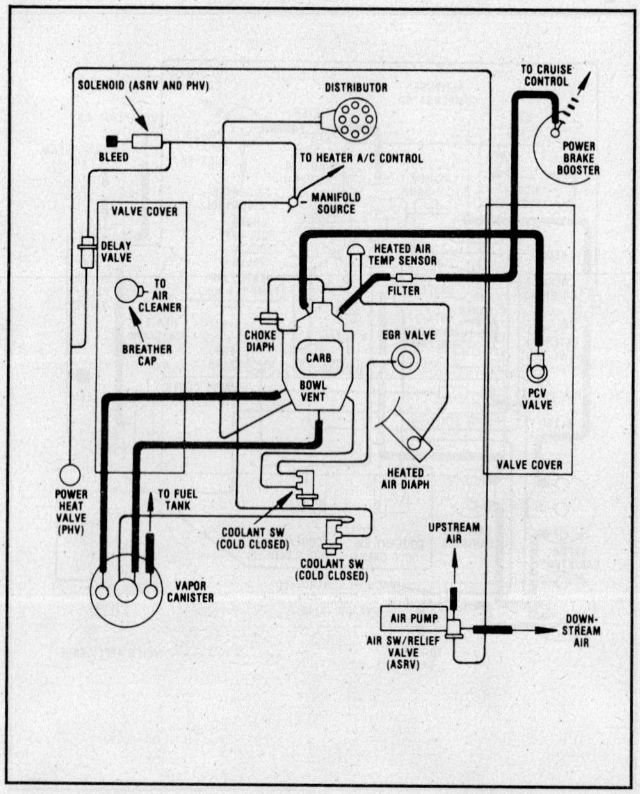

CHRYSLER CORP. VACUUM DIAGRAMS (Cont.)

Fig. 9: 5.2L California, High Altitude

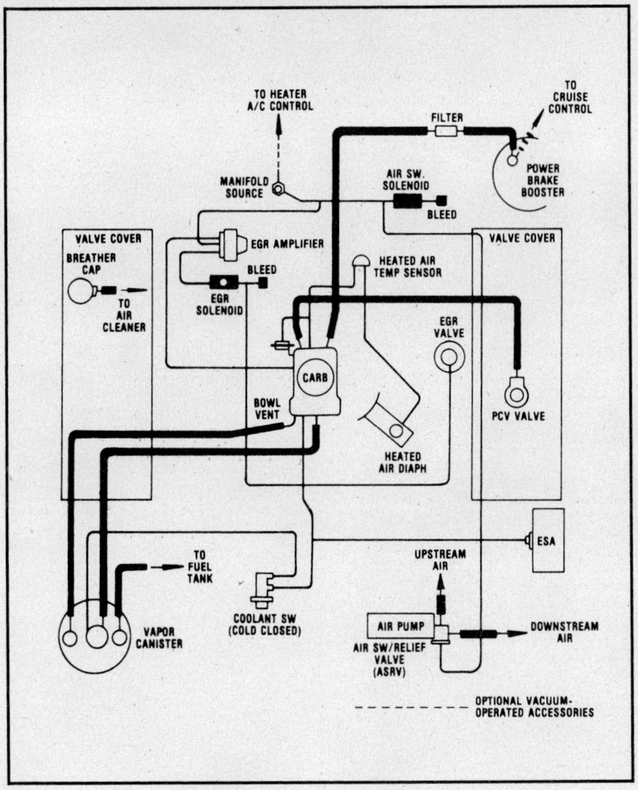

Fig. 11: 5.9L Federal High Altitude

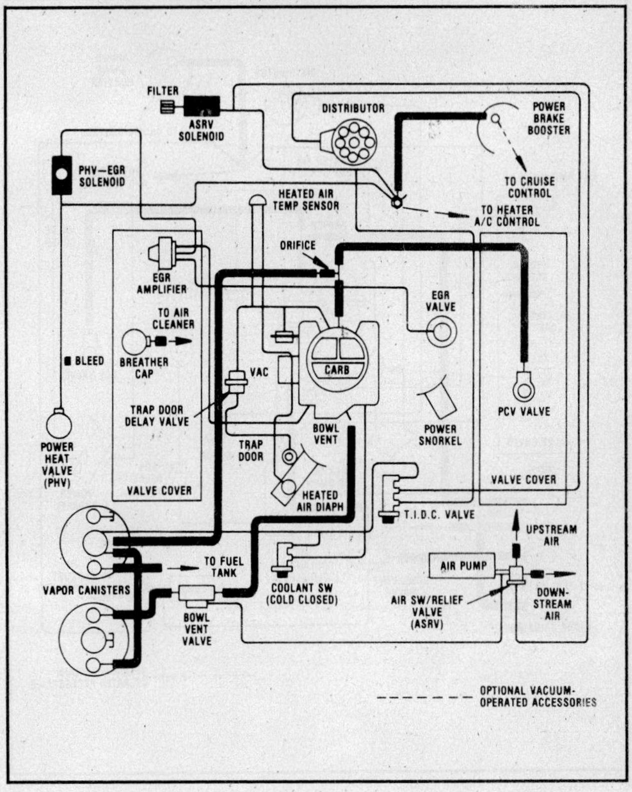

Fig. 10: 5.9L Federal Without ESA

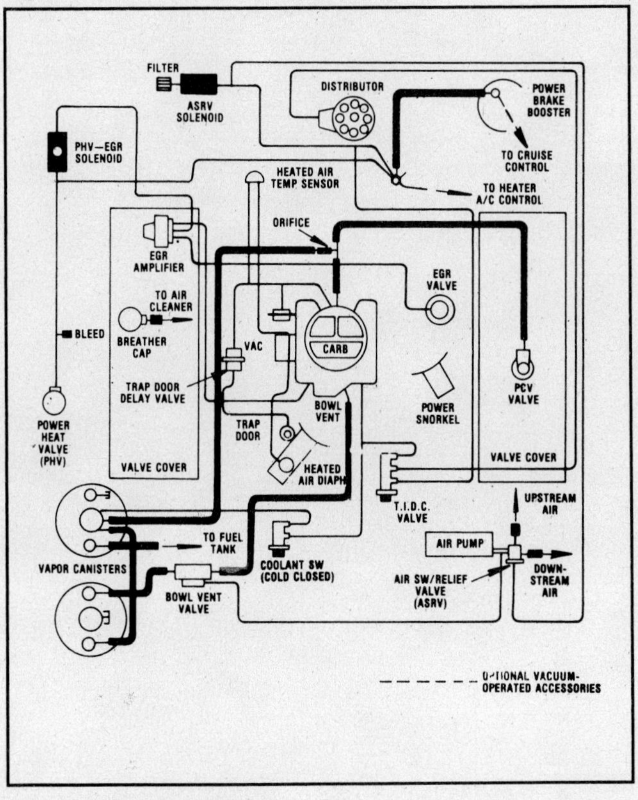

Fig. 12: 5.9L Federal, Heavy Duty Cycle

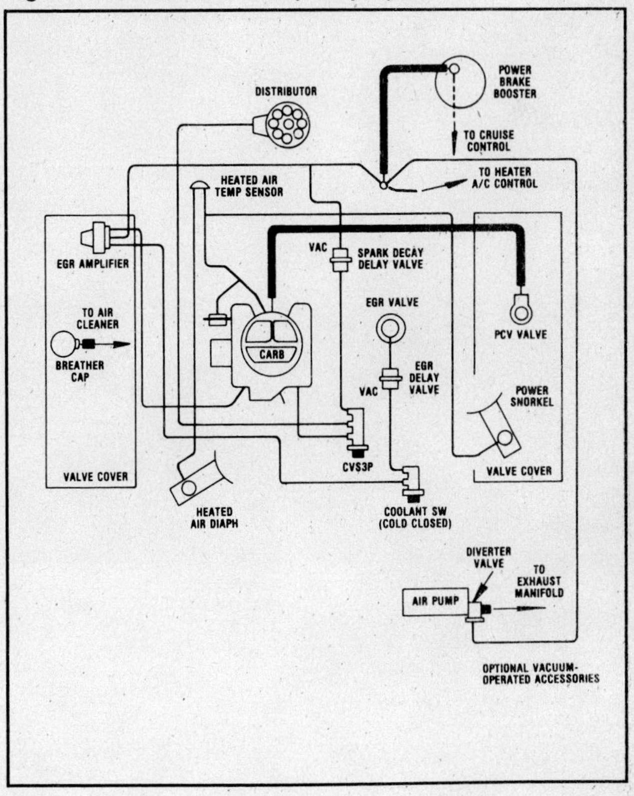

CHRYSLER CORP. VACUUM DIAGRAMS (Cont.)

Fig. 13: 5.9L California, Heavy Duty Cycle

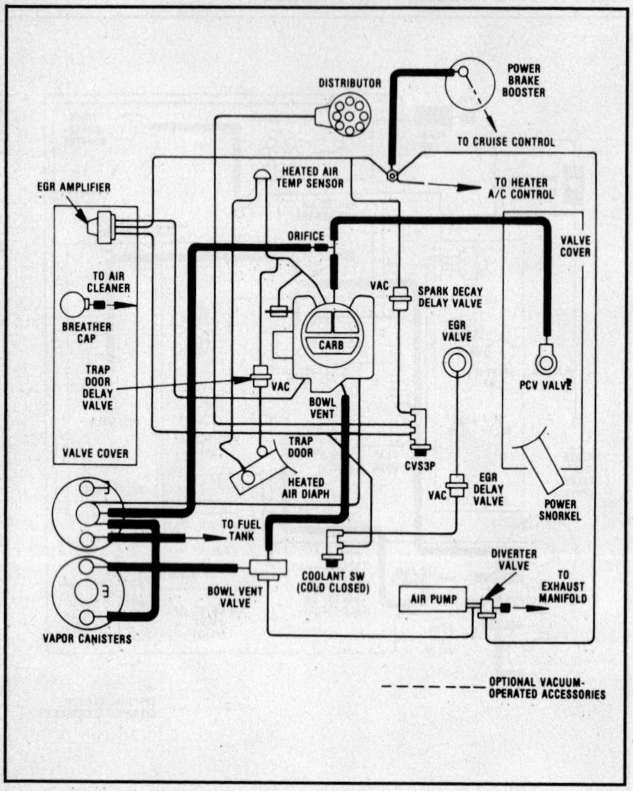

1985 Exhaust Emission Systems

FORD SYSTEMS

DESCRIPTION

Several systems are used to control emission of pollutants. System usage depends on model and engine-transmission combinations. Each system is designed to control a particular vehicle emission. In addition, specially calibrated carburetors, distributors and modified combustion chambers are used with these systems.

NOTE: **There are 2 light duty truck emission standards classifications: Light Duty and Heavy Duty Emissions. Light Duty refers to vehicles up through 8500 lbs. GVW; Heavy Duty refers to vehicles over 8500 lbs. GVW.**

THERMOSTATIC AIR CLEANER

Regardless of the type of thermostatic air cleaner used, air valve or thermostat, function is the same. System provides hot air from exhaust manifold shroud to carburetor during warm-up conditions.

AIR INJECTION

Air injection system consists of air pump, diverter valve, check valve, and various air distribution lines for injecting fresh air adjacent to exhaust valves or into converter. Such injection creates an afterburn, which further consumes unburned material in engine's exhaust.

EXHAUST GAS RECIRCULATION

Exhaust Gas Recirculation (EGR) system uses vacuum-operated EGR valve to introduce metered amounts of exhaust gas into engine's combustion chambers. This lowers peak combustion chamber temperatures and also reduces NOx formation.

ELECTRONIC ENGINE CONTROL SYSTEM (EEC-IV)

Center of EEC-IV system is Electronic Control Assembly (ECA). ECA receives information from several sensors and other electronic devices. Based on information received and operation program in ECA's memory, ECA generates output signals to control engine operation. Calibration module for EEC-IV systems is mounted inside ECA.

EEC-IV system controls 3 major areas of engine operation. These areas are, air/fuel mixture, ignition, and emission control. Additionally, system controls A/C compressor clutch operation and provides self-diagnostic capabilities. For additional information, see appropriate article in COMPUTERIZED ENGINE CONTROL section.

ELECTRIC CHOKE

Electric choke can be either all electric or electric assist. Depending on application, choke voltage is supplied by battery positive terminal or alternator stator terminal. All electric choke uses a resistance heating element to warm up choke bi-metal. Electric assist choke uses heating element and heated air inlet to heat choke bi-metal.

DECEL THROTTLE MODULATOR

This unit holds throttle partly open during deceleration, reducing emissions of hydrocarbons (HC).

CATALYTIC CONVERTER

This unit is used on all light duty emission models. It is connected into exhaust system so exhaust gases pass through converter. Inside converter, chemical reaction takes place which reduces exhaust emissions.

POSITIVE CRANKCASE VENTILATION

Positive Crankcase Ventilation (PCV) system controls crankcase blow-by gases. This system takes blow-by gasses from crankcase and recirculates them back into the combustion chamber for reburning. Key device in PCV system is vacuum-controlled PCV valve.

EVAPORATIVE EMISSION CONTROL

Fuel evaporative control system consists of special fuel tank, liquid vapor separator, non-vented filler cap, charcoal filled storage canister located in engine compartment, and hoses necessary for routing vapors from fuel tank to charcoal canister for storage.

With this system, fuel vapors are not allowed to evaporate from carburetor or fuel tank. Instead they are routed to charcoal canister for storage. Carburetor vacuum later purges canister of stored fuel vapors.

IDLE SPEED CONTROL

The purpose of the Idle Speed Control (ISC-E) system, used on the 2.0L Ranger, is to control engine RPM by means of a DC motor throttle actuator. It does not control any other engine function.

1985 Exhaust Emission Systems

FORD EXHAUST GAS RECIRCULATION

DESCRIPTION

Exhaust Gas Recirculation (EGR) system is used to reduce NOx emissions. This is accomplished by recycling exhaust gases back into the intake manifold, resulting in cooler combustion temperatures and controlled NOx emissions.

Fig. 1: Typical Ford EGR System for V8 Engines

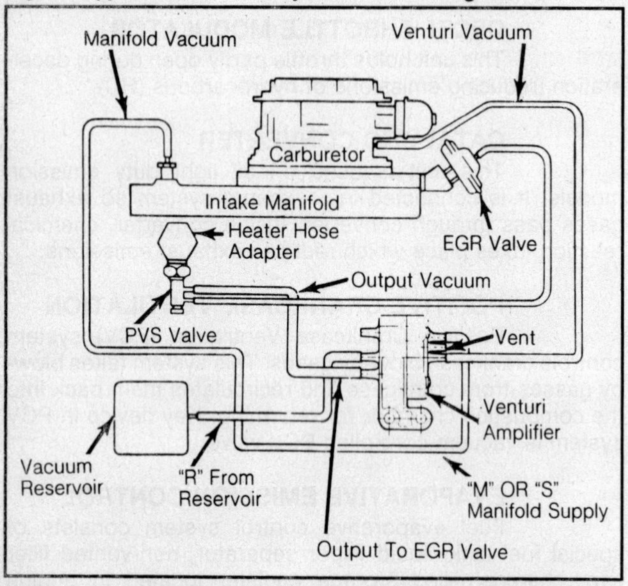

Lowers emissions by reducing combustion temperatures.

EGR system used by Ford consists of an EGR valve, vacuum amplifier, vacuum reservoir, ported vacuum switch (PVS) and connecting lines and hoses.

Fig. 2: Cutaway View of EGR Valve Without Backpressure Transducer

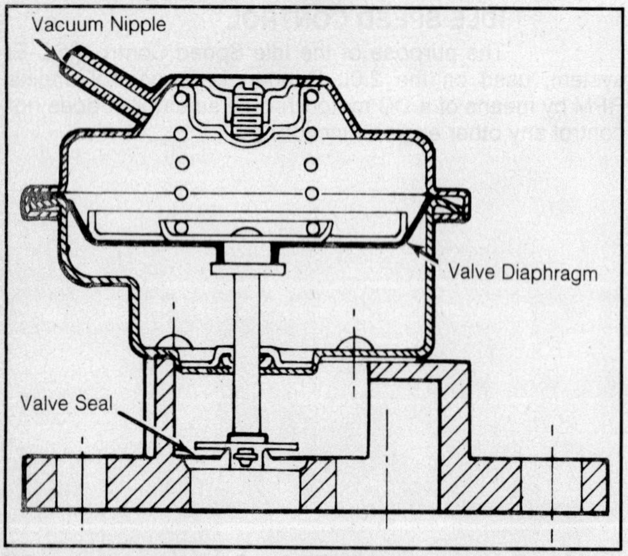

When testing, apply 8 in. Hg to EGR Valve and hold it for at least 30 seconds.

OPERATION

EGR system is controlled by EGR valve. When valve is open, exhaust gas enters manifold passages. When closed, no exhaust gas is allowed to enter intake manifold. Vacuum signals control opening and closing of EGR valve.

Light Duty emissions EGR systems use backpressure transducer to aid in controlling exhaust gas recirculation. This unit senses exhaust gas back pressure and modulates vacuum signal to EGR valve in response to amount of back pressure. Backpressure is used to provide information on engine operation modes. Backpressure transducer is integral with EGR valve.

Electronic Sonic EGR Valve

This valve operates like a ported valve, except tapered pintle is used for more exact flow control. Sensor mounted on top of this valve sends out electrical singals that tells Electronic Control Assembly (ECA) how far EGR valve is open.

Fig. 3: Electronic EGR Valve System

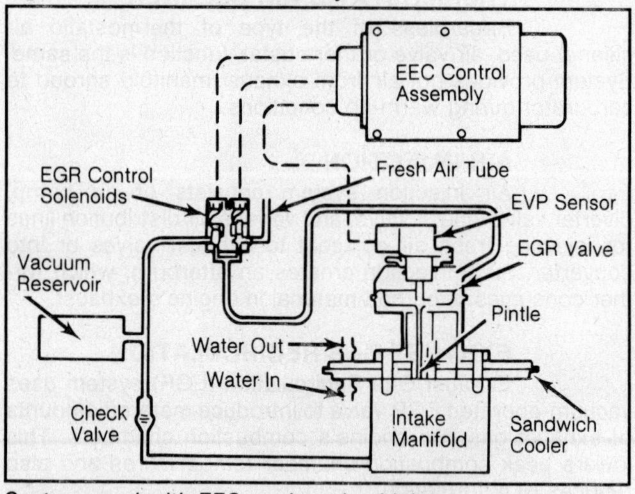

System used with EEC equipped vehicles.

ECA then signals EGR control solenoids to maintain or alter EGR flow as required. Source vacuum is from manifold and is bled off or applied to diahpragm by ECA. A cooler is sometimes used to reduce exhaust gas temperature, reduce detonation and allow better exhaust gas flow. This valve operates only at part throttle mode. It is closed in all other modes.

TESTING

EGR VALVE WITHOUT BACKPRESSURE TRANSDUCER

1) Check that all vacuum lines are properly routed, all connections are secure, and that vacuum hoses are not cracked, crimped or broken. When engine is cold there should be no vacuum to operate the valve. If there is vacuum, check PVS function. Replace if necessary. There should be no vacuum to valve at warm curb idle.

2) Vacuum should be available at or above part throttle with engine at operating temperature. If vacuum is not available, check PVS function and replace as necessary.

3) With engine at idle, apply 8 in. Hg vacuum to EGR valve. Valve stem should move to open valve and produce a rough idle. If valve stem moves but idle does not change, remove valve and clean inlet and outlet ports with wire brush.

4) With engine at idle, trap 4 in. Hg vacuum in EGR valve and hold. Vacuum should not drop more than 1 in. Hg in 30 seconds.

FORD EXHAUST GAS RECIRCULATION (Cont.)

5) If vacuum drops, replace valve. To test valve seat, insert blocking gasket (no flow holes) between valve and mounting base, then retighten valve. If idle improves, replace valve and remove blocking gasket. If idle does not improve, problem is not in EGR system.

Fig. 4: Integral Backpressure Transducer & EGR Valve

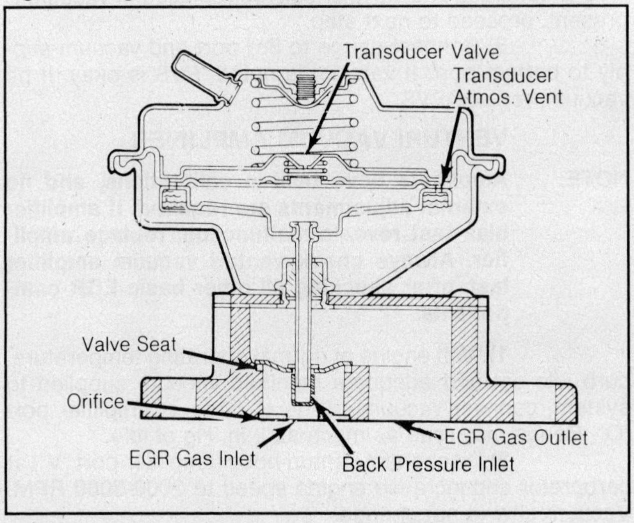

Valve cannot be opened by vacuum, until bleed hole is closed by exhaust backpressure.

EGR VALVE WITH INTEGRAL BACKPRESSURE TRANSDUCER

Signal Response Test

1) Check that all vacuum lines are properly routed, all connections are secure and that vacuum hoses are not cracked, crimped or broken. Disconnect vacuum line to EGR valve and plug line. Connect vacuum pump to EGR valve. Apply vacuum to valve. Vacuum (6 in. Hg) should bleed off and valve should not operate. If vacuum holds and valve stays open, replace valve.

2) When engine is cold there should be no vacuum to operate valve. If there is vacuum, check PVS function and replace if necessary. There should be no vacuum to valve at idle under any conditions.

3) Vacuum should be available at or above part throttle with engine at operating temperature. If vacuum is not available, check PVS function. Replace as necessary.

Valve Function Test

1) Clamp drive socket wrench into tailpipe. Socket outside diameter should be about 1/16" less than tailpipe inside diameter. Socket drive hole should be covered and socket should be inserted into tailpipe with open end facing out to ensure proper backpressure.

2) Do not block tailpipe fully or run engine faster than idle for prolonged periods of time. Be sure to remove socket from tailpipe at end of test.

3) Idle engine and apply vacuum to EGR valve gradually. EGR valve diaphragm should move smoothly and rough idle should occur. Trap 6 in. Hg vacuum in EGR valve and hold. Vacuum should drop more than 1 in. Hg in 30 seconds.

4) If vacuum does not drop or diaphragm does not move, replace valve. If diaphragm moves but idle does not change, remove valve and clean inlet and outlet ports with wire brush.

5) If valve is suspected of sticking, remove valve from engine. Cycle valve by pressing carefully with fingers against lower transducer plate. If valve sticks open when fingers are released, replace valve. If valve does not stick and correct vacuum signal is present at valve, check valve for carbon deposits and clean as necessary.

6) If engine has less than 6000 miles on it, is idling rough, and valve is suspected of being open, remove valve and check valve for foreign material. Tap base of valve on table while holding valve open with fingers. If foreign material falls from valve, make sure valve closes and reassemble valve to engine.

7) Reconnect vacuum line and check for rough idle. If rough idle continues and valve is still sticking, replace valve. If valve is not sticking, rough idle problem is not in EGR system.

ELECTRONIC SONIC EGR VALVE

1) Connect vacuum gauge to valve. Apply 6 in. Hg vacuum to valve and trap. Vacuum should not drop more than 1 in. Hg in 30 seconds. If so, replace valve "O" ring or EVP sensor.

2) As sonic valve is part of EEC system, check all circuitry as described in EEC article. See COMPUTERIZED ENGINE CONTROL section. Mechanical function can be checked as follows: Check vacuum lines for correct routing.

3) Disconnect vacuum hose at valve and connect vacuum gauge to hose. Accelerate engine to 2000-2500 RPM and release throttle. Repeat 8-10 times and check for consistent response.

4) If vacuum rises above zero, when engine is cold, diaphragm is leaking and valve should be replaced. With engine warm, vacuum should not rise above 15 in. Hg and should return to zero when throttle is released.

5) If vacuum does not go to 15 in. Hg, check vacuum source and service. If vacuum does not return to zero or is inconsistent, solenoid is worn and should be replaced.

CARBURETOR EGR PORT

1) Attach vacuum gauge directly to EGR carburetor port, using hose. Start engine, quickly open throttle to halfway position and close.

2) Observe vacuum gauge for quick rise and fall as throttle is opened and closed. If definite vacuum is evident, port is okay. If not, port is clogged and must be cleaned.

PORTED VACUUM SWITCH

PVS with 2 Connections

1) Detach both vacuum hoses from PVS, and connect vacuum gauge to top port on PVS. Connect other PVS nipple to manifold vacuum or external vacuum supply of at least 10 in. Hg. *See Fig. 5.*

2) Start engine and warm until engine operating temperature is reached. If no vacuum reading is noted, PVS should be replaced. If vacuum is present, PVS is okay.

PVS with 3 Connections

1) Disconnect EGR vacuum hose from PVS and connect manifold vacuum or external vacuum source to lowest port on PVS. *See Fig. 6.*

2) Detach distributor supply hose from center port, and attach vacuum gauge to center port.

3) Start engine and warm up until engine operating temperature is reached. If no vacuum is present, replace PVS. If present, PVS is okay.

FORD EXHAUST GAS RECIRCULATION (Cont.)

Fig. 5: Cutaway View of 2-Port PVS

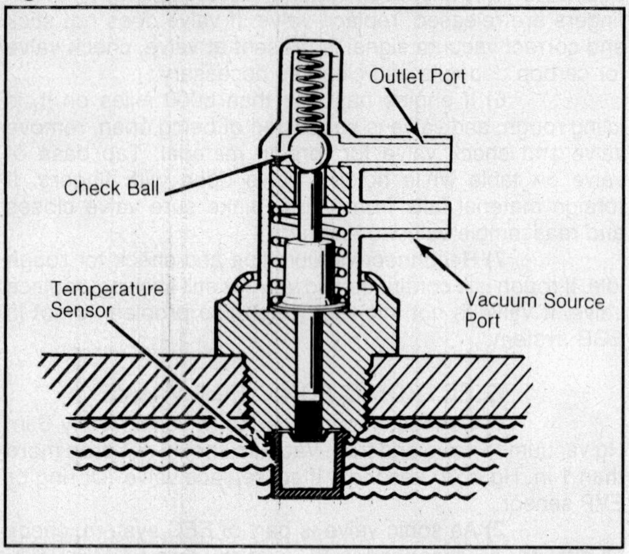

PVS will open when engine reaches operating temperature.

Fig. 6: Cutaway View of 3-Port PVS

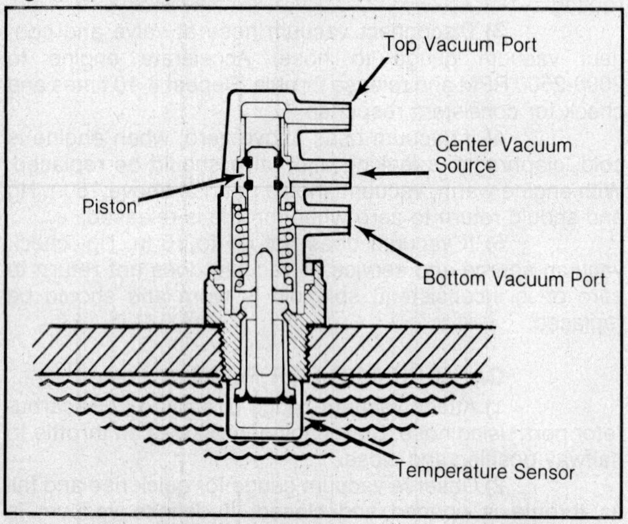

Warm engine should indicate vacuum at center PVS port.

Fig. 7: Cutaway View of 4-Port PVS

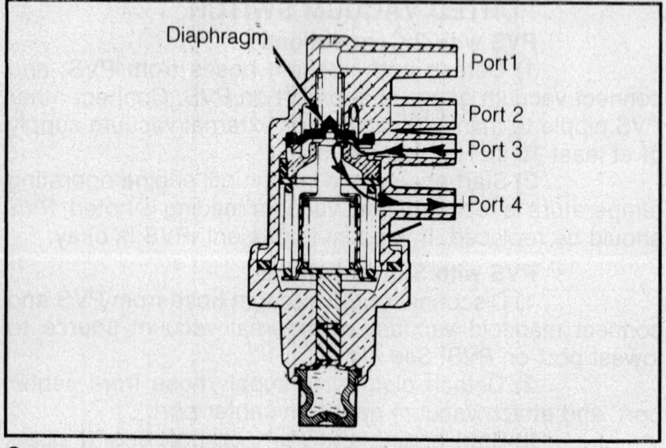

Connect vacuum gauge to 1st & 3rd port to check PVS.

PVS with 4 Connections

1) Disconnect vacuum hoses at PVS valve. Connect vacuum gauge to top port of PVS. Connect external vacuum source to 2nd port. *See Fig. 7.*

2) Start engine and warm up until engine operating temperature is reached. If no vacuum, this portion of PVS is damaged and valve should be replaced. If vacuum is present, proceed to next step.

3) Connect gauge to 3rd port and vacuum supply to bottom port. If vacuum is noted, PVS is okay. If no vacuum, replace PVS.

VENTURI VACUUM AMPLIFIER

NOTE: Amplifiers have built-in calibrations, and no external adjustments are required. If amplifier bias test reveals malfunction, replace amplifier. Always check venturi vacuum amplifier last, after checking all other basic EGR components.

1) With engine at normal operating temperature, curb idle set and adequate manifold vacuum supplied to system, connect vacuum gauge to hose at amplifier port "O". Gauge may read as much as 2 in. Hg at idle.

2) Disconnect venturi hose (amplifier port "V") at carburetor and increase engine speed to 2000-3000 RPM. Vacuum should not change.

3) While maintaining high engine speed, connect venturi hose. Vacuum should increase to 4 in. Hg. Return to idle. Gauge should return to initial reading. If amplifier does not perform as specified, replace amplifier.

Fig. 8: Testing Ford Venturi Vacuum Amplifier

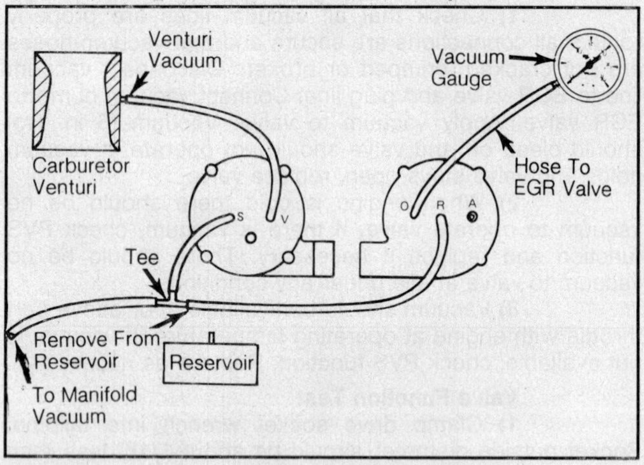

Amplifiers do not require external adjustments.

VACUUM AMPLIFIER RESERVOIR

When charged with 15-20 in. Hg vacuum, vacuum loss should not exceed .5 in. Hg in 60 seconds. If it does, replace reservoir.

REMINDER LIGHT RESET

1) Turn ignition off. Insert Phillips screwdeiver into hole in timer unit. While pressing screwdriver in, trun ignition to "RUN" position.

2) Light should be on. Hold screwdriver in for 5 seconds. Remove screwdriver. Light should go out in 2-10 seconds. If not repeat steps **1)** and **2)**.

3) Turn ignition off. Turn ignition to "RUN" position. Light should come on for 2-10 seconds. This varifies proper reset of light module.

FORD THERMOSTATIC AIR CLEANER

DESCRIPTION

Fresh air or heated air is made available to engine by ducting which directs air into air cleaner assembly. Air temperature is controlled by temperature-sensitive vacuum system that operates duct valve.

Vacuum-operated duct can select cool air from outside through pick-up tube, or warm air from shroud around exhaust manifold. System consists of shroud, air cleaner assembly with vacuum motor, duct and valve assembly, temperature sensor and cold-weather modulator (some models). *See Fig. 1.*

OPERATION

When engine is cold, air is selected from exhaust manifold shroud. In "open" position, vacuum applied to vacuum motor operates duct valve. *See Fig. 2.* Duct valve shuts off fresh air supply and opens, allowing heated air to enter air cleaner.

As engine warms up, sensor operates, preventing vacuum from being applied to vacuum motor. In this "closed" position, duct valve closes off supply of heated air, allowing air from outside to flow through pick-up tube into air cleaner. *See Fig. 2.*

Cold-weather modulator on some models, controls operation of duct valve under certain air temperature conditions for improved emission control.

TESTING

AIR CLEANER TEMPERATURE SENSOR

Temperature sensor should allow vacuum to close duct door to fresh air at ambient temperatures below

Fig. 2: Closed & Open Operation of Duct Valve

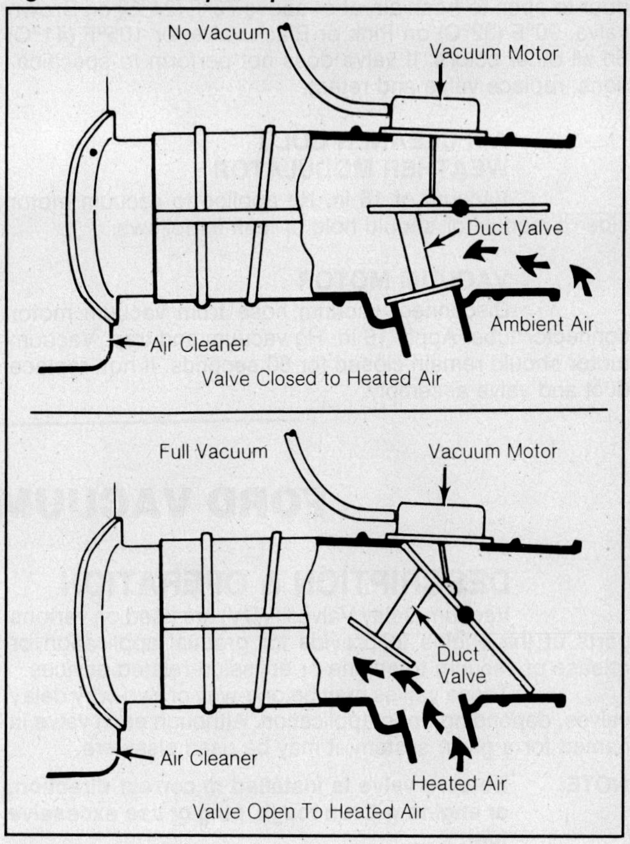

Fig. 1: Vacuum-Operated Air Cleaner Assembly Typical V8 Assembly Shown (Others Similar)

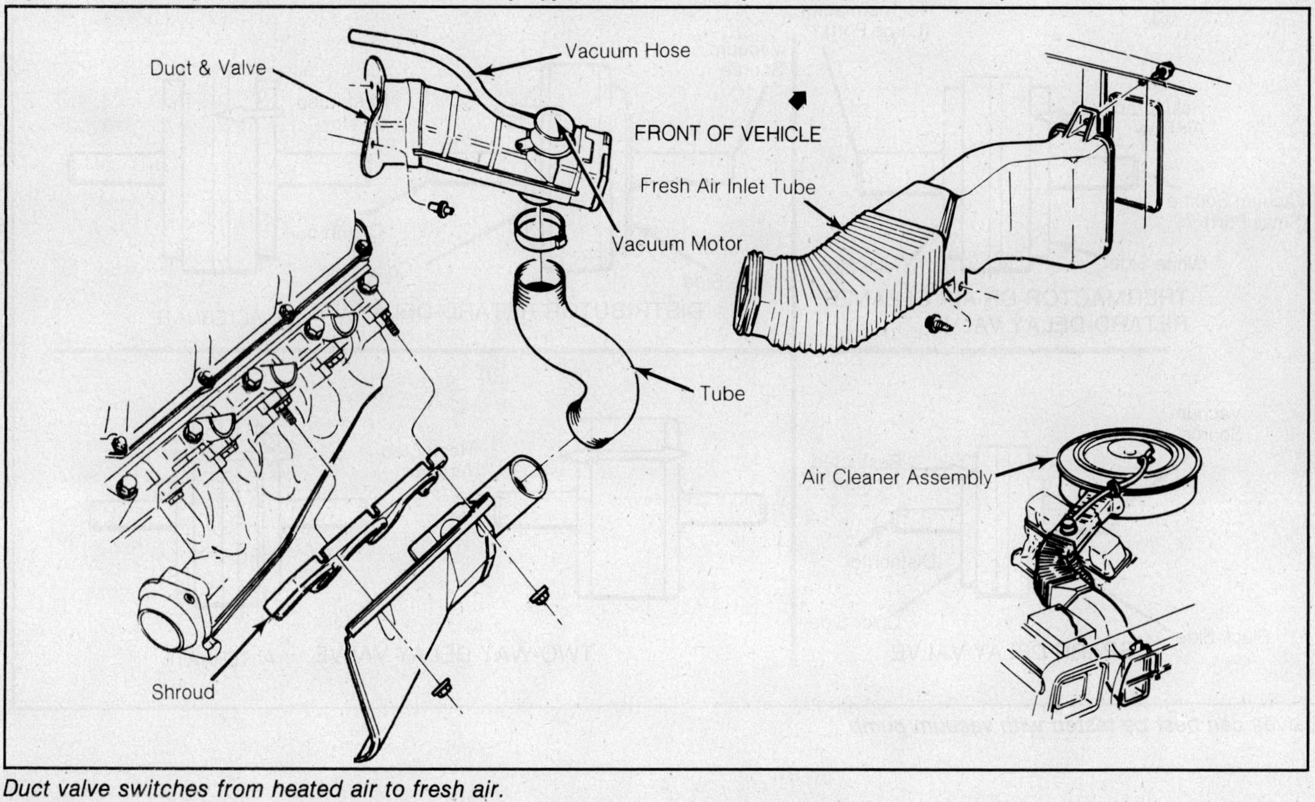

Duct valve switches from heated air to fresh air.

FORD THERMOSTATIC AIR CLEANER (Cont.)

75°F (24°C). Sensor should bleed off vacuum, allowing duct door to open to fresh air, at or above 75°F (24°C) on Brown valve, 90°F (32°C) on Pink or Black valve, or 105°F (41°C) on all other colors. If valve does not perform to specifications, replace valve and retest.

AIR CLEANER COLD WEATHER MODULATOR

Vacuum of 16 in. Hg applied to vacuum motor side of modulator should hold or leak as follows:

VACUUM MOTOR

Disconnect vacuum hose from vacuum motor connector tube. Apply 16 in. Hg vacuum and trap. Vacuum motor should remain closed for 60 seconds. If not, replace duct and valve assembly.

MODULATOR SWITCHING TEMPERATURE

Valve Color	Holds Vacuum	Leaks Vacuum
Black	Below 20°F (-7°C)	Above 35°F (2°C)
Blue	Below 40°F (4°C)	Above 55°F (13°C)
Green	Below 50°F (10°C)	Above 76°F (24°C)
Yellow	Above 65°F (18°C)	Below 50°F (10°C)

FORD VACUUM DELAY VALVES

DESCRIPTION & OPERATION

Vacuum Delay Valves (VDV) are used on various parts of the engine to provide for gradual application or release of vacuum to engine or emission-related devices.

These valves may be one-way or two-way delay valves, depending upon application. Although each valve is named for a given system, it may be used elsewere.

NOTE: Be sure valve is installed in correct direction, or engine will run rough, ping or use excessive fuel.

TESTING

1) Connect hand vacuum pump and hose to valve to be tested. Valves with both sides the same color are good if vacuum can be built up in both directions before bleeding off.

2) Valves with one side Black or White and the other side colored, are good if vacuum can be built up in one direction only before bleeding off.

NOTE: Use care to prevent oil or dirt from entering valves during testing.

Fig. 1: Four Types of Vacuum Delay Valves

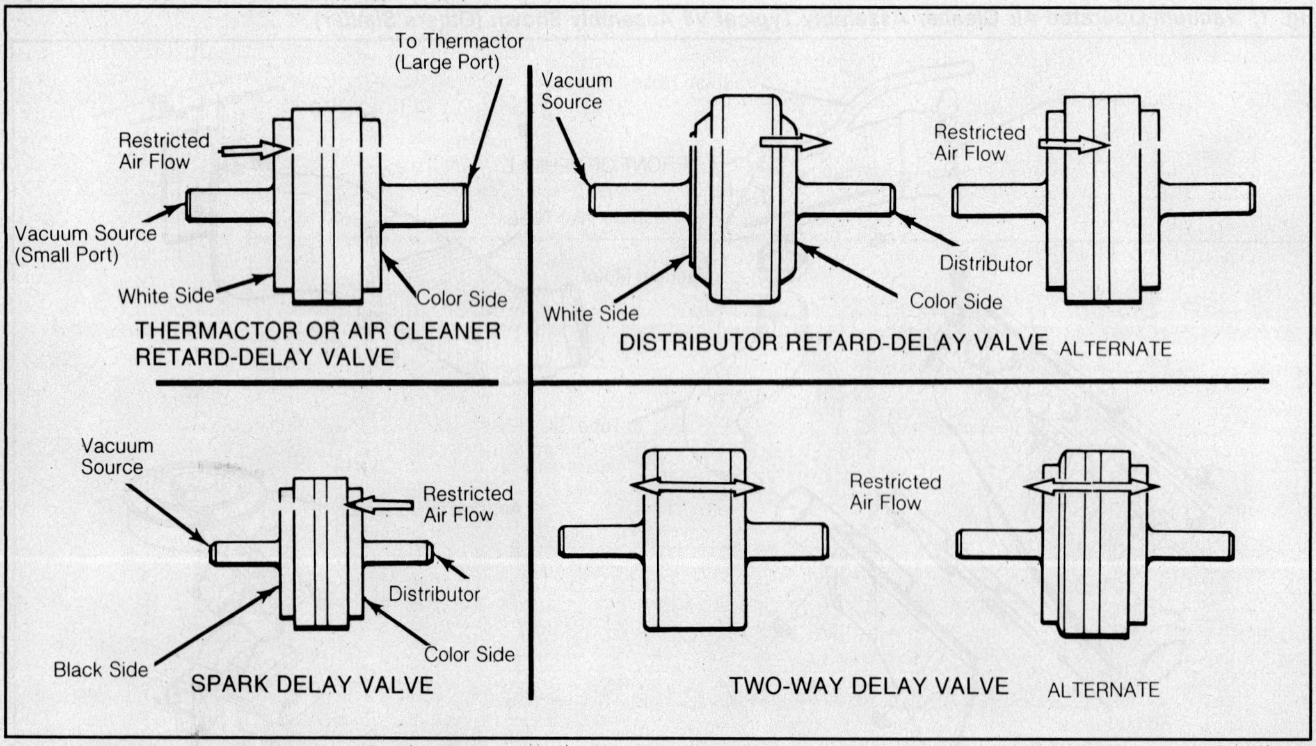

Valves can best be tested with vacuum pump.

FORD IDLE SPEED CONTROL

2.0L Federal

DESCRIPTION

The purpose of the Idle Speed Control (ISC-E) system, used on the 2.0L Ranger, is to control engine RPM by means of a DC motor throttle actuator. It does not control any other engine function.

DIAGNOSIS & TESTING

ENGINE RUNNING QUICK TEST

1) Start and run engine to stabilize idle. Upper radiator hose should be hot and pressurized. Carburetor should be off high cam.

Fig. 1: Meter Hook-Up for Reading Codes

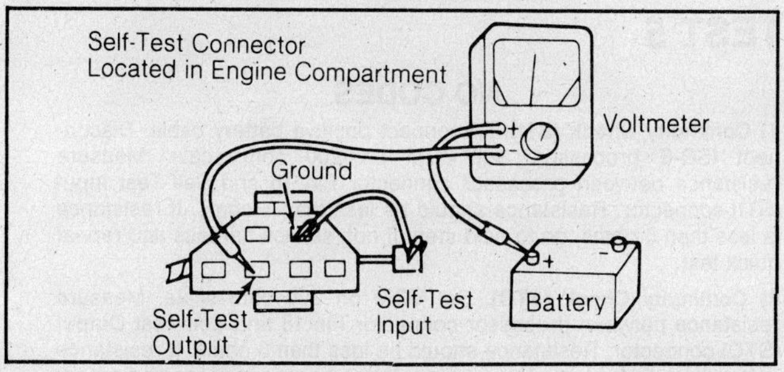

2) Turn ignition off. Connect a jumper wire from Self-Test Input (STI) to Pin 2. *See Fig. 1.*

3) Set analog VOM on a DC volatge range to read from 0 to 15 volts DC. Connect VOM from battery positive post to Pin 4 Self-Test Output (STO) in the Self-Test Connector.

4) Start and run engine to stable idle. Upper radiator hose should be hot and pressureized. Carburetor should be off high cam. Activate self-test.

5) Observe and record all service codes. Service codes are transmitted to the Self-Test Output terminal in the form of timed pulses. On the analog meter each pulse equals 1 meter sweep.

- One-half second on-time pulse for each digit.
- Two seconds off-time between digits.
- Four seconds off-time between codes.
- Eight to twelve seconds before fast and service codes.

Example: 6 pulses (sweeps) equals digit 6; two second pause then 8 pulses (sweeps) equals digit 8, this will equal code 68.

SERVICE CODES

Output Code	Go To
11	Test 3, Step **3)**
12	Test 4
13	[1] Adjust Minimum Speed Idle Screw
58	Test 2
68	Test 3
NO CODES	Test 5

[1] – See TUNE-UP section.

TEST 1

RPM CHECK

1) Turn ignition off. Disconnect self-test jumper. Connect tachometer and start engine. Read engine RPM. Engine RPM should be 775 to 825. If reading in correct go to next step. If not, go to step **3)**.

2) Turn ignition off. Disconnect engine coolant temperature switch. Start engine. Engine RPM should be 1175 to 1225. If reading is correct, ICS system is working properly, go to **Test 6**. If not, go to next step.

3) Engine Preparation. Run vehicle for 2 minutes at 2000 RPM. Varify water trmperature was above 128°F (53°C) during self-test (upper rediator hose hot and pressurized). If reading is correct go to next step. If not, repair engine cooling system.

4) ECT Switch Check. Disconnect vehicle harness from Engine Coolant Temperature (ECT) switch. Check contacts of ECT switch. Contact should be closed above 128°F (53°C). Measure resistance. If resistance is 5 ohms or less go to next step. If resistance is more than 5 ohms, replace ECT switch and retest.

5) Continuity Check. Disconnect vehicle harness from the ISC-E processor. Check circuits 354 and 60 for continuity. Mearure resistance. If resistance is 5 ohms or less go to next step. If resistance is more than 5 ohms, service or replace circuit and retest.

6) Short to Ground. Connect one lead of VOM to circuit 354 and the other to engine ground. Measure resistance. If resistance is more than 1000 ohms, replace ISC-E processor and retest. If resistance is 1000 ohms or less, repair or replace circuit.

Fig. 2: 2.0L ISC-E Wiring Diagram

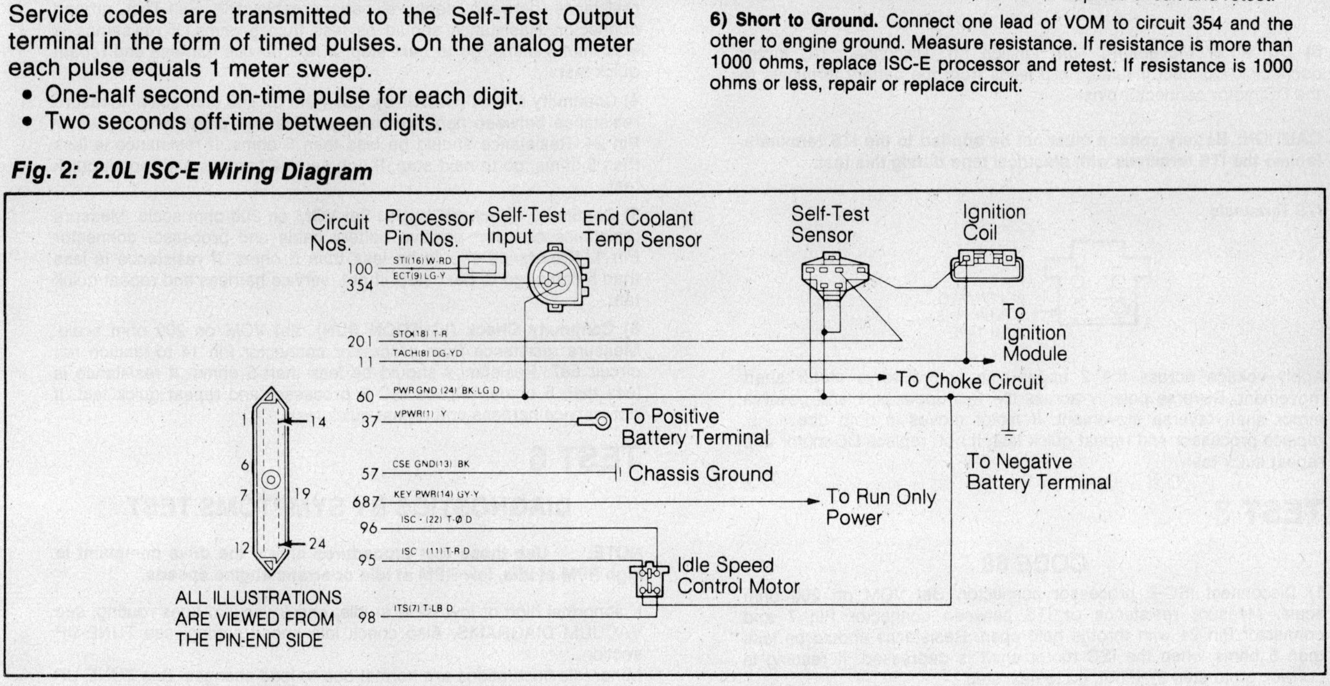

FORD IDLE SPEED CONTROL (Cont.)

TEST 2

CODE 58

1) Turn ignition off. Disconnect processor. Set VOM on 200 ohm scale. Measure resistance of the Idle Tracking Switch (ITS) between processor connector Pin 7 and processor connector Pin 24. Move throttle lever off the DC motor shaft. Resistance reading should be less than 5 ohms. Release the throttle lever to contact the DC motor shaft. If throttle does not contact shaft, depress shaft. Resistance reading should be greater than 5 ohms. If readings are correct go to step **3)**. If not, go to next step.

2) ITS Check. Ignition off. VOM on 200 ohm scale. Disconnect DC motor connector. Measure resistance of ITS from DC motor connector. Lift and release throttle lever. Resistance reading should be less than 5 ohms with the throttle lever lifted. Resistance should be greater than 5 ohms with the throttle contacting the DC motor shaft. If throttle does not contact shaft, depress shaft. If readings are correct service open in harness from DC motor connector to processor connector and repeat quick test. If not, replace DC motor and repeat quick test.

DC Motor Connector

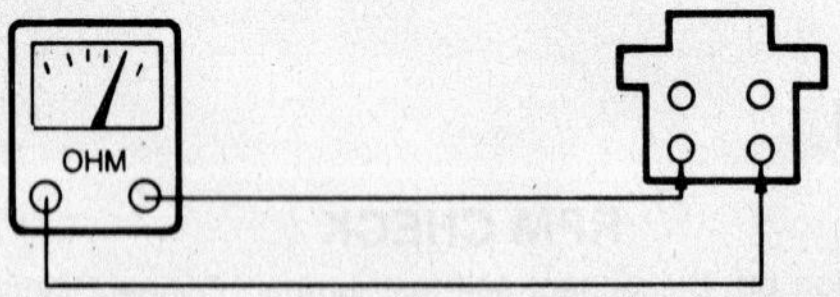

3) DC Motor Movement. Reconnect processor. Start engine an perform quick test. Check for motion of DC motor shaft during quick test. If motor shaft moves during test, replace processor and repeat quick test. If not, go to next step.

4) Continuity Check. Disconnect processor. Set VOM on 200 ohm scale. Measure continuity of harness from motor connector to processor connector. If resistance is 5 ohms or less for each, go to next step. If not, service harness and repeat quick test.

Processor Circuit

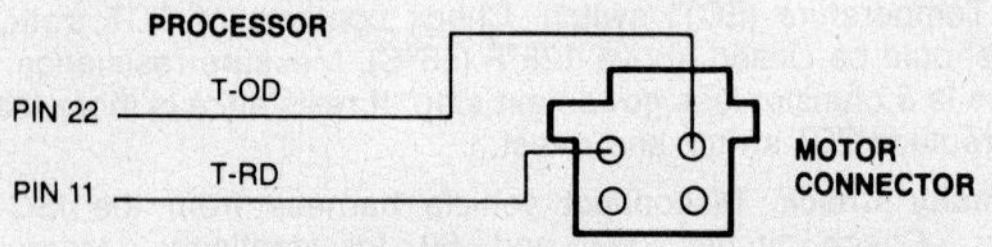

- Is resistance less than 5 ohms for each?

5) DC Motor Movement. Turn ignition off. Disconnect DC motor connector. Connect insulated clip leads from the battery terminals to the DC motor connector pins.

CAUTION: Battery voltage must not be applied to the ITS terminals. Isolate the ITS terminals with electrical tape during this test.

ITS Terminals

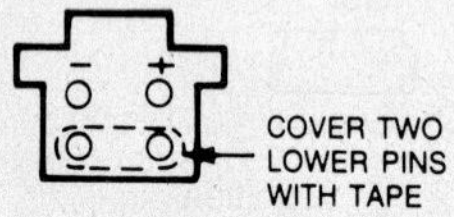

Apply voltage across the 2 upper pins and observe motor shaft movement. Reverse polarity across the two upper pins and observe motor shaft reverse movement. If motor moves in both directions, replace processor and repeat quick test. If not, replace DC motor and repeat quick test.

TEST 3

CODE 68

1) Disconnect ISC-E processor connector. Set VOM on 200 ohm scale. Measure resistance of ITS between connector Pin 7 and connector Pin 24 with throttle held open. Resistance should be less than 5 ohms when the ISC motor shaft is depressed. If reading is correct, go to step **3)**. If not, go to next step.

2) ITS Operation. Disconnect ISC motor from harness. Set VOM on 200 ohm scale. Measure resistance of ITS at motor connector (Yellow and Purple wires) with throttle held open. Resistance should be less than 5 ohms and change to greater than 5 ohms when the ISC motor shaft is depressed. If reading is correct, service harness and repeat quick test. If not, replace motor and repeat quick test.

3) Mechanical Idle Adjustment. Perform mechanical idle speed adjustment. Return to this step after adjustment. Rerun quick test. If code 68, replace ISC-E processor and repeat quick test. If code 11, system is OK.

TEST 4

CODE 12

Verifying DC Motor Movement. Bring vehicle to operating temperature. Initialize self-test. Visually verify DC motor movement during self-test. If there is movement, go to **Test 2** step **4)**. If not, set idle adjustment.

TEST 5

NO CODES

1) Continuity Check (STI). Disconnect positive battery cable. Disconnect ISC-E processor. Set VOM on 200 ohm scale. Measure resistance between processor connector Pin 16 and Self-Test Input (STI) connector. Resistance should be less than 5 ohms. If resistance is less than 5 ohms, go to next step. If not, service harness and repeat quick test.

2) Continuity Check (STO). Set VOM on 200 ohm scale. Measure resistance between processor connector Pin 18 and Self-Test Output (STO) connector. Resistance should be less than 5 ohms. If resistance is less than 5 ohms, go to next step. If not, service harness and repeat quick test.

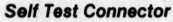

Self Test Connector

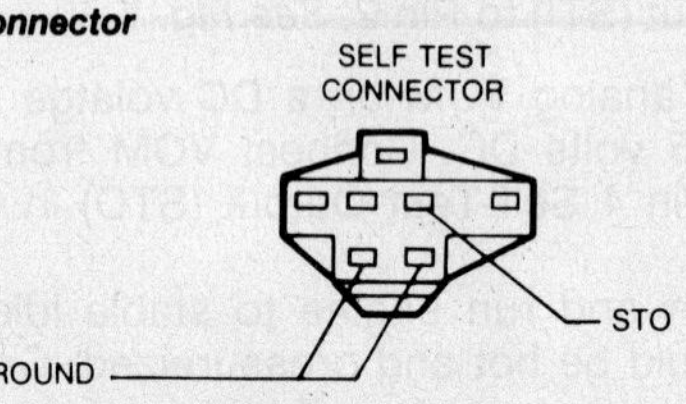

3) Continuity Check (GROUND). Set VOM on 200 ohm scale. Measure resistance between negative battery cable and Self-Test ground connector. Resistance should be less than 5 ohms. If resistance is less than 5 ohms, go to next step. If not, service harness and repeat quick test.

4) Continuity Check (GROUND). Set VOM on 200 ohm scale. Measure resistance between negative battery cable and processor connector Pin 24. Resistance should be less than 5 ohms. If resistance is less than 5 ohms, go to next step. If not, service harness and repeat quick test.

5) Continuity Check (POWER). Set VOM on 200 ohm scale. Measure resistance between positive battery cable and processor connector Pin 1. Resistance should be less than 5 ohms. If resistance is less than 5 ohms, go to next step. If not, service harness and repeat quick test.

6) Continuity Check (IGNITION RUN). Set VOM on 200 ohm scale. Measure resistance from processor connector Pin 14 to ignition run circuir 687. Resistance should be less than 5 ohms. If resistance is less than 5 ohms, relpace ISC-E processor and repeat quick test. If not, service harness and repeat quick test.

TEST 6

DIAGNOSTICS BY SYMPTOMS TEST

NOTE: Use these test procedures only if the drive complaint is high RPM at idle, low RPM at idle or erratic engine speeds.

If abnormal high or low RPM at idle, check vacuum hoes routing, see VACUUM DIAGRAMS. Also check idle speed setting, see TUNE-UP section.

Minor idle fluctuations are normal due to load changes. See TUNE-UP section.

FORD ALL-ELECTRIC & ELECTRIC ASSIST CHOKES

DESCRIPTION

NOTE: **If choke housing has no inlet air connection, either from external heat stove or from thermactor air system, vehicle is equipped with all-electric choke. However, if housing has air inlet connection, it can still include all-electric or electric assist choke.**

ALL-ELECTRIC CHOKE

12-Volt System

This 12-volt choke system is controlled by engine "RUN" signal from 3-terminal oil pressure switch. Vehicles without all-electric choke systems have 1-terminal oil pressure switch or sender.

The 3-terminal switch has 2 sets of contacts. The 2 outside terminals are for ungrounded, normally open contacts, which actuates choke. These contacts complete the circuit to ground when they are closed. This permits choke heater to operate, when ignition switch is in "RUN" position.

Center terminal is for case-grounded, normally closed contacts, which actuate oil pressure or engine light.

7.2-Volt System

This choke system operates in same manner, but receives its power from stator terminal (center tap) of alternator.

ELECTRIC ASSIST CHOKE

Many Light Duty emission models use hot air choke with electric assist. Electrically-heated choke thermostat spring housing acts as an aid to fast choke release.

Heater receives its voltage either from stator terminal on alternator or from battery through oil sensor switch. Heater only operates when engine is actually running.

Electric assist choke system consists of choke cap, thermostatic spring, bimetal temperature sensing disc and positive temperature coefficient (PTC) ceramic heater. *See Fig. 1.*

OPERATION

ELECTRIC ASSIST CHOKE

Current is constantly supplied to temperature sensing switch. System is grounded through ground strap connected to carburetor body. At temperatures below 54°F (12°C), switch is open. No current is supplied to ceramic heater located within thermostatic spring, allowing normal choking action to occur.

At temperatures from 54-74°F (12-24°C), depending on engine requirements, switch will remain open or will close to supply current to ceramic heater. Switch will always be closed at temperatures above 74°F (24°C). As heater warms, it causes thermostatic spring to pull choke plate open within 1 to 1.5 minutes.

ALL-ELECTRIC CHOKES

Although several different all-electric chokes are used on Ford Light Duty trucks, they operate similarly to electric assist chokes. Temperature ranges may vary between models. Ceramic heater is used to act upon bimetal thermostatic spring, which opens and closes choke.

TESTING

Remove air cleaner, check choke plate and choke linkage for free operation. Remove hot air supply tube at choke housing, and install Choke Tester (LRE34618). Perform hot and cold choke function per instructions contained in tester kit.

CHOKE CAP CONTINUITY

Alternator-Powered Choke

1) Disconnect electrical lead from choke cap. Turn ignition off. Connect one test lamp lead to positive battery terminal. Attach other lead to choke cap terminal. Test lamp should light. If test lamp lights, proceed to step **3)**. If test lamp does not light, use jumper wire to connect one end to choke clamp shroud and other end to battery negative terminal.

2) Test lamp should glow. If not, connect jumper wire directly to choke cap ground pin; if lamp glows, correct poor connections between choke clamp shroud and choke cap ground pin. If lamp does not glow, replace choke cap.

3) Leave test lamp connected and remove jumper wire. Test lamp should glow. If not, locate and repair open in ground circuit. Reconnect electrical lead to choke cap.

4) Connect test lamp between choke cap shroud and battery negative terminal. Start engine. Test lamp should glow. If not, locate and repair open circuit between choke cap and alternator stator terminal. If no open circuit is found, check alternator output and service as required. Stop engine and remove test equipment.

Battery-Powered Choke

1) Disconnect electrical lead from choke cap. Turn ignition off. Connect one test lamp lead to positive battery terminal. Attach other lead to choke cap terminal. Test lamp should light. If test lamp lights, proceed to step **3)**. If test lamp does not light, use jumper wire to connect one end to choke clamp shroud and other end to battery negative terminal.

2) Test lamp should glow. If not, connect jumper wire directly to choke cap ground pin; if lamp glows, correct poor connections between choke clamp shroud and choke cap ground pin. If lamp does not glow, replace choke cap.

3) Turn ignition off. Disconnect electrical connection from oil pressure switch and install jumper wire in electrical harness. Connect test lamp between battery negative terminal and choke cap terminal.

4) Turn ignition on, but do not start engine. Test lamp should glow. If not, locate and repair open circuit (fuse, fuse link, electrical connector, etc.). Turn ignition off.

5) Remove jumper wire and reconnect electrical connector to oil pressure switch. Turn ignition on, but do not start engine. Test lamp should not glow. If lamp glows, replace oil pressure switch.

6) With test lamp still connected, start engine. Test lamp should glow. If not, replace oil pressure switch.

CHOKE CAP RESISTANCE

1) Heat choke with choke tester for 3-5 minutes. Disconnect electrical connector from choke cap terminal. Connect ohmmeter between choke cap terminal and choke cap ground.

2) Ensure metal-to-metal contact, not metal oxide-to-metal contact. Ohmmeter reading should be under 30 ohms; but more than 0 ohms. If not to specifications,

FORD ALL-ELECTRIC & ELECTRIC ASSIST CHOKES (Cont.)

repeat test. If specifications are not met after second test, replace choke cap.

3) Replace air cleaner and reconnect vacuum lines. Choke cap should be quite warm. Reconnect ohmmeter as described in step **1)**.

4) On all models, use choke tester and cool cap by directing cold air towards oval insulator (not case) around cap terminal. Ohmmeter reading should gradually vary and then register sudden increase. Stop cooling.

5) Sudden increase should occur within 10 minutes after cooling began (choke tester used at maximum capacity and held close to cap). If sudden increase does not occur within 10 minutes, replace choke cap. If change does occur, warm oval insulator with choke tester.

6) Ohmmeter reading should again vary and then register sudden decrease. Stop warming cap. Sudden decrease should occur within 10 minutes after warming began (choke tester used at maximum capacity and held close to cap).

7) If sudden decrease does not occur within 10 minutes, replace choke cap. If change occurs, choke cap is operating properly.

Fig. 1: Ford Electric Assist Choke Assembly

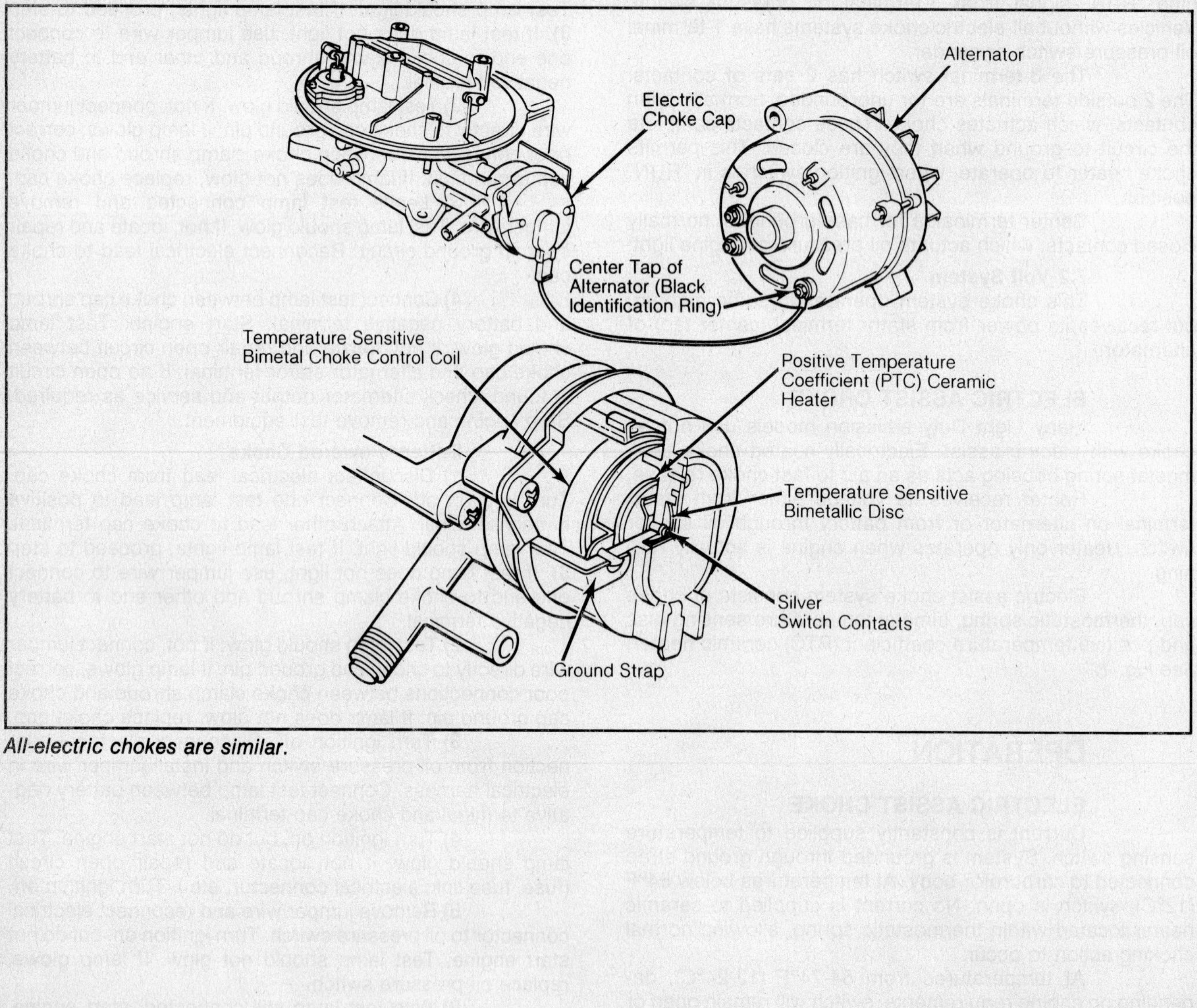

All-electric chokes are similar.

FORD DECEL THROTTLE CONTROL SYSTEM

DESCRIPTION

Decel throttle control (modulator) system keeps throttle valves open slightly during sudden deceleration to help reduce hydrocarbon and carbon monoxide emissions.

System consists of governor module or speed sensor, ported vacuum switch (some models), solenoid vacuum valve, throttle positioner (modulator) on throttle linkage, electrical wiring and vacuum hoses. *See Fig. 1*.

Some systems also utilize vacuum switch that notifies module or speed sensor when manifold vacuum is at predetermined level. System is electrically connected to ignition switch and to "TACH" terminal of ignition coil.

OPERATION

Manifold vacuum is routed through solenoid vacuum valve, which is normally closed, to vacuum throttle positioner (modulator).

Power is available to solenoid vacuum valve through an electronic sensor, but sensor ground circuit is open. When engine speed is higher than predetermined RPM setting, signal is sent to solenoid, which allows manifold vacuum to activate throttle positioner.

NOTE: **On some models, vacuum switch notifies sensor when manifold vacuum reaches predetermined value. Sensor then signals solenoid to activate throttle positioner (modulator).**

Vacuum pulls throttle positioner diaphragm, which pushes throttle to high idle position, during deceleration.

ADJUSTMENT

NOTE: **This adjustment is to be performed when replacing components found defective during "Testing" sequence.**

1) With engine at normal operating temperature, set transmission in Neutral (all transmissions).

2) Adjust carburetor to specified curb idle speed. On Auto. Trans. vehicles, this will be set to 150 RPM higher than specified curb idle speed (which is set with transmission in "D"), although transmission will remain in neutral. This is to keep minimum load on engine.

3) Disconnect system vacuum hose from throttle positioner diaphragm, and plug hose. Using "slave" hose, connect manifold vacuum source to diaphragm.

4) Allow one minute for engine speed to stabilize. If engine speed is within specifications, modulator is properly set. Go to step **7)**.

5) If RPM was not within specification, adjust throttle positioner by loosening lock nut and turning it until speed is within limits. Retighten lock nut.

NOTE: **On Carter 1-barrel carburetors, avoid damage to diaphragm by holding diaphragm shaft with 1/4" wrench while turning adjusting screw with 3/8" wrench.**

6) Detach manifold vacuum hose from positioner diaphragm, and allow engine to return to idle condition. Repeat procedure from step **2)** as required until proper function occurs.

7) Disconnect manifold vacuum hose from positioner diaphragm and allow engine to return to normal idle. Remove plug from original hose and reconnect it to throttle positioner fitting.

8) On Auto. Trans. vehicles, reset idle to specifications with transmission in "D". On all vehicles, stop engine. Install air cleaner assembly.

Fig. 1: Schematic of Ford Decel Throttle Control System

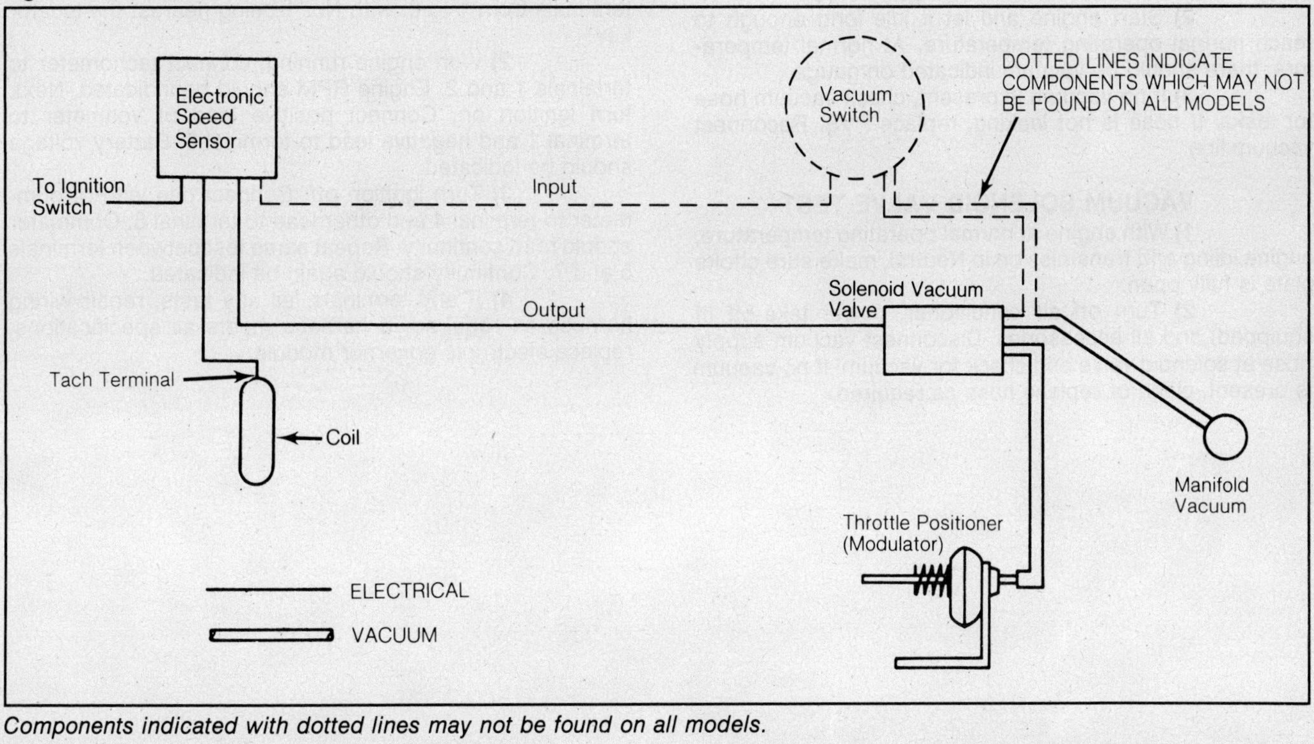

Components indicated with dotted lines may not be found on all models.

FORD DECEL THROTTLE CONTROL SYSTEM (Cont.)

TESTING

PRE-TEST SET-UP

1) If vehicle is equipped with vacuum delay valves, test for proper operation as instructed in FORD VACUUM DELAY VALVE article in this section.

2) All tests should be made with engine at operating temperature and all accessories off. Remove air cleaner and plug vacuum line. Check primary and secondary throttle linkage and choke linkage for freedom of movement. Connect tachometer to engine.

SYSTEM QUICK CHECK

1) With engine at idle, accelerate to 2000 RPM or more, then let it return to idle. Manifold vacuum should exceed 20.6 in. Hg since system includes a vacuum solenoid valve.

2) If vacuum diaphragm plunger extends and retracts, system is functioning properly. If not, continue with tests in sequence given.

THROTTLE POSITIONER (MODULATOR) DIAPHRAGM CHECK

1) Disconnect vacuum line from diaphragm. Connect external vacuum source to diaphragm. Apply and trap 19 in. Hg.

2) If diaphragm does not respond, or will not hold vacuum, replace diaphragm. If diaphragm responds and holds vacuum, proceed with testing.

3) Remove external vacuum source. If diaphragm does not return within 5 seconds, replace defective diaphragm. Reconnect vacuum line. If diaphragm returns in 5 seconds, it is not at fault.

PORTED VACUUM SWITCH (PVS) TEST

NOTE: **This switch may not be found on all models.**

1) Disconnect hose from PVS to solenoid vacuum valve, and connect external vacuum source.

2) Start engine and let it idle long enough to reach normal operating temperature. At normal temperature, there should be vacuum indicated on gauge.

3) If no vacuum is present, check vacuum hose for leaks. If hose is not leaking, replace PVS. Reconnect vacuum line.

VACUUM SOLENOID VALVE TEST

1) With engine at normal operating temperature, engine idling and transmission in Neutral, make sure choke plate is fully open.

2) Turn off air conditioner, power take-off (if equipped) and all accessories. Disconnect vacuum supply hose at solenoid valve and check for vacuum. If no vacuum is present, clean or replace hose as required.

3) If vacuum delay valve is used, remove valve and install straight connector. Disconnect wires to solenoid valve. With jumper wire, apply battery voltage to one of the solenoid terminals. Engine speed should not increase. If it does, replace solenoid valve.

4) With battery voltage on one terminal, use second jumper wire to ground other terminal of the valve. Engine speed should increase, if not, replace valve.

5) Remove ground jumper wire. Engine should return to idle within 15 seconds. If not, replace solenoid valve.

VACUUM SENSING SWITCH TEST

1) On models with vacuum sensing switch, check continuity between terminals while applying vacuum of less than 19.4 in. Hg.

2) If switch shows continuity (switch closed), replace switch. If not, apply more than 20.6 in. Hg to switch and recheck continuity. If no continuity now exists, replace switch.

NOTE: **Between 19.4 and 20.6 in. Hg, switch may be either open or closed.**

ELECTRONIC SPEED SENSOR MODULE TEST

1) Number harness terminals from 1 to 6 (or 8), starting with terminal 1 nearest the locator key. With ignition on, connect negative voltmeter lead to ground and touch positive lead, in turn, to terminals 1, 4, and 6. Battery voltage should be indicated at terminals 1 and 4. Terminal 6 should be 6-8 volts.

2) If voltage is less than 6 volts, service harness as necessary. If all tests are satisfactory, and problem still remains, replace electronic speed sensor module.

ELECTRONIC GOVERNOR MODULE CHECK

1) Check harness as follows: Number harness terminals from 1 to 8, with No. 1 being nearest the locator key.

2) With engine running, connect tachometer to terminals 1 and 2. Engine RPM should be indicated. Next, turn ignition on. Connect positive lead of voltmeter to terminal 1 and negative lead to terminal 8. Battery voltage should be indicated.

3) Turn ignition off. Connect one lead of ohmmeter to terminal 4 and other lead to terminal 6. Ohmmeter should read continuity. Repeat same test between terminals 5 and 7. Continuity should again be indicated.

4) If any terminals fail any tests, repair wiring harness as required. If harness meets all specifications, replace electronic governor module.

FORD VACUUM DIAGRAMS

INSTRUCTIONS

Located on front of engine, there is an Engine Code Information label containing engine calibration. Label may be any of several different styles. *See Fig. 1.* Using calibration number and Vacuum Diagram Index, determine which vacuum diagram to use for vehicle being serviced.

Fig. 1: Engine Code Information Label

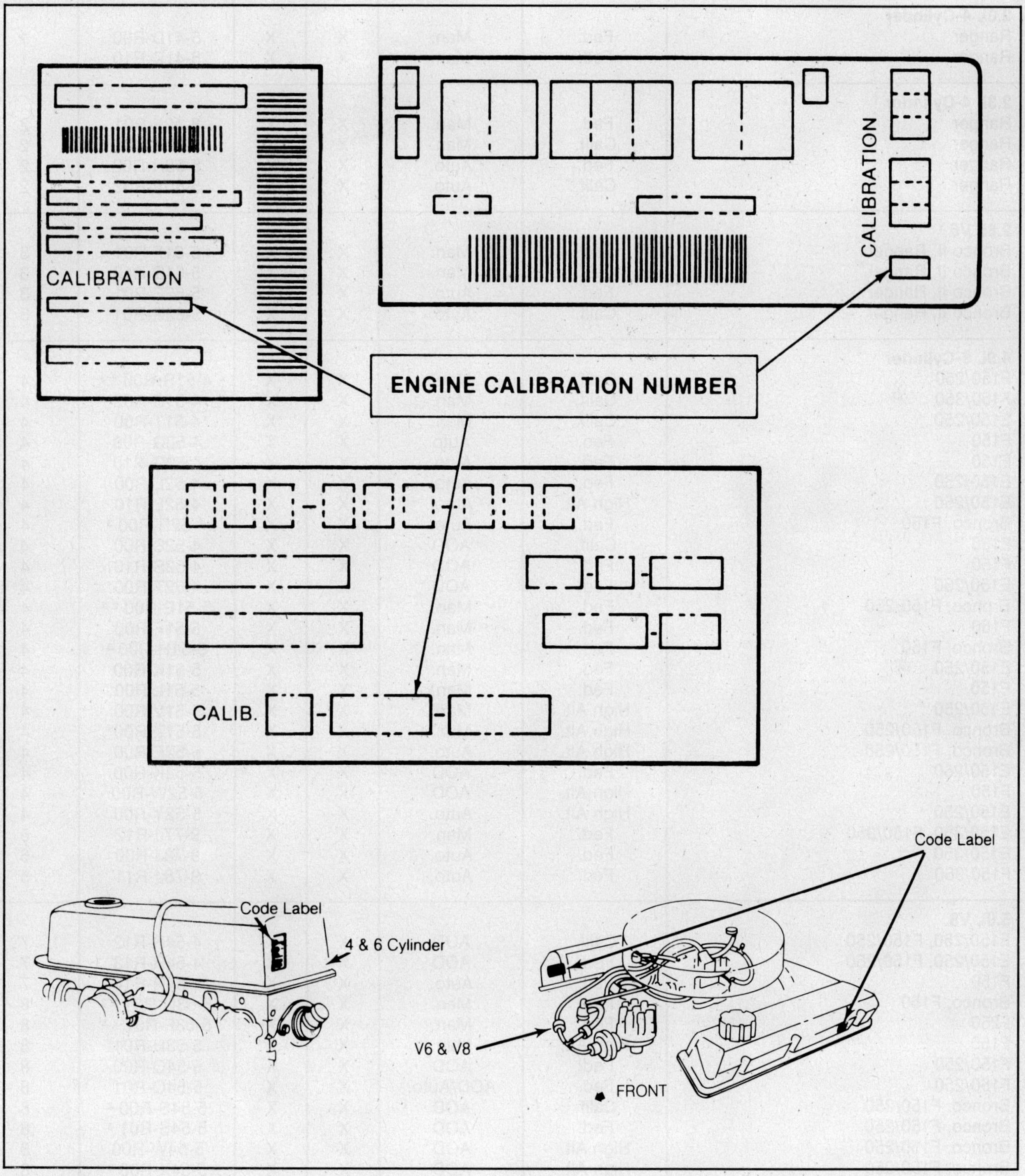

FORD VACUUM DIAGRAMS (Cont.)

1985 FORD MOTOR CO. VACUUM DIAGRAM INDEX

Engine & Model	Application	Transmission	A/C	Non A/C	Calibration	Fig. No.
2.0L 4-Cylinder						
Ranger	Fed.	Man.	X	X	5-41D-R00	1
Ranger	Fed.	Man.	X	X	5-41D-R10	1
2.3L 4-Cylinder [1]						
Ranger	Fed.	Man.	X	X	5-49F-R01	2
Ranger	Calif.	Man.	X	X	5-49S-R01	2
Ranger	Fed.	Auto.	X	X	5-50H-R02	2
Ranger	Calif.	Auto.	X	X	5-50S-R02	2
2.8L V6 [1]						
Bronco II, Ranger	Fed.	Man.	X	X	5-61F-R01	3
Bronco II, Ranger	Calif.	Man.	X	X	5-61S-R10	3
Bronco II, Ranger	Fed.	Auto.	X	X	5-62E-R01	3
Bronco II, Ranger	Calif.	Auto.	X	X	5-62R-R01	3
4.9L 6-Cylinder						
F150/250	Calif.	Man.	X	X	4-51R-R00 [2,3]	4
F150/350	Calif.	Man.	X	X	4-51S-R02	4
E150/250	Calif.	Man.	X	X	4-51T-R00	4
F150	Fed.	Auto	X	X	4-52G-R00	4
F150	Fed.	Auto.	X	X	4-52G-R10	4
E150/250	Fed.	Auto.	X	X	4-52L-R00	4
E150/250	High Alt.	Auto.	X	X	4-52L-R10	4
Bronco, F150	Fed.	Auto.	X	X	4-52R-R00 [3]	4
F150	Calif.	AOD	X	X	4-52S-R00	4
F150	Fed.	AOD	X	X	4-52S-R10	4
E150/250	Fed.	AOD	X	X	4-52T-R00	4
Bronco, F150/250	Fed.	Man.	X	X	5-51E-R00 [2,3]	4
F150	Fed.	Man.	X	X	5-51F-R00	4
Bronco, F150	Fed.	Man.	X	X	5-51H-R00 [3]	4
E150/250	Fed.	Man.	X	X	5-51K-R00	4
E150	Fed.	Man.	X	X	5-51L-R00	4
E150/250	High Alt.	Man.	X	X	5-51V-R00	4
Bronco, F150/250	High Alt.	Man.	X	X	5-51Z-R00	4
Bronco, F150/250	High Alt.	Auto.	X	X	5-52E-R00	4
E150/250	Fed.	AOD	X	X	5-52K-R00	4
F150	High Alt.	AOD	X	X	5-52W-R00	4
E150/250	High Alt.	Auto.	X	X	5-52Y-R00	4
E150/350, F150/350	Fed.	Man.	X	X	9-77J-R12	5
E150/350	Fed.	Auto.	X	X	9-78J-R00	6
F150/350	Fed.	Auto.	X	X	9-78J-R11	5
5.0L V8						
E150/250, F150/250	Calif.	AOD	X	X	4-54R-R12	7
E150/250, F150/250	Fed.	AOD	X	X	4-54R-R13	7
F150	Fed.	Auto.	X	X	4-54R-R14	7
Bronco, F150	Fed.	Man.	X	X	5-53D-R01 [2,3]	8
F250	Fed.	Man.	X	X	5-53F-R01 [2,3]	8
F150	High Alt.	Man.	X	X	5-53H-R01	8
F150/250	Fed.	AOD	X	X	5-54Q-R00	8
F150/250	Fed.	AOD/Auto.	X	X	5-54Q-R01	8
Bronco, F150/250	Calif.	AOD	X	X	5-54S-R00 [3]	8
Bronco, F150/250	Fed.	AOD	X	X	5-54S-R01 [3]	8
Bronco, F150/250	High Alt.	AOD	X	X	5-54W-R00	8
Bronco, F150/250	High Alt.	AOD	X	X	5-54X-R00 [3]	8

1985 Exhaust Emission Systems

FORD VACUUM DIAGRAMS (Cont.)

1985 FORD MOTOR CO. VACUUM DIAGRAM INDEX

Engine & Model	Application	Transmission	A/C	Non A/C	Calibration	Fig. No.
5.8L V8						
F150/350	Fed.	Auto.	X	X	4-64G-R00	9
Bronco, E150/350, F150/350	Fed.	Auto.	X	X	4-64G-R02 [2] [3]	9
Bronco, E150/350, F150/350	Fed.	Auto.	X	X	4-64T-R00	10,11
Bronco, F150/250	High Alt.	Auto.	X	X	4-64Z-R10 [2] [3]	12
F150/250	Fed.	Man.	X	X	5-63H-R00 [2] [3]	13
F150-250	High Alt.	Man.	X	X	5-63Y-R00 [2] [3]	14
F150/350	Fed.	Man.	X	X	2-75J-R20	15
E150/350, F150/350	Fed.	Auto.	X	X	2-76J-R20	15
7.5L V8						
E150/350, F150/350	Fed.	Auto./Man.	X	X	3-97J-R10	16
E150/350, F150/350	Fed.	Auto.	X	X	3-97J-R11	16
E150/350, F150/350	Calif.	Auto./Man.	X	X	4-98S-R00	17
E150/350, F150/350	Calif.	Auto.	X	X	4-98S-R10	17

1 – Aerostar information not available.
2 – 2WD models.
3 – 4WD models.

AOD – Auto. Trans. with overdrive.

EMISSION CONTROL DEVICE ABBREVIATIONS

A/CL-BI MET – Air Cleaner Bi-Metal Sensor
A/CL-DV – Air Cleaner Duct Valve
A/CL-CWM – Air Cleaner Cold Weather Modulator
ACV – Air Control Valve
AIR-BPV – Air By-Pass Valve
EGR – Exhaust Gas Recirculation
BPT – EGR Back Pressure Transducer
PCV – Positive Crankcase Ventilation
SOLV – Vacuum Solenoid Valve
VCV – Vacuum Control Valve
VCS – Vacuum Control Switch
VRESER – Vacuum Reservoir
V-REST – Vacuum Restrictor

Fig. 1: 2.0L 4-Cylinder
Calibration 5-41D-R00 & 5-41D-R10

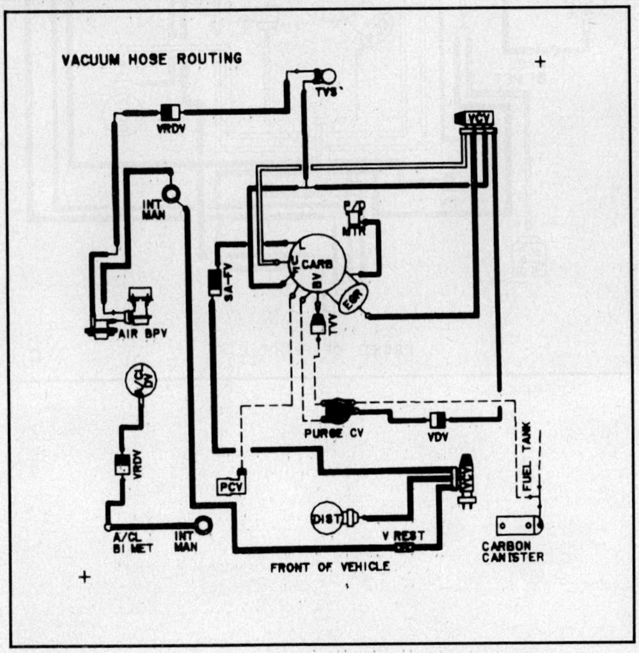

Fig. 2: 2.3L 4-Cylinder
(See Index for Calibration Numbers)

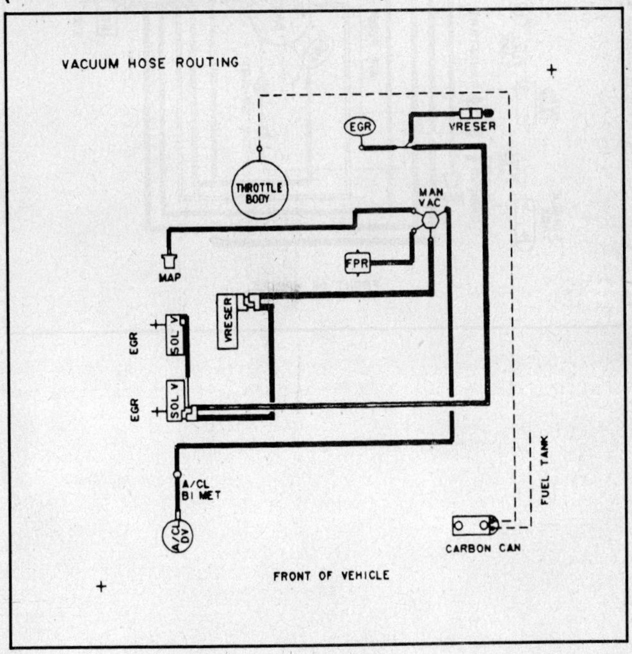

1985 Exhaust Emission Systems

FORD VACUUM DIAGRAMS (Cont.)

Fig. 3: 2.8L 4-Cylinder
(See Index for Calibration Numbers)

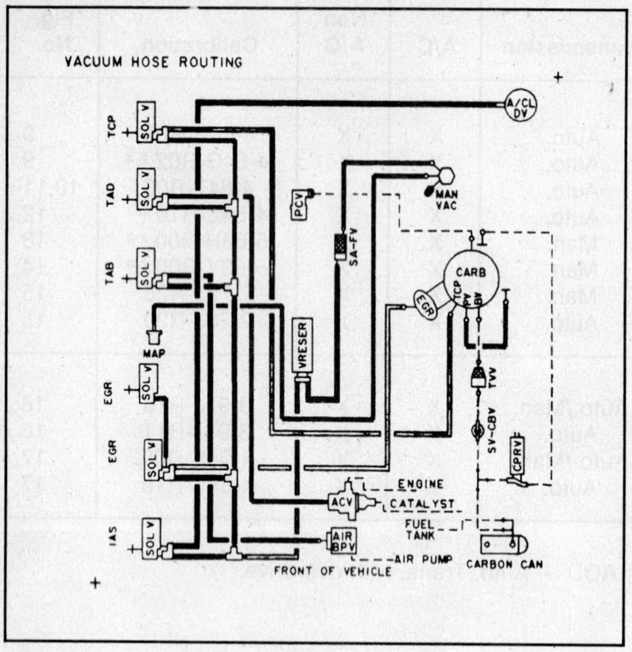

Fig. 4: 4.9L 6-Cylinder
(See Index for Calibration Numbers)

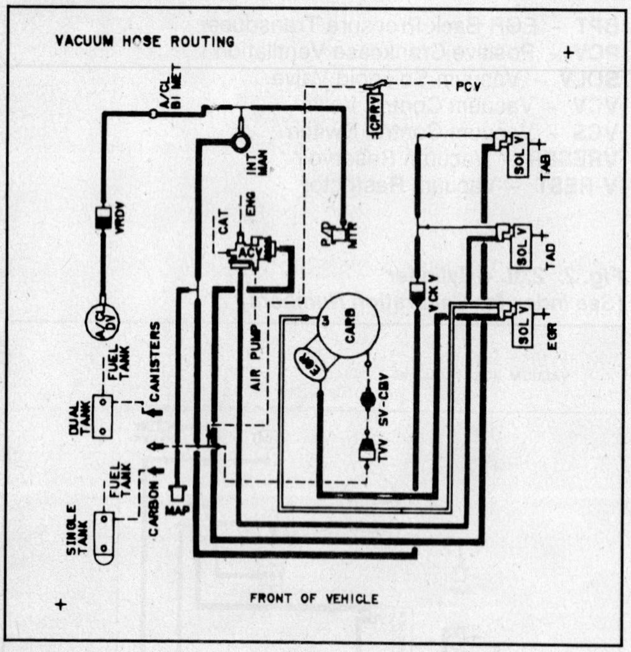

Fig. 5: 4.9L 6-Cylinder
Calibration 9-77J-R12 & 9-78J-R11

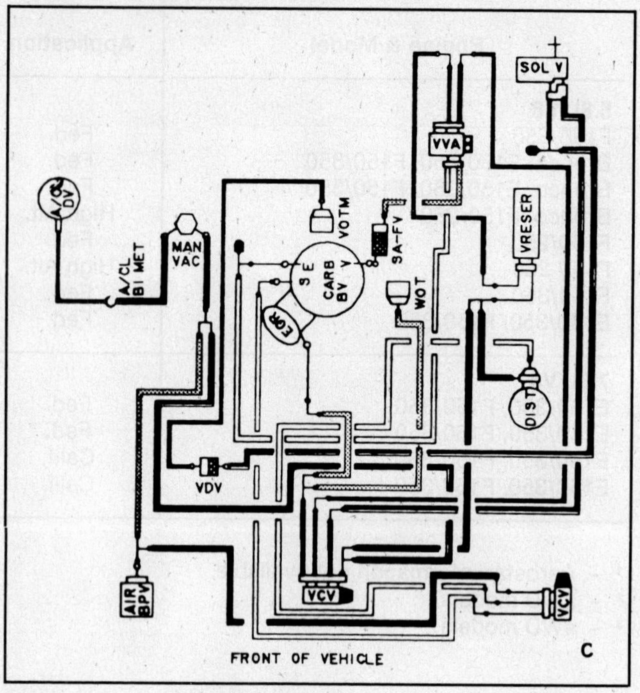

Fig. 6: 4.9L 6-Cylinder
Calibration 9-78J-R00

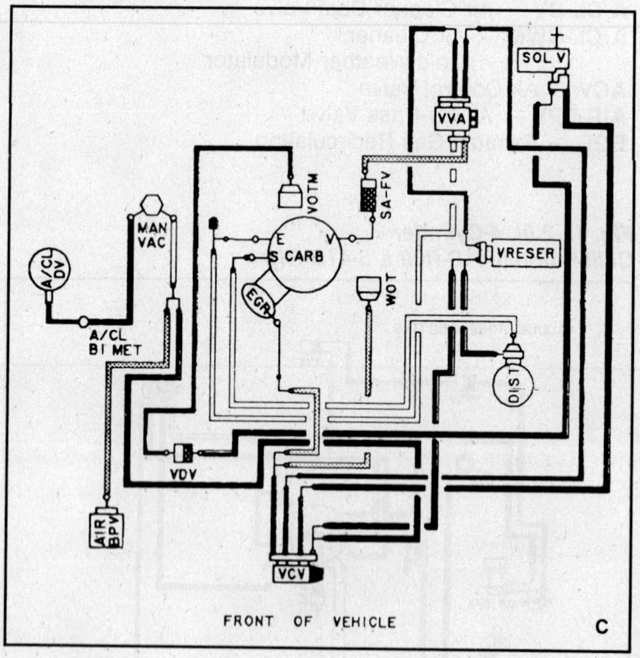

1985 Exhaust Emission Systems

FORD VACUUM DIAGRAMS (Cont.)

Fig. 7: 5.0L V8
(See Index for Calibration Numbers)

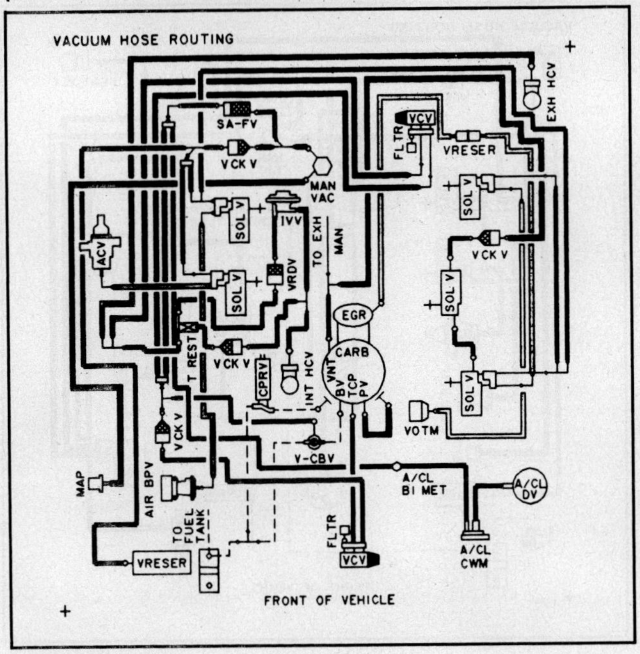

Fig. 8: 5.0L V8
(See Index for Calibration Numbers)

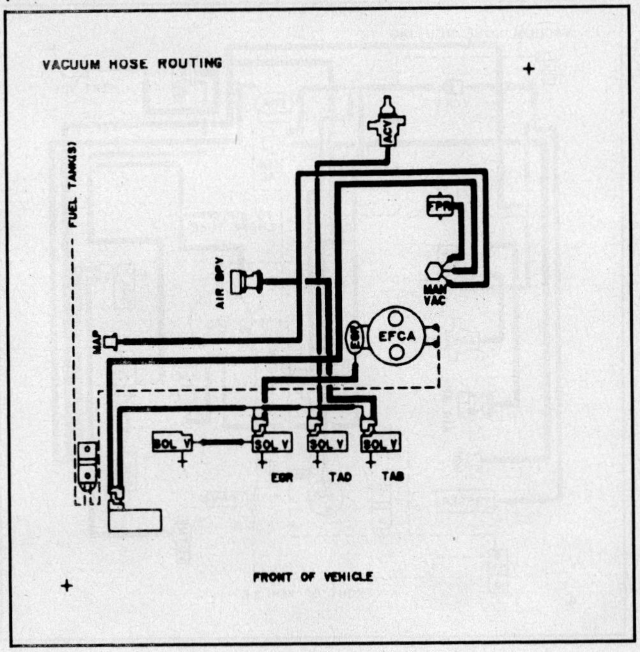

Fig. 9: 5.8L V8
Calibration 4-64G-R00 & 4-64G-R02

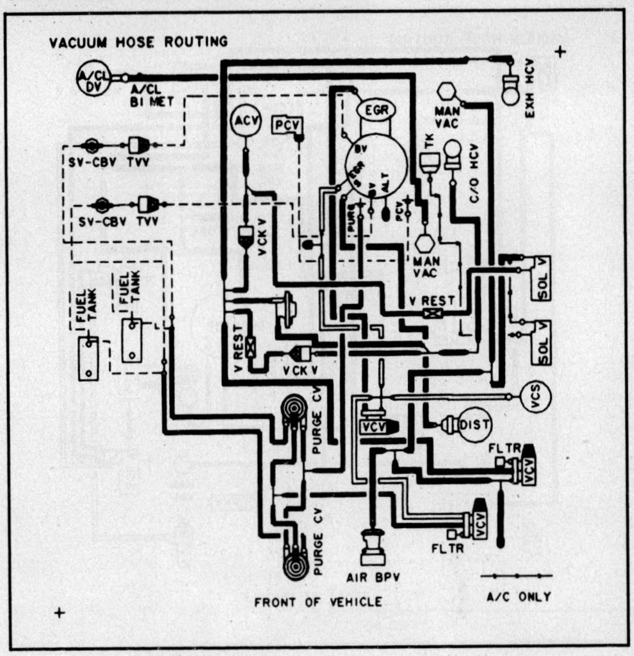

Fig. 10: 5.8L V8
Calibration 4-64T-R00

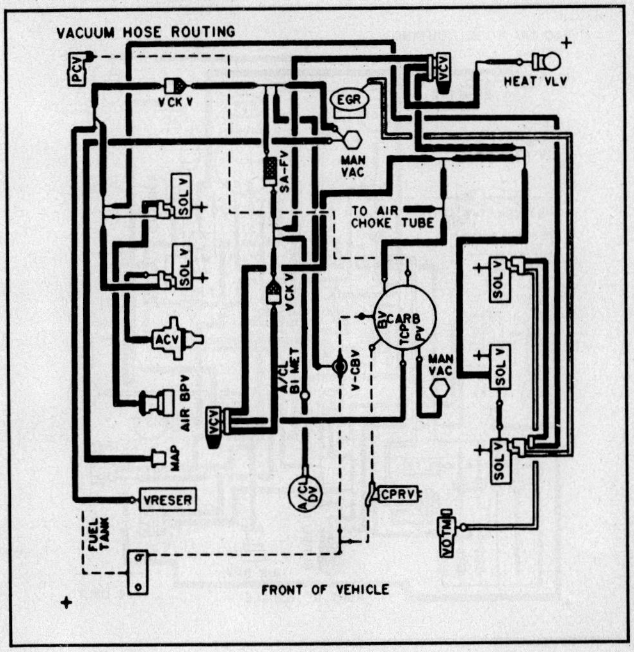

FORD VACUUM DIAGRAMS (Cont.)

Fig. 11: 5.8L V8 (E Series)
Calibration 4-64T-R00

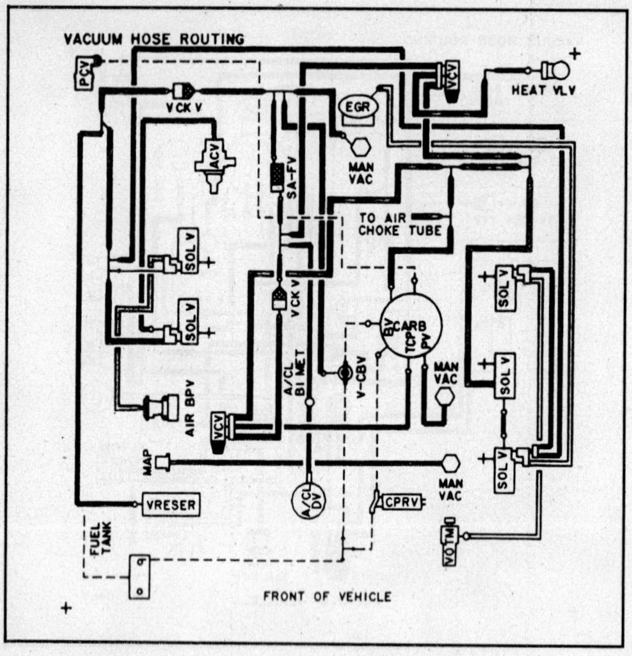

Fig. 13: 5.8L V8
Calibration 5-63H-R00

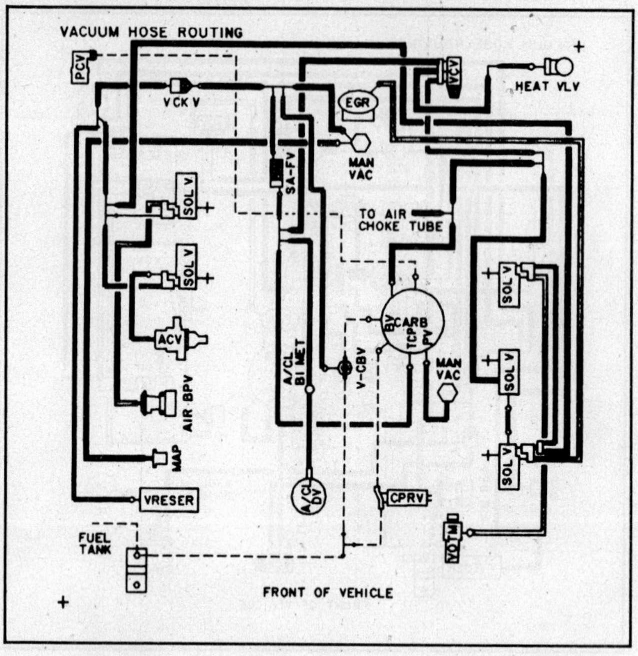

Fig. 12: 5.8L V8
Calibration 4-64Z-R10

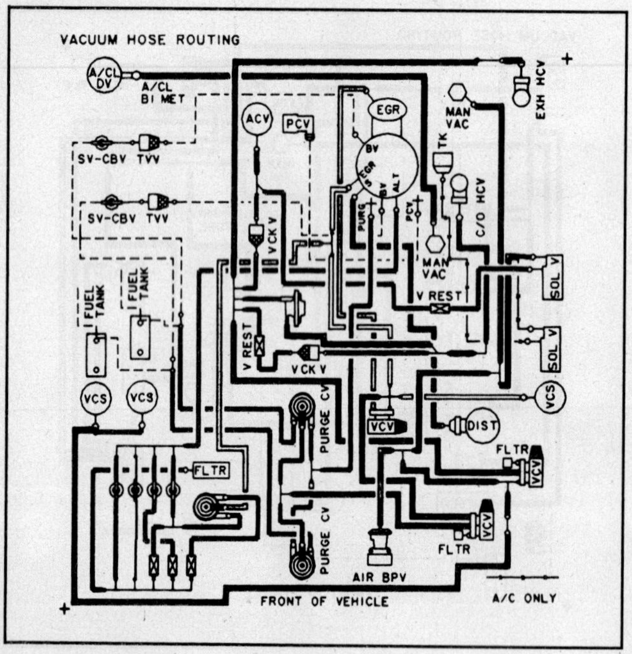

Fig. 14: 5.8L V8
Calibration 5-63Y-R00

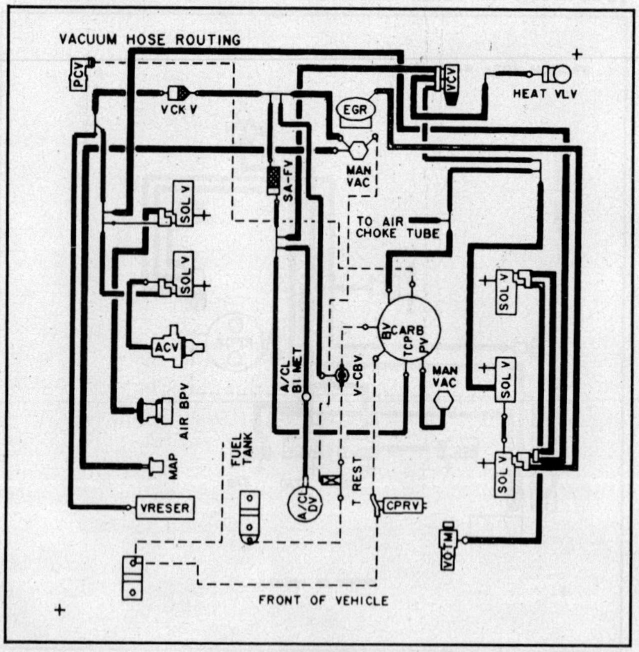

1985 Exhaust Emission Systems

FORD VACUUM DIAGRAMS (Cont.)

Fig. 15: 5.8L V8
Calibration 2-75J-R20 & 2-76J-R20

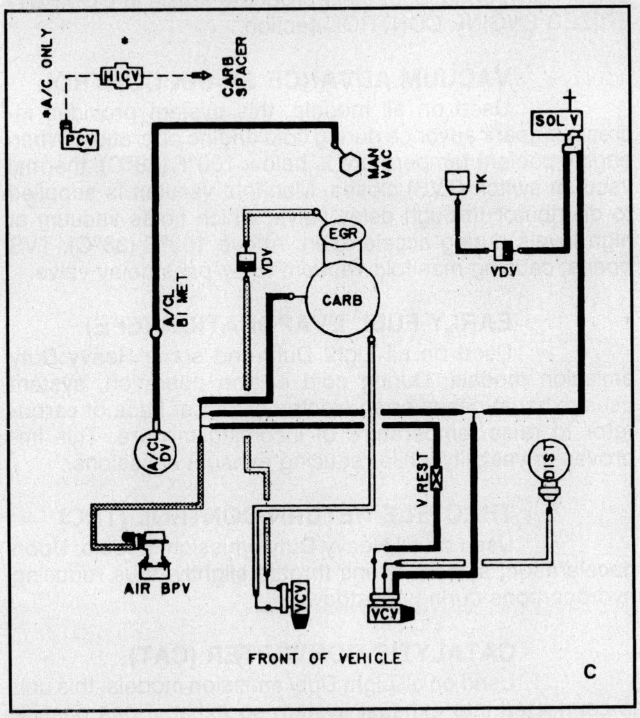

Fig. 16: 7.5L V8
Calibration 3-97J-R10 & 3-97J-R11

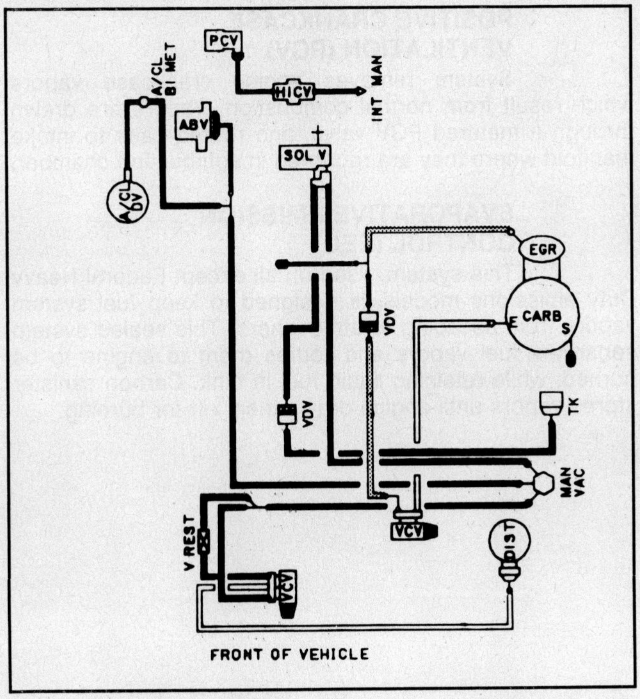

Fig. 17: 7.5L V8
Calibration 4-98S-R00 & 4-98S-R10

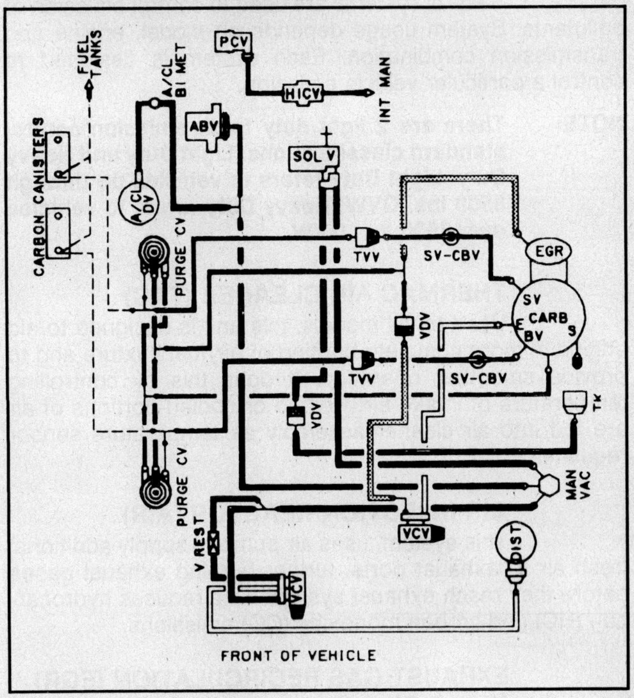

1985 Exhaust Emission Systems

GENERAL MOTORS SYSTEMS

DESCRIPTION

Several systems are used to control emission of pollutants. System usage depends on model, engine and transmission combination. Each system is designed to control a particular vehicle emission.

NOTE: **There are 2 light duty truck emission control standard classifications: Light Duty and Heavy Duty. Light Duty refers to vehicles up through 8500 lbs. GVW; Heavy Duty refers to vehicles over 8500 lbs. GVW.**

THERMAC AIR CLEANER (TAC)

Used on all models, this unit is designed to aid engine in more complete burning of air/fuel mixture and to provide smoother operation. It does this by controlling temperature of intake air. Heated or cooled portions of air are fed into air cleaner assembly as temperature sensor regulates.

AIR INJECTION REACTOR (AIR)

This system, uses air pump to supply additional fresh air to exhaust ports, further burning exhaust gases before they reach exhaust system. This reduces hydrocarbon (HC) and carbon monoxide (CO) emissions.

EXHAUST GAS RECIRCULATION (EGR) (Gas & Diesel)

This system recirculates exhaust gases into intake manifold and combustion chambers. This has the effect of lowering combustion temperatures, thereby lowering NOx emissions.

COMPUTER COMMAND CONTROL (CCC)

CCC is an electronically controlled exhaust emission system. It monitors several engine/vehicle functions and controls various operations, including transmission torque converter clutch (TCC). CCC system aids in control of exhaust emissions while maintaining good fuel economy and driveability.

Electronic Control Module (ECM) is the "brain" of the CCC system. ECM controls engine systems to maintain good vehicle performance under all normal driving conditions.

Primary objective of the system is to maintain an ideal air/fuel ratio of 14.7:1. With this ratio maintained, the catalytic converter can effectively control nitrogen oxides (NOx), hydrocarbons (HC) and carbon monoxide (CO). For additional information, see appropriate article in COMPUTERIZED ENGINE CONTROL section.

VACUUM ADVANCE SPARK CONTROL

Used on all models, this system provides increased spark advance during cold engine operation. When engine coolant temperature is below 100°F (38°C), thermal vacuum switch (TVS) closes. Manifold vacuum is supplied to distributor through delay valve, which holds vacuum at high levels during acceleration. Above 100°F (38°C), TVS opens, causing manifold vacuum to by-pass delay valve.

EARLY FUEL EVAPORATION (EFE)

Used on all Light Duty and some Heavy Duty emission models. During cold engine operation, system uses exhaust gases or an electric heater at base of carburetor to raise temperature of incoming mixture. This improves driveability while reducing exhaust emissions.

THROTTLE RETURN CONTROL (TRC)

Used on all Heavy Duty emission models. Upon deceleration, system opens throttle slightly, thus reducing hydrocarbons during coastdown.

CATALYTIC CONVERTER (CAT)

Used on all Light Duty emission models, this unit is connected into exhaust system so exhaust gas passes through converter. Inside converter, a chemical reaction takes place which reduces exhaust emissions.

POSITIVE CRANKCASE VENTILATION (PCV)

System removes engine crankcase vapors which result from normal combustion. Vapors are drawn through a metered PCV valve, and routed back to intake manifold where they are reburned in combustion chamber.

EVAPORATIVE EMISSION CONTROL (EEC)

This system, used on all except Federal Heavy Duty emissions models, is designed to keep fuel system vapors from escaping to atmosphere. This sealed system separates fuel vapors and routes them to engine to be burned, while retaining liquid fuel in tank. Carbon canister stores vapors until engine draws them off for burning.

1985 Exhaust Emission Systems

GENERAL MOTORS EXHAUST GAS RECIRCULATION

DESCRIPTION

Exhaust Gas Recirculation (EGR) is used on all Light Duty Emission models to reduce oxides of nitrogen (NOx) emissions. This process is accomplished by lowering combustion temperatures of burning gases. Recirculated and metered amounts of exhaust gases are reintroduced into engine through intake manifold, where they are mixed with air/fuel mixture.

Vacuum modulated system regulates exhaust gas recirculation according to manifold vacuum. Backpressure modulated system regulates timed vacuum according to exhaust backpressure level. Special control valve within the EGR valve housing responds as a pressure regulator.

California 4.3L, 5.0L and 5.7L engines use what is called "Pulse Width Modulation". This mains the ECM turns the solenoid on and off many times per second and varies the amount of "on" time to vary the amount of EGR. For more information, see COMPUTERIZED ENGINE CONTROL section.

OPERATION

VACUUM MODULATED EGR SYSTEM

With this system, amount of exhaust gas admitted into intake manifold depends on vacuum signal (ported vacuum), controlled by throttle position.

When throttle is closed (at idle or deceleration), there is no vacuum signal to EGR valve because EGR vacuum port is above the closed throttle valve. As the throttle valve is opened, ported vacuum signal is supplied to EGR valve, admitting exhaust gas into intake manifold.

BACKPRESSURE EGR SYSTEM

Negative Backpressure EGR Valve

Negative backpressure EGR valve assembly has same function as positive backpressure EGR valve, except that the bleed valve spring is moved from above the diaphragm to below, and valve is normally closed. Flow of valve is controlled by manifold vacuum, negative exhaust backpressure and carburetor ported vacuum signal.

When carburetor ported vacuum signal is applied to main vacuum chamber, partially opening valve, vacuum signal from manifold side (reduced by exhaust backpressure) is transmitted up the hollow stem of valve. This enables signal to act on diaphragm, opening bleed and causing transducer to modulate providing a specific valve flow. Thus flow of valve is a constant percentage of engine air flow.

VACUUM MODULATED (PORTED) EGR SYSTEM

Ported EGR Valve

This valve is controlled by a flexible diaphragm which is spring loaded to hold the valve closed. Ported manifold vacuum applied to the top of the diaphragm overcomes the spring pressure and opens the valve in the exhaust gas port. This allows exhaust gas to be pulled into the intake manifold and enter the engine cylinders.

EGR THERMAL VACUUM SWITCH

EGR-TVS, used on all models, closes to prevent EGR operations when engine coolant temperature is below 85°F (29°C). This improves cold engine driveability. When coolant temperature rises above 85°F (29°C), TVS opens to allow vacuum to be directed to EGR valve.

Fig. 1: Sectional View of Negative Backpressure EGR Valve

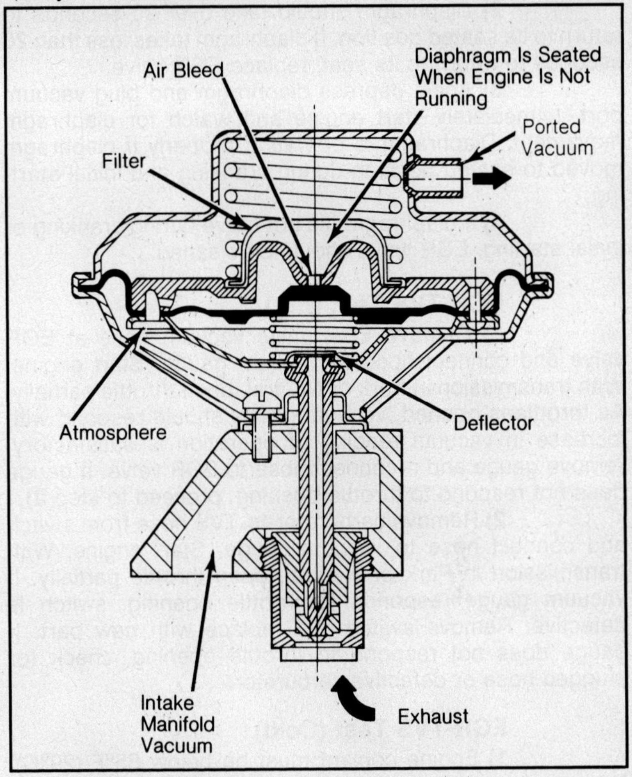

Fig. 2: Sectional View Ported EGR Valve

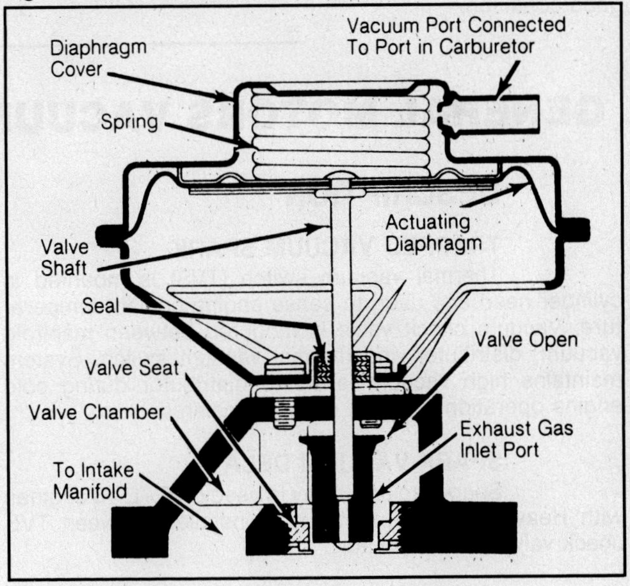

TESTING

FUNCTIONAL TESTS

Vacuum Modulated (Ported) & Negative Backpressure Types

1) Turn engine off. Disconnect vacuum hose from EGR valve. Place finger underneath valve and push up

GENERAL MOTORS EXHAUST GAS RECIRCULATION (Cont.)

to depress valve diaphragm. With diaphragm depressed, plug vacuum port on EGR valve.

2) Diaphragm should take over 20 seconds to return to its seated position. If diaphragm takes less than 20 seconds to return to its seat, replace EGR valve.

3) Again depress diaphragm and plug vacuum port. Immediately start engine and watch for diaphragm movement. Diaphragm is operating properly if diaphragm moved to seated position during cranking and initial starting.

4) If diaphragm did not move during cranking or initial starting, EGR valve should be cleaned.

EGR-TVS Test (Hot)

1) Remove EGR valve vacuum hose at EGR valve and connect hose to vacuum gauge. Start engine. With transmission in Park or Neutral, open throttle partially. As throttle is opened, vacuum gauge should respond with increase in vacuum reading. If operation is satisfactory, remove gauge and reconnect hose to EGR valve. If gauge does not respond to throttle opening, proceed to step **2)**.

2) Remove carburetor-to-TVS hose from switch and connect hose to vacuum gauge. Start engine. With transmission in Park or Neutral, open throttle partially. If vacuum gauge responds to throttle opening, switch is defective. Remove switch and replace with new part. If gauge does not respond to throttle opening, check for plugged hose or defective carburetor.

EGR-TVS Test (Cold)

1) Engine coolant must be below 85°F (29°C). Drain coolant to below level of switch. Disconnect vacuum lines and remove switch. Inspect switch to make sure it is in good condition.

2) Connect a vacuum hose to lower nipple of switch, marked "C" or "CARB". Connect vacuum gauge to upper nipple, marked "E" or "EGR". Place switch in water at 75°F (24°C) and submerge completely for 2 minutes while agitating water thoroughly. Apply 12 in. Hg to hose on lower nipple of switch. Under this condition, switch should be closed.

NOTE: **Leakage of up to 2 in. Hg in 2 minutes is allowable and does not mean a defective switch.**

3) If operation is satisfactory, reinstall switch. If switch is defective, replace with new part. Replace coolant and check level.

MAINTENANCE

EGR PASSAGE CLEANING

If inspection of EGR passages in intake manifold indicates excessive build up of exhaust deposits, passages should be cleaned. Care should be taken to ensure that all loose particles are completely removed to prevent them from clogging EGR valve or from being ingested into engine.

GENERAL MOTORS VACUUM ADVANCE SPARK CONTROL

DESCRIPTION

TRAPPED VACUUM SPARK

Thermal vacuum switch (TVS) is mounted in cylinder head and used to sense engine coolant temperature. Vacuum check valve is mounted between manifold vacuum, distributor and thermal vacuum switch. System maintains high vacuum levels to distributor during cold engine operation and cold engine acceleration.

Small sintered iron bleed orifice is provided in check valve to allow for leak-down to enable engine to be restarted if it stalls. (This applies to all models except: Light Duty California and High Altitude Emissions; 5.7L V8 with Heavy Duty emissions; all 7.4L V8 engines.)

SPARK VACUUM DELAY

Spark vacuum delay is used on 5.7L V8 engines with Heavy Duty emissions. It is installed between TVS check valve and distributor.

OPERATION

TRAPPED VACUUM SPARK

When engine temperature is below pre-set specified value, manifold vacuum signal is routed through check valve to distributor. Ports on TVS are blocked. Check valve will keep distributor vacuum at levels higher than manifold depression during vehicle acceleration.

When engine temperature is above pre-set value, TVS ports will be open to allow manifold vacuum to distributor. During this mode of operation, check valve will act as a connector.

SPARK VACUUM DELAY

As manifold vacuum increases, check valve opens and allows distributor vacuum to increase to same level. When vacuum decreases during vehicle acceleration, check valve closes and distributor vacuum will decrease at a rate controlled by internal bleed.

GENERAL MOTORS DIESEL EGR

DESCRIPTION

NOTE: California models with 6.2L diesel engines use an electronic EGR control system. See appropriate article in COMPUTERIZED ENGINE CONTROL section.

Purpose of the Exhaust Gas Recirculation (EGR) system is to limit formation of oxides of nitrogen (NOx) emissions. This is done by reducing high peak combustion temperatures at which NOx is formed. By reintroducing a small amount of exhaust gas back into the combustion chamber, high temperatures are avoided and thus NOx emissions formation is reduced.

EGR system consists of, EGR valve, exhaust pressure regulator (EPR), EGR solenoid, EPR solenoid, throttle position switch (TPS) and vacuum pump.

OPERATION

EGR valve installed on intake manifold, introduces exhaust gases to incoming fresh air at engine crossover. EPR valve installed between exhaust manifold and exhaust pipe, is used to increase exhaust backpressure during idle which increases exhaust flow through the EGR system.

TESTING

1) Warm-up engine to normal operating temperature. Remove air cleaner cover to observe operation of EGR valve.

2) With engine at idle, EGR valve should be open. If valve does not open, check and correct any electrical and hose connection which may be loose or disconnected.

3) Remove vacuum hose from EGR valve. Valve head should drop with noticeable reduction in noise. Reconnect hose.

4) At idle, hose to EGR valve should have about 20 in. Hg. If vacuum is not present, check output to vacuum pump at pump. Pump should produce a minimum of 20 in. Hg.

5) If vacuum is present at EGR valve but valve does not open and close as the hose is put on and taken off, EGR valve is stuck and should be checked and replaced if necessary.

6) Manually operate throttle lever at injection pump through 15° to 20° of travel. EGR valve should close when TPS reaches calibrated point.

7) Check Pink wire to TPS for 12 volts (key on). If 12 volts is not present, check for any loose connections, open wire and blown 20 amp gauge fuse. Correct any loose wire connections and/or change fuse.

8) With key on, Blue wire from TPS switch should also have 12 volts. Blue wire feeds EPR solenoid. At idle, if Pink wire has 12 volts but Blue wire does not, TPS is inoperative and should be changed.

9) With engine off, key on, operate throttle through 20° travel. At about 15°, TPS will cut out the 12 volts to Blue wire (EPR). At about 20°, TPS will cut in 12 volts to Yellow wire (EGR). If not, TPS is inoperative.

10) Check all electrical connections at EGR-EPR solenoid assembly. Check that all hoses are routed correctly and connected to the solenoids. If vacuum is present at solenoids and solenoids are receiving an electrical signal as previously mentioned and operation of TPS through the calibrated points does not operate the EGR and/or EPR valves, solenoid assembly is inoperative and should be replaced.

Fig. 1: Diesel EGR Valve

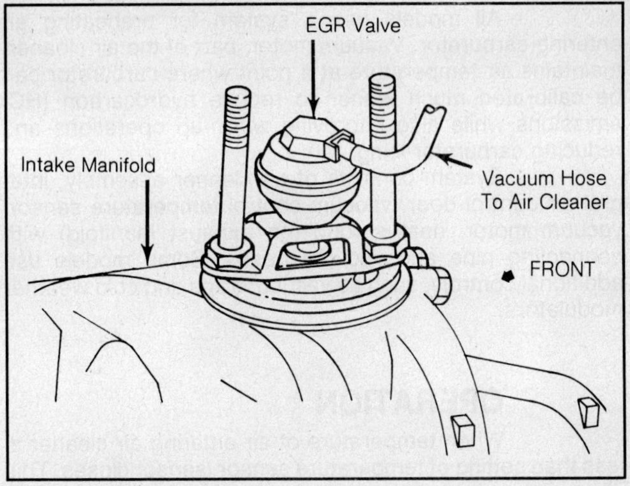

GENERAL MOTORS THERMOSTATIC AIR CLEANER

DESCRIPTION

All models use a system for preheating air entering carburetor. Vacuum motor, part of the air cleaner, maintains air temperature at a point where carburetor can be calibrated much leaner to reduce hydrocarbon (HC) emissions while also improving warm-up operations and reducing carburetor icing.

System consists of air cleaner assembly, integral air control door, vacuum control temperature sensor, vacuum motor, heat shroud (on exhaust manifold) with connecting pipe and vacuum hoses. Some models use additional controls, such as vacuum traps and cold weather modulators.

Fig. 1: General Motors V8 Engine Air Cleaner Assembly

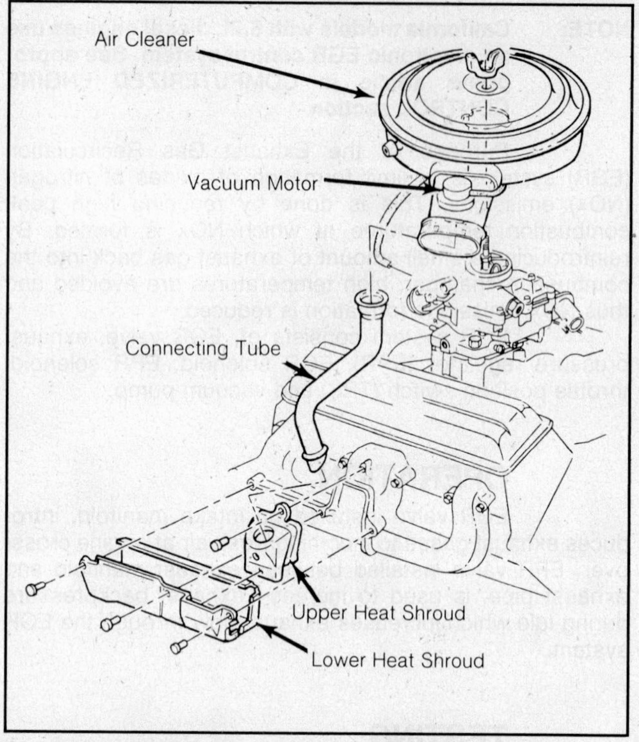

All Light Duty emission vehicles use preheated air to warm carburetor.

OPERATION

When temperature of air entering air cleaner is less than setting of temperature sensor, sensor closes. This allows engine vacuum to operate vacuum motor, which closes damper assembly to outside air. Heated air is then drawn from around exhaust manifold, through heat shroud and into air cleaner.

As air inside air cleaner warms, sensor valve begins to open. This bleeds off vacuum to vacuum motor. As vacuum to vacuum motor drops, air control door begins to open. This allows outside air to enter air cleaner. When air entering air cleaner reaches a specified temperature, air control door opens completely, thus closing off supply of heated air from around exhaust manifold.

TESTING

VACUUM CONTROL TEMPERATURE SENSOR TEST

1) With engine cold, check damper door. It should be in open snorkel position. Place thermometer inside air cleaner, near sensor.

2) With engine temperature below 80°F (27°C), start engine and run at idle. Damper door should be in closed snorkel position. When door starts to open, read thermometer in air cleaner. Temperature should be 100-140°F (38-59°C). If door does not begin to open at this temperature, replace sensor.

VACUUM MOTOR TEST

1) Check all hoses and connections for proper hook-up. With engine off, observe damper door through snorkel opening. Door should be open to outside air.

2) With external vacuum unit, apply 7 in. Hg vacuum to diaphragm assembly, through hose disconnected at sensor. Damper door should close when vacuum is applied. If not, check for vacuum leak, or binding linkage.

3) With vacuum applied, bend hose to trap vacuum in diaphragm assembly. Damper door should remain closed. If not, replace diaphragm assembly.

GENERAL MOTORS EARLY FUEL EVAPORATION

DESCRIPTION

Two Early Fuel Evaporation (EFE) systems are used on General Motors light and heavy duty trucks. EFE systems are used to provide heat to engine induction system during cold driveaway. Engines may be equipped with either electric heater type (4-cyl. & V6) or vacuum operated exhaust heat riser valve type (all others) EFE system.

Both electric and vacuum type systems provide rapid heating, resulting in faster fuel evaporation and more uniform fuel distribution. This also helps reduce choke "ON" time by warming engine faster.

OPERATION

Fig. 1: General Motors EFE System for 6-Cylinder Engines

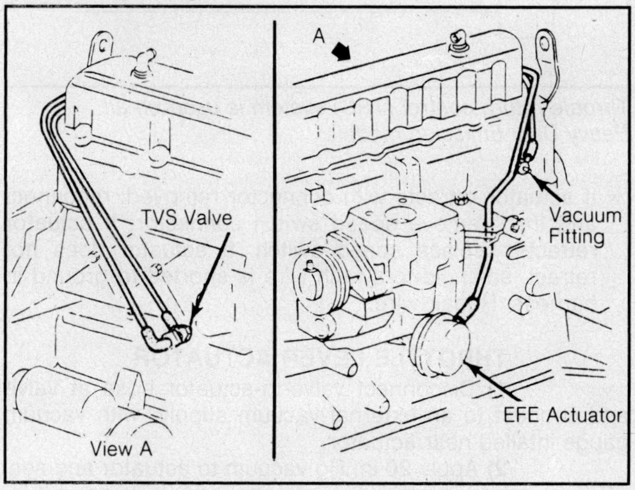

Fig. 2: General Motors EFE System for V8 Engines

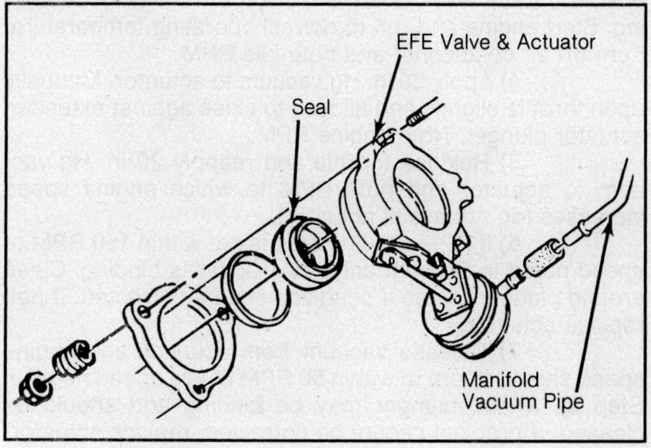

4-CYL. & V6 ENGINES

Electrical heater type system uses ceramic heater grid under primary bore of carburetor as an integral part of carburetor insulator and gasket. When engine coolant temperature is below given value, electrical current is supplied to heater through a relay.

6-CYL. & V8 ENGINES

Thermal vacuum switch is a normally closed switch which is sensitive to oil (6-Cyl.) or coolant (V8) temperature. With a cold engine, below 105°F (40°C), TVS is closed which allows manifold vacuum to actuator valve. Vacuum pulls diaphragm in actuator, closing EFE Valve.

This causes hot exhaust gases to be routed to base of carburetor. When engine temperature is above 105°F (40°C), thermal vacuum switch opens. This stops vacuum to actuator. Without vacuum, spring pushes actuator diaphragm to its at rest position and opens EFE valve.

Fig. 3: General Motors EFE System for 4-Cylinder Engines

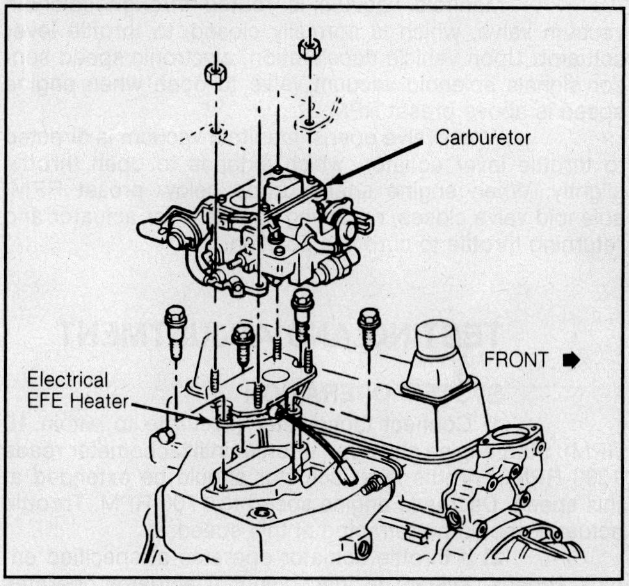

TESTING

VACUUM OPERATED TYPE

1) With engine cold, position transmission in "N" or "P" and apply parking brake. Start engine and observe movement of actuator rod and exhaust heat valve. Valve should move to its closed position.

2) If valve does not close, disconnect hose from actuator and apply 10 in. Hg vacuum to actuator. Valve should close and stay closed for at least 20 seconds. If valve does not stay closed for 20 seconds, replace actuator. Check valve rod and valve for proper operation. Repair as necessary.

3) When engine temperature reaches 105°F (40°C), exhaust heat valve should move to open position.

4) If valve does not open, disconnect hose at actuator and check for vacuum. If there is vacuum, replace TVS. If no vacuum is present, replace actuator.

ELECTRIC HEATER TYPE

With ignition on, engine off and engine cold, battery voltage should be available at EFE heater. If not, check EFE temperature switch and wiring back to ignition switch and ground. Repair as necessary.

MAINTENANCE

Periodically inspect vacuum hoses for damage, actuator for proper operation, linkage for binding and EFE valve for smooth operation.

GENERAL MOTORS THROTTLE RETURN CONTROL

DESCRIPTION

Throttle Return Control (TRC) system is used on all Heavy Duty emission models. Upon deceleration, system opens throttle slightly to reduce hydrocarbon emissions. System consists of throttle lever actuator, solenoid vacuum control valve and electronic speed sensor.

OPERATION

Manifold vacuum is routed through solenoid vacuum valve, which is normally closed, to throttle lever actuator. Upon vehicle deceleration, electronic speed sensor signals solenoid vacuum valve to open when engine speed is above preset RPM.

When valve opens, manifold vacuum is directed to throttle lever acuator, which extends to open throttle slightly. When engine speed drops below preset RPM, solenoid valve closes, retracting throttle lever actuator and returning throttle to curb idle position.

Fig. 1: Schematic of Throttle Return Control (TRC) System

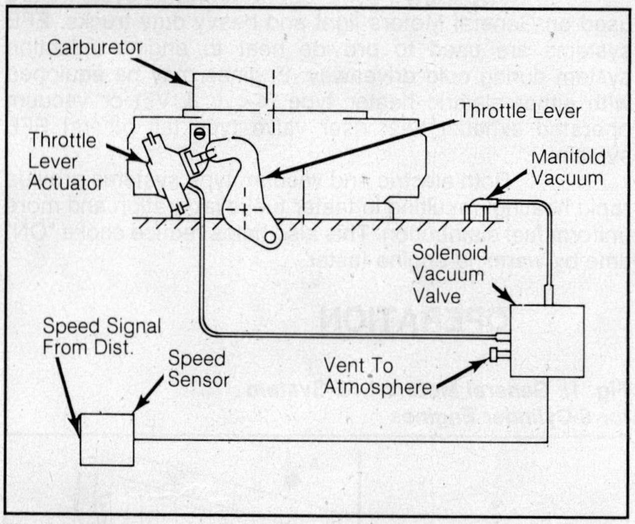

Throttle return control (TRC) system is used on all Heavy Duty Emission models.

TESTING AND ADJUSTMENT

SYSTEM OPERATION

1) Connect tachometer (accurate to within 10 RPM). Start engine and open throttle until tachometer reads 1890 RPM. Throttle lever actuator should be extended at this speed. Decrease engine speed to 1700 RPM. Throttle actuator should be retracted at this speed.

2) If throttle actuator operates at specified engine speeds, system is functioning. If actuator operates outside of RPM limits, replace speed sensor. If actuator does not operate at any speed, proceed with the following steps:

3) Using voltmeter, check for battery voltage at voltage wire terminal on solenoid valve and speed sensor. If voltage is present at one component only, repair wiring harness as required. If no voltage at both components, check engine harness connections at distributor and bulkhead connector and repair as required.

4) If battery voltage is present at solenoid valve and speed sensor, start engine and use jumper wire to ground solenoid-to-speed sensor connecting wire terminal at speed sensor. Throttle actuator should extend.

- If actuator did not extend, remove throttle actuator hose from solenoid and check solenoid orifice for blockage. If orifice is plugged, clean as required. If orifice is clear, replace solenoid.
- If actuator did extend, ground solenoid-to-switch wire terminal at speed switch. If actuator does not extend, repair speed switch-to-solenoid wire. If it extends, ensure speed switch ground wire reads ground with engine running and check speed switch-to-distributor wire connections. If actuator still does not extend with all wires properly connected and engine speed above 1890 RPM, replace speed sensor.

5) If throttle actuator remains extended at all speeds, remove electrical connector from solenoid.

- If actuator remains extended, check actuator vacuum orifice on solenoid valve for blockage. Clean orifice, and reconnect system. If actuator again remains extended, remove solenoid connector. If actuator does not retract, replace solenoid valve.
- If actuator retracts with connector removed, reconnect and then remove speed switch connector. If actuator retracts, replace speed switch. If actuator does not retract, solenoid-to-switch wire is shorted to ground in harness. Repair wire.

THROTTLE LEVER ACTUATOR

1) Disconnect valve-to-actuator hose at valve and connect to an external vacuum supply, with vacuum gauge intalled near actuator.

2) Apply 20 in. Hg vacuum to actuator and seal off vacuum source. If vacuum gauge reading drops, actuator is leaking and must be replaced.

3) To check actuator for proper operation, first ensure throttle lever, shaft and linkage work without binding. Start engine and run to normal operating temperature. Turn off air conditioner and note idle RPM.

4) Apply 20 in. Hg vacuum to actuator. Manually open throttle slightly and allow it to close against extended actuator plunger. Note engine RPM.

5) Release throttle and reapply 20 in. Hg vacuum to actuator and note RPM to which engine speed increases (do not assist actuator).

6) If RPM as just noted is not within 150 RPM of speed noted in Step **4)**, actuator plunger is binding. Clean around plunger to see if condition can be corrected. If not, replace actuator.

7) Release vacuum from actuator and engine speed should return to within 50 RPM of idle speed noted in Step **3)**. If not, plunger may be binding and should be cleaned. If problem cannot be corrected, replace actuator.

8) If engine RPM noted in Step **4)** is not to specified TRC speed, actuator must be adjusted.

9) To adjust actuator, apply 20 in. Hg vacuum to actuator. Manually open throttle slightly and allow it to close against extended actuator plunger. Turn hex-end of plunger to obtain specified speed.

NOTE: **See Emission Control Tune-Up decal for throttle lever actuator adjustment speeds.**

1985 Exhaust Emission Systems

GENERAL MOTORS VACUUM DIAGRAMS

MODEL IDENTIFICATION

Truck models, listed in tables, are identified using manufacturers letter and number designations. The letters identify vehicle model series (i.e., "C" is conventional chassis, including Pickup, Blazer and Suburban). The number reference identifies the vehicles load capacity. Refer to following charts for actual letter and number designations.

VEHICLE SERIES IDENTIFICATION

Vehicle Series	I.D. Letter
Conventional Chassis (2WD)	C
Conventional Chassis (2WD)	S
Conventional Chassis (4WD)	K
Conventional Chassis (4WD)	T
Conventional Van Chassis	G
Forward Control/Step Van Chassis	P
Astro & Safari Vans	M

VEHICLE LOAD CAPACITY

Chevrolet Number	GMC Number	Ton Capacity
10	15	1/2
10	1500	1/2
20	2500	3/4
30	3500	1
Astro	Safari	1/2

GENERAL MOTORS VACUUM DIAGRAM REFERENCE CHART

Vehicle Model, Series & Engine	Application	Transmission	Fig. No.
1.9L 4-Cylinder			
S10/15	Fed.	Man.	1
S10/15	High Alt.	Man.	2
2.2L 4-Cylinder Diesel			
S10/15	Fed.	Man.	3
S10/15	Calif.	Man.	4
2.5L			
No information.	.....	.....	.....
2.8L V6			
S10/15 & T10/15	Fed.	Man.	5
S10/15	Fed. & High Alt.	All	6
S10/15	Fed.	Auto.	7
T10	Fed.	Auto.	8
S10/15 & T10/15	Fed. & High Alt.	Auto.	9
S10/15 & T10/15	Fed. & High Alt.	Man.	10
S10/15 & T10/15	Fed.	Auto.	11
S10/15 & T10/15	Calif.	All	12
4.3L 6-Cylinder			
C10	Fed.	Auto.	13
C10/20 & K10	Fed. & High Alt.	Auto.	14
G10/20/30	Fed. & High Alt.	Auto.	15
M10	Fed. & High Alt.	Auto.	16
C10	Fed.	Auto.	17
C10	Fed. & High Alt.	Auto.	18
C10	Fed.	Man.	19
C10/20 & K10	Fed. & High Alt.	Man.	20
G10/20/30	Fed. & High Alt.	Man.	21
M10	Fed. & High Alt.	Man.	22
C10 & K10	Calif.	All	23
G10/20	Calif.	All	24
M10	Calif.	All	25
4.8L 6-Cylinder Heavy Duty			
C20/30, K20/30 & P20/30	Fed.	All	26
5.0L & 5.7L V8			
C10	Fed.	Auto.	27
C10/20 & K20	Fed.	Auto.	28
G10/20	Fed.	Auto.	29
C10/20 & K20	High Alt.	Auto.	30
G10/20/30	High Alt.	Auto.	31
C10/20 & K10	Fed. & High Alt.	Man.	32
G10/20	Fed. & High Alt.	Man.	33
C10	Fed.	Man.	34
C10 & K10/20	Fed.	Man.	35
C10 & K10	Fed.	Auto.	36
C10/20	Calif.	Auto.	37
G10/20/30	Calif.	Auto.	38

GENERAL MOTORS VACUUM DIAGRAMS (Cont.)

GENERAL MOTORS VACUUM DIAGRAM REFERENCE CHART

Vehicle Model, Series & Engine	Application	Transmission	Fig. No.
5.7L V8 Heavy Duty			
C20/30 & K20/30	Fed.	All	39
C20 & K20	Fed.	Auto.	40
G30	Fed.	Auto.	41
G30	Fed.	Auto.	42
P20/30	Fed.	All	43
C20/30, K20/30 & P30	Calif.	All	44
P30	Calif.	Man.	45
C20 & K20	Calif.	Auto.	46
G30	Calif.	Auto.	47
G30	Calif.	Auto.	48
6.2L V8 Diesel			
C10/20 & K10/20	Fed.	All	49
G20	Fed. & High Alt.	All	50
C10/20 & K10	Calif.	All	51
G20	Calif.	All	52
7.4L V8 Heavy Duty			
C20/30, K30 & P30	Fed.	All	53
P30	Fed.	All	54
C20/30 & K30	Calif.	All	55
P30	Calif.	All	56

EMISSION CONTROL DEVICE ABBREVIATIONS

AIR – Air Injection Reactor
DVTR – Diverter Valve
EFE – Early Fuel Evaporation
EGR – Exhaust Gas Recirculation
PCV – Positive Crankcase Ventilation
TRC – Throttle Return Control
TVS – Thermal Vacuum Switch

Fig. 1: 1.9L 4-Cyl. S10/15
Federal Manual Trans.

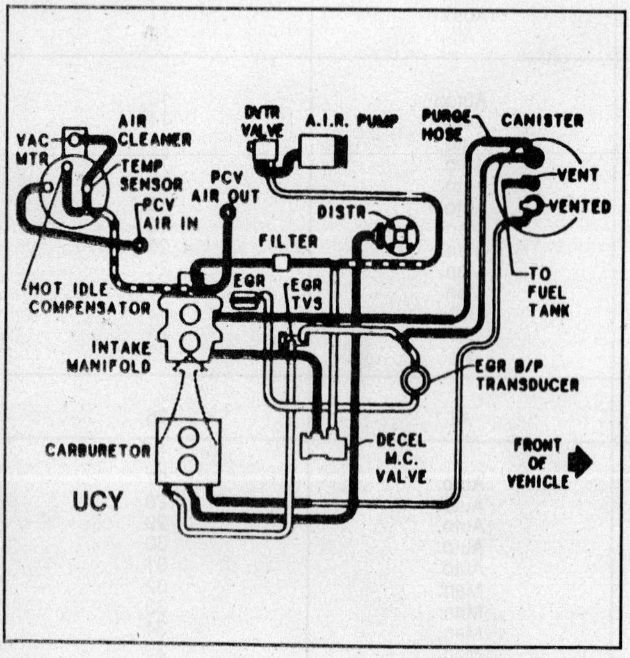

Fig. 2: 1.9L 4-Cyl. S10/15
High Altitude Manual Trans.

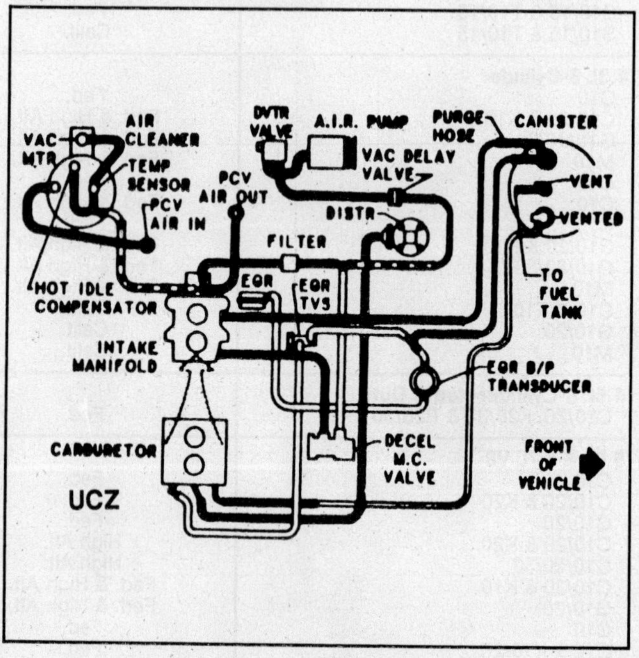

1985 Exhaust Emission Systems

GENERAL MOTORS VACUUM DIAGRAMS (Cont.)

Fig. 3: 2.2L 4-Cyl. Diesel S10/15
Federal Manual Trans.

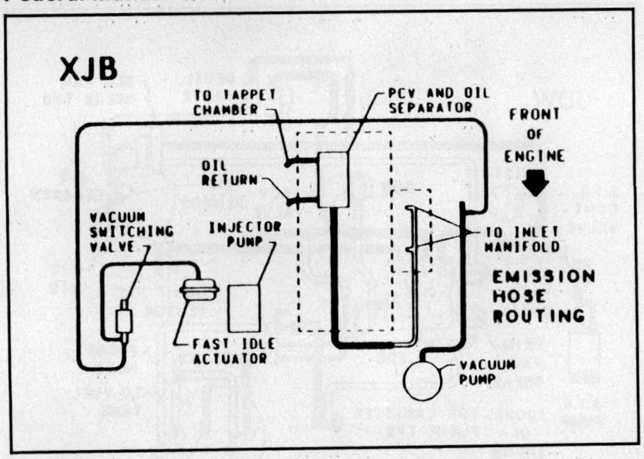

Fig. 4: 2.2L 4-Cyl. Diesel S10/15
California Manual Trans.

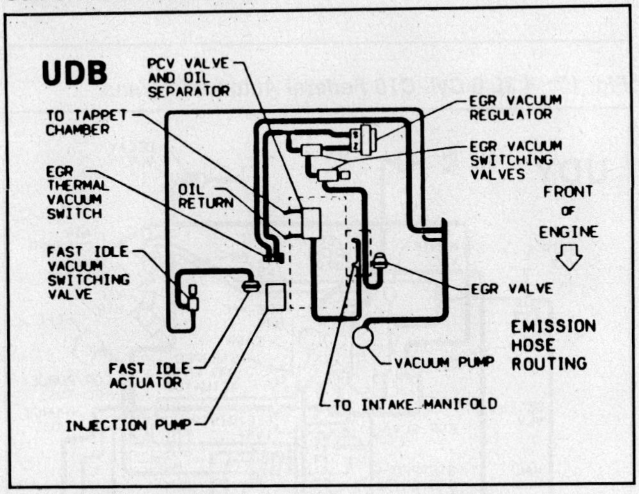

Fig. 5: 2.8L V6 S10/15 & T10/15
Federal Manual Trans.

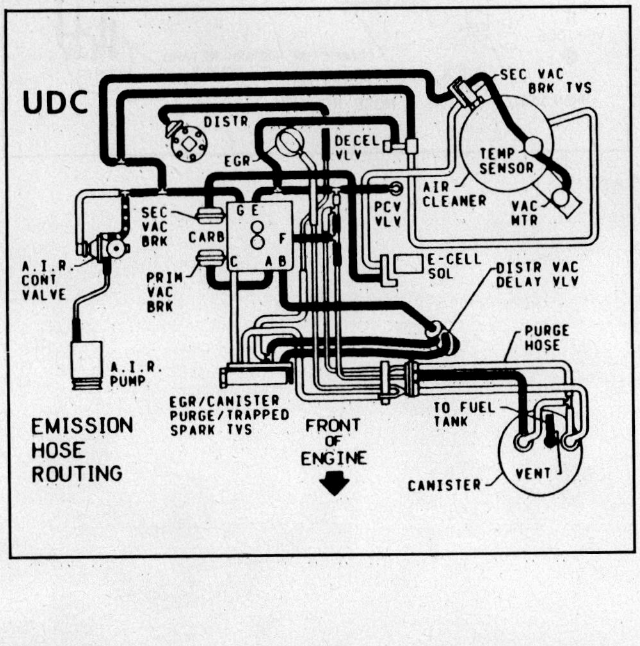

Fig. 6: 2.8L V6 S10/15
Fed. & High Alt. All Trans. (UDF, UDL, UDN)

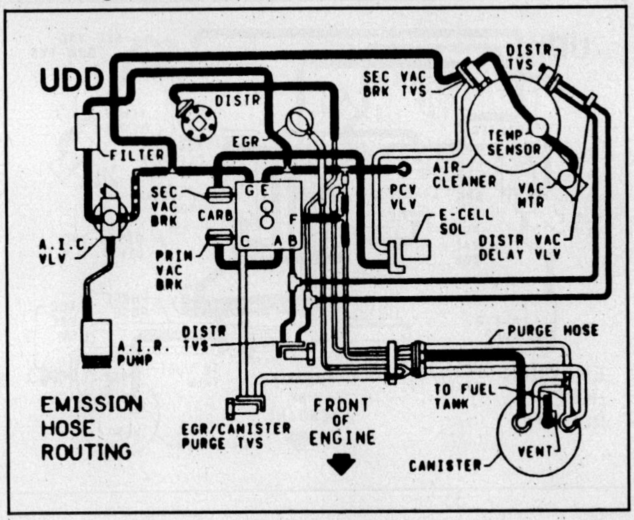

Fig. 7: 2.8L V6 S10/15 Federal Automatic Trans.

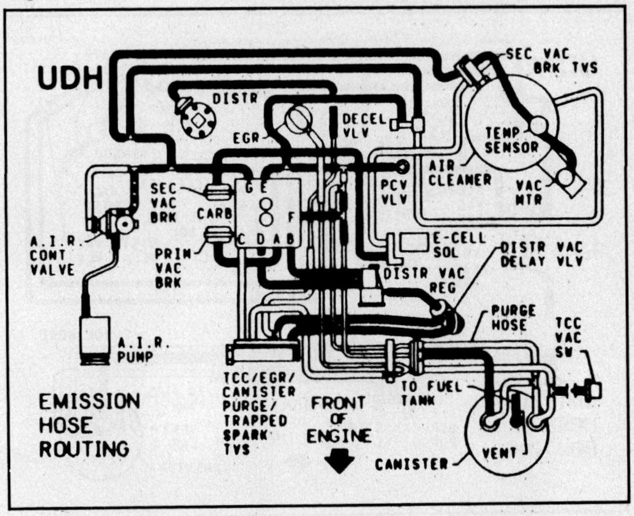

Fig. 8: 2.8L V6 T10 Federal Automatic Trans.

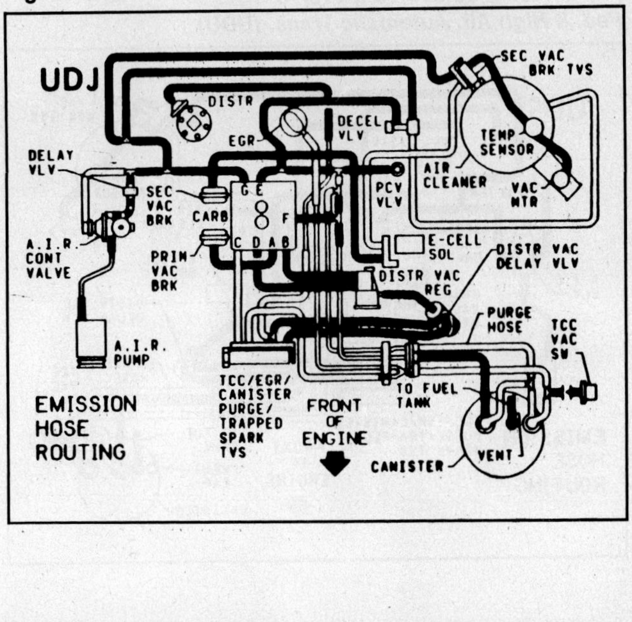

1985 Exhaust Emission Systems

GENERAL MOTORS VACUUM DIAGRAMS (Cont.)

Fig. 9: 2.8L V6 S10/15 & T10/15
Fed. & High Alt. Automatic Trans. (UDR, UDT)

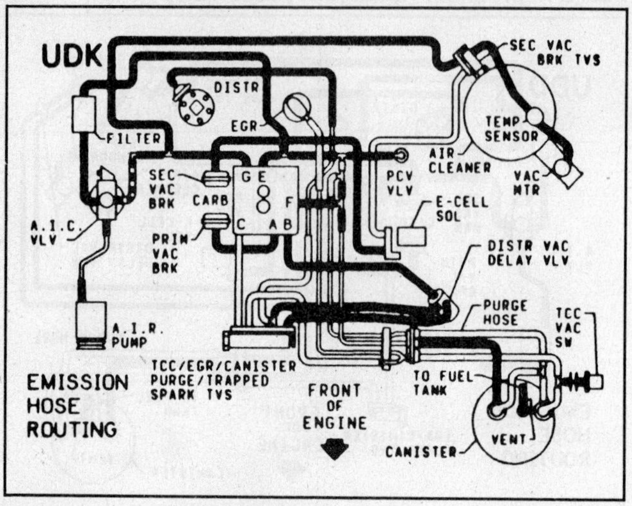

Fig. 10: 2.8L V6 S10/15 & T10/15
Fed. & High Alt. Manual Trans. (UDP)

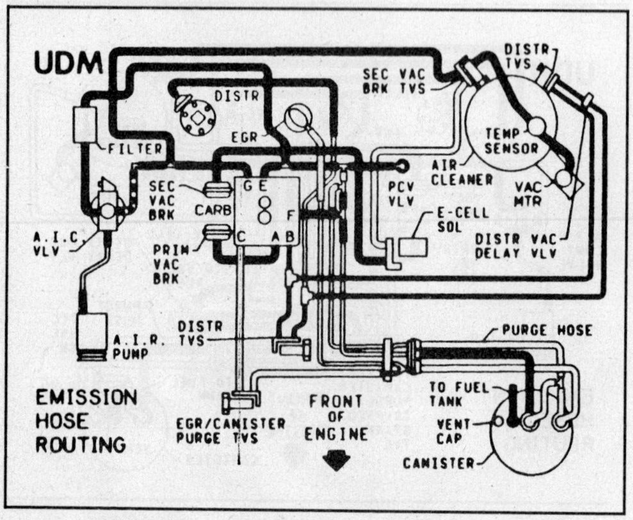

Fig. 11: 2.8L V6 S10/15 & T10/15
Fed. & High Alt. Automatic Trans. (UDU)

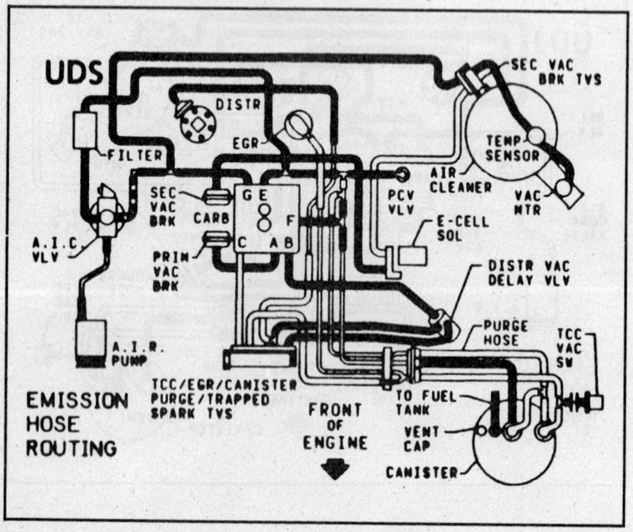

Fig. 12: 2.8L V6 S10/15 & T10/15
California Automatic Trans. (UDU)

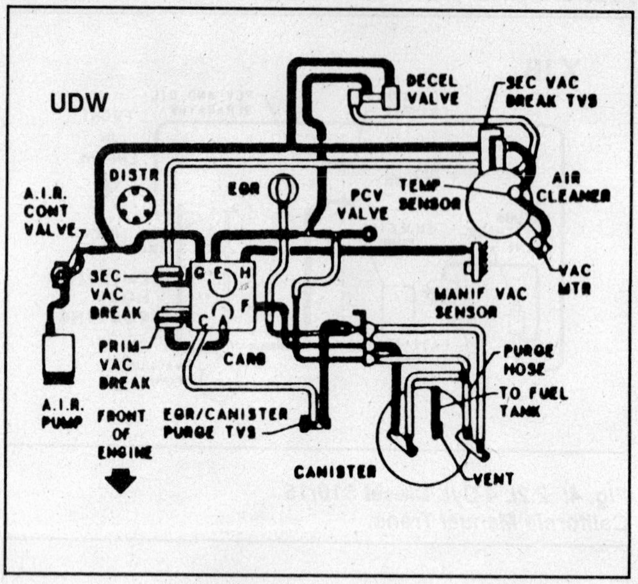

Fig. 13: 4.3L 6-Cyl. C10 Federal Automatic Trans.

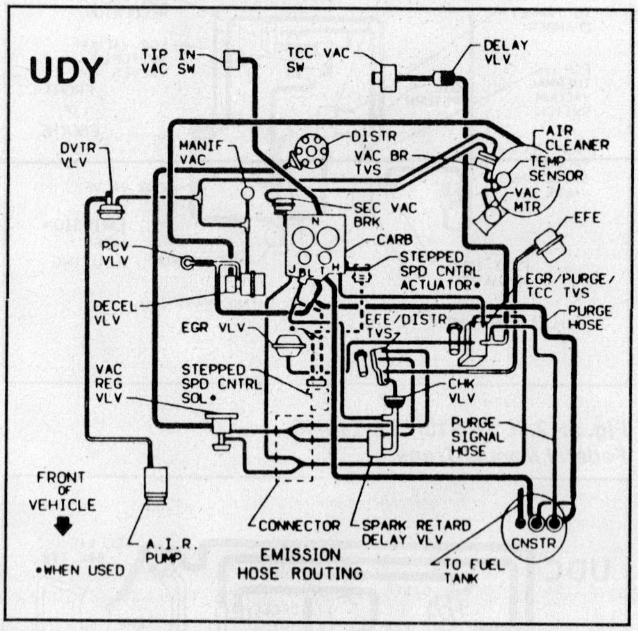

1985 Exhaust Emission Systems

GENERAL MOTORS VACUUM DIAGRAMS (Cont.)

***Fig. 14:* 4.3L 6-Cyl. C10/20 & K10**
Fed. & High Alt. Automatic Trans. (UFR, DZY)

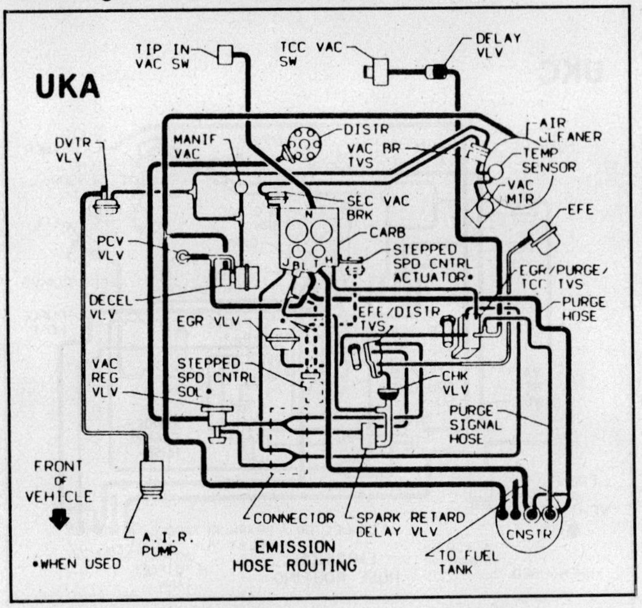

***Fig. 16:* 4.3L 6-Cyl. M10**
Fed. & High Alt. Automatic Trans. (UFT)

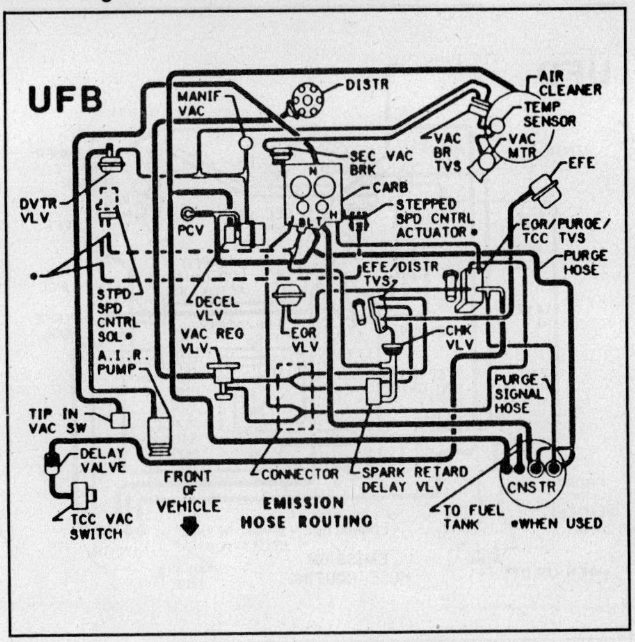

***Fig. 15:* 4.3L 6-Cyl. G10/20/30**
Fed. & High Alt. Automatic Trans. (UFA, UFF, UFS, UFW)

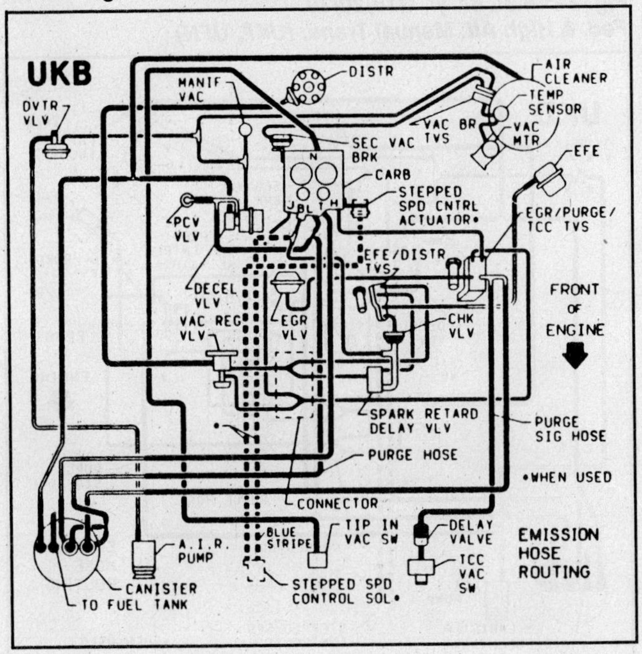

***Fig. 17:* 4.3L 6-Cyl. C10 Federal Automatic Trans.**

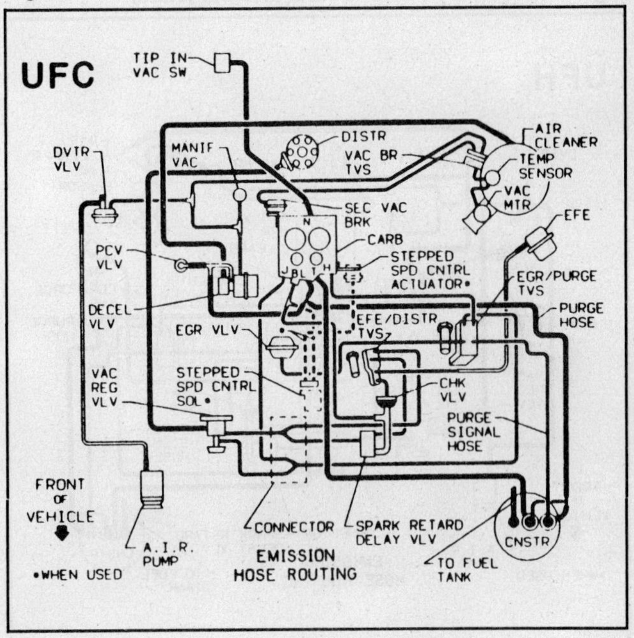

1985 Exhaust Emission Systems

GENERAL MOTORS VACUUM DIAGRAMS (Cont.)

Fig. 18: 4.3L 6-Cyl. C10
Fed. & High Alt. Automatic Trans. (UFU)

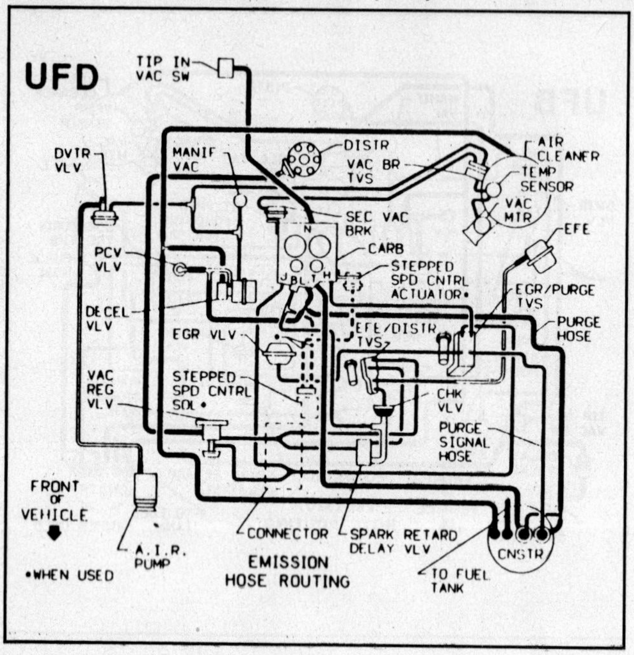

Fig. 20: 4.3L 6-Cyl. C10/20 & K10
Fed.& High Alt. Manual Trans. (UFJ, UFM)

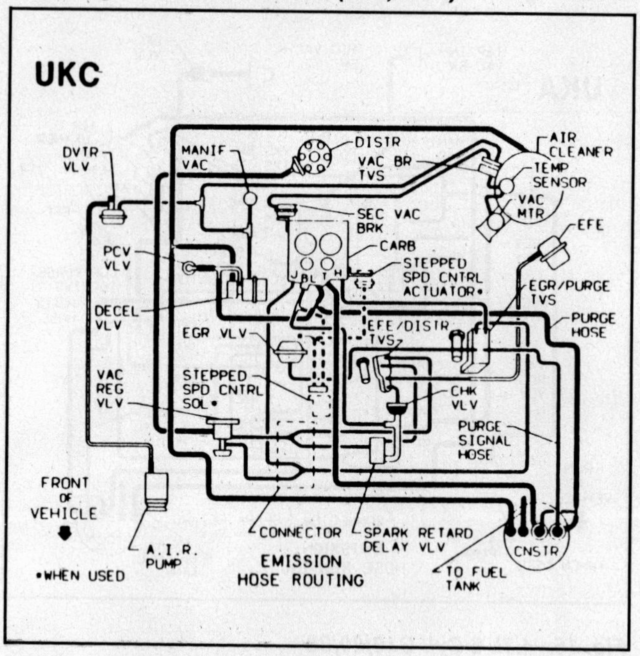

Fig. 19: 4.3L 6-Cyl. C10 Federal Manual Trans.

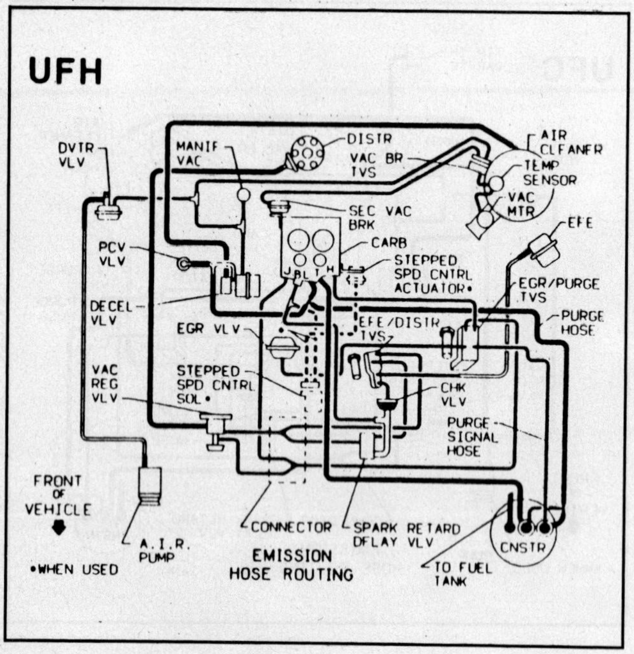

Fig. 21: 4.3L 6-Cyl. G10/20/30
Fed. & High Alt. Manual Trans. (UKF, UFN)

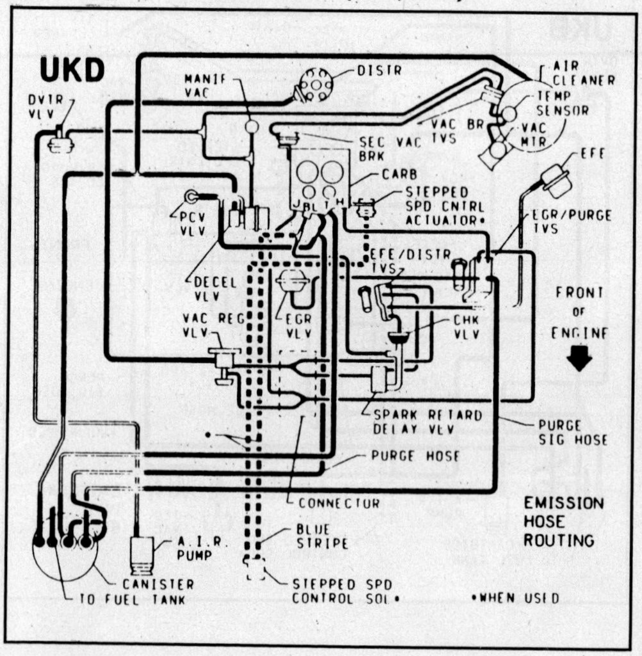

1985 Exhaust Emission Systems

GENERAL MOTORS VACUUM DIAGRAMS (Cont.)

Fig. 22: 4.3L 6-Cyl. M10 Fed. & High Alt. Manual Trans. (UFP)

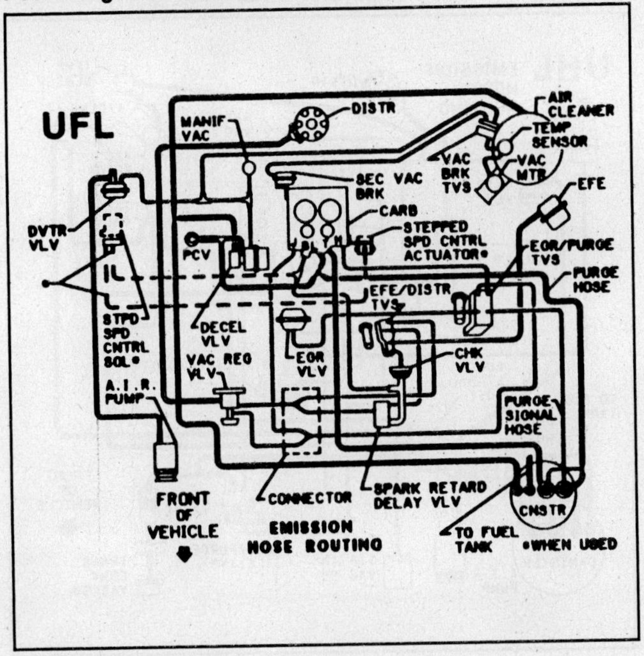

Fig. 23: 4.3L 6-Cyl. C10 & K10 California All Trans.

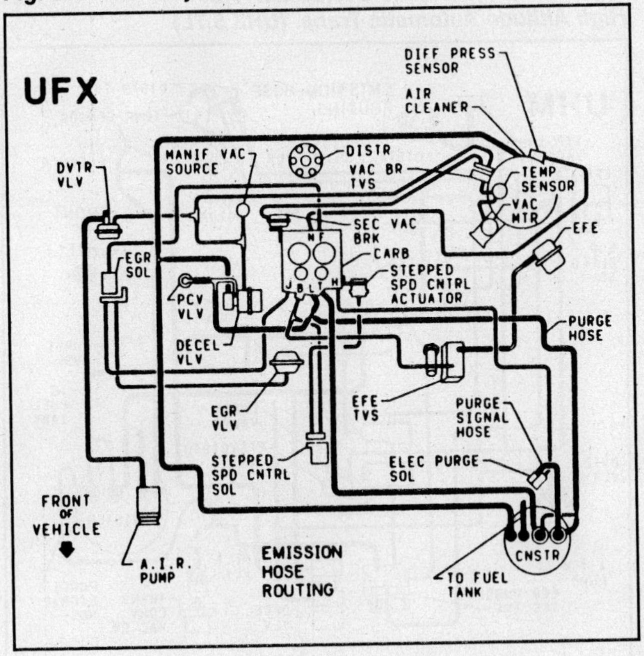

Fig. 24: 4.3L 6-Cyl. G10/20 California All Trans.

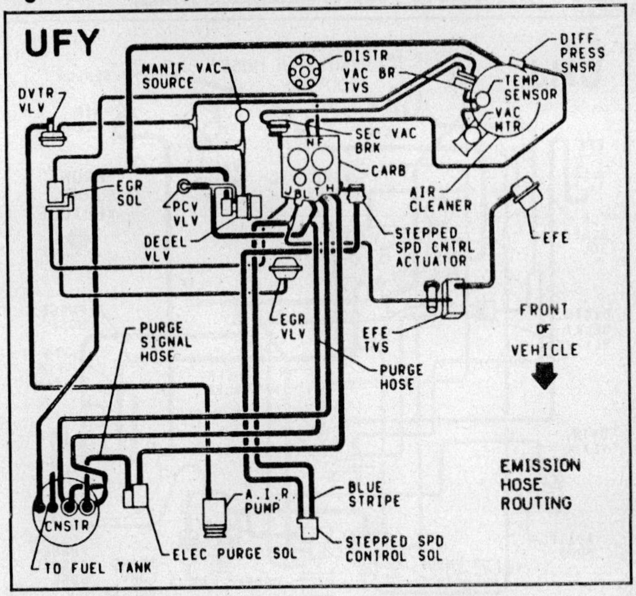

Fig. 25: 4.3L 6-Cyl. M10 California All Trans.

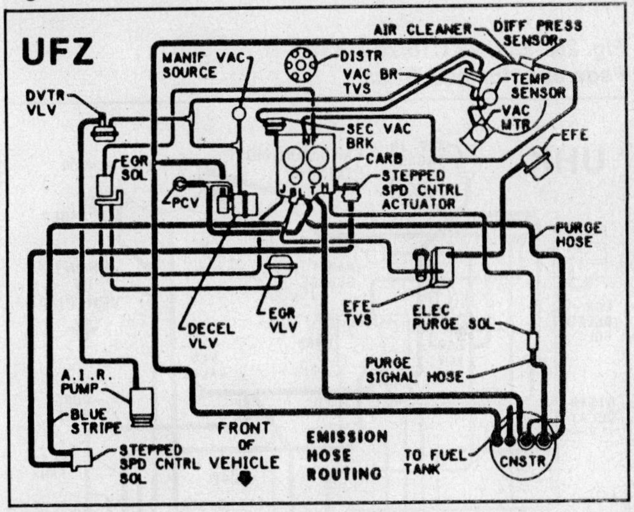

Fig. 26: 4.8L 6-Cyl. Heavy Duty C20/30 & K20/30 Federal All Trans. (UKR)

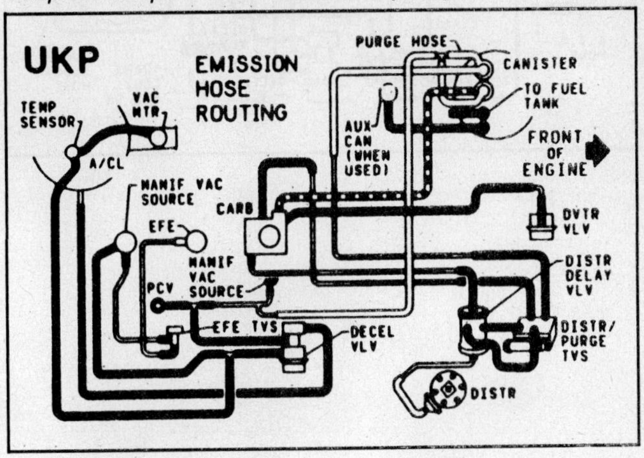

1985 Exhaust Emission Systems

GENERAL MOTORS VACUUM DIAGRAMS (Cont.)

Fig. 27: 5.0L V8 C10 Federal Automatic Trans.

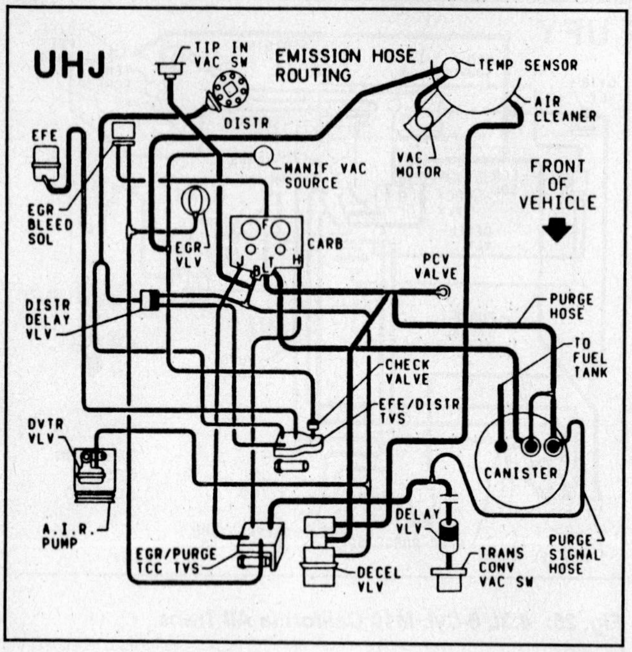

Fig. 28: 5.0L V8 C10/20 & K10 Federal Automatic Trans.

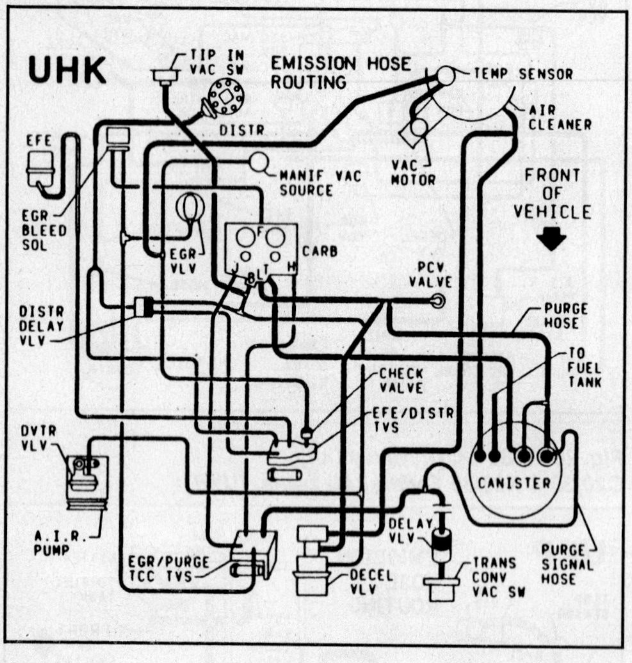

Fig. 29: 5.0L & 5.7L V8 G10/20/30 Federal Automatic Trans. (UHY 5.7L)

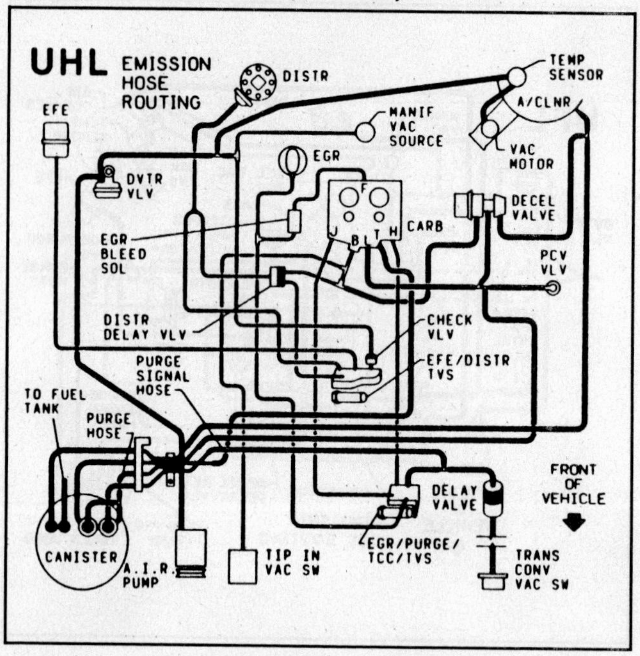

Fig. 30: 5.0L & 5.7L V8 C10/20 & K10/20 High Altitude Automatic Trans. (UHZ 5.7L)

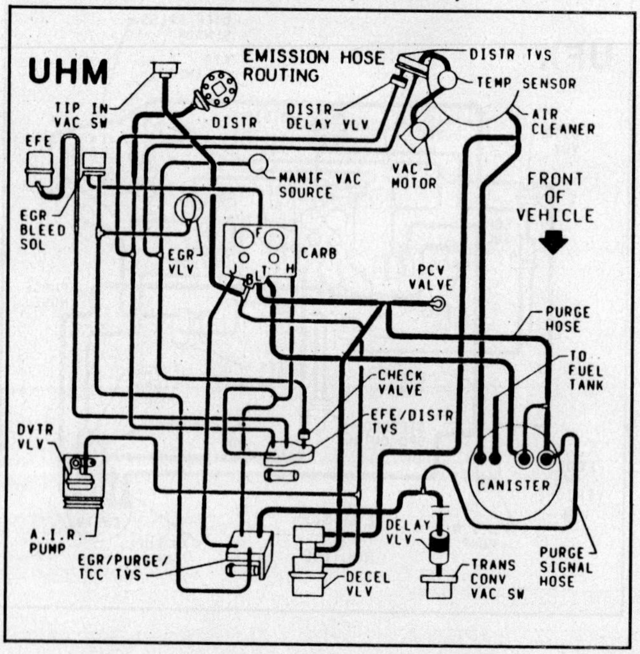

1985 Exhaust Emission Systems

GENERAL MOTORS VACUUM DIAGRAMS (Cont.)

***Fig. 31:* 5.0L & 5.7L V8 G10/20/30**
High Altitude Automatic Trans. (UJA 5.7L)

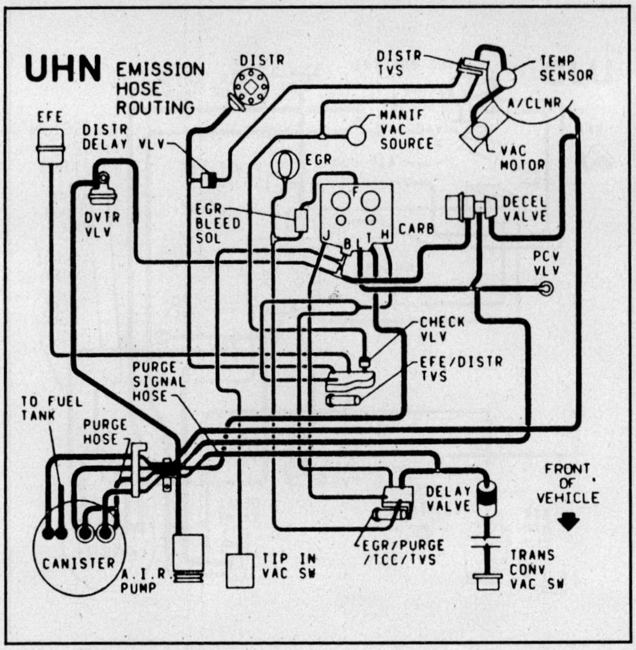

***Fig. 33:* 5.0L V8 G10/20**
Fed. & High Alt. Manual Trans. (UHW 5.0L)

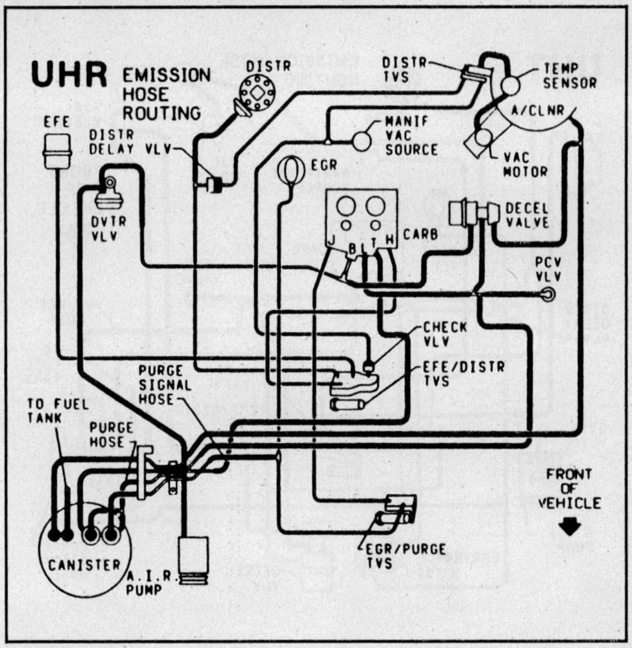

***Fig. 32:* 5.0L & 5.7L V8 C10/20 & K10**
Fed. & High Alt. Manual Trans. (UHU 5.0L, UJC 5.7L)

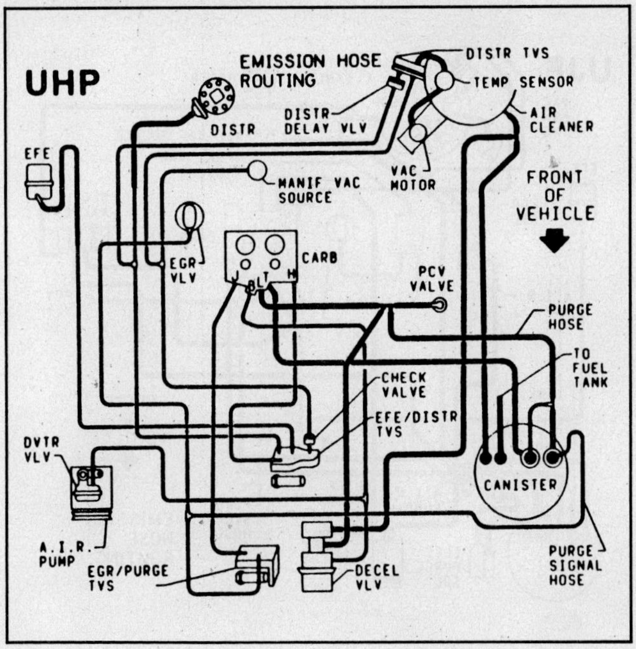

***Fig. 34:* 5.0L V8 C10 Federal Manual Trans.**

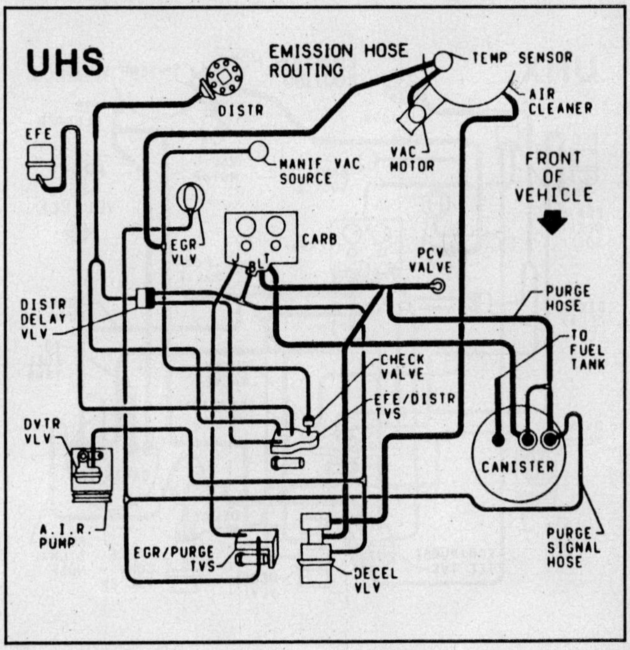

1985 Exhaust Emission Systems

GENERAL MOTORS VACUUM DIAGRAMS (Cont.)

Fig. 35: 5.0L & 5.7L V8 C10/20 & K10/20 Federal Manual Trans. (UJB 5.7L)

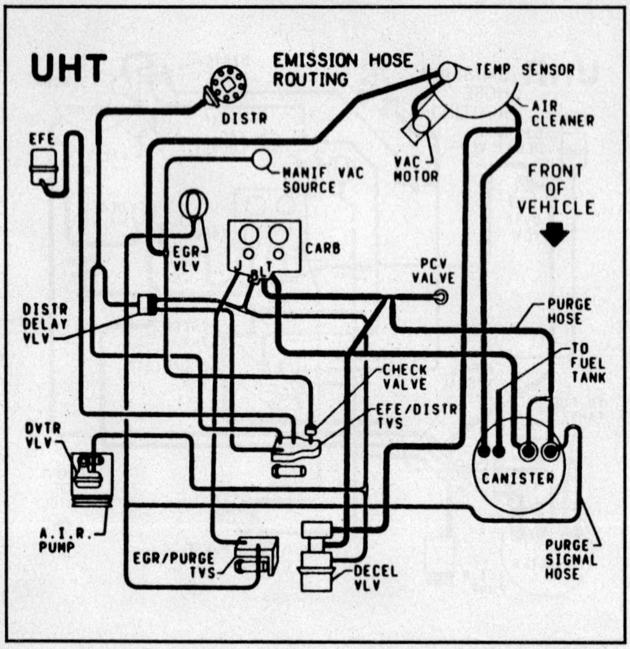

Fig. 37: 5.0L & 5.7L V8 C10 & K10 California Automatic Trans. (UJH 5.7L)

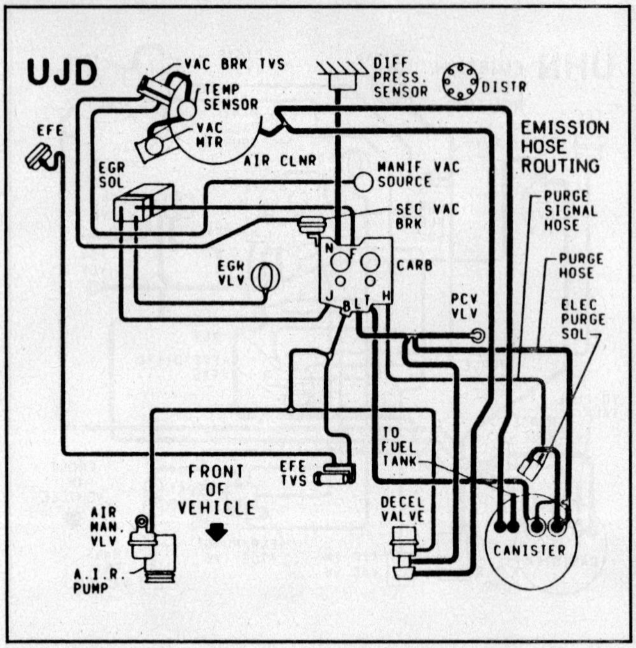

Fig. 36: 5.7L V8 C10 & K10 Federal Automatic Trans.

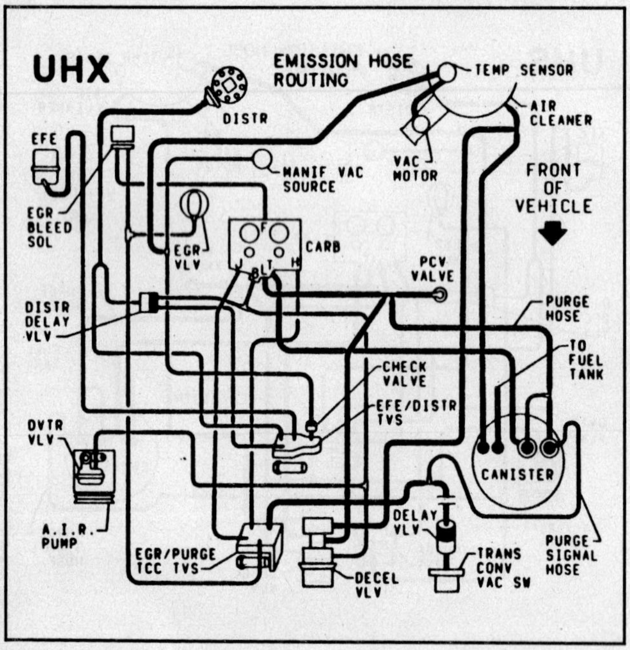

Fig. 38: 5.0L & 5.7L V8 G10/20/30 California Automatic Trans. (UJJ 5.7L)

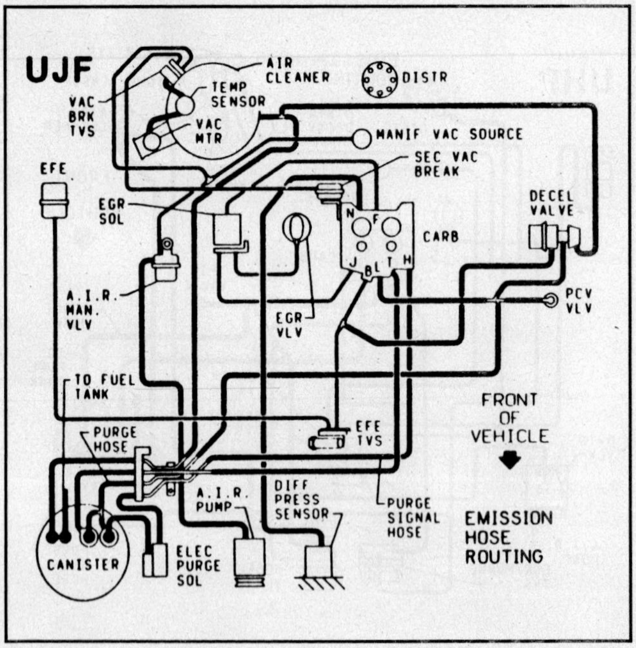

1985 Exhaust Emission Systems

GENERAL MOTORS VACUUM DIAGRAMS (Cont.)

Fig. 39: 5.7L V8 Heavy Duty C20/30 & K20/30 Federal All Trans.

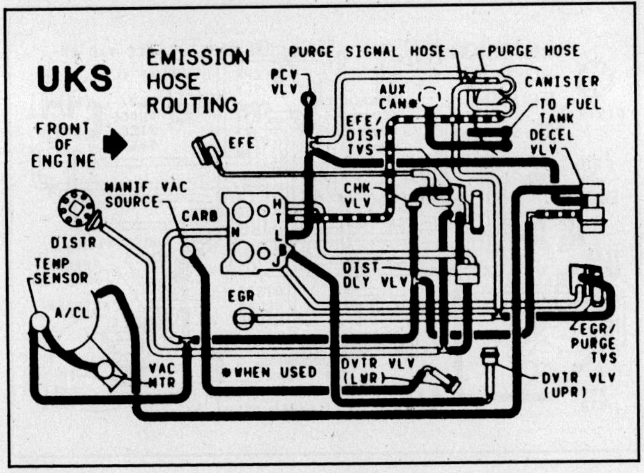

Fig. 40: 5.7L V8 Heavy Duty C20 & K20 Federal Automatic Trans.

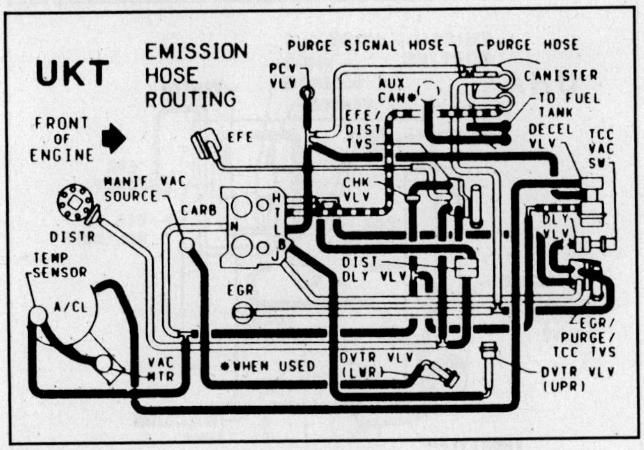

Fig. 41: 5.7L V8 Heavy Duty C30 Federal Automatic Trans. (UKX)

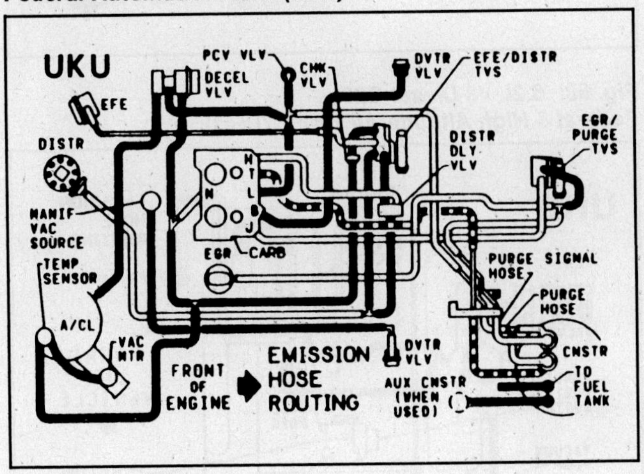

Fig. 42: 5.7L V8 Heavy Duty G30 Federal Automatic Trans.

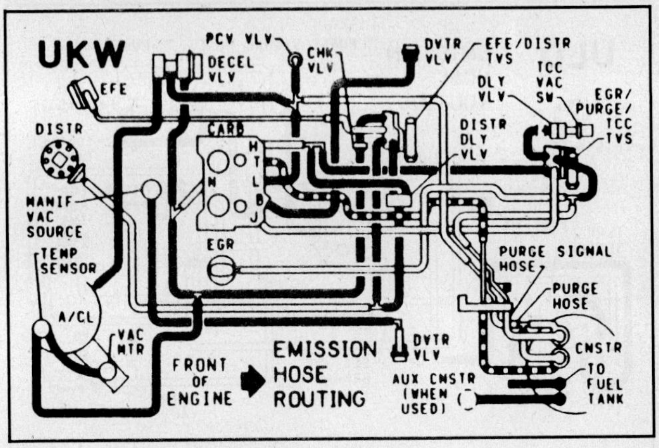

Fig. 43: 5.7L V8 Heavy Duty P20/30 Federal All Trans. (UJZ)

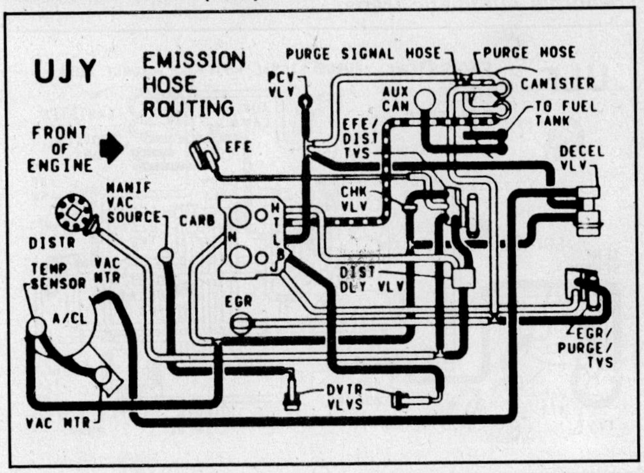

Fig. 44: 5.7L V8 Heavy Duty C20/30, K20/30 & P30 California All Trans.

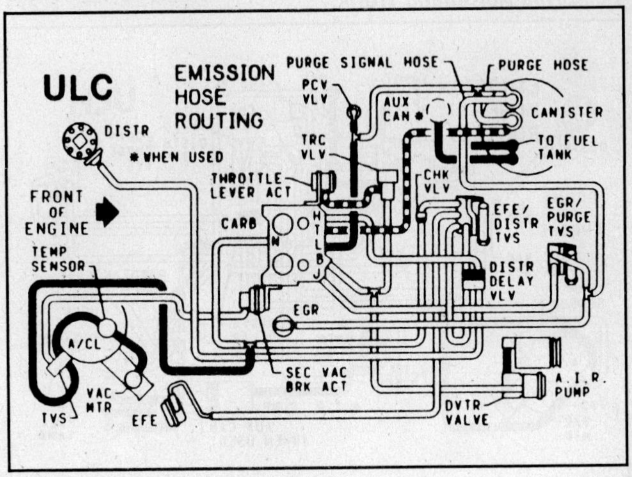

1985 Exhaust Emission Systems

GENERAL MOTORS VACUUM DIAGRAMS (Cont.)

Fig. 45: 5.7L V8 Heavy Duty G30
California Manual Trans.

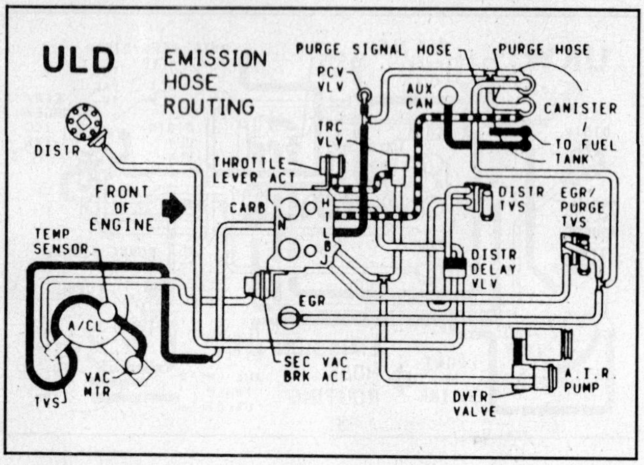

Fig. 46: 5.7L V8 Heavy Duty C20 & K20
California Automatic Trans.

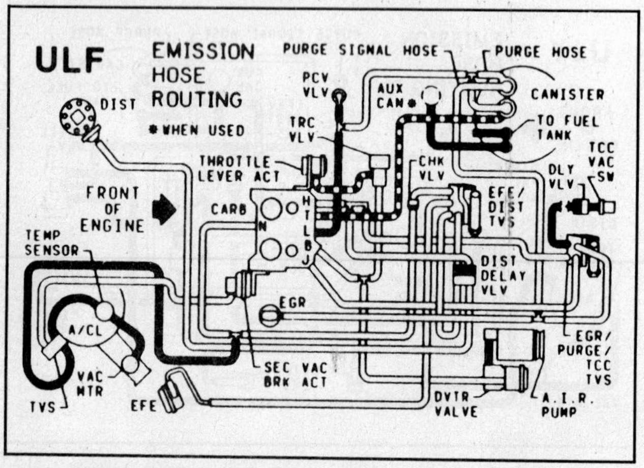

Fig. 47: 5.7L V8 Heavy Duty G30
California Automatic Trans.

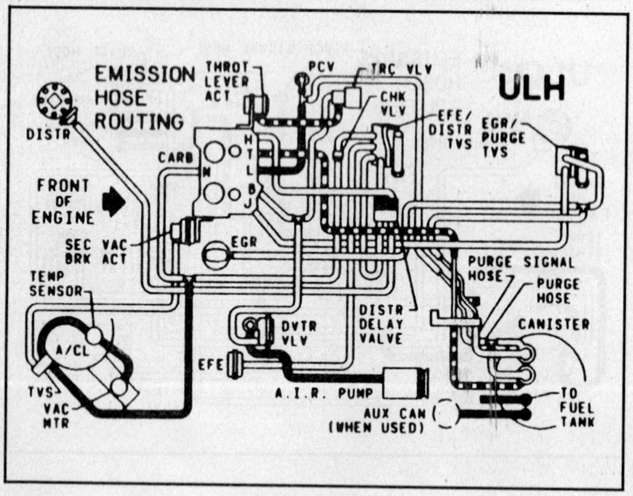

Fig. 48: 5.7L V8 Heavy Duty G30
California Automatic Trans.

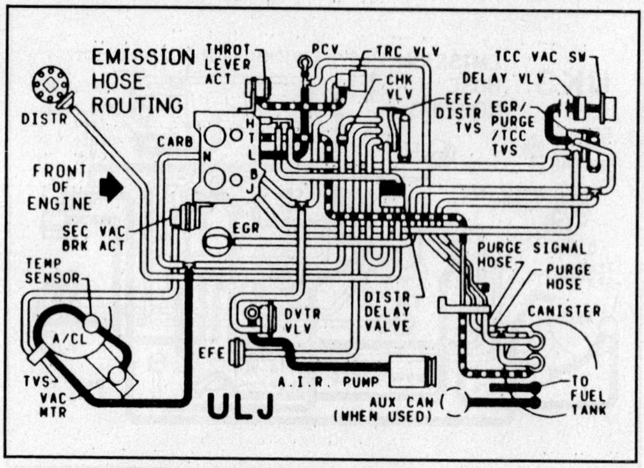

Fig. 49: 6.2L V8 Diesel C10/20 & K10/20
Federal All Trans. (UHC)

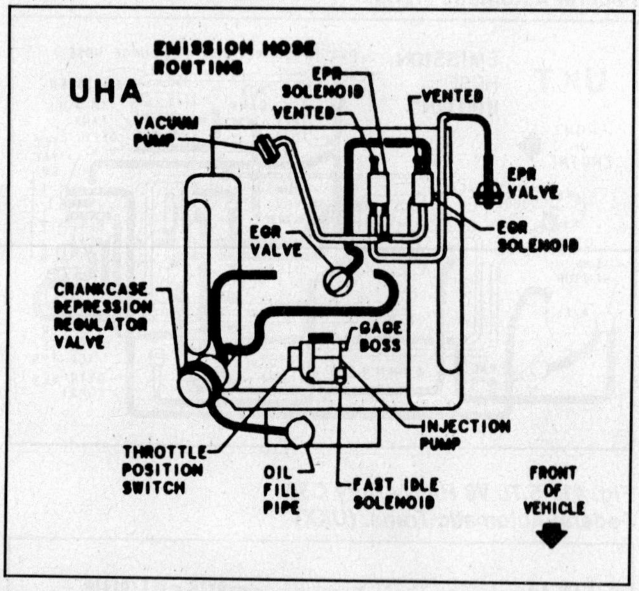

Fig. 50: 6.2L V8 Diesel G20
Federal & High Altitude All Trans. (UHD)

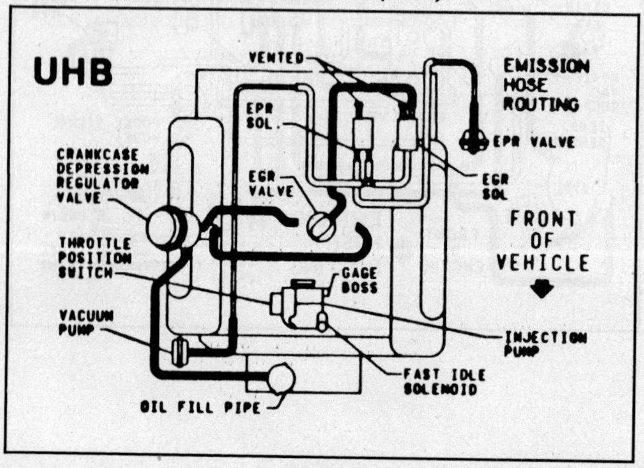

1985 Exhaust Emission Systems

GENERAL MOTORS VACUUM DIAGRAMS (Cont.)

Fig. 51: 6.2L V8 Diesel C10/20 & K10 California All Trans.

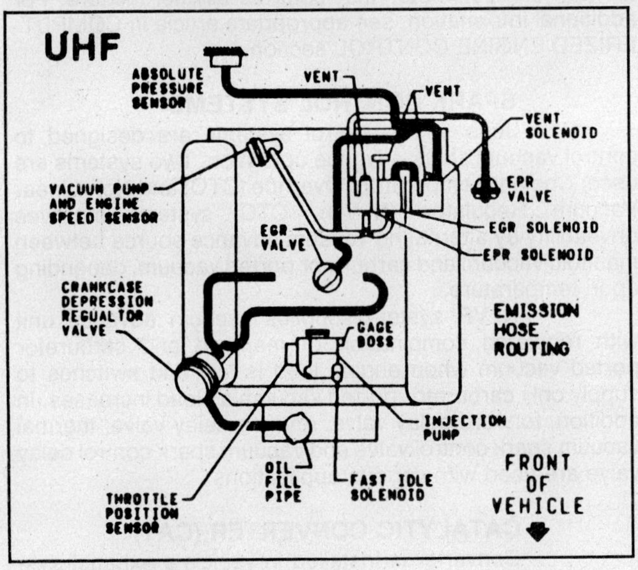

Fig. 52: 6.2L V8 Diesel G20 California All Trans.

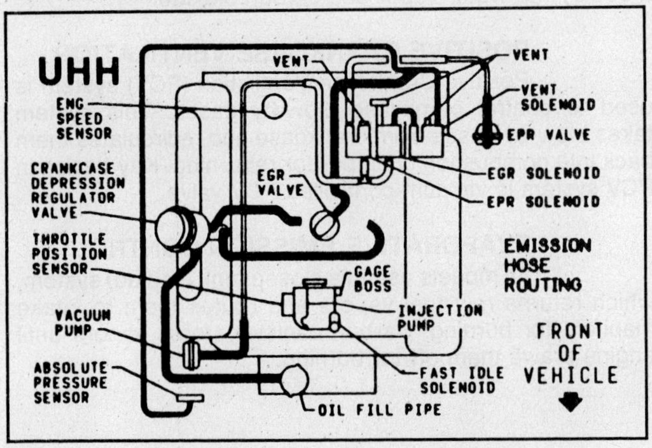

Fig. 53: 7.4L V8 Heavy Duty C20/30, K30 & P30 Federal All Trans.

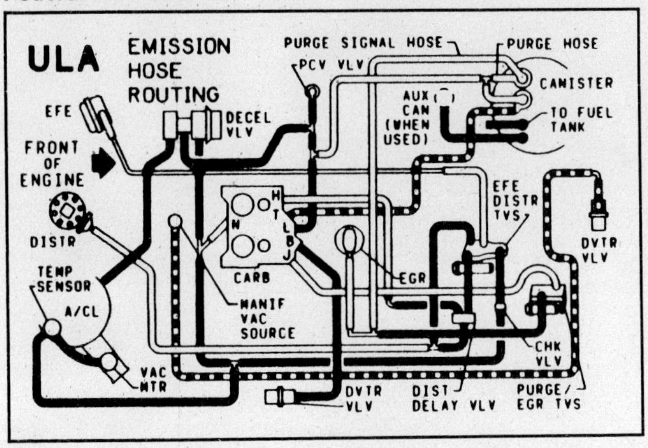

Fig. 54: 7.4L V8 Heavy Duty P30 Federal All Trans.

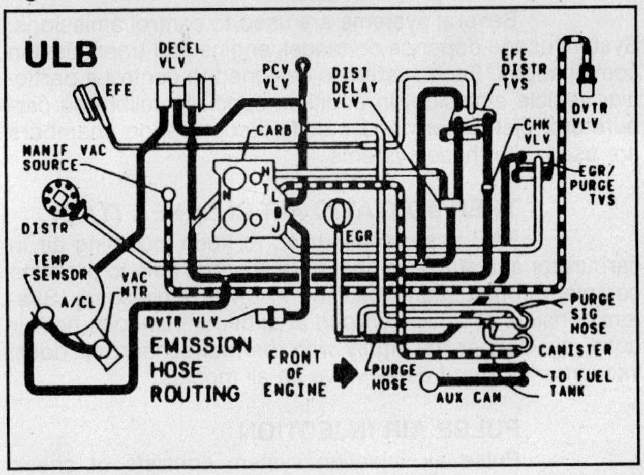

Fig. 55: 7.4L V8 Heavy Duty C20/30 & K30 California All Trans.

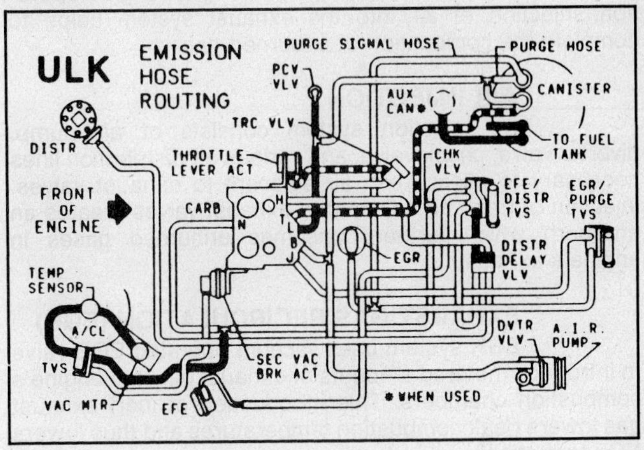

Fig. 56: 7.4L V8 Heavy Duty P30 California All Trans.

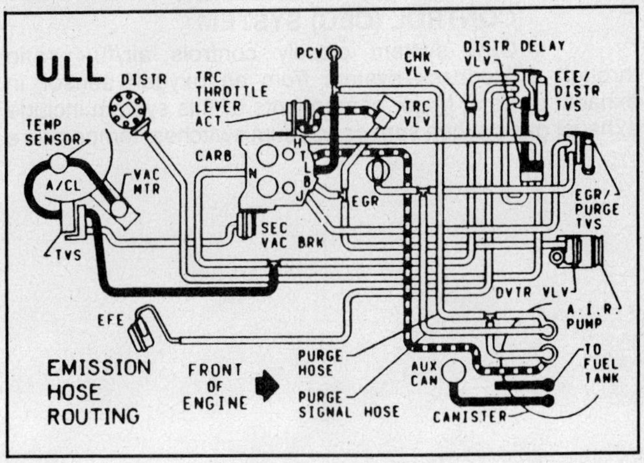

1985 Exhaust Emission Systems

JEEP SYSTEMS

DESCRIPTION

Several systems are used to control emissions. System usage depends on model, engine and transmission combinations. Each system is designed to control a particular vehicle emission. In addition, specially calibrated carburetors, distributors and modified combustion chambers are used with these systems.

THERMOSTATIC AIR CLEANER (TAC)

TAC assembly is used to keep incoming air in carburetor at a stable temperature which is able to promote complete combustion (resulting in fewer emissions). System consists of a heat shroud at exhaust manifold, hot air hose, air cleaner assembly with thermal sensor, air door, vacuum motor and delay valve on all models.

PULSE AIR INJECTION

Pulse air injection system consists of check valves, control valves, control valve solenoids and various lines and hoses. Air is injected either at the front exhaust pipe or at catalytic converter, depending on engine operation. Injection of air into the exhaust system helps to complete the combustion of unburned gases.

AIR INJECTION

Air injection system consists of air pump, diverter valve, check valve, and various air distribution lines necessary to inject fresh air adjacent to exhaust valves. Injection of fresh air adjacent to exhaust valves creates an afterburn which further consumes unburned gases in engine's exhaust.

EXHAUST GAS RECIRCULATION (EGR)

EGR system uses vacuum operated EGR valve to introduce metered amounts of exhaust gas into engine's combustion chambers. This introduction of inert exhaust gas lowers peak combustion temperatures and thus lowers NOx formations.

COMPUTERIZED EMISSION CONTROL (CEC) SYSTEM

CEC system closely controls air/fuel ratio through a feedback system from an oxygen sensor in exhaust system. Major components of this system include exhaust gas oxygen sensor, vacuum switches, temperature switches, Micro Computer Unit (MCU) and special carburetor with stepper motor that controls air/fuel mixture. For additional information, see appropriate article in COMPUTERIZED ENGINE CONTROL section.

SPARK CONTROL SYSTEMS

Jeep spark control systems are designed to control vacuum spark advance operation. Two systems are used: Coolant Temperature Override (CTO) and Non-Linear Vacuum Regulator (NLVR). CTO system improves driveability by alternating vacuum advance source between manifold vacuum and carburetor ported vacuum, depending upon temperature.

NLVR system supplies vacuum advance unit with regulated combination of manifold and carburetor ported vacuum when engine load is low and switches to supply only carburetor ported vacuum as load increases. In addition, forward delay valve, reverse delay valve, thermal vacuum spark control valve and vacuum spark control delay valve are used with various applications.

CATALYTIC CONVERTER (CAT)

Converter is installed in vehicle's exhaust system to aid in reduction of exhaust emissions. This unit changes unburned hydrocarbons (HC) and carbon monoxide (CO) into water vapor and carbon dioxide.

POSITIVE CRANKCASE VENTILATION

Positive Crankcase Ventilation (PCV) system is used to control crankcase blow-by gases. This system takes blow-by gases from crankcase and recirculates them back into combustion chamber for reburning. Key device in PCV system is vacuum-controlled PCV valve.

EVAPORATIVE EMISSION CONTROL

All models use this closed tank (sealed) system, which returns raw fuel vapors and routes them to intake manifold for burning. Carbon canister stores vapors until engine draws them off for burning.

JEEP EXHAUST GAS RECIRCULATION

DESCRIPTION

Purpose of the Exhaust Gas Recirculation (EGR) system is to limit formation of oxides of nitrogen (NOx) emissions. This is done by reducing high peak combustion temperatures at which NOx is formed. By reintroducing some exhaust gas back into combustion chamber, high temperatures are avoided and thus NOx emissions formation is reduced.

System consists of vacuum-operated EGR valve and coolant temperature override (CTO) switch. In addition, some models are equipped with air cleaner-mounted thermal vacuum switch (TVS), and some are equipped with an EGR vacuum dump valve.

OPERATION

When EGR valve receives vacuum signal from carburetor, through CTO switch, EGR valve opens and meters gases from exhaust manifold into intake manifold. Individual component operation is as follows:

EGR VALVE

EGR valve is mounted on spacer plate located beneath carburetor on 4-cylinder models, on machined surface at rear of intake manifold on V6 and V8 models, and on side of intake manifold on 6-cylinder models. Exhaust gas is drawn from exhaust crossover passage in V6, V8 and 4-cylinder engines and from an area near heat riser in 6-cylinder engines. Two types of EGR valves are used: Valve without backpressure sensor and valve with integral backpressure sensor.

EGR Valve w/o Integral Backpressure Sensor

EGR valves are calibrated by use of different shapes of valve pintles. Valve is normally held closed by spring (above diaphragm). Valve opens by overcoming spring tension when vacuum is sensed through coolant temperature override switch (CTO) and backpressure sensor (if used).

EGR Valve w/Integral Backpressure Sensor

Calibration is accomplished by use of different diaphragm spring loads and flow control orifices. This integral type unit combines EGR valve and backpressure sensor functions into one component. Restrictor plate is required with some engines.

Exhaust gas exerts backpressure inside exhaust manifold whenever engine is running. This pressure is conducted through hollow pintle stem into EGR diaphragm control chamber. If this pressure is great enough to overcome spring tension against diaphragm, diaphragm is moved against bleed valve and exhaust gas flow begins.

COOLANT TEMPERATURE OVERRIDE (CTO) SWITCH

Coolant temperature override (CTO) switch is located in coolant passage at right rear of cylinder head on 4-cylinder engines, at coolant passage of intake manifold, or at right rear corner of intake manifold near EGR valve on V8 engines, or at left front side of cylinder block on 6-cylinder engines.

Inner port of switch is connected to EGR spark port on carburetor and outer port is connected to EGR valve, or TVS. Switch opens at 100°F (38°C) for 4-cylinder engines, or 115°F (46°C) for 6-cylinder, V6 and V8 engines. Below these temperatures, no EGR is possible.

Fig. 1: Typical Jeep V8 Engine EGR System

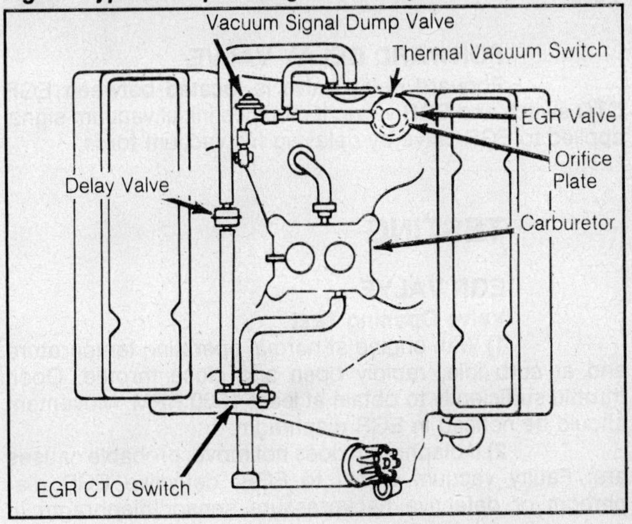

THERMAL VACUUM SWITCH (TVS)

Used only on 6-cylinder and V8 engines, this switch is located in air cleaner and acts as on-off switch for EGR system. It is controlled by ambient temperature in air cleaner. Switch controls vacuum passage between CTO switch and EGR valve. Below preset temperature, TVS blocks passage of vacuum delaying EGR operation and improving cold driveability.

Fig. 2: Typical Jeep 6-Cylinder Engine EGR System

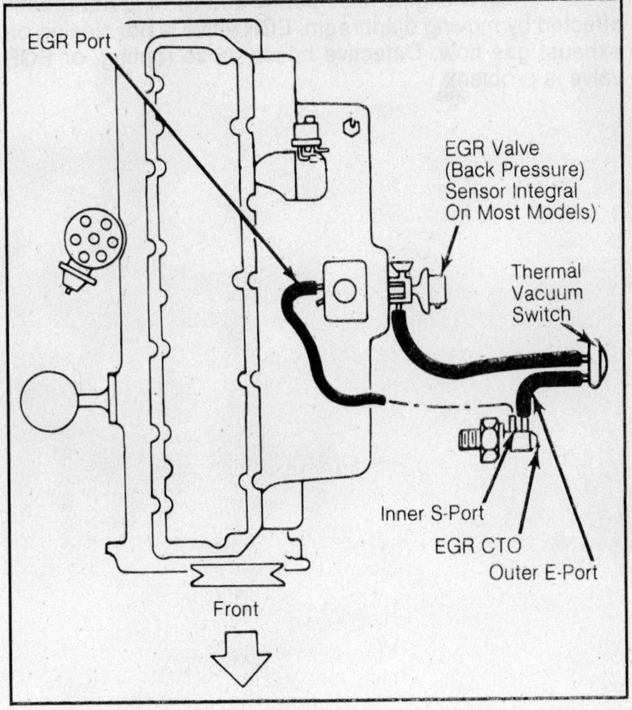

EGR DUMP VALVE

Used on some models, EGR dump valve is connected in series with vacuum source and EGR valve.

1985 Exhaust Emission Systems

JEEP EXHAUST GAS RECIRCULATION (Cont.)

Valve is used to eliminate EGR function at low vacuum levels. When vacuum drops below predetermined level, valve "dumps" vacuum rather than allowing it to flow to EGR valve.

FORWARD DELAY VALVE

Forward delay valve is located between EGR CTO switch and EGR valve. It modifies initial vacuum signal applied to EGR valve by delaying full vacuum force.

TESTING

EGR VALVE

Valve Opening Test

1) With engine at normal operating temperature and at curb idle, rapidly open and close throttle. Open throttle sufficiently to obtain at least 1500 RPM. Movement should be noticed in EGR diaphragm.

2) If diaphragm does not move, probable causes are: Faulty vacuum signal to EGR; defective EGR diaphragm or defective backpressure sensor diaphragm (if equipped); or leaks in vacuum lines or connections.

Valve Closing Test

1) With engine at normal operating temperature and at curb idle, manually depress EGR valve diaphragm. This should cause immediate engine speed drop, indicating that EGR valve had been properly cutting off exhaust gas flow at idle.

2) If there is no change in RPM and engine is idling properly, exhaust gases are not reaching combustion chamber. There is probably a plugged passage between EGR valve and intake manifold.

3) If engine idles poorly and RPM is not greatly affected by moving diaphragm, EGR valve is not closing off exhaust gas flow. Defective hoses, hose routing, or EGR valve is problem.

COOLANT TEMPERATURE OVERRIDE (CTO) SWITCH

NOTE: Engine coolant temperature must be below 100°F (38°C) to perform this test.

1) Check vacuum lines for leaks and correct routing. Disconnect vacuum line at back pressue sensor (if equipped) or at EGR valve, and attach this line to vacuum gauge.

2) Operate engine at 1500 RPM. No vacuum should be indicated on gauge. If vacuum is shown, replace CTO switch.

3) Idle engine until coolant temperature exceeds 100°F (38°C) on 4-cylinder engines, or 115°F (46°C) on 6-cylinder, V6 and V8 engines.

4) Accelerate engine to 1500 RPM. Carburetor ported vacuum should be shown on gauge. If not, replace CTO switch.

DUMP VALVE

1) With engine at normal operating temperature, remove dump valve vacuum hose from manifold and plug manifold connection.

2) Accelerate engine to 2000 RPM. Vacuum should be present at exhaust ports on bottom of valve. If not, replace valve.

3) Reconnect vacuum hose to manifold and accelerate engine to 2000 RPM. No vacuum should be felt at exhaust ports on bottom of valve. If vacuum is present, replace valve.

THERMAL VACUUM SWITCH

1) With air cleaner temperature below 40°F (-4°C), disconnect vacuum hoses from TVS and connect vacuum source to large outlet.

2) Apply vacuum to TVS. Vacuum should be held. If not, replace TVS.

3) Start engine and warm air cleaner to 55°F (13°C), or above. Vacuum should not be held. If it is held, replace TVS.

JEEP THERMOSTATIC AIR CLEANER

DESCRIPTION

All Jeep vehicles use a system for pre-heating air entering carburetor. This system is part of the air cleaner and maintains air temperature at a point where carburetor can be calibrated at leaner setting to reduce hydrocarbon emissions and improve engine performance during warm-up.

Jeep systems are vacuum-operated and consist of heat shroud on exhaust manifold, hot air duct, thermal sensor switch, vacuum motor, air valve assembly and reverse delay valve.

Fig. 1: Jeep Thermostatic Air Cleaner (TAC) Assembly

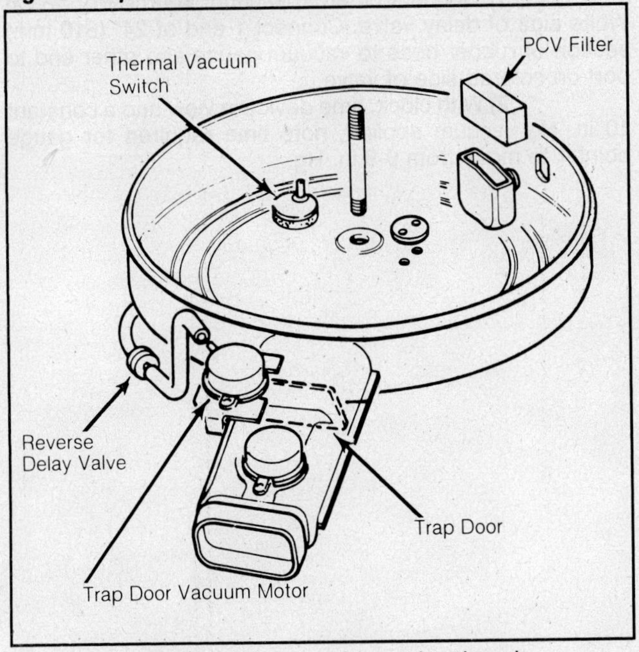

All Jeep vehicles use a system for pre-heating air entering carburetor.

OPERATION

During engine warm-up, temperature sensor switch applies vacuum to vacuum motor. Air diverter valve is held in the "ON" position. Exhaust manifold heated air flows to air cleaner. As temperature of incoming air increases to 90°F (32°C), temperature sensor opens vacuum line to atmosphere allowing spring pressure to push valve to "OFF" position. Air now flows from outside, through air cleaner duct to carburetor.

AIR CLEANER TRAP DOOR

On California vehicles, spring-loaded trap door is built into air cleaner to close off air cleaner when engine is shut off. Door is vacuum operated.

REVERSE DELAY VALVE

Reverse delay valve is installed in vacuum line in some vehicles to prevent trap door from closing during low engine vacuum periods. Valve provides about 9 seconds delay before allowing trap door to close.

Fig. 2: Cutaway View of Jeep Thermostatic Air Cleaner Assembly

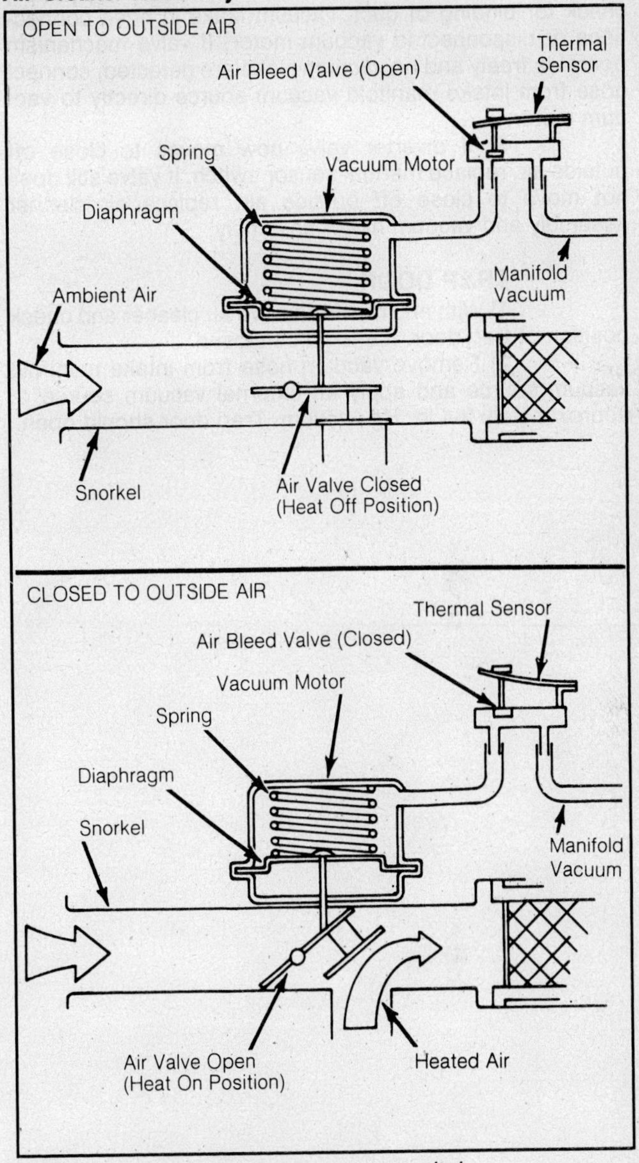

During warm-up, temperature sensor switch applies vacuum to vacuum motor.

TESTING

VACUUM MOTOR & TEMPERATURE SENSOR

1) Remove air cleaner assembly from vehicle and allow to cool to room temperature. Sight through air cleaner duct and observe position of air diverter valve. It should be fully open to outside air.

2) Reinstall assembly on carburetor and connect hot air duct and manifold vacuum hose. Start engine and observe position of air diverter valve. It should be fully closed to outside air.

3) Move throttle lever rapidly to 1/2 to 3/4 opening and release. Air diverter valve should open and then close again. Allow engine to warm to operating temperature and observe position of air diverter valve. It should be fully open to outside air.

JEEP THERMOSTATIC AIR CLEANER (Cont.)

4) If valve does not move to fully close off outside air at 83°F (28°C) or less with vacuum applied, check for binding of duct, vacuum leaks in hose connections or disconnected vacuum motor. If valve mechanism operates freely and no vacuum leaks are detected, connect hose from intake manifold vacuum source directly to vacuum motor.

5) If diverter valve now moves to close off outside air, replace thermal sensor switch. If valve still does not move to close off outside air, replace air cleaner assembly and vacuum motor assembly.

TRAP DOOR

1) With engine off, remove air cleaner and check position of trap door. It should be closed.

2) Remove vacuum hose from intake manifold vacuum source and apply an external vacuum source of approximately 2-4 in. Hg vacuum. Trap door should open.

3) If door does not open apply vacuum directly to vacuum motor. If door does not open, check for binding and adjust as necessary. If door swings freely, replace vacuum motor.

4) If door opens during step **3)**, check vacuum hose for blockage, cracks or leaks. Correct as necessary and retest as specified in step **2)**.

5) If hoses are not defective, remove reverse delay valve, join vacuum hose and retest from step **2)**. If door opens, replace reverse delay valve.

REVERSE DELAY VALVE

1) Connect external vacuum source to port on White side of delay valve. Connect 1 end of 24" (610 mm) section of rubber hose to vacuum gauge and other end to port on colored side of valve.

2) With clock, time device in view and a constant 10 in. Hg vacuum applied, note time required for gauge pointer to move from 0-8 in. Hg.

1985 Exhaust Emission Systems

JEEP PULSE AIR INJECTION SYSTEM

4.2L Engine

DESCRIPTION

Pulse air injection system is used to inject fresh air into exhaust system. When fresh air is injected into hot exhaust gases, combustion takes place. This reduces amount of unburned fuel that escapes to the atmosphere.

System consists of check valves, control valves, control valve solenoids, vacuum reservoir, vacuum lines and air lines. Pulse air system is capable of injecting air at both catalytic converter (downstream) or front exhaust pipe.

OPERATION

Pulse air system uses alternating positive and negative pressure pulsations in exhaust system to draw in fresh air through air cleaner. Check valves are used to allow fresh air into exhaust, but prevent exhaust from flowing back into intake system.

Air is switched between upstream and downstream injection by 2 vacuum-operated control valves. Each control valve is switched by an electrically operated-vacuum solenoid.

Vacuum solenoids are switched on and off by MCU according to engine operating conditions. Vacuum storage tank maintains vacuum supply to switching solenoids.

DIAGNOSIS & TESTING

1) Check condition of all hoses and lines in system. Reroute any kinked or restricted hoses. Repair or replace any cracked or broken hoses. To check system operation, feel for suction in injection hoses at air cleaner.

2) If problem exists, check to see if vacuum is being supplied to the valve. If vacuum is not present at valve(s) perform appropriate test(s). See appropriate article in COMPUTERIZED ENGINE CONTROL section.

Fig. 1: Jeep Pulse Air Injection System

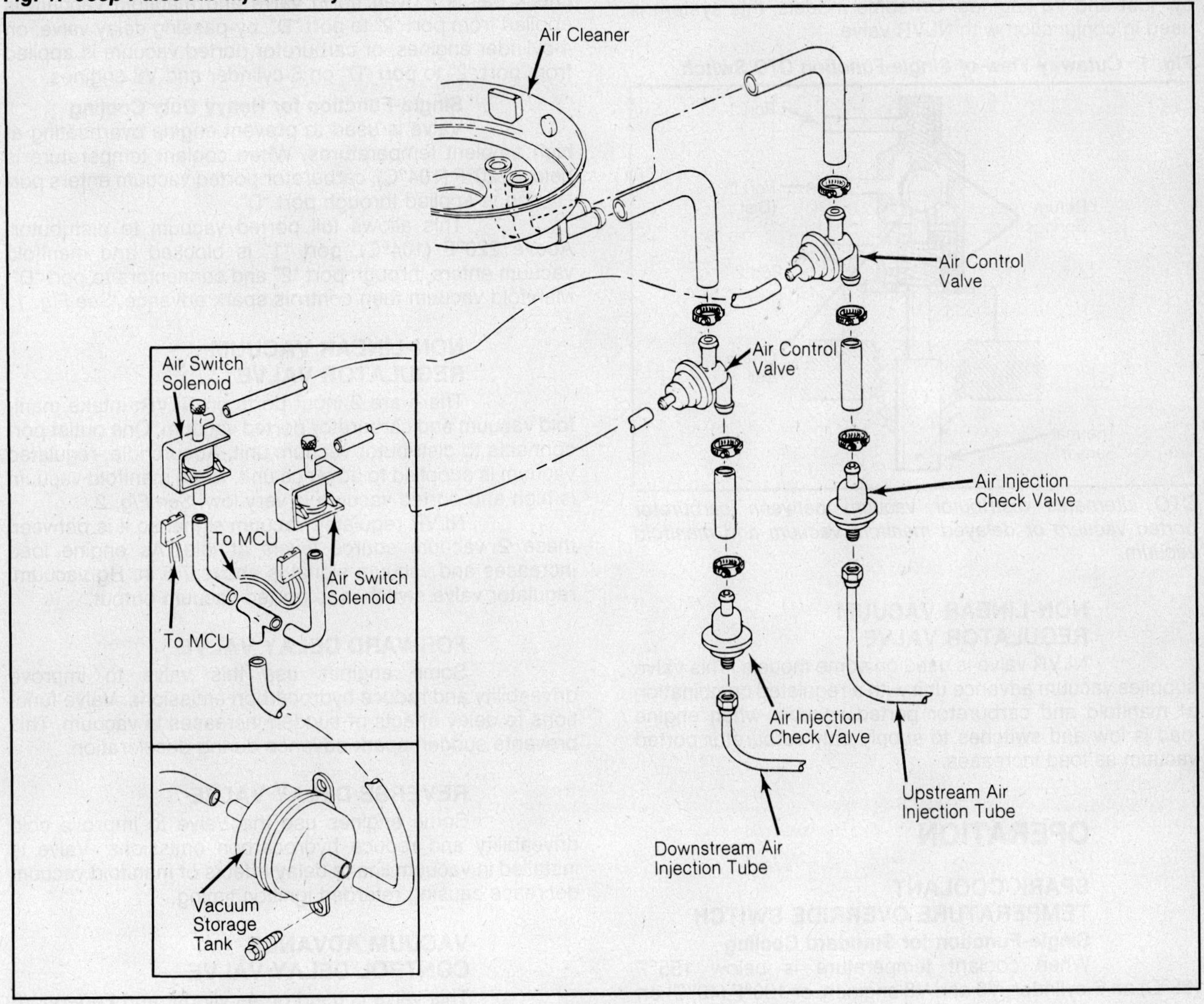

JEEP SPARK CONTROL SYSTEMS

DESCRIPTION

Jeep vehicles use spark control devices to assist ignition system in controlling exhaust emissions. They are Spark Control Temperature Override (CTO) valve, Non-Linear Vacuum Regulator (NLVR) valve, Forward Delay Valve, Reverse Delay Valve and on 4-cylinder and Federal V6 engines, Vacuum Spark Control Delay Valve. System application depends upon engine size, emissions category and vehicle model.

SPARK COOLANT TEMPERATURE OVERRIDE (CTO) SYSTEM

This system alternates distributor vacuum advance vacuum source between carburetor ported vacuum or delayed manifold vacuum and normal manifold vacuum, depending upon coolant temperature. Two types of CTO switches are used: single-function switch for models with standard cooling systems and single-function switch for heavy duty cooling systems.

CTO switch is threaded into left rear of block on 6-cylinder engines, and into thermostat housing on 4-cylinder and V8 engines. On some models, this system is used in conjunction with NLVR valve.

Fig. 1: Cutaway View of Single-Function CTO Switch

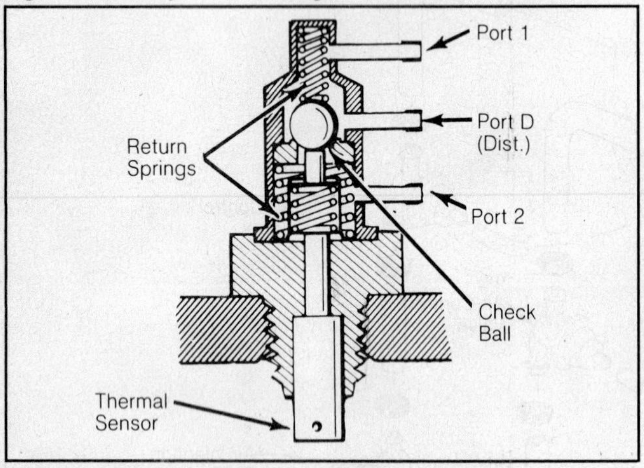

CTO alternates distributor vacuum between carburetor ported vacuum or delayed manifold vacuum and manifold vacuum.

NON-LINEAR VACUUM REGULATOR VALVE

NLVR valve is used on some models. This valve supplies vacuum advance unit with a regulated combination of manifold and carburetor ported vacuum when engine load is low and switches to supply only carburetor ported vacuum as load increases.

OPERATION

SPARK COOLANT TEMPERATURE OVERRIDE SWITCH

Single-Function for Standard Cooling

When coolant temperature is below 155°F (68°C) on 6-cylinder, V6 and V8 engines, or 120°F (49°C) on 4-cylinder engines, check ball is held against inner seat by spring tension. Manifold vacuum enters through port "1" and is applied through port "D". *See Fig. 1.*

Fig. 2: Jeep Non-Linear Vacuum Regulator Valve

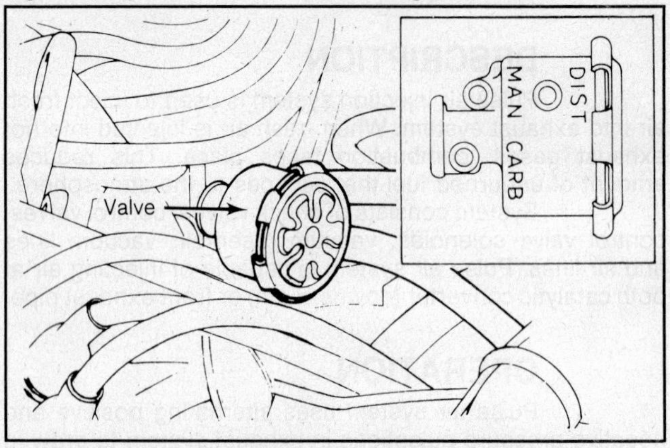

NLVR valve performs different functions depending upon engine loads.

When temperature goes above specified limits, check ball is moved up in valve and manifold vacuum is applied from port "2" to port "D", by-passing delay valve, on 4-cylinder engines, or carburetor ported vacuum is applied from port "2" to port "D" on 6-cylinder and V8 engines.

Single-Function for Heavy Duty Cooling

Valve is used to prevent engine overheating at high ambient temperatures. When coolant temperature is below 220°F (104°C), carburetor ported vacuum enters port "1" and is applied through port "D".

This allows full ported vacuum to distributor. Above 220°F (104°C), port "1" is blocked and manifold vacuum enters through port "2" and connectors to port "D". Manifold vacuum then controls spark advance. *See Fig. 1.*

NON-LINEAR VACUUM REGULATOR VALVE

There are 2 input ports on NLVR: intake manifold vacuum and carburetor ported vacuum. One outlet port connects to distributor vacuum unit. At curb idle, regulated vacuum is supplied to advance unit, when manifold vacuum is high and ported vacuum is very low. *See Fig. 2.*

NLVR regulates vacuum signal so it is between these 2 vacuum source levels at idle. As engine load increases and vacuum signal is above 7.5 in. Hg vacuum, regulator valve switches to ported vacuum output.

FORWARD DELAY VALVE

Some engines use this valve to improve driveability and reduce hydrocarbon emissions. Valve functions to delay effects of sudden increases in vacuum. This prevents sudden spark advance during deceleration.

REVERSE DELAY VALVE

Some engines use this valve to improve cold driveability and reduce hydrocarbon emissions. Valve is installed in vacuum line to delay effects of manifold vacuum decrease causing retarded ignition timing.

VACUUM ADVANCE CONTROL DELAY VALVE

This valve is used on 4-cylinder and Federal V6 engines to improve driveability when engine is cold. It is located in vacuum advance circuit. When vacuum is greater at port "4" than at port "1", air must flow through orifice to

JEEP SPARK CONTROL SYSTEMS (Cont.)

equalize pressure. This creates momentary delay that prevents sudden decrease in spark advance. When vacuum is greater at port "1" than at port "4", air flows freely through check valve and pressure is instantly equalized. *See Fig. 3.*

MAINTENANCE

Periodic maintenance is not normally required; should any switch or valve fail to function properly it should be replaced.

TESTING

SPARK COOLANT TEMPERATURE OVERRIDE SWITCH

Single-Function For Standard Cooling (6-Cylinder, V6 & V8 Engine)

Connect vacuum gauge to center port "D" of CTO switch. When coolant is below 155°F (68°C), manifold vacuum should register. Above 155°F (68°C), carburetor ported vacuum should register. If valve does not meet these requirements, it must be replaced. *See Fig. 1.*

Fig. 3: Jeep Vacuum Spark Control Delay Valve (4-Cylinder & V6 Engines)

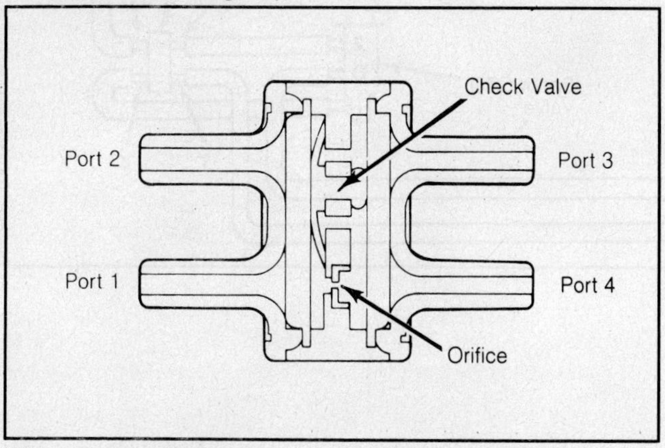

When testing disconnect vacuum hose from port "4".

Single-Function for Standard Cooling (4-Cylinder)

Disconnect vacuum hose from distributor vacuum advance mechanism and connect vacuum gauge to hose. Start engine. With coolant temperature below 120°F (49°C), manifold vacuum should register. Disconnect vacuum hose from port "4" of delay valve and cap. Manifold vacuum should not register until coolant temperature reaches about 120°F (49°C). If valve fails these tests it must be replaced. *See Fig. 3.*

NOTE: Ported vacuum is not available with throttle closed. Ported vacuum is available at part throttle (equivalent of 1000 RPM).

Single-Function for Heavy Duty Cooling

Connect vacuum gauge to center port "D" of CTO switch. When coolant is below 220°F (104°C), carburetor ported vacuum should register. Above 220°F (104°C), manifold vacuum should be indicated.

NON-LINEAR VACUUM REGULATOR VALVE

Connect vacuum gauge to distributor port "DIST" on NLVR. With engine at idle speed, a vacuum reading of 7 in. Hg vacuum should be shown. As throttle is opened and engine speed increases, ported vacuum level should be indicated. If not, replace NLVR. *See Fig. 2.*

FORWARD DELAY VALVE

1) Connect external vacuum source to port on Black (or Red) side of delay valve. Connect 1 end of a section of rubber hose to vacuum gauge and other end to port on colored side of valve.

2) With elapsed time device in view and a constant 10 in. Hg vacuum applied, note time required for gauge pointer to move from 0-8 in. Hg.

3) If valve fails to meet time limits, replace valve. If valve meets specifications, install so that Black (or Red) side is toward vacuum source.

FORWARD DELAY VALVE TIME LIMITS [1]

Valve Color	Min. Time	Max Time
Black/Purple	3.2	4.8
Black/Gray	8	12
Black/Brown	16	24
Black/Orange	1.5	2.5
Black/White	50	77
Black/Yellow	80	120
Black/Green	160	240

[1] - Time in seconds.

REVERSE DELAY VALVE

1) Connect external vacuum source to port on White side of delay valve. Connect 1 end of a section of rubber hose to vacuum gauge and other end to port on colored (non-White) side of valve.

2) With elapsed time device in view and a constant 10 in. Hg vacuum applied, note time required for gauge pointer to move from 0-8 in. Hg.

3) If valve fails to meet time limits, replace valve. If valve meets specifications, install with non-White side toward vacuum source.

VACUUM SPARK CONTROL DELAY VALVE

1) Connect tee fitting at ports "1" and "4". Connect vacuum gauge to each fitting. Start engine. Vacuum should be equal at both ports. *See Fig. 3.*

2) When throttle is suddenly depressed, vacuum at port "1" will instantly decrease and vacuum at port "4" should be maintained momentarily. If valve fails these tests, replace valve.

REVERSE DELAY VALVE TIME LIMITS [1]

Valve Color	Min. Time	Max. Time
White/Purple	3.2	4.8
White/Gray	8	12
White/Gold	12	18
White/Brown	16	24
White/Yellow	80	120
White/Red	300	450
White/Orange	1.5	2.5

[1] - Time in seconds.

JEEP SPARK CONTROL SYSTEMS (Cont.)

Fig. 4: Jeep (California) 4-Cylinder Spark Control System

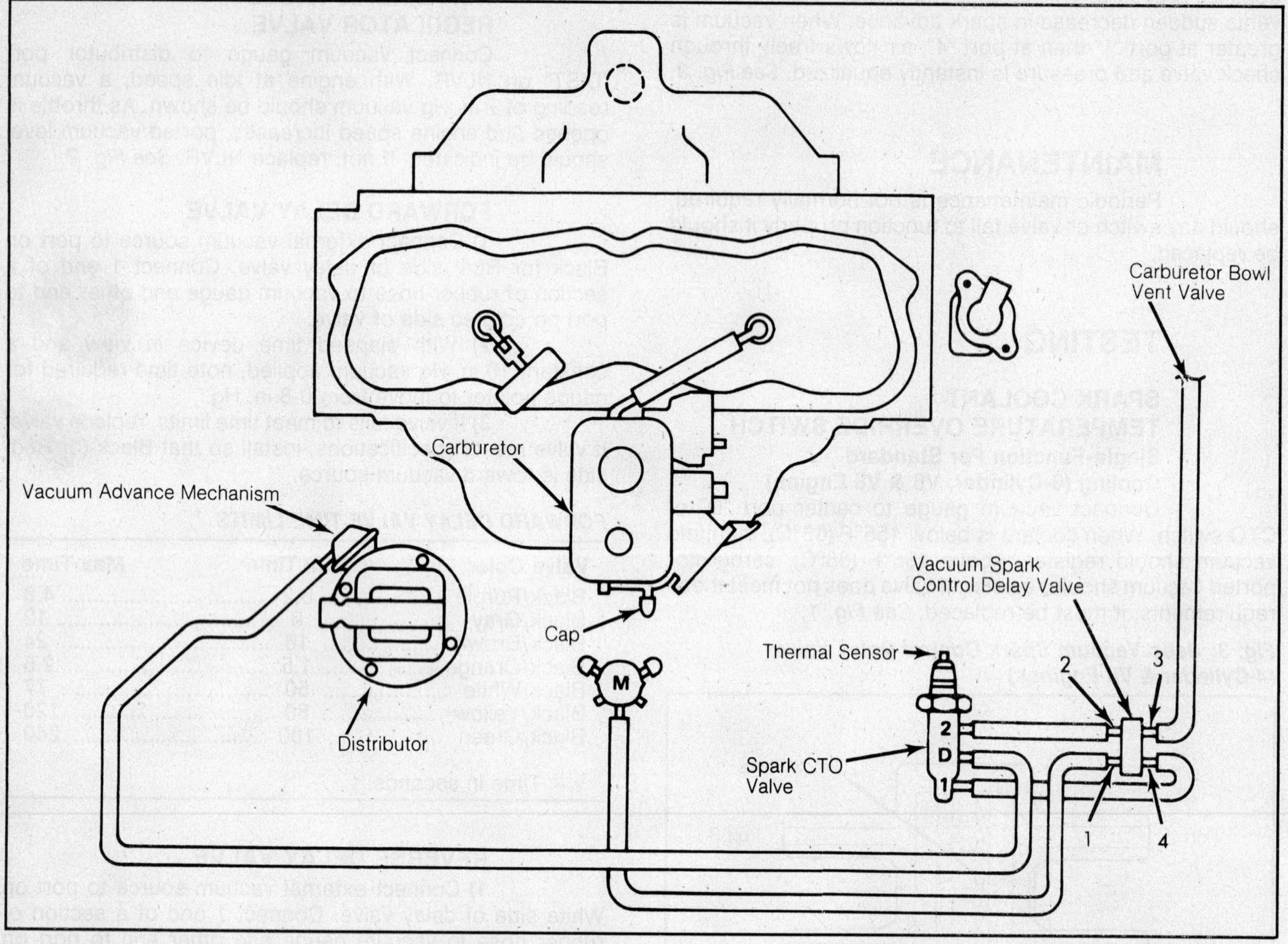

JEEP VACUUM DIAGRAMS

JEEP VACUUM DIAGRAM ABBREVIATIONS

CTO – Coolant Temperature Override; **EGR** – Exhaust Gas Recirculation; **HDC CTO** – Heavy Duty Cooling, Coolant Temperature Override; **PCV** – Positive Crankcase Ventilation; **TAC** – Thermostatic Air Cleaner; **VSD** – Vacuum Signal Dump

Fig. 1: 2.5L 4-Cylinder

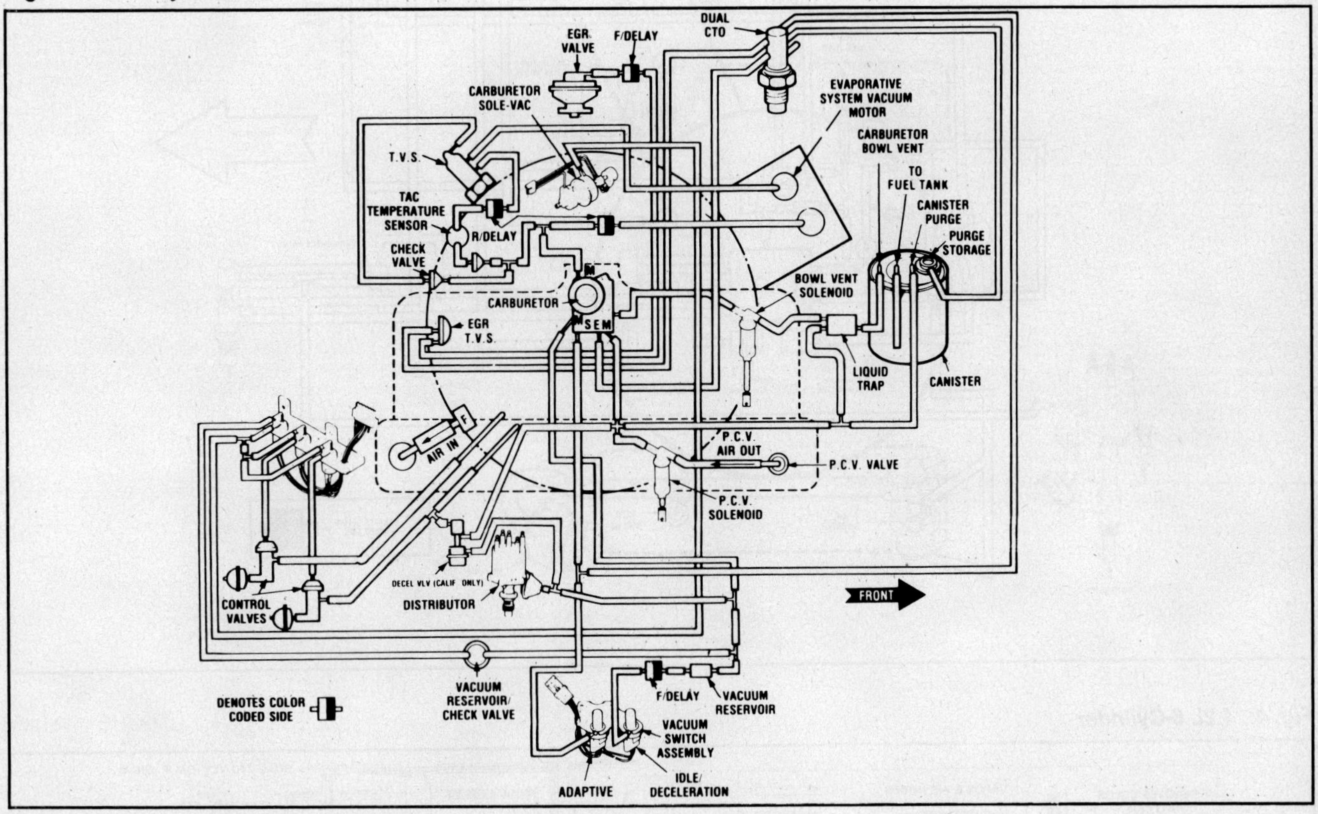

Fig. 2: 2.8L V6 California

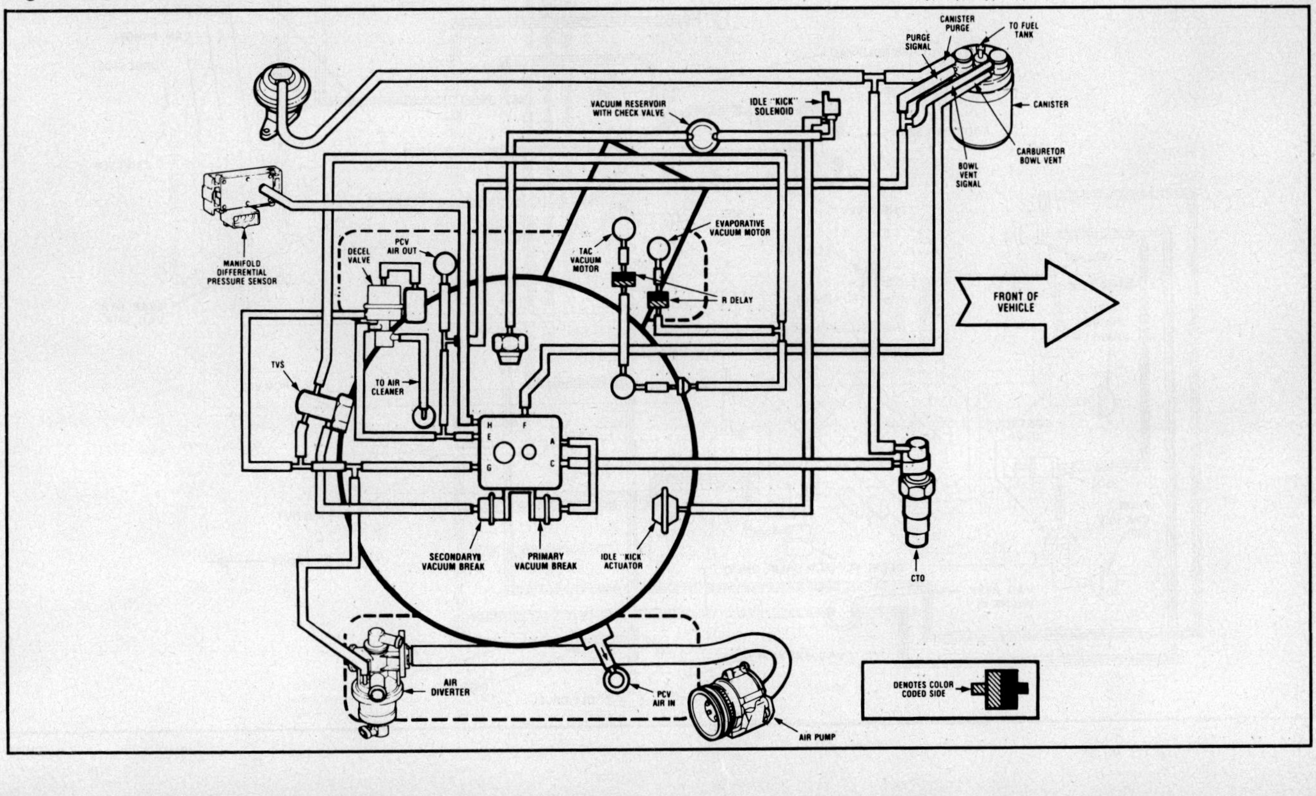

1984 Exhaust Emission Systems

JEEP VACUUM DIAGRAMS (Cont.)

Fig. 3: 2.8L V6 Federal

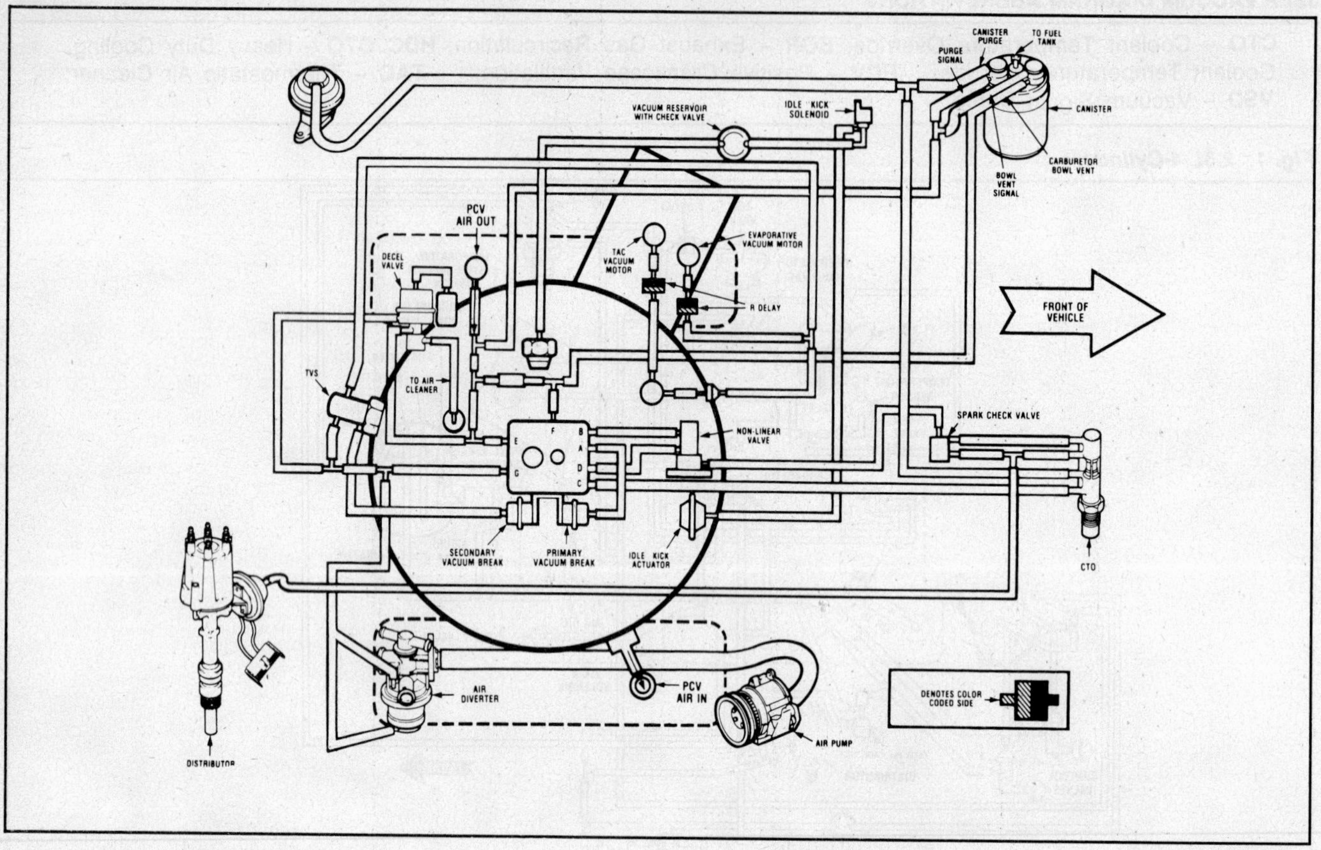

Fig. 4: 4.2L 6-Cylinder

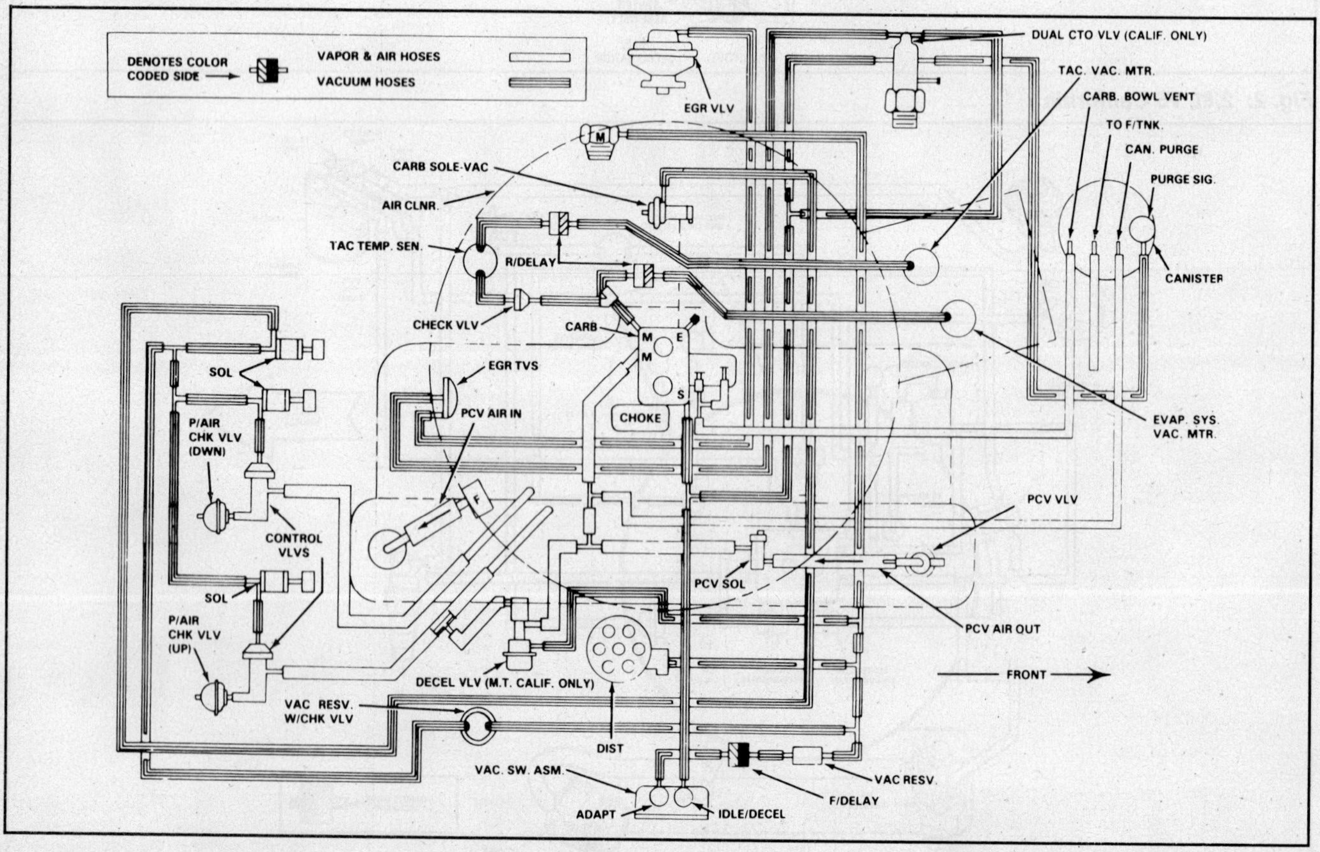

JEEP VACUUM DIAGRAMS (Cont.)

Fig. 5: 6.0L V8

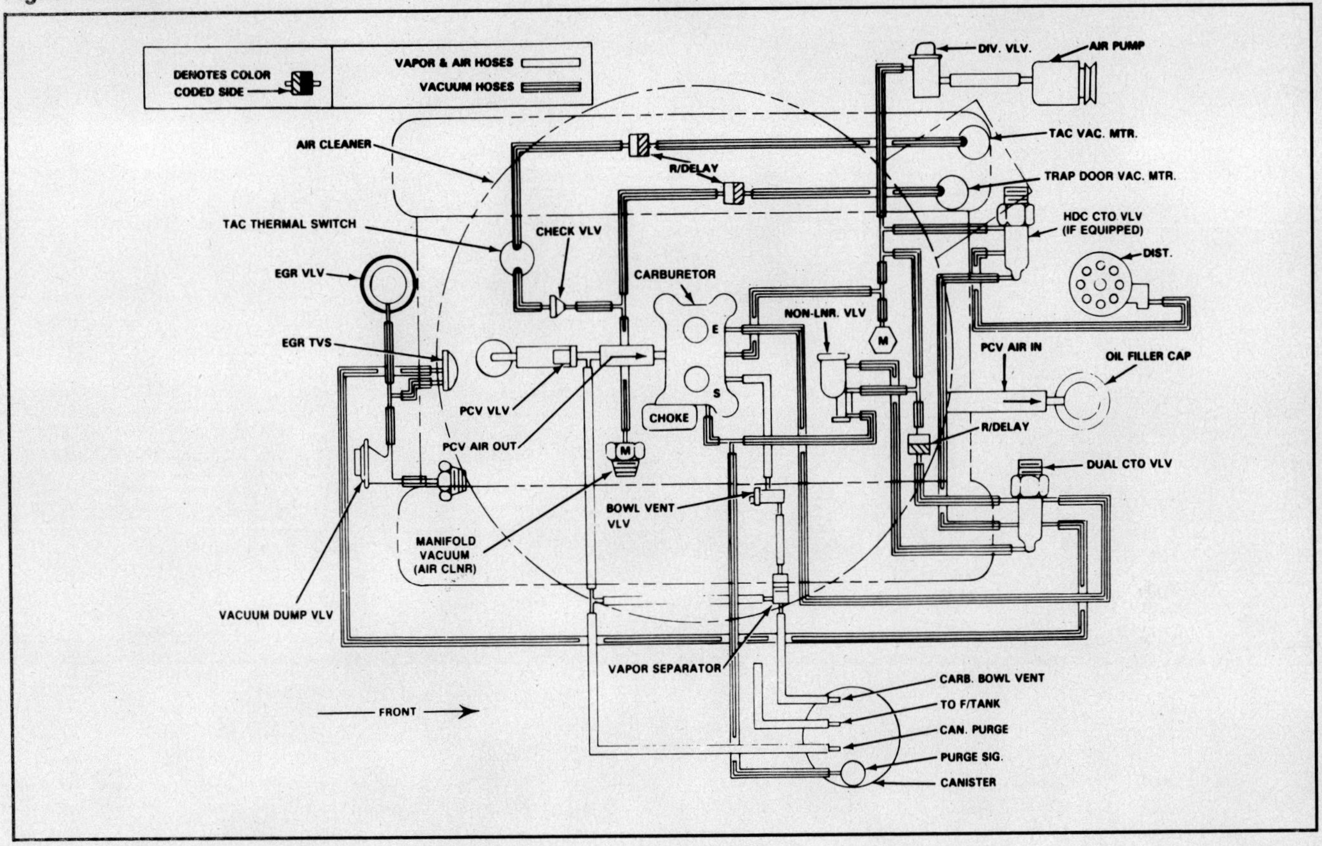

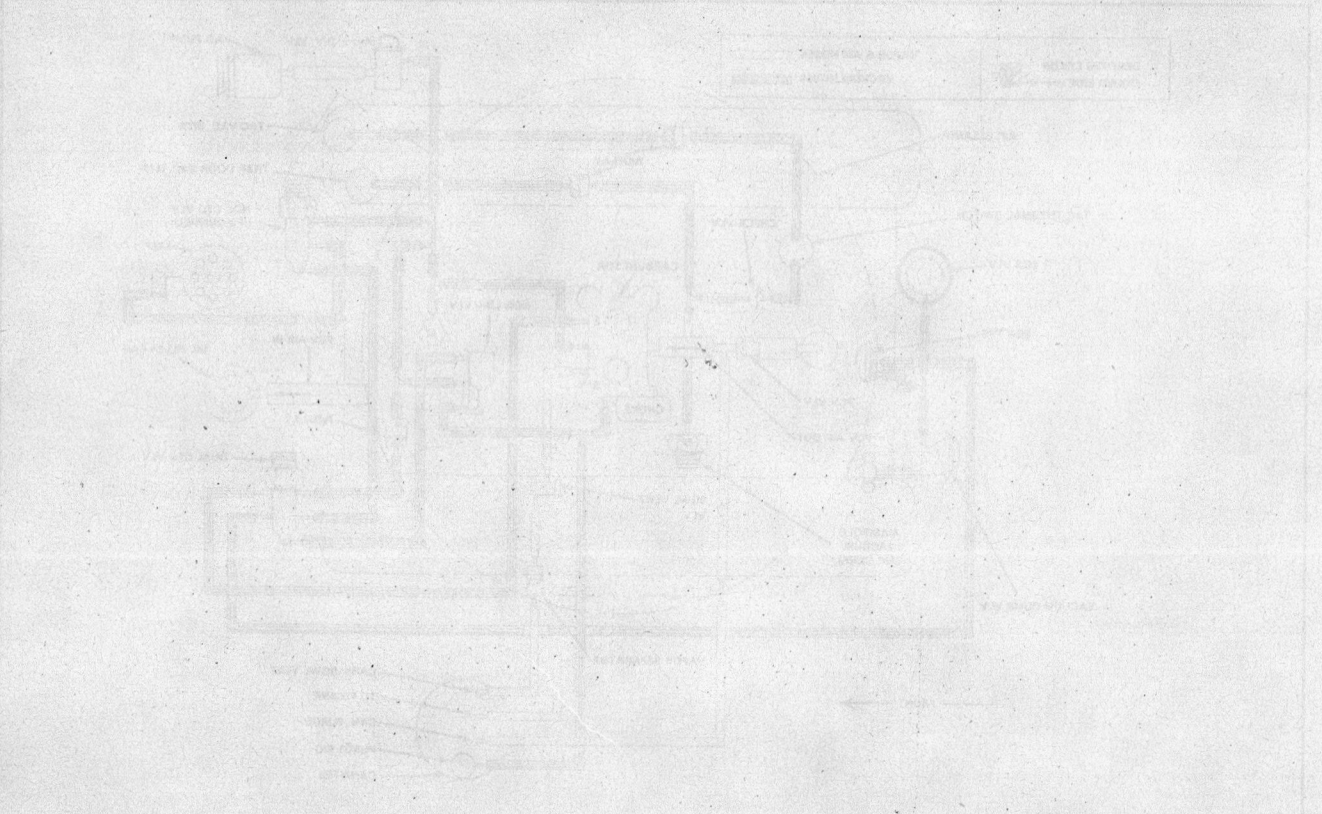

SECTION 4

ELECTRICAL

CONTENTS

NOTE: **ALSO SEE GENERAL INDEX.**

IMPORTANT: Because of the many model names used by vehicle manufacturers, accurate identification of models is important. See Model Identification at the front of this publication.

Ignition Systems

IGNITION SECONDARY QUICK CHECK CHART

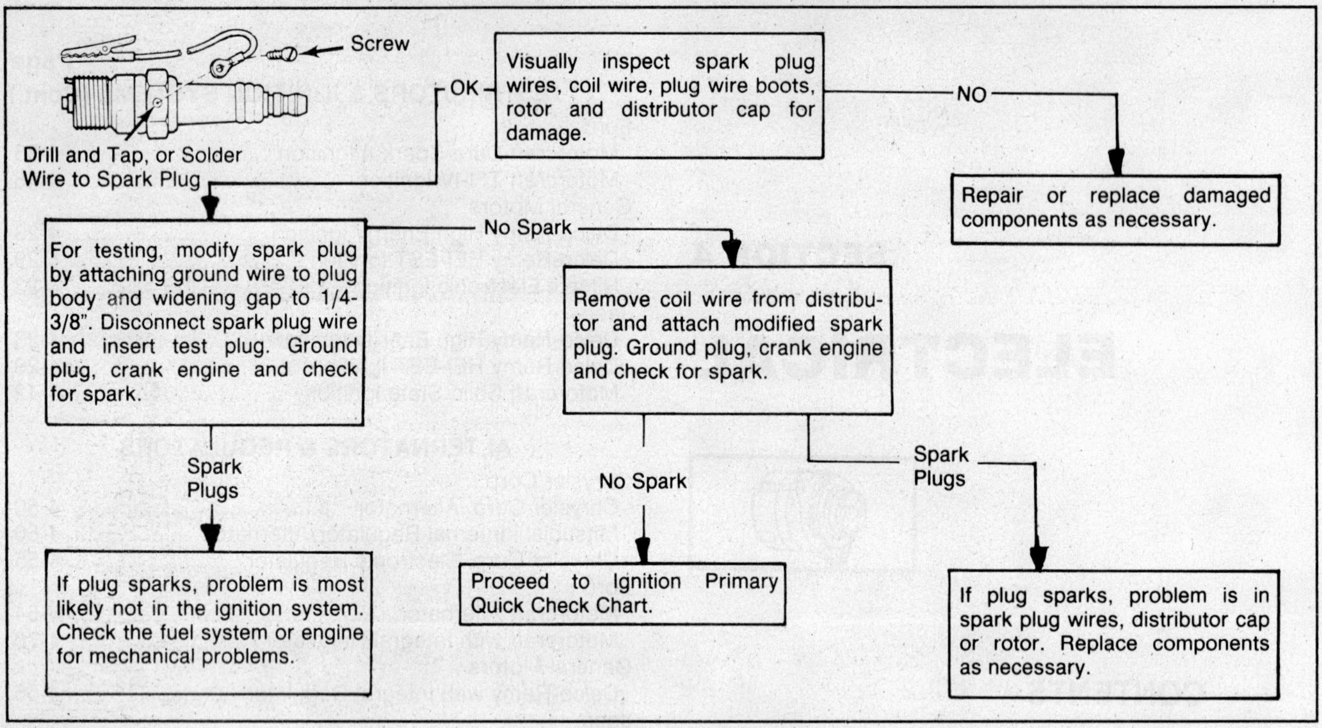

Screw
Drill and Tap, or Solder Wire to Spark Plug
OK
Visually inspect spark plug wires, coil wire, plug wire boots, rotor and distributor cap for damage.
NO
Repair or replace damaged components as necessary.
For testing, modify spark plug by attaching ground wire to plug body and widening gap to 1/4-3/8". Disconnect spark plug wire and insert test plug. Ground plug, crank engine and check for spark.
No Spark
Remove coil wire from distributor and attach modified spark plug. Ground plug, crank engine and check for spark.
Spark Plugs
If plug sparks, problem is most likely not in the ignition system. Check the fuel system or engine for mechanical problems.
No Spark
Proceed to Ignition Primary Quick Check Chart.
Spark Plugs
If plug sparks, problem is in spark plug wires, distributor cap or rotor. Replace components as necessary.

IGNITION PRIMARY QUICK CHECK CHART

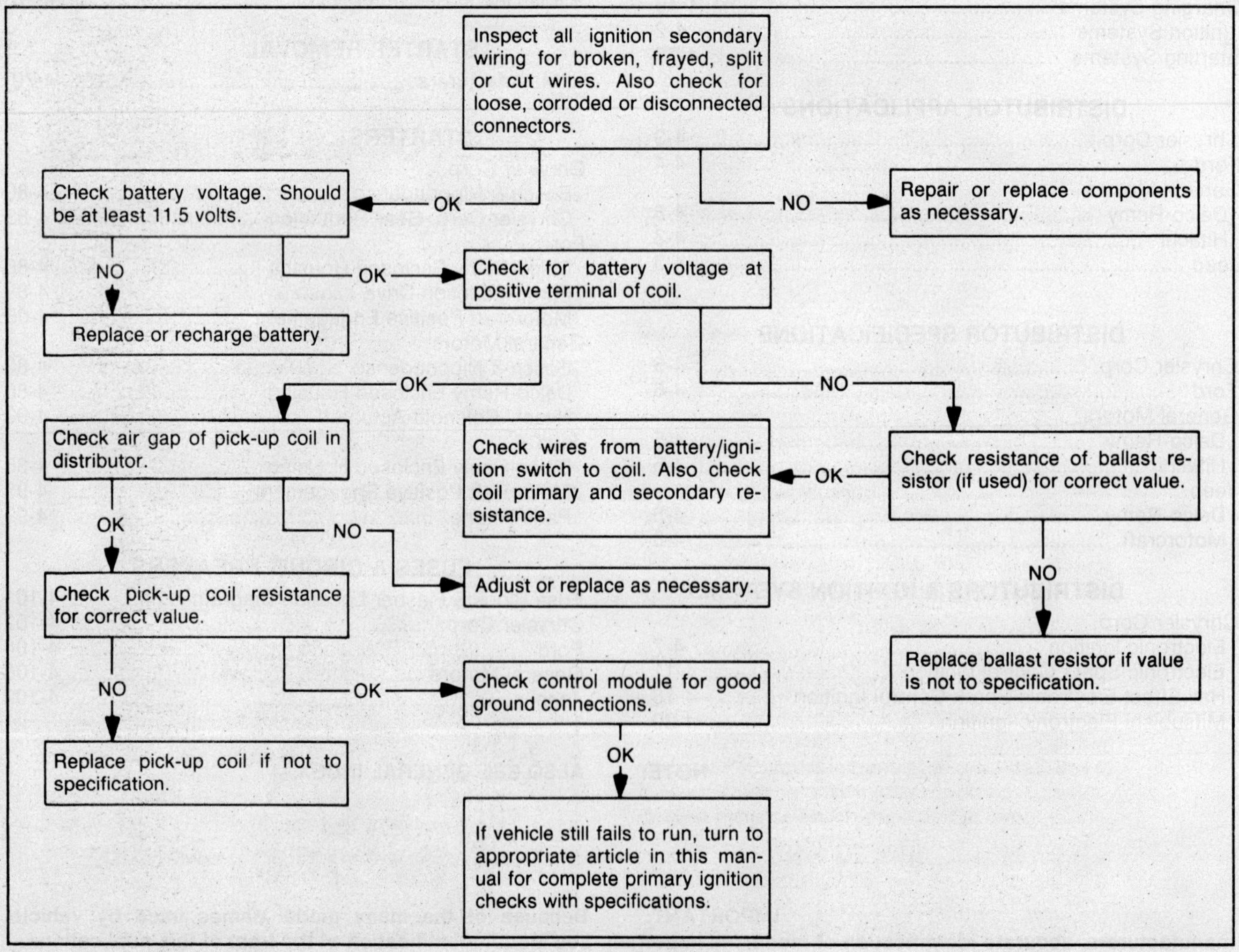

Inspect all ignition secondary wiring for broken, frayed, split or cut wires. Also check for loose, corroded or disconnected connectors.
OK
Check battery voltage. Should be at least 11.5 volts.
NO
Repair or replace components as necessary.
NO
Replace or recharge battery.
OK
Check for battery voltage at positive terminal of coil.
OK
NO
Check air gap of pick-up coil in distributor.
Check wires from battery/ignition switch to coil. Also check coil primary and secondary resistance.
OK
Check resistance of ballast resistor (if used) for correct value.
OK
NO
Adjust or replace as necessary.
Check pick-up coil resistance for correct value.
NO
NO
Replace ballast resistor if value is not to specification.
OK
Check control module for good ground connections.
Replace pick-up coil if not to specification.
OK
If vehicle still fails to run, turn to appropriate article in this manual for complete primary ignition checks with specifications.

Distributor Applications

ALL MANUFACTURERS

CHRYSLER CORP.

DODGE & PLYMOUTH

Application	Part No.
2.2L 4-Cylinder	5206975
2.6L 4-Cylinder	
Calif.	4243251
Fed.	4243792
3.7L 6-Cylinder	
Auto. Trans.	4145751
Man. Trans.	4091490
5.2L V8	
Calif. & High Alt.	4091140
Fed.	4289657
5.9L V8	
Fed. Light Duty & High Alt.	4145604
Calif. & Fed. Heavy Duty	4111950

[1] – "Light Duty" and "Heavy Duty" refer to emission control standards classifications. "Light Duty" refers to vehicles of 8500 lbs. GVW or less. Vehicles over this weight are referred to as "Heavy Duty".

JEEP

JEEP

Application	Part No.
2.5L 4-Cylinder	3242700
2.8L V6	
Calif.	89 83 501 870
Fed.	
Man. Trans.	89 83 501 493
Auto. Trans.	89 83 501 494
4.2L 6-Cylinder	3242409
6.0L V8	3233174

HITACHI

CHEVROLET & GMC

Application	Part No.
1.9L 4-Cylinder	
Man. Trans.	94240905
Auto. Trans.	94230979

DELCO-REMY

NOTE: SERIES IDENTIFICATION: The vehicle numbers used in this section have been abbreviated for common reference to both Chevrolet and GMC models. Chevrolet models use numerical designations as listed; GMC models are identified as follows: 10 = 1500, 20 = 2500, 30 = 3500 and S10 = S15.

CHEVROLET & GMC [1]

Application	Part No.
2.5L 4-Cylinder	
Astro/Safari	1103634
"S" Series	1103625
2.8L V6	
Fed.	
Man. Trans.	1103620
Auto. Trans.	1103621
High. Alt.	
Man. Trans.	1103635
Auto. Trans.	1103621
Calif.	1103644
4.3L V6	
Fed.	1103572
High Alt.	1103631
Calif.	1103573
4.8L 6-Cylinder	
Spring-Operated EFE	1103573
Vacuum-Operated EFE	1103636
5.0L V8 (VIN F)	1103460
5.0L V8 (VIN H)	
C 10	
Fed. Man. Trans.	1103641
C, K 10/20	1103465
G 10/20	
Man. Trans	1103465
Fed. Auto. Trans. (3-Spd.)	1103641
Fed. Auto. Trans. (4-Spd.)	1103465
High Alt. Auto. Trans.	1103465
5.7L (VIN L)	
Fed. & High Alt.	1103436
Calif.	1103460
5.7L (VIN M)	
Fed.	
Cast Iron Exh. Manifold	1103375
Stainless Steel Exh. Manifold	1103606
Calif.	1103420
7.4L V8	1103376

[1] – For 1.9L 4-cylinder engines, see HITACHI DISTRIBUTORS.

Distributor Applications

ALL MANUFACTURERS (Cont.)

MOTORCRAFT

FORD

Application	[1] Part No.
2.0L 4-Cylinder	E37E-FA
2.3L 4-Cylinder	E59E-CA
2.8L V6	E47E-AA
4.9L 6-Cylinder	
Bronco	E4TE-AA
E-150	E4TE-AA
E-250	
Man. Trans.	E4TE-AA
Auto. Trans.	
AOT	E4TE-AA
C6	
High Alt.	E4TE-AA
All Others	D9TE-ADA, EE5TE-MA
E-350	
Man. Trans.	D9TE-AEA, E5TE-NA
Auto. Trans.	D9TE-ADA, E5TE-MA
F-150	E4TE-AA
F-250	
Man. Trans.	
Under 8500 Lbs. GVW	E4TE-AA
Over 8500 Lbs. GVW	D9TE-AEA, E5TE-NA
Auto. Trans.	
Under 8500 Lbs. GVW	E4TE-AA
Over 8500 Lbs. GVW	D9TE-ADA, E5TE-MA
F-350	
Man. Trans.	D9TE-AEA, E5TE-NA
Auto. Trans.	D9TE-ADA, E5TE-MA
5.0L V8 EFI	
Man. Trans.	E5TE-EA
Auto. Trans.	E5TE-AA
5.0L V8 2-Bbl.	E5TE-BA
5.8L V8	
2-Bbl.	
Bronco	E4TE-AA
E-150	E4TE-CA
E-250	
Van	E4TE-CA
Wagon	E2TE-UA
E-350	E2TE-UA
F-150	E4TE-CA
F-250	
Under 8500 Lbs. GVW	E4TE-CA
Over 8500 Lbs. GVW	E2TE-UA
F-350	E2TE-UA
4-Bbl.	
Bronco	E4TE-EA
E-150	E4TE-EA
E-250	
Van	E4TE-EA
Wagon	E5TE-RA
E-350	E5TE-RA
F-150	E4TE-EA
F-250	
Under 8500 Lbs. GVW	E4TE-EA
Over 8500 Lbs. GVW	E5TE-RA
F-350	E5TE-RA
7.5L V8	
Fed.	E3HE-BA
Calif.	E4HE-AA

[1] – Basic part number is 12127. Table gives prefix and suffix only.

Distributor Specifications

ALL MANUFACTURERS

CHRYSLER CORP. DISTRIBUTOR ADVANCE SPECIFICATIONS
FOR DISTRIBUTOR RPM AND DEGREES, DIVIDE SPECIFICATIONS BY 2

Distributor Part No.	Rot.[1]	AUTOMATIC ADVANCE (Engine Degrees & RPM)						VACUUM ADVANCE (Engine Deg.)			
		Deg.	RPM	Deg.	RPM	Deg.	RPM	Deg.	In. Hg	Deg.	In. Hg
4111501	C	0.5-2.5	750	3.5-6.0	1400	7.5-9.5	2200	1.0-2.5	7.0	10-12	15
4111950	C	0.5-2.5	650	2.5-4.5	900	8-10	2200	1.0-2.5	7.0	10-12	15
4145604	C	0.5-2.5	600	1.5-3.5	1000	4-6	2200	1.0-2.5	7.0	10-12	15
4243792	C	0	600	6	1400	10	3000	0	3.1	10	11.8
4243251	C	0	600	6	1400	10	3000	0	5.1	7.5	11.8
4289657	C	0.5-1.5	900	2.0-3.5	1200	7.5-9.5	2100	1.0-2.5	7.0	10-12	15
4091140	C	Electronic Spark Advance									
4091490	C	Electronic Spark Advance									
4145751	C	Electronic Spark Advance									
5206975	C	Electronic Spark Advance									

[1] – C=Clockwise, as viewed from rotor end.

DELCO-REMY (GMC) DISTRIBUTOR ADVANCE SPECIFICATIONS
FOR DISTRIBUTOR RPM AND DEGREES, DIVIDE SPECIFICATIONS BY 2

Distributor Part No.	Rot.[1]	AUTOMATIC ADVANCE (Engine Degrees & RPM)						VACUUM ADVANCE (Engine Deg.)			
		Deg.	RPM	Deg.	RPM	Deg.	RPM	Deg.	In. Hg	Deg.	In. Hg
1103375	CC	0-3	700	7-9	1400	10-12	2100	0	3-6	5	7-9
1103376	CC	0-3	700	6-8	1400	9-11	2100	0	6-10	5	12-13
1103420	CC	0-3	1000	.....	.....	11-13	2000	0	9-11	5	12-14
1103436	CC	0-4	650	7-9	1200	10-12	2300	0	2-4	10	6-9
1103441	CC	0-3	700	11-13	2300	10-13	3000	0	2-3	12	5-10
1103460 [2]	CC	.....	.....	.....	.....	.....	.....	.....	.....	.....	.....
1103465 [3]	CC	0-2	700	3-5	1000	9-11	2100	0	2-4	10	6-9
1103536	CC	0-3	800	5-8	1200	12-14	2600	0	2-3	12	6-10
1103546	CC	0-3	700	10-12	2000	8-12	3000	0	2-3	12	6-10
1103547	CC	0-3	800	10-12	2200	8-12	3000	0	2-3	12	6-10
1103572 [3]	CC	0-2	800	5-7	1600	8-10	2000	0	3-6	5	7-9
1103573 [2]	CC	.....	.....	.....	.....	.....	.....	.....	.....	.....	.....
1103606	CC	0-3	600	4-6	850	9-11	1900	0	3-6	5	7-9
1103620	CC	0-3	600	6-8	1100	9-12	3000	0	2-4	10	5-7
1103621	CC	0-3	700	9-11	1700	7-11	4000	0	2-3	10	4-6
1103625 [2]	CC	.....	.....	.....	.....	.....	.....	.....	.....	.....	.....
1103631 [4]	CC	0-2	800	15-7	1600	8-10	2000	0	2-4	8	5-7
1103634 [2]	CC	.....	.....	.....	.....	.....	.....	.....	.....	.....	.....
1103635	CC	0-3	600	10-12	2400	9-12	3000	0	2-3	10	7-9
1103636	CC	0-2	700	3-5	1000	9-11	2100	0	7-10	5	12-13
1103641 [4]	CC	0-2	700	3-5	1000	9-11	2100	0	2-4	8	5-7
1103644 [2]	CC	.....	.....	.....	.....	.....	.....	.....	.....	.....	.....

[1] – CC=Counterclockwise, as viewed from rotor end.
[2] – HEI-EST distributor does not use vacuum or centrifugal advance mechanisms.
[3] – Used with E.S.S. system.
[4] – Used with E.S.C. system.

HITACHI DISTRIBUTOR ADVANCE SPECIFICATIONS
FOR DISTRIBUTOR RPM AND DEGREES, DIVIDE SPECIFICATIONS BY 2

Distributor Part No.	Rot.[1]	AUTOMATIC ADVANCE (Engine Degrees & RPM)						VACUUM ADVANCE (Engine Deg.)			
		Deg.	RPM	Deg.	RPM	Deg.	RPM	Deg.	In. Hg	Deg.	In. Hg
94240905	CC	2	1600	10	2600	16	3900	2	2-4	18	6-9
94230979	CC	2	1600	10	2600	16	3900	2	3-4	18	8-11

[1] – CC=Counterclockwise, as viewed from rotor end.

Distributor Specifications

ALL MANUFACTURERS (Cont.)

MOTORCRAFT (FORD) DISTRIBUTOR ADVANCE SPECIFICATION

Distributor Part Number (Basic Part No. is 12127)	Initial Ignition Timing (Degrees BTDC)	Total Advance @ 2500 Engine RPM (Including Initial Advance)	
		Hose Disconnected (Degrees BTDC)	Hose Connected (Degrees BTDC)
E37E-FA [1]	6	11-15	34-41
E37E-GA	9	15-20	34-46
E4TE-EA [2]	10	20-25	35-44
E4TE-RA	14	24-29	39-48
D9TE-ADA [3]	12	18-23	24-34
E2TE-UA [4]	8	13.5-16	19-25.5
E3HE-BA	8	23-27	39-49.5
E4HE-AA [5]	8	18-23	26-34

[1] – Calibration number 5-41D-R00 is 6° initial timing, 11-15° disconnected, 34-41° connected. Calibration number 5-41D-R10 is 6° initial timing, 11-15° disconnected, and 34-41° connected.
[2] – Calibration numbers 4-64G-R00 ("F" Series), 4-64G-R02 ("F" Series), 4-64G-R02 ("E" Series) are 10° initial timing, 20-25° disconnected, 35-44° connected.
[3] – Calibration numbers 9-78J-R00 ("E" Series) and 9-78J-R11 ("F" Series) are 12° initial timing, 18-23° disconnected, 24-34° connected.
[4] – Calibration numbers 2-75J-R20 and 2-76J-R20 are 8° initial timing, 13.5-16° disconnected, 19-25.5° connected.
[5] – Calibration numbers 3-98S-R00 and 4-98S-R10 are 8° initial timing, 18-23° disconnected, 26-34° connected.

CHRYSLER CORP. ELECTRONIC IGNITION

Dodge/Plymouth
All Federal V8 Models
High Altitude 5.9L V8

DESCRIPTION

All Federal models with V8 engines and High Altitude models with 5.9L V8 use Chrysler Corp. Electronic Ignition. This system consists of an electronic control unit (ECU), ignition switch, ignition coil and a 1.2 ohm ballast resistor. The distributor has vacuum and centrifugal advance mechanisms, pick-up coil assemblies and reluctor. *See Fig. 1.*

Fig. 1: Electronic Ignition Wiring Diagram

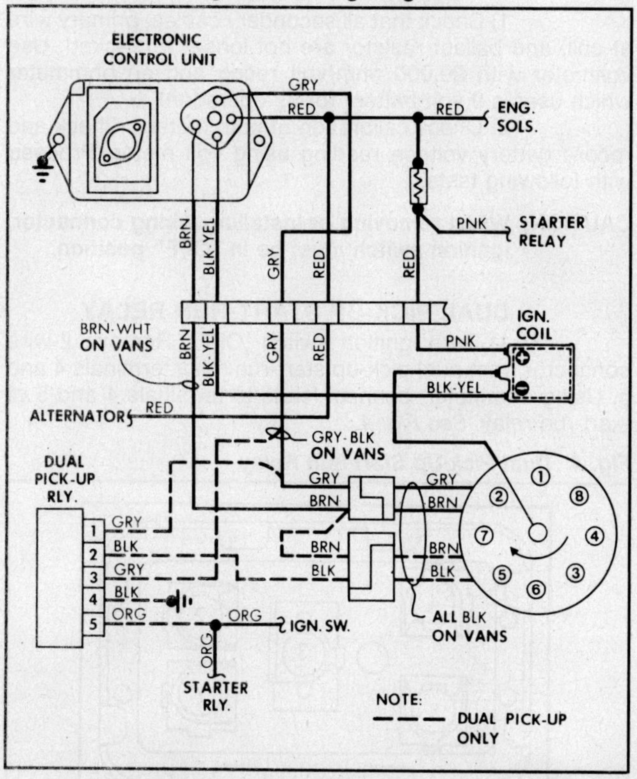

Distributors vary between models. Most models use a single pick-up coil assembly. All models with 5.9L V8 engines use 2 pick-up coil assemblies.

Models with dual pick-up coil assemblies also have a dual pick-up start-run relay, located between ECU and distributor.

Dual pick-up start-run relay permits use of dual pick-up distributor without electronic spark advance. This results in improved timing and increased fuel economy.

Control unit is connected to the rest of the system through a 4-wire connector. Distributor is connected to control unit by a 2-wire or by two 2-wire connectors (dual pick-up models).

OPERATION

DISTRIBUTOR

Single Pick-Up Models

Distributor has a toothed wheel, called a reluctor, having one tooth for each of the engine's 8 cylinders.

Fig. 2: Exploded View of Dual Pick-Up Distributor

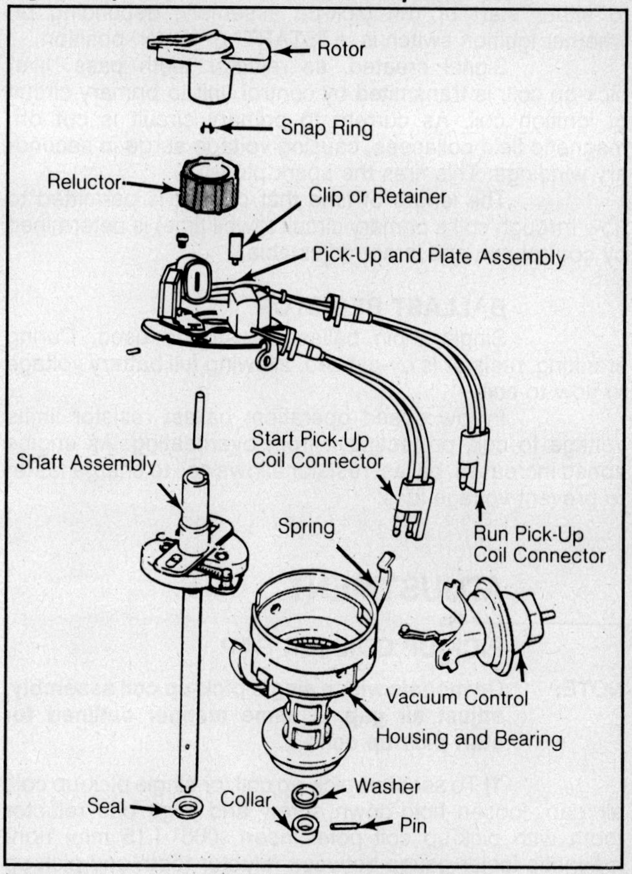

Reluctor has one tooth for each cylinder.

See Fig. 2. As reluctor rotates with distributor shaft, its teeth approach, become aligned with, and pass center pole piece of the pick-up coil.

This interruption of the magnetic field around the pick-up coil creates an electronic signal. This signal is transmitted to the control unit, which shuts off current flow to primary circuit of ignition coil as each signal is received.

Dual Pick-Up Models

This system operates identically to single pick-up models with one exception. Signals are sent by different pick-up coils during cranking and normal running conditions.

When cranking, system operates through start pick-up circuit of the dual pick-up start-run relay. Once engine begins to run, the relay switches back to the run pick-up circuit. Only one pick-up coil operates at a time.

Distributor pick-up coil connectors can be identified by their terminals. Run pick-up connectors have one male and one female terminal; start pick-up connectors have 2 male terminals.

ELECTRONIC CONTROL UNIT

Electronic control unit (ECU) is located in metal housing on firewall. Switching transistor is exposed on top for more efficient cooling.

Control unit is connected to rest of system by wiring harness and 4-wire connector. Control unit functions whenever ignition switch is turned to "START" or "RUN" positions.

Control unit furnishes current to distributor pick-up coil directly on single pick-up models. On dual pick-up

CHRYSLER CORP. ELECTRONIC IGNITION (Cont.)

models, current flows through dual pick-up start-run relay to either start or run pick-up assembly, depending on whether ignition switch is in "START" or "RUN" position.

Signal created, as reluctor teeth pass "live" pick-up coil, is transmited by control unit to primary circuit of ignition coil. As current to primary circuit is cut off, magnetic field collapses, causing voltage surge in secondary windings. This fires the spark plugs.

The length of time that current is permitted to flow through coil's primary circuit (dwell time) is determined by control unit and is not adjustable.

BALLAST RESISTOR

Single 2-pin ballast resistor is used. During cranking, resistor is by-passed, allowing full battery voltage to flow to coil.

In low speed operation, ballast resistor limits voltage to coil, protecting it from overheating. As engine speed increases, ballast resistor allows coil to charge faster to prevent voltage loss.

ADJUSTMENT

PICK-UP COIL AIR GAP

NOTE: **On models with a single pick-up coil assembly, adjust air gap in same manner outlined for start pick-up coils.**

1) To set **start** pick-up coil (or single pick-up coil) air gap, loosen hold-down screw and align one reluctor tooth with pick-up coil pole. Insert .006" (.15 mm) non-magnetic feeler gauge between reluctor tooth and pick-up coil pole. *See Fig. 3.*

2) Move pick-up coil assembly until contact is made between pick-up coil pole, feeler gauge and reluctor tooth. Tighten hold-down screw and remove feeler gauge. Gauge should not require force during removal.

Fig. 3: Checking Distributor Pick-Up Coil Air Gap

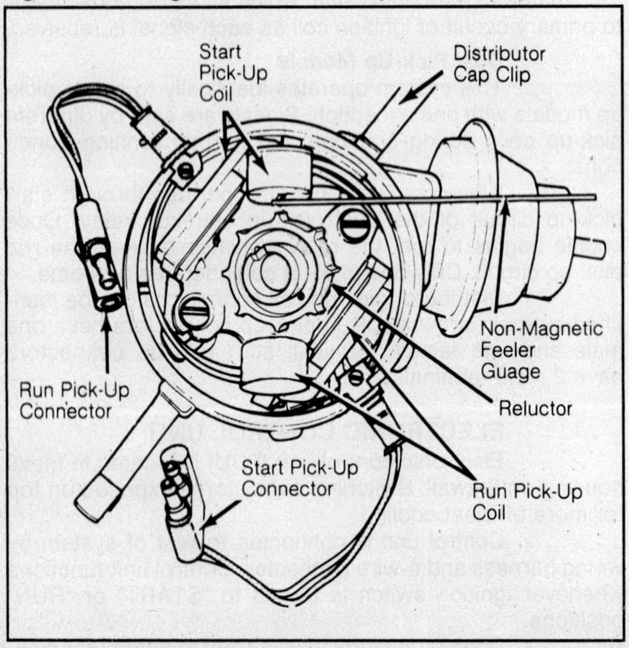

3) Check air gap of **start** pick-up coil (or single pick-up coil) using .008" (.20 mm) non-magnegic feeler gauge. It should not fit in gap. Do not force gauge into gap.

4) To adjust **run** pick-up coil air gap, use same procedure as for start pick-up coil. Set gap with .012" (.35 mm) feeler gauge and check it with .014" gauge.

TESTING

NOTE: **If tester (C-4166 with adapter C-4166-1 or C 4166A, or tester C-4503 with adapter C-4503-3) is available, use tester and follow manufacturer's instructions. If tester is not available, proceed as follows:**

1) Check that all secondary cables, primary wire at coil, and ballast resistor are not loose or cracked. Use voltmeter with 20,000 ohm/volt rating and an ohmmeter which uses a 9 volt battery for its operation.

2) Check calibration of both meters. Check and record battery voltage reading using volt meter. Proceed with following tests.

CAUTION: **When removing or installing wiring connector, ignition switch must be in "OFF" position.**

DUAL PICK-UP START-RUN RELAY

1) Turn ignition switch "OFF". Remove 2-wire connector from dual pick-up start-run relay terminals 4 and 5. Using ohmmeter, connect leads to terminals 4 and 5 of start-run relay. *See Fig. 4.*

Fig. 4: Dual Pick-Up Start-Run Relay

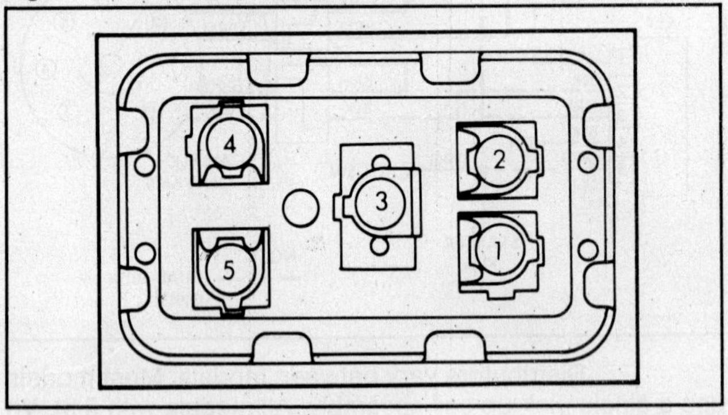

Note relay terminal locations.

2) Resistance reading should be 20-30 ohms. If not, replace dual pick-up start-run relay.

SYSTEM VOLTAGE CHECK

1) Remove coil secondary wire from distributor cap. Turn ignition switch "ON". Connect special jumper wire momentarily from ignition coil negative terminal to ground, while holding secondary wire 1/4" from engine ground. *See Fig. 5.* A spark should jump to ground.

2) If spark was present, go to WIRING HARNESS & CONNECTOR test. If no spark was obtained, turn ignition switch "OFF". Disconnect 4-wire harness connector from ECU.

3) Turn ignition switch "ON". Repeat step **1)**. If spark now results with connector removed, replace ECU.

4) If no spark was obtained in step **3)**, measure voltage at coil positive terminal. It should be within 1 volt of battery voltage. If so, check for battery voltage at coil negative terminal. If battery voltage is indicated, but no spark was noted in step **3)**, replace ignition coil.

5) If no battery voltage was present at ignition coil positive terminal in step **4)**, replace starter relay, and check wiring between battery positive terminal and coil positive terminal. If continuity does not exist, replace ballast resistor and repeat step **4)**.

Fig. 5: Special Jumper Wire with Capacitor

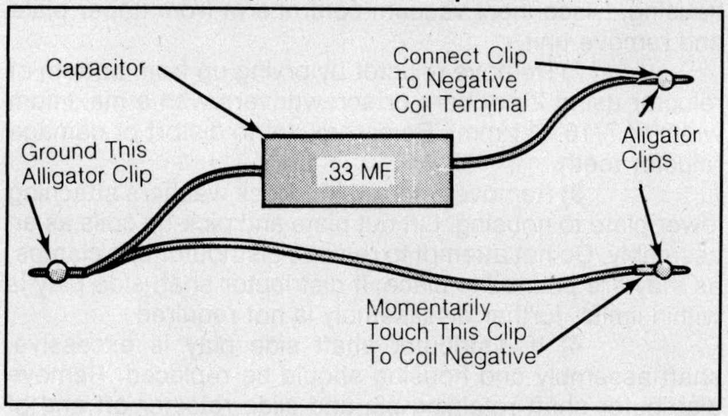

Wire is used for checking system voltage

Fig. 6: Checking Voltage at Cavity No. 2

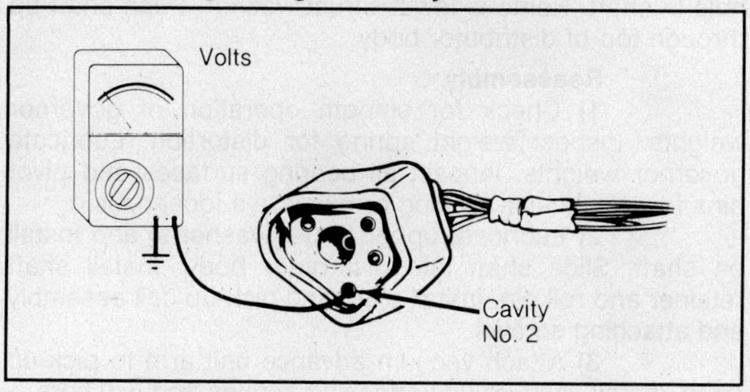

WIRING HARNESS & CONNECTOR

1) Measure voltage across battery terminals. Record this measurement. Turn ignition switch "OFF", then disconnect harness connector from ECU. Connect voltmeter negative lead to a good ground and then turn ignition "ON".

2) Connect positive lead to harness connector cavity 2. Voltmeter should read within 1 volt of battery voltage. *See Fig. 7.* If not, turn ignition switch "OFF" and move voltmeter negative lead from ground to coil negative terminal. There should be continuity.

3) If there is no continuity, check and repair wiring from harness connector to coil. Repeat step **2)**. If continuity is present, check again for battery voltage at harness connector cavity 2.

4) If battery voltage is obtained, go to step **5)**. If not, turn ignition off and check for continuity between cavity 1 of ECU harness connector and ignition switch. Trace circuit and repair as needed.

5) Turn ignition switch "OFF" and connect ohmmeter leads to cavities 4 and 5 of connector. *See Fig. 8.* Reading should be between 150 and 900 ohms. If reading is correct, go to step **7)**.

6) If resistance in step **5)** is incorrect, disconnect pick-up coil leads and measure resistance of each pick-up coil at connector terminals. If resistance is still incorrect, replace pick-up coil.

Fig. 7: Circuitry Checked if Cavity No. 2 Reading is Not Battery Voltage

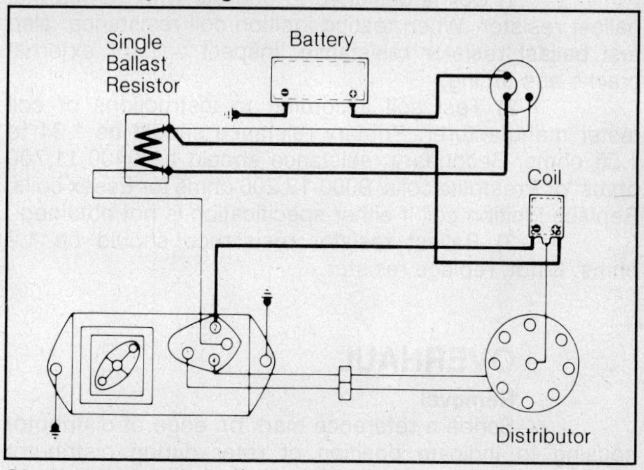

Check circuit indicated by heavy lines.

Fig. 8: Checking Resistance at Cavities No. 4 and 5

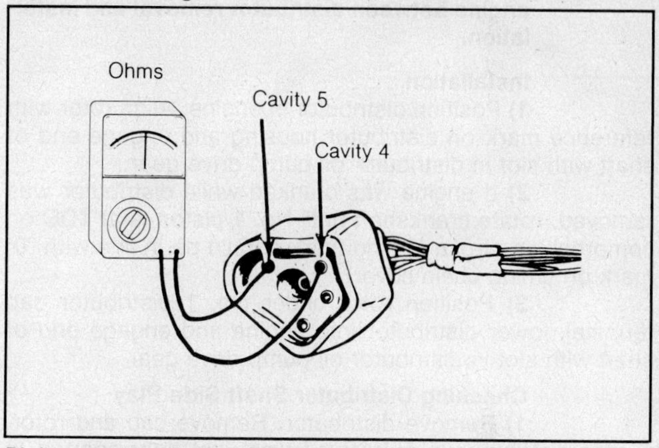

Pick-up coil resistance will be read.

7) If resistance in step **5)** or **6)** is correct, pick-up coils are good, but circuit between cavities 4 and 5 is open or shorted, or dual pick-up start-run relay is bad. Trace circuit for fault and test relay.

8) Connect one lead of ohmmeter to a good ground and check for short at each pick-up lead. If there is no short go to ECU GROUND CIRCUIT test. If pick-up is shorted, replace it.

ECU GROUND CIRCUIT

1) Connect one ohmmeter lead to a good ground and other lead to ECU connector pin 5 (not cavity 5 of harness connector). Ohmmeter should show full continuity.

2) If not, make sure control unit is making good contact with ground at hold-down bolts. If contact with ground is good, replace control unit.

CENTRIFUGAL ADVANCE CURVE

1) Install distributor in test stand. It is important that appropriate adapter for checking electronic type distributors be used. Adjust tester speed control to operate distributor at speeds called for in DISTRIBUTOR SPECIFICATION tables.

2) If advance is not correct, replace distributor shaft assembly (shaft, reluctor sleeve, governor weights).

CHRYSLER CORP. ELECTRONIC IGNITION (Cont.)

IGNITION COIL RESISTANCE CHECKS

1) Coil is designed to operate with an external ballast resistor. When testing ignition coil resistance, also test ballast resistor resistance. Inspect coil for external cracks and arcing.

2) Test coil according to instructions of coil tester manufacturer. Primary reistance should be 1.34 to 1.55 ohms. Secondary resistance should be 9400-11,700 ohms for Prestolite coils; 9000-12,200 ohms for Essex coils. Replace ignition coil if either specification is not obtained.

3) Ballast resistor resistance should be 1.2 ohms. If not, replace resistor.

OVERHAUL

Removal

Scribe a reference mark on edge of distributor housing to indicate position of rotor during distributor installation. Remove distributor.

NOTE: **Unless required for engine repair, do not crank engine between distributor removal and installation.**

Installation

1) Position distributor in engine. Align rotor with reference mark on distributor housing and engage end of shaft with slot in distributor oil pump drive gear.

2) If engine was cranked while distributor was removed, rotate crankshaft until No. 1 piston is at TDC on compression stroke (timing mark should be in line with "0" mark on timing chain cover).

3) Position rotor under No. 1 distributor cap terminal, lower distributor into engine and engage end of shaft with slot in distributor oil pump drive gear.

Checking Distributor Shaft Side Play

1) Remove distributor. Remove cap and rotor. Clamp distributor in soft-jawed vise, just tight enough to prevent distributor movement during testing.

2) Attach dial indicator to housing with indicator plunger against reluctor. Place a wire loop around shaft, resting against top of reluctor. Ensure that loop does not interfere with indicator or indicator holding bracket.

3) With a spring scale hooked in other end of loop, apply 1 1/2 lbs. of pull toward indicator, then 1 lb. away from indicator. Total dial reading must not exceed .006" (.15 mm). If it does, replace housing or shaft assembly.

Disassembly

1) Remove distributor cap. Using 2 screwdrivers, pry off rotor from shaft. Remove two screws and lockwashers attaching vacuum control unit to distributor housing. Disconnect vacuum control arm from upper plate and remove unit.

2) Remove reluctor by prying up from bottom of reluctor using 2 pry bars or screwdrivers with a maximum width of 7/16" (11 mm). Be careful not to distort or damage reluctor teeth.

3) Remove 2 screws and lock washers attaching lower plate to housing. Lift out plate and pick-up coils as an assembly. Do not attempt to remove distributor cap clamps, as they are peened in place. If distributor shaft side play is within limits, further dissasembly is not required.

4) If distributor shaft side play is excessive, shaft assembly and housing should be replaced. Remove distributor shaft retaining pin and slide retainer off end of shaft.

5) Use a small file to clean burrs from around hole in shaft. Remove lower thrust washer. Push shaft up through top of distributor body.

Reassembly

1) Check for smooth operation of governor weights. Inspect weight spring for distortion. Lubricate governor weights. Inspect all bearing surfaces and pivot pins for roughness, binding or excessive looseness.

2) Lubricate upper thrust washer(s) and install on shaft. Slide shaft into distributor body. Install shaft retainer and roll pin. Install plate and pick-up coil assembly and attaching screws.

3) Attach vacuum advance unit arm to pick-up plate. Install vacuum unit attaching screws and washers.

4) Position reluctor keeper pin in place on reluctor sleeve. Install reluctor and press firmly into place. Lubricate felt pad in top of reluctor sleeve with 1 drop of light engine oil before installing rotor. Install rotor and cap.

CHRYSLER CORP. ELECTRONIC SPARK CONTROL SYSTEM

Dodge/Plymouth 6-Cyl., High Alt. & Calif. V8

DESCRIPTION

Electronic Spark Control (ESC) system is governed by a Spark Control Computer (SCC). This system includes up to 6 engine sensors, specially calibrated carburetor and a dual pick-up distributor. ESC system is designed to burn a lean air/fuel mixture, with minimum of emissions.

SPARK CONTROL COMPUTER

Spark Control Computer (SCC), mounted on air cleaner, is the heart of the entire system. It gives the system capability of igniting lean fuel mixture according to different modes of engine operation by delivering an infinite number of variable advance curves.

SCC determines exact instant when ignition is required, then signals ignition coil to produce spark required to fire spark plugs.

SCC is basically an electronic printed circuit board, which receives signals from all sensors. Within milliseconds, it computes signals so that proper advance or retard is immediately achieved.

Fig. 1: Electronic Spark Control Computer

Vacuum transducer is mounted on computer housing.

SENSORS

Electronic Spark Control Computer uses up to 6 engine sensors to determine when to fire the spark plugs. These include 2 magnetic distributor pick-up coils (start and run), coolant temperature sensor, carburetor switch, vacuum transducer and charge temperature switch. Sensor signals are processed by a microprocessor. Sensor functions are as follows:

Magnetic Pick-Up Assembly

Pick-up coil assembly is located in distributor. Start pick-up coil supplies signal to computer, which will cause spark plugs to fire at fixed amount of advance during cranking only.

Once engine begins to run, the run pick-up coil takes over, supplying advance information to computer. Computer then modifies advance information to reflect other engine operating conditions supplied by remaining sensors.

Six-cylinder models with manual transmissions use only a run pick-up coil. Ignition signal information is provided by this pick-up at all times.

Coolant Temperature Sensor

Coolant sensor is located in cylinder head on six-cylinder models, at front of intake manifold on V8 engines. It informs computer when engine has reached predetermined temperature. This information is necessary to determine correct spark advance in accordance with engine operating temperature.

Vacuum Transducer

This sensor, located on spark control computer, signals computer to inform it of engine operating vacuum. Vacuum is one of the factors used to determine how much the computer will advance or retard ignition timing.

Carburetor Switch

Located on end of idle stop, carburetor switch informs computer when engine is at idle. When carburetor switch contacts throttle lever ground, computer will cancel spark advance and prevent air/fuel ratio from being adjusted.

Charge Temperature Switch

This sensor is located in No. 6 runner of intake manifold on six-cylinder models, on back of intake manifold on V8 engines. Switch will be closed whenever intake charge (air/fuel mixture) is below 60°F (16°C). This permits no EGR timer function and no EGR valve operation. When temperature is above 60°F (16°C), switch is open, allowing EGR timer to time out and EGR valve to operate.

OPERATION

Spark Control Computer has 2 functional modes, "Start" and "Run". "Start" mode operates while cranking and starting only. "Run" mode operates after engine has started and during normal engine operation.

Both modes never operate at same time. When cranking and starting, pick-up coil sends signal to computer which is in "Start" mode, "Run" mode is by-passed.

During "Start" mode, fixed advance is used. Advance is determined by distributor position (basic timing). After engine starts, pick-up coil continues to send signal to computer. Computer is now in "Run" mode and "Start" mode is by-passed. Amount of timing advance is now controlled by computer, based upon information received from engine sensors.

Amount of spark advance is determined by 2 factors, engine speed and engine vacuum. At what point it occurs, depends upon computer programming. Advance from vacuum will be provided when carburetor switch is open.

Spark advance programmed into computer is proportional to amount of vacuum and engine RPM. Advance from speed will be given by computer when carburetor switch is open and is programmed to engine RPM.

If for some reason "Run" mode does not work, "Start" mode will come back into service. This is called "Limp-in" mode, it allows the vehicle to be driven. Performance and economy will be greatly reduced because of the fixed timing.

If pick-up coil in distributor fails (both coils in dual coil distributors) or "Start" mode in computer fails, engine will not start or run.

TESTING

IGNITION SYSTEM STARTING TEST

1) Turn ignition switch "ON". Remove coil wire from distributor cap. Hold end of wire 1/4" from engine

CHRYSLER CORP. ELECTRONIC SPARK CONTROL SYSTEM (Cont.)

Fig. 2: Electronic Spark Control System Wiring Diagram

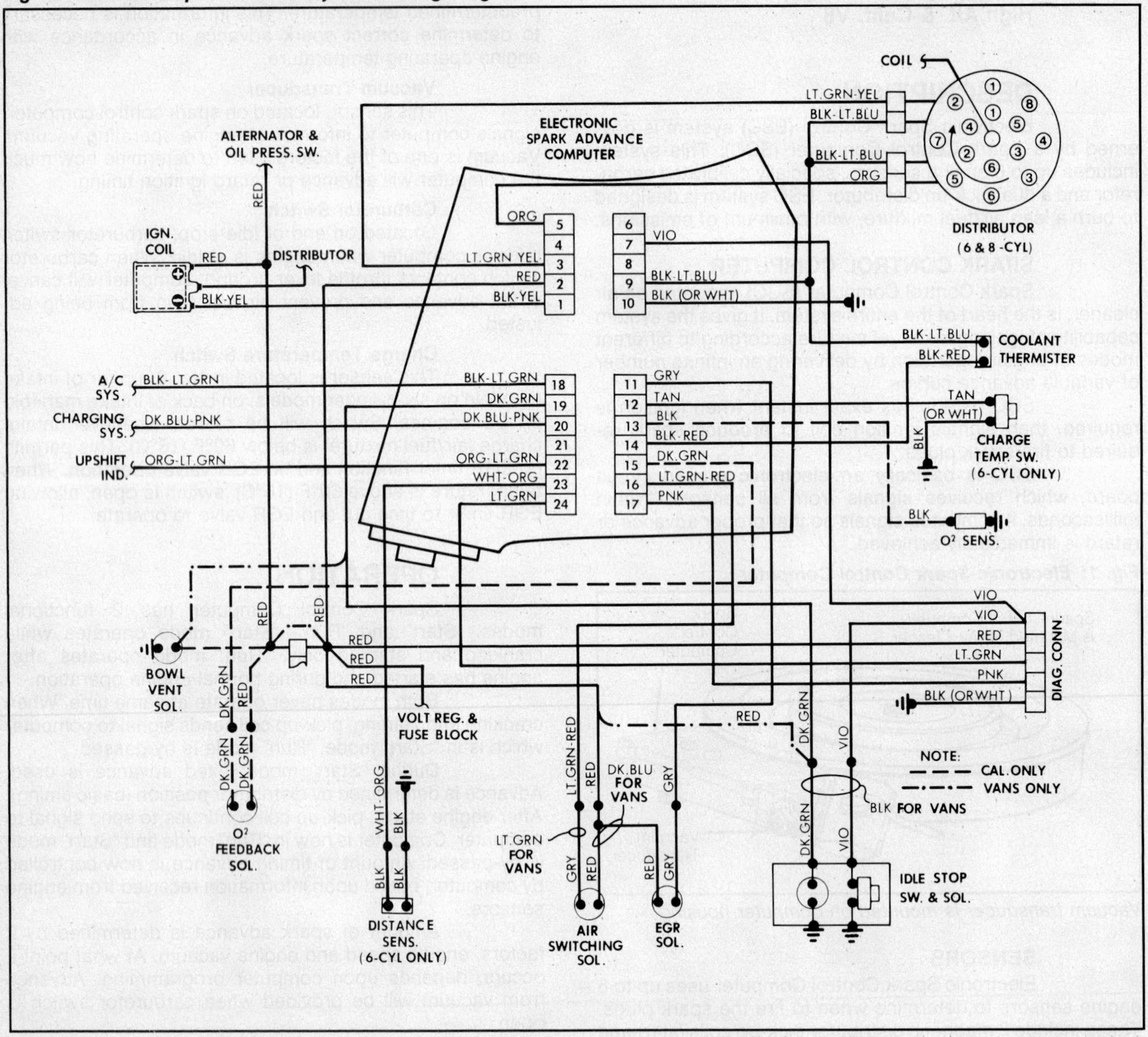

All except California 5.2L V8 with Electronic Spark Advance system.

ground. Using special jumper, intermittently ground coil negative terminal. Watch for spark at coil wire. If there is spark, it must be constant and bright blue. *See Fig. 4.*

2) If spark is good, continue to intermittently ground coil negative terminal, while slowly moving coil wire away from ground. Check for arcing at coil tower. If arcing occurs, replace ignition coil.

3) If spark is weak or not constant, or if there is no spark, proceed to FAILURE TO START TEST.

4) If spark is good and there is no arcing at coil tower, ignition system is producing necessary high secondary voltage. Make sure spark is getting to plugs by checking distributor rotor, cap, spark plugs, and plug wires.

5) If all this checks out, but engine still will not start, ignition system is not the problem. It will be necessary to check fuel system and engine mechanical components.

FAILURE TO START TEST

CAUTION: Perform IGNITION SYSTEM STARTING TEST first. Failure to do so may result in lost diagnostic time or incorrect test results.

1) Turn ignition switch off. Disconnect 10-wire connector from spark control computer. Repeat IGNITION SYSTEM STARTING TEST, step **1)**. If spark results, replace spark control computer.

2) If no spark is obtained, check voltage at coil positive terminal. Turn ignition switch to "ON" position. Connect positive voltmeter lead to coil positive terminal and ground negative lead. Reading should be within 1 volt of battery voltage. If not, check wiring between battery and coil positive terminal.

3) If voltage at positive coil terminal was correct, connect positive voltmeter lead to coil negative terminal and ground negative meter lead. Again, voltage

CHRYSLER CORP. ELECTRONIC SPARK CONTROL SYSTEM (Cont.)

Fig. 3: Electronic Spark Conrol System Wiring Diagram

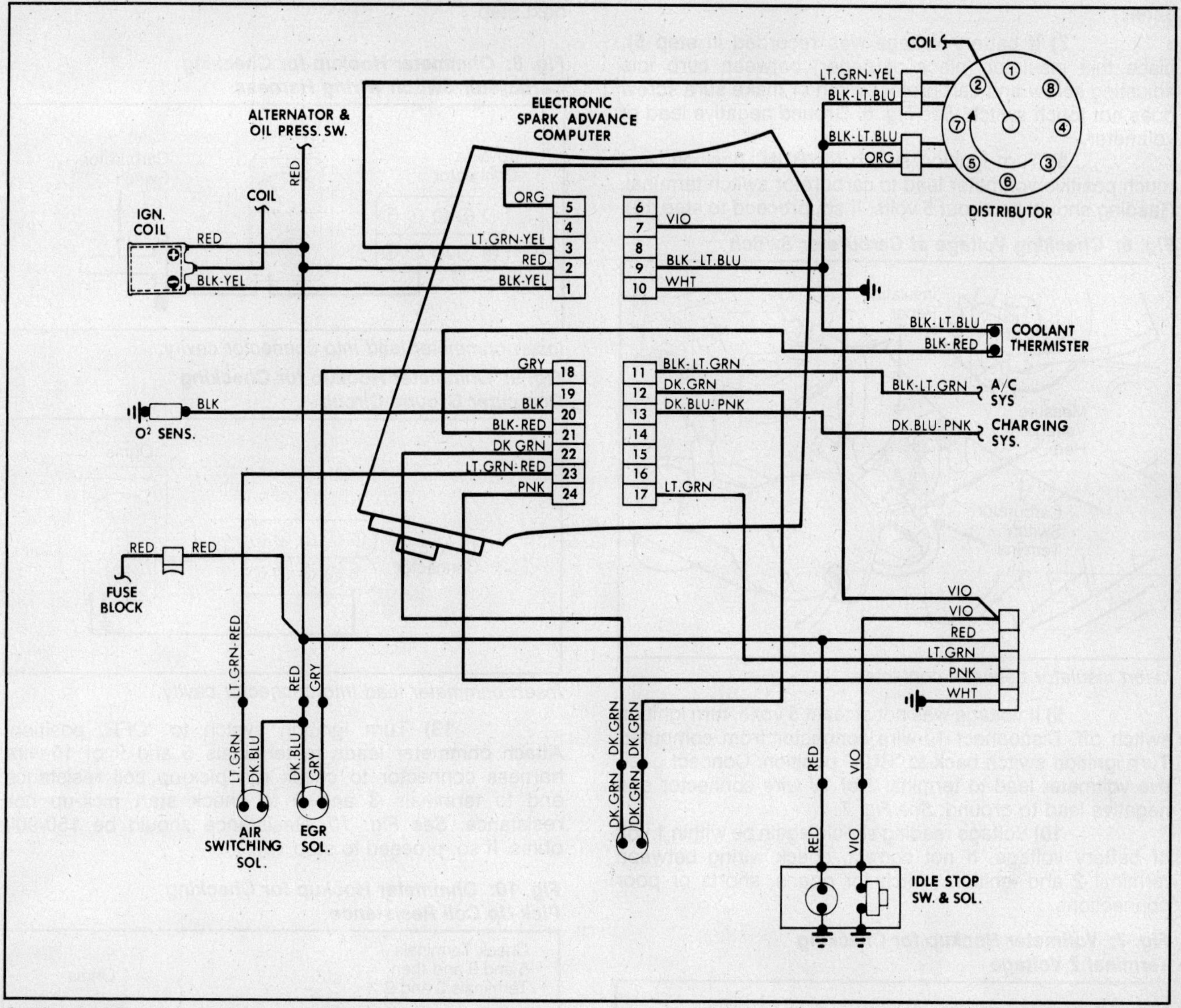

California 5.2L V8 with Electronic Spark Advance system.

Fig. 4: Special Jumper Wire with Capacitor

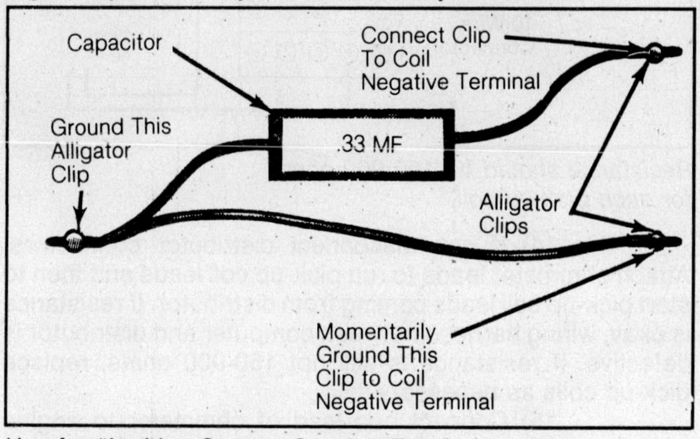

Use for "Ignition System Starting Test".

should be within 1 volt of battery voltage. If not, replace ignition coil.

4) If voltage was correct at negative coil terminal, but no spark resulted in IGNITION SYSTEM STARTING TEST, step **1)**, replace ignition coil.

5) If spark results, but engine will not start, turn ignition switch to "RUN" position. Connect positive voltmeter lead to terminal 1 of 10-wire connector and ground negative lead. *See Fig. 5.*

Fig. 5: Voltmeter Hookup for Checking Terminal 1 Voltage

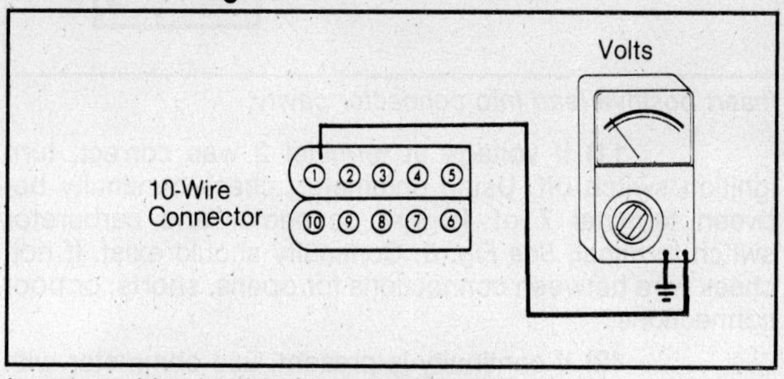

Insert positive lead into connector cavity.

6) Reading should be within 1 volt of battery voltage. If not, check wire for open and repair it, repeating

CHRYSLER CORP. ELECTRONIC SPARK CONTROL SYSTEM (Cont.)

step **5)** once more. Reconnect 10-wire connector to computer.

7) If battery voltage was recorded in step **5)**, place thin insulator (piece of paper) between curb idle adjusting screw and carburetor switch or make sure screw does not touch switch. *See Fig. 6.* Ground negative lead of voltmeter.

8) Turn ignition switch to "RUN" position, and touch positive voltmeter lead to carburetor switch terminal. Reading should be about 5 volts. If so, proceed to step **13)**.

Fig. 6: Checking Voltage at Carburetor Switch

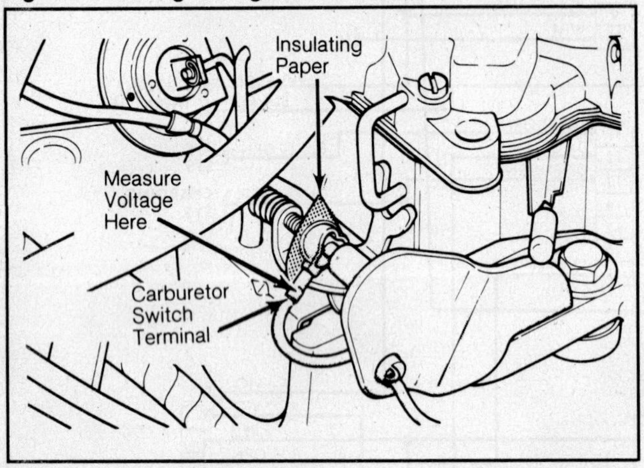

Insert insulator between contacts.

9) If voltage was not at least 5 volts, turn ignition switch off. Disconnect 10-wire connector from computer. Turn ignition switch back to "RUN" position. Connect positive voltmeter lead to terminal 2 of 10-wire connector and negative lead to ground. *See Fig. 7.*

10) Voltage reading should again be within 1 volt of battery voltage. If not correct, check wiring between terminal 2 and ignition switch for opens, shorts or poor connections.

Fig. 7: Voltmeter Hookup for Checking Terminal 2 Voltage

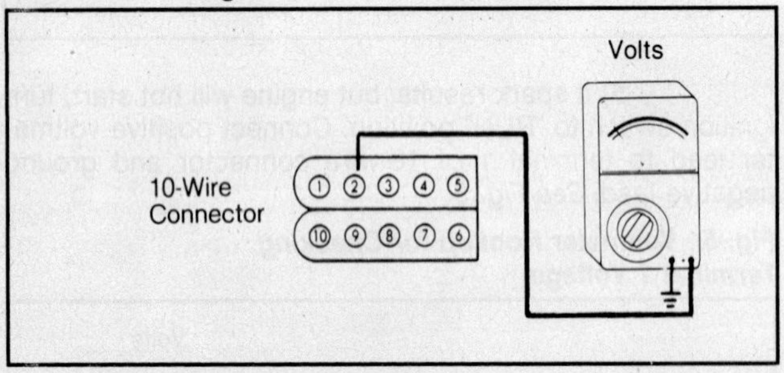

Insert positive lead into connector cavity.

11) If voltage at terminal 2 was correct, turn ignition switch off. Using ohmmeter, check continuity between terminal 7 of 10-wire connector and carburetor switch terminal. *See Fig. 8.* Continuity should exist. If not, check wire between connections for opens, shorts, or poor connections.

12) If continuity is present, use ohmmeter with leads attached to terminal 10 and engine ground to check continuity of ground circuit. *See Fig. 9.* If there is continuity, replace computer. If there is no continuity, check wire from terminal 10 to ground. If engine fails to start, proceed to next step.

Fig. 8: Ohmmeter Hookup for Checking Carburetor Switch Wiring Harness

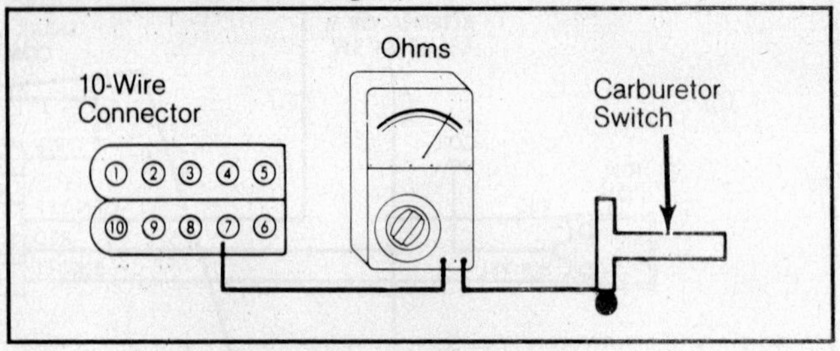

Insert ohmmeter lead into connector cavity.

Fig. 9: Ohmmeter Hookup for Checking Computer Ground Circuit

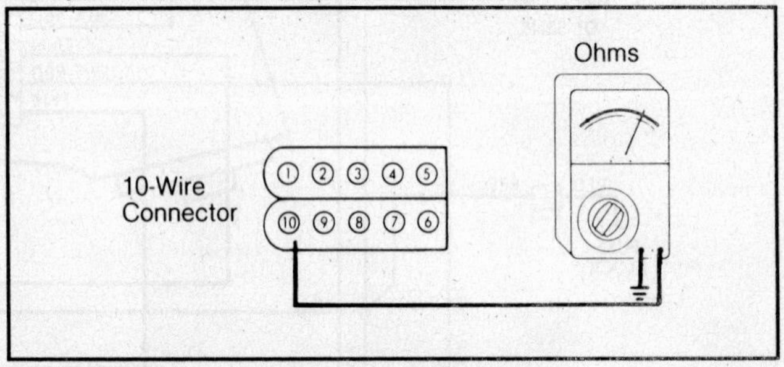

Insert ohmmeter lead into connector cavity.

13) Turn ignition switch to "OFF" position. Attach ohmmeter leads to terminals 5 and 9 of 10-wire harness connector to check run pick-up coil resistance and to terminals 3 and 9 to check start pick-up coil resistance. *See Fig. 10.* Resistance should be 150-900 ohms. If so, proceed to step **15)**.

Fig. 10: Ohmmeter Hookup for Checking Pick-Up Coil Resistance

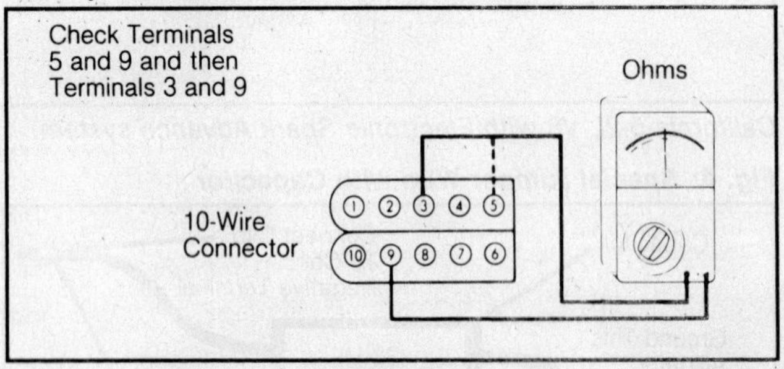

Resistance should be 150-900 ohms for each pick-up coil.

14) If not, disconnect distributor connectors. Attach ohmmeter leads to run pick-up coil leads and then to start pick-up coil leads coming from distributor. If resistance is okay, wiring harness between computer and distributor is defective. If resistance is still not 150-900 ohms, replace pick-up coils as necessary.

15) Connect one lead of ohmmeter to engine ground and touch other lead to each terminal of 2 leads coming from each of 2 distributor pick-up coils. There should be no continuity. If there is continuity, replace pick-up coils as necessary.

16) Remove distributor cap and check each reluctor-to-pick-up coil air gap. Check start pick-up coil

CHRYSLER CORP. ELECTRONIC SPARK CONTROL SYSTEM (Cont.)

gap with .006" (.15 mm) non-magnetic feeler gauge. Check run pick-up coil gap with .012" (.30 mm) gauge. *See Fig. 11.*

Fig. 11: Checking Distributor Pick-Up Air Gap

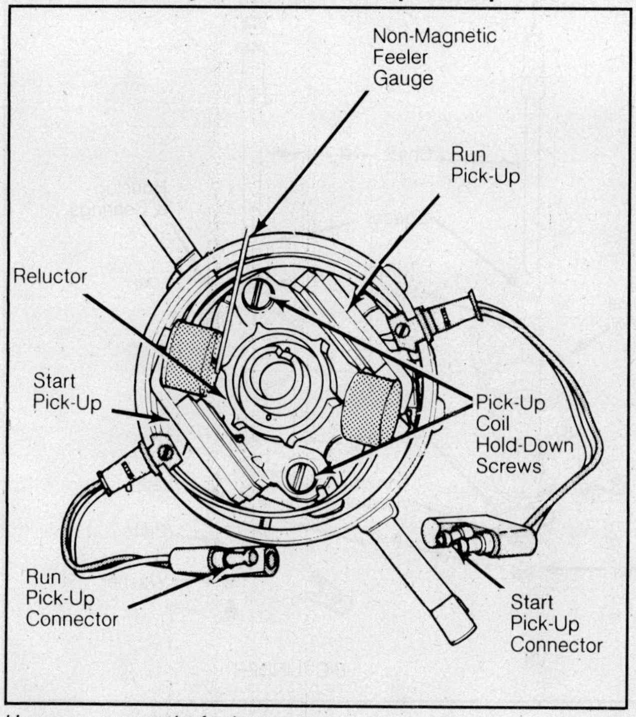

Use non-magnetic feeler gauge.

NOTE: To adjust gap, loosen pick-up coil hold-down screws, move pick-up coil against feeler gauge resting against reluctor tooth. Tighten hold-down screw, remove feeler gauge, and recheck gap.

17) Install distributor cap and reinstall all wiring. If engine fails to start, replace spark control computer. If it still fails to start, install original computer and retest.

IGNITION COIL RESISTANCE CHECKS

1) Test coil according to instructions of coil tester manufacturer. Primary reistance should be 1.34 to 1.55 ohms. Secondary resistance should be 9400-11,700 ohms for Prestolite coils, 9000-12,200 ohms for Essex coils.

2) Replace ignition coil if either specification is not obtained.

POOR PERFORMANCE TEST

Basic Advance Timing Test

1) Connect adjustable timing light and tachometer to engine. With parking brake set and transmission in neutral, start engine and run until normal operating temperature is reached.

2) Open and close throttle to ensure that linkage is not binding and that idle speed screw is against its stop. Connect jumper wire between carburetor switch and ground.

3) Check idle speed. Adjust only if idle is too high. Check ignition timing. If not within 2° of specification, loosen distributor hold-down screw and adjust timing. Tighten hold-down. Recheck timing and idle speed.

4) If idle speed is too high, repeat step **3)**.

Spark Advance of Computer

1) Set basic timing. Start engine and allow it to warm to normal operating temperature. Put transmission in neutral and set parking brake.

NOTE: The Spark Control Computer has various spark advance schedules incorporated into its microprocessor for operation at differing engine temperatures. Be sure engine is at normal operating temperature before testing.

2) Place thin insulator (piece of paper) between curb idle adjusting screw and carburetor switch. Make sure adjusting screw is not touching switch. *See Fig. 6.* Remove and plug vacuum line at vacuum transducer.

CAUTION: Use metal exhaust tube for step 3), as high temperatures could cause rubber hose to catch fire.

3) Connect auxiliary vacuum supply to vacuum transducer. Set to 10 in. Hg for 3.7L engines and 16 in. Hg for 5.2L engines. Increase engine speed to 2000 RPM. Wait 1 minute for specified accumulator clock up time and then check timing. Advance specifications are in addition to basic advance.

4) If computer fails to obtain specified settings, replace computer.

CARBURETOR SWITCH TEST

1) Grounding carburetor switch eliminates all spark advance on most systems. Turn key to "OFF" position. Disconnect 10-wire harness connector from computer.

2) With throttle completely closed, check continuity between terminal 7 and ground. If no continuity is indicated, check wire and carburetor switch. Recheck basic timing.

3) With throttle opened, check continuity between terminal 7 and ground. There should be no continuity.

CHARGE TEMPERATURE & COOLANT SWITCH

1) Turn ignition off. Disconnect wire from charge temperature switch. Connect one lead of ohmmeter to engine ground (or to switch's ground terminal). Connect other lead to center terminal of coolant switch. Check for continuity.

2) With cold engine, continuity should be present (resistance less than 100 ohms). If not, replace switch. Charge temperature switch must be cooler than 60°F (16°C) to obtain this reading.

3) With engine at normal operating temperature, terminal should show no continuity. If there is continuity, replace coolant switch.

COOLANT SENSOR

1) Resistance of sensor changes continually with engine temperature. This device is not a switch. Connect ohmmeter leads to coolant sensor terminals. Check resistance with engine cold and at operating temperature.

2) Resistance with engine cold should be 500-1100 ohms. Resistance at operating temperature should be more than 1300 ohms.

3) If resistance is outside of specifications, replace sensor.

CHRYSLER CORP. ELECTRONIC SPARK CONTROL SYSTEM (Cont.)

Fig. 12: Electronic Spark Control System Distributors

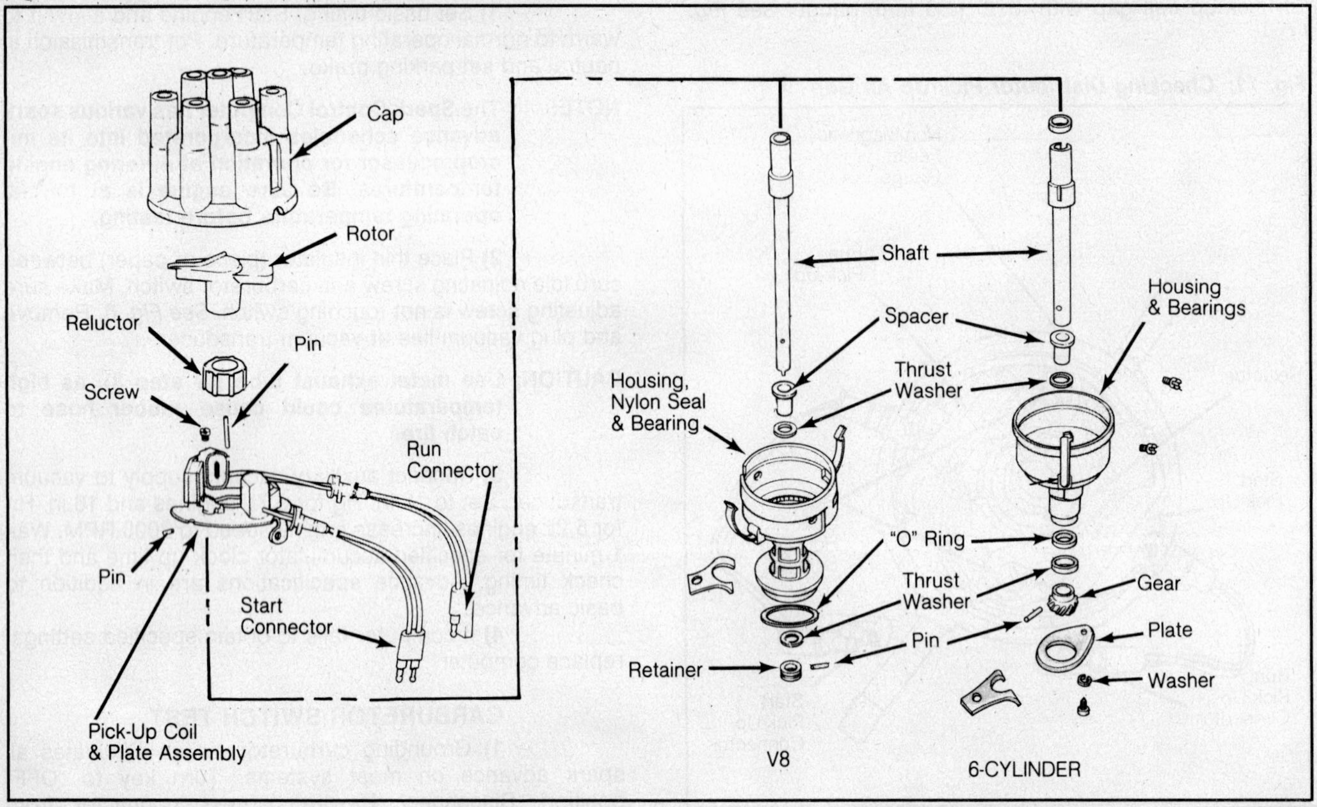

Note difference between start and run pick-up coil connectors.

ELECTRONIC EGR SYSTEM TEST

Spark Control Computer incorporates an electronic EGR control system. Check that engine temperature sensors are working properly, and proceed as follows:

1) With engine cold and ignition switch turned off, connect voltmeter positive lead to EGR solenoid Gray wire and negative lead to ground. Start engine.

2) Voltage should be less than 1 volt, remaining 1 volt until engine reaches normal operating temperature and electronic EGR schedule has timed out. Solenoid will then de-energize, and voltmeter should read charging system voltage.

3) If reading is not correct, replace solenoid and repeat test. If voltmeter indicates charging voltage before EGR schedule is complete, replace computer or externally mounted timer.

4) If engine is started while hot, EGR solenoid will only be energized during length of time delay schedule. It will then de-energize.

ELECTRONIC THROTTLE CONTROL SYSTEM TEST

Spark Control Computer also incorporates an electronic throttle system on Federal 6-cylinder and some 5.2L models. Solenoid, mounted on carburetor is energized when A/C, heater, electronic backlite, or electronic timers are activated.

The 2 timers, incorporated in the ignition system, operate when throttle is closed, plus time delay of 2 seconds, or after engine start condition (EGR time delay).

1) To test system, connect tachometer to engine. Start engine. Depress accelerator and let it up. Higher than curb idle speed should be seen for the length of EGR schedule.

2) If vehicle is equipped with A/C or electronic backlite, turn system on and depress accelerator for brief period. Higher than curb idle speed should result. Turn system off and normal idle speed should return.

NOTE: A/C clutch will cycle as it is running. This should not be mistaken as part of electronic control.

3) If speed increases do not occur, disconnect 6-way connector at carburetor. Check solenoid with ohmmeter, measuring resistance from terminal that contains Black wire to ground. Resistance should read 15-35 ohms. If not, replace solenoid.

4) Start vehicle and before delay has timed out, measure voltage of Black wire at 6-way connector. Charging voltage should be observed. If not, replace computer.

5) After time delay, turn A/C or backlite on. Charging voltage should be read. If not, check wiring back to instrument panel for open circuit.

OVERHAUL

Removal

1) When removing 6-cylinder distributor, rotate crankshaft until rotor is pointing toward cylinder block. Scribe a reference mark on the block to indicate position of rotor during distributor installation. Remove distributor.

2) On V8 models, scribe a reference mark on edge of distributor housing to indicate position of rotor during distributor installation. Remove distributor.

CHRYSLER CORP. ELECTRONIC SPARK CONTROL SYSTEM (Cont.)

NOTE: Unless required for engine repair, do not crank engine between distributor removal and installation.

Installation

1) On 6-cylinder models, install distributor in engine, carefully engaging drive gear with camshaft gear so that rotor is in line with reference mark when distributor is fully seated.

2) On V8 models, position distributor in engine. Align rotor with reference mark on distributor housing and engage end of shaft with slot in distributor oil pump drive gear.

3) On all models, if engine was cranked while distributor was removed, rotate crankshaft until No. 1 piston is at TDC on compression stroke (timing mark should be in line with "0" mark on timing chain cover).

4) On 6-cylinder models, position rotor just ahead of No. 1 distributor cap terminal and lower distributor into position, engaging drive gear with camshaft gear. With distributor fully seated, rotor should rotate into position under No. 1 cap terminal.

5) On V8 models, position rotor under No. 1 distributor cap terminal, lower distributor into engine and engage end of shaft with slot in distributor oil pump drive gear.

Checking Distributor Shaft Side Play

1) Remove distributor. Remove cap and rotor. Clamp distributor in soft-jawed vise, just tight enough to prevent distributor movement during testing.

2) Attach dial indicator to housing with indicator plunger against reluctor. Place a wire loop around shaft, resting against top of reluctor. Ensure that loop does not interfere with indicator or indicator holding bracket.

3) With a spring scale hooked in the other end of loop, apply 1 1/2 lbs. of pull toward indicator, then 1 lb. away from indicator. Total dial reading must not exceed .006" (.15 mm). If it does, replace the housing or shaft assembly.

Disassembly

1) Remove distributor cap. Using 2 screwdrivers, pry off rotor from shaft. Remove reluctor by prying up from bottom of reluctor using 2 pry bars or screwdrivers with a maximum width of 7/16" (11 mm). Be careful not to distort or damage reluctor teeth.

2) Remove 2 screws and lock washers attaching lower plate to housing. Lift out plate and pick-up coils as an assembly. Do not attempt to remove distributor cap clamps, as they are peened in place. If distributor shaft side play is within limits, further dissassembly is not required.

3) On 6-cylinder models, if distributor shaft side play is excessive, drive shaft or housing should be replaced. Check drive gear for excessive wear or damage to teeth.

4) If gear is damaged and shaft is to be reused, scribe a line on end of shaft from middle to edge, with end of mark centered between 2 gear teeth. Remove distributor drive gear retaining pin and slide gear off end of shaft.

5) On V8 models, if distributor shaft side play is excessive, shaft should be replaced. Remove distributor shaft retaining pin and slide retainer off end of shaft.

6) On all models, use a small file to clean burrs from around hole in shaft. Remove lower thrust washer. Push shaft up through top of distributor body.

Reassembly

1) Lubricate upper thrust washer(s) and install on shaft. Slide shaft into distributor body. On V8 models, install shaft retainer and roll pin.

2) On 6-cylinder models, install lower thrust washer and original gear, if used, on lower end of shaft. Install roll pin.

3) If a new drive gear is to be installed on old shaft, install gear with thrust washer in place. Position hole in new gear about 90 degrees from original hole in shaft. Center scribed line on shaft between 2 gear teeth.

NOTE: Hole in replacement gear is slightly higher than original hole in shaft. This design prevents weakening of shaft when new pin hole is drilled.

4) Place a .007" (.18 mm) feeler gauge between gear and thrust washer. Check that scribe mark is still centered between teeth and drill a .124-.129" (3.15-3.28 mm) hole in shaft. Install roll pin.

5) On all models, install plate and pick-up coil assembly and attaching screws. Position reluctor keeper pin in place on reluctor sleeve. Install reluctor and press firmly into place. Install keeper pin. Lubricate felt pad in top of reluctor sleeve (if equipped) with 1 drop of light engine oil before installing rotor. Install rotor and cap.

CHRYSLER CORP.
HALL EFFECT ELECTRONIC SPARK CONTROL

Chrysler Corp. 2.2L

DESCRIPTION

Electronic Spark Control system, used on Chrysler Corp. front wheel drive vehicles with 2.2L engines, features a Hall Effect distributor and spark control computer.

Fig. 1: Wiring Diagram of Chrysler Corp. Hall Effect Electronic Spark Control System

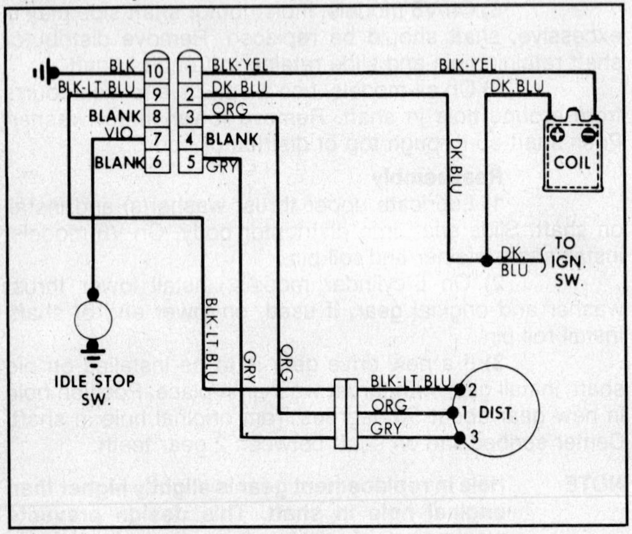

The computer is the heart of the system, providing capability of igniting a lean air/fuel mixture according to different modes of engine operation. It provides an infinite number of variable advance curves.

The computer contains an electronic printed circuit board, which simultaneously receives signals from various engine sensors, analyzes them to determine how the engine is operating and then advances or retards ignition timing.

The computer determines exact instant when ignition is required and then signals ignition coil to produce the electrical impulses that fire the spark plugs. The computer is located on the fenderwell.

The computer is connected to other fuel/ignition components by a 10-wire and 14-wire dual connector. Five engine sensors feed information to the computer. These include a vacuum transducer, mounted on the computer housing, the Hall Effect pick-up assembly in the distributor, engine coolant temperature sensor, carburetor switch and an oxygen sensor.

The computer used with the spark control system eliminates need for either vacuum advance units or centrifugal advance weights. Hall Effect distributor is connected to rest of the system by a 3-terminal connector. *See Fig. 2*. It sends small alternating current signals to the computer as rotor shutter blades enter and leave the gap in the Hall Effect switching unit pick-up assembly.

Carburetor switch senses when engine is at idle. Coolant temperature switch or sensor keeps the computer informed on engine operating temperatures. Vacuum transducer informs the computer of engine vacuum (load).

Fig. 2: Components of Hall Effect Distributor for Electronic Spark Control System

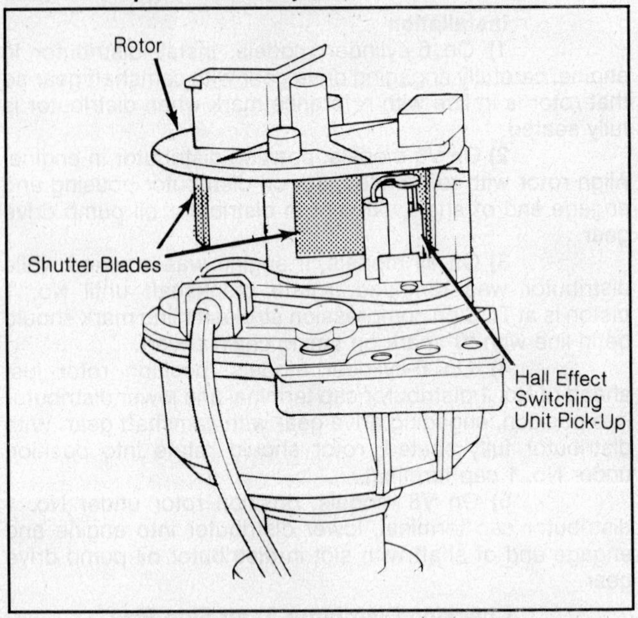

OPERATION

The computer has 2 functional modes, "START" and "RUN" modes. Start mode functions only during engine cranking and starting. Fixed amount of spark advance is provided, based on distributor position.

Run mode functions only when engine starts and is operating normally. Hall Effect pick-up assembly and 4 other sensors provide information to the computer, which then varies spark advance to match engine operating conditions. Spark timing and dwell cannot be adjusted in the run mode.

Engine sensors work together. If engine temperature drops below a predetermined temperature, coolant temperature switch signals the computer to prevent additional advance from the vacuum transducer signal. As temperatures rise, vacuum increases, and additional advance is called for. For maximum advance, the carburetor switch must remain open. During the time when advance will not occur quickly, vacuum advance is controlled by engine RPM and will build up at a slow rate. If the carburetor switch closes, this build-up of advance will be cancelled.

Hall Effect pick-up signal is a reference signal, providing maximum amount of advance, based on sensor input. At the proper time, the computer shuts off current to ignition coil primary circuit. As the magnetic field collapses, a high voltage surge occurs in the secondary, firing the spark plugs.

If run mode of the computer fails, system will go into start mode. This enables the vehicle to be driven in for repair. However, performance and fuel economy will be poor. If the Hall Effect pick-up or start mode of the computer fails, engine will not start or run.

ADJUSTMENTS

No adjustments can be made to the Hall Effect pick-up unit. Dwell and spark timing cannot be adjusted in run mode. Initial fixed timing (start mode) can be adjusted by changing distributor position.

CHRYSLER CORP.
HALL EFFECT ELECTRONIC SPARK CONTROL (Cont.)

TESTING

NOTE: Testing procedures for Chrysler Corp. Electronic Spark Control System are the same as for Chrysler Corp. Electronic Fuel Control. See CHRYSLER CORP. FWD ELECTRONIC FUEL CONTROL article in COMPUTERIZED ENGINE CONTROLS section.

OVERHAUL

DISASSEMBLY

1) Remove distributor with ignition wires from vehicle. Lightly clamp distributor in soft-jawed vise. Remove 2 screws holding splash shield to distributor housing. Remove distributor cap and rotor from shaft.

NOTE: When removing spark plug wires from distributor cap, do not pull on wires. Positive-locking wires must be released from inside cap. See Fig. 3.

2) Remove Hall Effect pick-up assembly lock springs (or clips) and lift pick-up assembly out. Mark drive gear (or distributor drive) position on distributor shaft. Using a pin punch, drive roll pin from shaft.

NOTE: Hall Effect pick-up assembly may be replaced without removing distributor from engine.

3) Remove drive gear (or distributor drive) and remove shaft from housing. If equipped, remove thrust washers, nylon spacers and block seals.

REASSEMBLY

To reassemble, reverse disassembly procedure. Correct rotor has "E.S.A." stamped in its top. Check rotor for proper grounding of shutter blades.

Fig. 3: Use Pliers to Release Positive-Locking Spark Plug Wire Terminals

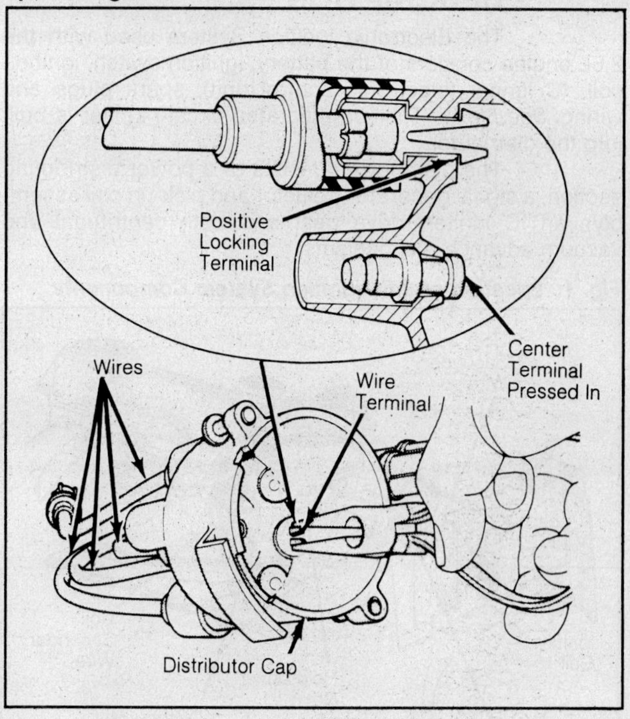

CHRYSLER CORP. (MITSUBISHI) ELECTRONIC IGNITION

Chrysler Corp. Models with 2.6L Engines

DESCRIPTION

The Electronic Ignition System used with the 2.6L engine consists of the battery, ignition switch, ignition coil, IC igniter (electronic control unit), spark plugs and wiring. *See Fig. 1.* The IC (integrated circuit) igniter is built into the distributor.

The distributor consists of a power distributing section, a signal generator (reluctor and pick-up coil assembly), an IC igniter, drive gear and both centrifugal and vacuum advance mechanisms.

Fig. 1: Location of 2.6L Ignition System Components

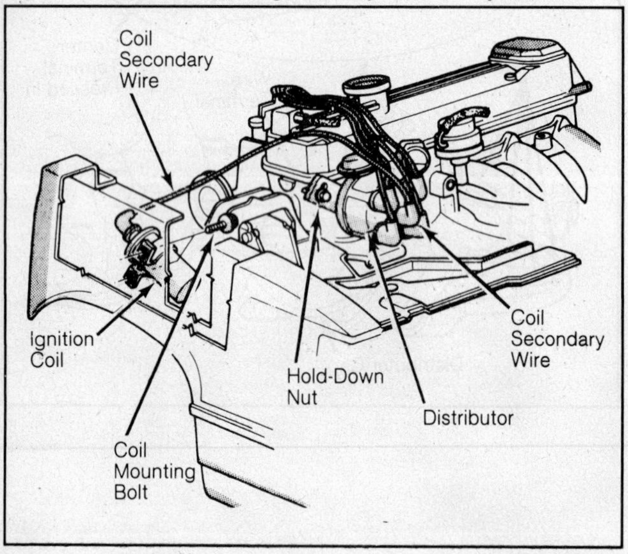

OPERATION

As the distributor shaft turns, a reluctor rotates inside a pick-up coil assembly. As the reluctor teeth pass the pick-up coil, a signal is generated similar to that produced by a small magneto generator.

The signal is produced in exact synchronization with distributor shaft rotation, four times per rotation and at equally spaced intervals.

The signal generated is sent to the IC igniter, which then switches current on or off in the ignition coil primary circuit. As current is shut off, the magnetic field in the coil primary collapses. This results in a voltage surge in the secondary, firing the spark plugs.

The centrifugal advance mechanism is located below the rotor assembly. As engine speed increases, the weights move outward, causing the reluctor to rotate ahead of the distributor shaft, advancing timing.

The vacuum advance has a spring-loaded diaphragm connected to the breaker assembly. As engine vacuum increases, the diaphragm pivots the movable breaker assembly in a direction opposite to shaft rotation. This, too, advances ignition timing.

ADJUSTMENTS

The only adjustments that can be made to this system are basic ignition timing (changing distributor position) and spark plug gap.

TESTING

IGNITION SYSTEM

1) Remove secondary wire from distributor center tower. Hold end of wire approximately 3/8" from a good engine ground. Crank engine and check for a bright blue spark at gap. *See Fig. 2.*

Fig. 2: Testing Ignition System for Spark

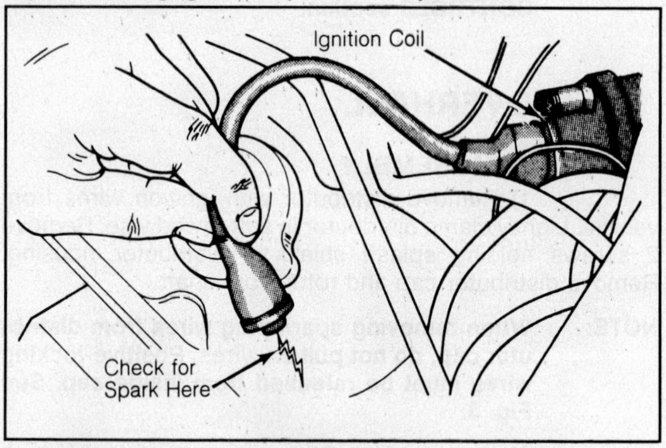

Hold end of wire approximately 3/8" from ground.

2) If spark does not occur, proceed to step **4)**. If spark does occur, slowly move secondary wire away from ground, checking for arcing at coil tower. If arcing occurs, replace ignition coil.

3) If spark was good and there was no arcing at coil tower, secondary voltage is good. Check distributor rotor and cap for damage, as well as, secondary wires and spark plugs. If all components are okay, check fuel system or check for mechanical damage to engine components.

4) If in step **2)** spark was weak, not constant, or there was no sparking, turn ignition switch "ON". Connect positive voltmeter lead to negative terminal of ignition coil. Connect negative lead to a good ground. Voltage reading should be battery voltage.

5) If voltage is battery voltage, proceed to step **6)**. If reading is less than 3 volts, IC igniter is defective. If there is no voltage indicated, check for open circuit in ignition coil or wiring harnesses.

6) If battery voltage was indicated in step **4)**, hold coil secondary wire about 1/4" from a good ground. Using a special jumper wire assembly, momentarily touch ignition coil negative terminal to ground. *See Fig. 3.* A spark should result.

Fig. 3: Special Ignition System Jumper Wire Assembly

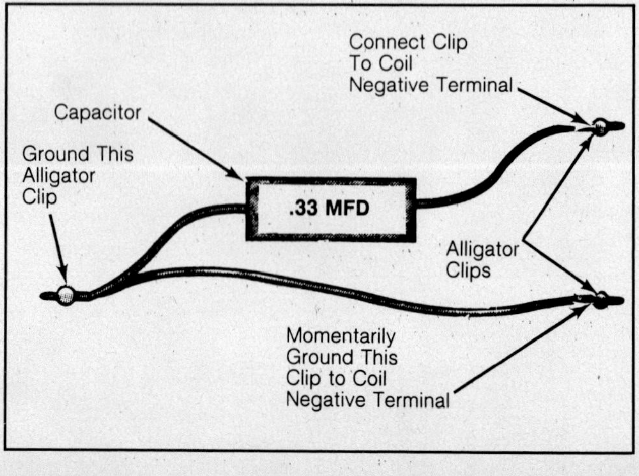

CHRYSLER CORP. (MITSUBISHI) ELECTRONIC IGNITION (Cont.)

7) If spark results, but engine does not start, proceed to step **9)**. If there was no spark, check for voltage at positive terminal of ignition coil with ignition switch on (voltmeter positive lead to positive terminal, negative lead to ground). Reading should be at least 12 volts.

8) If proper voltage is read, ignition coil is defective and must be replaced. If voltage was not to specifications, check wiring back to battery.

9) If in step **6)** a spark was produced, but vehicle will not start, replace IC igniter.

IC IGNITER

1) To check the IC igniter, connect one lead of 12-volt, 3-30 watt test lamp to output side of IC igniter. Attach battery positive terminal to IC igniter battery terminal, and the negative terminal to IC igniter base. Other test lamp lead should be attached to positive battery wire. *See Fig. 4*.

Fig. 4: Testing IC Igniter Operation

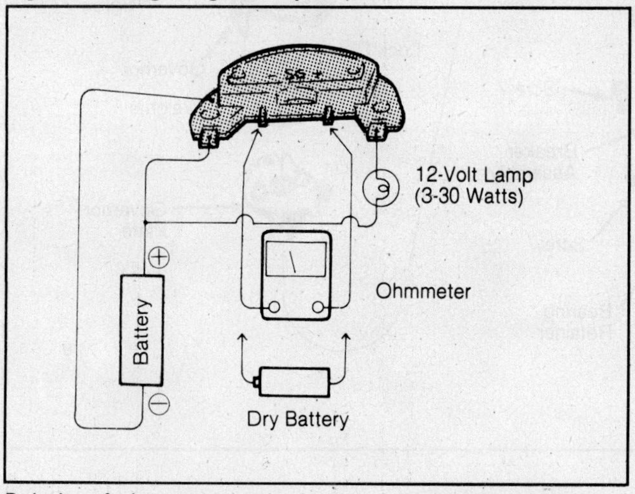

Polarity of ohmmeter or dry battery may be reversed.

2) Using a dry battery or ohmmeter, apply small voltage to signal input terminals of IC igniter. Test lamp should light when signal voltage is applied and go out when it is removed. If not, replace IC igniter.

3) If lamp does not operate as stated, IC igniter is defective. However, if lamp does operate properly, IC igniter still could be faulty. Part substitution is recommended as a final test in such cases.

PICK-UP COIL RESISTANCE

Connect an ohmmeter to terminals shown in *Fig. 5*. With ignition switch "OFF", resistance should read 920-1120 ohms. If not, replace pick-up coil assembly.

IGNITION COIL RESISTANCE

1) Connect ohmmeter leads to positive and negative terminals of ignition coil. Ignition switch should be "OFF" and wire should be removed from positive terminal of ignition coil to isolate it from system. Primary resistance should be 0.70-0.85 ohm.

2) With ignition switch still "OFF", connect ohmmeter leads to coil negative terminal and coil tower terminal. Secondary resistance should read 9,000-11,000 ohms.

3) If either reading is not within specified range, replace ignition coil.

Fig. 5: Measuring Pick-Up Coil Resistance

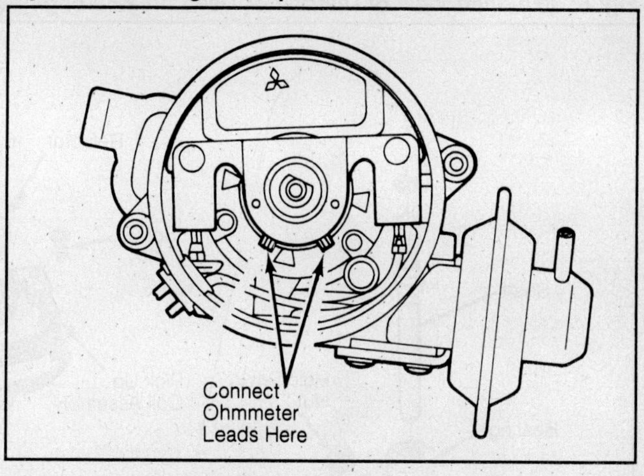

SECONDARY WIRE RESISTANCE

To check coil-to-distributor wire and spark plug wire resistance, connect ohmmeter leads to each end of wire. Resistance should be less than 22,000 ohms per wire. If not, replace wires.

CAUTION: Do not pull on wires when removing. Grasp wire's rubber cap. Do not bend wires as this could break the conductor.

CENTRIFUGAL ADVANCE MECHANISM

1) Run engine at idle speed and remove vacuum hose (non-striped) from vacuum controller. Slowly increase engine speed and check for advance.

2) If advance is excessive, check for deteriorated governor spring. A broken spring will result in abrupt advance. If advance is insufficient, check governor weights and cam for faulty operation.

VACUUM ADVANCE MECHANISM

1) Set engine speed at 2500 RPM. Check for advance by disconnecting and connecting distributor vacuum hose.

2) If available, connect a vacuum pump after removing distributor vacuum hose. Run engine at idle and slowly apply vacuum to check for advance.

3) If advance is excessive, check for deteriorated or sagging vacuum controller. If advance is insufficient or there is no advance, breaker plate is not operating properly or vacuum diaphragm is damaged.

OVERHAUL

DISASSEMBLY

1) Remove distributor cap and rotor. *See Fig. 6*. Remove centrifugal advance components as an assembly by removing screw in top of shaft. Due to extreme tightness of bolt, a socket or box wrench should be used for this purpose.

2) If governor assembly is further disassembled, be sure 2 different springs are properly identified for correct reassembly. Remove wire clamp screw and remove clamp. Remove 2 screws securing pick-up coil assembly and IC igniter and remove them as an assembly.

3) Remove 2 screws securing vacuum diaphragm assembly. Disengage vacuum diaphragm from

CHRYSLER CORP. (MITSUBISHI) ELECTRONIC IGNITION (Cont.)

Fig. 6: Exploded View of Distributor Used on 2.6L Engines

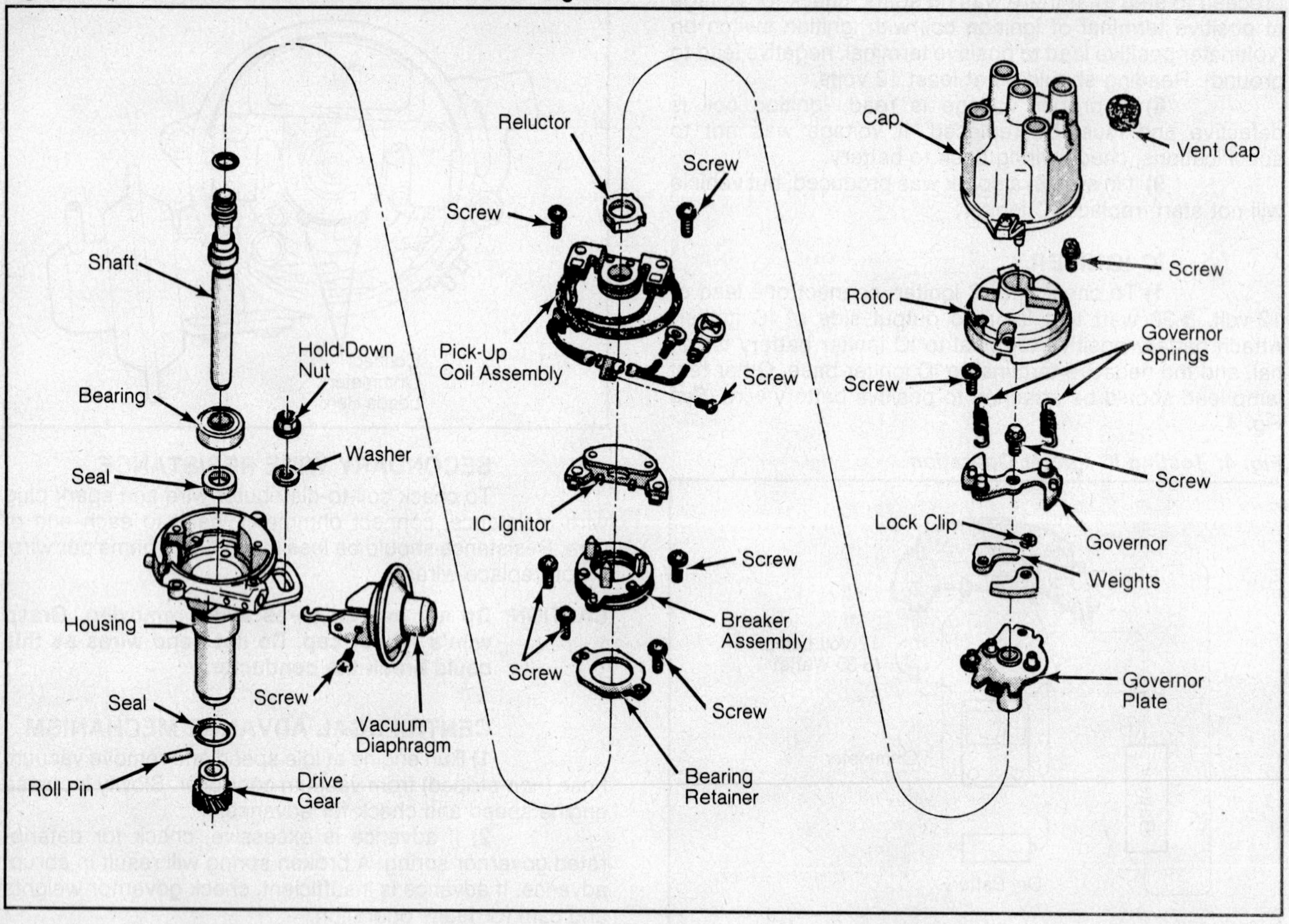

breaker assembly. Remove 2 screws retaining breaker assembly, and lift assembly from distributor housing.

4) Remove 2 screws from bearing retainer plate. Lift out plate. Mark location of drive gear on distributor shaft for later reassembly alignment. Drive out roll pin and remove drive gear. Lift distributor shaft and bearing assembly from housing. Remove housing seal.

REASSEMBLY

To reassemble, reverse disassembly procedure, noting the following: Check distributor cap for cracks, flashover, damage to carbon brush, and worn terminals. Remove light scaling from terminals. Be sure grease on back side of IC igniter is not removed, it is necessary for heat dissipation. Also, apply grease to all sliding surfaces.

DELCO-REMY HIGH ENERGY (HEI) IGNITION

Chevrolet & GMC
Federal 2.8L, 4.3L, 4.8L, 5.0L, 5.7L
Jeep Federal 2.8L V6

DESCRIPTION

NOTE: **Chevrolet and GMC light truck models with 5.0L 4-Bbl. (VIN H) engines are equipped with Electronic Spark Control to combat detonation. ESC models have 5-terminal electronic modules in the distributor, while non-ESC models have 4-terminal modules.**

The Delco-Remy High Energy Ignition (HEI) system consists of the battery, ignition switch, ignition coil, spark plugs, primary and secondary wiring, and a special distributor assembly.

The distributor housing and cap contain vacuum and centrifugal advance mechanisms, an electronic control module, pick-up coil, pole piece (with internal teeth), timer core (with external teeth), rotor, distributor shaft and a capacitor for radio noise suppression. Some distributor models also include an integral ignition coil.

Full battery voltage is present at the battery terminal of the distributor in either the "START" or "RUN" position, as no ballast resistance wire is used.

Fig. 1: Exploded View of HEI Distributor

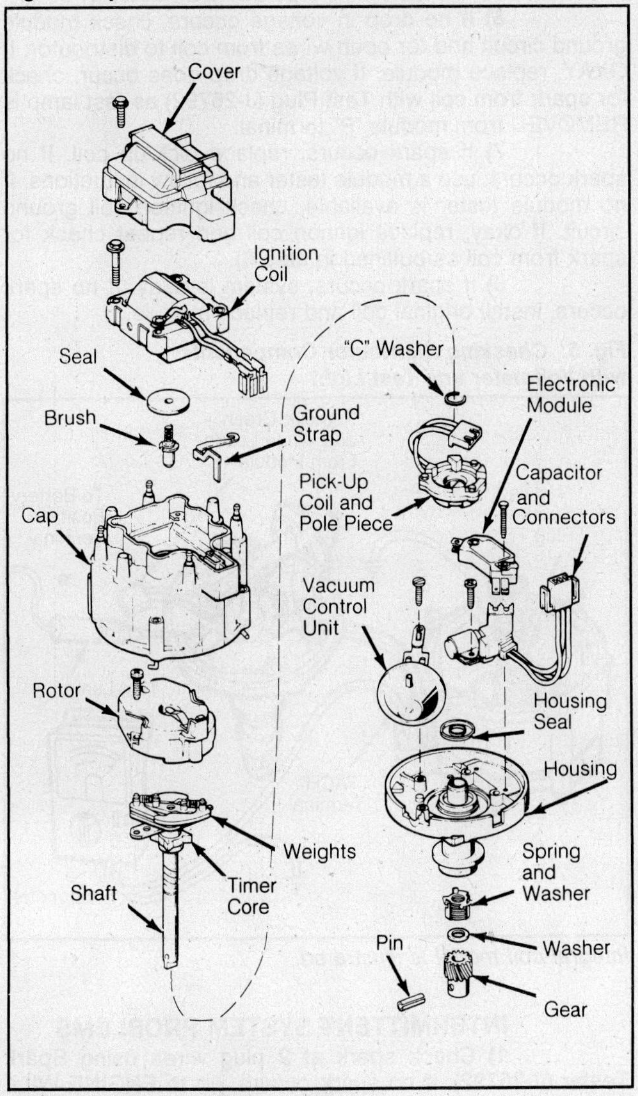

The timer core and pick-up coil pole piece have one tooth per cylinder.

OPERATION

The pick-up coil assembly consists of a permanent magnet, a pole piece, and a pick-up coil. The pick-up coil assembly is stationary, unless it is shifted by the vacuum control unit. The timer core position can also be shifted by the centrifugal weights.

The timer core, mounted on the distributor shaft, rotates with the shaft inside the pole piece portion of the pick-up coil assembly.

When the external teeth of the timer core line up with the internal teeth of the pole piece, a voltage is induced in the pick-up coil. This signals the electronic module inside the distributor, which opens the ignition coil primary circuit. *See Fig. 2.*

Fig. 2: Delco-Remy HEI System Wiring Diagram

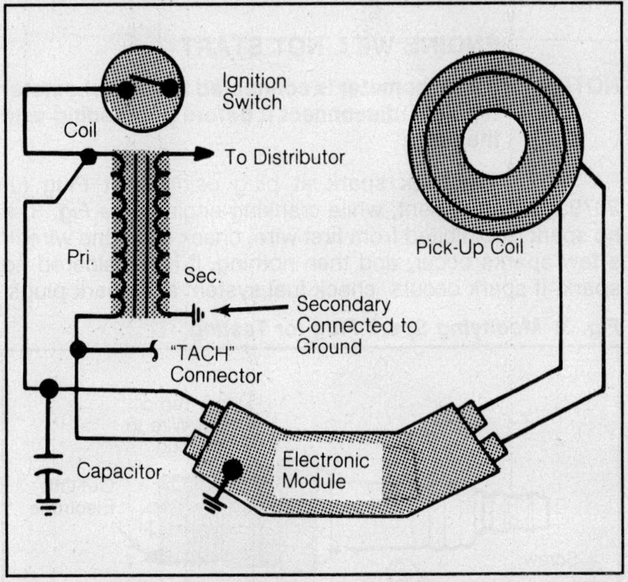

Module terminal letters may vary by model.

The magnetic field in the ignition coil primary circuit collapses, inducing high voltage in the coil's secondary circuit. This travels through the distributor cap contact, rotor and secondary wires to fire the spark plugs.

The electronic module automatically controls dwell period, stretching it with increasing engine speed. Dwell is not adjustable, and periodic checks of dwell are unnecessary. The HEI system features a longer spark duration, which is desirable for firing lean and EGR-diluted mixtures.

PRECAUTIONS

The following precautions MUST be observed during testing procedures:

- DO NOT ground tachometer terminal of distributor connector. Damage to the electronic module or ignition coil can result.
- Disconnect ignition switch connector at distributor be-

DELCO-REMY HIGH ENERGY (HEI) IGNITION (Cont.)

fore making compression checks.

- When using a timing light, connect at plug end of number 1 spark plug wire. DO NOT pierce plug boot.
- Remove spark plug wires, twist boot 1/2 turn and pull on boot (not on wire).

SYSTEM TESTING

1) Prior to diagnosis of HEI system, visually inspect spark plug wires, rotor contact button, plug wires boots, rotor and distributor cap for damage.

2) If a tachometer is connected to the tachometer terminal, disconnect it before proceeding with the test.

3) Check that wiring connector is properly attached to connector at side of distributor cap, and that spark plug leads are properly connected at both ends before continuing with test procedures.

4) If engine is difficult to start or misses, check position of battery terminal connector at distributor cap. Terminal must be inserted on side of connector opposite hold-down clip.

5) Intermittent no start condition may be caused by installation of a wrong pick-up coil or ignition coil.

ENGINE WILL NOT START

NOTE: **If a tachometer is connected to the tachometer terminal, disconnect it before proceeding with the test.**

1) Check spark at plug using Test Plug (J-26792), or equivalent, while cranking engine. *See Fig. 3*. If no spark is exhibited from first wire, check a second wire. If a few sparks occur, and then nothing, it is considered no spark. If spark occurs, check fuel system and spark plugs.

Fig. 3: Modifying Spark Plug for Testing

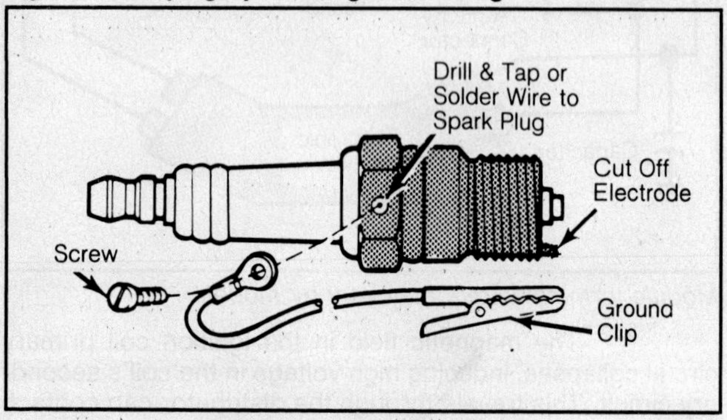

A commercial spark tester may also be used.

2) If no spark occurs, check voltage at ignition coil "B+" (battery) terminal while cranking engine. If reading is under 7 volts, repair primary wire circuit.

3) If reading is 7 volts or more, check "TACH" terminal voltage with ignition on. If reading is less than 1 volt, replace ignition coil. If reading is from 1 to 10 volts, replace module and check for spark. If spark occurs, system is OKAY. If no spark occurs, replace ignition coil.

4) If reading is more than 10 volts, check for spark at coil output terminal using Test Plug (J-26792) while cranking engine. *See Fig. 4*. If spark occurs, check cap and rotor for damage.

5) If no spark occurs, remove pick-up coil connector from module. Turn ignition on. With high input impedance voltmeter, observe voltage at "TACH" terminal while test lamp is momentarily connected to module "P" terminal (NOT MORE THAN 5 SECONDS). *See Fig. 5*.

Fig. 4: Checking for Spark at Ignition Coil Output Terminal

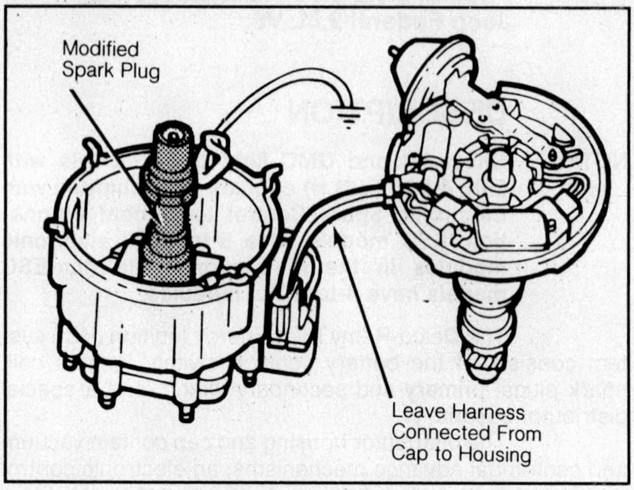

Integral coil model is shown.

6) If no drop in voltage occurs, check module ground circuit and for open wires from coil to distributor. If OKAY, replace module. If voltage drop does occur, check for spark from coil with Test Plug (J-26792) as test lamp is REMOVED from module "P" terminal.

7) If spark occurs, replace pick-up coil. If no spark occurs, use a module tester and follow instuctions. If no module tester is available, check ignition coil ground circuit. If okay, replace igntion coil and repeat check for spark from coil as outlined in step **6)**.

8) If spark occurs, system is okay. If no spark occurs, install original coil and replace module.

Fig. 5: Checking Distributor Components with Voltmeter and Test Light

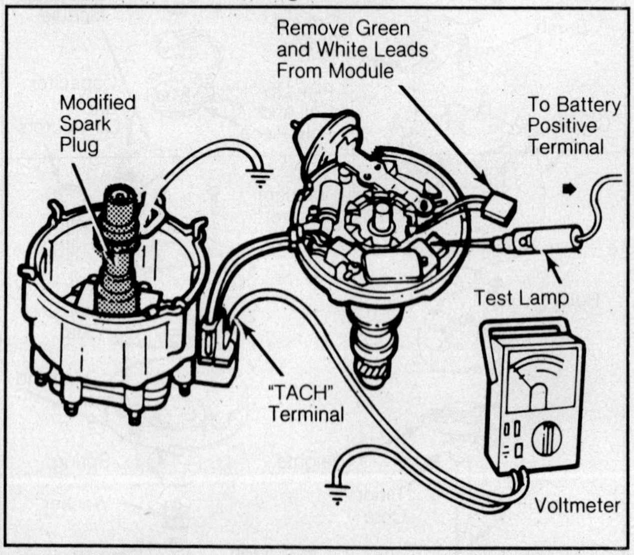

Integral coil model is illustrated.

INTERMITTENT SYSTEM PROBLEMS

1) Check spark at 2 plug wires using Spark Tester (J-26792). If no spark occurs, go to ENGINE WILL NOT START procedure. If spark occurs from 1 or both

DELCO-REMY HIGH ENERGY (HEI) IGNITION (Cont.)

spark plug wires check pick-up coil with ohmmeter and refer to testing pick-up coil in COMPONENT TESTING section in this article.

2) If pick-up coil is defective, replace it. If it is good, check for dwell increase from high to low RPM. If dwell did not increase, replace electronic module.

3) If dwell did increase, and trouble is not found, check fuel, coil and plug wires, also cap and plugs.

COMPONENT TESTING

ELECTRONIC MODULE

NOTE: When installing a new HEI module, use silicone lubricant on back of module and on housing under module.

An approved electronic module tester must be used to test the module. Use Module Tester (J-24642-E). Follow manufacturer's instructions.

INTEGRAL IGNITION COIL

Chevrolet & GMC Only

1) The ignition coil can be tested for shorted and open windings using an ohmmeter. Connect the ohmmeter between the positive terminal and coil frame (ground). Use the high resisitance scale. The ohmmeter should indicate infinite resistance. If not, replace the coil.

2) Connect the ohmmeter between the positive and negative terminals. Use the low resistance scale. The ohmmeter should indicate zero, or nearly zero. If not, replace the coil.

3) Connect the ohmmeter between the negative terminal and the high voltage terminal. Use the high resistance scale. The ohmmeter should indicate less than infinite resistance. If not, replace the coil. *See Fig. 6*.

EXTERNAL IGNITION COIL

Jeep Only

1) Connect ohmmeter leads to battery and "TACH" terminals. *See Fig. 7*. Primary resistance should read zero or nearly zero.

2) Now connect the leads to battery terminal and ground. On the high scale, an infinite reading should be indicated.

3) For secondary coil resistance, connect ohmmeter leads to "TACH" and secondary terminals. Ohmmeter should read less that infinite. *See Fig. 7*.

PICK-UP COIL

NOTE: Operation of the vacuum mechanism may cause a trigger wheel tooth and the pick-up coil pole piece to align and the ohmmeter pointer to deflect. This deflection should not be interpreted as the result of a faulty pick-up coil.

1) Identify the 2 pick-up coil lead wires. On most applications, these wires are 1 Green and 1 White. The pick-up coil connector must be disconnected from the module, then an ohmmeter is connected to 1 connector terminal and to the distributor housing. Next, the ohmmeter is connected to both terminals.

2) Connect external vacuum source to vacuum advance unit. If vacuum advance unit is inoperative, replace

Fig. 6: Coil Testing Connections with Integral Coil

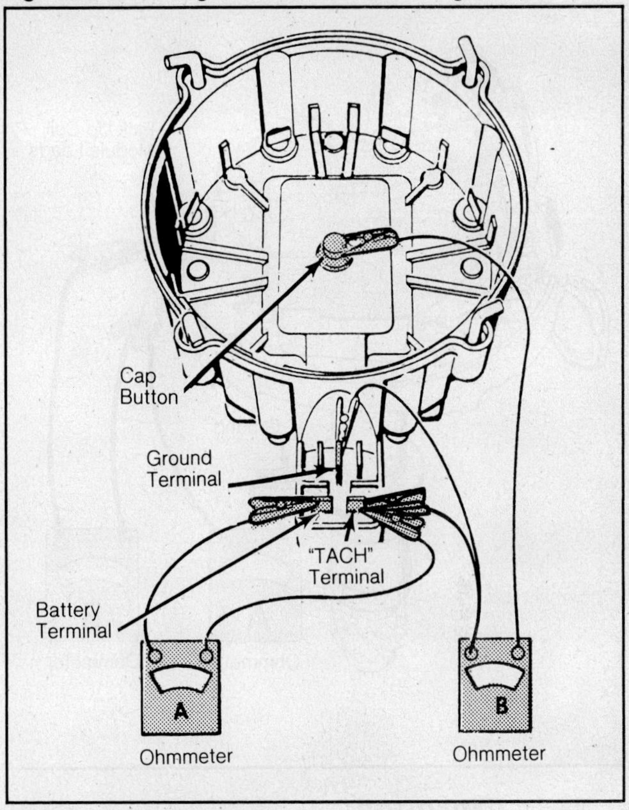

Be sure leads contact proper connections.

Fig. 7: Coil Testing Connection with External Coil

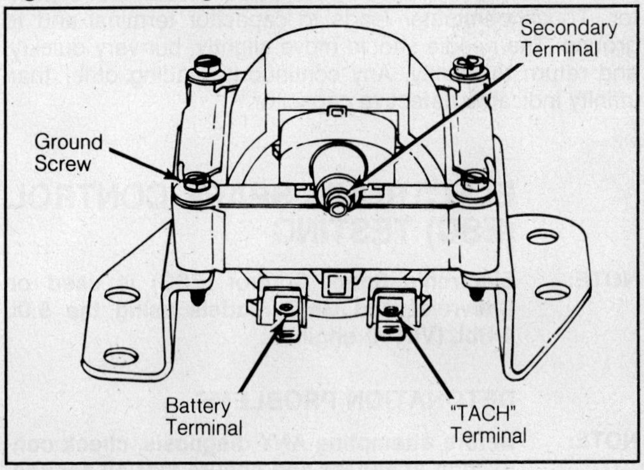

Touch coil mounting screw for ground.

unit. Connect an ohmmeter, using mid scale, to either pick-up coil terminal and the distributor housing.

3) Operate the vacuum pump and observe the ohmmeter throughout vacuum range. Reading should be infinite at all times. If not, replace pick-up coil. See meter "A" in *Fig. 8*.

4) Connect ohmmeter to both pick-up coil connector terminals. Operate vacuum pump and observe ohmmeter throughout the vacuum range. Also, flex wires by hand to locate any intermittent defective connections at pick-up coil and at terminals on ends of wires.

5) The ohmmeter should indicate a constant resistance in the 500-1500 ohm range at all times. If not, replace the pick-up coil. See meter "B" in *Fig. 8*

DELCO-REMY HIGH ENERGY (HEI) IGNITION (Cont.)

Fig. 8: Distributor Pick-Up Coil Testing Connections

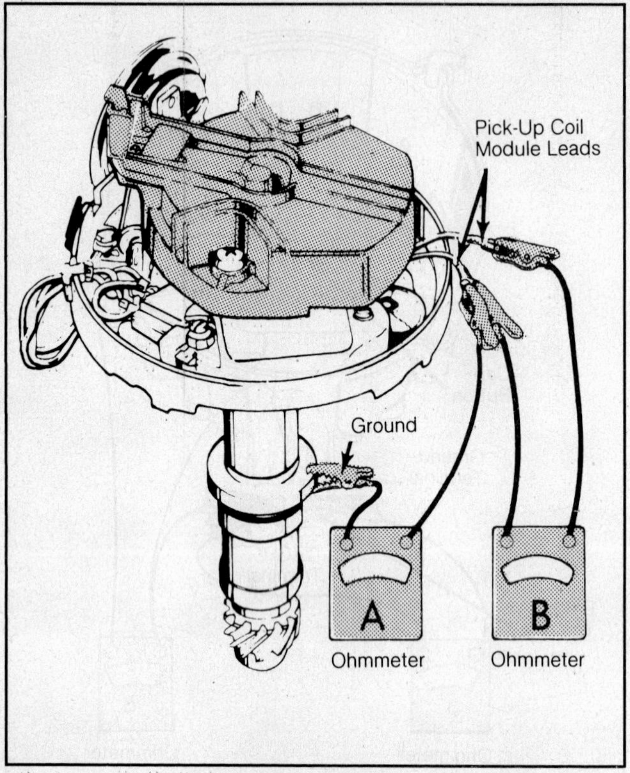

Fig. 9: Wiring Diagram for HEI System with Electronic Spark Control (ESC)

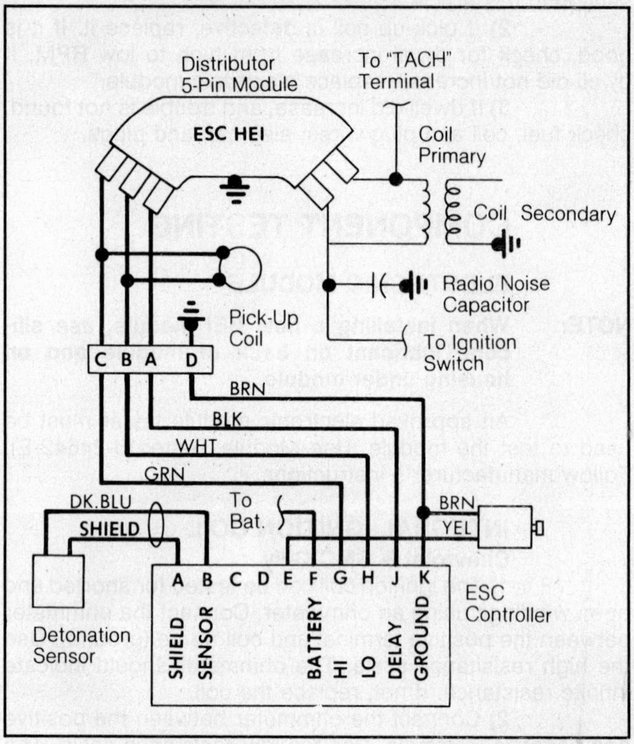

CAPACITOR

The capacitor is used for radio noise suppresion. Set ohmmeter in x1000 scale. Disconnect capacitor. Touch ohmmeter leads to capacitor terminal and to ground. The needle should move slightly, but very quickly, and return to infinity. Any continuous reading other than infinity indicates defective capacitor.

ELECTRONIC SPARK CONTROL (ESC) TESTING

NOTE: **Electronic Spark Control (ESC) is used on Chevrolet and GMC models using the 5.0L 4-Bbl. (VIN H) engine.**

DETONATION PROBLEMS

NOTE: **Before attempting ANY diagnosis, check connection at sensor and ensure that all connections are clean and tight. Also, trace-to-light detonation is acceptable.**

1) With engine running at fast idle speed, above 1000 RPM, and transmission in Neutral or Park, tap exhaust manifold lightly and repeatedly. Check for spark timing retard with a timing light. If retard is noted, check other engine detonation causes.

2) If no retard occurs, disconnect 10-pin connector from ESC controller, located in passenger compartment. Connect voltmeter leads between pins "B" and "K" of connector. With engine operating at 2000 RPM, voltage should read 80 millivolts (.08 volts). If so, proceed to step **5)**.

3) If voltage reading was lower than 80 millivolts, disconnect detonation sensor wire. Measure voltage from sensor terminal to ground. Reading should be more than 80 millivolts with engine operating at 2000 RPM.

4) If voltage reading in step **3)** is high or low, replace sensor. If OK, check wires from pins "A", "B", and "K" of 10-pin connector for open or short circuits. If OK, repair sensor connector. If not OK, replace or repair wiring harness.

5) If voltage reading in step **2)** was okay, try to start engine with 10-pin connector disconnected. If it starts, replace distributor's HEI module.

6) If engine will not start, reconnect 10-pin connector to ESC controller. Disconnect sensor wire from sensor, and insert a jumper wire into sensor wire connector. With engine running at fast idle speed, lay wire on top of distributor over ignition coil. If spark timing retard occurs, replace sensor.

7) If no spark retard occurs, connect voltmeter positive lead to pin "H" of 10-pin connector and negative lead to pin "K". With ignition switch on, voltage should read more than 0.2 volt. If voltage is more than 0.2 volt, replace ESC controller. If less than 0.2 volt, repair open wire from pin "H" in ESC harness.

POOR ENGINE PERFORMANCE

1) Disconnect 4-pin connector at distributor. Install a jumper wire between pins "A" and "C" of distributor connector. If problem remains, check other causes of poor engine performance.

2) If problem disappeared, remove jumper wire and reconnect 4-pin connector. Without disconnecting 10-pin ESC connector, attach jumper wire from pin "A" to pin "K". If problem remains, proceed to step **5)**.

3) If problem disappeared in step **2)**, remove jumper wire and disconnect sensor wire from sensor.

DELCO-REMY HIGH ENERGY (HEI) IGNITION (Cont.)

Measure voltage from sensor terminal to ground. Minimum reading is 80 millivolts at 2000 RPM. If okay, check for engine noises other than detonation that might cause input to sensor. Or, substitute with a known good sensor.

4) If voltage reading was either high or low in the previous step, disconnect wire from sensor. Measure voltage from terminal to ground, checking again. If high or low, replace sensor. If okay, check sensor wire and shield for open circuit. If okay, check sensor wire for an open and repair sensor connector. If not okay, repair harness.

5) If in step **2)**, the problem still existed, remove jumper wire from pins "A" and "K". With engine running, connect positive voltmeter lead to pin "F" and negative lead to pin "K" of 10-pin connector. If reading is under 11.6 volts, repair alternator charging circuit.

6) If over 11.6 volts, check wires in ESC harness from pins "H" and "K" for open circuits or poor connections. If okay, replace ESC controller; if not, replace or repair harness.

ENGINE STARTING PROBLEMS

1) Check all ESC harness connections, including 10-pin connector at ESC controller, 4-pin connector at distributor, 2-blade male connector to distributor, and 2-blade female connector to ignition switch lead (Pink wire). Repair connections as necessary.

2) If all connections are okay, disconnect 4-pin connector at distributor. Install jumper wire between pins "A" and "C" of distributor connector. If engine will not start, check other causes of engine failing to start.

3) If engine starts with jumper wire attached, remove jumper wire and reconnect 4-pin connector to distributor. With ignition switch on, connect voltmeter positive lead to pin "F" and negative lead to pin "K" on 10-pin connector. If under 7.0 volts, repair circuit between ignition switch and pin "F".

4) If over 7.0 volts are read, check wires in ESC harness from pins "G", "H", "J" and "K" of 10-pin connector for opens or shorts. If harness is okay, replace ESC controller.

OVERHAUL

DISTRIBUTOR

Disassembly

1) Disconnect wiring harness from cap. Disconnect coil wire. Remove distributor cap and disconnect vacuum hose from vacuum advance unit. *See Fig. 10.*

2) Mark rotor-to-distributor housing position and distributor housing-to-engine position for reassembly reference. Remove hold-down bolt and remove distributor housing from engine.

3) Remove rotor, 2 advance springs, weight retainer and advance weights. Mark distributor shaft and gear so they may be assembled in same position. Drive out roll pin from drive gear while supporting gear so no damage will occur to distributor shaft.

4) Remove gear, shim and tanged washer from distributor shaft, and clean any burrs from shaft. Remove distributor shaft from housing.

NOTE: **Do not attempt to service shaft bushings in housing.**

5) Remove 2 attaching screws holding module to housing, and position module to disconnect pick-up coil and wiring harness connectors. Remove "C" washer from housing, and lift pick-up coil assembly from advance unit and distributor shaft.

6) Remove 2 attaching screws, and remove vacuum advance mechanism. Disconnect capacitor lead, and remove attaching screw and capacitor. Remove wiring harness from position in distributor housing.

7) For integral coils, remove 3 coil cover attaching screws and lift off cover. Remove 4 ignition coil attaching screws, disconnect coil leads, and remove coil from cap. Remove ignition coil arc seal.

Fig. 10: Internal Components of HEI Distributor

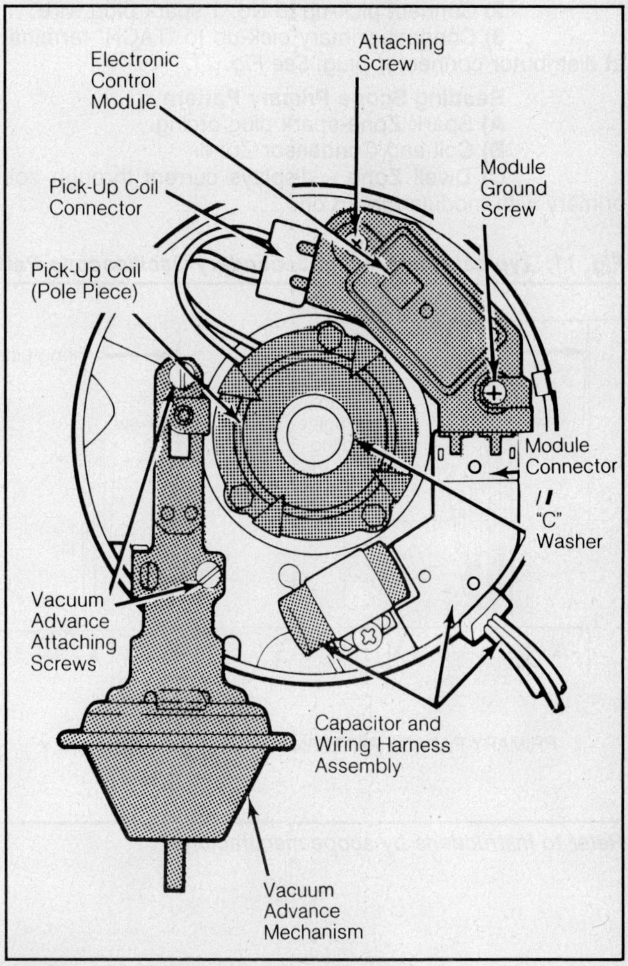

Number of module terminals will vary between regular and ESC systems.

Reassembly

1) Reverse disassembly procedures, while noting the following: Ensure there is special silicone lubricant between module and distributor base to provide heat transfer for module cooling. Lubricate felt washer with a few drops of engine oil.

2) After installation of distributor shaft, rotate to check for even clearance between external timer core teeth and internal pole piece teeth. Notch on side of rotor must engage tab on cam weight base.

DELCO-REMY HIGH ENERGY (HEI) IGNITION (Cont.)

TYPICAL DELCO-REMY OSCILLOSCOPE PATTERNS

TYPICAL PRIMARY PATTERNS

Scope Instructions for Primary Parade Only:

NOTE: Also refer to instructions furnished by scope manufacturer

1) Scope secondary pick-up cannot be connected on integral coils, because coil center tower terminal is inside distributor. See TYPICAL SECONDARY PATTERNS.

2) Connect pick-up to No. 1 spark plug wire.

3) Connect primary pick-up to "TACH" terminal at distributor connector plug. *See Fig. 11.*

Reading Scope Primary Pattern

A) Spark Zone-spark plug arcing.

B) Coil and Condensor Zone.

C) Dwell Zone - displays current through coil primary with module turned on.

TYPICAL SECONDARY PATTERNS

NOTE: A special adapter placed on top of the coil cap assembly may be used with some scopes to view the secondary pattern. The output voltage will read low with the adapter; this is normal. Refer to the scope manufacturer's instructions.

Secondary Voltage Patterns:

It is normal if dwell time varies from cylinder-to-cylinder. A 40 to 60 percent variation is shown below. It could be more, or it could be less. The voltage ripple shown may or may not appear; either is normal. Variation in dwell time or voltage ripple, as shown, does not necessarily indicate a bad module. See Fig. 11.

Fig. 11: Typical Primary and Secondary Oscilloscope Patterns

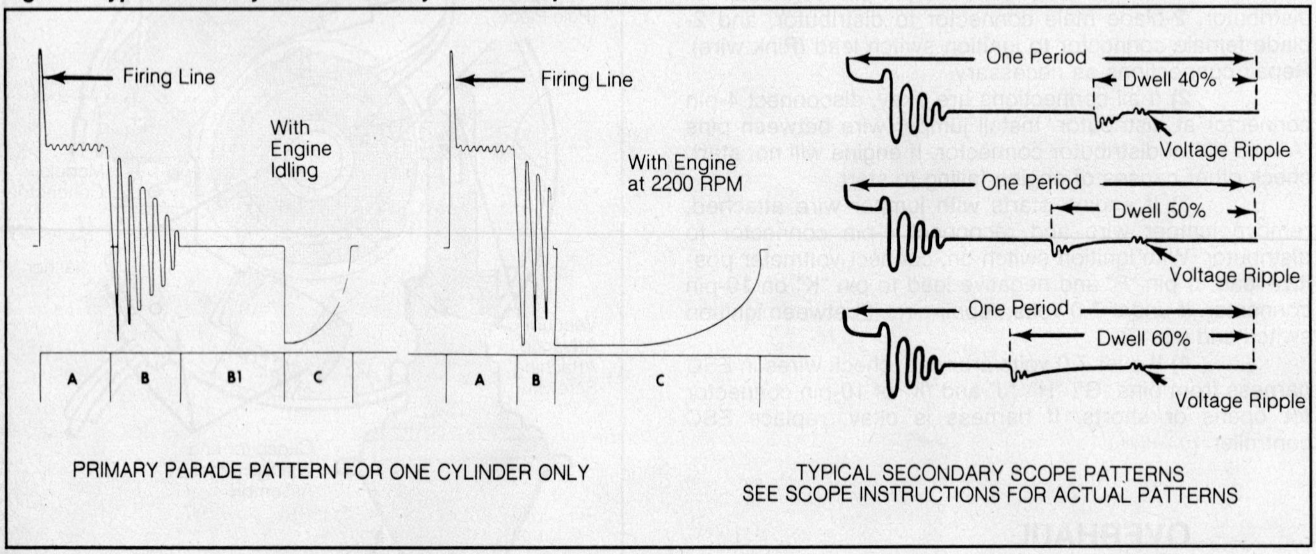

Refer to instructions by scope manufacturer.

DELCO-REMY HEI-EST IGNITION SYSTEM

Chevrolet & GMC
Calif. 2.5L, 2.8L, 4.3L, 4.8L, 5.0L, 5.7L
Jeep Calif. 2.8L V6

DESCRIPTION

The Delco-Remy HEI-EST system, a part of all General Motors Computer Command Control (CCC) systems, is designed to provide optimum performance through electronic control of air/fuel ratios, spark timing, air management and idle speed.

The system consists of an electronic control module (ECM), an HEI-EST distributor, an external ignition coil, and necessary wiring. The distributor has neither vacuum nor centrifugal advance mechanisms. *See Figs. 1 and 2.*

The distributor contains a 7-terminal HEI-EST electronic module, a timer core, pole piece, pick-up coil, and a radio noise suppression capacitor.

Fig. 1: Disassembled View of EST Distributor

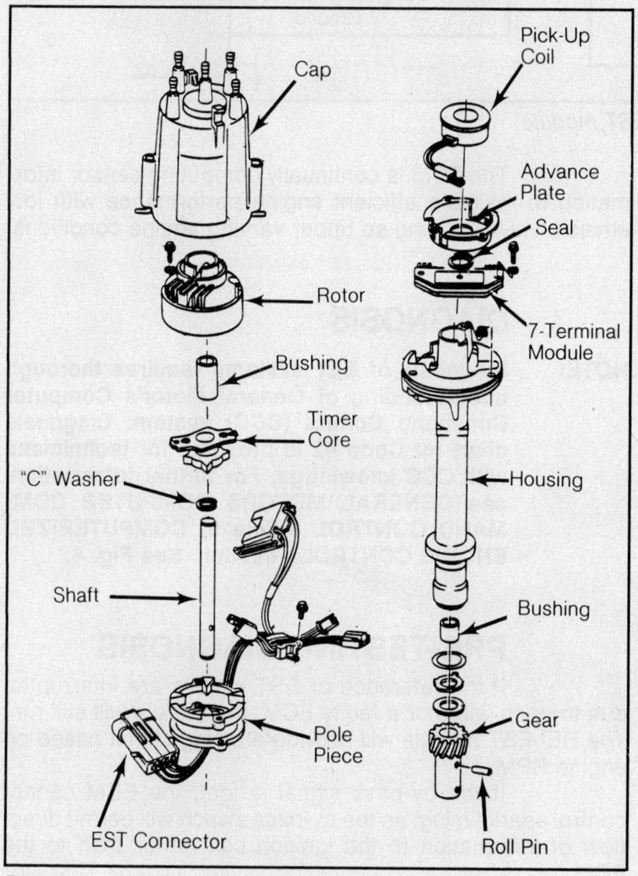

Distributor works with an external ignition coil.

The distributor is connected to the EST system by means of a 4-wire connector, leading to the CCC system's electronic control module (ECM).

The ECM (not the distributor HEI-EST module) receives voltage signals from a number of sensors. A typical system could be provided signals from oxygen, engine coolant temperature, throttle position, barometric pressure and manifold absolute pressure sensors, as well as, the distributor pick-up coil.

Fig. 2: Components of an HEI-EST Distributor

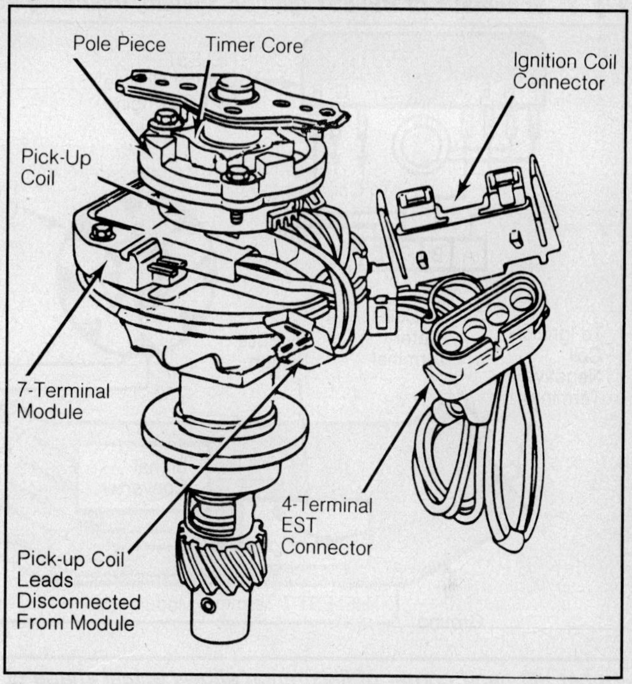

Timer core and pole piece have one tooth per cylinder.

CAUTION: Few components are interchangeable between HEI-EST and HEI distributors used on various engines. Be sure correct part is used, as similar appearance does not mean identical design or operation.

The HEI-EST distributor module has 7 terminals. The ignition coil battery terminal (positive) is connected to the module "+" terminal; the coil's "TACH" or negative terminal to the "C" terminal. *See Fig. 3.*

Terminals "N" and "P" are attached to the pick-up coil. HEI-EST module terminal "R" connects through the EST connector "B" to ECM terminal 10 (Distributor Reference Pulse Hi). Terminal "B" connects through terminal "C" to ECM terminal 11 (Ignition Module By-Pass).

Terminal "E" connects through connector "A" to ECM terminal 12 (EST). ECM terminal 13 (Distributor Reference Pulse Lo) connects to connector "D" and then to HEI-EST module ground.

OPERATION

During cranking or in event of EST ECM failure, a by-pass signal from ECM terminal 11 to HEI-EST module terminal "B" is either absent or low. *See Fig. 3.*

This notifies the HEI-EST module to take over control of spark advance and to ignore any EST information coming from the ECM. During this period, poor engine performance may result under some conditions, but the diagnostic "CHECK ENGINE" light will not come on.

The HEI-EST module will then convert pick-up coil RPM signals, and transmit them through the by-pass switch and terminal "C" directly to the negative "TACH" terminal of the ignition coil. These signals turn the coil primary circuit on and off, causing a surge in the secondary that fires the spark plugs.

When engine speed reaches 600 RPM or more (about 5-15 seconds after starting), the ECM transmits a

DELCO-REMY HEI-EST IGNITION SYSTEM (Cont.)

Fig. 3: Schematic of HEI-EST Ignition System, Including Relationship To Computer Command Control ECM

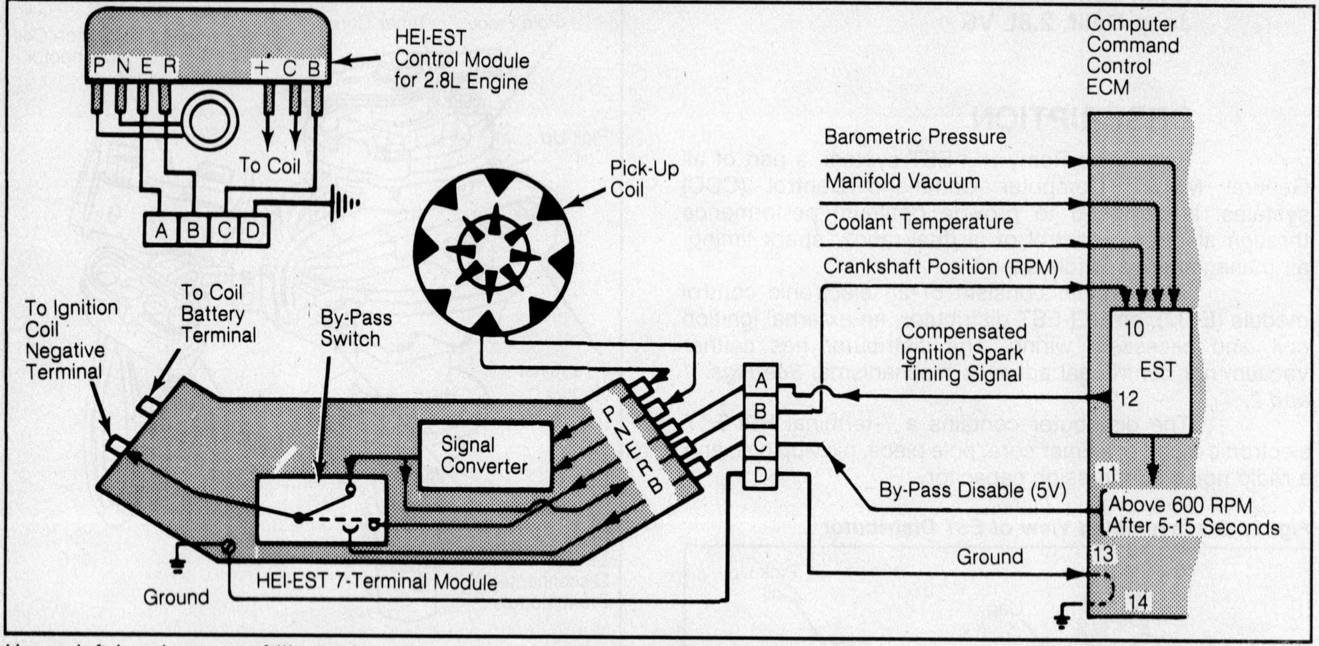

Upper left-hand corner of illustration shows actual shape of HEI-EST module.

constant 5-volt signal to the distributor HEI-EST module. This signal changes the position of the by-pass switch.

As a result, the pick-up coil's RPM signals can no longer flow directly to the ignition coil, as this circuit is now open. Instead, the signals are converted in the distributor module and routed through terminal "R" to ECM terminal 10.

The PROM (Programmed Read Only Memory) portion of the ECM carries the basic spark advance curve based on engine RPM. Spark timing is calculated by the ECM whenever an ignition pulse is present, however, spark advance information is only SENT TO the distributor when the engine is running (not during cranking).

Engine sensor values are used by the ECM to modify the PROM information, increasing or decreasing spark advance to achieve maximum performance with minimum emissions.

The coolant temperature sensor advances spark on a cold engine, and reduces advance as engine reaches normal operating temperature. If engine is too hot, spark is retarded to prevent detonation.

During light throttle operation, the throttle switch allows for additional advance. Additional adjustment by the ECM results from input from coolant temperature, engine RPM and manifold absolute pressure (MAP) sensors. When MAP is low, spark is at maximum advance.

As load increases and pressure increases, spark timing is retarded to allow the engine to maintain its performance and emission level.

After computation of all information from the various sensors, a compensated ignition spark timing signal is sent back to the distributor through the HEI-EST module's "E" terminal to the by-pass switch, "C" terminal, and ignition coil negative terminal.

Each time the signal is flashed on and off, the coil's primary circuit is turned on and off. As this occurs, a voltage surge is created in the secondary that fires the spark plugs.

The ECM is continually computing sensor information to maintain efficient engine performance with low emission levels, doing so under varying engine conditions.

DIAGNOSIS

NOTE: Diagnosis of EST systems requires thorough understanding of General Motor's Computer Command Control (CCC) system. Diagnosis chart for Code 42 is provided for technicians with CCC knowledge. For further information, see GENERAL MOTORS COMPUTER COMMAND CONTROL article in COMPUTERIZED ENGINE CONTROLS section. See Fig. 4.

PRE-TESTING DIAGNOSIS

If the reference or EST signals are interrupted due to open wires or a faulty ECM, the vehicle will still run. The HEI-EST module will provide a timing signal based on engine RPM.

If the by-pass signal is lost, the ECM cannot control spark timing, as the by-pass switch will permit direct flow of information to the ignition coil rather than to the ECM.

Normally, 5-15 seconds after starting a warm engine, the by-pass signal electronically operates a by-pass switch in the HEI-EST module. The HEI-EST module's RPM-controlled timing signal no longer can flow directly to the ignition coil, but is diverted to the ECM for modification by information from engine sensors.

Loss of the EST signal with the by-pass signal "ON", however, will stop the engine, because the HEI-EST module is no longer sending signals directly to the ignition coil, but to the ECM.

Any loss of the EST signal cuts all flow to the coil. If an attempt is made to restart the vehicle, the engine

DELCO-REMY HEI-EST IGNITION SYSTEM (Cont.)

Fig. 4: Procedure for CCC System Code 42

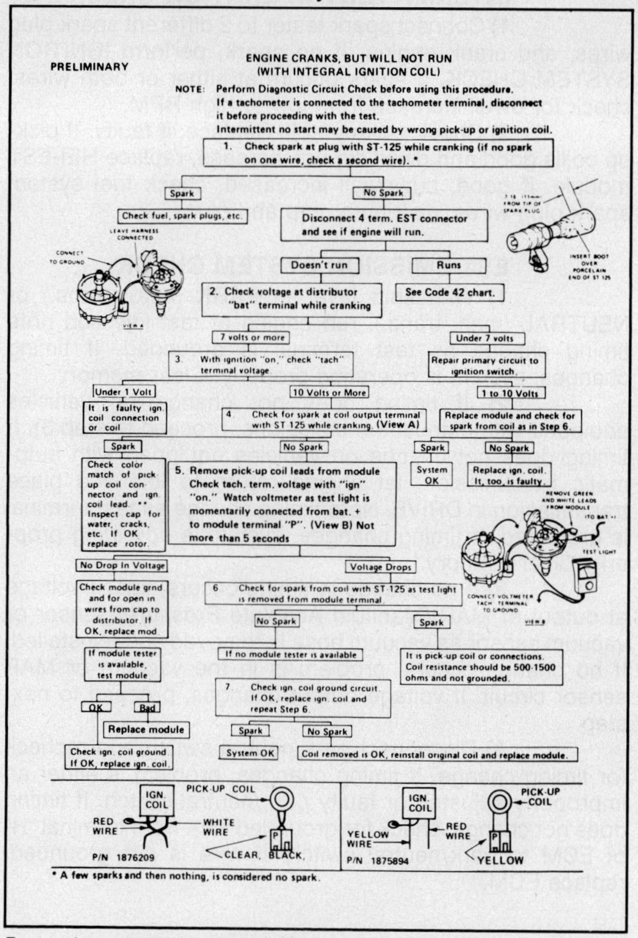

Procedure applies to 2.5L (TBI) equipped engines; others are similar. See COMPUTERIZED ENGINE CONTROLS section for correct application.

will run for a few seconds and then stop when the by-pass signal comes back on.

TESTING

IGNITION COIL RESISTANCE CHECK

Primary Resistance

1) Remove coil connector. Using the low scale, connect ohmmeter leads to coil's battery and "TACH" terminals. *See Fig. 5.* Resistance should be zero or nearly zero. If not, replace ignition coil.

2) Set ohmmeter on high scale, and connect leads to battery terminal and a good ground on coil. Reading should be infinity. If not, replace coil.

Secondary Resistance

With ohmmeter set in high range, connect leads to "TACH" terminal and to secondary terminal. Reading should be less than infinite (approximately 6,000 to 30,000 ohms). If reading is infinity, replace coil.

DISTRIBUTOR PICK-UP COIL SHORT AND RESISTANCE CHECKS

1) Disconnect pick-up coil leads from HEI-EST module "N" and "P" terminals (usually a Green and a White

Fig. 5: Ignition Coil Resistance Test Points

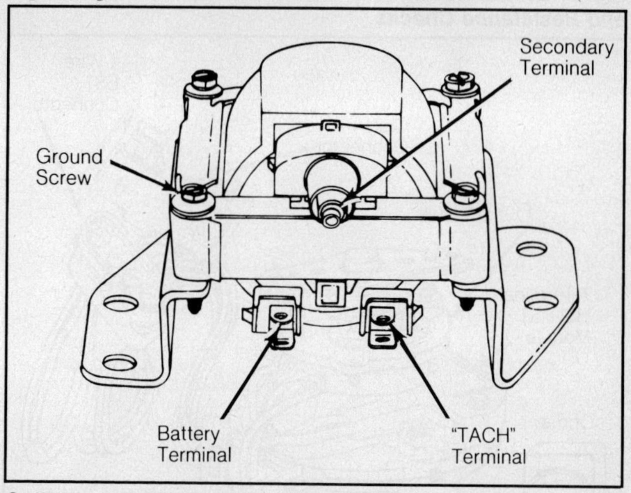

Coil primary wires must be removed for testing.

wire). To check for shorted pick-up coil, set ohmmeter in middle range.

2) Connect an ohmmeter lead to either pick-up coil wire terminal. Connect other lead to distributor housing. *See Fig. 6.* Reading should be infinite. If not, replace pick-up coil.

3) Connect ohmmeter leads to both pick-up coil leads, while flexing wires and connectors to locate intermittent opens. *See Fig. 6.* Resistance should read a constant unchanging value between 500 and 1500 ohms. If not, replace pick-up coil.

IGNITION SYSTEM CHECK

NOTE: Before making the following tests, secure an ignition spark tester. If tachometer is connected to ignition coil "TACH" terminal, disconnect it before performing tests. Use a digital voltmeter with 10 megohms impedance or larger.

1) Remove spark plug wire and attach spark tester to wire. Crank engine and check for spark at tester gap. If there is no spark, check a second wire in same manner. If sparks result, ignition system is not at fault. Suspect fuel system or spark plugs.

2) If no spark resulted in step **1)**, attach ignition tester to ignition coil secondary wire. Crank engine and recheck for spark at tester cap. If spark occurs, inspect distributor cap for water, cracks, or carbon tracking. If cap is OK, replace rotor.

3) If no spark occurred in either step **1)** or **2)**, remove distributor cap. Turn ignition system "ON". Check voltage at battery feed terminal (+) of HEI-EST module. Attach positive voltmeter lead to "+" terminal and negative lead to ground. Check for voltage while cranking engine.

4) If reading is less than 10 volts, repair primary circuit back to ignition switch. If 10 volts or more, turn ignition "ON". Move positive voltmeter lead from HEI-EST "+" terminal to module "C" terminal. Leave negative lead grounded.

5) If reading is under 1 volt, problem lies with open wire to ignition coil negative terminal, ignition coil connection or primary circuit of ignition coil. Repair or replace as necessary. If 10 volts or more is registered on voltmeter, proceed to step **7)**.

DELCO-REMY HEI-EST IGNITION SYSTEM (Cont.)

Fig. 6: Distributor Pick-Up Coil Short and Resistance Checks

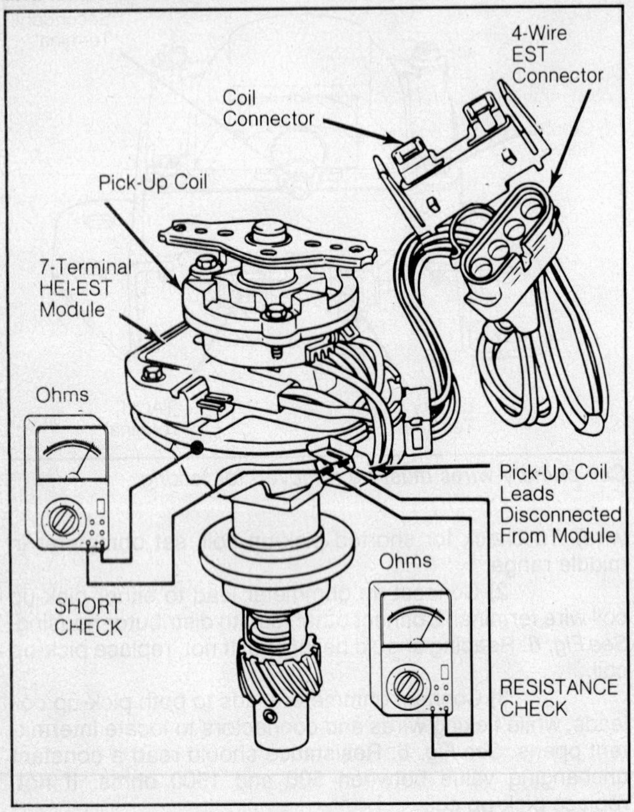

Notice ohmmeter test points.

6) If voltage reading on "C" terminal was 1-10 volts, replace distributor HEI-EST module and check for spark, following procedure outlined in steps **7)** through **10)**. However, if a spark results in step **10)**, ignition system is OK following module replacement. If there is still no spark, replace ignition coil also, as it too is defective.

7) If in step **5)**, 10 volts or more were read on module "C" terminal, remove pick-up coil connector from module. Turn ignition "ON". Check voltage again at module "C" terminal. Watch voltmeter as a test light is momentarily (not more than 5 seconds) connected to battery positive terminal to module "P" terminal.

8) If no drop in voltage occurs, check HEI-EST module ground. Also check for open in wires from distributor cap (coil) to distributor. If OK, replace HEI-EST module.

9) If voltage dropped, check for spark at tester gap (still attached to coil secondary terminal) when test light is removed from module "P" terminal. If spark occurs, either pick-up coil or its connections are defective.

NOTE: **Perform DISTRIBUTOR PICK-UP COIL SHORT and RESISTANCE CHECKS if not done previously. Resistance should be 500-1500 ohms.**

10) If no spark occurs and distributor module tester is available, check HEI-EST module. If OK, check ignition coil ground and coil-to-distributor wiring. If OK, replace ignition coil. If module is defective, replace.

11) If no module tester is available, replace HEI-EST module and repeat step **9)**. If spark results, system is OK. If no spark results, original module is OK. Reinstall module and replace coil.

INTERMITTENT OPERATION CHECK

1) Connect spark tester to 2 different spark plug wires, and crank engine. If no spark, perform IGNITION SYSTEM CHECK. If spark occurs at either or both wires, check for dwell increase from low to high RPM.

2) Check pick-up coil. Replace, if faulty. If pick-up coilis good and dwell did not increase, replace HEI-EST module. If good, but dwell increased, check fuel system spark plug wires, distributor cap and plugs.

EST EMISSION SYSTEM CHECK

1) With shift lever in PARK (auto. trans.) or NEUTRAL (man. trans.), run engine at fast idle and note timing change as test terminal is grounded. If timing changes, system is operating properly. Clear memory.

2) If timing does not change on vehicles equipped with manual transmissions, proceed to step **3)**. If timing does not change on vehicles equipped with automatic transmission, let engine return to idle and place transmission in DRIVE. Note timing change as test terminal is grounded. If timing changes, system is operating properly. Clear memory.

3) If no change in timing occurs, check voltage at output of MAP (Manifold Absolute Pressure) sensor or vacuum sensor as vacuum hose is removed and reinstalled. If no change occurs, problem is in the vacuum or MAP sensor circuit. If voltage output changes, proceed to next step.

4) Disconnect park/neutral switch and recheck for timing change. If timing changes, problem is either an improperly adjusted or faulty park/neutral switch. If timing does not change, check for grounded wire from terminal "H" of ECM to park/neutral switch. If wire is not grounded, replace ECM.

OVERHAUL

Disassembly

1) Remove coil connector and disconnect 4-wire EST connector. Turn 2 latches and lift off distributor cap.

2) Remove rotor and disconnect pick-up coil leads from HEI-EST module. *See Fig. 1.* Mark distributor shaft and gear for later reassembly. Drive out roll pin and remove distributor shaft from housing.

3) Remove retaining "C" washer, pick-up coil, magnet and pole piece. Remove 2 module attaching screws and capacitor screw. Lift module, capacitor and harness assembly from distributor housing. Disconnect wiring harness from module.

Reassembly

Assemble in reverse order, noting the following. Wipe distributor housing and module clean, and apply silicone grease between module and housing. Spin shaft to be sure timer core external teeth do not strike pole piece internal teeth.

HITACHI ELECTRONIC IGNITION SYSTEM

Chevrolet & GMC with Federal 1.9L Engines

DESCRIPTION

Hitachi electronic ignition is used with the 1.9L 4-cylinder engine. An engine speed sensor is incorporated within the system.

The distributor has both vacuum and centrifugal advance mechanisms. It also houses a reluctor, stator, magnet set, and a pick-up coil and control module assembly. *See Figs. 1 and 2.* The system makes use of a conventional ignition coil with positive, negative, and secondary terminals.

Fig. 1: Distributor Breaker Plate Assembly

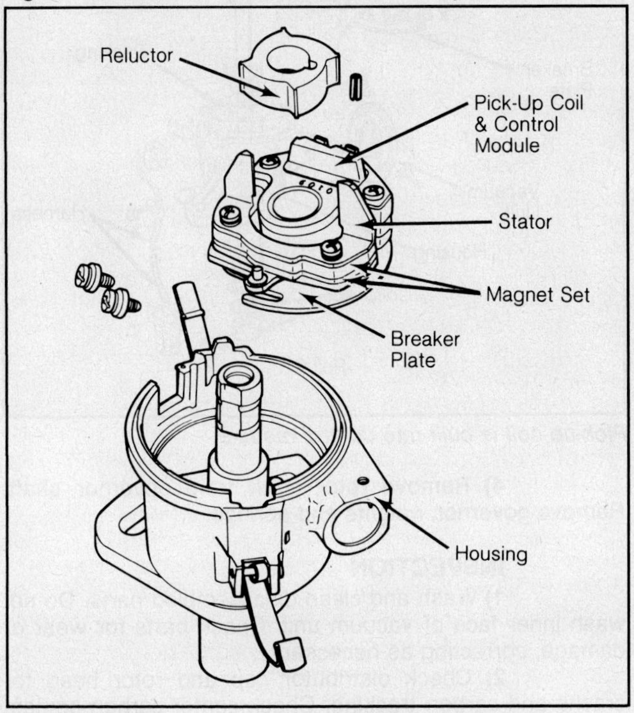

Note stator-to-pick-up coil and module relationship.

OPERATION

As the engine cranks, the distributor shaft turns, carrying with it the rotor shaft assembly. A reluctor (toothed wheel), mounted on the rotor shaft, turns inside a 2-pronged stator, which is attached to the magnet set.

As each reluctor tooth approaches and passes the stator upright prong, the magnetic field around the prong is broken. The pick-up coil and control module assembly is mounted inside the distributor, next to the magnet set and stator. Components are attached to the breaker plate assembly. *See Fig. 1.*

The build-up and collapse of the magnetic field causes the pick-up coil to send a signal to the control module. The module, in response, opens and closes the ignition coil primary circuit. Each time this occurs, a voltage surge occurs in the coil secondary circuit, firing the spark plugs.

ADJUSTMENT

PICK-UP COIL AIR GAP

Using a feeler gauge, measure air gap between each tooth of the reluctor and stator prongs. Air gap should read .012-.020" (.30-.50 mm). If not to specifications, loosen 2 screws and adjust position of stator and magnets until gap is correct. Tighten screws and recheck air gap.

TESTING

NOTE: When testing the ignition system, use either an ignition spark tester or modified spark plug (case grounded, with side electrode cut off).

IGNITION SYSTEM NO-START CHECK

1) Remove spark plug wire, and attach ignition tester to its end. Crank engine. If no spark, check a second spark plug wire in similar manner.

2) If spark resulted at either wire, ignition system is not at fault. Check fuel system, mechanical condition, and spark plugs. If no spark resulted at either wire, connect negative voltmeter lead to ground. In turn, touch positive lead to battery terminals of ignition coil and distributor, while cranking engine.

3) If voltage is below 7 volts, repair primary circuit (from battery terminals back to ignition switch and battery positive terminal. If voltage is above 7 volts, proceed to next step.

4) Turn ignition switch "OFF". Connect the ohmmeter leads to positive and negative terminals of ignition coil. Check for an open circuit in the coil. If open, replace ignition coil.

5) If ignition coil is not open, turn ignition switch "ON". Connect voltmeter negative lead to ground, and touch positive lead to ignition coil negative terminal. If voltage is below 5 volts, replace pick-up coil.

6) If voltage is above 5 volts at negative terminal of coil, remove secondary wire from top of distributor. Attach ignition spark tester to end of coil wire. Crank engine and check for spark at tester.

7) If spark results, check distributor cap. If cap is okay, replace rotor. If there is no spark, check distributor pick-up coil air gap. Clearance should be .012-.020" (.30-.50 mm) minimum on one side.

8) If gap is incorrect, adjust as necessary. If correct, replace control module (part of pick-up coil assembly). Repeat steps **1)** through **5)**.

9) If spark results at tester, no-start problem has been corrected. If no spark results, original module was not defective. Install original module, and replace ignition coil. Again, repeat steps **1)** through **5)**. Spark should result at tester.

IGNITION SYSTEM CHECK WHEN ENGINE RUNS ROUGH

1) Remove spark plug wire from spark plug. Attach ignition spark tester to end of spark plug wire. Crank engine and watch for spark at tester.

2) If there is no spark, refer to IGNITION SYSTEM NO-START CHECK. If spark occurs, check ignition timing. If necessary, adjust to correct. If timing is to specifications, check to see if dwell angle increased. If so, problem is not with ignition system. Check fuel system and spark plugs.

HITACHI ELECTRONIC IGNITION SYSTEM (Cont.)

3) If dwell angle did not increase, check distributor pick-up coil air gap. See PICK-UP COIL AIR GAP under ADJUSTMENTS. Adjust if necessary. If air gap is normal, replace control module.

IGNITION COIL PRIMARY RESISTANCE CHECK

1) Remove primary wires from ignition coil. Set ohmmeter in low range. Connect ohmmeter leads to coil positive and negative terminals (Leads may be touched to Red and White wire terminals in ignition coil harness connector).

2) Primary resistance should be .90-1.40 ohms. If not within specified range, replace ignition coil.

IGNITION COIL SECONDARY RESISTANCE CHECK

1) Remove primary wires and secondary wire from ignition coil. Set ohmmeter in high range. Connect ohmmeter leads to secondary tower and to either primary terminal (or White wire terminal in ignition coil harness connector).

2) Secondary resistance should measure 7300-11,100 ohms. If not, replace ignition coil.

IGNITION COIL INSULATION RESISTANCE CHECK

1) Set ohmmeter in highest range. Connect ignition coil harness to coil primary terminals, if previously removed. Connect ohmmeter leads to Red wire terminal in coil harness and to coil outer shell.

2) Insulation resistance should be 10 megohms or more. Even if tester needle deflects slightly, ignition coil is poorly insulated and must be replaced.

SPARK PLUG AND COIL WIRE RESISTANCE

1) Examine wires for broken insulation, terminals, corrosion, or other damage. Replace if necessary.

2) Set ohmmeter to high range. Connect ohmmeter leads to each end of spark plug and coil secondary wires. Resistance should be 31,500-73,500 ohms per foot.

OVERHAUL

DISASSEMBLY

1) Remove the cap, rotor, and packing. Remove cover. Remove screws attaching vacuum unit, and lift out vacuum unit from housing. *See Fig. 2.*

2) Remove screw attaching harness assembly. Disconnect connectors (Pink and White wires) from control unit. Remove harness assembly from housing. Using 2 screwdrivers to pry upward on reluctor, remove reluctor from rotor shaft.

3) Remove 2 screws securing breaker plate assembly, and lift assembly from housing. Remove pick-up coil and control module assembly. Remove governor shaft assembly, packing, and screw attaching rotor shaft assembly.

NOTE: **End of governor shaft is offset. To maintain original relationship of 2 shafts, scribe mark across rotor shaft and governor shaft before removal.**

Fig. 2: Exploded View of Hitachi Distributor

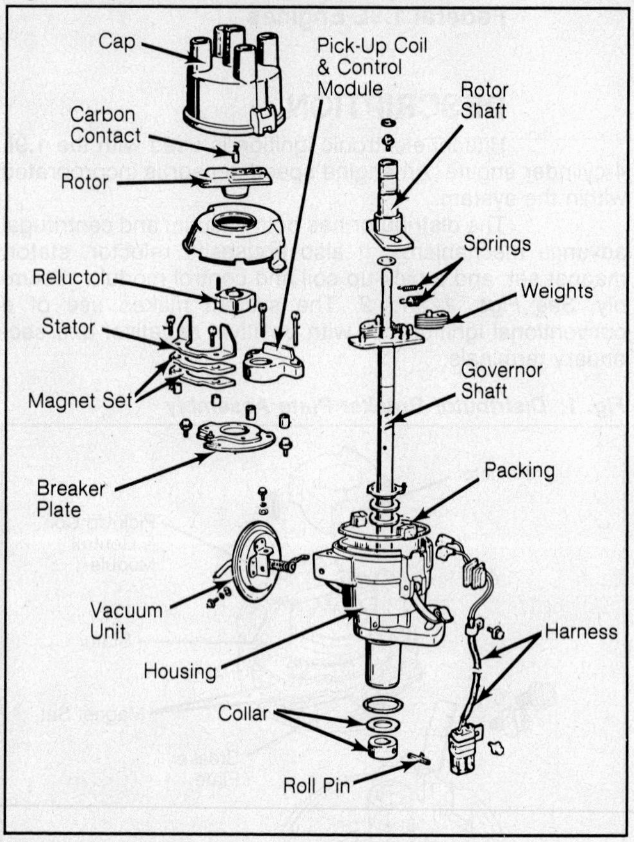

Pick-up coil is built into control module.

4) Remove rotor shaft from governor shaft. Remove governor weights and springs.

INSPECTION

1) Wash and clean disassembled parts. Do not wash inner face of vacuum unit. Check parts for wear or damage, correcting as necessary.

2) Check distributor cap and rotor head for cracks and carbon tracking. Check center carbon contact for wear.

REASSEMBLY

To reassemble, reverse disassembly procedure, noting the following points:

- Governor springs should be fitted to spring hanger pin of governor shaft assembly with smaller hook end downward.
- Correctly align rotor and governor shafts, according to scribe marks made during installation.
- Use a new roll pin when installing collar.
- When installing breaker assembly, the edge at cutaway portion of base must be flush with edge of base fixing screw slot.
- Roll pin should be installed so that slot is parallel with cutaway portion of reluctor, as viewed from above.
- Harness terminal should be connected to pick-up coil and control module assembly. *See Fig. 3.* Install gasket after setting cover to housing.

HITACHI ELECTRONIC IGNITION SYSTEM (Cont.)

Fig. 3: Attaching Harness to Control Module

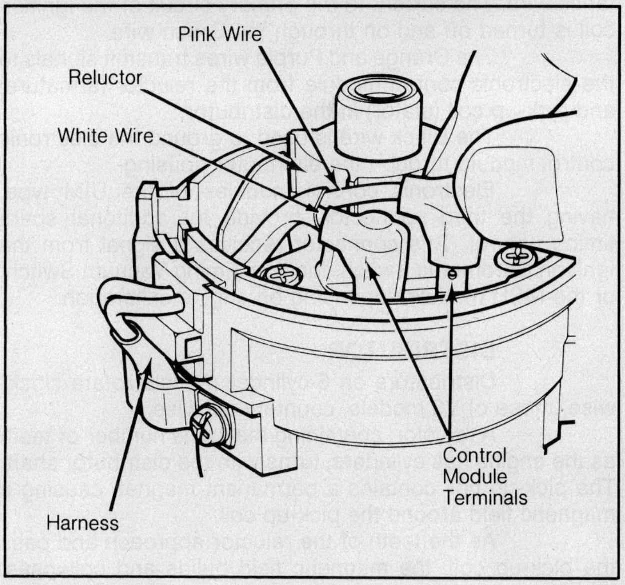

Notice wire colors and their location.

Fig. 4: Wiring Diagram of Hitachi System

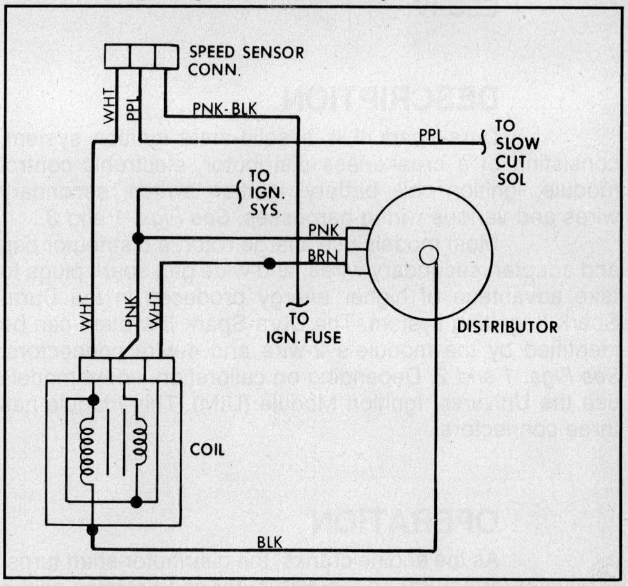

Also see chassis wiring in WIRING DIAGRAM section.

MOTORCRAFT DURA-SPARK II IGNITION SYSTEM

Ford, All Except Models Equipped with EEC-IV

DESCRIPTION

Dura-Spark II is a solid-state ignition system, consisting of a breakerless distributor, electronic control module, ignition coil, battery, ignition switch, secondary wires and various wiring harnesses. *See Figs. 1 and 3.*

Most models use a large rotor, a distributor cap and adapter, secondary wires, and wide gap spark plugs to take advantage of higher energy produced in the Dura-Spark II ignition system. The Dura-Spark II system can be identified by the module's 2-wire and 4-wire connectors. *See Figs. 1 and 2.* Depending on calibration, some models use the Universal Ignition Module (UIM). This module has three connectors.

OPERATION

As the engine cranks, the distributor shaft turns. A reluctor (armature) on the distributor shaft rotates past a pick-up coil (stator).

The reluctor has the same number of teeth as the engine has cylinders. As the teeth rotate past the pick-up coil, a signal is sent to the electronic control module.

Based on this signal, the module then determines when to turn current off and on in the primary windings of the ignition coil. This current collapse in the primary, causes a high voltage surge in the secondary.

This high voltage is routed to the spark plugs through the rotor, distributor cap and spark plug wires. A discussion of system components follows.

ELECTRONIC CONTROL MODULE

Each Dura-Spark II module has 6 wires (a 2-wire and a 4-wire connector). *See Figs. 1 and 2.* The Red and White wires are the ignition feed wires. The White wire is for cranking, and the Red wire is for operation after the engine is running.

The Red wire circuit contains a 1.1 ohm resistance wire. The current to the primary circuit of the ignition coil is turned off and on through the Green wire.

The Orange and Purple wires transmit signals to the electronic control module from the reluctor (armature) and pick-up coil (stator) in the distributor.

The Black wire is used to ground the electronic control module through the distributor housing.

Electronic control modules of the UIM type, having the third connector, provide for additonal spark timing control. This connector receives a signal from the Ignition Barometric Switch, Ignition Timing Vacuum Switch, or the MCU module depending on engine calibration.

DISTRIBUTOR

Distributors on 6-cylinder models rotate clockwise, those of V8 models, counterclockwise.

A reluctor, containing the same number of teeth as the engine has cylinders, turns with the distributor shaft. The pick-up coil contains a permanent magnet, causing a magnetic field around the pick-up coil.

As the teeth of the reluctor approach and pass the pick-up coil, the magnetic field builds and collapses. This causes a signal to be sent to the electronic control module.

In turn, the control module turns the ignition coil primary off and on, causing a high voltage surge in the secondary.

Dura-Spark II systems have an adapter between the distributor housing and cap. *See Fig. 3.* Distributor caps are larger than for conventional distributors, and have male terminals. Dura-Spark II distributors have both centrifugal and vacuum advance mechanisms.

On single diaphragm vacuum units, increased vacuum causes the movable pick-up coil to pivot on the lower plate assembly, advancing spark timing.

On dual diaphragm units, the outer (primary) diaphragm operates from carburetor vacuum to provide timing advance during normal idle off driving conditions. It is connected to the pick-up coil assembly.

The inner (secondary) diaphragm operates from intake manifold vacuum and acts to retard ignition timing.

Fig. 1: Dura-Spark II Ignition System Wiring Diagram

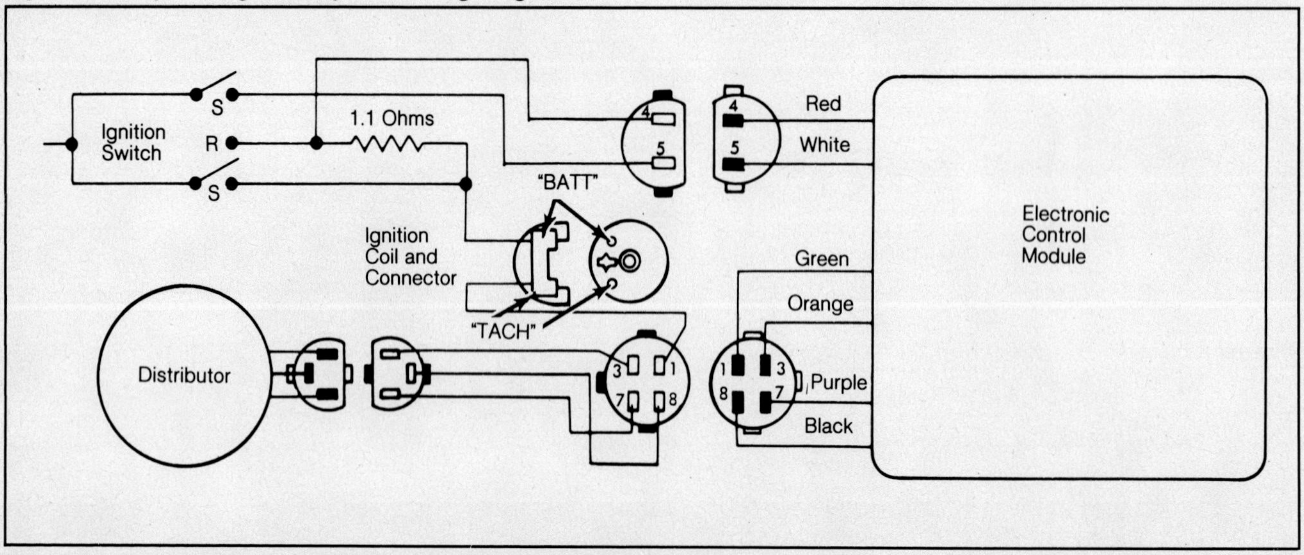

Electronic control module has a 2-wire and 4-wire connector.

MOTORCRAFT DURA-SPARK II IGNITION SYSTEM (Cont.)

The inner diaphragm is connected to the outer diaphragm rod by means of sliding linkage. Stronger intake manifold vacuum can override carburetor vacuum during closed throttle operation, retarding spark timing.

Fig. 2: Control Module and Distributor Connectors for Dura-Spark II System

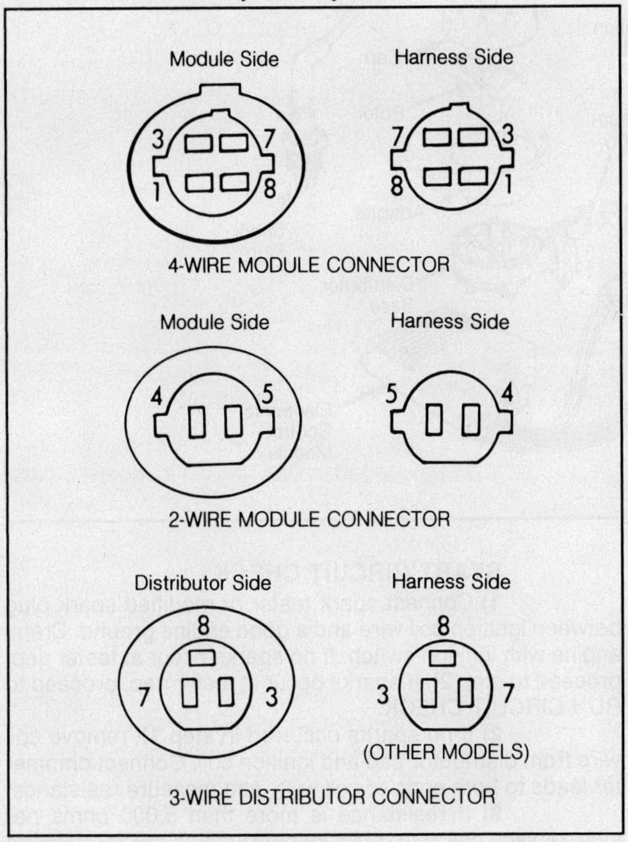

Compare terminal location to shape.

IGNITION COIL

Coils are oil-filled, and are energized whenever the ignition switch is in the "ON" or "START" position. They contain a positive "BATT" terminal, a negative "TACH" (sometimes called "DEC") terminal, and a single secondary terminal.

NOTE: **"DEC" refers to Distributor Electronic Control. This terminal is also referred to as the "Tach Test" terminal.**

A special connector attaches the Green wire from the control module to the negative terminal ("TACH") and the wire from the ignition switch to the positive terminal ("BATT").

RESISTANCE WIRE

The special ignition resistance wire in the Red wire circuit must be of specified length and diameter to reduce operating voltage.

CAUTION: **Under no circumstances should it be replaced by any other wire other than correct service resistance wire.**

When new wire is installed, old wire should be removed from system. Resistance value of wire is 1.0-1.1 ohms.

SYSTEM PROTECTION

Dura-Spark systems are protected against electrical currents produced or used by any other vehicle component during normal operation. However, damage to the ignition system can occur if proper testing procedures are not followed.

DURA-SPARK II SYSTEM PRECAUTIONS

Since the electronic control module and ignition coil are "ON" whenever the ignition switch is in the "ON" or "START" position, the system will generate a spark whenever the ignition switch is turned "OFF". This feature may be used as a diagnostic tool to check for continuity of circuit, coil and ignition switch. Some testing precautions follow:

CAUTION: **Since a spark may occur if distributor cap is removed with switch "ON", keep switch "OFF" during underhood operations, unless you plan to start the engine or perform a test requiring the switch to be "ON". This will prevent accidental engine rotation during service or test procedures.**

NOTE: **Silicone dielectric grease must be applied to all insulating areas at distributor (not on cap or rotor, if vehicle is equipped with FM radio), coil and spark plug boots.**

NOTE: **A 3/4" clearance must be maintained at distributor cap mounting edge, spark plug wire terminals, and coil tower to prevent high voltage arc to ground.**

NOTE: **When replacing spark plug wires, insure wire made of the same material is used for a replacement. Silicone/Silicone wire can be identified by the letters "SS" appearing on the wire in WHITE lettering. Silicone/EPDM wire can be identified by the letters "SE" appearing on the wire in BLACK lettering. The "SS" wire is used on cylinders subject to very high engine temperatures.**

NOTE: **When removing distributor cap and adapter, always remove the distributor cap first, then the adapter.**

ADJUSTMENTS

No adjustments are to be made to the ignition system except initial engine timing and spark plug gap.

TESTING

NOTE: **All wire colors shown refer to colors of electronic control module wires. For example, "the Green wire leading to the coil" would refer to any colored wire leading to the coil, that connects to the module's Green wire. Therefore, when making tests, wires must be traced back to control module for proper color identification. Also, when a test is completed and a problem is found, make the necessary repair and repeat the failed test to be sure that the problem has been corrected.**

MOTORCRAFT DURA-SPARK II IGNITION SYSTEM (Cont.)

Fig. 3: Schematic of Dura-Spark II Ignition System

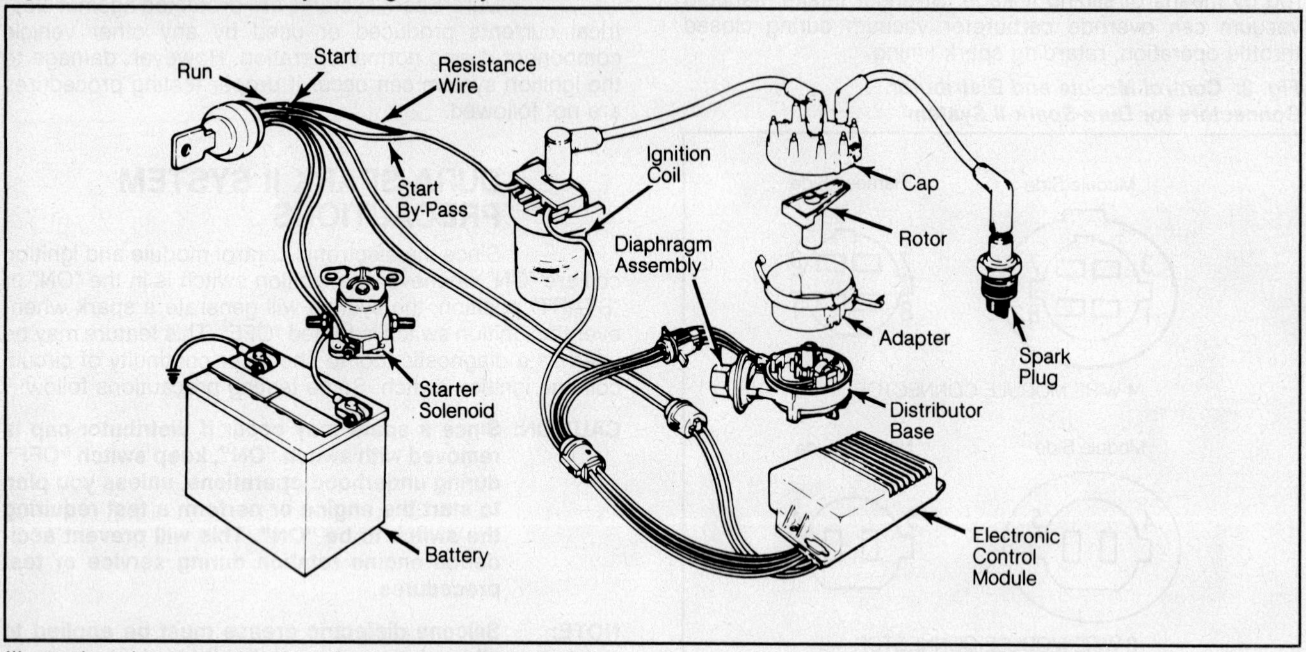

Illustration shows relationship of components to each other.

When checking the secondary voltage, do not remove the following spark plug wires while the engine is running or cranking:

- Plug No. 1 or 8 on V8 engines.
- Plug No. 3 or 5 on 6 cylinder engines.
- Plug No. 1 or 3 on 4 cylinder engines.

IGNITION SPARK TESTER

Either use an ignition spark tester, or modify a spark plug for use in testing ignition system. To modify plug, cut off side terminal, and install spring clip for grounding plug housing. *See Fig. 4*.

Fig. 4: Modified Spark Plug and Spark Tester

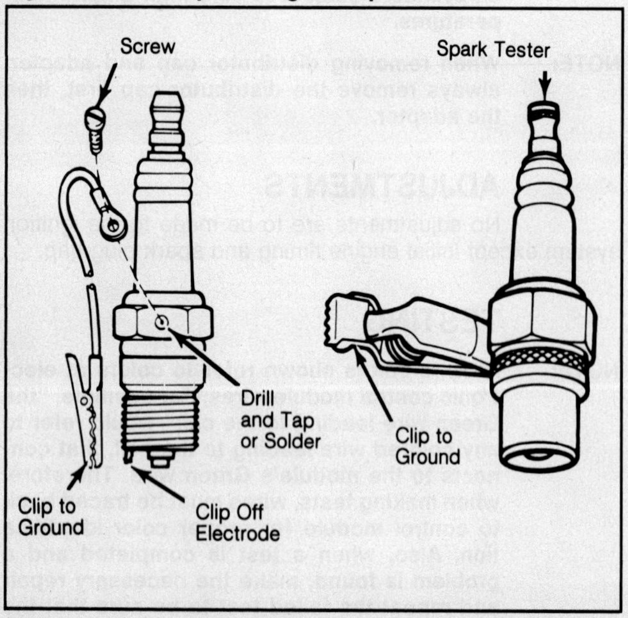

Testers may be purchased from most tool suppliers.

START CIRCUIT CHECK

1) Connect spark tester or modified spark plug between ignition coil wire and a good engine ground. Crank engine with ignition switch. If no sparks occur at tester gap, proceed to step **2)**. If sparks occur at tester gap, proceed to RUN CIRCUIT CHECK.

2) If no sparks occurred in step **1)**, remove coil wire from distributor cap and ignition coil. Connect ohmmeter leads to both ends of coil wire, and measure resistance.

3) If resistance is more than 5,000 ohms per inch, replace coil wire. Also, inspect ignition coil for damage or carbon tracking. Crank engine to verify distributor rotation and proceed to VOLTAGE SUPPLY CIRCUITS CHECK.

RUN CIRCUIT CHECK

1) Remove ignition coil wire from distributor cap, and install spark tester on wire. Turn ignition switch from "OFF" to "RUN" to "OFF" several times.

2) Sparks should occur at tester gap each time switch goes from "RUN" to "OFF" position. Remove spark tester and reconnect coil wire to distributor cap.

3) If sparks occur, check distributor cap, adapter, and rotor for cracks, carbon tracking or lack of silicone compound. Also check for roll pin retaining reluctor to sleeve in distributor shaft and check that Orange and Purple wires are not crossed between distributor and control module.

4) If no sparks occurred in step **1)**, proceed to CONTROL MODULE VOLTAGE CHECK.

CONTROL MODULE VOLTAGE CHECK

1) With ignition switch "OFF", carefully insert small straight pin in Red module wire. *See Fig. 5*. DO NOT allow straight pin to touch ground. Measure battery voltage at battery. Attach negative voltmeter lead to distributor base and positive lead to straight pin.

2) Turn ignition switch to "RUN" position. Measure voltage at straight pin in Red wire. After reading voltmeter, turn ignition switch "OFF" and remove straight pin.

MOTORCRAFT DURA-SPARK II IGNITION SYSTEM (Cont.)

Fig. 5: Checking Control Module "RUN" and "START" Circuits with Voltmeter

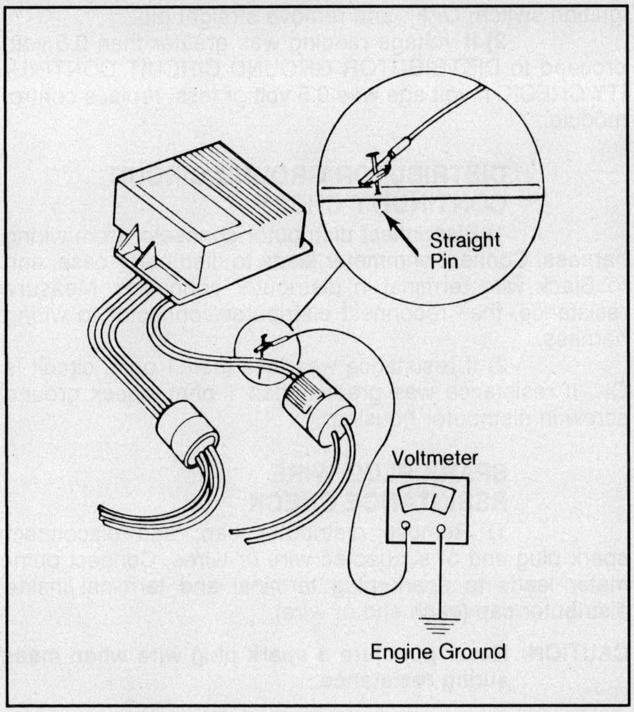

Do not let straight pin touch a ground.

3) Voltage at pin should read at least 90 percent of battery voltage. If so, proceed to BALLAST RESISTOR CHECK.

4) If reading was less than 90 percent of battery voltage, check wiring harness between control module and ignition switch. Also check for a worn or damaged ignition switch.

BALLAST RESISTOR CHECK

1) Disconnect control module 2-wire connector and remove coil connector from coil. Connect ohmmeter leads to "BATT" terminal of coil connector and to harness connector terminal mating with Red control module wire. Read ohmmeter, then reconnect all connectors.

2) If resistance is 0.8-1.6 ohms, problem is either intermittent or not in ignition system. If resistance was less than 0.8 or more than 1.6 ohms, replace resistance wire.

VOLTAGE SUPPLY CIRCUITS CHECK

1) If starter relay has an "I" terminal, disconnect cable between relay and starter motor at starter relay. If starter relay does not have an "I" terminal, disconnect wire to "S" terminal of starter relay. Insert small straight pins in Red and White control module wires.

CAUTION: Do not allow straight pins to contact an electrical ground.

2) Measure battery voltage at battery. Connect negative voltmeter lead to distributor base, and note voltmeter reading in each of the following situations:

- Positive voltmeter lead connected to pin in Red wire, with ignition switch in "RUN" position.
- Positive voltmeter lead connected to pin in White wire, with ignition switch in "START" position.
- Positive voltmeter lead connected to "BATT" terminal of ignition coil, with ignition switch in "START" position. *See Fig. 6*.

Fig. 6: Checking for Battery Voltage at Ignition Coil Positive ("BATT") Terminal

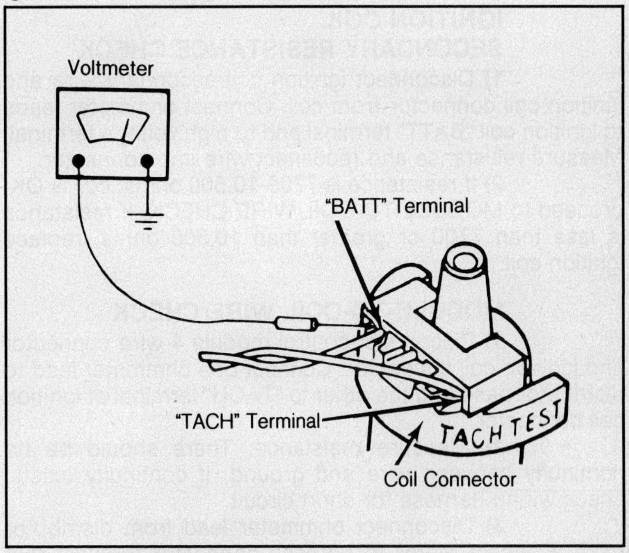

3) Turn ignition switch off. Reconnect any wires disconnected from starter relay. Remove voltmeter leads, and remove straight pins from wires.

4) If voltage readings were at least 90 percent of battery voltage, test result is okay, proceed to IGNITION COIL VOLTAGE SUPPLY CHECK. If reading was less than 90 percent of battery voltage, check for faulty wiring harness connectors or damaged ignition switch.

IGNITION COIL VOLTAGE SUPPLY CHECK

1) Connect negative lead of voltmeter to distributor base and positive lead to "BATT" terminal of ignition coil. *See Fig. 6*. Turn ignition switch to "RUN" position, and read voltmeter. Turn ignition switch "OFF".

2) If voltage was 6-8 volts, proceed to PICK-UP COIL & DISTRIBUTOR WIRING HARNESS CHECK. If voltage was less than 6 volts or more than 8 volts, proceed to IGNITION COIL PRIMARY RESISTANCE CHECK .

PICK-UP COIL & DISTRIBUTOR WIRING HARNESS CHECK

1) Disconnect control module 4-wire connector, and inspect for dirt, corrosion or damage. Connect ohmmeter leads to harness connector terminals that mate with Orange and Purple control module wires.

2) Resistance should be 400-1300 ohms. If so, proceed to CONTROL MODULE TO DISTRIBUTOR WIRING HARNESS CHECK. If resistance is not to specifications, proceed to PICK-UP COIL RESISTANCE CHECK.

CONTROL MODULE TO DISTRIBUTOR WIRING HARNESS CHECK

1) Disconnect 4-wire control module connector. Connect an ohmmeter lead to distributor base. Alternately, connect the other ohmmeter lead to wiring harness connector terminals that mate with Orange and Purple wires of control module connector.

MOTORCRAFT DURA-SPARK II IGNITION SYSTEM (Cont.)

2) If resistance is greater than 70,000 ohms, test result is OK. Proceed to IGNITION COIL SECONDARY RESISTANCE CHECK. If resistance was less than 70,000 ohms, check wiring harness between control module connector and distributor, including distributor grommet.

IGNITION COIL SECONDARY RESISTANCE CHECK

1) Disconnect ignition coil secondary wire and ignition coil connector from coil. Connect ohmmeter leads to ignition coil "BATT" terminal and to high voltage terminal. Measure resistance and reconnect wire and connector.

2) If resistance is 7700-10,500 ohms, coil is OK, proceed to MODULE-TO-COIL WIRE CHECK. If resistance is less than 7700 or greater than 10,500 ohms, replace ignition coil.

MODULE-TO-COIL WIRE CHECK

1) Disconnect control module 4-wire connector and ignition coil connector. Connect one ohmmeter lead to distributor base and the other to "TACH" terminal of ignition coil connector.

2) Measure resistance. There should be no continuity between wire and ground. If continuity exists, check wiring harness for short circuit.

3) Disconnect ohmmeter lead from distributor base. Connect meter to harness connector terminal that mates with Green wire and measure resistance. If wire shows any resistance, check wiring harness.

PICK-UP COIL RESISTANCE CHECK

1) Disconnect distributor connector from wiring harness. Connect ohmmeter leads to distributor connector terminals that mate with Orange and Purple wires of control module. Measure resistance of pick-up coil. Reconnect distributor connector to wiring harness.

2) Resistance should be 400-1000 ohms. If resistance is within this range, pick-up coil is OK. If resistance is not within specified range, replace pick-up coil assembly.

IGNITION COIL PRIMARY RESISTANCE CHECK

1) Disconnect ignition coil connector. Connect ohmmeter leads to "BATT" and "TACH" terminals of ignition coil. Measure resistance, and reconnect ignition coil connector.

2) If resistance is 0.8-1.6 ohms, coil is OK. Proceed to PRIMARY CIRCUIT CONTINUITY CHECK. If resistance is less than 0.8 or greater than 1.6 ohms, replace ignition coil.

PRIMARY CIRCUIT CONTINUITY CHECK

1) Insert a small straight pin in control module Green wire. Connect negative voltmeter lead to distributor base, and positive lead to pin in Green wire.

2) With ignition switch in "RUN" position, measure voltage. Turn ignition switch "OFF" and remove straight pin from Green wire.

3) If voltage reading was greater than 1.5 volts, proceed to GROUND CIRCUIT CONTINUITY CHECK. If voltage reading was 1.5 volts or less, inspect wiring between module and coil.

GROUND CIRCUIT CONTINUITY CHECK

1) Insert a small straight pin in control module Black wire. Connect negative lead of voltmeter to distributor base, and positive lead to straight pin in Black wire. With ignition switch in "RUN" position, measure voltage. Turn ignition switch "OFF", and remove straight pin.

2) If voltage reading was greater than 0.5 volt, proceed to DISTRIBUTOR GROUND CIRCUIT CONTINUITY CHECK. If volt age was 0.5 volt or less, replace control module.

DISTRIBUTOR GROUND CIRCUIT CONTINUITY CHECK

1) Disconnect distributor connector from wiring harness. Connect ohmmeter leads to distributor base, and to Black wire terminal in distributor connector. Measure resistance, then reconnect distributor connector to wiring harness.

2) If resistance was less than 1 ohm, circuit is OK. If resistance was greater than 1 ohm, check ground screw in distributor housing.

SPARK PLUG WIRE RESISTANCE CHECK

1) Remove distributor cap, and disconnect spark plug end of suspected wire or wires. Connect ohmmeter leads to spark plug terminal and terminal inside distributor cap (each end of wire).

CAUTION: Never puncture a spark plug wire when measuring resistance.

2) If resistance is less than 5000 ohms per inch, visually inspect wires for damage and remove spark plug for inspection and/or replacement. If resistance is greater than 5000 ohms per inch, disconnect suspected wire from distributor cap and again connect leads to each end of wire.

3) If resistance is now less than 5000 ohms per inch, inspect distributor cap and spark plug wire terminals for damage. Repair as necessary. If resistance is still greater than 5000 ohms per inch, replace wire(s).

OVERHAUL

DISASSEMBLY

1) Remove distributor cap, adapter, and rotor. Disconnect distributor wiring harness plug. Using a small gear puller or two screwdrivers, carefully pry armature from sleeve and plate assembly. Remove roll pin.

CAUTION: Do not pinch stator wires when removing armature.

2) On V8 engines, remove large wire retaining clip from base plate annular groove. Remove ground screw base, and pull up to remove rubber grommet from base.

3) Remove "E" clip securing diaphragm rod advance link to stator assembly. Lift diaphragm rod off post on stator assembly, and move it out against housing. Remove stator assembly.

4) On 6-cylinder models, remove "E" clip washer and wave washer, securing stator assembly to lower plate. Remove stator assembly ground screw and lift assembly from distributor.

REASSEMBLY

Reverse disassembly procedure. Using new roll pin, install roll pin in different groove, 180° from original groove.

MOTORCRAFT DURA-SPARK II IGNITION SYSTEM (Cont.)

Fig. 7: Components of Dura-Spark II Distributor

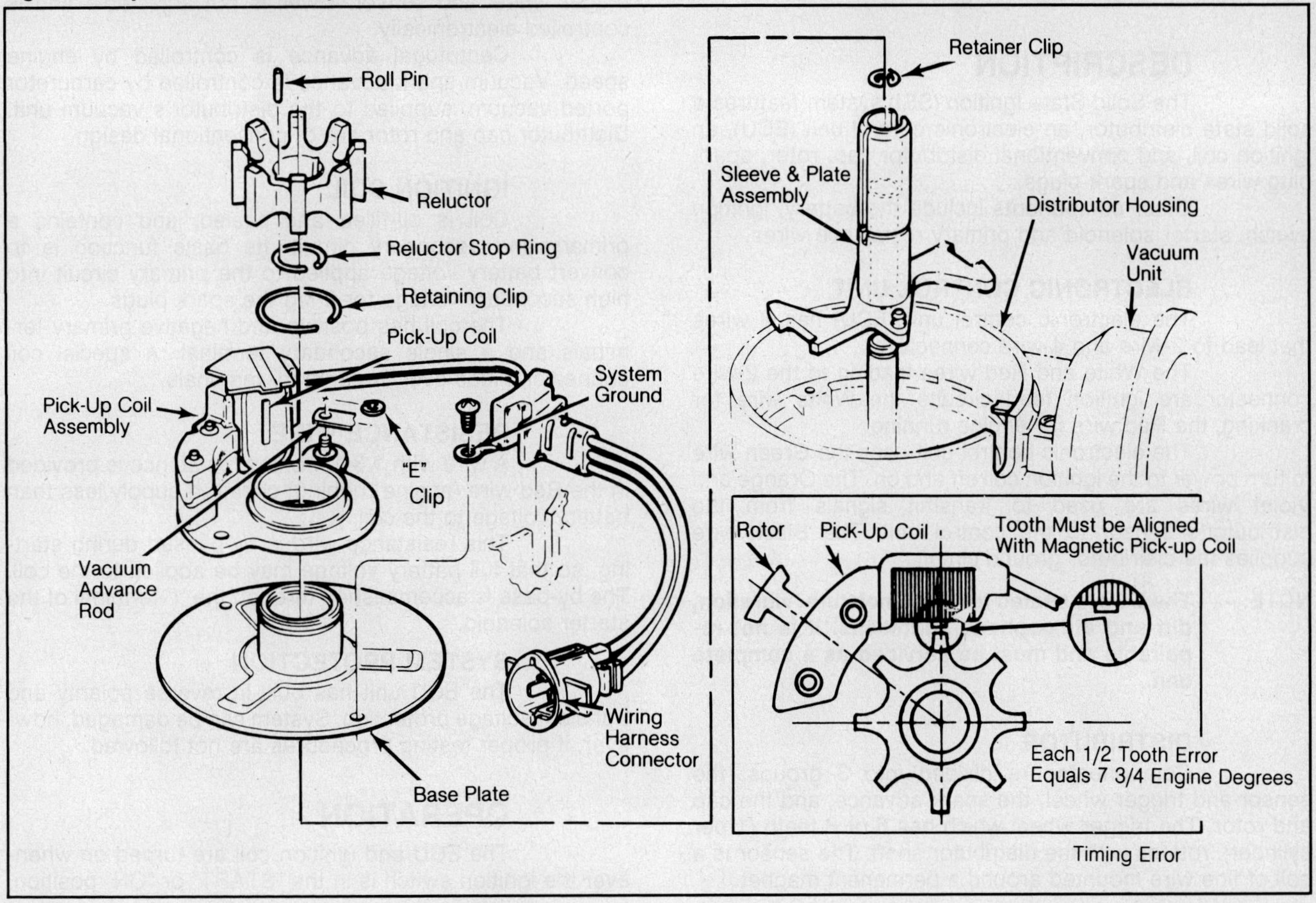

Reluctor shown, having 8 teeth, is for V8 engine.

MOTORCRAFT SOLID STATE IGNITION (SSI)

Jeep; All Except V6 Engine

DESCRIPTION

The Solid State Ignition (SSI) system features a solid state distributor, an electronic control unit (ECU), an ignition coil, and conventional distributor cap, rotor, spark plug wires and spark plugs.

Other components include the battery, ignition switch, starter solenoid and primary resistance wires.

ELECTRONIC CONTROL UNIT

The electronic control unit (ECU) has 6 wires that lead to 2-wire and 4-wire connectors.

The White and Red wires leading to the 2-wire connector are ignition feed circuits the White wire for cranking, the Red wire for engine running.

The electronic control unit uses the Green wire to turn power to the ignition coil off and on. The Orange and Violet wires are used to transmit signals from the distributor's sensor to the control unit. The Black wire supplies the distributor ground circuit.

NOTE: **The ECU is sealed to resist moisture, vibration, dirt and atmospheric conditions. It is not repairable and must be serviced as a complete unit.**

DISTRIBUTOR

Components are divided into 3 groups, the sensor and trigger wheel, the spark advance, and the cap and rotor. The trigger wheel which has 6 or 8 teeth (1 per cylinder), rotates with the distributor shaft. The sensor is a coil of fine wire mounted around a permanent magnet.

There are no contacting surfaces between the trigger wheel and sensor. Dwell is not adjustable and is controlled electronically.

Centrifugal advance is controlled by engine speed. Vacuum spark advance is controlled by carburetor ported vacuum, supplied to the distributor's vacuum unit. Distributor cap and rotor are of conventional design.

IGNITION COIL

Coil is oil-filled and sealed, and contains a primary and secondary circuit. Its basic function is to convert battery voltage applied to the primary circuit into high secondary voltage for firing the spark plugs.

The coil has positive and negative primary terminals and a single secondary terminal. A special coil connector slides over the primary terminals.

RESISTANCE WIRE

A wire with 1.3-1.4 ohms resistance is provided in the Red wire (engine running) circuit to supply less than battery voltage to the coil.

This resistance wire is by-passed during starting, so that full battery voltage may be applied to the coil. The by-pass is accomplished through the "I" terminal of the starter solenoid.

SYSTEM PROTECTION

The ECU unit has built-in reverse polarity and transient voltage protection. System can be damaged, however, if proper testing procedures are not followed.

OPERATION

The ECU and ignition coil are turned on whenever the ignition switch is in the "START" or "ON" position.

Fig. 1: Jeep Solid State Ignition (SSI) System

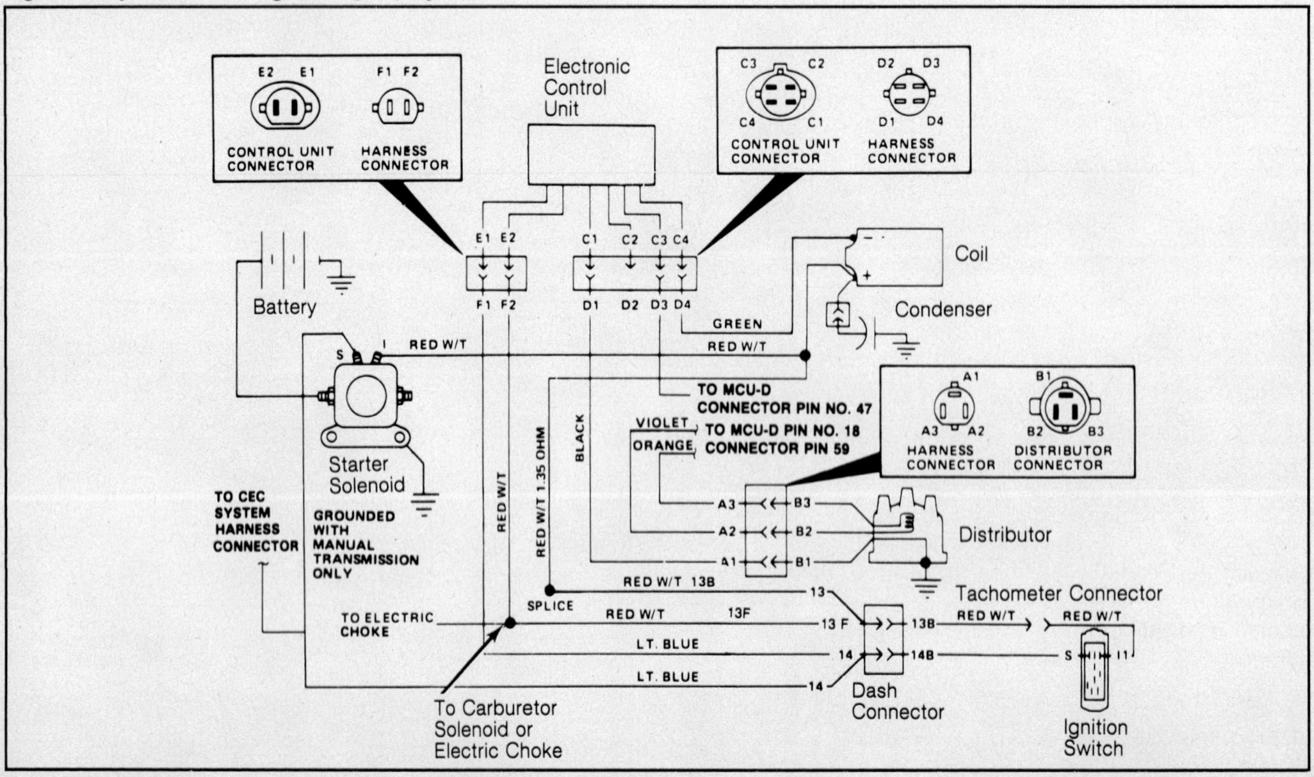

MOTORCRAFT SOLID STATE IGNITION (SSI) (Cont.)

When the engine begins turning the distributor shaft, the trigger wheel rotates with it.

As each tooth passes the sensor, it interrupts the magnetic field around the sensor. This continual build-up and collapse of the field provides a signal to the ECU.

The ECU receives this signal and turns the power to the ignition coil's primary circuit off and on as each tooth passes the sensor.

The collapse of the magnetic field in the ignition coil primary circuit induces a high voltage surge in secondary. This current flows from the coil to the distributor, rotor, cap and spark plug wires.

SOLID STATE IGNITION (SSI) SYSTEM NOTES

NOTE: **When disconnecting wire from spark plug or distributor cap, twist rubber boot slightly to loosen. Grasp boot (not wire) and pull off with steady, even force.**

NOTE: **When disconnecting control unit connectors, pull with firm, straight pull. Do not attempt to pry apart with screwdriver. When connecting, press together firmly to overcome hydraulic pressure of grease. If connector locking tabs weaken or break off, it is unnecessary to replace connector. Just press together firmly and bind with electrical tape or a harness tie strap to assure good connection.**

TESTING

SECONDARY CIRCUIT CHECK

CAUTION: **When checking secondary voltage, do not remove spark plug wires from spark plugs No. 3 on 4-cylinder, No. 1 or 5 on 6-cylinder and No. 3 or 4 on V8 Engines.**

1) Disconnect coil wire from distributor cap. Use insulated pliers to hold wire approximately 1/2" from engine block or intake manifold.

2) Crank engine and check for spark at gap. If no spark occurs, turn off ignition switch, and check resistance of secondary coil windings. SEE IGNITION COIL RESISTANCE CHECK, SECONDARY RESISTANCE. Replace ignition coil if outside specifications.

3) If spark occurred in step **2)**, connect coil wire to distributor cap. Remove wire from 1 spark plug. Using insulated pliers, hold wire 1/2" from engine head while cranking engine. Check for spark.

4) If spark occurs, check for fuel problems or incorrect timing. If no sparks occur, check for defective rotor or distributor cap or for defective spark plug wires.

CURRENT FLOW CHECK

1) Remove connector from ignition coil. Remove positive wire from connector, then negative wire. Connect ammeter between positive terminal of coil and disconnected positive wire. Connect jumper wire from negative terminal to good ground.

2) Turn ignition switch "ON". Current flow should be approximately 7 amps., but should not exceed 7.6 amps. If more than 7.6 amps., replace ignition coil.

3) With ammeter still connected to coil positive terminal, remove jumper wire from negative terminal. Connect coil Green wire to negative terminal. Current flow should be approximately 4 amps.

4) If less than 3.5 amps., check for poor connections in 4-wire and 3-wire connectors or for poor ground at distributor ground screw.

5) If current flow is greater than 5 amps., the control unit is defective and must be replaced. Start engine. Normal current flow with engine running is 2.0-2.4 amps. If outside of specifications, replace control unit.

COIL OUTPUT CHECK

1) Connect oscilloscope to engine. Start engine and observe secondary winding spark voltage. Remove 1 spark plug wire (not wire No. 3 on 4-cylinder, No. 1 or 5 on 6-cylinder engine nor wire No. 3 or 4 on V8 engines) from distributor cap. Run engine at 1000 RPM.

2) Observe voltage on oscilloscope. This voltage, referred to as open circuit voltage, should be 24,000 volts minimum.

NOTE: **Do not operate engine with spark plug disconnected for more than 30 seconds or damage may result to catalytic converter.**

SPARK PLUG REQUIRED VOLTAGE

1) Attach secondary voltage pick-up over coil high tension wire. Run engine at approximately 1000 RPM. Firing voltage should be relatively even and between 5000-16,000 volts.

2) If firing voltage is bad, check each cylinder. Maximum variation between cylinders is 3000 to 5000 volts.

IGNITION COIL RESISTANCE CHECK

Primary Resistance

1) Remove connector from positive and negative coil terminals. Be sure ignition switch is off. Set an ohmmeter on low scale and connect ohmmeter leads to positive and negative terminals.

2) Ohmmeter reading should be 1.13-1.23 ohms at 75°F (24°C). With coil temperature at 200°F (93°C), a 1.5 ohm reading is acceptable.

Secondary Resistance

1) Turn ignition switch off. Set ohmmeter to high scale (x1000 scale). Connect one lead to coil negative terminal and other lead to coil tower (remove coil secondary wire).

2) Ohmmeter reading should be 7700-9300 ohms with coil temperature at 75°F (24°C). With coil temperature at 200°F (93°C) or above, a maximum reading of 12,000 ohms is acceptable.

COIL PRIMARY CIRCUIT CHECK

1) Connect voltmeter positive lead to coil positive terminal and negative lead to ground. Turn ignition switch to "ON" position. Reading should be 5.5-6.5 volts. If voltage is too high (battery voltage), proceed to step **4)**. If voltage is too low (below 5.5 volts), disconnect condenser lead. If voltage is now correct, replace condenser. If voltage is still low, proceed to step **7)**.

2) If voltage was 5.5-6.5 volts in step **1)**, turn ignition switch to "START" position. Voltage should be the same as battery cranking voltage. If correct, check other systems (fuel, mechanical, etc.) for problems. If voltage is not correct proceed to next step.

MOTORCRAFT SOLID STATE IGNITION (SSI) (Cont.)

Fig. 2: Solid State Ignition Connectors

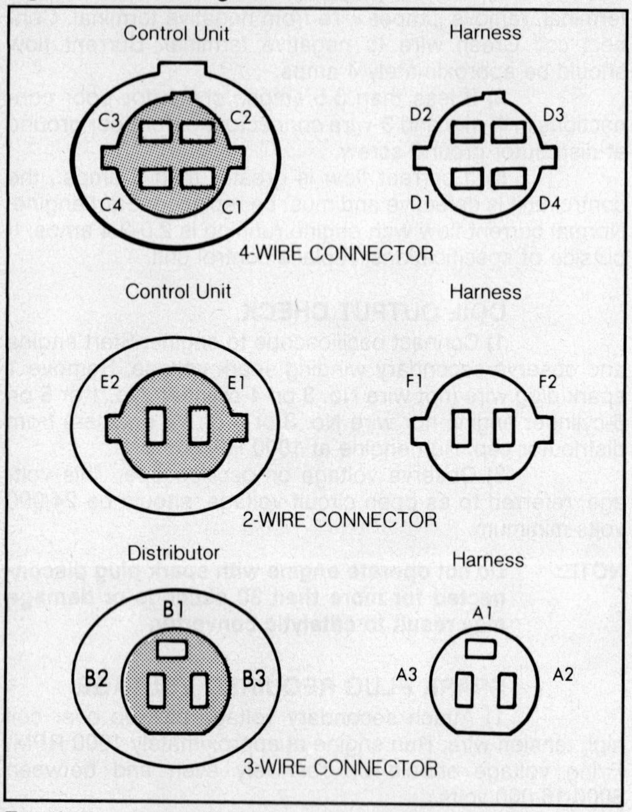

Terminals are identified for testing purposes.

3) Check wire connected to starter solenoid "I" terminal for shorts or opens. If wire is OK, check for defective starter solenoid. Replace solenoid if necessary.

4) With ignition switch in "ON" position and voltmeter still connected to coil positive terminal, disconnect wire connected to starter solenoid "I" terminal. If voltage drops to 5.5-6.5 volts, replace starter solenoid.

5) If voltage remains high, connect a jumper wire from coil negative terminal to ground. If voltage drops to 5.5-6.5 volt range, proceed to step **6)**. If voltage does not drop, resistance wire is defective. Replace resistance wire and retest, beginning with step **2)**.

6) With ignition switch "OFF", connect an ohmmeter lead to the coil negative terminal and the other lead to the Green wire terminal "D4" of the 4-wire harness connector. Also check from Black wire terminal "D1" to ground. If continuity is OK, replace the control unit. If no continuity is present, repair wire in harness and retest beginning at step **2)**.

7) With ignition switch "OFF", connect ohmmeter leads between coil positive terminal and dash connector "AV" (Red wire). If resistance is not 1.3-1.4 ohms, replace resistance wire. If ohmmeter reading is to specifications, proceed to next step.

8) With ignition switch still "OFF", connect ohmmeter leads between dash connector "AV" (Red wire) and ignition switch terminal "L1". Resistance should be less than 0.1 ohm. If reading is to specifications, repair feed wire or replace ignition switch.

9) If resistance is more than 0.1 ohm, check for opens in wire or for poor connections at connectors. Repair or replace as necessary.

CONTROL UNIT & SENSOR CHECK

1) Disconnect high tension coil wire from distributor cap. Attach a modified spark plug to coil wire (side electrode of plug cut off and ground wire attached to side of plug casing). If plug is not available, hold coil wire 1/2" from engine block, using insulated pliers.

2) Turn ignition switch "ON" and disconnect 4-wire connector from control unit. Watch for spark at modified spark plug, as connector is disconnected. If sparking occurs, proceed with next step. If no sparking occurs, proceed to step **6)**.

3) Turn ignition switch "OFF", and disconnect 4-wire connector at control unit. Connect an ohmmeter between the Orange and Violet wire terminals "D2" and "D3" of harness connector. Ohmmeter reading should be 400-800 ohms. If reading is correct, proceed to step **8)**. If reading is not correct, proceed to next step.

4) Disconnect and reconnect the 3-wire connector at the distributor. If ohmmeter reading is now correct, proceed to step **8)**. If reading is still not correct, proceed to next step.

5) Disconnect 3-wire connector at the distributor and connect ohmmeter leads between the Orange and Violet wire terminals "B2" and "B3" of distributor connector. If reading is now 400-800 ohms, repair harness between 3-wire and 4-wire connectors. If reading is still out of specifications, replace sensor in distributor.

6) With ignition switch "OFF" and 4-wire connector disconnected, connect ohmmeter leads to battery negative terminal (ground) and Black wire terminal "D1" in harness connector. Ohmmeter reading should be nearly zero (less than .002 ohms).

7) If ohmmeter reading is OK, recheck system starting at step **3)**. If reading is above specifications, check for the source of the bad ground, (ground cable resistance, distributor-to-engine block resistance, or ground screw in distributor to black wire terminal "D1").

8) With ignition switch "ON" and voltmeter connected to harness side of 4-wire connector Orange and Violet wire terminals "D2" and "D3", crank engine. Voltmeter reading should fluctuate.

9) If no voltage fluctuation occurs, check for defective trigger wheel, distributor shaft not turning, or missing trigger wheel retaining pin (shaft turning but not trigger wheel).

CONTROL UNIT POWER FEED CHECK

NOTE: **Before making this check, always check ignition coil primary circuit first.**

1) Disconnect 2-wire connector at control unit. Connect voltmeter negative lead to ground and positive lead to Red wire harness connector terminal "F2". Turn ignition switch on. Voltage reading should be battery voltage (within 0.2 volts). If reading is correct, replace control unit. If not, proceed to next step.

2) Locate and repair cause of voltage reduction (corroded connectors, defective ignition switch, etc.). If connectors are repaired and there is spark at coil wire, start engine. If connectors are repaired and there is no spark at coil wire, replace control unit.

3) Connect voltmeter negative lead to ground and positive lead to Light Blue wire at harness connector terminal "F1" in 2-wire connector. Crank engine. Voltmeter reading should be within 1 volt of battery cranking voltage. If not, check for bad connections, ignition switch or starter solenoid.

MOTORCRAFT SOLID STATE IGNITION (SSI) (Cont.)

4) Turn ignition switch off, connect 2-wire connector and disconnect 4-wire connector. Connect an ammeter to ground and to Black wire terminal "C1" of control unit (not harness) connector. Turn ignition switch on. Reading should be 0.9-1.1 amps. If reading is higher or lower than specified, replace control unit.

OVERHAUL

DISTRIBUTOR

Disassembly

1) Remove distributor cap and rotor. Using suitable gear puller (J 28509), remove trigger wheel (2 screwdrivers can be used to pry trigger wheel upward). Remove pin.

2) On 6-cylinder engines, remove sensor retainer and washers from pivot pin on base plate. On V8 engines, remove sensor snap ring from shaft. Remove retainer from vacuum unit-to-sensor drive pin and move vacuum lever aside.

3) Remove ground screw from harness tab. Lift sensor assembly from distributor housing. Only remove vacuum unit if it is to be replaced.

Reassembly

Reverse disassembly procedure, being sure to coat brass surface of rotor with silicone grease. If sensor or vacuum unit was replaced, check ignition timing.

Fig. 3: Exploded View of Jeep SSI Distributor

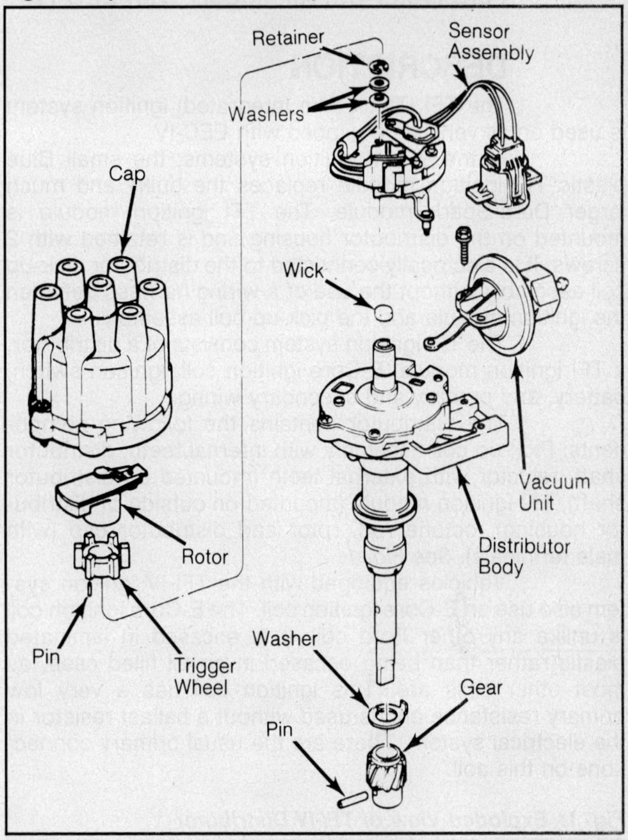

Reluctors have 1 tooth for each cylinder.

TYPICAL MOTORCRAFT IGNITION OSCILLOSCOPE PATTERNS

To analyze the Solid State (SSI) and Dura-Spark Ignition Systems using an oscilloscope, follow the procedures recommended by the manufacturer of the scope.

The electrical display patterns will appear similar to patterns of conventional breaker type ignition systems except as shown. *See Fig. 4.*

Fig. 4: Normal Oscilloscope Patterns Shown for Solid State Ignition (SSI) Systems

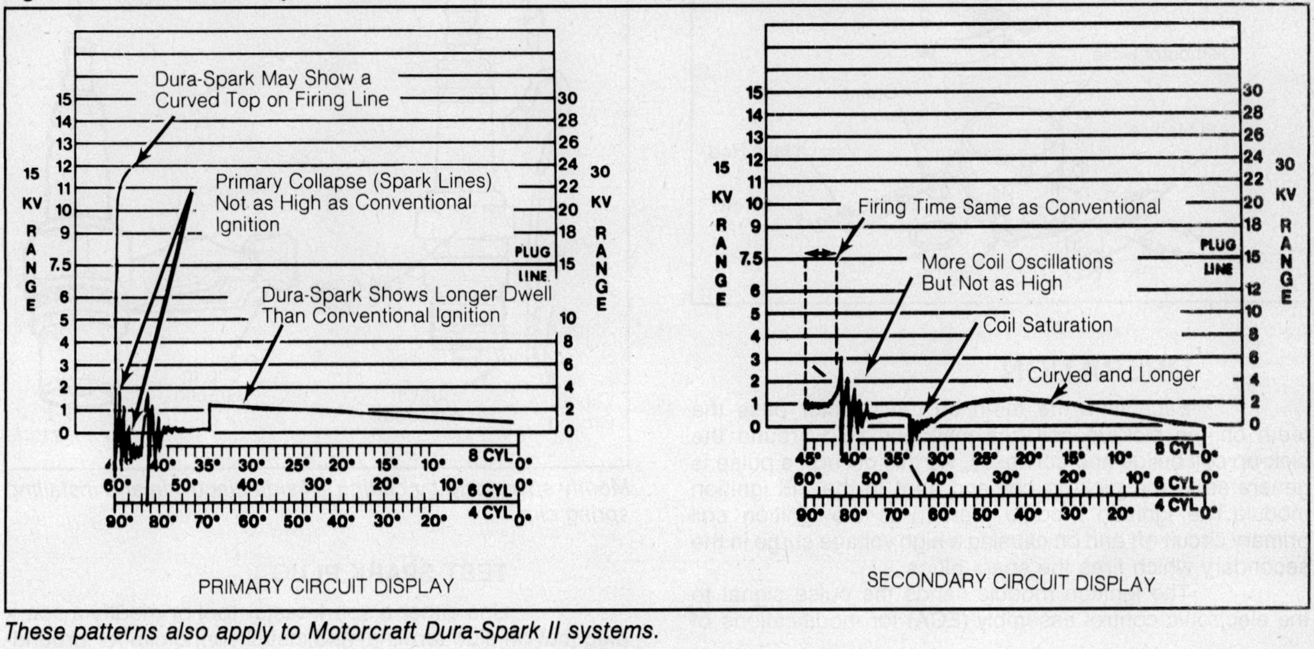

These patterns also apply to Motorcraft Dura-Spark II systems.

MOTORCRAFT TFI-IV IGNITION

Ford Motor Co. All Models With EEC-IV

DESCRIPTION

The TFI (Thick Film Integrated) ignition system is used on all vehicles equipped with EEC-IV.

In the TFI-IV ignition systems, the small Blue plastic TFI ignition module replaces the bulky and much larger Dura-Spark module. The TFI ignition module is mounted on the distributor housing and is retained with 2 screws. It is electrically connected to the distributor pick-up coil assembly without the use of a wiring harness between the ignition module and the pick-up coil assembly.

The TFI ignition system consists of a distributor, a TFI ignition module, E-Core ignition coil, ignition switch, battery, and primary and secondary wiring.

The distributor contains the following components: Pick-up coil assembly with internal teeth, distributor shaft, reluctor with external teeth (mounted on distributor shaft), TFI ignition module (mounted on outside of distributor housing), octane rod, rotor and distributor cap (with male terminals). *See Fig. 1.*

Vehicles equipped with the TFI-IV ignition system also use an E-Core ignition coil. The E-Core ignition coil is unlike any other Ford coil. It is encased in laminated plastic rather than being encased in an oil filled case, as most other coils are. This ignition coil has a very low primary resistance and is used without a ballast resistor in the electrical system. There are the usual primary connections on this coil.

Fig. 1: Exploded View of TFI-IV Distributor

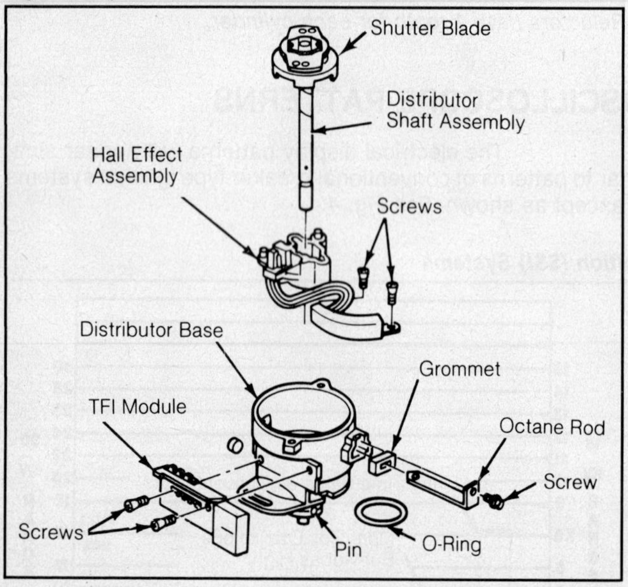

OPERATION

Each time the teeth on the reluctor pass the teeth on the pick-up coil, the magnetic field around the pick-up coil builds and collapses. As this occurs, a pulse is generated in the pick-up coil and sent to the TFI ignition module.The ignition module then turns the ignition coil primary circuit off and on causing a high voltage surge in the secondary which fires the spark plugs.

The ignition module sends the pulse signal to the electronic control assembly (ECA) for modifications of the timing signal. Then, a modified spark timing signal is returned to the ignition module. This signals the ignition module when to turn the ignition coil primary circuit on and off. This causes a high voltage surge in the secondary which fires the spark plugs.

After initial ignition timing has been set on TFI-IV models, adjustments for octane concerns can be made by installing the appropriate octane link in the distributor.

NOTE: Changing the timing by the use of octane rods can only be by Technical Service Bulletin authorization.

Fig. 2: TFI-IV Ignition System Wiring Diagram

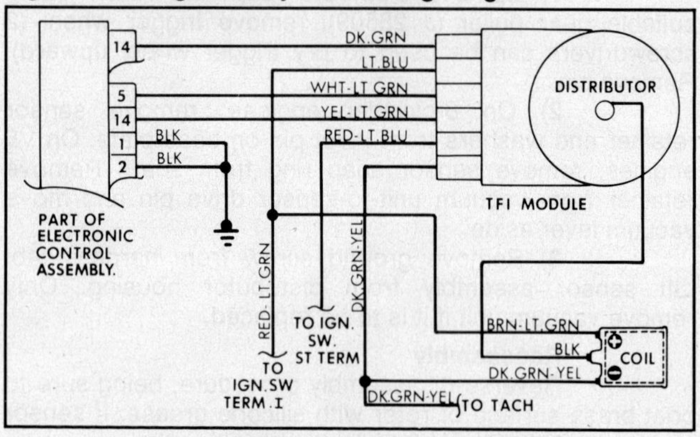

Also see chassis wiring in WIRING DIAGRAM Section.

TESTING

NOTE: When a test requires the inspection of a wiring harness, both a visual inspection and a continuity test should be performed. When making measurements of a wire or connector, it is a good idea to wiggle the wires while measuring.

Fig. 3: Modified Spark Plug and Spark Tester

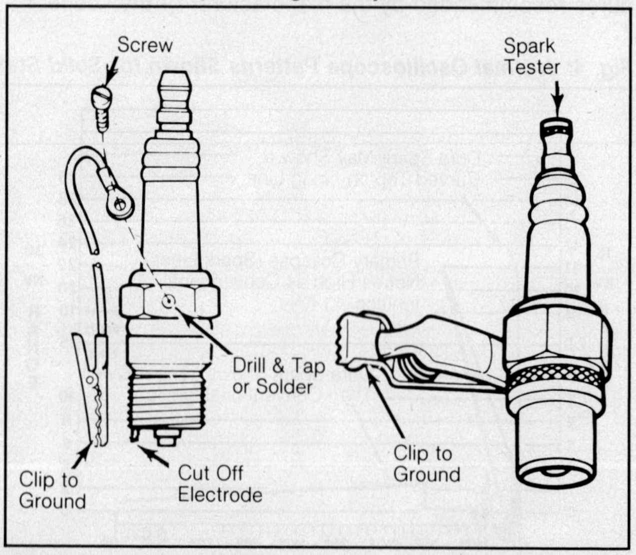

Modify spark plug by cutting off side electrode and installing spring clip.

TEST SPARK PLUG

Use either a spark tester tool or modify a spark plug (cut off side terminal and install spring clip for ground-

MOTORCRAFT TFI-IV IGNITION (Cont.)

ing plug housing) for use in testing ignition system. *See Fig. 3.*

IGNITION COIL SECONDARY VOLTAGE CHECK

1) Disconnect ignition coil secondary wire from distributor cap and attach spark tester to wire. Crank engine. Disconnect spark tester and reconnect secondary wire to distributor cap.

2) If sparks occurred at tester gap, inspect distributor cap and rotor for damage or carbon tracking. Crank engine to verify reluctor rotation. If no sparks occurred, measure resistance of ignition coil wire. Replace if greater than 5000 ohms per inch. Proceed to Ignition Coil Primary Circuit Switching Check.

IGNITION COIL PRIMARY CIRCUIT SWITCHING CHECK

NOTE: DO NOT allow straight pin to touch ground.

1) Insert a small straight pin in wire to ignition coil negative terminal about 1" from ignition module connector. Attach test light between straight pin and engine ground.

2) Crank engine. Remove test light and remove straight pin from wire. *See Fig. 4.* After test is completed, apply a small amount of silicone sealer to pin holes in wire.

Fig. 4: Testing Ignition Coil Primary Circuit Switching

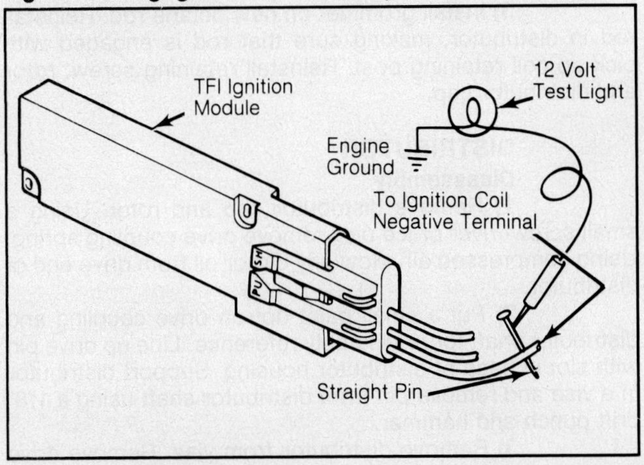

After test is completed, apply a small amount of silicone sealer to pin hole in wire.

3) If test light flashes, proceed to Ignition Coil Primary Resistance Check. If test light comes on but does not flash, proceed to Wiring Harness Check. If test light does not come on at all or is very dim, proceed to Wiring Harness Check.

IGNITION COIL PRIMARY RESISTANCE CHECK

1) With ignition switch in "OFF" position, disconnect ignition coil connector. Connect ohmmeter leads to positive and negative terminals of ignition coil. Measure resistance.

2) If resistance was .3-1 ohm, proceed to Ignition Coil Secondary Resistance Check. If resistance was less than .3 ohm or greater than 1 ohm, replace ignition coil.

IGNITION COIL SECONDARY RESISTANCE CHECK

1) With ignition switch in "OFF" position, disconnect ignition coil connector and secondary wire from ignition coil. Connect ohmmeter leads to ignition coil's negative and secondary terminals. Measure resistance.

2) If resistance was 8000-11,500 ohms, proceed to Wiring Harness Check. If resistance was less than 8000 ohms or greater than 11,500 ohms, replace ignition coil.

WIRING HARNESS CHECK

1) Disconnect ignition module connector from ignition module. Disconnect wire at "S" terminal of starter relay. Attach negative lead of voltmeter to distributor base and measure battery voltage at battery. With negative lead of voltmeter still connected to distributor base, check voltage in each of the following situations:

- Positive voltmeter lead connected to terminal 2 of ignition module connector with ignition switch in "RUN" position. *See Fig. 5.*
- Positive voltmeter lead connected to terminal 3 of ignition module connector with ignition switch in "RUN" position. *See Fig. 5.*
- Positive voltmeter lead connected to terminal 4 of ignition module connector with ignition switch in "START" position. *See Fig. 5.*

Fig. 5: Test Points for Wiring Harness Check

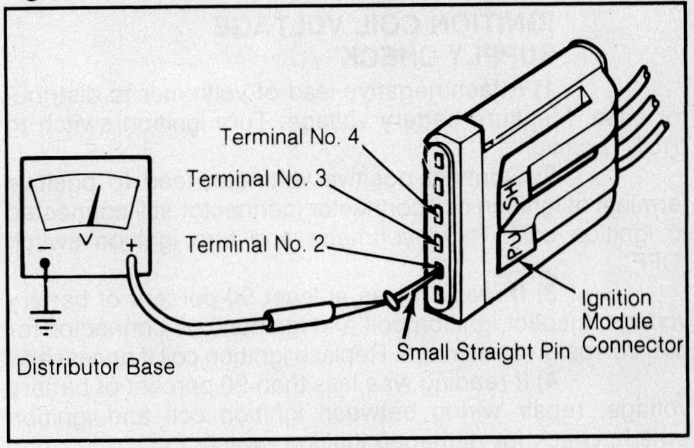

2) If reading was 90 percent of battery voltage or more, proceed to EEC Spark Signal Wire Continuity Check. If reading was less than 90 percent of battery voltage, inspect wiring harness and ignition switch.

EEC SPARK SIGNAL WIRE CONTINUITY CHECK

1) Disconnect connector from electronic control assembly (ECA). Disconnect ignition coil wire from distributor cap and connect spark tester to wire. Crank engine and check for spark.

2) If sparks did not occur, proceed to Distributor and Module Check. If sparks did occur, disconnect ignition module connector and check for continuity in Dark Green wire between ignition module connector and terminal of ECA.

3) If no continuity exists, repair wire or connectors as necessary. If continuity exists, proceed to testing procedures in FORD MOTOR CO. EEC-IV SYSTEM article in COMPUTERIZED ENGINE CONTROL section.

MOTORCRAFT TFI-IV IGNITION (Cont.)

DISTRIBUTOR & TFI-IV MODULE CHECK

1) Remove distributor from engine with secondary coil wire still connected to distributor. Remove module from distributor. Install new module on the distributor.

2) Connect jumper lead from the distributor base to a good engine ground. Connect vehicle harness to module. Connect spark tester to end of coil wire. Rotate distributor by hand and check for spark.

3) If sparks occur, reinstall distributor with new module. If no sparks occur, install new distributor using original module.

IGNITION COIL PRIMARY VOLTAGE CHECK

1) Attach negative lead of voltmeter to distributor base and measure battery voltage. Turn ignition switch to "RUN" position. Connect positive lead of voltmeter to coil connector negative terminal (connector still connected to coil). Measure voltage. Turn ignition switch to "OFF" position.

2) If reading was 90 percent of battery voltage or more, inspect wiring harness between ignition module and ignition coil negative terminal. If reading was less than 90 percent of battery voltage, inspect wiring harness between ignition module and ignition coil negative terminal and proceed to Ignition Coil Voltage Supply Check.

IGNITION COIL VOLTAGE SUPPLY CHECK

1) Attach negative lead of voltmeter to distributor base. Measure battery voltage. Turn ignition switch to "RUN" position.

2) Connect positive voltmeter lead to positive terminal of ignition coil connector (connector still connected to ignition coil). Read voltmeter and turn ignition switch "OFF".

3) If reading was at least 90 percent of battery voltage, inspect ignition coil and ignition coil connector for dirt, corrosion or damage. Replace ignition coil if necessary.

4) If reading was less than 90 percent of battery voltage, repair wiring between ignition coil and ignition switch, check for damaged ignition switch.

OVERHAUL

NOTE: **On models equipped with TFI-IV ignition systems, only the distributor cap, rotor, TFI module, distributor shaft O-ring and octane rod can be replaced. If any other component is found to be defective, the entire distributor assembly must be replaced.**

TFI IGNITION MODULE

Removal

1) Disconnect wiring harness connector from ignition module. Remove distributor cap with secondary wiring connected and position out of way. Remove distributor hold down bolt and remove distributor from engine. Engine may be equipped with security hold-down bolt for distributor. To remove bolt, use Distributor Hold-Down Wrench, tool T82L-12270-A.

2) With distributor on work bench, remove 2 screws retaining ignition module. Pull the right side of the ignition module down to the distributor mounting flange. Push ignition module back up and ignition module terminals will disengage from connector in distributor. Pull ignition module down and away from distributor to remove.

CAUTION: **Do not attempt to lift module from mounting surface prior to moving entire TFI module toward distributor flange. You will break the pins at the distributor/module connector.**

Installation

Reverse removal procedures and note the following: Coat the metal base plate of ignition module with about 1/32" of silicone grease before installing. Be sure that ignition module terminals are fully engaged in distributor connector. Tighten the 2 ignition module retaining screws to 9-16 INCH Lbs. (1.1-1.8 N.m).

OCTANE ROD

Removal & Installation

1) Remove distributor cap and rotor for visual access. Remove screw that retains octane rod to distributor housing.

2) Slide the octane rod and grommet out to a point at which the rod end can be disengaged from the pick-up coil retaining post.

3) Install grommet on new octane rod. Reinstall rod in distributor, making sure that rod is engaged with pick-up coil retaining post. Reinstall retaining screw, rotor and distributor cap.

DISTRIBUTOR

Disassembly

1) Remove distributor cap and rotor. Using a small screwdriver or ice pick remove drive coupling spring. Using compressed air, blow any dirt or oil from drive end of distributor.

2) Put a small paint dot on drive coupling and distributor shaft for reassembly reference. Line up drive pin with slot in base of distributor housing. Support distributor in a vise and remove pin from distributor shaft using a 1/8" drift punch and hammer.

3) Remove distributor from vise. Remove drive coupling from distributor shaft. Before removing shaft from disributor housing, remove any burrs from end of shaft. After all burrs have been removed, carefully remove shaft from distributor base.

4) Remove 2 screws retaining pick-up coil connector to housing. If TFI module has not been removed, remove pick-up coil connector from top of TFI module. Remove TFI module. Remove pick-up coil retainer from pick-up coil assembly. Remove pick-up coil assembly from distributor housing.

Reassembly

Reassemble distributor in reverse order of disassembly while noting the following: Be sure to align paint dots, made during disassembly, on housing and shaft. Apply a light coat of oil to distributor shaft before installing in housing. Be sure that connectors are securely connected to TFI module.

Charging Systems

TROUBLE SHOOTING

CONDITION	POSSIBLE CAUSE	CORRECTION
Vehicle Will Not Start	Dead battery	Check battery cells, alternator belt tension and alternator output
	Loose or corroded battery connections	Check that all charging system connections are tight and clean
	Ignition switch malfunction	Check and replace ignition switch as necessary
Alternator Light Stays ON With Engine Running	Loose or worn alternator drive belt	Check alternator drive belt tension and condition. See Belt Adjustment in TUNE-UP
	Loose alternator wiring connections	Check all charging system connections
	Short in alternator light wiring	See Indicator Warning Lights in SWITCHES, GAUGES & INSTRUMENT PANELS
	Defective alternator stator or diodes	See Bench Tests in ALTERNATORS & REGULATORS
	Defective regulator	See Regulator Check in ALTERNATORS & REGULATORS
Alternator Light Stays OFF With Ignition Switch ON	Blown fuse	See FUSES & CIRCUIT BREAKERS
	Defective alternator	See Testing in ALTERNATORS & REGULATORS
	Defective indicator light bulb or socket	See Indicator Warning Lights in SWITCHES, GAUGES & INSTRUMENT PANELS
Alternator Light Stays ON With Ignition Switch OFF	Short in alternator wiring	See On Vehicle Tests in ALTERNATORS & REGULATORS
	Defective rectifier bridge	See Bench Tests in ALTERNATORS & REGULATORS
Lights or Fuses Burn Out Frequently	Defective alternator wiring	See On Vehicle Tests in ALTERNATORS & REGULATORS
	Defective regulator	See Regulator Check in ALTERNATORS & REGULATORS
	Defective battery	Check and replace as necessary
Ammeter Gauge Shows Discharge	Loose or worn drive belt	Check alternator drive belt tension and condition. See Belt Adjustment in TUNE-UP
	Defective wiring	Check all wires and wire connections
	Defective alternator or regulator	See Bench Tests and On Vehicle Tests in ALTERNATORS & REGULATORS
	Defective ammeter, or improper ammeter wiring connections	See Testing in SWITCHES, GAUGES & INSTRUMENT PANELS
Noisy Alternator	Loose drive pulley	Tighten drive pulley attaching nut
	Loose mounting bolts	Tighten all alternator mounting bolts
	Worn or dirty bearings	See Bearing Replacement in ALTERNATORS & REGULATORS
	Defective diodes or stator	See Bench Tests in ALTERNATORS & REGULATORS
Battery Does Not Stay Charged	Loose or worn drive belt	Check alternator drive belt tension and condition. See Belt Adjustment in TUNE-UP
	Loose or corroded battery connections	Check that all charging system connections are tight and clean
	Loose alternator connections	Check all charging system connections
	Defective alternator or battery	See On Vehicle Tests and Bench Tests in ALTERNATORS & REGULATORS
	Defective alternator stator or diodes	See Bench Tests in ALTERNATORS & REGULATORS
	Add-on electrical accessories exceeding alternator capacity	Install larger capacity alternator
Battery Overcharged - Uses Too Much Water	Defective battery	Check alternator output and repair as necessary
	Defective alternator	See On Vehicle Tests and Bench Tests in ALTERNATORS & REGULATORS
	Excessive alternator voltage.	Check alternator output and repair as necessary

CHRYSLER CORP. ALTERNATORS

Dodge, Plymouth
(Exc. 2.6L Engine)

DESCRIPTION

The main components of the alternator are the stator, rotor, rectifiers, end shields and drive pulley. The built-in silicon rectifiers convert AC current (alternating current) into DC output current (direct current). The 114 amp model has 12 silicon rectifiers while all other models have 6 rectifiers.

IDENTIFICATION

CHRYSLER CORP. ALTERNATOR IDENTIFICATION

Tag Color Amp Output	Rated
Violet	41
Yellow	60
Brown	78
Yellow	114

SPECIFICATIONS

CHRYSLER CORP. SPECIFICATIONS

Rated Amp Output	[1] Minimum Amp Output
41	32@15 Volts
60	47@15 Volts
78	57@15 Volts
114	72@13 Volts

[1] – At 900 engine RPM for 114 amp alternator; 1250 RPM for all others. Voltage measured at the alternator.

OTHER SPECIFICATIONS

Rotation – Clockwise at drive end.
Field Coil Current Draw – 2.5-5.0 amps at 12 volts while rotating by hand.
Capacitor Capacity – .50 mfd. plus or minus 20%.

ON-VEHICLE TESTS

CHARGING CIRCUIT RESISTANCE

NOTE: **Before making test connections, disconnect negative battery cable at battery to avoid accidental shorting of charging or field circuits.**

1) Disconnect "BAT" lead at alternator. Connect a 0-150 ampere scale DC ammeter in series between alternator "BAT" terminal and disconnected "BAT" lead wire. Connect positive lead of voltmeter to disconnected "BAT" lead wire. Connect negative lead of voltmeter to positive post on battery.

2) Disconnect Green regulator field lead from alternator. Connect a jumper lead from alternator field terminal to ground. Connect a tachometer, and reattach battery ground cable. Connect a variable carbon pile to battery terminals (set in open or off position). *See Fig. 1.*

3) Start engine, and immediately reduce engine speed to idle. Adjust engine speed and set carbon pile to obtain 20 amps flowing in circuit. Voltmeter reading should not exceed 0.5 volts. If a high voltage drop is indicated, inspect, clean and tighten all connections in charging circuit.

NOTE: **If necessary, test voltage drop at each connection to locate connection with excessive resistance.**

Fig. 1: Charging Circuit Resistance Test Connections

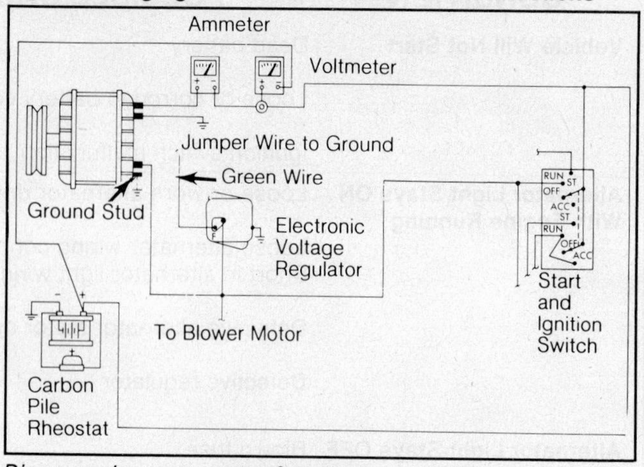

Diagram shows ammeter & voltmeter attaching points.

Fig. 2: Alternator Current Output Test Connections

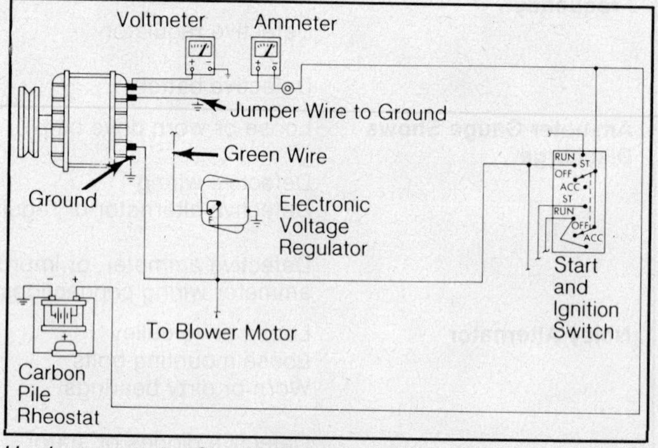

Hookup ammeter & voltmeter as shown.

CURRENT OUTPUT

1) Disconnect "BAT" lead at alternator. Connect a 0-150 ampere scale DC ammeter in series between alternator "BAT" terminal and disconnected "BAT" lead wire. Connect positive lead of voltmeter to "BAT" terminal. Connect negative lead of voltmeter to a good ground. Disconnect Green field wire to alternator. *See Fig. 2.*

2) Connect a jumper wire from alternator field terminal to ground. Connect a tachometer to engine and reconnect negative battery cable. Connect a variable carbon pile between battery terminals (set in open or off position). *See Fig. 2.* Start engine, and operate at idle speed immediately after starting.

3) Adjust engine speed and carbon pile until a speed of 900 RPM (114 amp) or 1250 RPM (all others) and a voltmeter reading of 13 volts (114 amp) or 15 volts (all others) is obtained. Do not allow voltage to exceed 16 volts. Observe ammeter. Current output should be within specifications. If output is less than specified, remove the alternator from the vehicle and proceed to BENCH TESTING.

CHRYSLER CORP. ALTERNATORS (Cont.)

BENCH TESTING

FIELD COIL CURRENT DRAW

1) Connect a jumper wire between 1 field terminal of alternator and negative terminal of a fully-charged battery. Connect ammeter positive lead to the other field terminal of alternator. Connect ammeter negative lead to battery positive terminal.

2) Connect a jumper wire from negative terminal of battery to alternator end shield. *See Fig. 3.* Slowly rotate alternator by hand. Observe ammeter reading. Field coil draw should be 2.5-5.0 amps at 12 volts.

3) A low coil draw is an indication of high resistance in field coil (brushes, slip rings or rotor coil). A high coil draw indicates possible shorted rotor coil or grounded rotor. No reading indicates an open rotor or defective brushes.

Fig. 3: Connections for Field Coil Current Draw Test

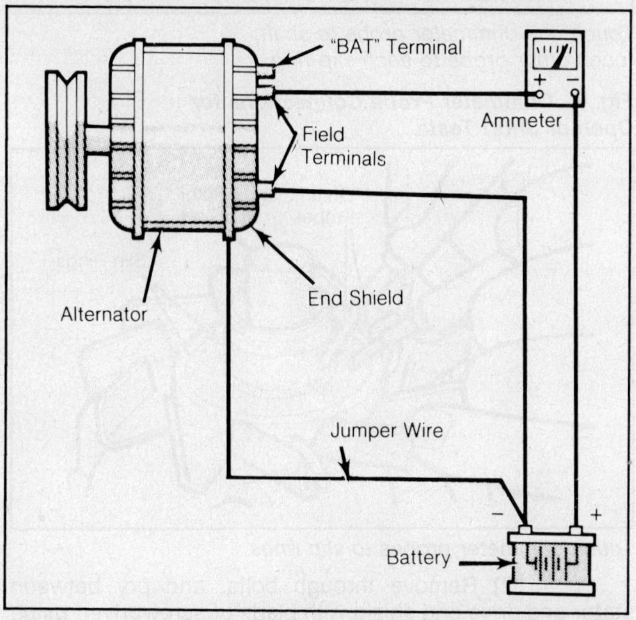

RECTIFIER (DIODE) TESTS

NOTE: **Do not break plastic cases of diodes, as they protect against corrosion. Always touch test probe to metal strap nearest diode. Rectifier diodes may be tested with a test lamp or tester C-3829A.**

Test Lamp Method

1) With rectifier end shield and stator assembly separated, test rectifiers with a 12V battery and suitable test lamp (No. 67 bulb, 4 candle power). Connect test lamp to battery positive terminal and to 1 test probe. Touch other test probe to negative battery terminal. Measure rectifier continuity with probes touching heat sink and rectifier top strap.

2) Now reverse probes. If lamp lights with current flow in one direction only, rectifier is satisfactory. If lamp lights with probes either way, rectifier is shorted. If lamp does not light at all, rectifier is open. Test each rectifier in both assemblies in same manner. Replace rectifier and heat sink assemblies, which have shorted or open rectifiers.

Tester C-3829A Method (Positive Rectifiers)

1) Remove alternator brushes and through bolts. Separate rectifier end housing and stator from drive end housing and rotor. With alternator on an insulated surface, connect test lead clip to alternator "BAT" output terminal. Plug tool into 110 volt AC power supply.

Fig. 4: View of Rectifier End Shield

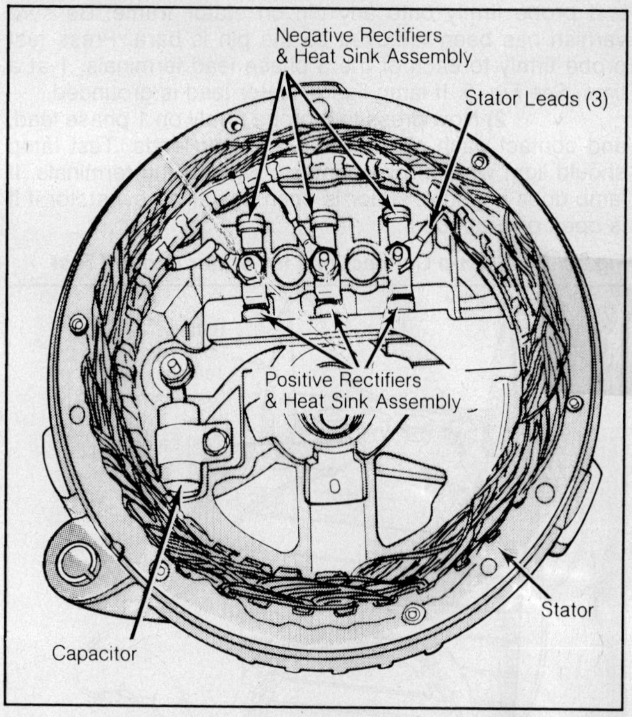

Note location of rectifiers and heat sink assemblies.

2) Touch the metal strap of each positive rectifier with test probe. Reading for satisfactory rectifiers will be 1 3/4 amperes or more and should be approximately the same for each rectifier. When 2 rectifiers are good and 1 is shorted, reading taken at good rectifiers will be low and reading at shorted rectifier will be zero.

3) Disconnect lead to rectifier reading zero, and retest. Reading of good rectifiers will now be within satisfactory range. When 1 rectifier is open, it will read approximately 1 ampere, while the 2 good rectifiers will read within satisfactory range.

Tester C-3829A Method (Negative Rectifiers)

1) Remove alternator brushes and through bolts. Separate rectifier end housing and stator from drive end housing and rotor. Connect test lead clip to rectifier end housing. Touch metal strap of each negative rectifier with test probe.

2) Test specifications and results will be approximately the same as for positive rectifiers, except meter will read on opposite side of scale. If a negative rectifier shows shorted condition, remove stator from rectifier end shield and retest. Stator winding could be grounded to stator laminations or rectifier end shield, indicating a shorted negative rectifier.

STATOR TEST

NOTE: **On 114 amp alternators, stator windings are "Delta" wound, and cannot be checked for opens and shorts with common shop equipment. If stator is not grounded, and all other components check correctly, suspect an open or a short in stator.**

CHRYSLER CORP. ALTERNATORS (Cont.)

1) Separate stator from both end shields. Press test probe firmly onto any pin on stator frame. Be sure varnish has been removed so the pin is bare. Press test probe firmly to each of the 3 phase lead terminals, 1 at a time. *See Fig. 5.* If lamp lights, stator lead is grounded.

2) Now press test probe firmly on 1 phase lead, and contact each of the other 2 stator leads. Test lamp should light when probe contacts each of the terminals. If lamp does not light, stator is open. Install a new stator if it is open or grounded.

Fig. 5: Test Lamp Connections for Stator Ground Test

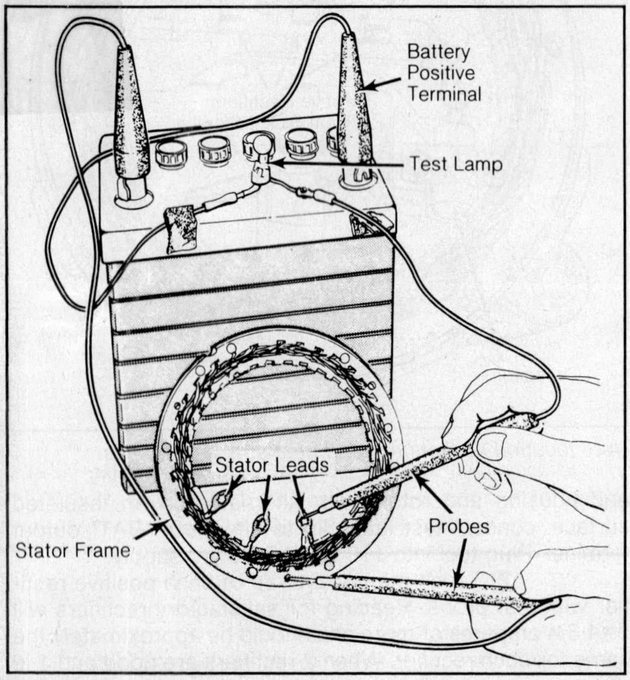

Touch test lamp probes to stator frame and stator leads.

ROTOR TEST

1) Test rotor for grounded, open or shorted field coils, using an ohmmeter. *See Figs. 6 and 7.* Test for grounds between each slip ring and rotor shaft. No continuity should exist.

2) Check for open field by connecting ohmmeter leads across slip rings. Normal resistance reading with rotor at room temperature is 1.7-2.1 ohms for 114 amp alternator and 1.5-2.0 ohms for all other models.

3) Readings between 2.5 and 3.0 ohms would result from rotors operating at high engine compartment temperatures. Readings above 3.5 ohms indicate high resistance, possibly requiring rotor replacement. If reading is below 1.7 ohms (114 amp alternator) or 1.5 ohms (all other models), the field coil is shorted.

OVERHAUL

DISASSEMBLY

1) Remove brush screws and insulating washers, and lift brush assemblies from end shield.

CAUTION: Stator is laminated. Do not burr stator or end shield.

Fig. 6: Ohmmeter Probe Connections for Rotor Ground Test

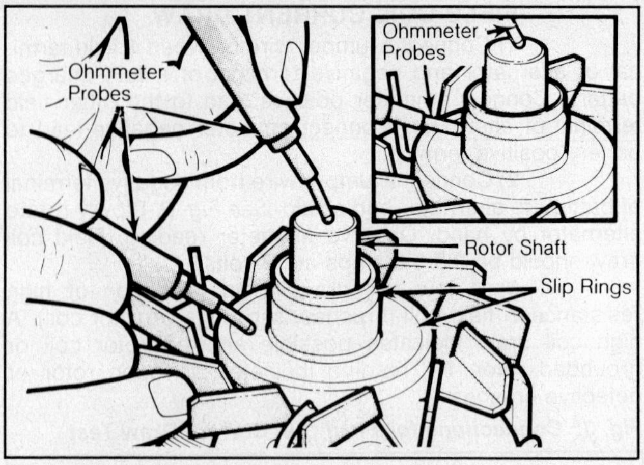

Touch one ohmmeter probe to shaft; touch other probe to each slip ring.

Fig. 7: Ohmmeter Probe Connections for Open or Short Tests

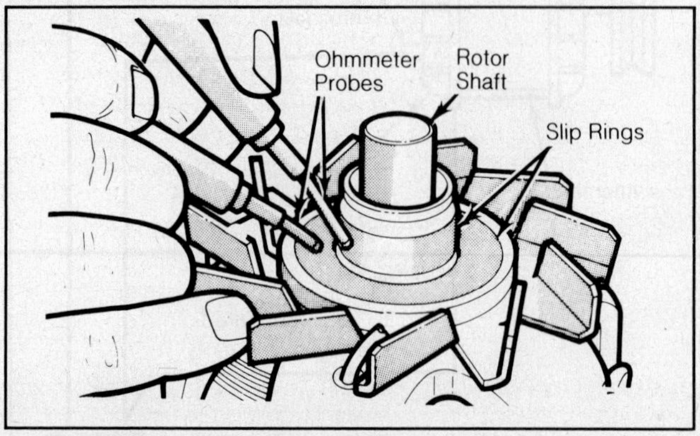

Touch ohmmeter probes to slip rings.

2) Remove through bolts, and pry between stator and drive end shield with blade of screwdriver, using slot provided. Carefully separate drive end shield, pulley and rotor assembly away from stator and rectifier end shield assembly. If negative heat sink diode straps are on top of positive heat sink straps, remove 4 hex head screws on negative rectifier and heat sink assembly. Remove heat sink assembly.

3) On all except 114 amp alternators, remove nut, washer and insulator from output ("BAT") terminal on outside of end shield. Turn end shield over, and remove capacitor, insulated washer and positive heat sink assembly. Remove insulator from "BAT" terminal hole.

4) On 114 amp alternators, reach inside end shield. Remove nut and insulator, attaching positive heat sink to end shield. Remove capacitor screw, capacitor and insulator.

5) From outside end shield, remove nut and insulator, attaching positive heat sink to end shield. Remove screws attaching negative heat sink to end shield. Remove positive and negative heat sink assemblies, noting location of insulators. Remove terminal block attaching screws and terminal block.

6) On all except 114 amp alternators, remove mica insulator from end shield and loosen 4 hex head screws on negative rectifier and heat sink assembly. Remove 2 outer screws and remove heat sink assembly.

Fig. 8: Installing Drive End Shield Bearing

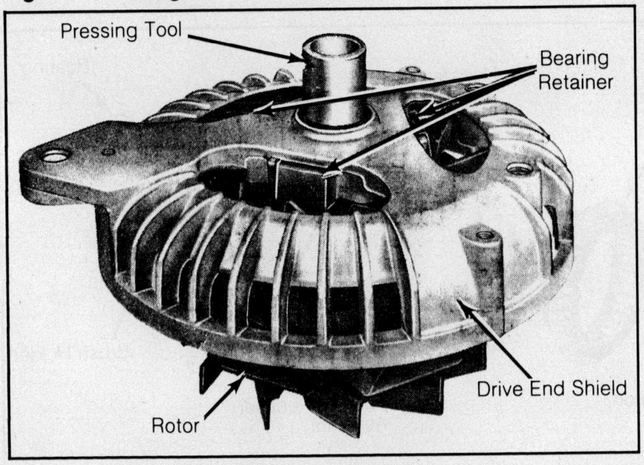

Support rotor shaft base, while pressing bearing into end shield.

7) Using a Puller (C-4068 or C-4333; C-4467 on 114 amp models), remove drive pulley from shaft. Remove screws attaching bearing retainer to drive end shield on 114 amp alternators. Separate bearing retainer from end shield. Support end shield and tap rotor shaft with plastic hammer to separate rotor from end shield.

8) Using puller, remove drive end ball bearing. If needle roller bearing in rectifier end shield must be replaced, it can be pressed out of end shield using an End Shield Support (C-3925) and Press Adapter (C-3770A).

SLIP RING REPLACEMENT

NOTE: Slip rings are not serviced as a separate item, only as part of the rotor assembly.

REASSEMBLY

ALL EXCEPT 114 AMP ALTERNATOR

1) Place grease retainer on rotor shaft, and press retainer onto shaft with Installer (C-3921). Press until grease retainer bottoms on rotor shaft. Position rectifier end shield bearing on base of Needle Bearing Installer (C-4201-1). Place end shield on top of bearing so it is properly aligned. With top part of Bearing Press (C-4201-2) placed on end shield, press into place until it bottoms.

NOTE: New bearings are pre-lubricated and should require no additional lubrication.

2) Insert drive end bearing in drive end shield. Install retainer plate to hold bearing in place. A metal spacer is supplied with replacement rotors and ball bearings (but is not a part of original alternator assembly). Place spacer on pulley end of rotor shaft first. Position bearing and drive end shield on rotor shaft. Support base of rotor shaft. Press bearing end shield into position on rotor shaft with an arbor press and Adapter (C-3858).

CAUTION: Ensure bearing is installed squarely to avoid damage to bearing and rotor shaft.

3) Install pulley on rotor shaft. Shaft of rotor must be supported, so all pressing force is on pulley hub and rotor shaft, (not on bearings). Do not hammer pulley on or apply more than 6800 lbs. (3084 kg).

4) If removed, install output terminal stud and insulator through end shield. Be sure mica insulators are in place and undamaged. Install positive heat sink assembly over studs. Guide rectifier straps over studs on terminal block. Install capacitor. Slide negative rectifier and heat sink assembly into place. Position straps and install screws.

5) Position stator over rectifier end shield and install winding terminals on terminal block. Press stator pins into each end shield. Route leads so they cannot contact rotor or sharp edge of negative heat sink. Position rotor and drive end shield over stator and rectifier end shield. Install through bolts. Compress both ends, and tighten through bolts evenly.

6) Install field brushes in insulated holders. Position vertical and horizontal field brushes properly in rectifier end shield. Place an insulating washer on each field brush terminal. Install lock washers. Be sure brushes are not grounded. Rotate pulley slowly by hand to ensure rotor blades do not hit stator leads.

114 AMP ALTERNATOR ONLY

1) Position rectifier end shield bearing on base of Support Tool (C-4330-1-3). Place end shield on top of bearing, so that it is properly aligned. With Bearing Installer (C-4330-2) placed on end shield, press into place until end shield touches base of press.

NOTE: New bearings are prelubricated and require no additional lubrication.

2) Insert drive end bearing in end shield. Position retainer, and tighten mounting screws, ensuring rotor spacer is in position. Place bearing and drive end shield on rotor shaft. Press end shield into position with arbor press and Adapter (C-3858).

3) Install pulley on rotor shaft. Support shaft so that pressing force is on pulley hub. Press pulley on shaft until it contacts inner race of drive end bearing. Do not hammer pulley on or exceed 6800 lbs. (3084 kg) of force. Position insulator and capacitor on positive heat sink mounting stub, and tighten attaching screw.

4) Position terminal block in rectifier end shield, and tighten screws. Position negative heat sink in end shield, ensuring that metal straps are placed over studs on terminal block. Install mounting screws and tighten.

5) Install insulator on positive heat sink stud, and place assembly into end shield. Ensure metal straps are properly positioned over studs on terminal block. From inside end shield, install insulator on positive heat sink stud and tighten nut.

6) From outside of end shield, install insulator on stud, and tighten mounting bolt. Position stator over end shield, and install terminals on terminal block. Route leads so they cannot contact rotor or sharp edges of negative heat sink.

7) Position rotor and drive end shield over end shield assembly, and align through bolts. Compress stator and both end shields manually. Install and tighten through bolts. Install field brushes in brush holder, with long terminal on bottom and short terminal on top. Install insulators and mounting screw.

8) Position brush holder assembly to end shield, making sure it is properly seated, and tighten mounting screw. Rotate pulley by hand to ensure rotor poles do not hit stator winding leads.

CHRYSLER CORP. ALTERNATORS (Cont.)

Fig. 9: Exploded View of Typical Chrysler Corp. Alternator

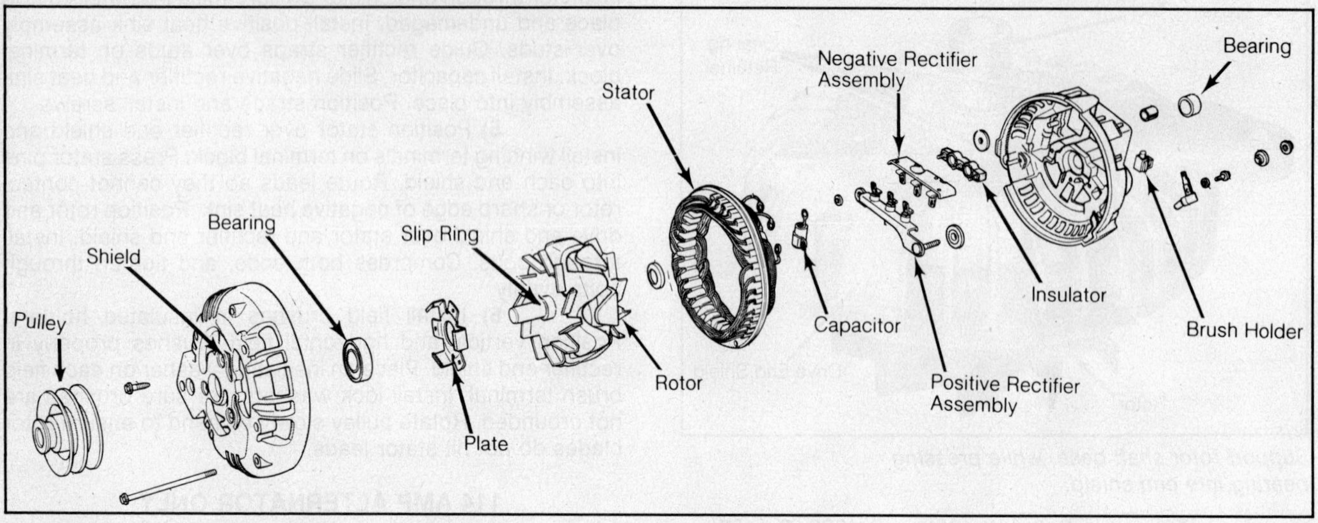

TIGHTENING SPECIFICATIONS

Application	INCH Lbs. (N.m)
Capacitor Bracket Screws	30-40 (3.4-4.5)
End Bearing Mount Screws	
114 Amp	19-29 (2.1-3.3)
Field Brush Screws	
All Exc. 114 Amp	15-35 (1.7-4.0)
114 Amp	30-40 (3.4-4.5)
Negative Heat Sink Mount Screw	
All Exc. 114 Amp	19-29 (2.1-3.3)
114 Amp	30-40 (3.4-4.5)
Plastic Insulator Nut	30-50 (3.4-5.6)
Positive Heat Sink Stud Nut	20-30 (2.3-3.4)
Terminal Block Mount Screws	
114 Amp Only	30-40 (3.4-4.5)
Through Bolts	
All Exc. 114 Amp	25-55 (2.8-6.2)
114 Amp	40-60 (4.5-6.8)
Winding Terminal Nut	11-17 (1.2-1.9)

CHRYSLER CORP. ELECTRONIC REGULATOR

Dodge, Plymouth
(Exc. 2.6L Engine)

DESCRIPTION

The electronic voltage regulator regulates electrical system voltage by limiting voltage generated by alternator. This is accomplished by controlling amount of current that is allowed to pass through alternator field winding. Regulator has no moving parts and requires no adjustment after it is set at factory.

Unit contains several semiconductor components, transistors and diodes plus some resistors and a capacitor. A large transistor is placed in series with alternator field winding and a control circuit which senses system voltage and turns transistor on and off as required.

As alternator speed and electrical system load conditions change, control circuit is turning transistor on and off many times per second most of the time engine is in operation.

The only time the transistor is not turning on and off rapidly is during low engine speed operation when high electrical loads are present. This requires the alternator field to be in the "ON" state continuously. Electronic regulator control circuit can also vary the regulated system voltage up or down as temperatures change.

TESTING

NOTE: **Battery specific gravity should be above 1.220 for a properly regulated voltage check. Charge battery or use a good test battery before testing regulator.**

NOTE: **Where Tester (C-4133) is available, use an Adapter (C-4341) to switch circuit of regulator to be tested. The adapter has a 3-position switch to select regulator part number or regulator installed. Follow manufacturer's test procedure.**

1) Connect positive lead of a voltmeter to positive post on battery. Connect negative lead of voltmeter to a good ground. Start and run vehicle at 1250 RPM with all lights and accessories turned off. Check voltmeter reading. Regulator is working properly if voltage readings are within specifications.

Voltage Regulator Specifications

Ambient Temperature [1]	Voltage Range
20°F (29°C)	14.9-15.9
80°F (27°C)	13.9-14.6
140°F(60°C)	13.3-13.9
Above 140°F (60°C)	Less than 13.6

1 – Ambient temperature is measured " (6.35 mm) from regulator.

2) If voltage is not within limits or is fluctuating, check that regulator has a good ground. With engine off, disconnect regulator terminals. Turn ignition switch to "ON" position. Do not start engine.

3) Battery voltage should be present at both regulator harness terminals. If so, replace regulator and repeat test.

ADJUSTMENT

The Electronic Voltage Regulator cannot be adjusted. If specifications are not obtained and investigation has shown the rest of electrical system to be satisfactory, then regulator must be replaced.

Fig. 1: Chrysler Corp. Test Connections for Voltage Regulator Test

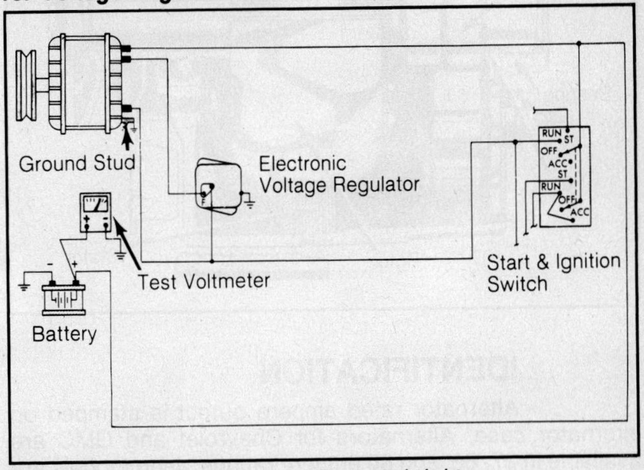

Be sure all connections are clean and tight.

Alternators & Regulators

DELCO-REMY WITH INTEGRAL REGULATOR

Chevrolet, GMC, Jeep

DESCRIPTION

Delco 10SI, 12SI, 15SI and 27SI integral regulator alternators feature a solid state regulator mounted inside alternator. These alternators are available with different outputs at idle and different maximum outputs.

Delcotrons consist of 2 separate housings (end frame assemblies), a rotor, stator, brushes, slip rings and diodes. Rotor is supported in drive end frames by ball bearings and in slip ring end frame by roller bearings. Bearings contain enough lubrication to eliminate need for periodic lubrication.

Fig. 1: Cutaway View Showing Internal Components of Delcotron Integral Regulator Alternator

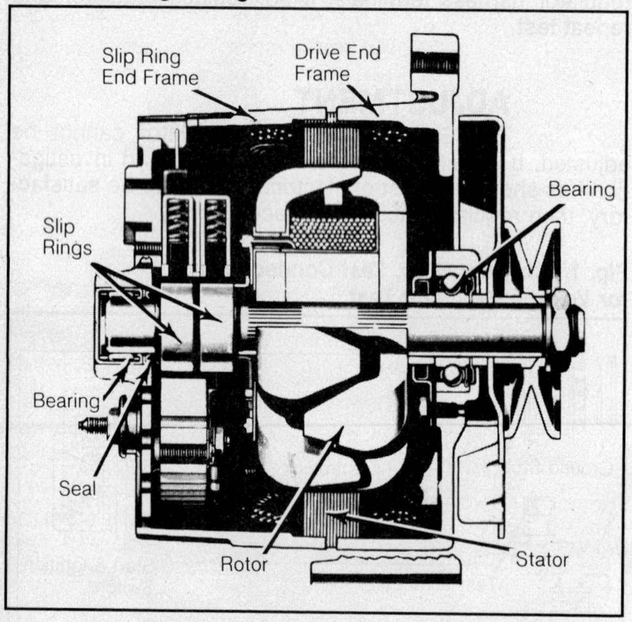

IDENTIFICATION

Alternator rated ampere output is stamped on alternator case. Alternators for Chevrolet and GMC are available in 37, 66, and 80 ampere ratings. Jeep models are rated at 42, 56, 78 and 85 amperes.

OPERATION

Two brushes carry current through slip rings to and from field coil mounted on rotor. Stator windings are assembled on the inside of a laminated core that forms part of the alternator frame.

A rectifier bridge, connected to stator windings, contains 6 diodes (3 positives and 3 negatives) molded into an assembly. This rectifier bridge changes stator A.C. voltage into D.C. voltage, which appears at output terminal.

The blocking action of the diodes prevents battery discharge back through alternator. Because of the blocking action, the need for a cut-out relay is eliminated. Alternator field current is supplied through a diode trio which is also connected to stator windings.

A capacitor is mounted in end frame, protecting rectifier bridge and diodes from high voltage and suppressing radio interference noise. Some vehicles are equipped with ammeters, others with voltmeters.

ADJUSTMENT

No periodic adjustments or maintenance of any kind is required on alternator assembly. Regulator voltage is preset, and no adjustment is possible.

CAUTION: **Do not attempt to polarize alternator. Do not short or ground any terminals except as instructed. Never operate alternator with battery out of circuit or output terminal open. Alternator and battery must share the same ground polarity.**

TESTING

NOTE: **Before making electrical checks, visually inspect all terminals for clean and tight connections. Check alternator mounting bolts and drive belt tension. Do not ground No. 2 lead wire. Battery must be in good condition to test charging system.**

UNDERCHARGED BATTERY

1) With ignition switch "ON", connect a voltmeter from alternator "BAT" terminal to ground, then from No. 1 terminal to ground, and last, No. 2 terminal to ground. A zero reading indicates an open between connection and battery.

2) Opens in the No. 2 lead may be between terminals at the crimp between harness wire and terminal, or in wire. *See Fig. 2.*

NOTE: **If preceding test is satisfactory, continue to next step.**

3) Disconnect battery ground cable. Connect an ammeter in circuit at "BAT" terminal of alternator.

4) Reconnect battery ground cable. Turn on all available accessories. Connect a carbon pile across battery. Operate engine at 2000 RPM and adjust carbon pile as required to obtain maximum current output.

5) If ampere output is within 10 amps of rated output as stamped on alternator case, alternator is good.

6) If output is not within 10 amps of rated output, ground field winding by inserting a screwdriver into test hole. *See Fig. 2.*

CAUTION: **Tab is within 3/4" (19 mm) of casting surface. Do not force screwdriver deeper than 1" (25 mm) into end frame. If test hole is not accessible, proceed to TESTING (ON BENCH) as described under OVERHAUL.**

7) Operate engine at moderate speed as required and adjust carbon pile for maximum output.

8) If output is now within 10 amps of rated output with fields grounded, regulator is defective and requires replacement.

9) If output is still not within 10 amps of rated output, check field winding, diode trio, rectifier bridge, and stator.

OVERCHARGED BATTERY

Connect a voltmeter from alternator terminal No. 2 to ground. If reading is zero, No. 2 lead circuit is open. If battery and No. 2 lead circuit check out good, alternator will have to be disassembled for further checks. *See Overhaul.*

DELCO-REMY WITH INTEGRAL REGULATOR (Cont.)

Fig. 2: Identification of Delcotron Terminal Locations

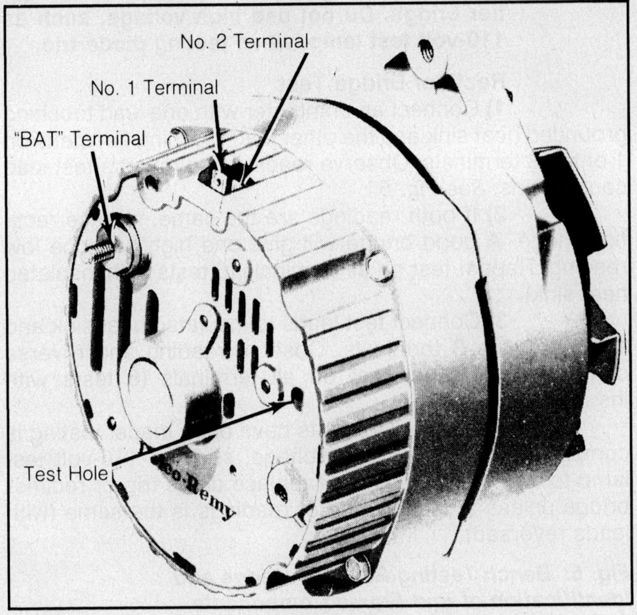

Visually inspect all terminals for clean, tight connections.

OVERHAUL

DISASSEMBLY

1) Scribe marks on housings for reassembly reference. Remove through bolts connecting housings. Separate front and rear housings by prying apart with screwdriver.

2) Place a piece of tape over slip ring end frame bearing to prevent entry of dirt. At this point brushes may drop onto rotor shaft and become contaminated with bearing lubricant. Clean brushes as soon as possible with a cleaner (acetone) to keep them from becoming grease soaked.

3) Place rotor in vise and tighten vise only enough to permit removal of shaft nut. Remove shaft nut, washer, pulley, fan and collar. Separate front housing from rotor shaft. Remove 3 stator lead attaching nuts and remove stator leads from bridge terminal.

4) Separate stator from rear housing. Remove diode trio lead clip attaching screw, and remove diode trio. Remove capacitor attaching screw and remove capacitor lead from bridge rectifier.

5) Remove bridge rectifier and battery terminal attaching screws and remove bridge rectifier. Remove 2 brush holder screws and 1 diode trio lead strap screw. Remove brush holder and brushes. Note location of brushes for reassembly.

6) Remove voltage regulator. Remove front bearing retaining plate screws. Press front bearing out of housing with collar. Press out rear bearing from housing by inserting collar inside housing and pressing bearing toward the outside.

INSPECTION

Wash all metal parts except bearings, stator and rotor. Inspect rotor slip rings. They may be cleaned with 400 grain polishing cloth, while rotor is being rotated. Slip rings may be lathe turned to .002" (.051 mm) maximum indicator reading.

Slip rings are not replaceable. Excessive damage will reguire rotor replacement. Inspect brushes for wear, replacing them if more than 50% worn.

TESTING (ON BENCH)

Rotor Field Winding Test

1) Check rotor for grounds or an open circuit, using a 110-volt test lamp or an ohmmeter. *See Fig. 3.* To check for grounds, connect ohmmeter leads to shaft and slip ring (each ring in turn). No continuity should exist.

2) To test for open field, connect ohmmeter leads to each slip ring. Continuity should be indicated.

3) To test for shorts, connect a 12-volt battery and ammeter in series with both slip rings. Current draw is used for this test.

4) Resistance should be 2.5-3.0 ohms. Excessive amperage draw or low resistance indicates shorted windings. If rotor tests okay, but alternator output is low, continue with tests.

Fig. 3: Bench Testing Rotor For Opens or Grounds Using an Ohmmeter

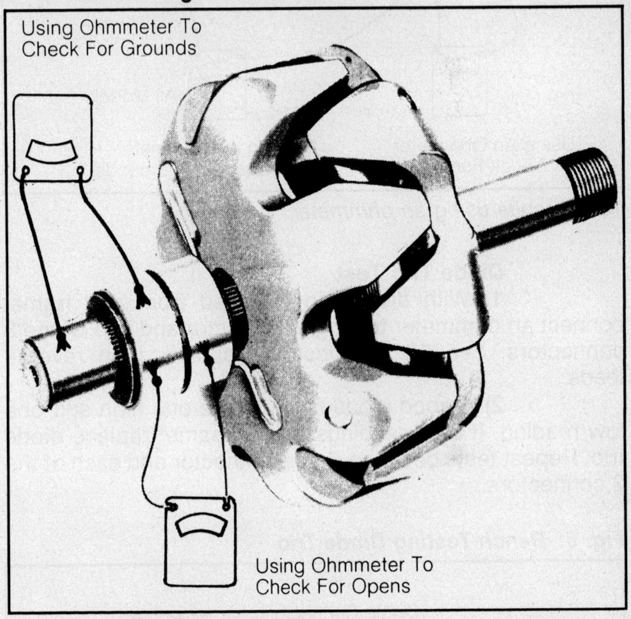

Check rotors using a 110-volt test lamp or an ohmmeter.

Stator Ground Test

1) Connect leads of 110-volt test lamp or an ohmmeter (x1000 scale) to any stator lead and to stator frame. Ohmmeter reading should be infinite. *See Fig. 4.*

2) If test lamp lights or if resistance is low, windings are grounded. Replace stator assembly.

NOTE: **Because of the delta stator winding design, 15 SI and 27 SI cannot be checked for open circuit.**

Stator Open Test

1) Connect a 110-volt test lamp or an ohmmeter (x1 scale) with leads touching any 2 stator leads. Make checks between 2 different sets of stator leads.

2) Readings should be equal. If test lamp does not light or if resistance is high, windings are open. *See Fig. 4.*

NOTE: **Delta windings on 15SI and 27SI model alternators cannot be checked for open with an ohmmeter.**

DELCO-REMY WITH INTEGRAL REGULATOR (Cont.)

Fig. 4: Bench Testing Stator for Open or Grounded Circuits

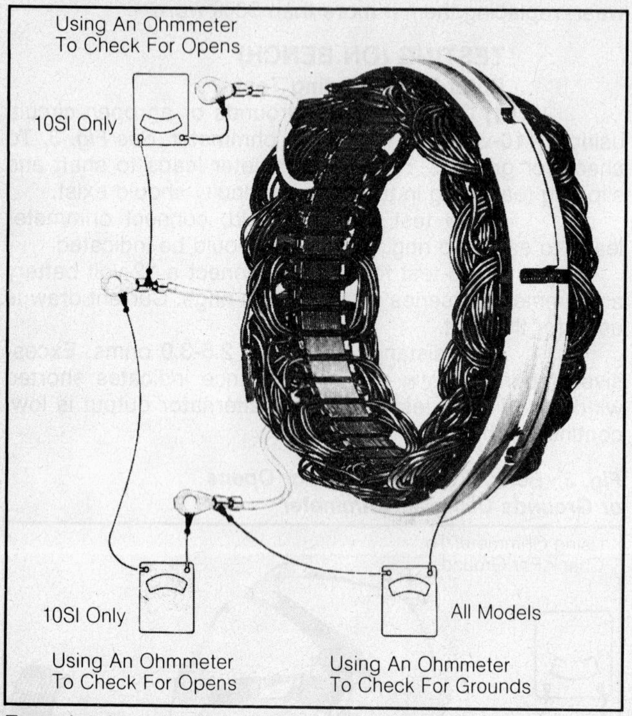

Test circuits using an ohmmeter.

Diode Trio Test

1) With diode trio removed from end frame, connect an ohmmeter to single connector and to 1 of the 3 connectors. *See Fig. 5.* Observe reading, then reverse leads.

2) A good diode trio will give one high and one low reading. If both readings are the same, replace diode trio. Repeat tests between single connector and each of the 2 connectors.

Fig. 5: Bench Testing Diode Trio

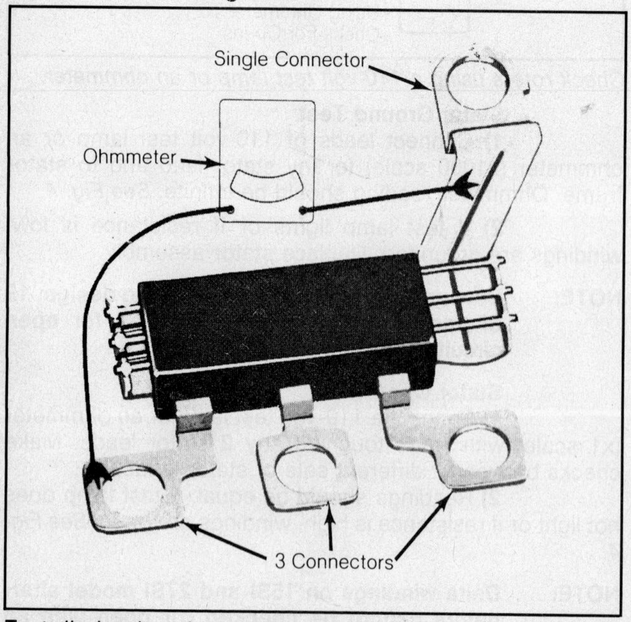

Test diode trio using an Ohmmeter

NOTE: Before replacing diode trio, also check rectifier bridge. Do not use high voltage, such as 110-volt test lamp, when testing diode trio.

Rectifier Bridge Test

1) Connect an ohmmeter with one lead touching grounded heat sink and the other lead touching flat metal on 1 of the 3 terminals. Observe reading and reverse test lead connections. *See Fig. 6.*

2) If both readings are the same, replace rectifier bridge. A good bridge will give one high and one low reading. Repeat test on all terminals (6 tests with insulated heat sink).

3) Connect test leads to insulated heat sink and 1 edge of the 3 terminals. Observe reading and reverse connections. Repeat test on all terminals (6 tests with insulated heat sink).

4) When all 12 tests have been made, testing is complete. Do not use high voltage, such as 110-volt test lamp to check bridge. Do not replace diode trio or rectifier bridge unless at least 1 pair of readings is the same (with leads reversed).

Fig. 6: Bench Testing Rectifier Bridge and Identification of End Frame Components

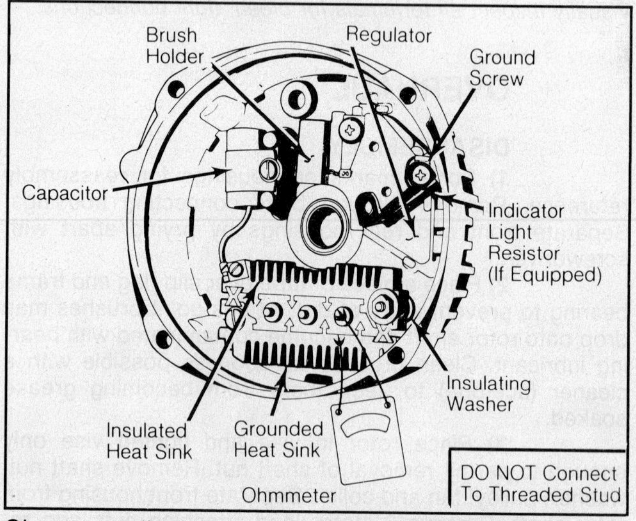

Observe reading and reverse test lead connections.

REASSEMBLY

1) On early production 15SI and 27SI models, fill cavity between retainer plate and bearing 1/4 full with lubricant (Delco-Remy 1948791 or equivalent). Series 10SI, 12SI and late production 15SI and 27SI use a sealed bearing and no lubrication is required.

2) Assemble bearing and slinger (flat washer on some models) in front housing. Press bearing in with collar that fits over outer race. If bearing retainer plate felt seal is hardened, replace retainer plate.

3) Install retainer plate and screws. Press rotor into end frame. Assemble collar, fan, pulley, washer and nut. Torque nut to 40-60 ft. lbs. (54-82 N.m).

4) If rear bearing was removed, support inside of rear housing with hollow cylinder. On 10SI and 27SI models, place flat plate over bearing. Press bearing into housing from outside, until bearing is flush with end frame.

5) On 15SI models, use thin-wall tube in space between grease cup and housing to push bearing in until flush with housing. Oil lip of replacement bearing seal, and press seal in with lip away from bearing.

DELCO-REMY WITH INTEGRAL REGULATOR (Cont.)

Fig. 7: Exploded View of Delcotron Alternator Model 10SI

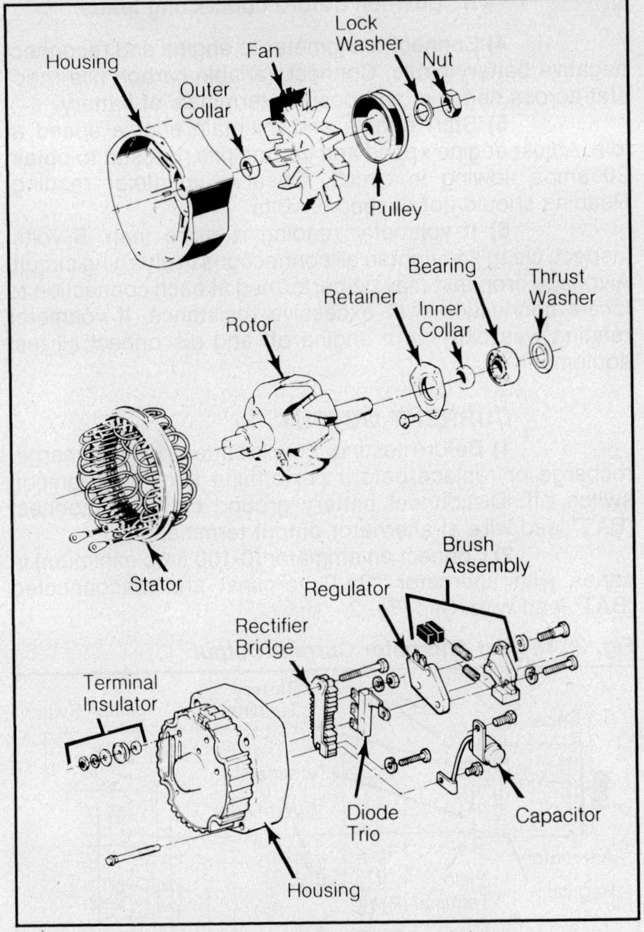

Alternator is used on Chevrolet, GMC and Jeep.

6) Install springs and brushes in brush holder. Install wooden toothpick in hole at bottom of holder to retain brushes. Install voltage regulator. Attach brush holder into rear housing, noting stack-up of parts. Allow toothpick to protrude through hole in rear housing

7) Install diode trio lead strap attaching screw and washer. Tighten brush holder screws. Position bridge rectifier on rear housing with insulator between heat sink and rear housing.

8) Install bridge rectifier and battery terminal screws. Connect capacitor lead to bridge rectifier. Position diode trio on end housing. Install diode trio lead clip screw, making sure insulating washer is over top of diode connector.

9) Install stator on rear housing. Attach stator leads to bridge rectifier terminals. Remove tape covering bearing and join front and rear housings with scribe marks aligned. Install through bolts and tighten. Remove toothpick from brush holder assembly.

ALTERNATOR OUTPUT

Stamped Amperage	Amperage @ 14V	Rated Output (Engine RPM)
37	22	2000
42	25	2000
56	30	2000
66	32	2000
78	55	2000
85	1	1

1 – Information not available from manufacturer. Police option.

MITSUBISHI INTERNAL REGULATOR/ALTERNATOR

Chrysler Corp. with 2.6L Engines

DESCRIPTION

The charging system consists of an alternator, internal voltage regulator, battery and connecting wires. The alternator has fifteen built-in rectifiers, that convert A.C. current into D.C. current. Current at output terminal is D.C. The alternator consists of a rotor, stator, rectifiers, end shields and drive pulley.

An electronic voltage regulator is built into interior of alternator rear housing. The regulator (using integrated circuits) limits output voltage generated by alternator, by controlling amount of current allowed to pass through alternator field winding. It also regulates system voltage in response to changes in ambient temperature. This regulator has no moving parts and requires no adjustments after initial setting at factory.

ON VEHICLE TESTS

NOTE: **Before starting any tests on charging system, ensure that battery is fully charged and terminals are clean. If battery will not charge fully, replace battery.**

CHARGING CIRCUIT RESISTANCE

1) Check battery for full charge, recharge or replace before performing test. Disconnect negative battery cable from battery. Disconnect "BAT" lead at alternator output terminal. *See Fig. 1.*

Fig. 1: Testing Charging Circuit Resistance

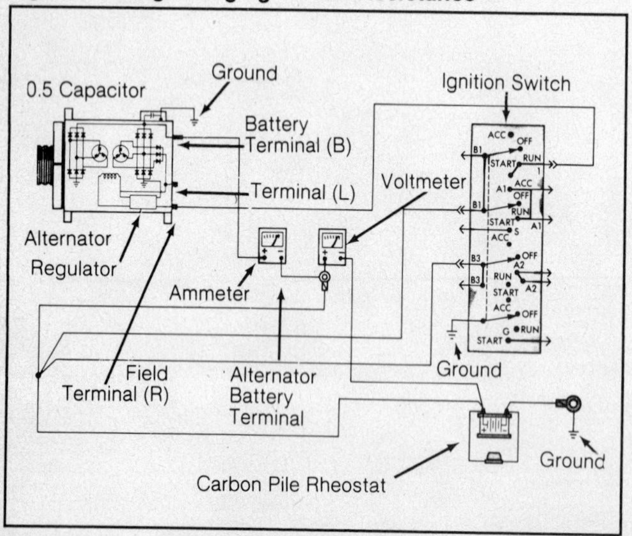

Disconnect negative battery cable before connecting test equipment.

2) Connect D.C. ammeter, set on 0-100 amp scale, in series between alternator "BAT" terminal and disconnected "BAT" lead wire. Connect ammeter positive lead to "BAT" terminal and negative lead to "BAT" lead.

3) Connect positive lead of voltmeter (range 0-18 volts minimum) to "BAT" lead wire. Connect negative voltmeter lead to positive battery post.

NOTE: **Be sure carbon pile rheostat is in "Open" or "Off" position before connecting leads.**

4) Connect tachometer to engine and reconnect negative battery cable. Connect variable carbon pile rheostat across negative and positive terminals of battery.

5) Start engine and maintain engine speed at idle. Adjust engine speed and carbon pile rheostat to obtain 20 amps flowing in circuit. Observe voltmeter reading. Reading should not exceed .5 volts.

6) If voltmeter reading is more than .5 volts, inspect, clean and tighten all connections in charging circuit. A voltage drop test may be performed at each connection to locate connection with excessive resistance. If voltmeter reading was okay, turn engine off and disconnect all test equipment.

CURRENT OUTPUT

1) Before testing, check battery for full charge, recharge or replace before performing test. Turn ignition switch off. Disconnect battery ground cable. Disconnect "BAT" lead wire at alternator output terminal.

2) Connect an ammeter (0-100 amp minimum) in series with alternator "BAT" terminal and disconnected "BAT" lead wire. *See Fig. 2.*

Fig. 2: Testing Alternator Current Output

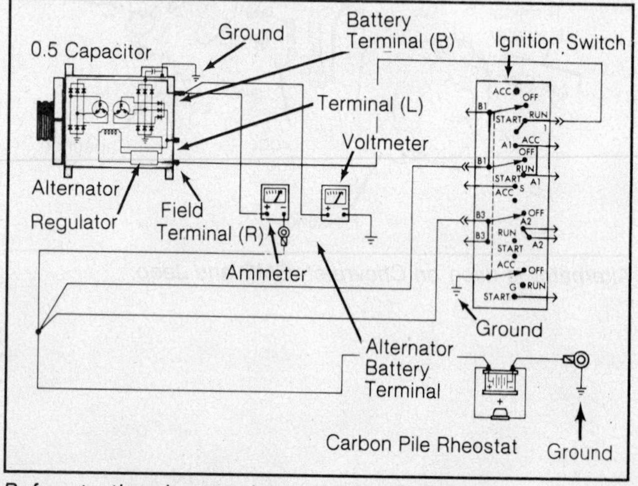

Before testing, be sure battery has full charge.

3) Connect positive lead to disconnected "BAT" terminal and negative lead to disconnected "BAT" lead. Connect positive lead of voltmeter (range 0-18 volts minimum) to "BAT" terminal of alternator. Connect negative lead to ground. Connect tachometer and reconnect battery ground cable.

NOTE: **Be sure carbon pile rheostat is in "Open" or "Off" position before connecting leads.**

4) Connect variable carbon pile rheostat between battery positive and negative terminals. Start engine and operate at idle speed.

CAUTION: **Do not permit voltage to exceed 16 volts.**

5) Adjust carbon pile rheostat and accelerate engine to specified speed. Measure current output. Compare ammeter readings with specifications. If reading is less than specified, remove alternator for bench testing. If test shows good, remove all test equipment.

MITSUBISHI INTERNAL REGULATOR/ALTERNATOR (Cont.)

NOTE: Battery specific gravity should be above 1.220 for a proper regulated voltage check. Charge battery or use a good test battery before testing regulator. DO NOT leave uncharged battery in circuit.

ELECTRONIC VOLTAGE REGULATOR

1) Check battery for full charge. Turn ignition switch off. Disconnect cable from battery terminal of alternator and connect ammeter between disconnected lead and battery terminal on alternator. *See Fig. 3.*

Fig. 3: Testing Voltage Regulator

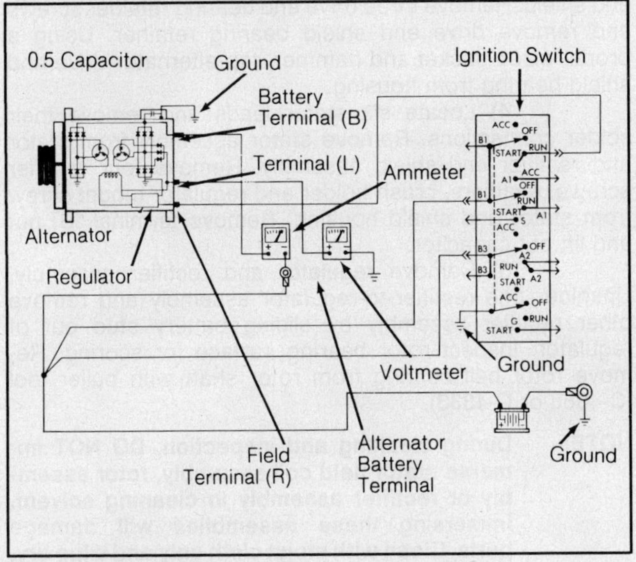

Check that voltage readings are in accordance with voltage chart.

2) Connect voltmeter between terminal "L" of alternator and good ground. Be sure voltmeter reading is zero. If pointer of voltmeter deflects (voltage is present), defective alternator or wiring is suspected.

3) Turn ignition switch on (DO NOT start engine). Voltmeter reading should be below battery voltage, approximately 1 volt or less. If any higher, defective alternator is suspected. Connect tachometer to engine. With ammeter terminals short circuited, start engine.

CAUTION: Be sure no starting current is applied to ammeter when engine is started.

4) Remove short circuit across ammeter terminals and increase engine speed to approximately 2000-3000 RPM. Check ammeter reading. If reading is 10 amps or less, take voltmeter reading without changing engine speed. This reading is charging voltage.

NOTE: The electronic voltage regulator compensates for temperature change. Check temperature around rear alternator bracket and adjust charging voltage accordingly.

5) If ammeter reading is more than 10 amps, continue to charge battery until reading falls to less than 10 amps. Replace battery with fully charged one, if necessary.

6) An alternate method is to limit charging voltage by connecting 1/4 ohm (25W) resistor in series with battery. After completion of test, disconnect all test equipment and connect battery cable.

BENCH TESTS

ROTOR ASSEMBLY

1) To check slip rings, inspect outside circumference of slip rings for roughness or foreign materials. Replace slip ring if badly worn or roughness is noted. Slip rings are not serviced as a separate item. They are serviced with rotor assembly.

NOTE: Standard outside diameter of slip ring is 1.30 in. (33 mm). Service limit is 1.26 in. (32.2 mm). Standard slip ring runout is .0012 in. (.03 mm). Service limit is .008 in. (.2 mm).

2) To test rotor field coils, using an ohmmeter, connect leads to field coil and slip ring (press pointer of probes on each slip ring) and check for continuity. Continuity should exist. If not, field coil is defective. Replace rotor assembly.

3) To test rotor for ground, connect ohmmeter leads to slip ring and rotor shaft or core and check for continuity. *See Fig. 4*. If there is continuity, slip ring is grounded. Replace rotor assembly.

Fig. 4: Ohmmeter Hookup for Testing Rotor for Ground

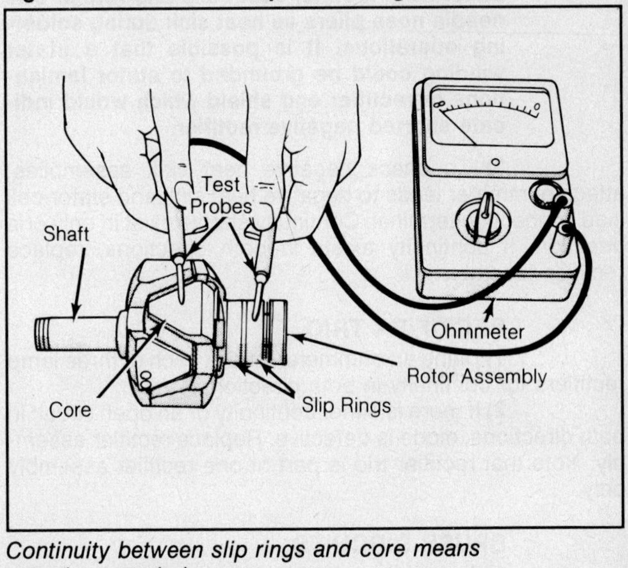

Continuity between slip rings and core means rotor is grounded.

STATOR ASSEMBLY

1) To test stator for open circuit, using an ohmmeter, connect leads to stator coil leads and check for continuity. Continuity should exist. If not, stator assembly is defective. Replace stator assembly.

2) To test stator coil for ground, check for continuity between stator coil leads and stator coil frame. If there is continuity, stator is grounded. Replace stator assembly.

RECTIFIER ASSEMBLY

1) Check positive heat sink assemblies with an ohmmeter. Check for continuity between positive heat sink and stator coil lead connection terminal. *See Fig. 5.*

2) Reverse ohmmeter leads. If continuity exists in both directions, diode is shorted. Replace rectifier assembly.

MITSUBISHI INTERNAL REGULATOR/ALTERNATOR (Cont.)

Fig. 5: Front View of Stator End Shield Assembly Showing Rectifier Testing Points

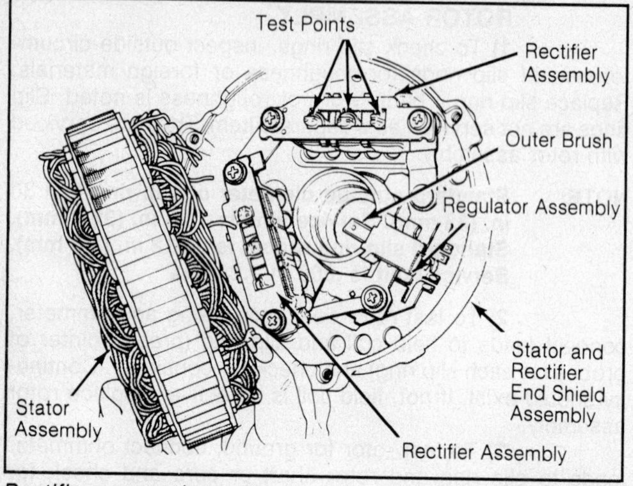

Rectifier connections should have continuity in one direction only.

NOTE: If negative rectifier shows shorted, unsolder stator from rectifier assembly and retest. Use needle nose pliers as heat sink during soldering operations. It is possible that a stator winding could be grounded to stator laminations or rectifier end shield which would indicate shorted negative rectifier.

3) To check negative heat sink assemblies, attach ohmmeter leads to negative heat sink and stator coil lead connection terminal. Continuity should exist in only one direction. If continuity exists in both directions, replace rectifier assembly.

RECTIFIER TRIO

1) Using an ohmmeter, check each of three lamp rectifiers for continuity in both directions.

2) If there is either continuity or an open circuit in both directions, diode is defective. Replace rectifier assembly. Note that rectifier trio is part of one rectifier assembly only.

BRUSH CIRCUITS

1) To test inner brush circuit, connect one ohmmeter lead to inner brush. Connect other ohmmeter lead to inner brush terminal. Continuity should exist. If continuity does not exist, replace brush assembly.

NOTE: Standard brush length is .709 in. (18 mm). Service limit is .315 in. (8 mm). Standard load of brush spring is .7 to 1.0 lbs. (.32 to .45 kg). Service limit is .5 lbs. (.23 kg).

2) To test outer brush circuit, connect one ohmmeter lead to outer brush. Connect other ohmmeter lead to outer brush terminal. Continuity should exist. If continuity does not exist, replace brush assembly.

OVERHAUL

DISASSEMBLY

1) Remove alternator assembly and place mounting lug in soft-jawed vise. Remove through bolts. Pry between stator and drive end shield with screwdriver blade. Carefully separate drive end shield, pulley and rotor assembly from stator and rectifier end shield assembly. *See Fig. 6.*

2) Place rotor in soft-jawed vise and remove pulley nut. Remove pulley, pulley fan, fan spacer and alternator drive end shield from rotor.

3) Remove front and rear dust seals from drive end shield. Remove three drive end bearing retainer screws and remove drive end shield bearing retainer. Using a proper sized socket and hammer, tap alternator drive end shield bearing from housing.

4) Locate six stator leads and remove their solder connections. Remove stator assembly from stator and rectifier end shield assembly. Remove four rectifier screws, rectifiers, brush holder and regulator mount screw from stator end shield housing. Remove terminal "B" nut and lift out capacitor.

5) Remove regulator and rectifier assembly. Unsolder one rectifier-to-regulator assembly and remove other rectifier assembly by sliding battery stud out of regulator. Inspect rotor bearing surface for scoring. Remove rotor ball bearing from rotor shaft with puller tool (C-4068 or C-4333).

NOTE: During cleaning and inspection, DO NOT immerse stator field coil assembly, rotor assembly or rectifier assembly in cleaning solvent. Immersing these assemblies will damage parts. Clean with moist cloth only and wipe dry.

REASSEMBLY

1) To reassemble, reverse disassembly procedure and note the following: Install new dust seals on each side of front bearing. Install new front and rear dust seals in alternator drive end shield.

2) When installing rotor, push brushes into brush holder. Insert a wire in end shield's brush retainer hole to hold brushes in raised position. Remove wire after rotor is installed.

3) Use socket on bearing inner race, drive bearing onto rotor shaft until it bottoms against flange.

4) After assembly, install alternator and adjust drive belt tension. During alternator installation, check clearance between alternator leg and front case. If clearance is more than .008 in. (0.2 mm), insert spacers .0078 in. (.198 mm) thick as required.

5) Tighten alternator support bolt nut to 15-18 ft. lbs. (20-24 N.m). Tighten brace bolt to 9-10 ft. lbs. (12-14 N.m). After tightening, coat all electrical connections with light mineral grease. Test current output.

MITSUBISHI INTERNAL REGULATOR/ALTERNATOR (Cont.)

Fig. 6: Exploded View of Chrysler (Mitsubishi) Alternator and Electronic Voltage Regulator

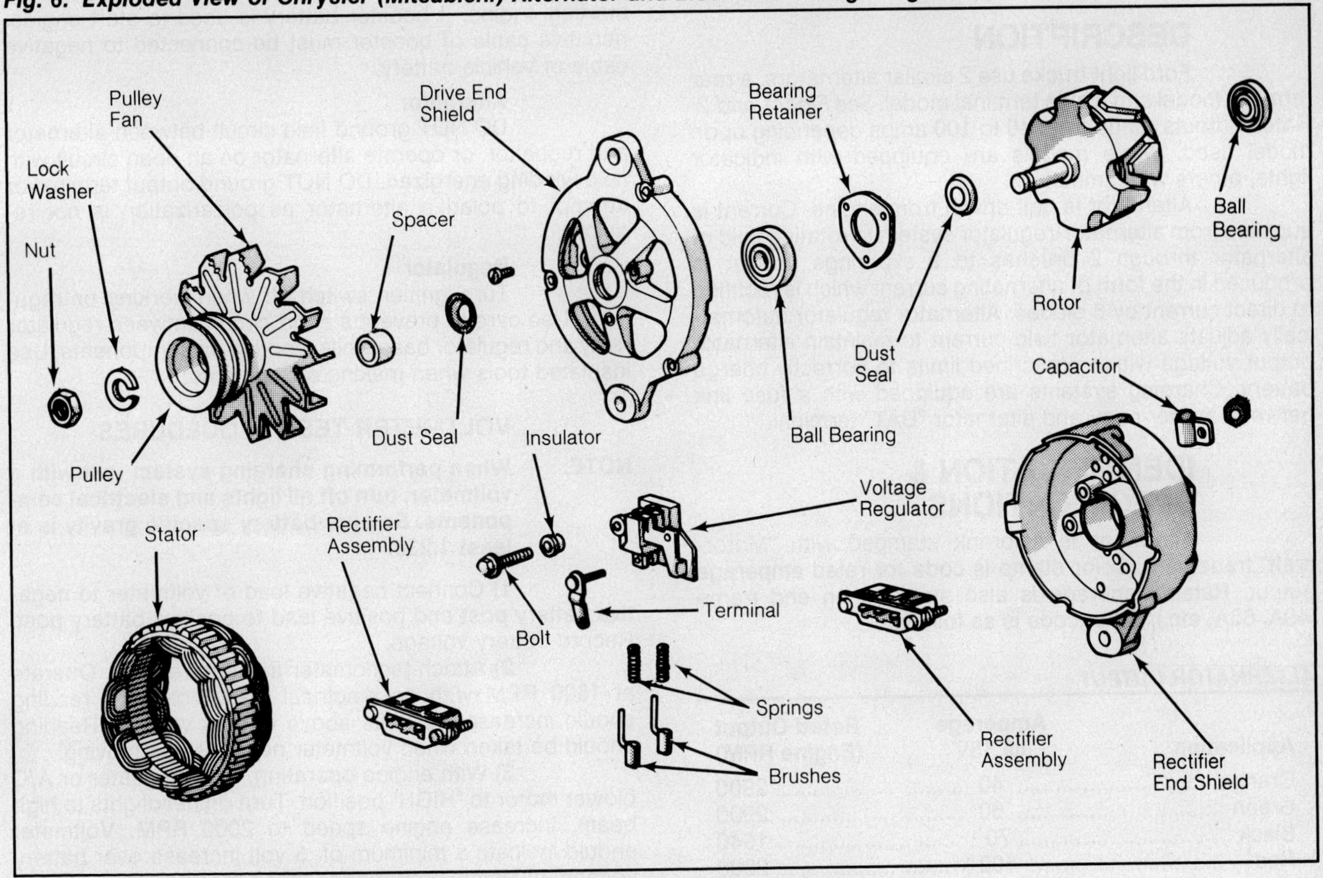

Check alternator for proper output, if not to specifications, disassemble and retest.

MITSUBISHI ALTERNATOR SPECIFICATIONS

Application	Specification
Model Identification Number	A4T25191
Rotation	[1] Clockwise
Rated Amp. Output	75 Amps.
Current Output	
@ 13.5 Volts & 500 RPM	17-25 Amps.
@ 13.5 Volts & 1000 RPM	63-70 Amps.
@ 13.5 Volts & 2000 RPM	74 Amps.
Regulator Voltage	
50°F (10°C)	12.8-13.4 Volts
68°F (20°C)	14.1-14.7 Volts

[1] – As viewed from pulley end.

MOTORCRAFT ALTERNATORS

Ford

DESCRIPTION

Ford light trucks use 2 similar alternators, a rear terminal model and a side terminal model. *See Figs. 1 and 2.* Rated outputs range from 40 to 100 amps depending upon model used. Some models are equipped with indicator lights, others with ammeters.

Alternator is belt driven from engine. Current is supplied from alternator-regulator system to rotating field of alternator through 2 brushes to 2 slip rings. Power is produced in the form of alternating current which is rectified to direct current by 6 diodes. Alternator regulator automatically adjusts alternator field current to maintain alternator output voltage within prescribed limits to correctly charge battery. Charging systems are equipped with a fuse link between starter relay and alternator "BAT" terminal.

IDENTIFICATION & SPECIFICATIONS

Alternator is color-ink stamped with "Motorcraft" trademark. Color stamp is code for rated amperage output. Rated amperage is also stamped on end frame (40A, 60A, etc.). Color code is as follows:

ALTERNATOR OUTPUT

Application	Amperage @ 15V	Rated Output (Engine RPM)
Orange	40	2900
Green	60	2900
Black	70 [1]	1640
Red	100 [1]	2900

[1] - Rated cold output.

ALTERNATOR SPECIFICATIONS

Alternator	Specification
Field Current at 12 Volts (All)	4.25 Amps
Slip Rings (All)	
Minimum Diameter	1.22"
Maximum Runout	.0005"
Brush Length Wear Limit	
All Models	1/4"
Pulley Nut Torque (All)	60-100 ft. lbs. (82-136 N.m)

ADJUSTMENT

ALTERNATOR REGULATOR

An electronic regulator is used on all charging systems. It is factory calibrated and cannot be adjusted.

TESTING PRECAUTIONS

When testing or servicing alternator or regulator, take following precautions to avoid damage to components.

Battery

DO NOT reverse battery connections. Negative terminal must be connected to ground. When charging battery, cables must be disconnected from battery before connecting charger. DO NOT use charger as a booster for starting engine. If booster battery is used to start engine, negative cable of booster must be connected to negative cable of vehicle battery.

Alternator

DO NOT ground field circuit between alternator and regualtor, or operate alternator on an open circuit with field winding energized. DO NOT ground output terminal or attempt to polarize alternator as polzarization is not required.

Regulator

Turn ignition switch off when working on regulator. Use care to prevent a short circuit between regulator relay and regulator base while working on components. Use insulated tools when making adjustments.

VOLTMETER TEST PROCEDURES

NOTE: **When performing charging system test with a voltmeter, turn off all lights and electrical components. Be sure battery specific gravity is at least 1.230.**

1) Connect negative lead of voltmeter to negative battery post and positive lead to positive battery post. Record battery voltage.

2) Attach tachometer and start engine. Operate at 1500 RPM with no electrical load. Voltmeter reading should increase 1-2 volts above battery voltage. Reading should be taken when voltmeter needle stops moving.

3) With engine operating, turn on heater or A/C blower motor to "HIGH" position. Turn on headlights to high beam. Increase engine speed to 2000 RPM. Voltmeter should indicate a minimum of .5 volt increase over battery voltage. If system conforms to these readings, operation is normal.

Fig. 1: Rear View Showing Alternator Terminal Location on Rear Terminal Models

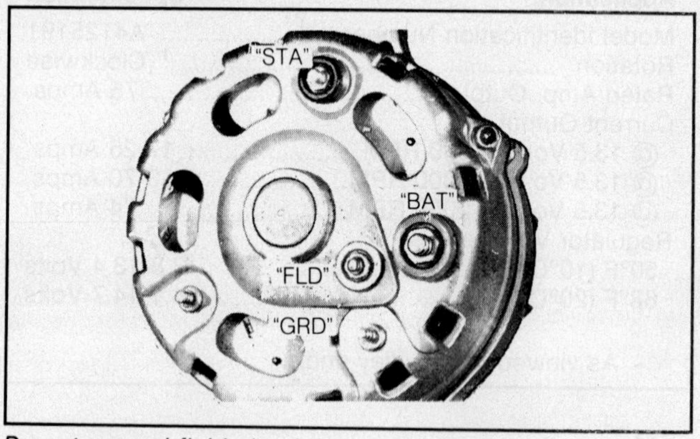

Do not ground field circuit between alternator and regulator.

TEST RESULTS

1) If voltmeter reading indicates over-voltage (more than 2 volts above battery voltage), shut off engine and check ground connections between regulator and alternator and/or regulator and engine. Clean and tighten connections and repeat test.

2) If over-voltage condition still exists, disconnect regulator wiring plug and repeat steps **2)** and **3)** of VOLTMETER TEST PROCEDURES. If condition is corrected, replace regulator and repeat test.

Alternators & Regulators

MOTORCRAFT ALTERNATORS (Cont.)

Fig. 2: Side View Showing Alternator Terminal Location on Side Terminal Models

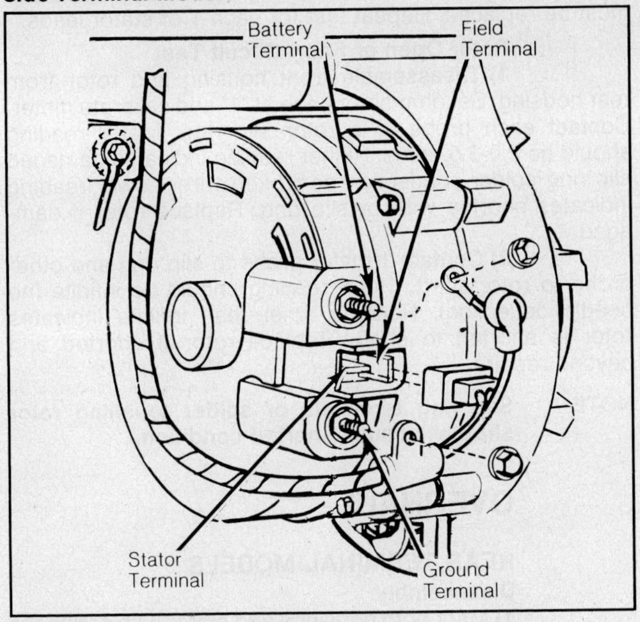

Connections must be clean and tight.

3) If over-voltage still exists with regulator disconnected, a short is indicated in wiring harness between alternator and regulator (Circuits "A" and "F"). Repair short circuit, and then reconnect regulator, repeating tests with regulator plug connected.

UNDER VOLTAGE & FIELD CIRCUIT TESTS

1) To determine if jumping procedure is safe, field circuit should be checked with regulator wiring plug disconnected and ohmmeter connected from "F" terminal of wiring plug to battery ground. Ohmmeter should indicate 3-250 ohms. *See Fig. 3.*

2) If load voltage did not increase 1/2 volt above base voltage, connect a jumper wire across "A" and "F" terminals of wiring plug and repeat test procedures.

3) If voltage is still under base voltage, remove jumper wire from wiring plug and leave plug disconnected from regulator. Connect jumper wire to "FLD" and "BAT" terminals on alternator and repeat test. If voltage increases more than 1/2 volt above battery voltage, repair wiring harness or replace regulator.

4) If voltmeter still indicates under-voltage, stop engine and move positive voltmeter lead to "BAT" terminal. If voltmeter now indicates base voltage reading, repair alternator. If voltmeter indicates zero volts, repair "BAT" wire or replace fuse link.

REGULATOR CIRCUIT TESTS

"S" Circuit With Ammeter

1) Connect positive voltmeter lead to regulator wiring plug "S" terminal position. Turn ignition "ON", but do not start engine.

2) Voltmeter should indicate battery voltage. If there is no voltage, "S" wire lead from ignition switch is open. Repair and retest system.

"S" & "I" Circuit With Indicator Light

1) Disconnect regulator wiring plug, and install a jumper wire between "A" and "F" terminals. With engine idling, connect negative lead of voltmeter to ground. Connect positive voltmeter lead, in turn, to "S" and then "I" terminals of regulator wiring plug.

Fig. 3: Test Wiring Connections for Field Circuit Test

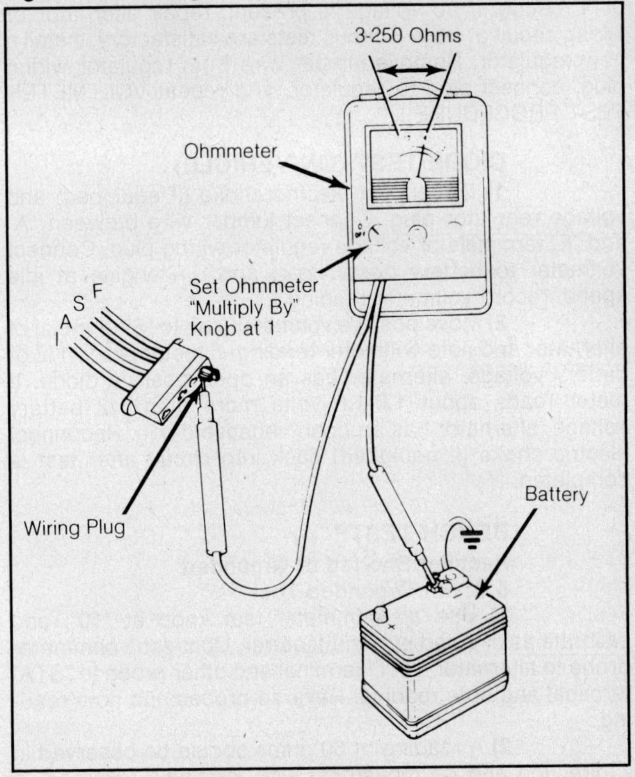

Field circuit should be checked with regulator wiring plug disconnected.

Fig. 4: Internal View Showing Stator Lead Connections on Rear Terminal Models

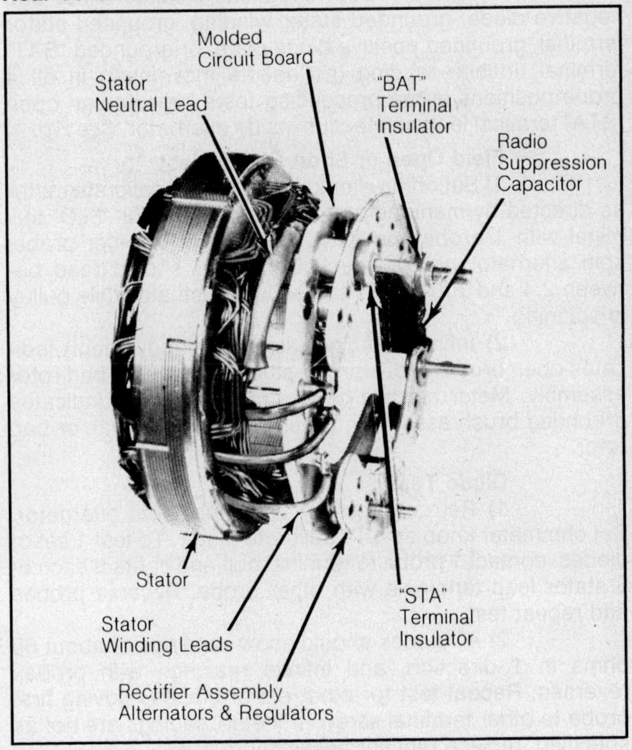

Be sure all connections are tight.

MOTORCRAFT ALTERNATORS (Cont.)

2) Voltage of "S" circuit should be about 1/2 that of "I" circuit. If no voltage is present, repair alternator or wiring circuit at fault. If circuit tests are satisfactory, install a new regulator. Remove jumper wire from regulator wiring plug, connect plug to regulator, and repeat VOLTMETER TEST PROCEDURE.

DIODE TEST (ON VEHICLE)

1) Disconnect electric choke (if equipped) and voltage regulator plug. Connect jumper wire between "A" and "F" terminals of voltage regulator wiring plug. Connect voltmeter to battery posts, start and run engine at idle speed, record voltmeter reading.

2) Move positive voltmeter lead to "S" terminal of alternator and note voltmeter reading. If meter reads 1/2 of battery voltage, alternator has an open positive diode. If meter reads about 1.0-1.5 volts more than 1/2 battery voltage, alternator has an open negative diode. Reconnect electric choke (if equipped) back into circuit after test is completed.

BENCH TESTS

Rectifier Shorted or Grounded & Stator Grounded Test

1) Use an ohmmeter, set knob at "10", and calibrate as directed by manufacturer. Connect 1 ohmmeter probe to alternator "BAT" terminal and other probe to "STA" terminal and note reading. Reverse probes and note reading.

2) A reading of 60 ohms should be observed in 1 direction and no movement with terminals reversed. A reading in both directions indicates a bad positive diode, grounded positive diode plate, or grounded "BAT" terminal.

3) Perform same test using "STA" and "GRD" terminals. Readings in both directions indicate either bad negative diode, grounded stator winding, grounded stator terminal, grounded positive diode plate, or grounded "BAT" terminal. Infinite reading (no needle movement) in all 4 probe positions in the preceeding tests indicates an open "STA" terminal lead connection inside alternator. *See Fig. 4.*

Field Open or Short Circuit Test

1) Set ohmmeter knob at "1" and calibrate meter as directed by manufacturer. Contact alternator "FLD" terminal with 1 probe and "GND" terminal with other probe, spin alternator pulley wheel. Ohmmeter should read between 2.4 and 100 ohms, and should fluctuate while pulley is spinning.

2) Infinite reading (no needle movement) indicates open brush lead, worn or stuck brushes, or bad rotor assembly. Meter reading of less than 2.4 ohms indicates grounded brush assembly, grounded field terminal, or bad rotor.

Diode Test

1) Remove rectifier assembly from alternator. Set ohmmeter knob at "10". Calibrate meter. To test 1 set of diodes, contact 1 probe to terminal bolt and contact each of 3 stator lead terminals with other probe. Reverse probes and repeat test.

2) All diodes should show readings of about 60 ohms in 1 direction, and infinite readings with probes reversed. Repeat test for other set of diodes, moving first probe to other terminal screw. If meter readings are not as specified, replace rectifier assembly.

Stator Coil Grounded Test

Set ohmmeter knob at "1000". Contact meter probes to 1 of stator leads and to stator laminated core. Meter should show infinite reading (no needle movement). If meter needle moved, stator winding is shorted to core and must be replaced. Repeat test for each 1 of stator leads.

Rotor Open or Short Circuit Test

1) Disassemble front housing and rotor from rear housing. Set ohmmeter knob at "1" and calibrate meter. Contact each probe to a rotor slip ring. Meter reading should be 2.0-3.5 ohms. Higher reading indicates damaged slip ring solder connection or broken wire. Lower reading indicates shorted wire or slip ring. Replace rotor if damaged.

2) Contact 1 meter probe to slip ring and other probe to rotor shaft. Meter reading should be infinite (no needle deflection). Reading other than infinite indicates rotor is shorted to shaft. Replace rotor if shorted and beyond repair.

NOTE: **Slip ring terminals or solder touching rotor shaft will cause shorted condition.**

OVERHAUL

REAR TERMINAL MODELS

Disassembly

1) Mark both housings and stator with scribe for reassembly. Remove through bolts and separate front housing and rotor from stator and rear housing. Remove all nuts and insulators from rear housing. Remove rear housing from stator and rectifier assembly. *See Fig. 5.*

2) Remove brush holder mounting screws, holder, brushes, springs, insulator and terminal. If replacement is necessary, press bearing from rear housing, supporting housing on inner boss. If rectifier assembly is being replaced, unsolder stator leads from rectifier terminals and separate stator from rectifier assembly.

NOTE: **Use 100 watt soldering iron.**

3) Original production alternators will have one of two types of rectifier assembly boards; one has circuit board spaced away from diode plates with diodes exposed. The other type is single circuit board with built-in diodes. If alternator rectifier has exposed diode board, remove screws from rectifier by rotating bolt heads 1/4 turn clockwise to unlock, and remove screws.

4) Push stator terminal straight out on a rectifier with diodes built into circuit board. Avoid turning screw while removing to make certain straight knurl will engage insulators when installing. Do not remove grounded screw.

5) Remove drive pulley nut, using Alternator Pulley Remover (T65P-10300-B). Pull lock washer, pulley, fan and spacer from rotor shaft. Remove rotor from front housing, and remove front bearing spacer. Do not remove rotor stop ring from shaft unless it is damaged.

6) Remove 3 screws holding front end bearing retainer and remove retainer. If bearing has lost lubricant or is damaged, support housing close to bearing boss and press out old bearing.

Reassembly

1) Rotor, stator and bearing must not be cleaned with solvent. Wipe these parts off with a clean, lint free cloth. Press front bearing in front housing bearing boss, putting pressure on bearing outer race only.

2) Install bearing retainer. If stop-ring on rotor drive shaft is damaged, install new stop-ring. Push new ring on shaft and into groove.

MOTORCRAFT ALTERNATORS (Cont.)

Fig. 5: Exploded View of Motorcraft Rear Terminal Alternator Assembly

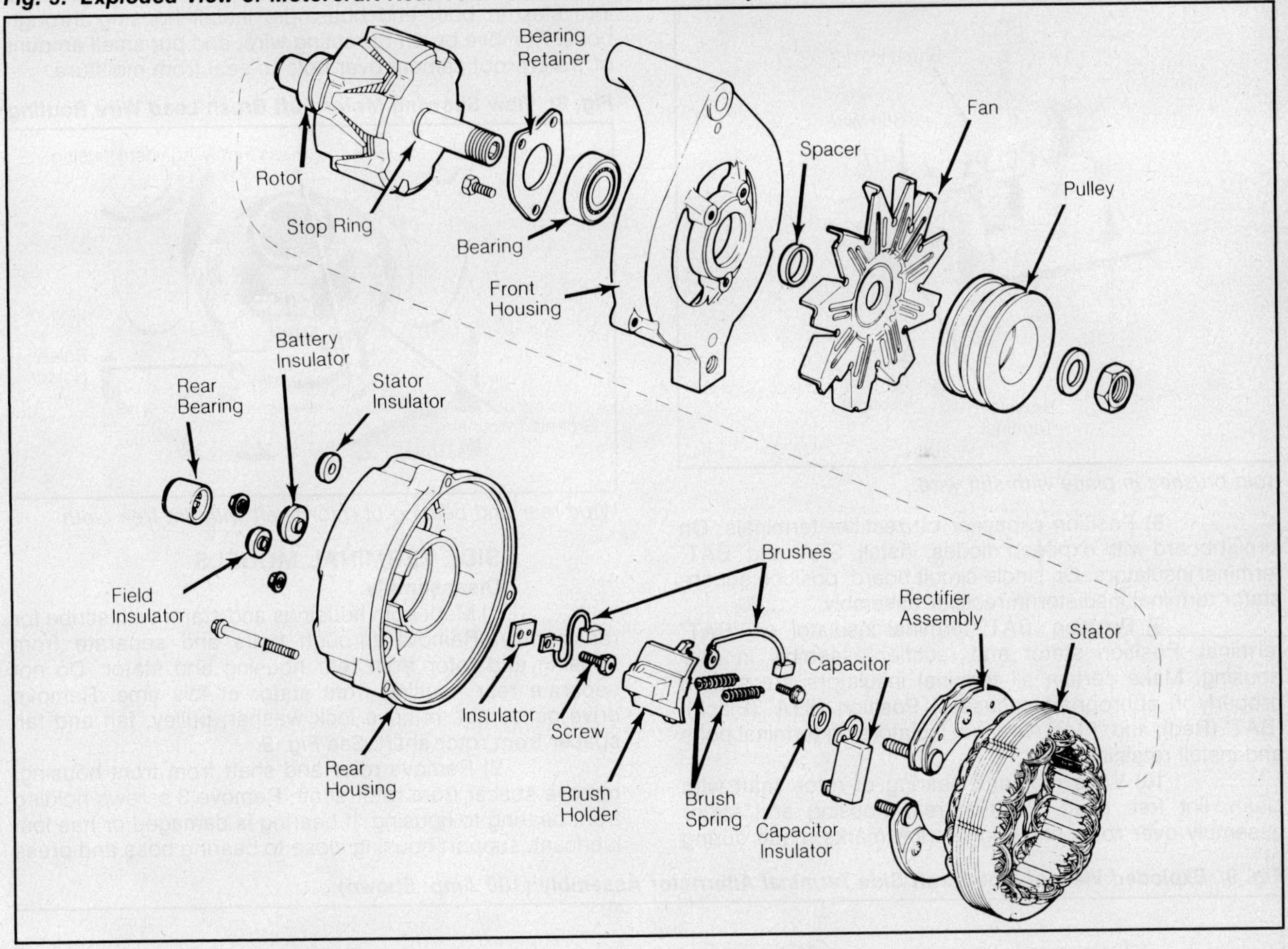

Fig. 6: Motorcraft Pulley Removal Procedure

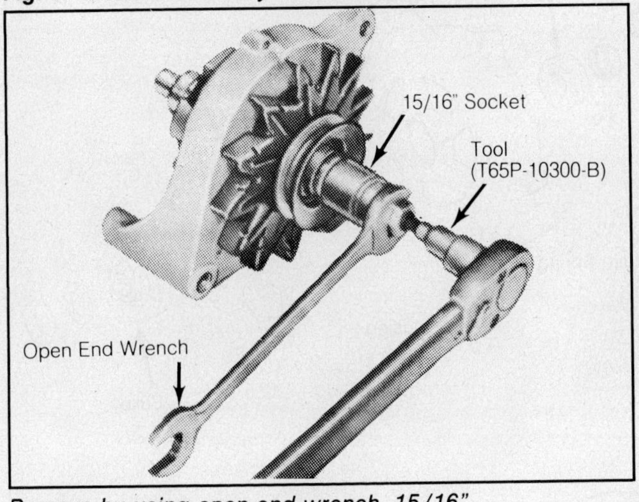

Remove by using open end wrench, 15/16" socket and puller (T65P-10300-B).

NOTE: **Do not open ring with snap ring pliers, as permanent damage will result.**

3) Position bearing spacer on rotor shaft with recessed side against stop ring. Position front housing, fan spacer, fan, pulley and lock washer on rotor shaft and install retaining nut. Tighten nut.

4) If rear housing bearing was removed, support housing on inner boss and press a new bearing flush with outer end surface. Place brush springs, brushes, brush terminal and terminal insulator in brush holder.

5) Hold brushes in position by inserting small piece of stiff wire in brush holder. Position brush holder assembly in rear housing and install mounting screws. Position brush leads in holder. *See Figs. 7 & 8.*

6) Wrap 3 stator winding leads around rectifier terminals and solder using 100 watt soldering iron and resin core solder. Position stator neutral lead eyelet on stator terminal screw and install screw in rectifier assembly. *See Fig. 4.*

7) For rectifier with diodes exposed, insert special screws through wire lug, dished washers and circuit board. Turn screws 1/4 turn counterclockwise to lock. For single circuit boards with built-in diodes, insert screws straight through wire lug, insulating washer and rectifier, into insulator.

NOTE: **Dished washers are to be used only on circuit board with exposed diodes. If dished washers are used on single circuit board, short circuit will occur. Flat insulating washers are to be used between stator terminal and board when single circuit board is used.**

MOTORCRAFT ALTERNATORS (Cont.)

Fig. 7: Assembled View of Brush Holder Assembly

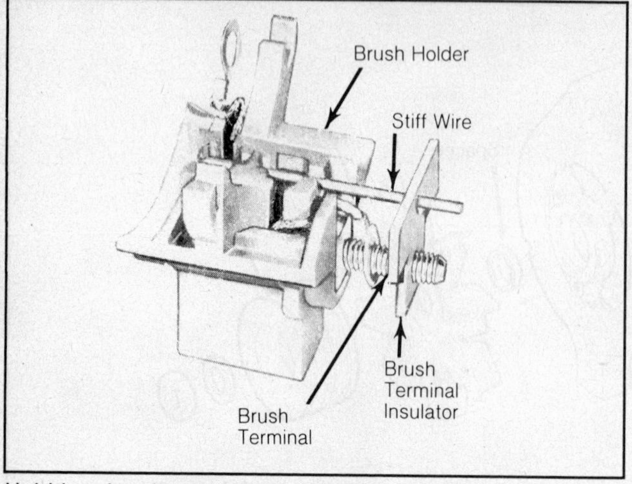

Hold brushes in place with stiff wire.

8) Position capacitor on rectifier terminals. On circuit board with exposed diodes, install "STA" and "BAT" terminal insulators. On single circuit board, position square stator terminal insulator in rectifier assembly.

9) Position "BAT" terminal insulator on "BAT" terminal. Position stator and rectifier assembly in rear housing. Make certain all terminal insulators are seated properly in appropriate recesses. Position "STA" (Black), "BAT" (Red), and "FLD" (Orange) isulators on terminal bolts and install retaining nuts.

10) Wipe rear end bearing of rotor shaft with clean, lint free cloth. Position rear housing and stator assembly over rotor and align scribe marks made during initial disassembly. Seat machined portion of stator core into step in both end housings. Install housing through bolts. Remove brush retracting wire, and put small amount of waterproof cement over hole to seal from moisture.

Fig. 8: View Showing Motorcraft Brush Lead Wire Routing

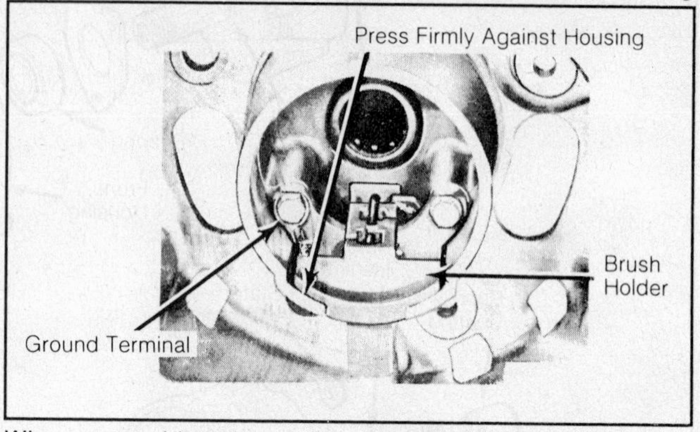

Wipe rear end bearing of rotor shaft with lint free cloth.

SIDE TERMINAL MODELS

Disassembly

1) Mark both housings and stator with scribe for reassembly. Remove through bolts and separate from housing and rotor from rear housing and stator. Do not separate rear housing from stator at this time. Remove drive pulley nut, remove lock washer, pulley, fan and fan spacer from rotor shaft. *See Fig. 9.*

2) Remove rotor and shaft from front housing, remove spacer from rotor shaft. Remove 3 screws holding front bearing to housing. If bearing is damaged or has lost lubricant, support housing close to bearing boss and press

Fig. 9: Exploded View of Motorcraft Side Terminal Alternator Assembly (100 Amp. Shown)

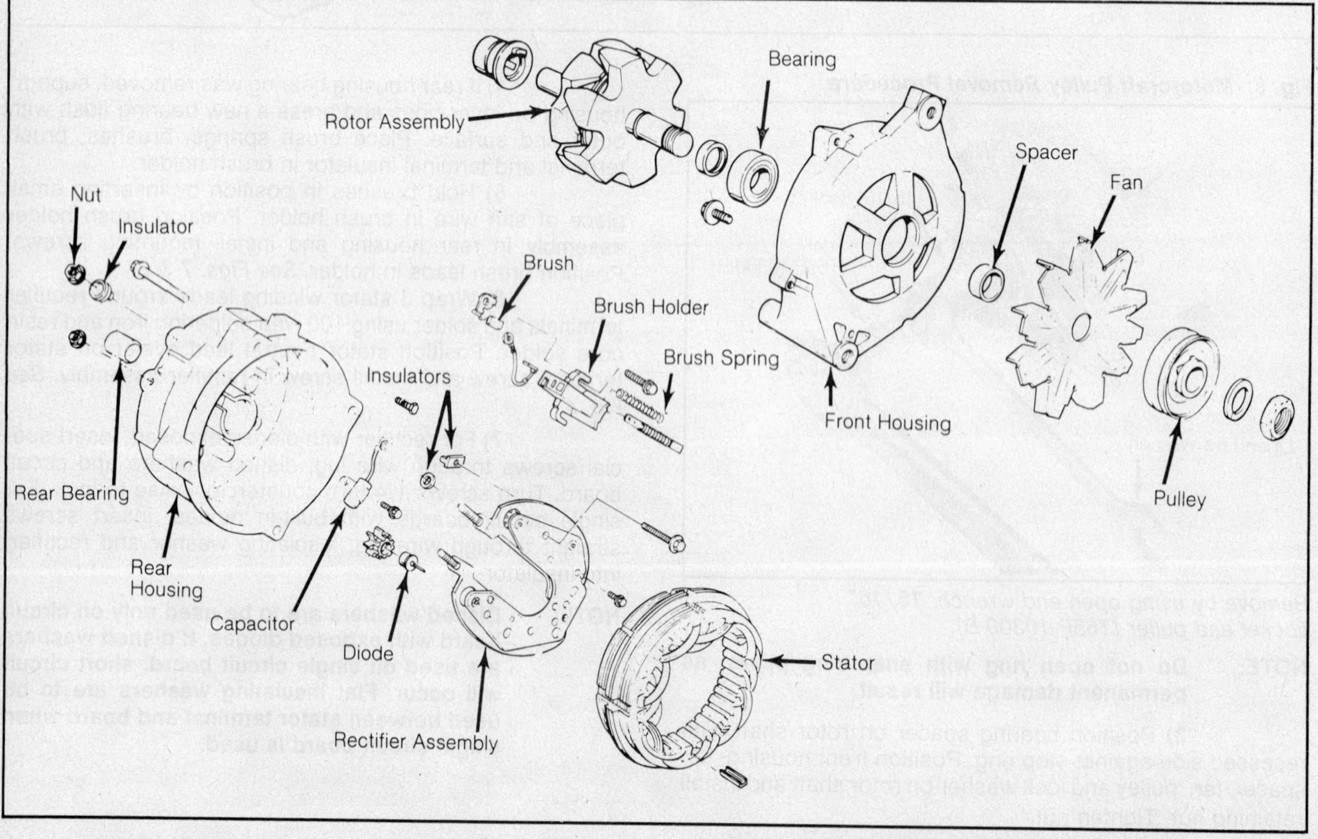

MOTORCRAFT ALTERNATORS (Cont.)

bearing from housing. Unsolder stator leads from rectifier assembly, using a 100 watt soldering iron.

3) Remove stator from rear housing. Unsolder brush holder from rectifier, using a 100 watt soldering iron. Remove capacitor lead-to-rectifier screw. Remove 4 rectifier-to-rear housing screws. Remove 2 terminal nuts and insulator from outside of housing, remove rectifier assembly from housing.

4) Remove 2 brush holder-to-housing screws, remove brushes and holder. Remove 2 rectifier insulators from bosses in housing. Clean all sealing compound from rear housing and brush holder. Remove capacitor from rear housing. If necessary to replace rear bearing, support rear housing near bearing boss and press bearing out of housing from inside.

Reassembly

1) Rotor, stator and bearings must not be cleaned with solvent. Wipe these parts off with a clean, lint free cloth. Press front bearing into front housing, putting pressure on bearing outer race only.

2) Install bearing retaining screws. Install inner space on rotor shaft and install shaft into front housing and bearing.

3) Install fan spacer, fan, pulley, lock washer, and nut onto rotor shaft. Tighten pulley nut. If rear bearing was removed, press new bearing in until it is flush with boss outer surface.

4) Position brush terminal, springs and brushes in brush holder and hold in position by inserting a small piece of stiff wire in brush holder.

5) Install brush holder to rear housing and install attaching screws. Push brush holder toward rotor shaft opening and tighten screws. Install capacitor to rear housing and install attaching screws.

6) Install 2 rectifier insulators on bosses, inside rear housing. Install insulator on "BAT" terminal of rectifier, position rectifier in rear housing.

7) Install outside insulator on "BAT" terminal, install nuts on "BAT" and "GRD" terminals finger tight. Install 4 rectifier attaching screws, but do not tighten. Tighten terminal nuts on "BAT" and "GRD" terminals, tighten 4 rectifier screws. Secure capacitor lead to rectifier. Press brush holder lead on rectifier pin and solder, using a 100 watt soldering iron.

8) Install stator in rear housing and align scribe marks. Press 3 stator leads onto rectifier pins and solder, using 100 watt soldering iron. Position rotor and front housing into stator and rear housing while aligning scribe marks.

9) Install 4 through bolts and tighten. Spin fan and pulley to ensure nothing is binding inside alternator. Remove brush retracting wire and put small amount of waterproof cement over hole to seal from moisture.

BRUSH REPLACEMENT

1) Mark both end housings and stator with a scribe. Remove 4 through bolts and separate front housing and rotor from rear housing and stator. Use a 100 watt soldering iron to detach brush holder lead from rectifier. Remove brush holder attaching screws and remove holder from rear housing. Remove any sealing compound.

2) To install, position holder to rear housing and insert wire, to retract brushes, through hole in rear housing. Install holder attaching screws, push holder toward rotor shaft and tighten screws. Press holder lead on rectifier pin and solder using a 200 watt soldering iron.

3) Install front housing and rotor to rear housing and stator while aligning scribe marks. Install 4 through bolts, spin fan and pulley to ensure nothing binds inside alternator. Remove wire, retracting brushes, and seal with a small amount of waterproof cement.

MOTORCRAFT WITH INTEGRAL REGULATOR

Ford Aerostar

DESCRIPTION

The integral alternator/regulator is belt-driven by the engine. Field current is supplied from the regulator, mounted on the rear of the alternator, to the rotating field of the alternator through 2 brushes and 2 slip rings.

The regulator automatically adjusts the alternator field current to maintain alternator output. The alternator is self current limiting. If equipped with a warning lamp, the regulator voltage control is turned on when the ignition switch is on and voltage is applied to the regulator "I" terminal through a resistor in the "I" circuit.

On warning lamp equipped vehicles, the warning lamp is connected across the terminals of a 500 ohm resistor at the instrument cluster. Current passes through the warning lamp when the ignition switch is in the "RUN" position and there is no voltage at terminal "S". When voltage at "S" rises to a preset value, the regulator switching circuits stop the flow of current into terminal "I" and the lamp turns off.

System voltage is sensed and alternator field current is drawn through terminal "A". If terminal "A" voltage is excessively high or low, or if terminal "S" voltage is abnormal, the regulator switching circuits will turn the warning lamp on, indicating a system fault.

The low voltage detector will sense a discharged battery or extreme discharge condition. It is normal for the warning lamp to flicker or come on during prolonged engine idle under heavy electrical load.

A fusible link is included in the charging system wiring on all models. It is used to prevent damage to the wiring harness and alternator if the wiring harness should

Fig. 1: Exploded View of Ford Integral Alternator/Regulator

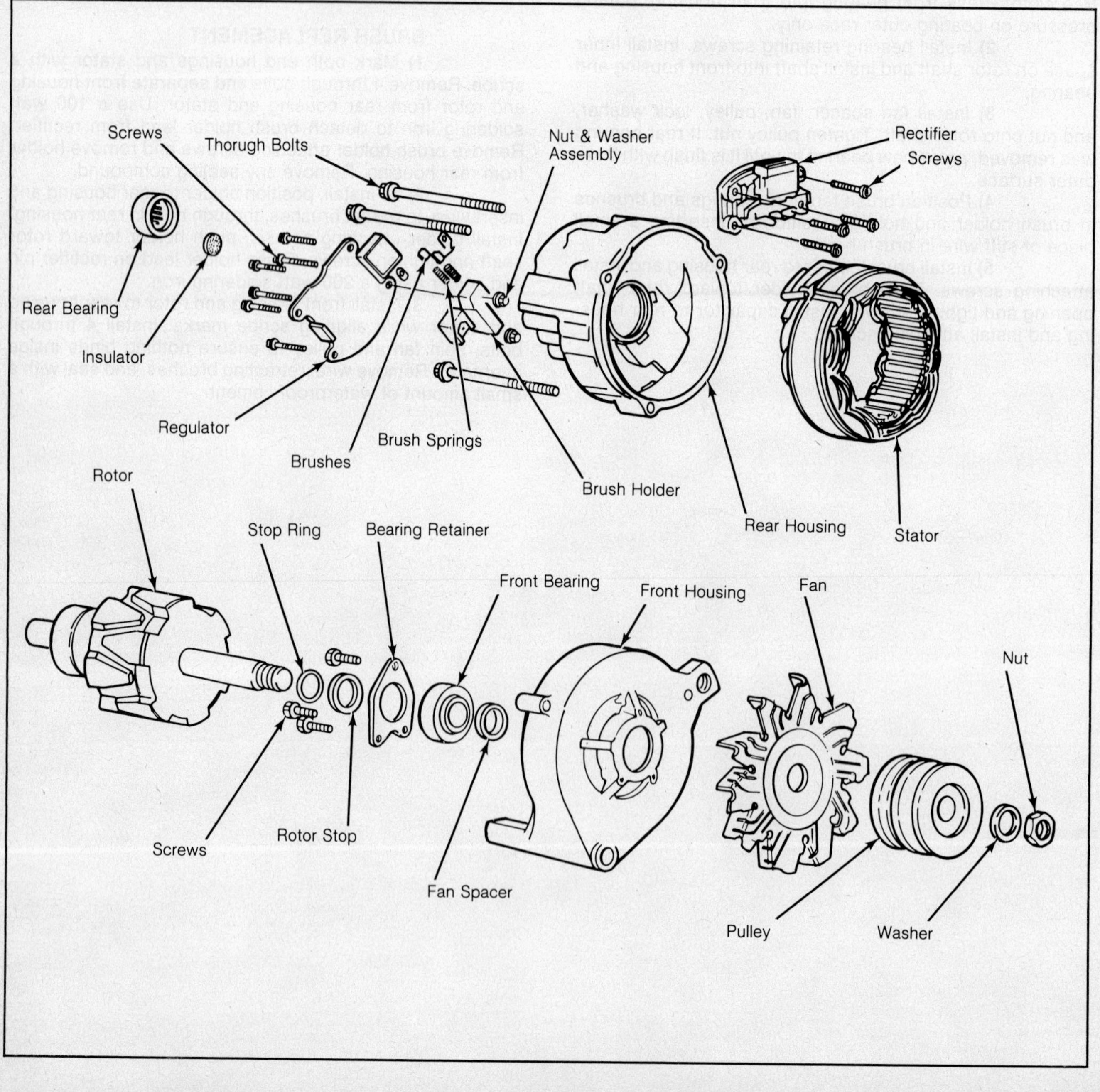

MOTORCRAFT WITH INTEGRAL REGULATOR (Cont.)

become grounded, or if booster battery is connected to the charging system incorrectly.

SPECIFICATIONS

ALTERNATOR OUTPUT

Amperage @15V	Watts @15V
40	600
40 HE	600
60	900
65	975

ALTERNATOR SPECIFICATIONS

Alternator	Specification
Slip Rings (All)	
Minimum Diameter	1.22" (31 mm)
Maximum Runout	0.0005" (.013 mm)
Brush Length Wear Limit	
All Models	.25" (6.35 mm)
Pulley Nut Torque (All)	60-100 ft.lbs. (82-135 N.m)

ADJUSTMENT

ALTERNATOR REGULATOR

A solid state regulator is used on all charging systems. It is factory calibrated and cannot be adjusted.

BENCH TESTING

If system diagnosis has isolated a problem in the intergral alternator/regulator, remove it from the vehicle for bench testing. In some cases it may be possible to replace a defective regulator or brushes without removing the alternator. Digital meters CANNOT be used to perform alternator testing

RECTIFIER SHORT OR GROUNDED & STATOR GROUNDED TEST

1) Disconnect battery and contact an ohmmeter probe to 1 of the alternator "B+" blade terminals and the other probe to the "STA" terminal. Then, reverse ohmmeter probes and repeat test.

2) Normally, there will be no needle movement in 1 direction, indicating rectifier diodes are being checked in reverse current direction and are not shorted. A low reading of about 6.5 ohms with probes reversed indicates that rectifier positive diodes are being checked in forward current direction.

3) A reading in both directions indicates a bad positive diode or shorted radio suppression capacitor. The radio suppression capacitor is built into the rectifier and is not individually serviceable.

4) Perform the same test using the "STA" blade terminal and alternator rear housing. A reading in both directions indicates either a grounded stator winding, a bad negative diode, a grounded stator lead wire or a shorted radio suppression capacitor.

Fig. 2: Rectifier Postive Diode Testing

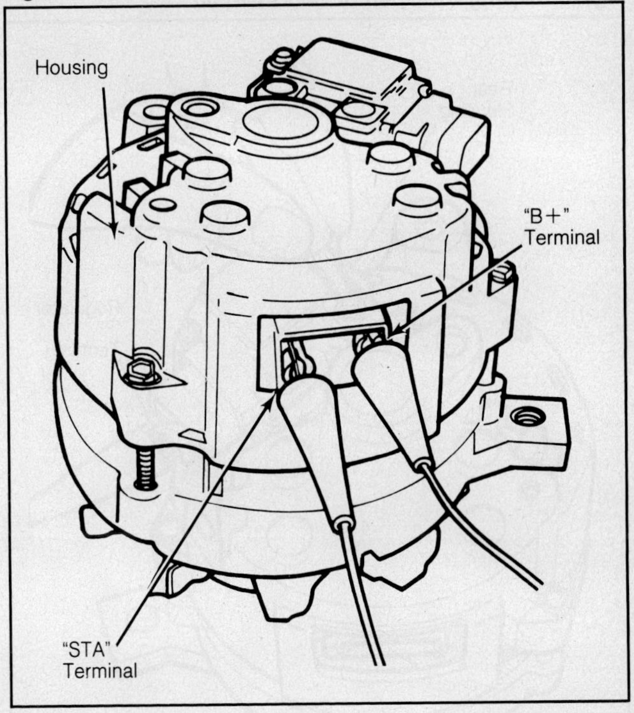

5) If there is no needle movement with probes in 1 direction and no needle movement or high resistance (significantly over 6.5 ohms) in the opposite direction as outlined in step **1)** and **4)**, a bad connection exists in the rectifier.

OPEN FIELD OR SHORT CIRCUIT TEST

1) Use an ohmmeter, set knob at "X1" and calibrate ohmmeter. Contact regulator "A" blade terminal with 1 probe and the regulator "F" screw head with the other probe. Then, spin alternator pulley. Reverse ohmmeter probes and repeat test.

2) In 1 probe direction, ohmmeter reading should be between 2.2 and 100 ohms and may fluctuate while pulley is turning. In the other probe direction, reading should fluctuate between 2.2 and about 9 ohms.

3) An infinite reading (no meter movement) in 1 direction and about 9 ohms in the other, indicates an open brush lead, worn or stuck brushes, a bad rotor or a loose regulator to brush holder attaching screw.

4) An ohmmeter reading of less than 2.2 ohms in both directions indicates a shorted rotor or bad regulator.

5) An ohmmeter reading significantly over 9 ohms in both directions indicates a defective regulator or loose "F" terminal screw.

6) Contact alternator rear housing with 1 ohmmeter probe and touch other probe to regulator "F" terminal. Reverse probes and repeat test.

7) Ohmmeter reading should be infinite in 1 probe direction and about 9 ohms in the other. A reading less than infinite in both directions indicates a grounded brush lead or defective regulator.

8) A reading significantly over 9 ohms in both directons indicates a defective regulator or a bad terminal "A" connection.

MOTORCRAFT WITH INTEGRAL REGULATOR (Cont.)

Fig. 3: Testing for Open or Short Circuit

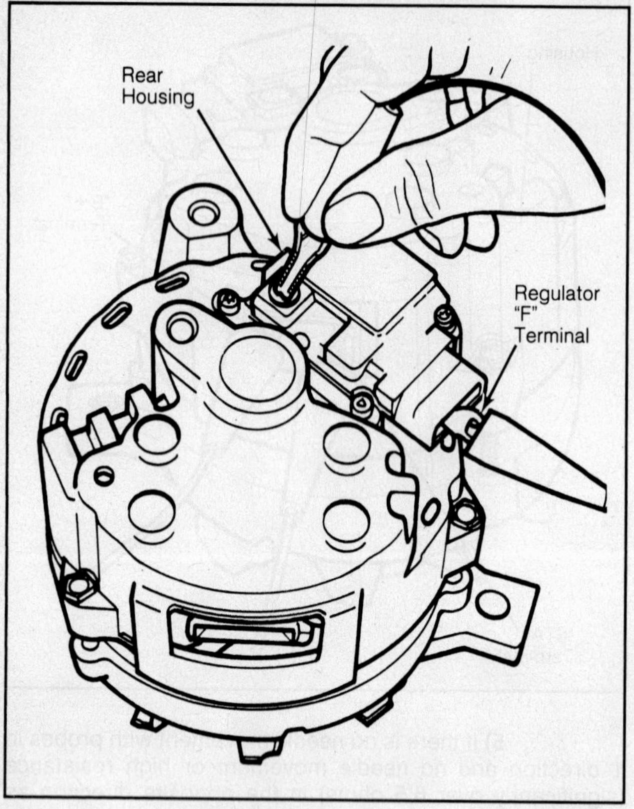

RECTIFIER TEST

1) Remove rectifier from alternator. Set ohmmeter knob at "X1" and calibrate meter. Contact 1 probe to 1 of the rectifier "B+" blade terminals and contact each of 3 stator terminals with other probe. Reverse probes and repeat test.

2) All diodes should show a low reading of about 7 ohms in 1 direction and an infinite reading with probes reversed. This reading may be checked against a good rectifier if one is available.

3) Perform the preceding test for negative diodes by contacting rectifier base plate and 3 stator terminals. If readings are not as specified, replace rectifier.

RADIO SUPPRESSION CAPACITOR OPEN OR SHORT TEST

NOTE: This is an open or short circuit test only and does not measure capacitance value. Actual capacitance value should be measured on a capacitance bridge at 1kHz at a maximum voltage of 350 mV RMS.

1) Contact a probe to 1 of rectifier "B+" blade terminals and contact the other probe to rectifier base plate. Reverse probes and repeat test.

2) One position should give an infinite reading, indicating reverse current direction through the diodes. The other position should give a reading of about 1000 ohms, indicating the forward current direction. The same reading in both directions indicates a defective rectifier.

3) To check capacitor, contact probes to rectifier "B+" terminal and base plate in the forward (1000 ohms) current direction. While observing meter indicator

Fig. 4: Testing Rectifier Assembly

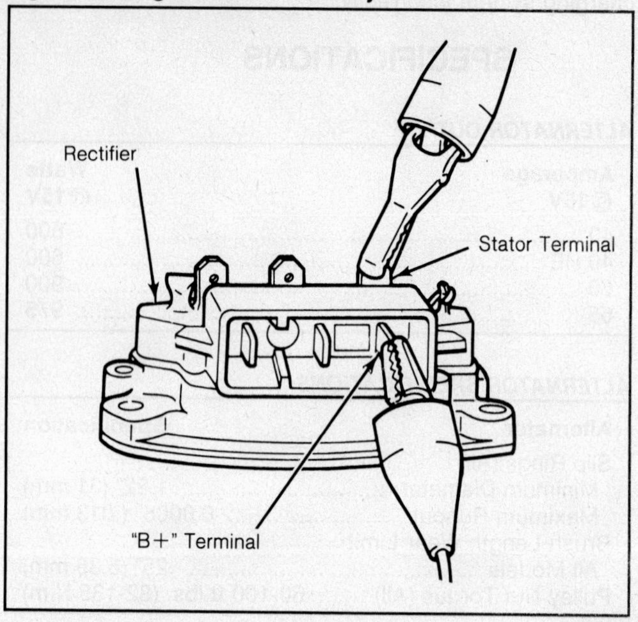

needle, reverse probes and again contact them to rectifier "B+" terminal and base plate.

4) Indicator needle should jump slightly (indicating that ohmmeter batteries are charging the capacitor) and then return to its original position (infinite reading). If needle does not jump, capacitor is open. Replace rectifier as a unit.

STATOR COIL GROUNDED TEST

1) Remove stator from alternator and disconnect it from the rectifier. Set ohmmeter knob to "X1000" and calibrate. Connect ohmmeter probes to 1 of the stator lead terminals and to the stator laminated core. Be sure probe makes a good electrical connection with the stator core. Meter should show an infinite reading.

2) If meter does not indicate an infinite reading, stator winding is grounded to the core and stator must be replaced.

Fig. 5: Testing Stator for Grounded or Shorted Winding

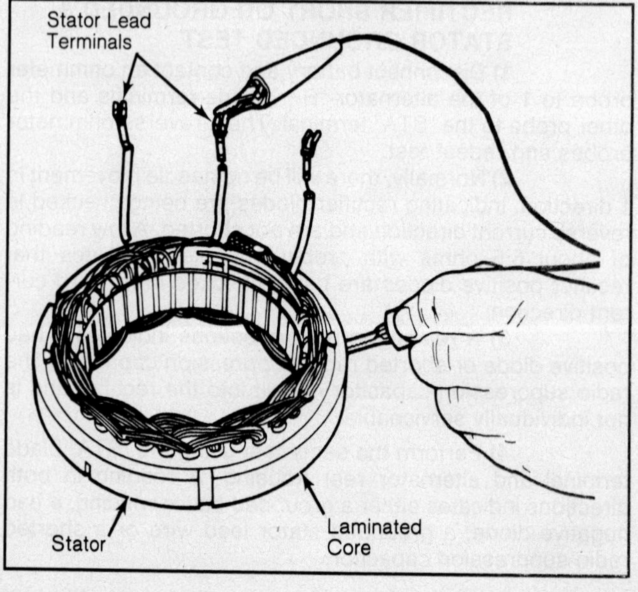

MOTORCRAFT WITH INTEGRAL REGULATOR (Cont.)

STATOR OPEN TEST

1) Disconnect stator from rectifier. Set ohmmeter knob at "X1" and calibrate. Connect 1 probe to a stator phase lead terminal. Touch the other probe to another stator lead terminal. Check meter reading.

2) Repeat this test with the other 2 stator lead combinations. If no meter movement occurs on a lead paired with either of the other phase leads, that phase is open and the stator must be replaced.

ROTOR OPEN OR SHORT TEST

1) Remove rotor from alternator. Set ohmmeter knob to "X1" and calibrate. Contact each ohmmeter probe to a rotor slip ring. Meter reading should be 2.0-3.9 ohms.

2) A higher reading indicates a damaged slip ring, welded connection or a broken wire. A low reading indicates a shorted wire or slip ring. Replace rotor if it is damaged and cannot be serviced.

3) Contact 1 ohmmeter probe to a slip ring and the other probe to the rotor shaft. Meter reading should be infinite. A reading other than infinite indicates rotor coil is grounded to shaft. Replace rotor if it is grounded and cannot be serviced.

Fig. 6: Testing Rotor for Open or Short Circuit

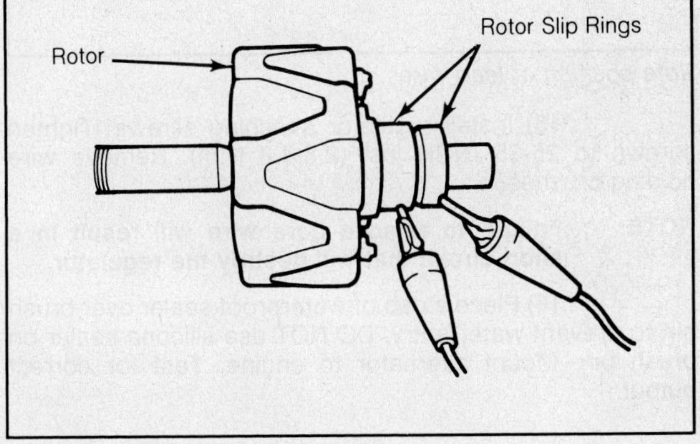

OVERHAUL

REMOVAL & DISASSEMBLY

1) Disconnect negative battery cable from battery. Disconnect wire harness attachments to integral regulator. Pull both connectors STRAIGHT OUT.

2) Loosen alternator pivot bolt and remove adjustment bolt from alternator. Disengage drive belt from pulley.

3) Remove alternator pivot bolt and alternator from vehicle. Remove alternator fan shield, if equipped.

4) Remove 4 screws (T20 Torx) attaching regulator to alternator rear housing. Remove regulator, with brush holder attached, from alternator. Remove "A" terminal insulator and 2 screws (T20 Torx) attaching regulator to brush holder.

5) Separate regulator, attaching nuts, brushes and brush springs from brush holder. Scribe a line across end housings and stator laminated core for reference during reassembly.

6) Remove 3 through bolts. Separate front housing and rotor from stator and rear housing. It may be necessary to tap front housing with a plastic hammer to loosen it from stator core.

7) Remove 3 stator lead terminals from rectifier. If terminals are soldered in place, unsolder connections using a 100 watt soldering iron. Use needle-nose pliers to pull stator lead terminal upward from rectifier. Separate stator from rear housing.

8) Remove 4 rectifier attaching screws (T20 Torx) and remove rectifier from housing. Using an arbor press, remove bearing from rear housing. Support housing close to bearing boss to prevent damage.

9) Remove drive pulley retaining nut from rotor using Alternator Pulley Holder (T65P-10300-P). Remove flat washer, drive pulley, fan and fan spacer from rotor shaft. Remove rotor from housing and remove housing from vise.

10) Remove front rotor stop from rotor shaft. DO NOT remove stop ring from shaft unless it is damaged. Remove screws attaching bearing retainer to front housing and remove retainer.

INSPECTION

CAUTION: When rebuilding an integral alternator, use only high temperature bearings. Use of standard parts will result in alternator failure.

1) Wipe stator, rotor and front bearing with a clean cloth. DO NOT clean these parts with solvent. Rotate front bearing on drive end of rotor shaft. Check for any scraping noise, looseness or roughness. Look for excessive lubricant leakage. If any of these conditions exist, replace bearing.

2) Inspect rotor shaft rear bearing surface for roughness or severe chatter marks. Replace rotor if shaft is not smooth.

3) Place rear bearing on slip ring end of rotor shaft and rotate bearing. Make same check for noise, looseness and roughness as was made for front bearing. Inspect rollers and cage for damage. Replace rear bearing if conditions exist.

4) Check slip rings for nicks and scratches. These may be removed by turning down slip rings. DO NOT go beyond a minimum diameter of 1.22" (31 mm). If rings are badly damaged, replace rotor.

5) Check all wire leads on both rotor and stator for loose or broken connections. Check windings for burned insulation. Replace parts that show signs of burned insulation.

6) Check pulley and fan for excessive looseness on rotor shaft and for cracks or other damage. Replace any pulley or fan that is loose, cracked or bent out of shape.

7) Check both front and rear housings for cracks, particularly in webbed areas at mounting ear. Replace a damaged or cracked housing. Wipe heat transfer grease from rectifier base and mounting area of rear housing with a clean cloth.

8) Replace brushes if they are worn shorter than 1/4" (6.35 mm) from surface of shunt. Remove sealing compound from brush pin hole in regulator.

ASSEMBLY & INSTALLATION

1) Install bearing into front housing. Press on outer race only. Position bearing retainer on front housing and install attaching screws. Tighten screws to 25-40 INCH lbs. (2.8-4.8 N.m).

MOTORCRAFT WITH INTEGRAL REGULATOR (Cont.)

2) If stop ring was removed from rotor shaft, install a new ring by sliding it over the end of the shaft and into groove farthest from pole piece. DO NOT open ring with snap ring pliers as permanent deformation of ring will result.

3) Install rotor stop on shaft with recessed side against stop ring. Install rotor in front housing and clamp housing in a vise equipped with protective jaws.

4) Install fan spacer, fan, drive pulley, flat washer and nut on rotor shaft. Tighten nut to 60-100 ft. lbs. (82-135 N.m). Remove rotor and housing from vise and check for free rotation of rotor.

5) Support rear housing close to bearing boss to prevent damage and install bearing using an arbor press. Press bearing into bore until it is flush with outside surface of housing.

6) Wipe rectifier base plate with a clean cloth. Apply 3/32" (2 mm) wide by 3/4" (20 mm) long strip of heat sink compound lengthwise across rectifier base plate.

7) Wipe rectifier mounting surface of rear housing with a clean cloth and seat rectifier into recessed mounting area.

CAUTION: Rectifier is cooled by conducting rectifier heat directly into rear housing. Failure to remove foreign material from mounting area or failure to apply heat sink compound may cause rectifier overheating.

8) Install rectifier attaching screws. Tighten screws to 25-35 INCH lbs. (2.8-4.0 N.m). Position stator in rear housing and align scribe marks made during disassembly. Push 3 stator terminals onto rectifier blade terminals.

9) Solder securely using resin core electrical solder if terminals were previously soldered. Work quickly to prevent overheating rectifier. Wipe rear end bearing surface of rotor shaft with a clean, lint-free coth.

10) Position rear housing and stator over rotor and align scribe marks. Seat machined portion of stator core into stop in both end housings. Install housing through bolts and tighten to 35-60 INCH lbs. (4.1-6.7 N.m).

11) Install springs and brushes in brush holder. Hold brushes in place by inserting a 1 3/8" (35 mm) piece of stiff insulated wire into brush holder pin hole. Position 2 nut and washer assemblies into retaining slots in brush holder.

12) Tip holder back slightly so that nut and washers fall to nut side of slots. Insert brush terminals past washers and into slots. Wipe regulator base plate with a clean cloth.

13) Position regulator against brush holder. Install regulator to brush holder attaching screws. Tighten screws to 20-30 INCH lbs. (2.3-3.4 N.m). Loop brush leads toward brush end of brush holder.

14) Install adhesive backed insulator onto "A" terminal screw head. Wipe regulator mounting surface of alternator rear housing with a clean cloth. Position regulator and brush holder onto rear housing.

Fig. 7: Alternator Brush Assembly

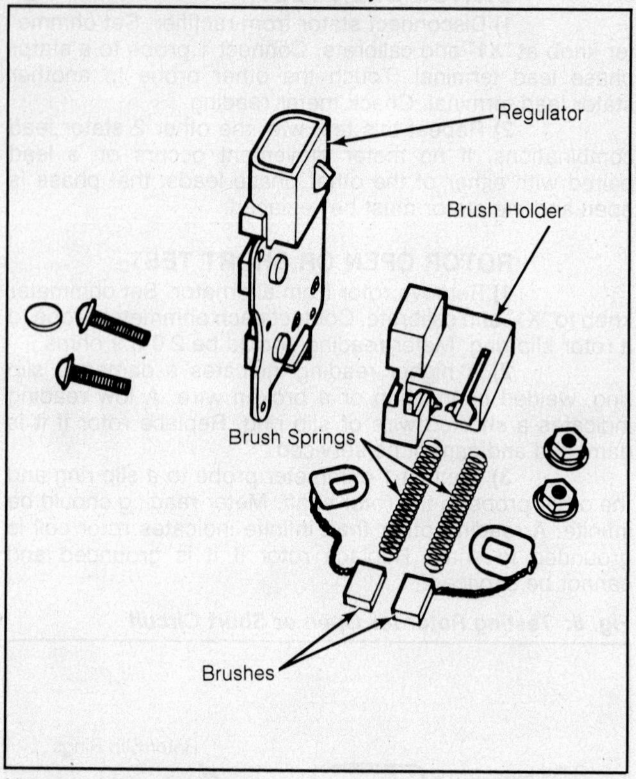

Note position of lead wires.

15) Install regulator attaching screws. Tighten screws to 25-35 INCH lbs. (2.8-4.0 N.m). Remove wire holding brushes.

NOTE: Failure to remove bare wire will result in a short circuit that will destroy the regulator.

16) Place a dab of waterproof sealer over brush pin to prevent water entry. DO NOT use silicone sealer on brush pin. Mount alternator to engine. Test for correct output.

TIGHTENING SPECIFICATIONS [1]

Application	INCH Lbs. (N.m)
Housing Through Bolts	35-60 (4.6.8)
Rectifier Mounting Screw	25-35 (2.8-4.0)
Brush Holder Mounting Screw	20-30 (2.3-3.4)
Regulator Mounting Screw	25-35 (2.8-4.0)
Bearing Retainer Screw	25-40 (2.8-4.5)
Drive Pulley Nut	60-100 (82-135)

1 – Drive pulley nut is tightened to 60-100 ft. lbs. (82-135 N.m).

PARIS-RHONE ALTERNATOR

Jeep Cherokee, Wagoneer
With 2.1L Turbo Diesel Engine

DESCRIPTION

Alternating current is generated by the stator as the stator rotates. The rectifier bridge changes the alternating current to direct current. The amount of D.C. voltage produced by the alternator is controlled by the solid state regulator. When the alternator output voltage is low, the regulator increases the current flowing through the field. This increases the alternator's output voltage at terminal "B". Field current is supplied directly from the stators output through the diode trio.

PRECAUTIONS

To avoid damaging the charging system, always abide the following precations:

- Do not attempt to polarize the alternator.
- Do not short circuit across terminals or connect ground to any terminals in the charging system except as specifically instructed.
- Never drive the alternator with the engine when the output terminal circuit is open or disconnected.
- Ensure that the alternator and battery have same ground polarity.
- When connecting a charger or a booster battery to vehicle battery, connect negative terminal to negative terminal and positive terminal to positive terminal.

Fig. 1: Exploded View of Paris-Rhone Alternator

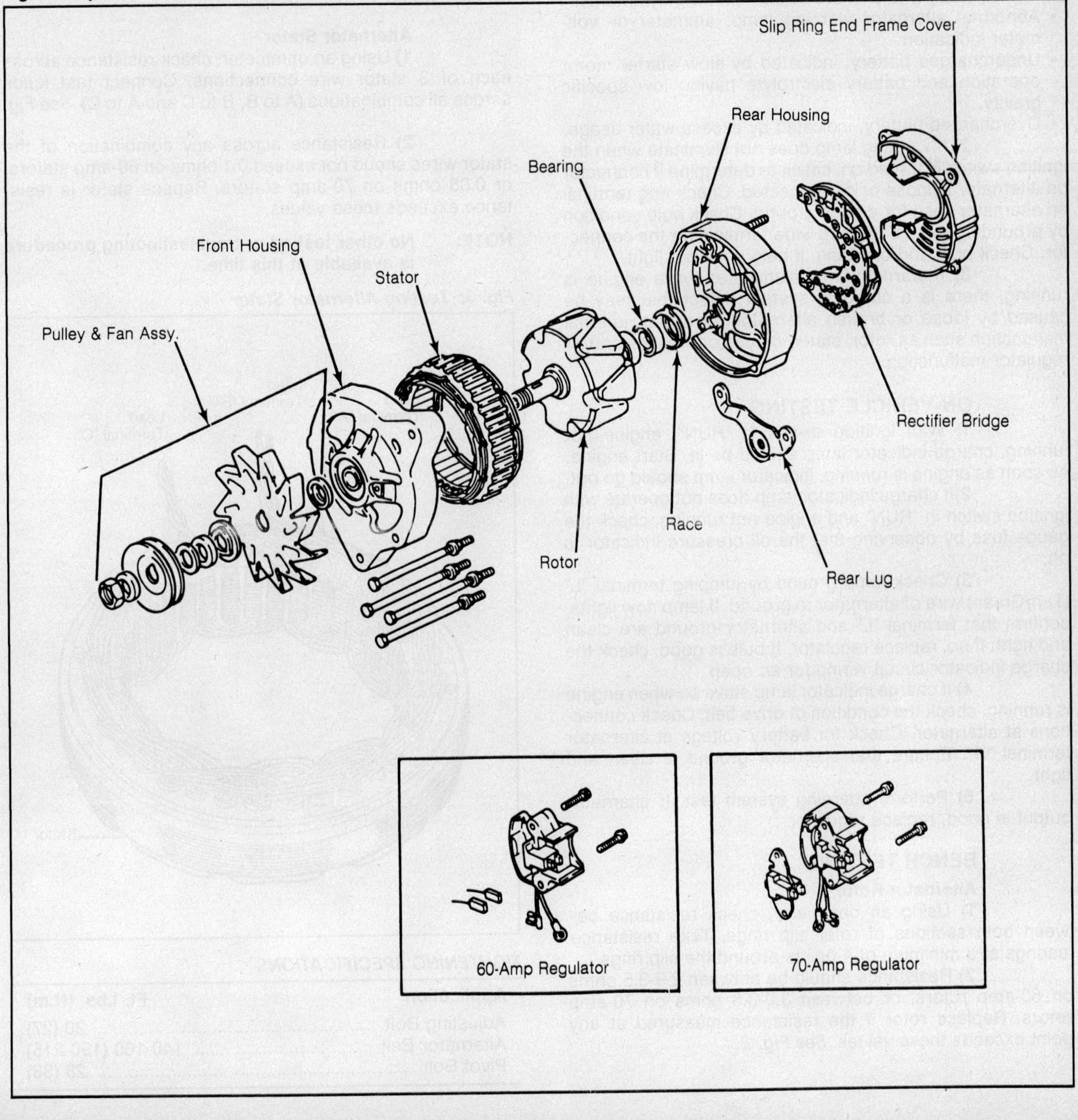

PARIS-RHONE ALTERNATOR (Cont.)

SPECIFICATIONS

ALTERNATOR CURRENT TEST SPECIFICATIONS

Engine RPM	Alternator RPM	60-Amp Model	70-Amp Model
700	1500	19 Amps	21 Amps
1400	3000	53 Amps	57 Amps
2800	6000	60 Amps	68 Amps

TROUBLE SHOOTING

1) Prior to performing any electrical test, visually inspect all charging system components and wiring for obvious problems. Malfunction of charging system is usually indicated by one or more of the following symptoms:

- Abnormal alternator warning lamp, ammeter or voltmeter indication.
- Undercharged battery, indicated by slow starter motor operation and battery electrolyte having low specific gravity.
- Overcharged battery, indicated by excess water usage.

2) If warning lamp does not illuminate when the ignition switch is turned on, check to determine if connector on alternator is loose or disconnected. Check ring terminal on alternator case for a good ground. Check bulb condition by grounding the .25" (6 mm) wide terminal on the connector. Check bulb and/or wiring, if bulb does not light.

3) If warning lamp illuminates while engine is running, there is a charging system defect that may be caused by loose or broken alternator drive belt, internal malfunction such as rotor, stator, diodes or brushes and/or regulator malfunction.

ON-VEHICLE TESTING

1) With ignition switch in "RUN", engine not running, charge indicator lamp should be lit. Start engine. As soon as engine is running, indicator lamp should go out.

2)If charge indicator lamp does not operate with ignition switch in "RUN" and engine not running, check the gauge fuse by observing that the oil pressure indicator is on.

3) Check lamp ground by jumping terminal "L" (Tan/Green) wire of alternator to ground. If lamp now lights, confirm that terminal "L" and alternator ground are clean and tight. If so, replace regulator. If bulb is good, check the charge indicator circuit wiring for an open.

4) If charge indicator lamp stays on when engine is running, check the condition of drive belt. Check connections at alternator. Check for battery voltage at alternator terminal "B". Ensure that alternator ground is clean and tight.

5) Perform charging system test. If alternator output is good, replace regulator.

BENCH TESTING

Alternator Rotor

1) Using an ohmmeter, check resistance between both sections of rotor slip rings. Take resistance readngs at a minimum of 4 points around the slip rings.

2) Resistance should be between 2.9-3.5 ohms on 60-amp rotors, or between 3.0-3.6 ohms on 70-amp rotors. Replace rotor if the resistance measured at any point exceeds these values. *See Fig. 2.*

Fig. 2: Testing Alternator Rotor

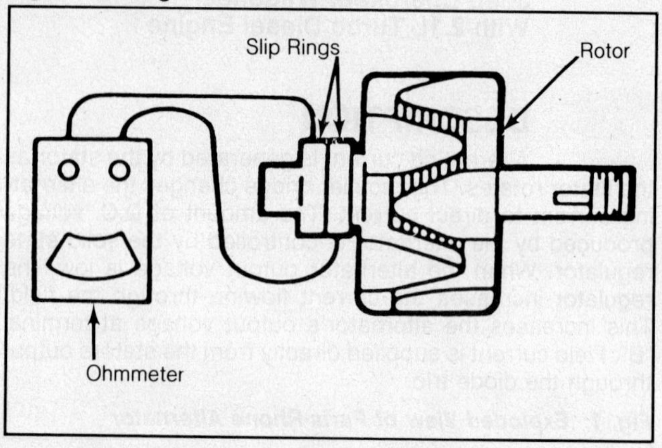

Alternator Stator

1) Using an ohmmeter, check resistance across each of 3 stator wire connections. Connect test leads across all combinations (A to B, B to C and A to C). *See Fig. 3.*

2) Resistance across any combination of the stator wires shoud not exceed 0.1 ohms on 60-amp stators, or 0.08 ohms on 70-amp stators. Repace stator is resistance exceeds these values.

NOTE: **No other testing or troubleshooting procedure is available at this time.**

Fig. 3: Testing Alternator Stator

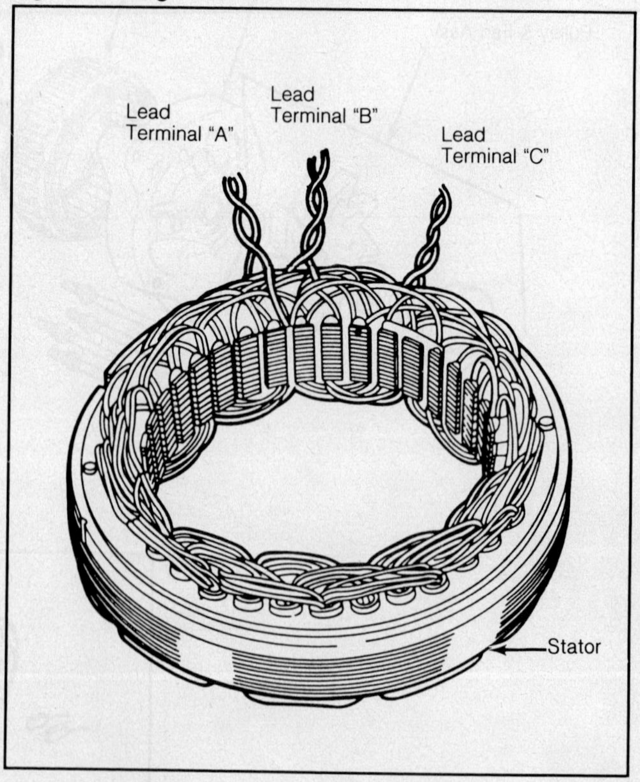

TIGHTENING SPECIFICATIONS

Application	Ft. Lbs. (N.m)
Adjusting Bolt	20 (27)
Alternator Belt	140-160 (190-215)
Pivot Bolt	28 (38)

TROUBLE SHOOTING

CONDITION	POSSIBLE CAUSE	CORRECTION
Starter Fails to Operate	Dead battery or bad connections between starter and battery	Check battery charge and all wires and connections to starter
	Ignition switch faulty or misadjusted	Adjust or replace ignition switch
	Open circuit between starter switch and ignition terminal on starter relay	Check and repair wires and connections as necessary
	Starter relay or starter defective	See Testing in STARTERS
	Open solenoid pull-in wire	See Testing in STARTERS
Starter Does Not Operate and Headlights Dim	Weak battery or dead battery cell	Charge or replace battery as necessary
	Loose or corroded battery connections	Check that battery connection are clean and tight
	Internal ground in starter windings	See Testing in STARTERS
	Grounded starter fields	See Testing in STARTERS
	Armature rubbing on pole shoes	See Overhaul in STARTERS
Starter Turns but Engine Does Not Rotate	Starter clutch slipping	See Overhaul in STARTERS
	Broken clutch housing	See Overhaul in STARTERS
	Pinion shaft rusted or dry	See Overhaul in STARTERS
	Engine basic timing incorrect	See Ignition Timing in TUNE-UP
	Broken teeth on engine flywheel	Replace flywheel and check for starter pinion gear damage
Starter Will Not Crank Engine	Faulty overrunning clutch	See Overhaul in STARTERS
	Broken clutch housing	See Overhaul in STARTERS
	Broken flywheel teeth	Replace flywheel and check for starter pinion gear damage
	Armature shaft sheared or reduction gear teeth stripped	See Overhaul in STARTERS
	Weak battery	Charge or replace battery as necessary
	Faulty solenoid	See On Vehicle Tests in STARTERS
	Poor grounds	Check all ground connections for tight and clean connections
	Ignition switch faulty or misadjusted	Adjust or replace ignition switch as necessary
Starter Cranks Engine Slowly	Battery weak or defective	Charge or replace battery as necessary
	Engine overheated	See ENGINE COOLING SYSTEMS
	Engine oil too heavy	Check that proper viscosity oil is used
	Poor battery-to-starter connections	Check that all connections between battery and starter are clean and tight
	Current draw too low or too high	See Bench Tests in STARTERS
	Bent armature, loose pole shoe screws or worn bearings	See Overhaul in STARTERS
	Burned solenoid contacts	Replace solenoid
	Faulty starter	Replace starter
Starter Engages Engine Only Momentarily	Engine timing too far advanced	See Ignition Timing In TUNE-UP
	Overrunning clutch not operating	Replace overrunning clutch. See Overhaul in STARTERS
	Broken starter clutch housing	See Overhaul in STARTERS
	Broken teeth on engine flywheel	Replace flywheel and check starter pinion gear for damage
	Weak drive assembly thrust spring	See Overhaul in STARTERS
	Weak hold-in coil	See Bench Tests in STARTERS
Starter Drive Will Not Engage	Defective point assembly	See Testing in STARTERS
	Poor point assembly ground	See Testing in STARTERS
	Defective pull-in coil	Replace starter solenoid
Starter Relay Does Not Close	Dead battery	Charge or replace battery as necessary
	Faulty wiring	Check all wiring and connections leading to relay
	Neutral safety switch faulty	Replace neutral safety switch
	Starter relay faulty	Replace starter relay

Starting Systems

TROUBLE SHOOTING (Cont.)

CONDITION	POSSIBLE CAUSE	CORRECTION
Starter Drive Will Not Disengage	Starter motor loose on mountings	Tighten starter attaching bolts
	Worn drive end bushing	See Overhaul in STARTERS
	Damaged engine flywheel teeth	Replace flywheel and check starter pinion gear for damage
	Drive yolk return spring broken or missing	Replace return spring
	Faulty ignition switch	Replace ignition switch
	Solenoid contact switch plunger stuck	Replace starter solenoid
	Faulty starter relay	Replace starter relay
	Insufficient clearance between winding leads to solenoid terminal and main contact in solenoid	Replace starter solenoid
	Starter clutch not disengaging	Replace starter clutch
	Ignition starter switch contacts sticking	Replace ignition switch
Starter Relay Operates but Solenoid Does Not	Faulty solenoid switch, switch connections or switch wiring	Check all wiring between relay and solenoid or replace relay or solenoid as necessary
	Broken lead or loose soldered connections	Repair wire or wire connections as necessary
Solenoid Plunger Vibrates When Switch is Engaged	Weak battery	Charge or replace battery as necessary
	Solenoid contacts corroded	Clean contacts or replace solenoid
	Faulty wiring	Check all wiring leading to solenoid
	Broken connections inside switch cover	Repair connections or replace solenoid
	Open hold-in wire	Replace solenoid
Low Current Draw	Worn brushes or weak brush springs	Replace brushes or brush springs as necessary
High Pitched Whine During Cranking Before Engine Fires but Engine Fires and Cranks Normally	Distance too great between starter pinion and flywheel	Align starter or check that correct starter and flywheel are being used
High Pitched Whine After Engine Fires With Key Released. Engine Fires and Cranks Normally	Distance too small between starter pinion and flywheel. Flywheel runout contributes to the intermittent nature	Align starter or check that correct starter and flywheel are being used

Starter Removal

ALL MODELS

REMOVAL & INSTALLATION

CHRYSLER CORP.

RWD Models

1) Disconnect ground cable at battery. Remove 1 bolt and 1 nut fastening starter motor heat shield. Remove battery cable at starter. Disconnect solenoid lead wires at terminals.

2) Remove 1 stud nut and 1 bolt attaching starter to flywheel housing. If equipped, slide auto. trans. cooling line bracket off stud. Remove starter from vehicle. DO NOT damage flywheel housing seal.

3) Prior to installation, test starter motor. Ensure starter and flywheel housing surfaces are free of dirt and oil. This ensures a good electrical connection.

4) When tightening starter motor attaching bolt, be sure to pull starter motor away from the engine to insure proper alignment. Reverse remaining removal procedure.

FWD Models

1) Disconnect negative battery cable. Remove heat shield clamp and heat shield, if equipped. On 2.2L engine, loosen air pump tube at exhaust manifold and swivel tube bracket away from starter.

2) Remove battery cable at starter. Disconnect solenoid lead wire. Remove bolts attaching starter to flywheel housing and rear bracket to engine or transaxle and remove starter from vehicle.

3) To install, position starter and install mounting bolts attaching starter to flywheel housing and rear bracket to engine. Connect battery cable to starter. Connect solenoid lead wire.

4) On 2.2L engine, swivel air pump tube toward starter and connect tube bracket to exhaust manifold. Install heatshield and clamp. Connect negative battery cable.

FORD MOTOR CO.

All Except 2.3L Turbo Diesel Engine

Disconnect negative battery cable. Raise vehicle. Disconnect relay to starter cable at starter terminal. Remove starter mounting bolts and remove ground cable. Remove starter from vehicle. To install, reverse removal procedure.

2.3L Turbo Diesel Engine

1) Open hood. Disconnect negative ground cables from both batteries. Remove air intake hose between air cleaner and intake manifold. Remove No. 1 glow plug relay from starter and position out of way.

2) Disconnect starter solenoid wiring. Remove bolt from alternator reinforcement bracket. Remove 2 starter mounting bolts, and remove starter from vehicle. To install, reverse removal procedure.

GENERAL MOTORS

1) Disconnect negative battery lead at battery. Raise vehicle. Remove starter braces and shields that may be in the way. Remove 2 starter motor attaching bolts, and allow starter motor to drop down.

2) Remove solenoid lead wires and battery cable from starter. To install, reverse removal procedure. Ensure that any shims removed are replaced.

JEEP

Delco-Remy Starter Motor

1) Disconnect negative battery cable at battery. Raise vehicle. From beneath vehicle, remove 2 starter motor mounting bolts. Allow starter to drop down.

2) Disconnect solenoid wires and battery cable. Remove starter from vehicle. To install reverse removal procedure. Replace any shims that were removed during removal.

Paris-Rhone Starter Motor
2.1L Turbo Diesel Engine

1) Disconnect battery negative cable. Disconnect starter solenoid wires on starter motor. Remove starter upper support bracket which is attached to starter and engine block.

2) Support left side of engine and remove left side engine mount. Remove starter lower rear support bracket which is attached to the starter and engine block.

3) To install, be sure starter locating dowel is properly seated in the aligning hole. Install starter mounting bolts and hand tighten only at this time. Install starter upper and lower support brackets. DO NOT tighten bolts at this time.

4) Tighten starter mounting bolts. Then, tighten starter upper and lower support bracket bolts. Install left side engine mount. Connect starter solenoid wires and battery cable. Install negative battery cable at battery.

Motorcraft Starter Motor

1) Disconnect negative battery cable at battery. Disconnect the cable from starter motor terminal. Remove attaching bolts and remove starter motor from vehicle.

2) To install, assemble bracket and bolt/washer to starter motor. Install motor and shim(s) to the cylinder block with dowel bolts. Ensure position of dust cover on man. trans. models is correct. Install bracket and mounting bolt/washer to engine block.

Starters

BOSCH & NIPPONDENSO

Chrysler Corp. FWD Models, Chevrolet & GMC 2.2L Diesel

DESCRIPTION

Chrysler Corp. models equipped with 2.2L engines use either a Bosch or Nippondenso direct drive starter motor with an overrunning clutch. Models with 2.6L engines and A-470 automatic transaxles use a Nippondenso reduction gear starter motor. Although structure of the starter motors differs, the electrical wiring is similar.

ON-VEHICLE TESTING

AMPERAGE DRAW TEST

NOTE: **Tests are performed with a Battery-Starter tester which incorporates a carbon pile rheostat. Engine should be at normal operating temperature and battery should be at full charge.**

1) Connect Battery-Starter tester and remote starter switch. Turn control knob to "OFF" position and set voltmeter selector to 16 volt position.

2) Turn function selector to Starter System Test (0-500 amp scale). Connect positive voltmeter lead to positive battery terminal and negative voltmeter lead to negative battery terminal.

3) Connect positive ammeter lead to positive battery terminal and negative ammeter lead to negative battery terminal. Disconnect coil wire from distributor cap and attach to a good ground to prevent engine from starting.

4) Crank engine. Note EXACT reading on voltmeter. Stop cranking engine. Turn tester control knob until EXACT reading is obtained on the voltmeter.

5) Observe ammeter reading. Ammeter should indicate starter amperage draw.

STARTER RESISTANCE TEST

1) Make sure battery is at full charge. Disconnect positive battery cable at battery. Connect an ammeter (0-300 scale) between disconnected battery lead and battery terminal.

2) Connect a voltmeter, graduated in tenths, between positive battery post and starter relay terminal on starter solenoid.

3) Crank engine and check reading on voltmeter and ammeter. Voltage reading should not exceed .3 volt.

4) A reading higher than .3 volt indicates a high resistance caused by loose circuit connections, defective cable, burned starter relay or solenoid switch contacts.

5) If current is high and starter cranks slowly, starter is defective and should be removed and repaired.

INSULATED CIRCUIT TEST

1) Make sure battery is at full charge. Set voltmeter selector to 4 volt position. Disconnect coil wire at distributor cap.

2) Connect voltmeter positive lead to positive battery terminal. Connect voltmeter negative lead to solenoid connector that connects to starter field coils.

NOTE: **It will be necessary to peel back rubber boot to gain access to connector. Voltmeter will read off scale until engine is cranked.**

3) Crank engine with a remote starter switch. Check voltmeter reading. A voltage drop of .3 volt or less indicates voltage drop is normal.

4) If voltmeter reads more than .3 volt, high resistance is indicated in starter insulated circuit.

5) Disconnect negative voltmeter lead from solenoid connector. Reconnect negative voltmeter lead to the following points and repeat test at each connection:

- Solenoid starter terminal.
- Solenoid battery terminal.
- Solenoid battery cable terminal.
- Starter relay and battery cable connection.

6) A small change will occur each time a portion of the circuit is removed from test. A definite change in voltmeter reading indicates the last part eliminated in test is at fault.

STARTER GROUND CIRCUIT

1) Connect voltmeter positive lead to starter housing. Connect voltmeter negative lead to battery negative terminal. Crank engine with a remote starter switch.

2) Voltmeter reading should not exceed .2 volt. A reading less than .2 volt indicates a voltage loss in ground cable which is normal.

3) A voltage loss of more than .2 volt indicates excessive voltage loss in starter ground circuit.

4) Disconnect voltmeter. Reconnect to the following points and repeat test at each connection: Starter drive housing, cable terminal at engine and battery cable clamp.

5) A small change will occur each time a portion of the circuit is removed from test. A definite change in voltmeter indicates last part eliminated in test is at fault.

BENCH TESTING

NO LOAD TEST

1) Place starter in a vise. Use a fully charged 12 volt battery. Connect an ammeter (0 - 100 scale) and a carbon pile rheostat in series with battery positive terminal and starter terminal.

2) Connect a voltmeter (16 volt scale) across starter. Rotate rheostat to full resistance position. Connect battery cable from negative battery terminal to starter housing.

3) Adjust rheostat until voltage shown on voltmeter is 11 volts. Check specifications for maximum amperage draw and minimum RPM.

ARMATURE FOR SHORT CIRCUIT

Place armature in a growler and hold a thin steel blade parallel and just above core while rotating armature slowly. If armature is shorted, blade will vibrate and be attracted to the core. Replace shorted armature.

ARMATURE FOR GROUND

Use test lamp and touch one lead to armature shaft and other lead to each commutator bar. *See Fig. 1.* If lamp lights, armature is grounded. Replace armature.

BOSCH & NIPPONDENSO (Cont.)

Fig. 1: Testing Starter Armature for Ground

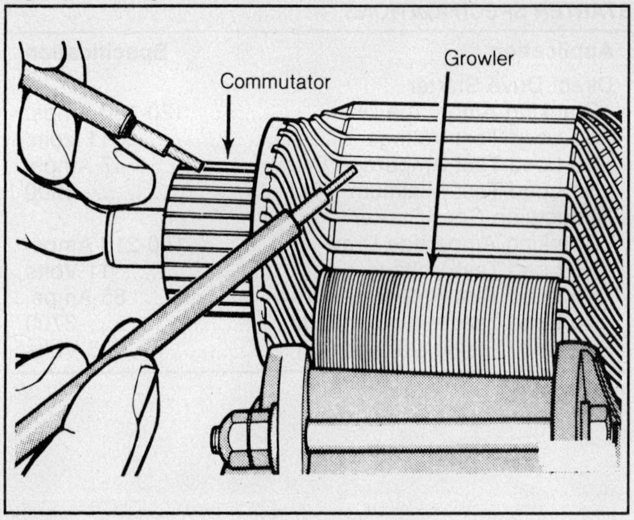

Fig. 2: Testing Field Coils for Ground

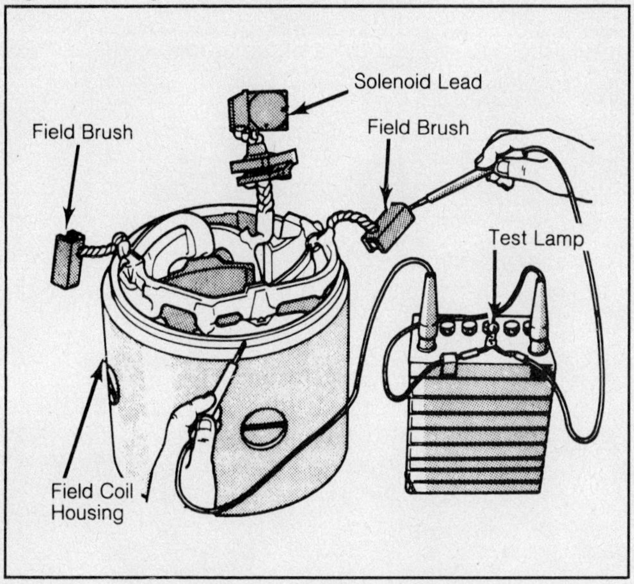

FIELD COILS FOR GROUND

Use test lamp and touch one probe to series field coil lead and other probe to field frame. *See Fig. 2.* If lamp lights, replace field coil housing assembly.

BRUSH HOLDERS FOR GROUND

1) Touch each of brush holders with one probe, while holding other probe against brush plate. Two brush holders are grounded 180° apart and should cause test lamp to light.

2) Other 2 brush holders should not cause lamp to light, as they are insulated. If these brush holders are grounded, replace brush plate assembly.

OVERHAUL

DISASSEMBLY

Bosch Starter

1) Disconnect field coil terminal nut. Remove solenoid mounting screws and work solenoid off shift fork. Remove solenoid. Remove screws and starter end shield bushing cap.

2) Remove bushing "C" washer and flat washer. Remove through bolts. Remove starter end shield. Slide 2 field brushes from holders by prying retaining springs back. Remove brush plate.

3) Slide field frame off starter over armature. Remove armature and clutch from drive end housing. Remove rubber seal. Remove clutch shift lever bolt and shift lever.

4) Press stop collar off snap ring using an arbor press and socket. Remove snap ring with snap ring pliers. Remove stop collar and clutch.

Nippondenso Starter

1) Remove nut from field coil terminal. Pull lead wire back. Remove 2 through bolts. Remove 2 screws from starter end shield. Remove upper left solenoid screw holding field coil wire retainer.

2) Remove starter end shield. Slide brushes from their holders by prying retaining springs back. Remove brush plate. Slide armature out of field frame. Remove field frame from gear housing.

3) Loosen gear housing to solenoid screws. Remove gear housing to solenoid screws. With a soft mallet, separate gear housing from solenoid. Remove reduction gear pinion roller retainer.

4) Remove reduction gear and clutch assembly from gear housing. Remove pinion gear from gear housing. Remove pinion gear rollers from gear housing. Remove solenoid ball and spring. Remove remaining solenoid cover screws. Remove cover from solenoid. Remove plunger from solenoid housing.

CLEANING

All Models

Clean armature, field coils, and brush end plate by wiping with a clean cloth. Grease dissolving solvent will damage insulation. Clean drive clutch using a brush moistened with solvent. Immersing drive clutch will wash lubricant out of assembly. Wash other parts in solvent.

REASSEMBLY

Bosch Starter

1) Install clutch and stop collar. Install snap ring with snap ring pliers. Using battery terminal puller, pull clutch stop collar over snap ring. Install clutch shift lever into drive end housing.

2) Install clutch shift lever bolt. Install and tighten shift lever nut. Install rubber seal into drive end housing. Install armature and clutch into drive end housing. Slide field frame over starter armature.

3) Install starter brush plate. Slide field brushes into their holders by prying retaining springs back. Install starter end shield. Install through bolts. Install flat washer and "C" washer.

4) Install starter end shield bushing cap. Work solenoid onto shift fork. Install solenoid mounting screws. Install field coil terminal lead to solenoid. Bench test before installation.

Nippondenso Starter

1) Install solenoid plunger into housing. Install cover to solenoid. Install solenoid cover screws. Leave upper left screw out at this time. Install solenoid ball and spring.

2) Coat rollers with grease and install into pinion roller retainer. Install pinion gear retainer and roller into

BOSCH & NIPPONDENSO (Cont.)

gear housing. Mesh pinion gear with reduction gear and install into gear housing.

3) Install gear housing to solenoid. Install 2 gear housing to solenoid screws. Install field frame to gear housing. Slide armature into field frame. Install brush plate.

4) Pry each brush spring back and slide brush into position. Install starter end shield. Install field coil wire retainer. Install upper left solenoid screw holding wire retainer. Position end shield and tighten screws.

5) Install through bolts and tighten. Install field coil terminal to field coil terminal stud. Push rubber boot onto terminal. Bench test starter prior to installation.

Fig. 3: Exploded View of Reduction Gear Starter

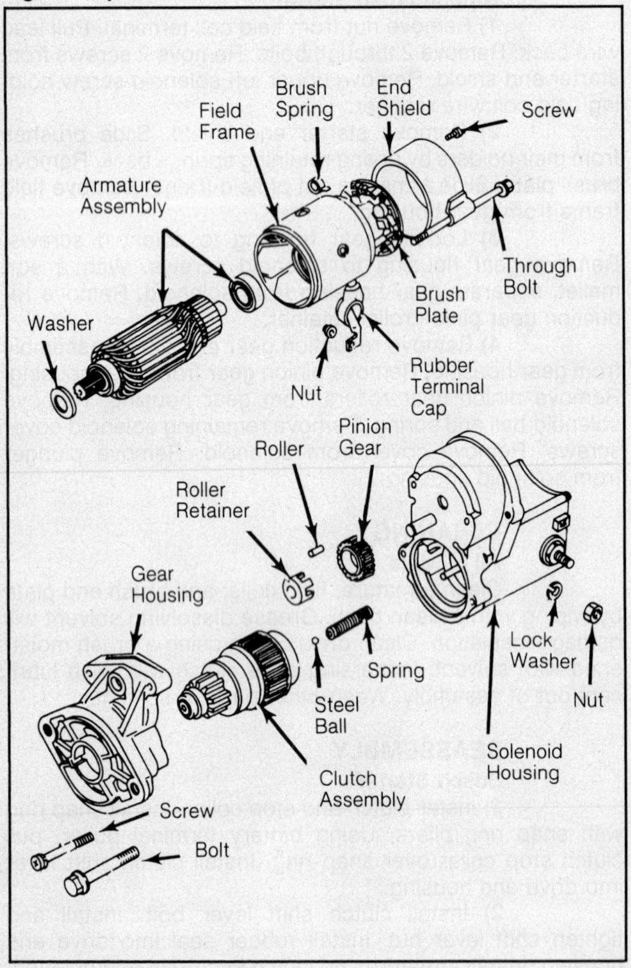

BOSCH & NIPPONDENSO STARTER SPECIFICATIONS

Application	Specification
Direct Drive Starter	
Cranking Amperage Draw	120-160 Amps.
No Load Test Voltage	11 Volts
No Load Test Amperage Draw	47 Amps.
No Load Test Minimum RPM	6600
Reductuion Gear Starter	
Cranking Amperage Draw	150-210 Amps.
No Load Test Voltage	11 Volts
No Load Test Amperage Draw	85 Amps.
No Load Test Minimum RPM	3700
Solenoid Closing Voltage (All)	7.5 Volts

CHRYSLER CORP. GEAR REDUCTION

Chrysler Corp. RWD Models

DESCRIPTION

The starter motor consists of 4 series parallel fields, 4 brushes and a solenoid-shifted, overrunning clutch. The starter has a 2-to-1 reduction gear set, built into the starter assembly, and located in a die cast aluminium housing. The starter consists of 2 separate circuits: The supply circuit, which provides heavy current to the motor, and the control circuit, which activates the solenoid.

TESTING

STARTER CONTROLS

NOTE: **Test solenoid and relay in order as described. Before performing test, disconnect coil wire from distributor cap and secure to a good ground to prevent engine from starting.**

Starter Solenoid

Connect a heavy jumper wire on starter relay between battery and solenoid terminals. If engine cranks, solenoid is good. Proceed to starter relay test. If engine does not crank or solenoid chatters, check wiring and connections from relay to starter for loose or corroded connections. Repeat test and if starter still fails to crank, starter must be removed for repairs.

Starter Relay

1) Position automatic transmission gear selector in "N" or "P" position and manual transmission in Neutral. Connect a jumper wire on starter relay between battery and ignition terminals.

2) If engine cranks, starter relay is good. If engine does not crank, connect a second jumper wire to starter relay ground terminal and a good ground. If engine still does not crank, replace starter relay.

3) If engine does crank, relay is functioning, transmission linkage is out of adjustment (automatic transmission) or neutral safety switch is defective (automatic transmission) or there is a poor ground between relay housing and its mounting surface.

CRANKING CIRCUIT RESISTANCE TEST

1) Make the following tests with engine cranking and all terminals connected. Connect a voltmeter at the following locations:

- Positive lead to battery positive post and negative lead to battery terminal on starter.
- Positive lead to starter housing and negative lead to negative post on battery.
- Positive lead to engine block and negative lead to battery ground cable.

2) Each of these 3 connections should show a voltmeter reading of .2 volt or less. If reading exceeds .2 volt, clean or repair cables and connections in circuit. Connect a voltmeter at the following locations:

- Positive lead to battery positive post and negative lead to cable clamp.
- Positive lead to battery negative post and negative lead to cable clamp.

3) If reading is other than zero on voltmeter, clean or repair cables and connections in circuit.

AMPERAGE DRAW TEST

NOTE: **Engine should be up to operating temperature before performing this test. Heavy oil or a tight engine will increase starter draw amperage.**

1) Connect a battery-starter tester and a remote starter jumper, both according to manufacturer's instructions. Turn variable resistor control knob to off or zero position. Crank engine long enough to read cranking voltage on voltmeter.

NOTE: **Do not crank engine excessively, or starter may overheat.**

2) Without cranking engine, turn variable resistor control knob on tester until voltmeter reads cranking voltage of previous test. With same voltmeter reading indicated, amperage reading will be equivalent to starter amperage draw test. See STARTER SPECIFICATIONS.

SOLENOID WINDINGS

1) Connect solenoid to a 6-volt DC power supply with an ammeter in series. Connect positive lead of power supply to solenoid terminal and positive lead of ammeter to solenoid sleeve.

2) Connect negative lead of power supply to other ammeter terminal. Turn current on and check draw against hold-in specifications. Check pull-in coil the same way, except connect positive ammeter lead to solenoid lead terminal.

3) Check draw against specifications. If either winding does not meet specifications, or if winding looks burnt or damaged, replace solenoid assembly.

NO LOAD TEST (ON BENCH)

Connect a test ammeter and carbon pile rheostat in series with battery positive post and starter terminal. Connect a voltmeter across starter. Rotate carbon pile to full resistance position. Connect battery cable from battery negative post to starter frame. Adjust rheostat until battery voltage shown on voltmeter reads 11 volts. Amperage draw should be as shown in specifications.

LOCKED RESISTANCE TEST

Mount starter in test bench. Follow test equipment manufacturer's instructions. With battery voltage adjusted to 4 volts, amperage draw should be as shown in specifications.

STARTER SPECIFICATIONS

Application	Amps
Amperage Draw Test	
3.7L & 5.2L	165-180
5.9L	180-200
Solenoid Winding Test (6 Volts @ 77°F)	
Pull-In Circuit	13-15
Hold-In Circuit	8-9
No Load Test (11 Volts @ 3700 RPM Minimum)	90
Locked Resistance Test (4 Volts)	475-550

OVERHAUL

DISASSEMBLY

1) Remove through bolts and end head assembly. By pulling outward, remove armature from gear hous-

CHRYSLER CORP. GEAR REDUCTION (Cont.)

ing and field frame assembly. Carefully pull field frame assembly from gear housing just far enough to expose terminal screw. Remove terminal screw. Completely remove field frame assembly.

2) Remove nuts and separate solenoid and brush plate assembly from gear housing. Remove nut, steel washer and sealing washer from solenoid terminal. Unwind solenoid lead wire from brush terminal. Remove screws attaching solenoid to brush plate. Remove solenoid from brush plate.

3) On brush plate, remove nut from battery terminal and remove terminal. From solenoid, remove solenoid contact and plunger assembly. Remove return spring from inside of solenoid moving core.

4) Remove dust cover from gear housing. Release retainer clip that positions driven gear on pinion shaft.

CAUTION: Retainer is under tension. Place cloth over assembly to catch it as it flies off.

5) Remove pinion shaft "C" clip. Push shaft toward rear of housing. Remove retainer ring and thrust washers. Remove clutch and pinion assembly. Remove the 2 shift fork nylon actuators as an assembly.

6) Remove driven gear and friction washer. Pull shifting fork forward and remove solenoid moving core. Remove shifting fork retainer pin and shifting fork assembly.

Fig. 1: Chrysler Corp. Shift Fork & Clutch Assembly

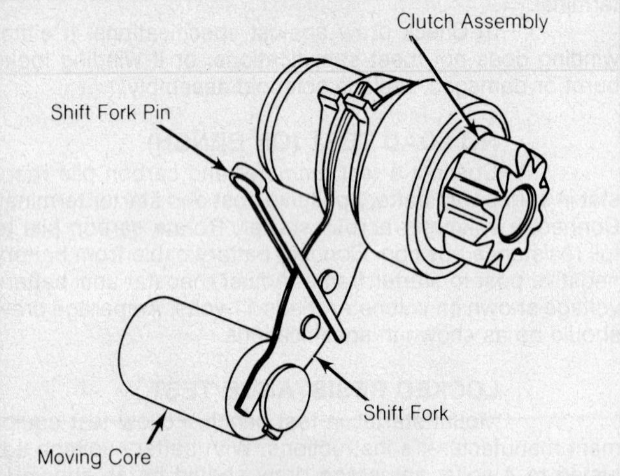

Remove shift fork assembly by removing retainer pin.

PARTS REPLACEMENT & TESTING

Brushes and Springs

Replace brushes if oil soaked or worn more than 1/2 length of new brushes. When soldering solenoid lead, use high temperature solder and resin flux. Measure spring tension with spring scale attached under spring near end. Pull on line parallel to edge of brush and note reading just as spring end leaves brush. Replace if tension is not within specifications.

SPRING TENSION

Application	Tension
All Models	32-36 ozs. (907-1021 g)

Starter Shaft Bushings

Inspect bearing surfaces for wear. Insert starter shaft into bushing and check for side play. Replace end head if its bushing is worn. Replace other bushings, using a Puller (C-3944). Service bushings are pre-sized and do not require burnishing or reaming.

Starter Clutch Unit

Pinion should rotate smoothly in 1 direction (not necessarily easy) and should not rotate in opposite direction. If not functioning properly, or if pinion is worn, chipped or burred, replace assembly.

CAUTION: Do not immerse in cleaning solvent. Unit is pre-lubricated and lubricant will wash out.

Armature

Check for shorted armature coils in growler. Check for grounded coils by touching 1 test light probe to armature shaft and other probe to each commutator bar. Lamp should not light. If lamp lights, armature coils are grounded and armature must be replaced. Commutator should be smooth and clean, and runout must not exceed .004" (.10 mm). If runout is excessive, reface in a lathe.

Field Coil Assembly

With field frame removed from starter, drill out rivet attaching field coil lead and shunt coil lead to frame. Insulate leads from frame. Test for ground with 110V test lamp by touching 1 probe to field coil lead and other probe to field frame. Lamp should not light. If lamp lights, field coils are grounded. Replace field coils and field frame as an assembly.

CLEANING

Do not immerse parts in cleansing solvent. Clutch outer housing and pinion gear may be cleaned with a cloth moistened with cleaning solvent and then wiped dry. Clean all corrosion from solenoid assembly and inside of solenoid housing. Clean terminal contacts and contactor with crocus cloth.

REASSEMBLY

1) Ensure that shift fork plates have approximately 1/16" side movement. Lubricate sparingly between plates with SAE 10 engine oil. Position shift fork in housing, bend 1 tip of pin at a 15° angle away from housing. Fork and retainer pin must operate freely after tip of pin is bent. Install solenoid moving core and engage shifting fork.

2) Start pinion shaft into drive housing. Install friction washer and drive gear, clutch and pinion assembly, thrust washer, retaining ring and thrust washer. Shift fork must engage clutch actuators properly and friction washer must be positioned on shoulder of pinion shaft splines before driven gear is positioned.

3) Install driven gear, retainer clip, pinion shaft "C" clip and starter solenoid return spring into bore of movable core. Install solenoid contact plunger assembly into solenoid. Contact spring must be positioned on shaft of solenoid contact and plunger assembly.

4) Assemble battery terminal stud in brush holder. Position seal on brush holder plate. Start solenoid lead wire through hole in brush holder. Install solenoid stud, insulating washer, flat washer, and nut.

5) Wrap lead wire tightly around brush terminal post. Solder with high temperature resin core solder and resin flux. Install brush holder to solenoid attaching screws. Install solenoid coil and brush plate assembly into starter gear housing. Install and tighten nuts.

CHRYSLER CORP. GEAR REDUCTION (Cont.)

6) Install armature thrust washer in brushes with brushes resting on washer tabs (washer will hold brushes out and facilitate armature installation). Install brush terminal screw. Position field frame in correct position on gear housing and install armature in field frame and gear housing.

Fig. 2: Exploded View of Reduction Gear Starter

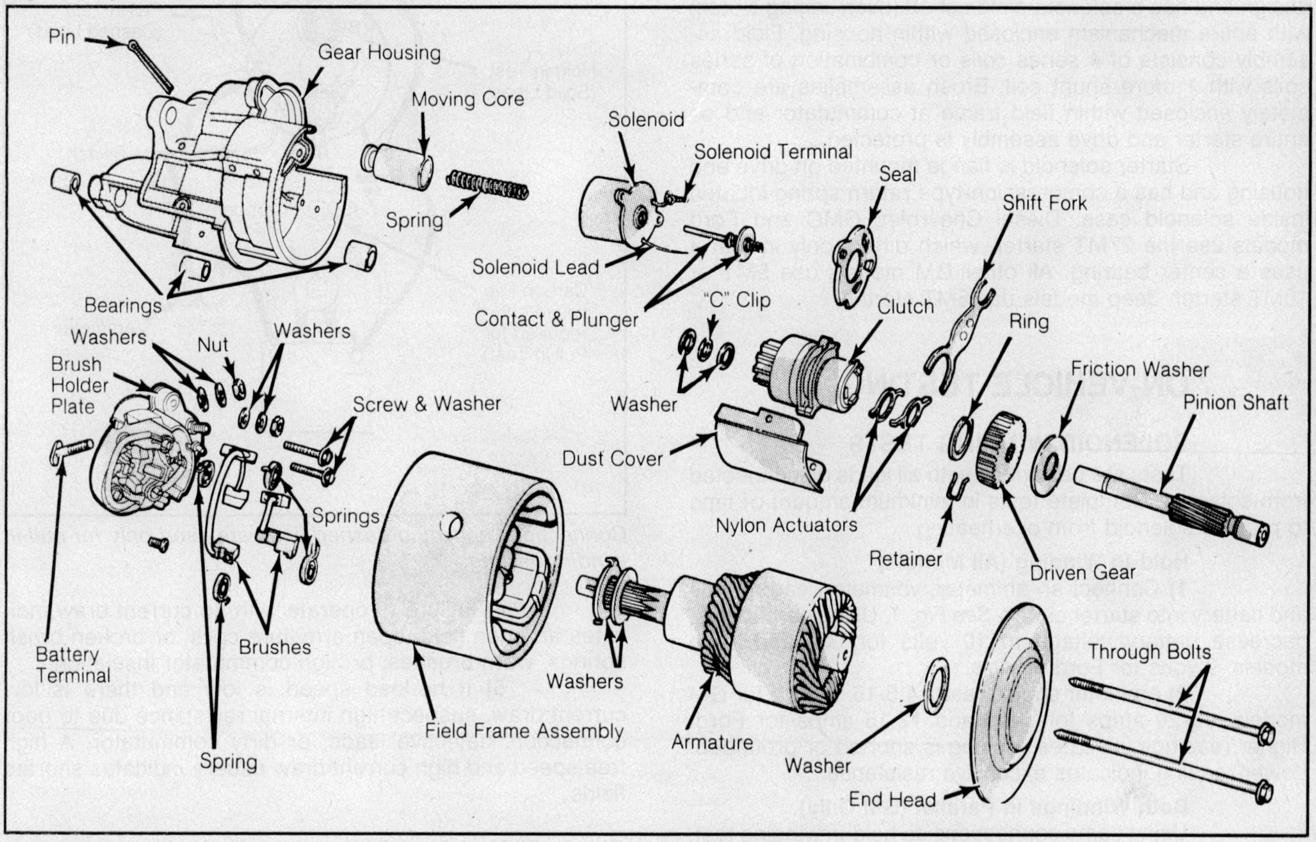

7) Carefully engage splines of shaft with reduction gear by rotating armature slightly. Install thrust washer on armature shaft. Position starter end head assembly and tighten through bolts securely.

DELCO-REMY ENCLOSED HOUSING

Chevrolet, Ford (6.9L Diesel), GMC, Jeep (2.8L V6)

DESCRIPTION

Starter is a 12-volt, 4-pole unit of conventional design and has a solenoid pinion shaft (overrunning clutch) with entire mechanism enclosed within housing. Field assembly consists of 4 series coils or combination of series coils with 1 more shunt coil. Brush assemblies are completely enclosed within field frame at commutator end so entire starter and drive assembly is protected.

Starter solenoid is flange mounted on drive end housing and has a compression-type return spring located inside solenoid case. Diesel Chevrolet, GMC and Ford models use the 27MT starter, which differs only in that it uses a center bearing. All other GM models use 5MT or 10MT starter. Jeep models use 5MT starter.

ON-VEHICLE TESTING

SOLENOID WINDING TESTS

Tests are performed with all leads disconnected from solenoid. Complete tests in minimum amount of time to prevent solenoid from overheating.

Hold-In Winding (All Models)

1) Connect an ammeter, voltmeter, carbon pile and battery into starter circuit. *See Fig. 1.* Using carbon pile, decrease battery voltage to 10 volts for GM and Jeep models, 9 volts for Ford models.

2) Ammeter should read 14.5-16.5 amps for GM models, 15-20 amps for Jeep and 12-16 amps for Ford. Higher readings indicates winding is shorted or grounded. Lower reading indicates excessive resistance.

Both Windings in Parallel (GM Only)

Using same connections as hold-in winding test, ground "M" terminal and using carbon pile adjust voltage to 10 volts. Amperage draw should be 41-47 amps.

Pull-In Windings (Ford and Jeep)

NOTE: Use carbon pile between battery and "M" terminal if its required to reduce voltage to specified testing voltage. If not, connect jumper directly from battery to "M" terminal.

Using solenoid test connections in dashed lines, decrease battery voltage to 9 volts for Ford, 5 volts for Jeep. *See Fig. 1.* Pull-in winding amperage draw should be 43-54 amps for Ford, 20-23 amps for Jeep.

STARTER NO LOAD TEST

1) To perform test, connect a tachometer, ammeter and voltmeter into start circuit. *See Fig. 2.* Adjust carbon pile to specified voltage indicated in table.

2) Read current draw and armature speed to ensure they are within specifications. Do not apply voltage greater than specified, as excessive voltage may cause armature to throw windings due to excessive speed.

3) Low free speed and high current draw indicates too much friction, shorted armature, or grounded armature or fields. Failure to operate with high current draw indicates a direct ground in terminal or fields or frozen bearings.

Fig. 1: All Models – Connections for Testing Solenoid Windings

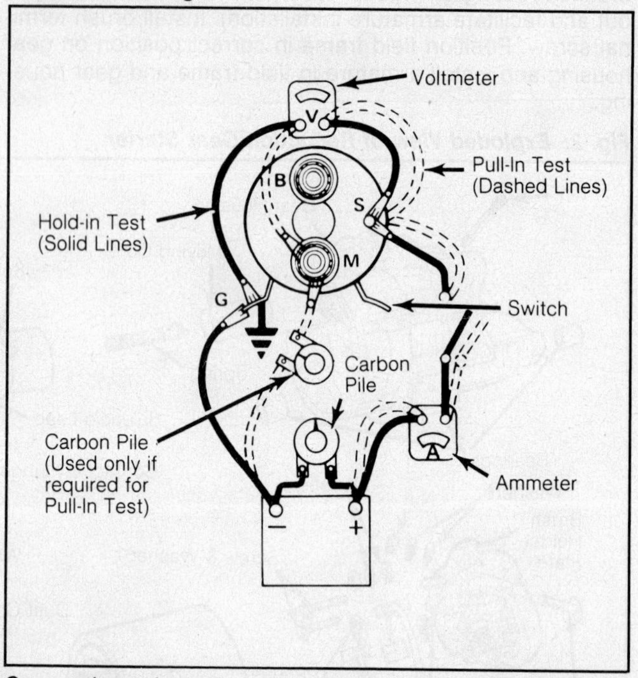

Connections shown in dashed lines are used only for pull-in winding testing.

4) Failure to operate with no current draw indicates an open field, open armature coils, or broken brush springs, worn brushes, or high commutator insulation.

5) If no-load speed is low and there is low current draw, suspect high internal resistance due to poor connection, defective leads, or dirty commutator. A high free speed and high current draw usually indicates shorted fields.

Fig. 2: All Models – Connections for No Load Test

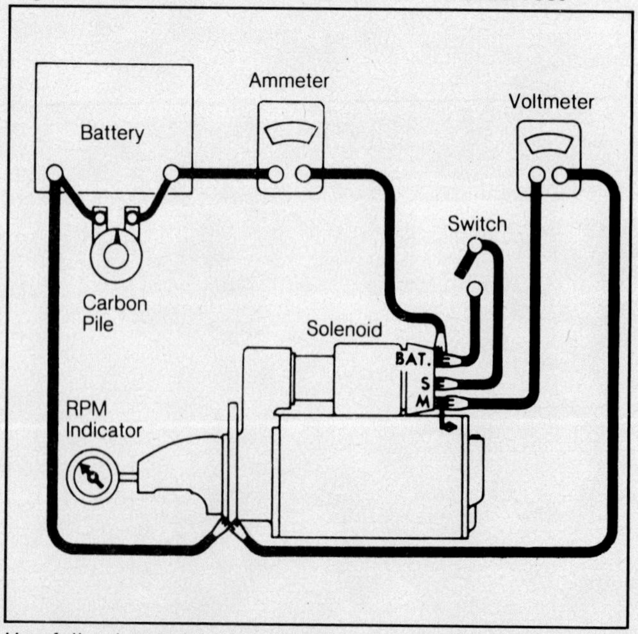

Use fully charged battery to make proper test.

DELCO-REMY ENCLOSED HOUSING (Cont.)

STARTER NO-LOAD SPECIFICATIONS [1]

Part No.	Amps.	RPM
1998427	50-75	6000-11,900
1998431	50-75	6000-11,900
1998437	60-90	6500-10,500
199843844	70-110	6500-10,700

[1] - Starter requires 10 volts for testing GM models, 9 volts for other models.

OVERHAUL

DISASSEMBLY

1) Disconnect field coil connector from solenoid motor terminal. Remove solenoid mounting screws and rotate solenoid 90° and remove along with solenoid plunger spring.

2) Remove 2 through bolts, commutator end frame, field frame assembly and washer. On diesel models, remove insulator. On gasoline models, remove armature assembly from drive housing and thrust collar from armature shaft.

3) On diesel models, remove shift lever pivot bolt, center bearing screws and drive gear housing from armature shaft. Shift lever and plunger assembly will now fall away from starter clutch.

4) Slide a 5/8" deep socket over pinion shaft and with a hammer, strike socket against retainer to drive retainer off snap ring. Remove snap ring from groove in armature shaft.

5) On diesel models, remove retainer, clutch assembly, fiber washer and center bearing. Remove roll pin and remove shift lever and plunger. On gasoline models, roller clutches are serviced as an assembly only.

CLEANING

Clean all parts by wiping with clean cloth. Do not clean armature, field coils, or drive assembly in any type of grease dissolving solvent as this will damage insulation and wash lubricant out of drive assembly.

BENCH TESTING

Armature

Test armature for shorted coils with a growler. Check for grounded coils using a self-powered test light. Place one test lead on armature core or shaft, and other test lead on commutator. Lamp should not light. If lamp lights, armature is grounded and should be replaced.

CAUTION: Some starters have molded-type commutator, insulation must not be undercut on these models as this may cause serious damage to commutator.

Field Coils

1) Using self-powered test light, place one test lead on field coil terminal strap, touch other test lead to field coil brush lead (check series coils and shunt coils separately at appropriate terminals).

2) Lamp should light. If lamp does not light, coils are open. Check for grounds by placing one test lead on field armature strap, touch other lead to armature core or shaft. If lamp lights, 1 or more coils are grounded.

CAUTION: Shunt coil ground lead must be disconnected and all field terminals insulated from frame when making this test.

Brushes, Springs & Holders

Replace brushes if worn to 1/2 of original length, or if oil-soaked or pitted. Check brush spring tension and replace springs if weak or distorted. Deformed or bent brush holders can be replaced by service units which are installed with screws and nuts.

Drive & Pinion

Pinion should turn freely in overrun direction and should not slip in drive direction. Check spring for correct tension and drive coilar for wear (these parts can be removed for replacement by forcing collar toward clutch and removing lock ring from end of tube). Replace drive assembly if pinion teeth are worn, chipped, or cracked.

Fig. 3: All Models (Except 5MT Starter) Brush Holder and Assembly

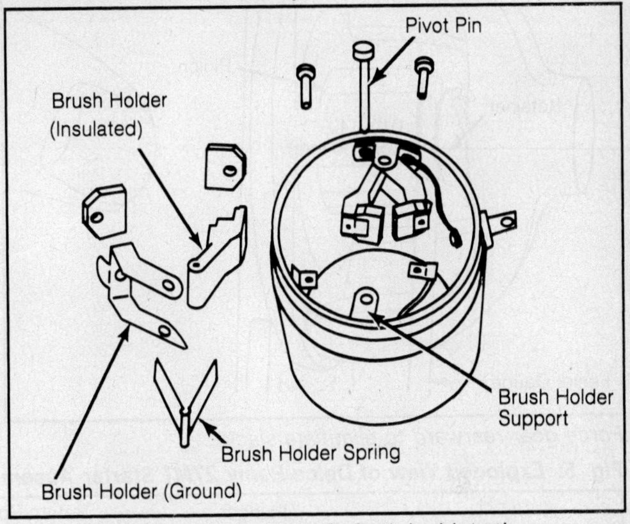

Replace brushes if worn to half of original length.

Pinion Clearance

1) Disconnect motor field coil connector and insulate it carefully. Connect a battery from solenoid switch terminal to solenoid frame. Momentarily flash a jumper lead from motor terminal to solenoid frame.

2) This shifts pinion into cranking position. Push pinion back toward commutator end to eliminate slack. Measure distance between pinion and pinion stop. When installing starter, check clearance between pinion and flywheel ring gear teeth.

3) Insert gauge .020" (.6 mm) diameter wire, about 3" (76 mm) long, with a 1/4" to 1/2" 90° bend in end between pinion tooth and ring gear. Center pinion tooth between flywheel teeth when making measurement.

PINION CLEARANCE

Application	Clearance
Pinion-to-Housing	[1] .010-.140" (.25-3.56 mm)
Pinion-to-Flywheel Clearance	.020" (.6 mm)

[1] - Measured between pinion stop (retainer) with pinion in engaged position.

DELCO-REMY ENCLOSED HOUSING (Cont.)

REASSEMBLY

1) On diesel model starters, assemble armature and clutch as follows: Lubricate drive end of armature shaft with silicone lubricant and install center bearing, fiber washer and clutch assembly onto armature, with pinion away from armature. Slide retainer onto shaft and install snap ring and thrust washer.

2) Position retainer and thrust washer with snap ring in between. Using pliers, grip retainer and washer and squeeze until snap ring is forced into retainer and is held in groove in armature shaft.

3) On all models, lubricate drive gear housing bushing with silicone lubricant. Engage shift lever yoke with clutch and slide complete assembly into drive gear housing.

4) Install center bearing screws and shift lever pivot bolt. Tighten securely. Install solenoid assembly on drive gear housing. Apply sealer (No. 1050026) to solenoid flange where it meets drive housing and field frame, using care not to damage brushes.

5) Position field frame against drive gear housing on alignment pin using care not to damage brushes. Lubricate commutator end frame bushing with silicone lubricant. Install washer on armature shaft and slide end frame onto shaft and install through bolts.

6) On diesel models, install insulator and then end frame onto shaft. Install through bolts, making sure they pass through bolt holes in insulator. Connect field coil connector to solenoid terminal. Check pinion clearance as outlined under, OVERHAUL and TESTING.

Fig. 4: All Models Checking Pinion-to-Housing Clearance

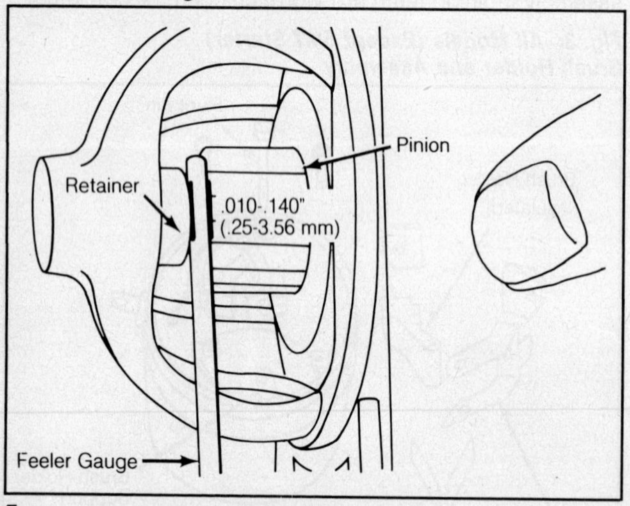

Force gear rearward to eliminate slack.

Fig. 6: All Models Exploded View of Shift Lever Assembly

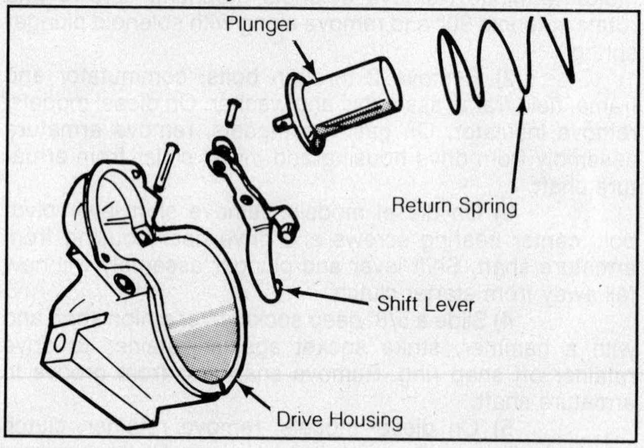

Fig. 5: Exploded View of Delco-Remy 27MT Starter Assembly

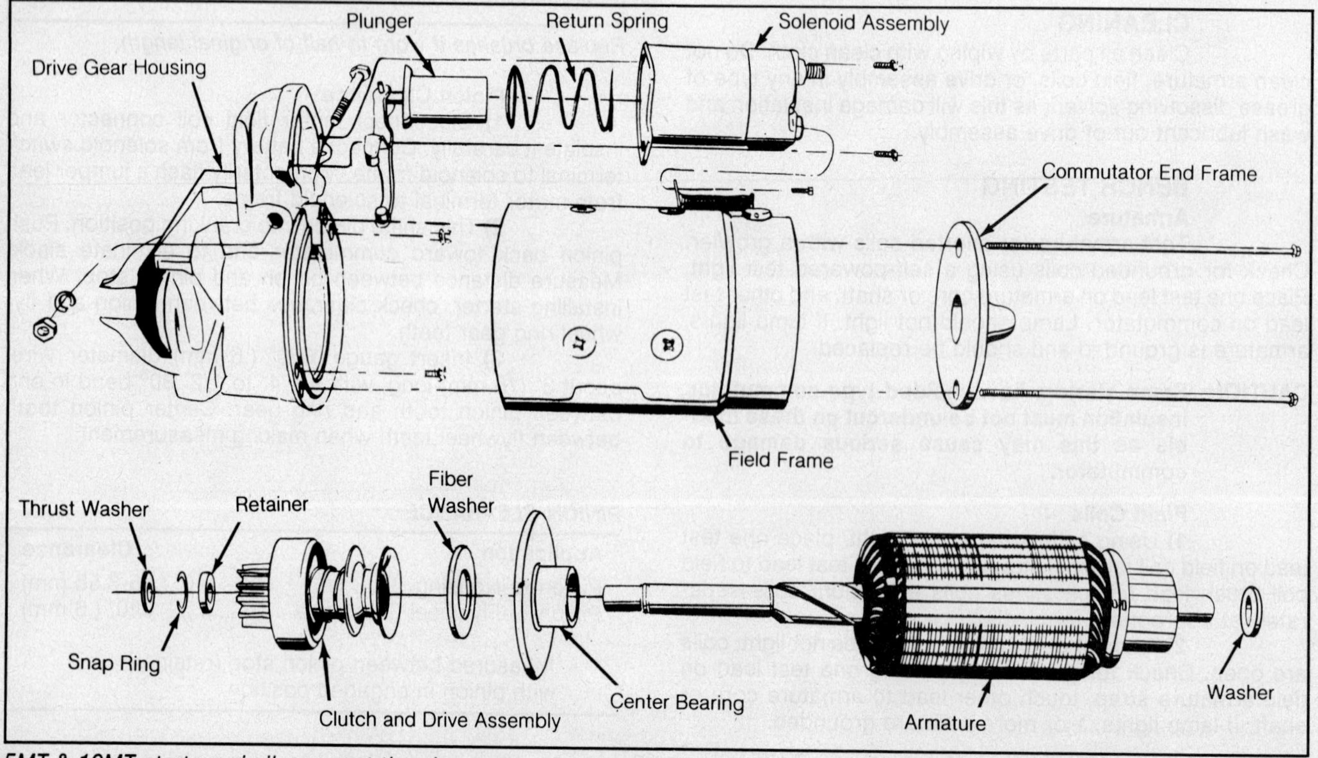

5MT & 10MT starters similar except they have no center bearing.

FORD REDUCTION DRIVE STARTER

Ranger & Bronco II
With 2.3L Turbo Diesel Engine

DESCRIPTION

Starter is a 12-volt unit that has the solenoid mounted on the starter housing. The solenoid is energized when the starter relay contacts are closed. This action engages the starter drive with the flywheel ring gear, starting the motor.

An overrunning clutch in the drive protects the starter from excessive speed when the engine starts. Current flows through the solenoid energizing coil until the plunger is at the end of its travel. The plunger then closes a set of contacts that by-pass the coil, letting the holding coil keep the starter drive engaged and passing current to the starter.

SPECIFICATIONS

LOAD TEST SPECIFICATIONS

Application	Specification
Voltage	12 Volts
Output (KW)	2.2
Rated Time	30 Sec.
Amperage	Less Than 500 Amps
Cranking Speed	150-220

NO LOAD SPECIFICATIONS

Application	Specification
Terminal Voltage	11 Volts
Current	130 Amps or Less
Speed	4000 RPM

ON-VEHICLE TESTS

STARTER LOAD TEST

1) Connect test equipment. *See Fig. 1.* Be sure that no current is flowing through the ammeter and heavy duty carbon pile rheostat portion of the circuit.

Fig. 1: Connecting Test Equipment

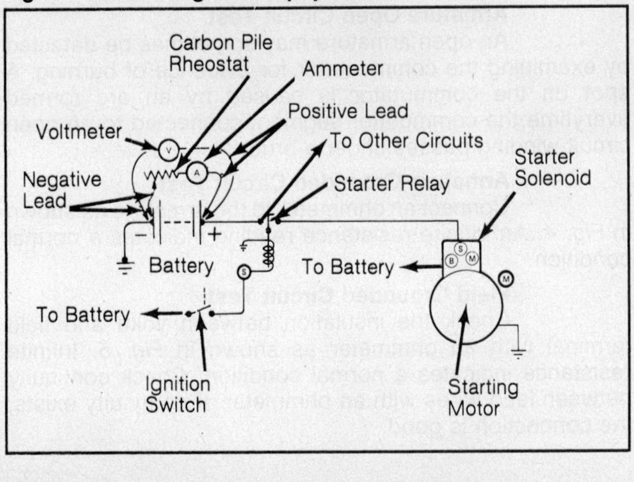

2) Crank engine with ignition off, and determine exact reading on voltmeter. This is accomplished by disconnecting push-on connectors at the starter solenoid and by connecting a remote control starter switch from the positive battery terminal to the "S" terminal of solenoid.

3) Stop cranking engine. Then reduce the resistance of the carbon pile until voltmeter indicates same reading as that obtained while the starter cranked the engine. The ammeter will indicate starter current draw under load.

STARTER MOTOR SPECIFICATIONS

Application	Measurement
Pinion Gap	.008-.079" (0.2-2.0 mm)
Brushes	
Standard Length	0.669" (17 mm)
Wear Limit	Visible Wear Mark
Armature	
Depth of Under Cut	
Standard	.016-.024" (0.4-0.6 mm)
Wear Limit	.008" (0.2 mm)
Brush Spring Install Lead	
Standard	2.9-3.7 lbs. (13-17 N)
Wear Limit	1.5 lbs. (7 N)
Current at No-Load	Less Than 50 Amps
Depth of Commutator	0.020-0.039" (0.50-.99 mm)
Under Cut Depth	0.020-0.039" (0.50-.99 mm)
Service Limit	.008" (0.2 mm) or Less
Commutator Diameter	1.524" (38.7 mm)
Service Limit	1.484 (37.7 mm)
Pinion Shaft End Play	.020" (0.50 mm)
Clearance Between Armature Shaft & Bearing	
Front	
Standard	.0028-.0039" (0.07-0.09 mm)
Wear Limit	.008" (0.2 mm)
Center	
Standard	.0118" (0.3 mm)
Rear	
Standard	.0028-.0039 (0.07-0.09 mm)
Wear Limit	.008" (0.2 mm)
Commutator Runout	
Standard	.0004" (0.01 mm)
Wear Lmit	.012" (0.3 mm)
Commutator O.D.	
Standard	1.5235" (38.7 mm)
Wear Limit	1.4842" (37.7 mm)

OVERHAUL

DISASSEMBLY

1) Remove starter from vehicle. Remove nut and washer from "M" terminal of starter solenoid and position field strap out of the way. Remove screws attaching solenoid to starter and remove solenoid.

2) Remove through bolts and screws, then remove rear bracket. Slide brushes from brush holder by prying back retaining springs. Remove the brush holder assembly.

3) Remove yoke assembly then, remove armature. Remove pinion shaft end cover from center cover. Measure pinion shaft end play using a feeler gauge. Retain this measurement for reassembly purposes. Remove retaining ring and washer from pinion shaft.

Starter

FORD REDUCTION DRIVE STARTER (Cont.)

4) Remove center bracket. Remove lever spring retainer and spring. Remove adjusting washer and reduction gear. Remove clutch shift lever and 2 lever holders. Press stop ring off snap ring using an arbor press and socket.

5) Remove snap ring with screwdriver, and then remove stop ring. Remove pinion and spring from pinion shaft. Remove overrunning clutch from front bracket.

Fig. 2: Exploded View of Ford Reduction Gear Starter

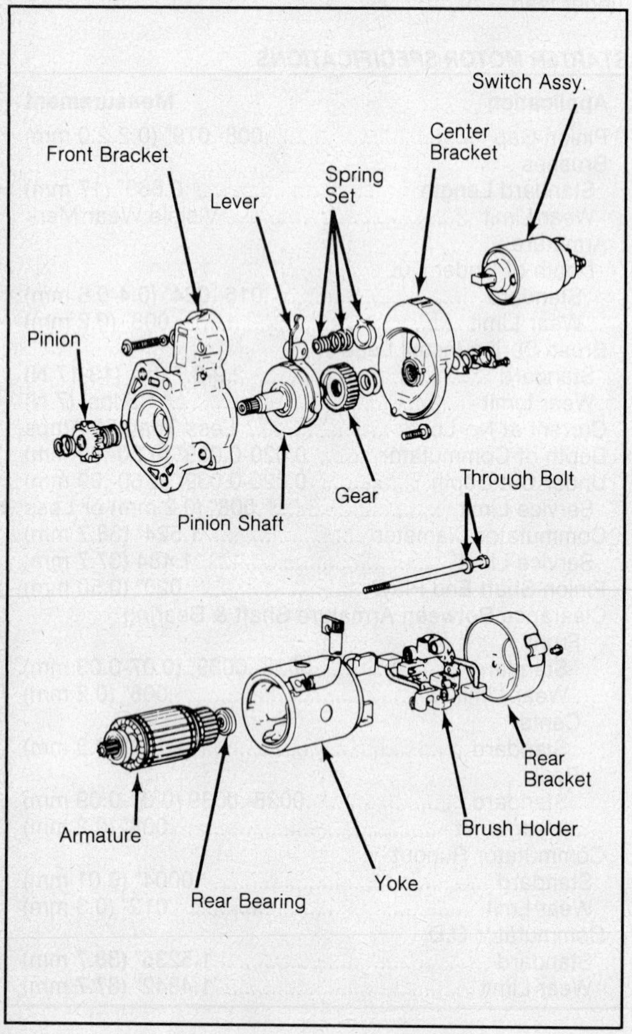

CLEANING & INSPECTION

1) Use a brush or air to clean field coils, armature, brush holder, brushes, drive assembly, brush end plate and drive end housing. Wash all other parts in solvent and throughly dry.

2) Inspect armature windings for broken or burned insulation and unwelded or open connections. Check armature for open circuits, shorts and grounds. Check commutator for runout.

3) Inspect armature shaft and bearings for scoring and excessive wear with Dial Indicator (4201-C). If commutator runout exceeds 0.002" (0.05 mm), or is rough, commutator should be refaced. Remove only enough metal to provide a smooth, even surface.

4) Check plastic brush holder for cracks or broken mounting pads. Replace brushes if worn to the mark. Inspect field coils for burned or broken insulation and continuity.

5) Check field brush connections. A brush kit and contact kit are available. All other assemblies are to be replaced rather than serviced. Examine wear pattern on starter drive teeth.

6) The pinion teeth must penetrate to a depth greater than 1/2 the ring gear tooth depth, to eliminate premature ring gear and starter drive failure. Replace starter drives and ring gears that have milled, pitted or broken teeth or show evidence of inadequate engagement.

STARTER MOTOR BENCH TESTS

Starter No-Load Test

1) Make test connections as shown in *Fig. 3*. Starter will run without a load. Be sure that no current is flowing through ammeter. Determine the exact reading on voltmeter.

2) Disconnect starter from battery. Reduce resistance of rheostat until voltmeter indicates same reading as that obtained while starter was running. Ammeter will indicate starter no-load current draw.

Fig. 3: Starter No-Load Test Connections

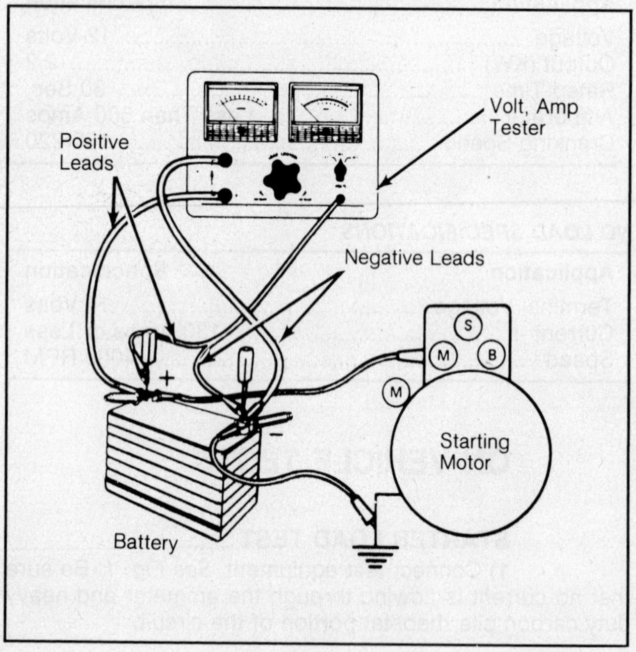

Armature Open Circuit Test

An open armature may sometimes be detected by examining the communtator for evidence of burning. A spot on the commutator is caused by an arc formed everytime the commutator segment connected to an open circuit winding passes under a brush.

Armature Grounded Circuit Test

Connect an ohmmeter to the armature as shown in *Fig. 4*. An infinite resistance reading indicates a normal condition.

Field Grounded Circuit Test

Check the insulation between yoke and field terminal with an ohmmeter as shown in *Fig. 5*. Infinite resistance indicates a normal condition. Check continuity between lead wires with an ohmmeter. If continuity exists, the connection is good.

FORD REDUCTION DRIVE STARTER (Cont.)

Fig. 4: Testing Armature for Grounded Circuit

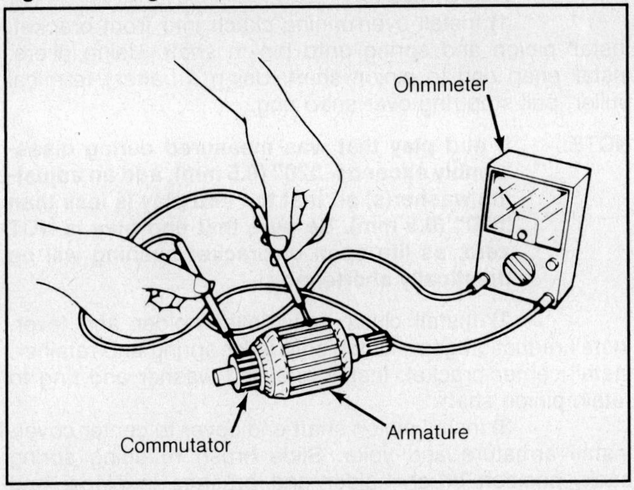

Contact probes at commutator segment and field winding.

Fig. 5: Testing Field for Grounded Circuit

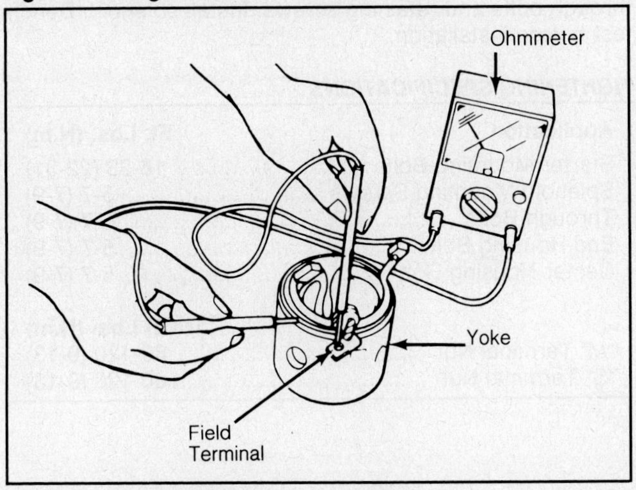

Fig. 6: Checking Depth of Mica Segments

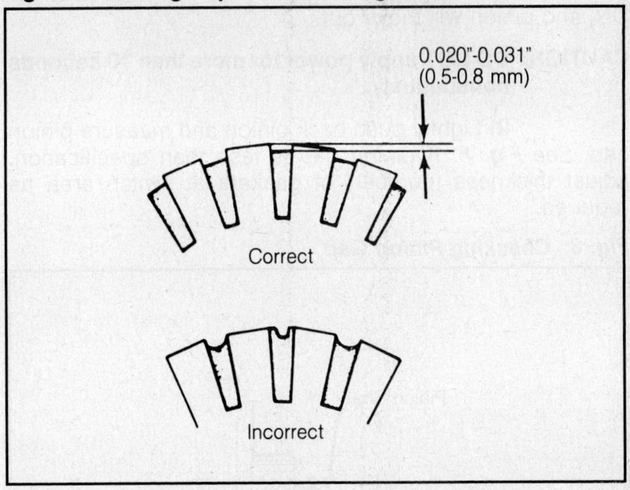

Fig. 7: Checking Brush Holder for Grounded Circuit

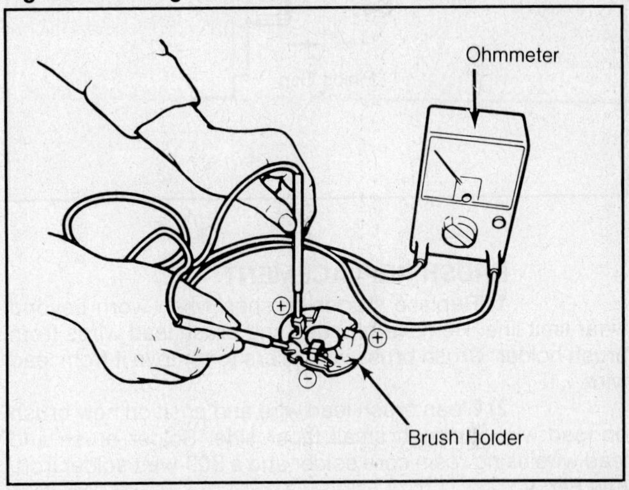

Overrunning Clutch Test

1) While holding clutch housing, rotate pinion. Drive pinion should rotate smoothly in 1 direction, but should not rotate in opposite direction. If clutch does not function properly, replacement is necessary.

2) Inspect pinion for wear or burrs. If pinion is worn or burred, replace overrunning clutch. If pinion is damaged, also inspect ring gear for wear or burrs.

Armature Short-Circuit Test

Place armature in a growler. Hold a thin steel blade parallel and just above armature while rotating armature slowly. A shorted armature will cause blade to vibrate and be attracted to the core. Replace if armature is shorted.

Mica Segment Depth Check

Check the depth of mica between segments. *See Fig. 6*. If depth is less than 0.0079" (0.2 mm), increase it to 0.0197-0.0315" (0.0-0.8 mm). Repair or replace as necessary.

Brush Holder Grounded Circuit Test

Using an ohmmeter, check insulation between positive brush holder and brush holder frame. *See Fig. 7*. An infinite resistance reading indicates a normal condition.

Solenoid Pull-In Test

1) Disconnect field coil wire from "M" terminal of solenoid. Connect a 12-volt battery between "S" terminal and "M" terminal.

CAUTION: This test must be performed quickly, less than 10 seconds, to prevent coil from burning.

2) If pinion moves out, the pull-in coil is good. If pinion does not move, replace solenoid.

Solenoid Hold-In Test

Disconnect field coil wire from "M" terminal of magnetic switch. Connect a 12-volt battery between "S" terminal and body. If pinion remains out, everything is in order. If pinion moves in, the hold-in circuit is open-circuited. Replacement is necessary.

Solenoid Return Test

Disconnect field coil wire from "M" terminal of magnetic switch. Connect a 12-volt battery between "M" terminal and body. Pull pinion out and release. If pinion quickly returns to its original position, solenoid is okay. If it doesn't, replacement is necessary.

CAUTION: This test must be performed quickly, in less than 10 seconds, to prevent coil from burning.

PINION CHECKING

1) Remove wire from "M" terminal on starter solenoid. Connect positive lead of a 12-volt source to

FORD REDUCTION DRIVE STARTER (Cont.)

terminal "S" and negative lead to terminal "M". Set switch to ON, and pinion will move out.

CAUTION: DO NOT apply power for more than 10 seconds continuously.

2) Lightly push back pinion and measure pinion gap. *See Fig. 8.* If pinion gap is less than specification, adjust thickness (number) of gaskets at switch area as required.

Fig. 8: Checking Pinion Gap

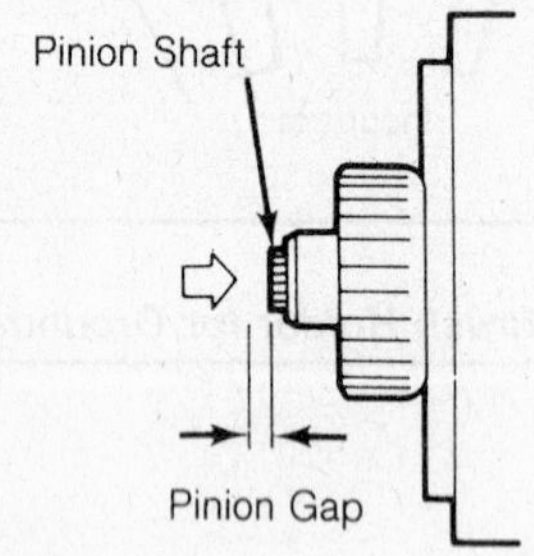

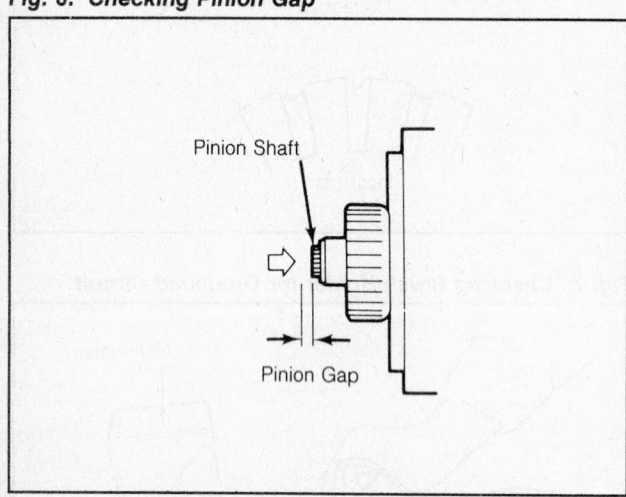

BRUSH REPLACEMENT

1) Replace starter brushes when worn beyond wear limit line. Remove brushes and brush lead wires from brush holder. Crush brush with pliers to remove it from lead wire.

2) Clean brush lead wire and position new brush on lead wire, through small taper side. Solder brush and lead wire using rosin core solder and a 300-watt solder iron. *See Fig. 9.*

Fig. 9: Replacing Starter Motor Brushes

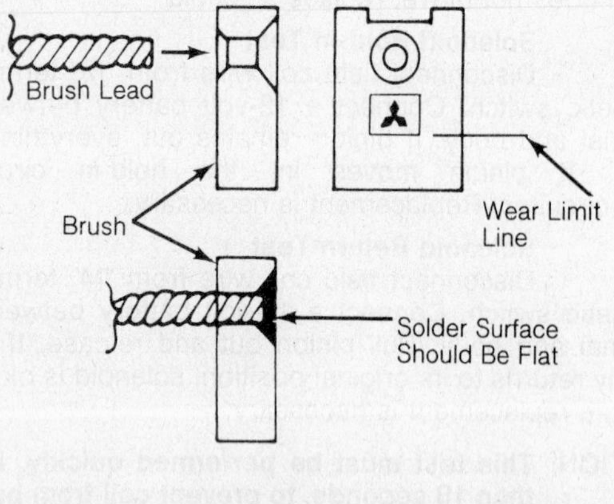

ASSEMBLY

1) Install overrunning clutch into front bracket. Install pinion and spring onto pinion shaft. Using pliers, install snap ring to pinion shaft. Using a battery terminal puller, pull stop ring over snap ring.

NOTE: If end play that was measured during disassembly exceeds .020" (0.5 mm), add an adjusting washer(s) so that the end play is less than .020" (0.5 mm). Be sure that end play is NOT zero, as life span of bracket bushing will be drastically shortened.

2) Install clutch shift lever holder and lever. Install reduction gear, clutch shift lever spring and retainer. Install center bracket. Install retaining washer and ring to retain pinion shaft.

3) Install pinion shaft end cover to center cover. Install armature and yoke. Slide brush retaining spring back, position brush holder and brushes in place, and release retaining spring.

4) Position rear bracket to housing and install through bolts and retaining screws. Install solenoid. Bench test before installation.

TIGHTENING SPECIFICATIONS

Application	Ft. Lbs. (N.m)
Starter Mounting Bolts	16-23 (22-31)
Solenoid Mounting Screws	5-7 (7-9)
Through Bolts	5-7 (7-9)
End Housing Bolts	5-7 (7-9)
Center Housing Bolt	5-7 (7-9)
	INCH Lbs. (N.m)
"M" Terminal Nut	80-120 (9-13)
"S" Terminal Nut	80-120 (9-13)

HITACHI SOLENOID-ACTUATED

General Motors "S" Series
With 2.8L V6 Engines

DESCRIPTION

The starter is a 4-pole, 4-brush type direct current series wound motor. The engagement mechanism is integral with the starter, and controls switching on and off of the motor and shifting of the starter pinion.

Starter incorporates an overrunning clutch. The shift lever mechanisim and solenoid plunger are enclosed in the drive housing to protect them from exposure to dirt, icing conditions and splash.

OPERATION

When the ignition switch is closed, the solenoid windings are energized. The resulting plunger and shift lever movement cause the pinion to engage the engine flywheel ring gear and the solenoid main contacts to close, so engine cranking takes place.

When the engine starts, pinion overrun protects the armature from excessive speed until the switch is opened. At this time the return spring causes the pinion to disengage.

TROUBLE SHOOTING & TESTING

STARTER MOTOR & SWITCH

Engage Switch Does Not Work When Starter Switch is Turned On

1) Check circuit. If circuit is faulty, correct condition. If circuit is okay, check starter switch. If contacts in switch are defective, replace contacts. If starter switch is okay, check engage switch coil.

2) If coil is open or burned, replace coil. If coil is okay, check plunger shaft. If shaft is bent or binding, repair or replace shaft.

Pinion Gear Does Not Properly Engage Ring Gear

1) Check battery. If charge is low, recharge. If battery is okay, check pinion and ring gear teeth. If teeth are worn or damaged, replace. If gear teeth are okay, check pinion gear movement.

2) If pinion return is incorrect, adjust. If pinion gear movement is okay, check armature shaft and bearing. Correct or replace as necessary. Check for foreign material on sliding portion of shaft.

Pinion Engages Ring Gear But Engine Will Not Turn Over

1) Check battery. If charge is low, recharge. If battery is okay, check brush contact with commutator face. If brush is in poor contact with face, correct or replace. If brush contact is okay, check pinion clutch.

2) If pinion clutch is slipping, replace. If pinion clutch is okay, check armature field coil. If field coil is open, correct or replace.

Starter Does Not Stop When Starter Switch Is Turned Off

Check engage switch contact point. If contact point is siezed, replace. If okay, check starter switch. Replace if defective.

Excessive Brush Sparking

1) Check brush contact with commutator face. If poor contact exists, correct. If contact is okay, check commutator. If commutator segment or phenol resin projects, correct or replace.

2) If soldering on commutator has loosened, correct. If commutator is okay, check armature shaft. If there is runout, replace bearing. If armature shaft is okay, check brush holder. If holder has loosened in mount, correct.

Fig. 1: Exploded View of Hitachi Starter

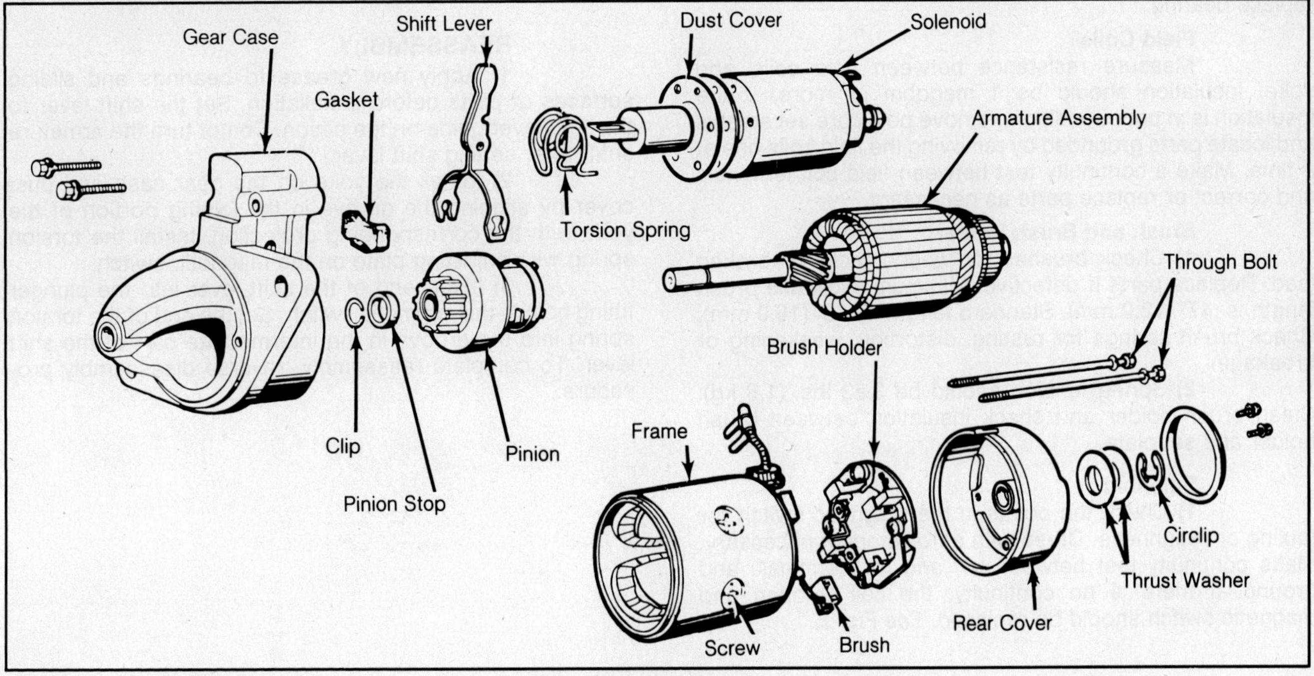

HITACHI SOLENOID-ACTUATED (Cont.)

OVERHAUL

DISASSEMBLY

1) Disconnect the lead from the "M" terminal of the solenoid. Remove the bolts attaching the solenoid. Remove the torsion spring from the solenoid. Remove the dust cover and remove the ring and thrust washer. *See Fig. 2.*

2) Remove the 2 screws and through bolts. Remove the rear cover assembly. Raise the brush spring, pull out the brush, and remove the brush holder assembly. Carefully remove the yoke from the gear case and remove the dust cover.

3) Remove the armature from the gear case toghether with shift lever and remove shift lever from the armature. Pull out the pinion stop clip and remove pinion stop. Remove pinion assembly.

PARTS INSPECTION & TESTING

Armature

1) Check the commutator face for roughness or burning and reface with fine sandpaper as necessary. If roughness or out-of-round is considerable, armature should be turned on a lathe. Mica insulators should be undercut to a depth of .020-.031" (.5-.8 mm).

2) Check for insulation between commutator coils and core using a growl tester. If the lamp of the tester comes on, coils are poorly insulated and must be replaced.

3) Make a continuity test between the segments of the commutator with growl tester. If lamp does not come on when tester leads are shorted across segments, coils are open and should be repaired or replaced.

4) Roll the armature on growl tester slowly while holding a strip of steel or a hacksaw blade over each segment of armature core. If the steel is pulled or vibrates, armature coils are shorted and must be repaired or replaced.

5) Check armature shaft for runout using a dial indicator. If beyond .0031" (.080 mm), replace. If clearance between shaft and bearing is more than .008" (.20 mm), replace bearing.

Field Coils

Measure resistance between field coils and yoke. Insulation should be 1 megohm or more. If the insulation is in poor condition, remove pole core set screws and locate parts grounded by removing the field coils one at a time. Make a continuity test between field coil terminals and correct or replace parts as necessary.

Brush and Brush Holder

1) Check brushes for wear, cracks or broken lead. Replace parts if defective. Minimum allowable brush length is .47" (12.0 mm). Standard length is .63" (16.0 mm). Check brush springs for rusting, distortion, weakening or breakage.

2) Spring tension should be 3.53 lbs. (1.6 kg). Clean brush holder and check insulation between brush holder and set plate.

Solenoid

1) Check the points in the magnetic switch for fouling or roughness. Dress with an oil stone if necessary. Make continuity test between "C" and "M" terminals and ground. If there is no continuity, the coil is open and magnetic switch should be replaced. *See Fig. 2.*

Fig. 2: Solenoid Test Connections

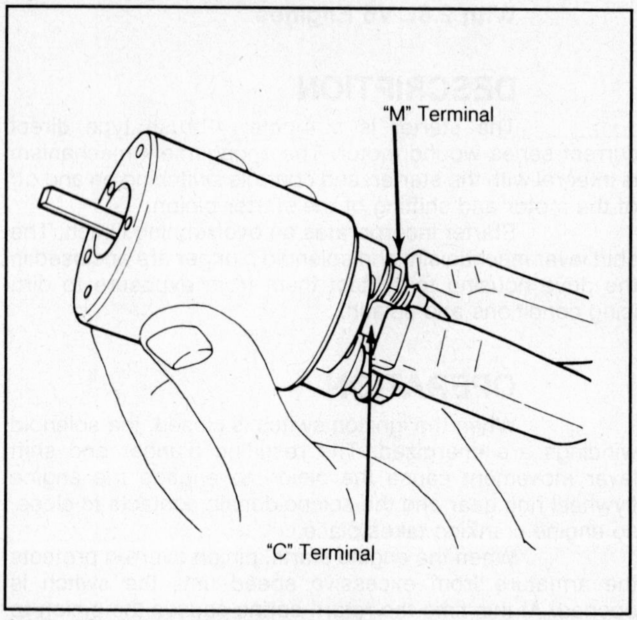

Apply 12 volts to test plunger action.

2) Apply 12 volts between "C" and "M" terminals of switch. Solenoid is okay when plunger is pulled when power is applied and returns smoothly when power is removed.

3) Check the gap between pinion and pinion stop when pinion is fully depressed due to action of the solenoid. Adjust if necessary by installing adjusting plate between magnetic switch and case. Standard gap is .012-.098" (.30-2.50 mm).

Pinion

Check pinion gear for wear or damage. Check sliding face of pinion for scuffs and replace if necessary. Check springs for damage or weakening. Check clutch for sticking or binding and replace if necessary.

REASSEMBLY

1) Apply new grease to bearings and sliding surfaces of parts before installation. Set the shift lever to the shift lever guide on the pinion. Do not turn the armature shaft after setting shift lever.

2) Install the yoke on the gear case and dust cover by aligning the groove in the joining portion of the yoke with the corresponding projection. Install the torsion spring with adjusting plate on the magnetic switch.

3) Insert end of the shift lever into the plunger fitting hole in the magnetic switch. Set the end of the torsion spring into the groove in the intermediate part of the shift lever. To complete reassembly, reverse disassembly procedure.

MOTORCRAFT POSITIVE ENGAGEMENT

Ford, Jeep 6-Cyl. & V8

DESCRIPTION

Unit is a 4-pole, 4-brush starter with 3 series coils and 1 shunt coil. Shunt coil is wound around a movable pole piece, which operates integral positive engagement drive mechanism.

Solenoids for Jeep vehicles with automatic and manual transmissions differ in their method of grounding solenoid pull-in windings.

TESTING

HOLD-IN WINDING TEST

Insert a piece of paper between contact points to serve as an insulator. Touch ohmmeter leads to starter frame and input terminal. Resistance should be 2.0-3.5 ohms. If not, replace field winding assembly.

PULL-IN WINDING TEST

1) Disconnect wire from solenoid "S" terminal. Connect ohmmeter test probes to "S" terminal and mounting bracket (ground terminal on Jeep vehicles with automatic transmission). *See Fig. 1.* If not to specifications, replace solenoid.

Fig. 1: Ford & Jeep Ohmmeter Test Connections for Solenoid.

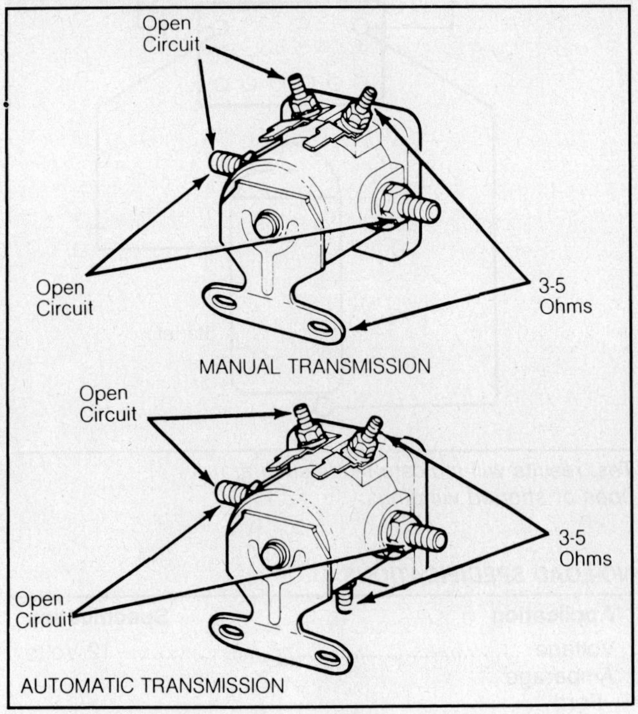

Connections must be clean and tight to make proper test.

2) Check for a poor ground by connecting ohmmeter leads to battery negative terminal and "S" terminal. If reading is greater than results received between "S" terminal and mounting bracket, solenoid has poor ground.

STARTER CRANKING CIRCUIT TESTS

Before performing tests, remove and ground coil secondary wire (disconnect at distributor). Place transmission in "Neutral" or "PARK" and apply parking brake. Be sure battery is fully charged. When making voltmeter connections, be sure to connect leads to battery posts or threaded terminals and not just to cable ends.

Fig. 2: Connections for Cranking Circuit Test Ford & Jeep

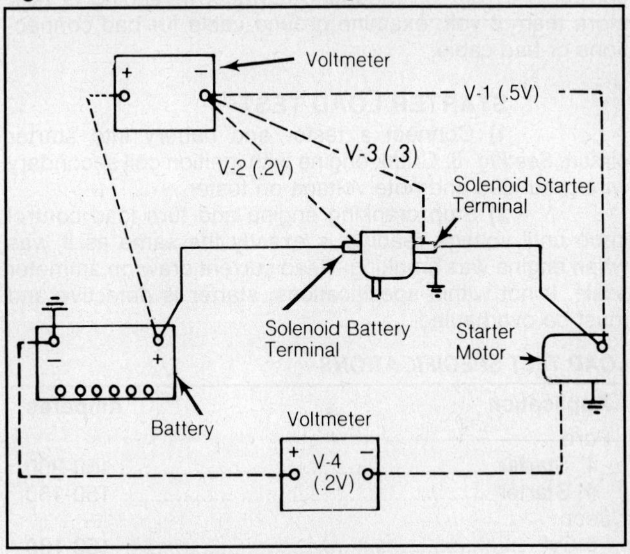

Voltages are shown for each connection.

Battery-to-Starter Motor Voltage Drop (V-1)

1) Connect voltmeter positive lead to battery positive post and negative lead to starter motor terminal. While cranking engine, note voltmeter reading. Reading should be .5 volts or less at specified load test amperage.

2) If reading is greater, move negative lead to starter cable at starter and retest. If voltage is now .5 volt or less, remove cable and clean connections, and retest at starter motor terminal. If voltage is still above specifications, test individual cables between battery and starter as follows:

Battery-to-Solenoid Voltage Drop (V-2)

1) Connect voltmeter positive lead to battery positive post and negative lead to battery terminal of solenoid. While cranking engine, note voltmeter reading. Reading should be .2 volt or less at specified load test amperage.

2) If just below or at specification, repair solenoid. If reading is greater, remove cable, clean connections, and retest. If reading is still above maximum .2 volt, replace cable.

Solenoid Voltage Drop (V-3)

1) Connect voltmeter positive lead to battery positive post and negative lead to starter CABLE at solenoid. While cranking engine, note voltmeter reading. Reading should be .3 volt or less at specified load test amperage.

2) If at or just below maximum reading, repair solenoid-to-starter cable. If reading is above maximum, move negative lead to starter TERMINAL at solenoid and retest.

3) If reading is now .3 volt or less, remove and clean cable connector, and retest. If still in excess of .3 volt, replace solenoid. If battery-to-starter circuit (V-1) reading is now greater than .5 volt, replace solenoid-to-starter cable.

MOTORCRAFT POSITIVE ENGAGEMENT (Cont.)

Starter Motor Ground Voltage Drop (V-4)

1) Connect voltmeter negative lead to starter motor housing and positive lead to battery negative post. While cranking engine, note voltmeter reading. Reading should be .2 volt or less at specified load test amperage.

2) If more, move positive lead to ground cable attaching bolt at engine and retest. If reading is now less than .2 volt, check starter motor for loose mounting bolts, corrosion or dirt on mounting surface. If reading is now more than .2 volt, examine ground cable for bad connections or bad cable.

STARTER LOAD TEST

1) Connect a tester and battery into starter circuit. *See Fig. 3.* Crank engine with ignition coil secondary wire grounded and note voltage on tester.

2) Stop cranking engine and turn load control knob until voltage reading is exactly the same as it was when engine was cranking. Read current draw on ammeter scale. If not within specifications, starter is defective and must be overhauled.

LOAD TEST SPECIFICATIONS

Application	Amperes
Ford	
4" Starter	150-200
4" Starter	150-180
Jeep	
6-Cyl.	150-180
V8	160-210

Fig. 3: Ford & Jeep Connections for Load Test

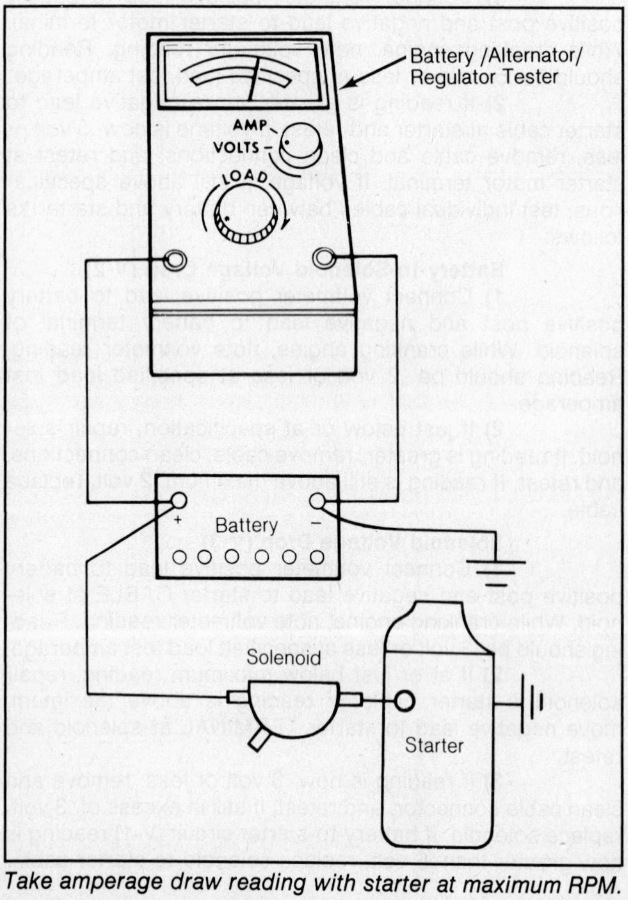

Take amperage draw reading with starter at maximum RPM.

STARTER NO-LOAD TEST

1) With tester and battery connected to starter, operate starter motor and note voltage reading and tachometer reading. *See Fig. 4.* Disconnect starter from battery. Turn load control knob until voltage reading is same as when starter is connected.

2) Read amperage draw, and if amperage reading is less than specifications, starter has high electrical resistance. If starter RPM is less than specifications, starter has high electrical resistance. If starter RPM is less than specifications starter has worn bushings or bent armature shaft.

Fig. 4: Ford & Jeep Connections for No-Load Test

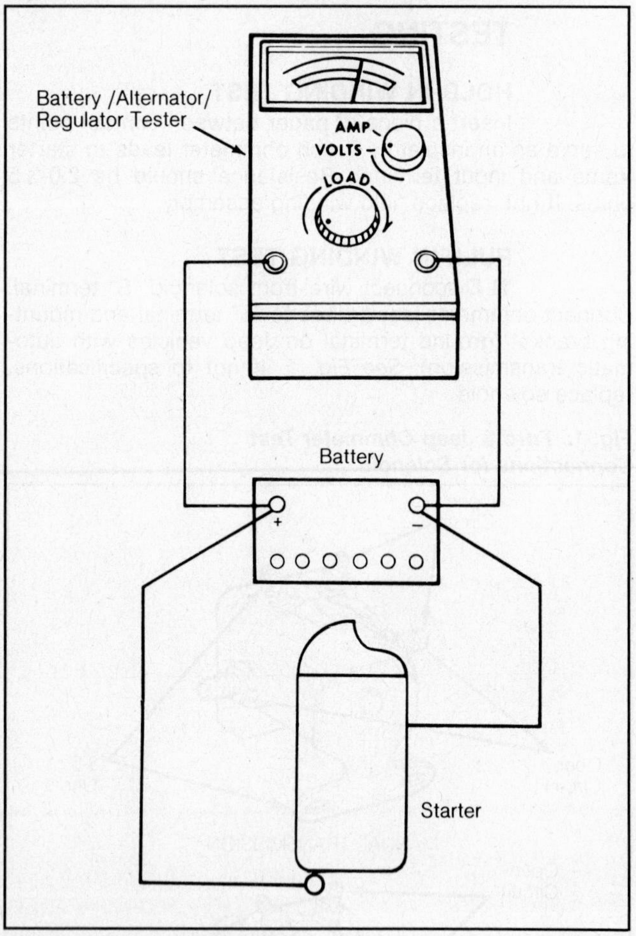

Test results will indicate faults such as open or shorted windings.

NO-LOAD SPECIFICATIONS

Application	Specification
Voltage	12 Volts
Amperage	
Ford	
4" Starter	70 Amps.
4" Starter	80 Amps.
Jeep	67 Amps.
RPM Range	7,380-9,356

MOTORCRAFT POSITIVE ENGAGEMENT (Cont.)

OVERHAUL

DISASSEMBLY

1) Remove cover screw, cover, through bolts, starter drive end housing and starter drive plunger lever return spring. Remove pivot pin retaining plunger lever and remove plunger lever and armature.

2) Remove stop ring retainer, stop ring from starter drive gear and starter drive gear assembly. Remove brush end plate and insulator assembly. Remove brushes from brush holder and lift out brush holder. Note location of brush holder with respect to end terminal.

3) Remove ground brushes-to-frame retaining screws. On field coil which operates drive gear actuating lever, bend edges on retaining sleeve and remove sleeve and retainers.

4) Remove 3 coil retaining screws with Generator Pole Screw Wrench (10044-A) and an arbor press. Cut field coil connection at switch post lead and remove small diameter ground wire from upper tab riveted to frame.

5) Remove pole shoes and coils from frame. Cut positive brush leads from fields coils as close to field connection point as possible.

PARTS REPLACEMENT & TESTING

Brushes & Springs

1) Check brush holders for broken springs and insulated brush holders for shorts to ground. Tighten any loose rivets. Replace brushes if worn to 1/4" in length. Measure spring tension with spring scale hooked under spring near end.

2) Pull on line parallel to edge of brush and note reading just as spring end leaves brush. Spring tension should be 40 ozs. (1.134 kg) on 4" starters, 80 ozs. (2.263 kg) on 4 1/2" starters. If replacing brushes, use a 300 watt soldering iron and rosin core solder.

Field Coil Assembly

Inspect field coils for burned or broken insulation and continuity. Check field brush connections and lead insulation. Check for grounds in field coil windings.

Armature

1) Check armature for shorted coils with a growler and a test light. Touch 1 test lead to armature core and the other to each commutator bar 1 at a time. If light lights, armature is shorted to ground and must be replaced.

2) Place switch on growler in GROWLER position and hold steel blade parallel to and touching armature core. Rotate armature and if blade vibrates at any point, that area is shorted and armature must replaced.

3) Inspect armature shaft for excessive wear. Inspect windings for broken or burned insulation. If commutator is rough or more than .005" (.13 mm) out of round, turn down in a lathe, removing only enough material to provide a smooth, even surface.

Fig. 5: Removing Pole Shoe Screw from Starter Housing.

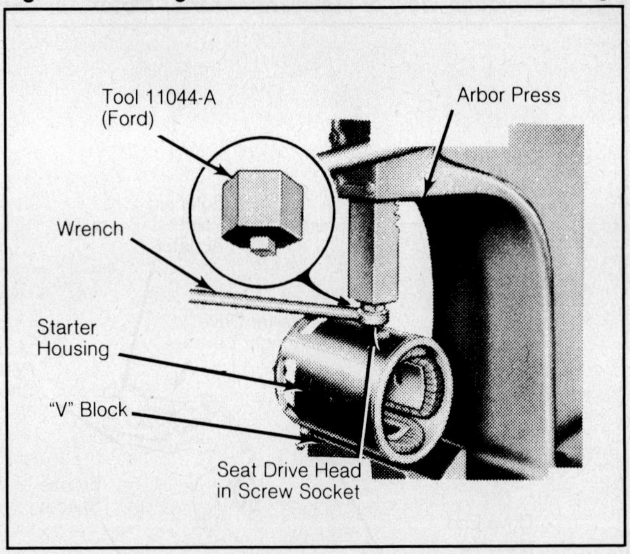

Use arbor press to hold generator pole screw wrench.

REASSEMBLY

1) Position 3 coils and pole pieces and install attaching screws. As pole shoe screws are tightened, strike frame with a soft hammer to seat and align pole shoes, then stake screws.

2) Install remaining coil and retainer. Bend tabs to secure coil to frame. Position new field brush lead on field coil terminal. Install clip to hold brush lead to terminal. Solder lead, clip and terminal together with a 300 watt iron and rosin core solder.

3) Ground coil around retaining sleeve by placing small diameter wire from coil under copper tab which attaches contact to frame. Install ground brushes to frame with screws.

4) Lubricate armature shaft splines with Lubriplate (or equivalent). Install drive gear assembly on armature shaft. Install new retaining stop ring and stop retainer.

5) Install armature in frame. Partially fill drive end housing bearing bore with grease and position drive gear plunger lever to frame and starter drive assembly and install pivot pin.

6) Install plunger lever return spring and drive end housing to frame. Install brush holder, brushes and springs. Install brush holder insulator.

7) Position end plate to frame and align plate locator with frame slot. Install and tighten through bolts. DO NOT pinch brush leads when installing end plate. Position drive gear plunger lever cover on starter and tighten cover screw.

MOTORCRAFT POSITIVE ENGAGEMENT (Cont.)

Fig. 6: Exploded View of Motorcraft Starter Motor Assembly Used On Ford & Jeep

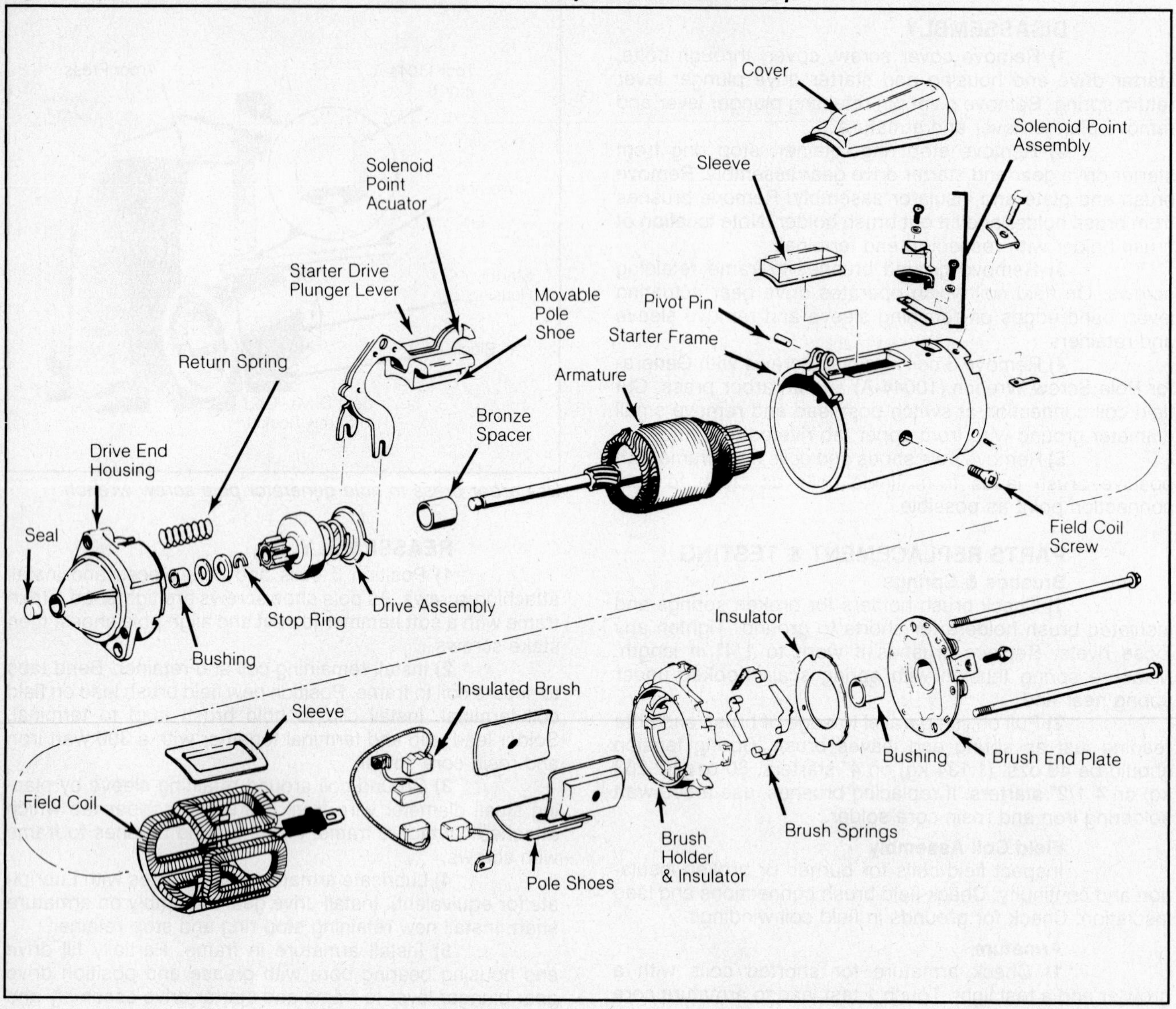

PARIS-RHONE

Jeep Cherokee, Wagoneer
With 2.1L Turbo Diesel

DESCRIPTION

Starter is a 4-pole, 4-brush type direct series wound motor. The engagement mechanism is integral with the starter and controls switching on and off of motor and shifting of the starter pinion.

OPERATION

1) With ignition switch in "S" position, battery voltage is applied from fusible link "D", to ignition switch, and to the coil of the starter relay to ground.

2) For vehicles equipped with man. trans., a grounding strap from the starter relay is used. On vehicles equipped with auto. trans., current flows to ground through the back-up/neutral saftey switch.

3) The coil of the starter relay energizes, closing relay contacts. With contacts closed, battery voltage is applied to the starter solenoid. Both windings within solenoid are energized.

4) The circuit through the pull-in windings is completed to ground through the starter motor. The windings work together magnetically to pull in the starter gear into the ring gear.

5) At the same time, the plunger also closes the solenoid switch contacts in the starter solenoid. Full battery voltage is applied directly to the starter motor and it cranks the engine. *See Fig. 2.*

SPECIFICATIONS

NOTE: **DO NOT consider the intial amperage draw that is required to begin engine craking. A very hot or very cold engine may draw 400 to 700 amperes for the first few revolutions. Take an amperage draw reading after the starter motor has obtained its maximum RPM.**

Fig. 1: Exploded View of Paris-Rhone Starter Motor

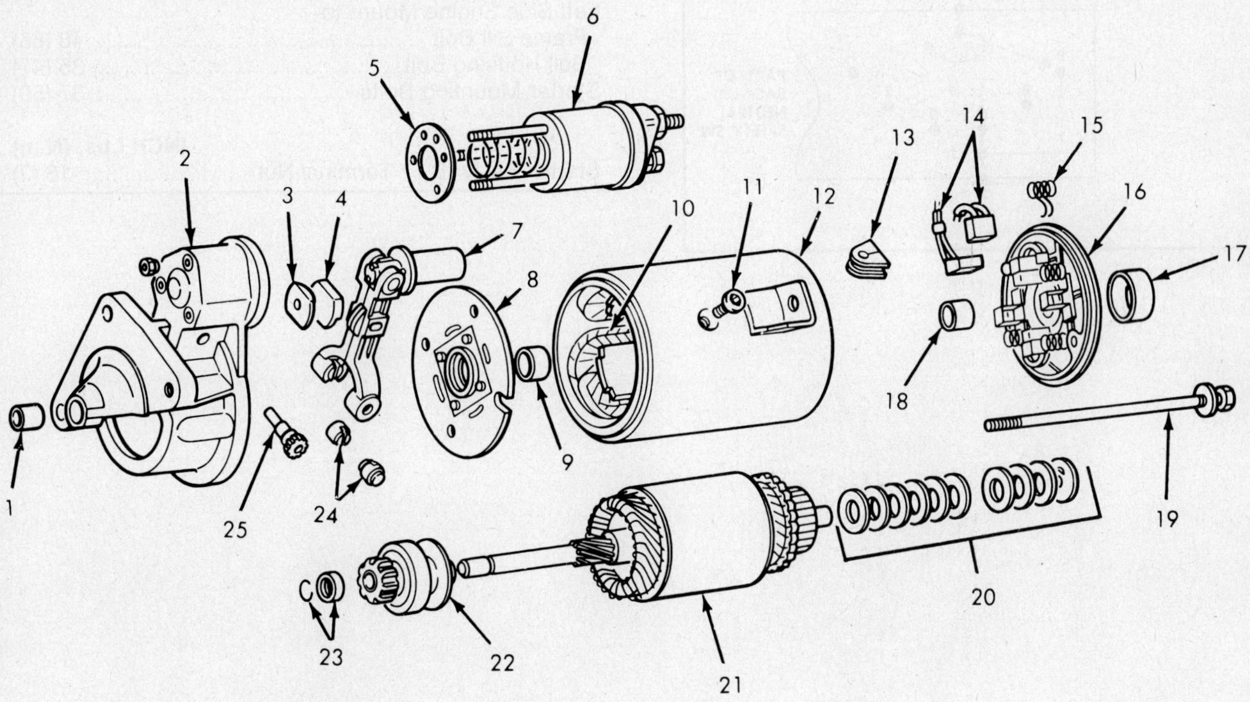

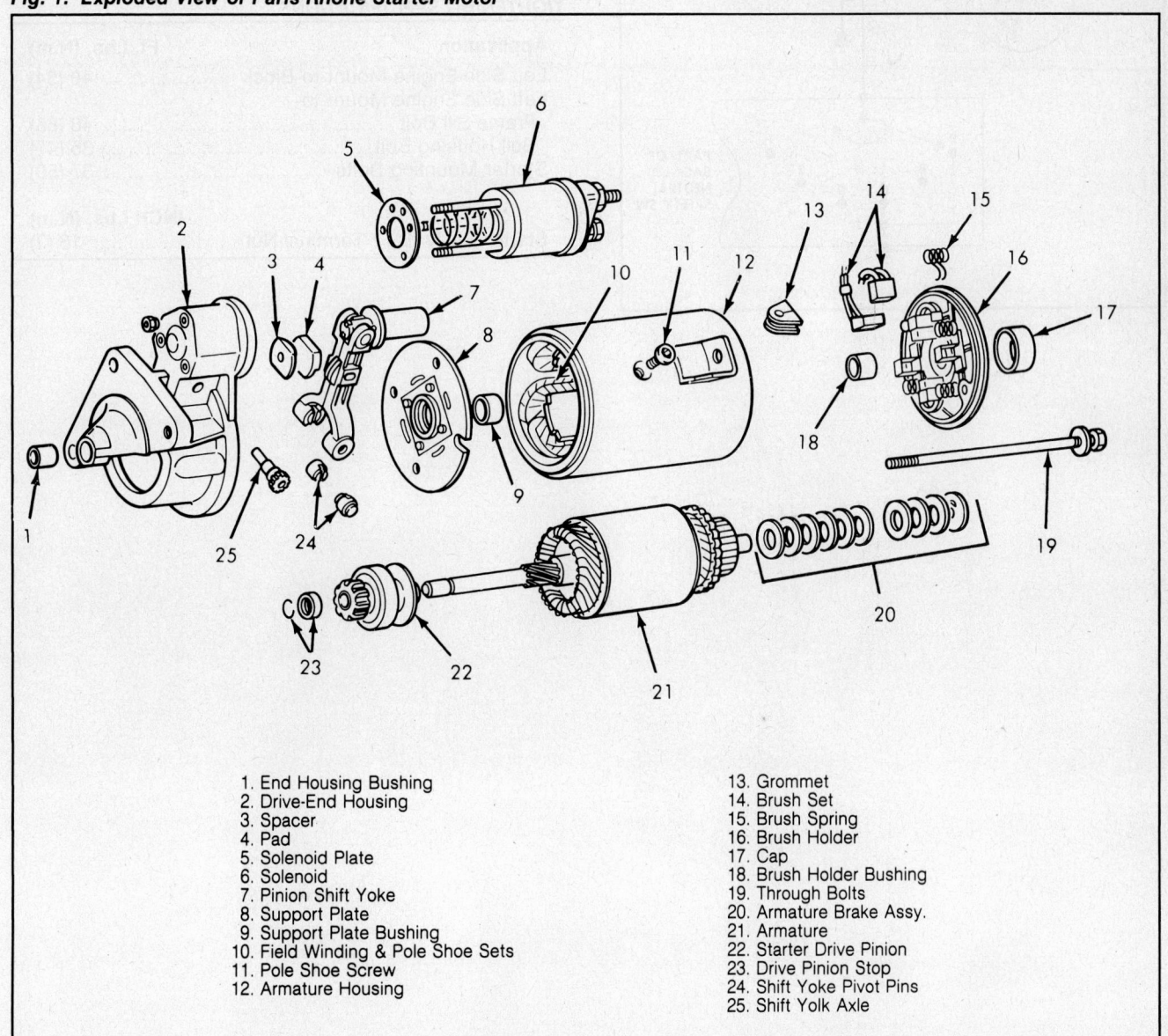

1. End Housing Bushing
2. Drive-End Housing
3. Spacer
4. Pad
5. Solenoid Plate
6. Solenoid
7. Pinion Shift Yoke
8. Support Plate
9. Support Plate Bushing
10. Field Winding & Pole Shoe Sets
11. Pole Shoe Screw
12. Armature Housing
13. Grommet
14. Brush Set
15. Brush Spring
16. Brush Holder
17. Cap
18. Brush Holder Bushing
19. Through Bolts
20. Armature Brake Assy.
21. Armature
22. Starter Drive Pinion
23. Drive Pinion Stop
24. Shift Yoke Pivot Pins
25. Shift Yolk Axle

Starters

PARIS-RHONE (Cont.)

Fig. 2: Wiring Diagram of Starting Circuit

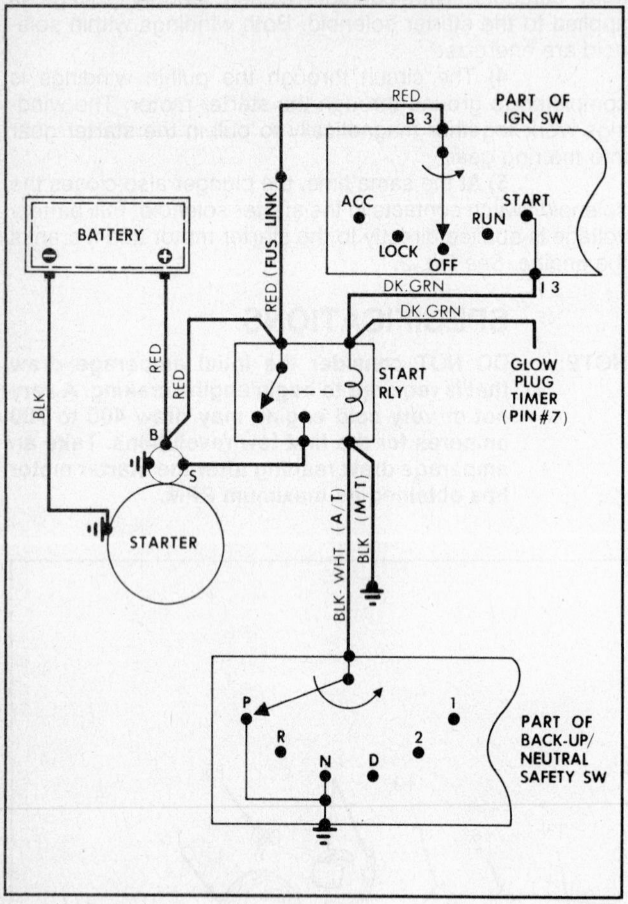

STARTER MOTOR SPECIFICATIONS

Application	Specification
Cold Cranking Voltage (Min.)	9.6 Volts
Cold Cranking Amps	350 Amps

TROUBLESHOOTING

- Check the battery for a broken or cracked casing.
- Check that all connections to battery and starter are clean and tight.
- Check electrolyte level of battery. Levels that are too high or too low may cause poor starter motor performance.
- Check battery by measuring specific gravity of electrolyte in each cell with a hydrometer.

NOTE: No other testing or troubleshooting procedures are available from manufacturer at this time.

TIGHTENING SPECIFICATIONS

Application	Ft. Lbs. (N.m)
Left Side Engine Mount-to-Block	40 (54)
Left Side Engine Mount-to-	
Frame Sill Bolt	48 (65)
Bell Housing Bolt	35 (47)
Starter Mounting Bolts	37 (50)
	INCH Lbs. (N.m)
Starter Relay "B+" Terminal Nut	18 (2)

Fuses & Circuit Breakers

FUSE BLOCK & FLASHER LOCATIONS

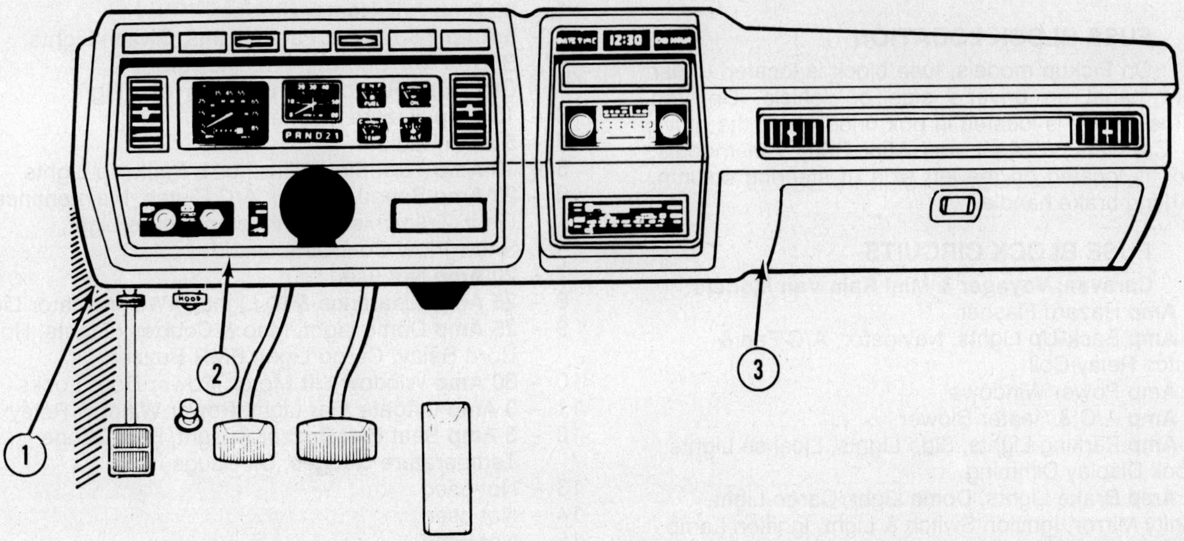

FUSE BLOCK & FLASHER LOCATIONS

Manufacturer & Model	Fuse Block	Hazard Flasher	Turn Signal Flasher
Chrysler Corp.			
Pickup Models	[2] Left of Steering Column	On Fuse Block	On Fuse Block
RWD Van Models	[3] Under Glove Box	Right of Fuse Block	Right of Fuse Block
FWD Van Models	[2] Left of Steering Column	Below Fuse Block	On Fuse Block
Ford Motor Co.			
Aerostar	[2] Left of Steering Column	Steering Column	On Fuse Box
Bronco & "F" Pickup Models	[2] Left of Steering Column	On Fuse Block	On Fuse Block
Bronco II & Ranger	[2] Left of Steering Column	Back of Fuse Block	Front of Fuse Block
Van Models	[2] Left of Steering Column	[1] Left Of Wiring Harness	Near Fuse Block
General Motors ★			
All Models	[2] Left of Steering Column	On Fuse Block	Near Fuse Block
Jeep			
All Models	[2] Left of Steering Column	On Fuse Block	On Fuse Block

★ – On some models, flashers may be located on convenience center behind glove box or near steering column.

Fuses & Circuit Breakers

CHRYSLER CORP.

FUSE BLOCK

FUSE BLOCK LOCATION

On Pickup models, fuse block is located under instrument panel on driver's side of vehicle. On Van models, fuse block is located in box underneath the glove box. On Caravan, Voyager and Mini Ram Van models, fuse block is located on the left side of steering column, under parking brake handle.

FUSE BLOCK CIRCUITS

Caravan, Voyager & Mini Ram Van Models

1 – **20 Amp** Hazard Flasher
2 – **20 Amp** Back-Up Lights, Navigator, A/C Fan & Clutch Relay Coil
3 – **30 Amp** Power Windows
4 – **30 Amp** A/C & Heater Blower
5 – **20 Amp** Parking Lights, Side Lights, License Lights Clock Display Dimming
6 – **20 Amp** Brake Lights, Dome Light, Cargo Light, Vanity Mirror, Ignition Switch & Light, Ignition Lamp Time Delay Relay, Door Courtesy Lights, Electric Mirrors
7 – **20 Amp** Horns, Cigar Lighter, Chimes, Digital Clock & Radio Memory, Navigator & Console Lamps
8 – **30 Amp** Power Seats, Power Door Locks, Power Sliding Door
9 – **5 Amp** Radio & Clock Display
10 – **20 Amp** Turn Signals, Heated Rear Window
11 – **20 Amp** Windshield Wipers/Washers
12 – **3 Amp** Instrument Cluster, A/C-Heater Control, Switch Title, Ash Tray, Cigar Lighter, Navigator Lamps & Radio
13 – **5 Amp** Fuel, Voltage, Oil & Temperature Gauges, Brake Warning, Seat Belt Warning Buzzer, Oil & Temperature Lamps, Chimes, Warning Lamp Module & Speed Control
14 – **6 Amp** Rear Washer/Wiper, Liftgate Release, Power Sliding Door
15 – **20 Amp** Spotlamp
16 – **20 Amp** Spotlamp

Fig. 1: Fuse Block for Caravan, Voyager and Mini Ram Van Models

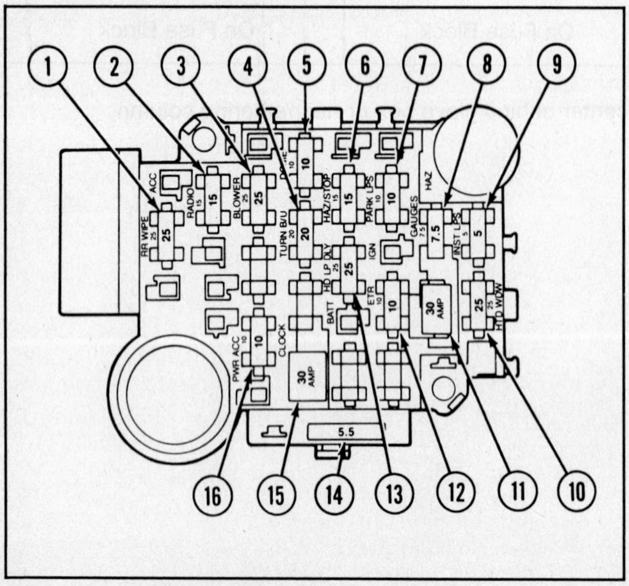

Fuse block located under parking brake handle.

Pickup Models

1 – **30 Amp** A/C-Heater Blower
2 – **5 Amp** Instrument Panel Lights, Switch Lights, Snow Plow Control, 4WD Indicator, Clock and Radio Dimming, Ash Tray Light
3 – **15 Amp** Hazard Flashers
4 – **5 Amp** Radio
5 – **15 Amp** Turn Signal Flasher & Back-Up Lights
6 – **20 Amp** Speed Control, A/C Clutch, Maintenance Light, Transmission Oil Temperature Light, Snow Plow Control Solenoids
7 – **20 Amp** Not used
8 – **25 Amp** Clearance & ID Lights, 4WD Indicator Light
9 – **25 Amp** Dome Light, Map & Courtesy Lights, Horn & Horn Relay, Cargo Light, EMR Buzzer
10 – **30 Amp** Window Lift Motor, Power Door Locks
11 – **3 Amp** Liftgate Ajar Light, Power Window Relay
12 – **3 Amp** Seat Belt Buzzer & Light, Fuel Gauge, Temperature Gauges, Oil Gauge
13 – Not used
14 – Not used
15 – Not used

Fig. 2: Fuse Block for Pickup & Ramcharger Models

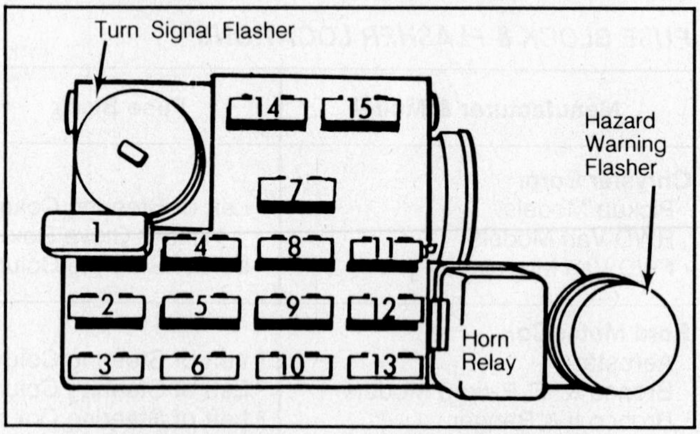

Fuse block under instrument panel on driver's side.

Ramcharger

1 – **30 Amp** A/C & Heater Blower Motor
2 – **3 Amp** Illumination Lamps
3 – **15 Amp** Hazard Flashers
4 – **10 Amp** Radio
5 – **15 Amp** Turn Signal Flasher, Back-Up Lamp & Switch
6 – **20 Amp** Speed Control, A/C Clutch, EMR Lamp
7 – **20 Amp** Trailer Lamps, EMR Memory
8 – **25 Amp** Fuse Cavity 2, Cigar Lighter, Exterior Lamps
9 – **20 Amp** Horn Relay, Cargo Lamp, Interior Lamps, Stop Lamps
10 – **30 Amp** Power Window Lift Motor, Door Lock Solenoid
11 – **3 Amp** Clock, 4WD Indicator, Liftgate Ajar
12 – **3 Amp** Seat Belt Buzzer, Cluster Warning Lamps
13 – Not Used
14 – Not Used
15 – Not Used

CHRYSLER CORP. (Cont.)

Fig. 3: Fuse Block for Van Models

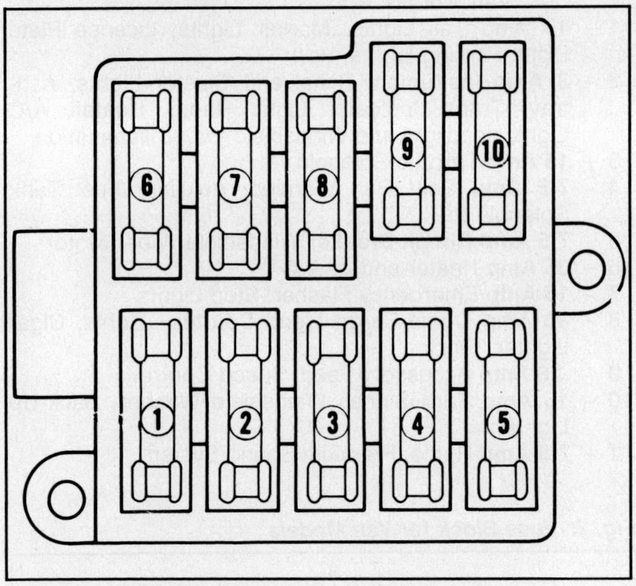

Fuse block located on the left side of the glove box.

Van Models

1 – **30 Amp** A/C & Heater Blower Motor
2 – **3 Amp** Illumination Lamps
3 – **15 Amp** Hazard Fasher
4 – **10 Amp** Radio
5 – **15 Amp** Turn Signal Flasher, Back-Up Lamp & Switch
6 - **20 Amp** Speed Control, A/C Clutch, EMR Lamp
7 – **20 Amp** Trailer Lamps, EMR Memory
8 – **25 Amp** Fuse Cavity 2, Cigar Lighter, Exterior Lamps
9 – **20 Amp** Horn Relay, Cargo Lamp, Interior Lamps, Stop Lamps
10 – **30 Amp** Power Windows, Power Door Locks
11 – **3 Amp** Clock, 4WD Indicator, Liftgate Ajar
12 – **3 Amp** Seat Belt Buzzer, Cluster Warning Lamps
13 – Not Used
14 – Not Used
15 – Not Used

CIRCUIT BREAKERS

Caravan, Voyager & Mini Ram Van Models

These models have 30-amp circuit breakers located on fuse block to protect fuse circuits 3 and 8. A 6-amp circuit breaker on fuse block protects fuse circuit 14.

Pickups & Ramcharger

A 30-Amp circuit breaker is used to protect fuse circuit 10.

Vans

A 30-amp circuit breaker is used to protect fuse circuit 10.

FUSIBLE LINKS

Mini Ram Van, Caravan & Voyager

A 20 gauge Orange fusible link, located at the rear of the battery is used to protect fuse circuit 1.

A 20 gauge Orange fusible link, located at the left shock tower, is used to protect the A/C circuits.

A 18 gauge Gray fusible link, located at the left shock tower, is used to protect the headlamp switch and fuse circuits 5, 6, 7, 8 and 12.

A 12 gauge Black fusible link, located at the left shock tower, is used to protect the charging system.

A 20 gauge Orange fusible link, located at the left shock tower, is used to protect the ignition switch and fuse circuits 2, 3, 4, 13, 14.

A 18 gauge Gray fusible link, located and the left side shock tower, is used to protect the starter system and fuse circuits 9, 10 and 11.

A 20 gauge Orange fusible link, located at the left side shock tower, is used to protect the heated rear window.

Pickups & Ramcharger

A 20 gauge Orange fusible link, located at the rear of the battery, is used to protect fuse circuit 3.

A 16 gauge Dark Blue fusible link, located at the rear of left front wheelhouse, protects the headlamp switch circuit and fuse circuits 2, 8, 9 and 10.

A 16 gauge Dark Blue fusible link for 60 amp alternators, or 12 gauge Black fusible for 100 amp alternators, located at the rear of left front wheelhouse, is used to protect the charging system.

There are two 20 gauge Orange fusible links, located at the rear of left front wheelhouse, used to protect various circuits to and from the ignition switch. One is used to protect the windshield wiper motor and fuse circuits 4, 5 and 6. The other is used to protect the electronic spark advance, electronic control unit and ignition switch.

In addition to the fuse circuits and fusible links, there are 2 fuses, located at the rear of the battery, used to protect other circuits. The fuse enclosed in the Black fuse holder is used to protect the hazard warning flasher. The fuse enclosed in the Clear or Natural fuse holder is used to protect the ammeter.

Vans

A 20 gauge Orange fusible link, located at the rear of left front wheelhouse, is used to protect the ignition switch, the electronic spark advance and control unit and fuse circuits 11 and 12.

In addition to the fuse circuits and fusible links, there are 2 fuses, located at the rear of the battery, used to protect other circuits. The fuse enclosed in the Black fuse holder is used to protect the hazard warning flasher. The fuse enclosed in the Clear or Natural fuse holder is used to protect the ammeter.

A 20 gauge Orange fusible link, located at the rear of left front wheelhouse, is used to protect the ignition switch, windshield wiper motor and fuse circuits 1, 4, 5 and 6.

A 20 gauge Orange fusible link, located at the rear of left front wheelhouse, isused to protect the ignition switch, the electronic spark advance and control unit and fuse circuits 11 and 12.

In addition to the fuse circuits and fusible links, there are 2 fuses, located at the rear of the battery, used to protect other circuits. The fuse enclosed in the Black fuse holder is used to protect the hazard warning flasher. The fuse enclosed in the Clear or Natural fuse holder is used to protect the ammeter.

FLASHER LOCATION

On all Chrysler models, the turn signal and hazard flasher units are located at the fuse block. In addition to flasher units, the horn relay is also located at the fuse block.

Fuses & Circuit Breakers

FORD

FUSE BLOCK

FUSE BLOCK LOCATION

On all models, fuse block is located under instrument panel to left of steering column.

FUSE BLOCK CIRCUITS

Aerostar

1 – **15 Amp** Stop Lamps, Emergency Flasher
2 – **6 Amp Circuit Breaker** Front Wiper/Washer
3 – **15 Amp** Exterior Lamps, Trailer Lamp Relay
4 – **15 Amp** Turn signal Flasher, Back-Up Lamps, Visor Vanity, Illuminated Entry Module, Trailer Tow Turn Signal Relay, Day and Night Mirror
5 – **20 Amp** Speed Control, Rear Wiper/Washer & Defroster, Clock Display, Washer Fluid Sensor, Warning Chime, Door Ajar, Heated Window
6 – Not Used
7 – **15 Amp** Interior Lamps, Radio Memory, Trip Computer, Headlamp High Indicator, Clock, Key Warning Buzzer
8 – **30 Amp** Heater and A/C Blower, A/C Clutch
9 – **20 Amp** Flash-to-Pass
10 – **15 Amp** Radio/Tape Player, Amplifier
11 – **20 Amp Fuse and 30 Amp Circuit Breaker** Rear Cigar Lighter, Power Door Locks
12 – **5 Amp** Instrument Panel Lamps, Auto. Trans. Floor Shift Illumination
13 – **20 Amp Circuit Breaker** Power Windows
14 – Not Used
15 – **20 Amp** Front Cigar Lighter, Horns
16 – **10 Amp** Tachometer Cluster, Fuel Computer, Speedometer, Electronic Day Illumination
17 – **10 Amp** Warning Lamps, Seat Belt Buzzer, Carburetor Circuits, Low Fuel Warning, Door Ajar

Fig. 1: Aerostar Fuse Block

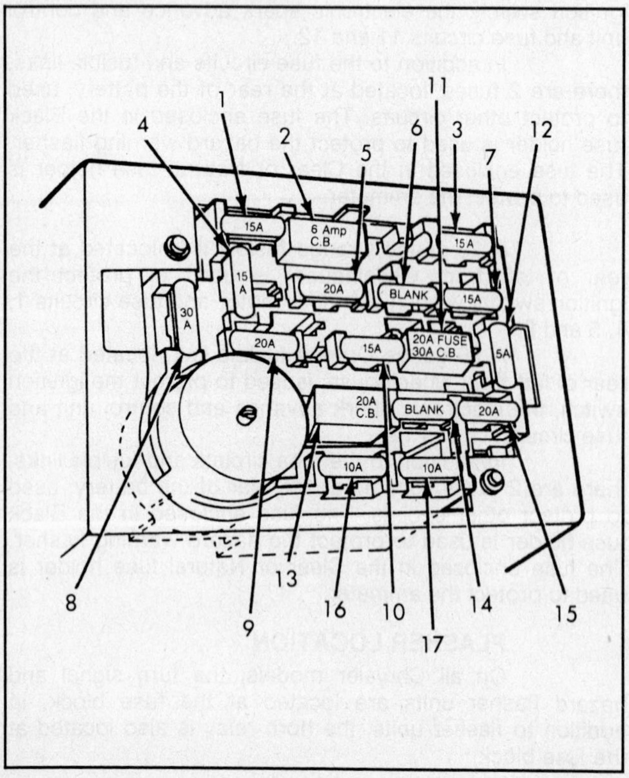

Van Models

1 – **15 Amp** Tail Lights, Marker Lights, License Plate Light, Parking Lights, Horn
2 – **3 Amp** Instrument Panel and Cluster Lights, Ashtray, Trans. Indicator Light, Radio, Heater, A/C Light, Headlight and Windshield Wiper Illumination
3 – **15 Amp** Throttle Solenoid
4 – **7.5 Amp** Seat Belt Warning, Auxiliary Fuel Tank Solenoid
5 – **7.5 Amp Circuit Breaker** Windshield Wiper Motor
6 – **35 Amp** Heater and/or A/C
7 – **15 Amp** Emergency Flasher, Stop Lights
8 – **20 Amp** Dome-Cargo Light, Courtesy Lights, Cigar Lighter, Clock
9 – **20 Amp** Accessory Feed, Speed Control
10 – **15 Amp** Turn Signal, Windshield Washer, Back-Up Lights
11 – **7.5 Amp** Radio, Premium Sound System

Fig. 2: Fuse Block for Van Models

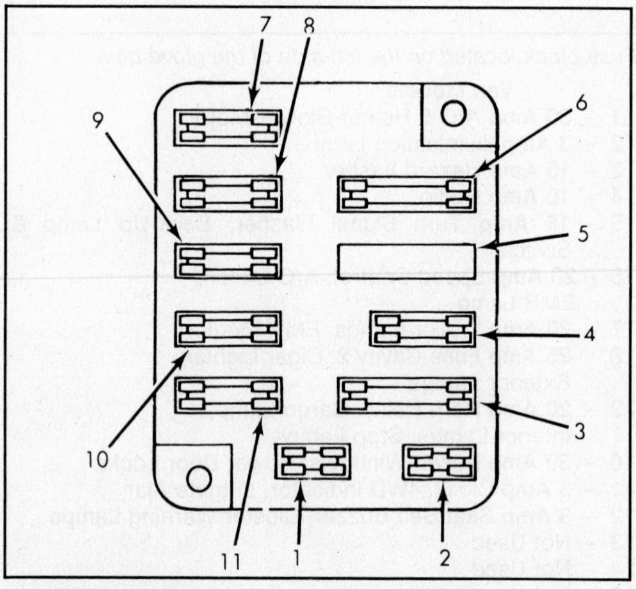

Fuse block under instrument panel at left side.

Bronco & "F" Series Pickups

1 – **15 Amp** Hazard & Stop Lights
2 – **15 Amp** Turn Signals & Back-Up Lights
3 – **30 Amp** Heater & A/C Blower Motor
4 – **5 Amp** Instrument Panel Lights
5 – **20 Amp Circuit Breaker ("F" Series)** Power Windows **25 Amp Circuit Breaker, (Bronco)** Power Tailgate
6 – **15 Amp** Warning Lights, Seat Belt Buzzer, Carburetor Circuits
7 – **10 Amp** Auxiliary Fuel Tank (Pickups)
8 – **20 Amp** Horn, Cigar Lighter
9 – **30 Amp Circuit Breaker** Power Door Locks, **25 Amp Fuse** Tailgate Key Switch (Bronco)
10 – **15 Amp** Interior Courtesy Lights
11 – **15 Amp** Tail Lights, Parking Lights, Trailer & Camper Option Lights, Instrument Panel Lights, Headlights On Buzzer (if equipped)
12 – **15 Amp** Radio
13 – **15 Amp** Accessories, Windshield Wipers, Speed Control, Auxiliary Battery & Heater, Defogger

FORD (Cont.)

Fig. 3: Fuse Block for Bronco and "F" Pickup Models

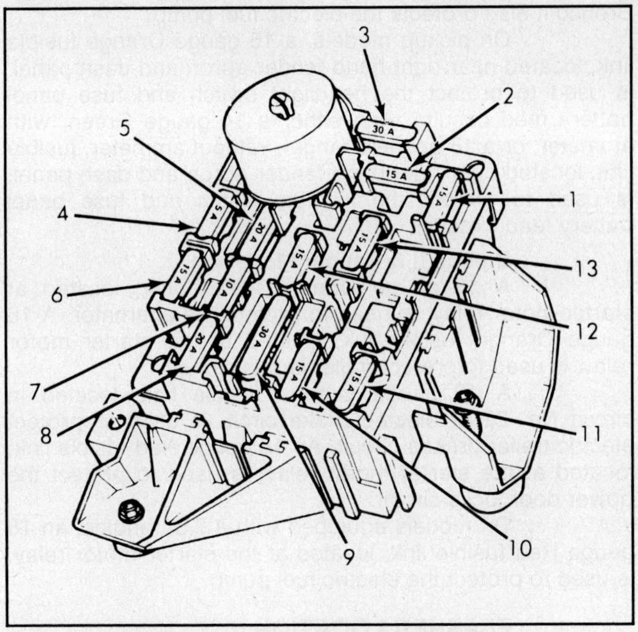

Fuse block under instrument panel at left side.

Bronco II & Ranger Models

1 – **15 Amp** Stop Lights, Emergency Warning Lights
2 – **15 Amp** Turn Signal Flasher, Back-Up Lights
3 – **30 Amp** A/C-Heater Blower, A/C Clutch
4 – **10 Amp** Radio
5 – **5 Amp** Instrument Panel Lights, Cluster Lights, Climate Control, Ashtray Light, Radio Illumination
6 – **20 Amp Circuit Breaker** Power Windows
7 – **30 Amp Circuit Breaker** Power Lumbar Seat
8 – **15 Amp** Warning Lights, Seatbelt Indicator & Buzzer, Carburetor Vent Solenoid
9 – **20 Amp** Cigar Lighter, Horns
10 – **15 Amp** Courtesy Lights, Dome Lights, Clock, Key Warning, Headlights On Buzzer
11 – **15 Amp** Tail Lights, Parking Lights, License Light, Headlight On Warning Buzzer
12 – **6 Amp Circuit Breaker** Wipers
13 – **15 Amp** Accessory Feed, Speed Control, 4WD Indicator

Fig. 4: Fuse Block for Bronco II and Ranger Models

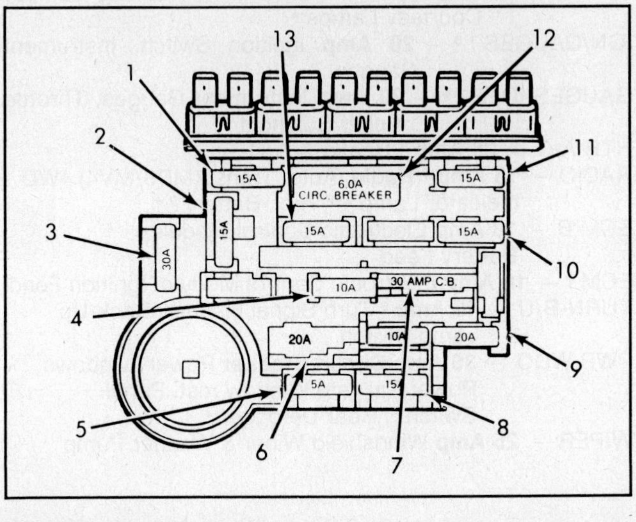

CIRCUIT BREAKERS

Aerostar

There are 3 circuit breakers, located at fuse block, used on Aerostar models. A 6-amp circuit breaker is used to protect the front wiper washer/wiper circuit. A 30-amp circuit breaker is used to protect the power door locks. A 20-amp circuit breaker is used to protect the power door locks.

Van Models

A 7.5-amp circuit breaker, located at the fuse block, protects windshield wipers. A 22-amp circuit breaker, located within headlight switch, protects the headlights. A 20-amp circuit breaker, located at the starter motor relay is used to protect the power door locks and windows.

Bronco & "F" Series Pickups

A 22-amp circuit breaker, located within headlight switch, protects the headlight circuit. A 7-amp circuit breaker, located within wiper switch, protects the windshield wiper circuit. Two 20-amp circuit breakers, located at the fuse block, are used to protect power window motors and power door lock circuits.

Bronco II & Ranger Models

A 22-amp circuit breaker, located within headlamp switch, is used to protect headlamps and high beam indicator circuits. A 30-amp circuit breaker, located in fuse block, is used to protect RPO power lumbar circuit. Also, a 4.5-amp circuit breaker, located in instrument panel above glove box, is used to protect liftgate wipers.

FUSIBLE LINKS

Aerostar

There are six 16 gauge Orange fusible links, located at the starter motor relay, used to protect various circuits. The circuits protected by these links are the auxiliary heater, alternator, trailer, heated backlite/power lumbar, headlamp switch battery feed, ignition switch battery feed.

There are two 20 gauge Blue fusible links, 2 located at the starter motor relay. These links protect the engine compartment lamp and the electronic engine control power relay.

On models equipped with 2.3L engine, two 20 gauge Blue fusible links, 1 located at the power relay and the other at the fuel pump relay, are used to protect the electronic engine control and the fuel pump.

On models equipped with 2.8L engine, there is a 20 gauge Blue fusible link, located in the left-hand fender "Go Way" connector to EEC-IV processor.

Van Models

A 14 gauge Green fusible link, located at the starter motor relay, is used to protect the auxiliary battery. An 18 gauge Red fusible link, located at the either the junction block or auxiliary battery relay, is used to protect the auxiliary heater or A/C.

A 16 gauge Orange for 40, 60 or 65 amp alternator, or a 14 gauge Green fusible link for 70 and 100 amp alternators, located at the starter motor relay, is used to protect the charging system.

A 20 gauge Blue fusible link, located in the choke wiring harness, is used to protect the electric choke. A 16 gauge Orange fusible link, located at the either the starter motor relay or junction block, is used to protect the trailer circuit.

Fuses & Circuit Breakers

FORD (Cont.)

An 18 gauge Red fusible link, located at the starter motor relay, is used to protect the carburetor circuits within the EEC system. A 14 gauge Green fusible link, located at the junction block, is used to protect camper circuits.

A 20 gauge Blue fusible link, located at the starter motor relay, is used to protect the engine compartment light. An 18 gauge Red fusible link, located at the starter motor relay, is used to protect the headlight switch battery feed circuit.

A 16 gauge Orange fusible link, located at the starter motor relay, is used to protect the ignition switch battery feed circuit. On models equipped with a 7.5L engine, there is a 16 gauge Orange fusible link, located at the starter motor relay, used to protect the electric fuel pump circuit.

Bronco & "F" Series Pickups

A 16 gauge Orange fusible link, located at the starter motor relay, is used to protect electric trailer brakes. A 16 gauge Orange fusible link, located at the junction block left-hand engine side of dash panel, is used to protect trailer light relay feed.

A 14 gauge Green fusible link, located at the dual battery relay, is used to protect the dual battery relay feed. On pickup models, a 14 gauge Green fusible link, located at the starter motor relay, is used to protect the 70 amp alternator.

On Bronco II models either a 14 Green or a 16 gauge Orange fusible link, located at the starter motor relay, is used to protect the alternator. A 16 gauge Orange fusible link, located at the junction block left-hand engine side of dash panel, is used to protect the camper battery feed, if not equipped with dual batteries.

On all models, an 18 gauge Red fusible link, located at the junction block left-hand engine side of dash panel, is used to protect marker lights relay feed circuit. An 18 gauge Red fusible link, located at the starter motor relay, is used to protect the electronic engine controls. On Bronco it also protects the electric fuel pump.

On pickup models, a 16 gauge Orange fusible link, located near right-hand fender apron and dash panel, is used to protect the headlight switch and fuse panel battery feed circuits. And either a 14 gauge Green, with ammeter, or a 16 gauge Orange , without ammeter, fusible link, located near right-hand fender apron and dash panel, is used to protect the ignition switch and fuse panel battery feed circuits.

Bronco II & Ranger Models

A 16 gauge .Orange fusible link, located at starter motor relay, is used to protect the alternator. A 16 gauge Orange fusible link, located at the starter motor relay, is used to protect trailer lamps circuit.

A 16 gauge Orange fusible link, located in circuit No. 22 of electric brake circit, is used to protect electric trailer brakes circuit. An 18 gauge Red fusible link, located at the starter motor relay, is used to protect the power door locks circuit.

On models equipped with a 2.3L engine, an 18 gauge Red fusible link, located at the starter motor relay, is used to protect the electric fuel pump.

FLASHER LOCATION

Hazard Flasher

On Aerostar models, the hazard flasher is taped to the steering column. On Van models, flasher is taped to main wiring assembly in left corner of instrument panel. On all other models, flasher is mounted on fuse block.

Turn Signal Flasher

On Van models, flasher is attached to lower reinforcement of instrument panel on left side of steering column. On all other models, flasher is located on fuse block.

GENERAL MOTORS

FUSE BLOCK

FUSE BLOCK LOCATION

On most models, fuse block is located under instrument panel on driver's side of vehicle. On other models access to fuse block is gained through an access within glove box.

FUSE BLOCK CIRCUITS

Blazer, Pickup, Van & Suburban Models

INST LPS – **5 Amp** Instrument Lamps, Rear Defogger Lamps, 4WD Indicator, Audio Alarm [3]

PWR ACC – **30 Amp Circuit Breaker** Power Door Locks, Power Tailgate [4], Rear Defogger [4,5], Power Windows [5], Rear Defogger [5], Tailgate [5]

HORN/DM – **20 Amp** Dome & Cargo Lamp, Clock, Lighter & Horn Relay Theft Deterrant [3]

GAUGES [3] – **20 Amp** Audio Alarm, Instrument Cluster Gauges, Brake Switch, Cruise Control

IGN – **20 Amp** Ignition [2], Diesel & Low Coolant [1,4,5], Cruise Control [1,4,5], Rear Defogger [1,4,5], Aux. Fuel Tank Selector Switch [1,4,5], Overspeed Warning [1,4,5], Auto. Trans. [1,4,5]

AUX HTR A/C – **25 Amp** Auxiliary Heater & A/C

STOP-HAZ – **15 Amp** [6] Hazard Flasher, Stop Lamps & Courtesy Lamps [2], Audio Alarm [3]

TAIL LPS [3] – **20 Amp**Tail Lamps, Headlamps

T/L CTSY – **20 Amp** Light Switch, Tail/Parking Lamps, Courtesy Lamps [4]

IGN/GAUGES [1,5] – **20 Amp** Ignition Switch, Instrument Gauges

GAUGES/IDLE [2,4] – **20 Amp** Instrument Gauges, Throttle Kicker Solenoid

HTR A/C – **25 Amp** [7] Heater & A/C

RADIO – **15 Amp** [8] Radio, Auto. Trans. (MD8/MV4) 4WD Indicator Lamp [2,4], Aux. Battery [2,4]

ECM B – **10 Amp** Electronic Control Module; Battery Feed

ECM I – **10 Amp** Electronic Control Module; Ignition Feed

TURN-B/U – **15 Amp** [9] Turn Signal Flasher, Back-Up Lamp Switch

PWR WDO – **30 Amp Circuit Breaker** Power Windows, Power Tailgate Window Inst. Panel Switch [4], Rear Defogger [4]

WIPER – **25 Amp** Windshield Wiper & Washer Pump

Fuses & Circuit Breakers

GENERAL MOTORS (Cont.)

CHOKE – **20 Amp** Electric Choke, Oil Pressure Switch [3]
[1] – Applies to GMC trucks only.
[2] – Applies to Chevrolet trucks only.
[3] – Applies to van models only.
[4] – Applies to Blazer & Suburban only.
[5] – Applies to GMC Jimmy Suburban only
[6] – On GMC Jimmy Suburban, fuse is 15-amp.
[7] – On van models, fuse is 20-amp.
[8] – On van models, fuse is 10-amp.
[9] – On van models, fuse is 20-amp.

NOTE: **An in-line fuse is used for the underhood lamp, if equipped.**

Fig. 1: Fuse Block for Blazer, Pickup, Suburban and Van Models

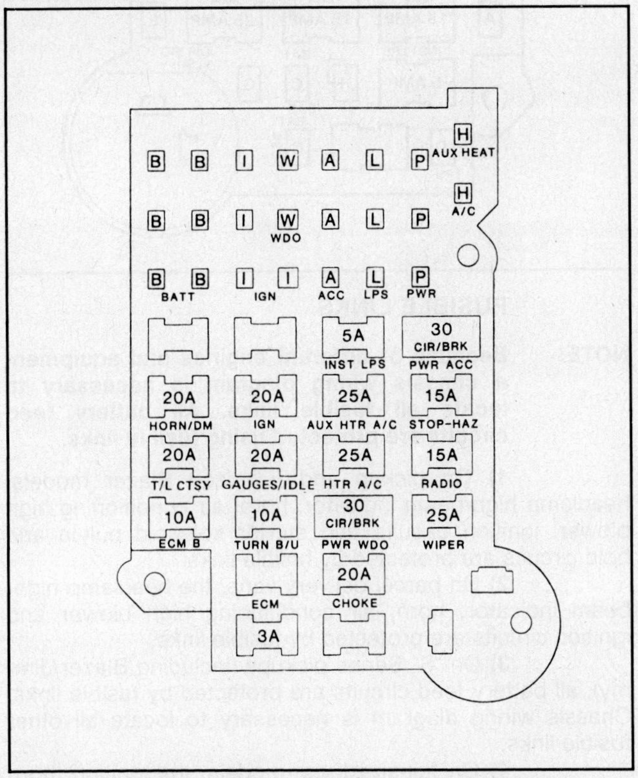

Fuse block located under left side of instrument panel.

Astro & Safari Models

INST LPS – **10 Amp** Instrument Panel Lamps, Radio Dial Lamps, Heater Lamps
PWR ACC – **30 Amp Circuit Breaker** Power Door Locks
HORN-DM – **20 Amp** Horn Relay, Digital Clock, Cigarette Lighter, Dome Lights
GAUGES – **20 Amp** Instrument Cluster Gauges, Brake Switch, Audio Alarm, Headlamp Switch Illumination
AUX HTR A/C – **25 Amp** Auxiliary Heater, Rear A/C
STOP-HAZ – **20 Amp** Stop Lamps, Hazard Flasher
TAIL LPS – **20 Amp** Headlamp Switch, Tail & Parking Lamps
TURN B/U – **20 Amp** Turn Signal Flasher, Back-Up Lamps
HTR A/C – **20 Amp** Front Heater & Air Conditioning
RADIO – **10 Amp** Radio
ECM B – **10 Amp** Electronic Control Module; Battery Feed
ECM I – **10 Amp** Electronic Control Module; Igniton Feed
PWR WDO – **30 Amp Circuit Breaker** Power Windows
WIPER – **25 Amp** Windshield Wiper & Pump
CHOKE – **20 Amp** Oil Pressure Switch

Fig. 2: Fuse Block for Astro & Safari Models

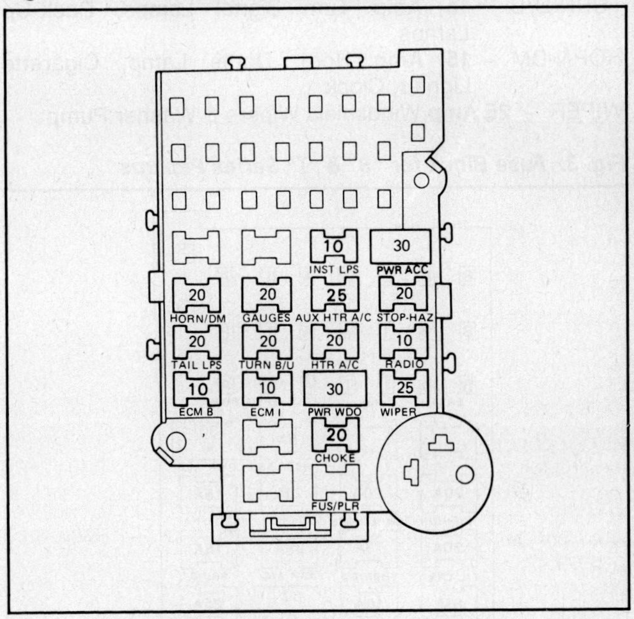

"S" & "T" Series Pickups

INST LPS – **5 Amp** Instrument Panel Lights, Headlamp Warning Buzzer, Rear Defogger Switch Lamp
PWR ACC – **30 Amp Circuit Breaker** Power Door Locks, Rear Defogger
HORN-DM – **20 Amp** Horn, Dome Lamps, Glove Box Lamp, Clock Left-Hand Courtesy Lamp, Lift Gate Release Solenoid, Lighter
IGN-GAUGES – **20 Amp** Ignition and Gauges, Rear Defogger Relay, Auto. Trans. Converter Clutch, Cruise Control
CHOKE – **20 Amp** Choke
STOP-HAZ – **15 Amp** Stop Lamps, Hazard Warning Lamps
T/L CTSY – **20 Amp** Light Switch, Tail/Park Lamps
TURN-B/U – **15 Amp** Turn Signal & Back-Up Lamps
HTR A/C – **25 Amp** Heating & Air Conditioning
RADIO – **15 Amp** Radio
ECM B – **10 Amp** Electronic Control Module; Battery Feed
ECM I – **10 Amp** Electronic Control Module; Ignition Feed
PWR WDO – **30 Amp Circuit Breaker** Power Windows
WIPER – **25 Amp** Windshield Wipers & Washers

NOTE: **For location of fuses on delivery vans, see fuse block located under instrument panel on driver's side. The following list details what size fuse protects which circuits.**

Delivery Van Models

CHOKE – **20 Amp** Electric Choke
ACC – **10 Amp** Radio (if equipped)
HTR-A/C – **25 Amp** Heater & Air Conditioning (if equipped)
STOP-HAZ – **15 Amp** Stop Lamps, Hazard Flashers

Fuses & Circuit Breakers

GENERAL MOTORS (Cont.)

GAUGES – **10 Amp** Fuel Gauge, Brake Warning Lamp, Oil Pressure Gauge, Trans. Downshift (MD 40), Choke Heater
TAIL LPS – **20 Amp** Light Switch, Tail Lamps
TURN-B/U – **15 Amp** Turn Signal Lamps, Back-Up Lamps
HORN-DM – **15 Amp** Horn, Dome Lamp, Cigarette Lighter, Clock
WIPER – **25 Amp** Windshield Wipers & Washer Pump

Fig. 3: Fuse Block for "S" & "T" Series Pickups

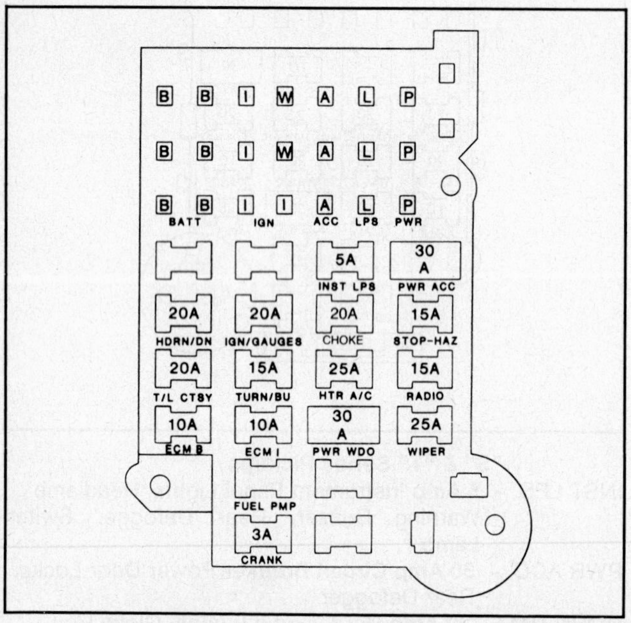

GAUGES – **10 Amp** Fuel Gauge, Brake Warning Lamp, Oil Pressure Gauge, Trans. Downshift (MD 40), Choke Heater
TAIL LPS – **20 Amp** Light Switch, Tail Lamps
TURN-B/U – **15 Amp** Turn Signal Lamps, Back-Up Lamps
HORN-DM – **15 Amp** Horn, Dome Lamp, Cigarette Lighter, Clock
WIPER – **25 Amp** Windshield Wipers & Washer Pump

CIRCUIT BREAKERS

All models have two 30-amp circuit breakers, 1 to protect power locks and rear defogger and another to protect power windows.

Fig. 4: Delivery Van Fuse Block

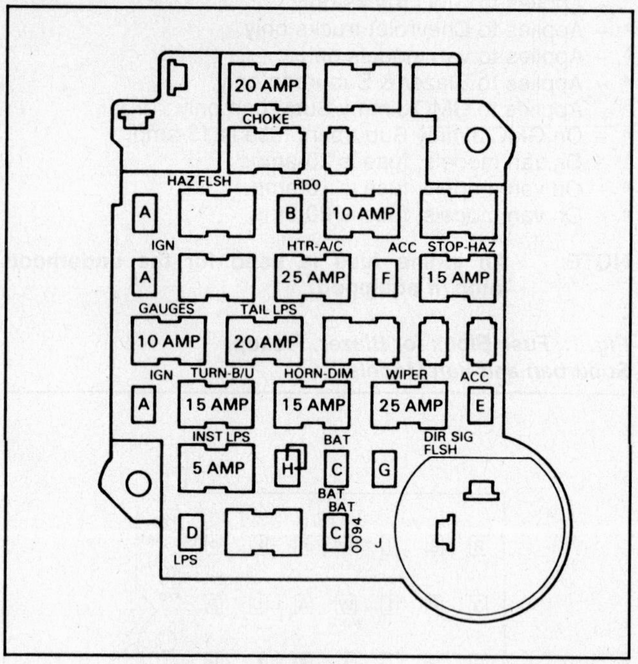

FUSIBLE LINKS

NOTE: **Because of different engines and equipment a chassis wiring diagram is necessary to locate all fusible links. All battery feed circuits are protected using fusible links.**

1) On pickup and full-sized Blazer models, headlamp high-beam indicator, horn, air conditioning high blower, ignition circuits and starter solenoid pull-in and hold circuits are protected by fusible links.

2) On parcel delivery vans, the headlamp high-beam indicator, horn, air conditioning high blower and ignition circuits are protected by fusible links.

3) On "S" Series pickups (including Blazer/Jimmy), all battery feed circuits are protected by fusible links. Chassis wiring diagram is necessary to locate all other fusible links.

4) On full-sized van models, the ignition, horn and headlamp high-beam indicator circuits and air conditioning high blower are all protected by fusible links.

5) On Astro/Safari models, all battery feed circuits are protected by fusible links. A chassis wiring diagram is necessary to locate all other fusible links.

FLASHER & RELAY LOCATION

On all models, buzzers, relays and flasher units are located on the underside of the instrument panel. Most are located beneath steering column while others may be located under glove box.

JEEP

FUSE BLOCK

FUSE BLOCK LOCATION

All Models

Fuse block is located under the instrument panel on driver's side of vehicle on all models.

FUSE BLOCK CIRCUITS

Cherokee & Wagoneer

1 – **25 Amp** Rear Washer/Wiper
2 – **15 Amp** Radio, Cigar Lighter
3 – **25 Amp** Blower Motor
4 – **20 Amp** Turn Signal, Back-Up Lights, Defogger Relay
5 – **10 Amp** Dome Lights, Courtesy Lights, Glove Box Light, Cargo Overhead Lights
6 – **15 Amp** Hazard Light Warning, Stop Lamps
7 – **10 Amp** Parking Lights, Head Light Warning, Instrument Panel Dimmer
8 – **7.5 Amp** Gauges, Seat Belt Warning
9 – **5 Amp** Instrument Panel Illumination
10 – **25 Amp** Rear Window Defogger
11 – **30 Amp Circuit Breaker** Power Door Lock, Power Seats, Trailer Towing Harness
12 – **10 Amp** ETR Radio, Power Antenna
13 – **25 Amp** Headlight Delay
14 – **5.5 Amp Circuit Breaker** Front Wipers
15 – **30 Amp Circuit Breaker** Power Windows
16 – **10 Amp** Clock

Fig. 1: Fuse Block Circuits for Cherokee & Wagoneer

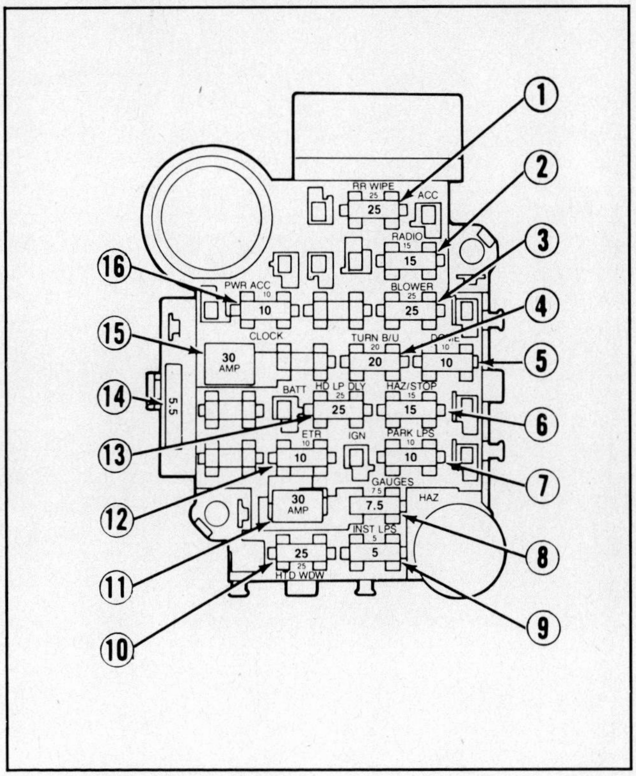

All Other Models

1 – **20 Amp All except CJ7 and Scrambler** Windshield Wipers **4.5 Amp CJ7 and Scrambler** Windshield Wipers
2 – **15 Amp** Turn Signals
3 – **10 Amp** Cigar Lighter and Radio
4 – **3 Amp** Instrument Panel & Accessory Lights
5 – **20 Amp Circuit Breaker** Interior Lights
6 – **20 Amp Circuit Breaker** Brake, Tail and Parking Lights
7 – **25 Amp** Air Conditioner, Heater and Eiectric Fan
8 – **3 Amp** Instruments
9 – **25 Amp** Seat Belt Warning and Back-Up Lights
10 – **20 Amp** Hazard Flasher, Clock and Stop Lights

Fig. 2: Fuse Block Circuits for all Jeep Models Except Cherokee and Wagoneer

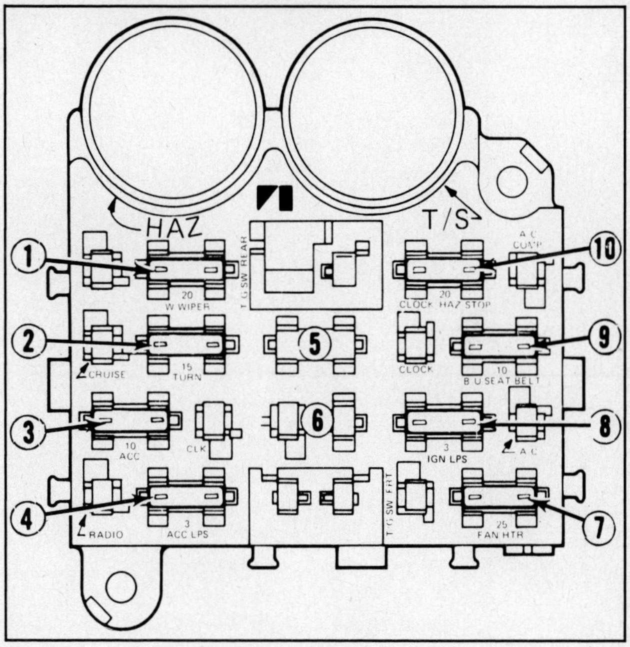

CIRCUIT BREAKERS

On all except Cherokee and Wagoneer, a 24 amp circuit breaker is located in the headlight switch to protect headlight circuit. There are 2 other circuit breakers located at the fuse block to protect light circuits.

On Cherokee and Wagoneer models, there are 3 circuit breakers located at the fuse block to protect power door locks and seats, windshield wiper motor and power windows.

IN-LINE FUSES

All Except Cherokee & Wagoneer

Six-cylinder models have a 4-amp in-line fuse protecting the cruise control. Models with V8 engines have a 1.5 amp in-line fuse protecting the cruise control.

FUSIBLE LINKS

All models are equipped with fusible links in the engine compartment to protect the battery feed within the starting and charging circuits.

FLASHER LOCATIONS

Hazard & Turn Signal Flasher

Hazard and turn signal flashers are located on fuse panel on all models.

SECTION 5

WIRING DIAGRAMS

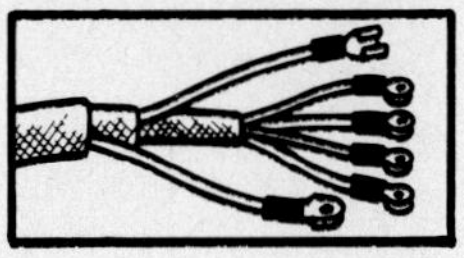

ARRANGEMENT OF DATA

Wiring diagrams on the following pages are arranged by manufacturer. Each manufacturer's diagrams are subdivided by vehicle models. Each group of similar models requires 4 pages of diagrams.

The first page includes the front lights and engine compartment. The additional pages work back from the engine compartment, including the fuse block, instrument panel, underdash area, accessories, rear lights and printed circuits.

CONTENTS

NOTE: ALSO SEE GENERAL INDEX.

IMPORTANT: Because of the many model names used by vehicle manufacturers, accurate identification of models is important. See Model Identification at the front of this publication.

MITCHELL'S WIRING DIAGRAMS

Mitchell obtains diagrams and wiring change bulletins from all the import manufacturers. These are all checked and redrawn in a consistent style for easy use. All diagrams are arranged with the front of the vehicle at the left side of the first page, and the taillights at the right edge of the last page. Accessories are shown near the end of the diagram. Components are shown in their approximate location in the vehicle, though due to crowded pages, it is not possible to shown exact positioning .

Several diagrams in this manual have been drawn in a new style. The improved layout allows space for internal switch details and connector shapes. Removing some of the wiring maze reduces eyestrain and wasted time from searching across several pages. Any wires that don't connect directly to their components are labeled so you know where they go. There is a component list at the front of the diagrams. It refers you to components, using grid numbers at the top and bottom of the pages.

HOW TO USE THE NEW DIAGRAMS

1) The front part of the diagram contains a reference list of the major electrical components. Find the component or system you wish to trace.

2) Use the grid numbers to find the component on the wiring diagram pages.

3) The vehicle locations shown at the bottom of the page will help you to find the approximate location of the component on the actual vehicle.

4) Find the circuit you need to service. The internals are shown for switches and relays so you can understand how the circuit operates.

5) If the wires are not drawn all the way to another component, a reference will tell you their destination.

6) Use the reference list and grid to find the other component rather than tracing a wire through several pages.

WIRING SYMBOLS

Standard wiring symbols are used on our diagrams. The list below will help clarify any symbols that are not easily understood at a glance. Most components are labeled "Motor", "Switch" or "Relay" in addition to being drawn with the standard symbol.

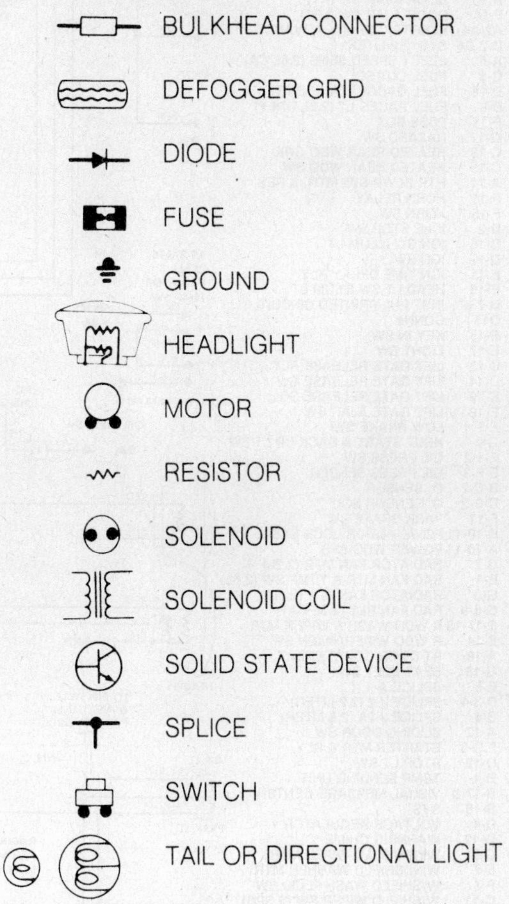

1985 Chrysler Corp.

CARAVAN, MINI RAM VAN & VOYAGER

COMPONENT GRID LOCATION

A-6	AIR SOL (2.6L)
B-15	A/C & HTR BLWR MTR RES
A-16	A/C HTR SW
G-4	A/C COND FAN RLY (2.2L)
E-5	A/C COND FAN RLY (2.6L)
G-14	A/C COMP CLUTCH (2.2L)
E-5	A/C COMP CLUTCH (2.6L)
F-4	A/C CYCLE SW (2.2 LITER)
D-5	A/C CYCLE SW (2.6. LITER)
D-6	A/C CUT-OUT SW (2.6L)
F-4	A/C LOW PRESS SW (2.2L)
D-5	A/C LOW PRESS SW (2.6L)
C-6	A/C OPEN THROT SOL (2.6L)
F-4	A/C WOT CUT-OFF SW (2.2L)
F-4	A/C WOT CUT-OFF SW (2.2L)
D-3	ALTERNATOR (2.2L)
C-5	ALTERNATOR (2.6L)
F-8	AMBIENT TEMP SW (2.6L CA)
G-7	BACK-UP LT SW
F-16	BEAM SELECT SW
B-17	BLOWER MTR SW
C-5	BOWL VENT SOL (2.6L)
D-12	BRAKE & CRUISE CTRL SW
D-3	CHOKE HTR (2.2L)
D-13	CLUTCH SW
F,G-3,4	CONDENSER FAN SYS (2.2L)
D,E-5,6	CONDENSER FAN SYS (2.6L)
D-4	COIL (2.2 LITER SYS)
B-5	COIL (2.6 LITER SYS)
A-8	CRUISE CTRL SERVO UNIT
D-4	DIAGNOSTIC CONN (2.2L)
A-6	DECELERATION SOL (2.6L)
E-11	DIRECTION FLASHER
F-17	DIR (TURN SIGNAL) SW
C-2	DISTRIBUTOR (2.2L)
D-5	DISTRIBUTOR (2.6L)
A-3	DISTANCE SENSOR (2.2L)
C-13	DOME LT
A-13	DOOR AJAR SW (RT)
F-14	DOOR AJAR SW (LFT)
A2-A4, D-2-D4	ELECTRIC SPARK ADVANCE SYS (2.2 LITER)
A-5	ELECT SPEED SENS (2.6L CA)
C-5	FUEL CUT SOL
D-19	FUEL GAUGE (TANK UNIT)
B-9	FUEL PACER LT (2.2L ONLY)
F-11	FUSE BOX
G-17	HAZARD SW
C-19	HEATED REAR WDO GRID
C-15	HEATED REAR WDO SW
A-14	HTR BLWR SW, MTR, & RES
F-11	HORN RELAY
F-15	HORN SW.
D-2	IDLE STOP SW
D-16	IGN SW ILLUM LT
D-17	IGN SW
E-11	IGN TIME DELAY RLY
E-15	HEAD LT SW ILLUM LT
D-7 & D18	INST PNL PRINTED CIRCUIT CONNs
E-15	KEY IN SW
E-17	LIGHT SW
D-13	LIFT GATE RELEASE RLY
D-14	LIFT GATE RELEASE SW
E-19	LIFT GATE RELEASE SOL
E-19	LIFT GATE AJAR SW
F-9	LOW BRAKE SW
G-7	NEUT START & BACK-UP LT SW
E-1-2	OIL PRESS SW
E-F-3	OIL PRESS SENDER
B-C-2	O_2 SENSOR
C-D-2	O_2 SENSOR SOL
F-11	PARK BRAKE SW
B-10-11	POWER DOOR LOCK SYS
A-10-11	POWER WDO SYS
G-2	RADIATOR FAN MTR (2.2L)
E-1	RAD FAN MTR & TEMP SW (2.6L)
G-3	RADIATOR FAN RLY (2.2L)
G-8-9	RAD FAN RLY (2.6L CA)
E-17-18	R WDO WASH & WIPER MTR
B-14	R WDO WIPER/WASH SW
A-18	RT DOOR COURTESY LT
G-18	SEAT BELT SW
E-3	SPLICE A-1
D-3-4	SPLICE J-2 (2.2 LITER)
B-6	SPLICE J-2A (2.6 LITER)
A-12	SLIDING DOOR SW
F,G-5	STARTER MTR & RLY
D-12	STOP LT SW
B-4	TEMP SENDING UNIT
B-17 & B-18	VISUAL MESSAGE CENTER SYS
D-4	VOLTAGE REGULATOR
G-12	WARNING CHIME
C-6	WINDSHIELD WIPER MTR
E-7	WINDSHIELD WASHER MTR
F-7	W/SHIELD WASH FLUID SW
C-11	W/SHIELD WIPER SW (2 SPD)
C-13	W/SHIELD WIPER INTERM SW
E-6	WIPER INTERM CTRL UNIT

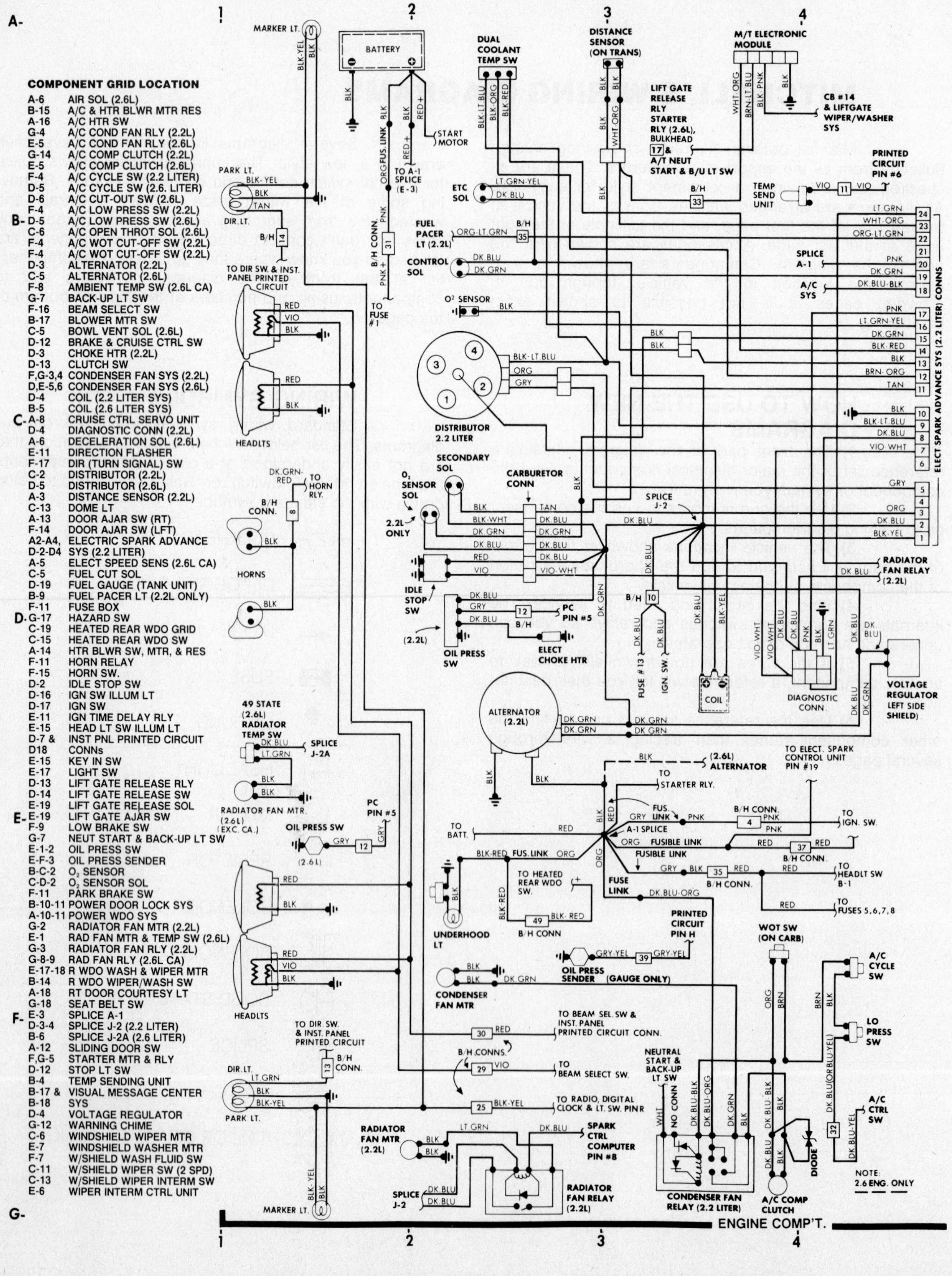

CARAVAN, MINI RAM VAN & VOYAGER (Cont.)

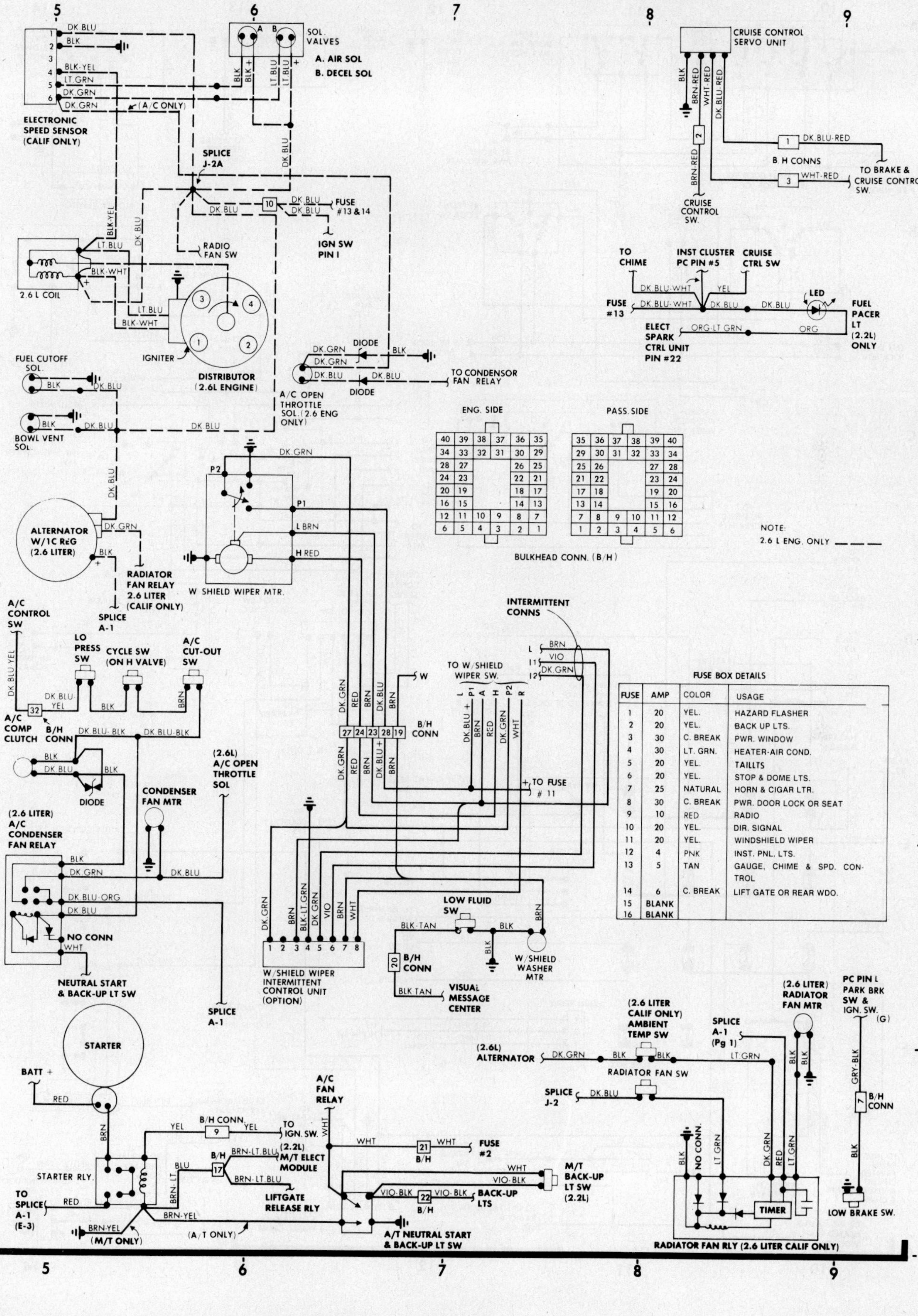

FUSE BOX DETAILS

FUSE	AMP	COLOR	USAGE
1	20	YEL.	HAZARD FLASHER
2	20	YEL.	BACK UP LTS.
3	30	C. BREAK	PWR. WINDOW
4	30	LT. GRN.	HEATER-AIR COND.
5	20	YEL.	TAILLTS
6	20	YEL.	STOP & DOME LTS.
7	25	NATURAL	HORN & CIGAR LTR.
8	30	C. BREAK	PWR. DOOR LOCK OR SEAT
9	10	RED	RADIO
10	20	YEL.	DIR. SIGNAL
11	20	YEL.	WINDSHIELD WIPER
12	4	PNK	INST. PNL. LTS.
13	5	TAN	GAUGE, CHIME & SPD. CONTROL
14	6	C. BREAK	LIFT GATE OR REAR WDO.
15	BLANK		
16	BLANK		

1985 Chrysler Corp.

CARAVAN, MINI RAM VAN & VOYAGER (Cont.)

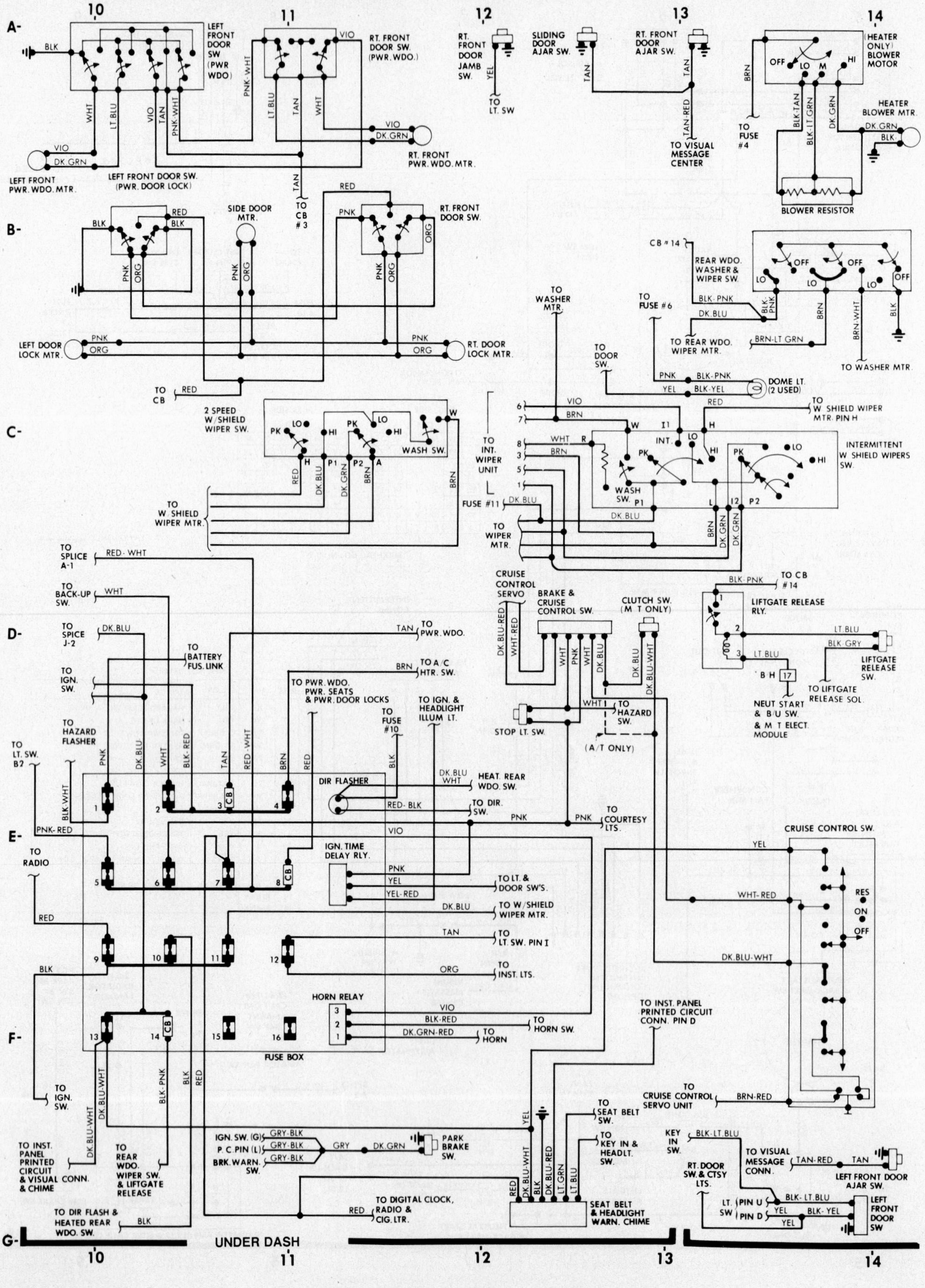

CARAVAN, MINI RAM VAN & VOYAGER (Cont.)

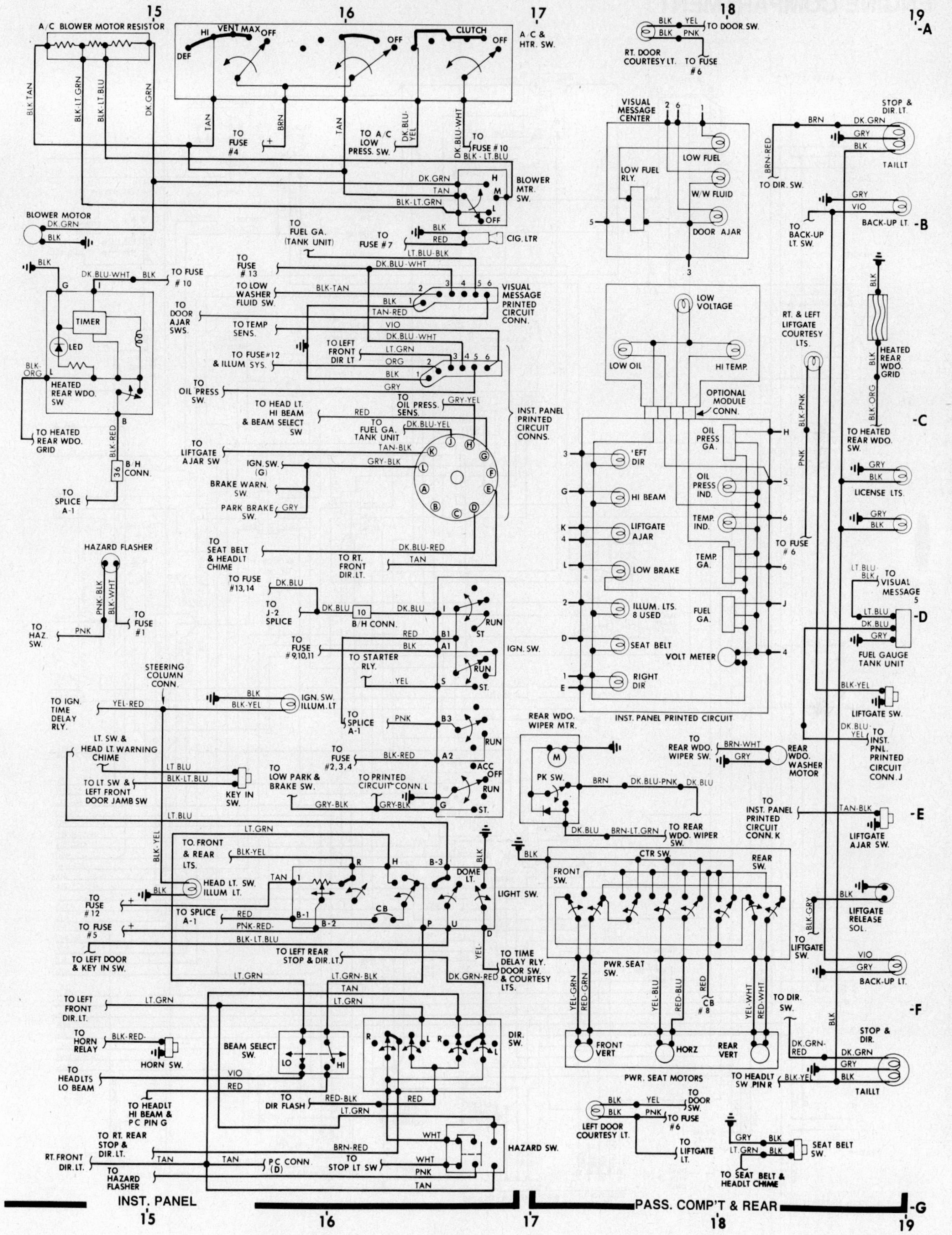

1985 Chrysler Corp.

RAM VANS & VOYAGER WAGONS

ENGINE COMPARTMENT

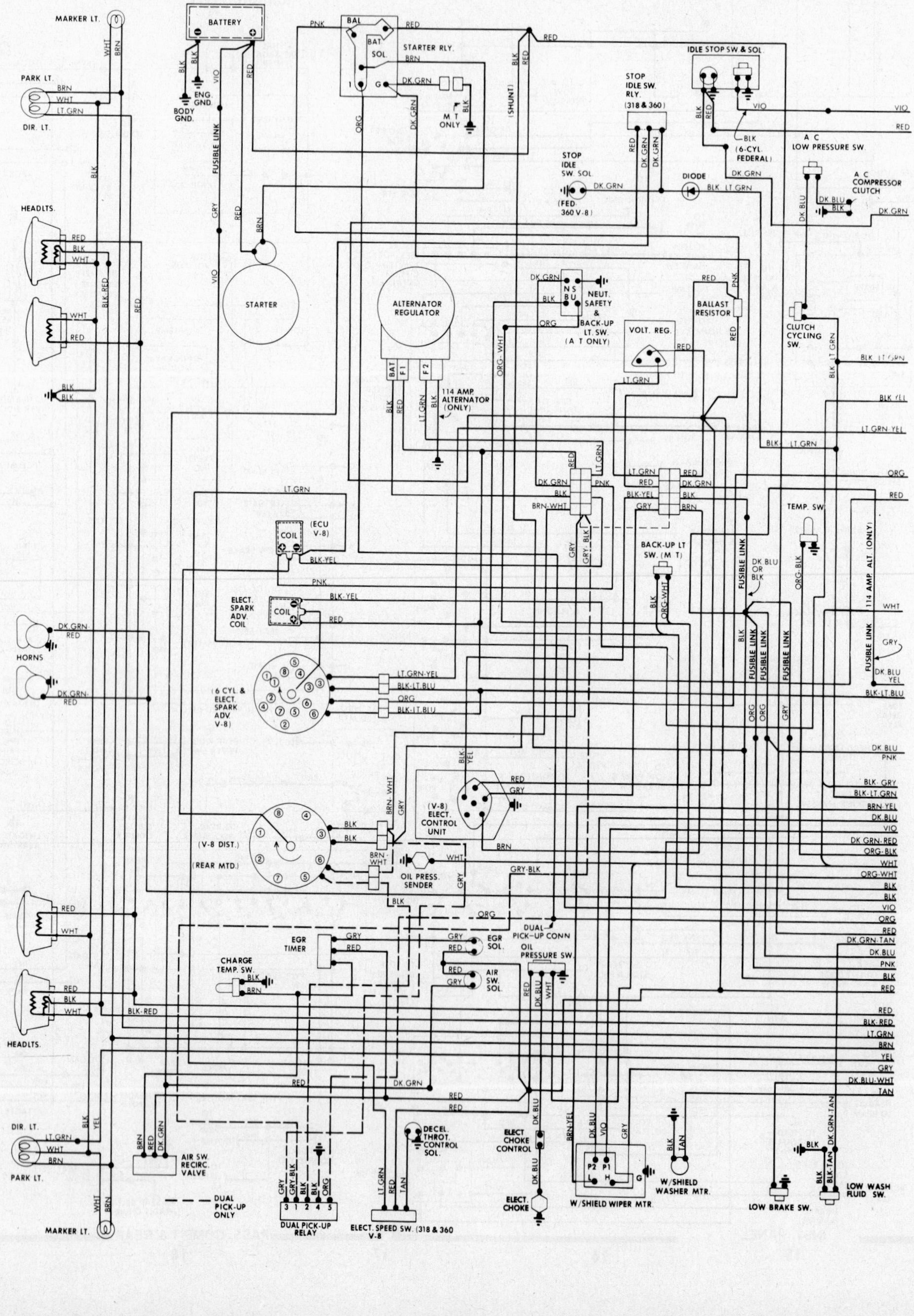

RAM VANS & VOYAGER WAGONS (Cont.)

FUSE BLOCK & UNDERDASH

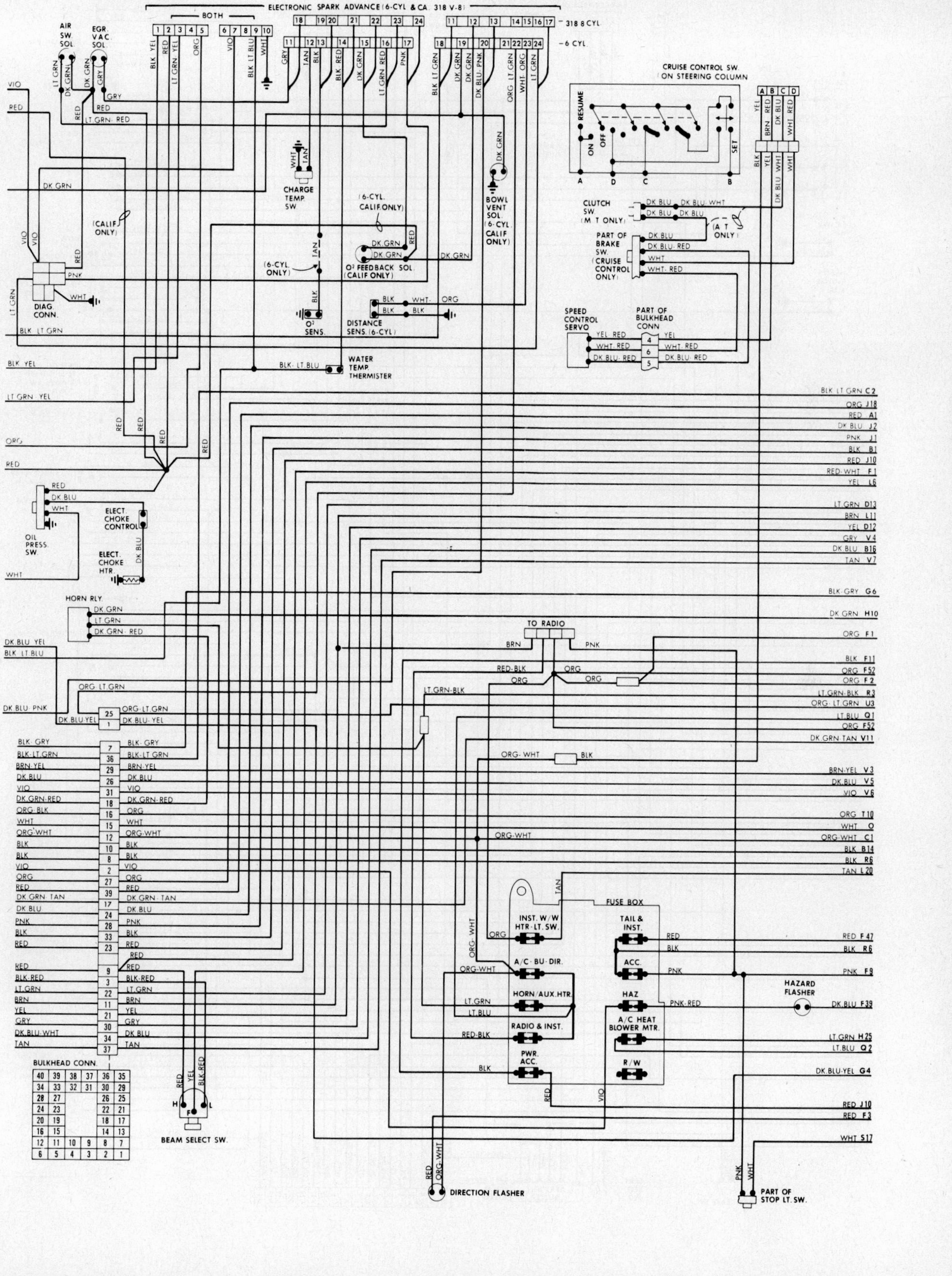

1985 Chrysler Corp.

RAM VANS & VOYAGER WAGONS (Cont.)

INSTRUMENT PANEL & UNDERDASH

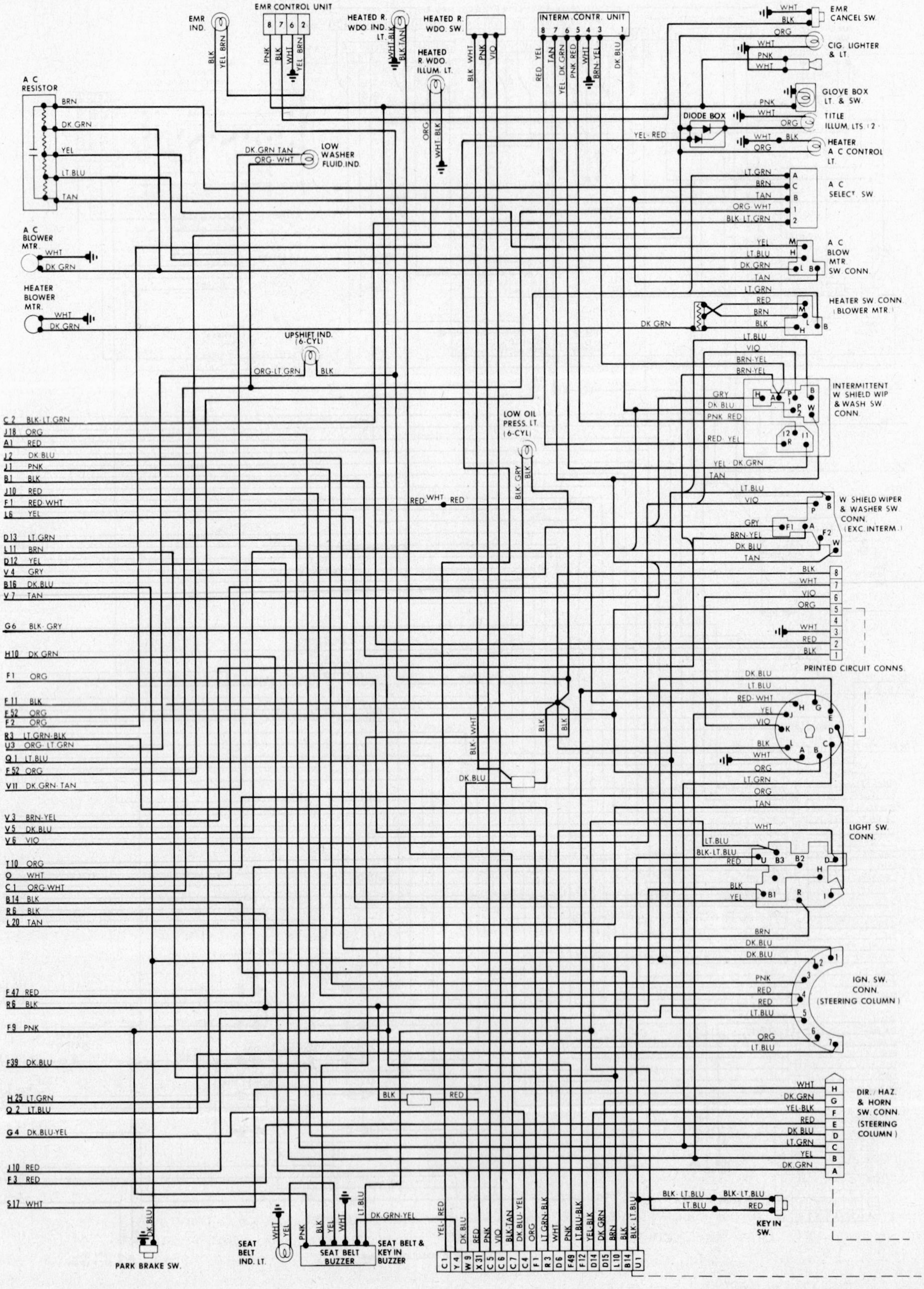

RAM VANS & VOYAGER WAGONS (Cont.)

REAR COMPARTMENT & ACCESSORIES

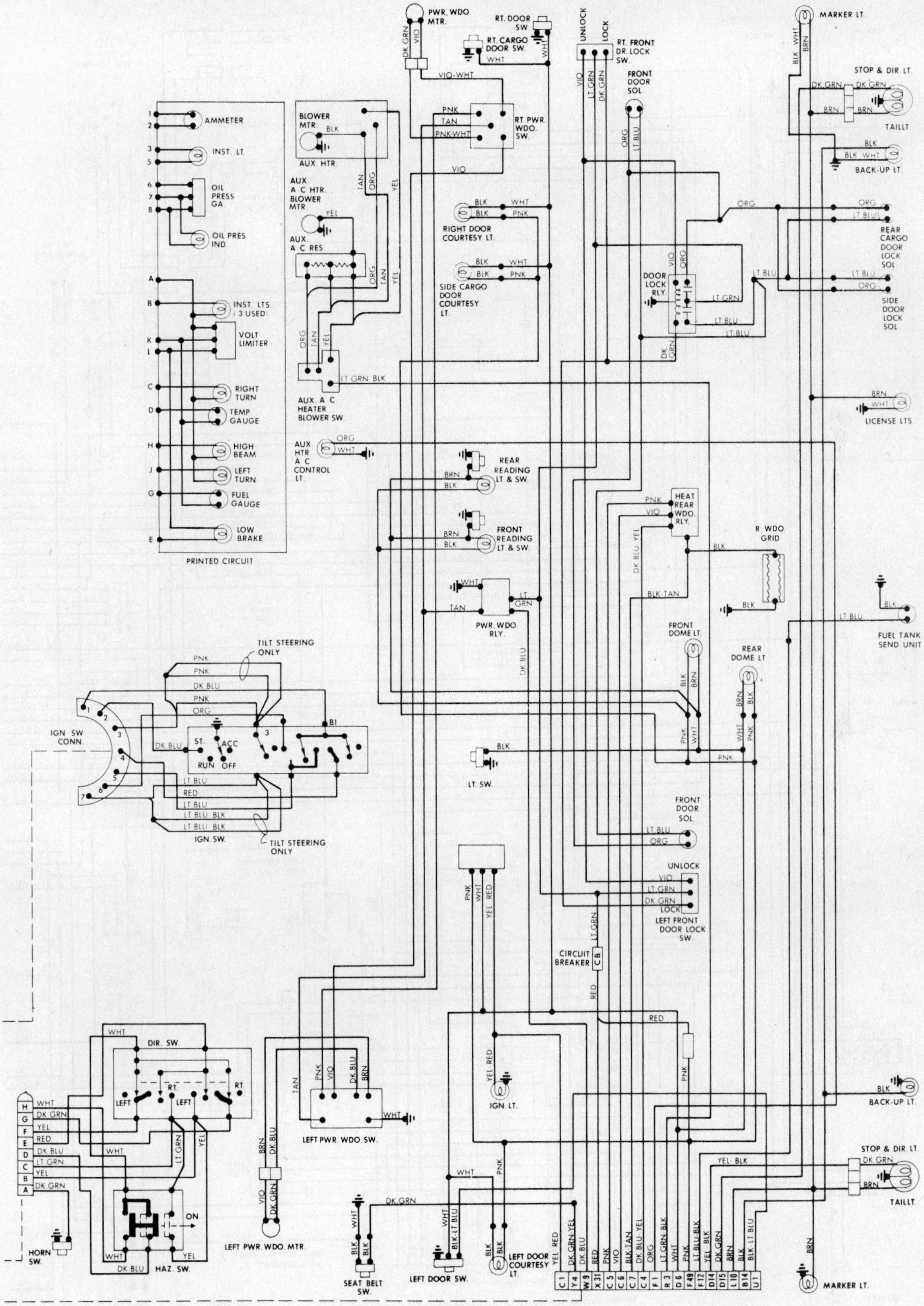

1985 Chrysler Corp.

CHASSIS CABS, PICKUPS & RAMCHARGER

ENGINE COMPARTMENT

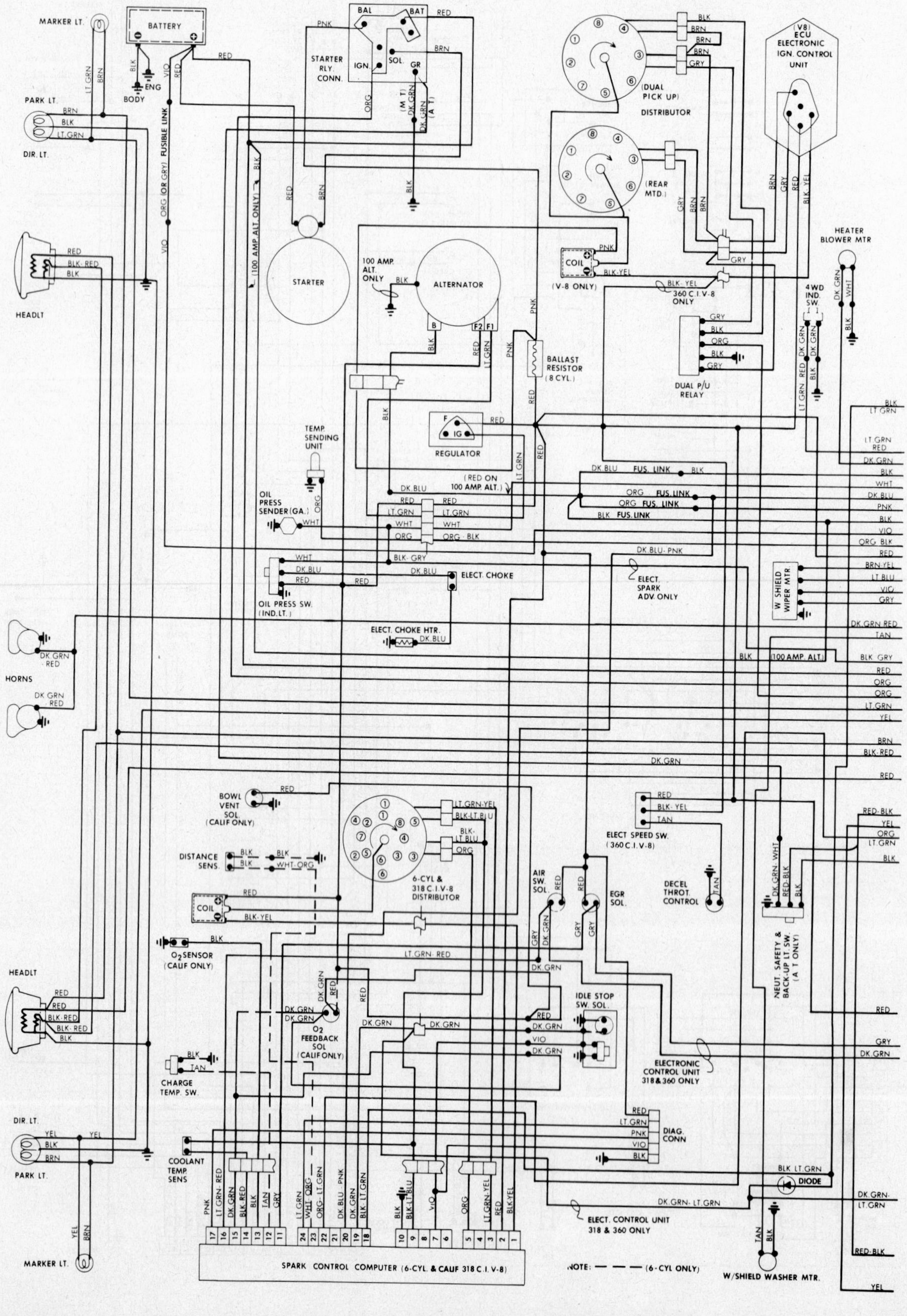

CHASSIS CABS, PICKUPS & RAMCHARGER (Cont.)

ENGINE COMPARTMENT & FUSE BLOCK

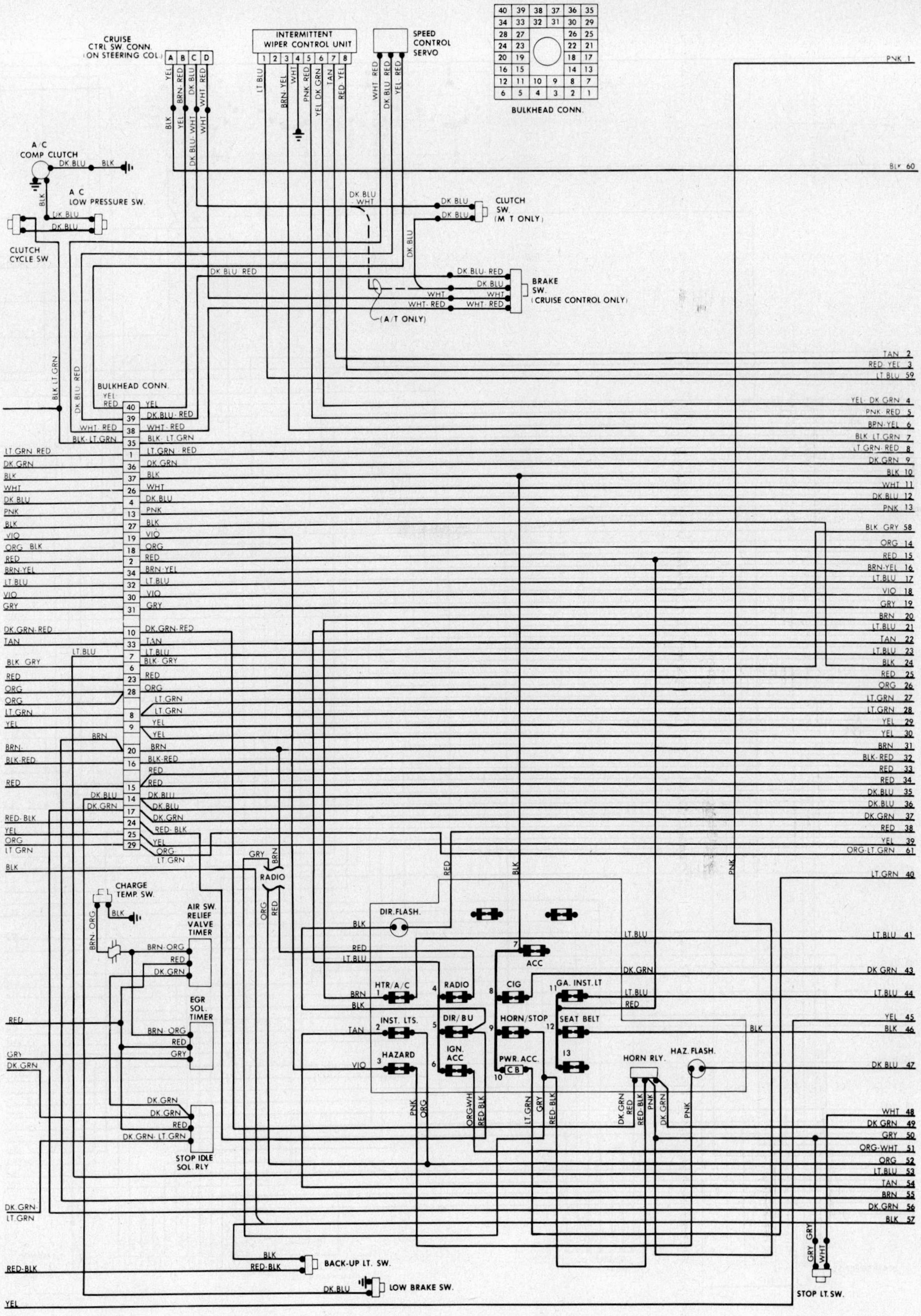

1985 Chrysler Corp.

CHASSIS CABS, PICKUPS & RAMCHARGER (Cont.)

UNDERDASH

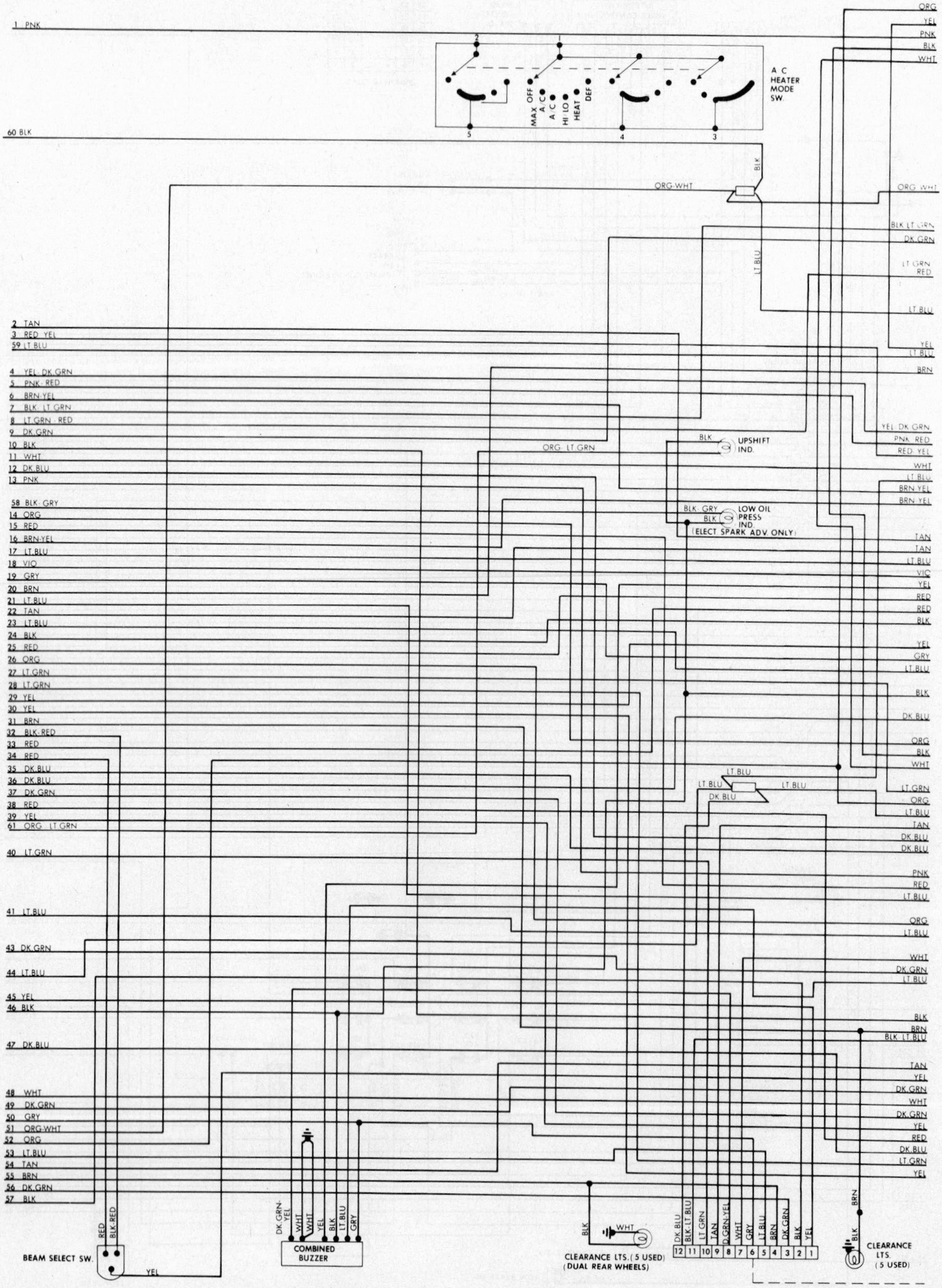

CHASSIS CABS, PICKUPS & RAMCHARGER (Cont.)

REAR COMPARTMENT & ACCESSORIES

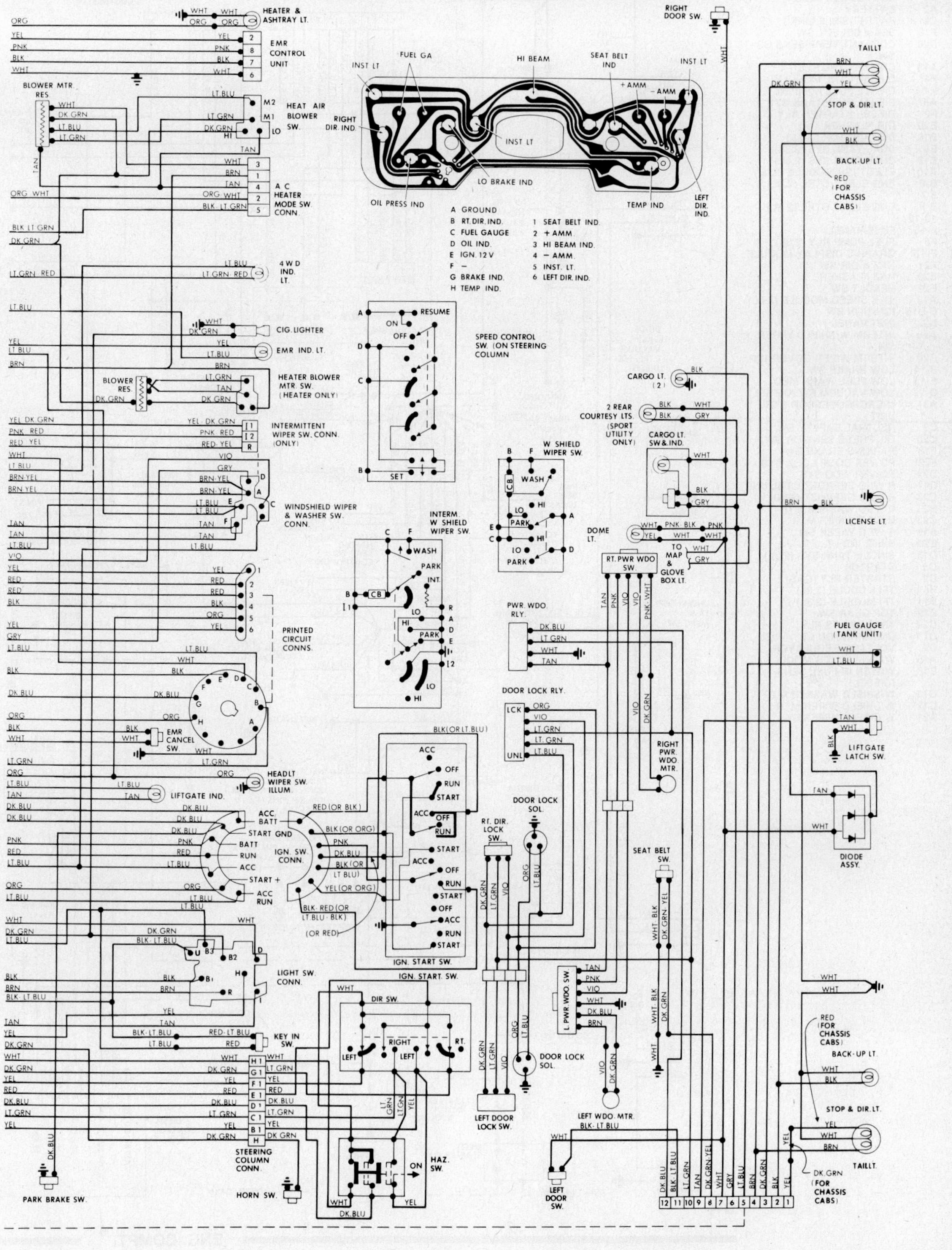

1985 Ford

BRONCO II & RANGER

COMPONENT LOCATIONS:

B1	A/C CYCLING SW
A18	A/C SYSTEM
D3	ALTERNATOR
D3	ALT FUSIBLE LINKS
A2	BATTERY
C2	BATT FUSIBLE LINKS
F18	BEAM SELECT SW
D20	COOLANT TEMP SENS OR SW
A13	CRUISE CTRL SYS
F4	DIESEL CTRL MODULE
E1	DIESEL FUEL PUMP RLY
A9	DIESEL FUEL TANK SYS
F2	DIESEL STARTER RLY
E20	DIR FLASHER
B10	DISTRIBUTOR (2.0L)
E9	DUAL TANK SYS (2.3L)
E18	DUAL TANK SYS (2.8L)
A10	ELECT IGN MODULE (2.0L)
B-F 5-7	ENG ELECT CTRL (2.3L)
B-F 10-12	ENG ELECT CTRL (2.8L)
F-16	FUSE PANEL
F6	FUEL PUMP RLY (2.3L)
F-13	GRAPHIC DISPLAY MODULE
F21	HAZ & DIR SW
E20	HAZ FLASHER
E21	HEADLT SW
A12	IDLE SPEED MODULE (2.0L)
B-D18	IGNITION SW
B22	INST PANEL
A20	INTERM W/SHIELD WIPER SW
B20	INTERM WIPER GOVERNOR
F-14	LOW BRAKE SW
E-13	LOW FUEL WARN MOD
D-12	LOW VACUUM SW (DIESEL)
A3	MICROPROCESSOR CTRL UNIT
C3	NEUTRAL SAFETY SW
C20	OIL PRESS SENS OR SW
F18	PARKING BRAKE SW
F22	POWER DOOR LOCK SYS
D22	POWER WDO SYS
D17	R WDO DEFROST CTRL UNIT
C23	R WDO DEFROST GRID
B23	R WDO WASHER MTR
C23	R WDO WIPER MTR
B19	R WDO WIPER SW
E21	SHIFT IND LT
D16	SINGLE TANK SYS (2.3L)
C3	STARTER
C2	STARTER RLY (GAS)
B6	TFI MODULE (2.3L)
B11	TFI MODULE (2.3L)
E19	TOP GEAR SW
C23	TRAILER LTS RLY
D1	UNDERHOOOD LT
D2	VOLTAGE REGULATOR
A15	WARN BUZZER MODULE
E18	WATER IN-FUEL SENS (DIESEL)
C13	W/SHIELD WASHER MTR
C12	W/SHIELD WIPER MTR
A21	W/SHIELD WIPER SW

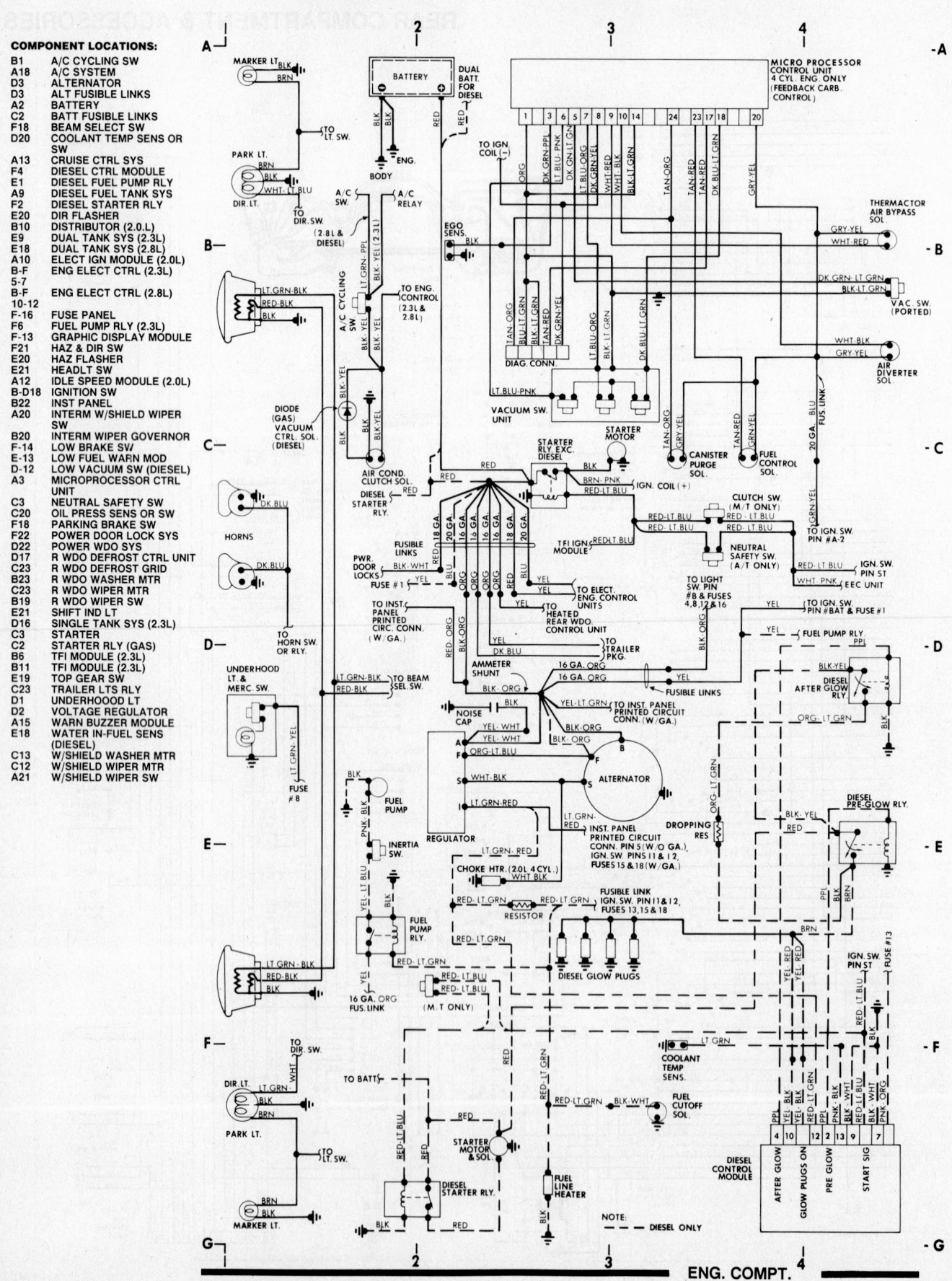

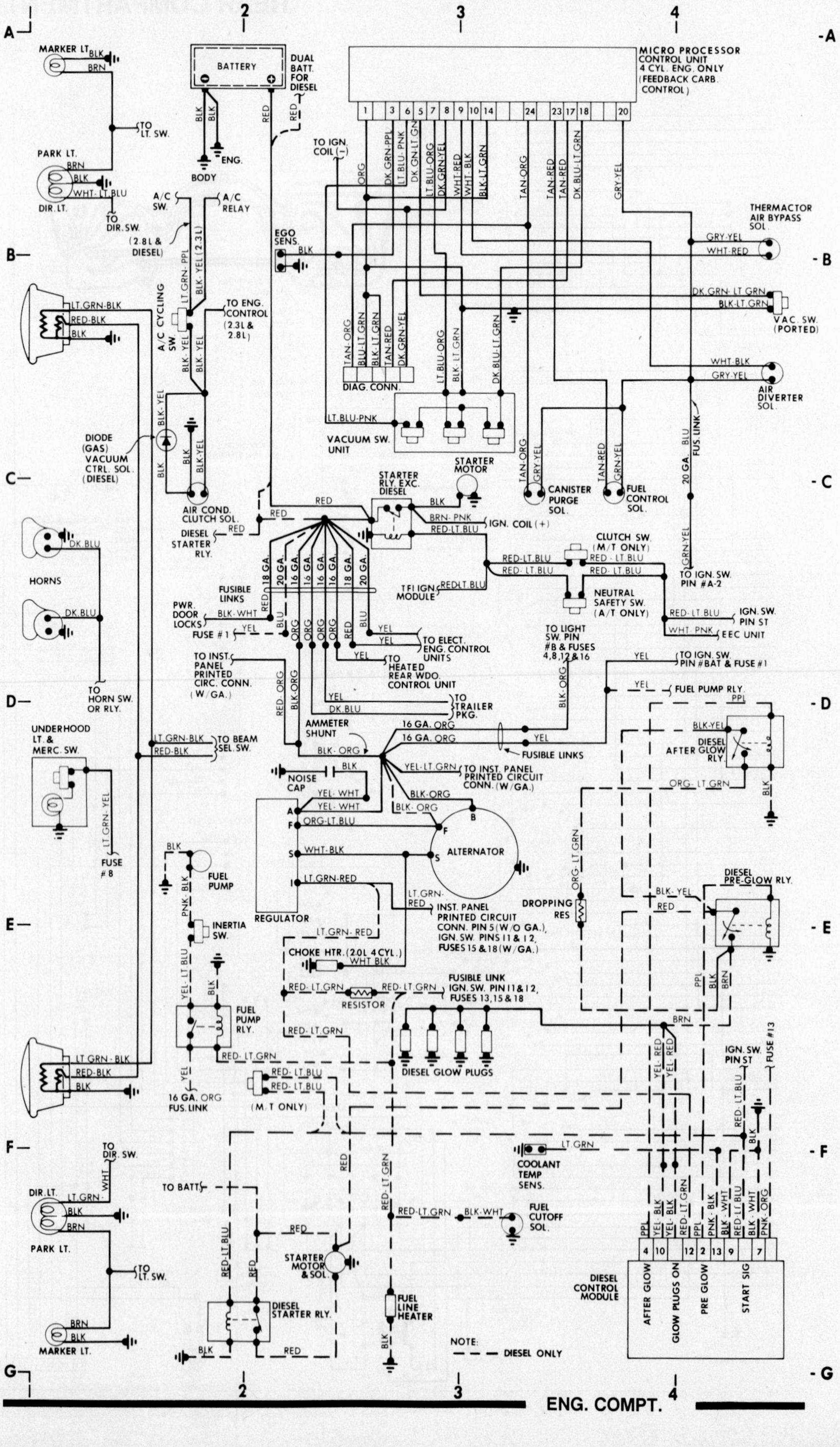

1985 Ford

BRONCO II & RANGER (Cont.)

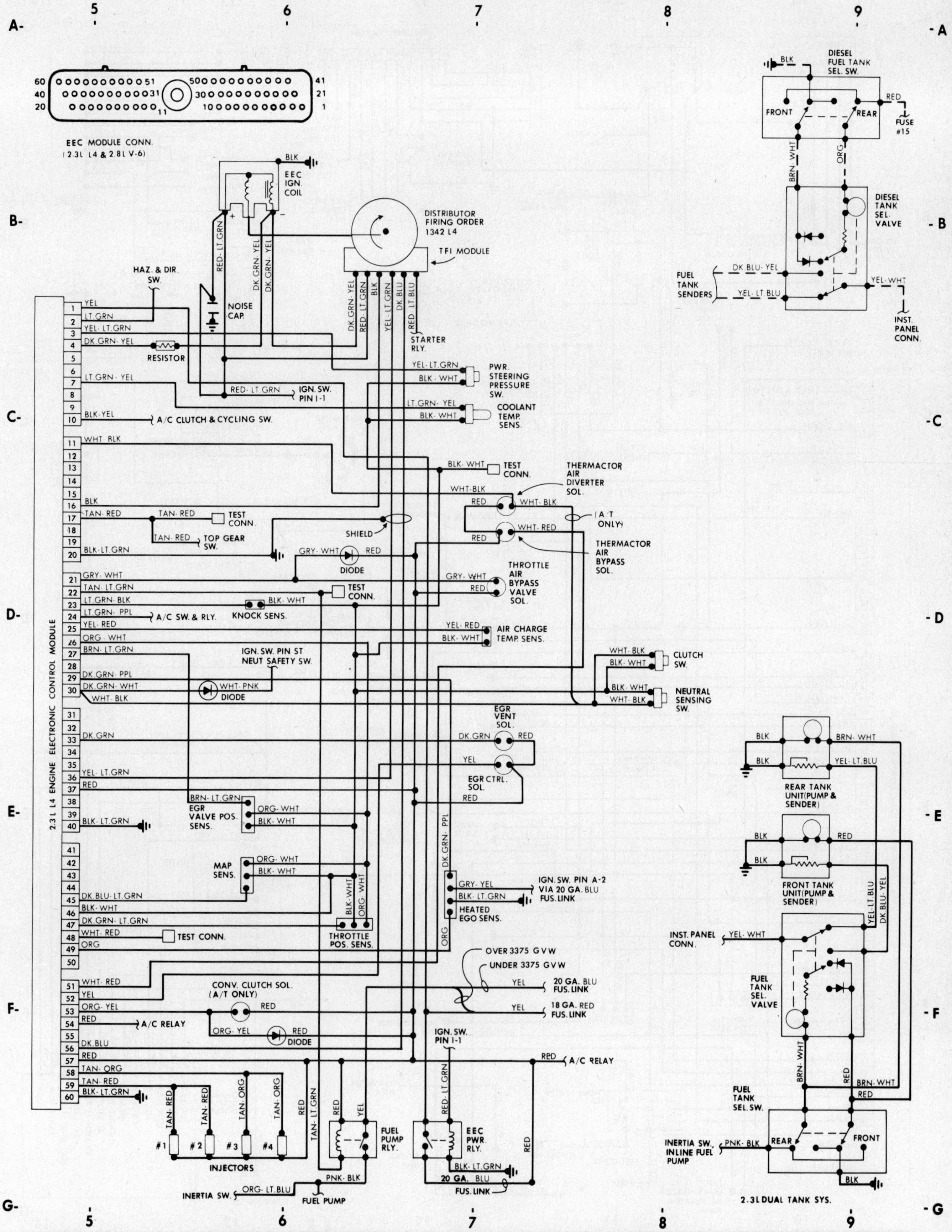

1985 Ford

BRONCO II & RANGER (Cont.)

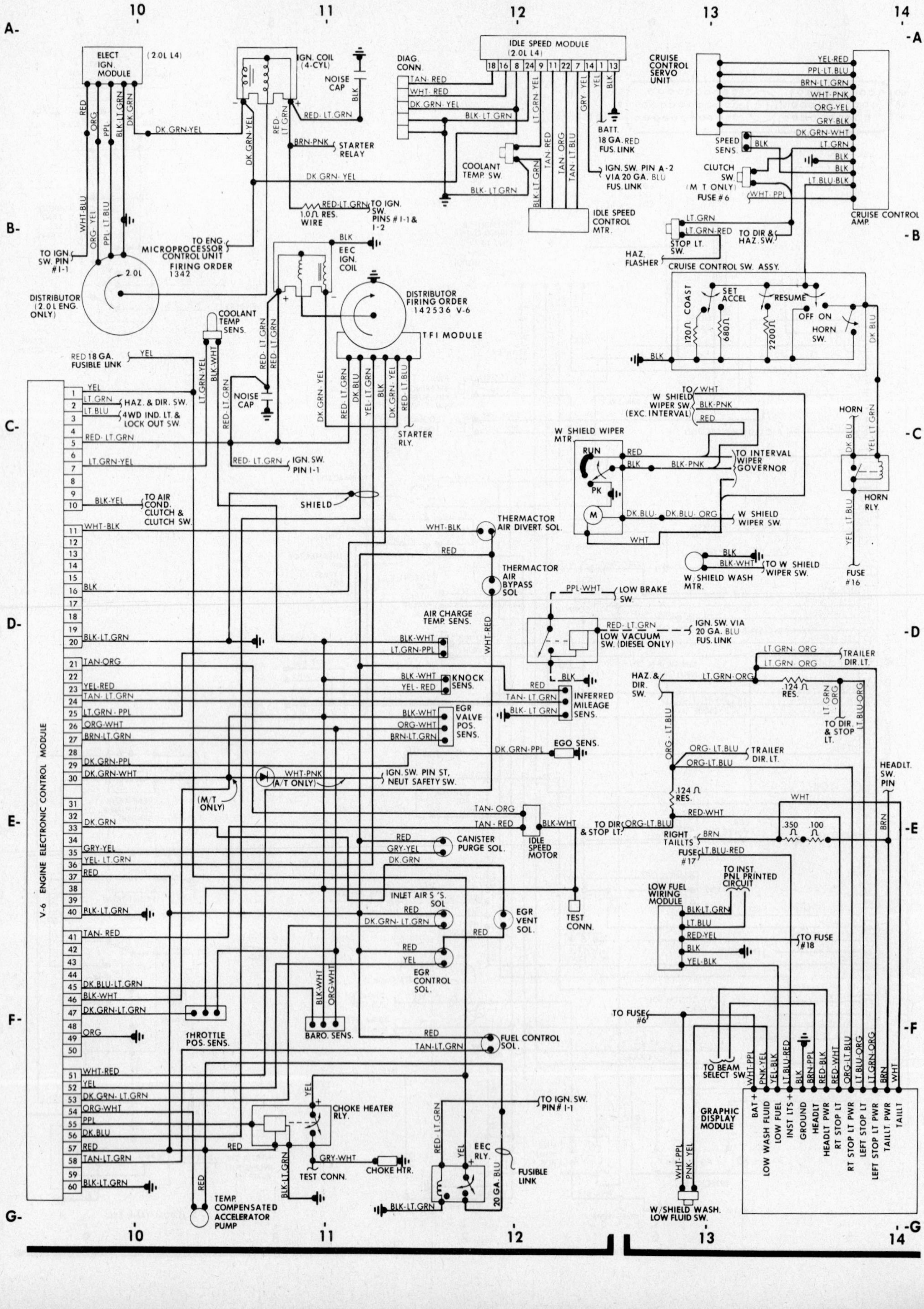

BRONCO II & RANGER (Cont.)

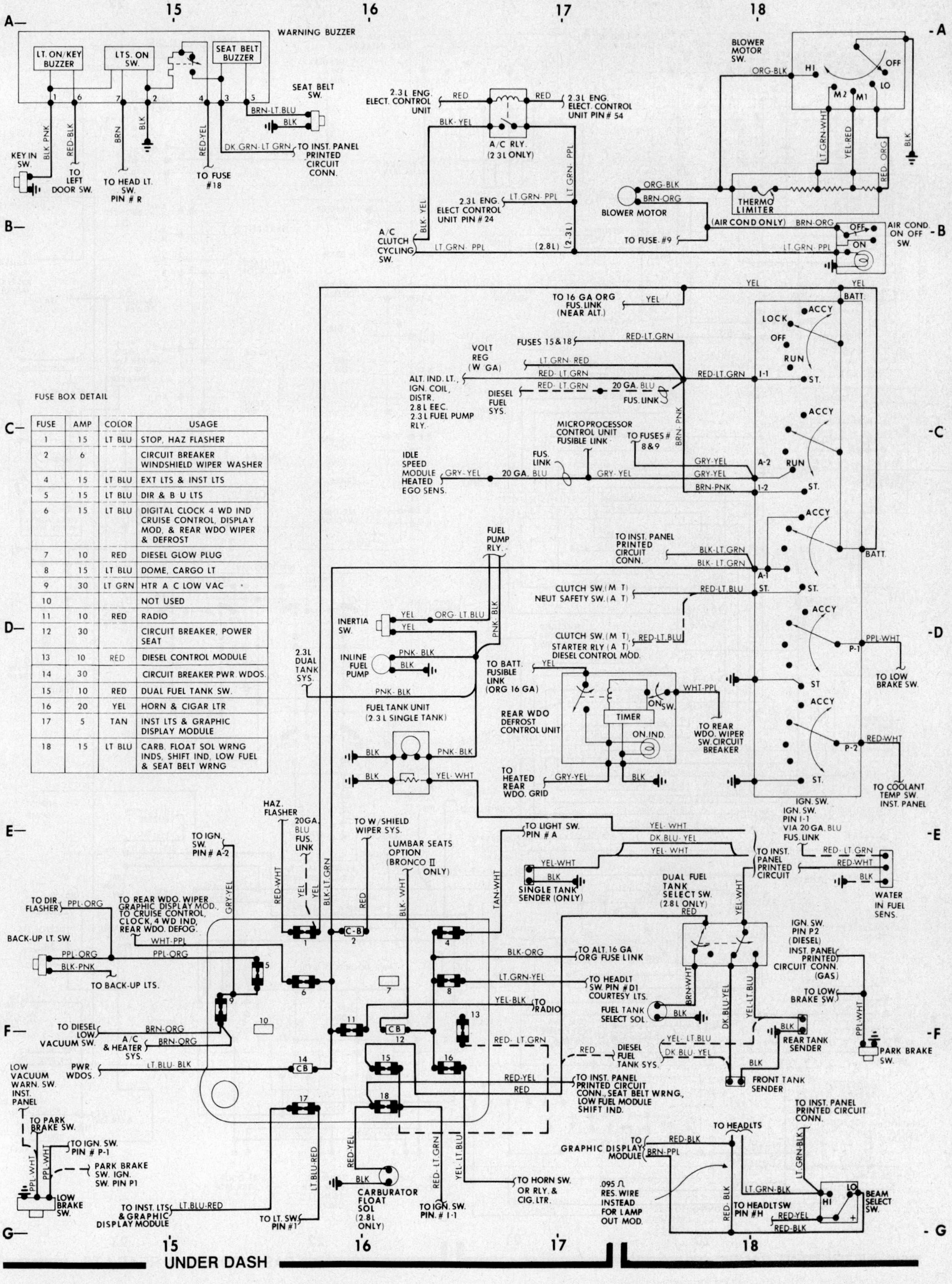

FUSE BOX DETAIL

FUSE	AMP	COLOR	USAGE
1	15	LT BLU	STOP, HAZ FLASHER
2	6		CIRCUIT BREAKER WINDSHIELD WIPER WASHER
4	15	LT BLU	EXT LTS & INST LTS
5	15	LT BLU	DIR & B U LTS
6	15	LT BLU	DIGITAL CLOCK 4 WD IND CRUISE CONTROL, DISPLAY MOD, & REAR WDO WIPER & DEFROST
7	10	RED	DIESEL GLOW PLUG
8	15	LT BLU	DOME, CARGO LT
9	30	LT GRN	HTR A C LOW VAC
10			NOT USED
11	10	RED	RADIO
12	30		CIRCUIT BREAKER, POWER SEAT
13	10	RED	DIESEL CONTROL MODULE
14	30		CIRCUIT BREAKER PWR WDOS.
15	10	RED	DUAL FUEL TANK SW.
16	20	YEL	HORN & CIGAR LTR
17	5	TAN	INST LTS & GRAPHIC DISPLAY MODULE
18	15	LT BLU	CARB. FLOAT SOL WRNG INDS, SHIFT IND, LOW FUEL & SEAT BELT WRNG

1985 Ford

BRONCO II & RANGER (Cont.)

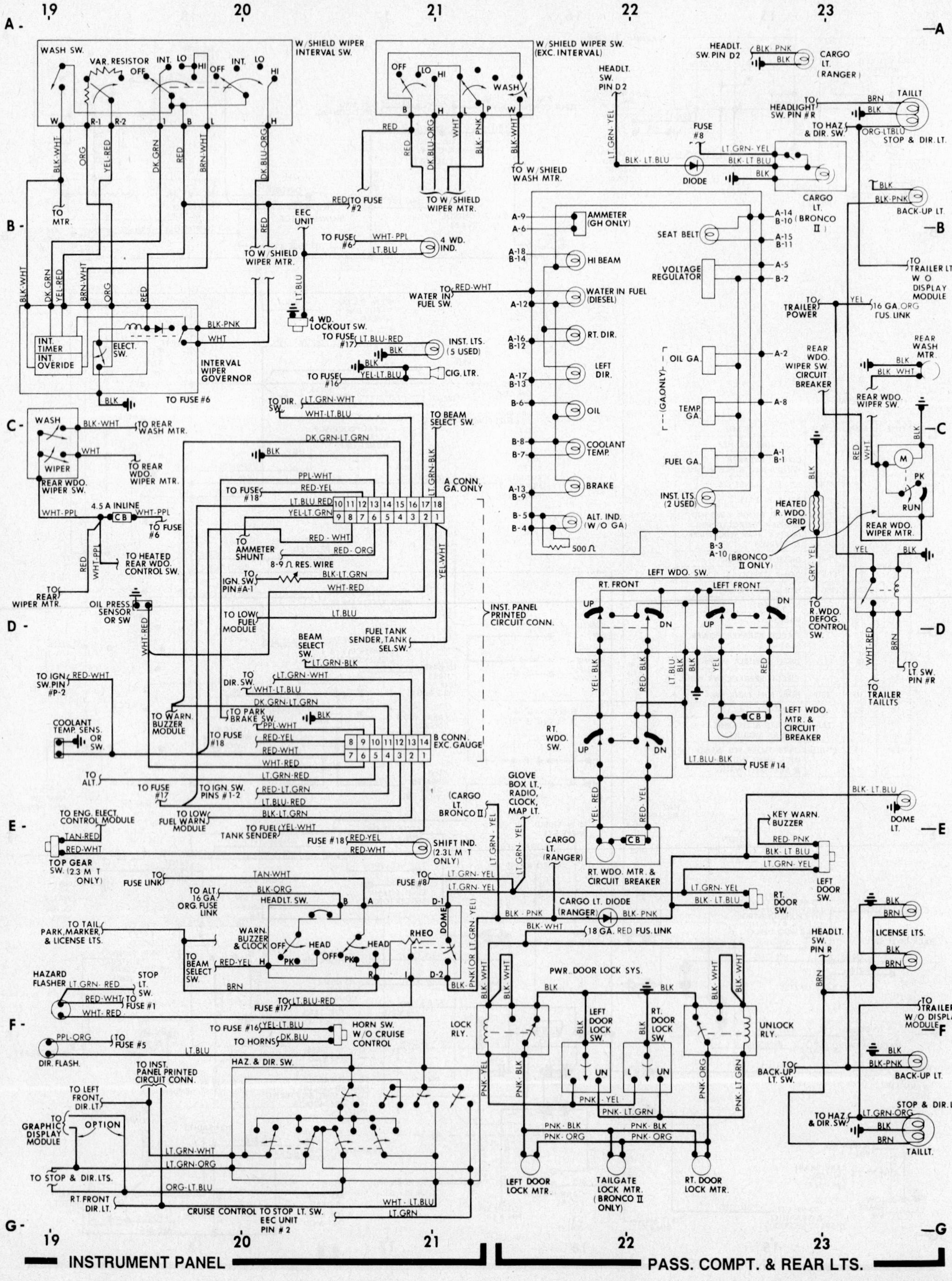

1985 Ford

E150/E350 ECONOLINE VANS & WAGONS

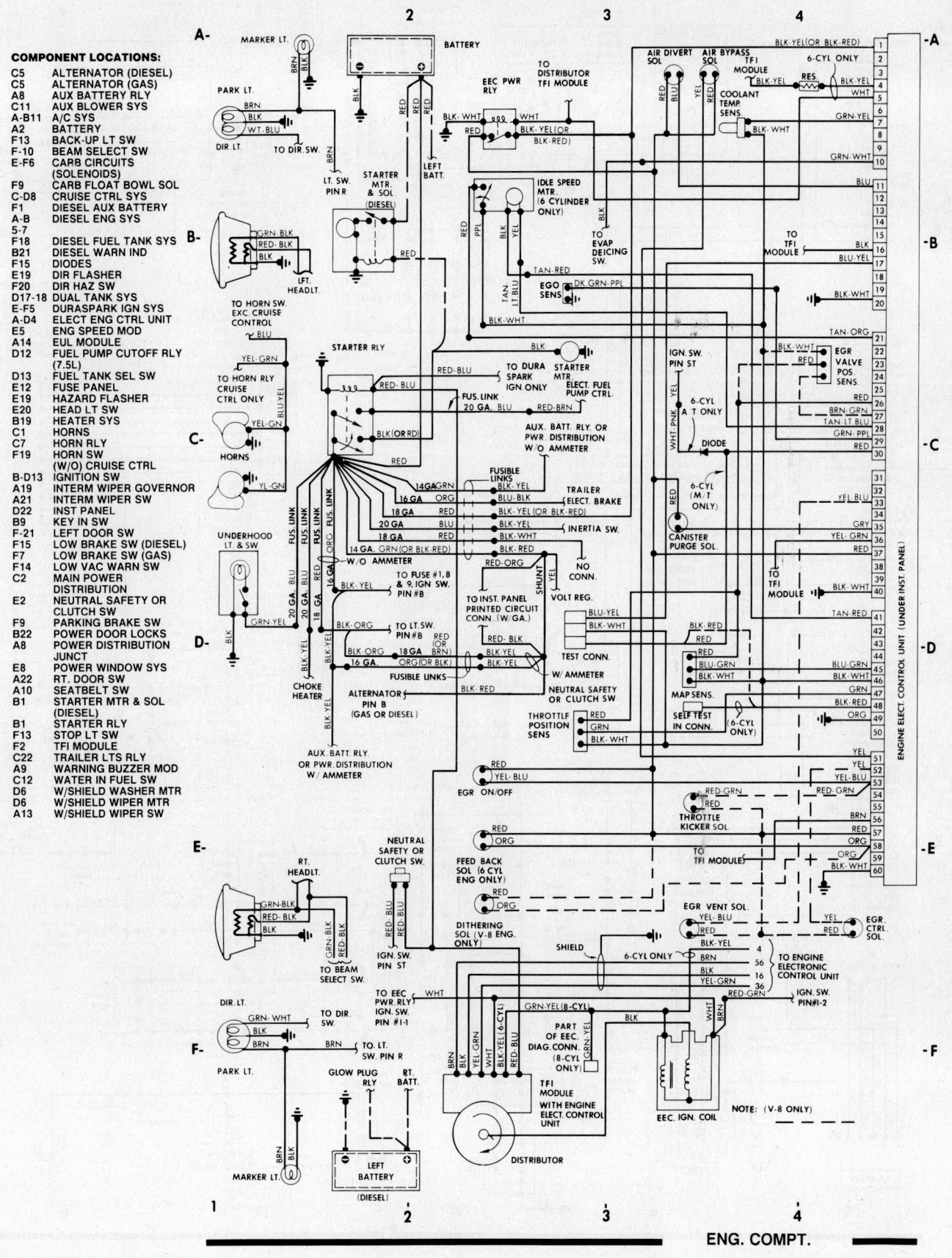

COMPONENT LOCATIONS:

C5 ALTERNATOR (DIESEL)
C5 ALTERNATOR (GAS)
A8 AUX BATTERY RLY
C11 AUX BLOWER SYS
A-B11 A/C SYS
A2 BATTERY
F13 BACK-UP LT SW
F-10 BEAM SELECT SW
E-F6 CARB CIRCUITS (SOLENOIDS)
F9 CARB FLOAT BOWL SOL
C-D8 CRUISE CTRL SYS
F1 DIESEL AUX BATTERY
A-B DIESEL ENG SYS
5-7
F18 DIESEL FUEL TANK SYS
B21 DIESEL WARN IND
F15 DIODES
E19 DIR FLASHER
F20 DIR HAZ SW
D17-18 DUAL TANK SYS
E-F5 DURASPARK IGN SYS
A-D4 ELECT ENG CTRL UNIT
E5 ENG SPEED MOD
A14 EUL MODULE
D12 FUEL PUMP CUTOFF RLY (7.5L)
D13 FUEL TANK SEL SW
E12 FUSE PANEL
E19 HAZARD FLASHER
E20 HEAD LT SW
B19 HEATER SYS
C1 HORNS
C7 HORN RLY
F19 HORN SW (W/O) CRUISE CTRL
B-D13 IGNITION SW
A19 INTERM WIPER GOVERNOR
A21 INTERM WIPER SW
D22 INST PANEL
B9 KEY IN SW
F-21 LEFT DOOR SW
F15 LOW BRAKE SW (DIESEL)
F7 LOW BRAKE SW (GAS)
F14 LOW VAC WARN SW
C2 MAIN POWER DISTRIBUTION
E2 NEUTRAL SAFETY OR CLUTCH SW
F9 PARKING BRAKE SW
B22 POWER DOOR LOCKS
A8 POWER DISTRIBUTION JUNCT
E8 POWER WINDOW SYS
A22 RT. DOOR SW
A10 SEATBELT SW
B1 STARTER MTR & SOL (DIESEL)
B1 STARTER RLY
F13 STOP LT SW
F2 TFI MODULE
C22 TRAILER LTS RLY
A9 WARNING BUZZER MOD
C12 WATER IN FUEL SW
D6 W/SHIELD WASHER MTR
D6 W/SHIELD WIPER MTR
A13 W/SHIELD WIPER SW

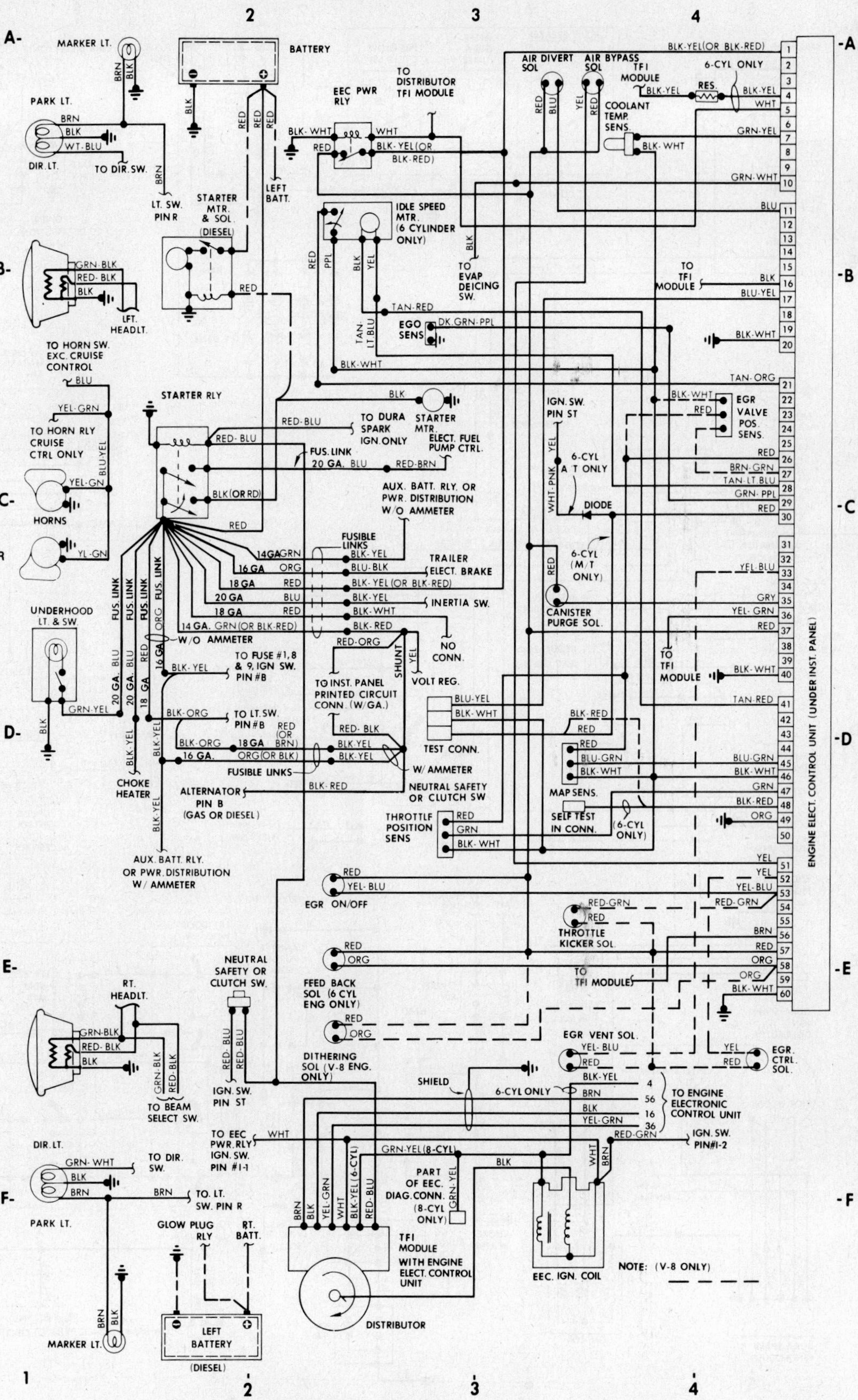

1985 Ford

E150/E350 ECONOLINE VANS & WAGONS (Cont.)

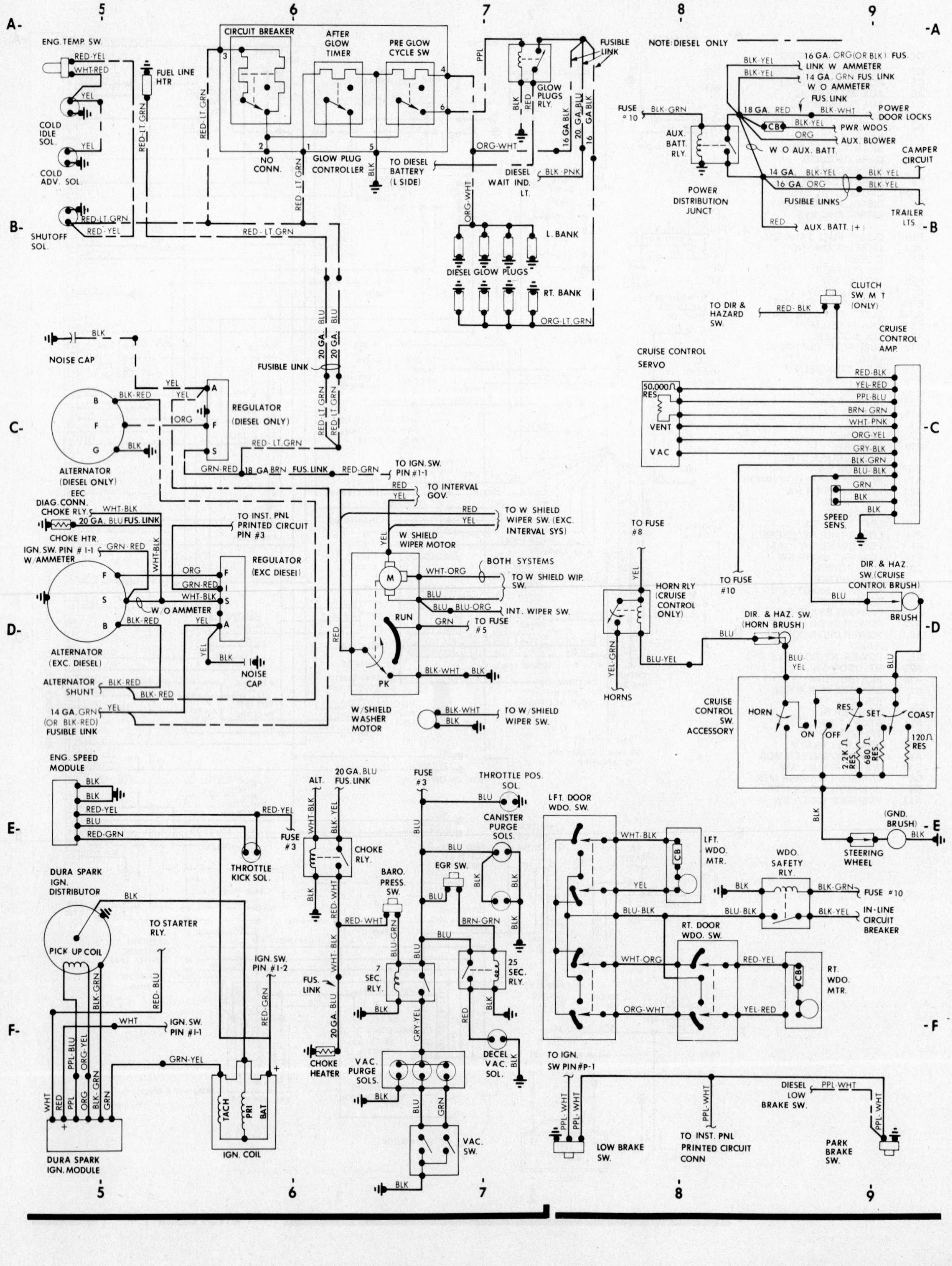

E150/E350 ECONOLINE VANS & WAGONS (Cont.)

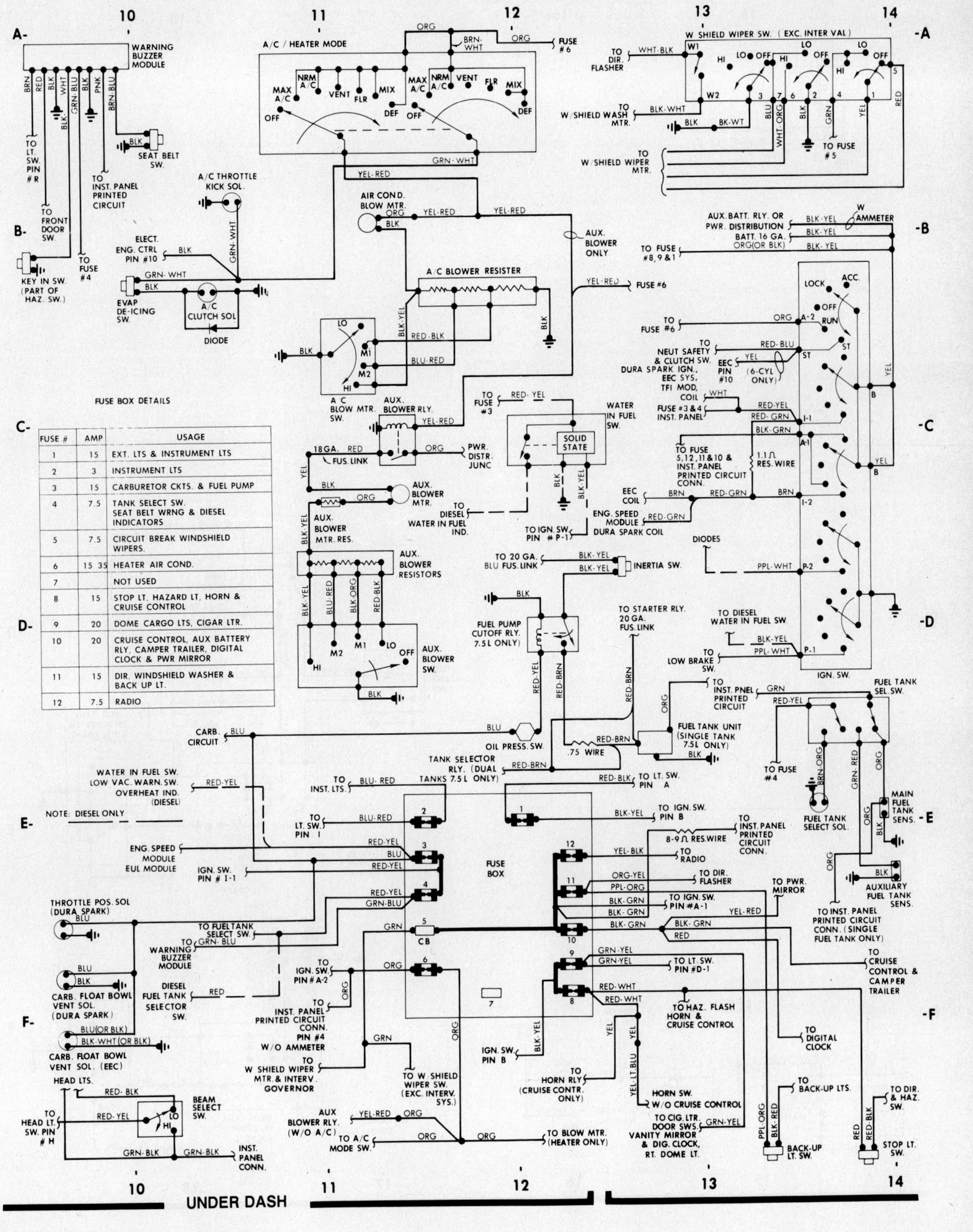

FUSE BOX DETAILS

FUSE #	AMP	USAGE
1	15	EXT. LTS & INSTRUMENT LTS
2	3	INSTRUMENT LTS
3	15	CARBURETOR CKTS. & FUEL PUMP
4	7.5	TANK SELECT SW. SEAT BELT WRNG & DIESEL INDICATORS
5	7.5	CIRCUIT BREAK WINDSHIELD WIPERS.
6	15 35	HEATER AIR COND.
7		NOT USED
8	15	STOP LT, HAZARD LT, HORN & CRUISE CONTROL
9	20	DOME CARGO LTS, CIGAR LTR.
10	20	CRUISE CONTROL, AUX BATTERY RLY, CAMPER TRAILER, DIGITAL CLOCK & PWR MIRROR
11	15	DIR. WINDSHIELD WASHER & BACK UP LT.
12	7.5	RADIO

1985 Ford

E150/E350 ECONOLINE VANS & WAGONS (Cont.)

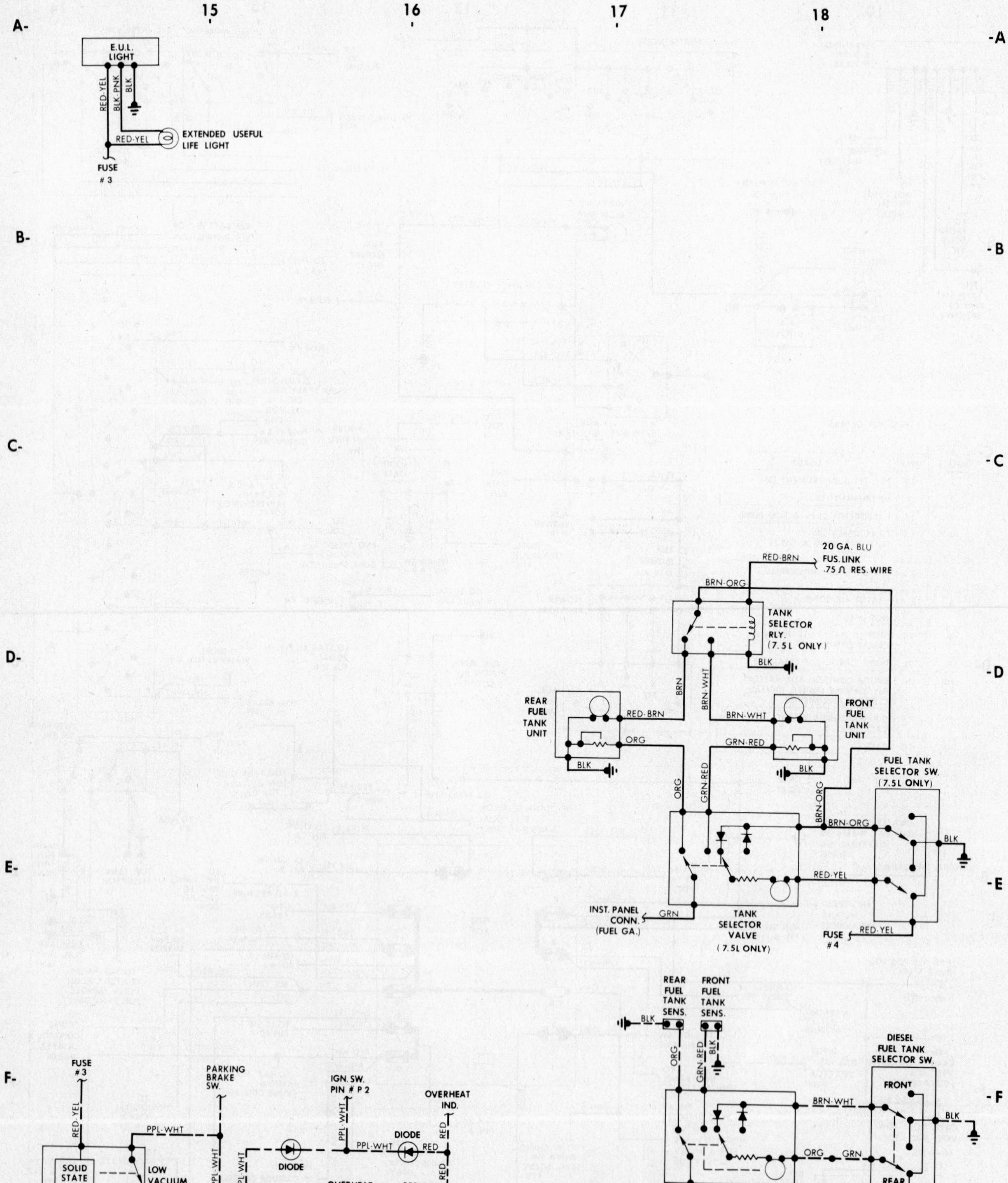

E150/E350 ECONOLINE VANS & WAGONS (Cont.)

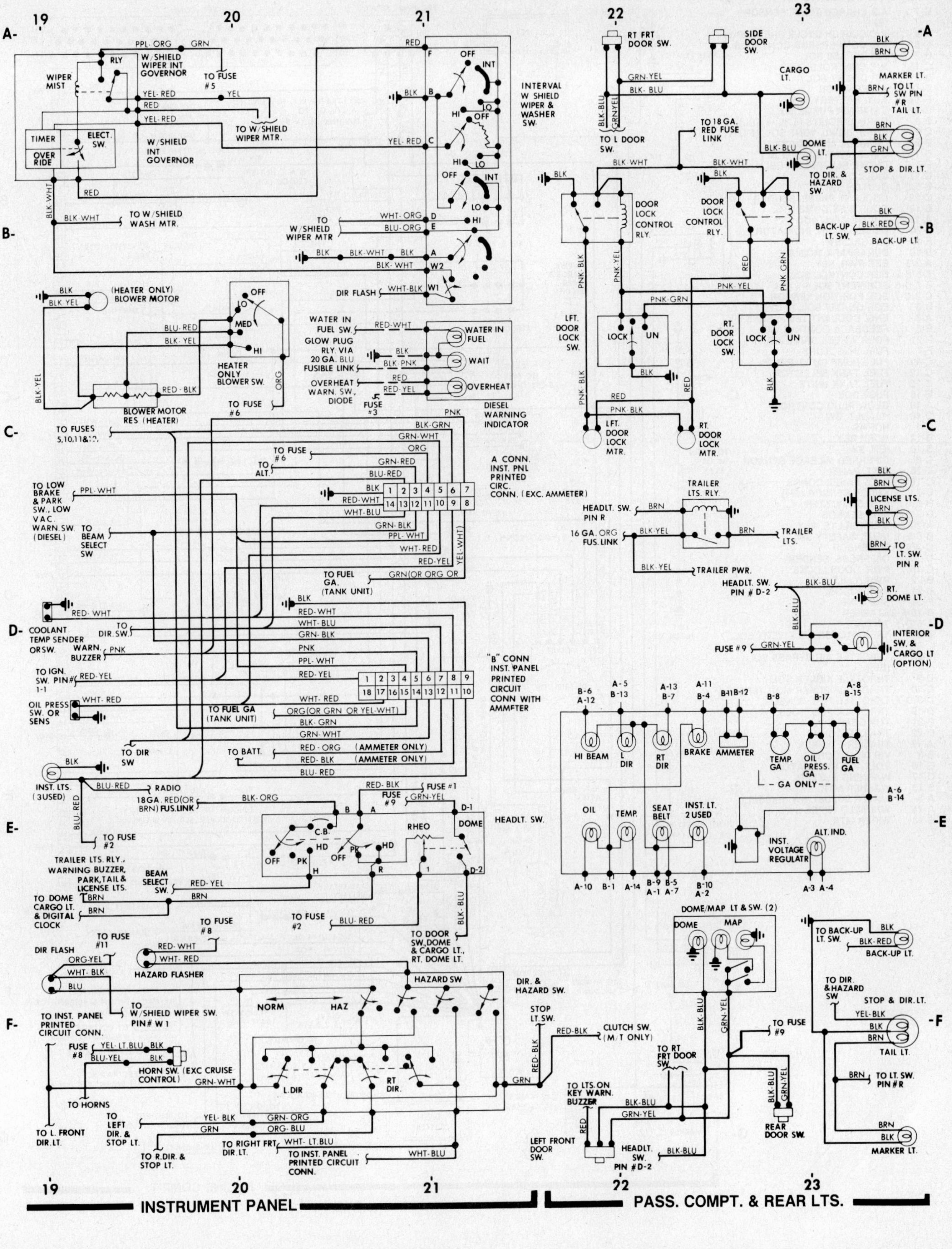

1985 Ford

BRONCO, F150/F350 PICKUPS & CHASSIS CABS

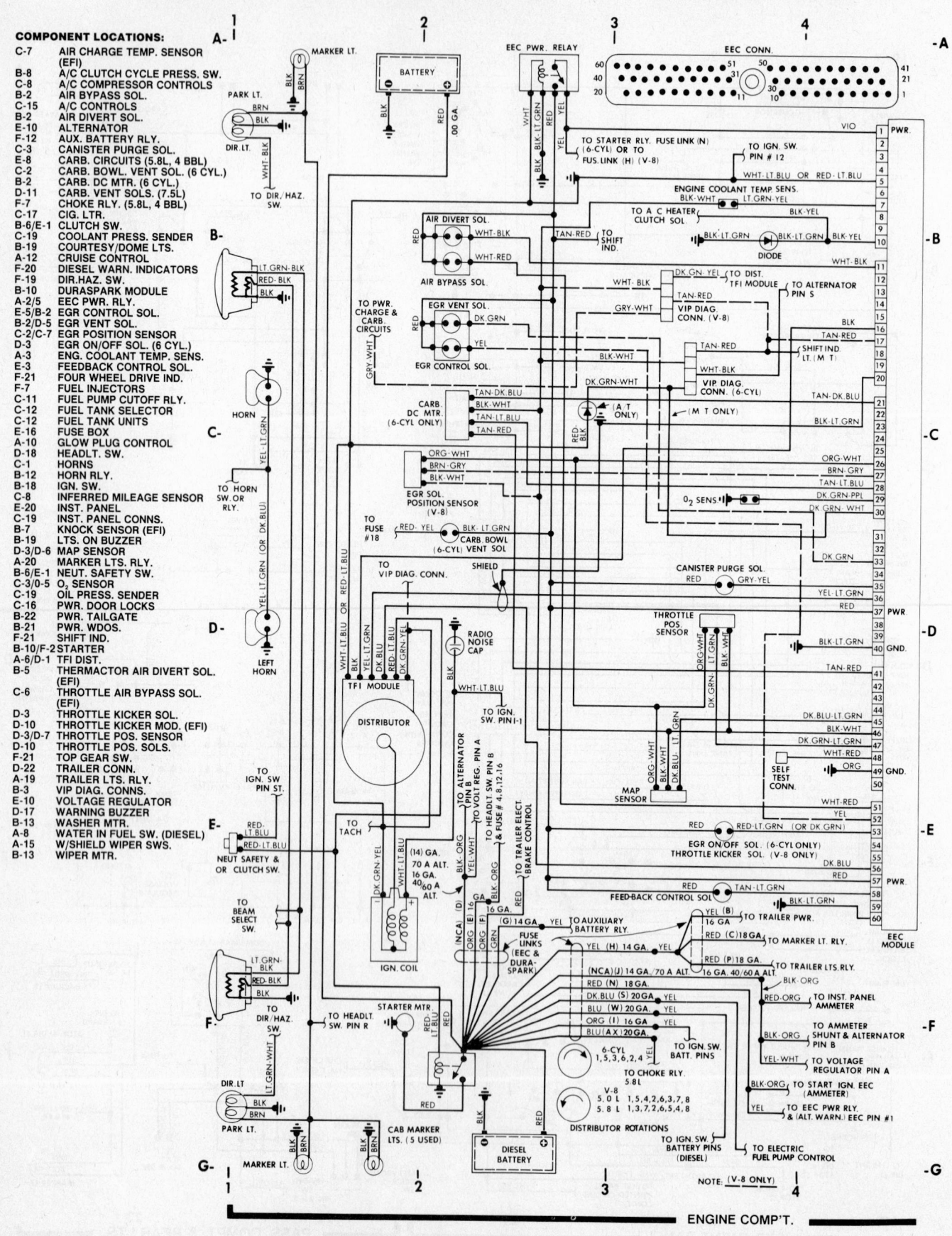

COMPONENT LOCATIONS:

C-7	AIR CHARGE TEMP. SENSOR (EFI)
B-8	A/C CLUTCH CYCLE PRESS. SW.
C-8	A/C COMPRESSOR CONTROLS
B-2	AIR BYPASS SOL.
C-15	A/C CONTROLS
B-2	AIR DIVERT SOL.
E-10	ALTERNATOR
F-12	AUX. BATTERY RLY.
C-3	CANISTER PURGE SOL.
E-8	CARB. CIRCUITS (5.8L, 4 BBL)
C-2	CARB. BOWL. VENT SOL. (6 CYL.)
B-2	CARB. DC MTR. (6 CYL.)
D-11	CARB. VENT SOLS. (7.5L)
F-7	CHOKE RLY. (5.8L, 4 BBL)
C-17	CIG. LTR.
B-6/E-1	CLUTCH SW.
C-19	COOLANT PRESS. SENDER
B-19	COURTESY/DOME LTS.
A-12	CRUISE CONTROL
F-20	DIESEL WARN. INDICATORS
F-19	DIR.HAZ. SW.
B-10	DURASPARK MODULE
A-2/5	EEC PWR. RLY.
E-5/B-2	EGR CONTROL SOL.
B-2/D-5	EGR VENT SOL.
C-2/C-7	EGR POSITION SENSOR
D-3	EGR ON/OFF SOL. (6 CYL.)
A-3	ENG. COOLANT TEMP. SENS.
E-3	FEEDBACK CONTROL SOL.
F-21	FOUR WHEEL DRIVE IND.
F-7	FUEL INJECTORS
C-11	FUEL PUMP CUTOFF RLY.
C-12	FUEL TANK SELECTOR
C-12	FUEL TANK UNITS
E-16	FUSE BOX
A-10	GLOW PLUG CONTROL
D-18	HEADLT. SW.
C-1	HORNS
B-12	HORN RLY.
B-18	IGN. SW.
C-8	INFERRED MILEAGE SENSOR
E-20	INST. PANEL
C-19	INST. PANEL CONNS.
B-7	KNOCK SENSOR (EFI)
B-19	LTS. ON BUZZER
D-3/D-6	MAP SENSOR
A-20	MARKER LTS. RLY.
B-6/E-1	NEUT. SAFETY SW.
C-3/0-5	O_2 SENSOR
C-19	OIL PRESS. SENDER
C-16	PWR. DOOR LOCKS
B-22	PWR. TAILGATE
B-21	PWR. WDOS.
F-21	SHIFT IND.
B-10/F-2	STARTER
A-6/D-1	TFI DIST.
B-5	THERMACTOR AIR DIVERT SOL. (EFI)
C-6	THROTTLE AIR BYPASS SOL. (EFI)
D-3	THROTTLE KICKER SOL.
D-10	THROTTLE KICKER MOD. (EFI)
D-3/D-7	THROTTLE POS. SENSOR
D-10	THROTTLE POS. SOLS.
F-21	TOP GEAR SW.
D-22	TRAILER CONN.
A-19	TRAILER LTS. RLY.
B-3	VIP DIAG. CONNS.
E-10	VOLTAGE REGULATOR
D-17	WARNING BUZZER
B-13	WASHER MTR.
A-8	WATER IN FUEL SW. (DIESEL)
A-15	W/SHIELD WIPER SWS.
B-13	WIPER MTR.

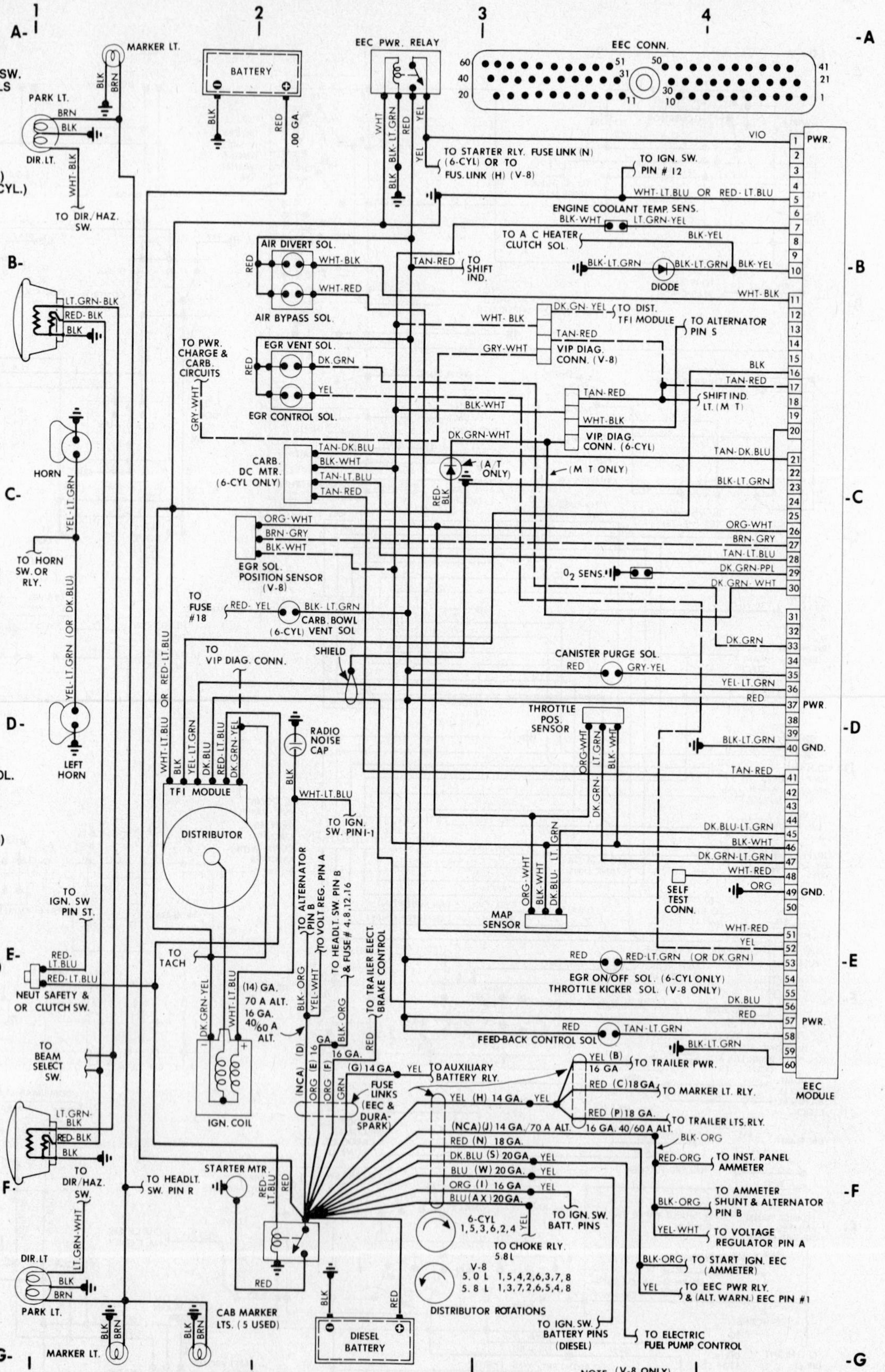

BRONCO, F150/F350 PICKUPS & CHASSIS CABS (Cont.)

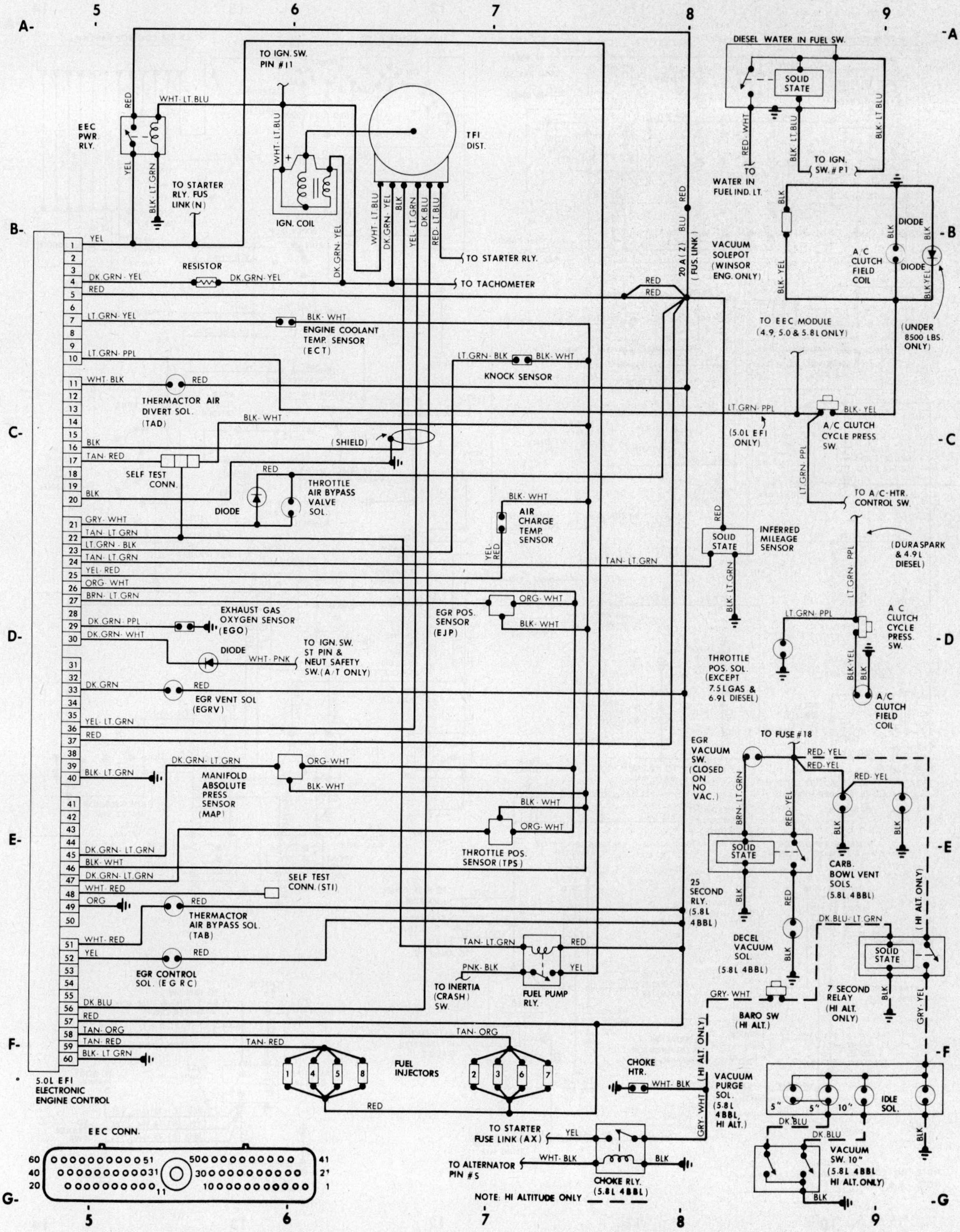

1985 Ford

BRONCO, F150/F350 PICKUPS & CHASSIS CABS (Cont.)

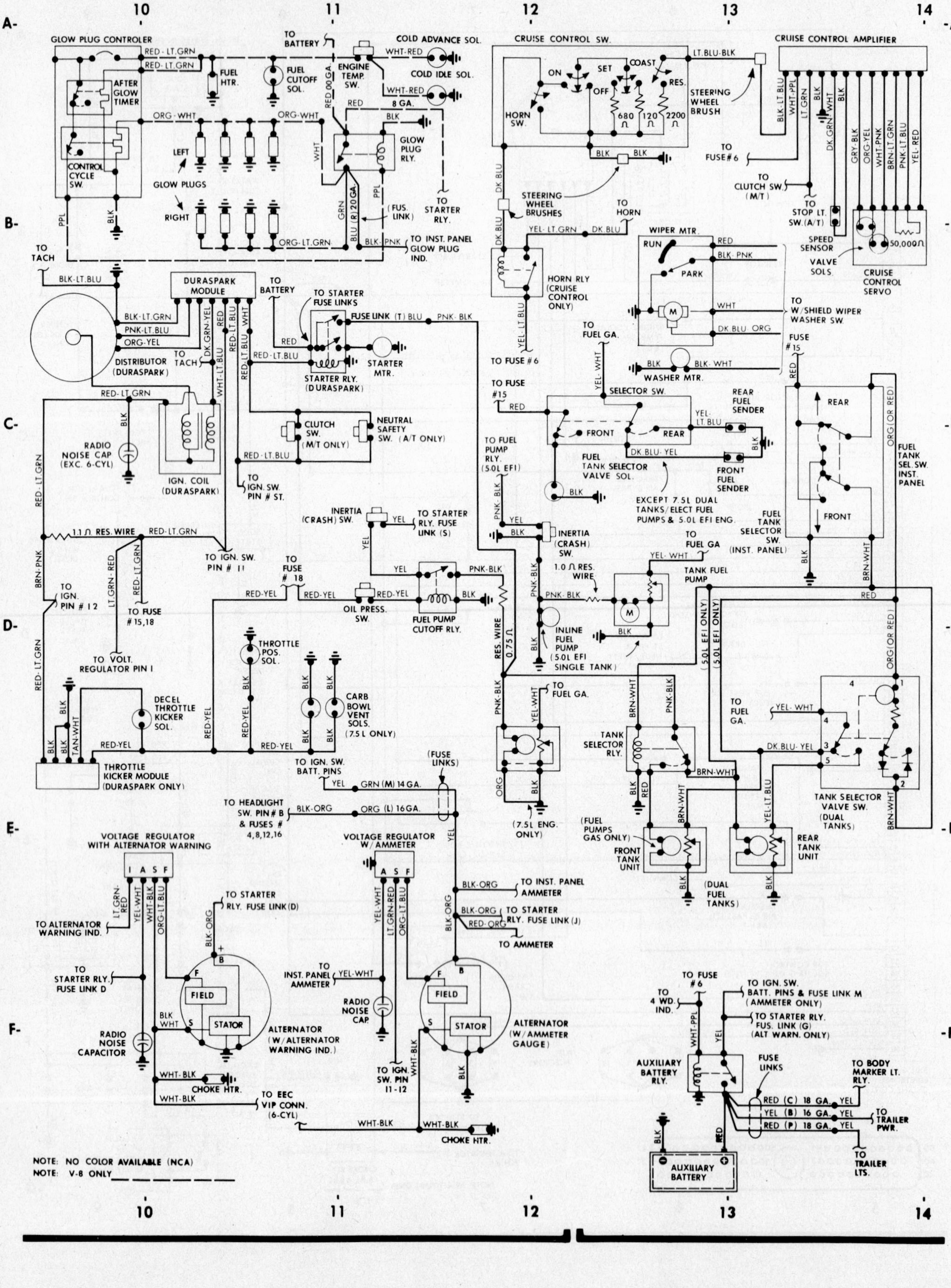

NOTE: NO COLOR AVAILABLE (NCA)
NOTE: V-8 ONLY ——————

BRONCO, F150/F350 PICKUPS & CHASSIS CABS (Cont.)

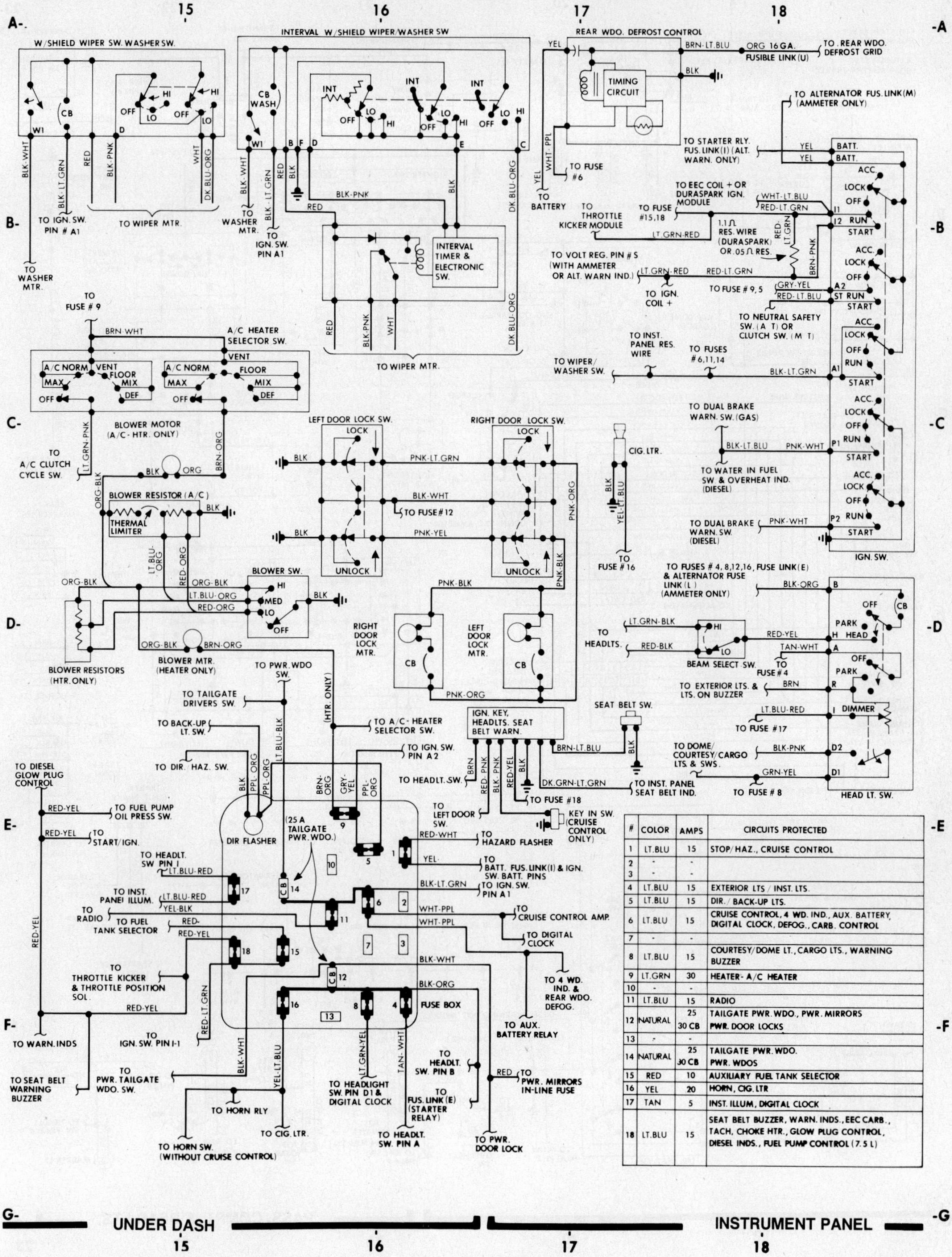

#	COLOR	AMPS	CIRCUITS PROTECTED
1	LT.BLU	15	STOP/HAZ., CRUISE CONTROL
2	-	-	
3	-	-	
4	LT.BLU	15	EXTERIOR LTS / INST. LTS.
5	LT.BLU	15	DIR./BACK-UP LTS.
6	LT.BLU	15	CRUISE CONTROL, 4 WD. IND., AUX. BATTERY, DIGITAL CLOCK, DEFOG., CARB. CONTROL
7	-	-	
8	LT.BLU	15	COURTESY/DOME LT., CARGO LTS., WARNING BUZZER
9	LT.GRN	30	HEATER - A/C HEATER
10	-	-	
11	LT.BLU	15	RADIO
12	NATURAL	25 30 CB	TAILGATE PWR. WDO., PWR. MIRRORS PWR. DOOR LOCKS
13	-	-	
14	NATURAL	25 30 CB	TAILGATE PWR. WDO. PWR. WDOS
15	RED	10	AUXILIARY FUEL TANK SELECTOR
16	YEL	20	HORN, CIG. LTR
17	TAN	5	INST. ILLUM, DIGITAL CLOCK
18	LT.BLU	15	SEAT BELT BUZZER, WARN. INDS., EEC CARB., TACH, CHOKE HTR., GLOW PLUG CONTROL, DIESEL INDS., FUEL PUMP CONTROL (7.5 L)

1985 Ford

BRONCO, F150/F350 PICKUPS & CHASSIS CABS (Cont.)

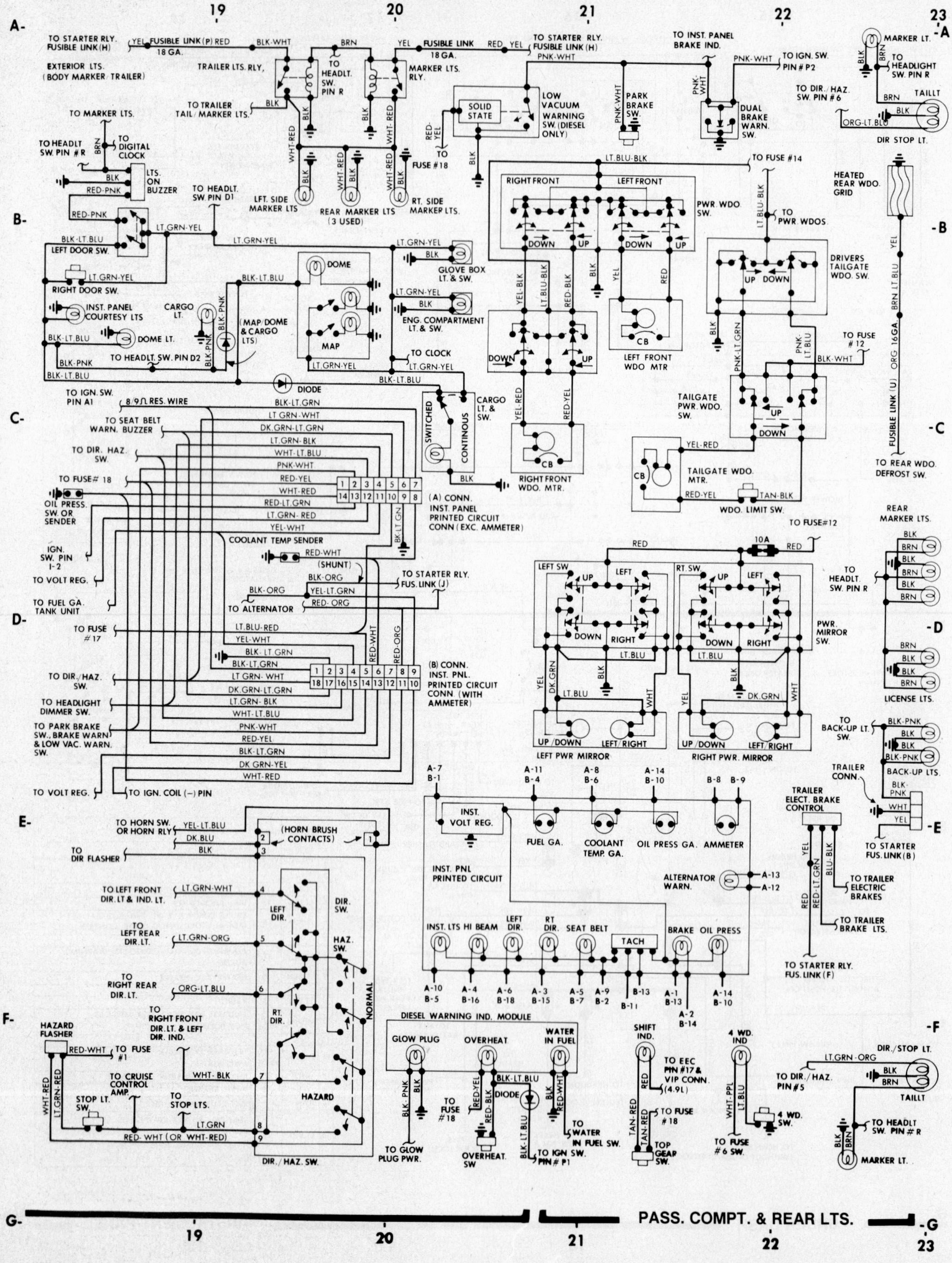

ASTRO & SAFARI

COMPONENT LOCATORS:

A14	A/C BLOWER SW
B2	A/C COMPRESSOR
A9	A/C COMP CTRL RLY (4 CYL)
B3	A/C HEATER BLWR MTR
A7	A/C HI BLWR RLY
B14	A/C RESISTORS
A15	A/C SELECTOR SW
B2	ALTERNATOR
A21	AUX HEATER SYS
E13	BACK-UP LT SW
A2	BATTERY
E17	BEAM SELECT SW
C3	BRAKE PRESS WARN SW
E13	BRAKE/STOP LT SW (A/T)
F13	CLUTCH START SW (M/T)
A20	COURTESY LTS
C7-9	CRUISE CTRL SYS
F16	DIR & HAZ SYS
A10	DIR FLASHER
B19	DOOR SWS
D-F 2-4	ELECT CTRL MOD (4 CYL)
D-F 5-7	ELECT CTRL MOD (6 CYL)
B5	ELECT SPARK CTRL (6 CYL FED)
A8	FUEL IDLER RLY (6 CYL)
C1	FUEL PUMP RLY
D1	FUEL TANK SENS & PUMP (4 CYL)
E9	FUEL TANK SENS (6 CYL)
E-F 10-11	FUSE PANEL
A10	HAZ FLASHER
A13	HEATER BLWR SW
A13	HEATER RESISTORS
A9	HORN RLY
F16	HORN SW
C15	IGNITION SW
A-B 16-18	INSTRUMENT CLSTR
A2	JUNCTION (ON FIREWALL)
F15	KEY IN SW
A12	LAMP DRIVER MOD
D15	LIGHT SW
E1	OIL PRESS SW (4 CYL)
F8	OIL PRESS SW (6 CYL)
F14	PARKING BRAKE SW
D-F 19,20	POWER DOOR LOCKS
F21	POWER MIRRORS
D21,22	POWER WINDOWS
B21	REAR A/C SYS
D16	RHEOSTAT
B2	STARTER
E13	STOP LT SW (M/T)
C3	TEMP SENS OR SW
A8	THROTTLE KICKER RLY (6 CYL)
C23	TRAILER WIRING
F8	VAC KICKER SOL (CAL)
A5	VAC KICKER SOL (FED)
E3	VEHICLE SPEED SENS (4 CYL)
A11	WARN BUZZER MOD
C3	W/SHIELD WASHER MTR
B3	W/SHIELD WIPER MTR
F17-18	W/SHIELD WIPER SW

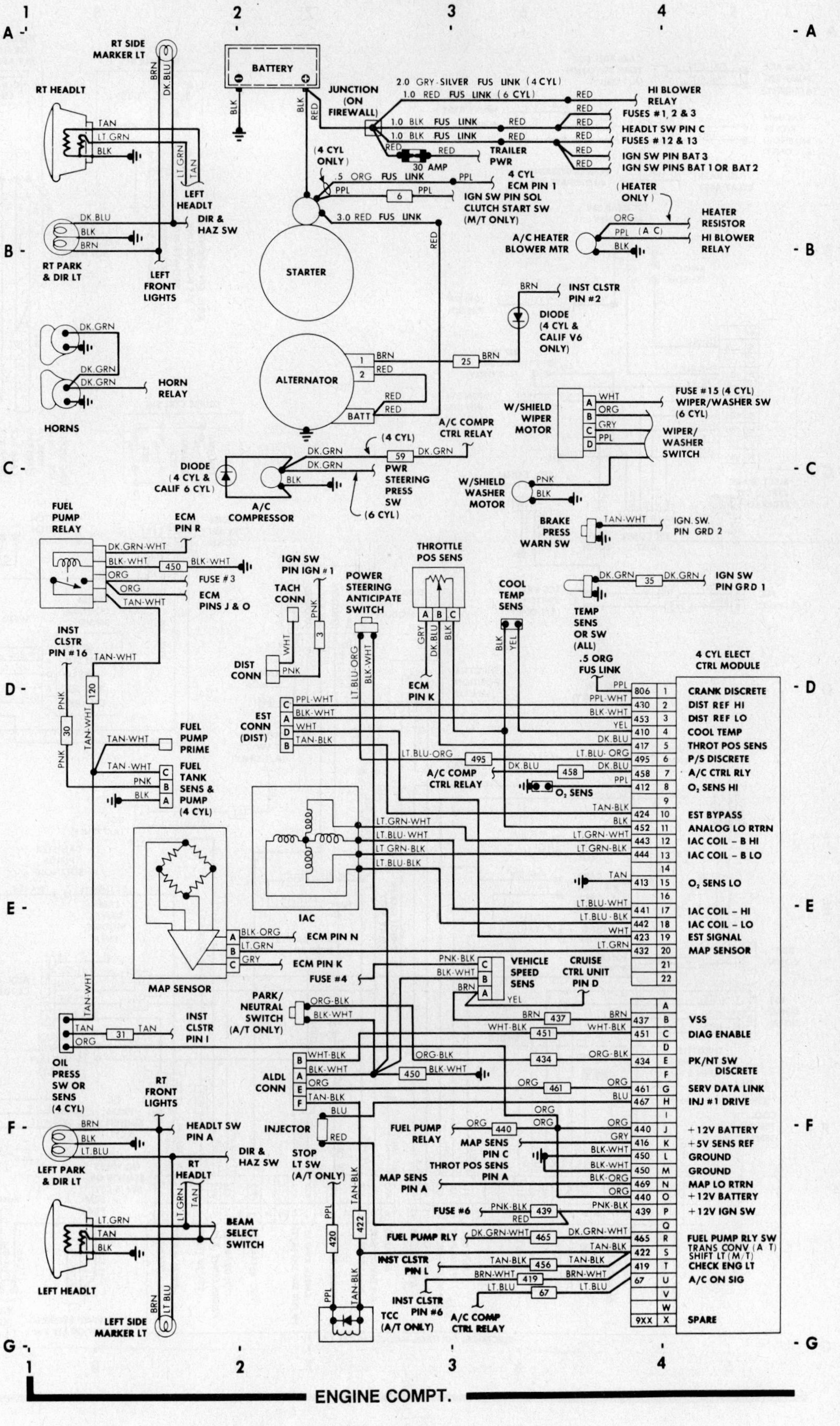

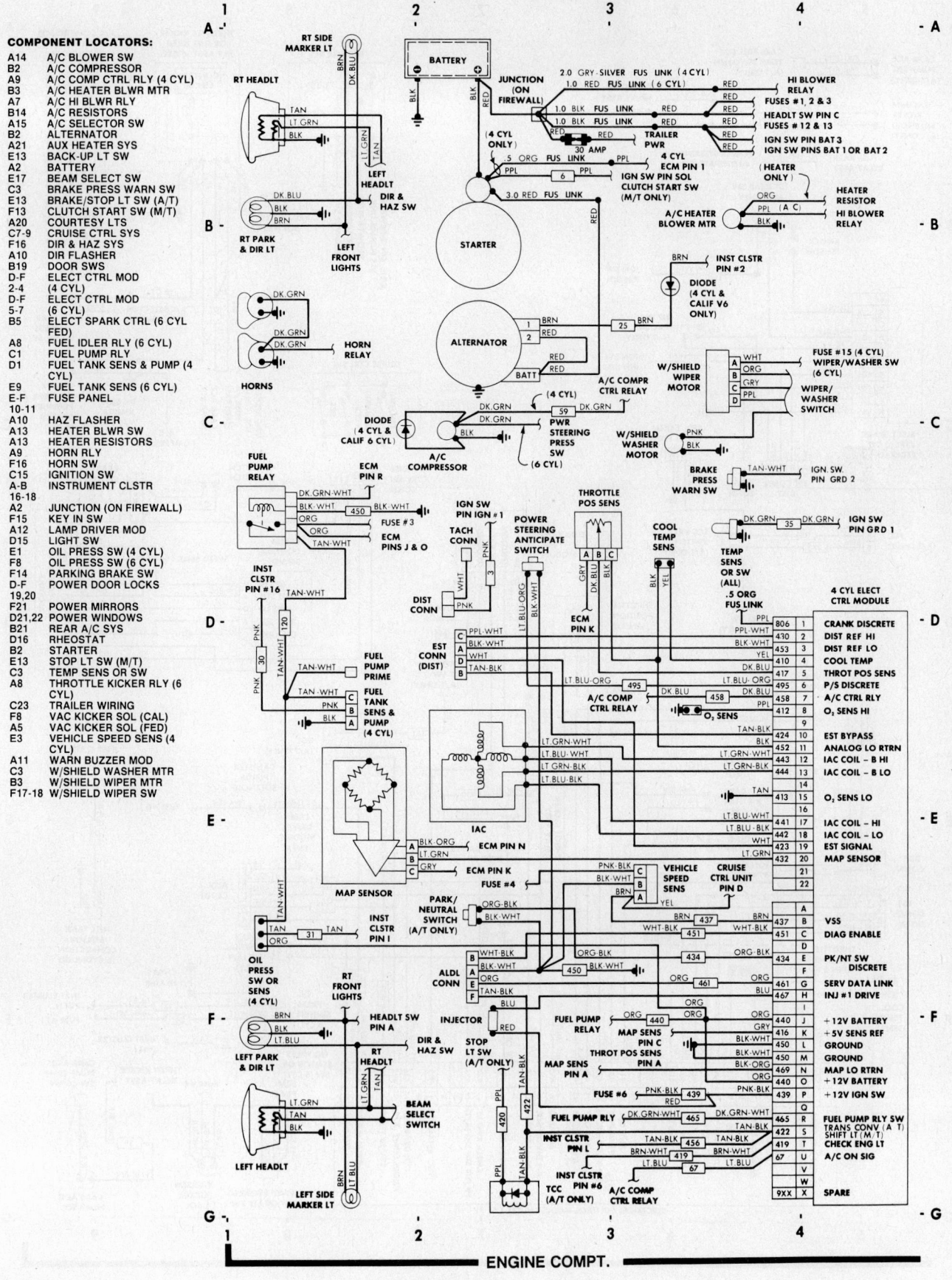

1985 General Motors

ASTRO & SAFARI (Cont.)

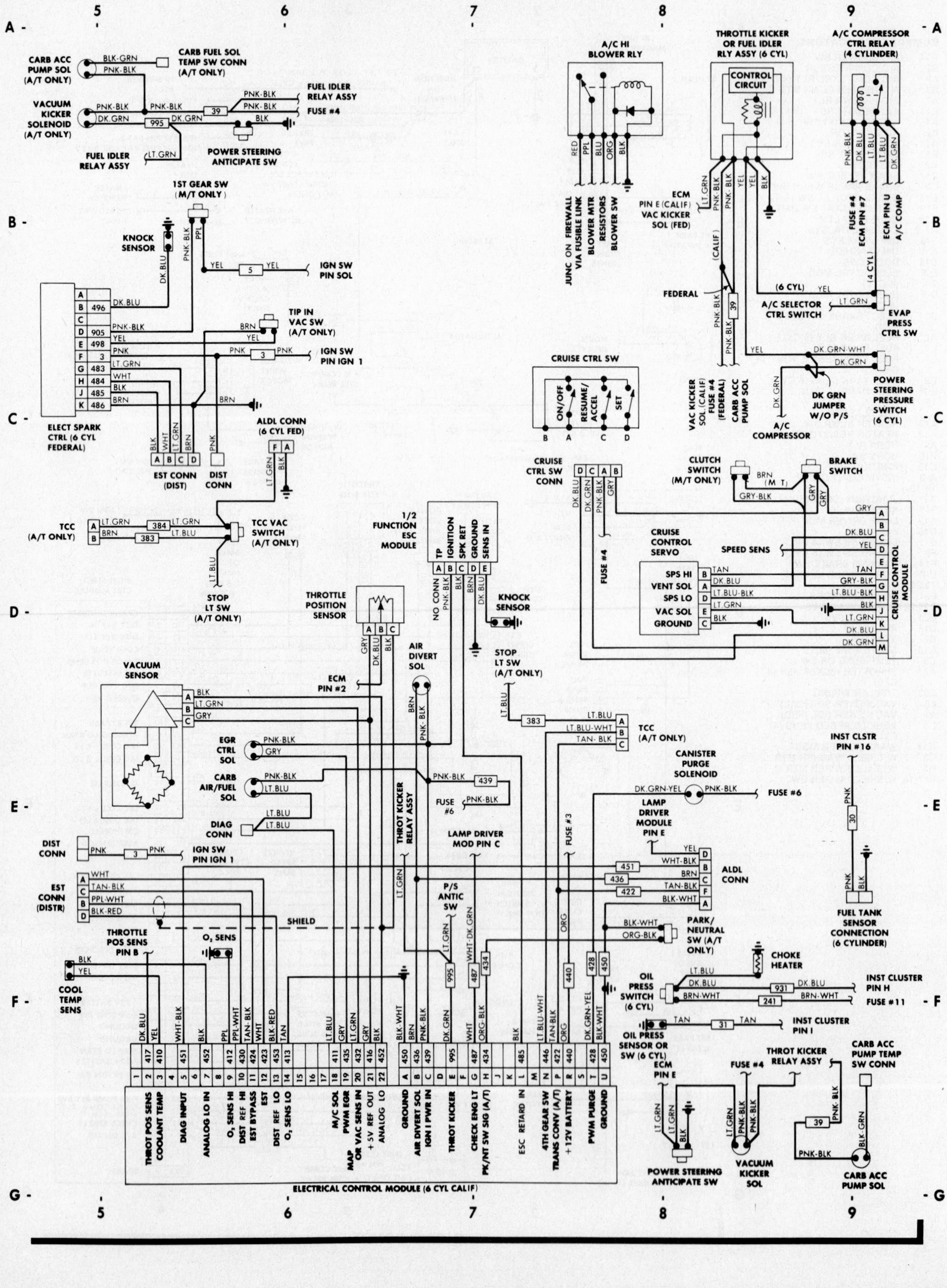

ASTRO & SAFARI (Cont.)

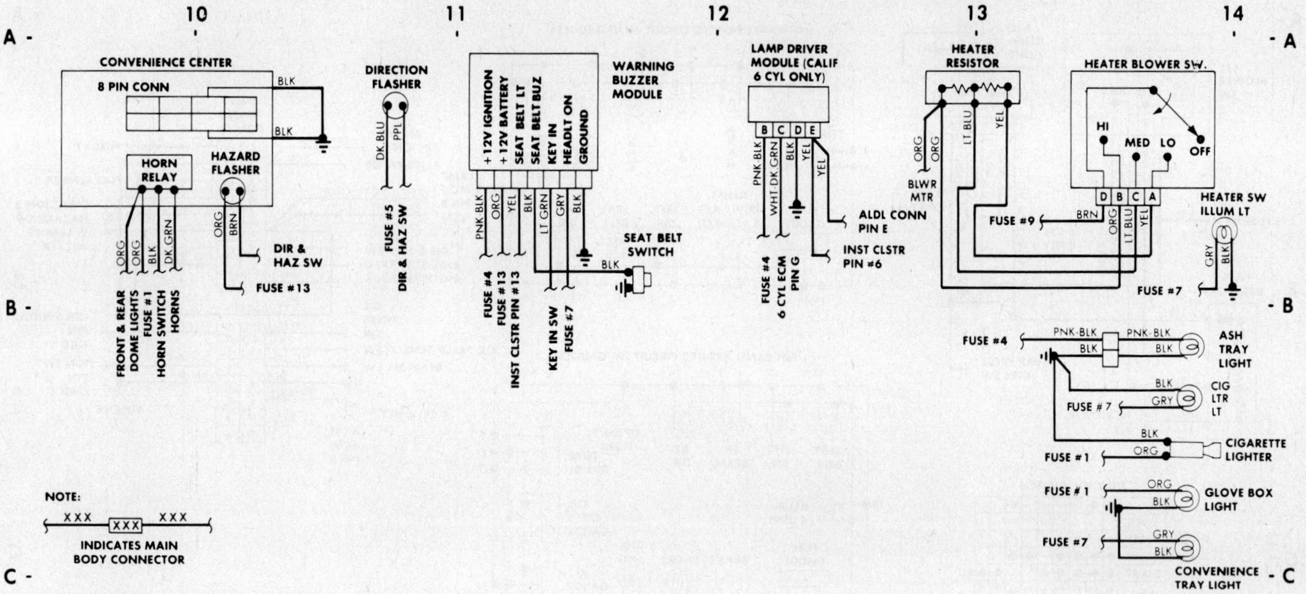

FUSE #	COLOR	AMP	USAGE
1	YEL	20	HORN, DOME LIGHTS
2	YEL	20	TAILLIGHTS
3	RED	10	ELECT CTRL MODULE
4	YEL	20	IGNITION GAUGES
5	YEL	20	TURN SIGS. BACK-UP LTS
6	RED	10	ELECT CTRL MODULE
7	RED	10	INSTRUMENT LTS
8	WHT	25	AUX HEATER, A/C
9	YEL	20	HEATER, A/C
10	CIRC BRKR	30	POWER WINDOWS
11	YEL	20	CHOKE
12	CIRC BRKR	30	POWER ACCESSORIES
13	YEL	20	STOP LTS, HAZARD
14	RED	10	RADIO
15	WHT	25	W/SHIELD WIPER

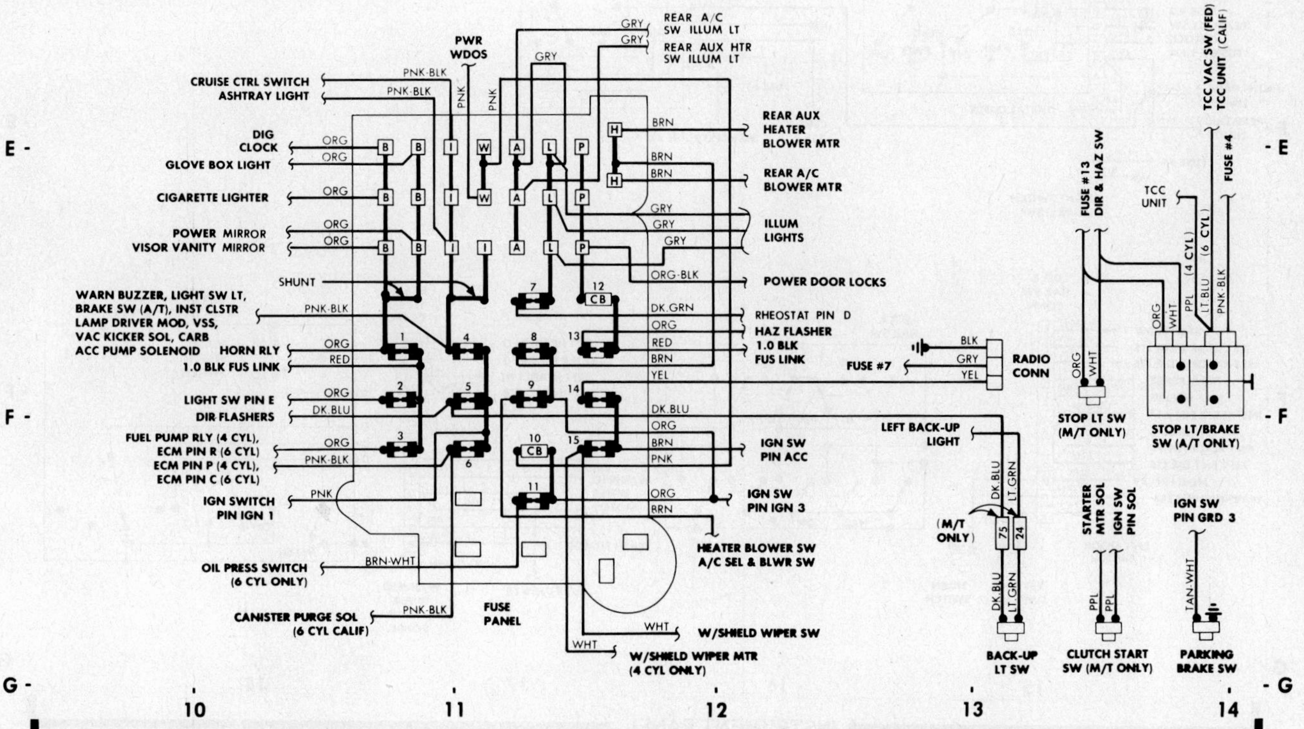

1985 General Motors

ASTRO & SAFARI (Cont.)

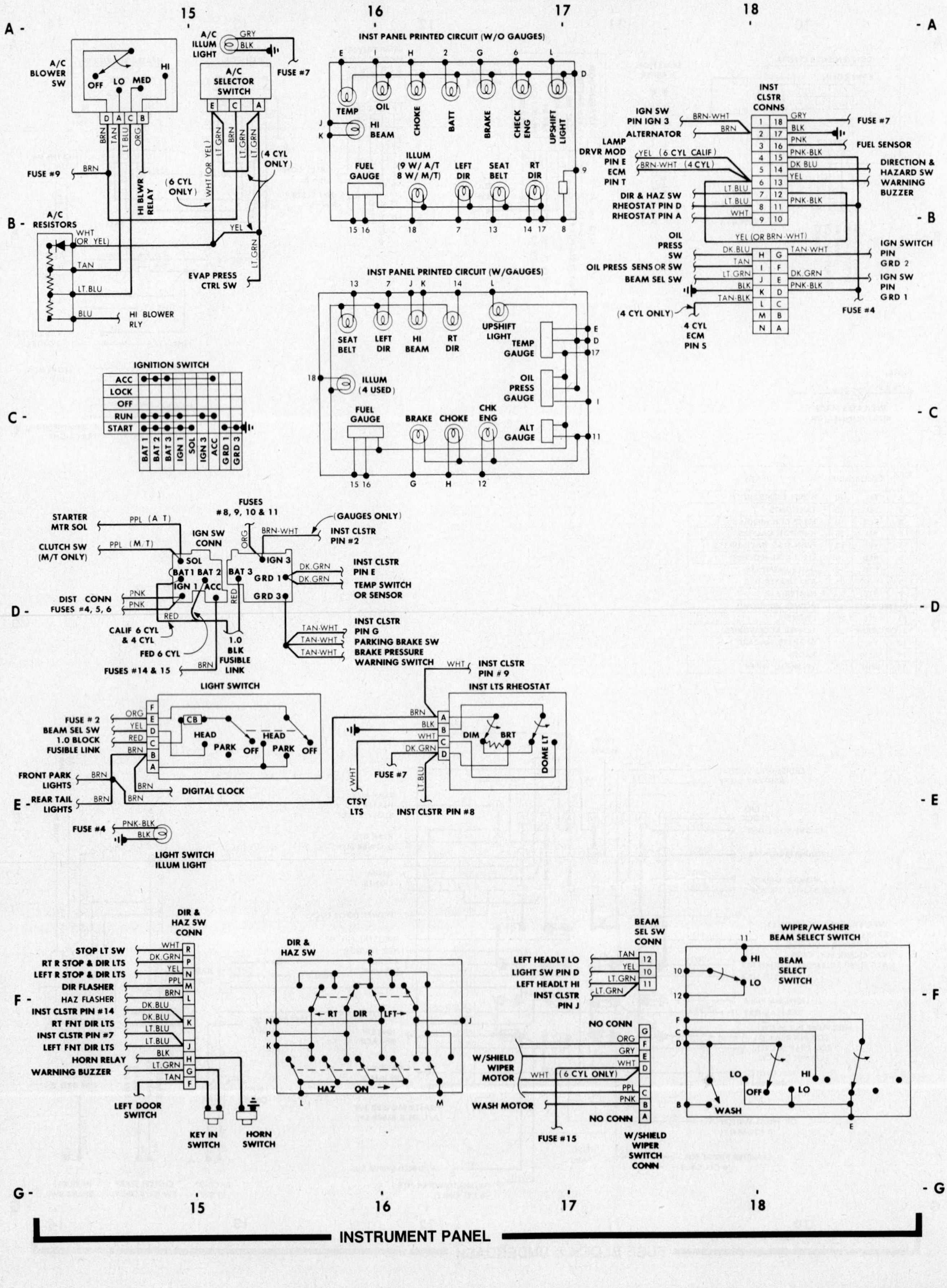

ASTRO & SAFARI (Cont.)

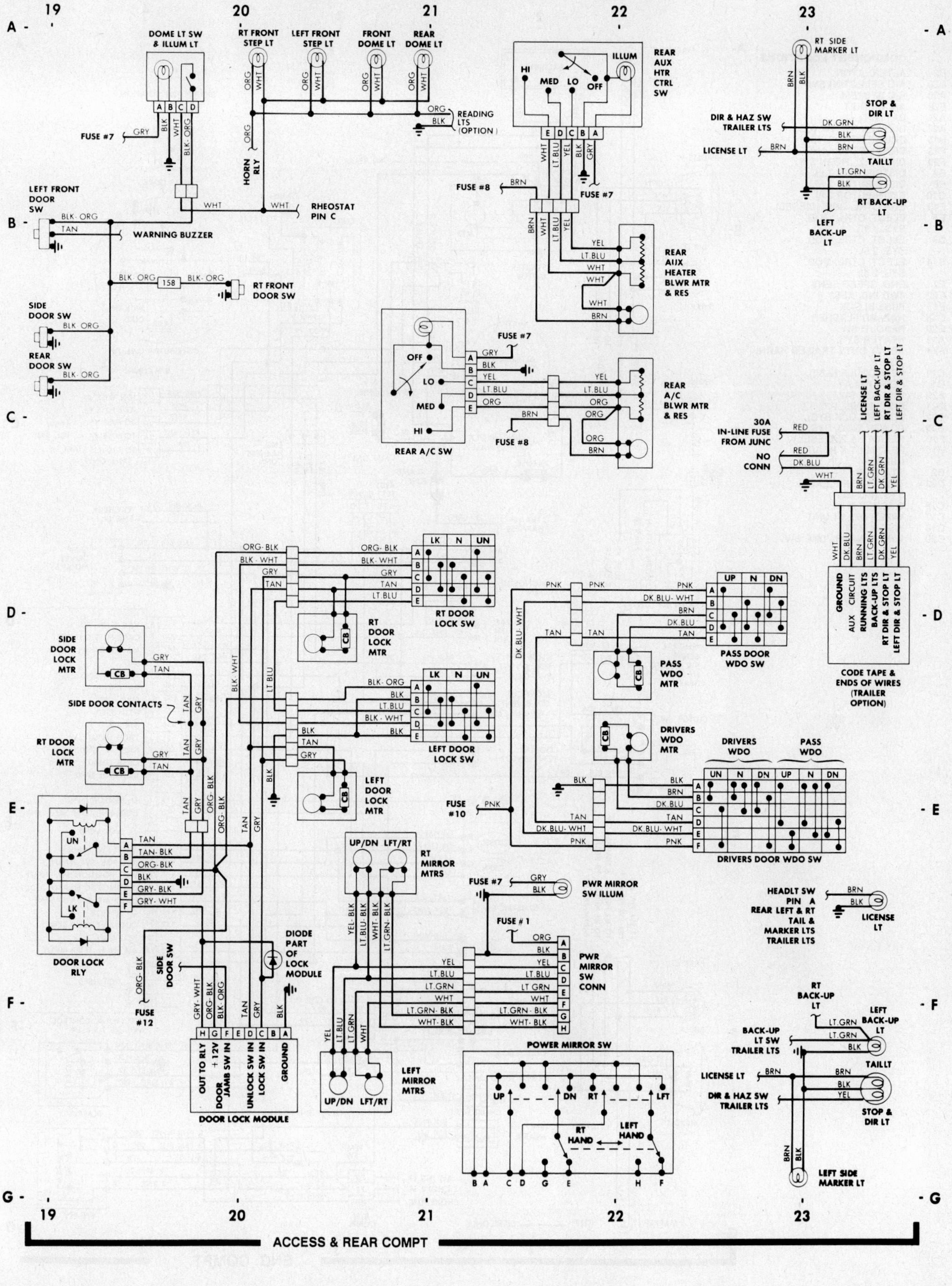

1985 General Motors

S10/S15 BLAZER/JIMMY & PICKUP

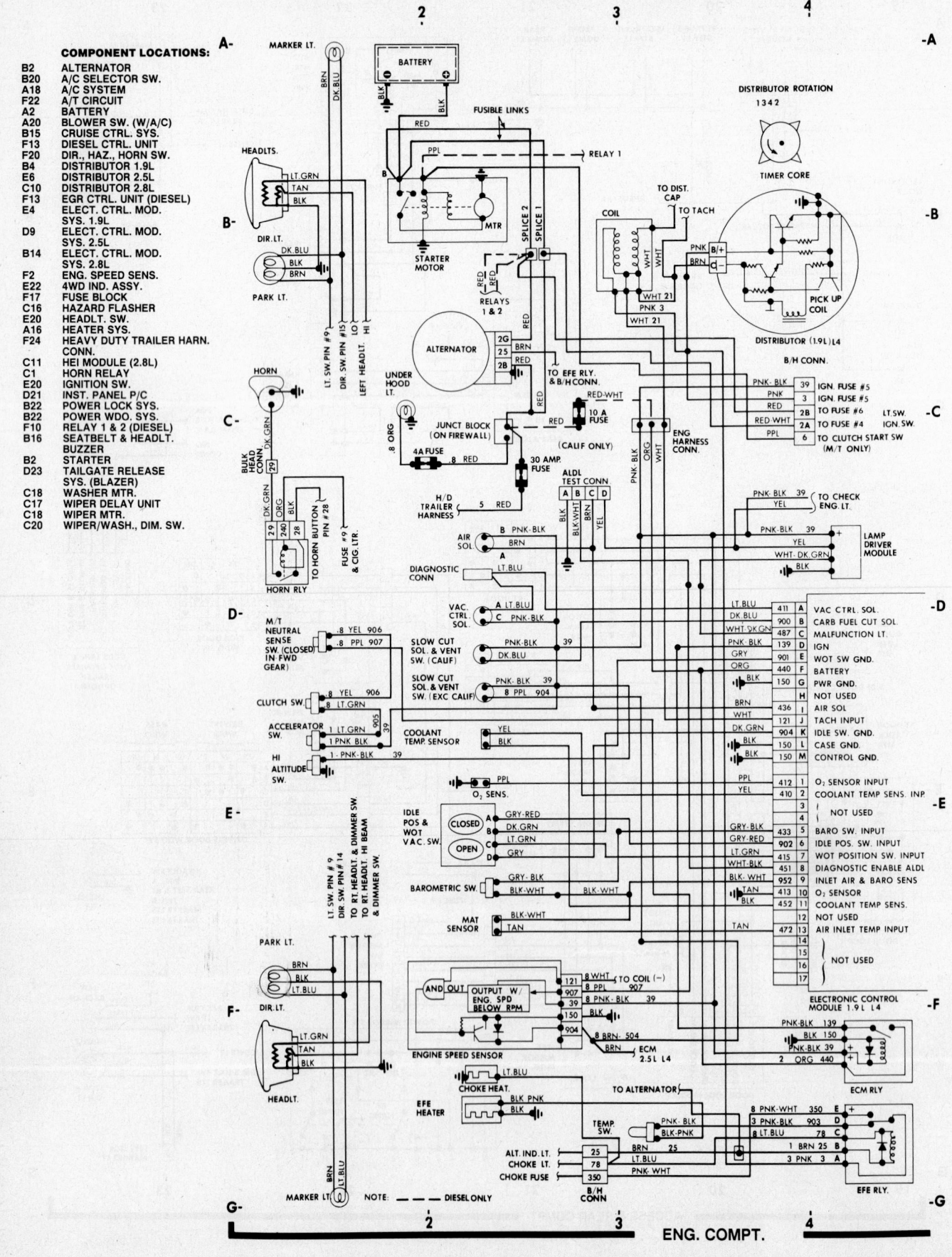

COMPONENT LOCATIONS:

B2	ALTERNATOR
B20	A/C SELECTOR SW.
A18	A/C SYSTEM
F22	A/T CIRCUIT
A2	BATTERY
A20	BLOWER SW. (W/A/C)
B15	CRUISE CTRL. SYS.
F13	DIESEL CTRL. UNIT
F20	DIR., HAZ., HORN SW.
B4	DISTRIBUTOR 1.9L
E6	DISTRIBUTOR 2.5L
C10	DISTRIBUTOR 2.8L
F13	EGR CTRL. UNIT (DIESEL)
E4	ELECT. CTRL. MOD. SYS. 1.9L
D9	ELECT. CTRL. MOD. SYS. 2.5L
B14	ELECT. CTRL. MOD. SYS. 2.8L
F2	ENG. SPEED SENS.
E22	4WD IND. ASSY.
F17	FUSE BLOCK
C16	HAZARD FLASHER
E20	HEADLT. SW.
A16	HEATER SYS.
F24	HEAVY DUTY TRAILER HARN. CONN.
C11	HEI MODULE (2.8L)
C1	HORN RELAY
E20	IGNITION SW.
D21	INST. PANEL P/C
B22	POWER LOCK SYS.
B22	POWER WDO. SYS.
F10	RELAY 1 & 2 (DIESEL)
B16	SEATBELT & HEADLT. BUZZER
B2	STARTER
D23	TAILGATE RELEASE SYS. (BLAZER)
C18	WASHER MTR.
C17	WIPER DELAY UNIT
C18	WIPER MTR.
C20	WIPER/WASH., DIM. SW.

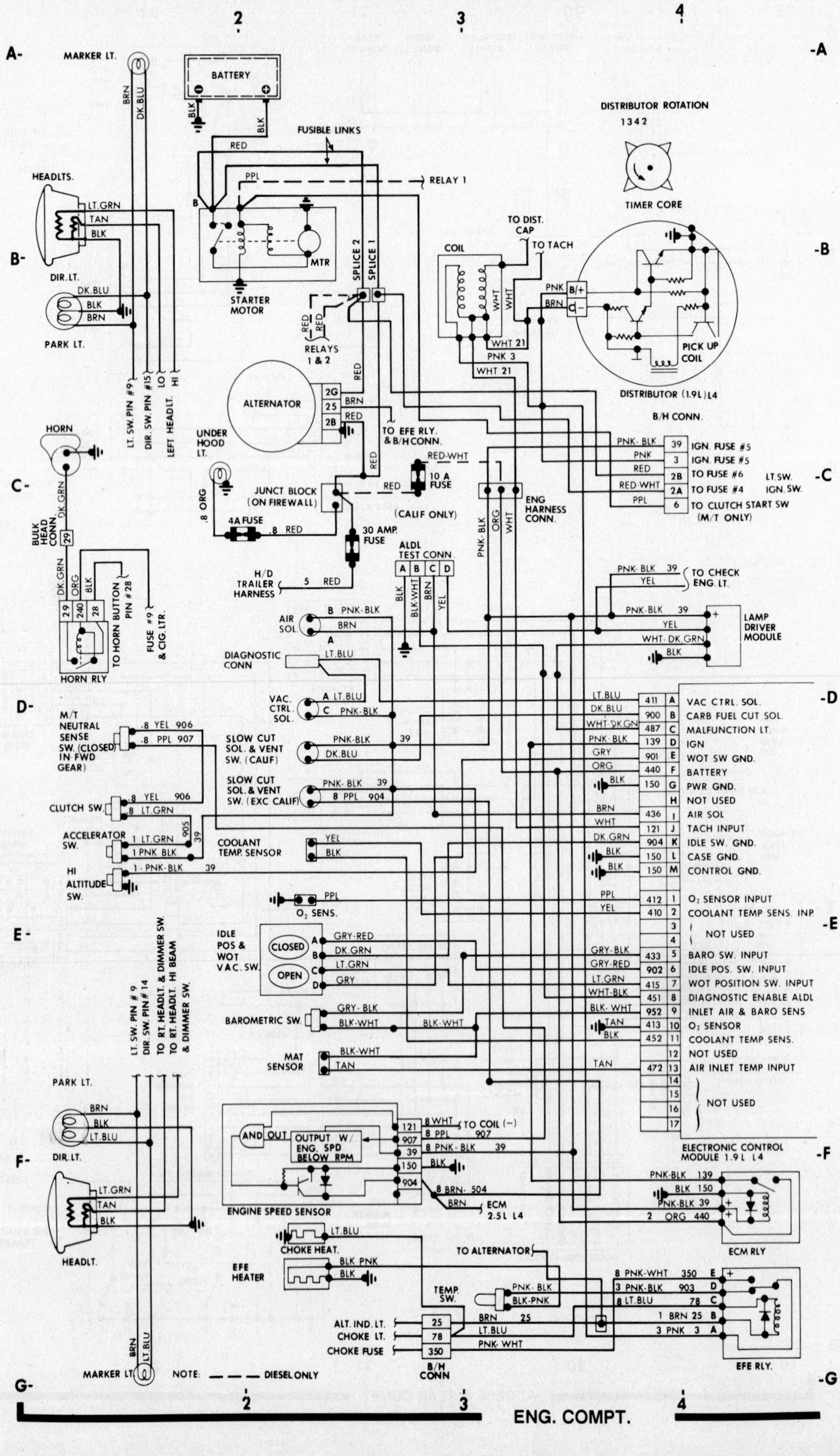

S10/S15 BLAZER/JIMMY & PICKUP (Cont.)

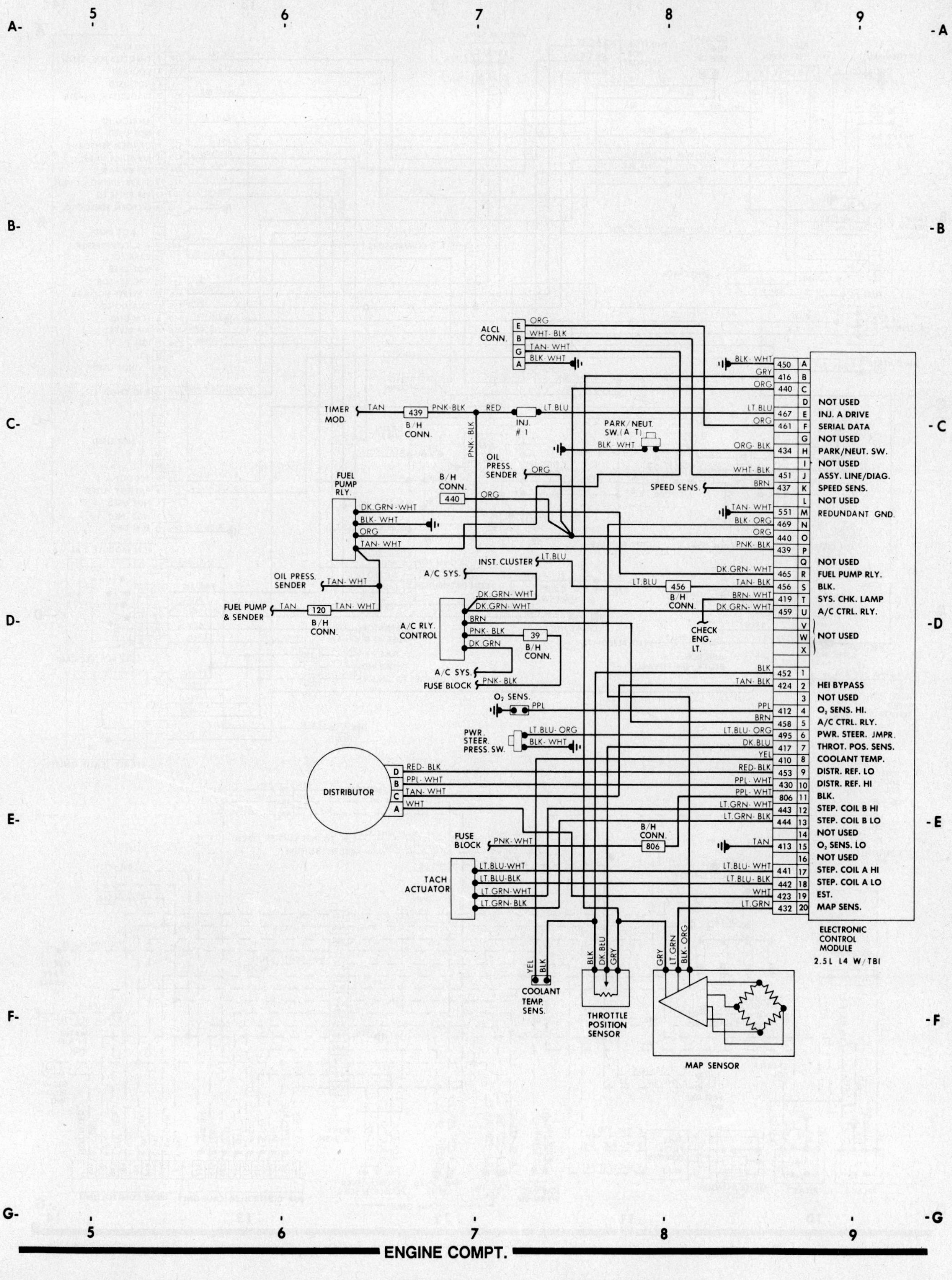

1985 General Motors

S10/S15 BLAZER/JIMMY & PICKUP (Cont.)

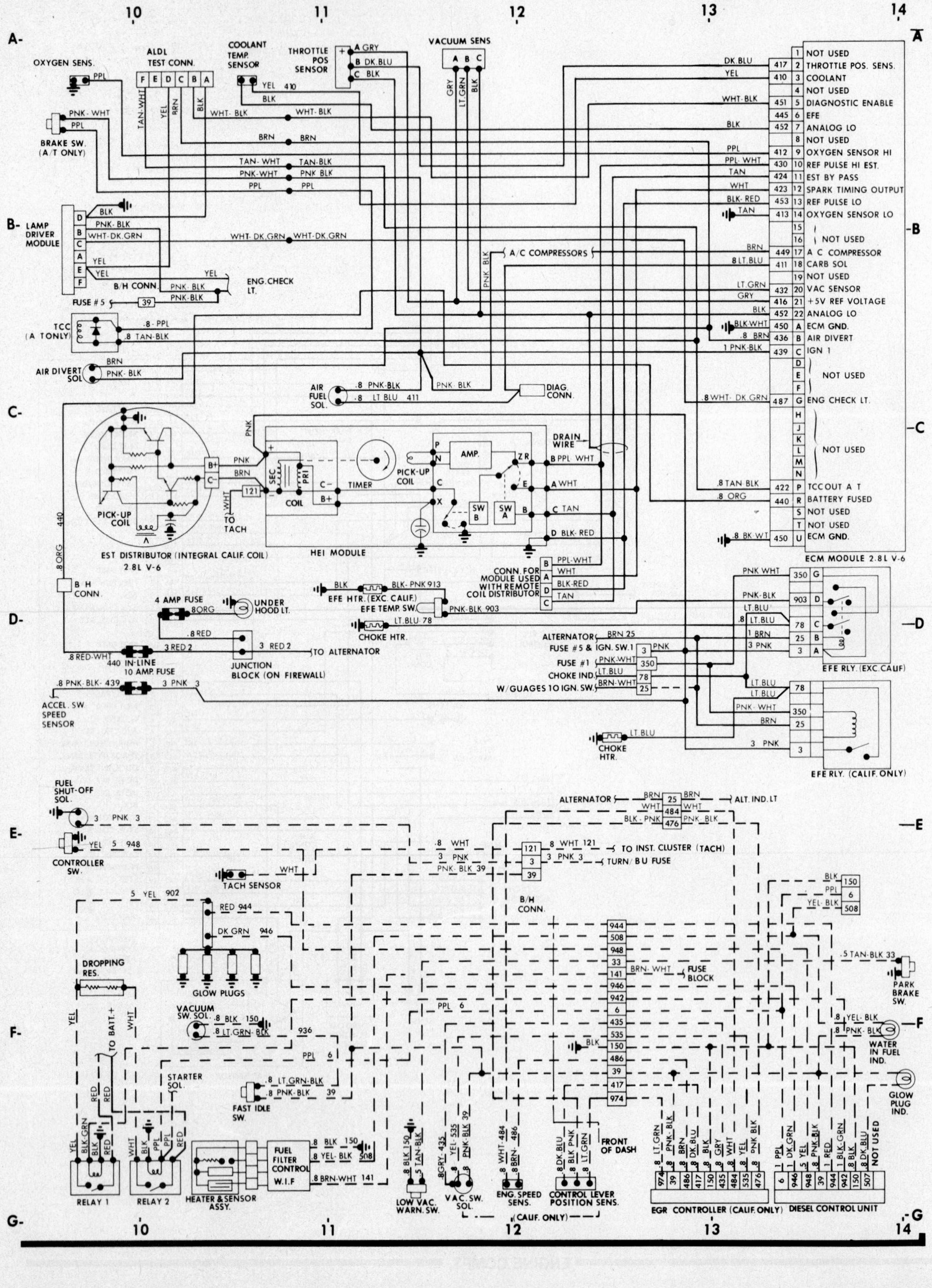

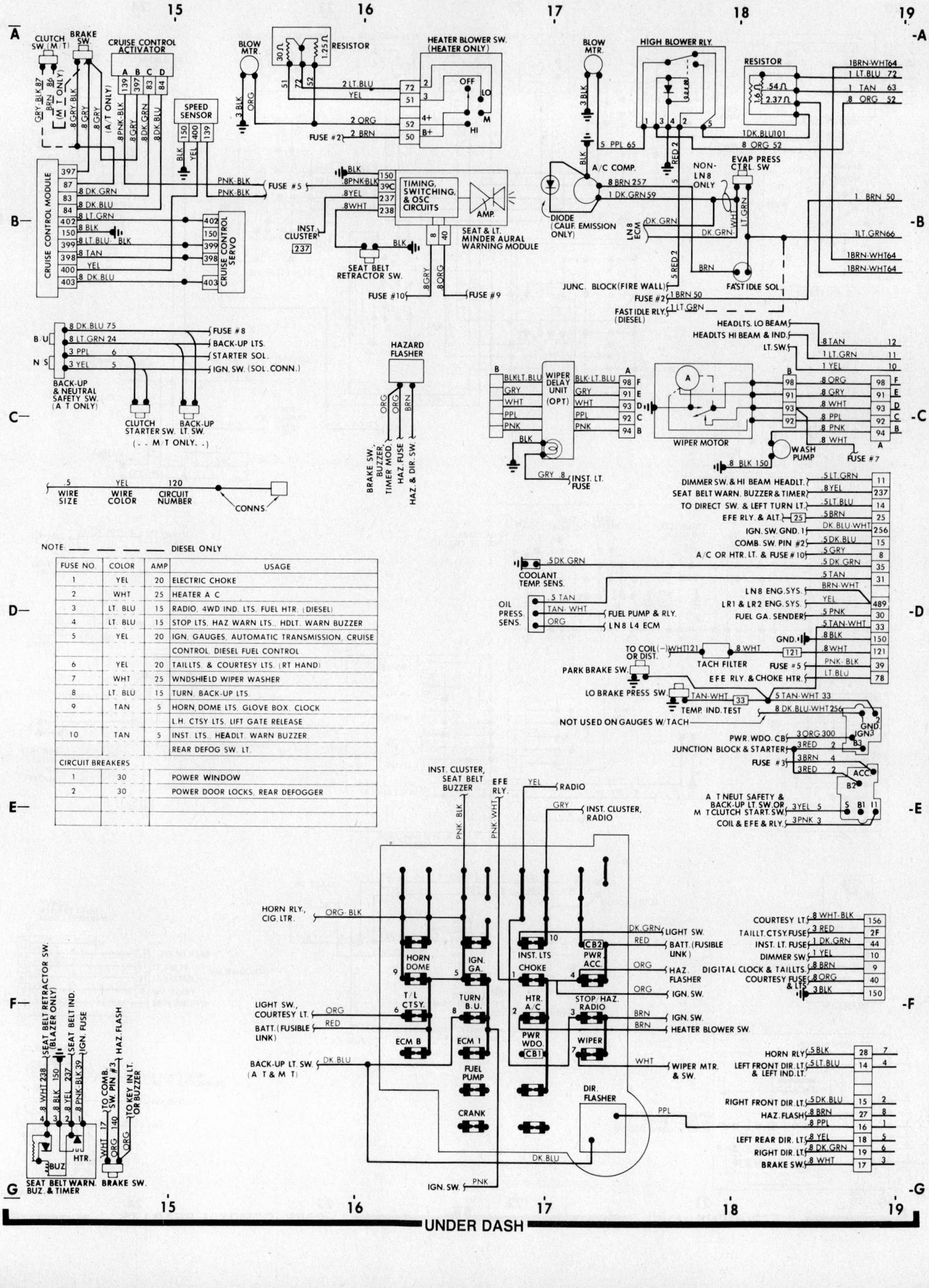

NOTE: — — — — DIESEL ONLY

FUSE NO.	COLOR	AMP	USAGE
1	YEL	20	ELECTRIC CHOKE
2	WHT	25	HEATER A C
3	LT. BLU	15	RADIO, 4WD IND. LTS. FUEL HTR. (DIESEL)
4	LT. BLU	15	STOP LTS, HAZ WARN LTS., HDLT. WARN BUZZER
5	YEL	20	IGN, GAUGES, AUTOMATIC TRANSMISSION, CRUISE
			CONTROL, DIESEL FUEL CONTROL
6	YEL	20	TAILLTS, & COURTESY LTS. (RT HAND)
7	WHT	25	WNDSHIELD WIPER WASHER
8	LT. BLU	15	TURN, BACK-UP LTS.
9	TAN	5	HORN, DOME LTS. GLOVE BOX, CLOCK
			L.H. CTSY LTS. LIFT GATE RELEASE
10	TAN	5	INST. LTS., HEADLT. WARN BUZZER.
			REAR DEFOG SW. LT.
CIRCUIT BREAKERS			
1	30		POWER WINDOW
2	30		POWER DOOR LOCKS, REAR DEFOGGER

1985 General Motors

S10/S15 BLAZER/JIMMY & PICKUP (Cont.)

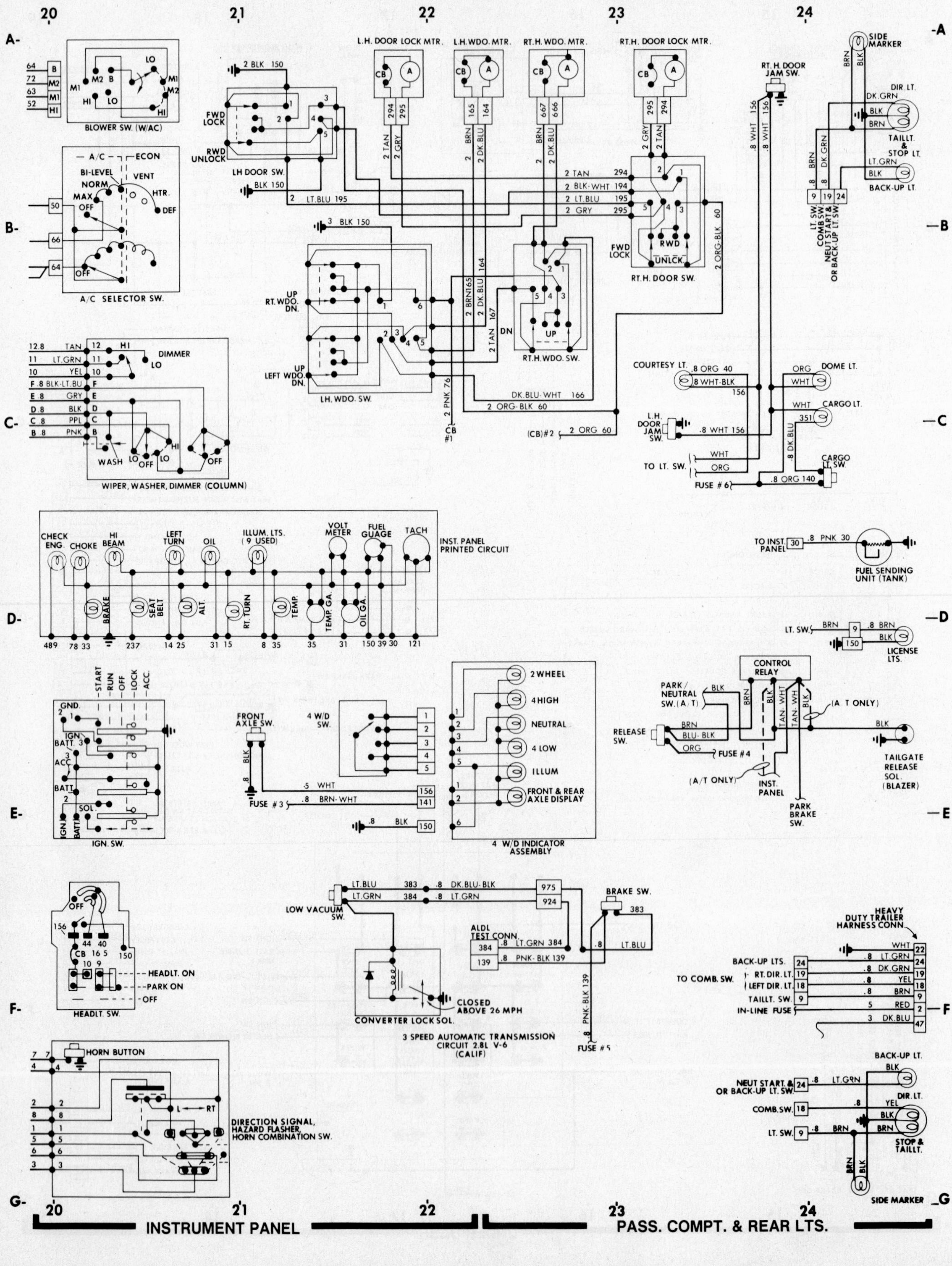

BLAZER, JIMMY, PICKUP & SUBURBAN

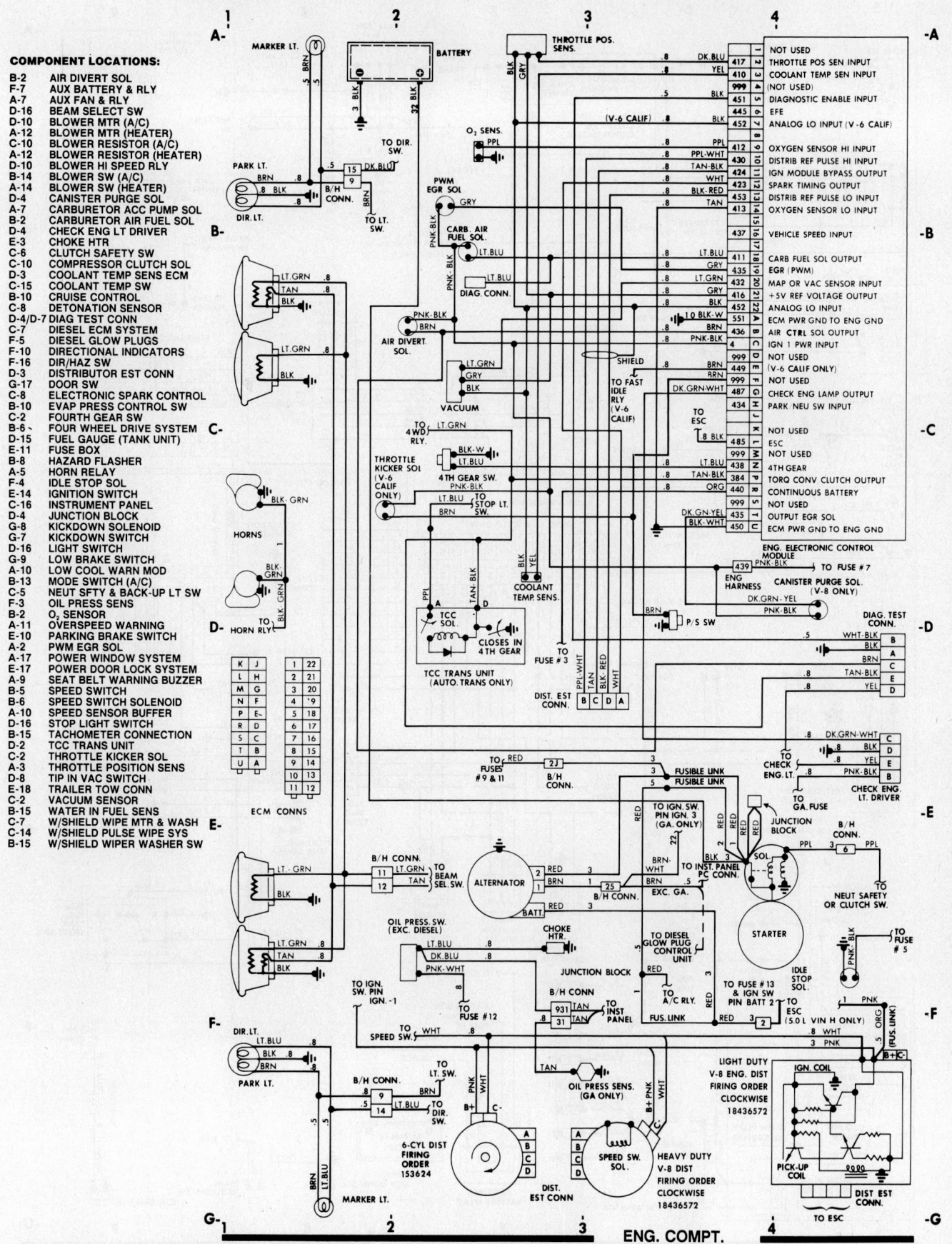

COMPONENT LOCATIONS:

B-2 AIR DIVERT SOL
F-7 AUX BATTERY & RLY
A-7 AUX FAN & RLY
D-16 BEAM SELECT SW
D-10 BLOWER MTR (A/C)
A-12 BLOWER MTR (HEATER)
C-10 BLOWER RESISTOR (A/C)
A-12 BLOWER RESISTOR (HEATER)
D-10 BLOWER HI SPEED RLY
B-14 BLOWER SW (A/C)
A-14 BLOWER SW (HEATER)
D-4 CANISTER PURGE SOL
A-7 CARBURETOR ACC PUMP SOL
B-2 CARBURETOR AIR FUEL SOL
D-4 CHECK ENG LT DRIVER
E-3 CHOKE HTR
C-6 CLUTCH SAFETY SW
C-10 COMPRESSOR CLUTCH SOL
D-3 COOLANT TEMP SENS ECM
C-15 COOLANT TEMP SW
B-10 CRUISE CONTROL
C-8 DETONATION SENSOR
D-4/D-7 DIAG TEST CONN
C-7 DIESEL ECM SYSTEM
F-5 DIESEL GLOW PLUGS
F-10 DIRECTIONAL INDICATORS
F-16 DIR/HAZ SW
D-3 DISTRIBUTOR EST CONN
G-17 DOOR SW
C-8 ELECTRONIC SPARK CONTROL
B-10 EVAP PRESS CONTROL SW
C-2 FOURTH GEAR SW
B-6 FOUR WHEEL DRIVE SYSTEM
D-15 FUEL GAUGE (TANK UNIT)
E-11 FUSE BOX
B-8 HAZARD FLASHER
A-5 HORN RELAY
F-4 IDLE STOP SOL
E-14 IGNITION SWITCH
C-16 INSTRUMENT PANEL
D-4 JUNCTION BLOCK
G-8 KICKDOWN SOLENOID
G-7 KICKDOWN SWITCH
D-16 LIGHT SWITCH
G-9 LOW BRAKE SWITCH
A-10 LOW COOL WARN MOD
B-13 MODE SWITCH (A/C)
C-5 NEUT SFTY & BACK-UP LT SW
F-3 OIL PRESS SENS
B-2 O_2 SENSOR
A-11 OVERSPEED WARNING
E-10 PARKING BRAKE SWITCH
A-2 PWM EGR SOL
A-17 POWER WINDOW SYSTEM
E-17 POWER DOOR LOCK SYSTEM
A-9 SEAT BELT WARNING BUZZER
B-5 SPEED SWITCH
B-6 SPEED SWITCH SOLENOID
A-10 SPEED SENSOR BUFFER
D-16 STOP LIGHT SWITCH
B-15 TACHOMETER CONNECTION
D-2 TCC TRANS UNIT
C-2 THROTTLE KICKER SOL
A-3 THROTTLE POSITION SENS
D-8 TIP IN VAC SWITCH
E-18 TRAILER TOW CONN
C-2 VACUUM SENSOR
B-15 WATER IN FUEL SENS
C-7 W/SHIELD WIPE MTR & WASH
C-14 W/SHIELD PULSE WIPE SYS
B-15 W/SHIELD WIPER WASHER SW

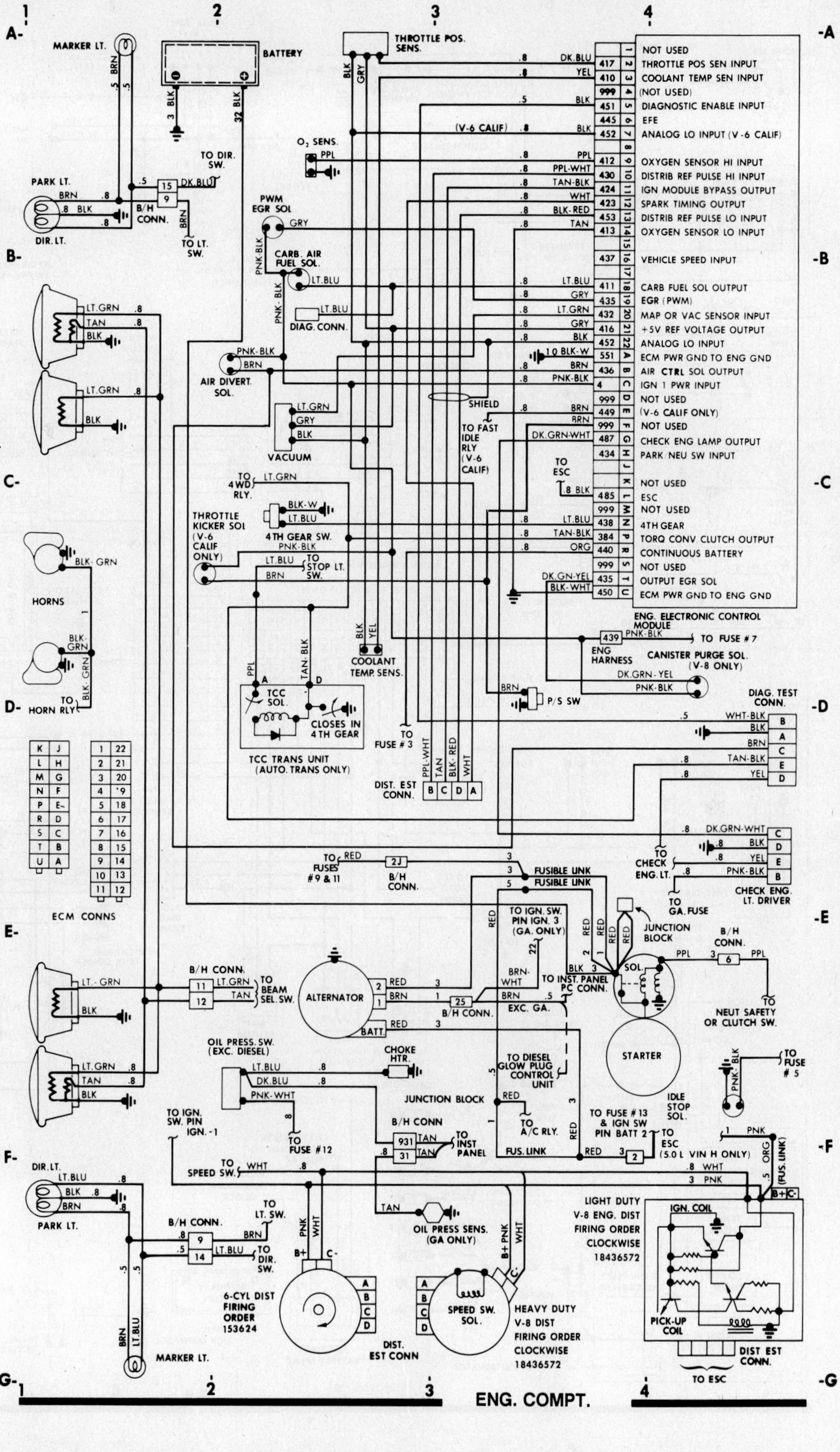

1985 General Motors

BLAZER, JIMMY, PICKUP & SUBURBAN (Cont.)

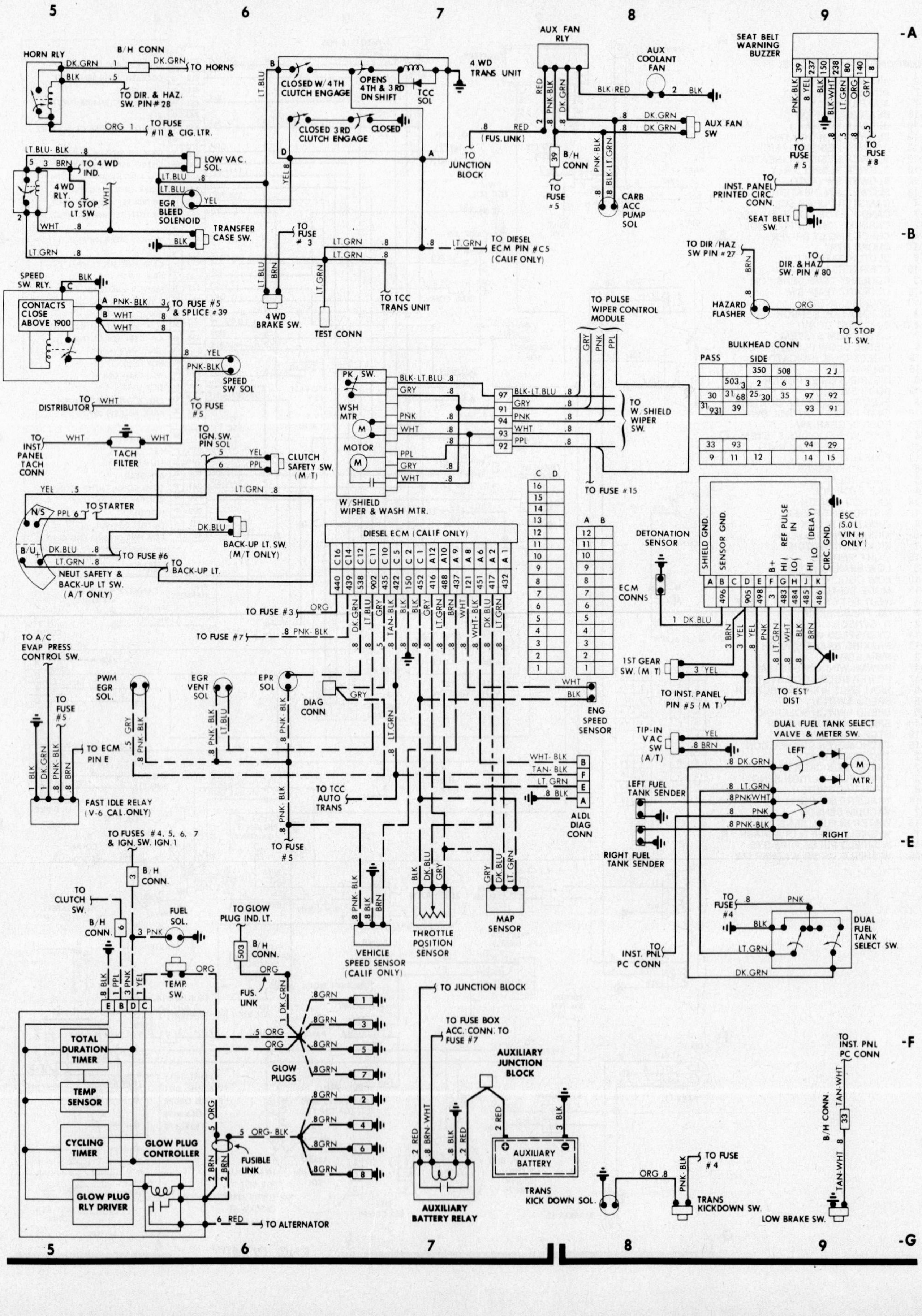

1985 General Motors

BLAZER, JIMMY, PICKUP & SUBURBAN (Cont.)

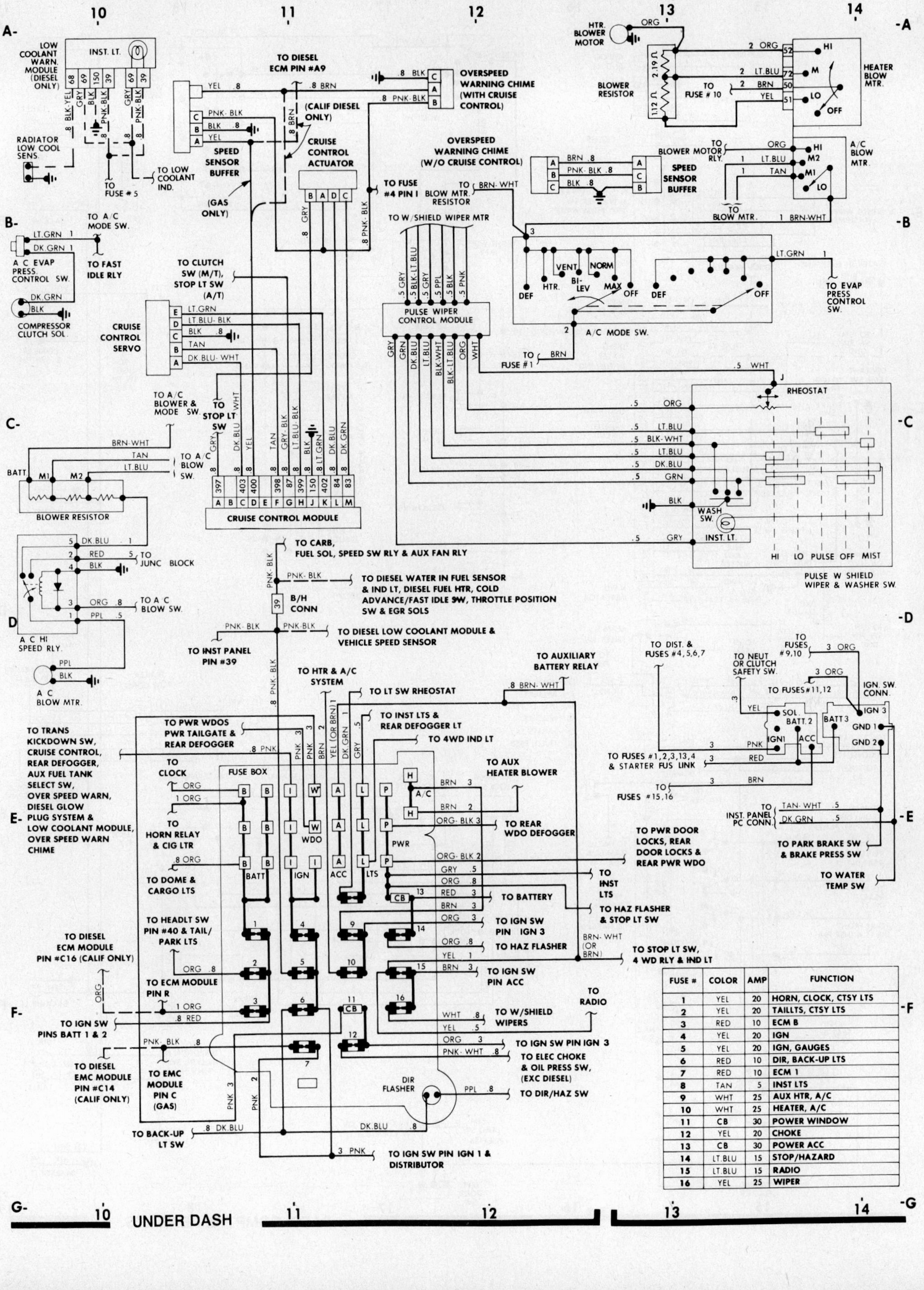

FUSE #	COLOR	AMP	FUNCTION
1	YEL	20	HORN, CLOCK, CTSY LTS
2	YEL	20	TAILLTS, CTSY LTS
3	RED	10	ECM B
4	YEL	20	IGN
5	YEL	20	IGN, GAUGES
6	RED	10	DIR, BACK-UP LTS
7	RED	10	ECM 1
8	TAN	5	INST LTS
9	WHT	25	AUX HTR, A/C
10	WHT	25	HEATER, A/C
11	CB	30	POWER WINDOW
12	YEL	20	CHOKE
13	CB	30	POWER ACC
14	LT.BLU	15	STOP/HAZARD
15	LT.BLU	15	RADIO
16	YEL	25	WIPER

UNDER DASH

1985 General Motors

BLAZER, JIMMY, PICKUP & SUBURBAN Cont.)

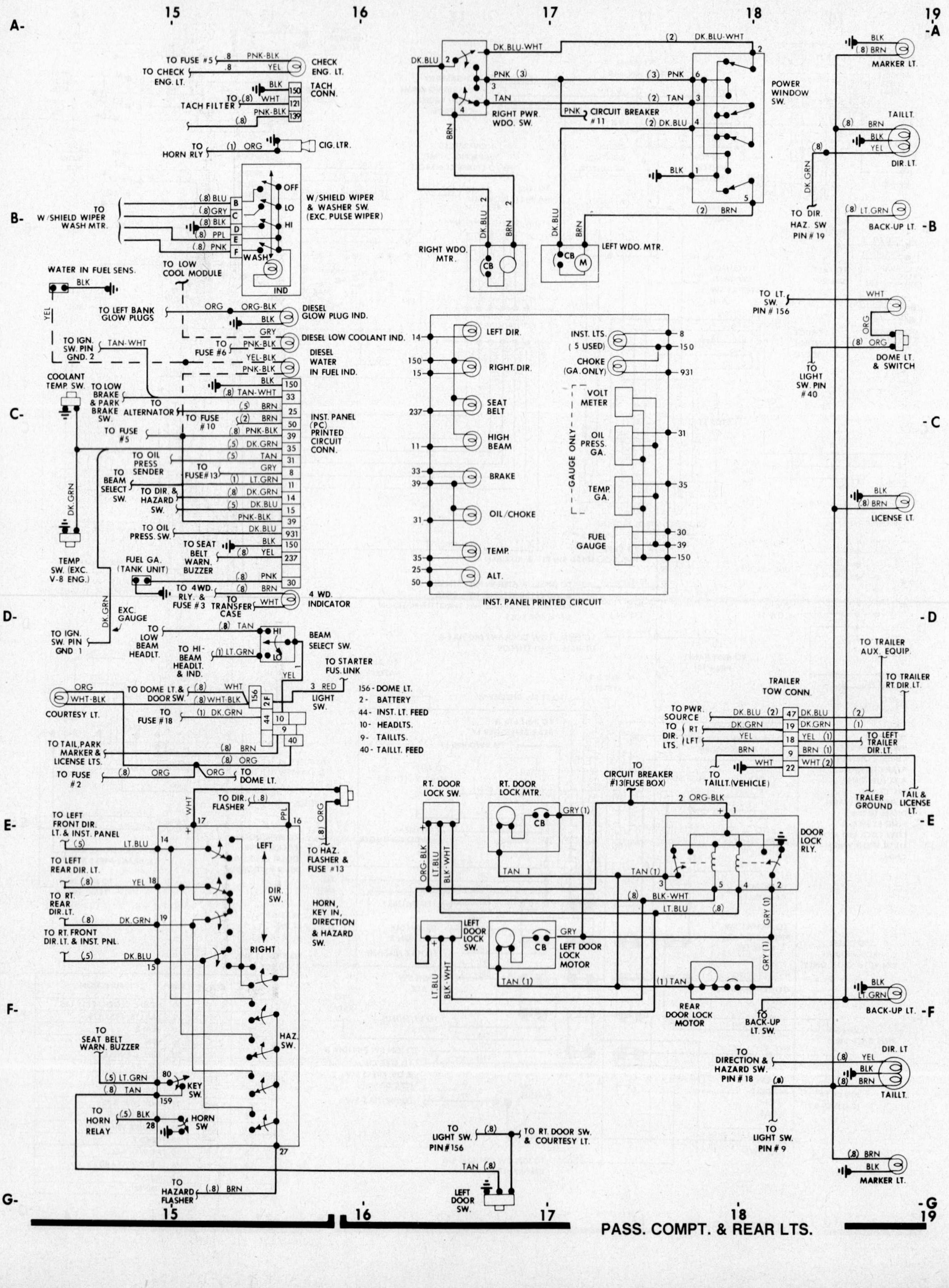

VANS, FRONT SECTIONS & HI-CUBES

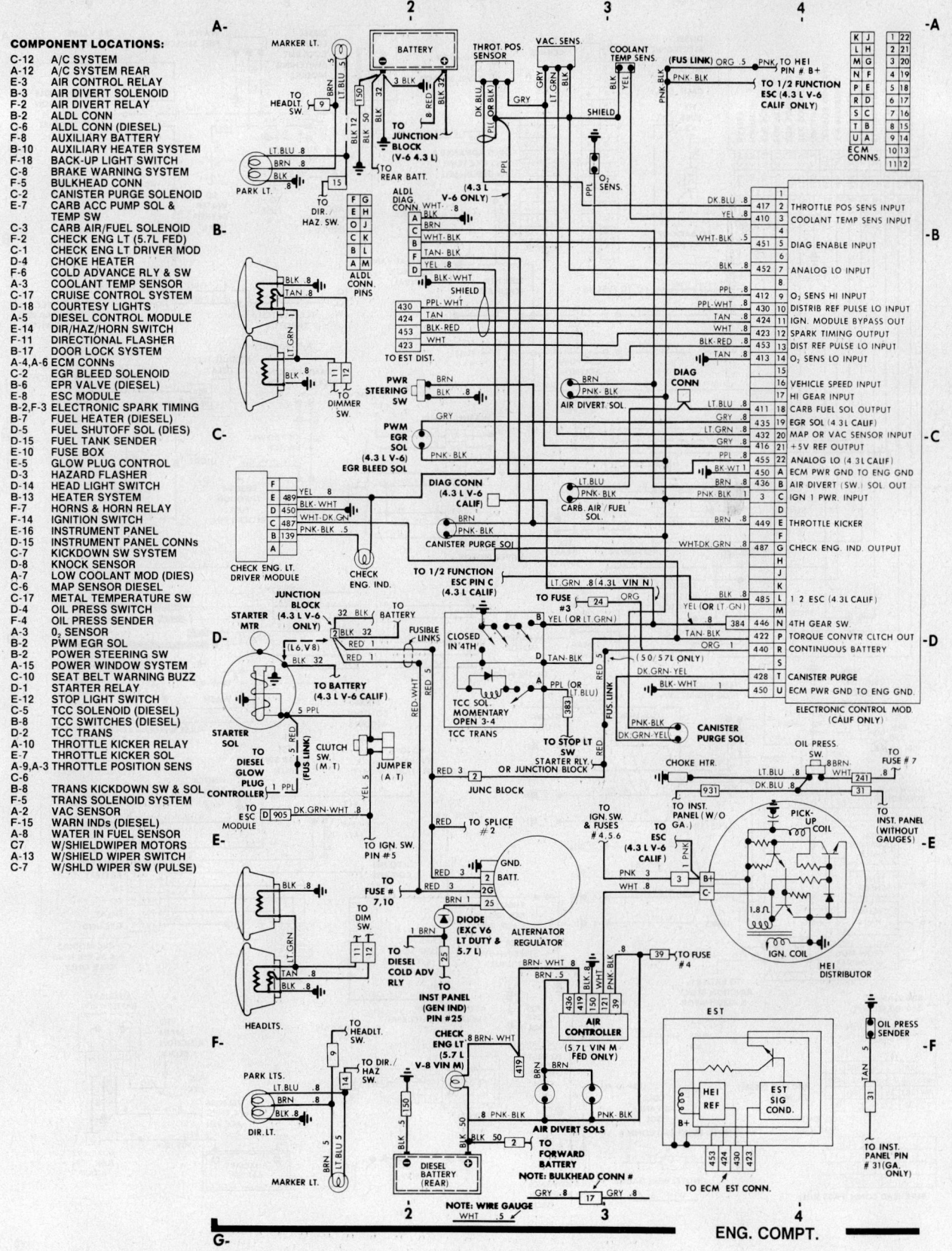

COMPONENT LOCATIONS:

- C-12 A/C SYSTEM
- A-12 A/C SYSTEM REAR
- E-3 AIR CONTROL RELAY
- B-3 AIR DIVERT SOLENOID
- F-2 AIR DIVERT RELAY
- B-2 ALDL CONN
- C-6 ALDL CONN (DIESEL)
- F-8 AUXILIARY BATTERY
- B-10 AUXILIARY HEATER SYSTEM
- F-18 BACK-UP LIGHT SWITCH
- C-8 BRAKE WARNING SYSTEM
- F-5 BULKHEAD CONN
- C-2 CANISTER PURGE SOLENOID
- E-7 CARB ACC PUMP SOL & TEMP SW
- C-3 CARB AIR/FUEL SOLENOID
- F-2 CHECK ENG LT (5.7L FED)
- C-1 CHECK ENG LT DRIVER MOD
- D-4 CHOKE HEATER
- F-6 COLD ADVANCE RLY & SW
- A-3 COOLANT TEMP SENSOR
- C-17 CRUISE CONTROL SYSTEM
- D-18 COURTESY LIGHTS
- A-5 DIESEL CONTROL MODULE
- E-14 DIR/HAZ/HORN SWITCH
- F-11 DIRECTIONAL FLASHER
- B-17 DOOR LOCK SYSTEM
- A-4,A-6 ECM CONNs
- C-2 EGR BLEED SOLENOID
- B-6 EPR VALVE (DIESEL)
- E-8 ESC MODULE
- B-2,F-3 ELECTRONIC SPARK TIMING
- B-7 FUEL HEATER (DIESEL)
- D-5 FUEL SHUTOFF SOL (DIES)
- D-15 FUEL TANK SENDER
- E-10 FUSE BOX
- E-5 GLOW PLUG CONTROL
- D-3 HAZARD FLASHER
- D-14 HEAD LIGHT SWITCH
- B-13 HEATER SYSTEM
- F-7 HORNS & HORN RELAY
- F-14 IGNITION SWITCH
- E-16 INSTRUMENT PANEL
- D-15 INSTRUMENT PANEL CONNs
- C-7 KICKDOWN SW SYSTEM
- D-8 KNOCK SENSOR
- A-7 LOW COOLANT MOD (DIES)
- C-6 MAP SENSOR DIESEL
- C-17 METAL TEMPERATURE SW
- D-4 OIL PRESS SWITCH
- F-4 OIL PRESS SENDER
- A-3 O_2 SENSOR
- B-2 PWM EGR SOL
- B-2 POWER STEERING SW
- A-15 POWER WINDOW SYSTEM
- C-10 SEAT BELT WARNING BUZZ
- D-1 STARTER RELAY
- E-12 STOP LIGHT SWITCH
- C-5 TCC SOLENOID (DIESEL)
- B-8 TCC SWITCHES (DIESEL)
- D-2 TCC TRANS
- A-10 THROTTLE KICKER RELAY
- E-7 THROTTLE KICKER SOL
- A-9,A-3 THROTTLE POSITION SENS
- C-6
- B-8 TRANS KICKDOWN SW & SOL
- F-5 TRANS SOLENOID SYSTEM
- A-2 VAC SENSOR
- F-15 WARN INDs (DIESEL)
- A-8 WATER IN FUEL SENSOR
- C7 W/SHIELDWIPER MOTORS
- A-13 W/SHIELD WIPER SWITCH
- C-7 W/SHLD WIPER SW (PULSE)

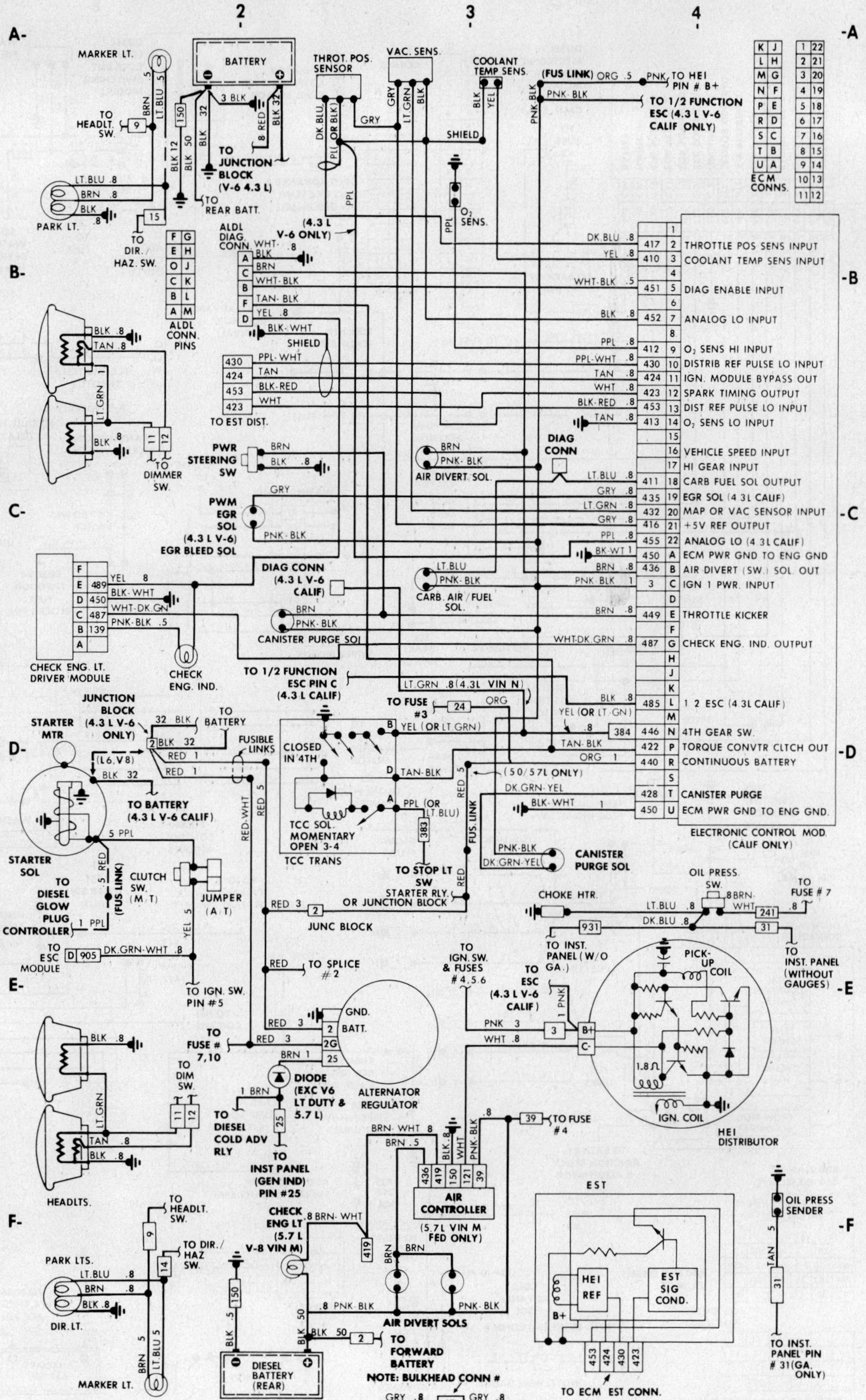

1985 General Motors

VANS, FRONT SECTIONS & HI-CUBES (Cont.)

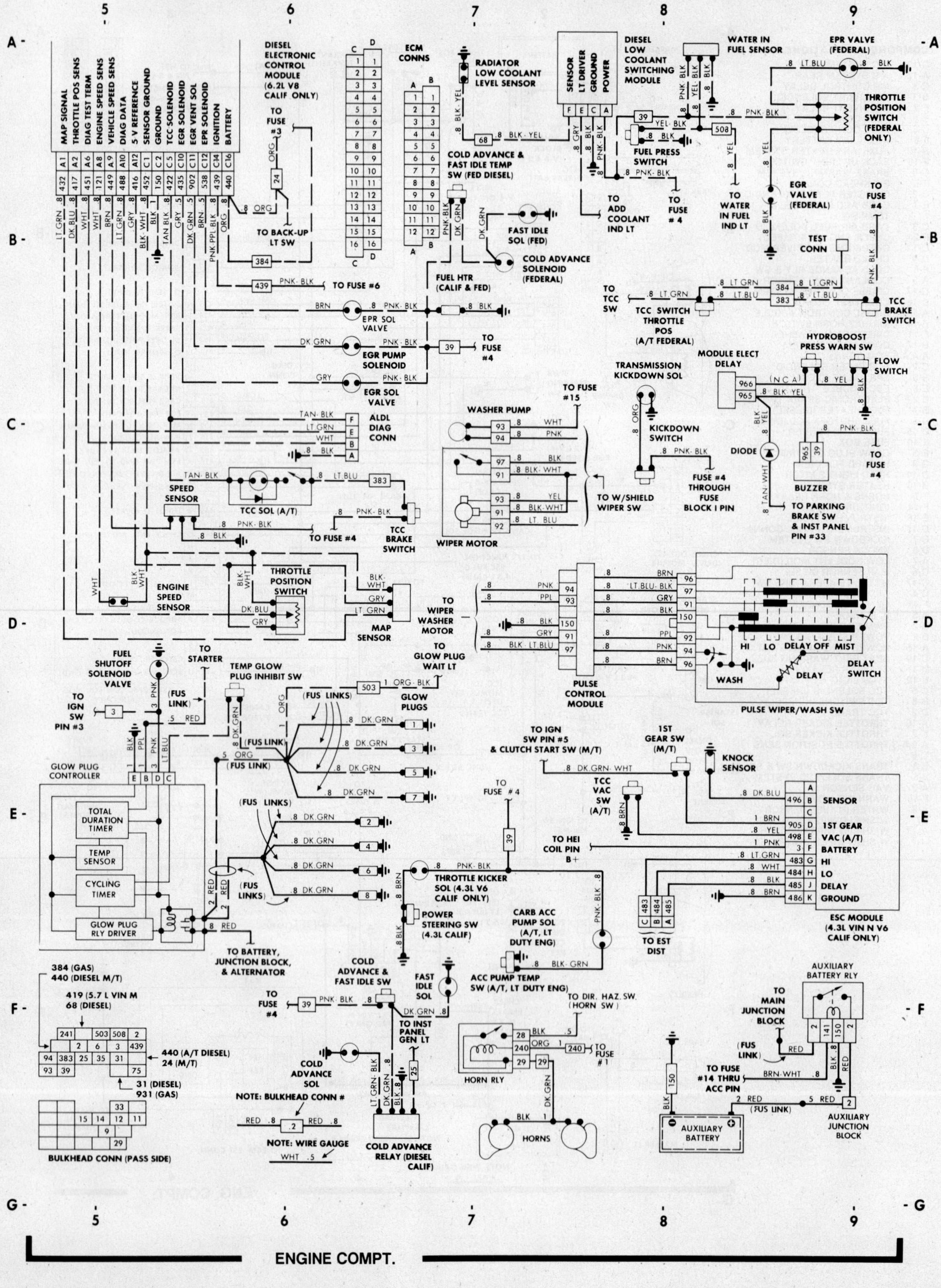

VANS, FRONT SECTIONS & HI-CUBES (Cont.)

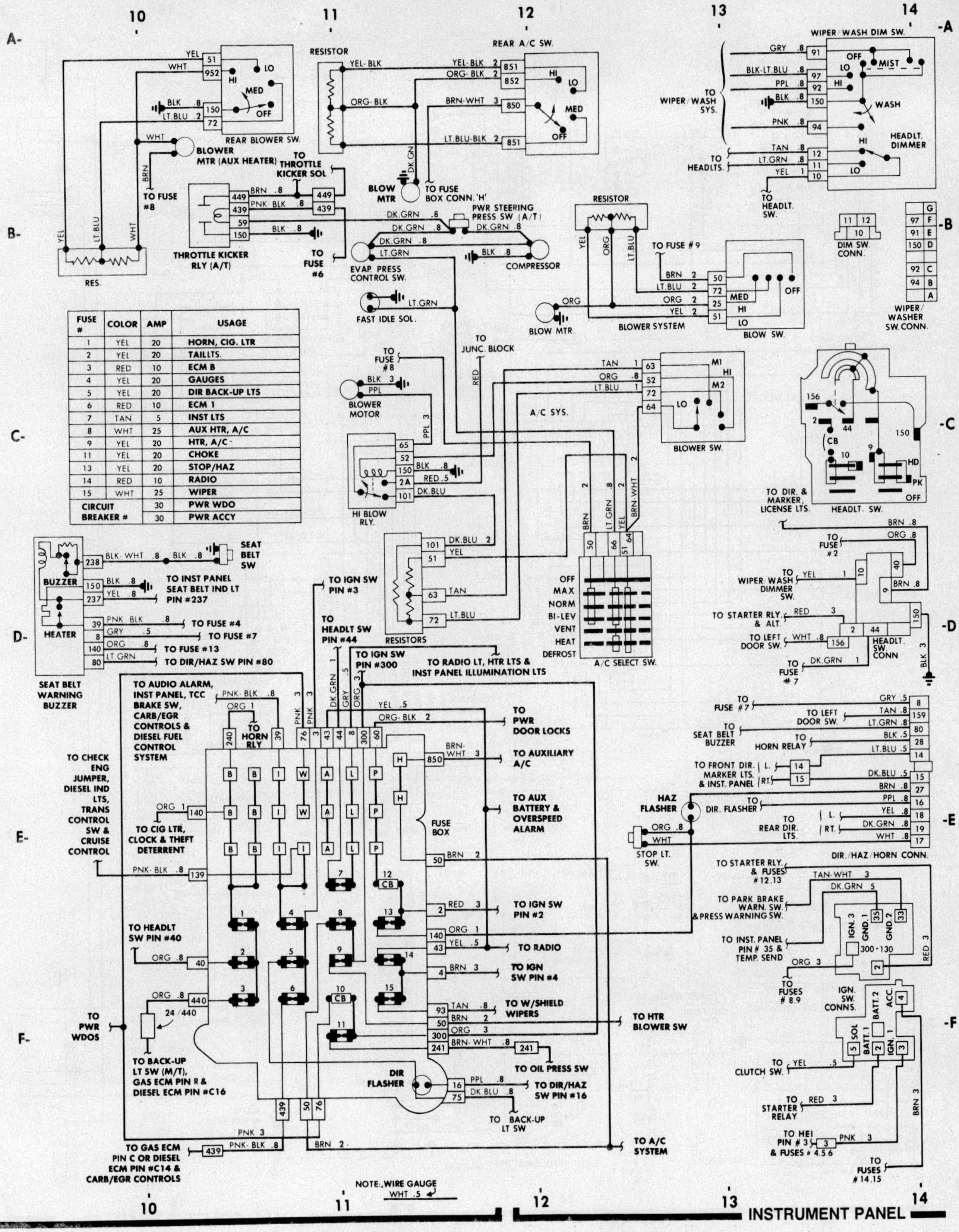

FUSE #	COLOR	AMP	USAGE
1	YEL	20	HORN, CIG. LTR
2	YEL	20	TAILLTS.
3	RED	10	ECM B
4	YEL	20	GAUGES
5	YEL	20	DIR BACK-UP LTS
6	RED	10	ECM 1
7	TAN	5	INST LTS
8	WHT	25	AUX HTR, A/C
9	YEL	20	HTR, A/C
11	YEL	20	CHOKE
13	YEL	20	STOP/HAZ
14	RED	10	RADIO
15	WHT	25	WIPER
CIRCUIT BREAKER #		30	PWR WDO
		30	PWR ACCY

INSTRUMENT PANEL

1985 General Motors

VANS, FRONT SECTIONS & HI-CUBES (Cont.)

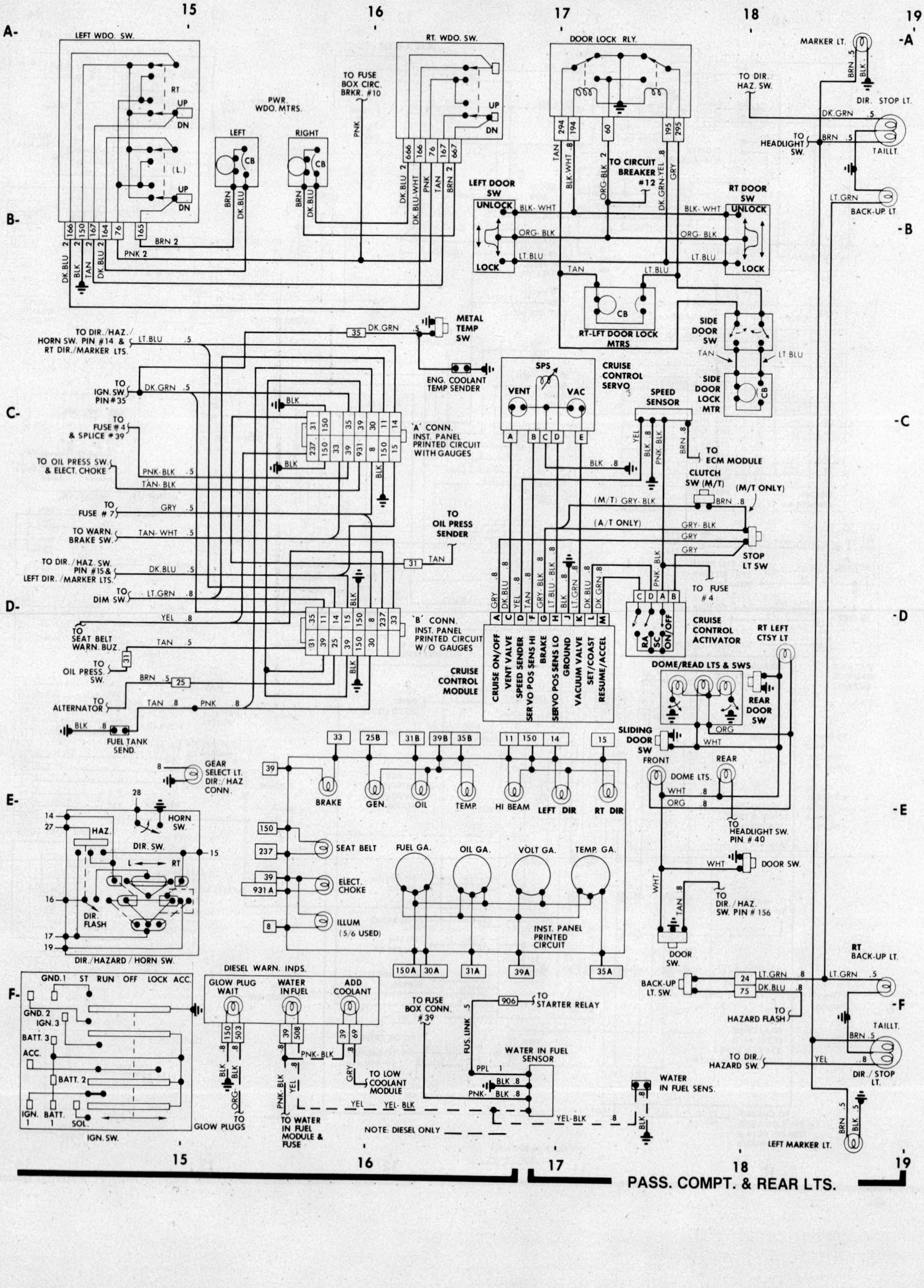

PARCEL DELIVERY VANS

ENGINE COMPARTMENT

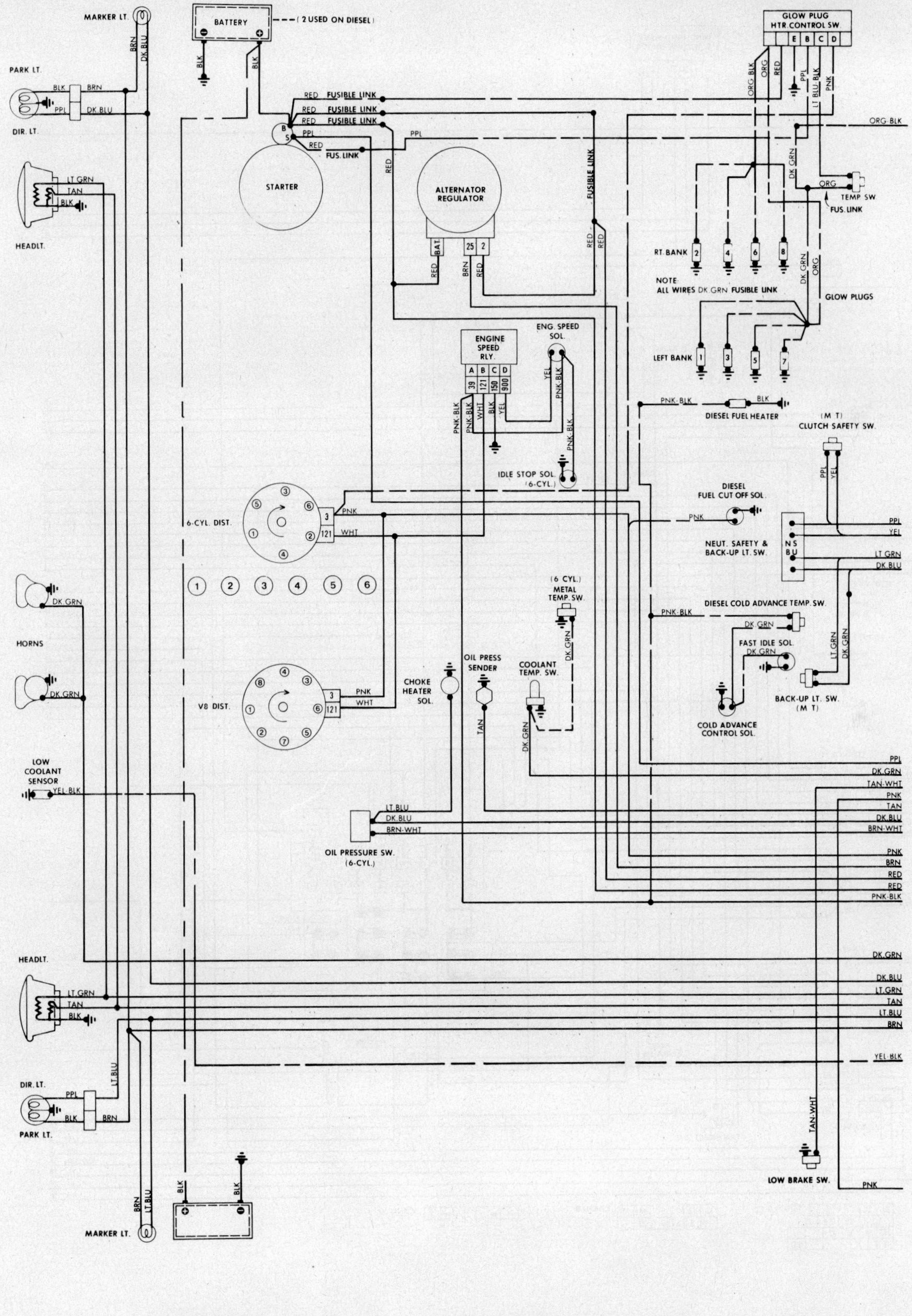

1985 General Motors

PARCEL DELIVERY VANS (Cont.)

FUSE BLOCK & UNDERDASH

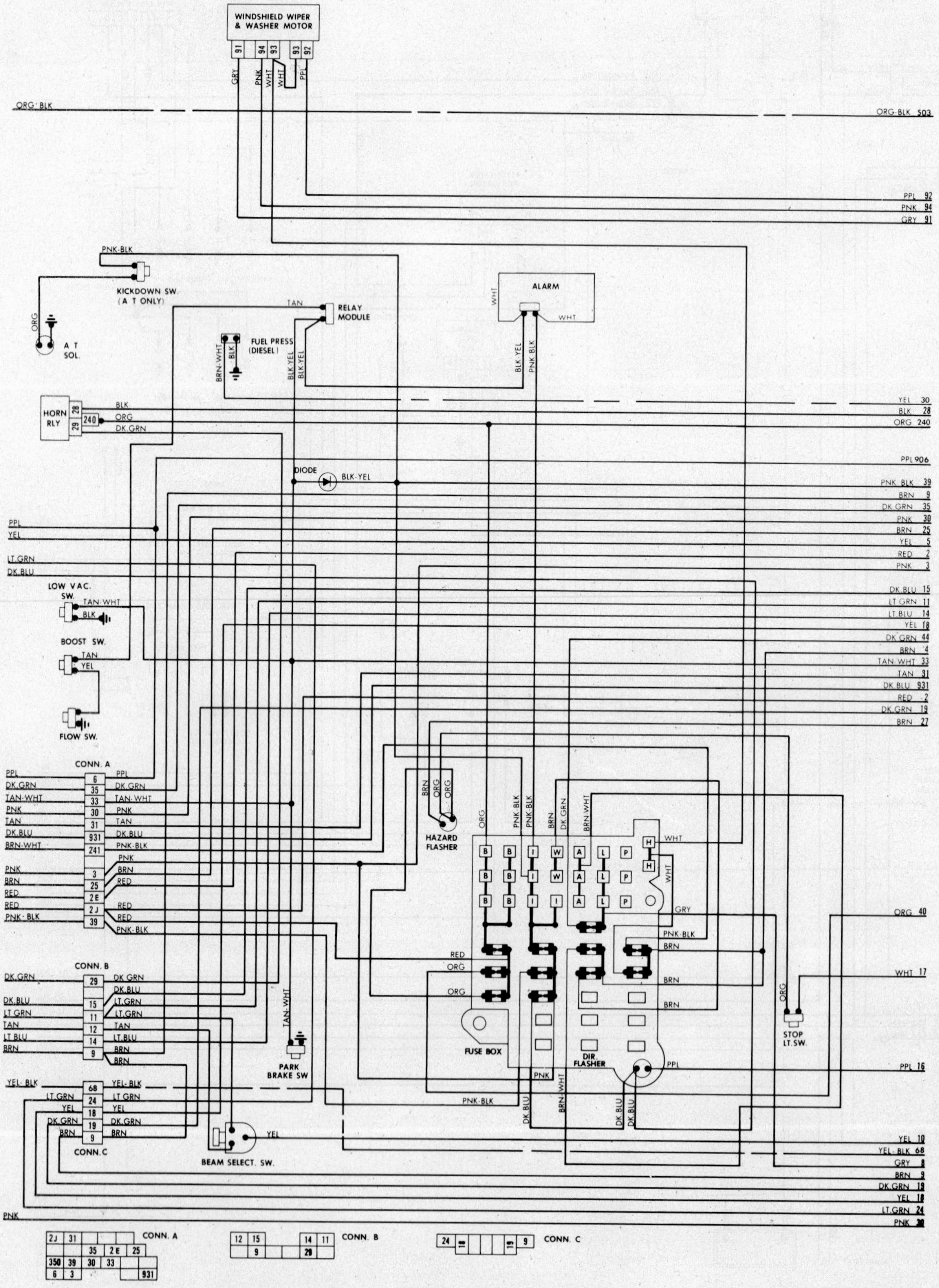

1985 General Motors

PARCEL DELIVERY VANS (Cont.)

INSTRUMENT PANEL & UNDERDASH

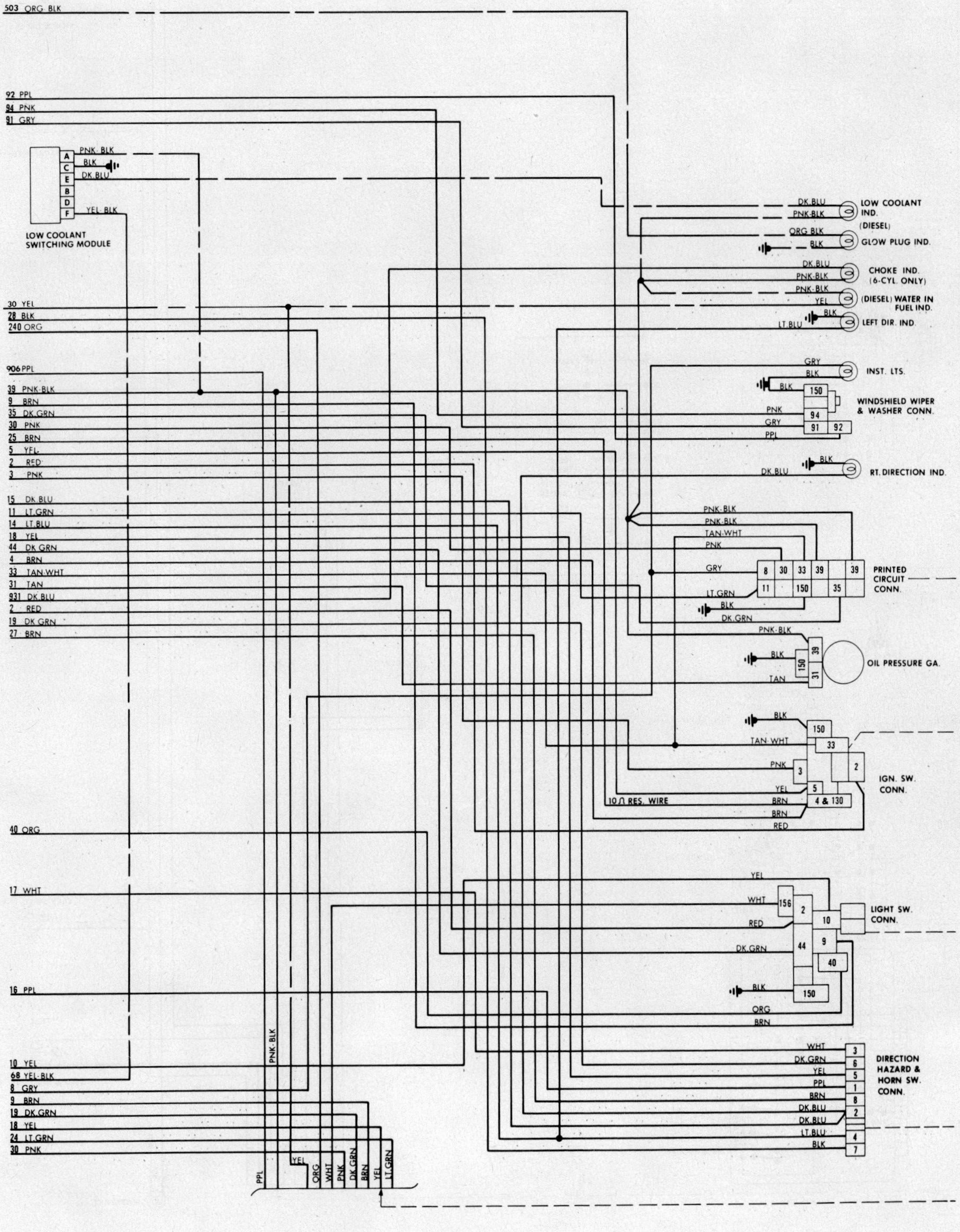

PARCEL DELIVERY VANS (Cont.)

UNDERDASH & REAR COMPARTMENT

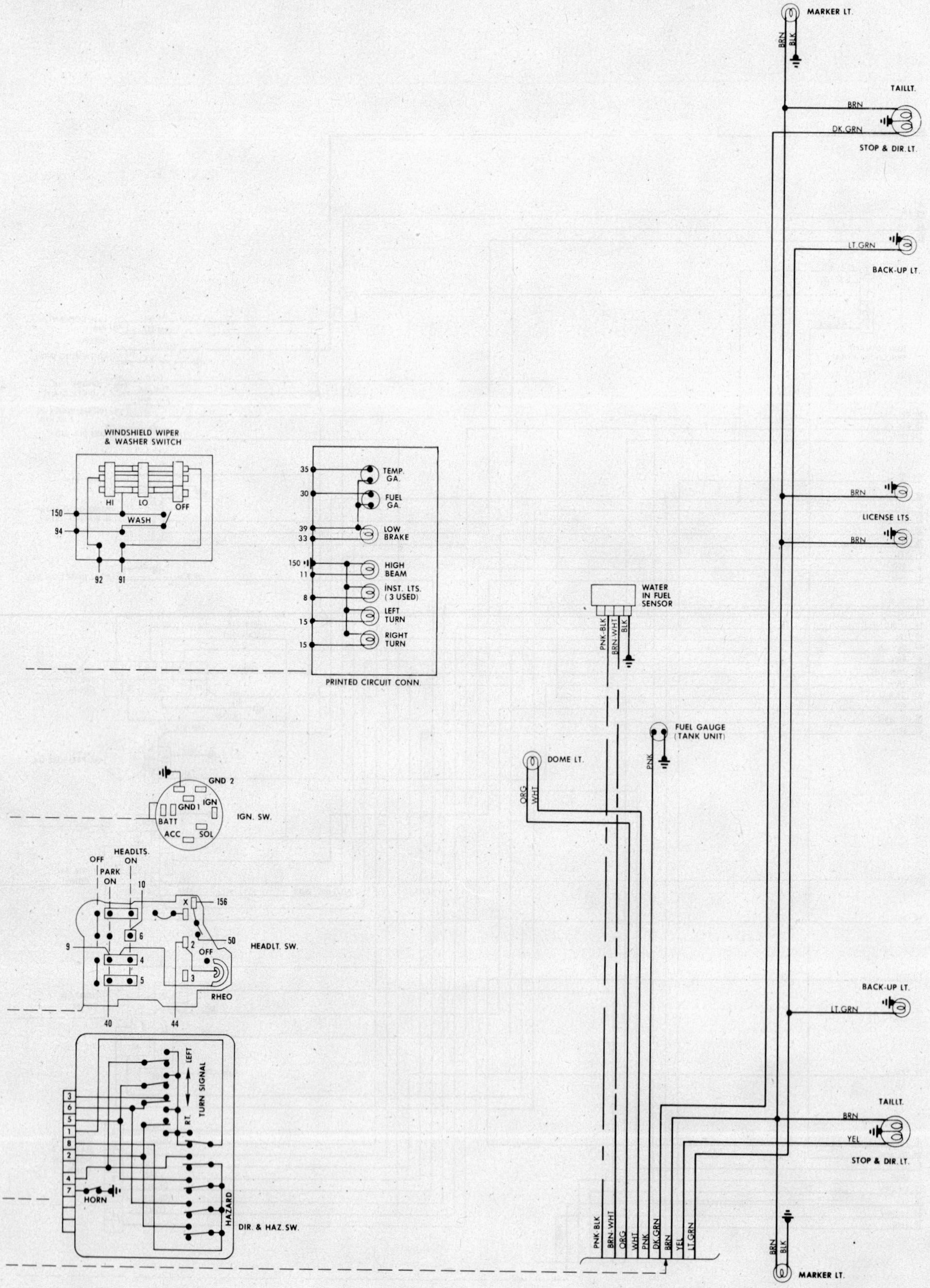

CJ7 & SCRAMBLER

ENGINE COMPARTMENT

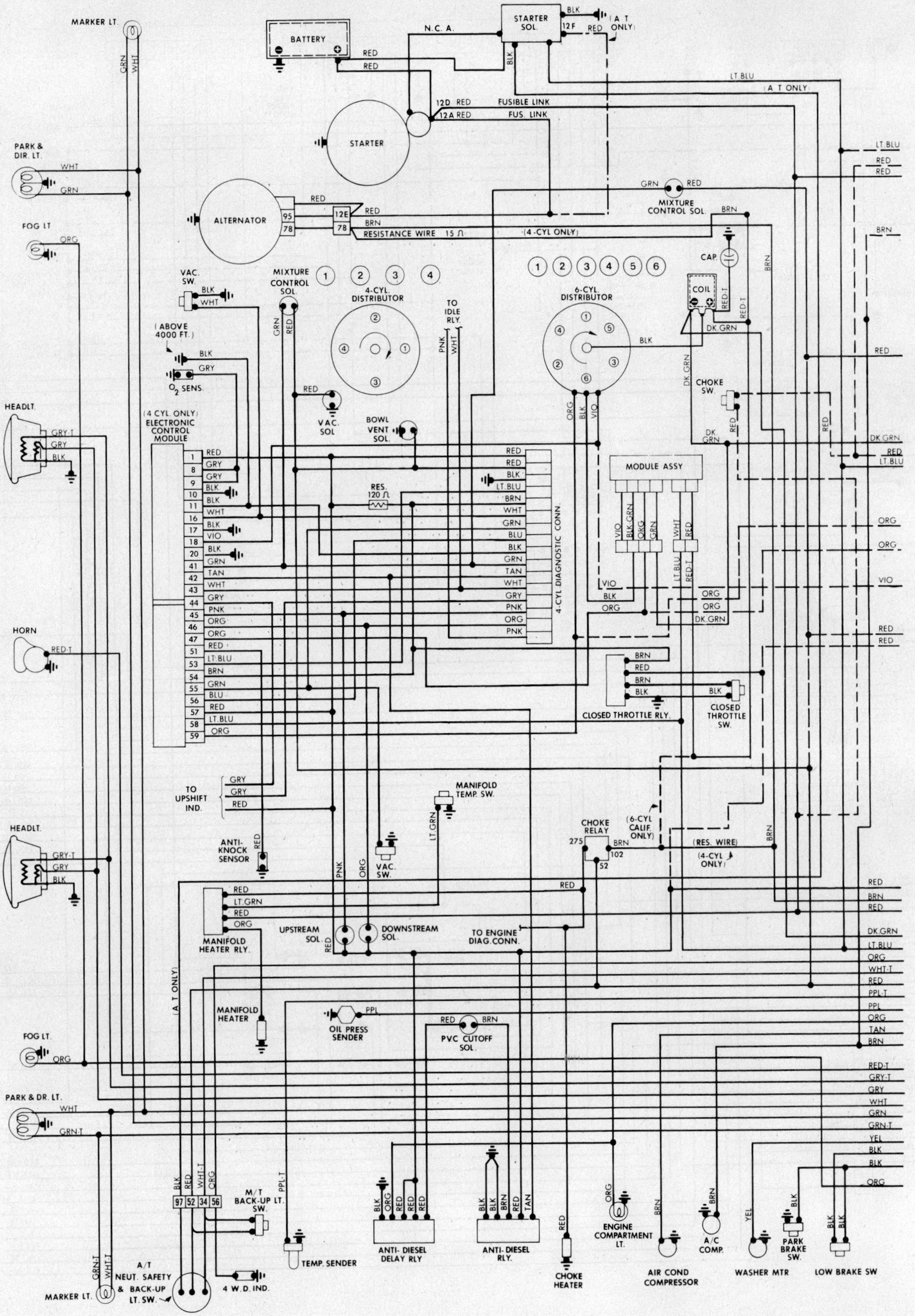

1985 Jeep

CJ7 & SCRAMBLER (Cont.)

ENGINE COMPARTMENT & FUSE BLOCK

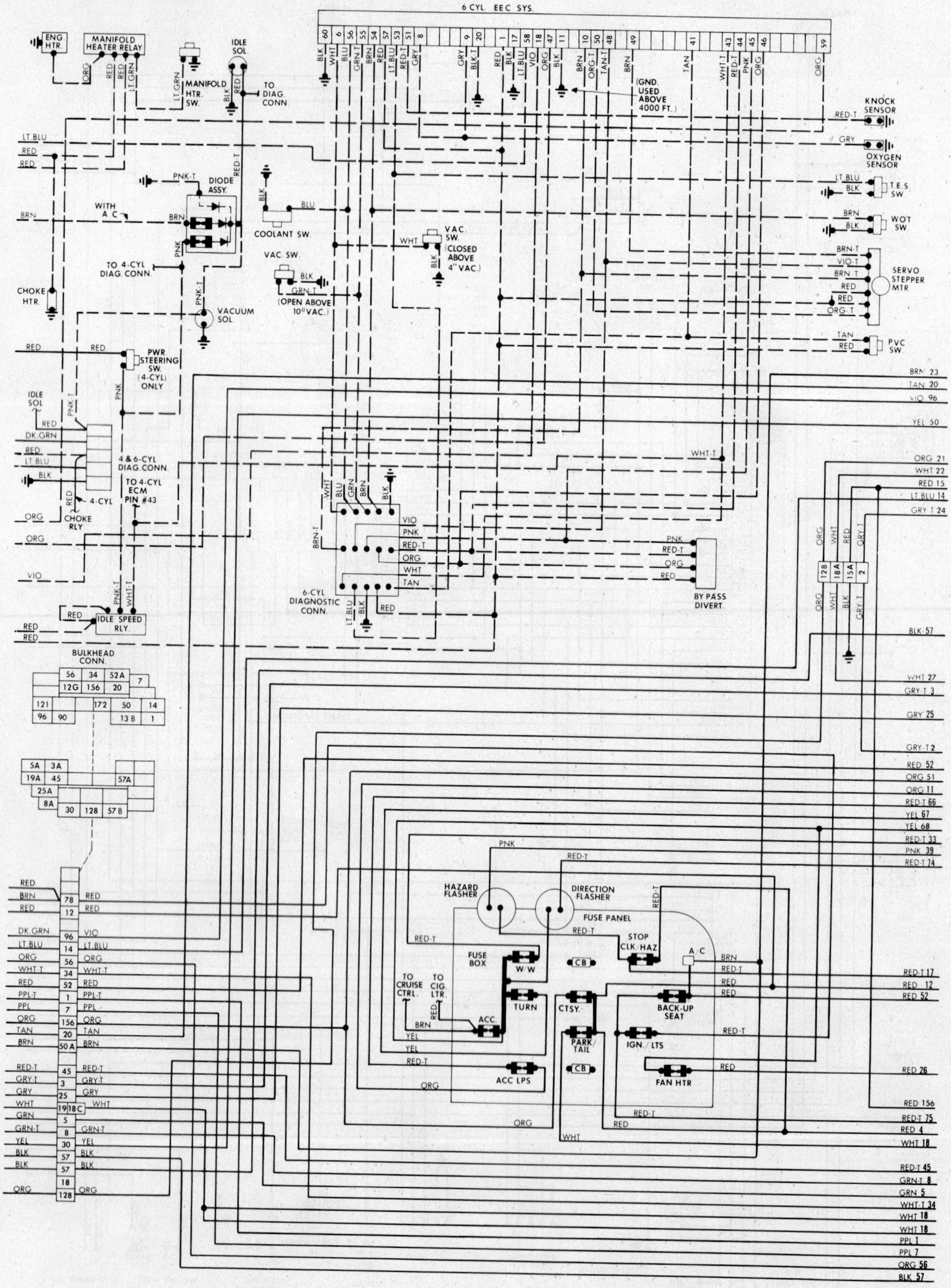

CJ7 & SCRAMBLER (Cont.)

INSTRUMENT PANEL & UNDERDASH

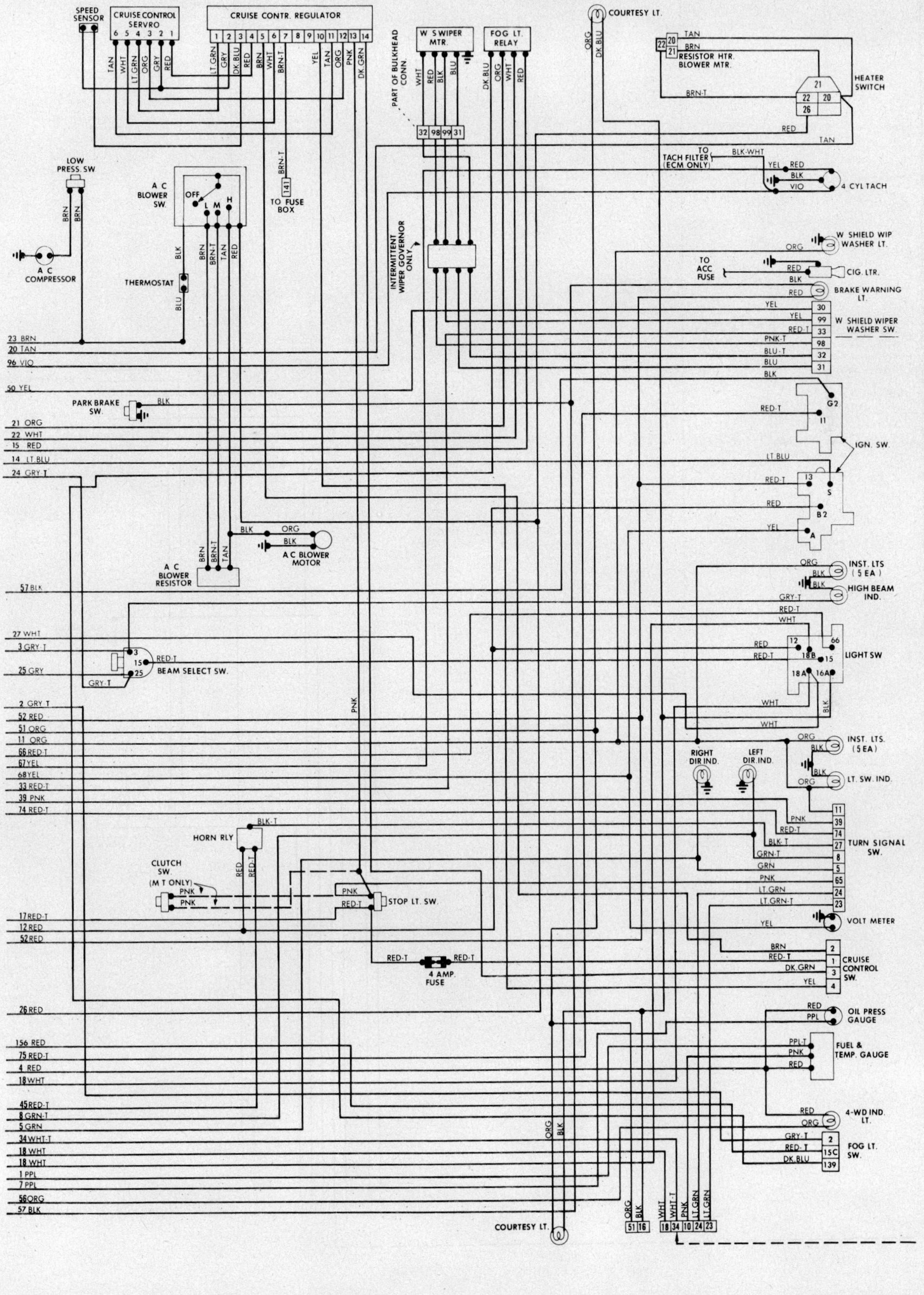

1985 Jeep

CJ7 & SCRAMBLER (Cont.)

REAR COMPARTMENT

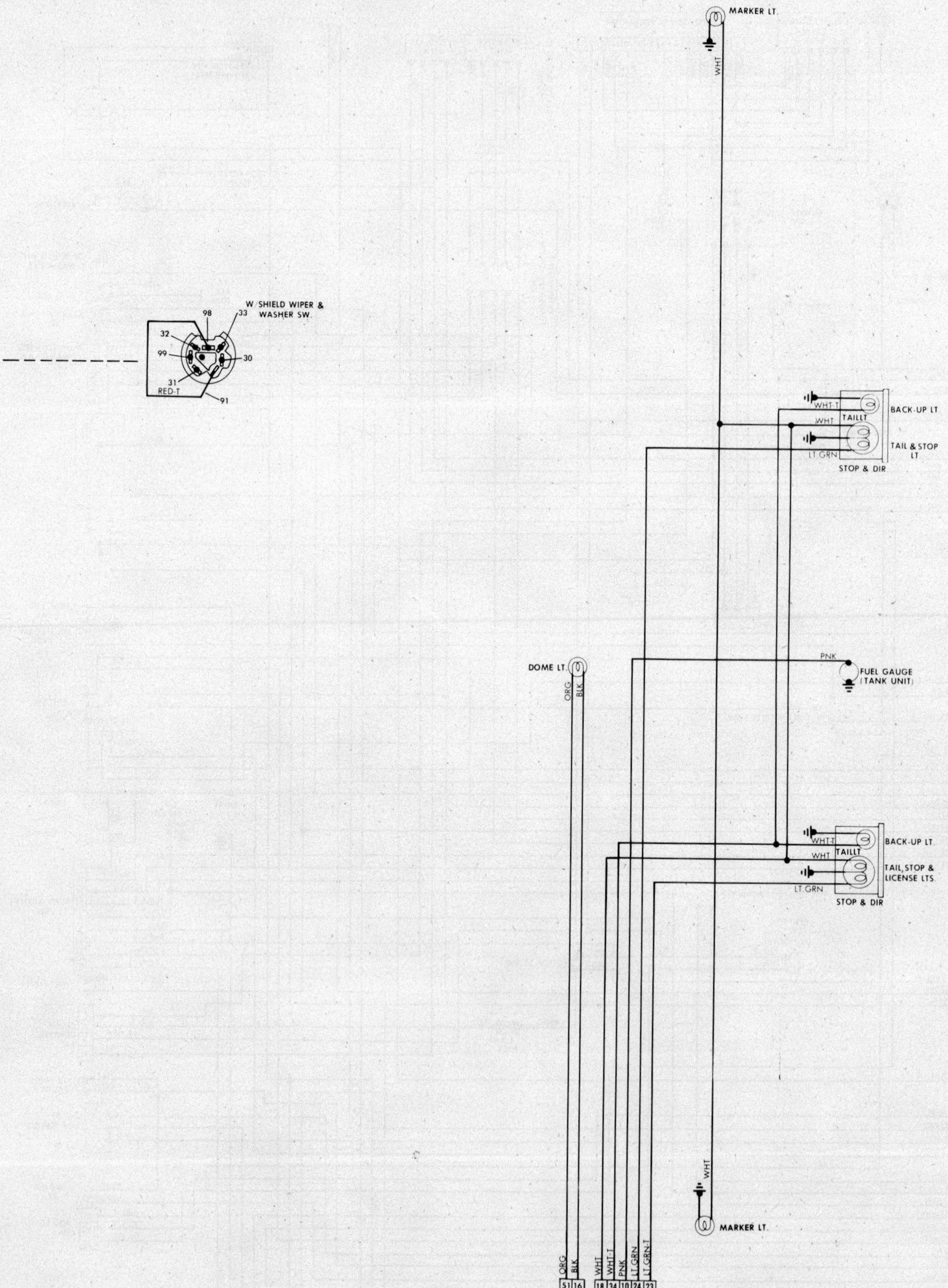

1985 Jeep

CHEROKEE & WAGONEER

COMPONENT LOCATIONS:

- B-17 A/C Select Sw.
- A-12 A/C Hi Speed Blower Rly. & Motor
- A-13 A/C Thermo Sw., Clutch Sol. & Thermo Stat. Sw.
- E-8 Alternator (Diesel)
- D-5 Alternator (Gas)
- G-7 Anti-Diesel Rly. & Timer
- A-14 Audio Alarm Module
- B-13 Auto Level Height Sens.
- F-14 Backup Lt. Sw. M/T Only
- E-23 Beam Select & Headlt. Sw.
- E-10 Bulkhead Conn. (B/H)
- D-5 Choke Htr. Rly. Sys.
- C-21 Clogged Oil Filter Sw.
- E-11 Clutch Sw.
- C-21 Coolant Temp. Sw.
- D-13 Cruise Control Sys.
- D-27 Dome Lt.
- F-23 Directional & Hazard Sw.
- A-26 Door Sw.'s (Right)
- G-26 Door Sw.'s (Left)
- E-6 Dura Spark Distributor (4 Cyl. Eng.)
- D-8 E Cell 2000 Hr Timer
- C-4 EEC Diag. Conn.
- D-6 EFE Rly. & Htr.
- F-5 Elect. Ignition Control Unit
- B-4 Eng. Diag. Conn.
- B-2 Fog Lt. Rly. & Fog Lts.
- F-20 Fog Lt. Sw.
- D-28 Fuel Ga. (Tank Unit)
- F-16 Fuse Box, Dir. & Hazard Flasher
- A-9 Fuse & Diode Module
- F-22 Gear Sel. Ind.
- F-8 Glow Plug System
- G-17 Headlt. Delay Module
- C-20 Heated Rear Wdo. Rly. & Sw.
- C-18 Heater Blower Motor Sw. & Resistor
- B-18 Heater Mode Sw.
- D-27 Heated Rear Wdo. Grid
- F-5 HEI Distributor & Coil
- G-10 Horn Rly. & Horns
- F-22 Horn Sw.
- B-8 Idle Sol.
- D-23 Ignition Sw.
- C-24 Inst. Pnl. Printed Ciruit Details
- C-23 Inst. Pnl. Printed Circuit Conn. A
- C-23 Inst. Pnl. Printed Circuit Conn. B
- F-26 Keyless Entry
- B-14 Key in Sw.
- D-28 License Lts.
- D-7 Low Brake Sw.
- C-2 Low Windshield Wash. Fluid Sens.
- B-5 Microprocessor Contr. Unit & Compts. (4 Cyl. Eng. Only)
- B-3 Neutral Safety & Backup Lt. Sw.
- D-20 Oil Press. Sender
- D-23 Park Brake Sw.
- C-15 Power Antenna Motor & Rly.
- F-12 Power Mirror Sys.
- A-7 Power Steering Sw.
- A-26 Power Seats
- E-25 Power Wdo. & Door Lock Sys.
- C-28 Rear Wdo. Washer Motor
- D-19 Rear Wdo. Wiper Washer Sw.
- C-27 Rear Wdo. Wiper Motor & Rly.
- A-4 Starter Sol. (V-6 Eng.)
- A-4 Starter Rly. (V-6 Eng.)
- E-11 Stop Lt. Sw.
- B-17 Sys. Sentry Display Module & Sys.
- A-8 Thermo Elect. Sw.
- D-6 Windshield Washer Motor
- C-8 Windshield Wiper Motor
- A-20 Windshield Wiper Sw. (Intermittent)
- A-22 Windshield Wiper Sw.

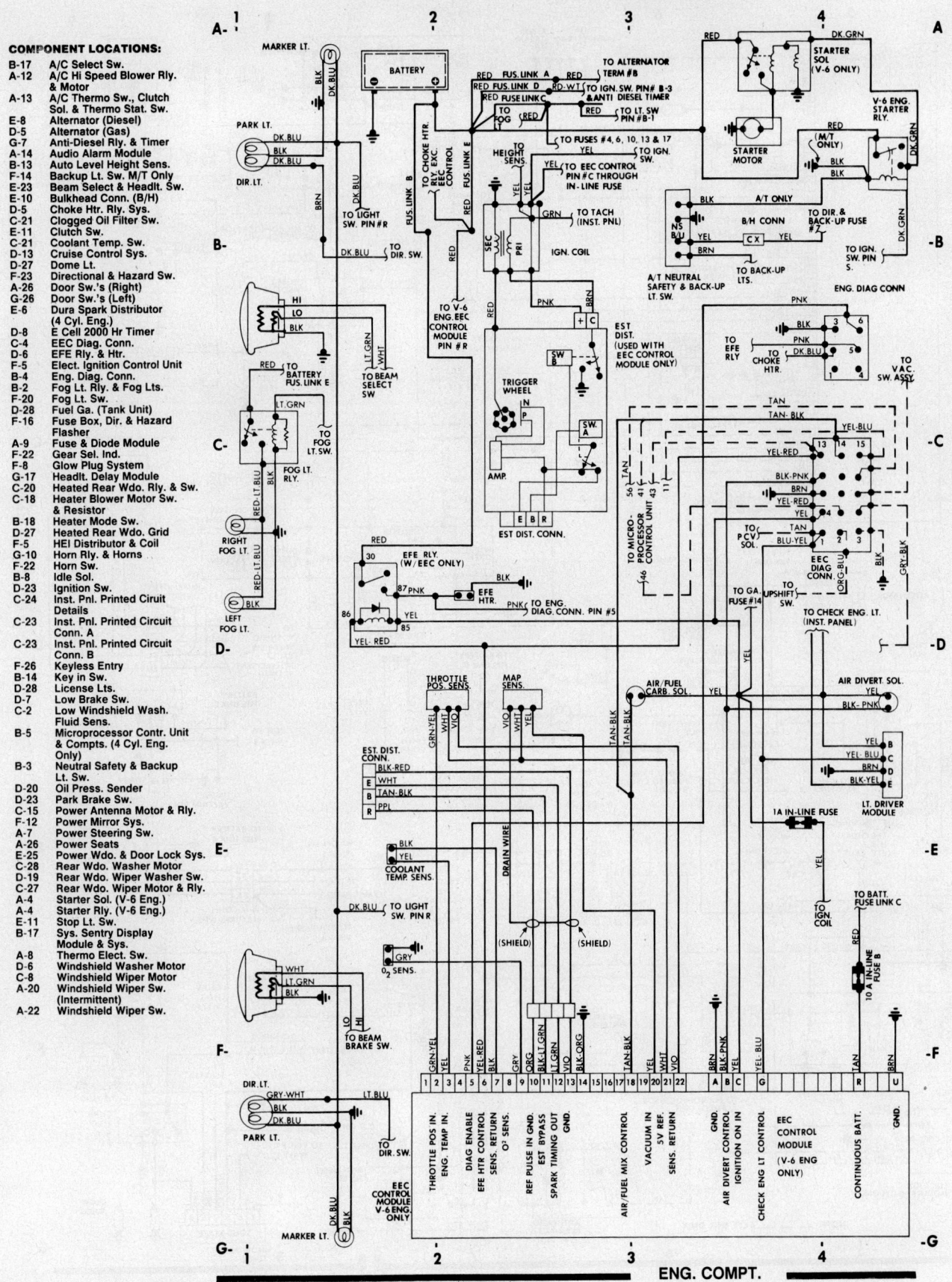

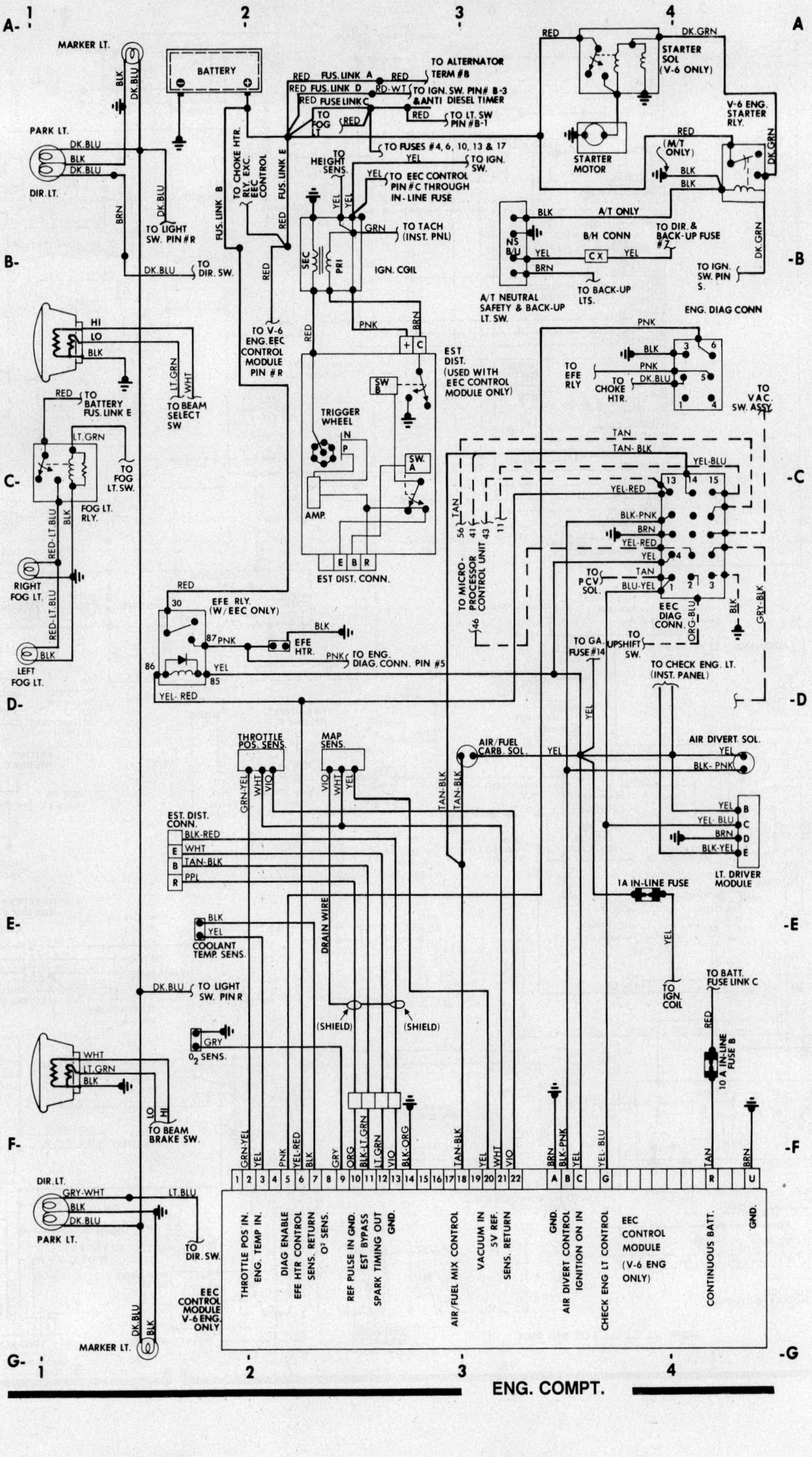

ENG. COMPT.

1985 Jeep

CHEROKEE & WAGONEER (Cont.)

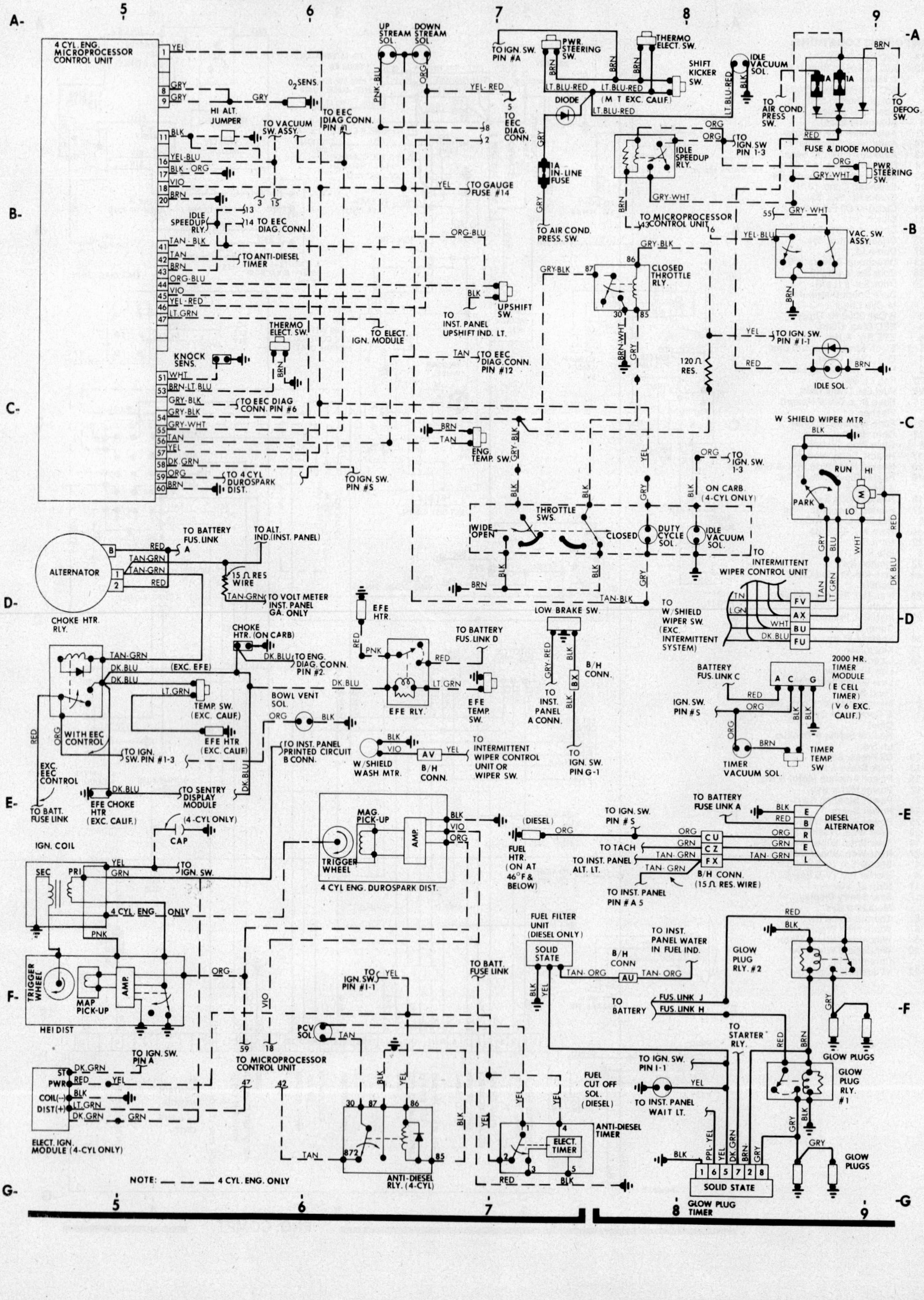

CHEROKEE & WAGONEER (Cont.)

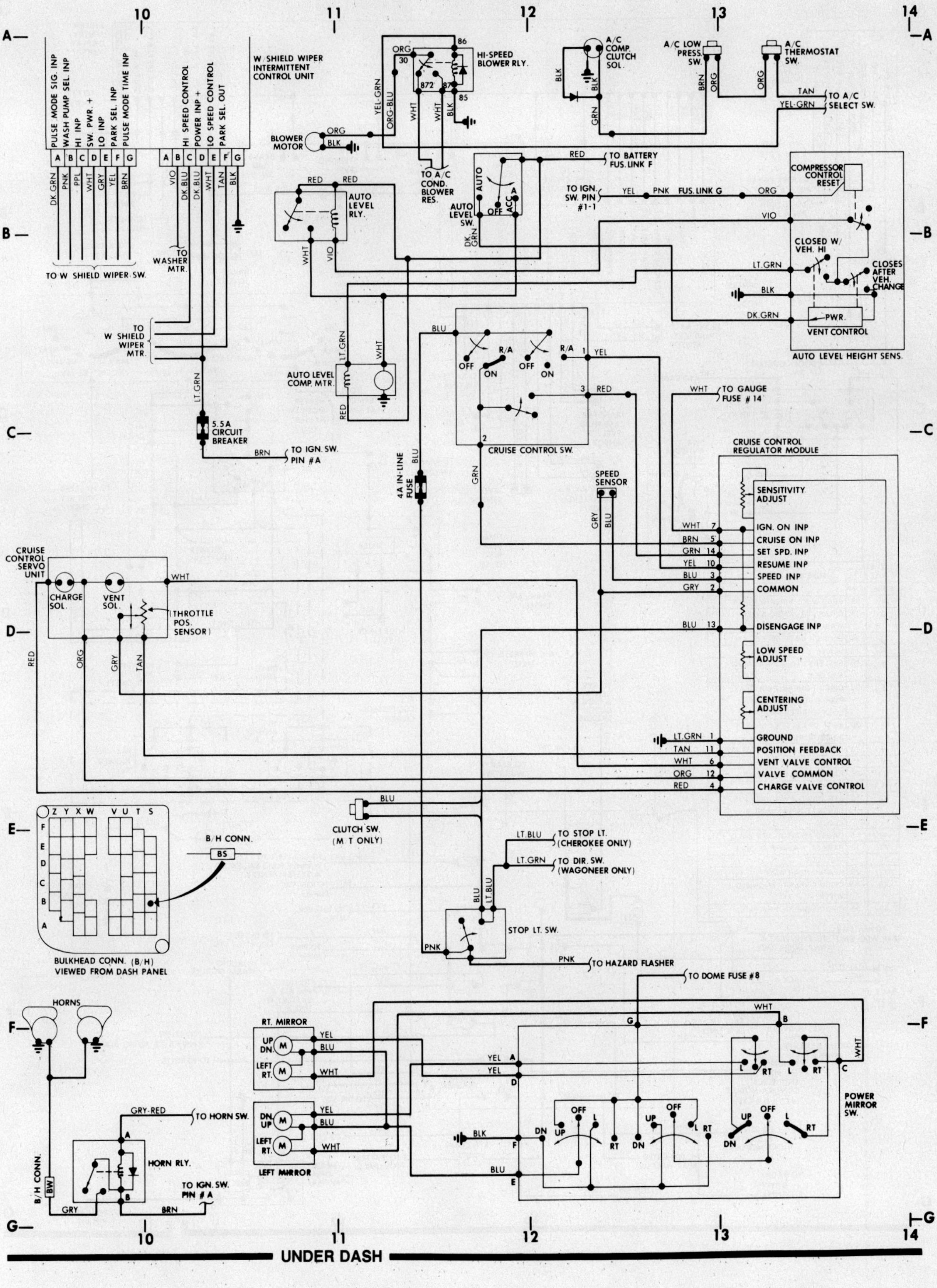

1985 Jeep

CHEROKEE & WAGONEER (Cont.)

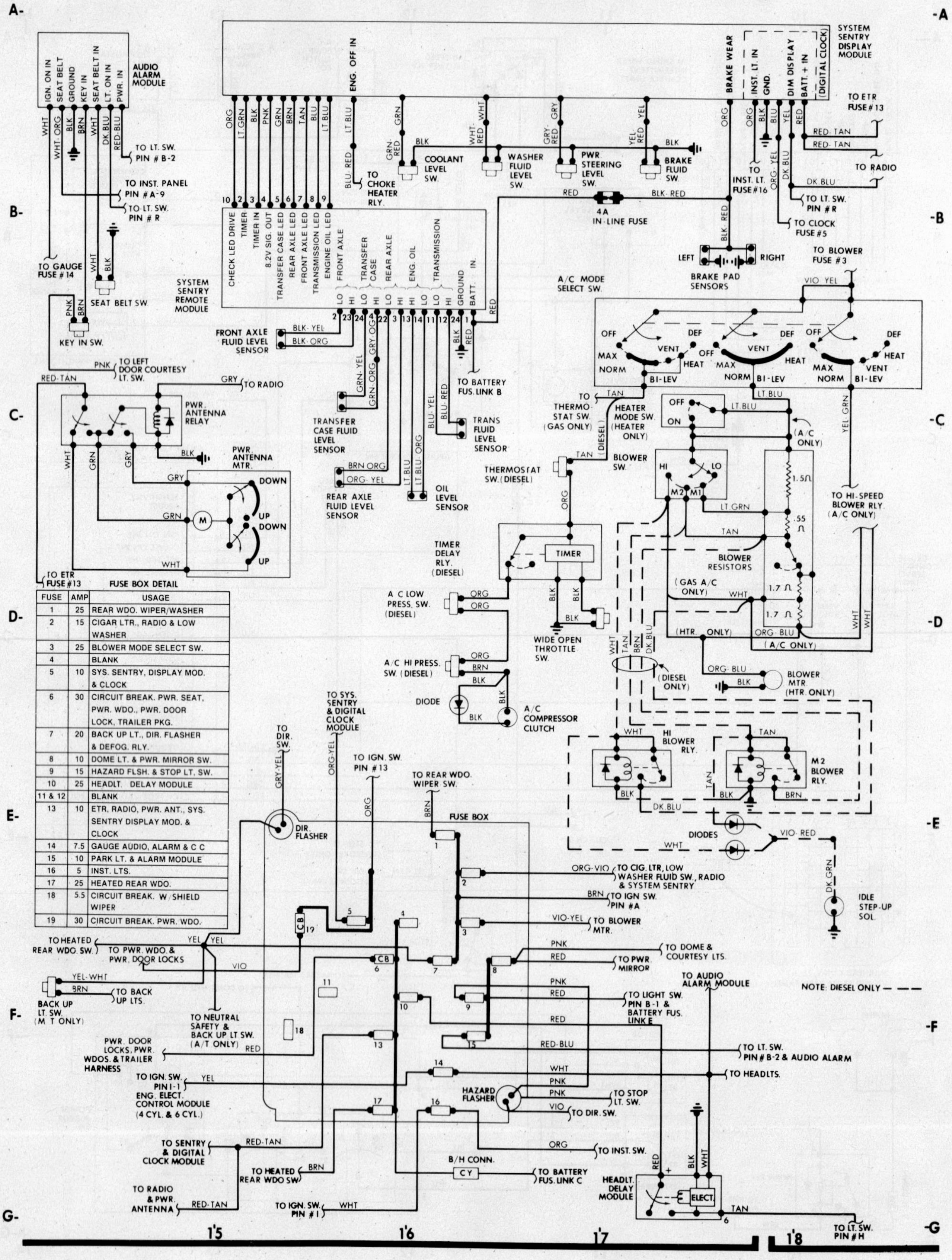

FUSE BOX DETAIL

FUSE	AMP	USAGE
1	25	REAR WDO. WIPER/WASHER
2	15	CIGAR LTR., RADIO & LOW WASHER
3	25	BLOWER MODE SELECT SW.
4		BLANK
5	10	SYS. SENTRY, DISPLAY MOD. & CLOCK
6	30	CIRCUIT BREAK. PWR. SEAT, PWR. WDO., PWR. DOOR LOCK, TRAILER PKG.
7	20	BACK UP LT., DIR. FLASHER & DEFOG. RLY.
8	10	DOME LT. & PWR. MIRROR SW.
9	15	HAZARD FLSH. & STOP LT. SW.
10	25	HEADLT. DELAY MODULE
11 & 12		BLANK
13	10	ETR, RADIO, PWR. ANT., SYS. SENTRY DISPLAY MOD. & CLOCK
14	7.5	GAUGE AUDIO, ALARM & C C
15	10	PARK LT. & ALARM MODULE
16	5	INST. LTS.
17	25	HEATED REAR WDO.
18	5.5	CIRCUIT BREAK. W/SHIELD WIPER
19	30	CIRCUIT BREAK. PWR. WDO.

CHEROKEE & WAGONEER (Cont.)

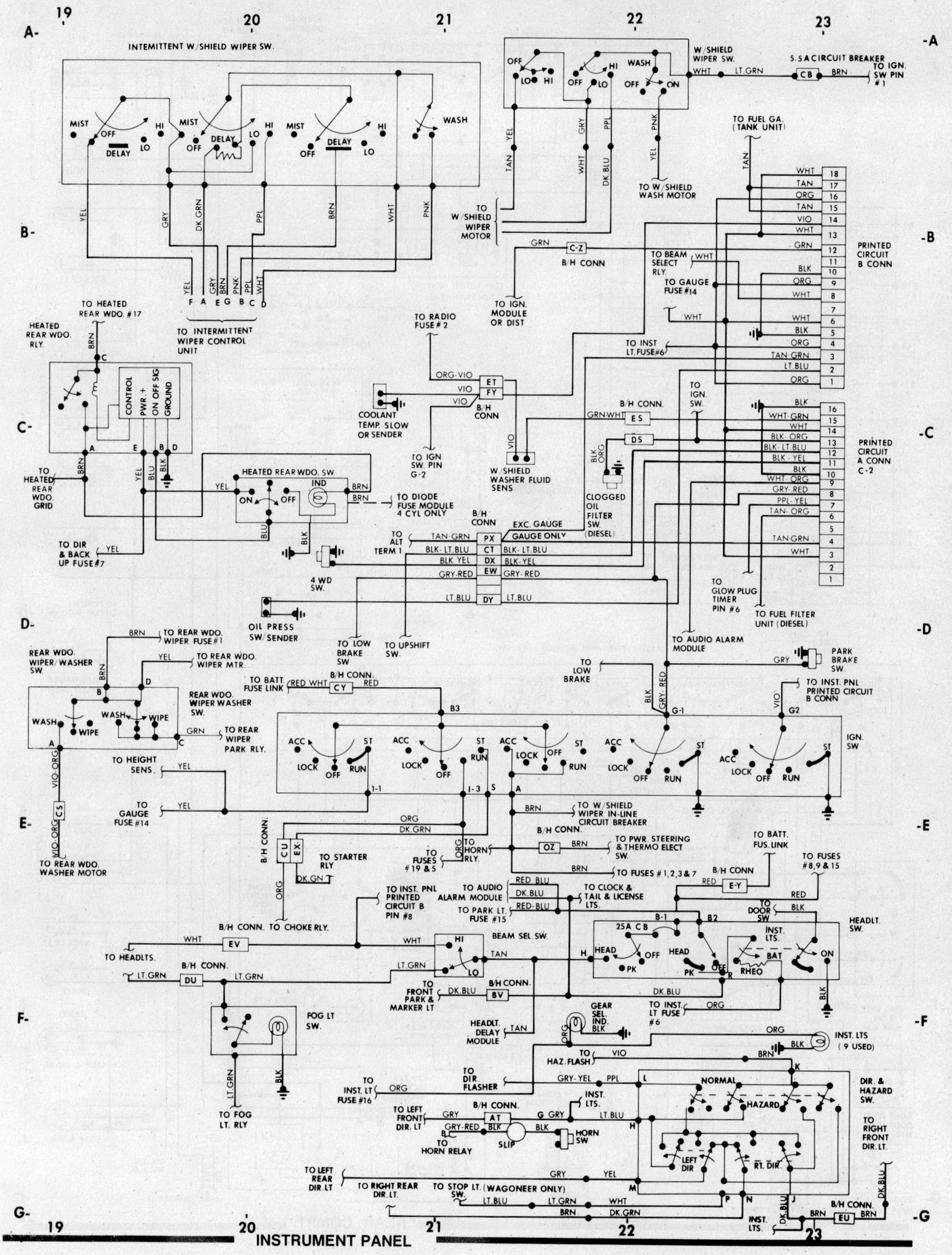

INSTRUMENT PANEL

1985 Jeep

CHEROKEE & WAGONEER (Cont.)

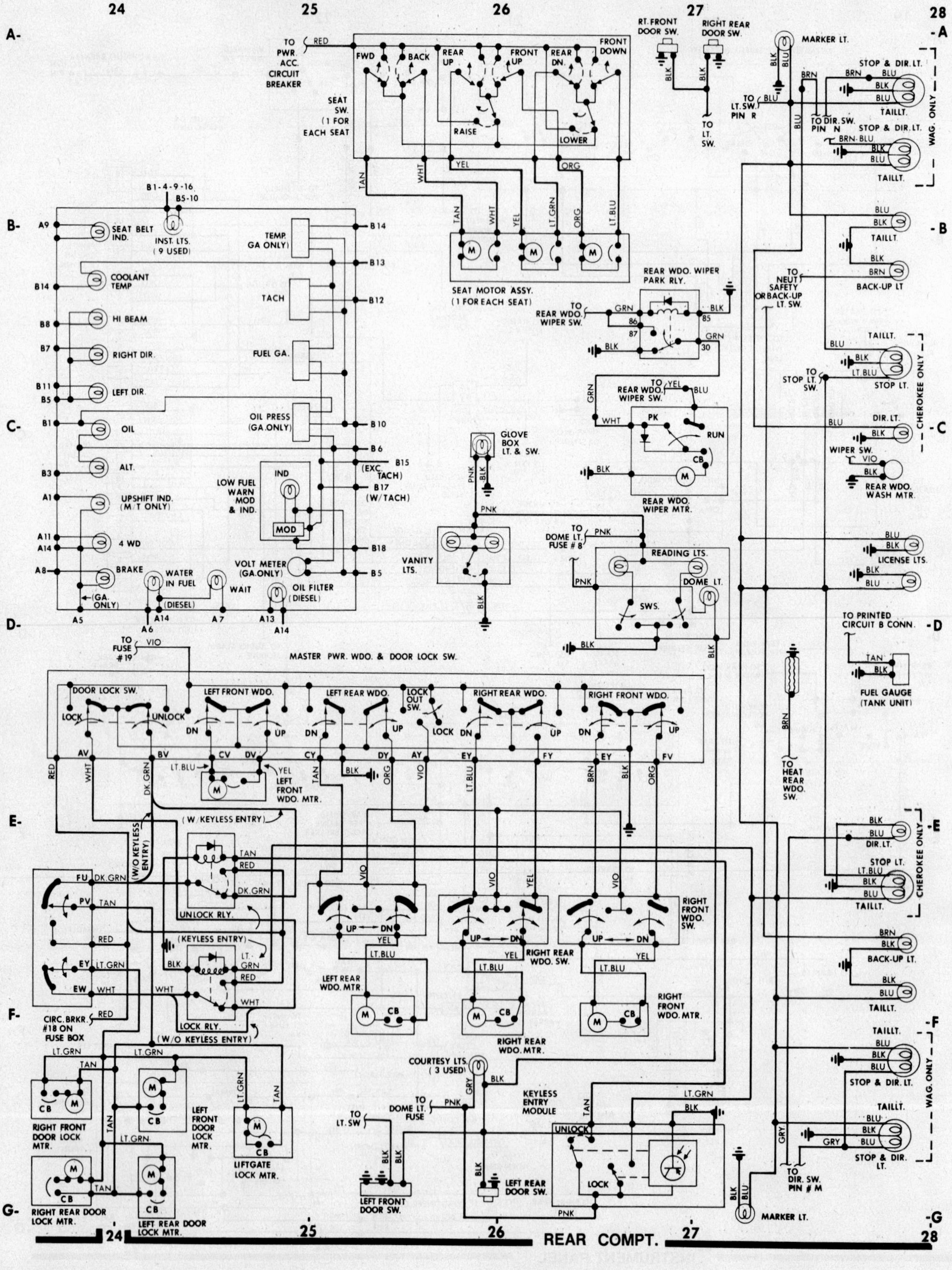

1985 Jeep

"J" TRUCKS & GRAND WAGONEER

ENGINE COMPARTMENT

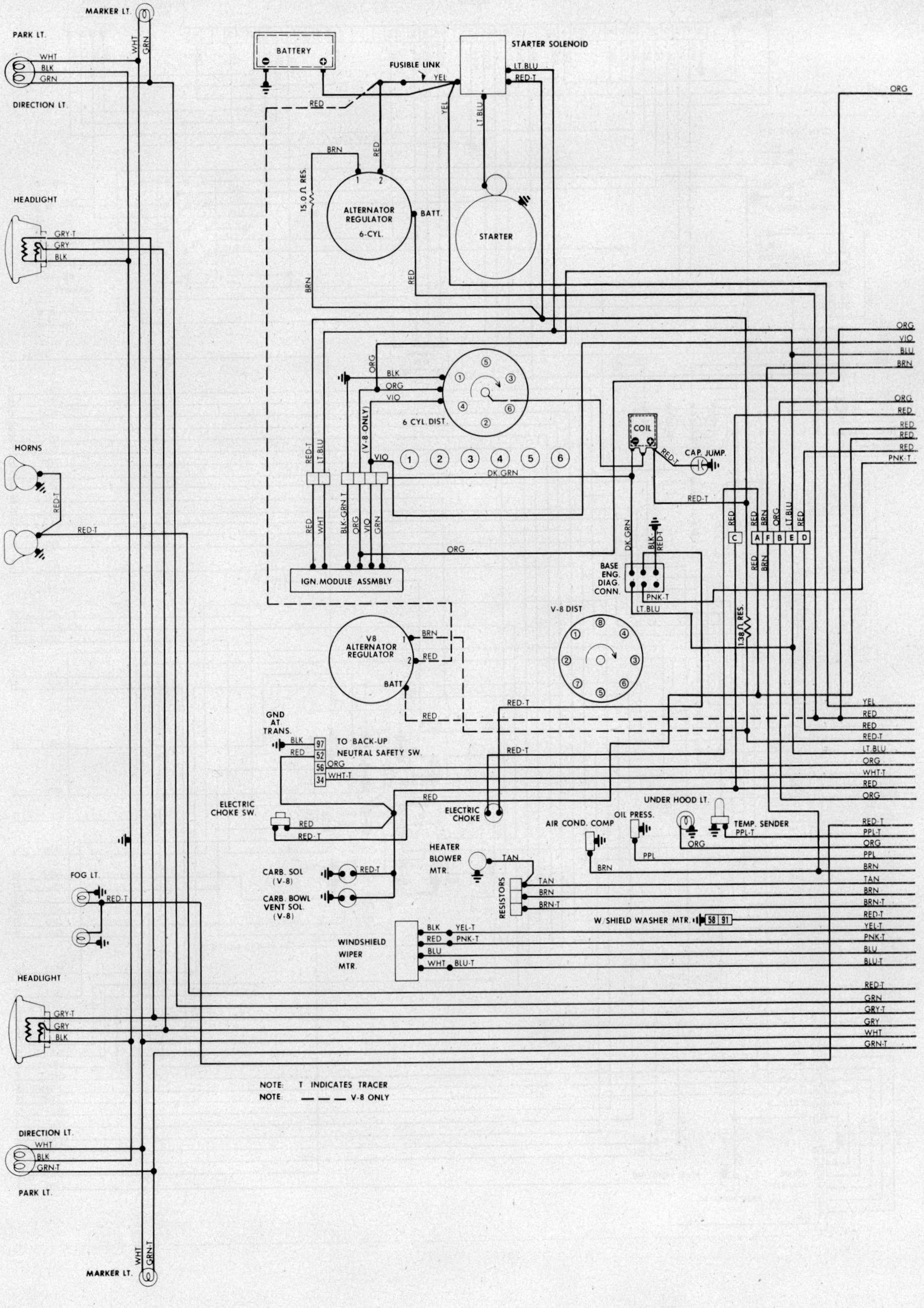

NOTE: T INDICATES TRACER

NOTE: — — — V-8 ONLY

1985 Jeep

"J" TRUCKS & GRAND WAGONEER (Cont.)

FUSE BLOCK & UNDERDASH

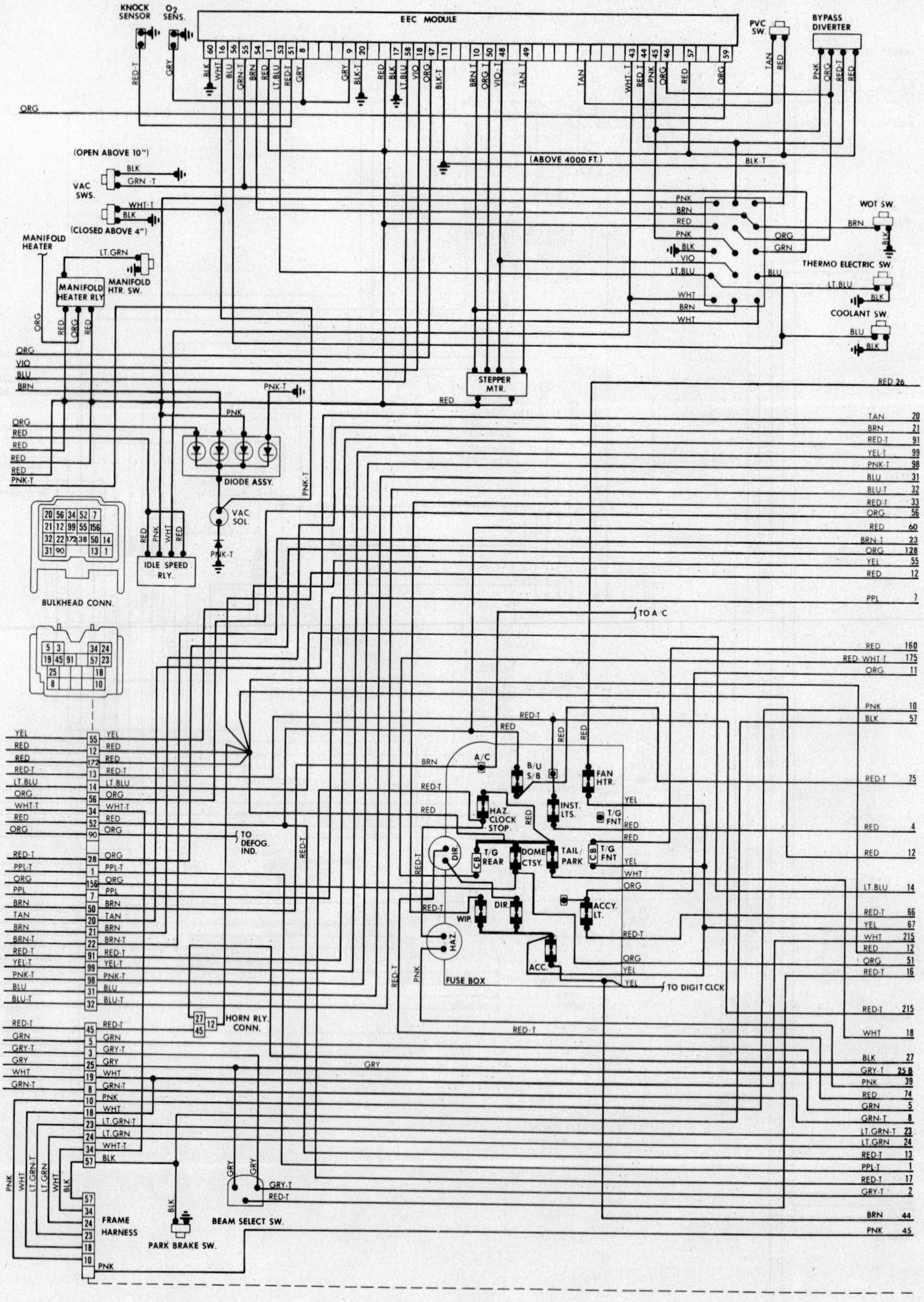

"J" TRUCKS & GRAND WAGONEER (Cont.)

INSTRUMENT PANEL & UNDERDASH

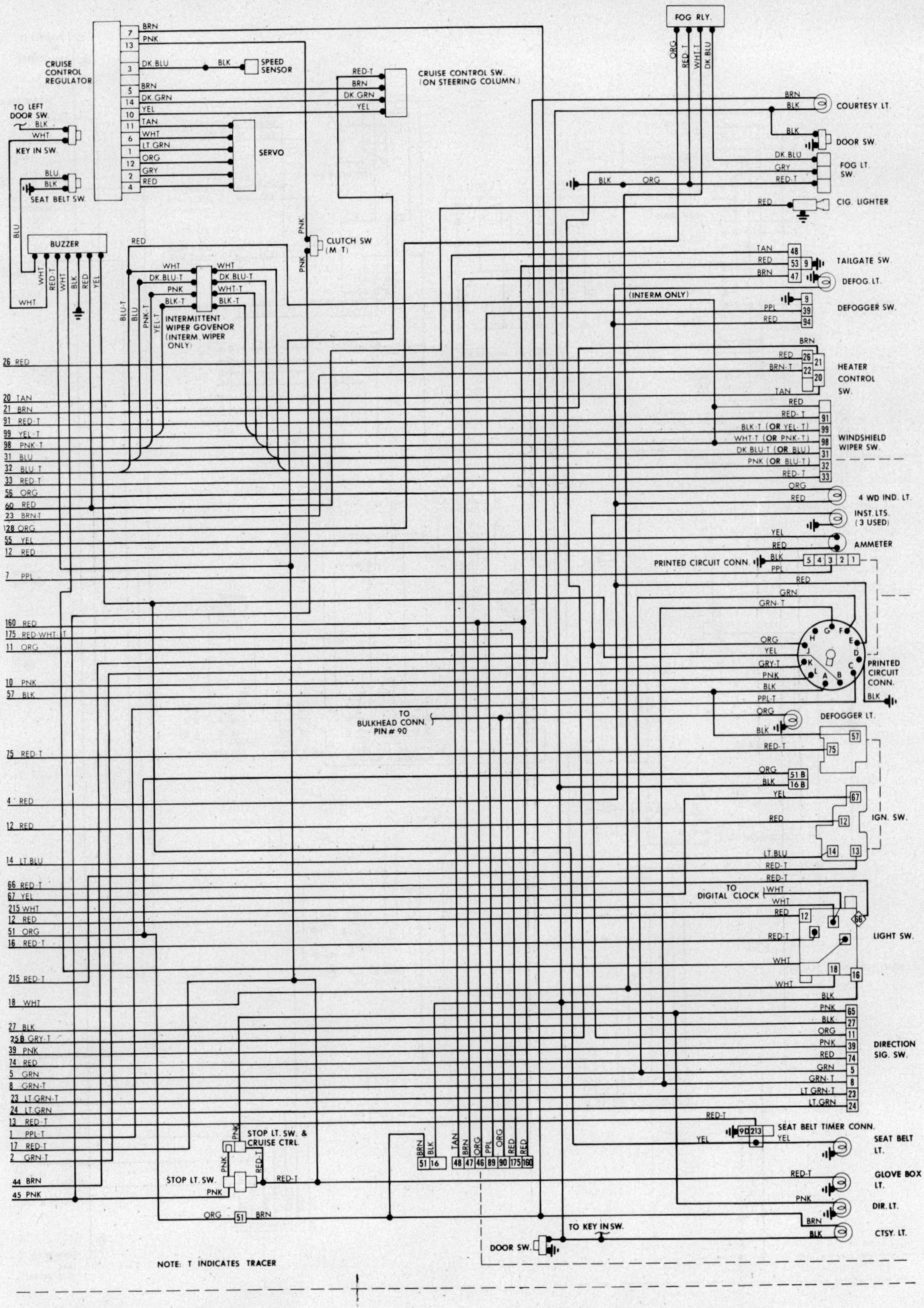

NOTE: T INDICATES TRACER

1985 Jeep

"J" TRUCKS & GRAND WAGONEER (Cont.)

REAR COMPARTMENT & ACCESSORIES

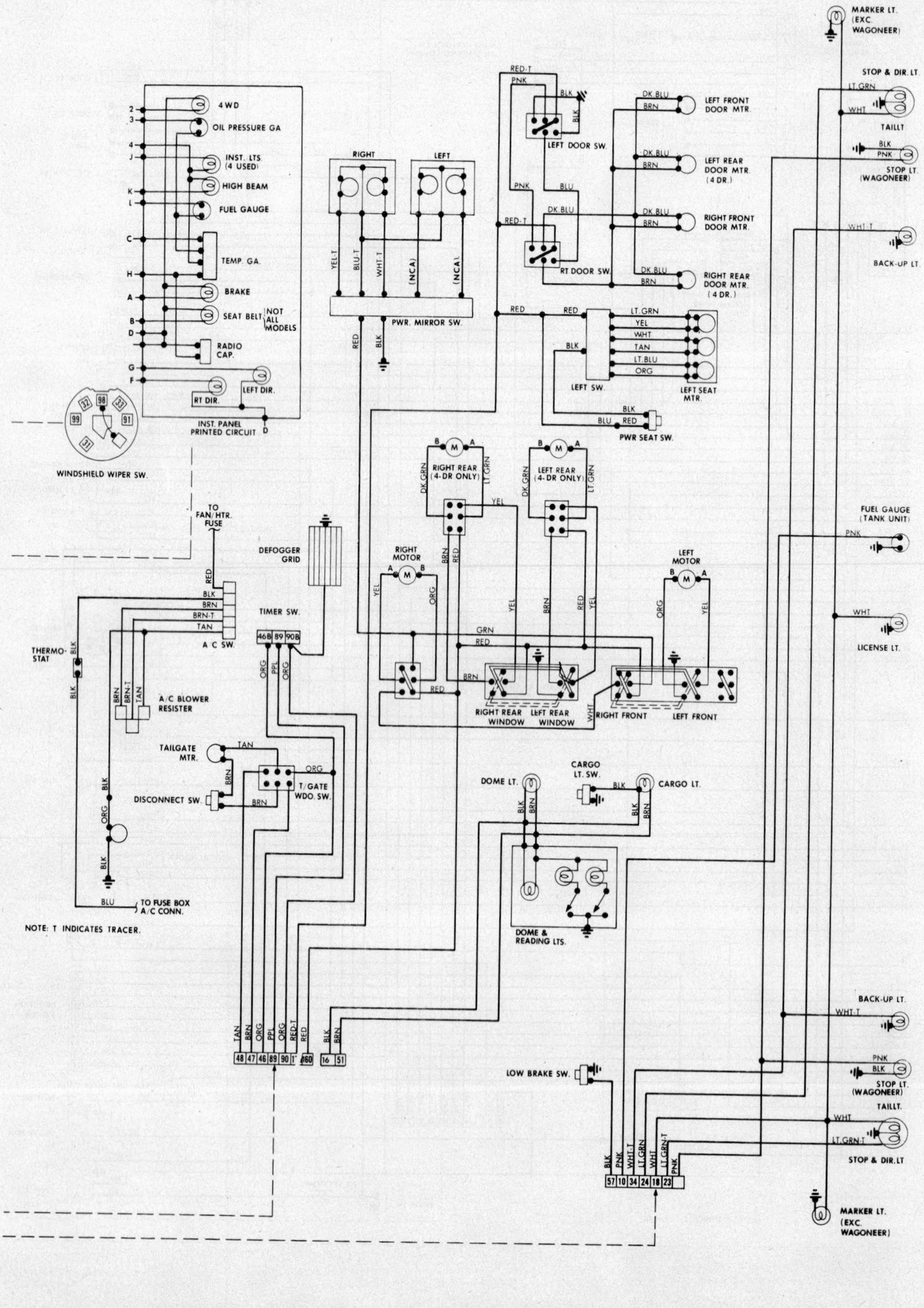

NOTE: T INDICATES TRACER.

SECTION 6

ACCESSORIES & EQUIPMENT

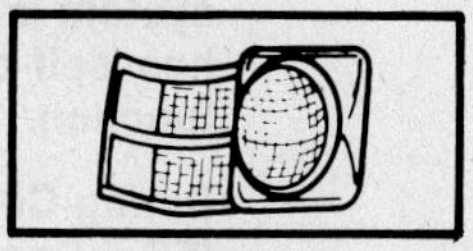

CONTENTS

NOTE: ALSO SEE GENERAL INDEX.

IMPORTANT: Because of the many model names used by vehicle manufacturers, accurate identification of models is important. See Model Identification at the front of this publication.

COMPRESSOR OIL CHECK

GENERAL NOTES

REFRIGERATION OIL

Refrigeration oil is highly refined, with a moisture content of less than 10 parts per million. Only new, moisture-free refrigeration oil should be used in any A/C system. To avoid water absorbtion, oil container must be tightly sealed when not in use. Excessive amounts of refrigerant oil in any A/C system may cause damage to system or reduction in cooling system capacity.

CHRYSLER CORP.

Chrysler replacement compressors contain 9-10 oz. of oil. Prior to installation of replacement compressor, drain approximately 4 oz. of oil from compressor to maintain proper total A/C system oil volume. Total system oil volume must not exceed 10 oz.

FORD

Ford replacement compressors contain 10 oz. of refrigerant oil. Prior to installation of replacement compressor, drain approximately 4 oz. of oil from compressor to maintain proper total A/C system oil volume.

GENERAL MOTORS

A/C systems using a 6-cylinder compressor (DA-6) contain 10 oz. of refrigerant oil. A/C systems using a 4-cylinder compressor (R-4) contain 6 oz. Compressors do not have an oil sump of any type. All oil is stored elsewhere in system. If accumulator is replaced in either system, add an additonal 2 oz. of oil to compensate for oil adsorbed by dessicant.

JEEP

A/C system compressor oil level us checked by inserting a special dipstick into the compressor oil sump. Oil is also stored in the evaporator and condenser. If either component is replaced, add an additonal 1 oz. of oil to compensate for oil adsorbed by dessicant.

COMPRESSOR OIL CHECK

CHRYSLER CORP.

NOTE: **It is not necessary to measure the A/C system oil level each time system is discharged, unless refrigerant charge has been depleted or significant oil loss has occured.**

During Compressor Replacement

1) Properly discharge system. Disconnect suction and discharge lines. Cap all openings to prevent moisture intrusion. Remove compressor from vehicle. Drain oil from suction and discharge ports. Discard used oil.

2) Add 5 oz. of oil through suction port. Install compressor onto vehicle. Using new gaskets, connect suction and discharge lines and tighten. Evacuate and recharge system.

During Component Replacement

After compressor has been installed and operated, oil will be distributed throughout system. Some oil will be trapped by system components. If evaporator, condenser or receiver/drier are replaced, add proper amount of oil. See CHRYSLER CORP. OIL LEVEL SPECIFICATIONS table.

CHRYSLER CORP. OIL LEVEL SPECIFICATIONS

Application	Amount
Evaporator	2 oz.
Condenser	1 oz.
Receiver/Drier	1 oz.

FORD

NOTE: **Oil level should be checked whenever the system is discharged for service, or if system has self-discharged due to component malfunction.**

During Compressor Replacement (FS-6 Compressor)

Remove compressor from vehicle, and pour oil from compressor manifold openings into a clean calibrated container. Compressor should contain approximately 6 oz. of oil.

During Component Replacement

After compressor has been installed and operated, oil will be distributed throughout system. Some oil will be trapped by system components. If evaporator, condenser, or accumulator/drier is replaced, add proper amount of oil. See FORD OIL LEVEL SPECIFICATIONS table.

FORD OIL LEVEL SPECIFICATIONS

Application	Amount
Evaporator	3 oz.
Condenser	1 oz.
Accumulator/Drier [1]	1 oz.

[1] - Amount of oil removed, plus amount indicated.

GENERAL MOTORS

NOTE: **Addition of oil is not required unless an obvious oil loss has occurred or a component is replaced. Check oil for evidence of contamination and determine if entire system requires servicing.**

No Evidence of Excessive Oil Leakage (DA-6 Compressor)

1) Properly discharge system. Remove compressor. Drain, measure and record amount of oil. Discard used oil.

2) Replace amount of oil drained, plus 1 ounce. If total amount is 8 oz. or more, an oil overcharge should be suspected.

Evidence of Excessive Oil Leakage (DA-6 Compressor)

1) Properly discharge system. Remove compressor and accumulator. Drain, measure and record total amount of oil from both components. Discard used oil.

2) If amount is less than 6 oz., add 6 oz. of new oil to system. If more than 6 oz., add same amount of oil as drained. If accumulator is being replaced, add an additonal 2 oz. of oil to compensate for oil adsorbed by dessicant.

Air Conditioning Servicing

COMPRESSOR OIL CHECK (Cont.)

No Evidence of Excessive Oil Leakage (R-4 Compressor)

Properly discharge system. Remove compressor. Drain, measure and record amount of oil drained. Discard used oil. Replace amount of oil drained, plus 1 ounce.

Evidence of Excessive Oil Leakage (R-4 Compressor)

1) Properly discharge system. Remove accumulator. Drain, measure and record amount of oil. If amount of oil removed is less than 3 oz., add 3 oz. of new oil to system. If more than 3 oz., add same amount of oil as drained.

2) If accumulator is being replaced, add an additonal 2 oz. of oil to compensate for that adsorbed by dessicant. It is not necessary to check compressor oil level, as a small amount of oil is retained by compressor.

During Component Replacement

After compressor has been installed and operated, oil will be evenly distributed throughout system. Some oil will be trapped by system components. If evaporator, condenser or accumulator is replaced, add proper amount of oil. See GENERAL MOTORS OIL LEVEL SPECIFICATIONS table.

GENERAL MOTORS OIL LEVEL SPECIFICATIONS

Application	Amount
Evaporator	3 oz.
Condenser	1 oz.
Accumulator [1]	2 oz.

[1] – Amount of oil removed, plus amount indicated.

JEEP

NOTE: **Oil level check should be performed when there has been an obvious loss of oil or when a component has been replaced, including the compressor.**

During Compressor Replacement

1) Remove oil filler plug. Look through filler plug hole and rotate clutch front plate to position piston connecting rod in center of filler plug hole. Insert special Dipstick (J 29642-12) into filler plug hole on right side of piston connecting rod, until dipstick contacts compressor housing. *See Fig 1.*

Fig. 1: Jeep Compressor Oil Check

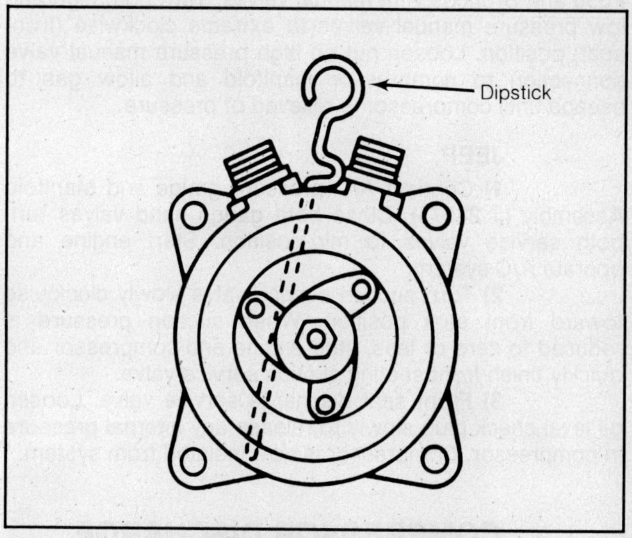

Insert dipstick on right side of connecting rod.

2) Remove dipstick and note number of marks covered with oil. Completely filled, 4 to 6 marks should be covered with oil. Correct oil level if necessary. Install oil filler plug.

During Component Replacement

After compressor has been installed and operated, oil will be distributed throughout system. A small amount of oil will be trapped by each system component. When replacing evaporator or condensor add 1 oz. of oil for each component replaced.

COMPONENT REPLACEMENT CAUTIONS

BEFORE SERVICING SYSTEM

Before disconnecting any lines or fittings, system must be completely discharged; however, if only compressor is being removed and compressor is equipped with stem-type service valves, compressor may be isolated from rest of system. See COMPRESSOR DISCHARGE and COMPRESSOR ISOLATION.

DISCONNECTING LINES & FITTINGS

After system is discharged, carefully clean area around coupling nut to prevent dirt from entering system. Always use two wrenches to avoid twisting or distorting lines and fittings (hold fitting with one wrench while loosening coupling nut with second wrench).

Cap or plug all lines and fittings immediately to prevent entry of moisture into system, do not remove these caps until connections are being made.

COMPONENT REPLACEMENT

After repaired or replacement component is installed, check and adjust compressor oil level. See COMPRESSOR OIL CHECK in this section. Certain component replacement requires additional refrigeration oil. Add specified amounts of oil directly to component prior to installation. If only valves or hoses are being replaced, addition of oil is not necessary.

CONNECTING LINES & FITTINGS

A new "O" ring should be used in all instances when connecting lines and fittings (dip "O" ring in clean refrigeration oil; ensure it is not twisted during installation). Always use two wrenches to avoid twisting or distorting lines and fittings, tighten coupling nuts securely.

PLACING SYSTEM IN OPERATION

1) After component replacement and/or system servicing has been completed and all connections have been made, evacuate system using a vacuum pump.

2) Charge system with fresh R-12 refrigerant according to vehicle manufacturers procedure. See REFRIGERANT CAPACITY.

3) Test system for leaks. Carefully check all new connections and components. Test system performance.

COMPRESSOR REPLACEMENT

COMPRESSOR ISOLATION

NOTE: **This procedure is to be performed on vehicles which have compressors equipped with stem-type service valves.**

FORD

This method can only be performed on F150, F350 and Broncos with manual valves. Turn both high and low pressure manual valves to extreme clockwise (front seat) position. Loosen nut on high pressure manual valve connection to compressor manifold and allow gas to escape until compressor is relieved of pressure.

JEEP

1) Connect A/C pressure gauge and Manifold Assembly (J 23575). Close both gauge hand valves turn both service valves to mid-position. Start engine and operate A/C system.

2) Turn suction service valve slowly clockwise toward front seat position. When suction pressure is reduced to zero or less, stop engine and compressor and quickly finish front seating suction service valve.

3) Front seat discharge service valve. Loosen oil level check plug slowly to release any internal pressure in compressor. Compressor is now isolated from system.

COMPRESSOR DISCHARGE

NOTE: **This procedure to be performed on vehicles which have compressors equipped with Schrader service valves. In these cases, compressor cannot be isolated and entire system must be discharged prior to compressor removal**

CHRYSLER CORP.

1) Install manifold gauge set, making sure all valves are closed. Install a long hose to manifold gauge set and run hose to oil collector can. Open compressor discharge and suction valves and allow refrigerant and oil to drain into collector can.

2) When system has been completely discharged, measure and record amount of oil collected in can. The amount measured should be added to system before it is recharged. Discard used oil.

FORD

1) Remove caps from compressor. Turn manifold gauge valves fully clockwise to close gauge set. Connect high and low pressure gauge hoses to compressor.

2) Slowly de-pressurize system by opening low pressure gauge valve. After system is nearly discharged, slowly open high pressure gauge valve. Open valve slowly to avoid losing an excessive amount of refrigerant oil.

GENERAL MOTORS

1) Remove cap from low-side service fitting and connect gauge set (J 5725-04). If gauge set is not being used, slowly discharge system by connecting a gauge hose to low-side service fitting on accumulator and discharging oil into bottle. *See Fig. 2.*

2) With low-side system fully discharged, check high-side system fitting (on line or muffler) for pressure. If pressure is found, discharge high-side using same procedure as for low-side.

Fig. 2: Discharging System Without Gauge Set

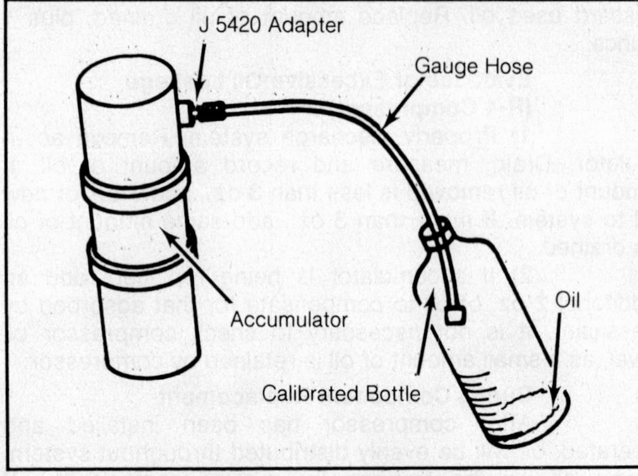

Slowly attach hose onto Schrader valve.

3) With system completely discharged, measure and note amount of oil collected. Discard used oil. If quantity of oil is 1/2 oz. or more, add this amount to system in addition to quantity required by component being replaced.

NOTE: **A restriction is indicated if pressure is found on high-side. The cause must be diagnosed and corrected before evacuating and charging system.**

COMPRESSOR REPLACEMENT

CHRYSLER CORP.

Removal

Slowly discharge system. Disconnect suction and discharge lines and cap all openings. Remove compressor from vehicle. Drain oil from suction and discharge ports. Discard used oil.

Installation

Add 5 oz. of new refrigerant oil through suction port. Install drain plug and tighten. Install compressor, using new gaskets connect suction and discharge lines and tighten. Evacuate and charge system.

FORD

Removal (2.0L & 2.3L Engines)

1) Slowly discharge system. Disconnect clutch lead. Disconnect refrigerant lines from compressor manifolds and cap all openings.

2) Loosen pivot bolt and remove front and rear adjusting bolts. Remove drive belts. Remove pivot bolt and remove compressor with braces attached.

Installation

If necessary, transfer clutch components to new compressor. Install front and rear braces. Reverse removal procedure to complete installation. Evacuate and charge system.

Removal (2.3L Diesel Engine)

1) Slowly discharge system. Raise vehicle on hoist. Loosen idler pulley and remove drive belt from

COMPRESSOR REPLACEMENT (Cont.)

compressor. Lower vehicle and remove drive belt. Remove compressor rear mounting bolts.

2) Disconnect suction and discharge hoses from compressor. Disconnect clutch lead. Remove outer mounting and bracket bolts. Remove compressor.

Installation

Install compressor on engine. Install new oiled "O" rings and connect suction and discharge hoses. Reverse removal procedure to complete installation. Evacuate and charge system.

Removal (2.8L Engine)

1) Remove carburetor air cleaner. Slowly discharge system. Remove clamp retaining A/C tube support clip. Disconnent refrigerant lines from compressor manifold and cap all openings.

2) Disconnect clutch lead. Loosen 5 compressor adjusting bolts and remove drive belt. Remove bolts attaching compressor to bracket. Remove compressor.

Installation

If necessary, transfer clutch components to new compressor. Install compressor on mounting bracket. Reverse removal procedure to complete installation. Evacuate and charge system.

Removal (4.9L Engine)

1) Slowly discharge system. Disconnect clutch lead. Disconnect refrigerant lines from compressor and cap all openings. Remove hex head bolt attaching compressor adjusting arm to mounting bracket.

2) Remove bolts securing braces to mounting bracket. Remove compressor with front and rear braces attached.

Removal (6.9L Engine)

Slowly discharge system. Disconnect refrigerant lines and cap all openings. Remove rear bolt and hose support. Loosen pivot and adjusting bolts. Remove drive belt and disconnect clutch lead. Remove compressor from vehicle.

Removal (V8 Engines)

Slowly discharge system. Disconnect clutch lead. Disconnent refrigerant lines from compressor manifold and cap all openings. Remove 5 bolts attaching compressor to brackets. Remove compressor.

Installation (4.9L, 6.9L & V8 Engines)

If necessary, transfer clutch components to new compressor. Install compressor on mounting bracket. Install new oiled "O" rings and connect suction and discharge hoses. Reverse removal procedure to complete installation. Evacuate and charge system.

GENERAL MOTORS

NOTE: "M" series refers to Astro and Safari vans.

Removal ("C" & "K" Series)

Discharge system. Remove connector attaching bolt. Remove connector and cap openings. Disconnect wiring to clutch actuating coil. Remove drive belt. Remove compressor mounting brackets and compressor. Drain and measure oil in compressor.

Removal ("G" Series)

1) Disconnect battery ground cable and compressor clutch connector. Purge system of refrigerant. Remove drive belt.

2) Remove 2 bolts and 2 clamps holding engine cover and remove engine cover. Remove air cleaner. Remove fitting and muffler assembly. Cap openings.

3) Remove compressor-to-bracket bolts. Remove engine oil tube support bracket bolt and nut from compressor. Remove clutch ground wire and remove compressor. Drain and measure oil in compressor.

Removal ("M" & "S" Series)

1) Discharge system. Disconnect battery ground cable and electrical connector at compressor. On vehicles equipped with 2.8L engine, remove compressor mounting bolts and remove compressor.

2) On vehicles equipped with 1.9L engine, remove power steering pump-to-engine bracket. Remove air cleaner. Remove A/C-to-engine bracket and compressor mounting bolts. Remove drive belt and manifold at rear of compressor. Remove compressor.

Installation (All Series)

Replace oil in compressor with amount equal to that removed. Reverse removal procedure, installing new "O" rings onto connector. Evacuate and charge system. Check operation.

JEEP

Removal

1) Isolate compressor. Disconnect battery negative cable. On vehicles with 4.2L engines, remove air cleaner. On all vehicles, remove discharge and suction hoses from compressor and cap all openings.

2) Remove drive belt(s) by loosening idler pulley or alternator on engines equipped with serpentine drive. Remove compressor from mounting bracket.

Installation

If a replacement compressor is being installed, check oil level and transfer magnetic clutch. Install compressor on mounting bracket. Reverse removal procedure to complete installation. Evacuate and charge system.

Air Conditioning Servicing

GENERAL SERVICE SPECIFICATIONS

REFRIGERANT CAPACITY

REFRIGERANT CAPACITY

Application	Ounces
Chrysler Corp.	
Pickups & Ramcharger	42
Vans	
FWD	38
RWD	
Front System Only	48
Front & Rear Systems	64
Ford	
Bronco, F150 & F350 Pickups	48
Bronco II & Ranger	40
E150 & E350 Vans	
Front (Main) System	56
Front & Rear (Auxiliary) System	68
General Motors	
Astro & Safari	48
Blazer & Pickups	48
"S" Series 2WD & 4WD	40
Suburban	
Front System	48
Front & Rear (Overhead) System	84
Vans	
Front System	48
Front & Rear (Overhead) System	72
Jeep	
CJ7 & Scrambler	40
All Others	36

COMPRESSOR BELT TENSION

COMPRESSOR BELT TENSION (Lbs.)[1]

Application	New Belt	Used Belt
Chrysler Corp.		
FWD Models		
2.2L	95	80
2.6L	115	80
RWD Models	120	65
Ford Motor Co.		
Aerostar, Bronco II & Ranger		
2.0L, 2.3L, 2.8L	150-190	140-160
2.2L Diesel	150-190	140-160
All Others	120-160	110-130
General Motors		
Astro & Safari		
2.5L	169	90
4.3L	152	69
"S" Series Pickups		
1.9L	157	90
2.2L Diesel	135	79
2.5L	152	90
2.8L	146	67
All Others		
V8 Diesel	175	55-100
All Other Engines	145	65-100
Jeep		
Serpentine Belt	180-200	140-160
All Other Belts	120-160	90-115

[1] – Using standard strand tension gauge.

CHRYSLER CORP.

DESCRIPTION

System is electrically-actuated and vacuum-operated. Turn signal lever on steering column incorporates a slide switch. The switch has "OFF", "ON", and "RESUME SPEED" positions. A "SPEED SET" button is located in the end of lever. System will not function under 30 MPH.

OPERATION

ENGAGING SYSTEM

Move slide switch to "ON" position, attain desired speed, and then momentarily depress and release "SPEED SET" button. Remove foot from accelerator, and speed will be maintained at selected level. Moving slide switch from "OFF" to "ON" while car is in motion establishes memory without system engagement at that speed.

DISENGAGING SYSTEM

A soft tap on brake pedal, normal clutch or brake application will disengage control unit; without erasing speed memory. Moving slide switch to "OFF" or turning ignition off also disengages system, but also erases speed memory.

RESUMING SPEED

Move slide switch to "RESUME" position.

CHANGING SPEED SETTING

To increase speed, accelerate to desired speed, and momentarily depress and release "SPEED SET" button. When unit is engaged, tapping button will increase speed in small amounts.

To decrease speed, tap brake pedal lightly to disengage system. When desired speed has been obtained, depress and release "SPEED SET" button. Decrease in speed can also be obtained by holding "SPEED SET" button depressed, until desired speed is attained. Releasing button engages system at that speed.

ACCELERATING FOR PASSING

Depress accelerator as necessary. When passing is completed, release accelerator. Vehicle will return to previously set speed.

TROUBLE SHOOTING

NO SPEED CONTROL WHEN BUTTON IS PRESSED

Slide switch in "OFF" position. Fuse blown. Faulty electrical circuit. Vacuum leak. Improper clutch or brake/speed control switch adjustment. Speed control throttle cable disconnected or not adjusted properly. Defective servo.

NO RESUME WHEN SLIDE SWITCH IS MOVED

Defective slide switch. Faulty electrical circuit.

Fig. 1: Wiring Diagram For FWD Speed Control System

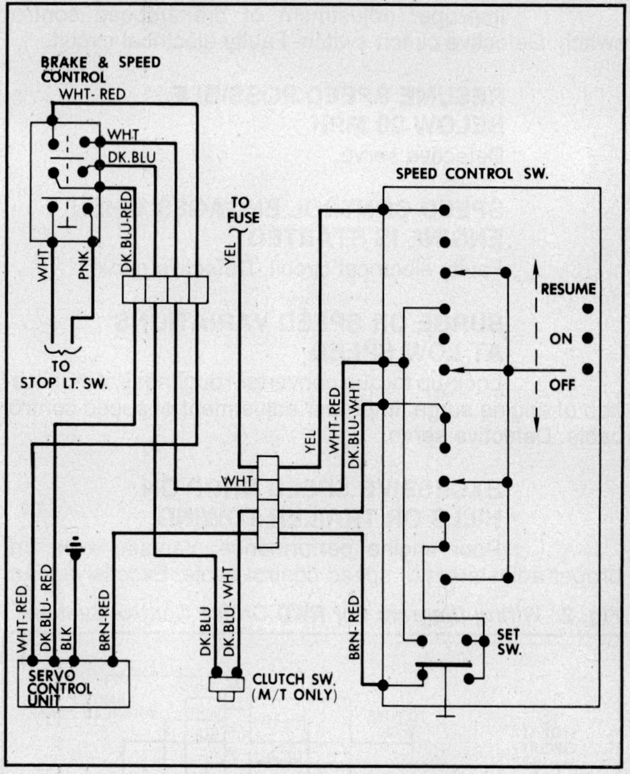

NO AUTOMATIC RELEASE WITH BRAKE PEDAL DEPRESSED

Speed control cable kinked or damaged. Defective or improperly adjusted brake/speed control switch. Faulty electrical circuit. Defective servo.

SPEED CONTROL ENGAGES WITHOUT ACTUATING SPEED SET BUTTON

Faulty electrical circuit. Defective servo.

CARBURETOR DOES NOT RETURN TO NORMAL IDLE

Speed control cable kinked or damaged. Speed control cable improperly adjusted. Standard throttle linkage faulty.

SPEEDOMETER NOISE, EXCESSIVE NEEDLE FLUTTER OR ERRATIC SERVO LOCK-IN PERFORMANCE

Speedometer cable kinked or damaged. Cable core bent or too long. Cable ferrule nut loose at speedometer head, transmission, or speed control servo. Noisy speedometer head assembly. Defective servo.

SPEED SETTING AFTER LOCK-IN TOO HIGH OR TOO LOW

Improper speed control throttle cable adjustment. Vacuum leak. Improper speed control lock-in adjustment. Defective servo.

CHRYSLER CORP. (Cont.)

UNIT DISENGAGES ON ROUGH ROAD

Improper adjustment of brake/speed control switch. Defective clutch switch. Faulty electrical circuit.

RESUME SPEED POSSIBLE BELOW 20 MPH

Defective servo.

SPEED CONTROL ENGAGES WHEN ENGINE IS STARTED

Faulty electrical circuit. Defective servo.

SURGE OR SPEED VARIATIONS AT LOW SPEED

Lock-up torque converter roughness. Amplification of engine surge. Improper adjustment of speed control cable. Defective servo.

EXCESSIVE SPEED DROP ON HILLS OR TRAILER TOWING

Poor engine performance. Vacuum leak. Improper adjustment of speed control cable. Excessive load.

Fig. 2: Wiring Diagram For RWD Cruise Control System

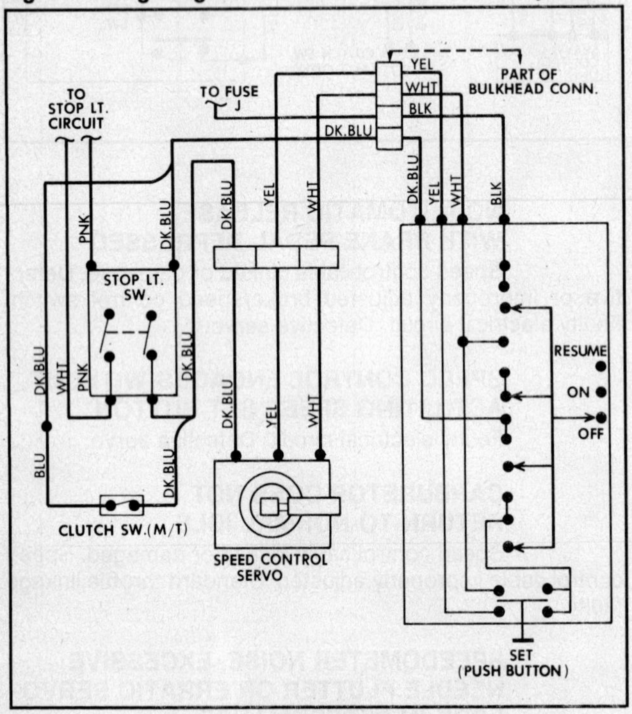

TESTING

SPEED CONTROL SWITCH

1) Disconnect 4-wire connector at steering column. Connect a 12-volt power source to Yellow wire (Black wire on RWD) terminal in speed control harness connector (male).

2) Connect a test lamp between connector Brown wire with Red tracer terminal (Yellow wire on RWD) and ground. Lamp should light when speed control switch is in "ON" position. Lamp should go out when "SPEED SET" button is depressed or when speed control switch is in "OFF" position.

3) Move test lamp lead to connector dark Blue wire with White tracer (dark Blue wire on RWD). Lamp should light with switch in "ON" position, and go out when switch is moved to "OFF" position.

4) Move test lamp lead to connector White wire with Red tracer (White wire on RWD). Lamp should not light with switch in "ON" position. Lamp should light when "SPEED SET" button is depressed and go out when button is released. Lamp should light when switch is in "RESUME" position and go out when switch is released.

BRAKE/SPEED CONTROL SWITCH

1) Disconnect double connector at switch pigtail and connect a 12-volt source to either terminal, then connect a test lamp from other terminal to ground.

2) Test lamp should light with brake pedal in normal position. If switch is correctly adjusted, test lamp light should go out when brake pedal is depressed a maximum of 3/8" (10 mm).

CLUTCH SWITCH

1) Disconnect double connector at switch pigtail and connect a 12-volt source to either terminal, then connect a test lamp from other terminal to ground.

2) Test lamp should light with brake pedal in free position. Test lamp light should go out when brake pedal is depressed.

Fig. 3: FWD Throttle Cable Adjustment

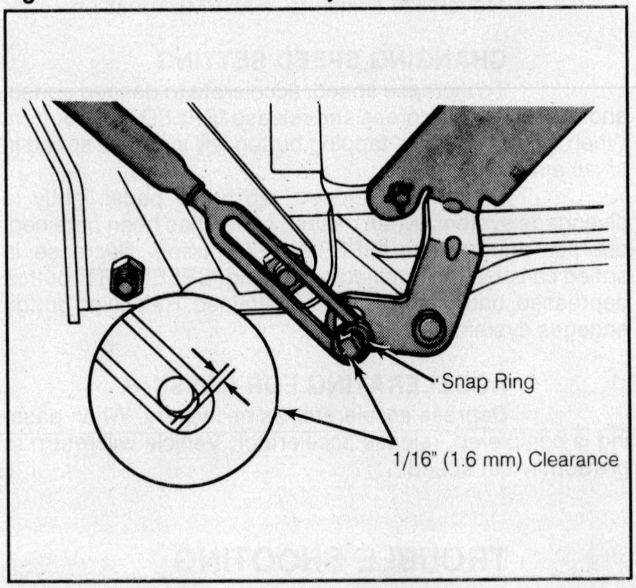

Remove all free play.

ADJUSTMENTS

SPEED CONTROL THROTTLE CABLE

FWD

1) Start engine and let run until it reaches normal operating temperature. Remove snap ring. Clearance between throttle stud and cable clevis should be 1/16" (1.6 mm). *See Fig. 3.* If necessary, loosen cable retaining clamp to adjust cable.

2) Pull all slack out of cable, using head of stud as a gauge. Do not move throttle away from curb idle position. Tighten retaining clamp nut to 45 INCH lbs. (5 N.m)

CHRYSLER CORP. (Cont.)

and move cable clevis back to round portion of stud. Install snap ring.

RWD

1) Start engine and let run until it reaches normal operating temperature. Carburetor should be at curb idle and choke off. Remove spring clip from the lost motion link stud. The clearance between stud and cable clevis should be 1/16" (1.6 mm).

2) Insert a gauge pin between cable clevis and stud. Loosen clamp at cable support bracket. *See Fig. 4.* Pull all slack out of cable, but do not move throttle away from curb idle position. Tighten clip at support bracket to 45 INCH lbs. (5 N.m). Remove gauge pin and install spring clip in stud of lost motion link.

Fig. 4: RWD Throttle Cable Adjustment

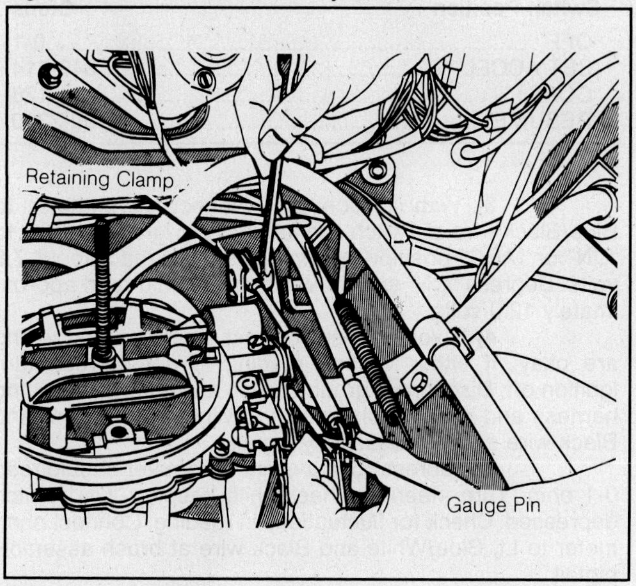

Remove all free play.

BRAKE/SPEED CONTROL SWITCH

FWD

1) With switch in retaining bracket, push switch forward as far as it will go. Brake pedal will move slightly forward. Slowly pull back on brake padal, until brake pedal will go no further.

2) This will cause the brake/speed control switch to ratchet backward to correct position. Very little movement is required, and no further adjustment is necessary.

RWD

1) Loosen switch mounting bracket. Insert .140" (3.6 mm) feeler gauge between brake push rod and switch, with brake pedal in fully released position.

2) Push switch bracket assembly toward brake push rod, until plunger is fully depressed and switch body contacts spacer. Tighten switch bracket bolt to 100 INCH lbs. (11 N.m). Remove feeler gauge.

SERVO LOCK-IN SCREW

NOTE: Lock-in accuracy will be affected by poor engine performance, adverse power-to-weight ratio, and improper slack in throttle control cable.

1) If speed drops more than 2 to 3 MPH when speed control is activated, lock-in adjusting screw should be turned counterclockwise approximately 1/4 turn for each 1 MPH correction required.

2) If speed increases more than 2 to 3 MPH, turn screw clockwise approximately 1/4 turn for each 1 MPH of correction required.

CAUTION: Do not turn adjusting screw more than 2 turns in either direction or damage to servo unit may occur.

Fig. 5: Adjusting Servo Lock-In Screw

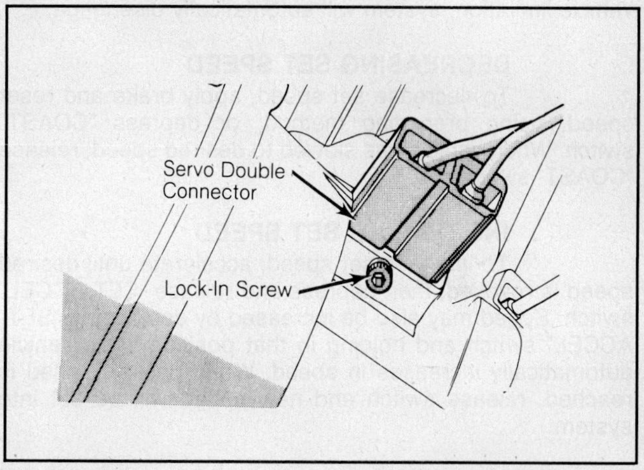

Do not adjust more than 2 turns in either direction.

FORD

DESCRIPTION

Ford cruise control system consists of 4 switches ("ON-OFF", "SET-ACCEL", "COAST", and "RESUME"), a servo assembly, speed control sensor, clutch position sensor switch (M/T), amplifier, wiring harness, vacuum dump valve, necessary wiring and vacuum hoses. Vehicles equipped with diesel engines also use a vacuum reservoir with an integrated check valve.

System switches are located in steering wheel spokes. Amplifier is located under instrument panel, and servo assembly is mounted on intake manifold. Speed sensor is located on left side of dash panel.

OPERATION

ENGAGING & DISENGAGING SYSTEM

System is operational at all speeds over 30 MPH. When "ON-OFF" switch is moved to "ON" position and "SET-ACCEL" switch is depressed, vehicle speed will be maintained until a new speed is set, brake pedal is depressed, clutch pedal is depressed (M/T), or "ON-OFF" switch is moved to "OFF" position.

The clutch position sensor switch (M/T) disengages speed control, preventing engine overspeed when clutch pedal is depressed. If actual vehicle speed falls more than 10 MPH below set speed, due to system malfunction or vehicle limitation, system will automatically disengage.

DECREASING SET SPEED

To decrease set speed, apply brake and reset speed, using preceding method, or depress "COAST" switch. When vehicle has slowed to desired speed, release "COAST" switch.

INCREASING SET SPEED

To increase set speed, accelerate until desired speed is reached, then depress and release "SET-ACCEL" switch. Speed may also be increased by depressing "SET-ACCEL" switch and holding in that position while vehicle automatically increases in speed. When desired speed is reached, release switch and new speed will be set into system.

RESUME FEATURE

When speed control system is deactivated by depressing brake or clutch pedal, previously set speed may be reestablished by depressing "RESUME" switch. Resume feature will not function if "ON-OFF" switch is moved to "OFF" position or vehicle speed drops below 30 MPH.

TESTING

NOTE: **Automatic Cruise Control Tester (Rotunda 007-00013) is available for diagnosing and testing factory installed Ford cruise control systems. The following tests are to be performed only if Automatic Cruise Control Tester (Rotunda 007-00013) is not used.**

CONTROL SWITCH TEST

Aerostar, Bronco II & Ranger

NOTE: **Horn and/or cruise control may operate intermittently if ground brush is missing.**

1) Check main feed fuse and brake lamp fuse. Replace if necessary. Remove steering wheel cover (horn pad on Aerostar series). With ignition off, connect an ohmmeter to White/Purple wire and to Black (Lt. Blue/Black on Aerostar) wire of switch connector at steering wheel. Depress "ON" switch.

2) Ohmmeter should read 0-1 ohms. If reading is not correct, replace switch assembly. Remove steering wheel and clean brush assembly and slip rings with solvent and lubricate. Reinstall steering wheel. Connect ohmmeter to Lt. Blue/Black wire and to Black wire of switch connector. Depress remaining switches and check resistances against table. If values are not correct, replace switch assembly.

CONTROL SWITCH RESISTANCES

Switch Position	Ohms
"OFF"	0-1
"SET ACCEL"	646-714
"COAST"	114-126
"RESUME"	2090-2310

3) With ignition off, connect a voltmeter to Blue/Black wire of switch connector. Turn ignition switch to "ON" or "ACC" position. Voltmeter should read about 7.8 volts. Depress "ON" switch. Voltmeter should read approximately 12.0 volts.

4) If voltages are correct, switches and wiring are okay. If either voltage reading is not correct, turn ignition off. Disconnect ground brush assembly from wiring harness and connect ohmmeter to White/Purple wire and Black wire at brush assembly pigtail.

5) Depress "ON" switch. Ohmmeter should read 0-1 ohm. Turn steering wheel while keeping "ON" switch depressed. Check for fluctuations in reading. Connect ohmmeter to Lt. Blue/White and Black wire at brush assembly pigtail.

6) Check for resistance values. See CONTROL SWITCH RESISTANCES table. Turn steering wheel while testing and check for fluctuations. If fluctuations are noted, remove steering wheel. Clean and lubricate brushes and slip rings. If no resistances are read, replace ground brush assembly.

7) If resistances are correct and no fluctuations occur, switches and ground brushes are okay. If replacement of switch assembly does not produce correct results, check slip ring for shorts. If necessary, replace entire wheel assembly and retest.

All Other Models

1) Disconnect 6-way connector at amplifier. Check battery voltage at Lt. Blue/Black wire when "ON" switch is depressed. Battery voltage should be available from Lt. Blue/Black wire leading from control switches.

2) Connect an ohmmeter between Lt. Blue/Black wire and ground. Check wire for continuity to ground with "OFF" switch depressed. If resistance higher than 1 ohm is found, wiring, slip rings or switch is at fault, or steering column may not be properly grounded.

3) To check steering column ground, connect an ohmmeter between a good body ground and steering column upper flange. Resistance should be less than 1/2 ohm. Rotate steering wheel, and check flexible coupling for resistance less than 1 ohm. If resistance higher than 3 ohms is noted, clean horn brush contacts and ground brush.

4) A resistance less than 1 ohm must be obtained before performing remaining tests. With ohmmeter connected between Lt. Blue/Black wire and ground, depress and hold "SET-ACCEL" switch. A reading of approximately 680 ohms should be indicated on ohmmeter.

5) Depress and hold "COAST" switch, a reading of approximately 120 ohms should be indicated on ohmmeter. Depress and hold "RESUME" switch, a reading of approximately 2200 ohms should be indicated.

SPEED SENSOR TEST

Aerostar, Bronco II & Ranger

1) Disconnect connector to speed sensor, and connect an ohmmeter between wire connector terminals (Dk. Green/White wire and Black wire) at speed sensor end. A reading of approximately 180-250 ohms should be obtained. A reading of 0 ohms indicates a shorted coil and a maximum reading indicates an open coil. Replace sensor in either case.

2) If ohmmeter reads 180 to 250 ohms and speedometer operates properly, speed sensor is probably good. A verified speed sensor can be substituted in place of existing sensor to check proper operation.

All Other Models

1) Disconnect 6-way connector at amplifier, and connect an ohmmeter between wire connector terminals (Dk. Green dashed and Black on Van models, Dk. Green/White and Black on all other models) at speed sensor end. A reading of about 40 ohms should be obtained.

2) A reading of 0 ohms indicates a shorted coil. A maximum reading indicates an open coil. Replace sensor in either case. If reading is 40 ohms and speedometer operates properly, speed sensor is probably good. A speed sensor of known quality can be substituted in place of existing sensor to check proper operation.

SERVO ASSEMBLY TEST

1) Disconnect ball chain from carburetor, if used. Separate 8-way connector at amplifier, then connect an ohmmeter between Orange/Yellow wire and Gray/Black wire at connector. A resistance of 40-125 ohms should be obtained.

2) Connect ohmmeter between Orange/Yellow wire and White/Pink wire at connector. A resistance of about 60-190 ohms should be obtained on Vans, and 60-90 on all other models. Reconnect ball chain to carburetor. Start engine with servo-to-amplifier connector disconnected. Verify that engine vacuum exceeds 2.5 in. Hg.

3) Connect Orange/Yellow wire of servo to battery positive terminal. Connect White/Pink wire to ground, and then momentarily touch Gray/Black wire of servo to ground. Servo throttle actuator should tighten bead chain or actuator cable and open throttle.

4) Throttle should remain in that position (or SLOWLY release tension). When White/Pink wire is removed from ground, servo should release tension immediately. If servo fails any of preceding tests, replace servo.

CAUTION: If Orange/Yellow wire is shorted to either White/Pink wire or Gray/Black dashed wire, it may cause damage to amplifier.

Fig. 1: Typical Servo Installation

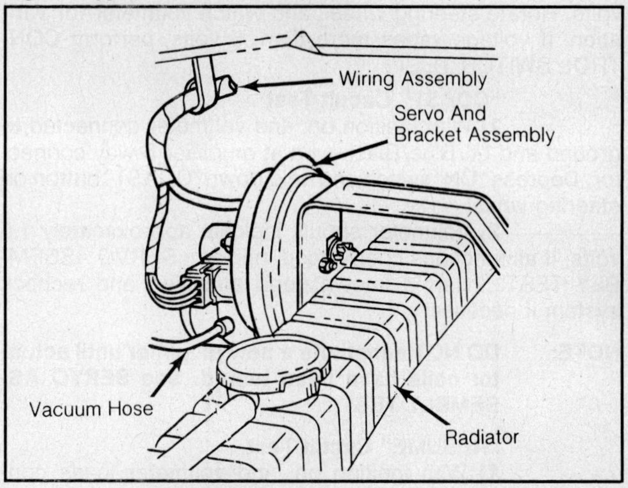

AMPLIFIER TEST

CAUTION: DO NOT use a test light to perform amplifier tests, as excessive current draw will damage electronic components. Use only a voltmeter of 5000 ohm/volt rating or higher.

"ON" Circuit Test (Aerostar, Bronco II & Ranger)

1) Turn ignition on and connect a voltmeter between White/Purple stripe wire and ground in 6-pin connector at amplifier. Connect voltmeter between Lt. Blue/Black wire and ground at amplifier 6-pin connector.

2) Voltmeter should read battery voltage when "ON" switch is depressed and held. If voltage is not available, perform control switch test. Release "ON" switch, voltmeter should read 7.8 volts. If meter reads 0 volts, check ground (Black wire) on amplifier.

3) If there is no ground on amplifier, check system ground connection and wiring. Also check No. 1 and 6 fuses and/or temporarily install a known good amplifier and recheck for good "ON" circuit.

All Other Models

1) Turn ignition on, and connect a voltmeter between ground and Lt. Blue/Black wire at amplifier 6-way connector. Voltmeter should read 12 volts when "ON" switch in steering wheel is depressed and held. If no voltage is present, see HORN RELAY TEST and CONTROL SWITCH TEST.

2) Release "ON" button. A 7.8 volt reading should remain on voltmeter, indicating "ON" circuit is engaged. If voltage does not remain, check for ground at amplifier, fuse and/or circuit breaker. Insert a known good amplifier and recheck "ON" circuit if necessary.

"OFF" Circuit Test

1) With ignition on, and voltmeter connected to ground and Lt. Blue/Black wire at amplifier 6-way connector, depress "OFF" switch on steering wheel. Voltage should drop to zero indicating "ON" circuit is de-energized.

2) If voltage does not drop to zero, perform CONTROL SWITCH TEST. If switches test good, install a known good amplifier and retest.

"SET-ACC" Circuit Test

1) With ignition on, and voltmeter connected to ground and Lt. Blue/Black wire at amplifier 6-way connector. Depress "ON" switch, then hold "SET-ACC" button on steering wheel.

Cruise Control Systems

FORD (Cont.)

2) Voltmeter should indicate approximately 4.5 volts. Rotate steering wheel, and watch voltmeter for variation. If voltage varies more than .5 volts, perform CONTROL SWITCH TEST.

"COAST" Circuit Test

1) With ignition on, and voltmeter connected to ground and Lt. Blue/Black wire at amplifier 6-way connector. Depress "ON" switch and hold down "COAST" button on steering wheel.

2) Voltmeter should indicate approximately 1.5 volts. If all functions check good, perform SERVO ASSEMBLY TEST. Insert a known good amplifier, and recheck system if necessary.

NOTE: DO NOT substitute a new amplifier until actuator coils have been tested. See SERVO ASSEMBLY TEST.

"RESUME" Circuit Test

1) With ignition on, and voltmeter leads connected to ground and to Lt. Blue/Black wire at amplifier 6-way connector, depress and hold "RESUME" switch. Voltmeter should indicate approximately 6.5 volts.

2) If all functions are okay, perform SERVO ASSEMBLY TEST. Insert a known good amplifier, and recheck system if necessary.

HORN RELAY CIRCUIT TEST

NOTE: Electrical connectors must remain connected during horn relay testing.

All Except Aerostar, Bronco II & Ranger

1) Locate Yellow wire on Vans or Yellow/Lt. Blue dot wire on Bronco and Pickups at connector "X". Check for battery voltage on pin side of connector. *See Fig. 2.*

2) Locate Blue/Yellow stripe wire on Vans or Dk. Blue wire on Bronco and Pickups at connector "Y". Check for battery voltage on socket side of connector. With voltmeter still connected to socket, depress horn switch.

3) Horn should sound, and voltmeter should indicate zero volts. If voltmeter still indicates battery voltage when horn switch is depressed, check horn switch or steering column wiring for an open circuit.

4) To by-pass horn switch and check horn relay, momentarily ground Blue/Yellow wire on Vans or Dk. Blue wire on Bronco and Pickups on socket side of connector "Y".

5) If horn still does not sound, check Yellow/Green stripe wire on Vans or Yellow/Lt. Green wire on Bronco and Pickups at connector "X" for battery voltage while relay is activated. If battery voltage is present when relay is activated, an open circuit is present between connector "X" and horn.

6) If battery voltage is present in step **1)** and horn relay failed to operate in step **3)**, replace relay.

Fig. 2: Wiring Diagram of Ford Cruise Control System

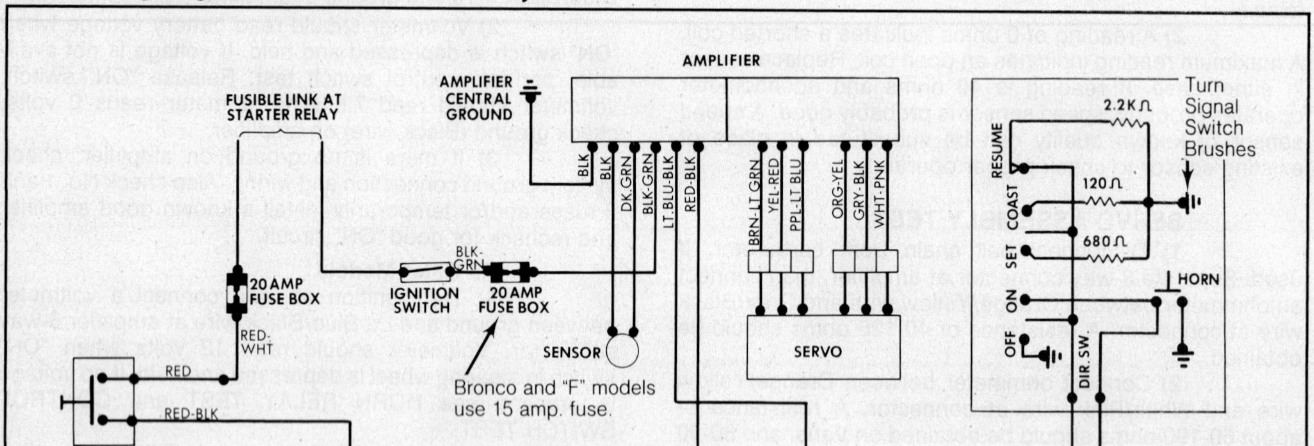

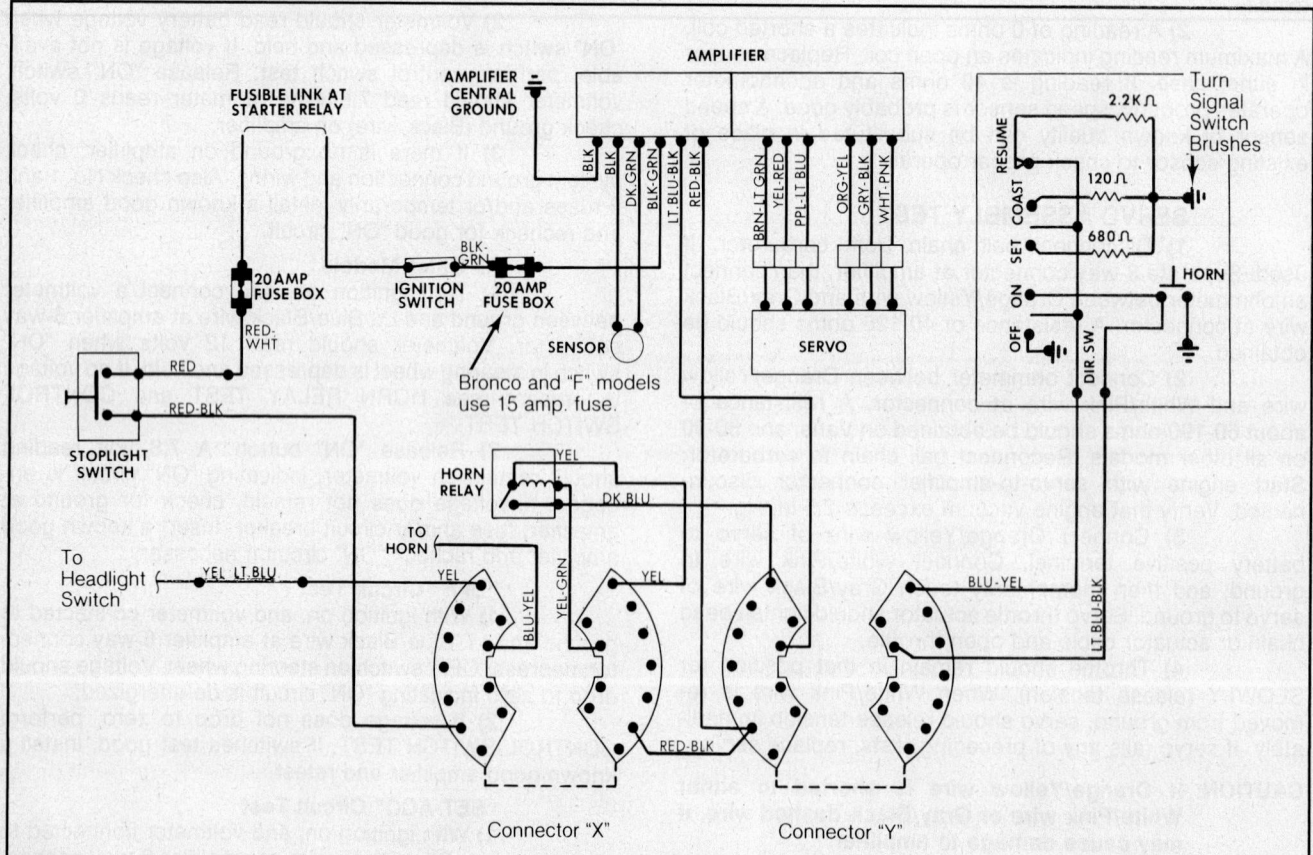

Diagram for Van models shown.

CLUTCH SWITCH TEST

NOTE: Switch operates magnetically. Do not use magnetized tools near switch. Use only a voltmeter of 5000 ohm/volt rating or higher to test switch. Test lamp will not indicate switch condition.

Vehicles With M/T

1) Ensure that clutch switch is depressed (switch closed) when clutch pedal is released, as Cruise control will not operate unless this condition exists. Correct if necessary, before performing test.

2) Disconnect clutch switch connector from speed control harness connector, and connect an ohmmeter to switch connector terminals. With clutch pedal released and switch plunger depressed (switch closed), resistance should be less than 5 ohms.

3) With clutch pedal depressed and switch plunger fully extended (switch open), resistance should be infinity (open circuit).

BRAKE LIGHT SWITCH TEST

NOTE: This test should be performed whenever brake application will not disengage speed control. On vehicles with M/T, ensure that clutch switch is working properly before performing this test.

1) Check for stop light operation with a maximum brake pedal effort of 6 lbs. (2.7 kg). Check brake pedal actuation and stop light switch if pedal effort required is excessive.

2) If stop lights operate correctly, check battery voltage at 6-way connector Black/Green wire on Vans and White/Purple stripe wire on Bronco and Pickups.

3) Depress pedal until stop lights are on, and check voltage at 6-way connector Red/Black wire on Vans and Lt. Green wire on Bronco and Pickups. If voltage readings differ by more than 1.5 volts, high resistance exists in stop light circuit and must be corrected.

4) Check stop light switch, supply circuit, fuses and bulbs for correct operation, if stop lights do not work.

VACUUM DUMP VALVE TEST

1) Vacuum dump valve should be checked whenever brake application does not release speed control. Disconnect vacuum hose from dump valve-to-servo, at servo unit. Connect hand vacuum pump to hose and pump up a vacuum.

2) If vacuum cannot be obtained, hose or dump valve leaks and should be replaced. Depress brake pedal. Vacuum should be released. If not, adjust or replace dump valve.

VACUUM RESERVOIR TEST

Diesel Engines Only

1) Locate vacuum reservoir on Left or Right fender. Disconnect vacuum hose at servo an connect a vacuum gauge with a minimum range of 0-25 in. Hg. Start engine and observe vacuum gauge.

2) Vacuum should be approximately 23 in. Hg., but not less than 20 in. Hg.. If reading is not within specifications, check for leaking vacuum hose or faulty vacuum pump.

3) Turn engine off after vacuum has stabilized above 20 in. Hg. Vacuum should hold steady. After 24 hours, vacuum should be a mimimum of 15 in. Hg.. If vacuum fails to hold, replace vacuum reservoir.

ADJUSTMENT

ACTUATOR CABLE

Aerostar, Bronco II & Ranger

Remove cable retaining clip. Disengage throttle positioner. Set carburetor at hot idle. Pull on actuator cable near servo to take up slack. While maintaining light tension on holding cable, insert cable retaining clip and snap securely.

Vehicles with 6.9L Engine

1) Set carburetor choke to hot idle position with throttle positioner solenoid disengaged. Snap molded speed control cable over accelerator cable end fitting attached to throttle ball stud.

2) Remove adjuster retaining clip, if used, from adjuster mounting tab. Insert speed control actuator cable adjuster mounting tab into slot provided in accelerator cable support bracket.

3) Pull cable through adjuster until a slight tension is felt, without pening throttle plate or increasing idle RPM. Insert retainer clip until engagement is felt, push downward until it locks.

BEAD CHAIN ADJUSTMENT

1) On vehicles equipped with solenoid anti-diesel valve, turn ignition switch to "OFF" position. On all vehicles, adjust bead chain to obtain .06-.25" (1.6-6.4 mm) actuator arm free travel when engine is at hot idle.

2) Adjust chain to eliminate as much slack as possible without keeping throttle lever from returning to idle. Cut off chain in excess of 4 beads.

VACUUM DUMP VALVE ADJUSTMENT

Aerostar, Bronco II & Ranger

Firmly depress brake pedal and hold in position. Push in dump valve until valve collar bottoms against retaining clip. Firmly pull brake pedal rearward. Clearance between dump valve housing and White plastic pad on brake pedal must be .05-.10" (1.27-2.54 mm) with brake pedal pulled to rearmost position.

Fig. 3: Vacuum Dump Valve Adjustment

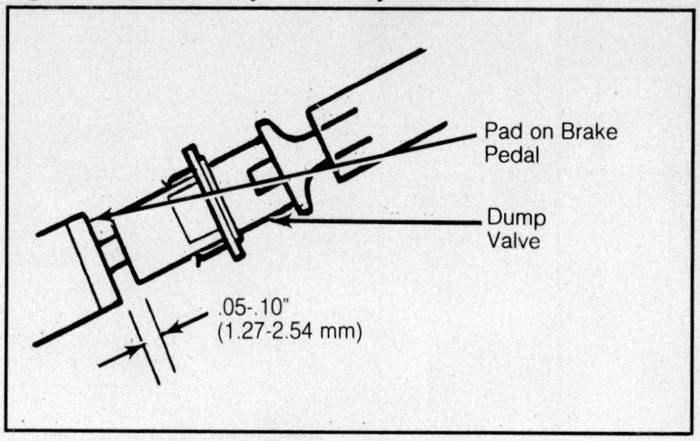

Bronco II and Ranger shown, other models similar.

All Other Models

1) Ensure brake pedal is against stop in released position. Move dump valve forward in retaining clip until 1/8" or less of valve plunger is exposed.

Cruise Control Systems

FORD (Cont.)

2) Tip of valve plunger should contact brake pedal adapter. Ensure brake pedal is against stop (released position). Depress brake pedal. If vacuum still does not release, replace dump valve.

Fig. 4: Bronco II & Ranger Wiring Diagram

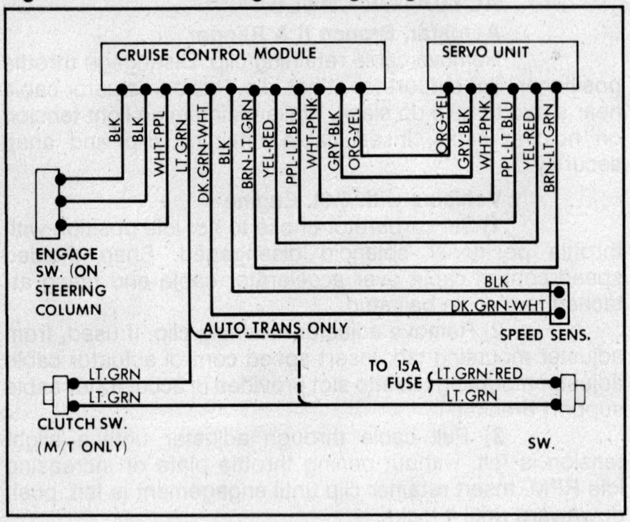

GENERAL MOTORS CUSTOM CRUISE III

DESCRIPTION

This system has capability to cruise, resume speed, accelerate, or coast-down. System consists of mode control switches, control module, servo unit, speed sensor, vacuum supply, electrical and vacuum release switches, and an electrical wire harness.

A vacuum operated servo unit is used to maintain desired speed. System control module monitors vehicle speed and servo position. Control module operates vacuum and vent valves in servo to maintain desired speed. A low speed limiter (contained within control module) prevents system engagement below 25 MPH.

OPERATION

The operation of control module is controlled by mode control switches, located on end of turn signal lever. System may be disengaged by turning off cruise control switch or by activating brake or clutch (M/T) release switch. A vacuum release valve, vents servo to atmosphere as either pedal is depressed, allowing servo unit to quickly return to throttle idle position.

CRUISE CONTROL SWITCH

The cruise control switch turns system on and off, and returns cruise control to last speed setting when momentarily moved towards "R/A" (Resume/Accelerate) position after braking. If slider switch is held for more than 1 second in "R/A" position, system enters acceleration mode. Vehicle may be accelerated by holding switch in "R/A" position.

When switch is released, vehicle will maintain selected cruise speed. Slider switch may be used to resume vehicle speed. With cruise control engaged and operating, quickly press switch to "R/A" position and release. This feature increases vehicle speed by approximately 1 MPH for each tap, up to 10 times. After 10 times, system must be reset to new speed to continue function.

SET/COAST SWITCH

The set/coast switch is located on end of turn signal lever and has 2 positions, normal and depressed.

SET Mode

With vehicle speed above 25 MPH (cruise control switch in "ON" position), depress and release set/coast switch. Speed will be set at speed vehicle was at when button was released. Speed will be maintained until cruise control switch is turned off, ignition is turned off or set/coast switch is fully depressed and held. Depressing brake or clutch pedal (M/T) releases cruise control, but will not shut system off.

COAST Mode

With set/coast switch fully depressed, control speed may be raised or lowered. To increase speed, accelerate to new speed, fully depress set/coast switch and release. New speed is set as switch is released. To decrease speed, depress and hold set/coast switch when vehicle has slowed to desired speed, release switch to set new speed.

TAP DOWN Mode

With cruise control engaged and operating, slow vehicle speed by "tapping" set/coast switch. Do not hold switch in depressed position as it will place system in coast mode. This feature decreases vehicle speed by approximately 1 MPH for each tap.

ELECTRONIC CONTROL MODULE

The control module monitors servo position, mode control switches, and output of speed sensor. In response to these inputs, control module electically signals opening and closing of vent and vacuum solenoid valves in servo. Control module is usually mounted on accelerator pedal bracket.

SERVO UNIT

The servo unit consists of a vacuum operated diaphragm, a normally open solenoid valve that vents diaphragm chamber to atmosphere, a normally closed solenoid valve that connects diaphragm chamber to vacuum source, and a variable inductance position sensor.

Steady Cruise State

Servo alters throttle position in response to signals from control module. With vacuum and vent valves closed, servo has constant vacuum on diaphragm and places no-flow requirement on vacuum source. Vacuum is trapped in diaphragm.

Vehicle Losing Speed

Servo alters throttle position in response to signals from control module. Control module energizes vacuum solenoid to open vacuum valve to vacuum source. This increases vacuum level in servo to increase throttle opening. Vent remains closed.

Vehicle Gaining Speed

Servo alters throttle position in response to signals from control module. Control module de-energizes vent solenoid to open vent valve to atmosphere, which reduces vacuum in servo and allows throttle return spring to decrease throttle opening. Vacuum valve remains closed.

Fig. 1: Servo Unit

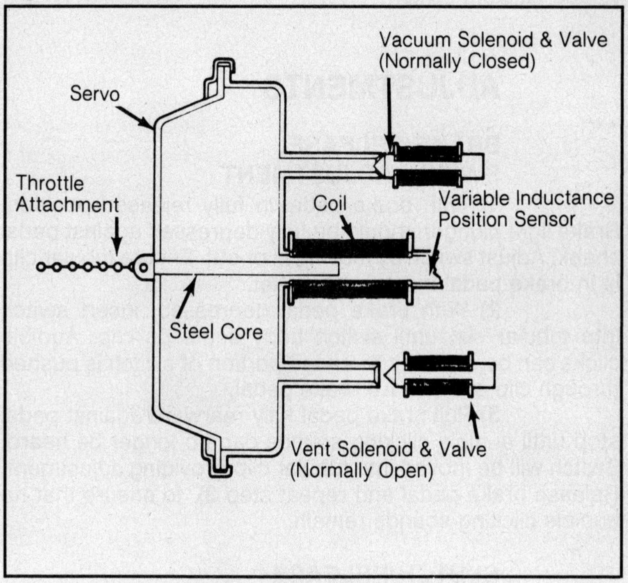

SPEED SENSOR

The vehicle speed sensor (VSS) buffer amplifier supplies vehicle speed to control module. Optic head portion of VSS is located in speedometer frame. A reflective blade is attached to speedometer cable/head assembly. Reflective blade spins like a propeller, with its blades passing through a light beam from an LED in optic head.

GENERAL MOTORS CUSTOM CRUISE III (Cont.)

As each blade enters LED light beam, light is reflected back to a photocell in optic head causing a low power speed signal to be sent to buffer for amplification and signal conditioning. This amplified signal is then sent to control module.

Fig. 2: Vehicle Speed Sensor (VSS)

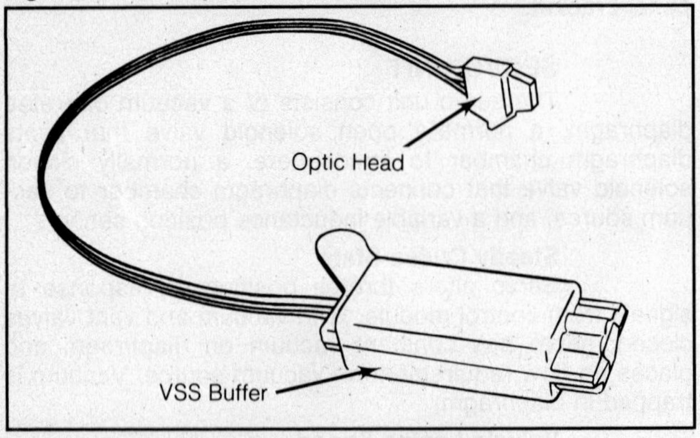

Buffer is located on speedometer cable.

ELECTRICAL & VACUUM RELEASE SWITCHES

These switches are used to disengage cruise control. An electrical release switch is mounted on brake and clutch pedal (M/T) brackets. Switches disengage system electrically as either pedal is depressed.

A vacuum release valve is also mounted on brake pedal bracket. This valve vents trapped vacuum in servo to atmosphere as brake pedal is depressed, allowing throttle to quickly return to idle position. This is done by routing a separate hose directly to servo from normally closed vacuum switch.

ADJUSTMENTS

BRAKE/RELEASE SWITCH ADJUSTMENT

1) With brake pedal in fully released position. Brake light plunger should be fully depressed against pedal shank. Adjust switch by moving in or out. Ensure tubular clip is in brake pedal mounting bracket.

2) With brake pedal depressed, insert switch into tubular clip until switch body seats on clip. Audible clicks can be heard as threaded portion of switch is pushed through clip and toward brake pedal.

3) Pull brake pedal fully rearward against pedal stop until audible clicking sounds can no longer be heard. Switch will be moved into tubular clip providing adjustment. Release brake pedal and repeat step **3)**, to ensure that no audible clicking sounds remain.

CLUTCH/RELEASE SWITCH ADJUSTMENT

Position switch slider forward on switch shaft. Fully depress clutch pedal to set switch.

LINKAGE CABLE ADJUSTMENT

1.9L, 2.5L & 2.8L Engines

With cable assembly installed on cable support and carburetor, install cable assembly to servo bracket, using second ball of servo chain on cable. With throttle fully closed (and ignition and fast idle cam off), adjust cable jam nuts until .040" (1 mm) clearance exists between throttle lever stud and end of cable slot. Tighten jam nuts.

4.3L & 4.8L Engines

With cable assembly installed and using second ball of servo chain, install servo assembly chain on cable assembly. With throttle fully closed (and ignition and fast idle cam off) adjust cable assembly jam nuts until .040" (1 mm) clearance exists between lever pin and end of cable assembly slot. Tighten jam nuts.

SERVO-TO-CARBURETOR ADJUSTMENT

V8 Gasoline Engines Only

With throttle fully closed (and ignition and fast idle cam off), adjust length so that rod assembles over end of stud. Install retainer.

SERVO ROD LINK ADJUSTMENT

V8 Diesel Engine Only

With engine off and idle screw against stop, assemble lower end of of rod link to throttle lever and upper end to hole closest to servo. This adjustment should provide a minimum of .040" (1 mm) slack.

TROUBLE SHOOTING

SYSTEM SURGES

Servo and throttle linkages should operate freely, smoothly and be properly adjusted. Check vacuum hose routing for pinches, leaks or restrictions. Perform SERVO TEST. Replace control module if no system problem is found.

CRUISE SET SPEED HIGH OR LOW

Check vacuum hose routing for pinches, leaks or restrictions. Adjust or replace as necessary. Check servo linkage for excess slack and adjust as described in this article. Replace control module, if no system problem is found.

EXCESSIVE CRUISE SPEED LOSS ON HILLS

Check hoses for vacuum leaks. If applicable, determine if check valve is funtional.

RESUME OR COAST DOES NOT OPERATE

If all other cruise control functions are working properly except resume or coast, replace control module.

DIAGNOSIS & TESTING

PRELIMINARY INSPECTION

Check system to ensure there are no bare, broken or disconnected wires or any pinched, damaged or disconnected vacuum hoses. Servo and throttle linkage should operate freely and smoothly. Servo linkage should be properly adjusted. If preliminary inspection does not reveal any problems, further testing is required.

CRUISE CONTROL DIAGNOSIS

1) Check throttle linkage to servo for proper adjustment. If not okay, adjust linkage. If adjustment is

GENERAL MOTORS CUSTOM CRUISE III (Cont.)

okay, check all electrical and vacuum connections for proper engagement. Check fuse.

2) If connections or fuse are not okay, repair or replace as necessary. If system is okay, perform SERVO TEST. If servo is not okay, repair or replace as necessary.

3) If servo is okay, perform CRUISE CONTROL SWITCH TEST. If switch is not okay, adjust, repair or replace as necessary. If switch is okay, perform CRUISE RELEASE SWITCH TEST.

4) If switch is not okay, repair or replace as necessary. If switch is okay, perform SET/COAST SWITCH TEST. If set/coast switch is not okay, repair or replace as necessary.

5) If set/coast switch is okay, perform SPEED SENSOR TEST. If speed sensor is not okay, repair or replace as necessary. If speed sensor is okay, replace control module.

SERVO TEST

1) Turn ignition off. Disconnect connector from control module assembly. Using an ohmmeter, probe between connector and cavity pins "F" (circuit 398) and "H" (circuit 399). Resistance should be between 20-30 ohms.

2) If reading is 20-30 ohms, continue test on step **5)**. If reading is not within specifications, disconnect servo electrical connector from servo. With ohmmeter probes between pins "B" (circuit 399) and "D" (circuit 398) on servo assembly. Resistance should be between 20-30 ohms.

3) If reading is not within specifications, replace servo. If reading is 20-30 ohms, check circuit 399 between pin "H" of control module and pin "B" of servo for loose connections or open wires. Repair or replace as necessary.

4) Check circuit 398 between pin "F" of control module and pin "D" of servo for loose connections or open wires. Repair or replace as necessary, continue test.

5) Using ohmmeter, probe between control module connector cavity pin "C" (circuit 430) and ground. Resistance should be infinity (open circuit). If continuity is indicated, locate short to ground and repair circuit 430 as necessary.

6) If no continuity is indicated, leave ohmmeter connected as is. Using a jumper wire, connect cavity "A" of servo connector to ground. Resistance should be 0 ohms.

7) If reading is not within specifications, locate open in circuit 430 between pin "C" of control module to pin "A" of servo. Repair or replace as necessary. If reading is within specifications, remove jumper wire and continue test.

8) Using an ohmmeter, probe between control module cavity pin "K" (circuit 402) and ground. Resistance should be infinity. If continuity is indicated, locate short to ground and repair circuit 402.

9) If no continuity is indicated, leave ohmmeter connected as is. Using a jumper wire, connect cavity "E" of servo connector to ground. Resitance should be 0 ohms.

10) If reading is not within specifications, locate open in circuit 402 between pin "K" of control module to pin "E" of servo. Repair or replace as necessary. If reading is within specifications, continue test.

11) Using an ohmmeter, probe connector cavity pin "C" (circuit 150) and ground. Resistance should be 0 ohms. If reading is 0 ohms, continue test on step **14)**.

12) If reading is not within specifications, disconnect electrical connector from control module. Using an ohmmeter, probe connector cavity "J" (circuit 150) and ground. Resistance should be 0 ohms.

13) If reading is not within specifications, locate open in circuit 150 between pin "J" of control module to ground (point G202). Repair or replace as necessary. If reading is 0 ohms, locate open in circuit 150 between pin "C" of servo to (S253) splice. Repair or replace as necessary.

14) Disconnect linkage, bead chain or cable from servo to throttle. Ensure electrical connector to servo is still disconnected. Start engine and let idle. Manually actuate servo vent and vacuum control valves by connecting jumper wires from battery positive post to pins "A" and "E" on servo assembly

15) Connect another jumper wire between pin "C" of servo and ground. With brake and clutch pedal (M/T) in free position, servo should fully pull in. If servo fails to pull in, go to step **18)**.

16) If servo pulls in, remove jumper wire from pin "E" on servo. Servo should stay in position. If servo stays in position, check connection of electrical connector at servo. If servo fails to remain in position, remove larger of two hoses and plug orifice of servo.

17) Reconnect jumper wire to pin "E" until servo fully pulls in, then remove jumper wire. If servo fails to stay in position, replace servo. If servo stays in position, check brake and/or clutch release valve for adjustment. Check hoses and valves for leaks, repair or replace as necessary. Check for proper system operation.

18) Remove larger of two hoses and plug orifice of servo. Servo should pull in. If servo fails to pull in, remove smaller hose from servo and check for vacuum. If vacuum is present, inspect connectors for leaks. If okay, replace servo.

19) If no vacuum is present, check connectors between servo and vacuum source. Repair or replace as necessary. If servo pulls in, check brake and/or clutch release valve for adjustment. Check hoses and valves for leaks, repair or replace as necessary.

SET/COAST SWITCH TEST

1) Turn ignition switch on. Place cruise control switch in "ON" position. Measure voltage at control module by probing pin "L" (circuit 84) and connecting other end of voltmeter to ground. If 12 volts are present, go to step **2)**. If no voltage is present, got to step **4)**.

2) Disconnect control module connector. Probe pin "L" (circuit 84) and other end of voltmeter to ground. If voltage is zero, check circuit 84 shorting to 12 volts in connector or malfunctioning control module. Repair or replace as necessary.

3) If 12 volts are present, disconnect connector (C235) and measure voltage at terminal "D" (circuit 84) on switch side of connector. If voltage is zero, check for short to 12 volts in wire. Repair or replace as necessary. If 12 volts are present, check for short in (C235) connector. If no short, replace switch. Check for proper system operation.

4) Depress and hold in set/coast switch. Measure voltage at pin "L" (circuit 84) of control module. If 12 volts are present, switch is okay. If voltage is zero, disconnect connector (C235) and measure voltage at terminal "B" (circuit 397) on switch side of connector.

5) If voltage is zero, go to step **7)**. If 12 volts are present, depress and hold in set/coast switch. Measure voltage at terminal "D" on switch side of connector. If voltage is zero, replace switch.

6) If 12 volts are present, check terminal "D" (circuit 84) of connector (C235) to pin "L" of control module. Locate open in circuit, repair and replace as necessary. Check for proper system operation.

GENERAL MOTORS CUSTOM CRUISE III (Cont.)

7) Measure voltage at terminal "A" (circuit 39) on harness connector side. If voltage is zero, locate open in circuit 39 or blown fuse. Repair or replace as necessary.

8) If 12 volts are present, ensure that cruise control switch is in "ON" position. If switch is on and zero volts are present at terminal "B" (circuit 397) on connector side of switch, replace switch.

CRUISE CONTROL SWITCH TEST

1) Turn ignition on. Place cruise control switch in "OFF" position. Measure voltage at control module by probing connector pin "A" (circuit 397) and connecting other end of voltmeter to ground. If 12 volts are present, go to step **2)**. If voltage is zero, go to step **3)**.

2) Disconnect cruise control switch connector (C235) and measure voltage at terminal "A" on harness side of connector and ground. If voltage is zero, locate open in circuit 39 or blown fuse. Repair or replace as necessary. If 12 volts are present, replace switch. Check for proper system operation.

3) Place cruise control switch in "ON" position. Measure voltage at control module by probing connector pin "A" (circuit 397) and connecting other end of voltmeter to ground. If 12 volts are present, switch is okay.

4) If voltage is zero, disconnect connector and measure voltage at terminal "B" on switch side of connector and ground. If 12 volts are present, locate open in circuit 397 between terminal "B" of connector (C235) and pin "A" of control module. Repair and replace as necessary.

5) If voltage is zero, measure voltage at terminal "A" on harness side of connector and ground. If 12 volts are present, replace switch. If voltage is zero, check fuse.

6) If fuse is okay, check wiring between fuse and switch. If fuse is blown, replace fuse. If fuse blows, check all branches of circuit 39 and locate short. Repair as necessary. If fuse does not blow, road test vehicle.

CRUISE RELEASE SWITCH TEST

1) Turn ignition on. Place cruise control switch in "ON" position. Measure voltage by probing pin "G" (circuit 86) and connecting other end of voltmeter to ground. If 12 volts are present, go to step **2)**. If voltage is zero, go to step **4)**.

2) Depress brake pedal and measure voltage by probing cruise release switch (circuit 86) and connecting other side of voltmeter to ground. If 12 volts are present, check cruise release switch and/or clutch switch (M/T) for adjustment. Adjust or replace as necessary.

3) If voltage is zero, cruise release switch is okay. If vehicle is equipped with clutch switch (M/T), ensure there is continuity through switch. Check for proper system operation.

4) Measure voltage by probing cruise release switch (circuit 86) amd connecting other end of voltmeter to ground. If 12 volts are present, locate open in circuit 86 between control module connector "G" pin and cruise release switch. Repair or replace as necessary. If vehicle is equipped with clutch switch (M/T), ensure there is continuity through switch.

5) If voltage is zero, measure voltage by probing cruise release switch (circuit 86) and connecting other end of voltmeter to a known good ground. If voltage is zero, perform CRUISE CONTROL SWITCH TEST. If 12 volts are present, check brake and/or clutch switch for adjustment. Adjust or replace as necessary.

SPEED SENSOR TEST

1) Turn ignition switch on and place cruise control switch in "ON" position. With speedometer turning (either through wheels or by hand), measure voltage by probing terminal "D" of control module with all connections mated. If voltage varies at around 4 volts, replace control module.

2) If voltage is not present, disconnect connector at VSS buffer. Measure voltage at connector cavity of wire that goes to terminal "D" of control module. Voltage reading should be 8.2 volts. If reading is correct, service vehicle speed sensor.

3) If voltage is incorrect, probe wire at terminal "D" with connector at VSS buffer still disconnected. If voltage reading is 8.2 volts, locate open in wire from control module to VSS buffer and repair as necessary. If voltage is incorrect, replace control module.

Fig. 3: General Motors Custom Cruise III Wiring Diagram

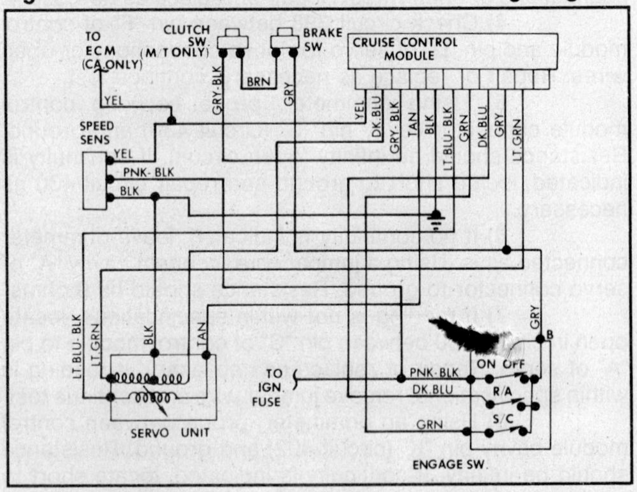

GENERAL MOTORS CUSTOM CRUISE III (Cont.)

CONTROL MODULE, SERVO & CRUISE CONTROL SWITCH CHECK

CONTROL SWITCH CONTINUITY CHECK

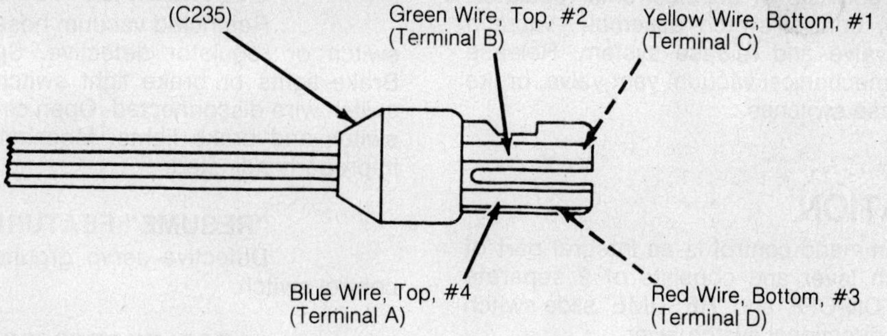

C – CLOSED
O – OPEN

SET/COAST (S/C) SW	POSITION SLIDER	1-2	1-3	1-4	2-3	2-4	3-4
NORMAL	OFF	O	O	O	O	O	O
NORMAL	ON	O	O	O	O	C	O
NORMAL	R/A	C	O	C	O	C	O
DEPRESSED	OFF	O	O	O	C	O	O
DEPRESSED	ON	O	O	O	C	C	C
DEPRESSED	R/A	C	C	C	C	C	C

CRUISE CONTROLLER (MODULE) CHECKS AT CONNECTOR

- IGNITION ON
- CONTROLLER DISCONNECTED

PIN	FUNCTION	VOLTAGE TO GND	RESISTANCE	CONDITIONS
G	BRAKE INPUT	12 V 0 V	– –	BRAKE (AND CLUTCH) NOT DEPRESSED SLIDER SWITCH "ON" BRAKE (AND/OR CLUTCH) DEPRESSED SLIDER SWITCH "ON"
L	SET/COAST INPUT	12 V 0 V 0 V	– – –	SLIDER SWITCH "ON" – SET/COAST DEPRESSED SLIDER SWITCH "ON" – SET/COAST NORMAL SLIDER SWITCH "OFF" – SET/COAST NORMAL
M	RESUME/ ACCEL. INPUT	12 V 0 V 0 V	– – –	SLIDER SWITCH "R/A" POSITION SLIDER SWITCH "ON" – SET/COAST DEPRESSED OR NORMAL SLIDER SWITCH "OFF" – SET/COAST DEPRESSED OR NORMAL
J	GROUND	–	0 Ω	MEASURED TO VEHICLE GROUND
A	ON/OFF INPUT	12 V 0 V	– –	SLIDER SWITCH "ON" SLIDER SWITCH "OFF" – SET/COAST DEPRESSED OR NORMAL
B	INDICATOR LAMP	12 V	–	CRUISE ARMED
F H	SPS HIGH SPS LOW	– –	20-30 Ω 0 Ω	MEASURED BETWEEN PINS F & H – SERVO CONNECTED MEASURED BETWEEN PINS F & H – SERVO DISCONNECTED
D	SPEED SIGNAL	→	→	SEE CHART (DIAGNOSTIC) ON SPEED SENDER TEST
K	VACUUM VALVE CONTROL	– –	30-50 Ω ∞ Ω	MEASURED TO GROUND – SERVO CONNECTED MEASURED TO GROUND – SERVO NOT CONNECTED
C	VENT VALVE CONTROL	– –	30-50 Ω ∞ Ω	MEASURED TO GROUND – SERVO CONNECTED MEASURED TO GROUND – SERVO NOT CONNECTED

SERVO CHECKS

- SERVO CONNECTOR DISCONNECTED
- MEASURE AT SERVO PINS

PIN	FUNCTION	RESISTANCE	CONDITIONS
D B	SPS HIGH SPS LOW	20-30 Ω	MEASURED BETWEEN PINS D AND B (IF MEASURED RESISTANCE IS NOT STATED VALVE, REPLACE SERVO)
A	VENT VALVE	30-50 Ω	MEASURED BETWEEN PINS A AND C (IF MEASURED RESISTANCE IS NOT STATED VALVE, REPLACE SERVO)
E	VACUUM VALVE	30-50 Ω	MEASURED BETWEEN PINS E AND C (IF MEASURED RESISTANCE IS NOT STATED VALVE, REPLACE SERVO)

Cruise Control Systems

JEEP CRUISE COMMAND

DESCRIPTION

Jeep vehicles use an electro-mechanical servo system. The system consists of an electronic regulator, speed sensor, servo, control switch assembly, vacuum storage can, check valve and release system. Release system consists of a mechanical vacuum vent valve, brake and clutch (M/T) release switches.

OPERATION

Cruise Command control is an integral part of the turn signal switch lever and consists of 2 separate switches. The first is "ON-OFF" and "RESUME" slide switch located on the flat of directional switch lever.

The second is a push button switch located at end of directional switch lever. To engage system, move slide switch to "ON" position and accelerate to desired speed. Depress and release button on end of switch lever. System will now maintain selected speed.

System will automatically disengage when brake or clutch pedal is depressed. It can be re-engaged to previously selected speed by accelerating to 30 MPH and moving slide switch to "RESUME" position, then releasing switch.

NOTE: **When slide switch is moved to "OFF" position, pre-set speed of "RESUME" function is canceled and must be reset when system is reactivated.**

A higher speed can be set by pressing on accelerator pedal until new speed is reached and then pushing control button. A lower speed can be achieved by lightly depressing brake pedal, allowing vehicle to slow to desired speed and then depressing and releasing push button. Operation of individual components is as follows:

ELECTRONIC REGULATOR

The electronic regulator receives an input voltage representing vehicle speed from the speed sensor, driven by the speedometer cable. The regulator has a low speed circuit that prevents operation at speeds below 30 MPH.

SPEED SENSOR

The speed sensor is installed between the upper and lower speedometer cables. It converts speedometer revolutions into a voltage input for the regulator.

SERVO

The servo is controlled by the regulator and uses manifold vacuum to control the throttle. A bead-link chain connects the servo cable to the throttle linkage.

CONTROL SWITCH

The control switch assembly is an integral part of the turn signal switch lever.

RELEASE SYSTEM

The release system deactivates cruise control system when brake or clutch pedal is depressed. Either a servo vent valve or a mechanical vacuum vent switch admits atmospheric pressure into servo when brake pedal is depressed.

TROUBLE SHOOTING

SYSTEM WILL NOT ENGAGE

Restricted vacuum hose or no vacuum. Control switch or regulator defective. Speed sensor defective. Brake lights or brake light switch defective. Brake light switch wire disconnected. Open circuit between brake light switch and brake lights. Mechanical vent valve position improperly adjusted.

"RESUME" FEATURE INOPERATIVE

Defective servo ground connection. Defective control switch.

"ACCELERATE" FUNCTION INOPERATIVE

Accelerate circuit in regulator inoperative. Defective control switch.

SYSTEM RE-ENGAGES WHEN BRAKE PEDAL IS RELEASED

Defective regulator. Mechanical vent valve not opening. Kink in mechanical vent valve hose. Brake light switch defective.

CARBURETOR THROTTLE DOES NOT RETURN TO IDLE POSITION

Improper linkage adjustment.

ROAD SPEED CHANGES MORE THAN 2 MPH WHEN SETTING SPEED

Centering adjustment wrong.

Fig. 1: Wiring Diagram for Jeep Cruise Command

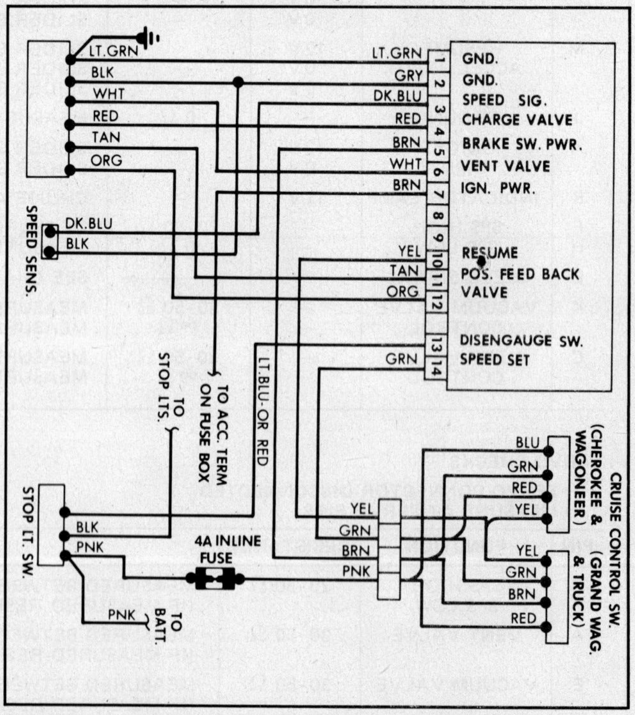

Diagram applies to Scrambler, Grand Wagoneer and Pickup models.

JEEP CRUISE COMMAND (Cont.)

Fig. 2: Cherokee & Wagoneer Control Switch Continuity Test Chart

SET/COAST (S/C) SW	POSITION SLIDER	1-2	1-3	1-4	2-3	2-4	3-4
Normal	Off	O	O	O	O	O	O
Normal	On	O	O	O	O	C	O
Normal	R/A	C	O	C	O	C	O
Depressed	Off	O	O	O	C	O	O
Depressed	On	O	O	O	C	C	C
Depressed	R/A	C	C	C	C	C	C

C - Closed

O - Open

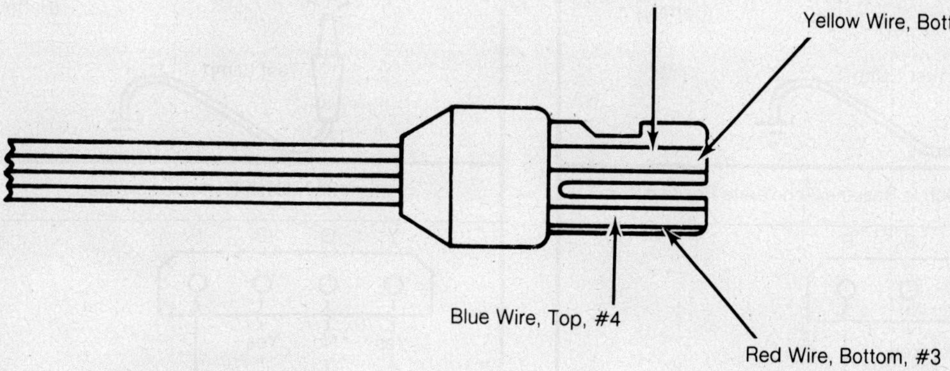

ENGINE ACCELERATES WHEN STARTED

Improper chain adjustment. Vacuum hose connections reversed at servo. Defective servo.

SYSTEM DISENGAGES ON LEVEL ROAD WITHOUT APPLYING BRAKE

Loose wire connection. Loose vacuum hose connection. Servo linkage broken. Defective brake light switch.

ERRATIC OPERATION

Reverse polarity. Defective servo. Defective regulator.

VEHICLE CONTINUES TO ACCELERATE WHEN "SET" BUTTON IS RELEASED

Servo or regulator defective.

SYSTEM ENGAGES BUT SLOWLY LOSES SET SPEED

Air leak at connections or in vacuum hoses. Air leak on vent valve on brake pedal.

DIAGNOSIS & TESTING

PRELIMINARY INSPECTION

Ensure that cruise control wire harness is properly connected to regulator before starting diagnosis or repair procedure, as this connection is disturbed when Cruise Command System Tester (AM PC-1-R) is used. A poor connection at this point may be improperly diagnosed as a regulator malfunction. Brake light and clutch switch should be properly adjusted.

CRUISE COMMAND SYSTEM TESTS

Testing is performed with Cruise Command System Tester (AM PC-1-R). Remove wire harness connector from regulator. Connect tester to wire harness connector. Perform the following tests as part of service diagnosis to determine the cause and correction of system malfunction. Various tester lamps are associated with specific components, circuits, etc.

CONTROL SWITCH CONTINUITY

Use a 12-volt test lamp to test control switch continuity. Connect test lamp to wires as indicated in Control Switch Test Chart. *See Fig. 2 or 3.*

JEEP CRUISE COMMAND (Cont.)

Fig. 3: CJ7, Scrambler, Grand Wagoneer & Truck Control Switch Continuity Test Chart

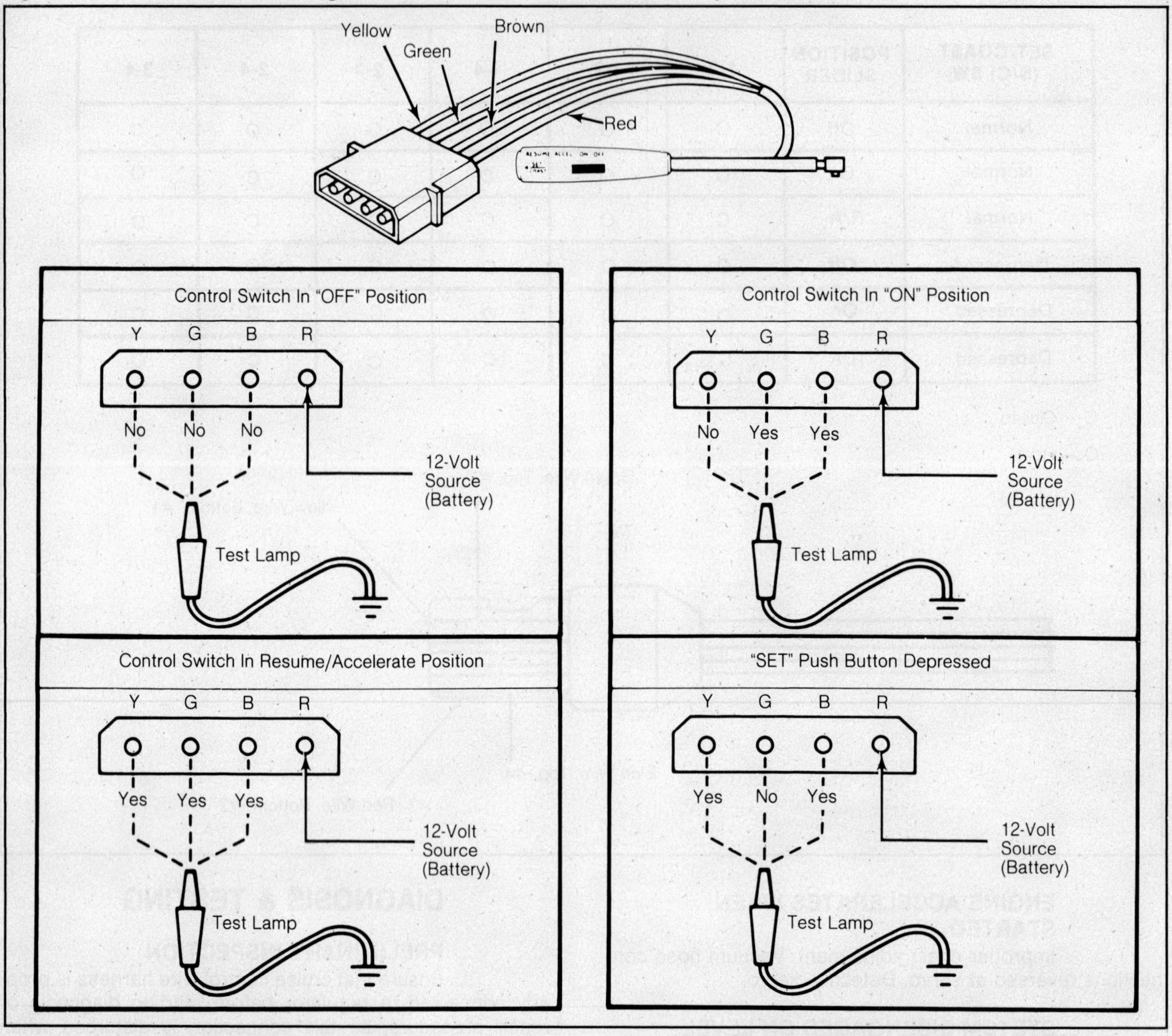

CORRECT POWER SOURCE

Cherokee & Wagoneer Models

1) With ignition switch and control switch off, all test lamps should be off. If any lamp is on, check that Brown (7) wire is connected directly to source of voltage, and check for bad control switch. With ignition switch off, and control switch on, lamps 2 and 3 should be on, lamps 1, 4, 5 and 6 should be off.

2) If lamp 2 is off, check speed sensor continuity, check speed sensor terminals to Gray and Dk. Blue wires, check terminals 2, 3, 5 and 7 (Gray, Dk. Blue and Lt. Green wires are not grounded). If lamp 3 is off, check brake light switch, check all Brown, Lt. Blue and Lt. Green wire connections.

All Other Models

With ignition switch and control switch off, all test lamps should be off. If one or more lamps are on, remove Brown (5) wire at regulator connector and check for direct source of voltage or repair defective control switch.

SYSTEM ELECTRICAL CONTINUITY

Cherokee & Wagoneer Models

1) With ignition and control switch on, lamps 2, 3 and 4 should be on. Lamps 1, 5 and 6 should be off. If lamp 2 is off, check speed sensor continuity, check speed sensor terminals to Gray and Dk. Blue wires, check terminals 2, 3, 5 and 7 (Gray, Dk. Blue and Lt. Green wires are not grounded).

2) If lamp 3 is off, check brake light switch and all Brown, Lt. Blue and Lt. Green wire connections. If lamp 4 is off, check terminals 2 and 11 at regulator connector, check continuity of throttle position feedback rheostat of servo.

All Other Models

1) With ignition and control switch on, lamps 1, 2, 3, and 4 should be on. Lamps 5 and 6 should be off. If lamp 1 is off, check for blown fuse in brake light switch to control switch circuit. Check Red, Brown and Green wires

JEEP CRUISE COMMAND (Cont.)

at control switch for continuity to switch. Check Dk. Green wire (14) at regulator connector for continuity to regulator.

2) If lamp 2 is off, check speed sensor for correct output voltage. Check Gray and Dk. Blue wire at speed sensor connector for continuity to regulator connector. Check terminals 2, 3, 5 and 7 at regulator connector for proper connection to wires.

3) If lamp 3 is off, check brake and clutch switch adjustment. If lamp 4 is off, check for defective connection at terminals 2 and 11 on regulator connector. Check operation of throttle position feedback rheostat on servo.

COAST CONTINUITY TEST

Cherokee & Wagoneer Models

1) With ignition and control switch on, and set switch depressed, lamps 1, 2, 3 and 4 should be on. Lamps 5 and 6 should be off. If lamp 1 is off, check voltage from brake light switch, check 4 Amp in-line fuse in Pink wire, check Pink, Brown and Dk. Green wires at control switch connector and Dk. Green (14) wire at regulator connector for good connections.

2) If lamp 2 is off, check speed sensor continuity, check speed sensor terminals to Gray and Dk. Blue wires, check terminals 2, 3, 5 and 7 (Gray, Dk. Blue and Lt. Green wires are not grounded).

3) If lamp 3 is off, check brake light switch, check all Brown, Lt. Blue and Lt. Green wire connections. If lamp 4 is off, check terminals 2 and 11 at regulator connector, check continuity of throttle position feedback rheostat of servo.

SERVO CHARGE VALVE SOLENOID CONTINUITY

CAUTION: **If engine is running, servo will move throttle to wide open position.**

All Except Cherokee & Wagoneer Models

1) With ignition and control switch on, and set switch depressed, lamps 2, 3, 4, 5 and 6 should be on. Lamp 4 will dim when servo moves throttle to wide open position with engine operating.

2) If lamp 2 is off, check speed sensor for correct output voltage. Check Gray and Dk. Blue wire at speed sensor connector for continuity to regulator connector. Check terminals 2, 3, 5 and 7 at regulator connector for proper connection to wires.

3) If lamp 3 is off, check brake and clutch switch adjustment. If lamp 4 is off, check for defective connection at terminals 2 and 11 on regulator connector. Check operation of throttle position feedback rheostat on servo.

4) If lamp 5 is off, check for defective connections at terminals 4 and 12 on regulator connector. If necessary, replace defective servo. If lamp 6 is off, check for defective connection at terminals 6 and 12 on regulator connector. If necessary, replace defective servo.

5) If all lamps are off after depressing set speed switch, check for blown fuse. Check for short circuits in Red, Pink and Brown wire circuits at control switch. If necessary, replace defective servo.

SYSTEM DISENGAGEMENT WITH BRAKE PEDAL DEPRESSED

Cherokee & Wagoneer Models

1) With ignition and control switch on, and brake pedal depressed, lamps 2 and 4 should be on. Lamps 1, 3, 5 and 6 should be off. Lamp 3 should be on when brake pedal is released.

2) If lamp 2 is off, check speed sensor continuity, check speed sensor terminals to Gray and Dk. Blue wires, check terminals 2, 3, 5 and 7 (Gray, Dk. Blue and Lt. Green wires are not grounded).

3) If lamp 4 is off, check terminals 2 and 11 at regulator connector, check continuity of throttle position feedback rheostat of servo.

All Except Cherokee & Wagoneer Models

1) With ignition and control switch on, and brake pedal depressed, lamps 1, 2 and 4 should be on. Lamps 3, 5 and 6 should be off. Lamp 3 should be on when brake pedal is released.

2) If lamp 1 is off, check for blown fuse in brake light switch to control switch circuit. Check Red, Brown and Green wires at control switch for continuity to switch. Check Dk. Green wire (14) at regulator connector for continuity to regulator.

3) If lamp 2 is off, check speed sensor for correct output voltage. Check Gray and Dk. Blue wire at speed sensor connector for continuity to regulator connector. Check terminals 2, 3, 5 and 7 at regulator connector for proper connection to wires.

4) If lamp 4 is off, check for defective connection at terminals 2 and 11 on regulator connector. Check operation of throttle position feedback rheostat on servo. If lamp 3 is off when brake pedal is released, check brake light switch adjustment.

"RESUME/ACCEL" FUNCTION

CAUTION: **If engine is running, servo will move throttle to wide open position.**

Cherokee & Wagoneer Models

1) With ignition and control switch "ON", move control switch to "R/A" position, lamps 2, 3, 4, 5 and 6 should be on. Lamp 1 should be off. Lamp 4 will dim when servo moves throttle to wide open position, if engine is running.

2) If lamp 2 is off, check speed sensor continuity, check speed sensor terminals to Gray and Dk. Blue wires, check terminals 2, 3, 5 and 7 (Gray, Dk. Blue and Lt. Green wires are not grounded).

3) If lamp 3 is off, check brake light switch, check all Brown, Lt. Blue and Lt. Green wire connections. If lamp 4 is off, check terminals 2 and 11 at regulator connector, check continuity of throttle position feedback rheostat of servo.

4) If lamp 5 is off, check for bad connection at White (6) and Orange (12) wire terminals. If necessary, replace servo. If lamp 6 is off, check for bad connection at Red (4) or Orange (12) wire terminals. If necessary, replace defective servo.

5) If all lamps are off after moving control switch to "R/A" position, check for blown fuse or fuses, check Red, Pink, Brown or White wires for shorts. If necessary replace defective servo.

All Other Models

1) With ignition and control switch on, move control switch to "R/A" position. All test lamps should be on. Lamp 4 will dim when servo moves throttle to wide open position, if engine is running.

2) If lamp 1 is off, check for blown fuse in brake light switch to control switch circuit. Check Red, Brown and Green wires at control switch for continuity to switch. Check

JEEP CRUISE COMMAND (Cont.)

Dk. Green wire (14) at regulator connector for continuity to regulator.

3) If lamp 2 is off, check speed sensor for correct output voltage. Check Gray and Dk. Blue wire at speed sensor connector for continuity to regulator connector. Check terminals 2, 3, 5 and 7 at regulator connector for proper connection to wires.

4) If lamp 3 is off, check brake light switch adjustment. If lamp 4 is off, check for defective connection at terminals 2 and 11 on regulator connector. Check operation of throttle position feedback rheostat on servo.

5) If lamp 5 is off, check for defective connections at terminals 4 and 12 on regulator connector. If necessary, replace defective servo. If lamp 6 is off, check for defective connection at terminals 6 and 12 on regulator connector. If necessary, replace defective servo.

6) If all lamps are off after moving control switch to "R/A" position, check for blown fuse. Check for short circuits in Red, Pink and Brown wire circuits at control switch. If necessary, replace defective servo.

SPEED SENSOR TEST

1) Disconnect wire harness connector at speed sensor. Connect a voltmeter (set on low AC scale) to wire terminals from speed sensor.

2) Raise front and rear wheels of vehicle off ground and support vehicle with safety stands. Operate engine (wheels spinning freely) at 30 MPH and note voltage.

3) Voltage should be approximately 0.9 volts. Increases of 0.1 volts per each 10 MPH increase in speed should also be noticed. Turn off engine and stop wheels. Lower vehicle. Connect speed sensor wire harness. Lower vehicle.

SERVO TEST

1) With ignition switch off, disconnect servo wire harness connector. Remove vacuum hose from brake pedal vent valve nipple on servo. Disconnect servo cable from throttle linkage at carburetor.

2) Connect an ohmmeter between ground and Red, then Orange, then White wire terminals of servo wire harness connector. *See Fig. 4.* Observe ohmmeter during each test, an infinite (open circuit) resistance should be indicated for each wire terminal.

3) If ohmmeter indicates less than infinite resistance on any terminal, servo has short circuit to ground and must be replaced. Short circuit will also cause damage to regulator and it must be replaced.

NOTE: **Without sufficient load, solid state circuitry in regulator will be damaged by excessive current flow. For this reason, perform steps 4)-8) with transmission in Park (Neutral for M/T).**

4) If servo does not have any short circuits to ground, connect a vacuum gauge to brake pedal vent valve nipple. Connect a jumper wire from chassis ground to Orange wire terminal in servo wire harness connector.

5) Connect a second jumper wire to battery positive terminal and start engine. Momentarily connect jumper wire and simultaneously touch Red and White wire terminals in servo wire harness connector.

6) Vacuum should be indicated on gauge while jumper wire is in contact with wire terminals. Perform this test several times to ensure that solenoid valves are working properly.

7) With no voltage applied, solenoid charge valve is closed and solenoid vent valve is open. With 12 volts applied, solenoid charge valve is open and vent valve is closed.

8) Turn engine off and remove jumper wires. If servo is defective, replace it. If okay, connect vacuum hose, wire harness connector and throttle linkage to servo.

Fig. 4: Servo Wire Harness Connector

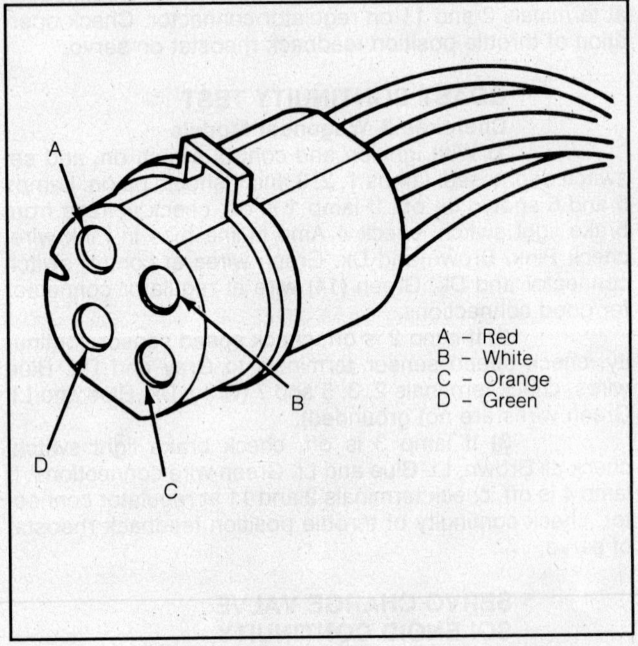

ADJUSTMENT

BRAKE LIGHT SWITCH ADJUSTMENT

All Models, Except Cherokee & Wagoneer

1) If equipped with A/C, remove screws attaching evaporator housing to instrument panel, move housing away from panel. On all models, depress and hold brake pedal in applied position. Push brake light switch through mounting bracket until it stops against brake pedal bracket.

2) Release brake pedal to set brake light switch in proper position. The switch plunger should be in "ON" position after 3/8-5/8" brake pedal travel. Measure brake pedal travel at center of brake pedal pad. If equipped with A/C, reposition and secure evaporator housing.

REGULATOR ADJUSTMENT

NOTE: **Regulator adjustments are preset by manufacturer, if other components in system appear to be funtioning properly and cruise control remains inoperative, perform following adjustments to determine if regulator is funtional.**

1) Remove regulator attaching screws or tie straps and move regulator downward for adjustment access. Turn centering adjustment screw to 10 o'clock position. Turn low speed adjustment screw to 10 o'clock position. Turn sensitivity adjustment screw fully clockwise.

CAUTION: **Adjustment potentiometers are extremely delicate. Carefully insert screwdriver and do not push or turn screws hard against wiper stops. Maximum movement is 3/4 of a turn.**

JEEP CRUISE COMMAND (Cont.)

2) Adjustments are not precisely correct for vehicle, but are acceptable to determine if regulator is functioning. Perform precise adjustments by road testing vehicle on level road. If adjustments have no effect on cruise control, replace regulator.

3) If actual engagement speed is more than 2 MPH or more above selected speed, stop vehicle and turn centering screw 1/16 of a turn counterclockwise. Recheck engagement speed and adjust as necessary.

4) If engagement speed is 2 MPH or more below selected speed, turn centering screw 1/16 of a turn clockwise. Recheck engagement speed and adjust as necessary.

VACUUM VENT VALVE

Depress brake or clutch pedal and hold in depressed position. Move vacuum vent valve toward bracket on pedal as far as possible. Release brake or clutch pedal.

Fig. 5: Regulator Adjustment Screws

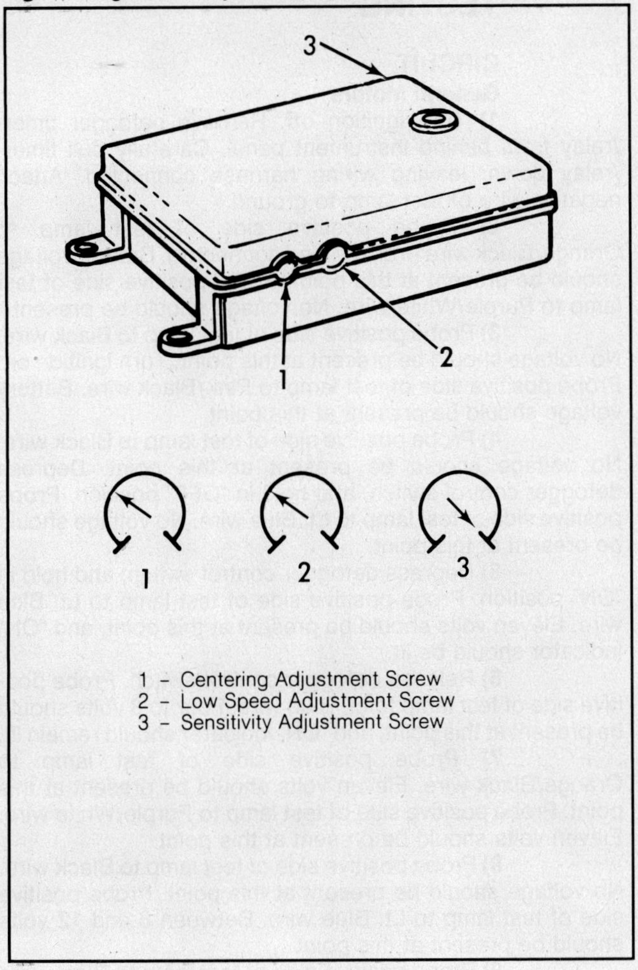

Defoggers

REAR WINDOW – ALL MANUFACTURERS

Chrysler Corp. Vans & Wagons; Ford Bronco & Bronco II; General Motors "S" Series Blazer/Jimmy; Jeep Cherokee, Grand Wagoneer, J10/20, Wagoneer

DESCRIPTION

Chrysler

Heated rear window system, consists of 2 bus bars, heating elements baked on inside of glass, a control switch, 25 amp fuse, and a continuous or timed relay.

Ford

A heated rear window defogger system is available on Bronco and Bronco II. System consists of a control assembly mounted in center of instrument panel, an indicator light, a series of grid lines baked on inside surface of rear window and system wiring.

The grid line consists of two layers. Layer 1 is Brown in color as viewed from outside. Layer 2 is Silver in color as viewed from interior.

General Motors

The heated rear window defogger is a 12 volt, 20 amp system consisting of a control assembly mounted in center of instrument panel, a timer/relay, a "SYSTEM ON" indicator light, a series of grid lines baked to inside surface of a tinted rear window and system wiring.

Jeep

A heated rear window defogger system is available on all series except CJ7 and Scrambler. System consists of 2 vertical bus bars and horizontal rows of heating elements fused to inside of glass, a control switch, an indicator light, and timer relay.

OPERATION

Chrysler

With ignition and control switches turned on, continuous relay will remain on until ignition or switch is turned off. Timed relay will operate 8 to 12 minutes. Relay is mounted to right of switch on lower dash panel. An indicator lamp on dash glows when system is operating.

Ford

A spring loaded switch turns system on or off, a timer controlled relay turns system off after approximately 10 minutes of operation. When switch is in "ON" position, normally open contacts in control assembly are mechanically closed thus providing current to grids, indicator lamp and triggering timing circuit.

The contacts will remain closed until timer turns system off, "ON/OFF" switch is turned off or if ignition switch is turned off. Power to grids and indicator light are supplied directly from battery side of starter motor through a fusible link which protects circuit.

Power for control timer comes from accessory terminal of ignition switch. Power is available when switch is in "RUN" or "ACC". This circuit is protected by a 15-ampere fuse, located in fuse block.

General Motors

Voltage is constantly applied through accessory circuit breaker, to relay contacts in defogger timer/relay. When ignition is turned on, power is supplied through instrument panel gauge fuse, to timer in defogger timer-/relay.

Depressing spring loaded control switch turns system on, and supplies power to defogger timer, closing relay contacts. Current flow then heats defogger grid wires.

Timer controlled relay turns system off after about 10 minutes of operation. If control switch is immediately depressed, timer will operate defogger for 5 additional minutes.

Jeep

The grid feed wire is connected to bus bar on left (driver's) side of window. Ground bus bar is on right side of vehicle. Timer/relay receives current from fuse block. A circuit breaker protects defogger circuit.

NOTE: **On Jeep models, the defogger switch and electric tailgate switch are serviced as an assembly.**

TESTING

CIRCUIT

General Motors

1) Turn ignition off. Remove defogger timer-/relay from behind instrument panel. Carefully pull timer-/relay down, leaving wiring harness connected. Attach negative wire of test lamp to ground.

2) Probe positive side of test lamp to Orange/Black wire (from behind connector). Battery voltage should be present at this point. Probe positive side of test lamp to Purple/White wire. No voltage should be present.

3) Probe positive side of test lamp to Black wire. No voltage should be present at this point. Turn ignition on. Probe positive side of test lamp to Pink/Black wire. Battery voltage should be present at this point.

4) Probe positive side of test lamp to Black wire. No voltage should be present at this point. Depress defogger control switch, and hold in "OFF" position. Probe positive side of test lamp to Lt. Blue wire. No voltage should be present at this point.

5) Depress defogger control switch, and hold in "ON" position. Probe positive side of test lamp to Lt. Blue wire. Eleven volts should be present at this point, and "ON" indicator should be lit.

6) Release defogger control switch. Probe positive side of test lamp to Lt. Blue wire. Four to 8 volts should be present at this point, and "ON" indicator should remain lit.

7) Probe positive side of test lamp to Orange/Black wire. Eleven volts should be present at this point. Probe positive side of test lamp to Purple/White wire. Eleven volts should be present at this point.

8) Probe positive side of test lamp to Black wire. No voltage should be present at this point. Probe positive side of test lamp to Lt. Blue wire. Between 8 and 12 volts should be present at this point.

9) Probe positive side of test lamp to Black wire on passenger's side of rear window defogger. No voltage should be present at this point. Probe positive side of test lamp to Black wire on driver's side of rear window defogger. Ten to 11 volts should be present at this point.

10) Probe positive side of test lamp to middle of defogger grid. Ten to 11 volts should be present at this point. Depress and release defogger control switch. "ON" indicator should go out. Install defogger timer/relay.

REAR WINDOW – ALL MANUFACTURERS (Cont.)

CONTROL SWITCH

Chrysler

With switch in "NORMAL" position, there should be continuity between 2 terminals. With switch in "ON" position, there should be continuity between all switch terminals. With switch in "OFF" position, there should be no continuity between terminals.

Ford

1) Remove instrument panel center finish panel. Remove 2 screws securing control assembly. Disconnect connector and remove control assembly.

2) Connect a jumper wire between ground pin and a good ground. Connect a jumper wire between ignition switch pin and battery pin. Connect a 12 volt test lamp between load (grid) pin and ground.

3) Apply power to battery pin. Test lamp should not light. Momentarily set switch to "ON" position. Test lamp should come on and stay on after switch returns to normal (center) position.

4) Test lamp should go off if switch is moved to "OFF" position, or a jumper wire is connected between ignition switch pin and battery pin, or after approximately 10 minutes have elapsed.

Jeep

1) On Cherokee & Wagoneer series, turn ignition switch on, and check for current at at "I" and "B" terminals. *See Fig. 1.* If there is no current, check circuit and repair as necessary. Ensure that switch has a good ground through wire connected to "G" terminal.

2) With a good ground circuit and ignition switch in "ON" position, current should be present at "L" terminal. If there is no current, replace control switch.

Fig. 1: Jeep Control Switch Terminals

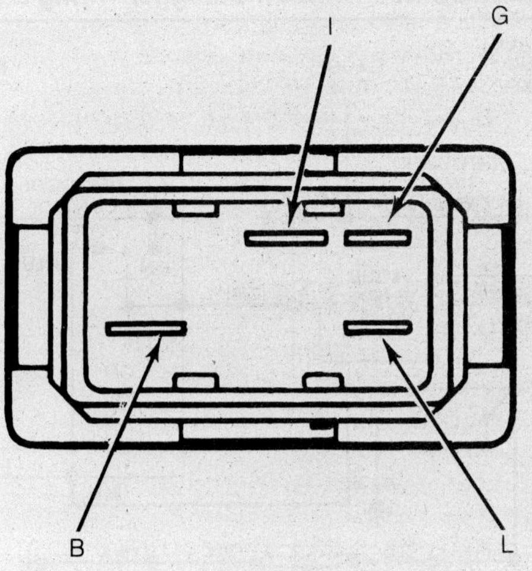

Jeep

On Grand Wagoneer & Truck series, turn ignition switch on, and press defogger switch. Separate wiring harness at connector under dash. Connect a 12-volt test lamp from Purple wire to ground. Test lamp should light. Turn defogger switch off. Test lamp should not light.

GRID

Chrysler

1) Using a voltmeter with a 0-15 volt range, contact bus bar connecting grid lines on right (Feed) side of glass with negative lead of voltmeter. Contact left bus bar with positive lead.

2) Turn ignition and control switches on. Reading should be 10-14 volts. Lower voltage indicates a poor ground. Attach negative lead to ground. Voltage reading should not vary.

3) Contact negative lead to left side bus bar. Probe each grid line at midpoint with positive lead. A 6 volt reading indicates line is good. A reading of 0 volts indicates a break in the line between the midpoint and the right bus bar.

4) A 10-14 volt reading indicates a break between midpoint and left bus bar. Move positive lead toward break and voltage will change when break is crossed.

Jeep

1) Use a 12-volt voltmeter, and connect positive lead to left (feed) side of vertical element on inside of glass. Connect negative lead to right side of vertical element. Voltage drop should be 11 to 13 volts with ignition on.

2) Connect negative lead of voltmeter to ground, meter reading should remain constant. Keeping negative lead connected to ground, carefully use positive lead to contact each grid at center of window.

3) A voltage reduction to 6 volts indicates a good grid. Voltage reduction of 12 volts at center of grid wire indicates a break between positive voltmeter lead and ground. No voltage reduction (0 volts) at center of grid wire indicates a break between center and feed wires.

4) Exact location of break can be determined by moving positive voltmeter lead left or right until an abrupt change in voltage is noticed.

All Manufacturers

NOTE: **On Jeep Grand Wagoneer and Trucks only, feed wire is connected on right side of window (passenger's side) and ground connection is on left side.**

1) Using a strong light source inside vehicle, visually inspect grid from outside vehicle. A broken grid will appear as a Brown spot.

2) Run engine at idle and set control switch to "ON" position. Indicator light should come on. Working inside vehicle with a 12 volt voltmeter, contact Red-Brown strips on back window.

3) Meter should read 10-13 volts. A lower voltage indicates a loose ground wire. Contact a good ground point with negative lead of meter, voltage reading should not change.

4) With negative lead grounded, probe each grid line at its mid-point position with positive lead. A reading of approximately 6 volts indicates a good grid line.

5) A reading of 0 volts indicates an in-line break between battery (positive) side of grid line. A reading of 12 volts indicates a broken circuit between grid line mid-point and ground.

INDICATOR LIGHT

Jeep

On Grand Wagoneer & Truck series, disconnect Orange wire from lamp. Connect jumper wire from accessory terminal to Orange wire. With ignition turned to "ACCESSORY" position, lamp should light.

REAR WINDOW – ALL MANUFACTURERS (Cont.)

RELAY

Chrysler

1) Remove relay. On continuous relay, ground housing. On timed relay, ground terminal "G". *See Fig. 2.* Connect jumper wire from terminal "B" to terminal "Y". Connect a 12 volt test lamp from terminal "L" of relay to ground.

2) Apply 12 volts to terminal "B". Test lamp should not light. If lamp comes on, replace relay.

3) Short terminal "B" and terminal "P" for a few seconds. Lamp should light and stay on for 8 to 12 minutes on timed relays and until turned off on continuous relays. If lamp does not light, replace relay.

Jeep

1) On Grand Wagoneer & Truck series, attach negative lead of voltmeter to ground. Probe Red wire with voltmeter positive lead. Battery voltage should be indicated. If no voltage is indicated, operate tailgate window.

2) If window operates, wire between relay and window switch is open. Probe Orange wire with voltmeter positive lead. No voltage should be indicated. Turn ignition switch on. Voltmeter should indicate voltage. If not, relay is defective or not receiving voltage from Purple wire.

3) If relay operates properly, it should remain energized for 8 to 12 minutes before opening. If time period is too short or too long, relay is defective. If relay did not energize, connect a jumper wire to a known good 12-volt source in tailgate and probe relay Purple terminal.

4) If relay "clicks", trace Purple wire for open or short. If relay does not click, check relay ground. If ground is satisfactory, relay should be replaced.

Fig. 2: Chrysler Relay Terminals

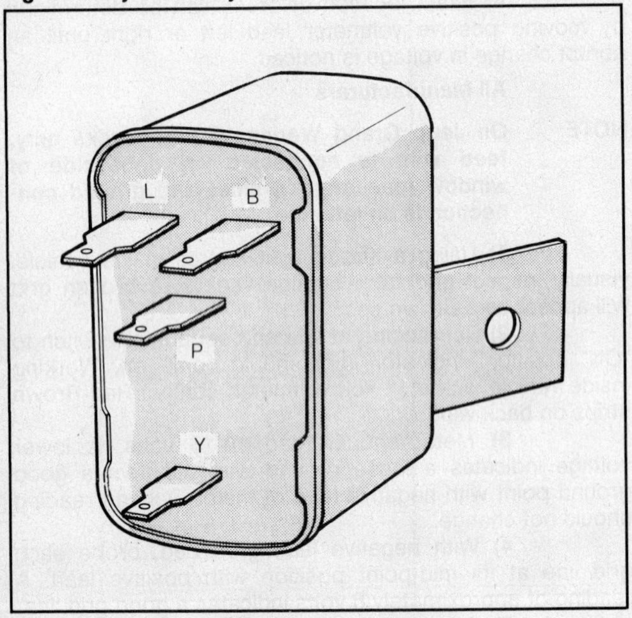

Fig. 3: Chrysler Rear Window Defogger Wiring Diagram

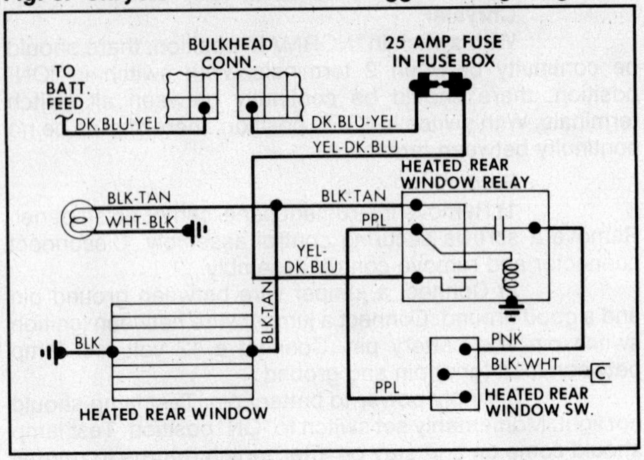

Fig. 4: Ford Rear Window Defogger Wiring Diagram

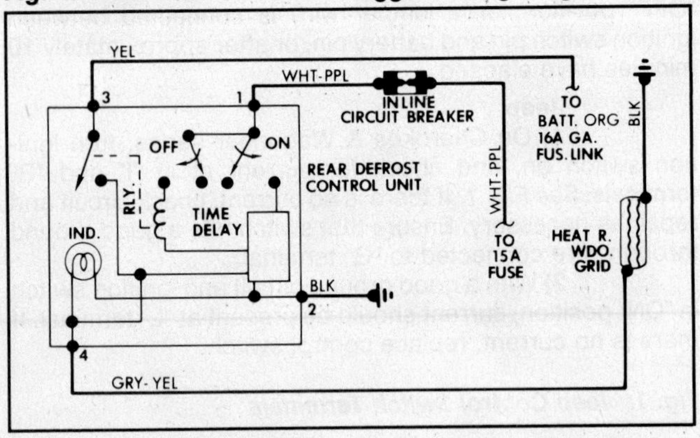

Fig. 5: GM/GMC Rear Window Defogger Wiring Diagram

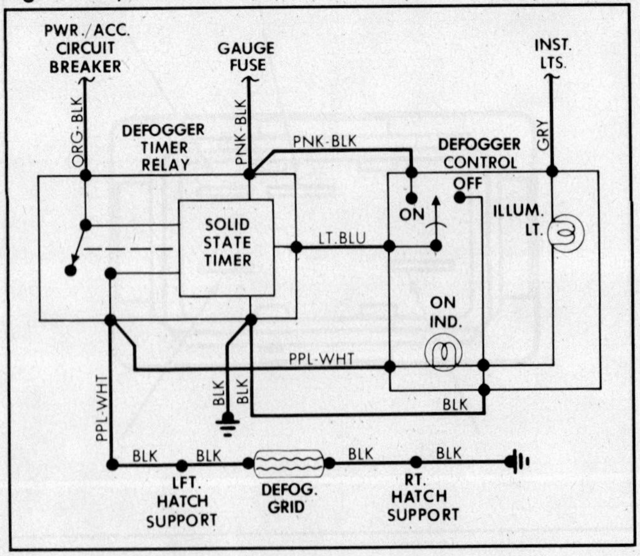

REAR WINDOW – ALL MANUFACTURERS (Cont.)

Fig. 6: Jeep Grand Wagoneer & Truck Rear Window Defogger Wiring Diagram

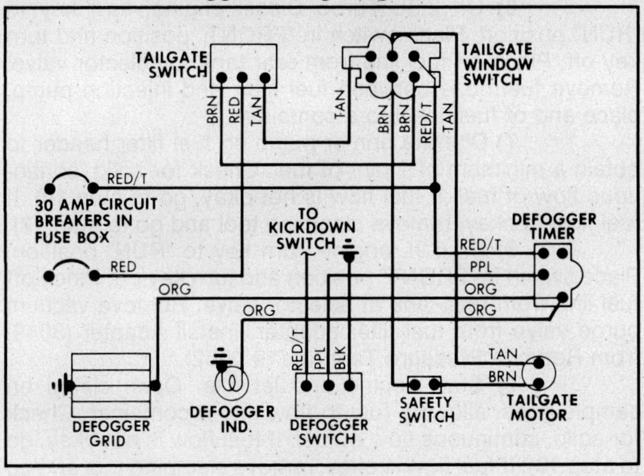

Fig. 7: Jeep Cherokee & Wagoneer Rear Window Defogger Wiring Diagram

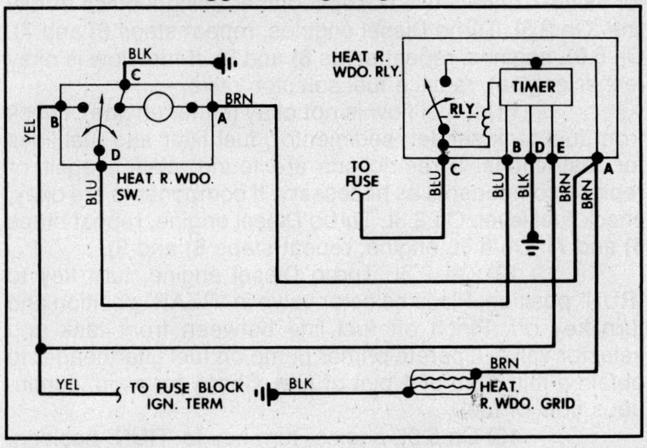

Fig. 8: Grid Continuity Voltage Drop

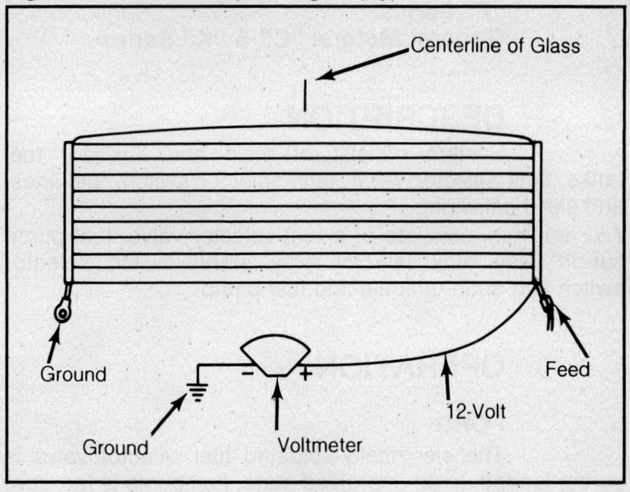

Electric Fuel Selector Valves

FORD & GENERAL MOTORS

Ford: Bronco, Bronco II, Ranger, "E" & "F" Series
General Motors: "C" & "K" Series

DESCRIPTION

System consist of main and auxiliary fuel tanks, tank selector valve, tank selector switch, fuel lines, and electrical wiring.
7.5L engines, consists of a fuel selector valve, fuel pump cut-off relay, tank selector relay, inertia switch, selector switch and an in-tank electric fuel pump.

OPERATION

FORD

The electrically-actuated fuel selector valve is spring-loaded. In de-energized state, fuel pump is fed from rear tank. When activated by battery voltage through selector switch, fuel feed transfers from rear to front tank.

An electrically-actuated, 6-port, fuel selector valve is used in vehicles equipped with 2.3L Turbo Diesel, 6.9L Diesel and 7.5L engines.

GENERAL MOTORS

Instrument panel-mounted switch controls both fuel selector valve and fuel gauge indication. Six port fuel selector valve is electrically-actuated. Depressing upper and lower halves of switch feeds fuel from right and left side fuel tanks respectively.

TESTING

FORD

Vehicles with Diesel Engines

1) Turn key to "RUN" position. Place switch in "FRONT" position. Disconnect selector valve connector. Check voltage between terminals 2 and 1. If okay, go to step **2)**. If no voltage is present, go to step **3)**.

2) Using a jumper wire, connect motor terminal 2 to battery positive post. Using a second jumper wire, connect motor terminal 1 to ground. Motor should run. Reverse jumper wires, motor should run in opposite direction. If motor does not run in one or both directions, replace motor. If motor runs in both directions, go to step **4)**.

3) Check voltage across fuse No.7 (No. 15 on 6.9L engines) in fuse block. If fuse is blown, repair shorts in selector valve circuit. Replace fuse, repeat test starting at step **1)**. If fuse is okay, check voltage between terminal 2 and ground. If okay, check for open ground circuit from motor, through switch to ground. If ground circuit is not okay, repair ground circuit. If ground circuit is okay, go to step **4)**

4) Remove selector valve switch knob and trim bezel. Remove switch mounting screws and disconnect switch from harness connector. With switch in "FRONT" position, check continuity between terminals 2 and 4, and between terminals 1 and 3. Place switch in "REAR" position, check continuity between terminals 1 and 4, and between terminals 2 and 3.

5) If continuity is not okay, replace selector valve switch. If continuity is okay, check continuity of Orange wire (circuit 974) and Brown/White wire (circuit 674) between selector switch and selector valve. If continuity is not okay, repair open circuits. If continuity is okay, go to step **6)**.

6) On 2.3L Turbo Diesel engine, turn key to "RUN" position. Place switch in "FRONT" position and turn key off. Pinch off fuel line from rear tank to selector valve. Remove fuel hose between fuel filter and injection pump, place end of fuel line into a container.

7) Operate primer pump on fuel filter header to obtain a minimum of 1 pint of fuel. Check for solid, continuous flow of fuel. If fuel flow is not okay, go to step **10)**. If fuel flow is okay, remove clamping tool and go to step **12)**.

8) On 6.9L engine, turn key to "RUN" position. Place switch in "FRONT" position and turn key off. Pinch off fuel line from rear tank at selector valve. Remove vacuum purge valve from fuel filter adapter. Install Adapter (3019) from Rotunda Pressure Test Kit (19 0002).

9) Start engine and let idle. Open clamp on sample hose, allowing fuel to flow into a container. Check for solid, continuous flow of fuel. If fuel flow is not okay, go to step **10)**. If fuel flow is okay, remove clamping tool and go to step **13)**.

10) Disconnect supply hose to engine at selector valve. Disconnect supply hose from front tank at selector valve. Connect two hoses together using a piece of fuel line. On 2.3L Turbo Diesel engines, repeat steps **6)** and **7)**. On 6.9L engines, repeat steps **8)** and **9)**. If fuel flow is okay (either engine), replace fuel selector valve.

11) If fuel flow is not okay (either engine), check front fuel tank sender, sedimentor, fuel filter and fuel lines for restrictions. If restrictions are found, clean, repair or replace components as necessary. If components are okay, check fuel level. On 2.3L Turbo Diesel engine, repeat steps **6)** and **7)**. On 6.9L engine, repeat steps **8)** and **9)**.

12) On 2.3L Turbo Diesel engine, turn key to "RUN" position. Place selector valve in "REAR" position and turn key off. Pinch off fuel line between front tank and selector valve. Operate primer pump on fuel filter header to obtain a minimum of 1 pint of fuel. Check for solid, continuous flow of fuel.

13) On 6.9L engine, turn key to "RUN" position. Place switch in "REAR" position and turn key off. Pinch off fuel line between front tank and selector valve. Remove vacuum purge valve from fuel filter adapter. Install Adapter (3019) from Rotunda Pressure Test Kit (19 0002). Start engine and let idle. Open clamp on sample hose, allowing fuel to flow into a container. Check for a solid, continuous flow of fuel.

14) If fuel flow is not okay (either engine), go to step **15)**. If fuel flow is okay (either engine), fuel supply system is okay. Connect fuel line to fuel injection pump. Remove clamping tool from front tank supply line and go to step **17)**.

15) Disconnect supply hose to engine at selector valve. Disconnect supply hose from rear tank at selector valve. Connect two hoses together using a piece of fuel line. On 2.3L Turbo Diesel engine, repeat steps **6)** and **7)**. On 6.9L engine, repeat steps **8)** and **9)**. On all vehciles, if fuel flow is okay, replace selector valve.

16) If fuel flow is not okay, check rear fuel tank sender and fuel lines to selector valve for restrictions. If restrictions are found, clean, repair or replace components and repeat step **15)**. If components are okay, check fuel tank fuel level and repeat step **15)**.

17) Disconnect fuel return hose from engine at selector valve and insert line into a container. Turn key to "RUN" position and place switch in "FRONT" or "REAR"

FORD & GENERAL MOTORS (Cont.)

position (problem tank). Start engine and check for a solid, continuous flow of fuel.

18) If fuel flow is okay, turn engine off. Connect fuel return line to selector valve and go to step **19)**. If fuel flow is not okay, check return line for restrictions. If restrictions are found, repair or replace as necessary and repeat step **17)**.

19) Disconnect fuel return line to problem tank at selector valve. Attach a 5/16" diameter hose to selector valve return port and insert end of hose into container. Start engine and check for a solid, continuous flow of fuel.

20) If fuel flow is okay, check fuel sender and fuel line to tank (front or rear) for restrictions. If restrictions are found, repair or replace as necessary. Run engine and check for smooth running. If fuel flow is not okay, replace fuel selector valve.

Fig. 1: Ford Six-Port Fuel Selector Valve

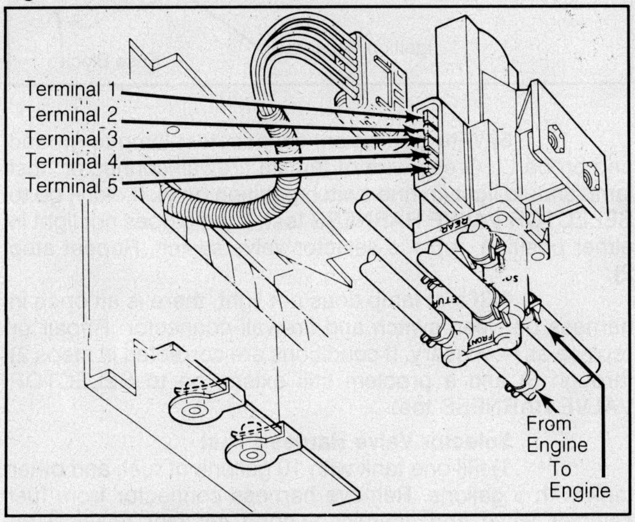

Terminals are not numbered on valve.

7.5L Engine

1) Turn key to "RUN" position. Place switch in "FRONT" position. Disconnect selector valve connector. Check for voltage between connector terminal 2 and ground. If voltage is present, go to step **3)**.

2) If no voltage is present, check voltage across fuse at fuse block. If fuse is blown, check selector valve circuit for shorts. Repair shorts, replace fuse and repeat step **1)**. If fuse is okay, go to step **6)**.

3) Check for voltage between selector valve connector terminals 2 and 1. If voltage is present, go to step **4)**. If no voltage is present, check for open ground circuit from valve connector, through selector switch to ground. If circuit is okay, go to step **6)**. If not okay, repair ground circuit, repeat test.

4) Place switch in "REAR" position, and check for voltage between connector terminal 1 and ground. If voltage is present, go to step **5)**. If no voltage is present, go to step **6)**.

5) Check for voltage between selector valve connector terminal 1 and 2. If voltage is present, go to step **8)**. If no voltage is present, check for open ground circuit from valve connector, through selector switch to ground. If circuit is okay, go to step **6)**. If not okay, repair ground circuit, repeat step **3)**.

6) Remove selector switch from instrument panel and disconnect switch from harness. With switch in "FRONT" position, check for continuity between terminals 2 and 4, and between terminals 1 and 3.

7) Place switch in "REAR" position and check for continuity between terminal 1 and 4, and between terminals 2 and 3. If switch is okay, go to step **10)**. If switch is not okay, replace switch.

NOTE: Selector valve will make a "zip" sound when shifting from one mode to another.

8) Using a jumper wire, connect selector valve terminal 2 to battery positive post. Using a second jumper wire, connect terminal 1 to ground. If valve is in "FRONT" mode, nothing will occur. Reverse jumper wires, valve should shift to "REAR" mode.

9) Reverse jumper wires once more, valve should shift to "FRONT" mode. If valve shifts into both modes, go to step **12)**. If valve does not shift into both modes, replace fuel selector valve.

10) On E series, check continuity of Brown/Orange wire (circuit 808) and Red/Yellow wire (circuit 739) between selector switch and selector valve. On F series, check continuity of Brown/White wire (circuit 674) and Orange wire (circuit 974) between selector switch and selector valve.

11) If continuity between selector switch and selector valve is okay, go to step **12)**. If continuity between selector switch and selector valve is not okay, repair open circuits as necessary.

12) Remove connector from oil pressure switch and insert temporary shorting wire between two connector terminals. Pinch off fuel line between rear tank and selector valve. Remove fuel hose to carburetor, and place end of fuel hose into a container.

NOTE: Fuel pump volume is approximately 1/2 gallon/minute.

13) Turn key to "RUN" position. Place switch in "FRONT" position. Check for a solid, continuous fuel flow. If fuel flow is not okay, go to step **14)**. If fuel flow is okay, remove clamping tool from rear supply line, go to step **18)**.

14) Disconnect supply hose to engine at selector valve. Disconnect supply hose from front tank at selector valve. Connect two hoses together using a length of fuel line. Repeat steps **12)** and **13)**. If fuel flow is okay, replace fuel selector valve.

15) If fuel flow is not okay, check front fuel tank sender, fuel lines and fuel filter for restrictions. If restrictions are found, clean, repair or replace components as necessary and repeat steps **12)** and **13)**.

16) If lines, filter and sender are okay, remove front fuel tank sender connector. Connect a 12-volt test lamp to pump terminal and to ground terminal of sender connector.

17) With key in "RUN" position and with switch in "FRONT" position, test lamp should light continuously and should go out as soon as rear tank is selected. Check fuel pump. If fuel pump is okay, continue test.

18) Remove connector from oil pressure switch and insert temporary shorting wire between two connector terminals. Pinch off fuel line between front tank and selector valve. Remove fuel hose to carburetor, and place end of fuel hose into a container.

19) Turn key to "RUN" position and place switch in "REAR" position. Check for a solid, continuous flow of fuel. If fuel flow is not okay, go to step **20)**. If fuel flow is okay, selector valve is operating properly.

FORD & GENERAL MOTORS (Cont.)

20) Disconnect supply hose to engine at selector valve. Disconnect supply hose from rear tank at selector valve. Connect two hoses together using a length of fuel line. Repeat steps **18)** and **19)**.

21) If fuel flow is okay, replace fuel selector valve. If fuel flow is not okay, remove rear fuel tank sender connector. Connect a 12-volt test lamp to pump terminal and to ground terminal of sender connector.

22) With key in "RUN" position and with switch in "REAR" position, test lamp should light continuously and should go out as soon as front tank is selected. Check fuel pump. If fuel pump is okay, fuel supply system is okay.

All Other Models

1) Turn ignition to "RUN" and place switch in "FRONT" position. Disconnect fuel selector valve. Using a 12-volt test lamp, check for voltage between wire harness terminal and ground. If test lamp comes on, go to step **3)** If lamp does not come on, check fuse at fuse block.

2) If fuse is blown, check fuel valve circuit and valve for short. Repair as necessary and replace fuse. If fuse is okay, check switch for continuity in auxiliary tank position. If no continuity, replace switch. If switch is okay, check wiring and valve for open circuit and repair as necessary.

3) Reconnect valve wire and place a paper clip on bottom end of valve. Paper clip should adhere to valve. If paper clip adheres, go to step **5)**. If paper clip does not adhere, ground valve case to frame rail with a jumper wire, and repeat paper clip test.

4) If paper clip still does not adhere, replace valve and solenoid assembly. If paper clip adheres, remove valve mounting bolts, and clean mounting surface. Install valve using zinc or cadmium plated bolts and washers.

5) Position switch in "MAIN" position and pinch off fuel hose from valve to main tank. Remove fuel line from carburetor, and place end of fuel line into a container. Remove battery feed from coil, and crank engine. Check fuel flow.

6) If fuel flows continuously, remove and replace valve solenoid assembly. If no fuel flows into container, check for plugged fuel line. If fuel lines are okay, fuel selector valve is operating correctly.

GENERAL MOTORS

Instrument Panel Harness Test

1) Ensure all electrical and ground connections are clean and tight. Disconnect selector valve harness at firewall, just right of steering column. *See Fig. 2.* With ignition on, connect a 12-volt test lamp to one terminal of female harness connector.

2) Connect other end of test lamp to remaining terminal. Test lamp should light in both switch positions. If okay, go to step **5)**. If test lamp does not light, go to next step.

3) Check for proper ground connection (Black or Black/Pink wire) at bus bar. Check for proper connection to ignition receptacle at fuse block. *See Fig. 2.*

4) If ground and power connections are okay, check for proper connection at selector valve switch. Check for bent terminals on back of switch and in switch connector. Check "B" on Pink wire and ground on Black wire in switch connector. Repeat step **2)**. If okay, go to next step.

Fig. 2: Selector Valve Wiring Harness

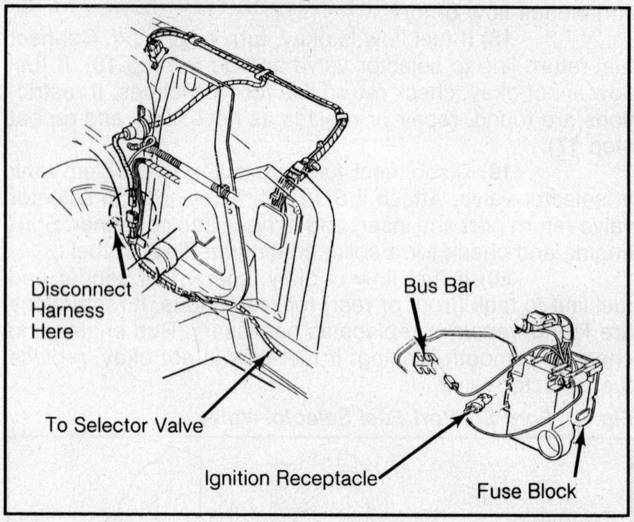

5) With ignition on, connect test lamp to ground and probe Lt. Green wire of female firewall connector, test lamp should light (in one switch position only). If okay, go to SELECTOR VALVE HARNESS test. If lamp does not light in either position, replace selector valve switch. Repeat step **2)**.

6) If test lamp does not light, there is an open in harness between switch and firewall connector. Repair or replace as necessary. If conditions are corrected in steps **2)** through **5)** and a problem still exists, go to SELECTOR VALVE HARNESS test.

Selector Valve Harness Test

1) Fill one tank with 10 gallons of fuel, and other tank with 5 gallons. Remove harness connector from fuel selector valve and connect a good selector valve. Turn ignition on and depress selector valve switch. Note gauge reading for right and left tanks.

2) If reading is different between tanks, replace selector valve. If no difference is shown, repair open circuit(s) in harness between selector valve and firewall connector. If fuel gauge operates, but not accurately, check fuel gauge.

REMOVAL & INSTALLATION

SELECTOR VALVE

Ford

Disconnect fuel hoses from selector valve. Remove electrical connections. Remove nut and ground wire. Remove valve attaching bolts, and remove valve. To install, reverse removal procedure. Ensure ground wire is securely fastened. Because solenoid is internally grounded, specified mounting bolts must be used.

General Motors

Disconnect battery negative cable. Remove hose shield and brace. Remove harness connector from selector valve. Remove fuel and vapor hoses, noting locations for reassembly reference. Remove 2 screws holding valve to frame, and remove valve. To install, reverse removal procedure.

ALL MANUFACTURERS

DESCRIPTION

Ignition switches are typically steering column mounted, and are actuated by ignition key locking cylinders.

SERVICING

Chrysler Corp. vehicles with column-mounted ignition switches and lock cylinders, require that steering wheel and turn signal switch be removed to gain access to ignition components.

On General Motors and Jeep vehicles, steering column must be removed or lowered. Steering wheel and turn signal switch must be removed to gain access to ignition components.

CAUTION: Lock plate is held by high spring pressure. Do not remove snap ring without using compressor tool. If steering shaft has American threads, use Compressor Tool (J-23653); if shaft has metric threads use Metric Forcing Screw (J-23653-4).

Ford vehicles require lowering of the steering column before servicing the ignition switch or lock cylinder.

CAUTION: Some steering columns are collapsible. Special care must be taken to avoid bumping, jolting or hammering on steering shaft and gearshift tube of these columns.

REMOVAL & INSTALLATION

LOCK CYLINDER

Removal (Chrysler Corp. FWD Models)

1) Remove ignition key. Remove screw and lift out buzzer/chime switch. Remove 2 screws attaching the ignition switch to column jacket. Remove ignition switch by rotating switch 90° on actuator rod and sliding off rod.

2) Remove 2 mounting screws from dimmer switch and disengage switch from actuator rod. Remove 2 screws that mount bellcrank. Slide bellcrank up into lock housing until it can be disconnected from the ignition switch actuator rod.

3) Turn ignition to "LOCK" position and remove key. Insert a small blade screwdriver into lock cylinder release holes. Push screwdriver in to release spring loaded lock retainers, while pulling lock cylinder out of housing.

Installation

Turn ignition to "LOCK" position and remove key. Insert cylinder into housing far enough to contact drive shaft. Press inward and move actuator rod up and down to align parts. When aligned, cylinder will move inward and a spring loaded retainer will snap into place, locking cylinder into housing.

Removal (Chrysler Corp. RWD Models)

1) Remove 2 retaining screws and the lock lever guide plate to expose the lock cylinder release hole. Turn ignition to "LOCK" position and remove key.

2) Insert a small diameter screwdriver into lock cylinder release hole and push in to release spring loaded lock retainer. At the same time pull lock cylinder out of housing.

Installation

Turn ignition to "LOCK" position and remove key. Insert cylinder into housing. When aligned, cylinder will move inward and a spring loaded retainer will snap into place, locking cylinder into housing.

Fig. 1: Typical Column Type Ignition Switch Lock Cylinder Removal

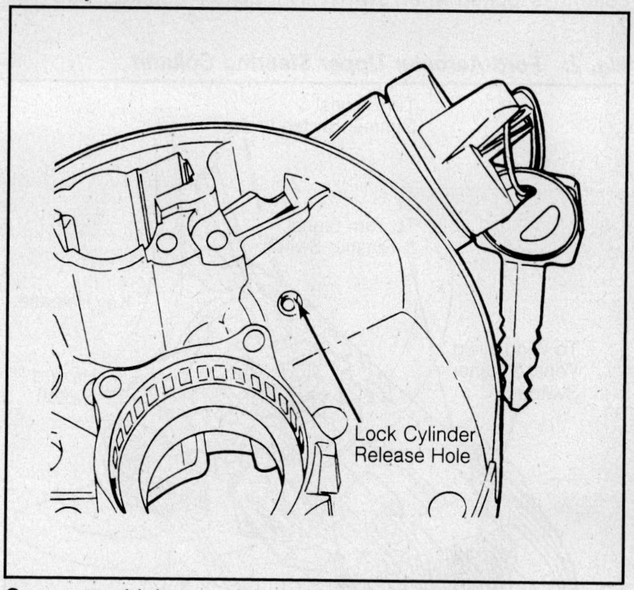

On most vehicles, push in to release lock retainer.

Removal (Ford Aerostar)

1) Turn ignition to "LOCK" position. Disconnect battery negative cable. Remove steering wheel. See appropriate article in steering section.

2) On models equipped with tilt steering, remove upper extention shroud by squeezing shroud at 6 and 12 o'clock positions, and pulling shroud free of retaining plate at 3 o'clock position.

3) On all models, remove steering column right side cover panel by removing 2 screws at bottom of panel. Remove upper column shroud (center column shroud on tilt column) by removing 4 screws at bottom of shroud.

4) Swing bottom panel of shroud open and remove 2 screws attaching shroud to retaining plate. Remove lock cylinder. Remove lower column shroud by raising left side of shroud up until turn signal switch window is above turn signal switch cut-out.

5) Raise right side of shroud until lock cylinder window clears cylinder housing. Slowly pull shroud from column. Disconnect ignition switch electrical connector.

6) Remove shear-type bolts attaching switch to lock cylinder housing by using a hammer and chisel to turn bolts 1 turn outward. Use pliers to grab and remove bolt from hole. Disengage ignition switch from actuator pin.

Installation

1) Align holes in base of switch casting with holes in lock cylinder housing. Turn ignition to "RUN" position and insert switch into switch carrier.

NOTE: It may be necessary to turn lock cylinder slightly to align actuator pin with "U" shaped slot in switch carrier.

2) Install, and tighten new shear bolts until bolt heads break off. To complete installation, reverse removal procedure. Rotate switch slightly during installation to align switch in cylinder.

ALL MANUFACTURERS (Cont.)

3) Check ignition switch functions. Verify that column is locked when switch is in "LOCK" position. *See Fig. 2.*

Fig. 2: Ford Aerostar Upper Steering Column

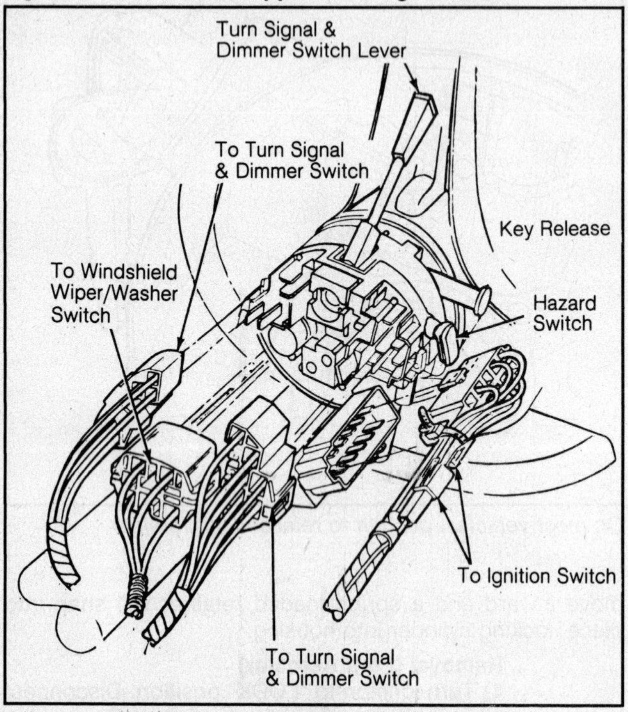

Removal (Ford Bronco II & Ranger)

1) Disconnect battery negative cable. Remove the trim shroud. Remove electrical connector from the key warning switch. Turn the ignition to "RUN" position.

2) Place a 1/8" diameter pin in the hole located in the outer edge of the lock cylinder housing. Depress the retaining pin, and pull out the lock cylinder.

Installation

1) Lubricate cylinder cavity with Ford lock cylinder lubricant. Turn ignition to "RUN" position. Depress retaining pin and insert it into lock cylinder housing.

2) Ensure cylinder is fully seated and aligned into interlocking washer before turning key to "OFF" position. Use key to rotate cylinder to ensure correct mechanical operation in all positions.

3) Install electrical connector into key warning switch. Connect battery negative cable. Check ignition switch functions and verify that column is locked in "LOCK" position.

Removal (All Other Ford Models)

1) Disconnect battery ground. On non-tilt column vehicles, remove steering wheel and trim pad. On models with A/T, place gearshift in "PARK" position (any position on vehicles with M/T). Insert key and turn cylinder to "ON" position.

2) Insert a 1/8" diameter pin in hole on outside of steering column casting near hazard warning button on tilt models. Insert pin in hole near base of lock cylinder on non-tilt models. On all models, depress pin and pull out on lock cylinder to remove.

Installation

Lubricate lock cylinder with grease. Turn lock cylinder to "ON" position. Depress retaining pin and insert cylinder into housing. Ensure that cylinder is fully seated and aligned with interlocking washer. Turn key, and check operation of lock cylinder.

Removal (General Motors)

Turn ignition to "RUN" position. Remove lock plate, turn signal switch and buzzer switch. Remove lock retaining screw and lock cylinder.

Installation

Position lock in housing. Turn key to "STOP" position while holding cylinder. Align cylinder with keyway in housing. Push lock in and install retaining screw.

Removal (Jeep)

Turn lock cylinder clockwise 2 detent positions beyond "OFF-LOCK" position. Compress lock cylinder retaining tab using a thin bladed screwdriver and remove lock cylinder.

Installation

Insert key in lock. Hold cylinder sleeve, and turn key clockwise until key stops. Insert cylinder lock into bore with cylinder tab aligned with keyway in housing. Push cylinder in until it bottoms. Rotate cylinder counterclockwise to engage lock sector, and push in until cylinder tab engages in housing groove.

IGNITION SWITCH

Removal (Chrysler Corp. FWD Models)

Remove ignition key. Remove screw and lift out buzzer/chime switch. Remove 2 screws attaching the ignition switch to column jacket. Remove ignition switch by rotating switch 90° on actuator rod and sliding off rod.

Installation

On models with A/T, place gearshift in "PARK" position. On all models, place ignition switch on ignition switch actuator rod and rotate 90° to lock rod into position. With lock cylinder and ignition switch in "LOCK" position, tighten ignition switch mounting screws.

Removal (Chrysler Corp. RWD Models)

Remove lock cylinder. Remove 3 retaining screws and ignition switch assembly.

Installation

Turn ignition to "OFF" position. On models with A/T, place gearshift in "PARK" position. On all models, feed wires down through space between housing and jacket. Position switch in jacket and tighten 3 mounting screws.

Removal (Ford Bronco II & Ranger)

1) Rotate lock cylinder key to "LOCK" position. Disconnect battery ground. On tilt columns, remove upper extension shroud by squeezing at the 6 and 10 o'clock positions and popping free of the retaining plate at the 3 o'clock position.

2) Remove 2 shroud halves by removing the 2 attaching screws. On all models, disconnect electrical connector from ignition switch. Drill out the 2 break-off head bolts holding the ignition switch to lock cylinder with a 1/8" drill bit.

3) Using an easy-out, remove bolts. Disengage the ignition switch from the actuator pin and remove switch.

Installation

1) Rotate ignition key to the "RUN" position. Install switch by aligning the holes on switch casting base with the holes in the lock cylinder housing. Minor movement of the lock cylinder to align the actuator pin with slot in switch carrier may be required.

ALL MANUFACTURERS (Cont.)

2) Install the new break-off head bolts and tighten until heads shear off. Connect the electrical connector to the igntion switch. To complete installation, reverse removal procedure.

Fig. 3: Rod-Actuated Ignition Switch

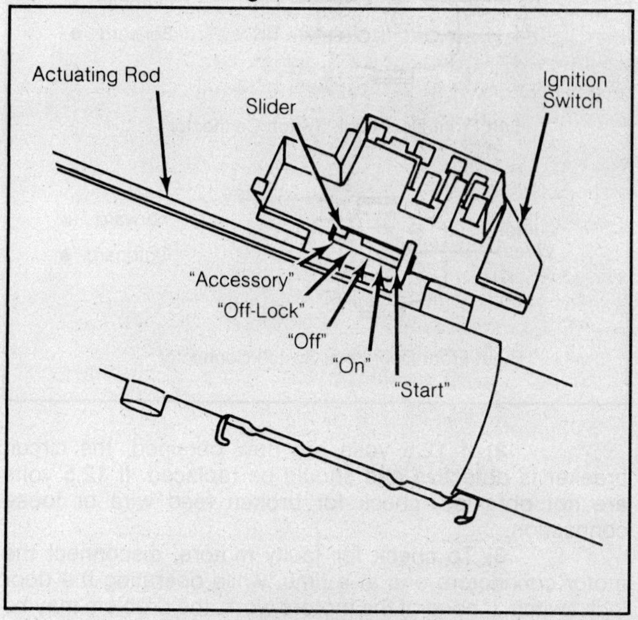

Removal (All Other Ford Models)

Disconnect battery ground. Remove steering column shroud and lower column. Disconnect switch wiring at multiple plug. Remove nuts securing switch to steering column. Lift switch vertically to disengage actuator, and remove switch.

Installation

With lock cylinder and switch in "LOCK" position, engage actuator rod in switch. Position switch on column and install retaining nuts, but do not tighten. Move switch up and down along column to locate mid-position of rod lash, and tighten retaining nuts.

Removal (General Motors "S" Series)

Lower steering column, and support column to avoid causing damage. Remove attaching screws. Disconnect actuating rod and wiring from switch and remove switch from steering column.

Installation

To install, move switch slider to far left position and then 2 detents to the right on non key-release switches. On key-release switches, move switch slider to the far left position. On all types, position rod in hole and install switch to steering column.

Removal (All Other General Motors Models)

Lower steering column, and support column to avoid causing damage. Remove lock cylinder. Pull switch actuating rod up until there is a definite stop, then move rod down one detent (into "LOCK" position). Remove 2 switch screws and switch assembly from vehicle.

Installation

Place lock and switch in "LOCK" position. Install actuating rod into switch, and install switch using mounting screws. Tighten slowly. Ensure switch position is not changed. To complete installation, reverse removal procedure.

Removal (Jeep)

Lower column and remove switch mounting screws. Disconnect harness connector. Remove switch.

Installation

Move switch slider to "ACC" position. Move switch slider back 2 clicks to "OFF-UNLOCK" position. Insert remote rod in switch slider, and position switch on column. Do not move slider. Install and tighten screws.

Power Door Locks

CHRYSLER CORP.

All Models

DESCRIPTION

Chrysler FWD vehicles are equipped with a motor-actuated door lock system. Operation of system is similar to that used in RWD vehicles. In addition, the left front door can be unlocked by actuation of remote door handle. The liftgate release consists of a latch with internal solenoid and push button switch. The solenoid is energized when push button is depressed.

Chrysler RWD vehicles are equipped with a solenoid-actuated door lock system. It can be locked or unlocked electrically by operating either left or right front locking knobs. When electrically-equipped, side and rear doors can be actuated by operation of front locking knobs. All doors must be closed before locking. They can be locked or unlocked manually with key or electrically as described.

The system combines a relay, circuit breaker, and button head terminals in door and post panels. All door wiring is contained in 1 wiring harness. The relay and the circuit breaker are mounted on the steering column support bracket on the underside of dash in vans and wagons. On trucks, relay and circuit breaker are mounted between fuse block and glove box on instrument panel support bracket. All components are serviced as complete assemblies.

TESTING

LIFTGATE DOOR LOCK TEST (FWD)

Ensure that lead wire is properly connected to solenoid. Connect a voltmeter between solenoid connector and ground. With switch depressed, at least 10 volts must be present. With solenoid removed, check plunger spring and plunger for free movement of at least 5/8".

DOOR LOCK SWITCH VOLTAGE TEST (FWD)

1) Remove door lock switch from trim panel. Carefully separate terminal block on wiring harness from switch body. Connect one lead of a 12-volt test lamp to Black wire terminal.

2) Touch other lead of test lamp to Red wire terminal. If lamp comes on, the wiring between battery and switch is okay. If lamp does not come on, check 30 amp main fuse (circuit breaker) or for a broken wire.

DOOR LOCK SWITCH TEST (FWD)

Connect jumper wires on right side switch connector. *See Fig. 1.* Operate door locks using left connector and jumper wires. Connecting "OR" to "RD" and "PK" to "BK" should lock doors. Connecting "PK" to "RD" and "OR" to "BK" should unlock doors. If door locks operate using jumper wires, the switches are at fault.

DOOR LOCK MOTOR TEST

1) With battery in normal operating condition, connect positive voltmeter lead to Lt. Green terminal of circuit breaker, and negative lead to ground. If reading of 12.5 volts is not obtained, connect positive lead to battery side of circuit breaker.

Fig. 1: FWD Door Lock Switch Connectors

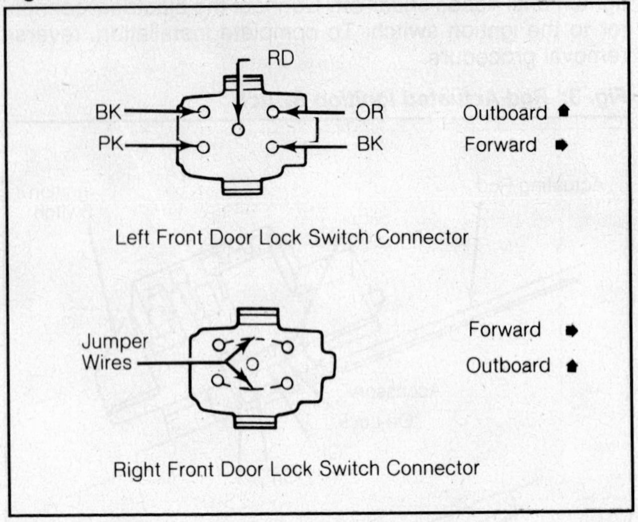

2) If 12.5 volts are now obtained, the circuit breaker is defective and should be replaced. If 12.5 volts are not obtained, check for broken feed wire or loose connection.

3) To check for faulty motors, disconnect the motor connectors one at a time, while operating the door lock switch. If none of the motors work, the problem may be caused by a shorted motor. Disconnecting defective motor will allow the remaining motors to operate.

Fig. 2: FWD Door Lock Motor

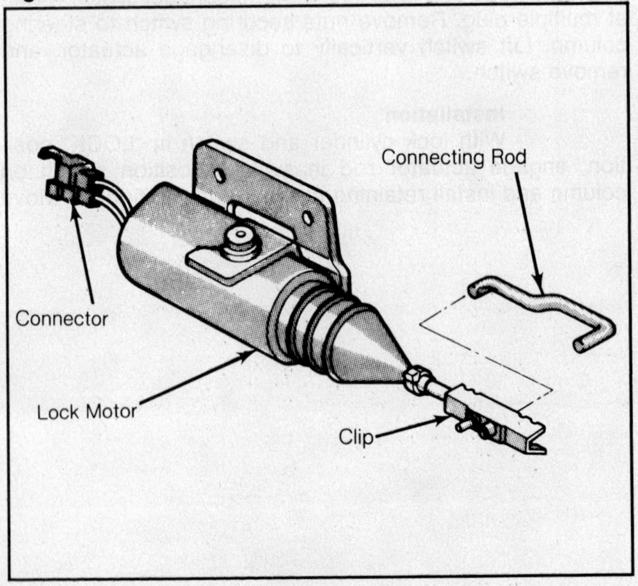

DOOR LOCK TEST (RWD)

1) With battery in normal operating condition and solenoid adjusted properly, connect positive lead of voltmeter to buss bar on relay assembly. Connect negative lead to ground.

2) With no load, voltage should be approximately 12.5 volts. When locks are operated, voltage should be 11 volts. If no voltage is read at relay, test circuit breaker as follows.

Power Door Locks

CHRYSLER CORP. (Cont.)

3) Connect positive voltmeter lead to Lt. Green terminal of circuit breaker, and negative lead to ground. If reading of 12.5 volts is not obtained, connect positive lead to battery side of circuit breaker.

4) If 12.5 volts are now obtained, the circuit breaker is defective and should be replaced. If 12.5 volts are not obtained, check for broken feed wire or loose connection.

5) To check for faulty solenoids, disconnect the solenoid connectors one at a time, while operating the door lock switch. If none of the solenoids work, the problem may be a shorted solenoid, defective door switch or faulty relay.

6) Disconnecting defective solenoid will allow the remaining solenoids to operate, provided the relay is not damaged.

ADJUSTMENT

DOOR LOCK LIFTGATE (FWD)

Adjust deck lid latch and striker so that deck lid latches with a moderate slam. Should latch fail to lock, replace latch assembly. With ignition switch in "ON" or "ACCY" position, depress deck lid unlock switch. Liftgate should unlock. Adjust as necessary.

DOOR LOCK SOLENOID (RWD)

Front Doors

Remove door trim panel. Loosen solenoid attaching screws. While pressing down on the lock knob, push up on the solenoid until the solenoid plunger bottoms out in the solenoid. Tighten screws, and test operation before installing trim panel.

Cargo Doors

Loosen solenoid mounting screws and slide solenoid to full down position. Raise solenoid link until latch is in locked position. Tighten solenoid mounting screws. Test operation before installing trim panel.

REMOVAL & INSTALLATION

DOOR LOCK MOTOR (FWD)

1) Remove inside door release handle, window regulator handle and door trim panel. Roll door water shield away from lower rear corner of door to reveal inside panel access opening.

2) Remove door lock link at door latch. Disconnect motor lead wires. Remove motor mounting bracket pop rivets and remove motor assembly from mounting. To install, reverse removal procedure.

CAUTION: Rubber boot on motor will restrict motor if it is twisted.

DOOR LOCK SOLENOID (RWD)

1) Remove trim panel on rear cargo doors, if used. Remove inside door release handle, window regulator handle and door trim panel.

Fig. 3: Solenoid for Electric Door Lock

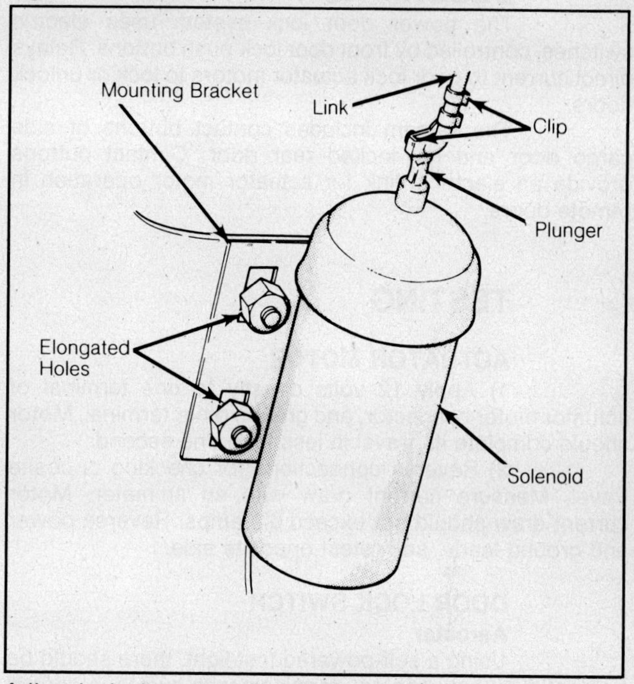

Adjust locks by solenoid position.

2) Roll door water shield away from lower rear corner of door to reveal inside panel access opening.

3) Remove solenoid link at solenoid. Disconnect solenoid lead wires. Remove mounting bracket attaching screws, and remove solenoid from mounting.

4) To install, reverse removal procedure and adjust if necessary.

Fig. 4: Power Door Lock Wiring Diagram

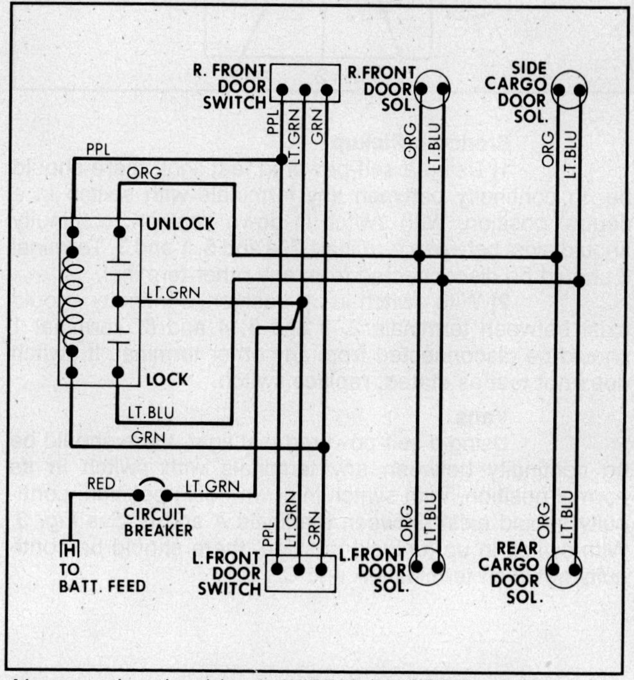

Also see chassis wiring in WIRING DIAGRAM section.

Power Door Locks

FORD

DESCRIPTION

The power door lock system uses electric switches, controlled by front door lock push buttons. Relays direct current to door lock actuator motors to lock or unlock doors.

The system includes contact buttons of side cargo door and key-locked rear door. Contact buttons provide an electrical link for actuator motor operation in remote doors.

TESTING

ACTUATOR MOTOR

1) Apply 12 volts directly to one terminal of actuator motor connector, and ground other terminal. Motor should complete its travel in less than one second.

2) Reverse connections for checking opposite travel. Measure current draw with an ammeter. Motor current draw should not exceed 6.2 amps. Reverse power and ground leads, and retest opposite side.

DOOR LOCK SWITCH

Aerostar

Using a self-powered test light, there should be no continuity between any terminals with switch in neutral position. With switch in "LOCK" position, continuity should exist between terminals 1 and 2. *See Fig. 1.* With switch in "UNLOCK" position, there should be continuity between terminals 2 and 3.

Fig. 1: Power Door Lock Switch

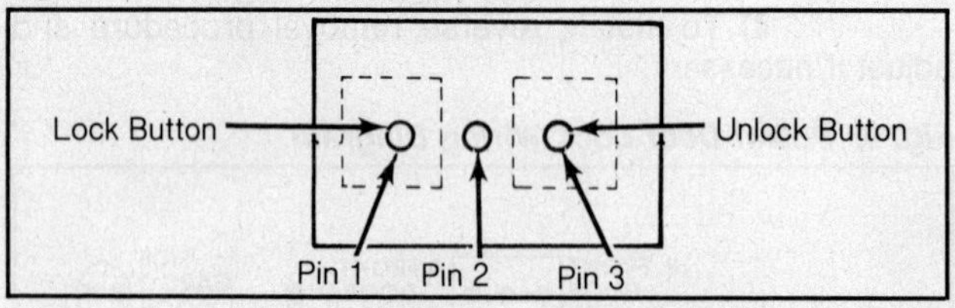

Bronco & Pickup

1) Using a self-powered test light, there should be no continuity between any terminals with switch in a neutral position. With switch in down position, continuity should exist between terminals 2, 4 and 5, 1 and 3. Terminal 6 should be disconnected from any other terminal.

2) With switch in up position, continuity should exist between terminals 2, 3 and 5, 4 and 6. Terminal 1 should be disconnected from any other terminal. If switch does not test as stated, replace switch.

Vans

Using a self-powered test light, there should be no continuity between any terminals with switch in its normal position. With switch in down (lock) position, continuity should exist between terminals A and B. *See Fig. 3.* With switch in up (unlock) position, there should be continuity between terminals A and C.

RELAYS

Aerostar & Vans

1) Remove both relay connectors. Relays are located on lower left side of instrument panel reinforcement. Ensure that terminal 1 of relay is grounded. If not, check relay case-to-ground screws for tightness.

2) If screws are tight, replace relay. With a test light connected between terminals 1 and 2, apply power to terminals 2 and 4 of each relay. *See Fig. 2.* Do not leave light connected for more than 2 minutes. Test light should light. If not, replace relay.

Fig. 2: Door Lock Relay Terminals (Aerostar & Vans)

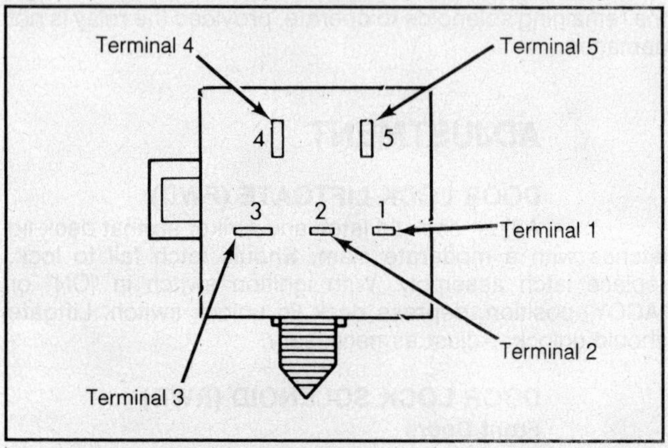

Do not leave test light connected more than 2 minutes.

REMOVAL & INSTALLATION

ACTUATOR MOTOR

Removal

Remove door trim panel. Disconnect actuator link from door latch. Remove actuator motor and swivel bracket from door by drilling out retaining rivet. Disconnect wiring at connector and remove motor.

Installation

To install, reverse removal procedure, noting that new pop rivet must retain actuator bracket securely.

DOOR LOCK CONTROL SWITCH

Removal (Bronco & Pickup)

To remove control switch, insert a small screwdriver into spring tab slot, located at top and bottom of switch housing. Apply pressure and assembly will pop out. Disconnect housing from wiring connector by separating locking fingers. To install, reverse removal procedure.

Removal (Aerostar & Vans)

Remove bezel retaining screw. Lift bottom of bezel from door trim panel. Remove switch and bezel assembly. Remove wiring connector retaining screw from rear of bezel. Pry switch from connector.

Installation (All Models)

To install, reverse removal procedure, ensure that switch is not binding with sheet metal or wires.

Power Door Locks

GENERAL MOTORS

DESCRIPTION

The electric door lock system consists of a lock actuator assembly at each door, switches and a relay. All doors lock and unlock manually or from door control switches. All components are serviced as complete assemblies.

The motor is a permanent magnet, 12-volt reversible type that is protected by an internal circuit breaker. Circuit breaker may require 1 to 3 minutes to reset. A 30 amp circuit breaker also protects wiring from door lock feed circuit to relay.

The relay assembly is a double-pull, double-throw relay externally grounded to body. It is located beneath right side of instrument panel behind glove compartment. Control switch is a 3-pin rocker type mounted on door armrests. Feed circuit to lock switches is protected by a 20 amp fuse.

TROUBLE SHOOTING

DOOR LOCKS INOPERATIVE FROM BOTH CONTROL SWITCHES, COURTESY LIGHT FUSE BLOWN

Install new courtesy light fuse and press door lock switch to "LOCK" position. If fuse blows, check for short in Lt. Blue wire between relay and switches. If system remains operative, check for short in Orange wire and in both Lt. Blue and Black wires between source and cross bar harness.

DOOR LOCKS INOPERATIVE, COURTESY LIGHT OPERATES

Ground test lamp. Check Orange/Black wire at relay connector. If lamp remains off, check circuit breaker and circuit to relay. With light on, press switch to "LOCK" position. If lamp remains off, check ground to body. If grounded, replace relay.

DOORS WILL UNLOCK BUT WILL NOT LOCK

With a test lamp grounded, check Lt. Blue wire terminal at relay. Press switch to "LOCK" position. If lamp comes on but system does not operate, replace relay. If lamp does not come on, check for short between relay and cross-body wiring harness.

DOORS WILL LOCK BUT WILL NOT UNLOCK

With a test lamp grounded, check Black wire at relay. Press switch to "UNLOCK" position. If lamp comes on but system does not operate, replace relay. If lamp does not come on, check for open in Black wire between relay and cross-body harness.

DOOR LOCKS OPERATE EXCEPT FOR ONE DOOR

Check for loose connection of Gray and Tan wires, or short in circuit. If both leads check to actuator motor, replace motor.

DOOR LOCKS OPERATE NORMALLY EXCEPT ONE DOOR WILL NOT UNLOCK/LOCK

Check ground. If okay, check for open circuit in Lt. Blue wire between switch and cross-body harness.

DOOR LOCKS INOPERATIVE AND RELAY CLICKS WHEN ACTIVATED

Check Black and Lt. Blue wires between switch and relay.

DOOR LOCKS INOPERATIVE OR LOCKS PULSATE AND RELAY CHATTERS WHEN SWITCH IS ACTIVATED

Gray and Tan wires are making contact between relay and lock actuator motor.

REMOVAL & INSTALLATION

DOOR LOCK MOTOR

1) Disconnect battery negative cable, remove door trim panel and disconnect electrical connector from motor.

2) Remove screws attaching motor to door. Remove door lock lever from rubber mount at top of motor actuator and remove motor through access hole. To install, reverse removal procedure.

Fig. 1: Power Door Lock Wiring Diagram

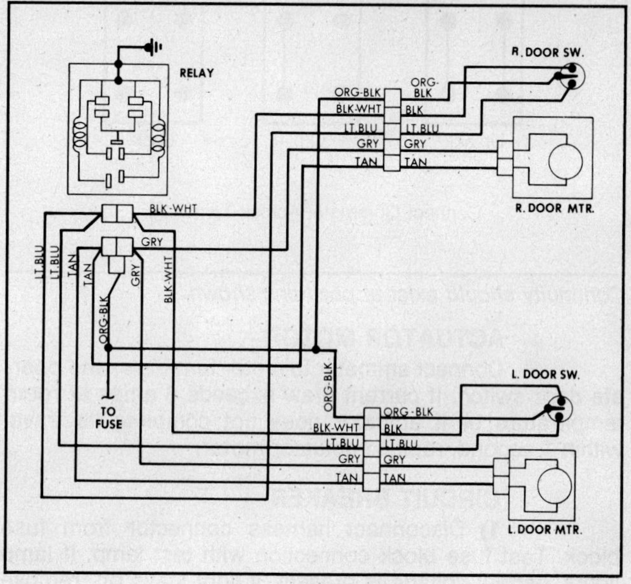

Power Door Locks

JEEP

All Models, Except CJ7 & Scrambler

DESCRIPTION

Jeep vehicles with power door locks use a battery-powered, motor-actuated lock system, controlled by rocker switches. Pressing up on the switch unlocks doors. Pressing down on the switch locks the doors.

Power door locks are protected by a 30 amp circuit breaker located in the fuse block. Two-door vehicles have the wiring harness running from door-to-door and is secured at the instrument panel with retainers.

Four-door vehicles have the wiring harness for the back doors connected to the front door harness of the side cowl panels. Power door locks do not lock or unlock the doors from outside the vehicle.

TESTING

SWITCH

Test switches for continuity using an ohmmeter. Connect ohmmeter across terminals as shown in *Fig. 1.* Continuity should exist between terminals in all positions.

Fig. 1: Checking Switch for Continuity

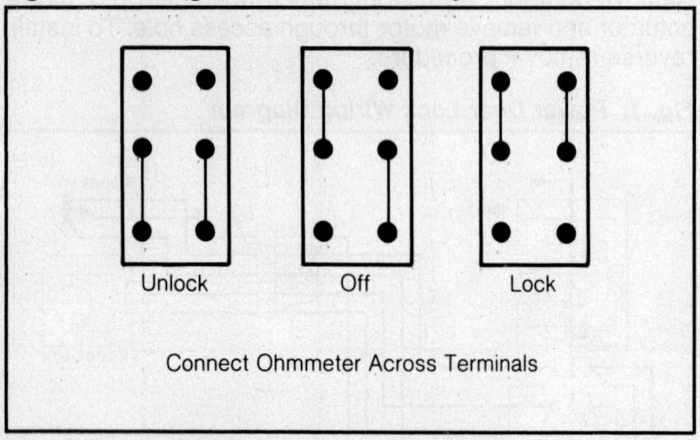

Continuity should exist at positions shown.

ACTUATOR MOTOR

Connect ammeter to motor terminals, and operate door switch. If current draw exceeds 8 amps at room temperature or if actuator does not complete its travel within 1 second, replace actuator motor.

CIRCUIT BREAKER

1) Disconnect harness connector from fuse block. Test fuse block connection with test lamp. If lamp lights, battery voltage is present. If light stays off, remove circuit breaker, and test with an ohmmeter.

2) If circuit breaker tests okay, check for battery voltage at circuit breaker connection at fuse block. If there is no battery voltage at connection, check for burnt fusible link in engine compartment.

REMOVAL & INSTALLATION

DOOR LOCK SWITCH

Disconnect battery negative cable. Remove door trim panel. Remove switch housing from inner door panel. Disconnect wiring and remove switch assembly. To disconnect, pry clips holding connector up. Depress retainer clips through holes in switch housing, and remove switch. To install, reverse removal procedure.

ACTUATOR MOTOR

Disconnect battery negative cable. Remove door trim panel. Remove actuator motor by drilling out rivets (attaching motor to door panel) using a 1/4" (6 mm) drill bit. Disconnect actuator rod from bellcrank. Disconnect wires from actuator motor, and remove motor. To install, reverse removal procedure, using new rivets.

Fig. 2: Wiring Diagram for Jeep Power Door Locks

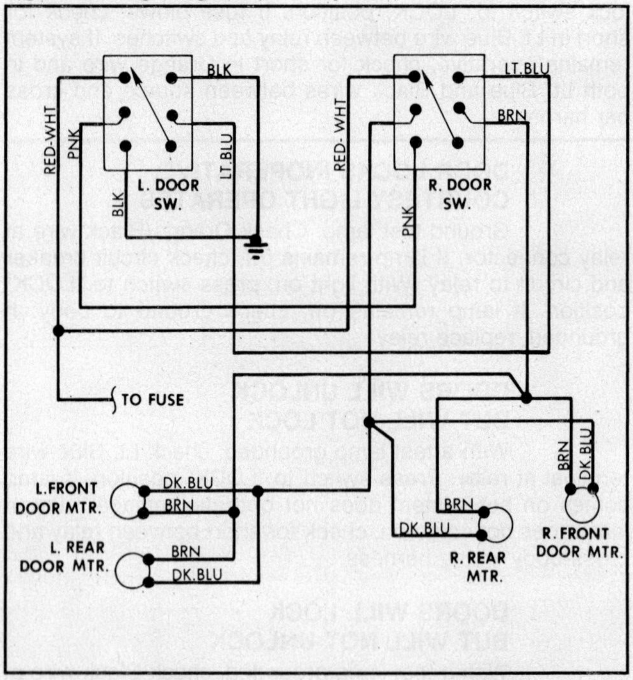

Power Mirrors

FORD & JEEP

DESCRIPTION

Power rearview mirror assemblies consist of door-mounted mirrors with internal motor drive and backing plate. System includes a door panel switch and necessary wiring components.

TROUBLE SHOOTING & TESTING

NOTE: The following tests apply to Jeep vehicles only.

MASTER SWITCH

1) Check power source line to switch connector. Check power source line between terminal "B" and ground of switch wiring connector. Check ground connection. Check ground connection between terminal "E" and ground of switch wiring connector.

2) With switch in "UP" position, continuity should exist between terminals "V 1" and "B" for left side mirror and between terminals "H 2" and "B" for right side mirror. Continuity should also exist between terminals "C" and "E".

3) With switch in "DOWN" position, continuity should exist between terminals "V 1" and "E" for left side mirror and between terminals "H 2" and "E" for right side mirror. Continuity should also exist between terminals "B" and "C".

4) With switch in "LEFT" position, continuity should exist between terminals "H1" and "E" for left side mirror and between terminals "V2" and "E" for right side mirror. Continuity should also exist between terminals "B" and "C".

5) With switch in "RIGHT" position, continuity should exist between "H1" and "B" for left side mirror and between terminals "V2" and "B" for right side mirror. Continuity should also exist between terminals "C" and "E".

Fig. 1: Jeep Master Switch Terminal Locations

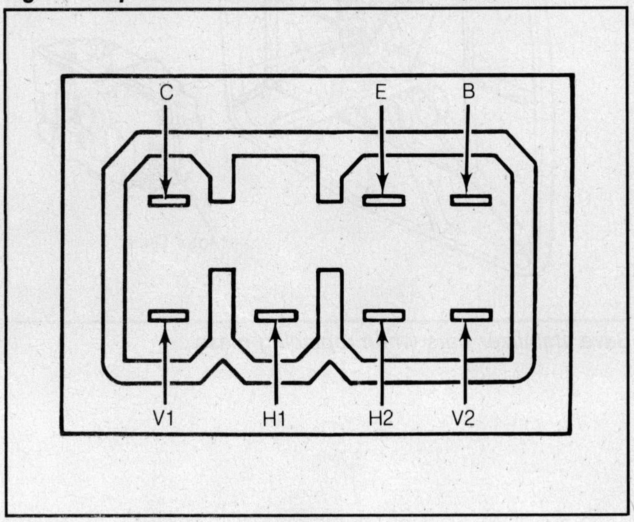

MIRROR MOTOR

Left Side

Using jumper wires, apply 12 volts to terminals "V 1" and "C", mirror should operate. Reverse jumper wires, mirror position should reverse. Apply 12 volts to terminals "H1" and "C", mirror should operate. Reverse jumper wires, mirror position should reverse. If mirror does not operate as indicated, replace mirror.

Right Side

Using jumper wires, apply 12 volts to terminals "V2" and "C", mirror should operate. Reverse jumper wires, mirror position should reverse. Apply 12 volts to terminals "H 2" and "C", mirror should operate. Reverse jumper wires, mirror position should reverse. If mirror does not operate as indicated, replace mirror.

Fig. 2: Jeep Mirror Motor Terminal Locations

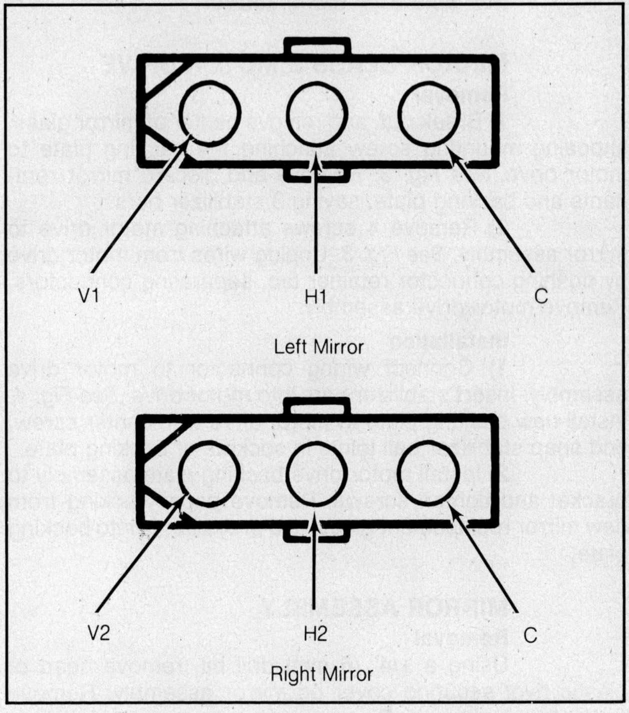

NOTE: The following tests apply to Ford vehicles only.

ONE MIRROR DOES NOT FUNCTION

1) Working underneath mirror, remove head of plastic rivet, using a 1/4" (6 mm) drill. Remove rivet stem remnants. Remove screw from cover, remove cover, and disconnect plug. Check function of mirror by connecting 12 volts to terminals of wire plug.

2) Yellow and Green wires provide up-down movement; Blue and White wires, right-left movement. If mirror does not function, replace motor drive. See MOTOR DRIVE REMOVAL.

3) If mirror functions when tested, but does not operate when connected to feed wire, remove left door panel. Test feed wire for continuity between switch plug and mirror plug. Repair or replace wiring, if necessary. If mirror functions through feed wire, but fails to respond to switch operation, replace switch.

BOTH MIRRORS DO NOT FUNCTION

1) Remove left door inner trim panel. Unplug accessory feed wire (Black and Yellow with Red stripe), and check for voltage. On vans, turn ignition switch on.

2) If no voltage is observed, check hot wire in-line fuse, check hot wire and ground connections. Repair as necessary. If voltage is present at accessory feed wire plug, reconnect wire. Check mirror functions and if satisfactory, install trim panel.

Power Mirrors

FORD & JEEP (Cont.)

3) If no voltage is observed, disconnect and check continuity of wiring, step-by-step, from hot wire lead to cowl/door harness connection, to switch wire feed connection, and to mirror feed wire connection. Replace or repair damaged wiring.

REMOVAL & INSTALLATION

NOTE: Removal procedure for Jeep vehicles were not available from manufacturer.

MIRROR GLASS & MOTOR DRIVE

Removal

1) Break out, and remove center of mirror glass, exposing mounting screw attaching the backing plate to motor drive. *See Fig. 3.* Remove and discard mirror remnants and backing plate, saving 3 stabilizer bars.

2) Remove 4 screws attaching motor drive to mirror assembly. *See Fig. 3.* Unplug wires from motor drive by pushing connector retainer tab, separating connectors. Remove motor drive assembly.

Installation

1) Connect wiring connector to motor drive assembly. Insert stabilizer bars into motor drive. *See Fig. 4.* Install new backing plate to motor drive with center screw, and snap stabilizer ball joints in sockets of backing plate.

2) Install motor drive/backing plate assembly to bracket and tighten screws. Remove paper backing from new mirror replacement glass, and press firmly into backing plate.

MIRROR ASSEMBLY

Removal

Using a 1/4" (6 mm) drill bit, remove head of plastic rivet securing cover on mirror assembly. Remove rivet stem remnants. Remove screw from cover, and remove cover. Disconnect electrical connector. Remove screws attaching mirror assembly to door, and remove mirror assembly.

Installation

To install, reverse removal procedure.

MIRROR SWITCH ASSEMBLY

Removal

Remove left door inner trim panel. Disconnect wiring harness from both switch wiring assemblies. Remove 2 bezel nuts securing bezel and switch assembly to door. Remove bezel and switch from door.

Installation

To install, reverse removal procedure.

NOTE: Some Pickups may use a snap-in bezel switch assembly. Insert screwdriver in slots at bezel edge to release retention springs. Then, disconnect wiring harness from switch, loosen set screw, and remove switch.

Fig. 3: Electric Mirror Mounting Screws

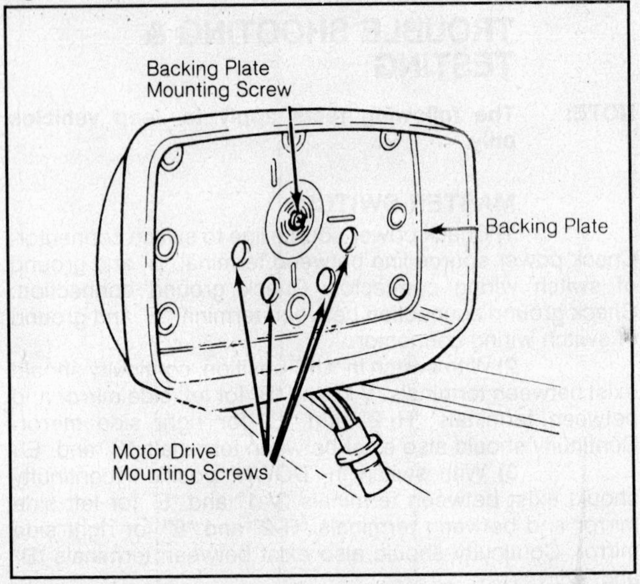

Mounting screws are located inside holes.

Fig. 4: Motor Drive Stabilizer Bars

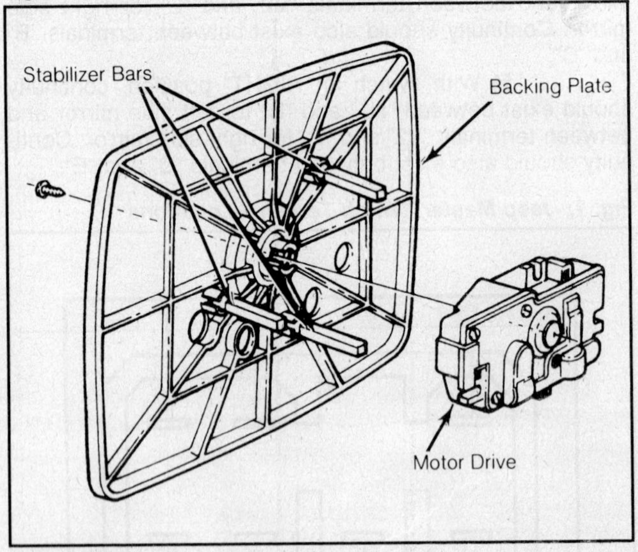

Save stabilizer bars when replacing glass.

Power Seats
CHRYSLER CORP.

All FWD Models

DESCRIPTION

Chrysler power seats can be adjusted 6 ways. The control switch is located on the inboard side of the driver's seat and consists of 3 switches which provide seat adjustment.

The front and rear switches are used to tilt the seat. The center switch moves the seat vertically and horizontally. The circuit is protected by a 30 amp circuit breaker located on the fuse block.

TESTING

ELECTRICAL CIRCUITS

1) With battery fully charged and all electrical connections cleaned and tightened, turn dome light on and operate seat switch. If dome light dims, seat may be jamming. Check for binding. If dome light does not dim, proceed to step **2)**.

2) Disconnect feed wire from instrument panel at fuse block side cowl circuit breaker. Connect 12-volt test lamp in series between feed wire and ground. If lamp lights, feed wiring is good. Remove test lamp and connect feed wire to circuit breaker.

3) Disconnect wiring from other side of circuit breaker and connect test lamp in series between circuit breaker and ground. If test lamp lights, circuit breaker is good. Remove test lamp and connect feed wire to circuit breaker.

4) Disconnect wiring harness at connector under seat. Connect test lamp between Red and Black wire in female connector. If test lamp lights, harness to seat is good. Remove test lamp and connect harness. Remove switch from seat harness.

5) To check front motor, connect an insulated jumper wire between Red terminal in center section and either the Red with Green tracer or Yellow with Green tracer connection in front section. Connect a second jumper wire between Black terminal in center section and open connection in front section.

6) If motor does not operate, reverse jumpers in front section. If motor still does not operate, the harness or complete 3-motor assembly is defective. To check center motor, connect an insulated jumper wire between Red terminal of center section and either the Red with Blue tracer or Yellow with Blue tracer connection in center section.

7) Connect a second jumper wire between Black terminal in center section and open connection in center section. If motor does not operate, reverse jumper wires. If motor still does not operate, harness or 3-motor assembly is defective.

8) To check rear motor, connect an insulated jumper wire between Red terminal in center section and either the Red with White tracer or Yellow with White tracer connection of rear section. Connect second jumper wire between Black terminal in center section and open connection in rear section.

9) If motor does not operate, reverse wires in rear section. If motor still does not operate, harness or 3-motor assembly is defective. If all motors and seat operate properly, the switch is bad.

REMOVAL & INSTALLATION

SEAT ASSEMBLY

1) Disconnect battery negative cable. Remove adjuster attaching bolts and nuts from floorpan. Move adjuster as required to gain access.

2) Disconnect wiring harness power lead at carpet. Remove seat assembly from vehicle. To install, reverse removal procedure and check seat operation.

MOTOR & CABLES

Removal

1) Remove seat assembly as previously outlined. Position adjuster full forward with front in full up position. If motor is not operable, grip plastic stop located near end of gear and screw assembly, manually adjust to desired position.

2) Remove front vertical lift assist spring and horizontal transmission pivot pin and cotter pin. Lift horizontal transmission away from transmission bracket and rotate transmission counterclockwise to disengage motor and cable from transmission.

3) Pull motor away from vertical transmission and remove plastic motor supports if motor is to be replaced. Transmissions are not serviceable and no maintenance is required. If transmission failed, replace entire seat adjuster assembly.

Installation

Install motor supports on new motor. With vertical transmission cables in place, slide cables and motor support into vertical transmission housings. With horizontal transmission cable in place, rotate horizontal transmission housing clockwise to insert cable and motor support into horizontal transmission housing. To complete installation, reverse removal procedure.

Fig. 1: Electrical Test Connections

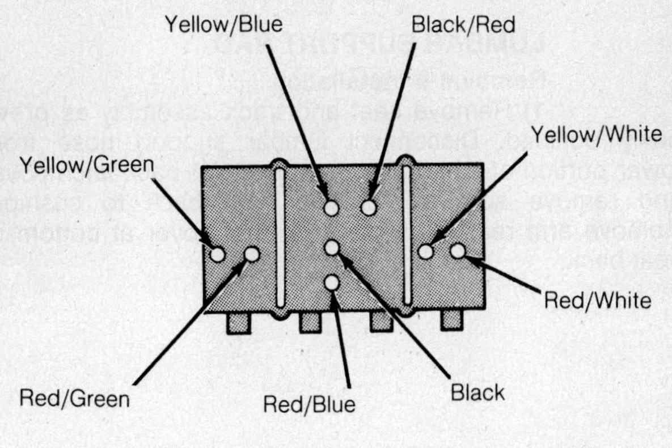

Power Seats

FORD

Aerostar, Bronco II

DESCRIPTION

Ford lumbar support power seat adjustment is controlled by a switch located on the inboard side of the driver's seat. The system consists of an electrically operated compressor, a lumbar support pad, control switch and necessary wiring. The lumbar support pad and compressor are located in seat assembly.

TESTING

NOTE: **Testing procedure not available from manufacturer.**

REMOVAL & INSTALLATION

SEAT & TRACK ASSEMBLY

Removal & Installation

1) Remove 4 seat track-to-floorpan screws and lift seat and track assembly from vehicle. Position seat upside down on a clean bench to remove seat tracks.

2) Disconnect latch tie rod assembly and assist spring from tracks. Remove 4 track-to-seat cushion screws from track assembly and remove tracks from seat cushion. To install, reverse removal procedure.

LUMBAR SUPPORT COMPRESSOR

Removal & Installation

Remove seat and track assembly. Remove front seat trim cushion as necessary to gain access to compressor mounting screws. Remove mounting screws, disconnect hose and electrical connector and remove compressor. To install, reverse removal procedure.

LUMBAR SUPPORT SWITCH

Removal & Installation

Remove seat and track assembly as previously outlined. Remove lumbar support switch bezel by carefully prying lower portion of bezel away from switch housing. Pull out and downward. Remove screws attaching switch to seat frame. Disconnect electrical connector and remove switch. To install, reverse removal procedure.

LUMBAR SUPPORT PAD

Removal & Installation

1) Remove seat and track assembly as previously outlined. Disconnect lumbar support hose from lower portion of seat back. Remove seat back latch cover and remove screws attaching seat back to cushion. Remove arm rest, if used. Unzip trim cover at bottom of seat back.

2) Remove moldings from seat back, if used. Cut hog rings from seat back trim cover and/or disengage plastic retainers from seat back frame. Remove trim cover. Disconnect hose from lumbar support pad. Using a screwdriver, bend lumbar support pad retaining tabs upward and remove pad. To install, reverse removal procedure.

Fig. 1: Bucket Seat with Lumbar Support

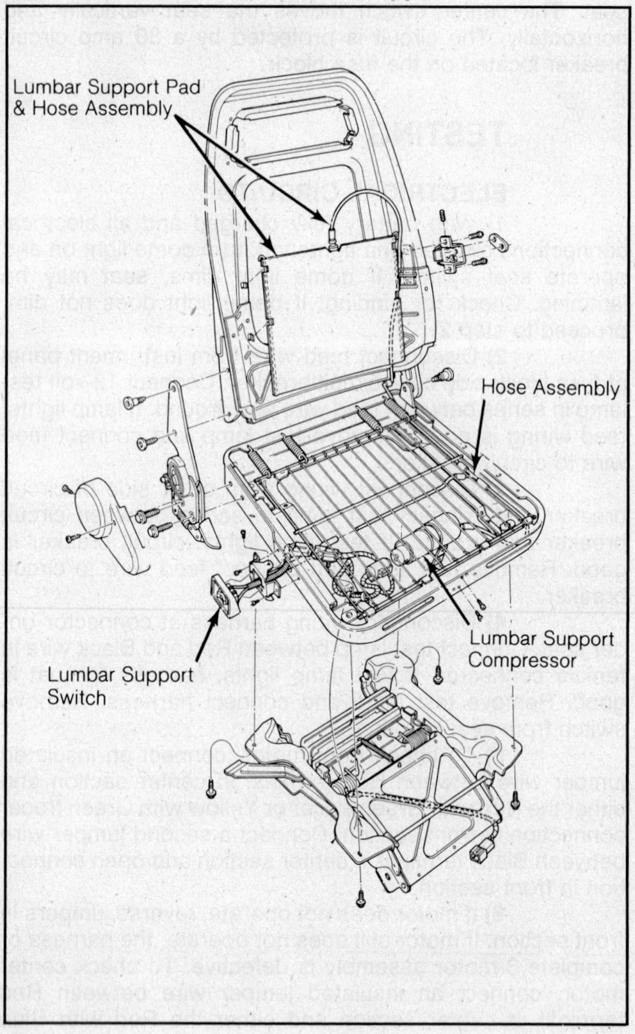

Power Seats

JEEP

All Models, Except CJ7 & Scrambler

DESCRIPTION

Jeep power seats can be adjusted 6 ways. The control switch is located on the left lower side of the driver's seat.

The switch has 3 levers; the middle lever raises or lowers the complete seat, as well as moving it forward or rearward. The 2 side levers raise or lower the front and back of the seat.

A permanent magnet reversible motor is connected by cables to rack and pinion assemblies located in the seat tracks. The circuit is protected by a 30 amp circuit breaker on the fuse block.

TESTING

ELECTRICAL CIRCUITS

1) With battery fully charged and all electrical connections cleaned and tightened, turn dome light on and operate seat switch. If dome light dims, seat may be jamming. Check for binding. If dome light does not dim, proceed to step **2)**.

2) Disconnect wiring harness at connector under seat. Connect 12-volt test lamp between Red and Black (ground) wire in female connector. If lamp lights, harness to seat is good. If lamp does not light, check for blown circuit breaker, continuity in Red and Black (ground) wires at connector, and for proper ground.

3) Reconnect harness under seat. Remove switch from seat harness. To check rear motor of switch, connect a covered jumper wire between Red terminal in center motor and either Lt. Blue or Orange connection in rear motor.

4) Connect a second jumper wire between Black (ground) terminal in center motor and open connection in front motor.

5) If motor does not operate, reverse jumpers in front motor. If motor still does not operate, the harness or complete 3-motor assembly is defective. To check center motor, connect a covered jumper wire between Red terminal of center motor and White or Tan terminal of center motor.

6) Connect a second jumper wire between Black (ground) terminal of center motor and open connection in center motor. If motor does not operate, reverse White and Tan jumper wires. If motor still does not operate, harness or 3-motor assembly is defective.

7) To check front motor, connect covered jumper wire between Red terminal in center motor and Green or Yellow connection of rear motor. Connect second jumper wire between Black (ground) terminal of center motor and open connection in rear motor.

8) If motor does not operate, reverse wires on rear motor. If motor still does not operate, harness or 3-motor assembly is defective. If all motors and seat operate properly, the switch is bad and should be replaced.

REMOVAL & INSTALLATION

SEAT ASSEMBLY

1) Disconnect battery negative cable. Remove nuts attaching seat assembly to floorpan.

2) Tilt seat, and disconnect wiring harness. Remove seat assembly from vehicle. To install, reverse removal procedure.

MOTOR

NOTE: **Whenever the motor, cable, and housing assemblies are removed or serviced, they must be synchronized to ensure proper operation.**

1) Remove seat assembly as previously outlined. Lay seat assembly on its back on a clean surface.

2) Remove motor mounting screws. Disconnect housings and cables from motor assembly, and remove motor. To install, reverse removal procedure.

Fig. 1: Electrical Test Connections

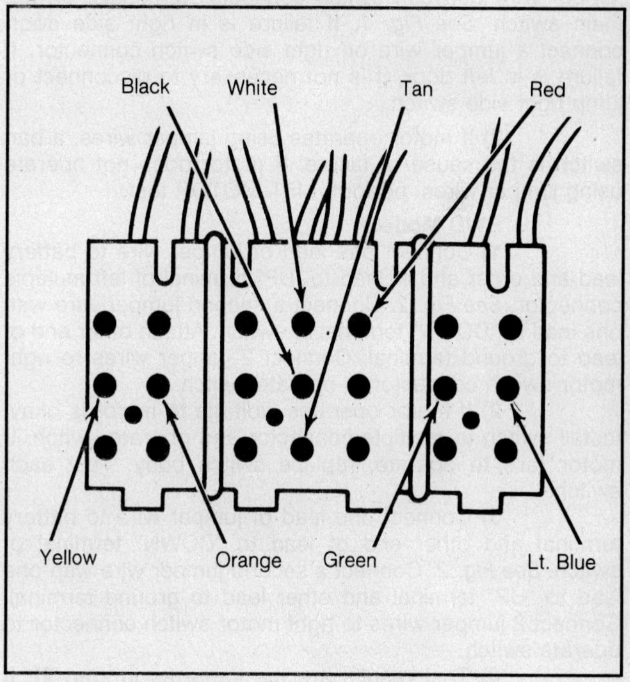

Driver's side connector shown.

Power Windows

CHRYSLER CORP. SIDE WINDOWS

DESCRIPTION

Electric window system consists of motors in each front door, switches to operate the motors, wiring harnesses and necessary connections. Window motors are permanent magnet type.

A battery connection (positive or negative) to either of the two motor terminals will cause the motor to rotate in one direction. Reversing current will cause motor to rotate in opposite direction. Each motor is grounded through the master switch.

TESTING

SWITCH VOLTAGE

1) Remove switch from trim panel. Separate multiple terminal block on wiring harness from switch body. Connect one lead of test lamp to battery wire terminal (Black wire on FWD models). Connect other lead to ground wire terminal (Tan wire on FWD models).

2) If test lamp comes on, wiring between battery and switch is okay. If lamp does not light, check 30 amp circuit breaker in fuse block, check for broken wire or poor ground.

MOTOR SWITCH

FWD Models

1) Check operation of lift motor by connecting a jumper wire between switch connector terminals, on left main switch. *See Fig. 1.* If failure is in right side door, connect a jumper wire on right side switch connector. If failure is in left door, it is not necessary to disconnect or jump right side switch.

2) If motor operates using jumper wires, a bad switch is the cause of failure. If motor does not operate using jumper wires, perform LIFT MOTOR test.

RWD Models

1) Connect one lead of jumper wire to battery lead and other end of lead to "UP" terminal of left multiple connector. *See Fig. 2.* Connect a second jumper wire with one lead to "DOWN" terminal of switch. Attach other end of lead to ground terminal. Connect 2 jumper wires to right motor switch connector to operate switch.

2) If motor operates, voltage to motor is okay. Install switch to multiple connector and operate switch. If motor fails to operate, replace switch body. Test each switch.

3) Connect one lead of jumper wire to battery terminal and other end of lead to "DOWN" terminal of switch. *See Fig. 2.* Connect a second jumper wire with one lead to "UP" terminal and other lead to ground terminal. Connect 2 jumper wires to right motor switch connector to operate switch.

4) Test results are the same as in step **2)**. If motor fails to run, perform LIFT MOTOR test.

LIFT MOTOR

1) Connect positive lead of test battery to either of the two terminals of motor. Connect negative lead to remaining terminal. Motor should now rotate in one direction to move window up or down.

2) If window is in up position, and leads are connected so motor rotates in up direction, no movement should occur. The reverse holds true, if leads are connected so motor rotates in down direction, and window is already down.

Fig. 1: FWD Motor Switch Tests

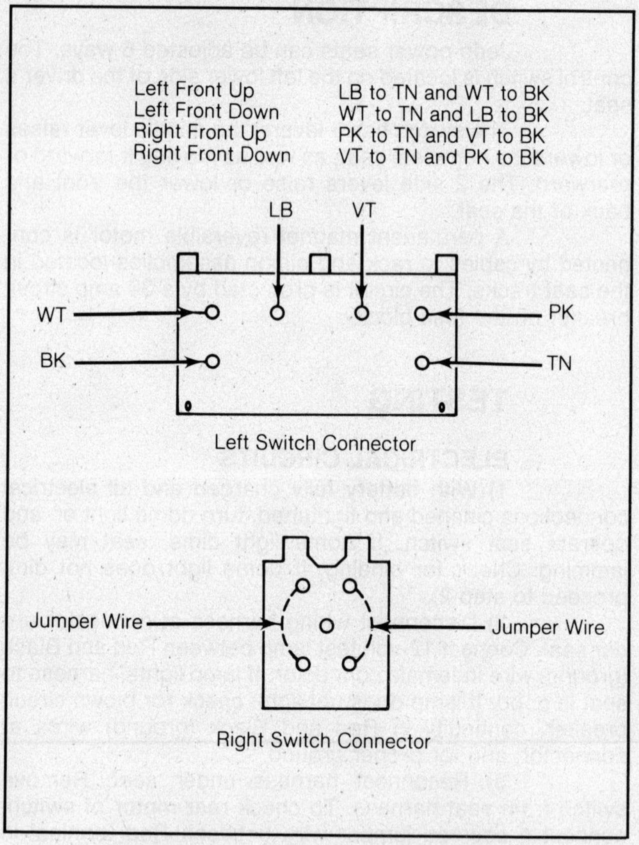

3) Reverse battery leads. Window should now move in desired direction. If not, remove motor and replace. If motor moved window, reverse leads again and ensure that motor moves window in both directions.

REMOVAL & INSTALLATION

WINDOW REGULATOR

Removal (FWD Models)

Remove trim panel and liner. Remove 2 nuts and remove glass from door. Disconnect electrical regulator at wiring harness and remove clip from inside panel. Drill out 5 power or 6 manual regulator attaching rivets. Remove 2 screws at sill. Rotate and remove regulator through access hole.

Installation

Mount regulator to door panel with 1/4"-20 X 1/2" screws and nuts, tightened to 90 INCH lbs. (10 N.m) to replace rivets.

Removal (RWD Models)

1) Raise window to full up position on vans or wagons. Remove trim panel and watershield. Remove lower trim panel on stereo-equipped vehicles. Remove down stop bumper bracket. Remove stereo speaker (if equipped). Remove vent wing. Lower glass to full down position on trucks.

2) Disconnect wiring connector from motor on trucks. Disconnect wiring connector from harness on vans and wagons. Disengage glass from regulator, and lower to door bottom. Drill out regulator rivets and remove regulator through access hole.

Installation

1) Mount regulator to door panel with 1/4"-20 X 1/2" screws and nuts, tightened to 90 INCH lbs. (10 N.m). Connect regulator wiring on vans and wagons. Slide glass into regulator arms and into rear glass run.

2) Install vent wing, and adjust. Raise glass to full up position. Install stereo speaker (if equipped). Install down stop bumper bracket. Test regulator function. Install trim panel and watershield.

MOTORS

Removal

Remove regulator as previously outlined. On FWD models, remove motor attaching screws and remove motor. On RWD models, secure regulator in a vise to prevent sector gear from rotating. Remove counterbalance spring. Remove 3 motor attaching screws and remove motor.

Installation

To install, reverse removal procedure, noting that counterbalance spring must be installed after motor is attached to regulator.

OVERHAUL

REGULATOR

Disassembly (RWD Models Only)

Secure regulator in vise to prevent sector gear from rotating. Remove counterbalance spring. Remove 3 screws attaching motor to regulator, and remove motor.

Inspection

Check regulator sector gear for chipped or broken teeth, and for severe wear. Check that all sliders and rivets are securely attached. Parts must not be bent or cracked. Check that sector gear rotates freely.

Reassembly

To reassemble, reverse disassembly procedure. Counterbalance spring must be installed after motor is attached to regulator.

Fig. 2: RWD Motor Switch Tests

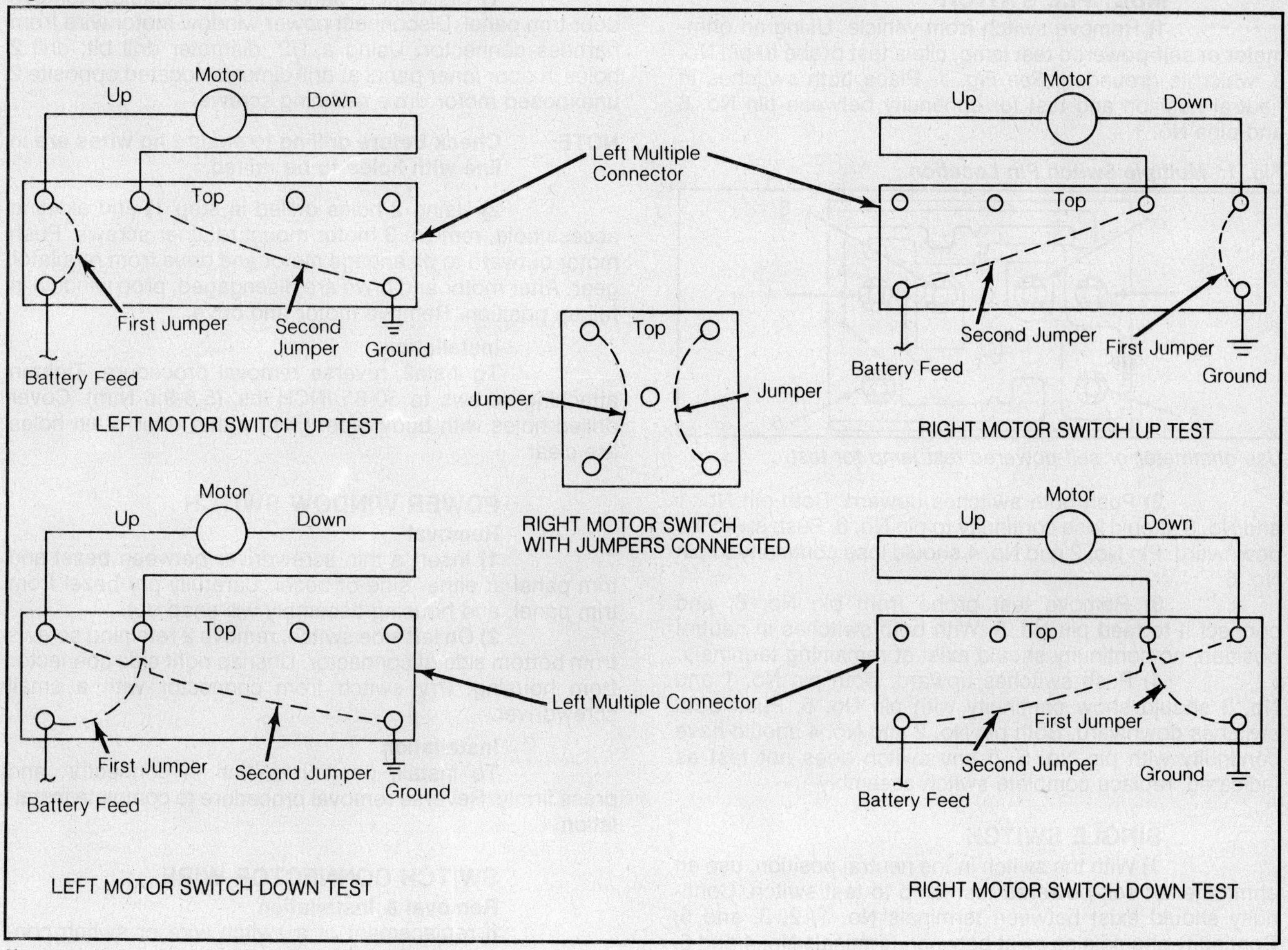

If motor does not run, see MOTOR LIFT test.

Power Windows

FORD SIDE WINDOWS

Bronco, Pickups

DESCRIPTION

Ford power window system consists of reversible 12-volt motors in each front door, switches to operate motors, wiring harness and necessary connections. Driver's door multiple switch controls both windows.

TESTING

MOTOR

1) Remove door trim panel. Disconnect motor lead. Disconnect regulator mechanism from motor. Connect a power source (battery) to motor with an ammeter in series. Operate motor and observe current draw.

2) Current draw should not fluctuate or exceed 4 amps. Reverse motor wire connections to observe reversed motor operation. Replace motor if current draw exceeds 4 amps.

MULTIPLE SWITCH

1) Remove switch from vehicle. Using an ohmmeter or self-powered test lamp, clip a test probe to pin No. 6, which is grounded. *See Fig. 1.* Place both switches in neutral position and test for continuity between pin No. 6 and pins No. 1-4.

Fig. 1: Multiple Switch Pin Location

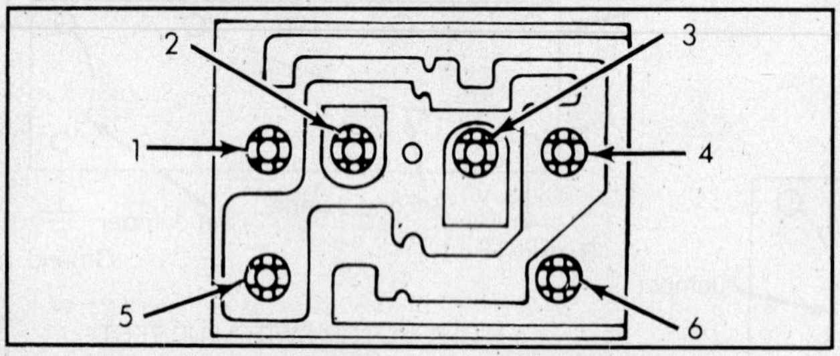

Use ohmmeter or self-powered test lamp for test.

2) Push both switches upward. Both pin No. 1 and No. 3 should lose continuity to pin No. 6. Push switches downward. Pin No. 2 and No. 4 should lose continuity to pin No. 6.

3) Remove test probe from pin No. 6, and connect it to feed pin No. 5. With both switches in neutral position, no continuity should exist at remaining terminals.

4) Push switches upward. Both pin No. 1 and No. 3 should show continuity with pin No. 5. Push both switches downward. Both pin No. 2 and No. 4 should have continuity with pin No. 5. If any switch does not test as indicated, replace complete switch assembly.

SINGLE SWITCH

1) With the switch in the neutral position, use an ohmmeter or self-powered test lamp to test switch. Continuity should exist between terminals No. 1, 2, 3, and 5. Continuity should also exist between terminals No. 4 and 6. *See Fig. 2.*

2) With switch pushed downward, continuity should exist between terminals No. 2, 4 and 5. Continuity should also exist between terminals No. 1 and 3. Terminal No. 6 should be disconnected from all other terminals.

Fig. 2: Single Switch Pin Locations

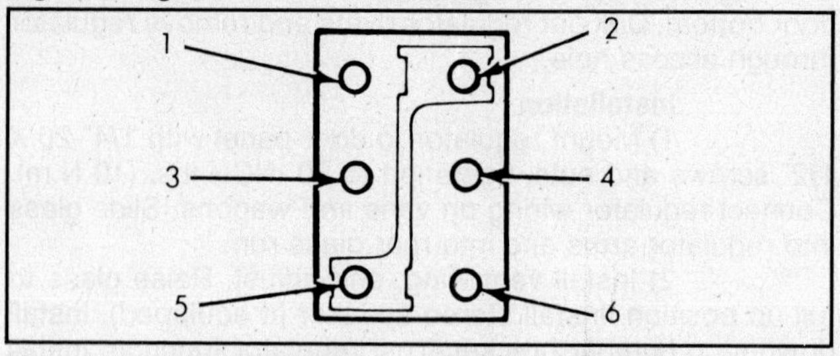

Use ohmmeter or self-powered test lamp for test.

3) With switch pushed upward, there should be continuity between terminals No. 2, 3, and 5. Continuity should also exist between terminals No. 4 and 6. Terminal No. 1 should be disconnected from all other terminals. If switch does not operate as specified, replace switch.

REMOVAL & INSTALLATION

MOTOR

Removal

1) Disconnect battery negative cable. Remove door trim panel. Disconnect power window motor wire from harness connector. Using a 1/2" diameter drill bit, drill 2 holes in door inner panel at drill dimples, located opposite 2 unexposed motor drive retaining screws.

NOTE: **Check before drilling to ensure no wires are in line with holes to be drilled.**

2) Using 2 holes drilled in step **1)** and existing access hole, remove 3 motor mount retainer screws. Push motor outward to disengage motor and drive from regulator gear. After motor and drive are disengaged, prop window in full up position. Remove motor and drive.

Installation

To install, reverse removal procedure. Tighten attaching screws to 50-85 INCH lbs. (5.6-9.6 N.m). Cover drilled holes with body tape. Ensure that door drain holes are clear.

POWER WINDOW SWITCH

Removal

1) Insert a thin screwdriver between bezel and trim panel at either side of bezel. Carefully pry bezel from trim panel, and housing assembly will snap out.

2) On left side switch, remove 2 retaining screws from bottom side of connector. Unsnap right side connector from housing. Pry switch from connector with a small screwdriver.

Installation

To install, position switch in connector, and press firmly. Reverse removal procedure to complete installation.

SWITCH CONNECTOR WIRE

Removal & Installation

If replacement of a switch wire or switch connector is necessary, insert a needle-like tool into edge of pin hole and bend terminal in. Pull wire and terminal from connector. To install terminal in connector, open terminal and insert it in connector.

FORD TAILGATE WINDOW

Bronco

DESCRIPTION

Power tailgate window system consists of a motor and regulator assembly inside the tailgate, a key-operated switch at the tailgate, an instrument panel switch, a limit switch to prevent window operation when tailgate is open, and necessary wiring and connections.

Circuit is protected by two 25 amp circuit breakers located in the fuse block. One circuit breaker protects the key switch.

ADJUSTMENTS

TAILGATE GLASS

Forward and rearward adjustments can be made by opening tailgate and loosening back window side glass attaching screws. Adjust glass as required, and tighten attaching screws.

Side-to-side adjustments are made by removing inside cover panel and loosening window glass to window bracket screws. After positioning the glass, tighten screws to 6-11 ft. lbs. (9-14 N.m)

TESTING

TAILGATE WINDOW MOTOR

1) Remove tailgate trim panel. Disconnect motor lead. Supply power to the motor lead connector with an ammeter attached in series.

2) Operate the motor and observe the current draw. The current draw should not exceed 4 amps and should not fluctuate. Raplace motor if current draw exceeds 4 amps.

INSTRUMENT PANEL TAILGATE SWITCH

1) Remove switch from vehicle. Use a self-powered test lamp or ohmmeter. With the switch in the neutral position, there should be continuity between terminals 1, 2, and 4. *See Fig. 1.*

2) With switch downward, there should be continuity between terminals 1 and 2 and between terminals 3 and 4. With switch upward, there should be continuity between terminals 1 and 3 and between terminals 2 and 4. If the switch does not test as listed, replace switch.

WINDOW SWITCH

1) Remove switch from vehicle. Use a self-powered test lamp or ohmmeter. With the switch in the neutral position, there should be continuity between terminals 1 and 3, 2 and 5, and 4 and 6. *See Fig. 1.*

2) With the toggle switch downward, there should be continuity between terminals 2, 4, and 5, and 1 and 3. Terminal 6 should be disconnected from any other terminal.

3) With the toggle switch pushed upward, there should be continuity between terminals 2, 3 and 5, and 4 and 6. Terminal 1 should be disconnected from any other terminal. If the switch does not test as specified, replace switch.

Fig. 1: Tailgate Instrument Panel & Window Switch Pin Positions

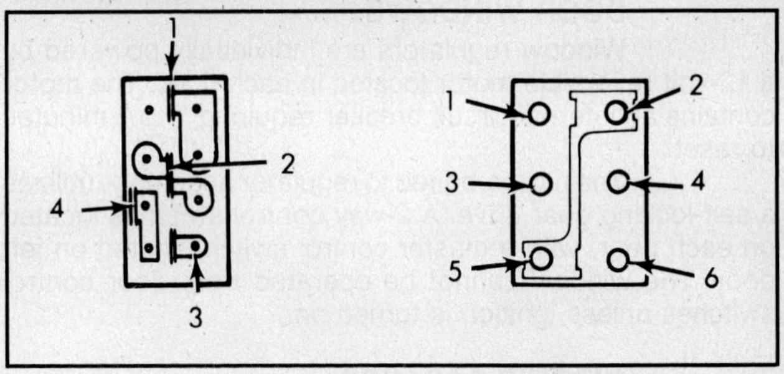

REMOVAL & INSTALLATION

REGULATOR SWITCH & MOTOR

Removal

1) Remove interior access cover from tailgate. Raise glass to full "UP" position. Disconnect wiring harness from switch and/or motor.

2) Remove clip attaching switch to lock cylinder, and remove switch. Remove motor mounting screws, and remove motor.

Installation

To install, reverse removal procedure. Check operation of switch and motor before installing access cover.

WINDOW REGULATOR

Removal

1) Raise glass to full "UP" position (if glass cannot be raised, lower tailgate and remove interior access cover). Using fingers, locate and remove 4 glass attaching nuts and screws at bottom edge of access opening.

2) Slowly slide glass from tailgate. Remove regulator attaching screw and washer assemblies. Remove regulator.

Installation

To install, reverse removal procedure, tightening screws to 72-132 INCH lbs. (9-14 N.m).

Fig. 2: Ford Bronco Power Tailgate Window Wiring Diagram

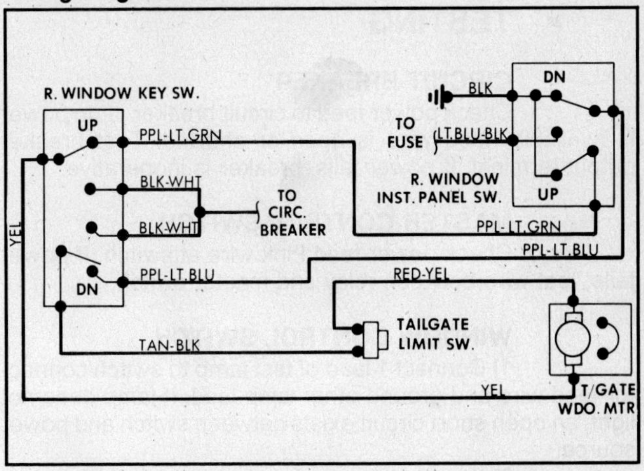

Power Windows

GENERAL MOTORS SIDE WINDOWS

DESCRIPTION

DOOR WINDOWS

Window regulators are individually powered by a 12-volt reversible motor located in each door. The motor contains an internal circuit breaker requiring 1 to 3 minutes to reset.

The motor, bolted to regulator assembly, utilizes a self-locking gear drive. A 2-way control switch is located on each door, with a master control switch located on left door. The window cannot be operated from door control switches unless ignition is turned on.

CIRCUIT BREAKER

A 30 amp circuit breaker is fuse block mounted.

CONTROL SWITCHES

In addition to individual control switches adjacent to individual windows, a master control switch is mounted on left door trim pad.

ACCESSORY JUNCTION BLOCK

Junction block is located on reinforcement at left shroud. It supplies current to power operated circuits. Current is supplied to junction block from circuit breaker. Power window harness plugs into junction block.

TROUBLE SHOOTING

WINDOWS WILL NOT OPERATE WITH IGNITION ON

Open circuit or short in power feed circuit. Switch defective.

RIGHT WINDOW OPERATES WITH MASTER SWITCH BUT WILL NOT OPERATE WITH RIGHT CONTROL SWITCH, LEFT WINDOW OPERATES

Open circuit or short in front harness power feed circuit.

TESTING

CIRCUIT BREAKER

Check power feed to circuit breaker. If no power is available, feed wire is open or shorted. Test breaker output terminal. If power fails, breaker is inoperative.

MASTER CONTROL SWITCH

Check power feed Pink wire at switch. If power fails, test wire between relay and master switch.

WINDOW CONTROL SWITCH

1) Connect 1 lead of test lamp to switch connector feed wire and ground other lamp lead. If lamp does not light, an open short circuit exists between switch and power source.

2) Insert 1 end of a jumper wire in switch connector and other end of jumper to motor lead in connector. Repeat procedure for motor lead terminal. If motor operates with jumper wire but does not operate with switch, replace switch.

WINDOW SWITCH TO WINDOW HARNESS

Disconnect harness connector from motor. Insert 1 end of a jumper wire in switch connector and other end of jumper to motor lead in connector. Using a test lamp, check for current at motor connector. If lamp does not light, switch to motor harness is shorted or has open circuit. Check other terminal using same procedure.

WINDOW MOTOR

Check power feed to motor terminals. If power is available, check motor ground. Inspect window regulator and channels for possible binding. Connect a jumper wire to other motor terminal. Motor should operate window up and down. If not, replace motor.

Fig. 1: Power Window Wiring Diagram

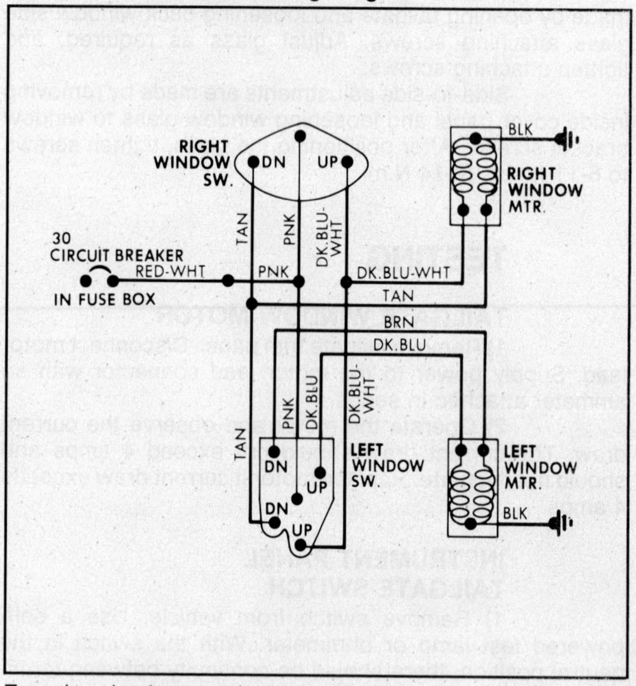

Two-door is shown, others are similar.

REMOVAL & INSTALLATION

NOTE: **Astro and Safari vans are classified as "M" series vehicles.**

WINDOW REGULATOR & MOTOR

CAUTION: **Disconnect electrical connections before removing regulator assembly from window.**

1) Raise window to full "UP" position and tape glass to door frame to prevent it from falling. Disconnect battery negative cable and remove door trim panel. On "S" series, remove door trim panel, armrest bracket and inner panel water deflector.

2) On "C" and "K" series, remove remote control bolts and place control assembly aside, if necessary. On all models, remove regulator-to-door panel attaching screws.

GENERAL MOTORS SIDE WINDOWS (Cont.)

3) On "C", "K" and "M" series, disconnect harness from regulator. On "C" and "K" series, slide regulator assembly rearward, disengaging rollers from sash panel. On "M" series, remove rivets attaching regulator to inner panel. On "C", "K" and "M" series, remove regulator assembly.

4) On "S" series, disconnect harness from motor. Disengage roller or regulator lift arm from glass run channel. Remove regulator through access hole.

CAUTION: Regulator lift arm is under tension from counterbalance spring, sector gear must be locked to avoid personal injury.

5) On "C" and "K" series, drill a hole through sector gear and back plate. Do not drill closer than 1/2" (13 mm) to edge of sector gear or back plate. On "C", "K" and "M" series, install sheet metal screw (No. 10 - 12 X 3/4") into hole to lock sector gear. Remove motor-to-regulator attaching screws (rivets on "M" series) and remove regulator from motor.

6) On "S" series, drill a hole through regulator sector gear and back plate and install a bolt and nut to lock sector gear. Using a 3/16" drill bit, drill out motor attaching rivets and remove rotor.

Installation

1) On "C", "K" and "M" series, lubricate motor drive gear and regulator sector teeth with a lubricant that is effective down to -20°F (-29°C). Ensure that motor pinion gear teeth mesh properly with sector gear. Remove screw locking sector gear. To complete installation, reverse removal procedure.

2) On "S" series, install motor on regulator using Riveter (J-29022) and install 3/16" rivets or install 3/16" nuts and bolts. Remove nut and bolt used to secure sector gear. To complete installation, reverse removal procedure.

Fig. 2: Power Window Regulator, Motor and Connector

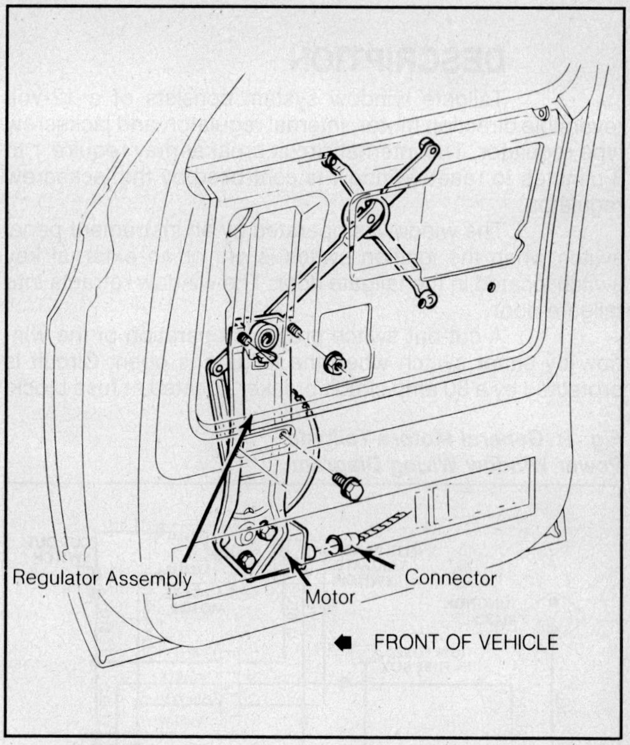

Power Windows

GENERAL MOTORS TAILGATE WINDOW

Chevrolet, GMC

DESCRIPTION

Tailgate window system consists of a 12-volt reversible direction motor, internal regulator, and jackscrew type regulator. The internal circuit breaker may require 1 to 3 minutes to reset. Window is controlled by the jackscrew regulator.

The window is operated by an instrument panel switch when the ignition switch is on, or an external key switch located in the tailgate door. The window retracts into tailgate door.

A cut-out switch prevents operation of the window by either switch when the tailgate is open. Circuit is protected by a 30 amp circuit breaker, located at fuse block.

Fig. 1: General Motors Tailgate Power Window Wiring Diagram

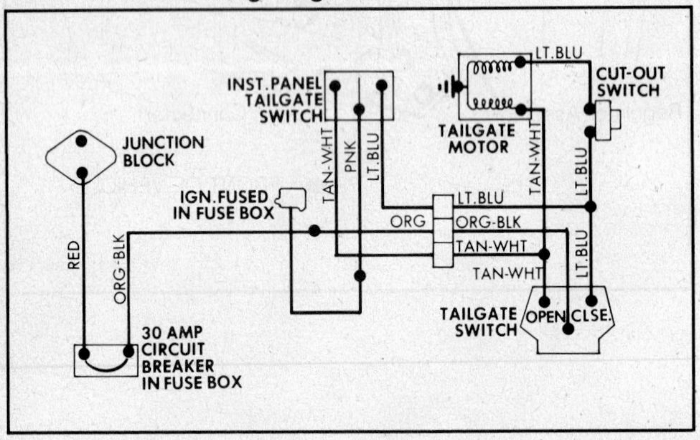

TESTING & TROUBLE SHOOTING

TAILGATE POWER WINDOW INOPERATIVE FROM PANEL OR TAILGATE KEY SWITCH

Check circuit breaker, and replace if bad. If good, check motor ground. If good, check the Tan/White and Lt. Blue wires for short. If not shorted, replace window motor.

TAILGATE POWER WINDOW INOPERATIVE FROM PANEL SWITCH, OPERATES FROM TAILGATE KEY SWITCH

1) If current from fuse block is good, ground 1 probe of 12-volt test lamp. Place tailgate panel switch in window "UP" position. Probe terminal for Lt. Blue wire at back of switch. If lamp does not light, replace switch.

2) If lamp lights, touch lamp probe to terminal for Tan/White wire at back of switch and press switch to "DOWN" position. If lamp does not light, replace switch. If lamp lights, check window motor ground to body and Lt. Blue and Tan/White wires between switch and motor.

NOTE: If switch operates from key switch, but not from panel switch, use same test procedure, replacing tailgate key switch if necessary.

TAILGATE WINDOW WILL NOT OPEN FROM PANEL SWITCH, OTHERWISE OPERATES

1) With ignition switch on, and tailgate open, place panel switch in "DOWN" position. Using a grounded 12-volt test lamp, probe Tan/White wire at panel switch.

2) If lamp does not light, replace switch. If lamp lights, probe Tan/White wire at window motor, with switch still in "DOWN" position. If lamp does not light now, check for open Tan/White wire between motor and panel switch. If lamp lights, system should operate normally.

TAILGATE WINDOW WILL NOT CLOSE FROM PANEL SWITCH, OTHERWISE OPERATES

1) With ignition switch on, and tailgate door open, place panel switch in "UP" position. Using a grounded 12-volt test lamp, probe terminal for Lt. Blue wire at back of switch. If lamp does not light, replace panel switch.

2) If lamp lights, probe terminal for Lt. Blue wire at cut-out switch. If lamp does not light, check for open Lt. Blue wire between instrument panel and cut-out switch. If lamp lights at cut-out switch terminal, check Lt. Blue wire between cut-out switch and motor. If wire is good, replace cut-out switch.

TAILGATE WINDOW WILL NOT OPEN FROM TAILGATE KEY SWITCH, OTHERWISE OPERATES

1) With ignition switch on, open tailgate door. Turn tailgate key switch to "DOWN" position. Using a grounded 12-volt test lamp, probe Tan/White wire at key switch.

2) If lamp does not light, replace key switch. If lamp lights, check for open Tan/White wire between key switch and window motor.

TAILGATE WINDOW WILL NOT CLOSE FROM TAILGATE KEY SWITCH, OTHERWISE OPERATES

1) With ignition switch on, and tailgate door open, place key switch in "UP" position. Using a grounded 12-volt test lamp, probe Lt. Blue wire at key switch. If lamp does not light, replace key switch. If lamp lights, probe Lt. Blue wire at cut-out switch.

2) If lamp does not light, check for open Lt. Blue wire between key switch and cut-out switch. If lamp lights, check for open in Lt. Blue wire between cut-out switch and window motor. If wire is okay, replace cut-out switch.

REMOVAL & INSTALLATION

WINDOW MOTOR

Removal

Disconnect drive cable and wiring harness from motor. Remove motor attaching screws and remove motor.

Installation

To install, reverse removal procedure.

CUT-OUT SWITCH

Removal

Disconnect left side remote control rod from center control by removing retaining clip. Remove side latch

GENERAL MOTORS TAILGATE WINDOW (Cont.)

retaining screws and disconnect cut-out switch wiring. Remove side latch assembly and screws holding latch to switch.

Installation
To install, reverse removal procedure.

JACKSCREW REGULATOR

CAUTION: If window glass is removed, or disengaged from regulator lift arms, the regulator lift arms must be secured before removing jackscrew. Regulator lift arms are under spring pressure and may cause injury if not secured.

Removal
Drill a 1/8" hole through sector gear and back plate. Install a sheet metal screw in hole to lock sector gears in position. Disconnect drive cable at jackscrew. Remove regulator jackscrew attaching screws and remove jackscrew assembly.

Installation
To install, reverse removal procedure.

Fig. 2: Power Tailgate Window Components

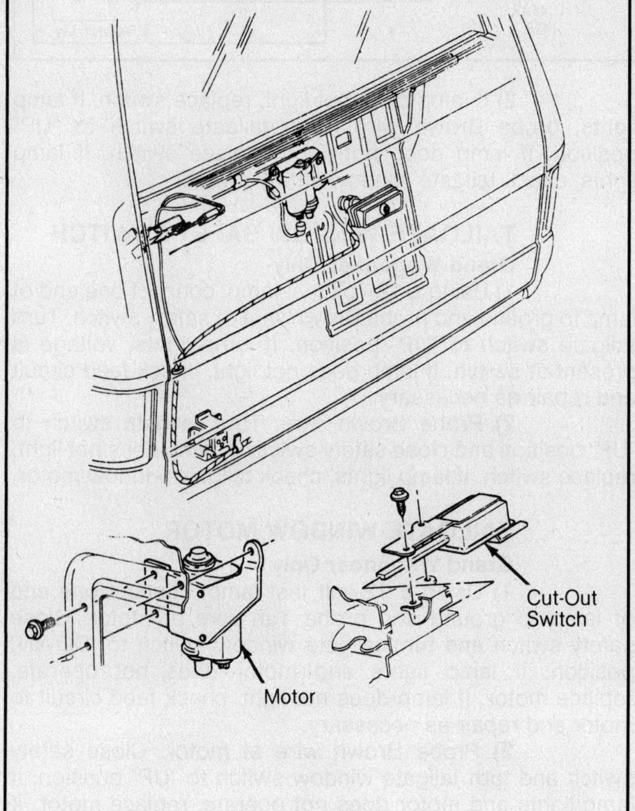

Power Windows

JEEP ELECTRIC WINDOWS

All Models, Except CJ7 & Scrambler

DESCRIPTION

All Cherokee and Wagoneers have a tape driven window regulator system. When motor is activated, the drive gear moves the flex rack along a T-track and raises or lowers the window glass.

On Grand Wagoneer, the system consists of an electrically-operated tailgate window and individual motors at all side windows. Tailgate window operates on 2 circuits, from an instrument panel switch or an external key switch at the tailgate.

Side windows are operated by individual switches at each door, or by a complete set of control switches at the instrument panel. The electric tailgate window system consists of a safety switch, gearbox-type regulator, 12-volt motor, wiring, connections and a 30 amp circuit breaker located at the fuse block.

The electric side window system consists of regulator motors, switches, actuators and actuator rods, wiring and connections, and a 30 amp circuit breaker located at the fuse block.

Fig. 1: Jeep Tailgate Wiring Diagram

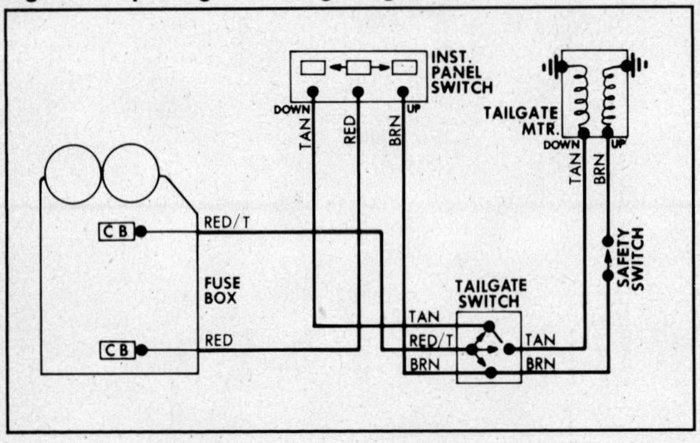

TESTING

NOTE: **Ensure that instrument panel tailgate switch is properly grounded as motor grounds through switch. The electric tailgate and defogger switch are serviced as an assembly.**

INSTRUMENT PANEL TAILGATE SWITCH

Grand Wagoneer Only

1) Turn ignition switch on. Using a 12-volt test lamp, connect one end of test lamp to ground and probe Red wire. If lamp does not light, repair feed circuit.

2) If lamp lights, probe Brown wire with switch in "UP" position. If lamp does not light, replace switch. If lamp lights, move switch to "DOWN" position and probe Tan wire. If lamp does not light, replace switch. If lamp lights, check tailgate window switch.

TAILGATE WINDOW SWITCH

Grand Wagoneer Only

1) Using a 12-volt test lamp, connect one end of lamp to ground and probe Red wire of tailgate window switch. If lamp does not light, repair feed circuit. If lamp lights, probe Tan wire. Turn tailgate switch to "DOWN" position.

Fig. 2: Jeep Power Window Wiring Diagram

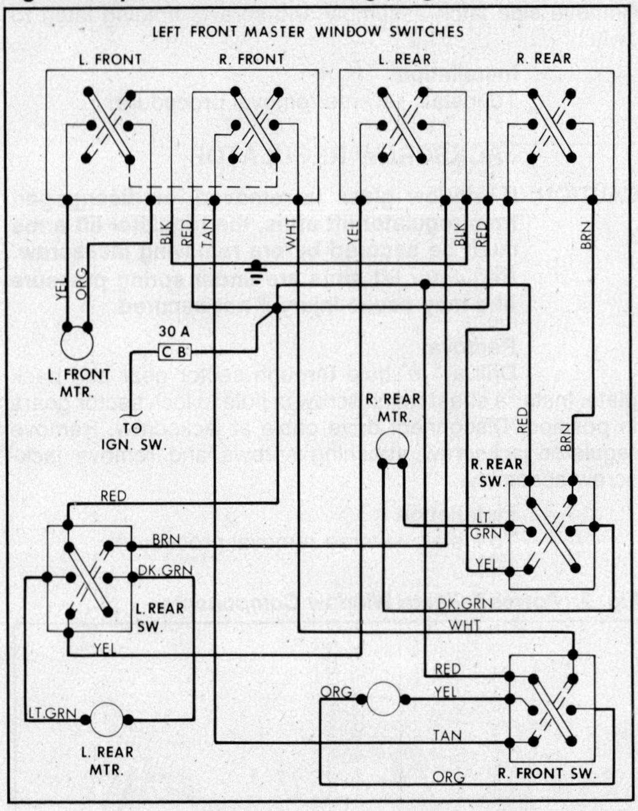

2) If lamp does not light, replace switch. If lamp lights, probe Brown wire. Turn tailgate switch to "UP" position. If lamp does not light, replace switch. If lamp lights, check tailgate window safety switch

TAILGATE WINDOW SAFETY SWITCH

Grand Wagoneer Only

1) Using a 12-volt test lamp, connect one end of lamp to ground and probe Brown wire of safety switch. Turn tailgate switch to "UP" position. If lamp lights, voltage is present at switch. If lamp does not light, check feed circuit and repair as necessary.

2) Probe Brown wire. Turn tailgate switch to "UP" position and close safety swicth. If lamp does not light, replace switch. If lamp lights, check tailgate window motor.

TAILGATE WINDOW MOTOR

Grand Wagoneer Only

1) Using a 12-volt test lamp, connect one end of lamp to ground and probe Tan wire at motor. Close safety switch and turn tailgate window switch to "DOWN" position. If lamp lights and motor does not operate, replace motor. If lamp does not light, check feed circuit to motor and repair as necessary.

2) Probe Brown wire at motor. Close safety switch and turn tailgate window switch to "UP" position. If lamp lights and motor does not operate, replace motor. If lamp does not light, check feed circuit to motor and repair as necessary.

MASTER SWITCH CIRCUIT

1) Remove escutcheon and housing from master switch. Separate terminal plate by releasing retainer hooks to expose terminal ends.

JEEP ELECTRIC WINDOWS (Cont.)

2) Turn ignition switch on. Using a 12-volt test lamp, connect one lead to Black wire and other lead to Red terminal. Repeat test at second Black wire.

3) If lamp does not light in either test, remove lead to Black terminal and connect to chassis ground. If lamp lights, an open exists between master switch and ground. If lamp does not light, it indicates a defective circuit breaker or an opening in the Red wire from circuit breaker to master switch.

CIRCUIT BREAKER TEST

1) Disconnect Yellow (Violet wire on Cherokee and Wagoneer) from circuit breaker and connect a 12-volt test lamp between Yellow (Violet) wire and ground. Turn ignition switch on. If lamp does not light, an open exists in Yellow (Violet) wire or ignition switch is defective.

2) Reconnect Yellow (Violet) wire to circuit breaker. Disconnect wire from circuit breaker and connect test lamp to circuit breaker terminal and ground. If lamp lights, circuit breaker is good. If lamp does not light, circuit breaker is defective.

CONTROL SWITCH & MOTOR TEST

Grand Wagoneer & Trucks Only

1) Connect test lamp between terminals of Orange and Yellow wires. Operate control switch "UP" and "DOWN".

2) If lamp lights in both switch positions, wires, individual door and master switches are not defective. Disconnect White and Green motor leads at terminal plate, and connect to Green and White leads.

3) Operate master switch. If window goes up and down, motor is okay, but switch is defective. If motor does not operate, remove trim panel and check connections and leads to motor. If motor operates, switch is defective.

SIDE WINDOW MOTOR

Connect test battery positive lead to one of the motor terminals. Connect negative lead to other terminal. Motor should now rotate in one direction to go "UP" or "DOWN". Reverse battery leads, motor should rotate in opposite direction. If window does not move, remove motor.

SWITCH VOLTAGE TEST

1) Turn ignition on. Remove switch from trim panel. Disconnect terminal block on wiring harness from switch body. Connect one lead of test lamp to Red wire terminal and other end to ground.

2) If lamp lights, the wiring circuit between battery and switch is functional. Check continuity in Black wire (ground). If lamp does not light, check circuit breaker. If okay, check for for a broken wire.

SWITCH UP & SWITCH DOWN TEST

1) Connect a jumper wire between Red (Violet on Cherokee and Wagoneer) lead and switch "UP" terminal. Connect a second jumper wire between switch ground terminal and "DOWN" terminal. This will test "UP" operation of switch.

2) If motor runs, voltage is present to motor. Connect switch to multiple connector and operate switch. If motor fails to run, replace switch. Test all switches in this manner.

3) To test "DOWN" operation of switch, connect first jumper wire between Red (Violet) lead and switch "DOWN" terminal, and second jumper wire between switch ground terminal and "UP" terminal. Repeat tests on all switches. Results are the same as "UP" test.

REMOVAL & INSTALLATION

TAILGATE WINDOW REGULATOR & MOTOR

Removal

1) Remove carpet and tailgate access cover plate. Remove retainers attaching regulator arms to channel. Disengage regulator arm pins from channel, and raise glass.

2) Carefully support glass in raised position. If regulator attaching screws are covered by sector gears, disconnect motor drive from gear regulator. Grasp regulator arm as far outboard as access hole will allow.

3) Push down on arm until holes in sector gears align with attaching screws and motor. Hold regulator in this position, and wedge a 1/4" screw between meshing teeth.

4) Remove regulator attaching screws, regulator, and motor. Release spring tension by using a large screwdriver to snap spring from under tension bracket.

Installation

To install, reverse removal procedure.

SIDE WINDOW MASTER SWITCH

Removal

1) Disconnect battery negative cable. Remove retaining screws and escutcheon. Remove switch housing screws.

2) Pull switch out to expose wires. Disconnect terminal plate from switch. Depress retainer clips through holes in switch housing, and remove switch.

Installation

To install, reverse removal procedure.

FRONT & REAR DOOR REGULATORS & MOTORS

Removal

1) Raise window half way up. Disconnect battery negative cable. Remove door trim panel and water shield.

2) Insert a drift punch into hole in door inner panel, or use masking tape to hold window half way up. Remove regulator arm retainer clip, and remove arm from bottom window channel.

3) Disconnect wires from motor. Remove inner door panel-to-regulator nuts and bolts. Remove regulator and motor assembly.

Installation

To install, reverse removal procedure.

Seat Belt Warning Systems

ALL MANUFACTURERS

DESCRIPTION & OPERATION

If driver's seat belt is not buckled, and ignition is turned to "ON" or "START" position, seat belt warning system will light "FASTEN SEAT BELTS" indicator and sound buzzer for 4 to 8 seconds.

If the driver's belt is buckled after buzzer sounds, buzzer will remain on 4 to 8 seconds. When ignition is turned to "ON" position, current is supplied through timer to buzzer circuit and indicator light circuit.

Light will always remain on until timer turns off current. Buzzer will only sound if driver's seat belt is not buckled before turning on ignition.

Fig. 1: Chrysler Seat Belt Warning System Wiring Diagram (FWD Models Shown)

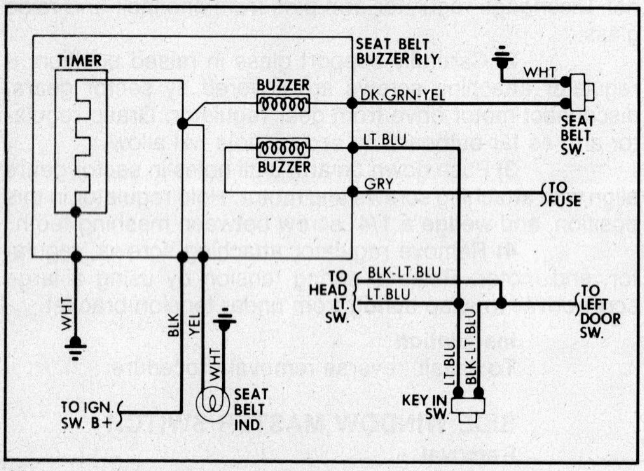

Also see chassis wiring in WIRING DIAGRAM section.

Fig. 2: Ford Seat Belt Warning System Wiring Diagram

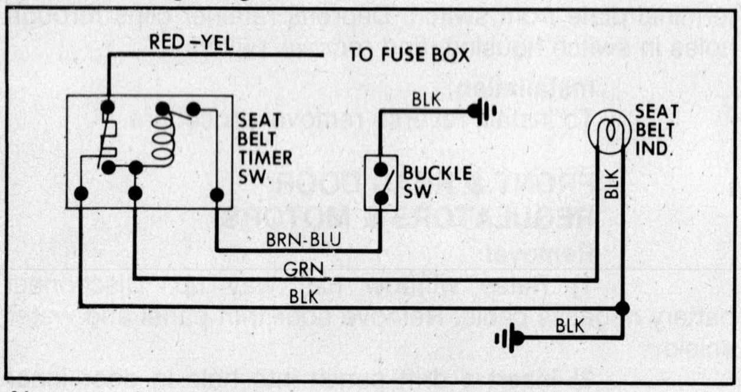

Also see chassis wiring in WIRING DIAGRAM section.

TROUBLE SHOOTING

NO SEAT BELT BUZZER OR LAMP

Check power from ignition switch. Replace timer/buzzer.

NO SEAT BELT BUZZER

Check seat belt switch. Test continuity between switch and timer/buzzer. Replace timer/buzzer.

NO WARNING LAMP

Check power and ground connections. Check for burned out indicator bulb. Replace timer/buzzer.

SEAT BELT BUZZER AND INDICATOR ALWAYS ON

Check for short to ground in seat belt switch or wire. Open ground connection for timer/buzzer. Replace timer/buzzer.

KEY BUZZER DOESN'T OPERATE

Check fuse. Check door jamb switch for proper operation. Check for open circuit.

KEY BUZZER ALWAYS ON

Check for short circuit to ground between key and door switch, or inoperative door switch.

Fig. 3: General Motors Seat Belt Warning System Wiring Diagram

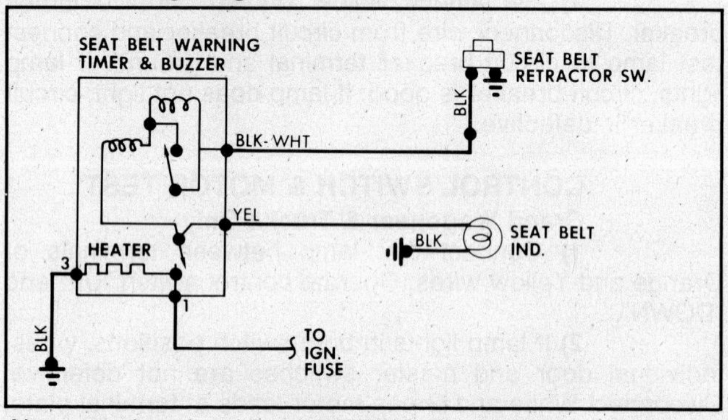

Also see chassis wiring in WIRING DIAGRAM section.

Fig. 4: Jeep Seat Belt Warning System Wiring Diagram (Grand Wagoneer & Trucks shown)

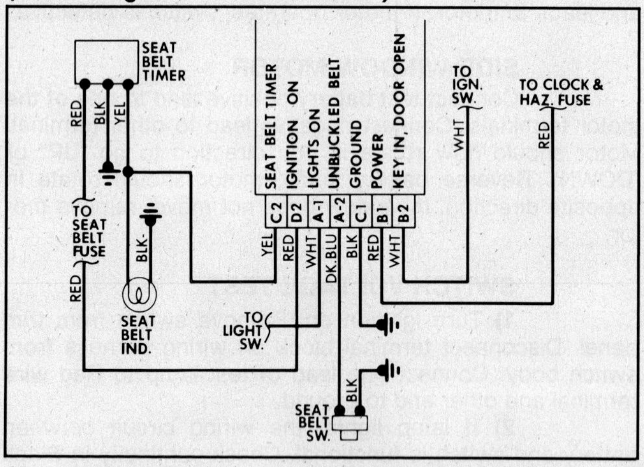

Also see chassis wiring in WIRING DIAGRAM section.

Sunroofs – Electric

JEEP

Grand Wagoneer

DESCRIPTION

Jeep electric sunroof features a sliding glass panel operated by an electric motor, and a manually operated sunscreen. System consists of sunroof assembly, electric motor mounted in the forward portion of the sunroof housing, a 2-position switch mounted in the windshield header and all necessary wiring.

Electrical feed is through air conditioning terminal of fuse block. Circuit is protected by air conditioning fuse and a 20 amp in-line fuse located in the wiring harness just below the "A" pillar.

ADJUSTMENT

MOTOR CLUTCH

1) Remove motor cap to gain access to adjusting screw. Cap is located in headliner just above and at center of windshield.

2) Loosen clutch plate adjusting screw jam nut using a deep socket. Tighten adjusting screw to 50 INCH lbs. (5.6 N.m). Tighten jam nut and install motor cap.

GLASS PARALLEL ALIGNMENT

NOTE: **Do not operate electric motor while the glass panel or cables are removed as cable damage could occur.**

1) Open glass about 1/2". Determine how much out-of-line front edge of glass is in relation to forward edge of roof panel opening. Note variation.

2) Open panel about 8" to gain access to cable and drive gear mechanism. Remove cable front cover and drive gear plate. Remove cable from track.

3) Move one side of glass panel slightly forward or backward as required to obtain parallel alignment with roof edge. Install cable in front track and insert cable in drive gear teeth.

4) Install drive gear plate and cable front cover. Close glass to within 1/4" of roof panel edge. Check alignment. Repeat steps as necessary to obtain proper parallel alignment.

REMOVAL & INSTALLATION

HALO ASSEMBLY

Removal & Installation

1) Open glass panel partially and remove halo assembly attaching screws. *See Fig. 1*. Grasp center of halo assembly and pull assembly downward to disengage front tabs from track.

2) Close glass panel fully. Slide halo assembly forward and remove assembly from vehicle. To install, reverse removal procedure.

GLASS PANEL

Removal & Installation

1) With halo assembly removed, close glass panel and remove outboard screws from front guide shoe assemblies. Loosen inboard screws and rotate guide shoes to disengage slide portion from track.

2) Release rear slide tension springs by rotating them to inboard position. Remove screws attaching rear guide shoes and retainers to tabs in glass panel and remove retainers.

3) From outside of vehicle, raise front of glass panel and slide panel forward and out of vehicle. To install, reverse removal procedure. Rear slide tension springs must be positioned under the spring lock roller.

Fig. 1: Exploded View of Jeep Power Sunroof Assembly

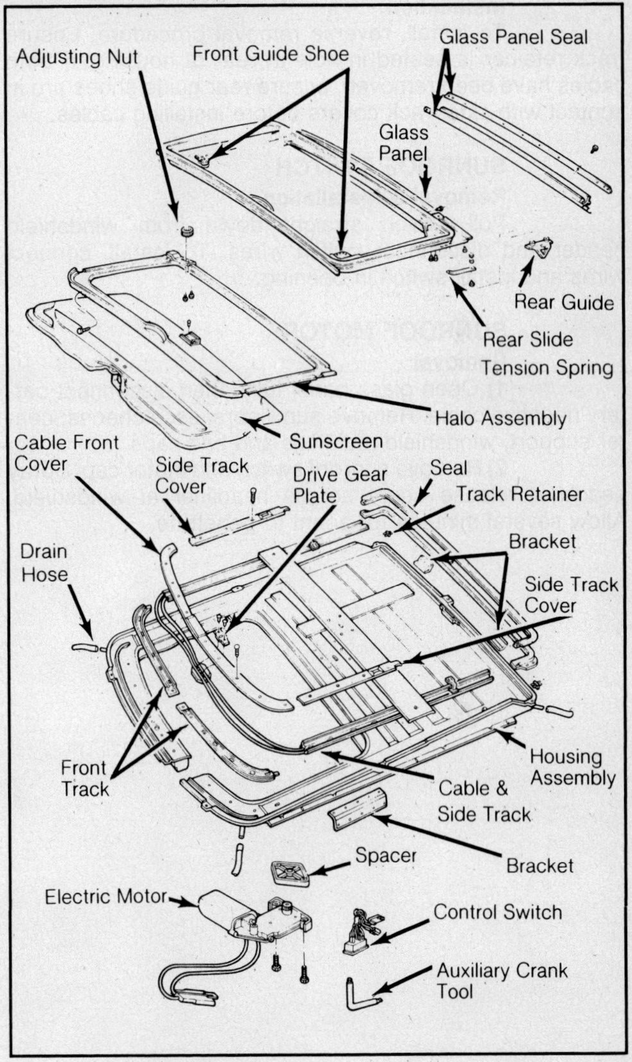

SUNSCREEN

Removal

Remove halo assembly and glass panel. Open sunscreen fully. Working from outside of vehicle, pull sunscreen upward at center of screen and slide screen forward and upward to remove.

Installation

Working from outside of the vehicle, curve sunscreen upward at center of screen. Slide screen rearward and downward into roof opening. Install glass panel and halo assembly.

Sunroofs – Electric

JEEP (Cont.)

CABLE & SIDE TRACK

Removal

1) Remove halo assembly, glass panel and sunscreen. Remove screws attaching cable front cover and remove cover.

2) Remove drive gear plate. Remove side track cover screws and remove side track cover.

3) Disengage cable from front track and motor gear and remove cable by pulling it up and out. Lift side track up and remove.

Installation

To install, reverse removal procedure. Ensure track retainer is seated in hole at rear of housing. If both cables have been removed, ensure rear guide shoes are in contact with side track covers before installing cables.

SUNROOF SWITCH

Removal & Installation

Pull switch straight down from windshield header and disconnect switch wires. To install, connect wires and install switch in opening.

SUNROOF MOTOR

Removal

1) Open glass panel fully, then disconnect battery negative cable. Remove sun visors, escutcheons, center support, windshield moldings and end caps.

2) Remove sunroof switch and motor cap. Spray headliner release agent across headliner at windshield. Allow several minutes for agent to penetrate.

NOTE: When removing headliner, use care to avoid separating foam backing from headliner. If backing begins to separate, apply more release agent.

3) Pull front edge of headliner downward. Remove motor mounting screws and remove motor.

Installation

To install, reverse removal procedure. Mask off top of windshield and spray trim adhesive on roof panel along top of windshield and install headliner. Check sunroof operation and adjust motor clutch if necessary.

Fig. 2: Front Guide Shoe and Rear Tension Spring

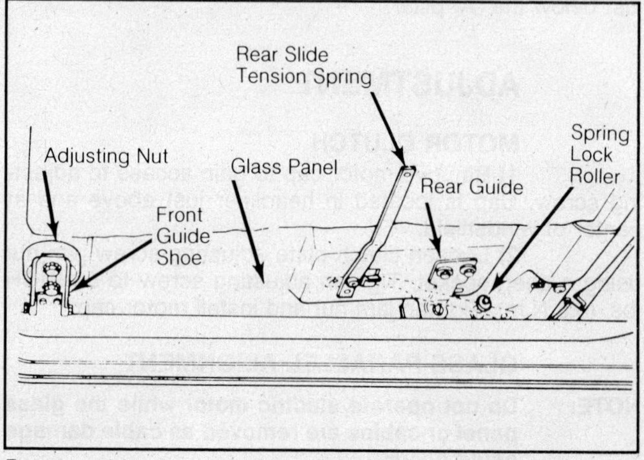

Rotate guide shoes to disengage slide portion from track.

CHRYSLER CORP.

DESCRIPTION & OPERATION

Fuel, temperature and oil pressure gauges operate on the constant voltage principle through a common voltage limiter, which provides intermittent current to the gauge system.

FUEL LEVEL GAUGE

A hinged float arm in fuel tank raises or lowers, depending on fuel level. It contacts a variable resistor in the fuel gauge sending unit. This provides a change of resistance in the fuel gauge circuit. This resistance registers on the instrument panel gauge in the form of a level reading.

TEMPERATURE & OIL PRESSURE

The operation of the temperature and oil pressure indicating systems is identical in operation to the fuel system, with the exception of the method of varying resistance of the sending units.

For temperature, the resistance of the disc in the sending unit varies with a direct relation to coolant temperature. When coolant temperatures are high, resistance is low. When coolant temperatures are low, resistance is high.

For oil pressure, the sending unit resistance is controlled by a diaphragm. The diaphragm is actuated as oil pressure increases or decreases.

OIL PRESSURE WARNING LIGHT

The oil pressure switch is mounted on the engine (location depends on engine type). When oil pressure is high, switch is held in the "OFF" or "OPEN" position.

This prevents current flow to the indicator light. When oil pressure is low, the switch is in the "ON" or "CLOSED" position, allowing current to flow to the indicator light.

ALTERNATOR INDICATOR SYSTEM

The alternator gauge is an ammeter, which senses the direction and rate of flow of electrical current to or from battery, and indicates whether battery is being charged or discharged. All FWD vehicles use a voltmeter as an alternator gauge.

TACHOMETER

The tachometer is a self-contained electronic unit connected to the ignition coil. The tachometer senses ignition firings and counts their number. This is shown on the face of the gauge. Gauge is marked off in RPM increments.

TESTING

VOLTAGE LIMITER

1) To quickly test voltage limiter in vehicle, connect one lead of a voltmeter or test lamp to temperature sending unit and other lead to a good ground.

2) Leave sending unit wire attached to sending unit. Turn ignition switch on. A fluctuating voltmeter or a flashing light indicates voltage limiter is operating.

FUEL GAUGE (FWD MODELS)

Check sending unit and wiring by grounding connector lead to sending unit, at sending unit. With ignition on, a grounded input will cause gauge to read maximum.

FUEL GAUGE (RWD MODELS)

With Tester

NOTE: Allow 2 minutes at each test point for gauge to settle. Tapping instrument cluster will help position needle.

1) Disconnect wire at fuel tank sending unit. Connect one lead of Gauge Tester (C 3826A) to wire terminal. Connect other lead to a good ground.

2) Turn ignition on, turn tester knob to "F" position, and observe instrument panel gauge. Gauge should read "FULL", plus 2 pointer widths or minus 1 pointer width.

3) Turn test knob to "1/2". Gauge should read "1/2" plus or minus 2 pointer widths. Turn knob to "E". Gauge should read "EMPTY", plus 1 pointer width or minus 2 pointer widths.

4) If panel gauge does not perform as described, continuity of circuit from tank sending unit to panel unit should be tested. Before replacing gauge, check printed circuit board for damage or defects.

5) If panel performs properly when tested but fails to operate properly when connected to vehicle system, inspect fuel tank sending unit ground strap for proper installation on fuel line. If ground continuity is good, remove tank unit for testing.

Without Tester

1) Disconnect wire from terminal on fuel tank sending unit. Attach wire to known good sending unit. Connect jumper wire between sending unit fuel pick-up tube and a good ground. To check fuel gauge, allow at least 2 minutes at each test point for gauge to settle.

2) Clip float arm of sending unit to its empty stop, and turn ignition to "ON" position. Gauge should read "EMPTY" plus 1 pointer width or minus 2 pointer widths. Move and clip sending unit float arm to full stop. Gauge should read "FULL" plus 2 pointer widths or minus 1 pointer width.

3) If fuel gauge does not perform as indicated, continuity of circuit from tank sending unit to panel should be tested, giving special attention to printed circuit board. Before replacing gauge, also check voltage limiter.

4) If panel gauge performs satisfactorily with Tester (C 3826A) or known good sending unit, check fuel tank and original fuel gauge sending unit by removing sending unit from tank. Connect sending unit wire and jumper wire as in step **1)**. If fuel gauge now checks within specifications, original unit is electrically okay.

5) Check ground strap from sending unit to fuel line for continuity. Check for deformed sending unit, improper installation, deformed mounting flange on fuel tank, or deformed bottom of fuel tank. Then recheck sending unit.

TEMPERATURE GAUGE

FWD Models

Remove connector from temperature sending unit. Turn ignition on. Grounding sending unit lead will cause temperature gauge to read maximum. If gauge does not respond, problem is in gauge or wiring.

RWD Models

1) Disconnect terminal from temperature sending unit or engine. Connect one test lead of Tester (C 3826A) to terminal and other lead to good ground. Turn ignition on, and turn tester knob to "E".

Fig. 1: Chrysler Corp. Instrument Cluster & Bezel

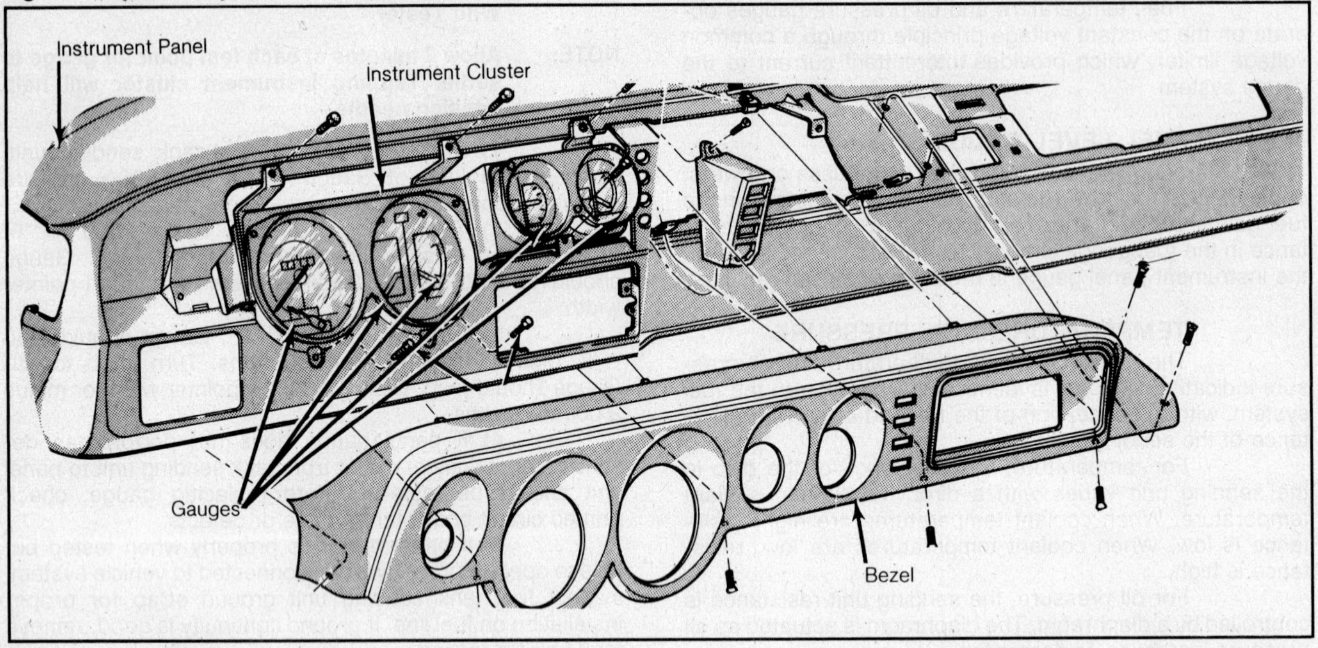

Van series is shown.

2) Temperature gauge should show "C", plus or minus 1/8". Turn tester knob to "1/2". Pointer should advance to driving range left of "1/2" position of dial.

3) Turn tester knob to "F". Gauge pointer should move to "H" position on dial. If gauge responds as stated, but does not operate with terminal attached to sending unit, replace sending unit.

4) If gauge does not respond, check for loose connections, broken wire, open printed circuit or faulty gauge.

AMMETER GAUGE

RWD Models

1) Turn ignition and headlights on (do not start engine). Ammeter needle should move toward the "D" or discharge scale. If no movement of the needle is observed, check terminals for loose wires.

2) If terminals are secure, ammeter is defective. If needle moves toward the "C" or charge side, the connections are reversed.

OIL PRESSURE WARNING LIGHT

FWD Models

1) Check low oil pressure warning light system by turning ignition to "ON" position and observing pressure light. If light comes on, start engine. If light stays on, immediately turn off engine, and use direct pressure gauge to check oil pressure.

2) If pressure is correct, check for grounded wire or replace oil pressure sending unit. If light does not come on, remove molded connector or single lead at oil pressure switch. If switch uses 3 terminals, connect center terminal of molded connector to ground.

3) If switch uses a single lead, connect lead to ground. If bulb comes on, with either system, replace sending unit. If bulb does not come on, light bulb is burned out or bulb socket, wiring, or connections are faulty.

RWD Models

1) Check low oil pressure warning light system by turning ignition to "ON" position and observing pressure light. If light comes on, start engine. If light stays on, immediately turn off engine, and use direct pressure gauge to check oil pressure.

2) If pressure is correct, check for grounded wire or replace oil pressure sending unit. Turn ignition to "ON" position. If light does not come on, disconnect lead of sending unit, and touch it to ground.

3) If bulb comes on, replace sending unit. If bulb does not come on, light bulb is burned out or bulb socket, wiring, or connections are faulty.

OIL PRESSURE GAUGE

RWD Models

1) Disconnect wire from oil pressure sending unit on engine. Connect one lead of Tester (C 3826A) to removed wire and other lead to good ground. Place tester knob in "E" position and turn ignition on. Do not start engine.

2) Oil pressure gauge should read "L" plus or minus 1/8". Turn tester knob to "1/2" position, oil pressure gauge should advance to "1/2" position on dial. With tester knob in "F" position, gauge should also advance to "H" position.

3) Should gauge respond to above tests, but fail to operate when connected to vehicle system, indications are of a defective sending unit. Should gauge fail to respond to above tests, check for loose connection, broken wire or faulty gauge.

BRAKE WARNING LIGHT

1) Brake warning system light comes on when ignition switch is on with parking brake applied, when one of the two service brake systems fails, or when ignition switch is positioned to "START".

2) Test system by applying parking brake and turning ignition "ON". If bulb fails to light, inspect for burned out bulb, disconnected socket, a broken or disconnected wiring.

CHRYSLER CORP. (Cont.)

3) Raise vehicle on hoist with an assistant inside. Have assistant observe warning light, as assistant depresses brake pedal. Light should come on when bleeder port on wheel cylinder is opened. If light fails to operate, inspect for burned out bulb, disconnected socket, bad brake line switch, broken or disconnected wiring.

REMOVAL & INSTALLATION

SPEEDOMETER

Removal & Installation
(FWD Models)

Disconnect speedometer cable in engine compartment. Remove 3 screws attaching speedometer to cluster. Pull speedometer rearward and disconnect from speedometer cable. To install, reverse removal procedure.

Removal & Installation
(Trucks)

Remove face plate and cluster mask-lens. Remove screws retaining speedometer to housing and remove speedometer. To install, reverse removal procedure.

Removal & Installation
(Vans & Wagons)

Disconnect negative battery cable. Remove 6 screws fastening instrument panel hood and bezel assembly to instrument panel. Pull bezel off upper retaining clips. Remove lens mounting plastic clips and remove lens. Remove mask. Remove speedometer mounting screws and remove speedometer through front cluster. To install, reverse removal procedure.

VOLTAGE LIMITER

Removal & Installation
(Trucks)

Reach up behind intrument cluster and pull out voltage limiter. Limiter is located left of speedometer cable. To install, reverse removal procedure.

Removal & Installation
(Vans & Wagons)

1) Disconnect battery negative cable. Remove 6 screws fastening instrument panel hood and bezel assembly to instrument panel. Pull bezel off upper retaining clips. Remove lens mounting clips and remove lens.

2) Remove mask. Remove nuts from fuel gauge Remove gauge through front of cluster. Unplug voltage limiter from printed circuit board. To install, reverse removal procedure.

GAUGES

Removal & Installation
(FWD Models)

Remove screws attaching gauges to cluster housing. Remove gauge assembly. To install, reverse removal procedure.

Removal & Installation
(Trucks)

Remove faceplate and cluster mask-lens. Remove instrument cluster. Locate terminals of gauge being serviced on circuit board side of cluster. Remove gauge attaching nuts and remove gauge. To install, reverse removal procedure.

Removal & Installation
(Vans & Wagons)

Disconnect battery negative cable. Remove 6 screws fastening instrument panel hood and bezel assembly to instrument panel. Pull bezel off upper retaining clips. Remove instrument cluster. Remove lens mounting plastic clips and remove lens. Remove mask. Remove mounting nuts of gauge being serviced and remove through front cluster. To install, reverse removal procedure.

INSTRUMENT CLUSTER

Removal & Installation
(FWD Models)

1) Remove instrument cluster bezel. Disconnect speedometer cable in engine compartment. On vehicles with A/T, remove instrument panel left cover and disconnect shift indicator wire.

2) Remove 5 screws attaching instrument cluster to instrument panel. Disconnect speedometer cable from speedometer. Disconnect cluster wiring connectors. Remove cluster past right side of steering coulmn. To install, reverse removal procedure.

Removal & Installation
(Trucks)

1) Cover steering column to prevent damage to paint. Remove faceplate. Remove 4 screws from steering column lower cover. Spread upper steering column cover out of locking tangs and slide downward. Disconnect shift actuator cable from steering column.

2) Loosen heater and A/C control. Pull rearward to clear forward mount on cluster housing. Remove 6 screws retaining cluster. Pull cluster rearward and disconnect 2 large connectors. Disconnect speedometer cable. Remove EMR and/or gate open lamp sockets. Remove cluster. To install, reverse removal procedure.

Removal & Installation
(Vans & Wagons)

1) Disconnect battery negative cable. Remove 6 screws fastening instrument cluster hood and bezel assembly. Pull bezel off upper retaining clips. Remove 5 cluster screws.

2) Carefully pull cluster out as far enough to disconnect speedometer cable by pushing spring clip toward cluster. Remove right and left printed cicuit board multiple connectors. Remove instrument cluster. To install, reverse removal procedure.

PRINTED CIRCUITS

Removal & Installation
(FWD Models)

Remove instrument cluster and remove circuit board. Remove lamp sockets and gauge clips. To install, reverse removal procedure.

Removal (Trucks)

1) Remove cluster mask-lens. Remove instrument cluster and remove ammeter, fuel, temperature and oil gauges. It is not necessary to remove speedometer.

2) Remove voltage limiter and radio capacitors. Remove all lamp socket assemblies by rotating counterclockwise. Remove screws attaching circuit board to cluster and remove circuit board.

Installation

To install, reverse removal procedure. Do not overtighten printed circuit board attaching screws.

Switches & Instrument Panels

CHRYSLER CORP. (Cont.)

Fig. 2: Chrysler Corp. Instrument Panel & Bezel

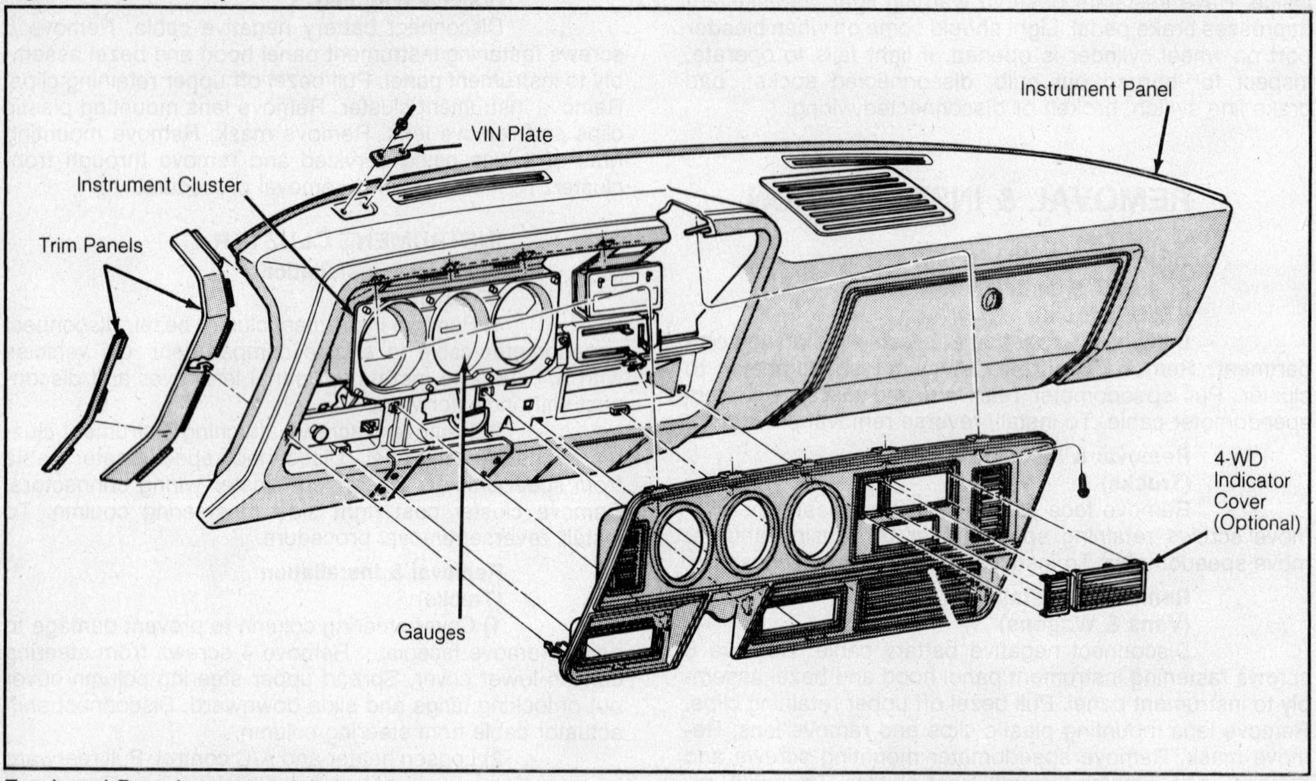

Truck and Ramcharger models are shown.

Removal (Vans & Wagons)

Remove instrument cluster. Remove lens mounting pins and remove lens and mask. Remove voltage limiter. Remove lamp socket assemblies. Remove all gauges except speedometer. Remove circuit board attaching screws and remove circuit board.

Installation

To install, reverse removal procedure. Do not overtighten printed circuit board attaching screws.

HEADLIGHT SWITCH

Removal & Installation (FWD Models)

1) Remove headlight and switch plate trim bezel. Remove 4 screws securing switch plate to lower panel. Pull assembly rearward an disconnect wiring connectors.

2) Remove knob and stem by depressing button on switch. Remove 2 screws attaching headlight switch plate to switch plate assembly. Remove headlight switch retainer and remove switch. To install, reverse removal procedure.

Removal & Installation (Trucks)

1) Remove cluster faceplate. Reaching under instrument panel, depress release button located on bottom of switch, and pull knob and stem out of front panel.

2) Remove wiper switch knob. Remove bezel. Remove spanner nut attaching switch to front panel. Reaching under instrument panel, lower switch down far enough to disconnect wiring harness. Remove switch. To install, reverse removal procedure.

Removal & Installation (Vans & Wagons)

1) Disconnect battery negative cable. Working under instrument panel, depress stem locking button located on bottom of switch and at same time pull knob and stem out of switch.

2) Remove instrument panel hood and bezel assembly. Remove switch bezel attaching screws. Remove nut attaching switch to panel, remove switch and disconnect wiring harness. To install, reverse removal procedure.

Switches & Instrument Panels

CHRYSLER CORP. (Cont.)

Fig. 3: Chrysler Corp. Instrument Panel & Bezel

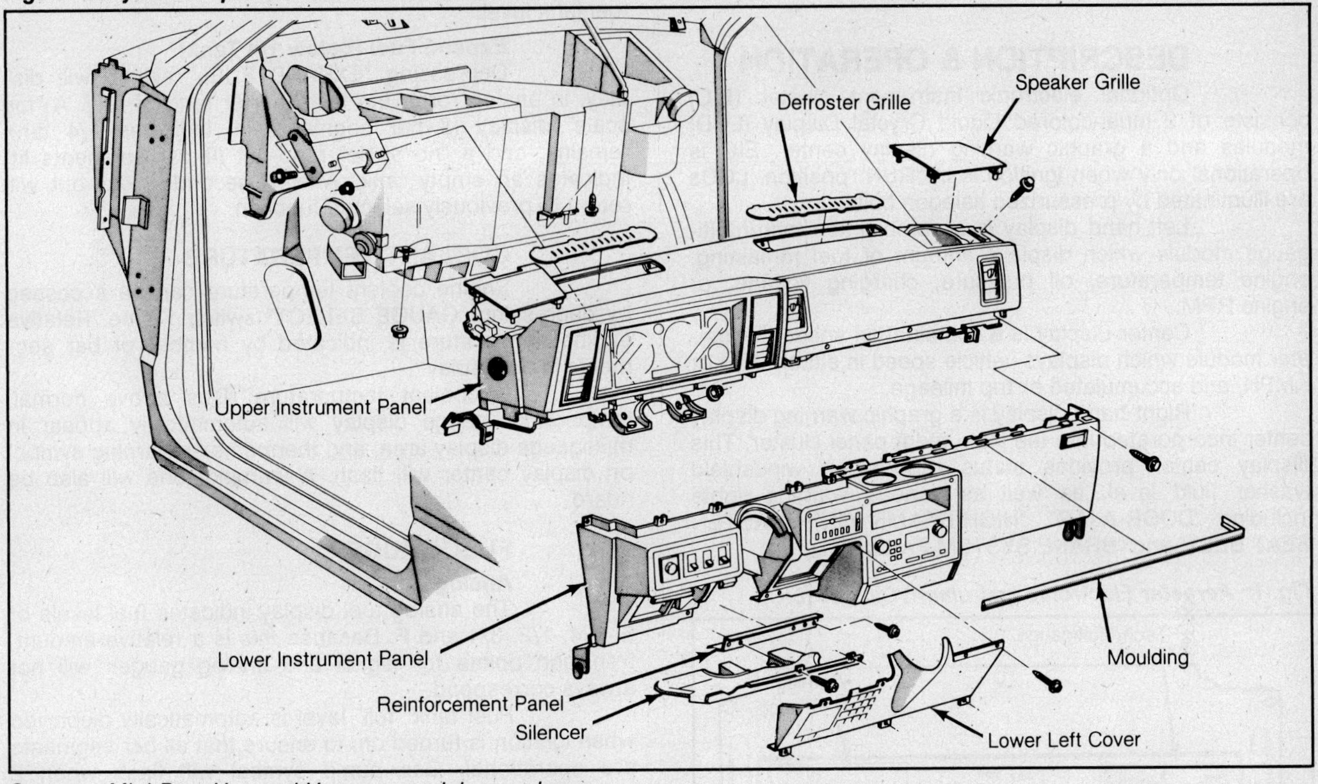

Caravan, Mini Ram Van and Voyager models are shown.

FORD ELECTRONIC INSTRUMENT CLUSTER

Aerostar

DESCRIPTION & OPERATION

Optional electronic instrument cluster (EIC) consists of 2 multi-colored Liquid Crystal Display (LCD) modules and a graphic warning display center. EIC is operational only when ignition is in "RUN" position. LCDs are illuminated by pressurized halogen bulbs.

Left-hand display is a combination tach/multi-gauge module which displays amount of fuel remaining, engine temperature, oil pressure, charging voltage, or engine RPM.

Center display is a combination speedo/odometer module which displays vehicle speed in either MPH or KMPH, and accumulated or trip mileage.

Right-hand display is a graphic warning display center incorporated into the instrument panel cluster. This display center provides status reports on windshield washer fluid level, as well as various warning lights including "DOOR-AJAR", "HIGH-BEAMS ON", "FASTEN SEAT BELT" and "BRAKE SYSTEM FAILURE".

Fig. 1: Aerostar Electronic Instrument Cluster (EIC)

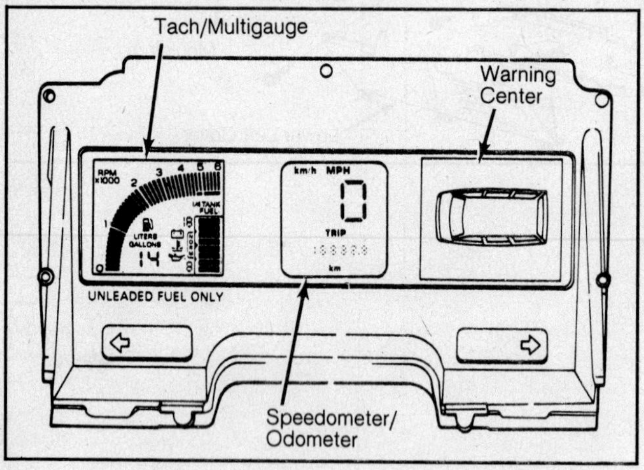

SWITCH CONTROL MODULE

English/Metric

Depressing "ENGLISH/METRIC" switch changes cluster read-out between English to metric gauge measurements.

Trip/Distance

Depressing "TRIP/DISTANCE" switch will display either trip or accumulated odometer mileage.

Trip Reset

Depressing "TRIP RESET" switch will cancel trip mileage recorded by speedometer module memory. This switch operates only when trip odometer read-out has been previously selected.

Gauge Select

The "GAUGE SELECT" switch controls display of 4 different gauges on tach/multigauge module.

Fuel tank "full" level will automatically be displayed when ignition is turned on. Depressing "GAUGE SELECT" switch 1 time will change display from fuel tank level to coolant temperature. Depressing switch 2 times will change display to oil pressure.

Depressing switch 3 times will change display to battery voltage. Depressing switch 4 times will "blank out" gauge. Depressing switch again will return display to fuel tank level.

Expand Fuel (Below 1/4 Tank)

Depressing "EXPAND FUEL" switch will display, in analog form, the last quarter tank of fuel. A "full scale" display (8 bar segments lit) indicates 1/4 tank remains, and a "no scale" read-out (0 bar segments lit) indicates an empty tank. After 5 seconds, read-out will return to previously selected function.

COOLANT TEMPERATURE

Engine coolant temperature can be accessed by depressing "GAUGE SELECT" switch 1 time. Relative engine temperature is indicated by number of bar segments lit on display.

If coolant temperature rises above normal, temperature gauge display will automatically appear in multigauge display area, and thermometer warning symbol on display center will flash. A warning tone will also be heard.

FUEL GAUGE

Analog

The analog fuel display indicates fuel levels of E, 1/4, 1/2, 3/4 and F. Because this is a relative amount, transition points for digital and analog gauges will not always correspond.

Fuel tank "full" level is automatically displayed when ignition is turned on, to ensure that all bar segments are operational. Gas pump symbol will flash when 2 gallons (6 liters) or less, remain in tank.

Digital

This display area indicates either number of gallons, or liters of fuel remaining, depending on position of "ENGLISH/METRIC" switch. Because analog read-out is a relative amount, digital and analog fuel transition points will not always correspond.

When ignition is turned on, complete fuel gauge read-out is displayed to ensure that all display segments are operational (display reads 88).

ODOMETER

Vehicle Distance

Accumulated mileage is stored in memory every 10 miles, and also when ignition is turned off. If speedometer module does not receive a valid odometer signal, "ERROR" will appear in odometer display area.

When a defective speedo/odometer module is replaced, an "S" symbol is displayed in upper right-hand corner of display, and a sticker must be affixed to driver's door pillar showing previous mileage.

Trip Distance

Depressing "TRIP/DISTANCE" switch will change accumulated mileage display to a 4 digit accumulated trip mileage display. If speedometer module does not receive a valid odometer signal, "ERROR" symbol will appear in odometer display area.

OIL PRESSURE

Oil pressure reading can be accessed by depressing "GAUGE SELECT" switch 2 times. Relative oil pressure is indicated by number of bar segments lit on multigauge display.

If oil pressure drops below normal, oil pressure display will automatically appear in display area, and

FORD ELECTRONIC INSTRUMENT CLUSTER (Cont.)

oil can warning symbol on display center will flash. A warning tone will also be heard.

SPEEDOMETER

The speedometer module receives speed and distance signals from a transmission-mounted magnetic speed sensor. Maximum speedometer reading is 85 MPH, or 199 KPH, depending on position of "ENGLISH/METRIC" switch.

When ignition is first turned on, entire speedometer read-out is displayed (display reads 188), to ensure that all display segments are operational.

If a defective speedometer module has been replaced, an "S" symbol is displayed in upper right-hand corner of speedometer display, and a sticker must be affixed to driver's door pillar showing previous mileage.

TACHOMETER

The moving tachometer bar graph receives a signal from ignition coil. When engine speed is below 2000 RPM, each bar segment represents a 100 RPM range. When engine speed is between 2000 and 4900 RPM, each bar segment represents a 200 RPM range. All engine speeds above 4900 RPM are displayed as 6000 RPM.

VOLTMETER

The voltmeter reading can be accessed by depressing "GAUGE SELECT" switch 3 times. Relative charging voltage is indicated by number of bar segments lit on display.

If battery charging rate is above or below normal, voltmeter display will automatically appear in multigauge display area, and battery warning symbol on display center will flash. A warning tone will also be heard.

TESTING

HOW TO USE THE DIAGNOSTIC TESTS

If a specific display problem exists or system malfunction occurs during self-test procedure, locate symptom on the appropriate diagnostic chart, and go to the recommended diagnostic test (A-FF). Follow test procedure to diagnose and correct the malfunction.

Throughout the article, references are made to particular pins. For example, pin 6A would refer to pin number 6 of the "A" (instrument cluster) circuit. *See Fig. 2.*

After correcting a symptom using the diagnostic test procedures, perform self-test procedure to recheck cluster operation.

HOW TO USE THE SELF-TESTS

If a general performance test of cluster operation is desired, and a specific display problem does not exist, go to the self-test procedure section. Follow the self-test procedure for each module.

Throughout the article, references are made to particular pins. For example, pin 6A would refer to pin number 6 of the "A" (instrument cluster) circuit. *See Fig. 2.*

TACH/MULTIGAUGE SELF-TEST

1) Turn ignition off. Depress and hold "GAUGE SELECT" switch while turning ignition on. Release "GAUGE SELECT" switch. System is now in microcomputer self-test mode. Depress "GAUGE SELECT" switch 1 time.

2) Absence of a tone, combined with 24 bar segments lit in tachometer bar graph display indicates a failed test. If test is failed, replace tach/multigauge module and recheck cluster operation. If test is passed, go to next step.

Diagrams 1-9 Self-Test Pattern

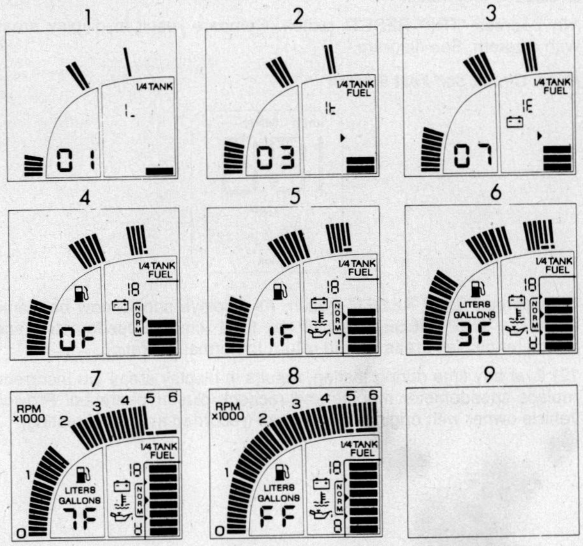

3) Depress "GAUGE SELECT" switch 2 times. Ensure "ENGLISH/METRIC" switch is in "ENGLISH" (released) position. Depress "GAUGE SELECT" switch 6 additional times to bring system into display self-test mode.

4) Depress "GAUGE SELECT" switch 9 times, comparing each result in display area with appropriate display diagram. See Diagrams 1-9.

5) If, at any time during these 9 tests, results in display areas are incorrect, replace tach/multigauge module. Recheck cluster operation.

6) If test is passed, tachometer display mode is automatically changed to reset circuit check mode. Depress "GAUGE SELECT" switch 1 time. Compare result in display area with diagram. See diagram.

Reset Circuit Self-Test Pattern

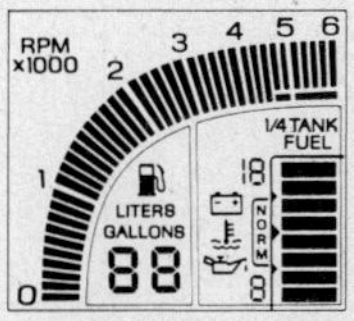

7) Depress "GAUGE SELECT" switch 1 time. All displays should now be blank. Depress "GAUGE SELECT" 1 time. Gauge display areas should return to normal operation.

8) If, at any time during testing, results in any display area are incorrect, replace tach/multigauge module. Recheck cluster operation.

FORD ELECTRONIC INSTRUMENT CLUSTER (Cont.)

SPEEDO/ODOMETER SELF-TEST

NOTE: For diagnostic & testing purposes of the speedo/odometer, 2 display areas will assume a new function: The right-hand digit (0-9 MPH) of the speedometer display area is the pass/fail indicator, and the outer right-hand digit of the odometer display is the test counter.

1) Turn ignition on. Depress "TRIP DISTANCE" switch. Record trip mileage shown. Turn ignition off. Depress and hold "TRIP RESET" switch, while turning ignition on. Release "TRIP RESET" switch. System is now in microcomputer self-test mode. Depress "TRIP RESET" switch 1 time.

2) Test counter (outer right-hand odometer digit) should indicate "1", and pass/fail indicator (right-hand digit of speedometer display area) will show a "P" (pass) or "F" (fail) condition. See diagram.

Microcomputer Self-Test Display

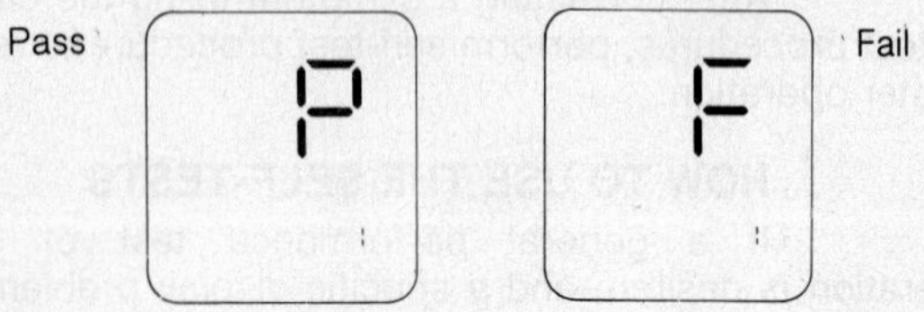

NOTE: A "P" (pass) indication should always be accompanied by a tone.

3) If an "F" (fail) condition is indicated, replace speedometer module and recheck cluster operation. Outer 2 left-hand odometer digits indicate software revision levels and jumper options. These 2 digits have no bearing on test results.

NOTE: If a defective speedometer module is replaced, an "S" symbol is displayed in upper right-hand corner of speedometer display, and a sticker must be affixed to driver's door pillar showing previous mileage.

4) Depress "TRIP RESET" switch 1 time. This will change microcomputer display mode to hot/cold start circuit display mode. The pass/fail indicator will show a "P" (pass) or "F" (fail) condition, and test counter should indicate "2". See diagram. Speedometer module should be replaced if an "F" (fail) indication appears.

Hot/Cold Start Circuit Self-Test Patterns

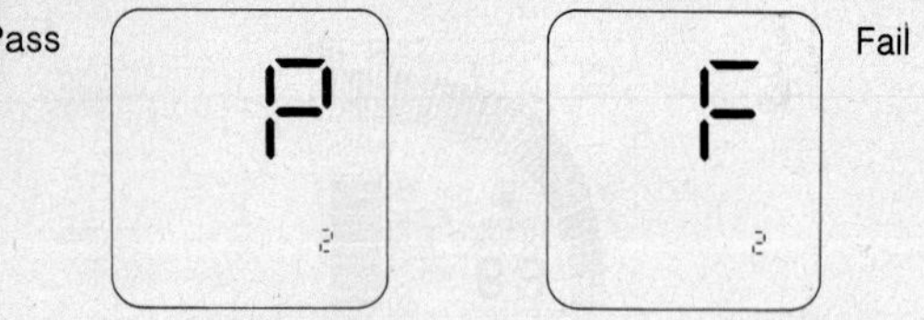

5) After completing hot/cold start circuit test, depress "TRIP RESET" switch 4 times. At this point, test counter should indicate "6". The hot/cold start circuit display mode has now been changed to trip odometer non-voluntary memory (NVM) check mode.

NOTE: Performing NVM check will reset trip mileage record to 0.

6) Depress "TRIP RESET" switch. Pass/Fail indicator will now show a "P" (pass) or "F" (fail) condition, and test counter should indicate "7". See diagram. If an "F" indication is displayed, replace speedometer module and recheck cluster operation.

Trip Odometer (NVM) Self-Test Pattern

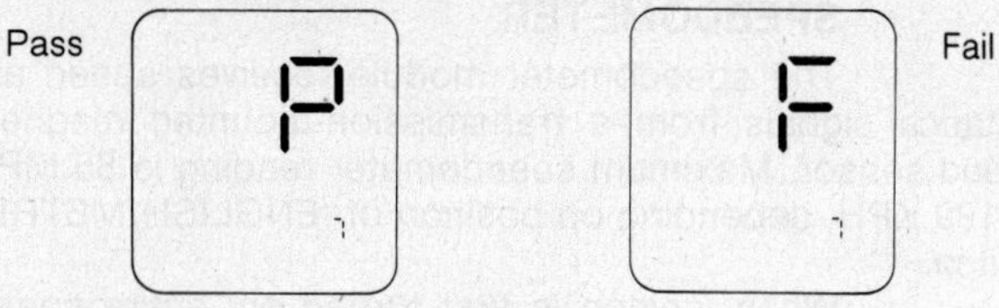

7) After completing trip odometer NVM check, depress "TRIP RESET" switch. This will change trip odometer NVM check to display test mode. Depress "TRIP RESET" switch 1 time. Compare result in display areas with diagram 10.

Display Diagrams 10-18 Self-Test Patterns

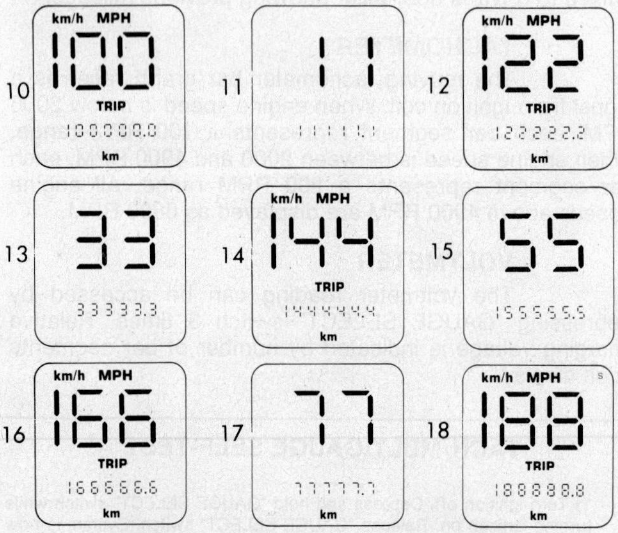

8) Continue to depress "TRIP RESET" switch 8 additional times, comparing each display area with appropriate diagram. See Diagrams 10-18.

9) If, at any time during testing, results in display areas are incorrect, replace speedometer module and recheck cluster operation. If test is passed, speedometer display mode is automatically changed to reset circuit self-test mode.

10) Depress "TRIP RESET" switch. Compare result in display areas with diagram. See diagram.

Reset Circuit Self-Test Pattern

11) Depress "TRIP RESET" switch. All displays should now be blank. Depress "TRIP RESET" switch a third time. Speedometer and odometer display areas should return to normal operation.

12) If, at any time during testing, results in display areas are incorrect, replace speedometer module and recheck cluster operation. Provide vehicle owner with original trip mileage (recorded at start of testing).

FORD ELECTRONIC INSTRUMENT CLUSTER (Cont.)

DIAGNOSTIC CHARTS

TACH/MULTIGAUGE MODULE DIAGNOSIS

Symptom	Test
Display Is	
Backlit But Blank	B
Dimly Lit	A
Incorrect At All Times	C
Missing Segments	C
Not Illuminated	A
Scrambled	C
Totally Blank	A
All Display Segments Stuck On	C
Module Does Not Respond To Buttons	T
No Signal Tone	
When Buttons Are Pushed	Y
When Driver Alert Is Displayed	Y

TACHOMETER DIAGNOSIS

Symptom	Test
No Tach Reading	E
Tach Reading Always High Or Low	D
Tach Reading Erratic	E

FUEL GAUGE DIAGNOSIS

Symptom	Test
Gauge Will Not Switch	
Between English And Metric	F
"CO" Displayed In Digital Display Area	G
"CS" Displayed In Digital Display Area	H
Inaccurate Fuel Reading	K
Incorrect Display When Tank Is	
Full	I
Empty	J

TEMPERATURE GAUGE DIAGNOSIS

Symptom	Test
Flashing Thermometer Symbol Is Displayed	L
Gauge Always	
Indicates "COLD"	N
Reads Above Or Below "Normal" Band	S
No Warning Tone When	
Thermometer Symbol Is Flashing	M

OIL PRESSURE GAUGE DIAGNOSIS

Symptom	Test
Flashing Oil Can Symbol Is Displayed	O
Gauge	
Always Indicates Low Pressure	Q
Indicates Erratic Pressure Readings	Q
No Warning Tone When	
Oil Can Symbol Is Flashing	P

VOLT GAUGE DIAGNOSIS

Symptom	Test
Does Not Display Charge Alert Symbol	R

SPEEDOMETER/ODOMETER MODULE DIAGNOSIS

Symptom	Test
All Segments Stuck On	V
Display Is	
Backlit But Blank	U
Dimly Lit	A
Incorrect At All Times	V
Missing Segments	V
Not Illuminated	A
Scrambled	V
Totally Blank	A
Display Will Not Switch	
Between English And Metric	W
Module Does Not Respond To Buttons	T
No Signal Tone	
When Buttons Are Pushed	X

SPEEDOMETER DIAGNOSIS

Symptom	Test
Display	
Constantly Reads Too High Or Too Low	Z
Reads 0 MPH At All Speeds	Y
Speed Jumps Up And Down Erratically	AA

ODOMETER DIAGNOSIS

Symptom	Test
Display Has "S" Illuminated In Upper R.H. Corner	CC
Display Reads "ERROR"	BB
Odometer Does Not Accumulate Mileage	DD
Odometer Counts 10 Miles	
Then Jumps Back 10 Miles	DD
Odometer Reading Is	
Constantly Too High Or Too Low	EE
More Or Less Than Actual Miles	FF

TRIP ODOMETER DIAGNOSIS

Symptom	Test
Display Will Not	
Reset	HH
Switch Between	
Total Mileage And Trip Mileage	GG

FORD ELECTRONIC INSTRUMENT CLUSTER (Cont.)

DIAGNOSTIC TESTING

TEST A

1) Turn ignition to "RUN" position. Check for backlighting of speedo/odometer and tach/multigauge modules. If other modules are properly lit, replace bad illumination bulbs. If other modules are dim or blank, go to step **2)**.

CAUTION: Halogen illumination bulbs are pressurized and may shatter if handled incorrectly. Wear eye protection when replacing or inspecting these bulbs.

2) Turn ignition to "RUN" position. Check for display backlighting. Turn ignition off. Turn headlights on. Move dimmer control to maximum brightness. Check for display backlighting.

3) If display is not illuminated in either condition, go to step **4)**. If only illuminated with ignition on, go to step **6)**. If only illuminated with headlights on, go to step **4)**. If illuminated, but very dimly, go to step **9)**.

4) Disconnect battery negative cable. Remove EIC. Reconnect harness (with cluster removed). Reconnect battery negative cable. Turn ignition to "RUN" position. Using a voltmeter, measure voltage between pins 4A (circuit 434) and 6A (circuit 57). *See Fig. 2.*

5) If voltage between pins 4A (circuit 434) and 6A (circuit 57) is greater than 10 volts, correct open in ground circuit 57 (pin 6A). If voltage is less than 10 volts, check power circuit 434 (pin 4A), fuse and relay.

6) Disconnect battery negative cable. Remove EIC. Reconnect harness (with cluster removed). Reconnect battery negative cable. Turn headlights on and move dimmer to maximum brightness.

7) Using a voltmeter, measure voltage between pins 4A (circuit 434) and 6A (circuit 57). *See Fig. 2.* If voltage between pins 4A (circuit 434) and 6A (circuit 57) is greater than 10 volts, correct open in ground circuit 57 (pin 6A). If voltage is less than 10 volts, go to next step.

8) Turn headlights on and move dimmer to maximum brightness. If instrument panel general illumination (switches, heater control panel, etc.) is not okay, check illumination relay and connecting circuits (434, 57 and 19). If general illumination is okay, check dimmer circuit 195 or dimmer fuse.

9) Disconnect battery negative cable. Remove EIC. Reconnect harness (with cluster removed). Reconnect battery negative cable. Turn ignition to "RUN" position. Check bulbs for burnt out filaments and replace bulbs as necessary.

CAUTION: Halogen illumination bulbs are pressurized and may shatter if handled incorrectly. Wear eye protection when replacing or inspecting these bulbs.

TEST B

1) Turn ignition to "RUN" position. If display is backlit but blank, check for proper operation of speedo/odometer. If speedo/odometer operates properly, go to step **2)**. If not operating properly, go to step **5)**.

2) Disconnect battery negative cable. Remove EIC, and prevent connector from shorting. Reconnect battery negative cable. Turn ignition to "RUN" position.

3) Using a voltmeter, check voltage at circuit 489 (Pin 1C). *See Fig. 2.* If greater than 10 volts, go to step **4)**. If less than 10 volts, check circuit 489 for open between cluster pin 1C and splice.

4) Using an ohmmeter, check for continuity between circuit 397 (Pin 2C) and battery negative cable. If continuity is present, replace tach/multigauge module and recheck cluster operation. If no continuity exists, check for open in cluster ground circuit 397 (Pin 2C).

5) Check for bad fuse in circuit 489. If fuse is bad, go to step **6)** before replacing fuse. If fuse is okay, go to step **2)**.

6) Before replacing fuse, turn ignition off and disconnect battery negative cable. Connect ohmmeter between circuit 489 and fuse ground. If continuity is present, replace fuse and recheck cluster operation. If continuity is not present, correct short in circuit 489. Replace fuse and recheck cluster operation.

TEST C

1) Turn ignition to "RUN" position and observe display. If all display segments light normally, and then display returns to normal operation, go to next step.

2) Ensure "ENGLISH/METRIC switch is in English released position. Depress and hold "GAUGE SELECT" switch in, while turning ignition to "RUN" position. Verify that display shows all zeros and note number of bar segments lit on tachometer display. Release "GAUGE SELECT" switch.

3) If 24 bar segments were lit on tachometer display, replace tach/multigauge module and recheck cluster operation. If module does not respond when "GAUGE SELECT" switch is depressed, go to Test T. If normal display was shown (8 bar segments lit on tachometer and 1 bar lit on multigauge), go to next step.

4) Ensure "ENGLISH/METRIC switch is in English (released) position. Depress and hold "GAUGE SELECT" switch in, while turning ignition to "RUN" position. Depress "GAUGE SELECT" switch several times until display shows 8 bar segments lit on tachometer, 1 bar lit on multigauge display and the number "61" appears in digital fuel gauge display area.

5) If all display areas are correct, system is okay. If display areas are incorrect, replace tach/multigauge module and recheck cluster operation.

TEST D

1) Ensure engine is operating properly and is not misfiring. Depress and hold "GAUGE SELECT" switch. After 5 seconds, a tone will be produced, and tach option display will appear. Display will remain as long as switch is depressed.

Typical Tach Option Display

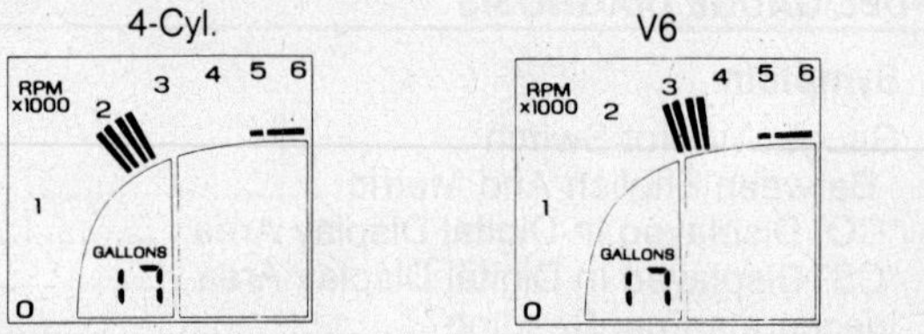

2) If option display appears. go to step **3)**. If option display does not appear, repeat step **1)** (ensure "GAUGE SELECT" switch is fully depressed). If, after repeating test, display does appear, go to step **1)** of Test W.

3) Note position of tach read-out. If tach option read-out bar segments point toward 2000 RPM, tachometer is wired for use with 4-cylinder engine. If tach option read-out bar segments point to 3000 RPM, tachometer is wired for use with V6 engine.

4) Verify that tachometer option display and engine match. If tachometer option and engine type match, replace tachometer and recheck cluster operation. If tachometer option and engine type do not match, tachometer wiring is incorrect. go to step **5)** or **7)** depending on engine type.

5) On vehicles with 4 cylinder engines, disconnect battery negative cable, and remove EIC. Check for continuity between pin 9C (circuit 398) and ground. *See Fig. 2.* Continuity should exist at this point. Check for continuity between pin 10C (circuit 644) and ground.

6) Continuity should not exist at this point. If continuity exists, replace tach/multigauge module and recheck cluster operation. If continuity is incorrect, rewire as necessary to create a ground at pin 9C (circuit 398) and an open at pin 10C (circuit 644).

7) On vehicles with V6 engines, disconnect battery negative cable, and remove EIC. Check for continuity between pin 9C (circuit 398) and ground, and between pin 10C (circuit 644) and ground. Continuity should not exist at either point.

8) If continuity is okay, replace tach/multigauge module and recheck cluster operation. If continuity is incorrect, rewire as necessary to create an open at both pin 9C (circuit 398) and 10C (circuit 644) and recheck cluster operation.

FORD ELECTRONIC INSTRUMENT CLUSTER (Cont.)

TEST E

1) Ensure engine is operating properly and is not misfiring. Disconnect battery negative cable, and remove EIC. Using an ohmmeter, measure resistance between pin 4C (circuit 11) and ignition coil. *See Fig. 2.* Move coil wiring side-to-side to check for intermittent connection.

2) If resistance is less than 100 ohms, replace tach/multigauge module and recheck cluster operation. If resistance is greater than 100 ohms, check wiring for open in circuit 11 (pin 4C).

TEST F

1) Turn ignition to "RUN" position. Depress "ENGLISH/METRIC" switch. If display responds, and labels change, system is okay. If display does not respond, go to next step.

2) Check that speedo/odometer display responds when "ENGLISH/METRIC" switch is depressed. If speedo/odometer display responds, go to step **3)**. If display does not respond, go to step **3)** of Test T.

3) Depress "ENGLISH/METRIC" switch several times. If fuel gauge sticks in "METRIC" mode, replace tach/multigauge module and recheck cluster operation. If fuel gauge sticks in "ENGLISH" mode, go to step **3)** of Test T.

TEST G

1) Disconnect battery negative cable. Lower fuel tank to gain access to fuel sending unit connector. Unplug fuel sending unit connector, and install a jumper wire between variable resistance terminal of sender and ground terminals.

2) Reconnect battery. Turn ignition to "RUN" position. If digital display reads "CO", remove jumper wire and go to step **4)**. If digital display reads "CS", remove jumper wire and go to next step.

3) Using an ohmmeter, measure resistance of fuel sending unit (across sending unit terminals). If resistance is 14-163 ohms, inspect sending unit terminals for loose or intermittent connection. If resistance is not between 14 and 163 ohms, replace sending unit and recheck cluster operation.

4) Disconnect battery negative cable. Remove EIC, and prevent connections from shorting. Connect jumper wire between variable resistance terminal and ground terminals of harness.

5) Check for continuity between pins 13C (circuit 29) and 14C (circuit 397) on cluster. *See Fig. 2.* If continuity exists, replace tach/multigauge module and recheck cluster operation. If continuity does not exist, correct open in fuel sending unit wiring (circuit 29).

TEST H

1) Disconnect battery negative cable. Remove EIC and prevent connections from shorting. Using an ohmmeter, measure resistance between pins 13C and 14C. *See Fig. 2.* If resistance is 14-163 ohms, replace tach/multigauge module and recheck cluster operation. If resistance is not between 14 and 163 ohms, go to next step.

2) Disconnect battery negative cable. Lower fuel tank to gain access to fuel sending unit connector. Unplug fuel sending unit connector. Measure resistance between pins 13C and 14C. If resistance is not 14-163 ohms, replace tach/multigauge module and recheck cluster operation. If resistance is higher than 163 ohms, go to next step.

3) Disconnect battery negative cable. Lower fuel tank to gain access to fuel sending unit connector. Unplug fuel sending unit connector. Measure resistance between pins 13C and 14C of cluster. If resistance is greater than 10,000 ohms, replace fuel sending unit and recheck cluster operation. If resistance is less than 10,000 ohms, correct short in harness.

TEST I

1) Ensure fuel tank is filled. Observe digital fuel gauge for "F" display. If a number, instead of an "F", is displayed, go to step **2)**. If "F" is displayed, system is okay.

2) Depress and hold "GAUGE SELECT" switch. After 5 seconds, a tone will be produced, and fuel option display will appear. Display will remain as long as switch is depressed.

Typical Fuel Option Display

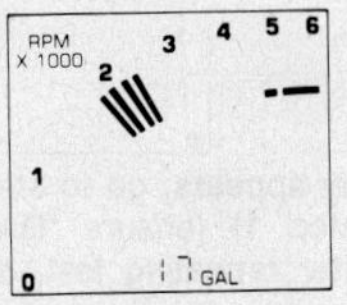

3) If option display appears. go to step **4)**. If option display does not appear, repeat step **2)** (ensure "GAUGE SELECT" switch is fully depressed). If, after repeating test, display does not appear, go to Test W.

4) Observe fuel read-out during option display mode. Fuel option read-out corresponds with size of fuel tank. Verify that proper fuel option display and tank size match.

5) If fuel option and tank size match, go to step **8)**. If fuel option and tank size do not match, go to step **6)** or **7)** depending on fuel tank size.

6) On vehicles with 15 gallon fuel tank, disconnect battery negative cable, and remove EIC. Check for continuity between pin 3C (circuit 396) and ground. *See Fig. 2.* Continuity should not exist at this point. Rewire as necessary to create an open at pin 3C (circuit 396) .

7) On vehicles with 17 gallon fuel tank, disconnect battery negative cable and remove EIC. Check for continuity between pin 3C (circuit 396) and ground. Continuity should exist at this point. Rewire as necessary to create a closed circuit 396 (pin 3C). Recheck cluster operation.

8) Verify that correct fuel tank filler neck is installed. Replace if necessary and recheck cluster operation. If filler neck is okay, disconnect battery negative cable. Lower fuel tank to gain access to fuel sending unit connector, and remove fuel sending unit.

9) Using an ohmmeter, measure resistance of fuel sending unit (across sending unit terminals). Resistance at empty stop should be 14-17 ohms. Resistance at FULL stop should be 156-163 ohms. If resistance values are okay, go to next step. If resistance values are incorrect, replace fuel sending unit and recheck cluster operation.

10) Inspect sending unit for free movment in tank. Check tank for damage and/or distortion. If tank is okay, replace tach/multigauge module and recheck cluster operation. If tank is distorted or damaged, repair or replace as necessary.

TEST J

1) Disconnect battery negative cable. Lower fuel tank to gain access to fuel sending unit connector, and remove fuel sending unit. Using an ohmmeter, measure resistance of fuel sending unit (across sending unit terminals). Resistance at empty stop should be 14-17. Resistance at full stop should be 156-163.

2) If resistance values are okay at both empty and full stops, go to step **3)**. If resistance values are incorrect at either empty, full, or both stops, replace fuel sending unit and recheck cluster operation.

3) Inspect sending unit for free movment in tank. Check tank for damage and/or distortion. If tank is okay, replace tach/multigauge module and recheck cluster operation. Replace tank if distorted or damaged.

FORD ELECTRONIC INSTRUMENT CLUSTER (Cont.)

TEST K

1) Depress and hold "GAUGE SELECT" switch. After 5 seconds, a tone will be produced, and fuel option display will appear. Display will remain as long as switch is depressed.

Typical Fuel Option Display

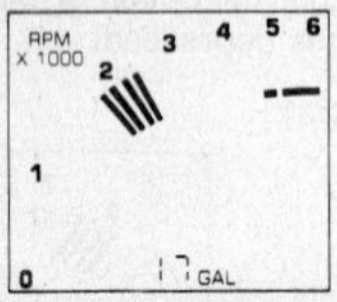

2) If option display appears, go to step **3)**. If option display does not appear, repeat step **1)** (ensure "GAUGE SELECT" switch is fully depressed). If, after repeating test, display does not appear, go to Test X.

3) Observe fuel read-out during option display mode. Digital fuel display should correspond with fuel tank size. Verify that proper fuel option display and tank size match.

4) If fuel option and tank size match, go to step **7)**. If fuel option and tank size do not match, go to either step **5)** or **6)** depending on fuel tank size.

5) On vehicles with 15 gallon fuel tank, disconnect battery negative cable, and remove EIC. Check for continuity between pin 3C (circuit 396) and ground. *See Fig. 2.* Continuity should not exist at this point. Rewire as necessary to create an open at pin 3C (circuit 396). If continuity does not exist, go to step **8)**.

6) On vehicles with 17 gallon fuel tank, disconnect battery negative cable and remove EIC. Check for continuity between pin 3C (circuit 396) and ground. If continuity does not exist, rewire as necessary to create a closed circuit 396 (3C). Recheck cluster operation. If continuity does exist, go to next step.

7) Disconnect battery negative cable. Lower fuel tank to gain access to fuel sending unit connector. Replace fuel sending unit with a 32-34 ohm resistor. Connect battery negative cable.

8) Turn ignition to "RUN" position. Gauge should indicate 2-3 gallons (9-11 liters) of fuel remaining. If gauge reading is okay, go to step **9)**. If gauge reading is inaccurate, go to step **11)**.

9) Disconnect battery negative cable. Remove EIC, and prevent connections from shorting. Jumper sending unit connector. Using an ohmmeter, measure resistance between pins 12A and 13A on cluster.

10) If resistance is greater than 1 ohm, correct short in circuit 29 (pin 13C). Recheck cluster operation. If resistance is 0-1 ohm, disconnect battery negative cable and check fuel sending unit for binding or sticking, replace if necessary.

11) If fuel sending unit is okay, check tank for damage and/or distortion. If tank is undamaged, problem is caused by other vehicle system(s). If tank is distorted or damaged, repair or replace as necessary.

TEST L

1) Unplug lead wire to temperature sending unit. Turn ignition to "RUN" position. Temperature gauge should indicate a cold engine (1 bar segment lit). If gauge display is okay, replace temperature sending unit and recheck cluster operation. If gauge is incorrect, go to next step.

2) Disconnect battery negative cable. Unplug wire to temperature sending unit. Remove EIC. Using an ohmmeter, measure resistance between pins 11C and 14C. *See Fig. 2.* If resistance is greater than 10,000 ohms, replace tach/multigauge module and recheck cluster operation. If resistance is less than 10,000 ohms, correct short in circuit 39 (pin 11C).

TEST M

Before testing, note the following:

- Driver warning tone is not active until engine is started, and reaches 600 RPM.
- Warning tone generator will not respond if another sound is being produced.
- Driver warning tone is only given for temperatures above normal.

Turn ignition on. Depress "GAUGE SELECT" switch. If tone is produced, system is okay. If no tone is produced, go to Test X.

TEST N

1) Unplug temperature sending unit. Jumper sending unit connector wires. Turn ignition to "RUN" position. Multigauge should show blinking thermometer symbol and light top and bottom 2 bar segments of multigauge.

2) If temperature gauge display is incorrect, go to step **3)**. If gauge display is okay, remove jumper wire and go to step **5)**.

3) Disconnect battery negative cable. Remove EIC. Ensure jumper wire is connected in place of temperature sending unit. Check continuity between pins 11C and 14C of cluster. *See Fig. 2.*

4) If continuity exists, replace tach/multigauge module and recheck cluster operation. If continuity does not exist, correct open in circuit 39. Recheck cluster operation.

5) Run engine at normal operating temperature. Measure temperature sending unit resistance. If resistance is less than 8000 ohms, replace tach/multigauge module and recheck cluster operation. If resistance is greater than 8000 ohms, go to next step.

6) Check cooling system and thermostat for proper operation. Check coolant level. Repair or replace cooling system components as necessary. If cooling system is okay, replace temperature sending unit and recheck cluster operation.

TEST O

1) Unplug wire to oil pressure sending unit. Turn ignition to "RUN" position. Depress "GAUGE SELECT" switch 2 times. Oil pressure gauge should indicate low pressure (oil can symbol flashing), and 1 bar segment should be lit on multigauge.

2) If oil pressure display is okay, replace oil pressure sending unit and recheck cluster operation. If oil pressure display is incorrect, go to next step.

3) Disconnect battery negative cable. Remove EIC. Measure resistance between pin 12C (circuit 31) and 14C (circuit 397). *See Fig. 2.* If resistance is greater than 10,000 ohms, replace tach/multigauge module and recheck cluster operation. If resistance is less than 10,000 ohms, correct short in circuit 31.

TEST P

Before testing, note the following:

- Driver warning tone is not active until engine is started, and reaches 600 RPM.
- Warning tone generator will not respond if another sound is being produced.

Turn ignition to "RUN" position. Depress "GAUGE SELECT" switch. If tone is heard, system is okay. If no tone is produced, go to Test X.

TEST Q

1) Verify that engine is not low on oil, and that oil pressure is okay. Unplug wire to oil pressure sending unit. Connect a jumper wire from sending unit lead wire to ground.

2) Turn ignition to "RUN" position. Oil pressure gauge should indicate low pressure (oil can symbol flashing), and 1 bar should be lit on multigauge. If display is okay, remove jumper wire and go to step **4)**. If display is incorrect, remove jumper wire and go to next step.

3) Disconnect battery negative cable. Remove EIC. Using an ohmmeter, check for continuity between pin 12C (circuit 31) and end of oil pressure sending unit connector. *See Fig. 2.* If continuity is present, go to step **4)**. If continuity is not present, correct open in circuit 31.

4) Secure unplugged cluster connectors from shorting. Unplug wire from oil pressure sending unit. Reconnect battery negative cable, and start vehicle. Using engine as ground, measure resistance of oil pressure sending unit.

5) Slowly increase and decrease engine RPM. Resistance of oil pressure sending unit should fluctuate between 9 and 40 ohms. If tested resistance is ever less than 9 or more than 40, replace oil pressure sending unit and recheck cluster operation. If tested resistance is okay, go to next step.

6) Disconnect battery negative cable. Measure resistance between sending unit case and battery ground. If resistance is less than 1 ohm, replace tach/multigauge module and recheck cluster operation. If resistance is greater than 1 ohm, correct poor engine ground.

FORD ELECTRONIC INSTRUMENT CLUSTER (Cont.)

TEST R

1) Turn ignition to "RUN" position, but do not start engine. Depress "GAUGE SELECT" switch 3 times. Multigauge should indicate charging system failure (battery symbol flashing). If display is correct, system is okay. If display is incorrect, go to next step.

2) Jumper "I" terminal of voltage regulator to battery ground. If display is now okay, repair or replace voltage regulator and recheck cluster operation. If display is still incorrect, turn ignition off. Unplug connector to voltage regulator, and turn ignition to "RUN" position.

3) Voltage at terminal "I" on connector should be about 12 volts. If voltage is okay, replace tach/multigauge module and recheck cluster operation. If 12 volts are not present, correct open in circuit 904.

TEST S

1) Ensure cooling cluster operation is okay. Run engine at normal operating temperature. Stop engine. Remove temperature sender wiring connector. Measure and record temperature sender resistance. If resistance is 1200-6000 ohms, go to step **2)**. If resistance is not between 1200 and 6000 ohms, replace temperature sender and recheck cluster operation.

2) Reconnect temperature sender wiring. Turn ignition to "RUN" or "ACC" position. Compare number of bar segments, with engine coolant temperature.

TEMPERATURE GAUGE BAR SEGMENTS

Coolant Temp. °F (°C)	No. Of Bar Segments Lit
0-120 (-17.8-48.9)	1
120-150 (48.9-65.6)	2
150-180 (65.6-82.2)	3
180-230 (82.2-110.0)	4
230-240 (110.0-115.6)	5
240-250 (115.6-121.1)	6
250-260 (121.1-126.6)	7
260-270 (126.6-132.2)	8

3) If display checks okay, system is operating properly. If number of bar segments lit does not correspond with engine temperature, remove EIC. Measure resistance between pin 14C (circuit 397) and 11C. *See Fig. 2.* Resistance should not vary more than 10 ohms from reading in step **1)**.

4) If resistance varies more than 10 ohms, check for poor connection and/or corrosion at temperature sender or in sender wiring. If resistance does not vary more than 10 ohms from reading in step **1)**, replace tach/multigauge module and recheck cluster operation.

TEST T

NOTE: If a defective speedometer module is replaced, an "S" symbol is displayed in upper right-hand corner of speedometer display, and a sticker must be affixed to driver's door pillar showing previous mileage.

1) Turn ignition to "RUN" position. Depress "GAUGE SELECT" switch. If tone is produced but tach/multigauge module does not respond, replace tach/multigauge module and recheck cluster operation. If tone is not produced, go to step **6)**.

2) Depress "EXPAND FUEL" switch on module. If tone is produced but tach/multigauge module does not respond, replace tach/multigauge module and recheck cluster operation. If tone is not produced, go to step **6)**.

3) Depress "TRIP DISTANCE" switch on module. If tone is produced but speedo/odometer module does not respond, replace module and recheck cluster operation. If tone is not produced, go to step **6)**.

4) Depress "TRIP RESET" switch on module. If tone is produced but speedo/odometer module does not respond, replace speedo/odometer module and recheck cluster operation. If tone is not produced, go to step **6)**.

5) Depress "ENGLISH/METRIC" switch on module. If tone is produced but speedo/odometer module does not respond, replace speedo/odometer module and recheck cluster operation. If tone is not produced, go to next step.

6) Unplug connector from affected switch module to vehicle wiring harness. Measure resistance between colored wire of affected module switch and Black wire (ground). **(Cont.)**

TEST T (Cont.)

MODULE SWITCH WIRE COLOR CHART

Wire Color	Module Switch
White	GAUGE SELECT
Orange	EXPAND FUEL
Purple	TRIP DISTANCE
Yellow	TRIP RESET
Brown	ENGLISH/METRIC

7) Resistance should be less than 10 ohms when switch depressed, and greater than 10,000 ohms when switch is released. If resistance of wire is incorrect, replace switch module assembly and recheck cluster operation. If resistance of wire is okay, go to next step.

8) Disconnect battery negative cable and remove EIC. Check for continuity between mating switch module connector and cluster connector. If continuity is not present, correct open in connector wiring. If continuity is present, go to next step.

9) Check for continuity of switch module ground between mating switch module and cluster connectors (between cluster pins 14B and 14C, and Black/White wire at switch connector). *See Fig. 2.*

10) If continuity is not present, correct open in ground circuit (397). If continuity is present, replace module that affected switch and wire are connected to, and recheck cluster operation.

TEST U

NOTE: If a defective speedometer module is replaced, an "S" symbol is displayed in upper right-hand corner of speedometer display, and a sticker must be affixed to driver's door pillar showing previous mileage.

1) Turn ignition to "RUN" position. If display is backlit but blank, check multigauge operation. If multigauge operates properly, go to step **2)**. If multigauge does not operate properly, go to step **7)**.

2) Disconnect battery negative cable, and remove EIC. Secure unplugged cluster connectors from shorting. Reconnect battery negative cable. Turn ignition to "RUN" position.

3) Measure voltage at pins 14A and 13B. *See Fig. 2.* If voltage is more than 10 volts at both pins, go to step **4)**. If voltage is less than 10 volts at either pin, correct open at pin 13B (circuit 54) and/or pin 14A (circuit 489) as necessary. Recheck cluster operation.

4) Disconnect battery negative cable, and remove EIC. Secure unplugged cluster connectors from shorting. Reconnect battery negative cable. Check voltage at pin 13B (circuit 54).

5) If voltage at pin 13B (circuit 54) is more than 12 volts, go to step **6)**. If voltage at pin 13B (circuit 54) is less than 12 volts, correct open in circuit 54.

6) Using an ohmmeter, check for continuity between pin 14B (circuit 397) and battery negative cable. If continuity is present, replace speedo/odometer module, and recheck cluster operation. If continuity is not present, correct open in circuit between cluster and ground.

7) Check for bad fuse in circuit 489 (pin 12B) and/or circuit 54 (pin 13B). If fuse is okay, go to step **2)**. If fuse is blown, go to next step.

8) Before replacing fuse, turn ignition off and disconnect battery negative cable. Check for short between circuit side of fuse and ground. If a short condition is present, correct short. If short condition is not present, replace fuse and recheck cluster operation.

TEST V

NOTE: If a defective speedometer module is replaced, an "S" symbol is displayed in upper right-hand corner of speedometer display, and a sticker must be affixed to driver's door pillar showing previous mileage.

1) Turn ignition to "RUN" position, and observe speedometer display. If all display segments light up, and then go out, go to step **2)**. If display is missing segments, or segments are half-lit, replace speedo/odometer module and recheck cluster operation.

2) Place "ENGLISH/METRIC" switch in "ENGLISH" position. Depress and hold "TRIP RESET" switch while turning ignition to "RUN" position. Observe display reaction. Release "TRIP RESET" switch.

(Cont.)

FORD ELECTRONIC INSTRUMENT CLUSTER (Cont.)

TEST V (Cont.)

3) If display did not enter test mode (did not respond to switch being depressed) go to Test T, step **1)**. If all read-outs are displayed as zeros, go to step **4)**. If display reads "F" on right-hand digit of speedometer, replace speedo/odometer module and recheck cluster operation.

4) Ensure "ENGLISH/METRIC" switch is in "ENGLISH" position. Depress and hold "TRIP RESET" switch while turning ignition to "RUN" position. Repeatedly depress "TRIP RESET" switch until all zeros are displayed. See diagram.

Test Display For Zeros

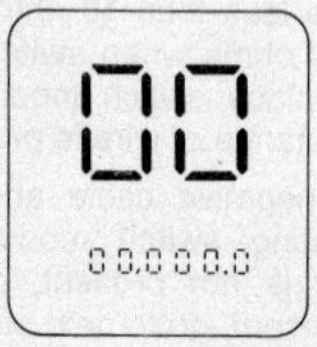

5) If any segments are half-lit, missing or scrambled, replace speedo/odometer module and recheck cluster operation. If display is complete, depress "TRIP RESET" switch to advance display through test displays. When test display of eights is shown, all labels and symbols should be displayed and display should read "188". See diagram.

Test Display For Eights

6) If any segments are half-lit or scrambled, replace speedo/odometer module and recheck cluster operation. If all segments appear correct throughout testing, system is okay.

TEST W

NOTE: **If a defective speedometer module is replaced, an "S" symbol is displayed in upper right-hand corner of speedometer display, and a sticker must be affixed to driver's door pillar showing previous mileage.**

1) Turn ignition to "RUN" position. Depress "ENGLISH/METRIC" switch. If labels in all display areas change from English and metric, system is okay. If display does not change when switch is depressed, go to next step.

2) Depress "ENGLISH/METRIC" switch several times. If display remains in "ENGLISH" mode, go to step **3)**. If display remains in "METRIC" mode, replace speedo/odometer module and recheck cluster operation.

3) Unplug connector at push switches. Using an ohmmeter, measure resistance between Brown and Black/White wires (ground) of connector leading to switches.

4) Resistance with "ENGLISH/METRIC" switch depressed should be less than 10 ohms. Resistance with "ENGLISH/METRIC" switch released should be greater than 10,000 ohms. If resistance values are okay, go to step **5)**. If resistance values are incorrect, replace switch module and recheck cluster operation.

5) Disconnect battery negative cable, and remove EIC. Check for continuity between switch module connector and pin 5B (circuit 273). *See Fig. 2.*

6) If continuity is present, replace speedo/odometer module and recheck cluster operation. If continuity is not present, correct open in circuit 273.

TEST X

NOTE: **If a defective speedometer module is replaced, an "S" symbol is displayed in upper right-hand corner of speedometer display, and a sticker must be affixed to driver's door pillar showing previous mileage.**

Before testing, note the following:

- Driver warning tone is not active until engine is started, and reaches 600 RPM.
- Warning tone generator will not respond if another sound is being produced.

1) Turn ignition to "RUN" position. Depress each module switch ("GAUGE SELECT", "EXPAND FUEL", "ENGLISH/METRIC", etc.). If tone is produced for all switches, system is okay.

2) If tone is not produced when any module switches are depressed, go to step **3)**. If tone is produced for some switches, go to step **7)**.

3) Check for "fasten seat belt" and "key in ignition" warning tones. If tones are produced, go to step **4)**. If tones are not produced, repair/replace tone generator module and recheck cluster operation.

4) Disconnect battery negative cable. Remove cluster and secure connectors from shorting. Reconnect battery negative cable. Turn ignition to "RUN" position. Verify that "fasten seat belt" warning tone is operating.

5) After tone has stopped, connect a jumper between pin 2B and ground, and listen for tone (test 1). *See Fig. 2.* Remove jumper wire. Connect a jumper between pin 6B and ground, and listen for a tone (test 2).

6) If tone is produced during both tests, replace tach/multigauge module and recheck cluster operation. If tone is not produced in either test, correct open in circuit 183 (pin 2B) and recheck cluster operation.

7) Identify which switch groups do not produce a tone when depressed. If "ENGLISH/METRIC", "TRIP DIST" and "TRIP RESET" switches (speedo/odometer wiring circuit) do not produce a tone, go to step **8)**. If "GAUGE SELECT" and "EXPAND FUEL" switches (tach/multigauge wiring circuit) do not produce a tone, go to step **11)**.

8) Disconnect battery negative cable. Remove cluster and secure connectors from shorting. Reconnect battery negative cable. Turn ignition to "RUN" position. Verify that "fasten seat belt" warning tone is operating.

9) After tone has stopped, connect a jumper between pin 2B and ground. If tone is produced, replace speedo/odometer module and recheck cluster operation.

10) If tone is not produced, correct open in circuit 183 (between pin 2B and tone generator) and recheck cluster operation.

11) Disconnect battery negative cable. Remove cluster and secure connectors from shorting. Reconnect battery negative cable. Turn ignition to "RUN" position. Verify that "fasten seat belt" warning tone is operating.

12) After warning tone has stopped, connect a jumper between pin 6C and ground. If tone is produced, replace tachometer/multigauge module and recheck cluster operation. If tone is not produced, correct open in circuit 183 (between pin 6C and tone generator) and recheck cluster operation.

TEST Y

NOTE: **If a defective speedometer module is replaced, an "S" symbol is displayed in upper right-hand corner of speedometer display, and a sticker must be affixed to driver's door pillar showing previous mileage.**

1) Turn ignition to "RUN" position, and observe display. If all display segments come on and then go out, go to step **2)**. If segment display is incorrect, replace speedo/odometer module and recheck cluster operation.

2) Check for proper advancement of speedometer reading while vehicle is moving forward. If speedometer display operates properly, go to step **3)**. If display does not advance correctly, replace speedo/odometer module and recheck cluster operation.

3) If vehicle is not equipped with cruise control, go to step **4)**. Test drive vehicle and check cruise control system operation. If system does not operate properly, go to step **4)**. If system operates properly, go to step **8)**.

(Cont.)

FORD ELECTRONIC INSTRUMENT CLUSTER (Cont.)

TEST Y (Cont.)

4) Disconnect speed sensor connector. Measure resistance across connector leads. If resistance is less than 500 ohms, correct short in wiring circuit 150, and recheck cluster operation.

5) If resistance is greater than 500 ohms, check resistance across speed sensor terminals. If resistance is less than 200 ohms, or more than 230 ohms, replace sensor and recheck cluster operation. If resistance is 200-230 ohms, go to next step.

6) Disconnect speed sensor from transmission. Check driven gear for damage and verify that retainer clip is in position. Replace driven gear and/or retainer clip as necessary and recheck cluster operation. If driven gear and retainer clip are okay, go to next step.

7) Check drive gear on transmission output shaft for wear and/or damage, replace as necessary, and recheck cluster operation. If gear is okay, go to next step.

8) Reconnect speed sensor wiring. Disconnect battery negative cable and remove cluster. Check resistance between pin 3B and pin 14B of connector. *See Fig. 2*.

9) If resistance is 160-230 ohms, replace speedo/odometer module and recheck cluster operation. If resistance is less than 160 ohms, or more than 230 ohms, correct open in circuit 150 and recheck cluster operation.

TEST Z

NOTE: If a defective speedometer module is replaced, an "S" symbol is displayed in upper right-hand corner of speedometer display, and a sticker must be affixed to driver's door pillar showing previous mileage.

1) Verify that correct size tires are installed on vehicle. If tire size is okay, record odometer reading. Test drive vehicle over a known distance and record odometer reading again. If odometer reading varies from actual mileage, go to next step.

2) Remove speed sensor from transmission and verify that correct drive and driven gears are installed. If correct drive and driven gears are installed, replace speedo/odometer module and recheck cluster operation.

TEST AA

NOTE: If a defective speedometer module is replaced, an "S" symbol is displayed in upper right-hand corner of speedometer display, and a sticker must be affixed to driver's door pillar showing previous mileage.

1) Remove speed sensor from transmission. Check that gear teeth are not damaged, that gear does not slip on shaft, and that retainer clip is in position. Replace driven gear and/or retainer clip as necessary and recheck cluster operation. If gear and retainer clip are okay, go to next step.

2) Measure resistance across harness wires of connector. If resistance is less than 500 ohms, correct short in wiring circuit 150, and recheck cluster operation.

3) If resistance is greater than 500 ohms, check resistance across speed sensor terminals. If resistance is less than 200 ohms, or more than 230 ohms, replace sensor and recheck cluster operation. If resistance is 200-230 ohms, go to next step.

4) Reconnect speed sensor wiring. Disconnect battery negative cable and remove cluster. Check resistance between pin 3B and pin 14B of connector. *See Fig. 2*.

5) If resistance is 160-230 ohms, replace speedo/odometer module and recheck cluster operation. If resistance is less than 160 ohms, or more than 230 ohms, correct open in circuit 150 and recheck cluster operation.

TEST BB

NOTE: If a defective speedometer module is replaced, an "S" symbol is displayed in upper right-hand corner of speedometer display, and a sticker must be affixed to driver's door pillar showing previous mileage.

Turn ignition to "RUN" position. Check odometer display. If odometer display reads "ERROR", replace speedo/odometer module and reheck cluster operation.

TEST CC

NOTE: If a defective speedometer module is replaced, an "S" symbol is displayed in upper right-hand corner of speedometer display, and a sticker must be affixed to driver's door pillar showing previous mileage.

1) To determine if speedo/odometer module is original or replacement, turn ignition to "OFF" position. Depress and hold "TRIP RESET" switch while turning ignition to "RUN" position.

2) Observe option code on odometer read-out. Compare option code display with module type to determine if speedo/odometer module is original or replacement. See diagram and table.

Option Code Display

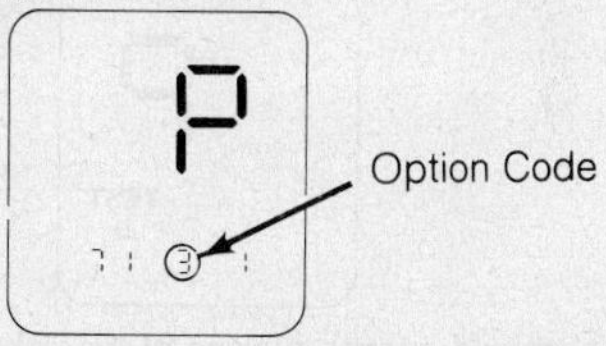

OPTION CODE DISPLAY

Option Code	Module Type
2	Replacement
3	Replacement
6	Original
7	Original
E	Original
O	Replacement
R	Replacement

3) If "S" symbol is displayed on an original speedo/odometer module, replace the module and recheck cluster operation. If an "S" symbol is displayed on replacement module, system is okay.

TEST DD

NOTE: If a defective speedometer module is replaced, an "S" symbol is displayed in upper right-hand corner of speedometer display, and a sticker must be affixed to driver's door pillar showing previous mileage.

1) Test drive vehicle at least 10 miles to check for proper odometer operation. If odometer accumulates 10 miles then jumps back 10 miles, replace speedo/odometer module and recheck cluster operation.

2) If odometer will not accumulate mileage, check for proper speedometer operation. If operation is not okay, go to Test Y. If operation is okay, replace speedo/odometer module and recheck cluster operation.

FORD ELECTRONIC INSTRUMENT CLUSTER (Cont.)

TEST EE

NOTE: If a defective speedometer module is replaced, an "S" symbol is displayed in upper right-hand corner of speedometer display, and a sticker must be affixed to driver's door pillar showing previous mileage.

1) Verify symptom by test driving vehicle. If symptom exists, turn vehicle off. Depress and hold "TRIP RESET" switch while turning ignition to "RUN" position. Display should show all zeros (test 1).

2) Release "TRIP RESET" switch and note speedometer display. A "P" symbol should appear in place of the right-hand speedometer digit, and "1" should appear in the odometer "tenths" position (test 2).

Computer Self-Test Display

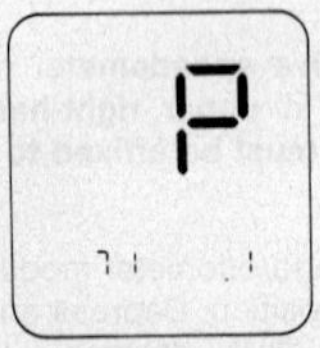

3) If either test (1 or 2) is failed, replace speedo/odometer module, and recheck cluster operation. If display passes both tests, depress "TRIP RESET" switch 4 times and note display.

Memory Self-Test Display

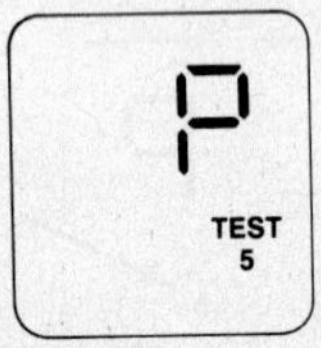

4) A "P" symbol should appear in place of the right-hand speedometer digit, and "5" should appear in the odometer "tenths" position. If test is failed, replace speedo/odometer module, and recheck cluster operation. If display is okay, go to next step.

5) Check speedometer for correct operation. If okay, replace speedo/odometer module, and recheck cluster operation. If speedometer constantly reads too high or too low, go to Test Z. If speedometer display is erratic, go to Test AA.

TEST FF

Odometer symptoms are diagnosed and corrected by performing the following tests in this order; Z, V and EE. If tests Z, V and EE are performed and no problems exist, system is okay.

TEST GG

NOTE: If a defective speedometer module is replaced, an "S" symbol is displayed in upper right-hand corner of speedometer display, and a sticker must be affixed to driver's door pillar showing previous mileage.

1) Turn ignition to "RUN" position. After "fasten seat belt" warning tone has stopped, depress "TRIP DIST" switch. If tone is present, replace speedo/odometer module and recheck cluster operation. If tone is not present, go to next step.

2) Unplug connector at push button switches. Measure resistance between Purple and Black/White wires. Resistance should be less than 10 ohms when switch is depressed, and greater than 10,000 ohms when switch is released.

3) If resistance is incorrect, replace switch assembly and recheck cluster operation. If resistance is okay, disconnect battery negative cable, and remove EIC. Check for continuity between mating switch module connector and cluster circuit 288 (pin 7B). *See Fig. 2.*

4) If continuity is not present, correct open in circuit 288 (pin 7B). If continuity is present, replace speedo/odometer module, and recheck cluster operation.

TEST HH

NOTE: If a defective speedometer module is replaced, an "S" symbol is displayed in upper right-hand corner of speedometer display, and a sticker must be affixed to driver's door pillar showing previous mileage.

1) Turn ignition to "RUN" position. After "fasten seat belt" warning tone has stopped, depress "TRIP RESET" switch. If tone is present, replace speedo/odometer module and recheck cluster operation. If tone is not present, go to next step.

2) Unplug connector at push button switches. Measure resistance between Yellow wire and Black/White wire. Resistance should be less than 10 ohms when switch depressed, and greater than 10,000 ohms when switch is released.

3) If resistance of wire is incorrect, replace switch assembly and recheck cluster operation. If resistance is okay, disconnect battery negative cable and remove EIC. Check for continuity between mating switch module connector and cluster circuit 286 (pin 6B). *See Fig. 2.*

4) I continuity is not present, correct open in circuit 286 (pin 6B). If continuity is present, replace speedo/odometer module and recheck cluster operation.

Fig. 2: Instrument Cluster and Switch Module Circuits

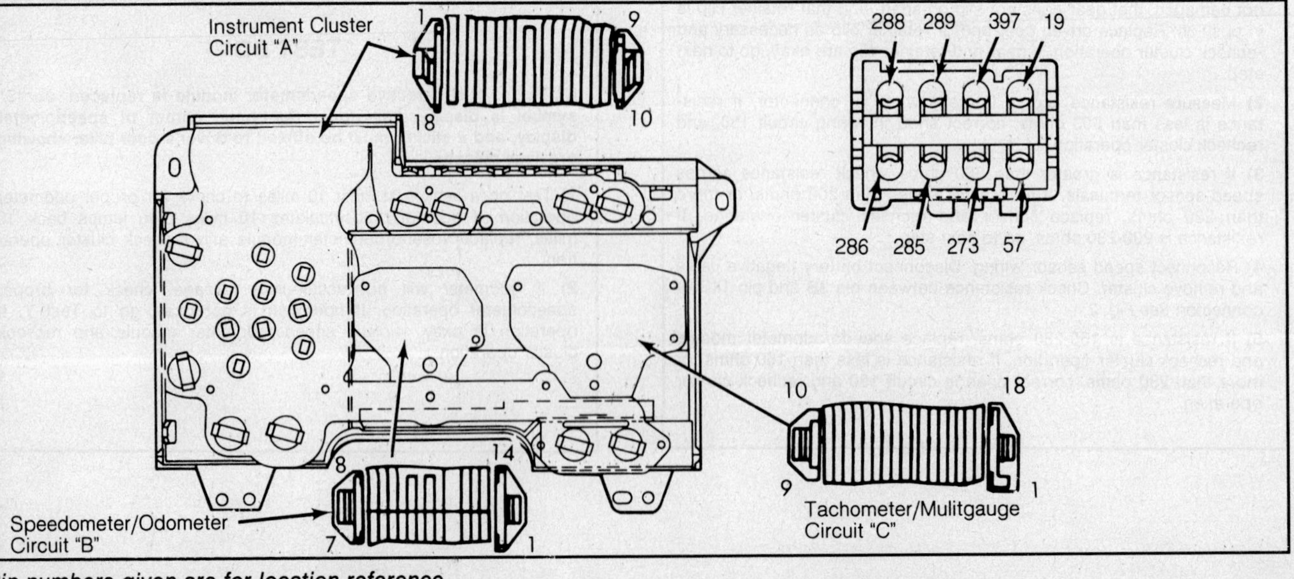

Pin numbers given are for location reference.

FORD ELECTRONIC INSTRUMENT CLUSTER (Cont.)

REMOVAL & INSTALLATION

CLUSTER BUTTON PANEL

Removal & Installation

Disconnect battery negative cable. Remove button panel face plate. Pull button panel from instrument panel. Disconnect wiring connector. To install, reverse removal procedure.

ELECTRONIC INSTRUMENT CLUSTER (EIC)

Removal

Disconnect battery negative cable. Remove cluster trim. Remove 4 cluster mounting screws. Pull top of cluster toward steering wheel. Unplug 3 connectors behind cluster. Pull bottom of cluster out.

Installation

Insert bottom of cluster into instrument panel aligning pins. To complete installation, reverse removal procedure.

Fig. 3: Exploded View of Aerostar EIC

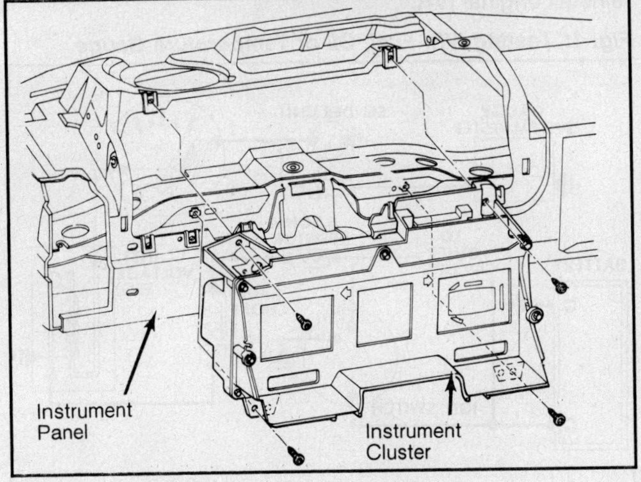

ELECTRONIC MODULE

Removal

Remove EIC. Remove 5 screws attaching lens/mask assembly to cluster. Remove 3 screws from back of module. Lift flex circuit from locator pins. Remove module from cluster.

Installation

Using alcohol and a lint-free cloth, remove dust and/or fingerprints from module displays and cluster lens. To install, reverse removal procedure.

HEADLIGHT SWITCH

Removal & Installation

1) Main light switch is located in left side instrument panel control pod. To remove, disconnect battery negative cable. Remove 5 screws attaching cluster finish panel to cluster.

2) Remove 3 screws attaching left side control cluster. Disconnect wiring connector. Remove 2 screws attaching light switch to control pod.

FORD STANDARD INSTRUMENT CLUSTER

DESCRIPTION & OPERATION

NOTE: **Service procedures for Aerostar with optional electronic instrument cluster are located in FORD ELECTRONIC INSTRUMENT PANEL article in this section.**

AMMETER GAUGE

Gauge senses both direction and flow rate of electrical current to or from battery, indicating whether a charge or discharge condition exists. A shunt-type ammeter is used. Ammeter is non adjustable. If found defective it should be replaced as a unit.

FUEL GAUGE

Gauge pointer is operated by flow of current heating a wire-wound bi-metal strip inside gauge. Current flow is controlled by a variable resistance, float-type sending unit in fuel tank.

As amount of fuel decreases, more circuit resistance is produced, allowing less current flow and heat to bi-metal strip. This causes pointer to move a shorter distance.

INSTRUMENT VOLTAGE REGULATOR

Instrument Voltage Regulator (IVR) is used in-line with all gauges except ammeter. It controls and maintains an average pulsating voltage, received by each gauge, of 5 volts. To prevent radio interference, a supression choke is used in-line between printed circuit and IVR.

OIL PRESSURE GAUGE

Gauge circuitry consists of an IVR, oil pressure gauge and a pressure-operated sending unit. As oil pressure increases, sending unit resistance decreases, causing an increase in current flow and gauge pointer movement.

OIL PRESSURE INDICATOR LIGHT

The light is connected between oil pressure switch unit on engine and coil terminal of ignition. Warning light should come on when ignition is first turned on.

It should go out after engine is started, indicating oil pressure has reached a safe level. Warning light should also come on any time oil pressure drops below normal.

TEMPERATURE GAUGE

System consists of a variable resistance-type sending unit and a gauge. As coolant temperature increases, resistance in sending unit decreases. This allows an increase of current flow and gauge pointer movement. It is possible, under certain driving conditions, for pointer to read at top of normal band and still have coolant temperature within limits.

TESTING

GAUGES

Oil Pressure Indicator Light

1) Turn ignition on, but do not start engine. Indicator light should come on. Start engine. Warning light should go out within 3 or 4 seconds.

2) To test oil pressure switch, turn ignition on, but do not start engine. If indicator light does not come on, disconnect wire from oil pressure switch terminal and touch to ground.

3) If light now comes on, oil pressure switch is defective. If light does not come on, check for bad bulb or open wiring in bulb circuit.

Oil Pressure Gauge

1) Remove connector from oil pressure sender unit and connect to matching terminals on Gauge Tester (Rotunda 21 0015). Attach tester ground wire to vehicle frame. Turn vehicle ignition to "ACC" position.

2) Turn tester switch to "IVR CHECK" position. A flashing light indicates IVR and wiring are functional. Turn tester switch to either "HIGH" or "LOW" position. Center line of gauge pointer should be within oil pressure White band of tester.

3) If center of pointer registers in White band, system is operating properly and oil pressure sending unit must be replaced. If pointer center line is outside of low band, replace gauge. If outside high band, replace IVR and repeat test. If still outside high band, replace gauge and reinstall original IVR.

Fig. 1: Testing IVR, Fuel, Oil or Temperature Gauge

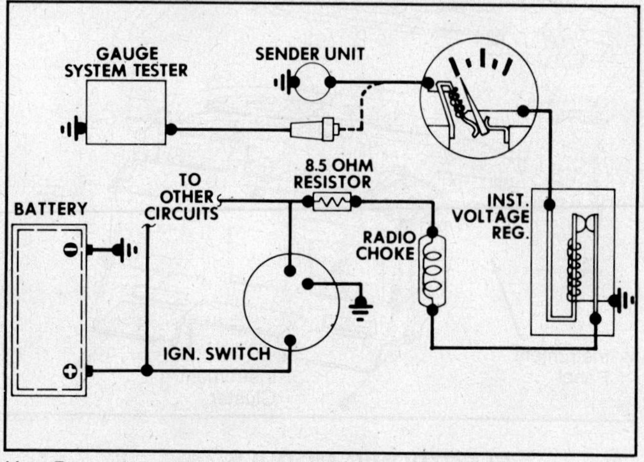

Use Rotunda gauge tester 21 0015.

Ammeter

1) With engine off, turn headlights on. Meter pointer should move toward "D" (discharge) side of gauge. If pointer does not move, check connections at rear of meter housing, printed circuit connections and multiple connector at printed circuit.

2) If connections are good, replace ammeter. If ammmeter pointer moves toward "C" (charge) side of gauge with lights on and engine off, reverse ammeter connections.

Fuel Level Gauge

1) Using Gauge Tester (Rotunda 21 0015), test fuel level gauge and instrument voltage regulator (IVR). Disconnect connnector from fuel sender and attach to tester. Turn ignition to "ACC" position.

2) Set tester switch to "IVR CHECK" position. If light flashes on and off, IVR and wiring are functional. If "IVR CHECK" light is on steady, check IVR ground screw. If ground screw is secure, replace IVR. If "IVR CHECK" light does not come on, check for open wiring in gauge circuit and/or circuit wiring.

3) With tester switch in either "HIGH" or "LOW" position, center line of gauge pointer should be within either

FORD STANDARD INSTRUMENT CLUSTER (Cont.)

"Full" or "Empty" White band on tester. If so, fuel indicating system is working properly and replacement of fuel sender is necessary.

4) If pointer is outside "Empty" White band, replace fuel gauge. If outside "Full" White band, replace IVR and retest. If still outside "Full" White band, replace fuel gauge and reinstall original IVR.

Temperature Gauge

1) Disconnect connector from temperature sender and connect to Gauge Tester (Rotunda 21 0015). Attach other tester lead to ground on vehicle. Turn ignition to "ACC" position. Turn tester switch to "IVR CHECK" position. A flashing light indicates IVR and wiring are functional.

2) Place tester switch in either "HIGH" or "LOW" position. Center line of pointer should be within "H" or "C" (White temperature level) test band. If so, indicating system is operating properly and sending unit requires replacement. If center line is outside White band, replace IVR and retest. If outside upper White band, replace gauge and retest.

NOTE: **If system still does not operate properly, check engine coolant level, proper operation of thermostat and fan belt tension.**

REMOVAL & INSTALLATION

SPEEDOMETER & GAUGES

Removal & Installation (All Models)

Instrument cluster must be removed to allow any repair or replacement of speedometer or gauges.

INSTRUMENT CLUSTER

Removal (Aerostar)

Disconnect battery negative cable. Remove 7 screws attaching cluster housing to cluster. Remove cluster housing. Remove 4 screws attaching cluster to instrument panel. Disconnect wiring harness connectors from rear of cluster. Disconnect speedometer cable.

Installation

Apply a 3/16" ball of silicon lubricant to drive hole of speedometer head. To complete installation, reverse removal procedure. Check operation of all gauges, lamps and signals.

Removal (Bronco II & Ranger)

1) Disconnect battery negative cable. Remove 2 screws attaching steering column shroud to panel. Remove shroud. Remove lower instrument panel trim. Detach cluster trim cover attaching screws and remove cover. Remove 4 screws attaching cluster to panel. Pull cluster slightly away from panel.

2) Disconnect speedometer cable at speedometer. If there is not enough room, detach cable at transmission. Disconnect wiring harness connector from printed circuit. Disconnect any light bulbs from sockets and remove instrument cluster.

Installation

Apply a 3/16" ball of silicone lubricant to drive hole of speedometer head. To complete installation, reverse removal procedure. Check operation of all gauges, lamps and signals.

Removal & Installation (All Vans, Except Aerostar)

1) Disconnect battery negative cable. Remove 2 steering column shroud-to-panel retaining screws and remove shroud. On vehicles with tilt steering columns, loosen bolts attaching column to band "C" support to provide additional clearance for cluster removal.

2) Remove 7 screws retaining cluster to instrument panel. Position cluster away from panel for access to rear of cluster. Disconnect speedometer cable. Disconnect multiple feed plug from printed circuit board and remove instrument cluster from instrument panel.

NOTE: **In some cases, it may be necessary to remove speedometer cable at the transmission, pulling cable through cowl.**

3) To install, reverse removal procedure. Apply approximately 3/16" diameter ball of silicone lubricant in drive hole of speedometer head.

Removal & Installation (Bronco & Pickups)

1) Disconnect battery negative cable. Using a hook to release knob lock tab. Remove knob from wiper-washer, headlight, windshield wiper and fog lamp switch, if used.

2) Remove steering column shroud. If equipped with A/T, remove loop on selector indicator cable assembly from retainer pin. Spread cable retaining clips with a hook tool. Remove bracket screw from cable bracket. Slide bracket from slot in tube.

3) Remove cluster trim cover and 4 cluster attaching screws. Disconnect speedometer cable, wire connector from printed circuit and 4WD indicator light (if equipped). Remove instrument cluster. To install, reverse removal procedure.

INSTRUMENT VOLTAGE REGULATOR & PRINTED CIRCUIT

Removal (Bronco II & Ranger)

Remove instrument cluster. Snap off printed circuit connector buttons from IVR. Remove attaching screw and instrument voltage regulator. Remove all retaining nuts and lamp bulbs and remove printed circuit.

Installation

To install, carefully position circuit to back of cluster and engage with plastic locating pins. To complete installation, reverse removal procedure.

Removal (All Vans, Except Aerostar)

Remove instrument panel. Snap off printed circuit connector buttons from IVR. Disconnect multiple feed plug and remove attaching screw, then remove IVR. Remove gauge retaining nuts, light bulbs, and printed circuit board.

Installation

To install, reverse removal procedure. Printed circuit board must be carefully positioned to back of cluster and engaged with plastic locating pins.

HEADLIGHT SWITCH

Removal & Installation (Bronco II & Ranger)

Disconnect battery negative cable. Pull headlight switch knob to "ON" position. Depress shaft release button and remove knob and shaft assembly. Remove finish panel. Unscrew mounting nut. Remove switch from under

FORD STANDARD INSTRUMENT CLUSTER (Cont.)

Fig. 2: Exploded View of Van Instrument Cluster (Except Aerostar)

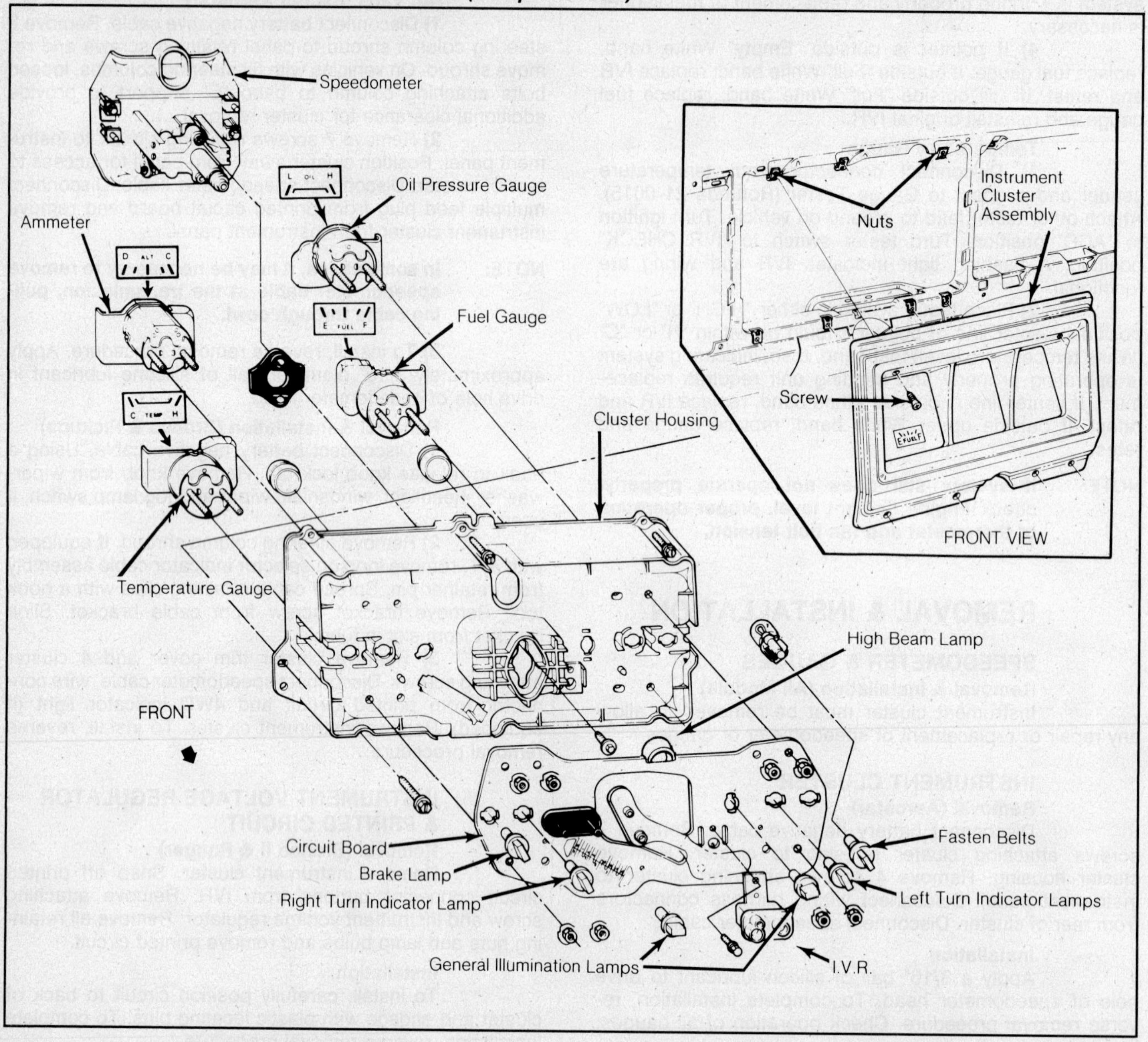

instrument panel. Remove wiring from switch. To install, reverse removal procedure.

Removal & Installation (All Other Models)

1) Disconnect battery negative cable. On Bronco and Pickups, remove wiper-washer, headlight and fog light switch knob, if used. Remove steering column shroud. Remove center finish panel. Remove switch from back side of instrument panel.

2) On Vans (except Aerostar), remove knob and shaft by pulling knob into fully "ON" position, and press knob release button on switch housing. Pull knob and shaft from switch and unscrew mounting nut. Remove bezel and switch. Remove wiring connector. To install, reverse removal procedure.

FORD STANDARD INSTRUMENT CLUSTER (Cont.)

Fig. 3: Exploded View of Bronco & Pickups Instrument Cluster (Rear View)

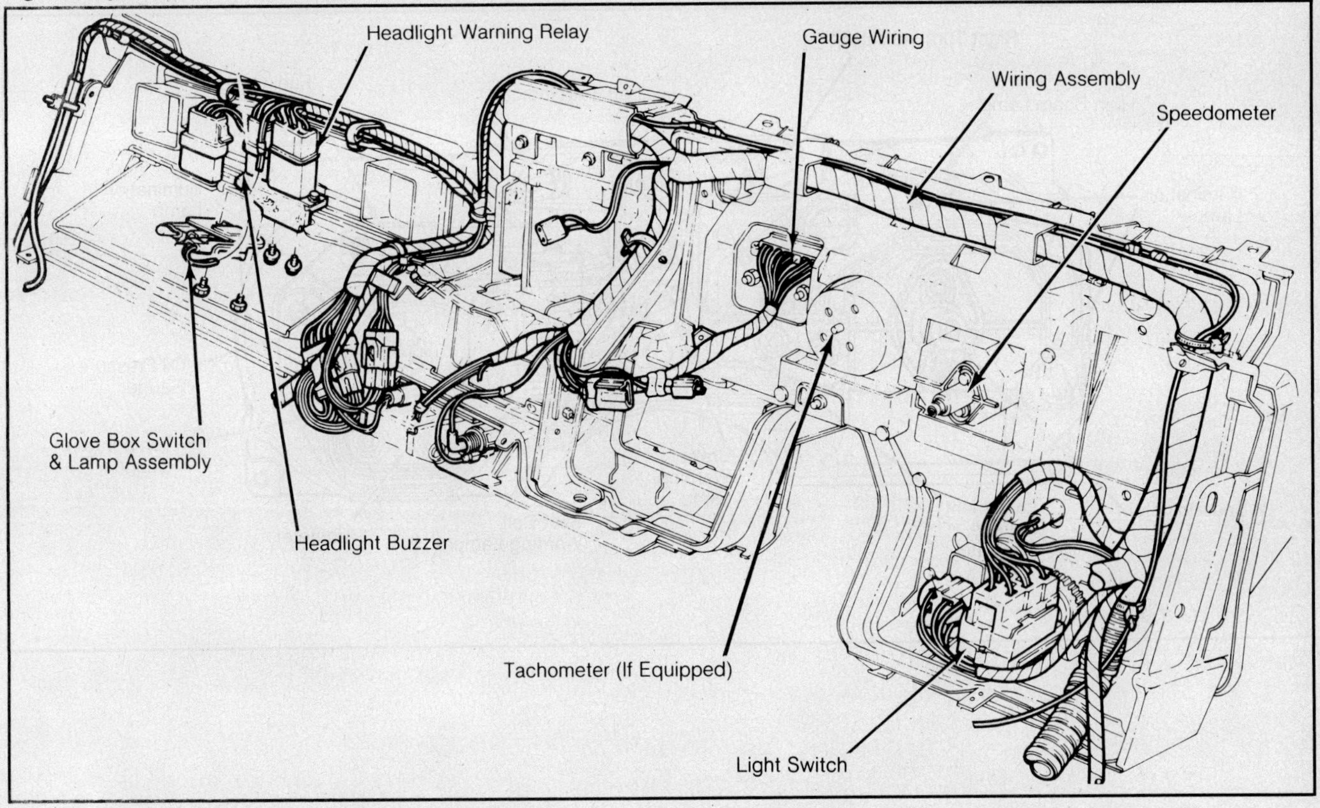

Fig. 4: Aerostar Instrument Cluster Printed Circuit

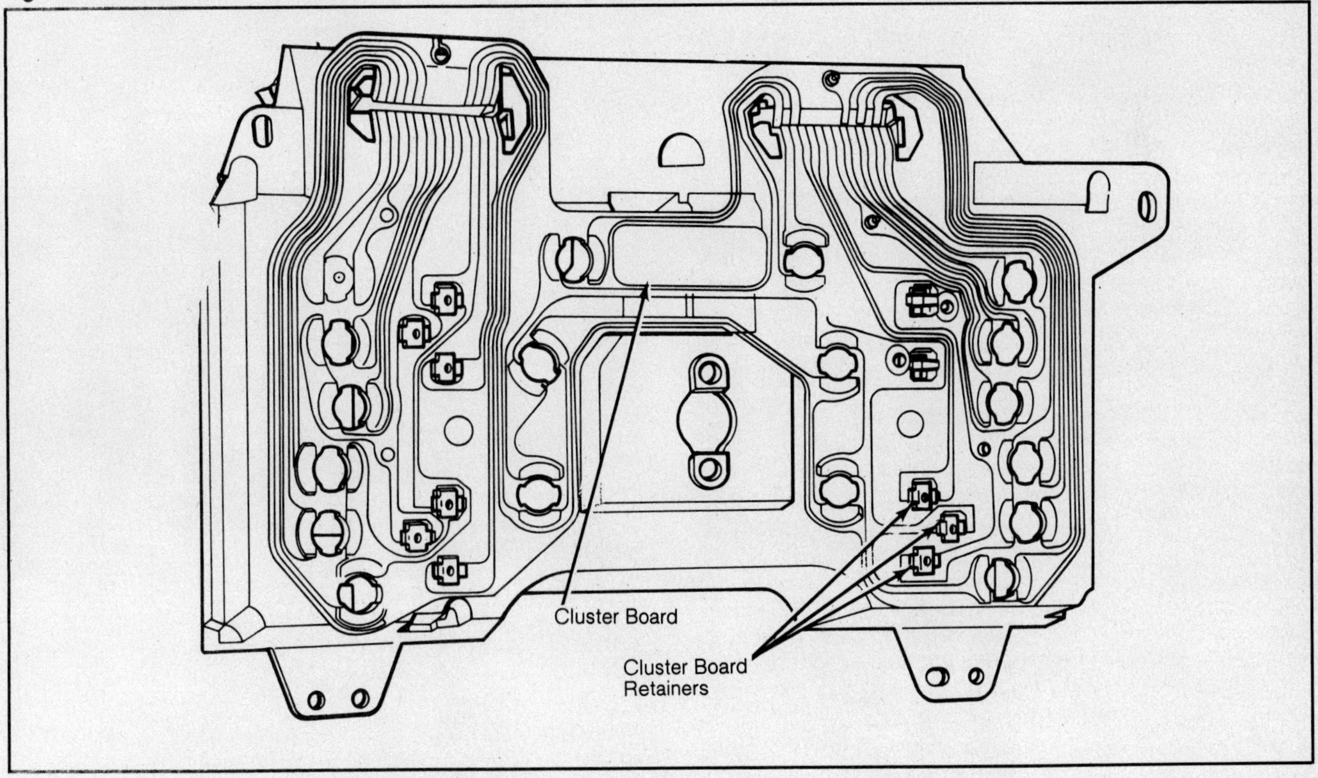

Ensure 9 cluster board retainers are in position.

FORD STANDARD INSTRUMENT CLUSTER (Cont.)

Fig. 5: Rear View of Bronco II and Ranger Instrument Cluster

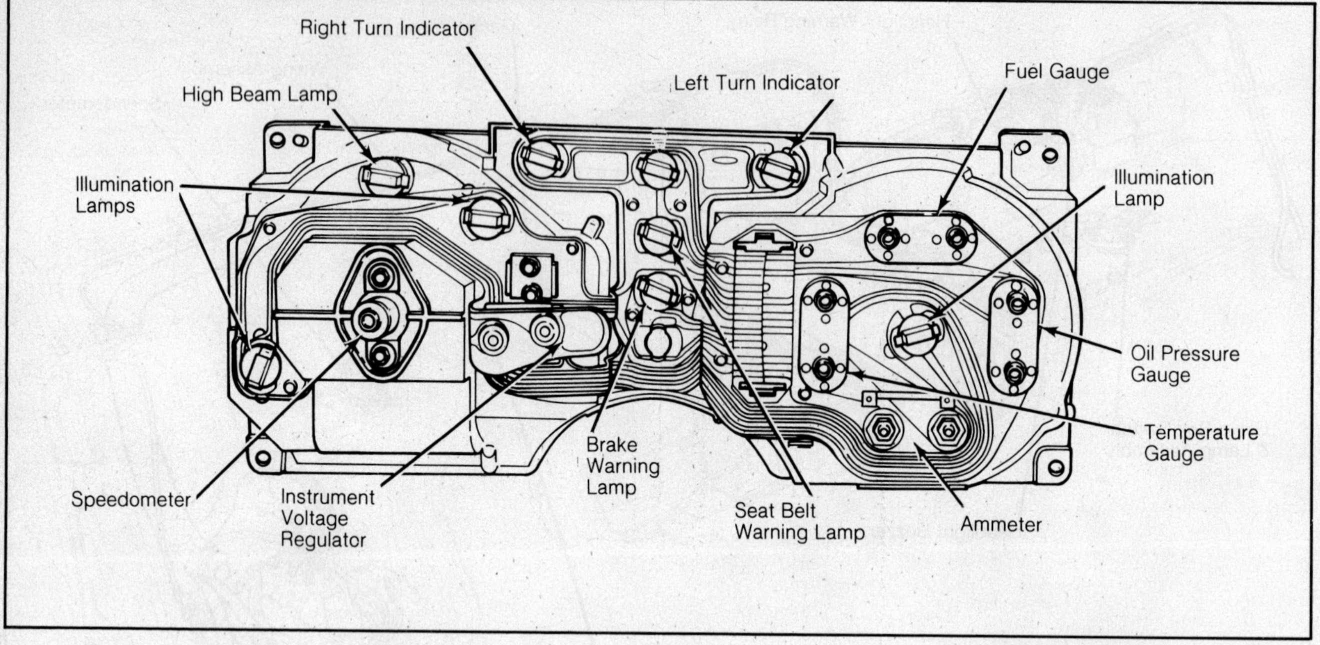

GENERAL MOTORS

NOTE: **Astro and Safari vans are "M" series vehicles.**

DESCRIPTION

All instruments and gauges are installed in instrument cluster. "C", "K" and "S" series can be serviced in vehicle. "G" and "M" series require removal of entire instrument cluster from vehicle prior to servicing. Indicator lamps and illuminating bulbs may be replaced without removing instrument cluster from vehicle on all except "M" series.

TESTING & TROUBLE SHOOTING

INDICATOR WARNING LIGHTS

Oil Pressure Indicator

1) Indicator light is inoperative with ignition switch on and engine not running. Check for burned out bulb, open light circuit or defective oil pressure switch.

2) Indicator light is on and engine is running above idle speed. Indicates low oil pressure, defective oil pressure switch or ground condition between light and switch.

Fig. 1: "G" & "M" Series Instrument Cluster

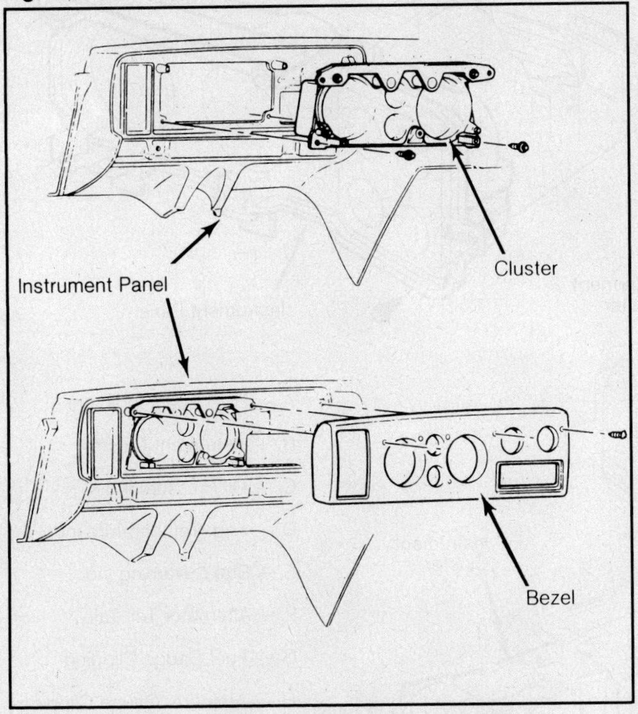

"G" series cluster is shown, "M" series is similar.

Temperature Indicator

1) If "HOT" indicator light is inoperative when cranking engine, check for burned out light bulb, open light circuit or a defective ignition switch.

2) When light is on with engine running, check for coolant temperature above 258°F (125°C), grounded condition between light and switch, defective temperature sender or ignition switch.

Charging Indicator

1) If light is on with ignition off, check for shorted positive diode. If light is not on with ignition on and engine not running, check for burned out bulb, open in light circuit or open in field.

2) If light is on with engine running above idle speed, check for no alternator output, shorted negative diode or loose or broken alternator belt.

Fig. 2: "S" Series Instrument Cluster

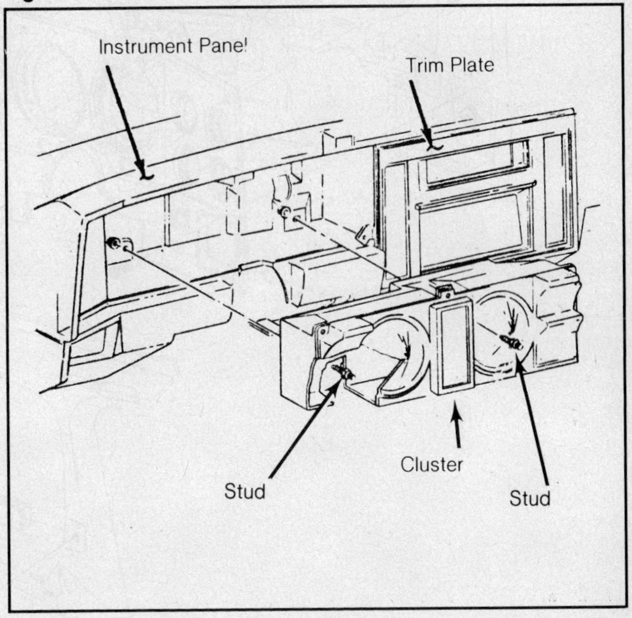

FUEL GAUGE

1) Using Gauge Tester (J 24538A). Disconnect feed wire from fuel gauge tank terminal and connect one test lead to wire and ground other lead. Turn ignition on. If gauge responds but not accurately, proceed to step **2)**. If gauge does not respond, go to step **3)**. If gauge responds accurately, go to step **5)**.

2) Remove gauge and check for loose nuts at gauge terminals. If nuts are loose and gauge reads between 1/4 and 1/2 with 90 ohms from tester, tighten nuts and install gauge. If gauge is inaccurate in other ways and/or nuts are tight, replace gauge.

3) Disconnect front body connector. Connect tester to lead that goes to gauge. If gauge responds accurately, check wiring between rear compartment and front body connector. If gauge does not respond, go to step **4)**.

4) Remove gauge. Check for bad connections at gauge terminal or instrument cluster connector. If connections are good, replace gauge. If bad, repair connections and install gauge.

5) Check rear compartment connector and wires to sender. If okay, replace sender. If not okay, repair wire or connector.

OIL PRESSURE GAUGE

1) Disconnect oil gauge sender wire and connect gauge tester to sender wire and ground. Turn ignition on. If gauge responds to tester accurately, replace sender. If gauge does not respond, go to step **2)**. If gauge responds but not accurately, go to step **4)**.

GENERAL MOTORS (Cont.)

Fig. 3: General Motors "C" & "K" Series Instrument Cluster

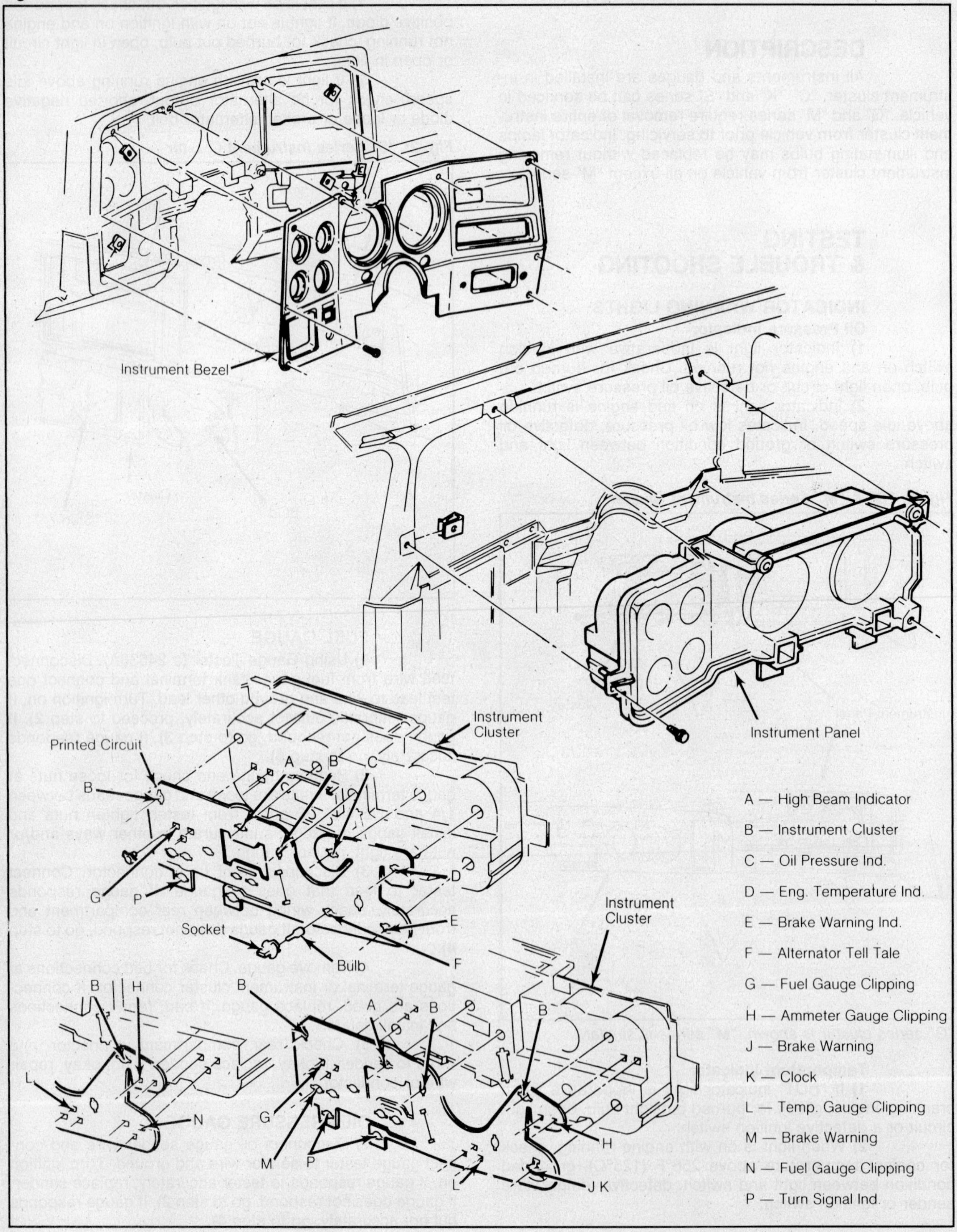

2) Disconnect oil gauge lead at engine harness connector. Connect tester to lead that goes to gauge. If gauge responds to tester accurately, check wiring between sender connector and engine harness connector. If gauge does not respond, go to step **3)**.

3) Remove gauge. Check for bad connections at gauge terminals or instrument cluster connector. If connections are good, replace gauge. If bad, repair connections and install gauge.

4) Remove gauge and check for loose nuts at gauge terminals. If nuts are loose and gauge reads slightly below midscale with 90 ohms from tester, tighten nuts and install gauge. If gauge is inaccurate in other ways and/or nuts are tight, replace gauge.

TEMPERATURE GAUGE

1) Disconnect temperature gauge sender wire and connect gauge tester between sender wire and ground. Turn ignition on. If gauge responds to tester accurately, replace sender. If gauge does not respond or is inaccurate, go to step **2)**. If gauge responds well beyond "HOT", go to step **4)**.

2) Disconnect temperature gauge lead at engine harness connector. Connect tester to lead that goes to gauge. If gauge responds to tester accurately, check wiring between sender connector and engine harness connector. If gauge does not respond, go to step **3)**.

3) Remove gauge. Check for bad connections at gauge terminals or instrument cluster connector. If connections are good, replace gauge. If bad, repair connections and install gauge.

4) Remove gauge and check for loose nuts at gauge terminals or lack of ground connection to gauge. If connections are good, replace gauge. If connections are bad, repair connections and install gauge.

AMMETER GAUGE

If gauge fails to read correctly, test charging system. See DELCO-REMY ALTERNATORS article in ELECTRICAL section.

SPEEDOMETER

1) If speedometer is noisy, check for kinked, pinched or burnt casings. Check for bent cable tips, improper or insufficient lubrication of cable, or rough drive gear.

2) If speedometer whines, driven gear stem in transmission could be binding with adapter. If calibration is incorrect, possible causes include incorrect transmission adapter, incorrect drive gear or sleeve, over or undersize tires, and faulty speedometer head.

REMOVAL & INSTALLATION

SPEEDOMETER & GAUGES

Removal & Installation (All Series)

All instruments and gauges are installed in instrument cluster. On "C", "K" and "S" series, they may be serviced in vehicle. On "G" and "M" series, entire cluster must be removed for service.

INSTRUMENT CLUSTER

Removal & Installation
("C" & "K" Series)

1) Disconnect battery negative cable, and remove headlight switch control knob and radio control knobs. Remove steering column cover, and 8 screws attaching bezel. Remove bezel.

2) Reach up under instrument panel cluster and disconnect speedometer by depressing tang on rear of speedometer head and pulling cable free.

3) Remove cluster from vehicle for further disassembly as required. To install, reverse removal procedure.

Removal & Installation ("G" Series)

1) Disconnect battery negative cable. Reach up under instrument panel cluster and disconnect speedometer cable by depressing tang while pulling cable free.

2) Remove clock set stem knob. Remove bezel attaching screws and remove bezel. Remove lower cluster attaching screws. Pull top of cluster away from instrument panel and lift out bottom of cluster. Unplug harness connector from printed circuit and remove cluster.

3) To install, reverse removal procedure. Esure that clips at top of cluster slip into instrument panel opening after bottom of cluster is installed.

Removal & Installation ("M" Series)

1) Disconnect battery negative cable. Remove steering column lower trim plate. Remove 5 screws securing instrument cluster trim plate panel. Pull panel outward, allowing it to hang to left side by wiring.

2) Remove A/C control assembly fasteners. Move control aside for easier access. Remove alarm assembly (if equipped). Remove cluster trim panel. Remove fasteners attaching cluster to instrument panel.

3) Pull cluster outward 3-4 inches and disconnect speedometer, speed sensor and all electrical connections. To install, reverse removal procedure.

Removal & Installation ("S" Series)

1) Disconnect battery negative cable. Remove 5 screws and remove instrument cluster trim plate. Remove instrument panel face plate. Remove lens and speedometer cable.

2) Disconnect electrical connector from instrument cluster and remove cluster. To install, reverse removal procedure.

PRINTED CIRCUITS

Removal & Installation (All Series)

1) Remove instrument cluster, all cluster light assemblies and printed circuit retaining screws.

2) If necessary, remove fuel, temperature and ammeter terminal nuts retaining printed circuits to rear of cluster. Remove printed circuits from rear of cluster.

3) To install, reverse removal procedure. Printed circuit retaining screws serve as ground for printed circuit. They must be properly installed to provide proper ground connection.

HEADLIGHT SWITCH

Removal & Installation
("C" & "K" Series)

1) Disconnect battery negative cable. Reach up behind instrument cluster, depress shaft retaining button and remove switch knob and rod. Remove cluster bezel screws at left end, and pull out on bezel. Hold switch nut with wrench.

GENERAL MOTORS (Cont.)

2) Disconnect multiple wiring connectors at switch terminals. To remove switch, turn while holding switch nut. To install, reverse removal procedure.

Removal & Installation ("G" Series)

1) Disconnect battery negative cable. Reach up behind instrument panel and remove switch knob and shaft by depressing retaining button. Remove switch retaining nut from front of panel and push switch through panel opening.

2) Remove multiple electrical connector at switch terminals. To install, reverse removal procedure. Ensure ground ring is installed on switch.

Removal & Installation ("S" Series)

1) Disconnect battery negative cable. Pull headlight switch out. Reach up under instrument panel and depress switch shaft retainer button while pulling on switch control shaft knob.

2) Remove 3 screws and remove switch trim plate. Use a large bladed screwdriver to remove light switch ferrule nut from front of instrument panel. Disconnect connector from bottom of light switch. To install, reverse removal procedure.

JEEP

DESCRIPTION

CHEROKEE & WAGONEER

Instrument panel is composed of speedometer housing, panel lights, high beam indicator, turn signal indicators, brake failure/parking brake warning indicator, temperature gauge, and combination fuel gauge and constant voltage regulator (CVR). Other gauges include tachometer, voltmeter and oil pressure gauge.

CJ7 & SCRAMBLER

Instrument panel is composed of speedometer housing, panel lights, high beam indicator, turn signal indicators, brake failure/parking brake warning indicator, temperature gauge, and combination fuel gauge and constant voltage regulator (CVR). Other gauges include tachometer, voltmeter and oil pressure gauge.

GRAND WAGONEER & TRUCKS

Instrument cluster is composed of speedometer housing, panel lights, high beam indicator, turn signal indicators, ammeter, oil pressure gauge, temperature and fuel gauges, constant voltage regulator (CVR), brake failure warning bulb, lock-out verification light (Quadra-Trac), emergency drive indicator, heater control lights, wiper/washer control lights, and blower motor fan switch.

OPERATION

AMMETER

Used to indicate current flow into and out of battery, depending on vehicle electrical load. It is standard equipment on all but CJ7 and Scrambler.

FUEL LEVEL GAUGE

System consists of a fuel gauge, sending unit in fuel tank, appropriate wiring and constant voltage regulator (CVR). Gauge is grounded through variable resistor of sending unit. A float attached to a slide rheostat follows fuel level and varying resistance increases or decreases indicator reading.

TEMPERATURE GAUGE

System consists of gauge and sending unit, appropriate wiring and constant voltage regulator (CVR). Gauge is grounded through variable resistor of sending unit. Changes in coolant temperature vary resistance in sending unit, increasing or decreasing indication on gauge.

VOLTMETER

Available on Cherokee, CJ7, Scrambler and Wagoneer, system consists of a voltmeter and related wiring. Voltmeter indicates regulated voltage to provide an indication of charging system's ability to maintain battery charge.

OIL PRESSURE GAUGE

Consists of magnetic-type gauge, a variable resistance sending unit and wiring on Jeep CJ7 and Scrambler. There are 2 coils in gauge, one directly grounded, other connected to sending unit. Resistance is controlled in sending unit by oil pressure. Magnetic fields are created around both coils in gauge. Needle is attracted to coil having greater current flow.

On all others, oil pressure gauge system consists of CVR-powered gauge, variable resistance sending unit, and CVR. Gauge needle, attached to bi-metal strip, responds to temperature changes. It moves as current flows from CVR through heating coil around bi-metal strip, and to ground at sending unit on engine.

CONSTANT VOLTAGE REGULATOR

On Cherokee, CJ7, Scrambler and Wagoneer, CVR is built into fuel gauge. On all others, it is built into temperature gauge. CVR provides equal regulated voltage to each gauge.

The CVR's function is to regulate variable input voltage available from vehicle battery or charging system to provide a constant 5-volt output to gauges. CVR does not produce a steady DC voltage output, but rather a pulsating voltage averaging 5 volts. Output voltage averaging lower or higher than 5 volts will result in proportionately higher or lower gauge readings.

TESTING

OIL PRESSURE GAUGE

1) To test accuracy of oil pressure gauge, use Tester (J 24538). Disconnect wire from sending unit. Connect one lead of tester to ground and other lead to sending unit wire.

2) Adjust tester to selected ohm value listed in OIL PRESSURE SENDING UNIT RESISTANCES table. Compare results with specifications shown in table.

OIL PRESSURE SENDING UNIT RESISTANCES

Application	psi	Ohms
CJ7 & Scrambler	0	234-246
	20	149-157
	40	100-106
	60	65-69
	80	32-35
Grand Wagoneer & Trucks	0	69-77
	10	35-38
	60	13-15
	80	9-11

OIL PRESSURE GAUGE RESISTANCES

Application	psi	Ohms
Cherokee & Wagoneer	0	1
	40	46
	80	87

FUEL GAUGES

1) To test accuracy of fuel gauge, use Tester (J 24538). Disconnect wire from sending unit. Connect one lead of tester to ground and other lead to sending unit wire. Compare results with specifications shown in FUEL GAUGE SENDING UNIT RESISTANCES table.

2) If within specifications, measure resistance across terminal test points on fuel gauge, as listed in FUEL GAUGE SENDING UNIT RESISTANCES (INTERNAL) table. Compare results with specifications shown in table.

JEEP (Cont.)

FUEL GAUGE SENDING UNIT RESISTANCES

Application	Indication	Ohms
CJ7 & Scrambler	Empty	73
	1/2 Full	23
	Full	10
Grand Wagoneer & Trucks	Empty	61
	1/2 Full	23
	Full	10

FUEL GAUGE RESISTANCES (INTERNAL)

Application	Test Points	Ohms
CJ7 & Scrambler	"S" to Ground	68-72
	"S" to "I"	19-21
	"S" to "A"	19-21
	"I" to "A"	0
	"I" to Ground	49-51
	"A" to Ground	49-51
Cherokee & Wagoneer	Empty	1
	1/2 Full	44
	Full	88
Grand Wagoneer & Trucks	"S" to "A"	19-21

TEMPERATURE GAUGES

1) To test accuracy of temperature gauge, use Tester (J 24538). Disconnect wire from sending unit. Connect one lead of tester to ground and other lead to sending unit wire. Compare results with specifications shown in TEMPERATURE SENDING UNIT RESISTANCES table.

2) If within specifications, measure resistance across terminal test points on temperature gauge. See FUEL GAUGE RESISTANCES (INTERNAL) table.

TEMPERATURE SENDING UNIT RESISTANCES

Application	Needle Position	Ohms
CJ7, Grand Wagoneer, Scrambler & Trucks	"C"	73
	Start of Band	36
	End of Band	13
	"H"	9

TEMPERATURE GAUGE RESISTANCES (INTERNAL)

Application	Test Points	Ohms
Cherokee & Wagoneer	100°	1365
	220°	94
	260°	55
CJ7 & Scrambler	"S" to "A"	19-21
Grand Wagoneer & Trucks	"S" to Ground	68-72
	"S" to "I"	19-21
	"S" to "A"	19-21
	"I" to "A"	0
	"I" to Ground	49-51
	"A" to Ground	49-51

Fig. 1: Testing Temperature Gauge

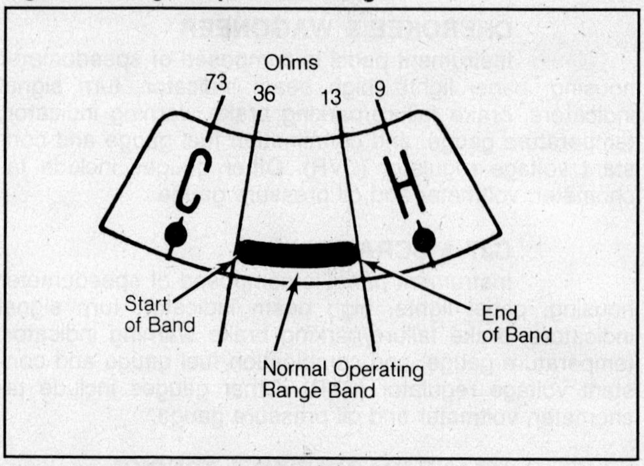

When known resistance is sent to gauge, needle should move to position on chart.

VOLTMETER

Connect voltmeter of known accuracy across battery terminals. Turn ignition switch on, and compare indication of test voltmeter with indication of vehicle voltmeter. Replace if readings vary.

REMOVAL & INSTALLATION

SPEEDOMETER & GAUGES

Instrument panel must be removed to gain access to speedometer and gauges for repair or replacement.

INSTRUMENT CLUSTER

Removal & Installation (Cherokee & Wagoneer)

1) Disconnect battery negative cable. Remove 4 instrument panel bezel attaching screws and remove bezel. Remove cigarette lighter housing attaching screws. Remove switch housing attaching screws.

2) Remove instrument cluster attaching screws. Disconnect speedometer cable. Pull out cluster and disconnect multiple plugs. Remove instrument cluster. To install, reverse removal procedure.

Removal & Installation (CJ7 & Scrambler)

Disconnect battery negative cable. Separate speedometer cable from speedometer head. Remove attaching screws and remove cluster. Note position of all lamps and electrical wires. Remove cluster electrical connectors. To install, reverse removal procedure.

Removal (Grand Wagoneer & Trucks)

1) Disconnect battery negative cable. Remove cluster retaining screws. Disconnect speedometer cable. Disconnect cluster terminal pin plug by pulling it straight off. Disconnect 4-terminal connector. Mark ammeter wires for installation reference and disconnect ammeter.

2) Disconnect blower motor wire connector. Tag hoses from heater control according to their numbered location and disconnect from heater control. Remove heater control panel lamps. Disconnect heater temperature control wire from lever. Remove cluster assembly.

Installation

To install, reverse removal procedure. Install ammeter wires in original locations, and ensure that nuts are tight.

Fig. 2: Jeep Instrument Cluster

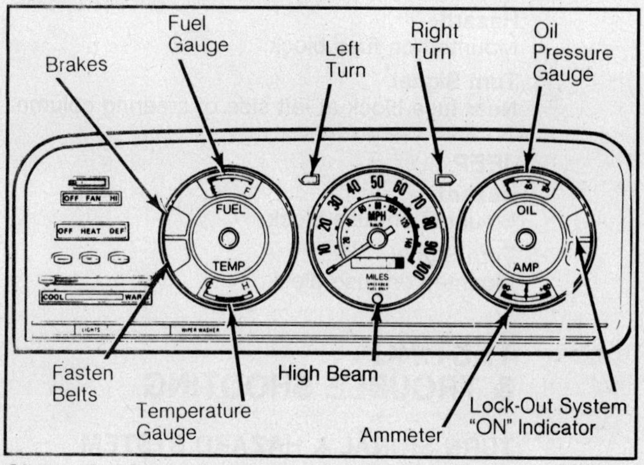

Cluster for Grand Wagoneer and Trucks shown.

PRINTED CIRCUITS

NOTE: CJ7 and Scrambler use direct wiring for all gauges and cluster lamps.

Removal & Installation (Cherokee & Wagoneer)

1) Remove instrument cluster lens and bezel cover. Remove all gauges and tachometer, if used. Remove gauge pin connector clips from cluster housing. Remove lamp sockets from circuit board.

2) Remove circuit board ground clip at back of speedometer housing. Remove printed circuit board. To install, reverse removal procedure.

Fig. 3: Rear View of Jeep Instrument Cluster

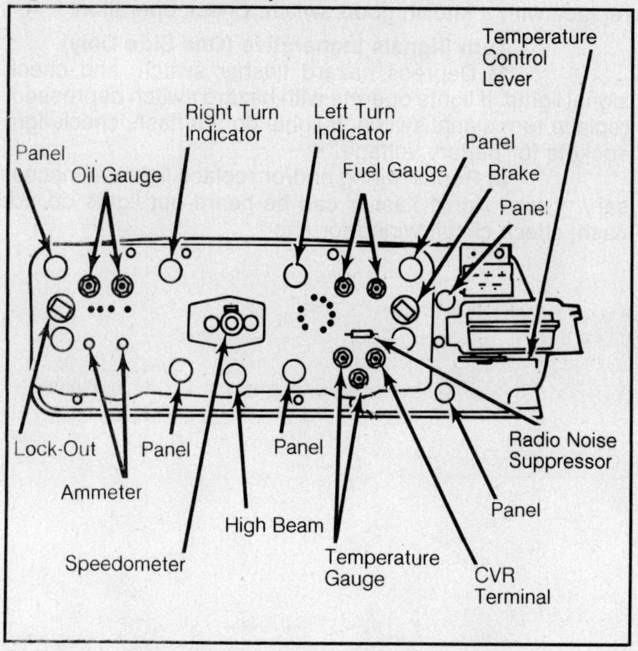

Cluster for Grand Wagoneer and Trucks shown.

Removal & Installation (Grand Wagoneer & Trucks)

1) Remove instrument cluster, radio noise suppressor, and all lamps from cluster. Remove circuit board and gauge assembly. Remove retaining nuts from ammeter and oil pressure gauge. Lift ammeter, oil pressure gauge and plate out of cluster as an assembly.

2) Remove retaining nuts from fuel and temperature gauges. Remove large ground screw from circuit board above speedometer. Remove speedometer, fuel gauge and temperature gauge as an assembly. To install, reverse removal procedure. Ensure that ammeter nuts are tight.

CONSTANT VOLTAGE REGULATOR

Removal & Installation

CVR is an integral part of fuel gauge on CJ7 and Scrambler. It is an integral part of temperature gauge on all others. If regulator requires replacement, entire gauge must be replaced.

HEADLIGHT SWITCH

Removal & Installation (Cherokee & Scrambler)

Disconnect battery negative cable. Pull control knob to full "ON" position. Reach up under instrument panel, depress knob release button and pull knob out of switch. Remove retaining nut. Disconnect wiring harness and remove switch. To install, reverse removal procedure.

Removal & Installation (All Others)

Disconnect connector plug from switch. Pull control knob to second position. From behind instrument panel, depress knob release button and pull knob out of switch. Remove retaining nut and bezel. Remove switch through rear of instrument panel. To install, reverse removal procedure.

Fig. 4: Jeep Headlight Switch & Harness Connector

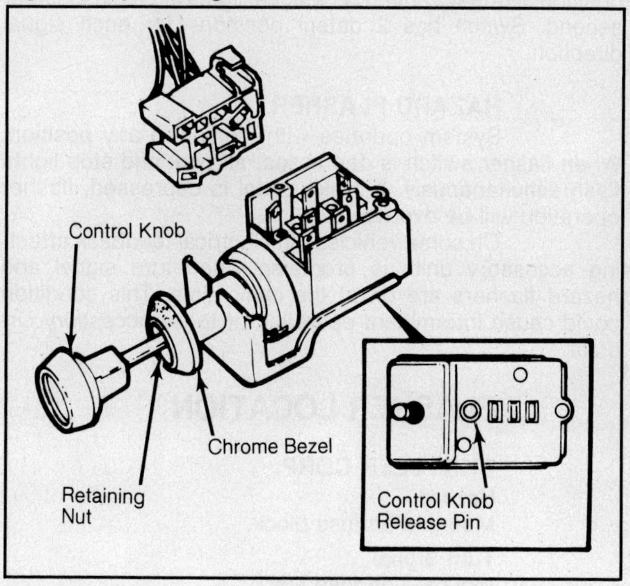

Remove switch through rear of instrument panel.

Turn Signal & Hazard Flasher Systems

ALL MANUFACTURERS

DESCRIPTION

Turn signal and hazard flasher systems are integral and use a common switch assembly mounted within upper steering column housing. For wiring diagrams of individual models, see appropriate article in WIRING DIAGRAM section.

Two flasher units are used. The hazard flasher is a variable load type and will operate regardless of number of lights burned out. If one signal light is burned out, signal circuit will not function on that side due to insufficient current draw to operate flasher.

Fig. 1: Typical Wiring Diagram of Turn Signal and Hazard Flasher System

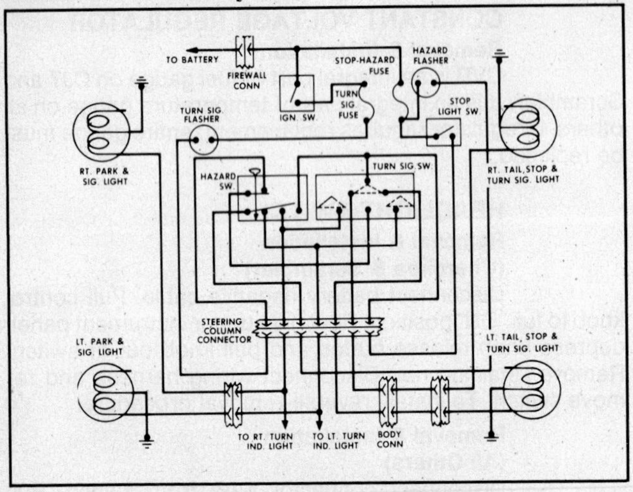

OPERATION

TURN SIGNALS

System operates only when ignition is in "ON" position. Normal frequency of signal lights is 1-2 flashes per second. Switch has 2 detent positions for each signal direction.

HAZARD FLASHER

System operates with ignition in any position. When flasher switch is depressed, all park and stop lights flash simultaneously. If brake pedal is depressed, flasher operation will be overriden.

On some vehicles, an electrical feedback affecting accessory units is produced when turn signal and hazard flashers are on at the same time. This condition could cause intermittent operation of these accessory circuits.

FLASHER LOCATION

CHRYSLER CORP.

Hazard
Mounted on fuse block.

Turn Signal
Mounted on fuse block.

FORD

Turn Signal
On fuse block under steering column.

Hazard
On rear side of fuse panel on all except "E" series. In wiring harness near left side cowl on "E" series.

GENERAL MOTORS

Hazard
Mounted on fuse block.

Turn Signal
Near fuse block at left side of steering column.

JEEP

Hazard
Mounted on fuse block.

Turn Signal
Mounted on fuse block.

TESTING & TROUBLE SHOOTING

TURN SIGNAL & HAZARD SYSTEM

Hazard Flasher Inoperative

1) Check turn signal operation. If operation is okay, check hazard circuit fuse. If fuse is defective, check for short in hazard circuit. If fuse is okay, check for battery voltage to hazard flasher. Replace flasher if necessary.

2) If system is still inoperative, check for battery voltage to hazard switch in steering column. Repair circuit between flasher and switch if necessary. To check switch, unplug at column connector and replace with a known good switch. Check operation.

Turn Signals Inoperative

1) Check hazard flasher operation. If all lights flash, check turn signal system fuse and flasher. If fuse is defective, check for shorts between fuse and signal lights.

2) If fuse and flasher are okay, check for continuity in switch wiring and battery voltage to and from switch. To check switch, unplug at column connector and replace with a known good switch. Check operation.

Turn Signals Inoperative (One Side Only)

1) Depress hazard flasher switch, and check signal lights. If lights operate with hazard switch depressed, replace turn signal switch. If lights do not flash, check light sockets for battery voltage.

2) Repair wiring and/or replace lights as necessary. If turn signal flasher can be heard but lights do not flash, check circuit wiring for short.

DESCRIPTION

Standard 2-speed and intermittent wiper motors have permanent magnetic fields and are controlled by feeding power to different brushes for low and high speed. Motor speed is selected by rotating switch knob.

Some FWD vehicles are equipped with rear wiper/washer systems. A 6 amp circuit breaker is integral with wiper switch in protecting wiper system on RWD vehicles.

Washer system is electrically operated and consists of an electric pump, sealed motor, reservoir, rubber hoses and nozzles.

NOTE: **All motors are essentially the same. The intermittent wiper system utilizes a delay mode, a faster wipe speed, and an extra wipe feature. Delay mode is 2-15 seconds. The extra wipe is after wash cycle has ended.**

TROUBLE SHOOTING

WINDSHIELD WIPER SYSTEM

Wiper Inoperative

Binding linkage. Faulty wiper switch. Open or grounded wiring. Faulty motor.

Motor Runs But Output Crank Does Not Turn

Stripped intermediate gear or output gear. Output gear slips on output shaft. Crank arm not fastened properly to output gear shaft.

Motor Does Not Shut Off

Defective park switch.

Blades Will Not Park

Motor park switch open. Faulty instrument panel switch. Arm set at incorrect position. Open park wiring circuit.

Motor Will Not Run, Circuit Breaker Does Not Cycle

Open circuit in wiring. Loose bulkhead connector. Motor not grounded. Faulty circuit breaker, instrument panel switch or motor.

Motor Will Not Run, Circuit Breaker Cycles

Grounded wiring. Binding linkage. Faulty motor or instrument panel switch circuit breaker.

Motor Stops In Any Position When Switch Is Turned Off

Motor park switch open. Open park wiring circuit. Faulty instrument panel switch.

Motor Will Not Stop When Switch Is Turned Off

Defective park switch.

WASHER SYSTEM

Pump Runs But No Fluid Comes Out

No fluid in reservoir. Nozzle jet plugged or under intake grille. Broken hose or faulty pump.

System Operates Intermittently

Loose or faulty wiring connections. Faulty switch or motor.

System Output Low

Low aimed nozzles. Pinched or leaking hoses. Poor electrical connections. Defective motor.

Pump Motor Does Not Run

Broken wires. Faulty motor or switch. Poor ground. Loose wiring terminals.

TESTING

REAR WIPER MOTOR

FWD Models Only

1) Disconnect feed wire connector from wiper motor. With ignition on, check for battery voltage at Blue wire. With ignition on and rear wiper switch on, check for battery voltage at Blue and Brown wires.

2) If battery voltage is not present, check fuse, rear wiper switch and wiring. If battery voltage is present, replace rear wiper motor.

WINDSHIELD WIPER MOTOR WILL NOT RUN

1) Check for blown fuse. If new fuse blows, disconnect motor wiring connector and replace fuse. If fuse does not blow, motor is defective and should be repaired. If fuse blows, switch or wiring is at fault.

2) Position panel switch in low-speed position. If motor can be heard running, check motor output shaft. If shaft is not turning, gearbox assembly requires replacement.

3) If shaft is turning, check drive link to output shaft for worn parts or disconnected components. If motor cannot be heard running, connect a voltmeter or test lamp between motor terminal "L" and ground.

4) If voltage is present and panel switch circuit breaker is not cycling on RWD vehicles, check for open ground circuit. Ensure ground strap is making good contact, and that motor mounting is free of paint and nuts are tight.

5) Common brushes may not be making good contact with commutator and may require freeing-up or repositioning of spring. Armature may have an open circuit.

6) If no voltage is present, check wiring and switch in FWD vehicles. If voltage is present only part-time in RWD vehicles, circuit breaker is cycling. Problem may be a faulty circuit breaker or a short in wiring, motor, or switch panel.

7) Remove wiper arms and blades, disconnect harness at motor and connect an ammeter between battery and terminal "L". If motor runs with average ammeter reading below 6 amps, motor is okay. Correct problem in switch panel or wiring.

8) If motor does not run and draw is more than 6 amps, check wiper linkage for binding. Disconnect drive link from motor. If motor runs and draws less than 3 amps, repair linkage.

9) If motor fails to run or draws more than 3 amps, check motor and gearbox for internal jamming. If no internal jamming exists, check motor for brush leads shorting to housing or armature for burned or blackened windings which could indicate an internal short.

WINDSHIELD WIPER MOTOR RUNS IN LOW SPEED ONLY

Position switch in high position and connect test lamp between terminal "H" and ground. If lamp does not light, an open exists in wiring or switch. If lamp lights, brush is not making contact with armature.

Wiper/Washer Systems

CHRYSLER CORP. (Cont.)

Fig. 1: Two-Speed Intermittent Wiper Motor Terminals

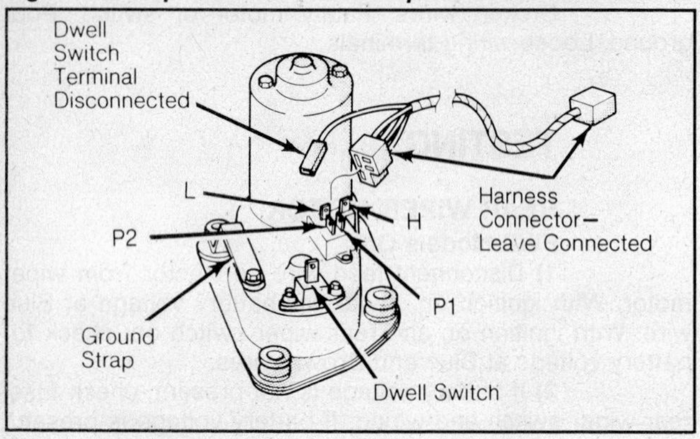

Standard terminal motor is similar.

WINDSHIELD WIPER MOTOR RUNS IN HIGH SPEED ONLY

Position switch in low position and connect test lamp between terminal "L" and ground. If lamp does not light, an open exists in wiring or switch. If lamp lights at terminal "L", brush is not making contact with armature.

MOTOR CONTINUES TO RUN WITH SWITCH IN OFF OR PARK POSITION

Remove wiring harness and connect a jumper wire from terminal "P2" to terminal "L", then connect a jumper from "P1" to battery. If motor now runs to park position and stops, panel switch is defective. If motor continues to run and does not park, gearbox assembly requires replacement.

MOTOR WILL NOT STOP IN PARK POSITION WHEN SWITCH IS IN OFF POSITION

1) Remove wiring connector and clean terminals. If problem continues, place switch in park position and connect a voltmeter or test lamp between terminal "P1" and "L". If 12 volts are present or test lamp lights, check for voltage at "P2".

2) If voltage at "P2" is zero or test lamp does not light, motor park switch is defective and gearbox assembly must be replaced. If 12 volts are present or lamp lights, an open exists in panel switch or wiring.

WINDSHIELD WIPER 2-SPEED WIPER SWITCH

1) Disconnect wiring from switch and remove switch from instrument panel. Use a continuity tester or ohmmeter to check for continuity between contact terminals of switch. SEE SWITCH CONTINUITY table.

SWITCH CONTINUITY

Off	Low	High
[1]B to B/U	B to B/U	B to B/U
B to P1	B to P1	B to P1
A to P2	B to A	B to H
H-Open	P2-Open	P2-Open
	H-Open	A-Open

[1] – B to W (Wash) on FWD.

2) For test purposes, first position is "OFF", "LOW" is first detent from "OFF" position and "HIGH" is second detent from "OFF" position. Ground is formed by case of wiper switch.

Fig. 2: Chrysler 2-Speed Wiper Wiring Diagram

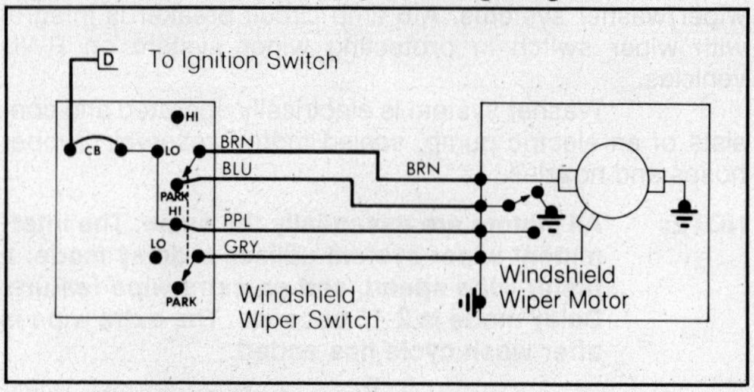

RWD wiring diagram is shown.

WINDSHIELD WIPER INTERMITTENT SWITCH

1) Disconnect wiring from switch and remove switch from instrument panel. Use a continuity tester or ohmmeter to check for continuity between contact terminals of switch. For test purposes, first position is "OFF", next is slide for "DELAY WIPE", "LOW" is first detent and "HIGH" is second detent.

2) Ensure case of wiper switch is grounded. Resistance at maximum delay position should be between 270,000 ohms and 330,000 ohms, for both FWD and RWD vehicles. Resistance at minimum delay position should be zero with ohmmeter set on high scale.

3) Positive lead of ohmmeter connected to "P2" and negative lead connected to "G" should show low resistance, on RWD vehicles. See Fig. 4. Negative lead of ohmmeter connected to "P2" and positive connected to "G" should show an open circuit or very high resistance, on RWD vehicles.

4) If there is the same resistance in both minimum and maximum delay positions, switch is defective.

INTERMITTENT SWITCH CONTINUITY (FWD)

Off	Delay	Low	High
B to P1	B to P1	B to P1	B to P1
A to P2	B to I_1	B to A	B to H
	R to I_1		
	I_2 to G		

INTERMITTENT SWITCH CONTINUITY (RWD)

Off	Delay	Low	High
B-P1	B-I_1	B-A	B-A
A-G	[1] R-I_1	P2-G	[2] P2-G
	P2-G		H-G

[1] – Through variable resistor I_1.
[2] – Through diode G, and ohmmeter on high scale.

CHRYSLER CORP. (Cont.)

Fig. 3: Chrysler Corp. Wiper Motor Exploded View

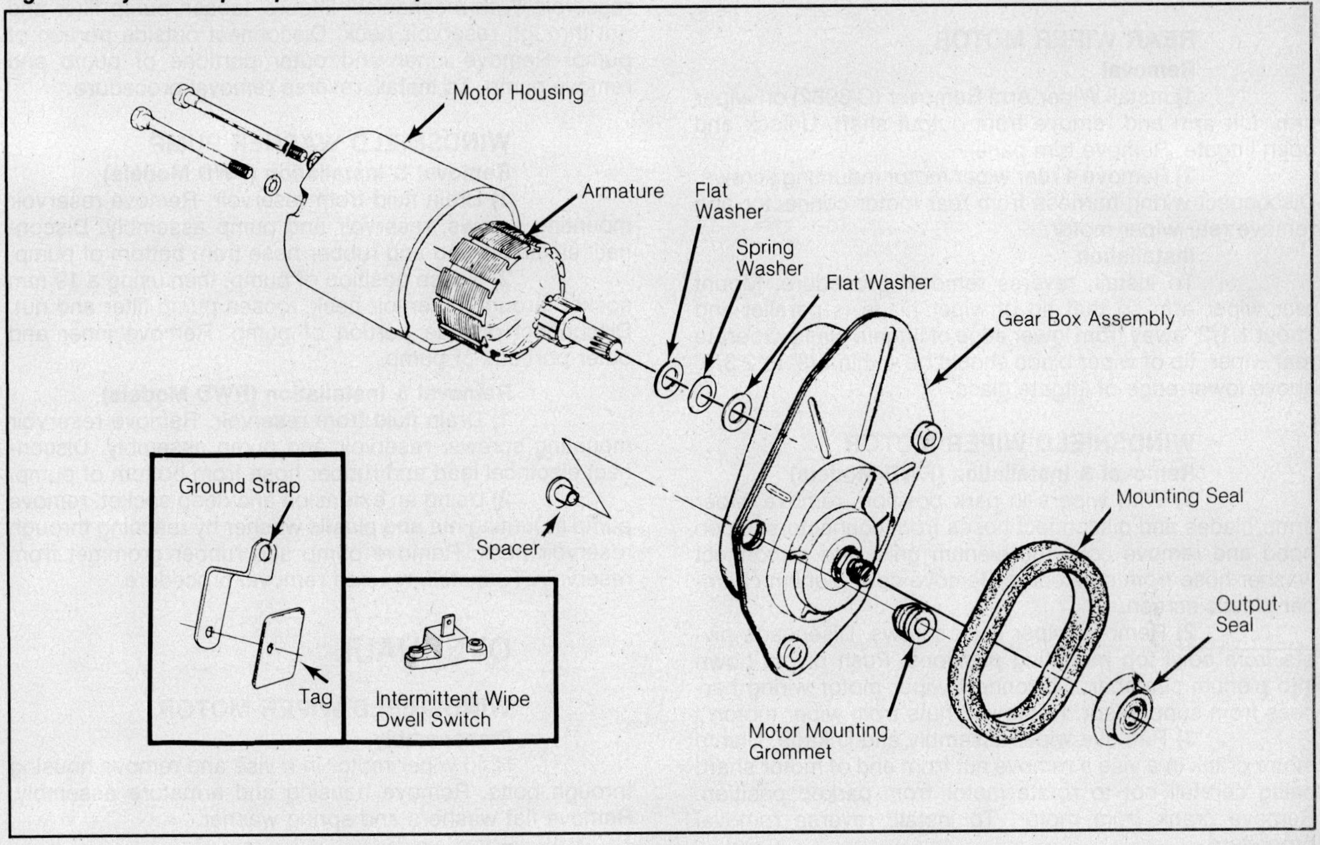

Fig. 4: Chrysler Intermittent Wiper Diagram (RWD Models Shown; FWD Models Similar)

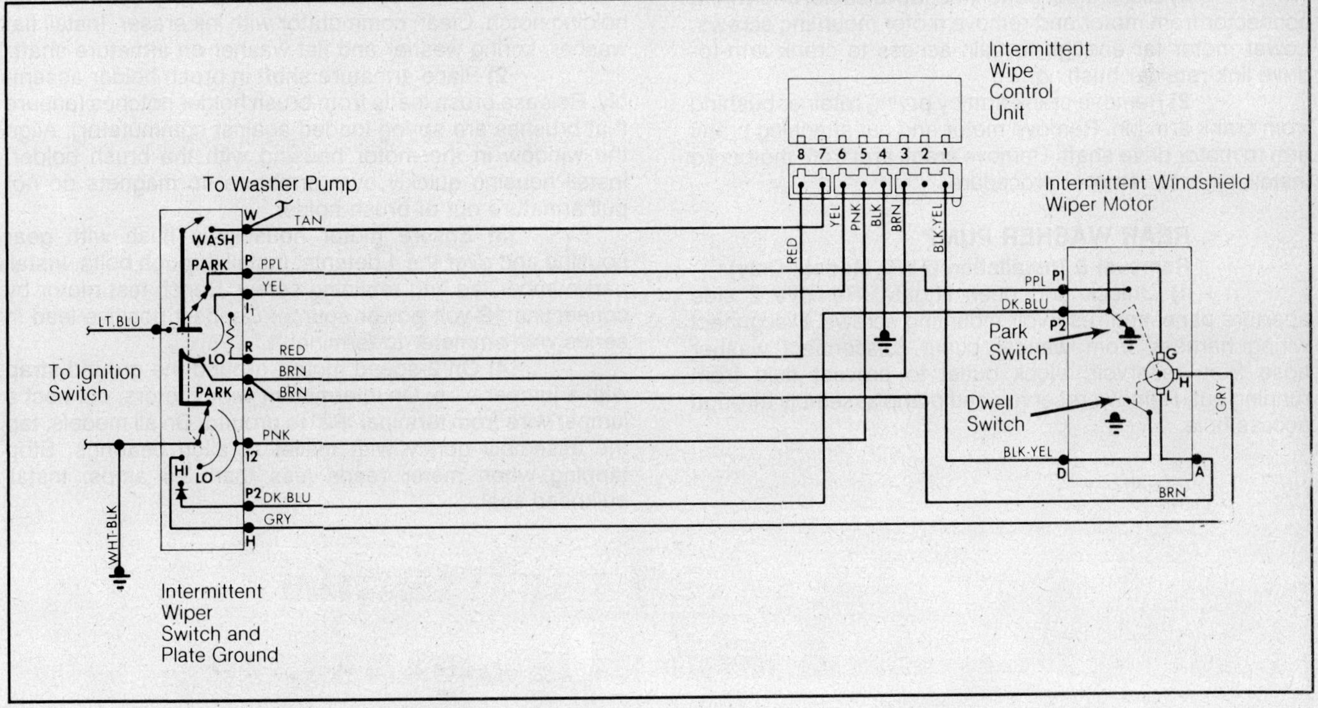

Also see chassis wiring in WIRING DIAGRAM section.

REMOVAL & INSTALLATION

REAR WIPER MOTOR

Removal

1) Install Wiper Arm Remover (C 3982) on wiper arm. Lift arm and remove from output shaft. Unlock and open liftgate. Remove trim panel.

2) Remove 4 rear wiper motor mounting screws. Disconnect wiring harness from rear motor connector and remove rear wiper motor.

Installation

To install, reverse removal procedure. Mount rear wiper arm so that tip of wiper blade is parallel and about 1 1/2" away from lower edge of liftgate glass. Operate rear wiper, tip of wiper blade should be within 7/8" to 2 3/8" above lower edge of liftgate glass.

WINDSHIELD WIPER MOTOR

Removal & Installation (FWD Models)

1) With wipers in park position, remove wiper arms/blades and disconnect hoses from connectors. Open hood and remove cowl top plenum grille and disconnect washer hose from connector. Remove cowl plenum chamber plastic screen.

2) Remove wiper pivot screws. Disengage pivots from cowl top mounting positions. Push pivots down into plenum chamber. Disconnect wiper motor wiring harness from suppressor. Remove 3 nuts from wiper motor.

3) Remove wiper assembly and linkage. Clamp motor crank in a vise a remove nut from end of motor shaft, being carefull not to rotate motor from parked position. Remove crank from motor. To install, reverse removal procedure.

Removal & Installation (RWD Models)

1) Disconnect battery negative cable, and wiring connector from motor and remove motor mounting screws. Lower motor far enough to gain access to crank arm-to-drive link retainer bushing.

2) Remove crank arm by prying retainer bushing from crank arm pin. Remove motor and nut attaching crank arm to motor drive shaft. Remove crank arm from motor. To install, reverse removal procedure.

REAR WASHER PUMP

Removal & Installation (FWD Models Only)

1) Unlock and open liftgate. Remove 2 side aperture panel and reservoir mounting screws. Disconnect wiring harness from washer pump. Disconnect washer hose from reservoir, block outlet to prevent fluid from running out. Remove reservoir and pump assembly through access hole.

2) Work filler tube off reservoir and empty reservoir. With mechanical fingers, loosen pump filter and nut through reservoir neck. Disconnect outside portion of pump. Remove inner and outer portions of pump and remove pump. To install, reverse removal procedure.

WINDSHIELD WASHER PUMP

Removal & Installation (FWD Models)

1) Drain fluid from reservoir. Remove reservoir mounting screws, reservoir and pump assembly. Disconnect electrical lead and rubber hose from bottom of pump.

2) Notice position of pump, then using a 19 mm socket through reservoir neck, loosen pump filter and nut. Disconnect outside portion of pump. Remove inner and outer portions of pump.

Removal & Installation (RWD Models)

1) Drain fluid from reservoir. Remove reservoir mounting screws, reservoir and pump assembly. Disconnect electrical lead and rubber hose from bottom of pump.

2) Using an extension and deep socket, remove pump mounting nut and plastic washer by reaching through reservoir neck. Remove pump and rubber grommet from reservoir. To install, reverse removal procedure.

OVERHAUL

WINDSHIELD WIPER MOTOR

Disassembly

Hold wiper motor in a vise and remove housing through bolts. Remove housing and armature assembly. Remove flat washers and spring washer.

Reassembly

1) Hold gear box in vise with brush holder up. Pull brushes back in brush slots and push brush lead into holding notch. Clean commutator with ink eraser. Install flat washer, spring washer and flat washer on armature shaft.

2) Place armature shaft in brush holder assembly. Release brush leads from brush holder notches (ensure that brushes are spring loaded against commutator). Align the window in the motor housing with the brush holder. Install housing quickly over armature so magnets do not pull armature out of brush holder.

3) Ensure motor housing is flush with gear housing and over the 4 detents. Install through bolts. Install part number tag and retaining screw. Bench test motor by connecting 12-volt power source. Connect positive lead in series with ammeter to terminal "L".

4) On 2-speed motor, ground the ground strap with a jumper wire. On intermittent wipe motors, connect a jumper wire from terminal "P2" to ground. On all models, tap the assembly gently with mallet to align bearings. Stop tapping when meter reads less than 2.5 amps. Install bulkhead seal.

Wiper/Washer Systems

FORD – AEROSTAR, BRONCO II & RANGER

DESCRIPTION

Windshield wipers are actuated by a permanent magnet, rotary-type electric motor. The 2 wiper arms and blades are mounted on pivot shafts at each side of windshield.

Pivot shafts are connected to motor by linkage arms and attaching clips. Both standard and interval wiper/washer systems feature a lever-type wiper/washer switch mounted on steering column.

The Bronco II rear window wiper system consists of a motor mounted inside liftgate, an articulating arm and blade assembly, an instrument panel mounted control switch, and an in-line circuit breaker.

OPERATION

STANDARD SYSTEM

Switch has "OFF", "LOW" and "HI" positions. Switch must be in "LOW" or "HI" to operate washer.

INTERMITTENT SYSTEM

"LOW" and "HI" speed operation is same as standard wiper system. When wiper switch is in "INTERVAL" position, wipers make single swipes separated by a pause. The control knob on end of wiper control switch sets length of pause from 1 to 12 seconds.

To operate washer, pull control lever out. If lever is in "LOW" or "HI" position, washers operate with no change in wiper operation. If wiper control switch is in "OFF" or "INTERVAL" position, wipers will run as long as lever is pulled. When lever is released, washers will stop immediately but wipers will operate 1 to 4 cycles and then return to "OFF" or "INTERVAL" operation.

TESTING

WIPER MOTOR CURRENT DRAW

1) Disconnect battery negative cable. Disconnect linkage from motor and disconnect electrical plug to test motor on vehicle. Connect negative lead from ammeter to battery positive post.

2) Connect positive lead first to low speed connection and then to high speed connection at connector plug. *See Fig. 1.* In either case, current draw should not exceed 3 amps.

CIRCUIT BREAKER

1) Before connecting circuit breaker to volt-amp tester, short leads together and adjust current draw until it equals circuit breaker rating. Connect breaker to ammeter. Leave breaker connected to tester for 10 minutes. Hold current reading on ammeter at rated current. If circuit breaker opens during 10 minutes, replace circuit breaker.

2) Short tester leads together and adjust current draw until it is twice rated current. Connect breaker. Hold current reading on ammeter at twice rated current. Circuit breaker should open and current drop to zero within 30 seconds.

Fig. 1: Motor Current Draw Test

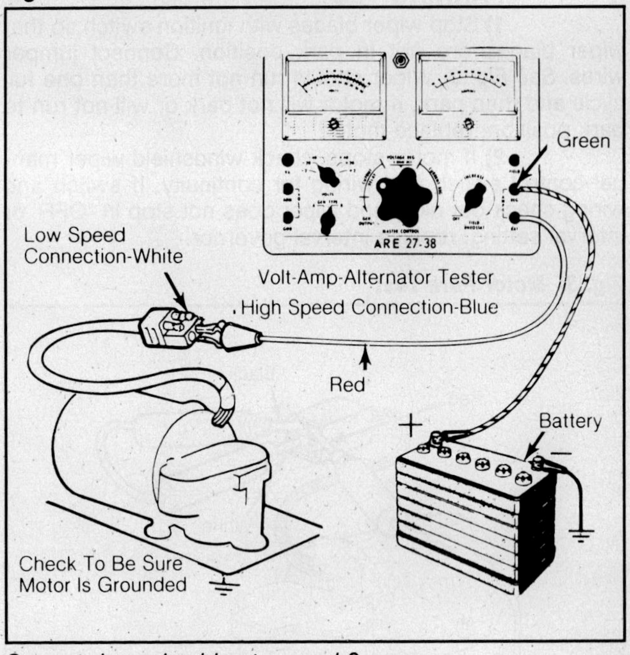

Current draw should not exceed 3 amps.

SWITCH CONTINUITY

1) Check continuity between switch terminals. *See Fig. 2.* Either a self-powered test light or an ohmmeter can be used with standard system. An ohmmeter must be used with interval system.

2) To detect marginal operation of switch, move switch lever while each reading is taken. If switch does not exibit continuity or exibits poor continuity in any switch position, replace switch.

WIPER SWITCH CONTINUITY

Switch Position	Standard Switch	Interval Switch
"OFF"	[1] P-L	
"LOW"	B-L	B-L
"HIGH"	B-H	[2] B-H-L
"WASH"	B-W	B-W
"INTERVAL"		B-I

[1] – No continuity between terminals P and L.
[2] – No continuity between terminals H and L.

Fig. 2: Wiper Switch Connector Terminals

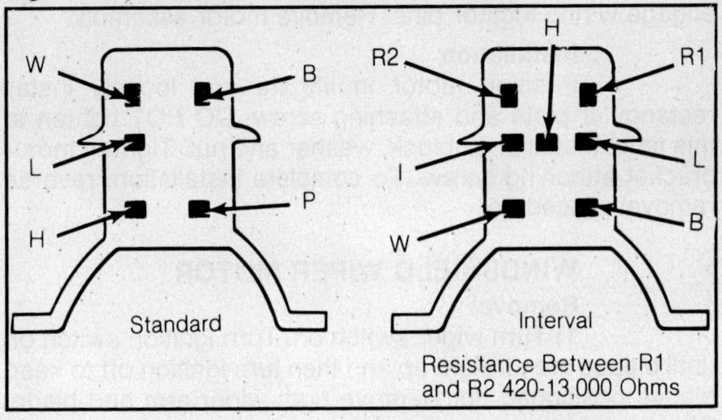

FORD – AEROSTAR, BRONCO II & RANGER (Cont.)

PARKING TEST

1) Stop wiper blades with ignition switch so that wiper blades are not in park position. Connect jumper wires. *See Fig. 3.* Wiper should run not more than one full cycle and then park. If motor will not park or will not run to park position, replace motor.

2) If motor stops, check windshield wiper manual control switch and wiring for continuity. If switch and wiring check out okay and wiper does not stop in "OFF" or interval setting, replace interval governor.

Fig. 3: Motor Park Test

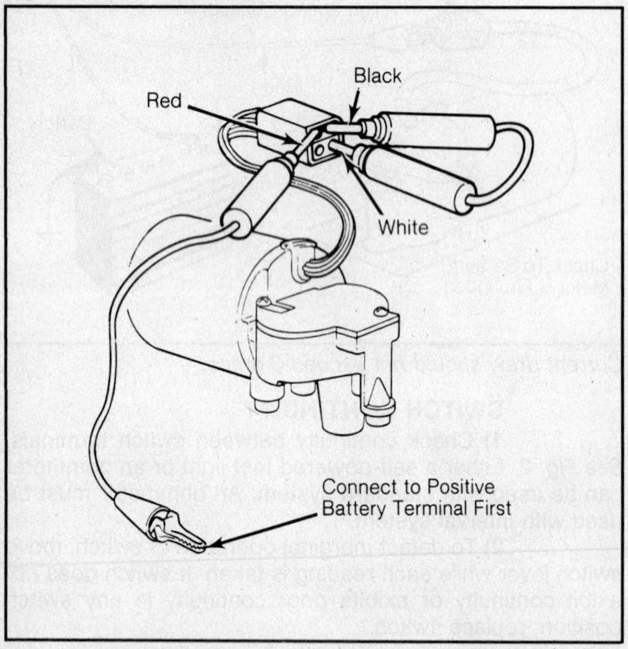

Wipers should run not more than one full cycle and park.

REMOVAL & INSTALLATION

REAR WIPER MOTOR

Removal

1) Disconnect battery negative cable. Remove wiper arm and blade assembly. Remove pivot shaft attaching nut, washer and pivot block. Remove liftgate inner trim panel.

2) Remove motor bracket attaching screw and rectangular plate. Disconnect electrical connector and disengage wiring locator pins. Remove motor assembly.

Installation

Position motor in liftgate and loosely install rectangular plate and attaching screw. DO NOT tighten at this time. Install pivot block, washer and nut. Tighten motor bracket attaching screw. To complete installation, reverse removal procedure.

WINDSHIELD WIPER MOTOR

Removal

1) Turn wiper switch on. Turn ignition switch on until blades are straight up and then turn ignition off to keep blades positioned up. Remove right wiper arm and blade. Disconnect battery negative cable. Remove right pivot nut and allow linkage to drop into cowl.

Fig. 4: Rear Wiper Motor

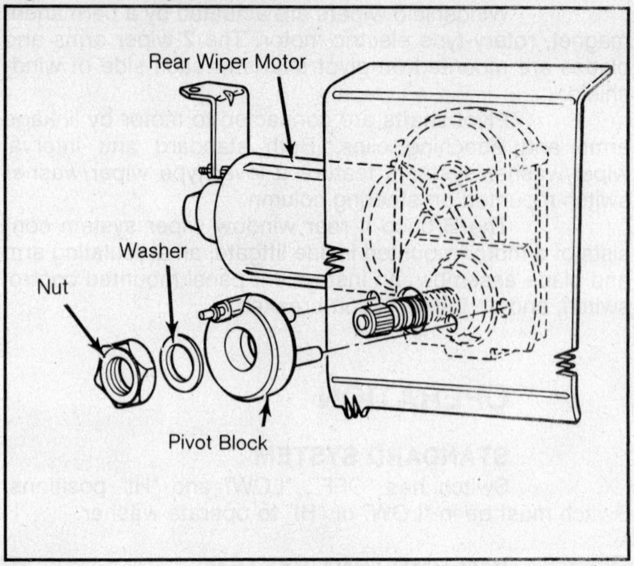

Used in Bronco II only.

2) Remove linkage access cover. Reach through access cover opening and unsnap wiper motor clip. Push clip away from linkage until it clears nib on crank pin. Push clip off linkage. Remove wiper motor wiring connector. Remove wiper motor attaching screws and remove motor.

Installation

To install, reverse removal procedure. Install clip to linkage first. DO NOT attempt to install linkage to motor crank pin and then install clip. Clip is properly installed if nib is protruding through center of clip.

REAR WIPER CONTROL SWITCH

Removal & Installation

Disconnect battery negative cable. Remove headlamp switch knob and bezel. Pull finish panel away from instrument panel and disconnect electrical connector. Remove screw attaching wiper switch to finish panel and remove. To install, reverse removal procedure.

WINDSHIELD WIPER CONTROL SWITCH

Removal & Installation

Disconnect battery negative cable. Remove trim shrouds. Disconnect quick connect electrical connector. Peel back foam sight shield, remove two cross-recessed screws holding switch and remove wiper/washer switch. To install, reverse removal procedure.

INTERVAL GOVERNOR

Removal & Installation

Disconnect battery negative cable. Remove steering coulmn shroud. Unplug governor connector from wiper control switch. Unplug instrument panel wiring harness connector from governor. Remove mounting screws and remove governor. To install, reverse removal procedure.

FORD – AEROSTAR, BRONCO II & RANGER (Cont.)

Fig. 5: Aerostar, Bronco II & Ranger Windshield Wiper System Wiring Diagram

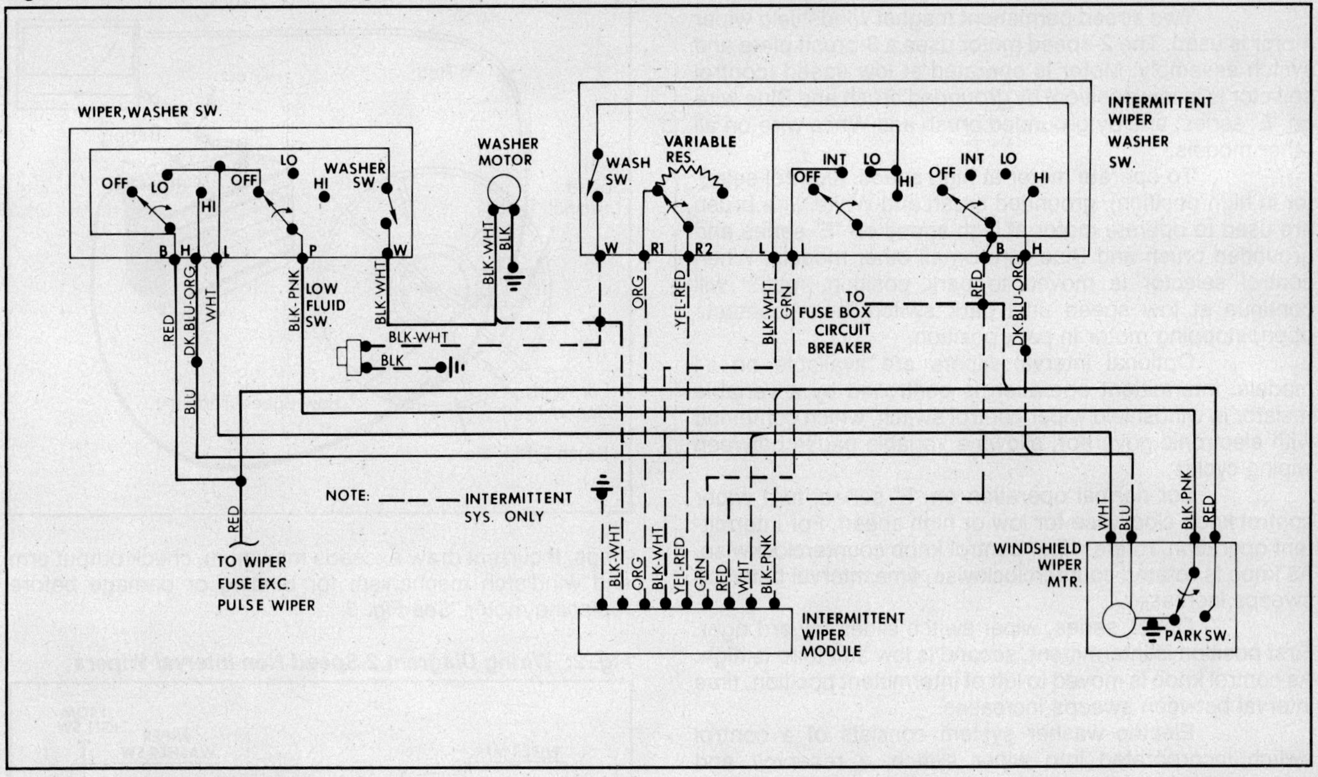

WIPER ARMS

Removal

Raise blade away from windshield and move slide latch away from pivot shaft. This unlocks wiper arm from pivot shaft and holds blade off of glass. Pull off wiper arm.

Installation

1) To install, push main arm head over pivot shaft. Ensure pivot shaft is in park position. Hold main arm head onto pivot shaft while raising blade end of wiper arm and push slide latch into lock under pivot shaft head.

2) Lower blade to windshield. If blade does not touch windshield, slide latch is not completely in place.

PIVOT SHAFT AND LINKAGE

Removal

1) Perform wiper motor removal procedure up to and including removal of wiper linkage from motor crank pin. Slide right pivot shaft and linkage assembly out through right access opening.

2) Remove left wiper arm and blade. Remove left linkage access cover. Remove left pivot nut, lower linkage and slide out through left access opening.

Installation

Install clip completely on right linkage. Ensure clip is completely on. DO NOT put linkage on and then attempt to install clip. Slide left pivot shaft and linkage through access opening and position pivot shaft in place. Reinstall left wiper pivot shaft nut and linkage cover.

WASHER PUMP AND RESERVOIR

Removal & Installation (Rear System)

Remove right side quarter trim panel. Disconnect filler hose. Disconnect pump electrical connector. Remove screws attaching reservoir to quarter panel and remove. To install, reverse removal procedure.

Removal & Installation (Front System)

Disconnect lock tab wire connector and hose. Remove retaining screws and lift assembly from fender or radiator support. Disconnect washer and radiator overflow hoses. To install, reverse removal procedure.

FORD – EXCEPT AEROSTAR, BRONCO II & RANGER

DESCRIPTION

Two speed permanent magnet windshield wiper motor is used. The 2-speed motor uses a 3-brush plate and switch assembly. Motor is operated at low speed (control selector is in low position) by grounded brush and Blue wire on "E" series, and by grounded brush and White wire on all other models.

To operate motor at high speed, (control selector in high position), grounded brush and White wire brush are used to operate motor at high speed on "E" series and grounded brush and Blue wire on all other models. When control selector is moved to park position, motor will continue at low speed until park switch lower contacts open, stopping motor in park position.

Optional interval wipers are available on all models. Intermittent operation is controlled by a variable resistor in windshield wiper control switch, which combined with electronic governor, allows a variable pause between wiping cycles.

For normal operation on "F" series, turn wiper control knob clockwise for low or high speed. For intermittent operation, rotate wiper control knob counterclockwise. As knob is rotated counterclockwise, time interval between sweeps increases.

On "E" series, wiper switch slides toward right. First position is intermittent, second is low and third is high. As control knob is moved to left of intermittent position, time interval between sweeps increases.

Electric washer system consists of a control switch incorporated into wiper switch, a reservoir and motor assembly, nozzles and connecting hoses.

Circuit breaker is located in wiper control switch on systems using rotary switch and is fuse panel-mounted for systems using slide control switch. Amperage ratings for rotary and slide circuit breakers are 7 and 7.5 amps respectively.

TESTING

WIPER MOTOR CURRENT DRAW

"E" Series

1) Disconnect linkage from motor. Install Connector Sleeves (Kit No. C4AZ-14294-B) between motor terminals and volt-amp meter. Connect positive (Red) lead of meter to center terminal on motor end plate and Green lead of meter to battery positive post.

2) Connect a jumper wire between battery negative post to low speed terminal on motor end plate. Check and record current draw. Move jumper wire from low speed terminal to high speed terminal. Measure and record current draw.

3) Maximum allowable current draw for either speed is 3.5 amps. If current draw exceeds maximum, check output arm and windlatch mechanism for binding or damage before replacing motor. *See Fig. 1.*

Bronco & "F" Series

1) Disconnect linkage and electrical connections from motor. Connect Green lead of volt-amp meter to battery positive post, and positive (Red) lead of meter to low speed connection at electrical plug. Measure and record current draw.

2) Move Red lead of meter to high speed connection at electrical plug. Check and record current draw. Maximum allowable current draw for either speed is 3.0 amps. If current draw exceeds maximum, check output arm and windlatch mechanism for binding or damage before replacing motor. *See Fig. 3.*

Fig. 1: Testing Motor Current Draw – "E" Series

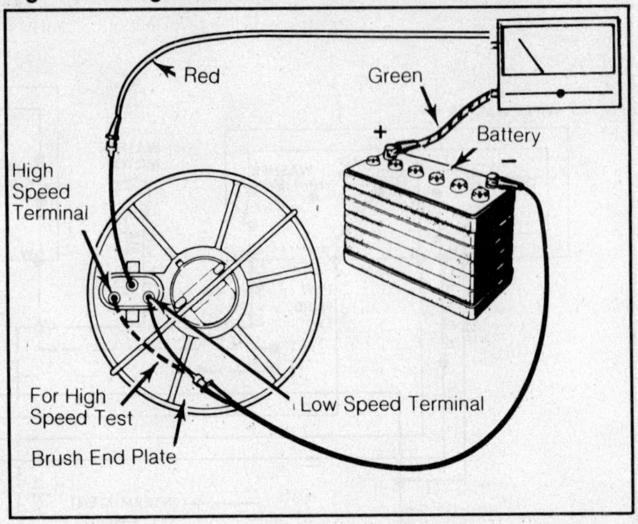

Fig. 2: Wiring Diagram 2-Speed Non-Interval Wipers

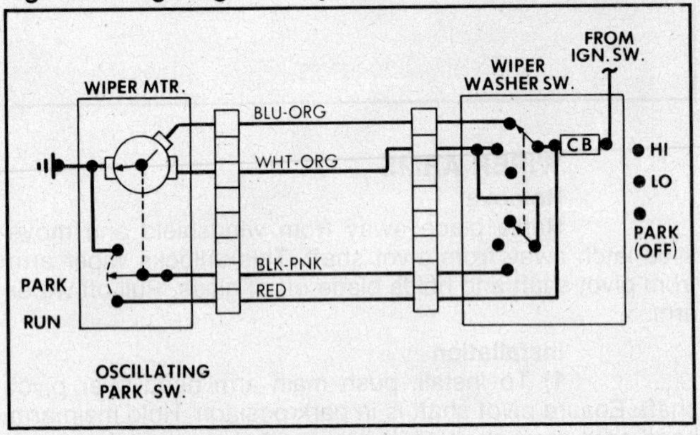

Bronco and "F" Series are shown.

CIRCUIT BREAKER

Rotary-Type Switch

1) Short tester leads together and adjust current draw to 7 amps. Connect leads to switch. *See Fig. 5.* Leave leads attached for 10 minutes.

2) Current should not be broken during 10 minute test period. If current is broken during test, replace rotary switch. If current is not broken during test, remove leads from switch and short tester leads together. Adjust current draw to 14 amps.

3) Connect leads to switch. Current should fall to 0 within 20 seconds. If current has not broken within 20 seconds, remove leads from switch and replace wiper switch assembly.

WIPER SWITCH CONTINUITY

1) Use appropriate SWITCH CONTINUITY table and corresponding figure to check continuity between switch terminals. *See Fig. 6, 7 or 8.* Either a self-powered test light or an ohmmeter can be used to test a standard 2-speed switch. Only an ohmmeter can be used to test switch on intermittent-type system.

FORD – EXCEPT AEROSTAR, BRONCO II & RANGER (Cont.)

2) If switch does meet continuity specifications, replace switch. To detect marginal switch operation, slide switch (or rotate knob) while obtaining readings.

Fig. 3: Testing Motor Current Draw – Bronco & "F" Series

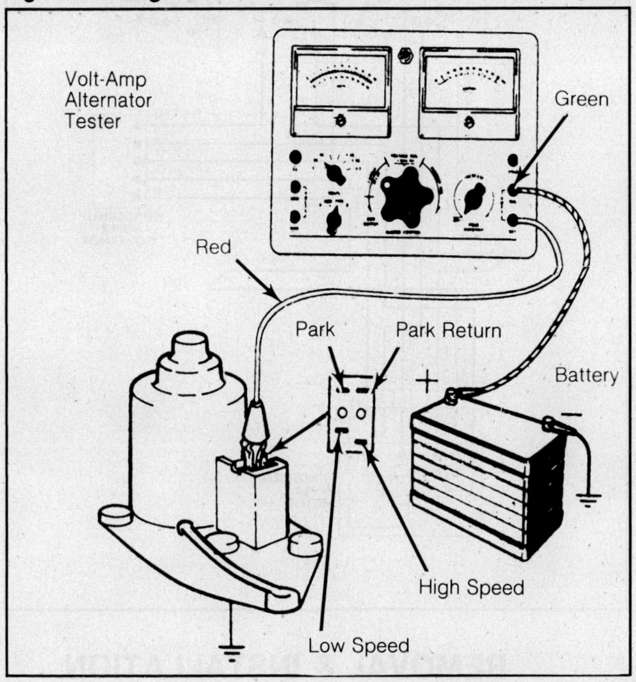

Fig. 4: Wiring Diagram 2-Speed Non-Interval Wipers

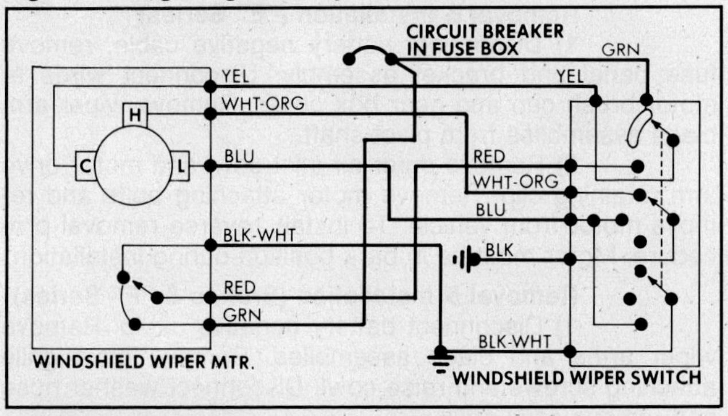

"E" Series are shown.

ROUND BLADE-TYPE SWITCH CONTINUITY

Switch Position	Terminals
Off	C-D, A-B
Low	A-B-D
High	A-B-E
Wash	A-B-W1

Intermittent Switch Position	Intermittent Terminals
Off (Park)	A-B, D-E
Low	[1] A-B, D-E-F
High	[1] D-E-F, A-B-C
Intermittent	E-F, A-B
Wash	A-B-W1

[1] – Variable resistance between terminals D and E should be a minimum of 200-1000 ohms and a maximum of 5600-8400 ohms.

Fig. 5: Circuit Breaker Test

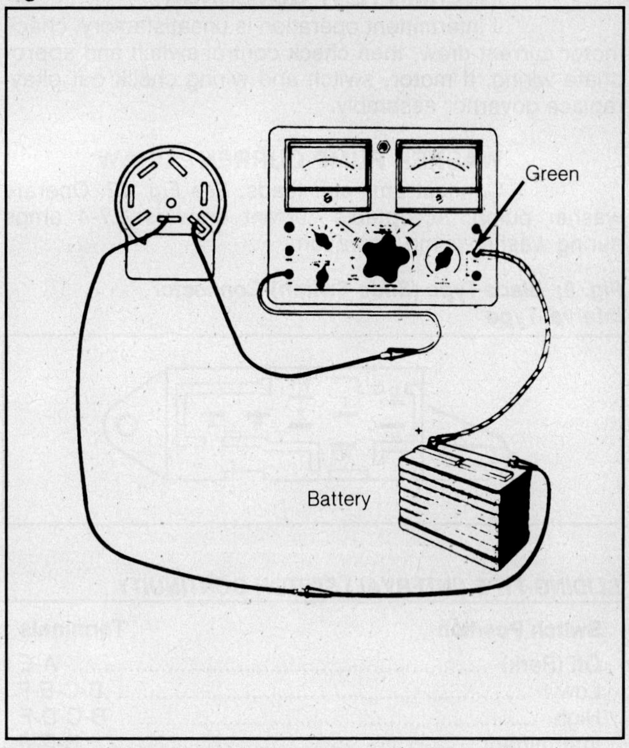

Test is for systems with rotary control switch only.

Fig. 6: Round Blade-Type Switch Connector

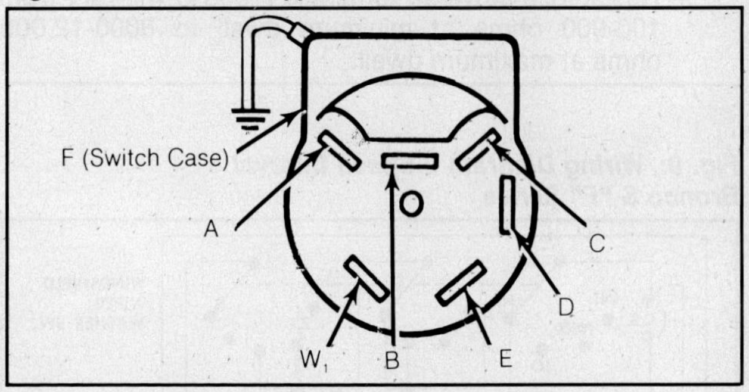

Fig. 7: Blade-Type (Slide Switch) Connector Non-Interval Type

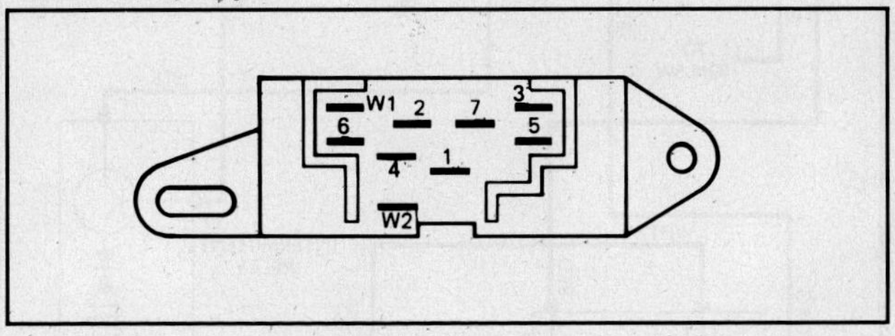

SLIDING-TYPE (NON-INTERVAL) SWITCH CONTINUITY

Switch Position	Terminals
Off (Park)	1-5, 3-7
Low	1-4, 2-7
High	1-4, 2-6
Wash	W1-W2

Wiper/Washer Systems

FORD – EXCEPT AEROSTAR, BRONCO II & RANGER (Cont.)

INTERMITTENT GOVERNOR

If intermittent operation is unsatisfactory, check motor current draw, then check control switch and appropriate wiring. If motor, switch and wiring check out okay, replace governor assembly.

WASHER PUMP CURRENT DRAW

Connect ammeter leads. *See Fig. 12.* Operate washer pump. Acceptable current draw is 1.7-4 amps during washer pump operation.

Fig. 8: Blade-Type (Slide Switch) Connector Interval-Type

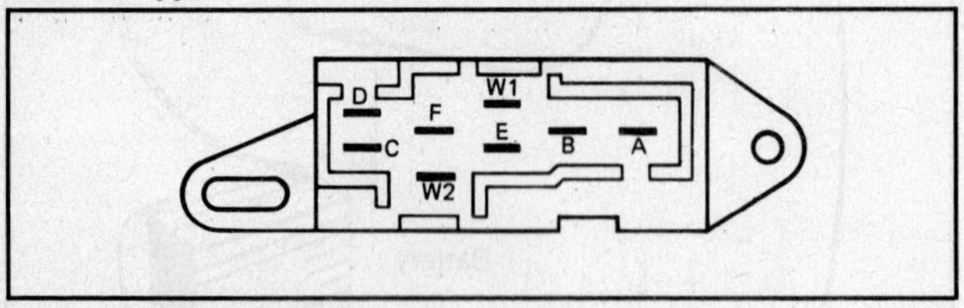

SLIDING-TYPE (INTERVAL) SWITCH CONTINUITY

Switch Position	Terminals
Off (Park)	A-E
Low [1]	B-C-E-F
High	B-C-D-F
Intermittent	B-E-F
Wash	W1-W2

[1] – Resistance between terminals F and C will vary from 100-900 ohms at minimum dwell to 8000-12,000 ohms at maximum dwell.

Fig. 9: Wiring Diagram 2-Speed Interval Bronco & "F" Series

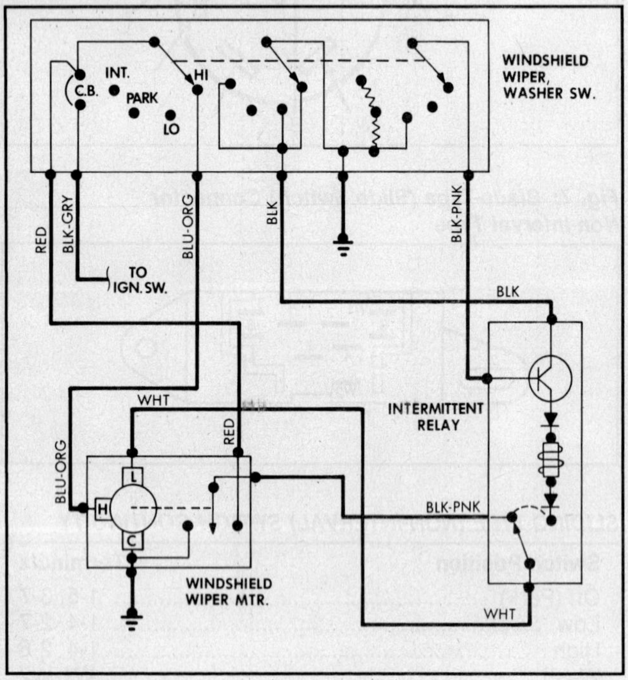

Fig. 10: Wiring Diagram 2-Speed Interval (Depressed Park) "E" Series

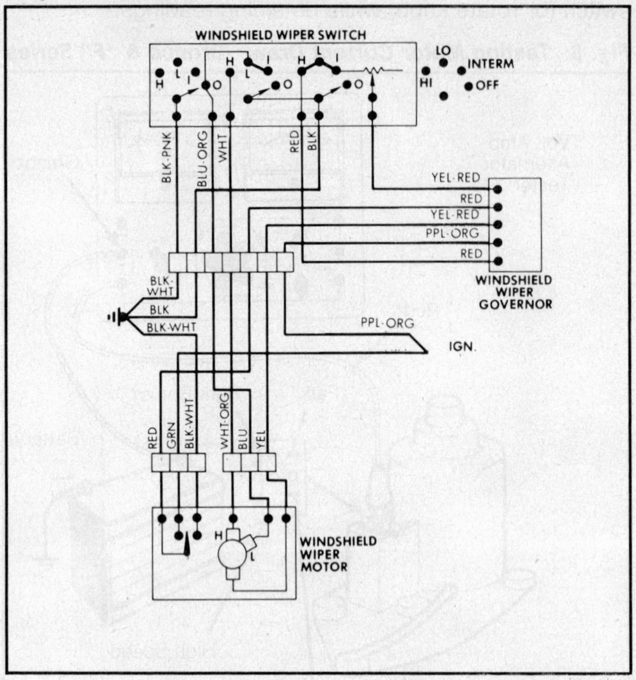

REMOVAL & INSTALLATION

WIPER MOTOR

Removal & Installation ("E" Series)

1) Disconnect battery negative cable, remove fuse panel and bracket assembly. Disconnect wires at motor brush cap and gear box cover. Remove wiper arm blade assemblies from pivot shaft.

2) Remove outer air inlet cowl and motor drive arm retaining clip. Remove motor attaching bolts and remove motor from vehicle. To install, reverse removal procedure. Motor must be in park position during installation.

Removal & Installation (Bronco & "F" Series)

1) Disconnect battery negative cable. Remove wiper arms and blade assemblies. Remove cowl grille attaching screws and raise cowl. Disconnect washer hose and remove cowl grille.

2) Remove wiper linkage clips from motor output arm. Disconnect wiring. Remove motor attaching screws and motor. To install, reverse removal procedure.

WIPER CONTROL SWITCH

Removal & Installation ("E" Series)

1) Disconnect battery negative cable. Remove switch knob and bezel. Depress lock button on top of light switch and pull shaft and knob from switch.

2) Remove screws at bottom of finish panel and pry 2 upper retainers away from instrument panel assembly. Disconnect electrical connection from switch. Remove switch attaching bolts and switch. To install, reverse removal procedure.

Removal & Installation (Bronco & "F" Series)

Disconnect battery negative cable. Remove switch knob, bezel nut and bezel. Pull switch out from under instrument panel. Disconnect electrical connection from switch. Remove switch from vehicle. To install, reverse removal procedure.

FORD – EXCEPT AEROSTAR, BRONCO II & RANGER (Cont.)

Fig. 11: Motor Park Test

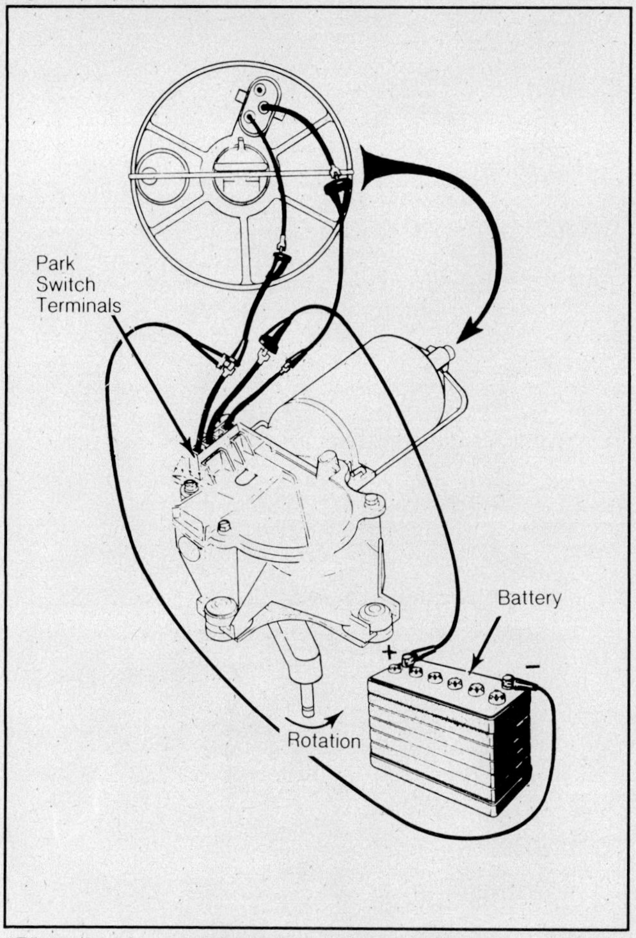

"E" series shown, others are similar.

Fig. 12: Washer Pump Current Draw Test

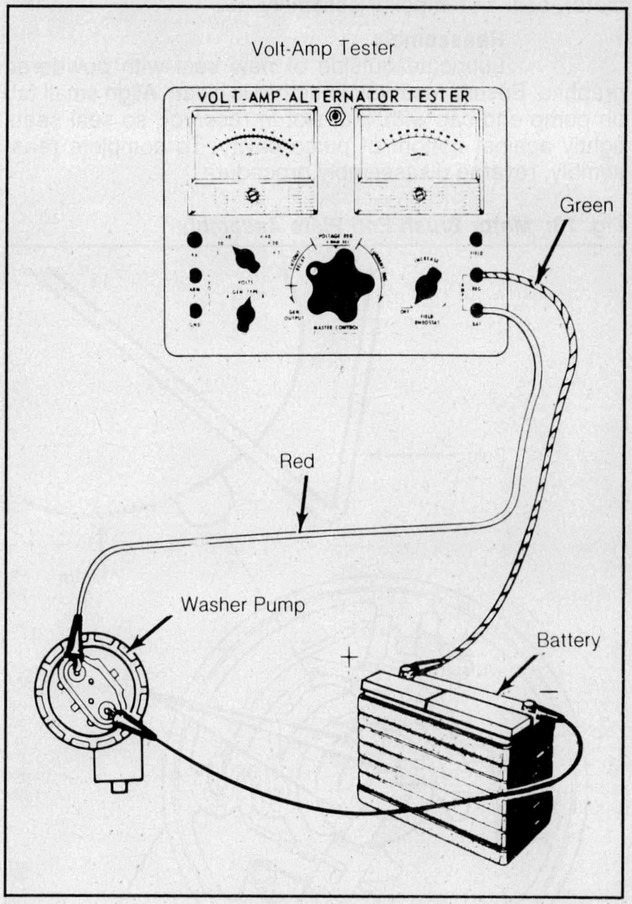

INTERMITTENT GOVERNOR

Removal & Installation

Governor is mounted on lower flange of instrument panel. Remove rear window defogger switch assembly (if equipped) to gain access to right side governor attaching screw. Disconnect wiring from governor and remove attaching screws. To install, reverse removal procedure.

WASHER PUMP & RESERVOIR

Removal & Installation

1) Using a small screwdriver, disconnect lock tab wire connector. Remove hose and drain reservoir. Remove pump retaining screws.

2) Remove reservoir attaching screws. To install, reverse removal procedure. Fill reservoir before electrical connections are made.

OVERHAUL

WIPER MOTOR

NOTE: **Wiper motor for "F" series and Bronco is not serviceable, and must be replaced as a unit. Wiper motor for "E" series is serviceable only in kits of major sub-assemblies. Available kits include cover/switch assembly and brush end plate.**

COVER/SWITCH ASSEMBLY

Disassembly & Reassembly

Remove 4 cover retaining screws. Remove assembly. Replace with appropriate kit. Ensure ground strap is under cover screw. Tighten screws to 15-25 INCH lbs. (1.7-2.8 N.m).

NOTE: **"E" series switch assembly is identified by the letter "U" stamped on the outside surface.**

BRUSH END PLATE

Disassembly & Reassembly

1) Observe and record position of bale retainer. Pry retainer off using a screwdriver. Remove end plate and plug. Replace with appropriate kit. When installing new kit, use a fine wire probe through hub opening to position brushes on commutator.

2) Rotate end plate until key is positioned in notch, and assemble plug. DO NOT over-bend bale retainer during installation.

WASHER MOTOR, SEAL & IMPELLER

Disassembly

Remove reservoir assembly from vehicle. Pry out retaing ring with a small screwdriver. Using pliers, grip

FORD – EXCEPT AEROSTAR, BRONCO II & RANGER (Cont.)

one part of wall surrounding electrical terminal and pull out motor, seal and impeller assembly.

Reassembly

Lubricate outside of new seal with powdered graphite. Ensure reservoir chamber is clean. Align small tab on pump end cap with with slot in reservoir so seal seats tightly against bottom of pump cavity. To complete reassembly, reverse disassembly procedure.

Fig. 13: Motor Brush End Plate Assembly

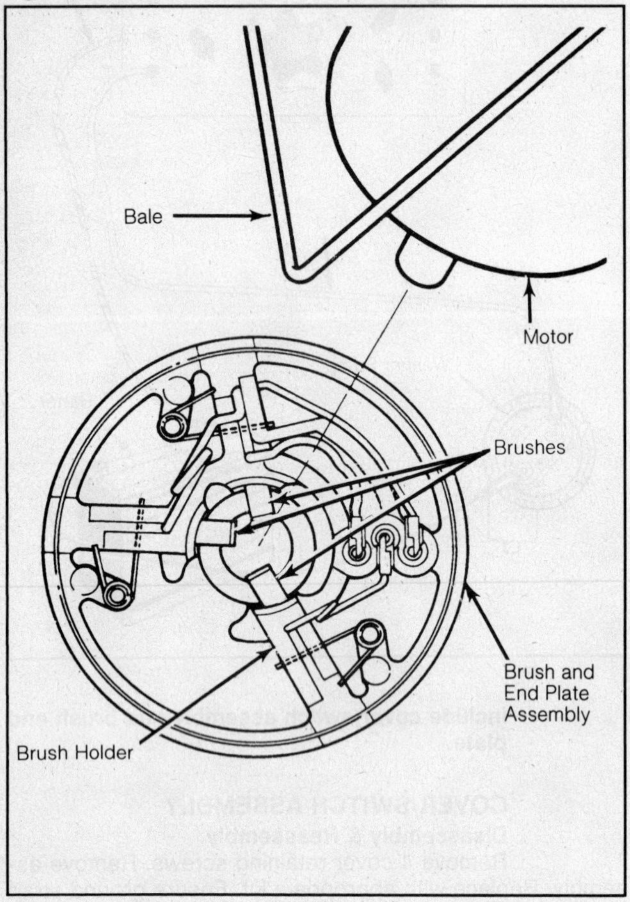

"E" series shown, others are similar.

Wiper/Washer Systems

GENERAL MOTORS – ASTRO & SAFARI

DESCRIPTION

The internal components of 2-speed non-depressed park-type wiper system include a field magnet, armature, drive gear, park switch actuator, brush holder assembly, and a radio noise suppression capacitor.

Pulse and demand wash functions are controlled by a printed circuit board enclosed in wiper housing cover. All motor components are enclosed in a die-cast aluminum housing with a plastic cover. A ground strap on one motor mounting bolt hole provides ground for a capacitor.

The washer pump consists of permanent magnet motor and pump assembly. The washer pump assembly is mounted in bottom of fluid reservoir.

OPERATION

When ignition switch is on, power is supplied to both low and high speed fixed contacts in steering column switch. When wash button is pushed, a demand wash is actuated (in 1.5 second intervals) for as long as button is held. This is followed by approximately 6 seconds of dry wipes.

Rotating control switch will vary delay time. Instantaneous wipe can be obtained by rotating switch to mist positon. Armature is grounded through common brush via ground strap.

Constant Speed Operation

When column switch is in "LOW" or "HIGH" position, respective brush circuit is completed and wiper motor runs at desired speed.

Park Operation

When column switch is turned to "OFF" position, low speed brush circuit is completed through a park switch on brush assembly. When blades reach park position, large gear moves park switch actuator and opens normally closed park switch.

Washer Operation

Actuating washer portion of column switch completes washer pump motor circuit to ground. With column switch in wash position, wiper switch is mechanically moved to "LOW" position. This dual function starts wiper motor and washer operation at same time. The washer pump runs when switch is activated.

TESTING & DIAGNOSIS

SWITCH VOLTAGE

1) Turn ignition on. Attach voltmeter negative lead to ground. With wiper switch in each position, probe appropriate terminals with positive lead. See WIPER SWITCH TEST table. Record voltage reading at each terminal.

WIPER SWITCH TEST

Switch Position	12 Volts At Terminal
Off	"1"
Low, Pulse Or Mist	"1", "3"
High	"1", "3", "4"

2) Voltage readings at terminals not shown on chart should be 0 volts. If voltage readings are not correct in all switch positions, check continuity of each harness wire, and replace as necessary. If wiring is okay, replace switch.

WIPER MOTOR

1) Disconnect motor wiring. Ensure that wiper motor mounting screws are secure. Check system fuses. Ensure that washer hoses are clear of debris. Repair or replace components as necessary.

2) If fuses, mounting screws and hoses are okay, perform tests in order listed. If wiper does not operate in any of the following tests, circuit board or motor is defective.

Mist Mode

Apply battery voltage to terminal "1". *See Fig 2.* Connect a 5 ohm resistor between terminal "2" and ground. Connect a 360 ohm resistor between battery voltage source and terminal "3". Motor should now operate in mist mode.

Fig. 2: Motor Terminal Identification

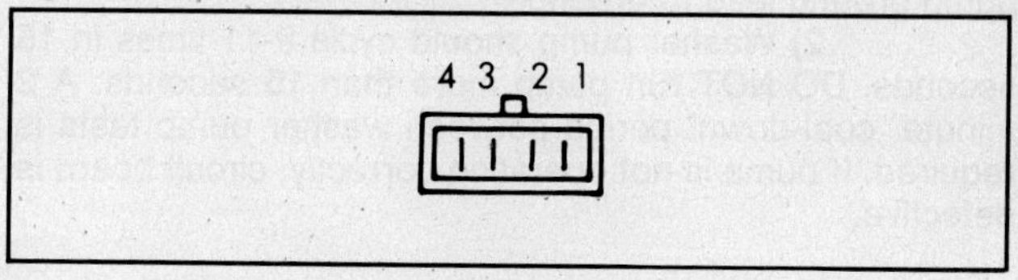

Fig. 1: Exploded View of Positive Park Wiper Motor

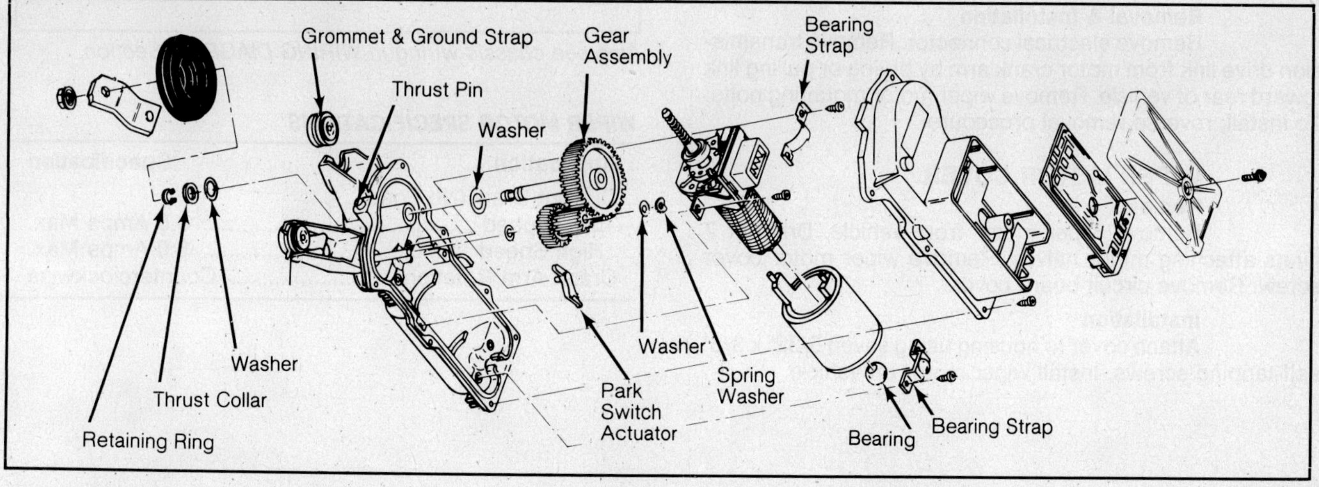

Wiper/Washer Systems

GENERAL MOTORS – ASTRO & SAFARI (Cont.)

Off/Park Mode

1) Apply battery voltage to terminal "1". *See Fig 2.* Connect a 5 ohm resistor between terminal "2" and ground. Connect terminal "3" directly to ground.

2) Motor should now be in off/park mode. If motor is not operating correctly, verify that park switch actuator is not broken. If park switch is okay, circuit board is defective.

Pulse Wipe Mode

1) Apply battery voltage to terminal "1". *See Fig 2.* Connect a 5 ohm resistor between terminal "2" and ground. Connect a variable resistor (10,000 to 500,000 ohm) between battery voltage source and terminal "3" (pulse time will depend upon position of resistor control).

2) Motor should now operate in pulse wipe mode. Check pulse wipe mode with resistor in several positions. If motor is not operating correctly, circuit board is defective.

Low Speed Mode

Apply battery voltage to terminal "1". *See Fig 2.* Connect a 5 ohm resistor between terminal "2" and ground. Connect a 360 ohm resistor between battery voltage source and terminal "3". Motor should now operate in low speed mode.

High Speed Mode

Apply battery voltage to terminal "1". *See Fig 2.* Connect a 5 ohm resistor between terminal "2" and ground. Connect a 360 ohm resistor between battery voltage source and terminal "3". Apply battery voltage to terminal "4". Motor should now operate in high speed mode.

NOTE: **Damage to circuit board will result if terminal "4" is connected before terminal 3.**

Wash Mode

1) Apply battery voltage to terminals 1 and 3. *See Fig 2.* Connect a known good washer pump (do not use pump of vehicle being tested) to terminal 2. Connect washer pump ground lead to ground.

2) Washer pump should cycle 9-11 times in 15 seconds. DO NOT run pump more than 15 seconds. A 2 minute "cool-down" period between washer pump tests is required. If pump is not operating correctly, circuit board is defective.

REMOVAL & INSTALLATION

WIPER MOTOR

Removal & Installation

Remove electrical connector. Remove transmission drive link from motor crank arm by prying or pulling link toward rear of vehicle. Remove wiper motor mounting bolts. To install, reverse removal procedure.

WIPER MOTOR COVER

Removal

Remove wiper motor from vehicle. Drill out 7 rivets attaching motor halves. Remove wiper motor cover screw. Remove circuit board cover.

Installation

Attach cover to housing using seven 5/32" x 3/8" self-tapping screws. Install wiper motor on vehicle.

WIPER MOTOR HOUSING

Removal

1) Remove wiper motor from vehicle. Drill out 7 rivets attaching motor halves. Remove wiper motor cover screw. Remove circuit board cover. Remove circuit board by slowly lifting outboard edge of cover.

2) Remove housing cover. Mark position of crank arm relative to shaft. Remove crank arm lock nut, crank arm, shaft seal, thrust collar and washer. Check gear assembly shaft for burrs, and file if necessary.

3) Push end of gear shaft through housing and remove gear assembly and washer. Remove spring washer and flat washer. Remove intermediate gear and flat washer. Remove park switch actuator.

4) Drill out 4 rivets attaching bearings and bearing straps. DO NOT allow metal chips to fall in motor. Remove 2 screws holding brush assembly in place. Remove 2 screws attaching armature/brush assembly (to avoid having to realign brushes onto commutator).

Installation

To install, reverse removal procedure. Use parts supplied in service package. After wiper motor is fully assembled, place thrust pin in casting with insert about 1/32" above rear of pin.

NOTE: **Use WIPER MOTOR HOUSING removal and installation procedures to replace wiper gear assembly, intermediate gear assembly, wiper magnet assembly, park switch actuator, brush holder assembly and motor armature.**

Fig. 3: Positive Park Pulse Wiper System Wiring Diagram

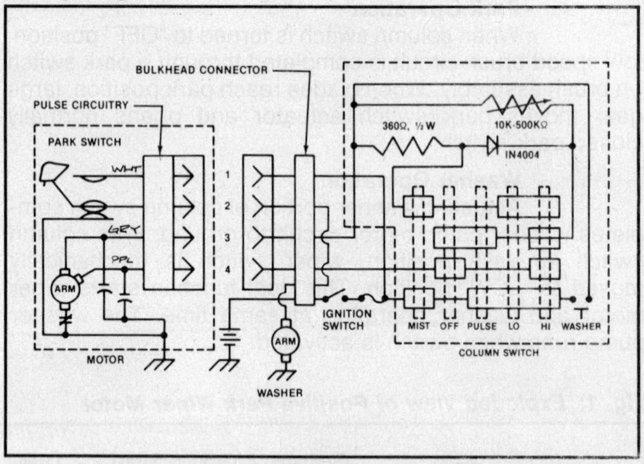

Also see chassis wiring in WIRING DIAGRAM Section.

WIPER MOTOR SPECIFICATIONS

Application	Specification
Current Draw (No Load)	
Low Speed	3.5 Amps Max.
High Speed	5.0 Amps Max.
Crank Arm Rotation	Counterclockwise

GENERAL MOTORS – INTEGRAL WIPER/WASHER MOTOR

"C", "G" & "K" Series

DESCRIPTION

Two speed motor, permanent magnet-type, consists of parts-field magnets, armature and drive gear within upper and lower housings. The washer pump is assembled on outside surface of upper half of housing and is an integral part of wiper motor assembly. Wiper motor is protected by an automatic reset circuit breaker. Vehicle wiring is protected by fuse in fuse block.

OPERATION

The washer pump system consists of a spring loaded piston enclosed in a plastic cylinder housing with an actuator plate extending from cylinder housing. A valve assembly, consisting of two exhaust and one intake check valve, is attached to end of cylinder housing.

A tang on piston actuator plate holds plate in a lock-out position, (no pumping action). To start pump, push washer button which will energize relay. This pulls relay armature toward coil allowing ratchet gear pawl to engage ratchet gear and begin rotation. This sequence starts pumping action.

Fig. 1: Washer Actuator Plate and Valve Assembly

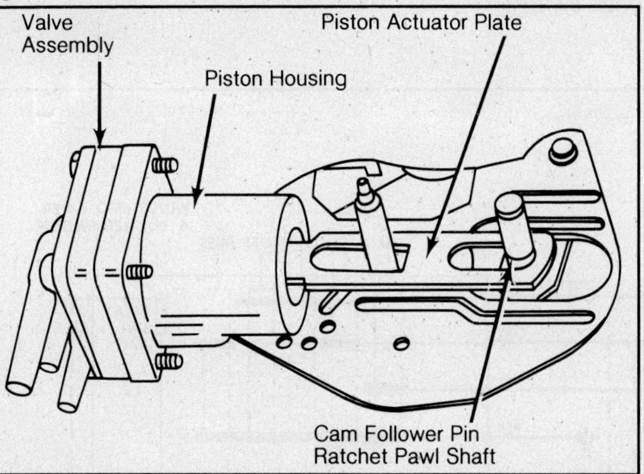

Tang holds plate in lock-out position.

TROUBLE SHOOTING

ALL SERIES

Wiper Inoperative

Check fuse, wiring harness, wiper ground and dash connections.

Wiper Operates At One Speed Only

Check for open wiring between terminals 2 or 3 and dash switch. Check dash switch and if not operable, check low and high brush leads.

Wiper Blades Will Not Return To Park

Check for open wire from terminal 5 to dash switch. If not open, dash switch or wiper park switch needs replacing.

Wiper Will Not Shut Off

Disconnect wiring from terminals 4 and 5. Replace park switch assembly if motor stops. If motor still runs, remove wires from terminals 1, 2 and 3. Connect a 12 volt lead to terminal 1 only and if motor does not run it indicates a ground in wires from wiper motor to terminal 2 or 3 at dash switch. If it runs, check for internal ground in high or low brushes.

Washer Pump Will Not Run

1) Turn ignition switch on. Ensure washer solution is adequate, then push wash button and listen for relay to energize. With ignition still on, and wiring connected to wiper terminals, connect test lamp lead to ground and probe terminals 6 and 7.

2) If light is off at both terminals; check for open in circuit to pump. If light is on at only one terminal, replace coil/park switch assembly. If light is on at both terminals but one light is dim, ground dim light terminals. If pump runs, check for open in wire between pump and dash switch or for a defective dash switch.

NOTE: Delay wiper system is available as optional equipment. A separate control assembly provides a variable delay of 1 to 20 seconds.

REMOVAL & INSTALLATION

WIPER MOTOR

Removal ("C" & "K" Series)

1) Ensure wiper motor is in park position and disconnect battery negative cable. Disconnect electrical harness at motor and hoses at washer pump. Reach through access hole in cowl grille and loosen wiper drive rod attaching screws.

2) Remove drive rod from wiper motor crank arm. Remove screws attaching wiper motor to instrument panel and remove motor assembly.

Installation

To install, reverse removal procedure. Lubricate crank arm pivot prior to installation.

Removal ("G" Series)

1) Ensure wiper motor is in park position, then disconnect battery negative cable. Remove wiper arms from wiper linkage. Remove cowl panel cover. Loosen nuts holding linkage to crank arm and lift linkage off arm. Disconnect wiring to motor.

2) Remove left defroster outlet from flex hose and position hose to one side. Remove screw securing left hand heater duct to engine cover shroud and slip heater duct down and out. Remove washer hoses, then remove screws securing wiper motor to cowl and lift wiper motor from under dash.

Installation

To install, reverse removal procedure. Ensure wiper motor is in park position before installing. Lubricate wiper motor crank arm pivot prior to installation.

OVERHAUL

Repairs to motor/gear box section of wiper assembly are limited to switch, armature, cap and brush holder assembly plus external parts, crankarm, spacer/seal (plastic) and output shaft seal.

Wiper/Washer Systems

GENERAL MOTORS – INTEGRAL WIPER/WASHER MOTOR (Cont.)

Fig. 2: Motor Terminal Check Diagram

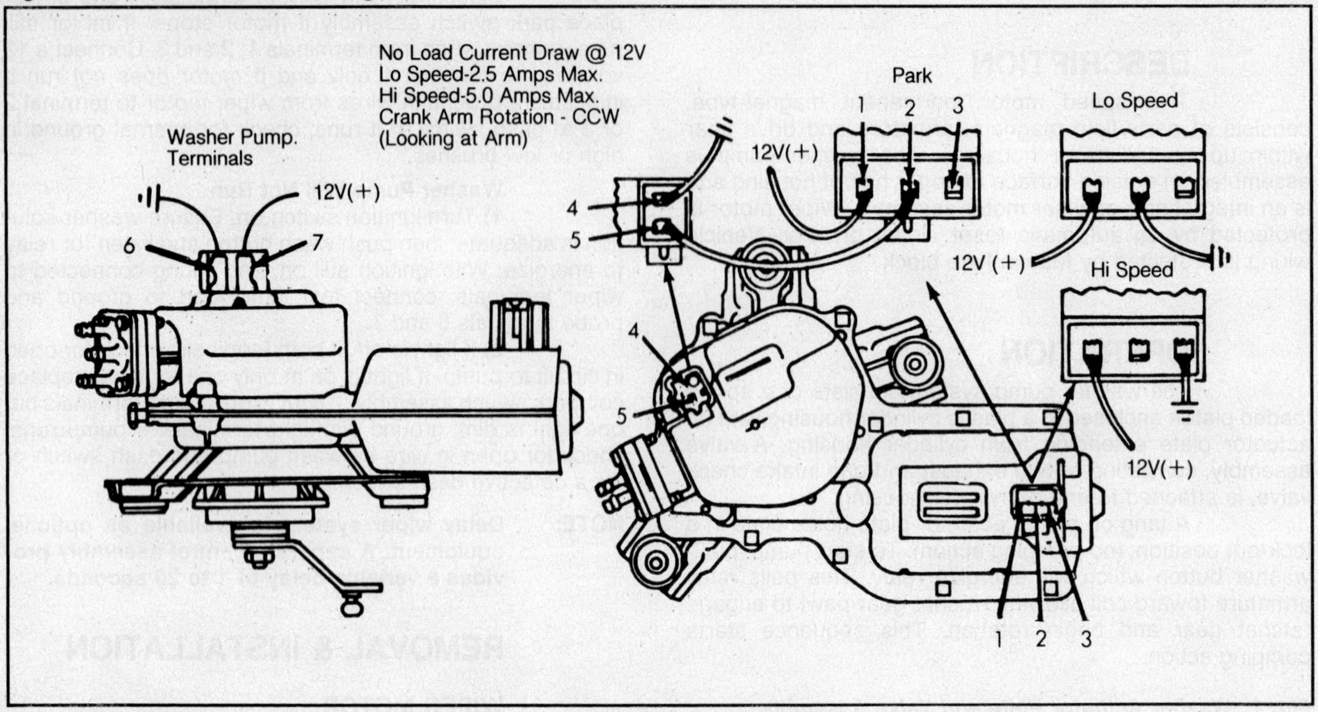

Connections operate wipers independently of vehicle wiring and dash switch.

Fig. 3: Wiper/Washer System Wiring Diagram

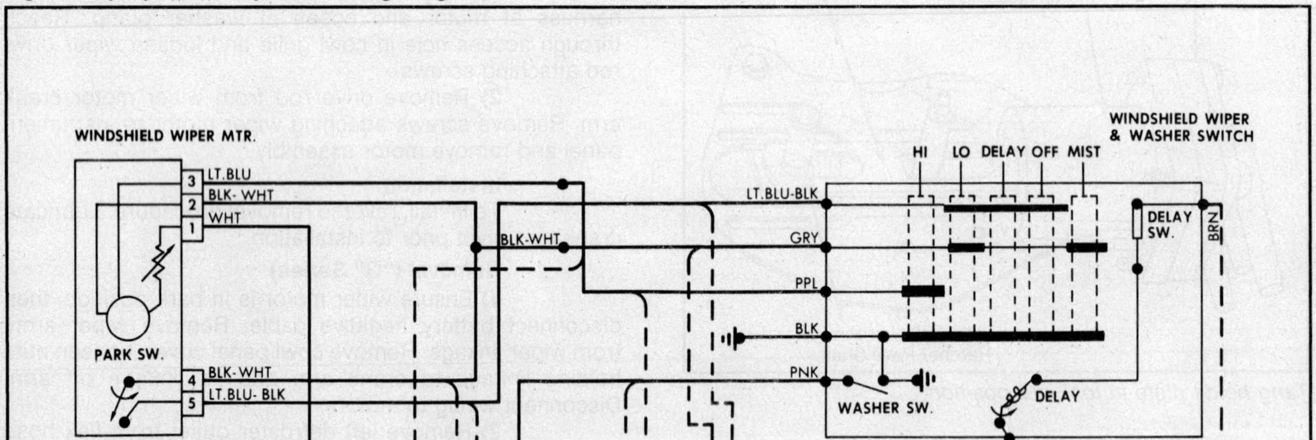

Diagram is for "C" and "K" series, including Blazer, Pickup and Suburban.

Wiper/Washer Systems

GENERAL MOTORS – INTEGRAL WIPER/WASHER MOTOR (Cont.)

Fig. 4: Wiper/Washer System Wiring Diagram

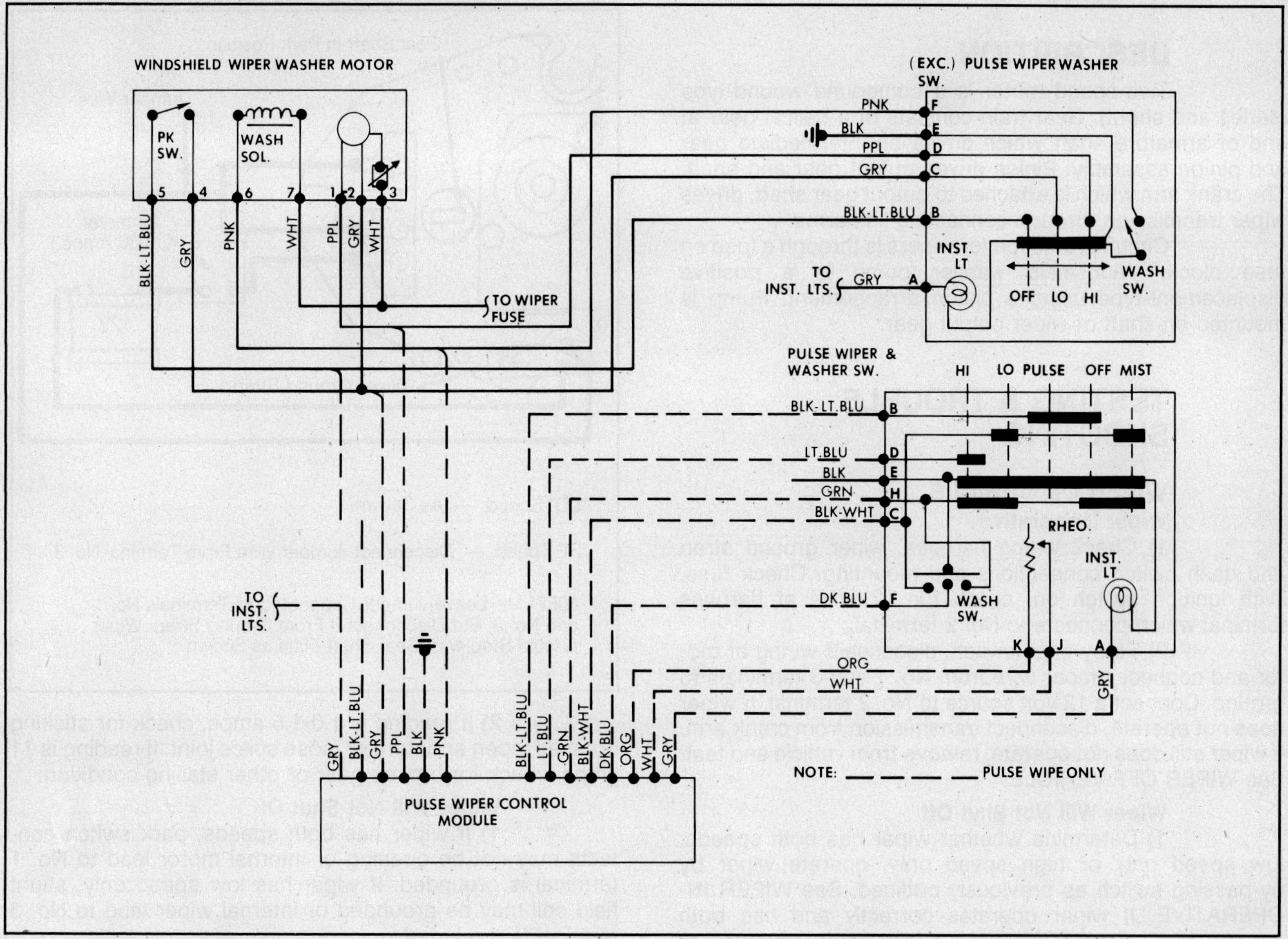

Diagram is for "C" series.

GENERAL MOTORS SQUARE MOTOR

"P" Series

DESCRIPTION

Two-speed motor is a compound wound-type (series and shunt). Gear train consists of a helical gear at end of armature shaft which drives an intermediate gear and pinion assembly. Pinion drives output gear and shaft. The crank arm which is attached to output gear shaft, drives wiper tranmission through connecting link arms.

Circuit protection for wipers is through a fuse on fuse block. Windshield washer pump is a positive displacement-type using a piston arrangement. Pump is mounted on shaft of wiper output gear.

TESTING & TROUBLE SHOOTING

WIPER ON VEHICLE

Wiper Inoperative

1) Check wiring harness, wiper ground strap and dash switch connections and mounting. Check fuse. With ignition switch on, check for 12 volts at harness terminal which connects to No. 2 terminal.

2) To by-pass switch, disconnect wiring at motor and connect jumper wire from No. 1 and 3 terminals to ground. Connect a 12 volt source to No. 2 terminal. If wiper does not operate, disconnect transmission from crank arm. If wiper still does not operate, remove from vehicle and test. See WIPER OFF VEHICLE.

Wiper Will Not Shut Off

1) Determine whether wiper has both speeds, low speed only or high speed only, operate wiper by by-passing switch as previously outlined. See WIPER INOPERATIVE. If wiper operates correctly and has both speeds, lead to switch from No. 1 terminal is grounded or switch is faulty.

2) If wiper has low or high speed only, lead to switch from No. 3 terminal is open or switch is faulty. If wiper still does not operate, remove from vehicle and test. See WIPER OFF VEHICLE.

Operates Low Speed Only & Shuts Off With Dash Switch In High Position

Reverse harness leads connected to No. 1 and 3 terminals.

Does Not Return To Park With Wiper Off

Check ground strap connection. Park switch contacts may be dirty, bent or broken.

Speed Normal In Low, But Too Fast In High

Terminal board resistor may be open. Remove from vehicle to test terminal board.

Wiper Operates Intermittently

Loose ground strap or dash switch mounting.

WIPER OFF VEHICLE

NOTE: Use ammeter with reading of 30 amps (minimum) in feed wire circuit.

Wiper Inoperative

1) Connect an ammeter and battery to No. 2 terminal and a jumper wire from No. 1 and 3 terminals to ground. Wiper should operate at low speed. If ammeter reading is 0, check for loose splice joints or loose solder connection at No. 2 terminal.

Fig. 1: Jumper Wire Testing Connections

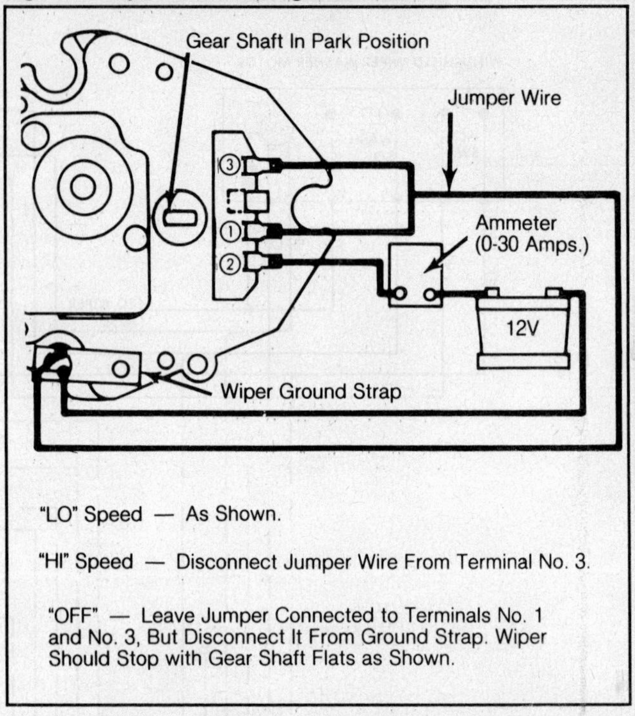

2) If reading is 1.0-1.5 amps, check for sticking brushes, open armature or loose splice joint. If reading is 11 amps, check for broken gear or other stalling condition.

Wiper Will Not Shut Off

1) If wiper has both speeds, park switch contacts may not be opening or internal motor lead to No. 1 terminal is grounded. If wiper has low speed only, shunt field coil may be grounded or internal wiper lead to No. 3 terminal is grounded.

2) If wiper has high speed only, shunt field is open or internal lead to No. 3 terminal is open.

Wipers Operate Intermittently

Check for sticking brushes, loose splice joints or other loose connections.

Fig. 2: General Motors Square Motor Wiper System Wiring Diagram

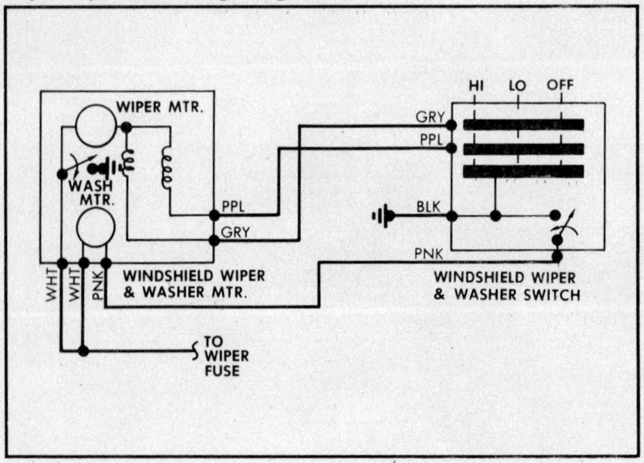

GENERAL MOTORS SQUARE MOTOR (Cont.)

OVERHAUL

GEAR BOX

Disassembly

1) Remove washer pump. Remove pump drive cam by wedging shaft with 2 screwdrivers. Clamp crank arm in vise and remove retaining nut. Arm must be secure in vise to avoid stripping wiper gears.

OVERHAUL

GEAR BOX

Disassembly

1) Remove washer pump. Remove pump drive cam by wedging shaft with 2 screwdrivers. Clamp crank arm in vise and remove retaining nut. Arm must be secure in vise to avoid stripping wiper gears.

2) Remove crank arm, seal cap, retaining ring and end play washers. Drill out gear box cover rivets and remove cover.

3) Remove output gear and shaft assembly. Slide intermediate gear and pinion off shaft. Remove terminal board and park switch by unsoldering motor leads and drilling out rivets holding terminal board and park switch ground strap to plate.

Reassembly

1) Lubricate gear teeth with suitable cam lubricant. Position cover over locating dowel pins. Reconnect ground strap.

2) Place wiper in park position. Install crank arm on output shaft so identification marks line up with marks in cover. Clamp crank in vise and tighten retaining nut. To complete reassembly, reverse disassembly procedure.

WIPER MOTOR

Disassembly

Disassemble gear box, remove through bolts, tap motor frame lightly and remove motor from mounting plate. Release brush spring tension and slide armature and end plate from motor frame. Pull end plate from armature. Remove end play adjusting washers and note arrangement for proper reassembly.

NOTE: A thrust plug is located between armature shaft and end plate.

Reassembly

Lubricate armature shaft bushings with light machine oil. Install washers with concave side of washers toward each other. End play is automatically controlled by proper installation of washers. To complete reassembly, reverse disassembly procedure.

WASHER PUMP

Dissembly

1) Squeeze solenoid cover and remove. Remove ratchet dog retaining screw. Hold solenoid plunger in position and lift solenoid assembly and ratchet dog from pump frame. Separate ratchet dog from solenoid mounting plate.

2) Disconnect ratchet pawl spring, remove pawl retaining ring and slide ratchet pawl off cam follower shaft. Remove ratchet dog from pump frame, move ratchet wheel spring out of shaft groove and slide ratchet wheel off its shaft.

3) Separate pump and pump actuator plate from frame by pulling pump housing until grooves in housing clear frame. Remove actuator plate from ratchet wheel and cam follower shafts. Remove screws attaching valve assembly to pump housing and remove valve.

Reassembly

Position gasket between housing and valve plate in housing and valve plate grooves. Install triple "O" ring between valve body and pipe assembly. To complete reassembly, reverse disassembly procedure.

MOTOR SPECIFICATIONS

Application	Specification
Operating Voltage	12 Volts
Current Draw (No Load Max.)	
"LO" Speed	4 Amps
"HI" Speed	3.5 Amps
Current Draw (Stall, Cold)	12 Amps
Crank Arm Speed (Minimum)	
"LO" Speed	31 RPM
"HI" Speed	55 RPM

Fig. 3: Exploded View of Wiper Motor and Drive Assembly

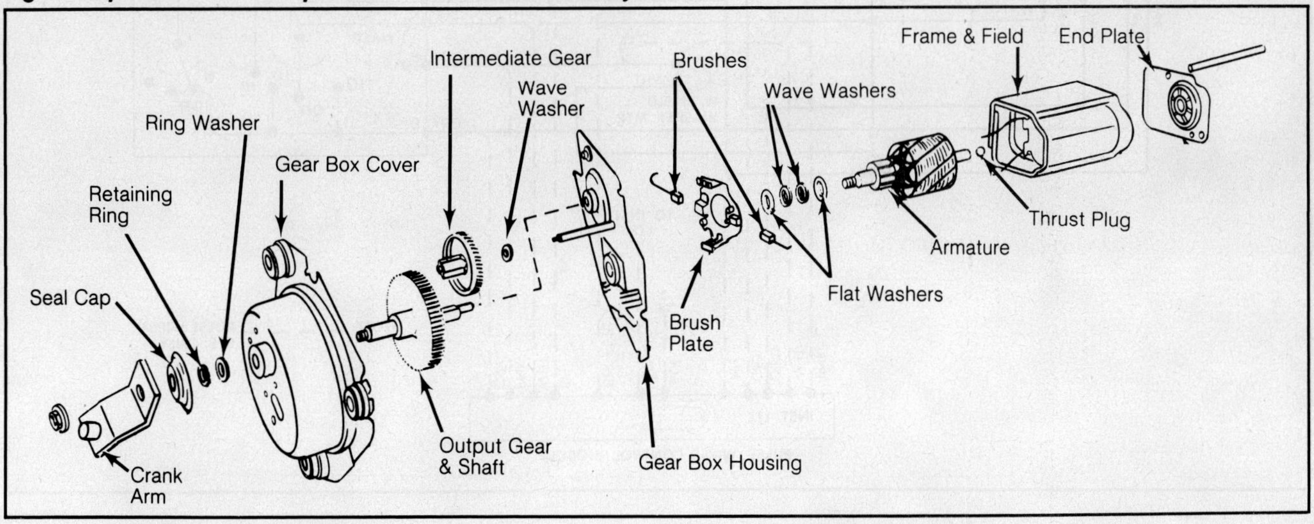

Wiper/Washer Systems

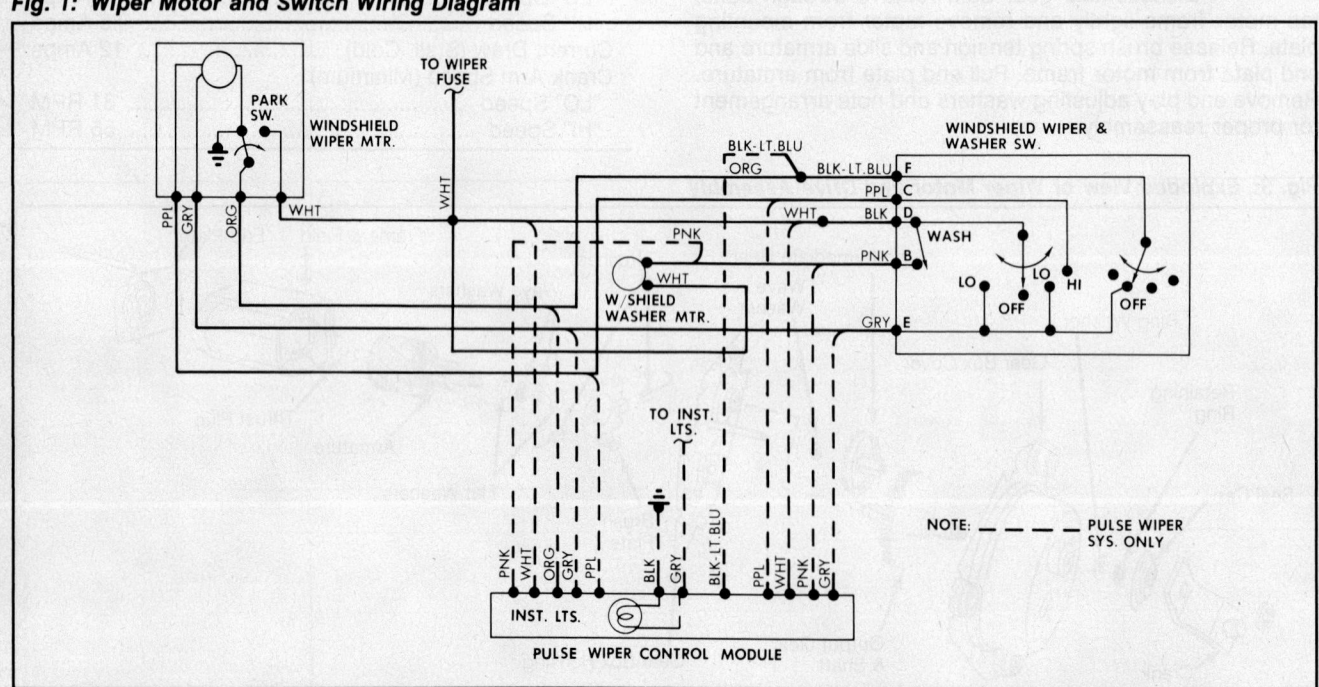

GENERAL MOTORS – "S" SERIES

DESCRIPTION

Wiper system is a permanent magnet positive park system with a dynamic brake and separate washer assembly. Washer system consists of a permanent magnet (PM) motor and pump assembly that is mounted to solution jar by a nut located inside jar. The motor can be operated only when ignition switch is in "RUN" or "ACCESSORY" position.

TESTING & TROUBLE SHOOTING

WIPER SYSTEM

Wiper Inoperative

1) With ignition switch on, and wiper switch on "HIGH", ground 12 volt test lamp amd touch probe to wiper terminal No. 1. If lamp lights, proceed to step **3)**. If lamp does not light, check fuse.

2) If fuse is okay, repair open in feed circuit between fuse box and wiper motor. If fuse is blown, replace fuse. If fuse blows, check for short in wiring or high amperage draw in motor.

3) If lamp came on in step **1)**, place switch in "LOW". Connect jumper wire to ground. If wiper runs, repair open in ground strap. If wiper does not run, problem is in motor. Repair or replace motor as necessary.

Wiper Has Low Speed Only

1) With ignition switch on, and wiper switch in "HIGH" position, remove connector from wiper terminal. Connect 12 volt source to high speed terminal No. 1. If wiper is inoperative, repair wiper motor.

2) With wiper in "HIGH", check for open wire from wiper terminal No. 1 to column switch and repair. If wire is okay, replace column switch.

Wiper Has High Speed Only

1) With ignition switch on, and wiper switch in "LOW" position, remove connector from wiper terminal. Connect 12 volt source to terminal No. 2. If wiper does not run, repair wiper motor.

2) If wiper runs in "LOW", check for open in wire from wiper terminal No. 2 to column switch and repair. If wire is okay, replace column switch.

Wiper Works at Same Speed in Both "LOW" and "HIGH" Positions

1) With ignition switch on, and wiper switch in "LOW" or "HIGH" position, remove connector from wiper terminal. Connect 12 volt source to low or high terminals. If wiper runs at one speed, repair wiper motor. Check for low or high speed brushes shorting.

2) If wiper runs in both "HIGH" and "LOW", check for open in wires from terminals No. 1 and No. 2 to column switch and repair. If there are no opens, replace column switch.

Wipers Will Not Park

1) With ignition switch on, and wiper switch in "PARK" position, remove connector from wiper terminal. Connect jumper from terminal No. 2 to No. 3 and 12 volt source to terminal No. 4. If wiper is inoperative or does not park, repair wiper motor.

2) Check park switch actuator and brush holder. If wiper runs and parks in step **1)**, turn column switch off. Check current flow between terminals No. 2 and No. 3 on harness. If lamp lights, check for open in wire from terminal No. 4 to fuse block and repair.

3) If there is no current flow in step **2)**, check for open in wires from terminal No. 3 to column switch and repair. If there are no opens, replace column switch.

Wiper Will Not Shut Off

1) With ignition on and wiper switch off, remove connector from wiper terminal. Connect jumper from terminals No. 2 and No. 3 and 12 volts to terminal No. 4.

Fig. 1: Wiper Motor and Switch Wiring Diagram

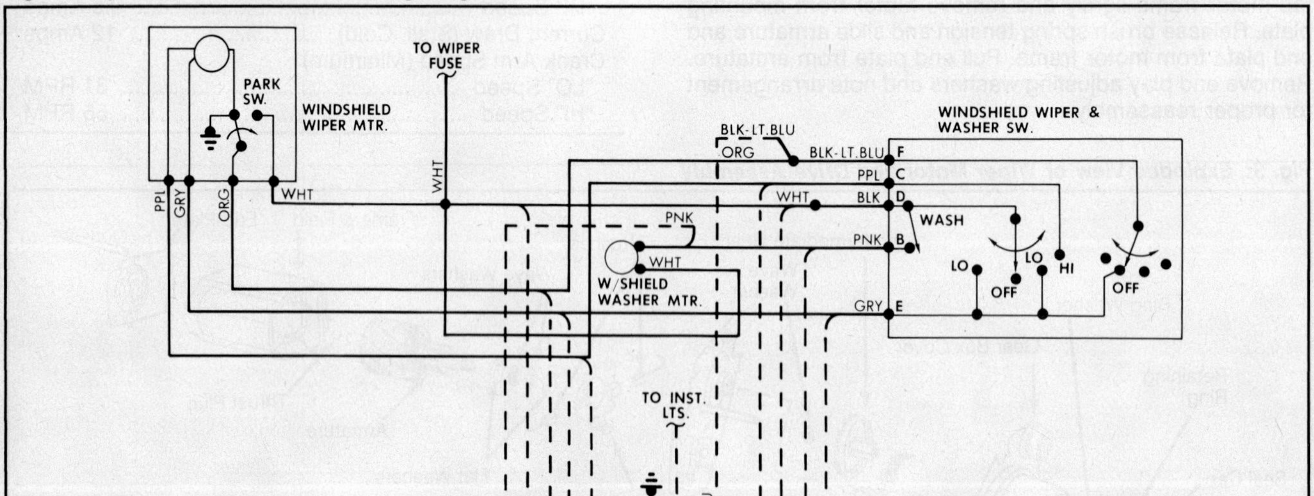

2) If wiper still runs, repair wiper motor (check park switch actuator and brush holder assembly). If wiper parks, replace column switch.

Intermittent Wiper Condition

1) Remove wiper fuse from fuse block and connect an ammeter accross fuse block terminals. Operate wipers in "HIGH" with windshield dry. Current draw will fluctuate. If current draw is below 5.0 amps, a weak circuit breaker is indicated. Replace brush holder assembly.

2) If current draw exceeds 5.0 amps, remove wiper arms and blades and repeat test. If current still exceeds 5 amps, go to step **3)**. If current draw is okay, replace wiper blade elements and repeat test. If current draw is okay, problem is corrected.

3) If current draw exceeded 5.0 amps in step **2)**, disconnect wiper linkage from motor crank arm and repeat test. If current draw is okay, wiper transmission linkage is binding. Repair or replace as needed.

4) If current draw exceeds 5.0 amps with linkage disconnected, repair wiper motor. Check for shorted or grounded armature.

Wiper Motor Runs But Blades Do Not Move

1) Check wiper linkage connection to crank arm. If linkage disconnected, connect linkage and check system.

2) If linkage is connected, wiper gear is stripped. Repair motor.

Wiper Motor Parks But Above Normal Position

1) With ignition switch on, and wiper switch in "PARK" position, remove connector from wiper terminal. Check for open between terminal No. 3 and ground. If there is an open, repair open in motor or replace holder assembly.

2) If there is no open, check arm and blade location and/or transmission linkage.

Fig. 2: Windshield Wiper Motor Components

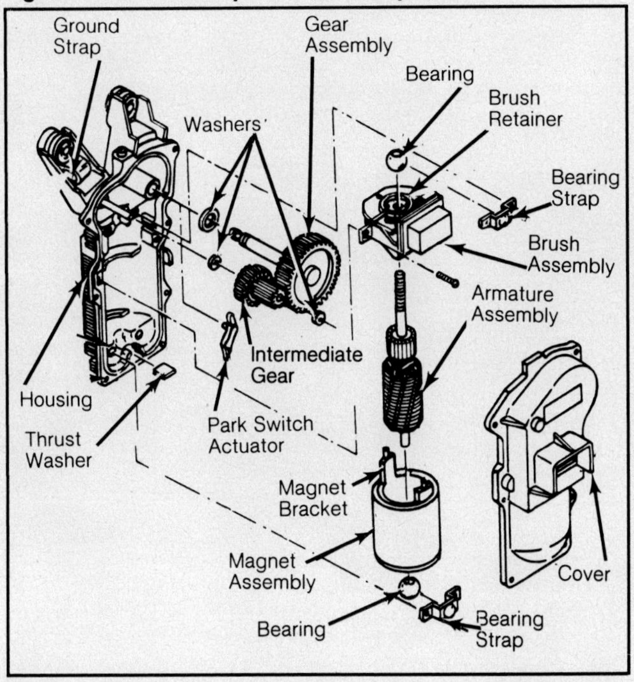

Replace rivets with self-tapping screws when reassembling.

REMOVAL & INSTALLATION

WIPER MOTOR

Removal

1) Disconnect battery negative cable. Remove wiper arms. Remove cowl vent and grille. Loosen but do not remove transmission drive link to motor crank arm attaching nuts.

2) Detach drive link from motor crank arm. Disconnect motor electrical leads. Remove motor attaching screws. Rotate motor upward and outward to remove.

Installation

Install motor by reversing removal procedure. Check operation of system.

WIPER MOTOR COVER

Removal

Remove wiper motor. From housing side, drill ends off 7 rivets holding cover to housing with an 11/64" drill bit. Remove cover.

Installation

To install, attach cover to housing with self-tapping screws.

WIPER HOUSING

Removal

1) Remove wiper motor. Remove wiper motor cover. Remove crank gear lock nut, crank arm, shaft seal, thrust collar and washer. Push end of gear shaft through housing and remove gear assembly and washer.

2) File burr from retaining ring groove and where crank arm seats on shaft. Remove intermediate gear and washers. Drill ends off 4 rivets holding bearings and bearing straps in place with an 11/64" drill bit. Be careful not to get metal chips into motor.

3) Remove 6-point socket screws holding brush assembly in place. Remove armature, brush and magnet

Fig. 3: Wiper Motor Brush Retainer Assembly

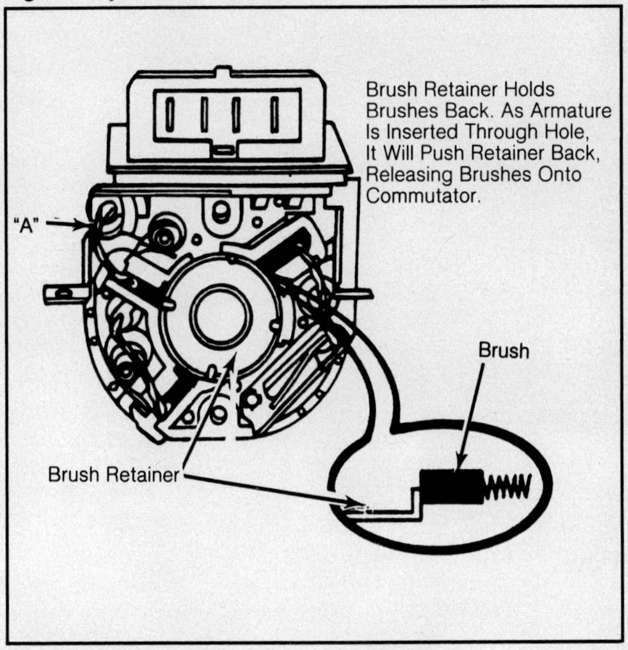

Brush Retainer Holds Brushes Back. As Armature Is Inserted Through Hole, It Will Push Retainer Back, Releasing Brushes Onto Commutator.
"A"
Brush
Brush Retainer

Braided contact wire "A" must be behind brush retaining spring.

GENERAL MOTORS – "S" SERIES (Cont.)

assembly together to avoid realignment of brushes. Alignment is shown in *Fig. 3*.

Installation

To install, reverse removal procedure. Use new housing, retaining ring and self-tapping screws. Position thrust pin casing with insert about 1/32" above rear of pin. *See Fig. 4.*

Fig. 4: Wiper Thrust Pin Adjustments

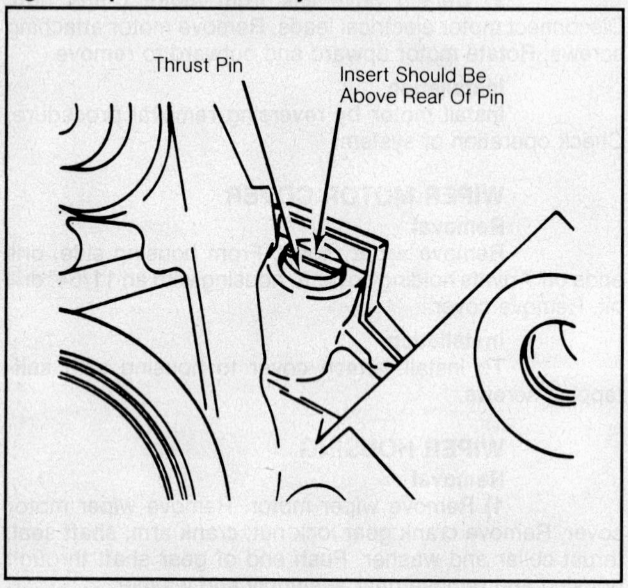

Check thrust pin insert protrusion.

JEEP

DESCRIPTION

Jeep vehicles use a 2-speed electric motor, which is a compound wound (series and shunt) type. A crank arm, attached externally to gear shaft, operates linkage which activates wiper blades.

All models have an optional intermittent feature. All models use an electric washer system consisting of a motor, reservoir, and necessary hoses and nozzles.

The pump assembly is mounted in bottom of reservoir. The motor case is grounded to vehicle body and is energized by a feed wire from control switch.

Some Cherokee and Wagoneer models are equipped with rear wipers. The rear motor is a single-speed motor with an automatic park feature. The circuit is protected by a separate 4.5 amp circuit breaker attached to brake pedal support.

TROUBLE SHOOTING

ALL EXCEPT CJ7 & SCRAMBLER

Wiper Inoperative or Operates at One Speed Only

1) If wiper does not operate on either speed, check for binding or interference of linkage. If okay, place wiper switch on "LOW" and then on "HIGH" setting. Connect a test lamp between terminals of wiring harness plug that connects to motor.

2) Check for power at White wire with tracer and Black (ground) wire terminal for low speed. Check between Dk. Blue with tracer and Black wire terminal for high speed.

3) If lamp does not light, check ignition switch, wiper switch, harness or terminals for open circuits. If lamp lights, check for loose or misaligned connection between wiring harness plug and motor plug. If okay, replace wiper motor.

Wipers Do Not Park

1) Disconnect motor and connect Black lead to White lead. Apply 12 volts to Red lead. Replace motor if it fails to park. If it parks, turn ignition switch on, and wiper switch to "PARK".

2) Connect a test lamp to Lt. Green wire with tracer and to ground at motor plug on Cherokee and Wagoneer. Between Pink wire with tracer and ground on Grand Wagoneer and Trucks.

3) Check continuity between Tan wire with tracer and White wire with tracer on Cherokee and Wagoneer. Check between Yellow wire with tracer and White wire with tracer on Grand Wagoneer and Trucks.

4) If test lamp does not light, check harness connections between motor and instrument panel switch. If okay, replace panel switch. If not okay, repair harness connection.

Wiper Motor Quits While Wiping

1) With engine idling and blower motor on high, operate wipers at high speed setting for 5 cycles consisting of 3 seconds of water and 57 seconds of drying.

2) If motor struggles to a complete stop, clean glass and replace blades. Repeat test. If motor stops, test circuit breaker in panel switch. If motor stopped suddenly in original test, check circuit breaker. Repeat test. If motor stops, replace motor.

All Functions Okay Except Intermittent Wipe

1) If blades stop and start erratically, test circuit breaker. If not, check wiper switch continuity. If continuity is not present, check continuity of wiring between switch, governor and ground. Repair wiring or replace governor as necessary.

2) If operation is intermittent on low speed only, check for loose connections at governor by disconnecting governor and connecting switch directly to instrument panel harness.

3) If all functions except pulse and mist work, replace governor. If functions are not okay, recheck wiring and replace governor.

Windshield Washer Does Not Operate

1) If motor runs but does not pump, check fluid level. If level is okay, check for split, loose, pinched or kinked hoses. Check for restrictions at nozzles. Check for reversed wire leads to motor. If pump is still inoperative, replace pump motor.

2) If motor does not run, check for blown fuse. Replace fuse, if necessary. If fuse is okay, disconnect plug at reservoir and check for power by connecting a test lamp across connector terminals. Energize washer circuit by closing washer and ignition switches.

3) If no power is present, check for open ground wire or defective wiper/washer switch. Repair or replace as necessary. If power is present, reconnect plug to motor and check for tight connection. If motor does not run, replace pump motor.

Fig. 1: Jeep 2-Speed Wiper System Wiring Diagram

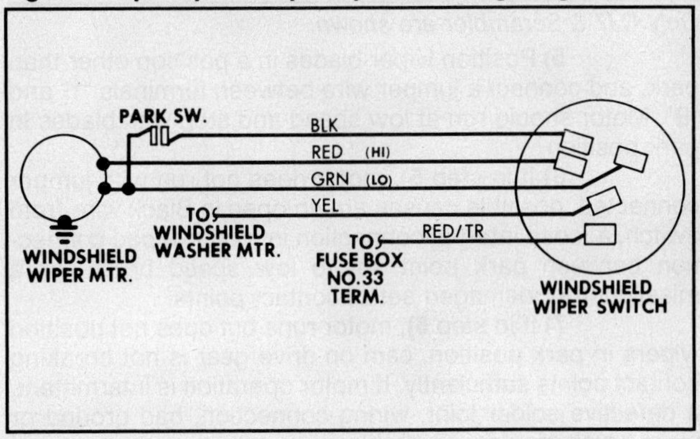

Only CJ7 and Scrambler are shown.

TESTING

CJ7 & SCRAMBLER

NOTE: **The wiper motor must be grounded for proper operation during all test procedures.**

Intermittent Governor Test

1) Special electronic testing equipment is required to check governor. However, check all other components in event of unsatisfactory intermittent wiper cycle. If all components function properly, install new governor.

2) The 6" governor lead plugs into wiper control switch. The shorter 4" lead plugs into instrument panel switch.

Wiper Motor Test

1) Turn ignition on. Use a test lamp to check for 12 volts at switch terminal "B". *See Fig. 2.* If test lamp lights but motor does not operate, ensure ground is good by connecting a jumper wire from motor ground strap to a good body ground.

Wiper/Washer Systems

JEEP (Cont.)

2) If motor still will not operate, disconnect jumper wire. Disconnect wiring from switch. Connect a jumper wire between terminals "2" and "B", which should give low speed operation of motor.

3) If motor does not operate on low speed, possible causes are an open condition in Green wire leading from switch, a loose internal connection in motor, or a stuck low speed brush.

4) Connect a jumper wire between terminals "3" and "B", which should give high speed operation of motor. If motor does not operate on high speed, possible causes are an open condition in Red wire leading from switch, a loose internal connection in motor, or a stuck high speed brush.

Fig. 2: Jeep Identification of Test Connections

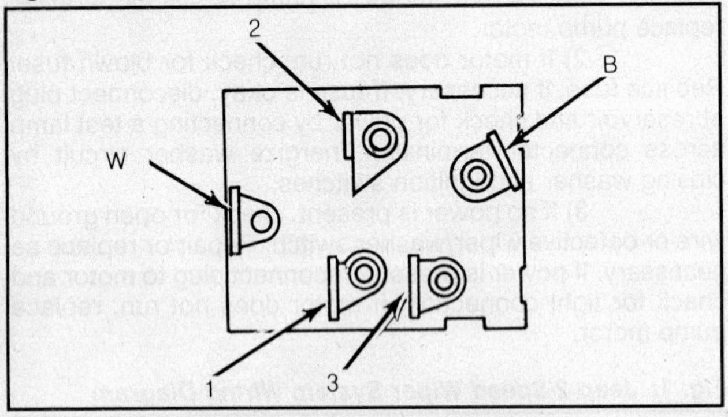

Only CJ7 & Scrambler are shown.

5) Position wiper blades in a position other than park, and connect a jumper wire between terminals "1" and "B". Motor should run at low speed and stop with blades in park position.

6) If in step **5)**, motor does not run with jumper connected, possible causes are an open in Black wire from switch, a loose internal connection in motor, a bad connection between park point set to low speed brush, or a misaligned or damaged set of contact points.

7) If in step **5)**, motor runs but does not position wipers in park position, cam on drive gear is not breaking contact points sufficiently. If motor operation is intermittent, a defective solder joint, wiring connection, bad ground or worn brush may cause problem.

GRAND WAGONEER & TRUCK

Wiper Switch Test

1) Check wiper switch continuity, using a continuity light (J 21008) or an ohmmeter. Continuity should exist at switch positions indicated in *Fig. 3.*

2) Using an ohmmeter, check variable resistance between terminals "4" and "5" of intermittent system. If intermittent wipe cycle is not working, but system operates properly on low and high speeds. Turn switch knob counterclockwise as far as possible. Ohmmeter should indicate 5600-8400 ohms.

3) As knob is turned clockwise, resistance should decrease to a minimum of 100-900 ohms. Replace switch if continuity or resistance tests fail. If operation is proper, check wiring.

Circuit Breaker Test

1) Two tests are available for 7 amp circuit breaker. Connect wiper switch as shown in *Fig. 3.* Adjust current draw until it equals circuit breaker rating. Leave switch connected for 10 minutes. Current reading on ammeter should remain at rated current.

2) If circuit breaker opens during 10 minute period, replace switch assembly. Adjust current draw until it is twice circuit breaker rating (14 amps). Current reading on ammeter should drop to zero within 15 seconds. If it takes longer for circuit breaker to open, replace switch assembly.

Intermittent Governor Test

1) Special electronic testing equipment is required to check governor. However, check all other components in event of unsatisfactory intermittent wiper cycle. If all components function properly, install new governor.

2) The 6" governor lead plugs into wiper control switch. The shorter 4" lead plugs into instrument panel switch.

Current Draw Test

1) Remove wiper arms and blades, and disconnect motor lead. Connect negative lead of ammeter to positive battery post. *See Fig. 3.* Connect other ammeter test lead to Blue wire with tracer (low speed) of motor harness.

2) Current draw should be approximately 1 amp, but not more than 3 amps. Connect ammeter lead to Blue wire terminal (high speed). Current draw should remain level, but never over 3 amps.

Park Test

1) Disconnect motor from harness connection. Temporarily, connect a battery jumper wire to either Blue wire or Blue wire with tracer. This will move wiper arms and blades away from normal park position. Insert a jumper wire from White to Black wire terminals.

2) Contact a battery jumper wire to Red wire terminal of motor harness. Motor should operate until wipers have reached normal park position. If not, replace wiper motor.

REMOVAL & INSTALLATION

REAR WIPER SWITCH

Removal & Installation (Cherokee & Wagoneer)

Remove instrument panel bezel and switch housing panel. Disconnect switch connector, slightly depress switch mounting tabs and remove switch. To install, reverse removal procedure.

WINDSHIELD WIPER SWITCH

Removal & Installation (CJ7 & Scrambler)

On vehicles with A/C, remove screws attaching evaporator assembly to instrument panel and lower evaporator assembly. Remove wiper control knob. Remove nut and switch. Mark wire color locations for installation reference and disconnect wires. To install, reverse removal procedure.

Removal & Installation (Grand Wagoneer & Trucks)

1) Disconnect negative battery cable. Locate small notch at base of knob and insert a small screwdriver to release one-way friction spring. This spring allows knob to be installed, but prevents removal unless spring tension is released.

2) Remove slotted trim nut from front of switch. Push switch through instrument panel, disconnect wiring harness and remove switch. To install, reverse removal procedure.

JEEP (Cont.)

Fig. 3: Testing Wiper/Washer System

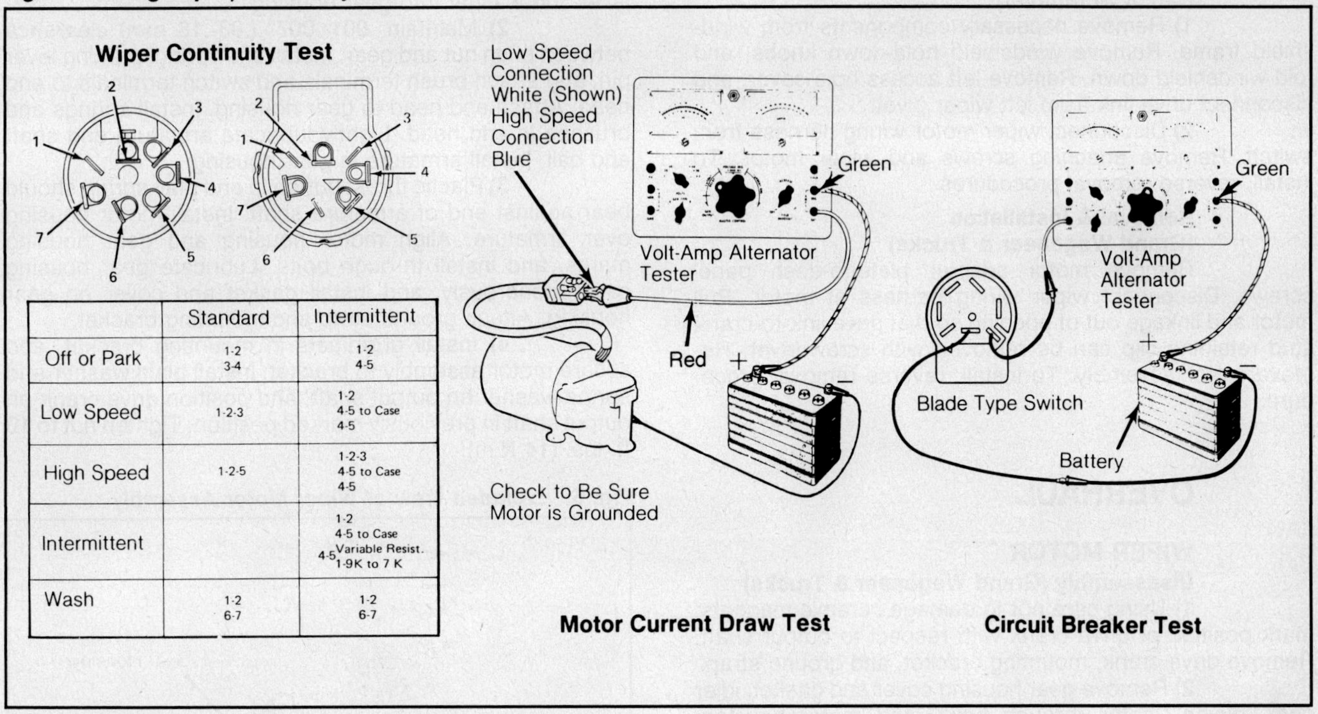

	Standard	Intermittent
Off or Park	1-2 3-4	1-2 4-5
Low Speed	1-2-3	1-2 4-5 to Case 4-5
High Speed	1-2-5	1-2-3 4-5 to Case 4-5
Intermittent		1-2 4-5 to Case 4-5 Variable Resist. 1.9K to 7 K
Wash	1-2 6-7	1-2 6-7

Only Grand Wagoneer and Trucks are shown.

Fig. 4: Jeep 2-Speed Wiper System Wiring Diagram

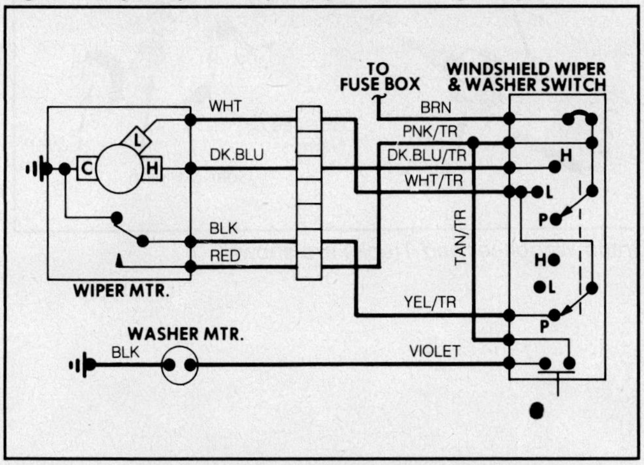

System is standard for Grand Wagoneer and Trucks.

Fig. 5: Jeep 2-Speed Wiper System Wiring Diagram

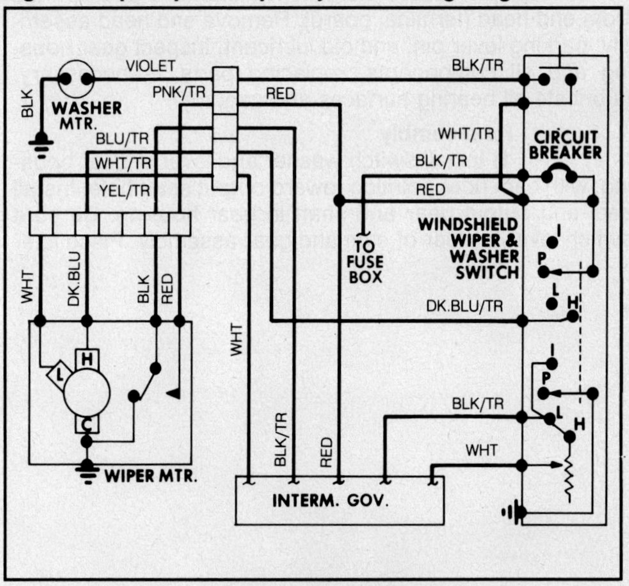

Grand Wagoneer and Trucks with intermittent governor.

REAR WIPER MOTOR

Removal & Installation (Cherokee & Wagoneer)

1) Remove wiper arm from pivot pin by depressing tab and pulling arm straight out. Disconnect washer hose. Remove pivot pin retaining nut and interior trim panel. Remove rear wiper motor attaching screws and remove wiper motor.

2) To install, reverse removal procedure. Wiper blade should be parallel to window in parked position (3/8"-3/4" from bottom of window) and come no closer than 3/16" to window seal when operated on a wet window.

WINDSHIELD WIPER MOTOR

Removal & Installation (Cherokee & Wagoneer)

Remove wiper arm assemblies by lifting blades off windshield and pulling out tab that locks blade in up position. Remove cowl trim panel. Disconnect washer hose. Remove cowl mounting bracket attaching nuts and pivot pin screws. Disconnect wiring harness and remove wiper motor. To install, reverse removal procedure.

JEEP (Cont.)

Removal & Installation
(CJ7 & Scrambler)

1) Remove necessary components from windshield frame. Remove windshield hold-down knobs, and fold windshield down. Remove left access hole cover, and disconnect drive link from left wiper pivot.

2) Disconnect wiper motor wiring harness from switch. Remove attaching screws and wiper motor. To install, reverse removal procedures.

Removal & Installation
(Grand Wagoneer & Trucks)

Remove motor adapter plate-to-dash panel screws. Disconnect wiper wiring harness at motor. Pull motor and linkage out of opening so that drive link-to-crank stud retaining clip can be removed with screwdriver. Remove motor assembly. To install, reverse removal procedure.

OVERHAUL

WIPER MOTOR

Disassembly (Grand Wagoneer & Trucks)

1) Using care not to damage ceramic magnets, mark position of drive crank with respect to output shaft. Remove drive crank, mounting bracket, and ground strap.

2) Remove gear housing cover and gasket, idler gear, pinion, motor through bolts, and motor housing. Remove end play spring, output gear and shaft, switch lever, washer, and seal from gear housing.

3) Disassemble brushes, harness and springs from end head (terminal board). Remove end head assembly, parking lever pin, and old lubricant. Inspect gear housing and all components, replacing parts as necessary. Lubricate all bearing surfaces and gears.

Reassembly

1) Install switch washer and lever in gear housing, with cam rider pointing toward output shaft hole. Install seal and output gear and shaft in gear housing. Be sure switch lever is clear of cam and gear assembly. Place idler gear and pinion on shaft, and insert shaft through switch lever and washer into gear housing.

2) Maintain .001-.007" (.03-.18 mm) clearance between push nut and gear. Install end spring, parking lever pin, and attach brush terminals and switch terminals to end head. Attach end head to gear housing. Install springs and brushes in end head. Lightly lubricate armature end shaft and ball. Install armature in gear housing.

3) Plastic thrust button in end play spring should bear against end of armature shaft. Install motor housing over armature. Align motor housing and gear housing marks, and install through bolts. Lubricate gear housing cavity generously, and install gasket and cover on gear housing. Attach ground strap and mounting bracket.

4) Install grommets in mounting bracket, and secure motor assembly to bracket. Install plain washer and spring washer on output shaft, and position drive crank on output shaft in previously marked position. Tighten nut to 10 ft. lbs. (14 N.m).

Fig. 6: Exploded View of Wiper Motor Assembly

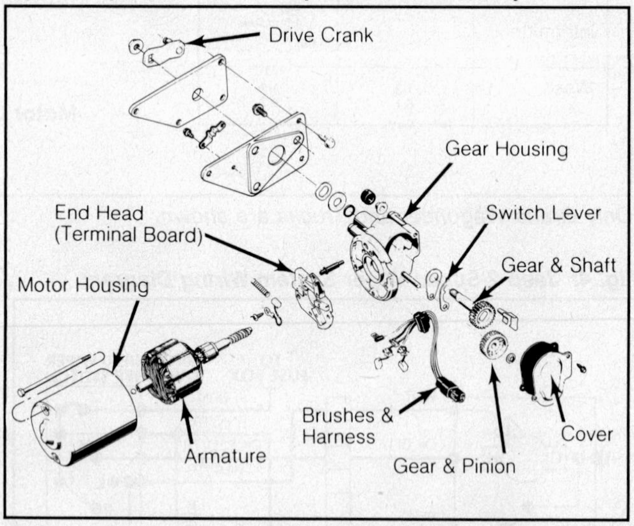

Grand Wagoneer and Trucks are shown.

FORD, GENERAL MOTORS & JEEP

DESCRIPTION

Ford vehicles equipped with 2.3L Turbo Diesel and 6.9L Diesel engines use a vacuum pump to supply vacuum to power-assist brake booster. The pump is driven by a single drive belt off alternator pulley.

General Motors vehicles equipped with 2.2L and 6.2L Diesel engines use vacuum pumps to assist in maintaining a proper vacuum level for accessories. This is accomplished by using either belt driven or gear driven mechanical-type pumps.

Jeep vehicles equipped with 2.1L Turbo Diesel use an oil pump-driven vacuum pump to assist in maintaining a proper vacuum level for accessories.

OPERATION

GENERAL MOTORS

Belt Driven Pump

The belt driven pump is a diaphragm-type pump that requires a belt adjustment at regular intervals. It is driven by alternator belt.

Gear Driven Pump

The gear driven pump is a diaphragm-type pump driven by a cam inside drive housing assembly to which it mounts. The drive housing assembly has a drive gear on lower end that meshes with camshaft gear in engine. This drive gear causes cam in drive housing to rotate. The drive gear also powers engine oil pump.

JEEP

Gear Driven Pump

The gear driven pump is a diaphragm-type pump driven by a cam inside drive housing assembly to which it mounts. The drive housing assembly has a drive gear on lower end that meshes with oil pump gear in engine. This drive gear causes cam in drive housing to rotate.

DIAGNOSIS & TESTING

FORD, GENERAL MOTORS & JEEP

1) Block wheels, apply parking brake and place transmission in Park (A/T) or Neutral (M/T). On Ford vehicles, disconnect vacuum pump hose from brake booster and install a vacuum gauge. *See Fig. 1.*

2) On General Motors and Jeep vehicles, connect vacuum gauge to pump inlet. *See Fig. 1.* Disconnect outlet hose from oultlet tube on pump and plug end of hose, if used. DO NOT plug outlet tube with engine idling.

3) Minimum vacuum reading should be 21 in. Hg at sea level, within 30 seconds. For higher altitudes, compensate vacuum reading according to graph. *See Fig. 1.*

4) If vacuum pump checks okay, go to step **5**). If vacuum reading is low or fluctuating, check gauge and connections for leaks. If pump is belt driven, check belt tension and pulley fit to shaft. Check idle speed. Recheck vacuum pump. If vacuum reading is still low, replace vacuum pump. If vacuum checks okay, go to next step.

5) Remove plug from outlet hose and reconnect hose to pump outlet tube, if used. Reconnect vacuum hose with a tee and vacuum gauge located near pump inlet. *See Fig. 2.* With engine ilding, vacuum may be 3 in. Hg less than that measured in step **1**).

Fig. 1: Vacuum Pump Diagnosis

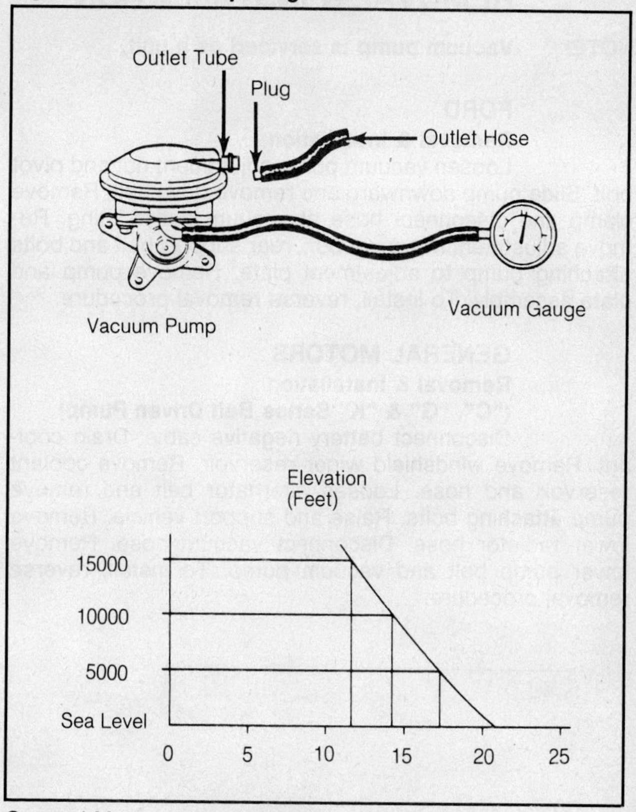

General Motors pump is shown, Jeep is similar.

6) If vacuum reading is okay, remaining problems are not in vacuum system. If vacuum reading is lower than specified, check hoses for leaks and repair as necessary. If vacuum reading is still low, check vacuum accessories for leaks. Repair or replace as necessary.

Fig. 2: Vehicle Vacuum System Diagnosis

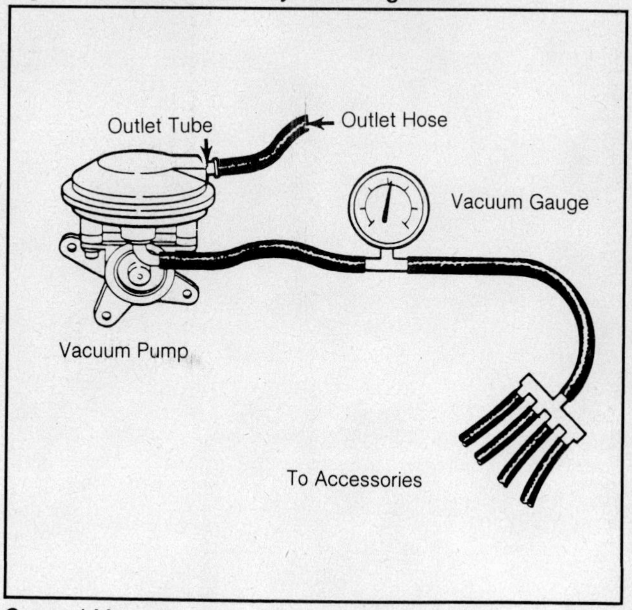

General Motors pump is shown, Jeep is similar.

Vacuum Pumps

FORD, GENERAL MOTORS & JEEP (Cont.)

REMOVAL & INSTALLATION

NOTE: Vacuum pump is serviced as a unit.

FORD

Removal & Installation

Loosen vacuum pump adjustment nut and pivot bolt. Slide pump downward and remove drive belt. Remove clamp and disconnect hose at vacuum outlet fitting. Remove adjustment nut, pivot bolt, rear support bolt and bolts attaching pump to adjustment plate. Remove pump and plate assembly. To install, reverse removal procedure.

GENERAL MOTORS

Removal & Installation
("C", "G" & "K" Series Belt Driven Pump)

Disconnect battery negative cable. Drain coolant. Remove windshield wiper reservoir. Remove coolant reservoir and hose. Loosen alternator belt and remove pump attaching bolts. Raise and support vehicle. Remove lower radiator hose. Disconnect vacuum hose. Remove lower pump bolt and vacuum pump. To install, reverse removal procedure.

Removal & Installation
("S" Series Belt Driven Pump)

Disconnect battery negative cable and vacuum hose. Loosen and remove vacuum pump belt. Remove vacuum pump pulley-to-hub attaching bolts. Remove pump and bracket from engine. Remove bracket from pump. Press off hub when replacing pump. To install reverse removal procedure.

Removal & Installation
("C", "G" & "K" Series Gear Driven Pump)

Remove vacuum hose from pump inlet. Remove bolt and clamp holding drive assembly to engine block. Lift pump and drive assembly out of vehicle. Cover hole to prevent foreign materials from falling into engine. To install, reverse removal procedure.

JEEP

Removal & Installation
(Cherokee and Wagoneer)

Remove vacuum hose from pump inlet. Remove bolts holding drive assembly to engine block. Remove pump and drive assembly from vehicle. Cover drive assembly hole to keep dirt and moisture out of engine. To install, reverse removal procedure.

SECTION 7

ENGINES

CONTENTS

ENGINE TROUBLE SHOOTING

NOTE: **ALSO SEE GENERAL INDEX.**

IMPORTANT: **Because of the many model names used by vehicle manufacturers, accurate identification of models is important. See Model Identification at the front of this publication.**

Engine Trouble Shooting

GASOLINE ENGINE TROUBLE SHOOTING

CONDITION	POSSIBLE CAUSE	CORRECTION
Engine Lopes At Idle	Intake manifold-to-head leaks	Replace manifold gasket, see ENGINES
	Blown head gasket	Replace head gasket, see ENGINES
	Worn timing gears, chain or sprocket	Replace gears, chain or sprocket
	Worn camshaft lobes	Replace camshaft, see ENGINES
	Overheated engine	Check cooling system, see COOLING
	Blocked crankcase vent valve	Remove restriction
	Leaking EGR valve	Repair leak and/or replace valve
	Faulty fuel pump	Replace fuel pump
Engine Has Low Power	Leaking fuel pump	Repair leak and/or replace fuel pump
	Excessive piston-to-bore clearance	Install larger pistons, see ENGINES
	Sticking valves or weak valve springs	Check valve train components, see ENGINES
	Incorrect valve timing	Reset valve timing, see ENGINES
	Worn camshaft lobes	Replace camshaft, see ENGINES
	Blown head gasket	Replace head gasket, see ENGINES
	Clutch slipping	Adjust pedal and/or replace components, see CLUTCHES
	Engine overheating	Check cooling system, see COOLING
	Auto. trans. pressure regulator valve faulty	Replace pressure regulator valve
	Auto. trans. fluid level too low	Add fluid as necessary, see TRANSMISSIONS
	Improper vacuum diverter valve operation	Replace vacuum diverter valve
	Vacuum leaks	Inspect vacuum system and repair as required
	Leaking piston rings	Replace piston rings, see ENGINES
Faulty High Speed Operation	Low fuel pump volume	Replace fuel pump
	Leaking valves or worn valve springs	Replace valves and/or springs, see ENGINES
	Incorrect valve timing	Reset valve timing, see ENGINES
	Intake manifold restricted	Remove restriction
	Worn distributor shaft	Replace distributor
Faulty Acceleration	Improper fuel pump stroke	Remove pump and reset pump stroke
	Incorrect ignition timing	Reset ignition timing, see TUNE-UP
	Leaking valves	Replace valves, see ENGINES
	Worn fuel pump diaphragm or piston	Replace diaphragm or piston
Intake Backfire	Improper ignition timing	Reset ignition timing, see TUNE-UP
	Faulty accelerator pump discharge	Replace accelerator pump
	Improper choke operation	Check choke and adjust as required
	Defective EGR valve	Replace EGR valve
	Fuel mixture too lean	Reset air/fuel mixture, see TUNE-UP
	Choke valve initial clearance too large	Reset choke valve initial clearance
Exhaust Backfire	Vacuum leak	Inspect and repair vacuum system
	Faulty vacuum diverter valve	Replace vacuum diverter valve
	Faulty choke operation	Check choke and adjust as required
	Exhaust system leak	Repair exhaust system leak
Engine Detonation	Ignition timing too far advanced	Reset ignition timing, see TUNE-UP
	Faulty ignition system	Check ignition system, see ELECTRICAL
	Spark plugs loose or faulty	Retighten or replace plugs
	Fuel delivery system clogged	Inspect lines, pump and filter for clog
	EGR valve inoperative	Replace EGR valve
	PCV system inoperative	Inspect and/or replace hoses or valve
	Vacuum leaks	Check vacuum system and repair leaks
	Excessive combustion chamber deposits	Remove built-up deposits
	Leaking, sticking or broken valves	Inspect and/or replace valves
External Oil Leakage	Fuel pump improperly seated or worn gasket	Remove pump, replace gasket and seat properly
	Valve cover gasket broken	Replace valve cover gasket
	Oil filter gasket broken	Replace oil filter and gasket
	Oil pan gasket broken or pan bent	Straighten pan and replace gasket
	Timing chain cover gasket broken	Replace timing chain cover gasket

Engine Trouble Shooting

GASOLINE ENGINE TROUBLE SHOOTING (Cont.)

CONDITION	POSSIBLE CAUSE	CORRECTION
External Oil Leakage (Cont.)	Rear main oil seal worn	Replace rear main oil seal
	Oil pan drain plug not seated properly	Remove and reinstall drain plug
	Camshaft bearing drain hole blocked	Remove restriction
	Oil pressure sending switch leaking	Remove and reinstall sending switch
Excessive Oil Consumption	Worn valve stems or guides	Replace stems or guides, see ENGINES
	Valve "O" ring seals damaged	Replace "O" ring seals, see ENGINES
	Plugged oil drain back holes	Remove restrictions
	Improper PCV valve operation	Replace PCV valve
	Engine oil level too high	Remove excess oil
	Engine oil too thin	Replace with thicker oil
	Valve stem oil deflectors damaged	Replace oil defelctors
	Incorrect piston rings	Replace piston rings, see ENGINES
	Piston ring gaps not staggered	Reinstall piston rings, see ENGINES
	Insufficient piston ring tension	Replace rings, see ENGINES
	Piston ring grooves or oil return slots clogged	Replace piston rings, see ENGINES
	Piston rings sticking in grooves	Replace piston rings, see ENGINES
	Piston ring grooves excessively worn	Replace piston and rings, see ENGINES
	Compression rings installed upside down	Replace compression rings correctly, see ENGINES
	Worn or scored cylinder walls	Rebore cylinders or replace block
	Mismatched oil ring expander and rail	Replace oil ring expander and rail, see ENGINES
	Intake gasket dowels too long	Replace intake gasket dowels
	Excessive main or connecting rod bearing clearance	Replace main or connecting rod bearings, see ENGINES
No Oil Pressure	Low oil level	Add oil to proper level
	Oil pressure sender or gauge broken	Replace sender or gauge
	Oil pump malfunction	Remove and overhaul oil pump, see ENGINES
	Oil pressure relief valve sticking	Remove and reinstall valve
	Oil pump passages blocked	Overhaul oil pump, see ENGINES
	Oil pickup screen or tube blocked	Remove restriction
	Loose oil inlet tube	Tighten oil inlet tube
	Loose camshaft bearings	Replace camshaft bearings, see ENGINES
	Internal leakage at oil passages	Replace block or cylinder head
Low Oil Pressure	Low engine oil level	Add oil to proper level
	Engine oil too thin	Remove and replace with thicker oil
	Excessive oil pump clearance	Reduce oil pump clearance, see ENGINES
	Oil pickup tube or screen blocked	Remove restrictions
	Oil pressure relief spring weak or stuck	Eliminate binding or replace spring
	Main, rod or cam bearing clearance excessive	Replace bearing to reduce clearance, see ENGINES
High Oil Pressure	Improper grade of oil	Replace with proper oil
	Oil pressure relief valve stuck closed	Eliminate binding
	Oil pressure sender or gauge faulty	Replace sender or gauge
Noisy Main Bearings	Inadequate oil supply	Check oil delivery to main bearings
	Excessive main bearing clearance	Replace main bearings, see ENGINES
	Excessive crankshaft end play	Replace crankshaft, see ENGINES
	Loose flywheel or torque converter	Tighten attaching bolts
	Loose or damaged vibration damper	Tighten or replace vibration damper
	Crankshaft journals out-of-round	Re-grind crankshaft journals
	Excessive belt tension	Loosen belt tension
Noisy Connecting Rods	Excessive bearing clearance or missing bearing	Replace bearing, see ENGINES
	Crankshaft rod journal out-of-round	Re-grind crankshaft journal
	Misaligned connecting rod or cap	Remove rod or cap and re-align
	Incorrectly tighten rod bolts	Remove and re-tighten rod bolts

Engine Trouble Shooting

GASOLINE ENGINE TROUBLE SHOOTING (Cont.)

CONDITION	POSSIBLE CAUSE	CORRECTION
Noisy Pistons and Rings	Excessive piston-to-bore clearance	Install larger pistons, see ENGINES
	Bore tapered or out-of-round	Rebore block
	Piston ring broken	Replace piston rings, see ENGINES
	Piston pin loose or seized	Replace piston pin, see ENGINES
	Connecting rods misaligned	Re-align connecting rods
	Ring side clearance too loose or tight	Replace with larger or smaller rings
	Carbon build-up on piston	Remove carbon
Noisy Valve Train	Worn or bent push rods	Replace push rods, see ENGINES
	Worn rocker arms or bridged pivots	Replace rocker arms or pivots, see ENGINES
	Dirt or chips in valve lifters	Remove lifters and remove dirt/chips
	Excessive valve lifter leak-down	Replace valve lifters, see ENGINES
	Valve lifter face worn	Replace valve lifters, see ENGINES
	Broken or cocked valve springs	Replace or reposition springs
	Too much valve stem-to-guide clearance	Replace valve guides, see ENGINES
	Valve bent	Replace valve, see ENGINES
	Loose rocker arms	Retighten rocker arms, see ENGINES
	Excessive valve seat run-out	Re-face valve seats, see ENGINES
	Missing valve lock	Install new valve lock
	Push rod contacting cylinder head	Replace with shorter push rod
	Excessively worn camshaft lobes	Replace camshaft, see ENGINES
	Plugged valve lifter oil holes	Eliminate restriction or replace lifter
	Faulty valve lifter check ball	Replace lifter check ball, see ENGINES
	Rocker arm nut installed upside down	Remove and reinstall correctly
	Valve lifter incorrect for engine	Remove and replace valve lifters
	Faulty push rod seat or lifter plunger	Replace plunger or push rod
Noisy Valves	Improper valve lash	Re-adjust valve lash, see ENGINES
	Worn or dirty valve lifters	Clean and/or replace lifters
	Worn valve guides	Replace valve guides, see ENGINES
	Excessive valve seat or face run-out	Re-face seats or valve face
	Worn camshaft lobes	Replace camshaft, see ENGINES
	Loose rocker arm studs	Re-tighten rocker arm studs, see ENGINES
	Bent push rods	Replace push rods, see ENGINES
	Broken valve springs	Replace valve springs, see ENGINES
Burned, Sticking or Broken Valves	Weak valve springs or warped valves	Replace valves and/or springs, see ENGINES
	Improper lifter clearance	Re-adjust clearance or replace lifters
	Worn guides or improper guide clearance	Replace valve guides, see ENGINES
	Out-of-round valve seats or improper seat width	Re-grind valve seats
	Gum deposits on valve stems, seats or guides	Remove deposits
	Improper spark timing	Re-adjust spark timing
Broken Pistons/Rings	Undersize pistons	Replace with larger pistons, see ENGINES
	Wrong piston rings	Replace with correct rings, see ENGINES
	Out-of-round cylinder bore	Re-bore cylinder bore
	Improper connecting rod alignment	Remove and re-align connecting rods
	Excessively worn ring grooves	Replace pistons, see ENGINES
	Improperly assembled piston pins	Re-assemble pin-to-piston, see ENGINES
	Insufficient ring gap clearance	Install new rings, see ENGINES
	Engine overheating	Check cooling system
	Incorrect ignition timing	Re-adjust ignition timing, see TUNE-UP
Excessive Exhaust Noise	Leaks at manifold to head, or to pipe	Replace manifold or pipe gasket
	Exhaust manifold cracked or broken	Replace exhaust manifold, see ENGINES

Engine Trouble Shooting

DIESEL ENGINE TROUBLE SHOOTING

NOTE: **Diesel engine mechanical diagnosis is the same as gasoline engines for items such as noisy valves, bearings, pistons, etc. The following troubie shooting covers only items pertaining to diesel engines**

CONDITION	POSSIBLE CAUSE	CORRECTION
Engine Won't Crank	Bad battery connections or dead batteries	Check connections and/or replace batteries
	Bad starter connections or bad starter	Check connections and/or replace starter
Engine Cranks Slowly, Won't Start	Bad battery connections or dead batteries	Check connections and/or replace batteries
	Engine oil too heavy	Replace engine oil
Engine Cranks Normally, But Will Not Start	Glow plugs not functioning	Check glow plug system, see FUEL
	Glow plug control not functioning	Check glow plug controller, see FUEL
	Fuel not injected into cylinders	Check fuel injectors, see FUEL
	No fuel to injection pump	Check fuel delivery system
	Fuel filter blocked	Replace fuel filter
	Fuel tank filter blocked	Replace fuel tank filter
	Fuel pump not operating	Check pump operation and/or replace pump
	Fuel return system blocked	Inspect system and remove restriction
	No voltage to fuel solenoid	Check solenoid and connections
	Incorrect or contaminated fuel	Replace fuel
	Incorrect injection pump timing	Re-adjust pump timing, see FUEL
	Low compression	Check valves, pistons, rings, see ENGINES
	Injection pump malfunction	Inspect and/or replace injection pump
Engine Starts, Won't Idle	Incorrect slow idle adjustment	Reset idle adjustment, see TUNE-UP
	Fast idle solenoid malfunctioning	Check solenoid and connections
	Fuel return system blocked	Check system and remove restrictions
	Glow plugs go off too soon	See glow plug diagnosis in FUEL
	Injection pump timing incorrect	Reset pump timing, see FUEL
	No fuel to injection pump	Check fuel delivery system
	Incorrect or contaminated fuel	Replace fuel
	Low compression	Check valves, piston, rings, see ENGINES
	Injection pump malfunction	Replace injection pump, see FUEL
	Fuel solenoid closes in RUN position	Check solenoid and connections
Engine Starts/Idles Rough Without Smoke or Noise	Incorrect slow idle adjustment	Reset slow idle, see TUNE-UP
	Injection line fuel leaks	Check lines and connections
	Fuel return system blocked	Check lines and connections
	Air in fuel system	Bleed air from system
	Incorrect or contaminated fuel	Replace fuel
	Injector nozzle malfunction	Test and/or replace nozzles, see FUEL
Engine Starts and Idles Rough Without Smoke or Noise, But Clears After Warm-Up	Injection pump timing incorrect	Reset pump timing, see FUEL
	Engine not fully broken in	Put more miles on engine
	Air in system	Bleed air from system
	Injector nozzle malfunction	Check nozzles, see FUEL
Engine Idles Correctly, Misfires Above Idle	Blocked fuel filter	Replace fuel filter
	Injection pump timing incorrect	Reset pump timing, see FUEL
	Incorrect or contaminated fuel	Replace fuel
Engine Won't Return to Idle	Fast idle adjustment incorrect	Reset fast idle, see TUNE-UP
	Internal injection pump malfunction	Replace injection pump, see FUEL
	External linkage binding	Check linkage and remove binding
Fuel Leaks on Ground	Loose or broken fuel line	Check lines and connections
	Internal injection pump seal leak	Replace injection pump, see FUEL
Loss of Engine Power	Restricted air intake	Remove restriction
	EGR valve malfunction	Replace EGR valve
	Blocked or damaged exhaust system	Remove restriction and/or replace components
	Blocked fuel tank filter	Replace filter
	Restricted fuel filter	Remove restriction and/or replace filter

DIESEL ENGINE TROUBLE SHOOTING (Cont.)

CONDITION	POSSIBLE CAUSE	CORRECTION
Loss of Engine Power (Cont.)	Blocked vent in gas cap	Remove restriction and/or replace cap
	Tank-to-injection pump fuel supply blocked	Check fuel lines and connections
	Blocked fuel return system	Remove restriction
	Incorrect or contaminated fuel	Replace fuel
	Blocked injector nozzles	Remove nozzle and remove blockage, see FUEL
	Low compression	Check valves, rings, pistons, see ENGINES
Cylinder Knocking Noise	Injector nozzles sticking open	Test injectors and/or replace, see FUEL
	Very low nozzle opening pressure	Test injectors and/or replace
Loud Engine Noise With Black Smoke	Basic timing incorrect	Reset timing, see FUEL
	EGR valve malfunction	Replace EGR valve
	Internal injection pump malfunction	Replace injection pump, see FUEL
	Incorrect injector pump housing pressure	Check pressure and adjust, see FUEL
Engine Overheating	Cooling system leaks	Check cooling system and repair leaks
	Belt slipping or damaged	Check tension and/or replace belt
	Thermostat stuck closed	Remove and replace thermostat, see COOLING
	Head gasket leaking	Replace head gasket
Oil Light on at Idle	Low oil pump pressure	Check oil pump operation, see ENGINES
	Oil cooler or line restricted	Remove restriction and/or replace cooler
Engine Won't Shut Off	Injector pump fuel solenoid does not return fuel valve to OFF position	Remove and check solenoid and replace if needed
	VACUUM PUMP DIAGNOSIS	
Excessive Noise	Loose pump-to-drive assembly screws	Tighten screws
	Loose tube on pump assembly	Tighten tube
	Valves not functioning properly	Replace valves
Oil Leakage	Loose end plug	Tighten end plug
	Bad seal crimp	Remove and re-crimp seal

Chrysler Corp. Engines

2.2 LITER 4-CYLINDER

IDENTIFICATION CODING

ENGINE IDENTIFICATION

Engine may be identified from the Vehicle Identification Number (VIN) stamped on a Gray metal tab located on top left corner of instrument panel, visible through windshield.

The VIN number contains 17 characters. The 8th character identifies the engine and the 10th character establishes the model year. In addition, the engine identification number is stamped on left rear side of cylinder block, below cylinder head.

ENGINE IDENTIFICATION CODE

Engine	Code
2.2L 2-Bbl.	C

SPECIAL ENGINE MARKS

Information identifying undersize and oversize components will be found at various locations on engine. It is decoded as follows:

- Camshaft bearing caps painted Green with "O/S J" stamped on rear of oil gallery plug on air pump end of cylinder head indicate oversize camshaft journals.
- Camshafts painted Green with "O/S J" stamped on air pump end of camshaft indicate an oversize camshaft journal diameter of 1.395-1.396" (35.433-35.458 mm).

ENGINE REMOVAL

See ENGINE REMOVAL at end of ENGINE section.

CYLINDER HEAD & MANIFOLDS

INTAKE & EXHAUST MANIFOLDS

Removal

1) Disconnect battery and drain cooling system. Remove air cleaner and disconnect vacuum lines, electrical wiring, and fuel lines from carburetor. Remove throttle linkage and power steering pump belt.

2) Remove power brake unit vacuum hose from intake manifold. Remove water hoses from water crossover. Raise vehicle and disconnect exhaust pipe from manifold. Remove power steering pump and set aside.

3) Remove intake manifold support bracket. Remove EGR tube. Lower vehicle. Remove intake manifold bolts and remove intake manifold. Remove exhaust manifold nuts and remove exhaust manifold.

Installation

1) Clean all gasket surfaces and inspect for cracks and surface flatness. Gasket surfaces must be flat within .006" (.15 mm) per foot of manifold length. Coat manifold side of intake and exhaust manifold gasket with sealer. Install gasket on cylinder head.

2) Position exhaust manifold on cylinder head and install nuts. Tighten retaining nuts by starting in center and working outward in both directions. Position intake manifold on cylinder head and install bolts. Raise vehicle. Tighten retaining bolts by starting in center and working outward in both directions. Reverse removal procedure to complete installation.

Fig. 1: Intake and Exhaust Manifold Installation

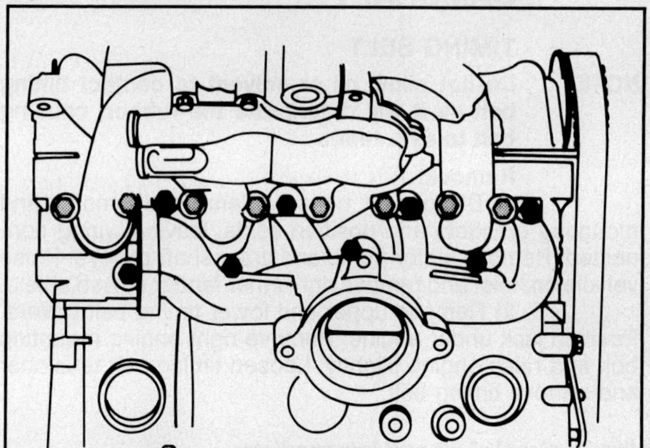

Begin tightening in center and work outward.

CYLINDER HEAD

Removal

1) Remove intake and exhaust manifolds. Remove water pump and crankshaft pulleys. Raise vehicle and remove right inner fender splash shield. Remove upper and lower timing belt covers. Position jack under engine.

2) Remove right engine mounting bolt and raise engine slightly. Loosen timing belt tensioner and remove timing belt. Install Camshaft Sprocket Holder (C-4687) and hold sprocket while removing sprocket bolt. Remove camshaft sprocket.

3) Remove camshaft cover. Remove air pump pulley, making sure not to turn camshaft. Disconnect dipstick tube from thermostat housing and carefully rotate bracket away from stud. Do not bend bracket.

4) Remove cylinder head bolts in reverse order of tightening sequence. *See Fig. 2.* Remove cylinder head and gasket.

Fig. 2: Cylinder Head Tightening Sequence

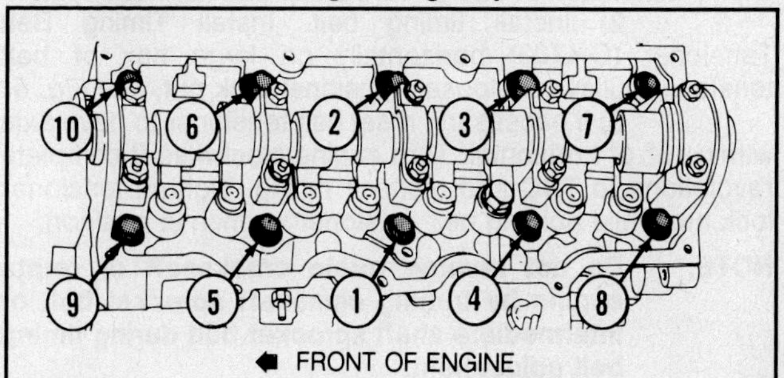

Remove head bolts in reverse order of tightening sequence.

Installation

1) Clean all gasket surfaces. Check cylinder head and block for flatness. Cylinder head flatness must be within .004" (.10 mm). Install gasket and cylinder head.

2) Tighten cylinder head bolts as follows: Tighten bolts to 30 ft. lbs. (41 N.m). *See Fig. 2.* Tighten bolts to 45 ft. lbs. (61 N.m). Retighten bolts to 45 ft. lbs. (61 N.m). Turn cylinder head bolts an additional 1/4 turn.

3) Reverse removal procedure to complete installation. Adjust timing belt. See TIMING BELT INSTALLATION in this article.

Chrysler Corp. Engines

2.2 LITER 4-CYLINDER (Cont.)

CAMSHAFT

TIMING BELT

NOTE: Do not allow oil or solvent to contact timing belt as it will deteriorate the rubber, causing belt to skip teeth.

Removal

1) Disconnect battery. Remove alternator and mounting brackets and position aside, leaving wiring connected. Remove water pump and crankshaft pulleys. Raise vehicle on hoist and remove right inner fender splash shield.

2) Remove upper and lower timing belt covers. Position jack under engine. Remove right engine mounting bolt and raise engine slightly. Loosen timing belt tensioner and remove timing belt.

Fig. 3: Crankshaft and Intermediate Sprocket Timing Marks

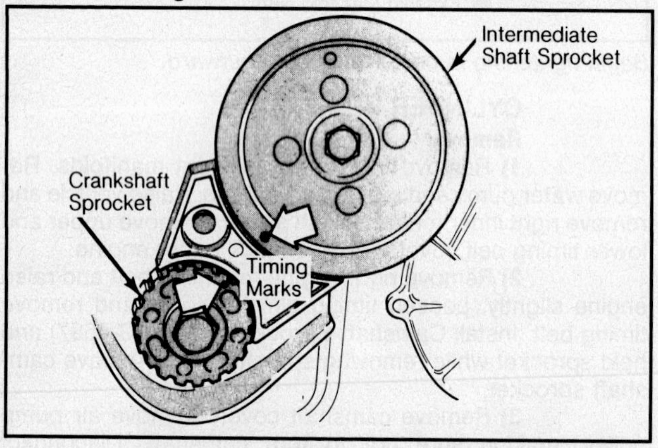

Installation

1) Remove spark plugs and place No. 1 cylinder on TDC. Align timing marks on crankshaft and intermediate sprockets. *See Fig. 3*. Turn camshaft sprocket until arrows on hub are in line with No. 1 camshaft cap-to-cylinder head line. Small hole must be at 12 o'clock position. *See Fig. 4*.

2) Install timing belt. Install Timing Belt Tensioner (C-4703) horizontally on large hex of belt tensioner pulley and loosen tensioner lock nut. *See Fig. 5*.

3) If necessary, reset belt tensioner to have axis within 15° of horizontal. Turn engine clockwise 2 complete revolutions to TDC and recheck timing. Tighten tensioner lock nut while holding belt tensioner wrench in position.

NOTE: Do not reverse rotate crankshaft or rotate engine by turning camshaft sprocket bolt or intermediate shaft sprocket bolt during timing belt adjustment.

CAMSHAFT

CAUTION: Do not cock camshaft during removal as damage to camshaft and/or bearing thrust surfaces could result.

Removal

1) Remove timing belt cover and timing belt. Install Camshaft Sprocket Holder (C-4687) and hold camshaft sprocket while removing sprocket bolt. Remove sprocket, then remove camshaft cover.

2) On each rocker arm, rotate camshaft until base circle of cam is in contact with rocker arm. Install spring compressor and compress valve spring. Remove rocker arms and keep in order for reinstallation.

3) Loosen camshaft bearing cap bolts several turns. Using soft-faced mallet, tap rear of camshaft to loosen bearing caps. Remove camshaft cap nuts and bearing caps so that cam does not cock in cylinder head. Remove camshaft and oil seals.

Installation

1) Check bearing cap oil holes for blockage. Install camshaft into cylinder head and align bearing caps in proper sequence, with bearing cap No. 1 at timing belt end and bearing cap No. 5 at transmission end.

2) Make sure arrows on bearing caps No. 1, 2, 3, and 4 point toward timing belt to prevent bearing cap breakage. Apply anaerobic sealer to No. 1 and No. 5 bearing caps at sealing surfaces. Install bearing cap bolts and tighten.

Fig. 4: Camshaft Timing Marks

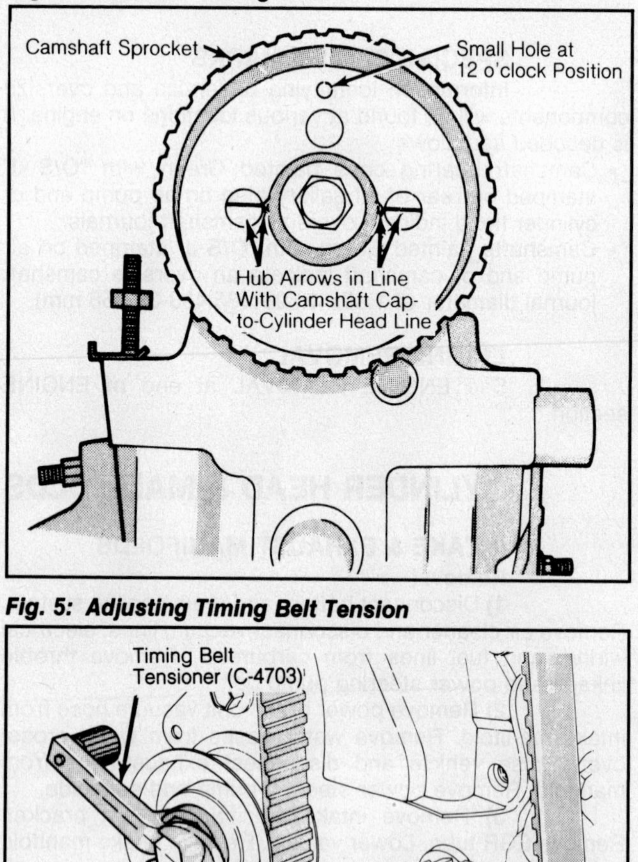

Fig. 5: Adjusting Timing Belt Tension

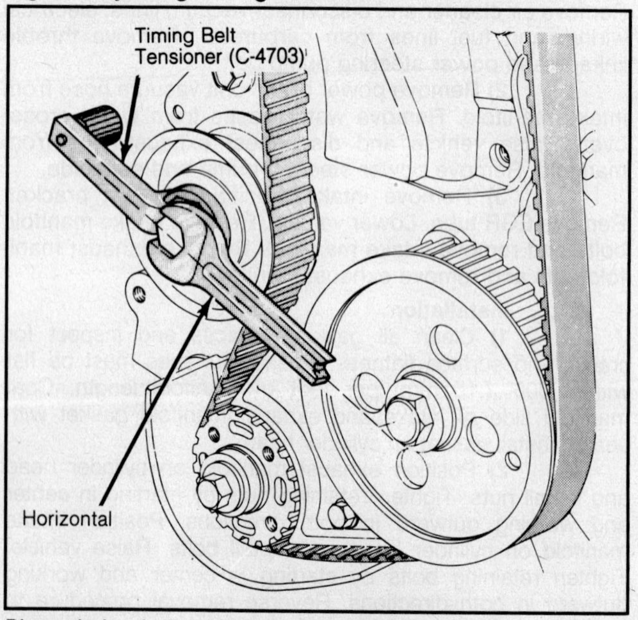

Place timing belt tensioner horizontally on pulley.

3) Mount dial indicator at timing belt end of camshaft and slide cam rearward. Zero dial indicator. Slide cam all the way forward and read dial indicator reading. End play should be .006" (.15 mm) maximum. If end play exceeds specification, camshaft and/or cylinder head should be replaced.

4) Shaft seal lip surface must be free of varnish, dirt or nicks. Polish shaft with 400 grit paper if necessary. Lightly coat outside diameter of new oil seal with Loctite (P/N 4057987) for steel case seal.

5) Use soapy water for rubber-coated steel case seal. Using Oil Seal Installer (C-4680), install oil seal flush with front of oil seal retainer. Reverse removal procedure to complete installation.

INTERMEDIATE SHAFT

Removal

1) Remove fuel pump and distributor. Remove timing belt cover and remove timing belt. Install Intermediate Sprocket Holder (C-4687). Remove sprocket bolt and sprocket.

2) Install Oil Seal Remover (C-4679) and remove oil seal, being careful not to nick shaft seal surface or seal bore. Remove intermediate shaft retainer bolts, retainer, and intermediate shaft. Remove intermediate shaft front and rear bushings using Bushing Remover (C-4697-2).

Installation

1) Install intermediate shaft rear and front bushings using Bushing Installer (C-4686-1), until tool is flush with block. Install intermediate shaft, retainer, and bolts, then tighten. Lightly coat outside diameter of new oil seal with Loctite (P/N 4057987) for steel case seal.

2) Use soapy water for rubber-coated steel case seal. Using Oil Seal Installer (C-4680), install oil seal flush with front oil seal retainer.

3) Install intermediate sprocket and Sprocket Holder (C-4687). Install sprocket bolt and tighten. Align intermediate shaft, crankshaft, and camshaft sprocket timing marks. *See Figs. 3 and 4*. Align slot in oil pump shaft parallel to centerline of crankshaft.

4) Remove distributor cap and align rotor to No. 1 firing position and install in engine. Install fuel pump and distributor cap. Reverse removal procedure to complete installation.

VALVE TIMING

See TIMING BELT INSTALLATION procedure in this article.

VALVES

VALVE ARRANGEMENT

E-I-E-I-E-I-E-I (Front-to-rear).

VALVE GUIDE SERVICING

NOTE: **Replace guides only if guide does not clean up with .031" (0.80 mm) oversize reamer, or if guide is loose in head.**

1) Insert valve with valve head positioned .40" (10 mm) above cylinder head gasket surface. Attach dial indicator to cylinder head and position against valve head at right angle to valve stem. Zero indicator.

2) Move valve toward and away from indicator. Valve guide wear should not exceed .02" (0.5 mm) for intake valve guides and .27" (0.7 mm) for exhaust valve guides.

3) If valve guide wear is excessive, ream or replace valve guides. Replacement valves are available in .006" (.15 mm), .016" (.40 mm) and .031" (.80 mm) oversize.

VALVE GUIDE REPLACEMENT

NOTE: **Cylinder head must be supported with alignment fixture when pressing guides in or out.**

1) Thoroughly clean cylinder head gasket surface and alignment fixture top surface of any foreign material. Position cylinder head on fixture with head gasket side down, so valve guides are vertical. *See Fig. 6*.

Fig. 6: Cylinder Head Alignment Fixture

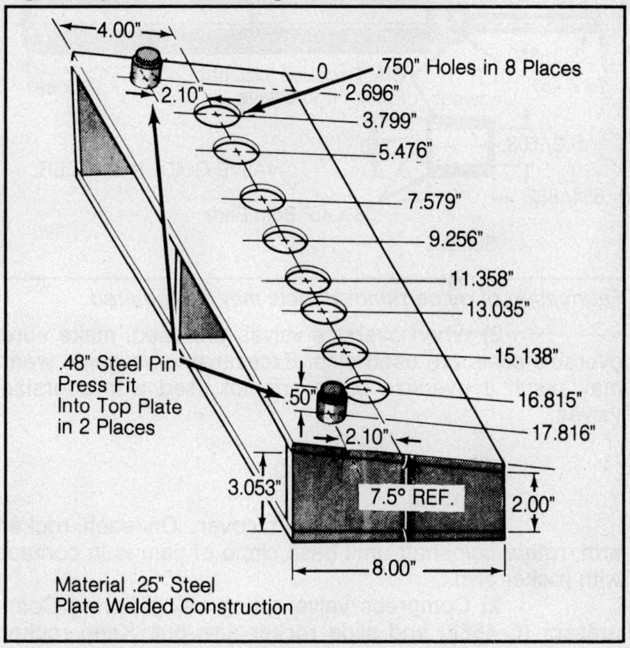

Measurements are in inches.

2) Position valve guide remover on guide and press out using a press with a rated 3-ton capacity. *See Fig. 7*. Ream cylinder head guide bores to .499-.500" (12.68-12.70 mm) diameter. Thoroughly clean guide bores and replacement guides.

3) Place new guides in dry ice for a minimum of 30 minutes. Long guides are for exhaust valves and short guides are for intake valves. Lubricate guide bores with engine oil. Place guide on installation tool and carefully align in guide bore.

4) Make sure groove on valve guide is at upper end for valve stem seal retention. Press guide in slowly until tool seats on cylinder head. The inside diameter of guide is pre-drilled for correct stem-to-guide clearance, so reaming is not required.

VALVE STEM OIL SEALS

Removal

Oil seals are installed on all valve guides and must be replaced whenever valve service is performed. See VALVE SPRING REMOVAL in this article for removal of oil seals.

Installation

1) Lightly coat valve stems with engine oil and install new seals. Push seals firmly and squarely over guide so center bead of seal seats in groove on valve guide. Lower edge of seal must rest on valve guide boss.

2.2 LITER 4-CYLINDER (Cont.)

Fig. 7: Valve Guide Removal and Installation Tools

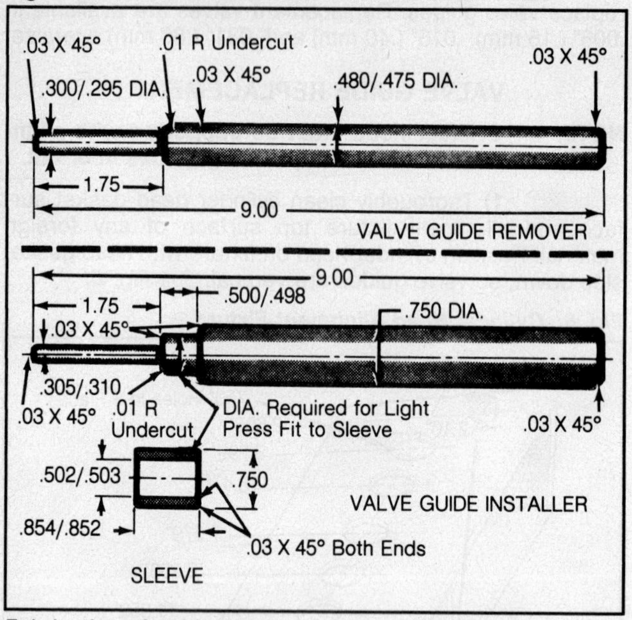

Fabrication of guide removal tools may be required.

2) When oversize valves are used, make sure oversize seals are used also. Excessive valve guide wear may result if oversize seals are not used with oversize valves.

VALVE SPRINGS

Removal

1) Remove camshaft cover. On each rocker arm, rotate camshaft until base circle of cam is in contact with rocker arm.

2) Compress valve spring using Spring Compressor (C-4682) and slide rocker arm out. Keep rocker arms in order for reinstallation. Remove hydraulic lash adjuster. Rotate crankshaft until piston of cylinder being serviced is at TDC.

3) Remove spark plug. Install air line adapter to spark plug port and apply 90-120 psi air pressure to hold valves closed. Install spring compressor and compress valve spring. *See Fig. 8.*

Fig. 8: Removing and Installing Valve Spring Assembly

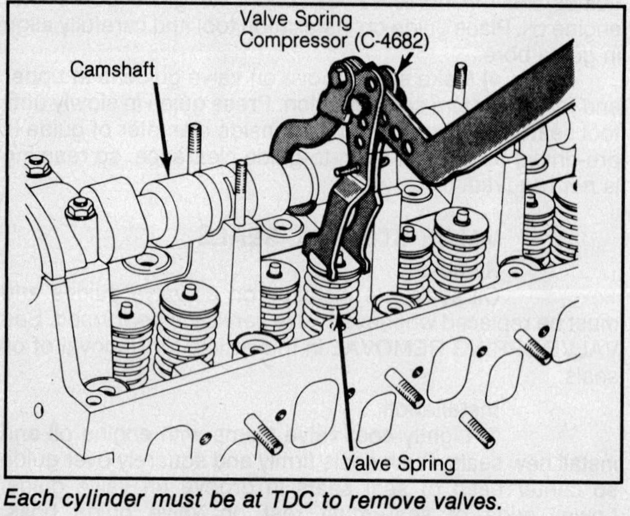

Each cylinder must be at TDC to remove valves.

4) Remove valve locks, retainer, valve spring and valve spring seat. Remove oil seal by gently prying oil seal side-to-side, using screwdriver blade, until seal is dislodged from valve guide groove.

Installation

Test valve springs using Spring Tester (C-647). Replace springs if not within specifications. Install oil seals, valve spring seats, valve springs, and retainers. Compress valve spring and install valve locks. Reverse removal procedure to complete installation.

VALVE SPRING INSTALLED HEIGHT

Measure valve spring installed height from lower edge of valve spring to upper edge of spring. Do not include valve spring seat or retainer. Specified height is 1.62-1.68" (41.2-42.7 mm). If valve seats have been reground, an additional spring seat may be required to maintain proper spring height.

VALVE STEM INSTALLED HEIGHT

1) Measure valve stem installed height from tip of valve stem to spring seat. *See Fig. 9.* Specified height is 1.960-2.009" (49.76-51.04 mm). Check height after grinding valves or seats.

Fig. 9: Measuring Valve Stem Installed Height

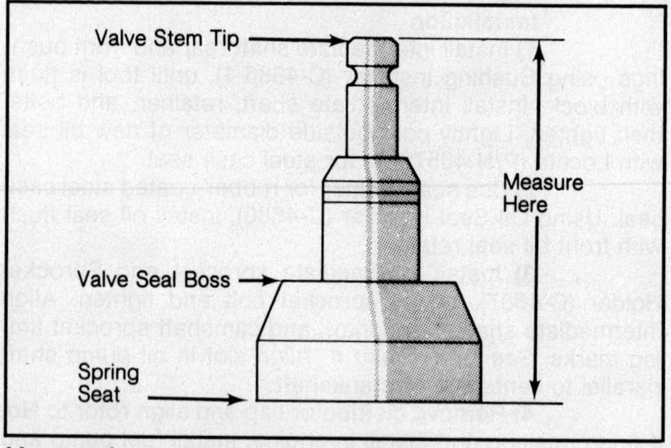

Measure from spring seat to tip of stem.

Fig. 10: Measuring Spring Retainer Clearance

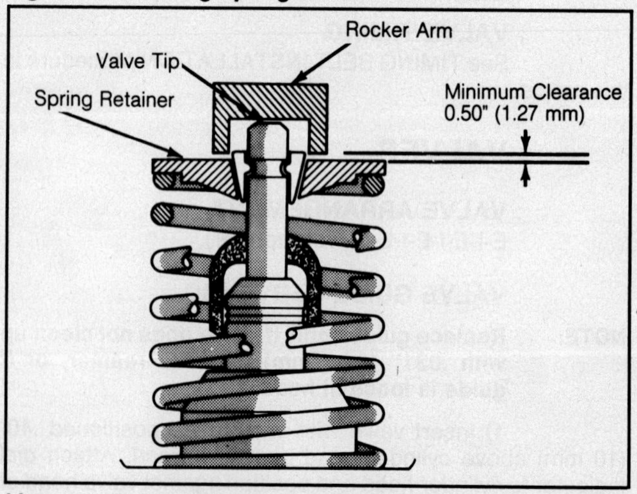

Measure clearance between rocker arm and spring retainer.

2) If necessary, grind valve stem tip to obtain specified height. If more than .020" (.50 mm) must be ground from valve tip, check clearance between rocker arm and valve spring retainer. *See Fig. 10.* If clearance is below .050" (1.27 mm), valve and/or head must be replaced.

ROCKER ARM ASSEMBLY

CAUTION: It is possible for valve spring retainers to become dislodged when compressing valve spring. Ensure that locks are properly installed.

Removal

1) Remove camshaft cover. On each rocker arm, rotate camshaft until base circle of cam is in contact with rocker arm.

2) Compress valve spring using spring compressor and slide rocker arm out. Keep rocker arms in order for reinstallation. Remove lash adjusters. Keep lash adjusters in order for reinstallation.

Installation

1) Partially fill lash adjusters with engine oil. Install lash adjusters in original positions. Compress valve spring and slide rocker arms in place.

2) Check clearance between projecting ears of rocker arms (either side of valve stem tip) and valve spring retainer. A minimum clearance of .020" (.50 mm) must be present. If clearance is not sufficient, grind rocker arm ears as required to obtain clearance.

HYDRAULIC VALVE LASH ADJUSTERS

NOTE: Lash adjusters are serviced as complete assemblies. Parts are not interchangeable.

No adjustment of lash adjusters is required. Servicing of adjusters requires only that care and cleanliness be exercised in handling of parts. If disassembled for cleaning purposes, reassemble using new spring clip. Adjusters must be full of oil prior to installation. Oiling holes in cylinder head must be free of any obstruction.

DRY LASH

Dry lash is the amount of clearance between base circle of an installed camshaft and the rocker arm pad, with lash adjuster completely collapsed. Remove and drain adjuster of any engine oil to perform this check. Install adjuster completely collapsed.

Measure clearance between base circle and rocker arm pad using feeler gauge. Specified clearance is .024-.060" (.62-1.52 mm). If not within specifications, check wear on parts and replace as required. Refill adjusters with engine oil before final assembly and allow 10 minutes for adjusters to bleed down before rotating camshaft.

PISTONS, PINS & RINGS

OIL PAN

See OIL PAN REMOVAL at end of ENGINE section.

PISTON & ROD ASSEMBLY

Removal

1) Remove cylinder head and oil pan. Place piston at bottom of stroke and cover top of piston to collect cuttings. Remove ridge at top of cylinder bore using ridge reamer.

2) If necessary, mark connecting rods and caps for cylinder identification and reinstallation in original positions. Remove rod cap nuts and rod cap. Push piston and rod assembly out top of cylinder block.

Installation

1) Lightly coat piston rings and cylinder bores with engine oil. Ensure "TOP" mark on upper and intermediate piston rings point toward top of piston. Ensure ring gaps are properly spaced on upper and intermediate rings. Oil ring rail gaps are installed 180° apart from each other. *See Fig. 11.*

Fig. 11: Piston Ring Gap Spacing

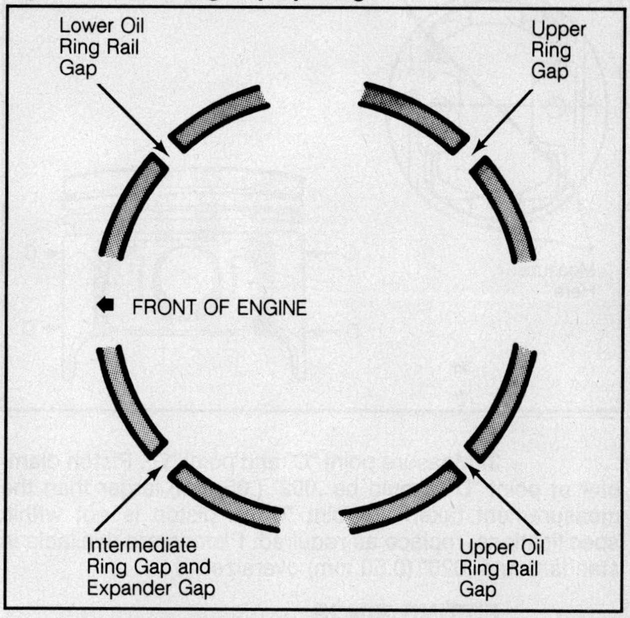

Install rings with "TOP" mark facing top of piston.

2) Rotate crankshaft so connecting rod journal is at center of cylinder bore. Install rod bolt protectors before installing piston and rod assembly in block. Using ring compressor, compress rings. Install piston in cylinder bore with indent on piston and oil hole in connecting rod pointing toward timing belt side of engine. *See Fig. 12.*

Fig. 12: Piston and Rod Installation

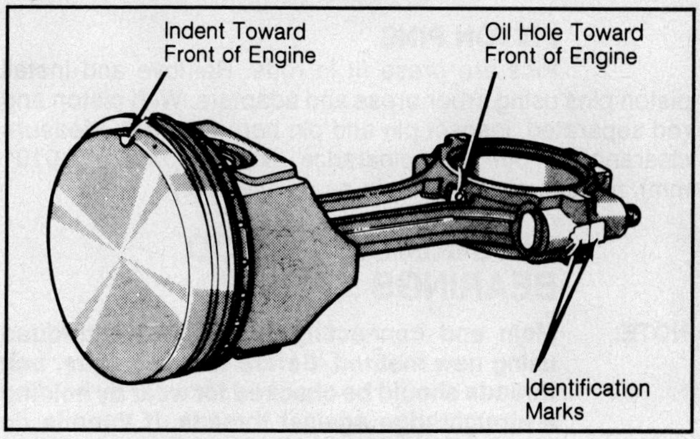

Piston indent and connecting rod oil hole face front of engine.

FITTING PISTONS

1) Measure cylinder bore at 3 points: 3/8" down from top, 3/8" up from bottom of bore, and at center of bore. Measure in line with thrust face and at 90° angle to thrust face. Cylinder bore wear limit is .0027" (.069 mm). Maximum cylinder out-of-round is .002" (.051 mm), maximum cylinder bore taper is .005" (.13 mm).

Chrysler Corp. Engines

2.2 LITER 4-CYLINDER (Cont.)

2) Measure pistons with pins removed at points "A", "B", "C" and "D". *See Fig. 13*. First, measure point "B". Piston diameter should be 3.443-3.445" (87.44-87.51 mm). Now measure point "A": Due to elliptical shape of piston skirt, point "A" should be .012-.014" (.31-.36 mm) less than measurement taken at point "B".

Fig. 13: Measuring Piston Fit

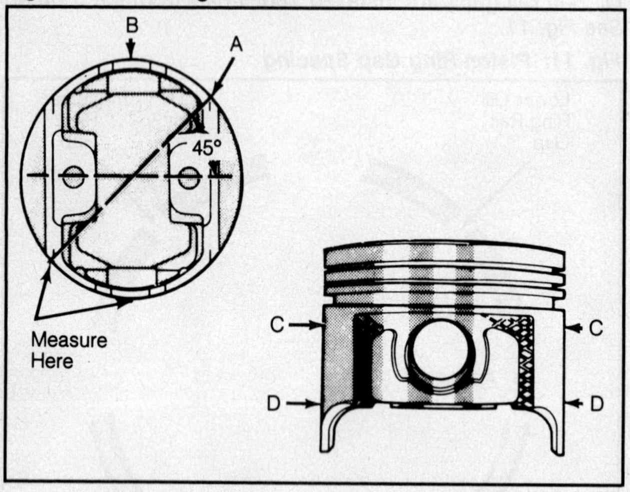

3) Measure point "C" and point "D". Piston diameter at point "D" should be .002" (.05 mm) larger than the measurement taken at point "C". If piston is not within specifications, replace as required. Pistons are available in standard and .020" (0.50 mm) oversize.

FITTING RINGS

CAUTION: Avoid damaging ring or cylinder bore.

1) Place cylinder block upside down. Position ring in cylinder block bore that it will be used in. Using head of piston, push ring squarely 5/8" deep into bore.

2) Measure gap between ends of ring using feeler gauge. With ring lands clean, measure ring side clearance. If not within specifications, substitute another ring set until rings are within specifications.

PISTON PINS

Pins are press fit in rods. Remove and install piston pins using arbor press and adapters. With piston and rod separated, inspect pin and pin bore for wear. Measure clearance. If pin bore clearance exceeds .00075" (.0191 mm), replace piston and pin as an assembly.

CRANKSHAFT & ROD BEARINGS

NOTE: Main and connecting rod bolts are torqued using new method. Before torquing bolts, bolt threads should be checked for wear by holding a straightedge against threads. If threads do not fully touch straightedge, bolt should be replaced.

CONNECTING ROD BEARINGS

1) Use Plastigage method to check rod bearings. Turn crankshaft until connecting rod to be checked just starts moving toward top of engine. Place Plastigage across full width of lower bearing, 1/4" off center and away from oil holes.

2) Install rod cap and tighten nuts to 40 ft. lbs. (55 N.m), then tighten an additional 1/4 turn. Remove rod cap and determine amount of clearance. Clearance should be .0008-.0034" (.019-.087 mm).

3) If clearance exceeds specifications, bearings must be replaced. New bearings are available in standard, .001" and .002" undersize for use with standard size crankshaft. Bearings are also available in .010", .011", and .012" undersize for use with reconditioned crankshaft.

4) Check rod journal for out-of-round condition. If journals are more than .003" (.08 mm) out-of-round, crankshaft must be reconditioned or replaced. When all bearings have been checked and/or replaced, measure rod side clearance using feeler gauge. Clearance should be .005-.013" (.13-.32 mm).

MAIN BEARINGS

1) Check main bearing clearances using Plastigauge method. To accurately determine bearing clearance, weight of crankshaft must first be eliminated. A .010" (.25 mm) minimum thickness cardboard shim (matchbook cover) should be used for this purpose.

2) Remove crankshaft main bearing cap(s) on either side of bearing being checked. See MAIN BEARING CLEARANCE CHECK table. When checking clearance of No. 1 or No. 5 main bearings, remove adjacent main bearing cap only.

3) Place a cardboard shim between the bearing shell(s) and cap(s) which were removed. Install these "shimmed" bearing cap(s) and tighten to 10-15 ft. lbs. (14-20 N.m).

MAIN BEARING CLEARANCE CHECK

When Checking	Shim
Number 1 Bearing	Number 2 Bearing
Number 2 Bearing	Number 1 & 3 Bearings
Number 3 Bearing	Number 2 & 4 Bearings
Number 4 Bearing	Number 3 & 5 Bearings
Number 5 Bearing	Number 4 Bearing

4) Remove main bearing cap and place Plastigage across full width of lower bearing, 1/4" off center and away from oil holes. Install main bearing cap with bearing and tighten bolts to 30 ft. lbs. (41 N.m), then tighten an additional 1/4 of a turn.

5) Remove main cap and determine amount of clearance. Clearance should be .0003-.0031" (.007-.080 mm). If clearance exceeds specifications, bearings must be replaced.

6) New bearings are available in standard, .001" and .002" undersize for use with standard size crankshaft. Bearings are also available in .010", .011", and .012" undersize for use with reconditioned crankshaft.

7) Check crankshaft journal for out-of-round condition. If journals are more than .0005" (.013 mm) out-of-round, crankshaft must be reconditioned or replaced. When all bearings have been checked and/or replaced, measure crankshaft end play.

THRUST BEARING END PLAY

Mount dial indicator on front of engine with stem on nose of crankshaft. Move crankshaft all the way rearward and zero dial indicator. Move crankshaft all the way forward and read dial indicator reading. End play should be .002-.007" (.05-.18 mm).

CRANKSHAFT SPROCKET OIL SEAL

Removal

1) Remove timing belt cover and remove timing belt. Remove crankshaft sprocket bolt. Install Centering Button (L-4524) on end of crankshaft before installing puller.

2) Install Crankshaft Sprocket Puller (C-4685) and remove crankshaft sprocket. Install Oil Seal Puller (C-4679) and remove oil seal, being careful not to nick shaft seal surface or seal bore.

Installation

1) Shaft seal lip surface must be free of varnish, dirt or nicks. Polish shaft with 400 grit paper if necessary. Lightly coat outside diameter of new oil seal with Loctite (P/N 4057987) for steel case seal.

2) Use soapy water for rubber-coated steel case seal. Using Oil Seal Installer (C-4680), install oil seal flush with front of oil seal retainer. Reverse removal procedure to complete installation.

REAR MAIN BEARING OIL SEAL

Removal

Engine or transmission must be removed for seal service. Using large screwdriver, pry out seal from crankshaft oil seal retainer, being careful not to nick or damage flange seal surface or retainer bore.

Installation

Lightly coat outside diameter of new oil seal with Loctite (P/N 4057987). Position seal and Oil Seal Installer (C-4681) flush with retainer. Tap seal into place with plastic hammer.

ENGINE OILING

CRANKCASE CAPACITY

Crankcase capacity is 4 quarts (3.8L) with or without filter change.

NORMAL OIL PRESSURE

Normal oil pressure should be 50 psi (3.52 kg/cm^2) at 2000 RPM.

OIL PRESSURE REGULATOR VALVE

Valve is serviceable, but not adjustable.

OIL PUMP

Removal

Remove oil pan. Remove bolt holding oil pick-up tube to No. 3 main bearing cap bolt. Remove bolt on pump cover holding oil pick-up tube to oil pump. Remove pick-up tube and "O" ring. Remove 2 bolts holding oil pump to cylinder block and remove pump.

Disassembly

Remove oil pump cover-to-pump housing bolts and remove pump cover. Remove inner rotor and outer rotor. Remove oil pressure relief valve pin, cup, spring, and valve from oil pump housing.

Inspection

1) Install inner and outer rotor into pump housing. Check inner rotor end play by placing straightedge across pump housing. Using feeler gauge, measure clearance between inner rotor and straightedge. Clearance should be .001-.004" (.03-.10 mm).

2) Using a micrometer, measure outer rotor thickness. Minimum thickness should be .825" (20.96 mm). Now measure rotor diameter. Minimum diameter should be 2.469" (62.70 mm).

3) Using a feeler gauge, measure inner rotor-to-outer rotor clearance. Maximum clearance should be .010" (.25 mm). Measure outer rotor-to-pump housing clearance. Maximum clearance should be .014" (.35 mm). Place straightedge across pump cover and measure pump cover wear using feeler gauge. Maximum clearance should be .003" (.08 mm).

4) Measure regulator valve spring. Free length is 1.95" (49.5 mm), loaded measurement is 15-25 lbs. at 1.34" (67-89 N at 34 mm). If any measurement is not within specifications, replace oil pump as an assembly.

Reassembly

Install outer rotor with large chamfered edge facing down into pump housing. Install inner rotor. Install pump cover, attaching bolts and tighten. Insert pressure relief valve, spring, cup, and pin into pump housing.

Installation

1) Reverse removal procedure, making sure to install new "O" ring seal on pick-up tube. Align slot in oil pump shaft parallel to centerline of crankshaft. Apply Loctite (P/N 515) between pump and block.

2) Install pump full depth and rotate back and forth to ensure full surface contact between pump and block. Hold pump in fully seated position and tighten bolts to 17 ft. lbs. (23 N.m). Reverse removal procedure to complete installation.

Fig. 14: Exploded View of Oil Pump Assembly

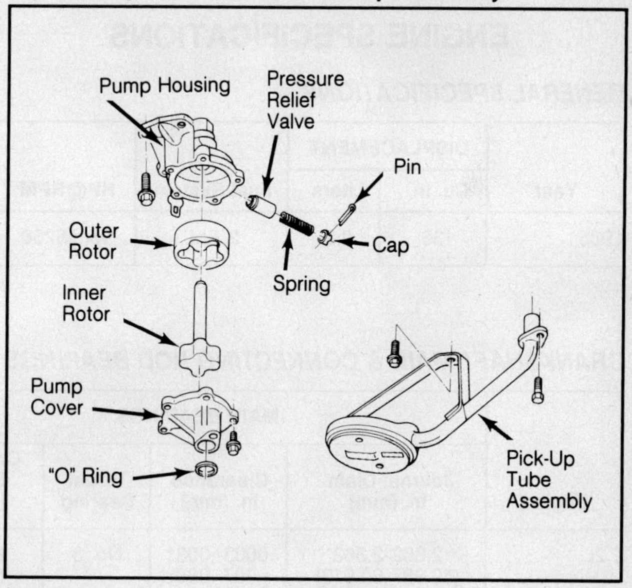

Install new "O" ring on oil pick-up tube.

Chrysler Corp. Engines

2.2 LITER 4-CYLINDER (Cont.)

ENGINE COOLING

WATER PUMP

Removal

Disconnect negative battery cable and drain cooling system. Remove upper radiator hose. Remove A/C compressor from engine bracket and set aside. Remove alternator and set aside. Disconnect lower hose and by-pass hose. Remove bolts holding water pump to engine and remove water pump.

Installation

Install water pump on engine. Tighten top bolts to 21 ft. lbs. (28 N.m). Tighten lower bolt to 50 ft. lbs. (68 N.m). Reverse removal procedure to complete installation.

NOTE: **For further information on cooling system capacities and other cooling system components, see appropriate article in ENGINE COOLING SYSTEMS section.**

TIGHTENING SPECIFICATIONS

Application	Ft. Lbs. (N.m)
Camshaft Bearing Cap Bolt	14 (19)
Camshaft Cover Bolt	9 (12)
Camshaft Sprocket Bolt	65 (88)
Connecting Rod Cap Nut	[1] 40 (54)
Crankshaft Sprocket Bolt	50 (68)
Cylinder Head Bolt	
Step 1	30 (41)
Step 2	45 (61)
Step 3	[2] 45 (61)
Exhaust Manifold Nut	17 (23)
Front Oil Seal Retainer Bolt	9 (12)
Intake Manifold Bolt	17 (23)
Intermediate Retainer Bolt	9 (12)
Intermediate Sprocket Bolt	65 (88)
Main Bearing Cap Bolt	[3] 30 (41)
Oil Pump-to-Block Bolt	17 (23)
Rear Oil Seal Retainer Bolt	9 (12)
Water Pump Housing	
Lower	50 (68)
Upper	21 (28)

[1] – Then tighten an additional 1/4 turn.
[2] – Tighten in 3 steps, then tighten an additional 1/4 turn.
[3] – Then tighten an additional 1/4 turn.

ENGINE SPECIFICATIONS

GENERAL SPECIFICATIONS

Year	DISPLACEMENT		Fuel System	HP@RPM	Torque	Compr.	BORE		STROKE	
	Cu. In.	Liters			Ft. Lbs.@RPM	Ratio	In.	mm	In.	mm
1985	135	2.2	2-Bbl.	96@5200	119@3200	9.0:1	3.44	87.5	3.62	92.0

CRANKSHAFT MAIN & CONNECTING ROD BEARINGS

Engine	MAIN BEARINGS				CONNECTING ROD BEARINGS		
	Journal Diam. In. (mm)	Clearance In. (mm)	Thrust Bearing	Crankshaft End Play In. (mm)	Journal Diam. In. (mm)	Clearance In. (mm)	Side Play In. (mm)
2.2L	2.362-2.363 (59.987-60.013)	.0003-.0031 (.007-.080)	No. 3	.002-.007 (.05-.18)	1.968-1.969 (49.979-50.005)	.0008-.0034 (.019-.087)	.005-.013 (.13-.32)

2.2 LITER 4-CYLINDER (Cont.)

ENGINE SPECIFICATIONS (Cont.)

PISTONS, PINS, RINGS

	PISTONS		PINS	RINGS		
Engine	Clearance In. (mm)	Piston Fit In. (mm)	Rod Fit In. (mm)	Ring No.	End Gap In. (mm)	Side Clearance In. (mm)
2.2L	.0005-.0015 (.013-.038)	.0002-.00075 (.006-.019)	.0007-.0017 (.018-.043)	1	.011-.021 (.28-.53)	.0015-.003 (.038-.078)
				2	.011-.021 (.28-.53)	.0015-.004 (.038-.093)
				3	.015-.055 (.38-1.4)	[1] .....

[1] – Oil ring side clearance must not exceed .008" (.20 mm).

VALVES

Engine Size & Valve	Head Diam. In. (mm)	Face Angle	Seat Angle	Seat Width In. (mm)	Stem Diameter In. (mm)	Stem Clearance In. (mm)	Valve Lift In. (mm)
2.2L							
Intake	1.60 (40.64)	45°	45°	.069-.088 (1.75-2.25)	.3124 (7.935)	.0009-.0026 (.022-.065)	.....
Exhaust	1.39 (35.4)	45°	45°	.059-.078 (1.50-2.00)	.3103 (7.881)	.0030-.0047 (.076-.119)	.....

VALVE SPRINGS

		PRESSURE Lbs. @ In. (Kg @ mm)	
Engine	Free Length In. (mm)	Valve Closed	Valve Open
2.2L	2.39 (60.8)	90-100@1.65 (41-45@41.91)	144-156@1.22 (65-71@30.99)

CAMSHAFT

Engine	Journal Diam. In. (mm)	Clearance In. (mm)	Lobe Lift In. (mm)
2.2L	1.375-1.376 (34.94-34.96)	.....	.....

2.6 LITER 4-CYLINDER

ENGINE CODING

ENGINE IDENTIFICATION

Engine may be identified from Vehicle Identification Number (VIN). VIN is stamped on Gray metal tab located on upper left corner of instrument panel, near windshield. Engine Identification Number is located on left side of block between core plug and rear of block (radiator side of vehicle).

Engine serial number is located on right side of block adjacent to exhaust manifold stud. In addition, VIN code appears as part of production or unit number stamped on right side of engine forward facing surface, below cylinder head. VIN consists of 17 characters. The 8th character identifies engine and 10th character establishes model year.

ENGINE IDENTIFICATION CODE

Engine	Code
2.6L 2-Bbl.	G

ENGINE REMOVAL

See ENGINE REMOVAL at end of ENGINE section.

CYLINDER HEAD & MANIFOLDS

EXHAUST MANIFOLD

Removal

1) Disconnect battery. Drain cooling system. Remove air cleaner assembly. Loosen power steering pump and remove belt. Raise vehicle. Disconnect exhaust pipe and air injection tube assembly from exhaust manifold.

2) Lower vehicle. Disconnect air injection tube assembly from air pump and move to one side. Unbolt power steering pump assembly and set aside. Remove heat shield from exhaust manifold.

3) Remove exhaust manifold retaining nuts and remove assembly from vehicle. Remove carburetor air heater from manifold assembly. Remove bolts holding exhaust manifold and front catalytic converter together.

Installation

1) Clean all gasket surfaces. Check gasket surfaces for flatness using a straightedge. Gasket surfaces must be flat within .006" (.15 mm) per foot of manifold length. Inspect manifold and front catalytic converter for cracks or distortion.

2) Install new gasket between exhaust manifold and front catalytic converter. Tighten mounting bolts to 24 ft. lbs. (32 N.m). Install carburetor air heater on exhaust manifold assembly. Tighten bolts to 80 INCH Lbs. (9 N.m).

3) Lightly coat exhaust manifold gasket with sealer on cylinder head side. Install new exhaust manifold gasket on cylinder head. Install manifold assembly. Tighten 4 center mounting nuts to 150 INCH Lbs. (17 N.m).

4) Tighten 4 outer mounting nuts to 150 INCH Lbs. (17 N.m). Install heat shield. Tighten mounting bolts to 80 INCH Lbs. (9 N.m). To complete installation, reverse removal procedure.

CYLINDER HEAD & INTAKE MANIFOLD

Removal

1) Disconnect battery. Drain cooling system and remove upper radiator hose. Disconnect heater hoses. Disconnect plug wires and remove distributor. Remove valve cover-to-carburetor bracket.

2) Remove fuel lines and fuel pump. Remove valve cover. Remove all vacuum hoses and wiring from engine. Unhook accelerator linkage at carburetor. Remove water pump belt and pulley. Rotate crankshaft to TDC on No. 1 cylinder.

3) Mark face of timing chain link that is in line with timing mark on camshaft sprocket. Use White paint to make mark. Remove camshaft sprocket and distributor drive gear from camshaft. Disconnect pulse air feeder hoses from underneath vehicle.

4) Unbolt power steering pump and set aside with hoses connected. Disconnect ground wire. Remove dipstick tube. Remove exhaust manifold shield. Disconnect exhaust pipe from exhaust manifold. Remove exhaust manifold as previously described.

5) Loosen cylinder head bolts in sequence. *See Fig. 1*. Loosen bolts in sequence to avoid warping cylinder head. Remove bolts and lift cylinder head assembly out of vehicle. Remove intake manifold from head.

Fig. 1: Cylinder Head Bolt Removal Sequence

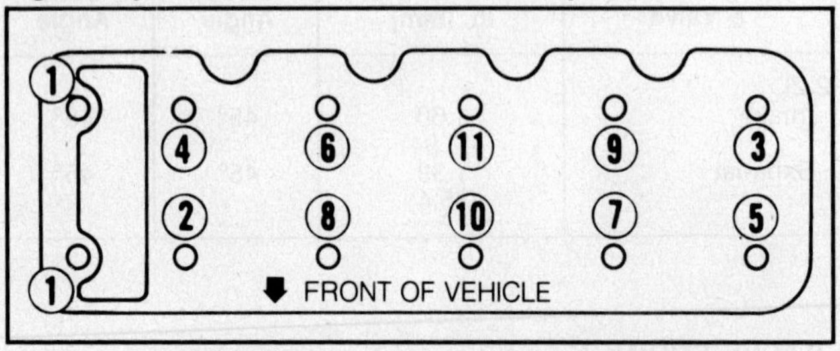

Loosen head bolts in sequence to prevent warping.

Installation

1) Clean gasket surfaces of cylinder block and head. Check head for warpage with straightedge. Maximum allowable warpage of cylinder head is .004" (.10 mm).

2) Install new cylinder head gasket, using no sealant. Install intake manifold. Install cylinder head assembly and tighten cylinder head bolts in reverse order. *See Fig. 1*. Tighten all head bolts, except 2 bolts to chain case cover, to 30 ft. lbs. (40 N.m) on 1st step.

3) For cold engine, tighten bolts to 69 ft. lbs. (94 N.m) on 2nd step. For hot engine, tighten bolts to 76 ft. lbs. (103 N.m) on 2nd step. Tighten cylinder head-to-chain case cover bolts to 159 INCH Lbs. (18 N.m).

4) Check valve clearance with engine cold. Readjust valve clearance after checking hot torque setting of cylinder head bolts. Hot intake and jet valve clearance is .006" (.15 mm) and hot exhaust valve clearance is .010" (.25 mm).

5) To complete installation, reverse removal procedure. Install breather and semi-circular seal in back of cylinder head and apply sealant to seal. *See Fig. 2*. Use new gasket for valve cover.

CAMSHAFT

Removal

1) Disconnect negative battery cable. Drain cooling system. Remove upper radiator hose and disconnect heater hoses. Remove breather hoses, purge hose and vacuum hoses. Remove air cleaner and duct assembly.

2) Remove fuel line and fuel pump. Disconnect spark plug cables and remove distributor. Remove

Chrysler Corp. Engines

2.6 LITER 4-CYLINDER (Cont.)

carburetor-to-valve cover bracket and separate carburetor linkage. Remove water pump pulley shield, valve cover and breather. Remove semi-circular seal.

Fig. 2: Installing Breather & Semi-Circular Seal

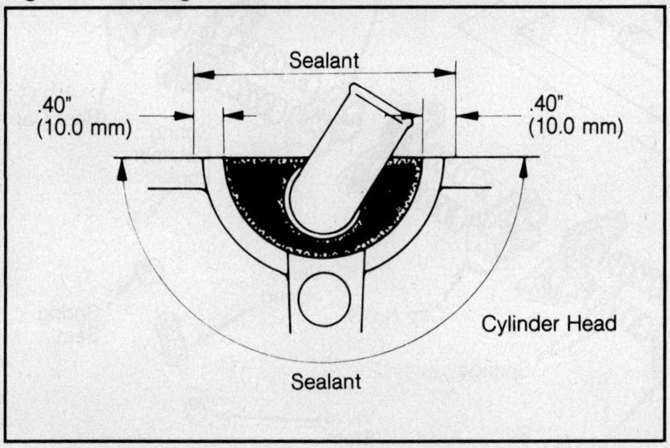

Apply sealer at application points marked.

3) Remove water pump belt and pulley. Turn crankshaft until No. 1 piston is at TDC on compression stroke. Make mating mark on timing chain in line with timing mark on camshaft sprocket using White paint. Remove camshaft sprocket bolt, washer and distributor drive gear. *See Fig. 3.*

NOTE: DO NOT remove rocker arm mount bolts from camshaft bearing caps. Remove rocker arms, rocker shafts and bearing caps as an assembly. If wave washer is replaced for any reason, dished portion of washer must face front of engine.

4) Remove camshaft sprocket with timing chain and place on sprocket holder. Remove rocker arm mount bolts with rocker arms, rocker shafts, and bearing caps as an assembly. Remove camshaft. *See Fig. 4.*

Installation

1) Check camshaft journals for wear, scratches or seizure. Check lobes, rocker arms and bearing caps for damage or wear. Limit of camshaft lobe wear is 1.64" (41.7 mm) or wear of .020" (.50 mm).

2) If cylinder head bearing surfaces are excessively worn, scratched or binding, replace cylinder head assembly. Lubricate camshaft lobes and bearing journals. Install camshaft onto cylinder head.

3) Install complete rocker arm shaft assembly with mating marks on bearing caps and rocker shafts in proper position. Marks on cap are .08" (2 mm) diameter castings while marks on shafts are .12" (3 mm) holes. Position camshaft so dowel pin on front end is positioned at top center. *See Fig. 5.*

4) Install camshaft bearing caps with arrows pointing toward timing chain end and in numerical order. Starting at center, tighten all bolts to 85 INCH Lbs. (10 N.m) in sequence of center (No. 3), No. 2, No. 4, front (No. 1), and rear (No. 5) caps. Repeat sequence, tightening to 175 INCH Lbs. (20 N.m).

5) Install camshaft sprocket and distributor drive gear onto camshaft. Carefully set camshaft timing. Tighten camshaft sprocket locking bolt. Set valve clearance temporarily to cold engine setting.

Fig. 3: Camshaft, Timing Chain and Silent Shaft Assemblies

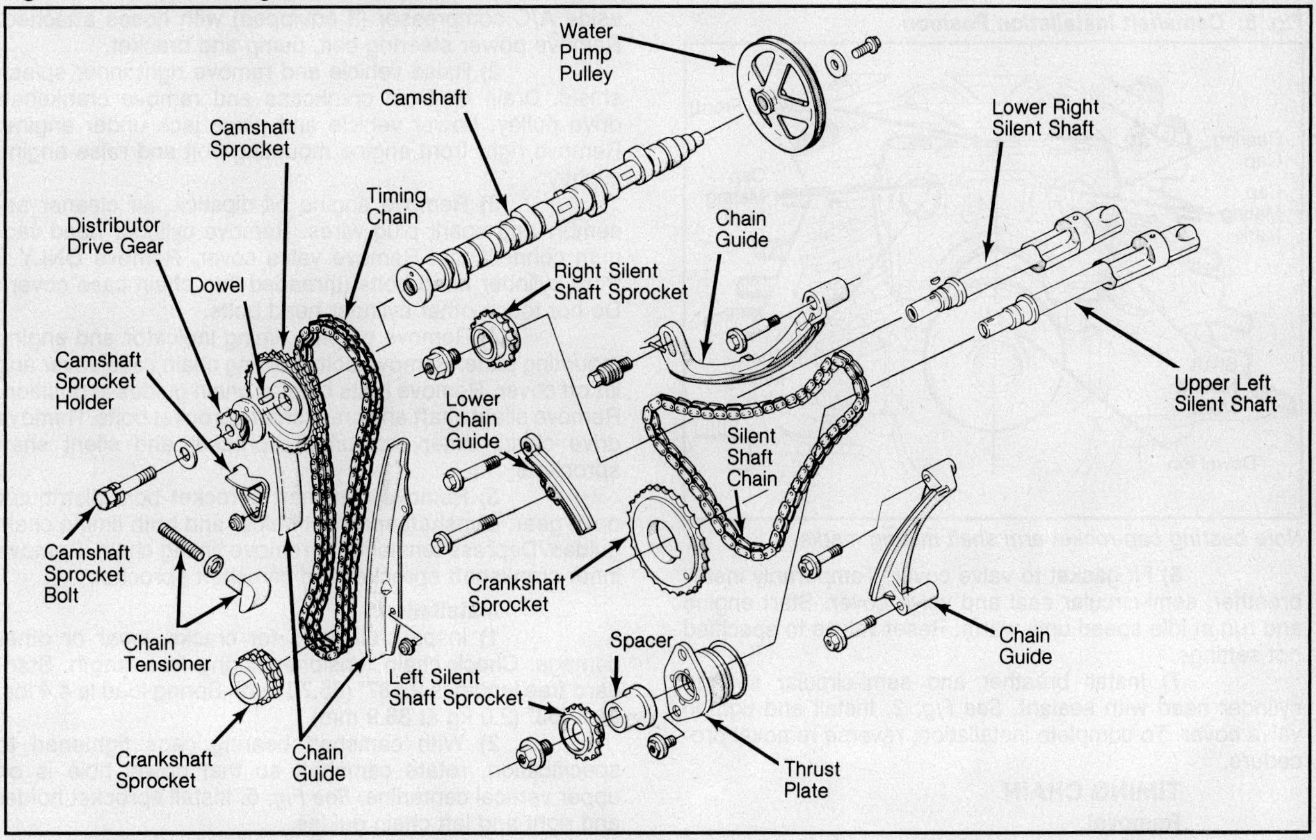

To remove, mark timing chain with White paint on chain links aligned with marks on camshaft and crankshaft sprockets.

2.6 LITER 4-CYLINDER (Cont.)

Fig. 4: Rocker Arm and Valve Assembly

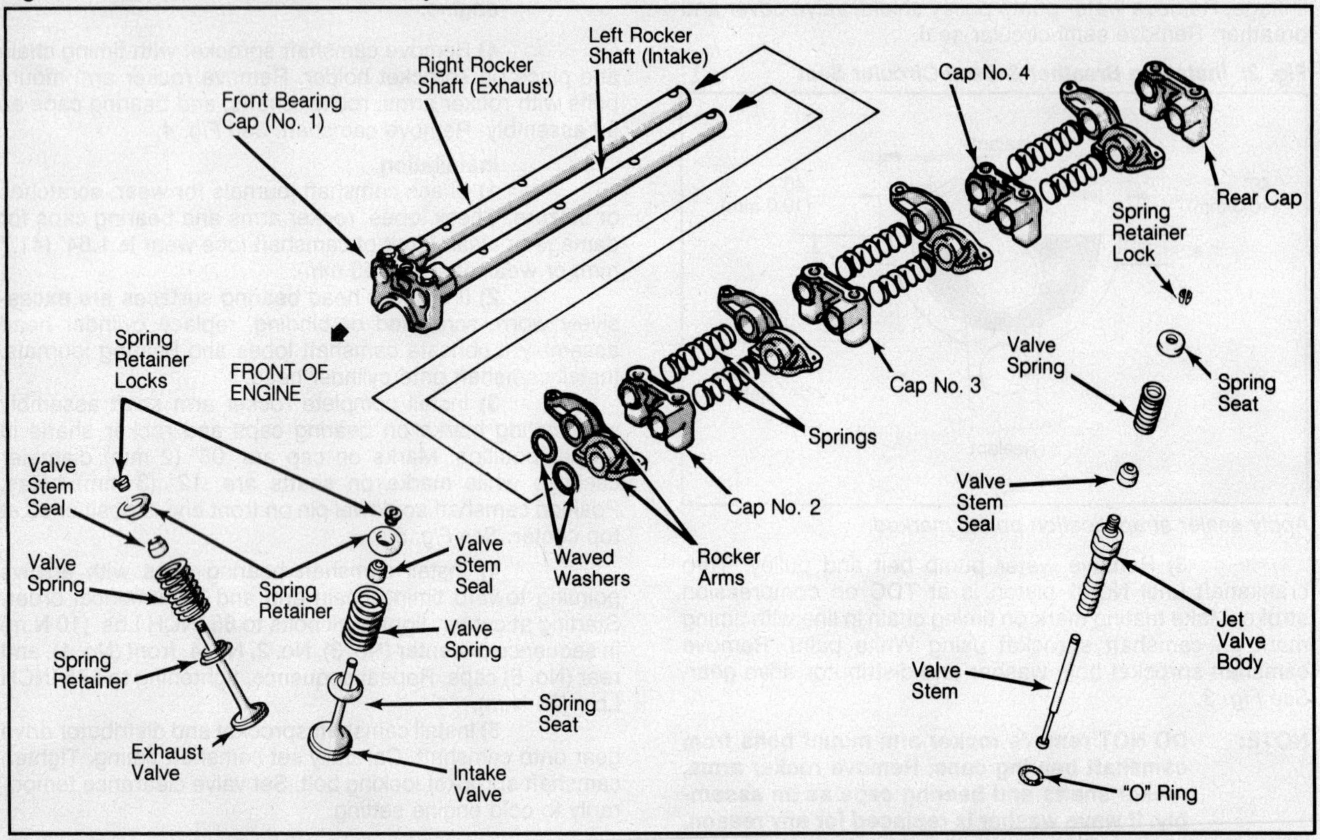

Mark rocker arm shafts for reassembly and note number of oil holes at bottom of shafts.

Fig. 5: Camshaft Installation Position

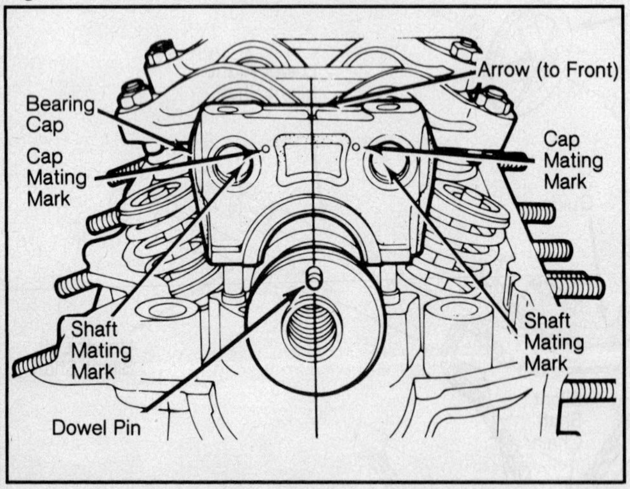

Note bearing cap-rocker arm shaft mating marks.

6) Fit gasket to valve cover. Temporarily install breather, semi-circular seal and valve cover. Start engine and run at idle speed until warm. Reset valves to specified hot settings.

7) Install breather and semi-circular seal to cylinder head with sealant. *See Fig. 2.* Install and tighten valve cover. To complete installation, reverse removal procedure.

TIMING CHAIN

Removal

1) Disconnect negative battery cable. Remove alternator belt, alternator and distributor. Remove and set aside A/C compressor (if equipped) with hoses attached. Remove power steering belt, pump and bracket.

2) Raise vehicle and remove right inner splash shield. Drain oil from crankcase and remove crankshaft drive pulley. Lower vehicle and place jack under engine. Remove right front engine mounting bolt and raise engine slightly.

3) Remove engine oil dipstick, air cleaner assembly and spark plug wires. Remove cylinder head vacuum connections. Remove valve cover. Remove ONLY 2 front cylinder head bolts (threaded into chain case cover). Do not touch other cylinder head bolts.

4) Remove oil pan, timing indicator and engine mounting plate. Remove bolts holding chain case cover and lift off cover. Remove bolts holding chain guides in position. Remove silent shaft and crankshaft sprocket bolts. Remove drive chain, outer crankshaft sprocket and silent shaft sprockets.

5) Remove camshaft sprocket bolt, distributor drive gear, camshaft sprocket holder and both timing chain guides. Depress tensioner to remove timing chain. Remove inner crankshaft sprocket and camshaft sprocket.

Installation

1) Inspect all parts for cracks, wear or other damage. Check chain tensioner spring free length. Standard free length is 2.587" (65.70 mm). Spring load is 4.4 lbs. at 1.453" (2.0 kg at 36.9 mm).

2) With camshaft bearing caps tightened to specification, rotate camshaft so that dowel hole is on upper vertical centerline. *See Fig. 5.* Install sprocket holder and right and left chain guides.

3) Rotate crankshaft until No. 1 piston is at TDC on compression stroke. Install tensioner spring and shoe on oil pump body. Install timing chain on camshaft and crankshaft sprockets.

4) Ensure timing marks are aligned. Timing marks on sprockets are punch marks near gear teeth. Timing marks on chain are middle of each PLATED link. *See Fig. 6*. Holding chain and sprocket assembly in both hands, align crankshaft sprocket to keyway and slide into place.

Fig. 6: Camshaft Sprocket Alignment and Installation

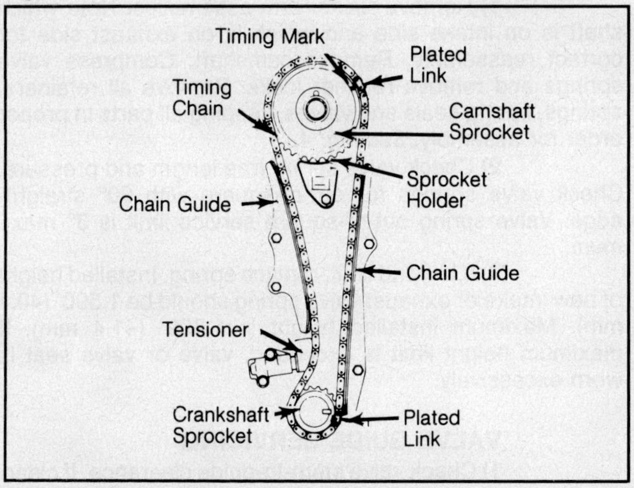

Sprocket timing marks are punch marks.

5) Align camshaft sprocket dowel hole with camshaft dowel hole. Install dowel pin and distributor drive gear. Install sprocket bolt on camshaft and tighten. Install silent shaft chain drive sprocket on crankshaft.

6) Install silent shaft chain to oil pump sprocket and to silent shaft sprocket. Ensure timing marks on gear teeth (punch marks) are aligned with marks (plated links) of chain. *See Fig. 7*.

7) Holding parts with both hands, align crankshaft sprocket timing mark with plated chain link. Install oil pump and silent chain sprockets to their respective shafts.

Fig. 7: Silent Shaft Drive Chain Installation

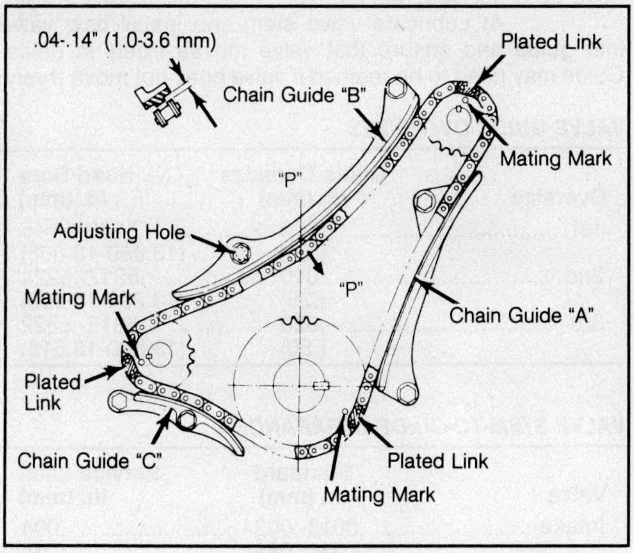

Timing marks on chain and sprockets must be aligned.

8) Install oil pump and silent shaft sprocket bolts. Loosely install three chain guides. Adjust silent shaft tension by tightening chain guide "A" and "C". Then shake oil pump and silent shaft sprockets to collect all chain slack at point "P". *See Fig. 7*.

9) Adjust position of chain guide "B" so that when chain is pressed inward with finger tips, clearance between chain guide "B" and chain links will be .04-.14" (1.0-3.6 mm). Tighten chain guide "B" mounting bolts.

10) Install new chain case cover gaskets to cover. Trim as required to fit at top and bottom. Coat cover and gaskets with sealant. Install gasket and cover to cylinder block. Reinstall front 2 cylinder head bolts.

11) To adjust tension with engine installed, proceed as follows: Remove cover from access hole in chain case cover. Loosen special bolt "B". *See Fig. 8*.

12) Apply finger pressure only (no tools) on boss in direction indicated. Tighten special bolt "B" to 175 INCH Lbs. (20 N.m). Complete reassembly by reversing disassembly procedure.

Fig. 8: Silent Shaft Chain Adjustment with Engine Installed

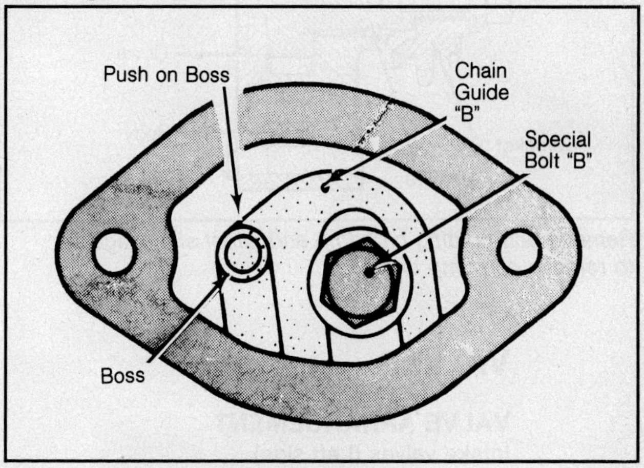

When adjusting use finger pressure only.

SILENT SHAFTS

Right Silent Shaft

1) With chains removed, remove oil pump mounting bolts. *See Fig. 9*. Remove bolt holding oil pump driven gear and silent shaft together. Remove oil pump and withdraw right silent shaft from bore.

2) To install, reverse removal procedure. Prime oil pump and ensure oil pump mating marks align and that Woodruff key on shaft fits keyway in driven gear.

NOTE: If bolt holding oil pump driven gear is difficult to remove, remove oil pump and silent shaft as an assembly and then remove lock bolt.

Left Silent Shaft

1) Remove thrust plate supporting left silent shaft. Thrust plate is removed by threading two .31" (7.9 mm) bolts evenly into tapped plate holes. Withdraw left silent shaft from cylinder block.

2) To install, reverse removal procedure. Install silent shafts into cylinder block taking care not to damage inner bearings. Install thrust plate on left silent shaft using new "O" ring. Install oil pump.

3) If silent shaft inner bearings are worn, use Camshaft Bearing Remover (MD998251) to draw bearing from cylinder block. For installation, use Camshaft Bearing Installer (MD998250) to press bearing straight into block.

4) Silent shaft clearances are as follows: Outer diameter to outer bearing clearance is .0008-.0024" (.020-.060 mm). Inner diameter to inner bearing clearance is .0020-.0035" (.050-.090 mm).

Chrysler Corp. Engines

2.6 LITER 4-CYLINDER (Cont.)

Fig. 9: Cutaway View of Gear Type Oil Pump

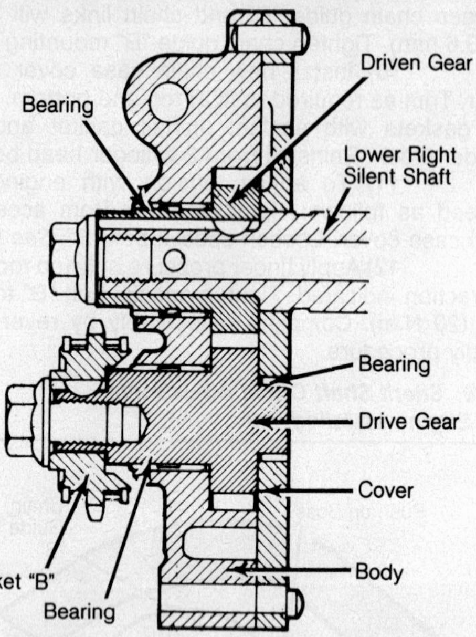

Remove bolt holding oil pump and silent shaft together to remove oil pump and shaft.

VALVES

VALVE ARRANGEMENT

Intake valves (Left side).
Exhaust valves (Right side).
Jet valves (Left side).

JET VALVES

Removal

Remove jet valve assembly with Jet Valve Socket (MD998310). Remove jet valve spring retainer lock, using Jet Valve Spring Pliers (MD998309). Remove valve spring retainer and valve spring.

CAUTION: Ensure Jet Valve Socket (MD998310) is not tilted in relation to center of jet valve. Valve stem may be bent by pressure against valve spring retainer and cause incorrect jet valve operation.

Inspection

1) Ensure valve slides freely in jet body but has no play. Check face of jet valve and jet body seat for damage. Check jet valve spring for cracks or damage. Replace jet valve and jet valve body as assembly if either part is defective.

2) Jet valve stem diameter should be .169" (4.29 mm). Angle of face and seat is 45°. Valve spring free length is 1.165" (29.59 mm). Spring load should be 5.50 lbs at .846" (2.5 kg at 21.49 mm).

Installation

1) Install new jet valve stem seal on jet body, using Seal Installer (MD998308). Do not reuse old seal. Oil jet valve stem and insert valve in body, using care not to damage stem seal lips. Ensure valve slides smoothly in body.

2) Place spring and retainer on valve body. Compress with Spring Pliers (MD998309) and install retainer lock. Install new "O" ring seal in groove of jet body. Oil "O" ring and threaded portion of jet body. Screw jet valve assembly into head by hand and tighten with Jet Valve Socket (MD998310).

VALVE SPRINGS

1) Remove rocker arm assemblies. Note which shaft is on intake side and which is on exhaust side for correct reassembly. Remove camshaft. Compress valve springs and remove retainer locks. Remove all retainers, springs, spring seals and valves, keeping all parts in proper order for assembly. *See Fig. 4.*

2) Check valve spring free length and pressure. Check valve springs for out-of-square with 90° straight-edge. Valve spring out-of-square service limit is 3° maximum.

3) If beyond limit, replace spring. Installed height of new intake or exhaust valve spring should be 1.590" (40.4 mm). Maximum installed height is 1.629" (41.4 mm). If maximum height limit is exceeded, valve or valve seat is worn excessively.

VALVE GUIDE SERVICING

1) Check valve stem-to-guide clearance. If clearance exceeds service limits, check valve guide and valve stem for wear. If guide is to be replaced, 3 oversizes are available. Guide should be driven out from top of head down through combustion chamber.

2) With head at room temperature, press old guide out with push rod of Valve Guide Remover/Installer (MD998115). Valve guide bore hole in cylinder head must be bored to size for outside diameter of new guide.

3) Press new guide into head from top. Use Valve Guide Remover/Installer (MD998115) with collar. Use of Valve Guide Remover/Installer (MD998115) will press guide into head to correct installed height. Properly installed guide will have .55" (13.9 mm) of length remaining above head boss surface. *See Fig. 10.*

4) Lubricate valve stem and install new valve into guide and ensure that valve moves freely in guide. Guide may need to be reamed if valve does not move freely.

VALVE GUIDE OVERSIZES

Oversize	Guide Oversize In. (mm)	Cyl. Head Bore In. (mm)
1st	.002 (.05)	.5138-.5145 (13.050-13.068)
2nd	.010 (.25)	.5217-.5224 (13.250-13.268)
3rd	.020 (.50)	.5315-.5322 (13.500-13.518)

VALVE STEM-TO-GUIDE CLEARANCE

Valve	Standard In. (mm)	Service Limit In. (mm)
Intake	.0012-.0024 (.031-.061)	.004 (.10)
Exhaust	.002-.0035 (.05-.089)	.006 (.15)

2.6 LITER 4-CYLINDER (Cont.)

Fig. 10: Valve Guide Installation and Height

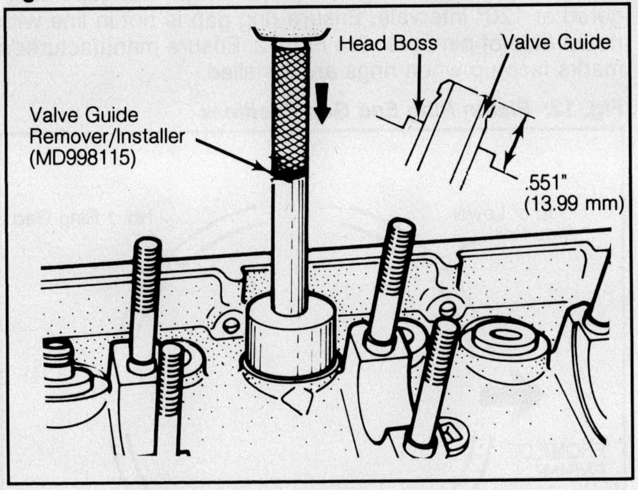

VALVE STEM OIL SEALS

1) Cylinder head must be removed from engine. After installing valve spring seat, lubricate new valve stem oil seal with engine oil and place on valve guide.

2) Using Seal Installer (MD998005), lightly tap seal into correct position as tool bottoms on head. Do not use old seals or twist seals when installing. *See Fig. 11*.

Fig. 11: Valve Stem Oil Seal Installation and Height

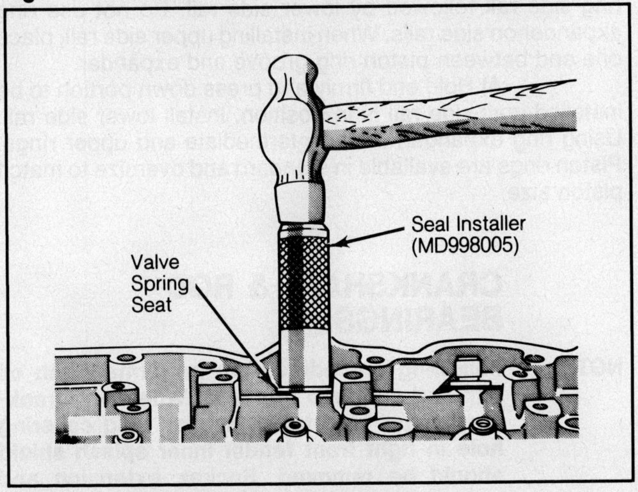

Install new seal with light taps until installer bottoms on cylinder head.

VALVE SEAT SERVICING

1) Check valve seat for damage or wear. Replace or rework seat, as necessary. If reworking seat, check valve guide first. Make proper replacement, if required, then check seat for necessary corrections.

2) Recondition valve seat with grinder or cutter to specified contact width. After rework, valve should be lapped into seat. Use valve grinding compound.

3) Valve seat sink (wear of seat inward allowing valve to seat too deep in head) must be checked by measuring installed height of valve spring. Measure between spring seat and retainer with all spring components installed.

4) Remove valve seat by thinning down with cutter. Machine seat bore to proper size for oversize seat. Cool new oversize seat insert with liquid nitrogen. Quickly press chilled insert into head. Replacement seats are available in .012" (.30 mm) and .024" (.60 mm) oversizes, which are marked "30" and "60" respectively.

CAUTION: Do not try to press seat insert into head when both are at same temperature. Valve seat bore of cylinder head will be damaged and seat insert will have loose fit.

VALVE CLEARANCE ADJUSTMENT

NOTE: After overhaul or other service procedures, perform all valve adjustments AFTER checking hot torque on cylinder head bolts. Emission levels and engine performance will be adversely affected by incorrect jet valve adjustment. Jet valve adjustment must be done prior to intake valve adjustment.

Jet Valves

1) Engine must be warm for correct adjustment. Rotate engine until No. 1 piston is at TDC on compression stroke. Back off intake valve adjusting screw on No.1 cylinder at least 2 full turns.

2) Loosen nut on jet valve adjusting screw of No. 1 cylinder. Back off jet valve adjusting screw (counterclockwise) until .006" (.15 mm) feeler gauge fits between screw and top of jet valve stem.

3) Tighten adjusting screw (clockwise) until tip of screw just touches feeler gauge. If screw is hard to turn, be careful to avoid compressing spring. Jet valve could be forced down as jet valve spring tension is low.

4) Hold adjusting screw in place and tighten lock nut. Recheck jet valve clearance. Adjust jet valve clearance on No. 3, No. 4 and No. 2 cylinders in same manner as described for cylinder No. 1.

Intake & Exhaust Valve

1) Be sure engine is warm. Position piston at TDC of compression stroke on cylinder at which valves are being adjusted. Loosen valve adjuster lock nuts. Adjust valve clearance by turning adjusting screw while measuring clearance with feeler gauge. Repeat for each cylinder.

2) Hot engine settings are .006" (.15 mm) for intake valves and .010" (.25 mm) for exhaust valves. After adjustment, tighten lock nut securely while holding adjusting screw with screwdriver.

PISTONS, PINS & RINGS

OIL PAN

See OIL PAN REMOVAL at end of ENGINE section.

PISTON & CONNECTING ROD ASSEMBLY

Removal

1) Remove cylinder head and oil pan. With piston at bottom of stroke, check top of cylinder bore for ridge. Cover piston with cloth to catch cuttings and remove ridge with ridge reamer.

2) Mark piston and rod assemblies for installation in original locations. Ensure connecting rods and rod caps are marked for reassembly in their original locations.

3) Rotate engine until connecting rod is straight down. Remove connecting rod caps and bearings. Push

2.6 LITER 4-CYLINDER (Cont.)

connecting rod and piston assembly upward through top of cylinder block.

Installation

1) Lubricate all internal surfaces with engine oil before installing. Ensure arrows on top of pistons point toward timing chain. Matching marks on connecting rods and caps must align and be on right side of engine.

2) Use ring compressor to compress rings. Ensure piston ring end gaps are positioned properly. *See Fig. 12.* Apply light coat of engine oil to pistons and rings. Rotate crankshaft so connecting rod journal is at center of bore.

3) Cover rod bolts before installing piston and rod assembly in bore. This will protect crankshaft journals from damage. Tap lightly on piston dome with wood hammer handle while guiding connecting rod onto crankshaft.

4) Install rod cap onto proper piston and connecting rod assembly. Ensure cap and rod markings are on same side. Tighten attaching bolts. Install cylinder head and oil pan.

FITTING PISTONS

1) After checking block for distortion, cracks or scratches, measure cylinder bores at 3 levels (90° apart). Top and bottom levels should be .38" (10 mm) into cylinder.

2) If any cylinder bore is distorted from standard size, block must be rebored and oversize pistons installed. Standard bore size is 3.587" (91.10 mm). Maximum out-of-round or taper is .0008" (.02 mm).

NOTE: **Pistons are available in standard, .010" (.25 mm), .020" (.50 mm), .030" (.75 mm) and .040" (1.00 mm) oversizes. Oversize pistons are stamped on crown to indicate amount of oversize.**

3) Check outside diameter of piston by measuring at point .08" (2 mm) from bottom of skirt and 90° to pin bore (across thrust face). Determine amount of cylinder reboring required to meet specified clearance.

FITTING PISTON PINS

NOTE: **When removing or installing piston pin, connecting rod should be in firm contact with body of Pin Installer (MD998184 & MD998183).**

1) Inspect and replace any piston pin showing signs of fracture, etching or wear. Check piston pin-to-rod bore fit. Lubricate pin and small end of rod bore with engine oil.

2) Set connecting rod and piston with arrow on piston and mark on connecting rod facing up. Using correct guide bar (marked 4G54) and push rod, press piston pin into bore, using 1600-3800 lbs. (720-1710 kg) force at normal room temperature.

FITTING PISTON RINGS

NOTE: **Upper and intermediate (No. 1 and No. 2) piston rings have same thickness, but different cross section. Oil ring expander end gap should be at least 45° from side rail gaps, but not on piston pin center or on thrust direction.**

1) Measure piston ring side and end gap clearance for all pistons. Replace rings as necessary. Check ring end gap after using piston to position ring in cylinder bore at least .63" (16 mm) from bottom of bore.

2) Install rings on pistons with end gaps staggered at 120° intervals. Ensure ring gap is not in line with thrust face of pin bore. *See Fig. 12.* Ensure manufacturer's marks face up when rings are installed.

Fig. 12: Piston Ring End Gap Positions

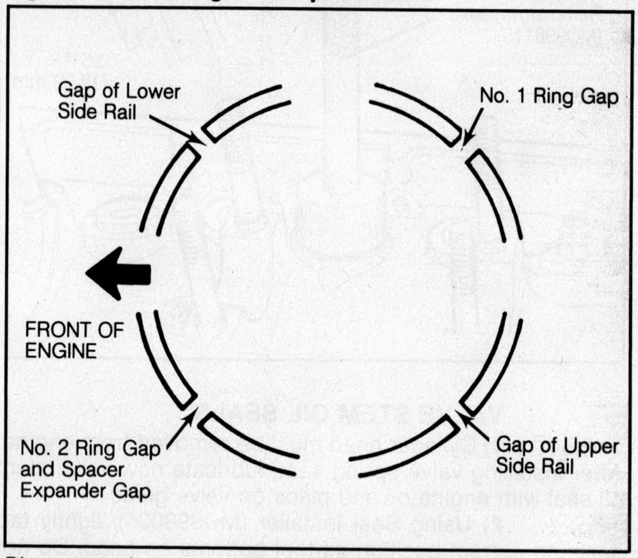

Place manufacturer's marks up when piston rings are installed.

3) Install oil ring expander first, then upper oil ring side rail followed by lower side rail. Do not use ring expander on side rails. When installing upper side rail, place one end between piston ring groove and expander.

4) Hold end firmly and press down portion to be installed until side rail is in position. Install lower side rail. Using ring expander, install intermediate and upper rings. Piston rings are available in standard and oversize to match piston size.

CRANKSHAFT & ROD BEARINGS

NOTE: **Following procedures are performed with oil pan and oil pump removed. Whenever crankshaft must be rotated, access plug covering hole in right front fender inner splash shield should be removed. Socket, extension and ratchet may then reach crankshaft sprocket bolt to turn crankshaft.**

CONNECTING ROD BEARINGS

1) Inspect bearings for seizure, improper contact, or other damage. Replace defective bearings. Measure outside diameter of crankshaft connecting rod bearing journals to determine if out-of-round or tapered.

2) Turn crankshaft until connecting rod to be checked starts moving toward top of engine. Use Plastigage method to measure bearing clearances. If clearance exceeds specifications, replace bearing.

3) Undersize bearings are available in .010" (.25 mm), .020" (.50 mm), and .030" (.75 mm) undersizes. After inspection and/or replacement, tighten rod bearing caps. Check connecting rod-to-crankshaft side clearance. Clearance should be .004-.010" (.10-.25 mm).

Chrysler Corp. Engines

2.6 LITER 4-CYLINDER (Cont.)

CONNECTING ROD JOURNALS

Size	Diameter [1] In. (mm)
Standard	2.0860-2.0866 (52.985-53.000)
1st Undersize	2.0762-2.0767 (52.735-52.750)
2nd Undersize	2.0663-2.0669 (52.485-52.500)
3rd Undersize	2.0565-2.0571 (52.235-52.250)

[1] - Maximum out-of-round is .0004" (.010 mm).

MAIN BEARINGS

NOTE: **No. 1 main bearing is at timing chain end and No. 5 bearing is at transmission end of block. When using Plastigage to check main bearings, remove weight from crankshaft by supporting counterweight with jack or preferably by shimming adjacent bearings. Do not turn crankshaft with Plastigage installed.**

1) Inspect each bearing for seizure, improper contact, or damage. Replace defective bearings. Measure outside diameter of crankshaft main bearing journals to determine if out-of-round or tapered.

2) Use Plastigage method to measure bearing clearance. Always install caps with arrow facing toward timing chain end. If clearance exceeds limits, replace bearing. Undersize bearings are available in .010" (.25 mm), .020" (.50 mm), and .030" (.75 mm) undersizes.

3) After inspection and/or replacement, tighten main bearing caps in three stages. Start at center bearing (No. 3) and then caps No. 2, No. 4, No. 1, and No. 5.

4) On installation, note that upper bearings are grooved except for No. 3 bearing, which is thrust bearing. All lower bearings are ungrooved and go in bearing caps. Ensure locating tangs and oil holes line up.

CRANKSHAFT MAIN BEARING JOURNALS

Size	Diameter [1] In. (mm)
Standard	2.3616-2.3622 (59.985-60.000)
1st Undersize	2.3518-2.3524 (59.735-59.750)
2nd Undersize	2.3419-2.3425 (59.485-59.500)
3rd Undersize	2.3321-2.3327 (59.235-59.250)

[1] - Maximum out-of-round or taper is .0004" (.010 mm)

THRUST BEARING END PLAY

1) Check crankshaft end play with crankshaft bearing caps installed. Mount dial indicator to front of engine and locate tip on nose of crankshaft. Move crankshaft to rear of its travel. Zero dial indicator.

2) Move crankshaft forward and read end play on gauge. Replace center main thrust bearing shells (both ungrooved) if end play is out of specification. Range of crankshaft end play is .002-.007" (.05-.18 mm).

REAR OIL SEAL

1) Remove bolts holding crankshaft rear oil seal case to cylinder block. Remove case with seal, separator and gasket. Remove separator and oil seal from case.

2) Install new seal using Seal Installer (MD998376). Install separator into case, ensuring .16" (4 mm) oil hole in separator is located at oil pan (lower) side of seal case. Examine crankshaft journal that runs in oil seal and chamfer over which seal must pass. Damage at either point can cause seal failure.

3) Coat new gasket lightly with grease and install. Lubricate seal lip with engine oil and install seal over end of crankshaft. Rotate housing right and left during installation to ensure seal lip surface is flat. Install housing bolts and tighten.

FRONT OIL SEAL

1) Remove crankshaft drive pulley. Pry out oil seal. Use care not to nick or damage sealing surfaces.

2) Install new oil seal, coating outside diameter lightly with Loctite Stud N' Bearing Mount or equivalent. Install crankshaft drive pulley and tighten to specification.

ENGINE OILING

CRANKCASE CAPACITY

Crankcase capacity is 4 1/2 quarts (4.3L) without oil filter; 5 quarts (4.7L) including filter.

NORMAL OIL PRESSURE

Normal oil pressure should be 50-64 psi (3.5-4.4 kg/cm^2) at 2000 RPM. Minimum at idle is 4 psi (28 kg/cm^2)

PRESSURE REGULATOR VALVE

Pressure regulator valve is located in oil pump body and is not adjustable.

OIL PUMP

Gear-type oil pump is used on 2.6L engine to provide force-feed lubrication system. Driven gear of oil pump also drives right silent shaft. *See Fig. 13*. For removal of oil pump, see SILENT SHAFTS in this article. Dissassembly is done as oil pump is removed from block.

Inspection

Check drive gear-to-housing clearance. Check drive and driven gear end play. Check drive and driven gear-to-bearing clearance in body and at cover. Remove end cap and check oil pump relief valve spring free length is 1.85" (46.9 mm). Ensure spring load is 9.5 lbs. at 1.575" (4.3 kg at 40 mm).

Installation

Ensure new gasket is used. Refill oil pump assembly with oil before installation. Pump reassembly is done as pump is installed on block. For installation of oil pump, see SILENT SHAFTS in this article.

Chrysler Corp. Engines

2.6 LITER 4-CYLINDER (Cont.)

Fig. 13: Mating Marks for Oil Pump Gears

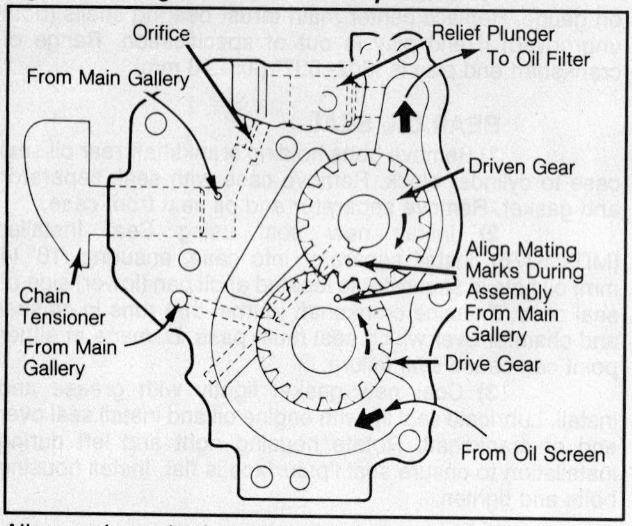

Align marks and prime oil pump during installation.

OIL PUMP SPECIFICATIONS

Application	Clearance In. (mm)
Gears-to-Housing Clearance	.004-.006 (.11-.15)
Gears-to-Bearing Clearance (Oil Pump Body)	.0008-.002 (.020-.05)
Driven Gear End Play	.0016-.0039 (.040-.100)
Drive Gear End Play	.0020-.0043 (.050-.110)

ENGINE COOLING

WATER PUMP

Removal

1) Drain cooling system. Remove radiator hose, by-pass hose and heater hose from water pump. Remove drive pulley cover. Remove locking bolt and pivot bolts. Pull up on slotted side (front of car) of water pump to relieve belt tension.

2) Remove drive belt. Remove water pump assembly from engine. Remove 4 bolts holding pump to body. Discard gasket and clean all gasket surfaces. Remove and discard "O" ring and clean "O" ring groove.

Installation

1) Install new gasket on water pump body. Position pump assembly on body and tighten 4 bolts. Use new "O" ring and position pump on engine with drive belt. Install pivot and locking bolts. Adjust belt tension and tighten bolts.

2) Reverse removal procedure to complete reassembly. When refilling cooling system, check anti-freeze freezing point and fill cooling system with required amount of anti-freeze (Mopar-4106794 or Prestone II).

3) If, after repair, radiator coolant level must be checked, install pressure cap and start engine. Run until upper radiator hose feels hot. Stop engine and add more coolant, as necessary, to completely fill system.

NOTE: For further information on cooling system capacities and other cooling system components, see appropriate article in ENGINE COOLING SYSTEMS at end of ENGINE section.

TIGHTENING SPECIFICATIONS

Application	Ft. Lbs. (N.m)
Camshaft Sprocket Bolt	40 (54)
Connecting Rod Cap Bolt	34 (46)
Crankshaft Drive Pulley Bolt	87 (118)
Cylinder Head Bolt	
Step 1 (Cold or Hot)	34 (46)
Step 2	
(Cold)	69 (93)
(Hot)	76 (103)
Main Bearing Cap Bolt [1]	58 (78)
Oil Pump Sprocket Bolt	25 (34)
Silent Chain Sprocket Bolt	25 (34)
Water Pump Drive Pulley Bolt	40 (54)
	INCH Lbs. (N.m)
Camshaft Bearing Cap Bolt	175 (20)
Chain Case Cover Bolt	159 (18)
Chain Guide Bolt	159 (18)
Cylinder Head-to-Chain Case Cover Bolt	159 (18)
Engine Mount Plate Bolt	159 (18)
Exhaust Manifold Nut	150 (17)
Intake Manifold Nut	150 (17)
Jet Valve	168 (19)
Oil Pump Mount Bolt	71 (8)
Water Pump Mounting Bolt	203 (23)

1 – Tighten in 3 even steps.

ENGINE SPECIFICATIONS

GENERAL SPECIFICATIONS

Year	DISPLACEMENT Cu. In.	DISPLACEMENT Liters	Fuel System	HP@RPM	Torque Ft. Lbs.@RPM	Compr. Ratio	BORE In.	BORE mm	STROKE In.	STROKE mm
1985	156	2.6	2-Bbl.	104 @ 4800	142 @ 2800	8.7:1	3.59	91.1	3.86	98.0

Chrysler Corp. Engines

2.6 LITER 4-CYLINDER (Cont.)

ENGINE SPECIFICATIONS (Cont.)

VALVES

Engine Size & Valve	Head Diam. In. (mm)	Face Angle	Seat Angle	Seat Width In. (mm)	Stem Diameter In. (mm)	Stem Clearance In. (mm)	Valve Lift In. (mm)
2.6L [1]							
Intake	1.81 (45.72)	45°	45°	.035-.051 [2] (.90-1.29)	.315 (8.00)	.0012-.0024 (.03-.06)	.413 (10.5)
Exhaust	1.50 (38.10)	45°	45°	.035-.051 [3] (.90-1.29)	.315 (8.00)	.0020-.0035 (.05-.09)	.413 (10.5)

1 – If jet valve or body are bad, replace both as assembly only.
2 – Margin for new valve is .047" (1.2 mm), service limit is .028" (.7 mm).
3 – Margin for new valve is .079" (2 mm), service limit is .039" (1 mm).

PISTONS, PINS, RINGS

Engine	PISTONS Clearance In. (mm)	PINS Piston Fit In. (mm)	PINS Rod Fit In. (mm)	RINGS Ring No.	RINGS End Gap In. (mm)	RINGS Side Clearance In. (mm)
2.6L	.0008-.0016 (.020-.040)	Slip Fit	Press Fit	1	.010-.018 (.25-.45)	.0024-.0039 (.061-.099)
				2	.010-.018 (.25-.45)	.0008-.0024 (.020-.061)
				3	.008-.035 (.20-.40)	[1]

1 – Free to rotate after assembly.

CRANKSHAFT MAIN & CONNECTING ROD BEARINGS

Engine	MAIN BEARINGS Journal Diam. In. (mm)	MAIN BEARINGS Clearance In. (mm)	MAIN BEARINGS Thrust Bearing	MAIN BEARINGS Crankshaft End Play In. (mm)	CONNECTING ROD BEARINGS Journal Diam. In. (mm)	CONNECTING ROD BEARINGS Clearance In. (mm)	CONNECTING ROD BEARINGS Side Play In. (mm)
2.6L	2.362 [1] (59.99)	.0008-.0028 (.020-.067)	No. 3	.002-.007 (.05-.18)	2.087 (53.01)	.0008-.0028 (.020-.067)	.004-.010 (.10-.25)

1 – Maximum taper or out-of-round is .0004" (.010 mm).

VALVE SPRINGS

Engine	Free Length In. (mm)	PRESSURE Lbs. @ In. (Kg @ mm) Valve Closed	PRESSURE Lbs. @ In. (Kg @ mm) Valve Open
2.6L	1.869 [1] (47.47)	61@1.59 (271@40)	....

1 – Valve spring free length service limit is 1.830" (46.48 mm).

CAMSHAFT

Engine	Journal Diam. In. (mm)	Clearance In. (mm)	Lobe Lift In. (mm)
2.6L	1.375 (34.94)	.002-.004 [1] (.05-.10)	.413 (10.5)

1 – Camshaft end play is .005-.013" (.13-.33 mm).

Chrysler Corp. Engines

3.7 LITER 6-CYLINDER

ENGINE CODING

ENGINE IDENTIFICATION

The engine can be identified by a number stamped on right side of block below No. 6 spark plug. The first digit indicates model year. The next 3 digits indicate cubic inch displacement.

The engine can also be identified by the eighth character of the Vehicle Identification Number (VIN). The VIN is located on a label on upper left corner of instrument panel, near windshield.

VIN ENGINE CODES

Application	VIN Code
3.7L 1-Bbl.	H

ENGINE REMOVAL

See ENGINE REMOVAL at end of ENGINE section.

SPECIAL ENGINE MARKS

Information identifying undersize and oversize components will be found at various locations on engine. Coding and location is as follows:

- "M" or "R" followed by number indicates which main or rod journals are .001" (.03 mm) undersize. Found on center crankshaft counterweight.
- "M-10" or "R-10" indicates all main or rod journals are .010" (.25 mm) undersize. Found on center crankshaft counterweight.
- "A" Indicates all cylinder bores .020" (.51 mm) oversize. Found on top of front pad on right side of block.
- "♦ " indicates .008" (.20 mm) oversize valve lifters. Found on top of front pad on right side of block.
- "O/S" Indicates .005" (.13 mm) oversize valve stems and is stamped on the thermostat boss at front of cylinder head.

MANIFOLDS & CYLINDER HEAD

MANIFOLD ASSEMBLY

Removal

1) Label and disconnect all lines, hoses and linkages from carburetor and air cleaner. Remove carburetor air heater. Remove air cleaner and carburetor. Disconnect exhaust pipe at manifold.

2) Remove nuts and washers securing manifolds to cylinder head and remove manifolds as an assembly. Remove stud nut and bolts securing manifolds together and separate manifolds.

Installation

1) Clean all gasket mating surfaces. Install new gasket between intake and exhaust manifold. Install bolts and stud nut securing manifolds together, but do not tighten at this time.

2) Remove air injection tube, if used. Coat new manifold-to-cylinder head gasket on both sides with gasket sealer and install on cylinder head. Position manifold assembly on cylinder head.

3) Install steel conical washer on center stud with cup side facing nut. Install brass washers at each end of exhaust manifold with flat sides facing manifold. Install triangular washers on remaining studs. Install nuts with cone side facing washers. Snug all bolts and nuts to approximately 10 INCH Lbs. (1 N.m).

4) Tighten intake-to-exhaust manifold stud nut first, then remaining manifold bolts. Starting at center of manifold assembly and working outward, tighten manifold-to-cylinder head nuts.

5) Connect exhaust pipe to manifold. Install carburetor air heater, air injection tube (with new gasket), carburetor, linkages, lines, hoses and air cleaner.

CYLINDER HEAD

Removal

1) Drain cooling system and remove air cleaner. Label and disconnect all wiring, hoses, lines and linkages from carburetor, distributor, manifolds and cylinder head.

2) Disconnect exhaust pipe at manifold. Remove valve cover and rocker arm shaft assembly. Label push rods to ensure installation in original location, then remove. Remove cylinder head and manifolds as an assembly. Remove manifolds from cylinder head.

Installation

Clean all gasket mating surfaces. Install cylinder head gasket. Do not use gasket sealer on head gasket. Install cylinder head. Install cylinder head bolts (clean and lightly oiled). Tighten bolts in 2 steps. *See Fig. 1.* To complete installation, reverse removal procedure.

Fig. 1: Cylinder Head Bolt Tightening Sequence

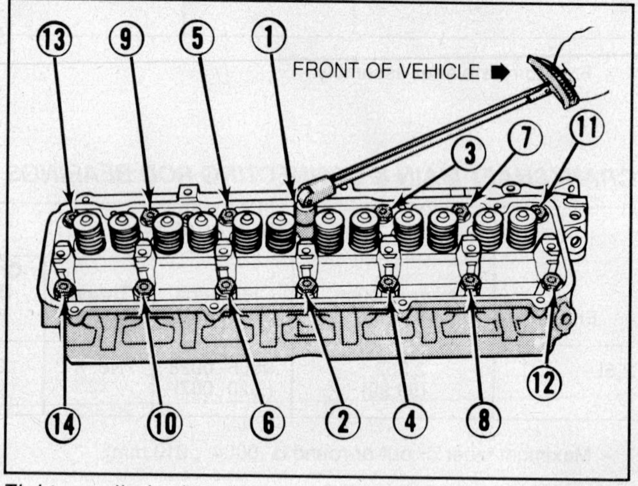

Tighten cylinder head bolts in 2 steps.

VALVES

VALVE ARRANGEMENT

E-I-E-I-E-I-I-E-I-E-I-E (Front-to-rear).

ROCKER ARM SHAFT ASSEMBLY

Removal

Remove valve cover. Remove bolts and retainers attaching shaft assembly to cylinder head. Remove rocker arms and shaft assembly. Label push rods to ensure installation in original location, then remove.

Installation

Install shaft assembly with oil hole positioned upward and toward front of engine. *See Fig. 2.* Install

3.7 LITER 6-CYLINDER (Cont.)

retainers between rocker arms so that they seat on shaft and not on extended bushing of rocker arm. Install long retainer in center position and special bolt at rear of engine. Install valve cover.

Fig. 2: Rocker Arm Shaft Assembly

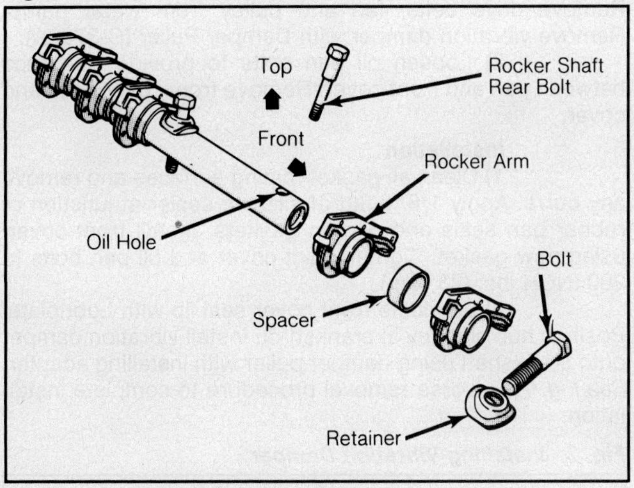

Install long retainer in center position.

VALVE SPRINGS

CAUTION: When removing valves from cylinder head, always remove burrs from valve stem lock grooves to prevent damage to valve guides.

Removal

With cylinder head removed, compress valve springs using valve spring compressor. Remove valve retainer locks, spring retainers, springs and oil seals. Identify valves to ensure installation in original locations.

Inspection

1) Valve springs should be tested whenever they are removed from cylinder head. Using valve spring tester, check spring tension. *See Fig. 3.* Replace springs that do not meet specifications.

2) Inspect each spring for squareness, using a steel square and flat surface. Replace spring if more than 1/16" (1.6 mm) out of square.

Installation

1) Coat valve stems with engine oil and insert in cylinder head. If valves or seats are reground, check valve stem height using Valve Gauge (C-3746). If valve is too long, grind valve tip down until length is within limits.

2) Install new oil seals firmly and squarely down over valve guides. Do not bottom out intake seals on guide tops. Intake oil seals require 1/16" (1.5 mm) gap between top of guide and inner top surface of seal. Install valve springs, retainers and locks.

VALVE SPRING INSTALLED HEIGHT

1) If valves or seats are reground, measure installed height of spring. Measure from bottom surface of spring seat in cylinder head (if spacers are installed, measure from top of spacer) to bottom surface of spring retainer.

2) If height is not within limits, install a 1/16" (1.5 mm) spacer between valve spring and cylinder head to correct spring height.

Fig. 3: Testing Valve Spring Tension

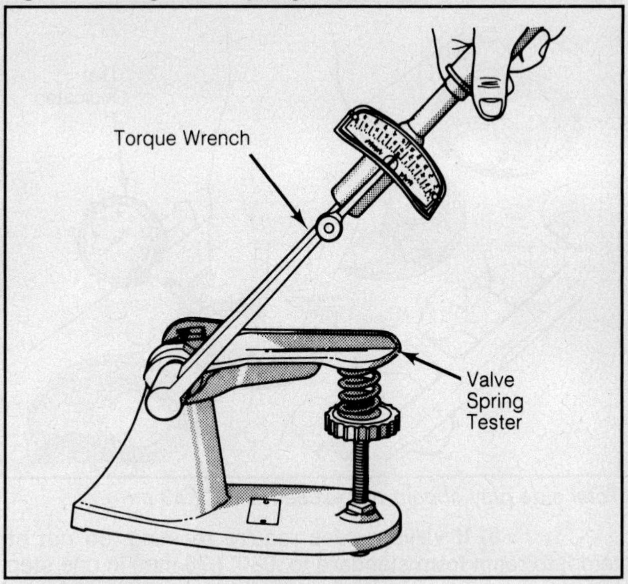

Use torque wrench and spring tester.

VALVE SPRING INSTALLED HEIGHT SPECIFICATIONS

Application	In. (mm)
All	1 5/8 - 1 11/16 (41.3-42.9)

VALVE STEM OIL SEALS

Cup-type oil seals are used on all valves. Long seal is used on intake valve and short seal is used on exhaust valve. If seals are removed for any reason, replace with new seals. *See Fig. 4.*

Fig. 4: Intake and Exhaust Valve Assemblies

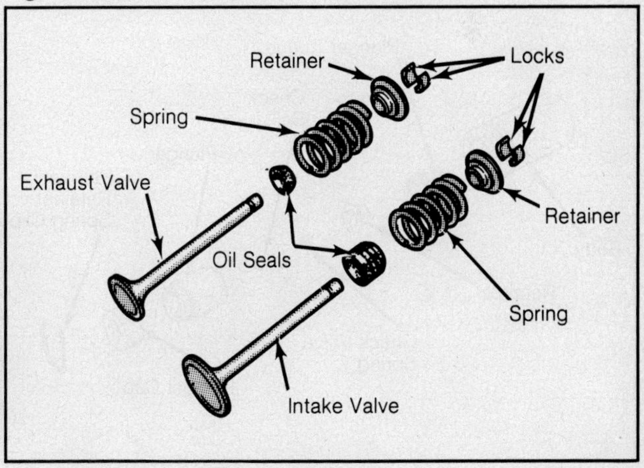

Short seal is used on exhaust valves.

VALVE GUIDE SERVICING

1) With valve spring assembly removed and valve guide cleaned, install Sleeve (C-3973) over valve stem. Install valve in cylinder head.

2) Attach dial indicator to cylinder head, and position at right angle to valve stem being measured. *See Fig. 5.* Total side play should not exceed .017" (.43 mm).

3.7 LITER 6-CYLINDER (Cont.)

Fig. 5: Measuring Valve Stem-to-Guide Clearance

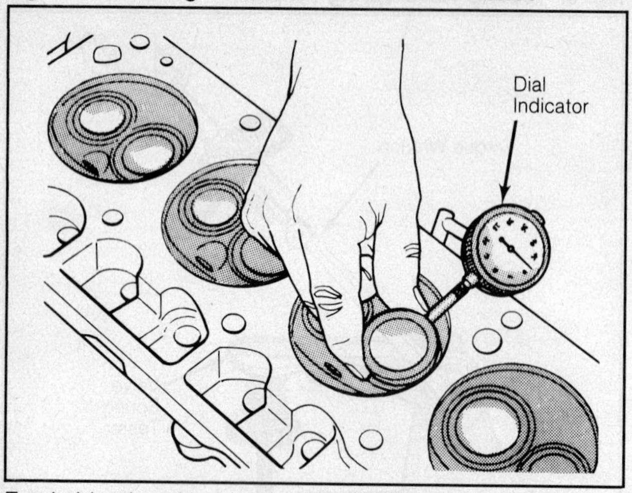

Total side play should not exceed .017" (.43 mm).

3) If valve guides require reaming, do not attempt to ream from standard to .030" (.76 mm) in one step. Use step-up procedure when reaming to .030" (.76 mm) oversize.

4) Replacement valves with oversize stems are available in .005" (.13 mm), .015" (.38 mm), and .030" (.76 mm) oversize.

HYDRAULIC VALVE LIFTERS

1) Prior to testing, disassemble lifter and clean all parts to remove varnish and carbon. Reassemble lifter.

2) To test, remove cap from plunger and plunger from lifter body. Fill lifter body with clean kerosene and install plunger. Unseat check valve to permit complete installation of plunger. Replace cap. *See Fig. 6.*

Fig. 6: Hydraulic Lifter Assembly

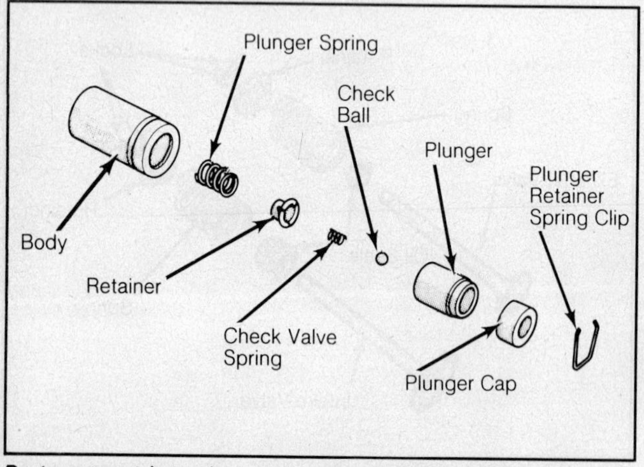

Parts are not interchangeable between lifters.

3) Place lifter upright in Lifter Tester (C-4343). Test leakdown by compressing tool. If plunger collapses immediately, disassemble, clean and retest. If rapid leakdown still occurs, replace lifter.

4) Check all lifters for wear and replace as necessary. If lifter or lifter bore in cylinder block is scuffed, scored, or shows signs of sticking, ream bore to next oversize and replace with oversize lifter.

CAMSHAFT

ENGINE FRONT COVER

Removal

1) Drain cooling system and remove radiator. Remove drive belts, fan and pulley from water pump. Remove vibration damper with Damper Puller (C-3732A).

2) Loosen oil pan bolts to provide clearance between pan and front cover. Remove front cover bolts and cover.

Installation

1) Clean all gasket mating surfaces and remove any burrs. Apply 1/8" bead of silicone sealer at junction of rubber pan seals and oil pan gaskets. Install front cover, using new gasket. Tighten front cover and oil pan bolts to 200 INCH lbs. (23 N.m).

2) Lubricate front cover seal lip with Lubriplate. Position hub slot key in crankshaft. Install vibration damper onto crankshaft using damper puller with installing adapter. *See Fig. 7.* Reverse removal procedure to complete installation.

Fig. 7: Installing Vibration Damper

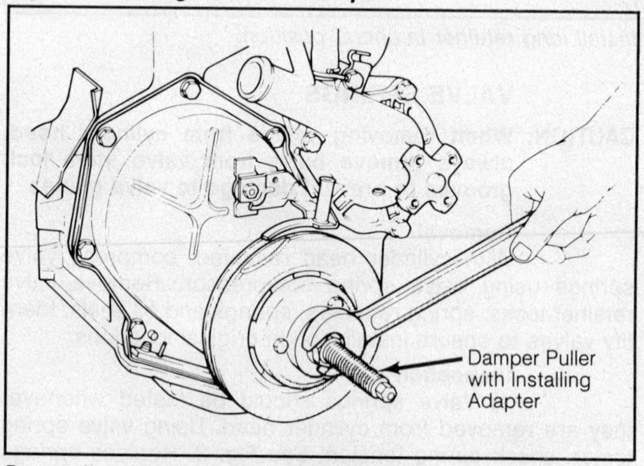

Press vibration damper onto crankshaft, using damper puller and adapter.

FRONT COVER OIL SEAL

Removal

Disconnect battery. Drain cooling system and remove radiator and fan assembly. Remove power steering pulley. Remove crankshaft pulley and vibration damper. Pry seal out from behind lip, using care not to damage crankshaft seal surface of front cover.

Installation

1) Install new seal by installing the threaded shaft part of Seal Installer (C-4251) into threads of crankshaft. Place seal into opening with seal spring facing the engine.

2) Place Installing Adapter (C-4251-2) with the thrust bearing and nut on the shaft. Tighten nut until tool is flush with the timing chain cover. Reverse removal procedure to complete installation.

TIMING CHAIN

Checking For Stretch

1) Remove front cover. Place torque wrench and socket on camshaft sprocket bolt. Using 30 ft. lbs. (41 N.m) torque (with head installed), or 15 ft. lbs. (20 N.m) torque (with head removed), turn camshaft sprocket in normal direction of rotation to remove chain slack. Do not allow crankshaft to rotate.

2) Place a steel ruler next to timing chain to measure amount of chain movement. Apply same torque in reverse direction, and measure amount of chain movement. *See Fig. 8.* If movement exceeds 1/8" (3 mm), replace timing chain.

Removal

Remove front cover. Remove camshaft sprocket attaching bolt, then remove timing chain and camshaft sprocket.

Installation

Turn crankshaft to line up timing mark of crankshaft sprocket with centerline of camshaft. Install camshaft sprocket and timing chain with timing marks aligned. *See Fig. 9.* Tighten camshaft sprocket bolt. Reverse removal procedures to complete installation.

Fig. 8: Measuring Timing Chain Stretch

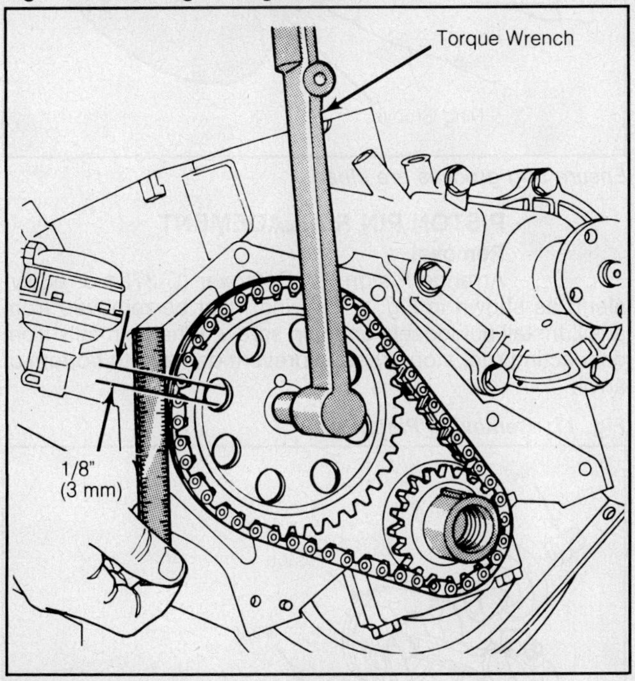

Do not allow crankshaft to rotate.

Fig. 9: Aligning Timing Chain Sprockets

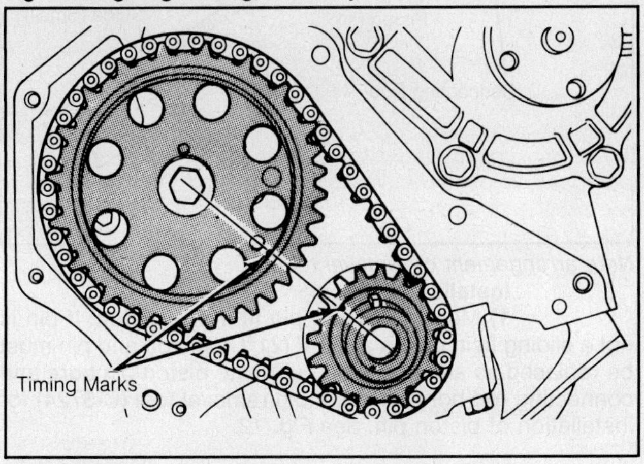

Timing marks on sprockets must align as shown.

VALVE TIMING

CAUTION: Do not rotate crankshaft further than indicated, as valve spring might bottom and cause serious valve train damage.

1) Rotate crankshaft until No. 6 exhaust valve is closing and No. 6 intake valve is opening.

2) Insert a 1/4" (6.35 mm) spacer between rocker arm and valve stem tip of No. 1 intake valve. Spring load on spacer should bleed down lifter, bottoming lifter plunger.

3) Install dial indicator on No. 1 intake valve, so indicator point is in contact with the valve spring retainer. Dial indicator stem must be parallel with valve stem. Zero dial indicator.

4) Rotate crankshaft clockwise until dial indicator shows .010" (.25 mm) of lift. If valve timing is correct, the timing of the crankshaft pulley should read from 12° BTDC to TDC.

5) If reading is not within specified limits, inspect sprocket index marks, timing chain wear and accuracy of "TDC" mark on timing indicator.

CAMSHAFT

Removal

1) Remove air cleaner, valve cover and rocker shaft assembly. Label push rods to ensure installation in original location, then remove. Remove lifters, using Valve Lifter Remover (C-4129). Keep lifters in order for installation in original location.

2) Remove timing chain and sprockets, distributor, oil pump and fuel pump. Install a long bolt in end of camshaft to aid in removal. Remove camshaft, using care not to damage camshaft bearings.

Installation

If camshaft is being replaced, check lifters for "dished" wear, and replace as necessary. Lubricate camshaft lobes and bearing journals. Carefully install camshaft in cylinder block. Reverse removal procedure to complete installation.

CAMSHAFT BEARINGS

Removal

Remove engine from vehicle. Remove camshaft from engine. Drive out rear cam bearing welch plug. Using camshaft bearing installer/remover, remove bearing shells from cylinder block.

Installation

1) Using bearing installer/remover, install bearings into place in cylinder block. Be sure oil hole(s) in bearings align with oil hole(s) in cylinder block.

2) Insert remaining bearings in similar manner. Install No. 1 bearing 3/32" (2.4 mm) inward from front surface of block. Apply Loctite or equivalent locking compound to new welch plug at rear of camshaft. Install plug. Be sure plug does not leak.

PISTONS, PINS & RINGS

OIL PAN

See OIL PAN REMOVAL at end of ENGINE section.

Chrysler Corp. Engines

3.7 LITER 6-CYLINDER (Cont.)

PISTON & ROD ASSEMBLY

Removal

1) With cylinder head and oil pan removed, use ridge cutter to remove any ridge or deposits on upper end of cylinder bore. Piston must be at bottom of stroke and covered with cloth to collect cuttings.

2) Ensure connecting rods and caps are marked for cylinder identification. Rotate crankshaft so connecting rod is centered in cylinder bore. Remove connecting rod cap.

3) Cover rod cap bolts with rubber hose to protect crankshaft. Push piston and rod assembly out through top of cylinder block. Use care not to nick crankshaft journal or cylinder wall. Install rod caps on mating rods.

Installation

1) Compression ring gaps must be located on piston, so they will be on left side of engine and staggered about 60° apart.

NOTE: **Neither gap should line up with oil ring gaps, and "ID" mark on each compression ring must face top of piston.**

2) Rotate oil ring expander so gaps are on right side of engine. Rotate steel rails so gaps are opposite and positioned above piston pin holes.

3) Immerse pistons and rings in clean engine oil. Slide ring compressor over piston and tighten. Do not allow position of rings to change. Lightly oil cylinder bores.

4) Rotate crankshaft so connecting rod journal is in center of cylinder bore. Position piston and rod assembly into bore. Notch on top of piston and oil squirt hole in connecting rod must point toward front of engine.

5) Carefully guide connecting rod onto crankshaft journal. Tap piston head lightly with hammer handle to seat connecting rod and bearing against crankshaft. Install and tighten rod cap and bearing.

FITTING PISTONS

1) With piston and cylinder bores dry and clean, measure for piston-to-cylinder wall clearance. Measurements should be taken at 70°F (21°C).

2) Measure piston skirt diameter 90° to piston pin axis. Measure cylinder bore halfway down cylinder and 90° to crankshaft centerline.

3) Check cylinder bore for taper or out-of-round condition using a micrometer or cylinder bore gauge.

4) Cylinder bore must not be more than .005" (.13 mm) out-of-round. Taper must not exceed .010" (.25 mm). If not within limits, bore and hone cylinders. Pistons are available in standard and .020" (.51 mm) oversize.

5) After boring and honing operations, always wash cylinders thoroughly with scrub brush and soapy water, then rinse well. Oil the bores after cleaning to prevent rust.

FITTING RINGS

1) Using a feeler gauge, check ring end gap in cylinder bore. Ring must be square in bore and about 2" from bottom of cylinder bore.

2) Install rings on piston, starting at bottom with oil ring expander and rails, then working upward until top compression ring is installed. "ID" mark on each compression ring must face upward.

3) Using a feeler gauge, check side clearance of ring in ring groove of piston. *See Fig. 10.* Steel oil ring rails should not bind in ring groove and side clearance must not be excessive.

Fig. 10: Measuring Piston Ring Side Clearance

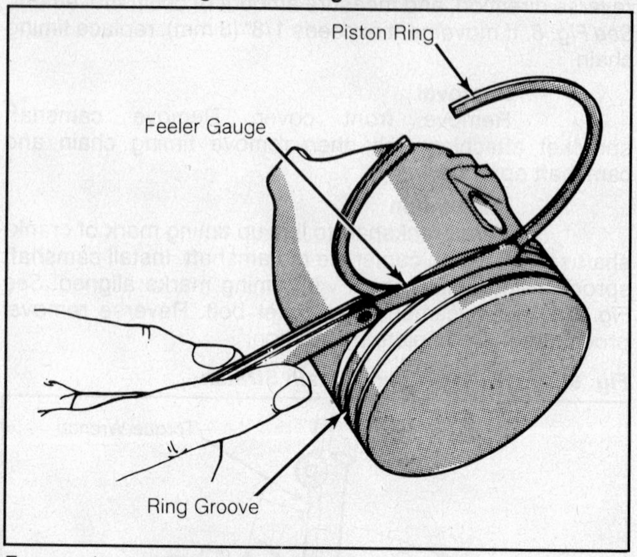

Ensure ring grooves are clean.

PISTON PIN REPLACEMENT

Removal

Arrange Piston Pin Remover (C-3724 or equivalent) as shown in *Fig. 11.* Spring must be removed from anvil. Install nut loosely on main screw. When pin falls from connecting rod, stop press to prevent damage to bottom of anvil.

Fig. 11: Removing Piston Pin

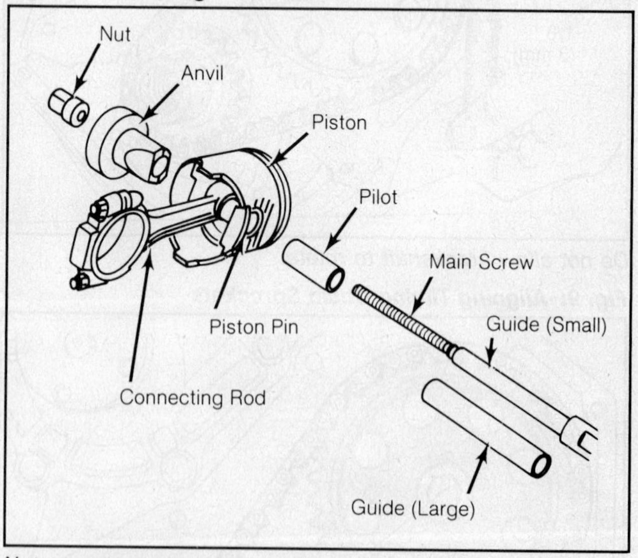

Note arrangement of removal tool.

Installation

1) Measure piston pin fit in the piston. If pin is not a sliding fit in piston at 70°F (21°C), piston and pin must be replaced as an assembly. Lubricate piston pin bore and connecting rod bore. Arrange pin removal tool (C-3724) for installation of piston pin. *See Fig. 12.*

3.7 LITER 6-CYLINDER (Cont.)

Fig. 12: Installing Piston Pin

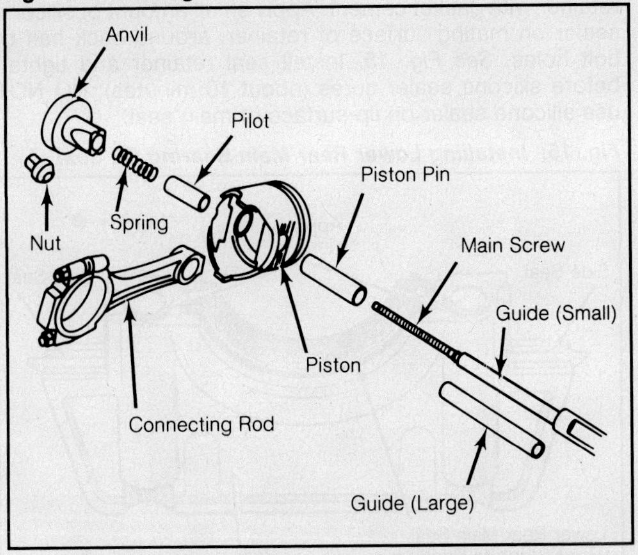

Pin must be a sliding fit in piston at 70F (21C).

2) Install spring inside pilot. Install spring and pilot in anvil. Position notch on piston and oil hole in connecting rod on same side (front of engine). *See Fig. 13.* Press pin into position until pin bottoms against pilot on tool.

Fig. 13: Correct Rod-to-Piston Relationship

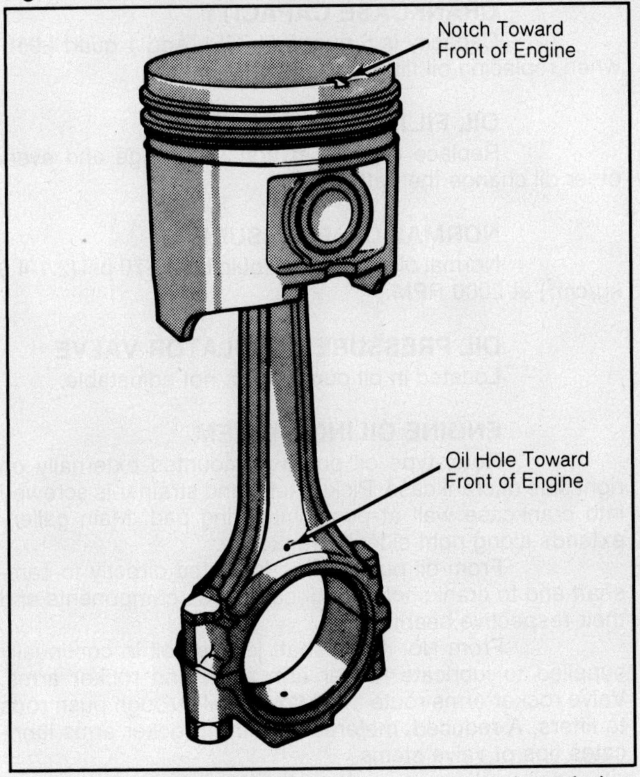

When removing and installing pistons, cover rod cap bolts with rubber hose to protect crankshaft and cylinders.

Checking Pin Fit

Arrange piston pin tool parts as for removal of pin. Place assembly in vise, securing main screw butt end between vise jaws. Attach torque wrench to nut, and test torque up to 15 ft. lbs. (20 N.m). If connecting rod moves downward on piston pin, replace connecting rod.

CRANKSHAFT & ROD BEARINGS

CONNECTING ROD BEARINGS

NOTE: **Use Plastigage method for checking bearing clearances. Be sure oil film is removed from surfaces to be checked.**

1) Ensure rod caps are marked for cylinder identification. Rotate crankshaft until connecting rod to be checked starts moving toward top of engine. Remove rod cap. Place strip of Plastigage across full width of lower bearing, about 1/4" off center of cap, and away from oil holes.

2) With Plastigage in place, install and tighten rod cap to specification. Do not rotate crankshaft. Remove cap. Measure compressed width of Plastigage (with scale furnished) to determine bearing clearance. Out-of-round or taper on any journal must not exceed .001" (.03 mm).

3) New bearings are available in standard, .001" (.03 mm), .002" (.05 mm), .003" (.08 mm), .010" (.25 mm), and .012" (.31 mm) undersize. Always install new bearings in pairs.

4) Install connecting rod bearings so small, formed tang fits into machined groove in connecting rod.

MAIN BEARINGS

1) Check main bearing clearances one at a time. To accurately determine clearance, weight of crankshaft must first be eliminated (when checking with engine installed). A .010" (.25 mm) minimum thickness cardboard shim (matchbook cover) should be used for this purpose.

2) Remove crankshaft main cap(s) on either side of bearing being checked. See MAIN BEARING CLEARANCE CHECK table. Place cardboard shim between bearing shell(s) and cap(s) which were removed. Install "shimmed" bearing cap(s) and tighten to 10-15 ft. lbs. (14-20 N.m).

3) Remove main cap of bearing to be checked. Use Plastigage method, tightening main cap to specification.

MAIN BEARING CLEARANCE CHECK

When Checking	Shim
Number 1 Bearing	Number 2 Bearing
Number 2 Bearing	Number 1 & 3 Bearings
Number 3 Bearing	Number 2 & 4 Bearings
Number 4 Bearing	Number 3 Bearing
Number 5 Bearing	Number 4 Bearing

4) When installing new bearings, always install in pairs. New bearings are available in standard, .001" (.03 mm), .002" (.05 mm), .003" (.08 mm), .010" (.25 mm), and .012" (.31 mm) undersize.

5) Lower main bearings 1, 2 and 4 are interchangeable. Upper main bearings 1, 2 and 4 are interchangeable. Upper (grooved face) main bearings are not interchangeable with lower (plain face) main bearings.

3.7 LITER 6-CYLINDER (Cont.)

Thrust bearings are not interchangeable with any other bearing. *See Fig. 14.*

Fig. 14: Main Bearing Identification

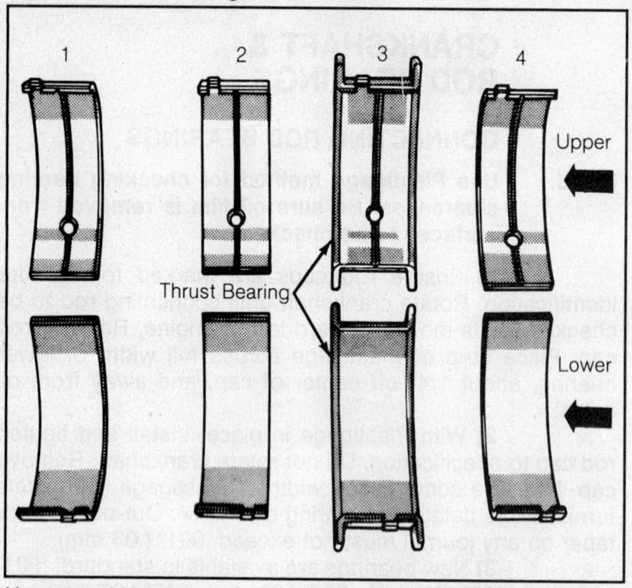

Upper and lower bearing halves are not interchangeable.

6) Replace main bearings one at a time. To extract upper main bearing from cylinder block, insert Pin (C-3059) into oil hole of crankshaft journal. Rotate crankshaft clockwise, allowing pin to push upper bearing out of cylinder block.

7) When installing a new upper main bearing, slightly chamfer sharp edges from plain side of new bearing, then start bearing in place. Using pin, install upper bearing in reverse order of removal procedures.

CRANKSHAFT END PLAY

Check crankshaft end play. If not within specifications, replace thrust bearing (No. 3 main bearing).

REAR MAIN BEARING OIL SEAL

Removal

1) Remove oil pan. Remove rear seal retainer and rear main bearing cap. Remove lower seal from seal retainer.

2) Remove upper seal by pressing on seal end with a small screwdriver, then pull seal from cylinder block. Use care not to damage crankshaft.

Installation

1) Lightly oil upper seal lip with engine oil. Hold seal tightly against crankshaft with paint stripe on seal positioned to rear of engine. Position shim protector (supplied with seal) between lip of seal and edge of groove in block.

2) Slide seal into groove, rotating crankshaft as needed. Use care not to damage seal lip, or allow back of seal to become nicked or shaved by groove in block. If seal is damaged in any way, it must be discarded and replaced with another new seal. Install rear main bearing cap.

3) Clean seal retainer and wipe dry. Apply 1/8" bead of silicone sealer in bottom of retainer groove, starting and finishing 1/2" from ends of groove. Install lower seal half into retainer with paint stripe to rear.

4) Hold side seals in position in grooves of retainer with gasket cement. Apply small amount of silicone sealer on mating surface of retainer, around back half of bolt holes. *See Fig. 15.* Install seal retainer and tighten before silicone sealer cures (about 10 minutes). DO NOT use silicone sealer on lip surface of main seal.

Fig. 15: Installing Lower Rear Main Bearing Oil Seal

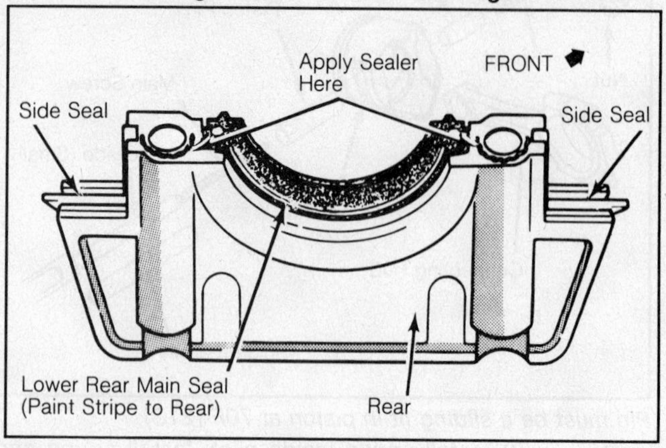

ENGINE OILING

CRANKCASE CAPACITY

Capacity is 5 quarts (4.75L). Add 1 quart (.95L) when replacing oil filter.

OIL FILTER

Replace oil filter at first oil change and every other oil change thereafter.

NORMAL OIL PRESSURE

Normal oil pressure should be 30-70 psi (2.1-4.9 kg/cm^2) at 2000 RPM.

OIL PRESSURE REGULATOR VALVE

Located in oil pump body, not adjustable.

ENGINE OILING SYSTEM

Rotor-type oil pump is mounted externally on right side of crankcase. Pickup tube and strainer is screwed into crankcase wall at pump mounting pad. Main gallery extends along right side of crankcase.

From oil pump, oil is force-fed directly to camshaft and to crankshaft to lubricate these components and their respective bearings.

From No. 4 camshaft journal, oil is continually supplied to lubricate rocker arm shaft and rocker arms. Valve rocker arms route a full flow of oil through push rods to lifters. A reduced, metered flow from rocker arms lubricates tips of valve stems.

OIL PUMP

Removal

Carefully remove oil pump cover, using care not to allow outer rotor to drop out. Remove outer rotor. Remove oil pump.

3.7 LITER 6-CYLINDER (Cont.)

Fig. 16: Engine Oiling System

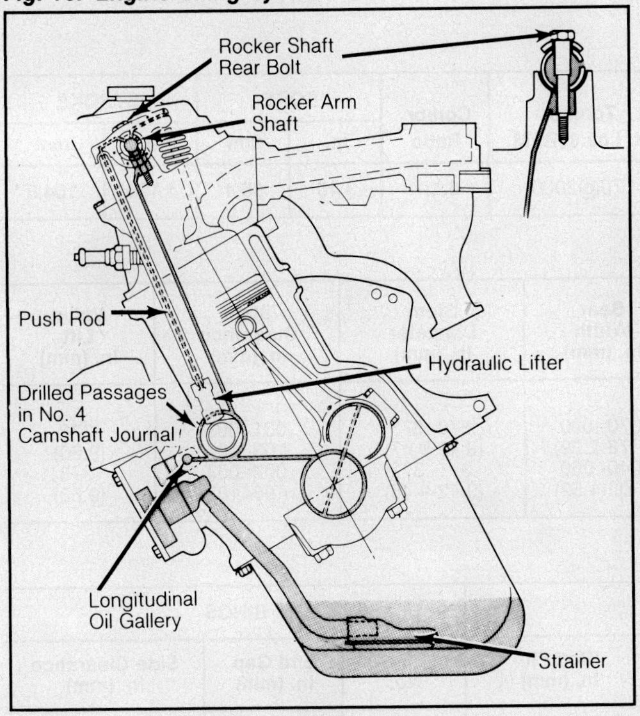

Disassembly

While supporting gear to eliminate load on aluminum body of pump, press off pump drive gear. Pump may now be completely disassembled. *See Fig. 17.*

Fig. 17: Oil Pump Assembly

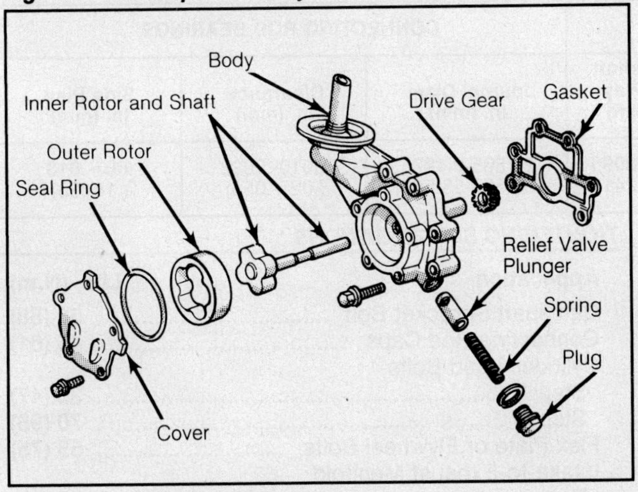

Inspection

1) Clean all parts thoroughly. Replace pump assembly if mating surface of cover is scratched or grooved. Check wear of cover with a straightedge and feeler gauge. Replace pump assembly if wear is excessive.

2) Replace shaft and both rotors if inner rotor thickness, outer rotor thickness or outer rotor diameter indicate excessive wear.

3) Measure outer rotor-to-pump body clearance with a feeler gauge. If clearance exceeds limit, replace pump assembly.

4) Install inner rotor in pump body. Place a straightedge over pump body, between bolt holes. Using a feeler gauge, measure clearance over inner rotor. Replace pump assembly if clearance is excessive.

5) Install both rotors in pump body. Using a feeler gauge, check clearance between tips of inner and outer rotors. Excessive clearance requires replacement of shaft and both rotors.

6) Make following inspection of relief valve assembly: Check relief valve plunger for wear and binding in bore. Check spring for free length of 2 1/4" (57.2 mm). Spring tension should be 22.3-23.3 lbs. (1.56-1.63 kg/cm^2) when compressed to 1 19/32" (40.5 mm).

OIL PUMP SPECIFICATIONS

Application	In. (mm)
Pump Cover Wear	.0014 (.036) Max.
Inner Rotor Thickness	.826 (20.98) Min.
Outer Rotor Thickness	.826 (20.98) Min.
Outer Rotor Diameter	2.47 (62.74) Min.
Outer Rotor-to-Pump Body	.013 (.33) Max.
Clearance Over Inner Rotor	.003 (.076) Max.
Rotor Tip Clearance	.009 (.23) Max.

Reassembly

1) Reassemble pump in reverse order of disassembly, using new parts as required. When pressing drive gear onto shaft, note the following:

2) Install inner rotor and shaft assembly into pump body. Insert a 1/32" thick washer in the inner rotor shaft hole. Using the washer to support the shaft, press drive gear onto the shaft. Remove the washer.

Installation

1) Prime inside of pump with engine oil. Using new gasket, install and tighten oil pump onto cylinder block. Install outer rotor into pump body.

2) Ensure all internal parts are well lubricated. Install and tighten pump cover, using a new seal ring between cover and pump body.

ENGINE COOLING

WATER PUMP

Removal

Drain cooling system. Remove all drive belts. Remove fan, spacer, pulley and bolts as an assembly. Position by-pass hose lower clamp in center of hose. Disconnect heater hose. Remove water pump bolts and remove water pump.

Installation

To install water pump, reverse removal procedures, using new gasket.

NOTE: **For information on cooling system capacities and other cooling system components, see appropriate cooling system article at end of ENGINE section.**

Chrysler Corp. Engines

3.7 LITER 6-CYLINDER (Cont.)

ENGINE SPECIFICATIONS

GENERAL SPECIFICATIONS

Year	DISPLACEMENT		Fuel System	HP@RPM	Torque Ft. Lbs.@RPM	Compr. Ratio	BORE		STROKE	
	Cu. In.	Liters					In.	mm	In.	mm
1985	225	3.7	1-Bbl.	95@3600	170@2000	8.4:1	3.40	86.4	4.125	104.8

VALVES

Engine Size & Valve	Head Diam. In. (mm)	Face Angle	Seat Angle	Seat Width In. (mm)	Stem Diameter In. (mm)	Stem Clearance In. (mm)	Valve Lift In. (mm)
3.7L							
Intake	1.615-1.625 (41.02-41.28)	44.5-45°	45-45.5°	.070-.090 (1.78-2.29)	.372-.373 (9.45-9.47)	.001-.003 (.03-.08)	.378 (9.60)
Exhaust	1.355-1.365 (34.42-34.67)	42.5-43°	45-45.5°	.040-.060 (1.02-1.52)	.371-.372 (9.42-9.45)	.002-.004 (.05-.10)	.378 (9.60)

PISTONS, PINS, RINGS

Engine	PISTONS	PINS		RINGS		
	Clearance In. (mm)	Piston Fit In. (mm)	Rod Fit In. (mm)	Ring No.	End Gap In. (mm)	Side Clearance In. (mm)
3.7L	.0005-.0015 (.013-.038)	.00035-.00085 (.0009-.0216)	.0007-.0017 (.018-.043)	1 & 2	.010-.020 (.25-.51)	.0015-.003 (.038-.080)
				3	.015-.055 (.38-1.40)	.0002-.005 (.005-.130)

CRANKSHAFT MAIN & CONNECTING ROD BEARINGS

Engine	MAIN BEARINGS				CONNECTING ROD BEARINGS		
	Journal Diam. In. (mm)	Clearance In. (mm)	Thrust Bearing	Crankshaft End Play In. (mm)	Journal Diam. In. (mm)	Clearance In. (mm)	Side Play In. (mm)
3.7L	2.7495-2.7505 (69.837-69.863)	.0010-.0025 (.025-.064)	No. 3	.0035-.0095 (.089-.241)	2.1865-2.1875 (55.537-55.563)	.0010-.0022 (.025-.056)	.007-.013 (.18-.33)

CAMSHAFT

Engine	Journal Diam. In. (mm)	Clearance In. (mm)	Lobe Lift In. (mm)
3.7L			
No. 1	1.998-1.999 (50.75-50.77)	.001-.003 (.03-.08)	.....
No. 2	1.982-1.983 (50.34-50.37)		
No. 3	1.967-1.968 (49.96-49.99)		
No. 4	1.951-1.952 (49.56-49.58)		

VALVE SPRINGS

Engine	Free Length In. (mm)	PRESSURE Lbs. @ In. (Kg @ mm)	
		Valve Closed	Valve Open
3.7L	1.92 (48.8)	49-57@1.69 (22-26@42.86)	137-150@1.31 (62-68@33.34)

TIGHTENING SPECIFICATIONS [1]

Application	Ft. Lbs. (N.m)
Camshaft Sprocket Bolt	50 (68)
Connecting Rod Caps	45 (61)
Cylinder Head Bolts	
Step 1	35 (47)
Step 2	70 (95)
Flex Plate or Flywheel Bolts	55 (75)
Intake-to-Exhaust Manifold	
Bolts	20 (27)
Stud Nut	30 (41)
Main Bearing Caps	85 (115)
Rear Main Bearing Seal Retainer	30 (41)
Rocker Arm Shaft Bolts	25 (34)
Water Pump Bolts	30 (41)
	INCH Lbs. (N.m)
Fan Bolts	200 (23)
Manifold Assembly-to-Cylinder Head	120 (14)
Oil Pump	
Cover-to-Body	130 (15)
Pump-to-Cylinder Block	200 (23)

[1] – All critical bolts must be clean and lightly oiled.

ENGINE CODING

ENGINE IDENTIFICATION

Engine identification number is stamped on a pad located at rear of the right engine mount. First digit indicates model year. The next 3 digits indicate engine size in cubic inches.

Engine can also be identified by the eighth character in the Vehicle Identification Number (VIN). VIN is located on a plate attached to upper left corner of instrument panel, near windshield.

VIN ENGINE CODES

Application	VIN Code
5.2L 2-Bbl.	T
5.9L 4-Bbl.	
Federal	W
California	I
Heavy Duty	V

ENGINE REMOVAL

See ENGINE REMOVAL at end of ENGINE section.

SPECIAL ENGINE MARKS

Information identifying undersize and oversize components will be found at various engine locations. It is decoded as follows:

- "M" or "R" followed by number, indicates which main or rod bearing journal is .001" (.03 mm) undersize. This mark will be stamped on No. 8 crankshaft counterweight on 5.2L engines and on No. 3 crankshaft counterweight on 5.9L engines.
- "MX" or "RX" indicates all main or rod bearing journals are .010" (.25 mm) undersize. Marked on No. 8 crankshaft counterweight (5.2L), or No. 3 crankshaft counterweight (5.9L).
- "A" indicates .020" (.51 mm) oversize cylinder bores. Follows engine identification number.
- "♦ " indicates .008" (.20 mm) oversize lifters. Located on top pad, front of engine, and stamped on flat ground on outside surface of each oversize lifter bore.
- "X" indicates .005" (.13 mm) oversize valve stems. Found on milled pad near two 3/8" tapped holes on each end of cylinder head.

MANIFOLDS & CYLINDER HEAD

INTAKE MANIFOLD

Removal

1) Drain cooling system and disconnect battery ground cable. Remove alternator, air cleaner and fuel line. Disconnect accelerator linkage. Remove vacuum hose between carburetor and distributor.

2) Remove distributor cap and wires. Disconnect by-pass hose and heater hoses. Remove PCV and fuel evaporation hoses. Remove valve covers.

3) Disconnect coil and temperature sending unit wiring. Remove intake manifold, coil and carburetor as an assembly.

Installation

1) Clean all gasket mating surfaces. Lightly coat intake manifold side gaskets with sealer, on 5.2L engines only. Do not use any sealer on side gaskets on 5.9L engines.

2) Install manifold side gaskets. Coat front and rear intake manifold end gaskets and cylinder block with a quick-dry cement.

3) Install end gaskets, ensuring end holes in gaskets are locked into tangs of head gasket. Place a 1/4" drop of silicone sealer at each of the 4 intake manifold-to-cylinder head gasket corners.

4) Position intake manifold on engine. Inspect gaskets for correct positioning, and install bolts finger tight.

5) Tighten bolts to 25 ft. lbs. (34 N.m). Tighten bolts to 40 ft. lbs. (54 N.m). *See Fig. 1.*

Fig. 1: Intake Manifold Tightening Sequence.

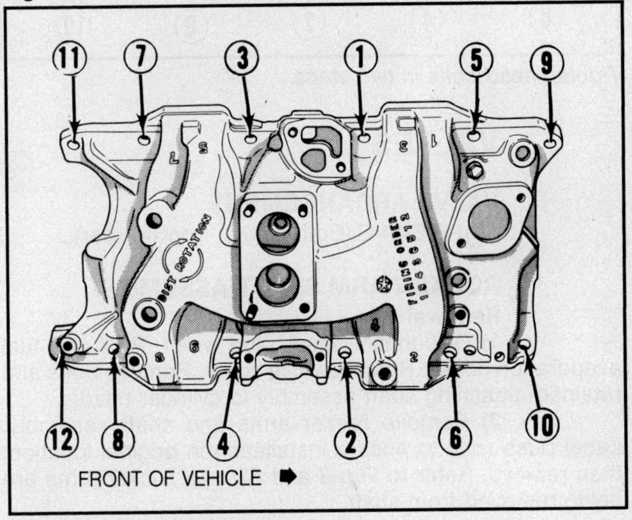

Tighten bolts as indicated in text.

EXHAUST MANIFOLDS

Removal

Disconnect exhaust pipe from exhaust manifold. Remove bolts, nuts and washers securing manifold to cylinder head. Remove manifold. Replace any studs that come out during manifold removal with new studs.

Installation

1) Install new studs, if necessary. Apply sealant to coarse threads of studs to prevent coolant leaks. Position manifold on studs and install conical washers and nuts.

2) Install conical washers and bolts to inner end of outer manifold arms. Install remaining bolts (without washers) to center arm of manifold.

3) Starting at center arm of exhaust manifold and working outward, tighten manifold. Connect and tighten exhaust pipe.

CYLINDER HEAD

Removal

1) Drain cooling system and disconnect battery ground cable. Remove intake and exhaust manifolds. Remove rocker arm shaft assemblies.

2) Label push rods to ensure installation in original location, then remove. Remove head bolts and remove cylinder head.

Installation

1) Clean all gasket surfaces of cylinder block and head. Coat new head gaskets with sealer and install on cylinder block. Install cylinder head.

5.2 & 5.9 LITER V8 (Cont.)

2) Install and tighten head bolts in 2 steps. *See Fig. 2.* Reverse removal procedure to complete installation.

Fig. 2: Cylinder Head Tightening Sequence

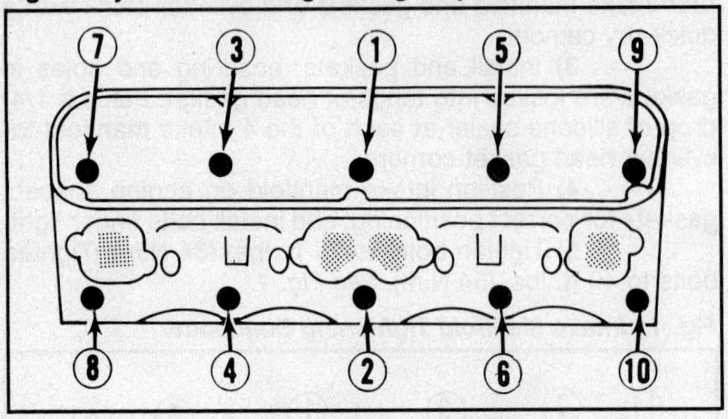

Tighten head bolts in two steps.

VALVES

VALVE ARRANGEMENT

E-I-I-E-E-I-I-E (Both banks, front-to-rear).

ROCKER ARM SHAFT ASSEMBLY

Removal

1) Disconnect spark plug wires, PCV and fuel evaporation hoses. Remove valve cover. Remove bolts and retainers attaching shaft assembly to cylinder head.

2) Remove rocker arms and shaft assembly. Label push rods to ensure installation in original location, then remove. Refer to *Fig. 3* and *Fig. 4* if rocker arms are being removed from shaft.

Installation

1) Install rocker arm and shaft assembly with notch on end of rocker arm shaft pointing to centerline of engine and toward front of engine on left bank, to rear of engine on right bank.

Fig. 3: Identifying Rocker Arms

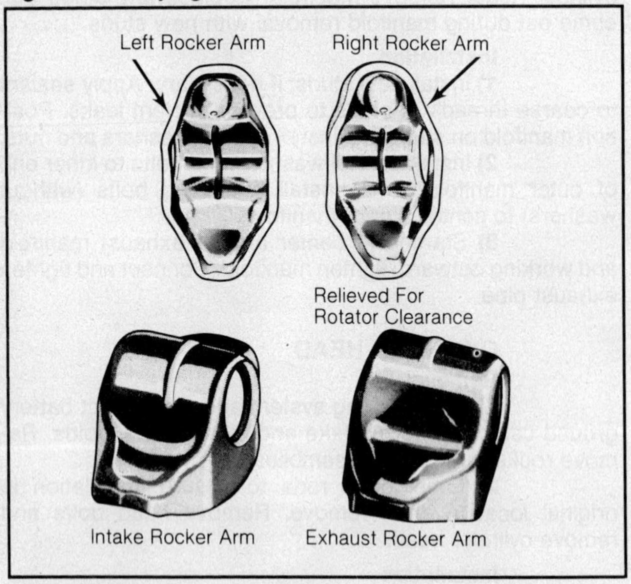

Note difference in rocker arms.

2) Ensure that long, stamped steel retainers are installed in number two and four positions. Tighten bolts to 200 INCH Lbs. (23 N.m). Reverse removal procedure to complete installation.

Fig. 4: Location of Rocker Arms

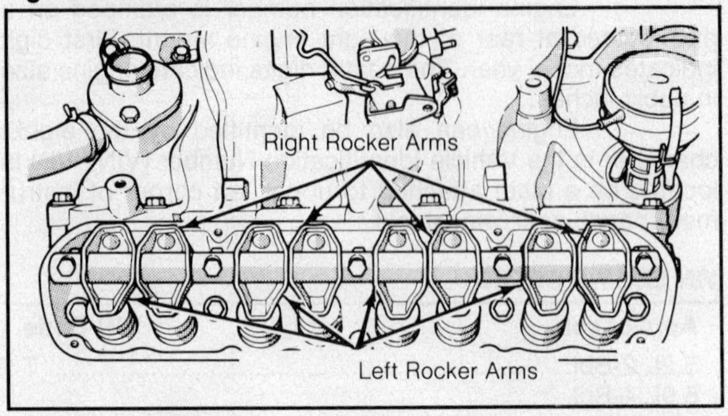

Install long retainers in number two and four positions.

VALVE SPRINGS

CAUTION: Installing incorrect exhaust valve springs on engines with positive rotators can cause severe engine damage.

Removal

1) With cylinder head removed, compress valve springs using valve spring compressor. Remove retainer locks, valve spring retainers, valve springs and valve stem oil seals.

2) Before removing valves, remove any burrs from valve stem lock grooves to prevent damage to valve guides. Label valves to ensure installation in original locations, then remove.

Inspection

1) Valve springs should be tested whenever they are removed from cylinder head. Using a valve spring tester, check spring tension. Replace springs that do not meet specifications.

2) Inspect each spring for squareness, using a steel square and flat surface. Replace spring if more than 5/64" (2 mm) out-of-square.

Installation

1) Lubricate valve stems and install valves in cylinder head. If valves or seats have been reground, check valve stem height using Gauge (C-3968). *See Fig. 5.*

2) If valve is too long, grind tip of valve stem until length is within limits. Do not grind valve stem tip on exhaust valves.

3) Install oil seals on valve stems and over valve guides. Install springs and retainers. See VALVE SPRING COLOR CODE table. Compress valve springs with compressor and install locks.

VALVE SPRING COLOR CODE

Application	Color Code
Intake Valve (All)	Blue
Exhaust Valve (5.2L)	White
Exhaust Valve (5.9L)	Yellow

VALVE SPRING INSTALLED HEIGHT

1) If valves or seats are reground, measure installed height of springs. Measure from bottom surface of spring seat (if spacers are installed, measure from top of spacer) to bottom of spring retainer.

Fig. 5: Measuring Valve Stem Length

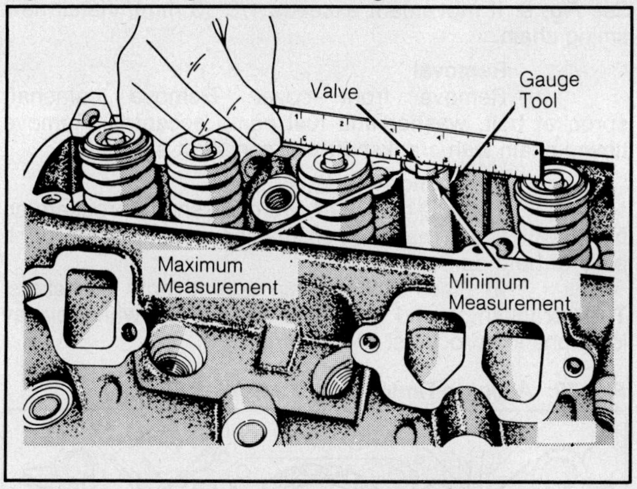

Do not grind valve stem tips on exhaust valves.

2) If installed height is incorrect, install a 1/16" (1.7 mm) spacer between valve spring and cylinder head to correct spring height.

VALVE SPRING INSTALLED HEIGHT SPECIFICATIONS

Application	In. (mm)
Intake Valves	1 5/8-1 11/16 (41.27-42.86)
Exhaust Valves	1 29/64-1 33/64 (36.9-38.5)

VALVE STEM OIL SEALS

Cup-type oil seals are used on all valves. If seals are removed for any reason, new seals must be used upon reassembly. See VALVE SPRINGS for removal and installation procedures.

VALVE GUIDE SERVICING

1) With valve spring assembly removed and valve guide cleaned, install Sleeve (C-3937) over valve stem. Install valve in cylinder head.

2) Attach dial indicator to cylinder head, and position indicator at right angle to valve stem being measured. *See Fig. 6.* Total side play should not exceed .017" (.43 mm).

3) If valve guides require reaming, do not attempt to ream guides from standard to .030" (.76 mm) oversize in one step. Use step-up procedure when reaming to .030" (.76 mm) oversize.

4) Replacement valves with oversize stems are available in .005" (.13 mm), .015" (.38 mm) and .030" (.76 mm) oversize.

HYDRAULIC VALVE LIFTERS

1) Prior to testing, disassemble lifter. Clean lifter inside and out to remove varnish and carbon deposits.

2) To test, remove cap from plunger and plunger from lifter body. *See Fig. 7.* Fill lifter body with clean kerosene. Unseat check valve to permit complete installation of plunger. Install cap.

3) Place lifter upright in Lifter Tester (C-4343) and check leakdown by compressing tool. If lifter collapses immediately, disassemble, clean and retest. If rapid leakdown still occurs, replace lifter.

4) If lifter or lifter bore in cylinder block is scuffed, scored, or shows signs of sticking, ream bore to next oversize and replace with oversize lifter.

Fig. 6: Measuring Valve Stem-to-Guide Clearance

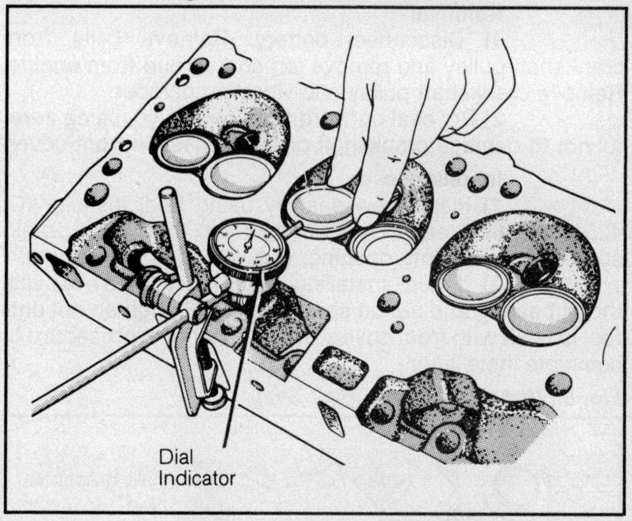

Total side play should not exceed .017" (.43 mm).

Fig. 7: Hydraulic Lifter Assembly

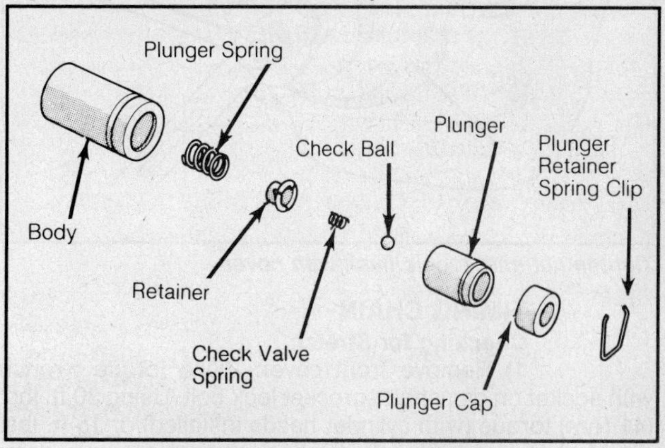

Parts are not interchangeable between lifters.

CAMSHAFT

ENGINE FRONT COVER

Removal

1) Disconnect battery. Drain cooling system, remove radiator and water pump assembly. Remove power steering pump, if used. Remove crankshaft pulley and vibration damper.

2) Remove fuel lines and fuel pump. Loosen oil pan bolts and remove front bolts on each side. Remove front cover and gasket, using care not to damage oil pan gasket.

Installation

1) Check that mating surfaces of cover and cylinder block are clean and free from burrs. Apply a 1/8" bead of silicone sealer to oil pan gasket.

2) Apply Lubriplate to front cover oil seal lip. Install front cover and attaching bolts, but do not tighten bolts at this time.

3) Install vibration damper onto crankshaft to align oil seal, then tighten damper center bolt. Tighten front cover bolts, then oil pan bolts. Reverse removal procedure to complete installation.

FRONT COVER OIL SEAL

Removal

1) Disconnect battery. Remove belts from crankshaft pulley and remove fan and shroud from engine. Remove crankshaft pulley and vibration damper.

2) Pry seal outward from behind lip, being careful not to damage crankshaft or seal recess in front cover.

Installation

1) Install new seal by using Seal Installer (C-4251). Install threaded shaft of tool into threads of crankshaft. Place seal into opening, with spring facing engine.

2) Place Installing Adapter (C-4251-3) with thrust bearing and nut on shaft. *See Fig. 8.* Tighten nut until tool is flush with front cover. Reverse removal procedure to complete installation.

Fig. 8: Installing Front Cover Seal

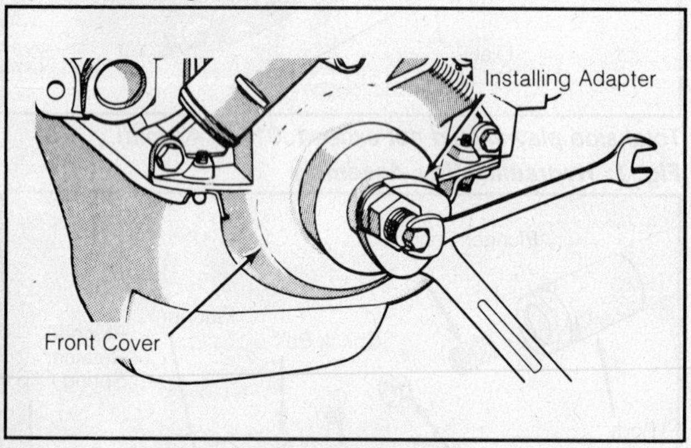

Tighten nut until tool is flush with cover.

TIMING CHAIN

Checking for Stretch

1) Remove front cover. Place torque wrench with socket on camshaft sprocket lock bolt. Using 30 ft. lbs. (41 N.m) torque (with cylinder heads installed) or 15 ft. lbs. (21 N.m) torque (with cylinder heads removed), turn camshaft sprocket in normal direction of rotation to remove chain slack. Do not allow crankshaft to rotate.

Fig. 9: Measuring Timing Chain Stretch

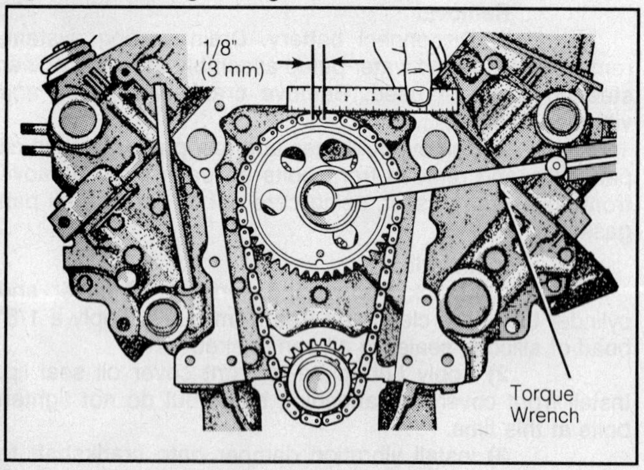

Do not allow crankshaft to rotate.

2) Place a steel ruler next to timing chain to measure amount of chain movement. Apply same torque in reverse direction, and measure amount of chain movement. *See Fig. 9.* If movement exceeds 1/8" (3 mm), install new timing chain.

Removal

Remove front cover. Remove camshaft sprocket bolt, washer and fuel pump eccentric. Remove timing chain with crankshaft and camshaft sprockets.

Installation

1) Place camshaft and crankshaft sprockets on bench with timing marks on an imaginary centerline through bore of both sprockets.

2) Place timing chain around both sprockets. Turn crankshaft and camshaft to line up with keyway locations in sprockets.

Fig. 10: Aligning Timing Chain Sprocket Marks

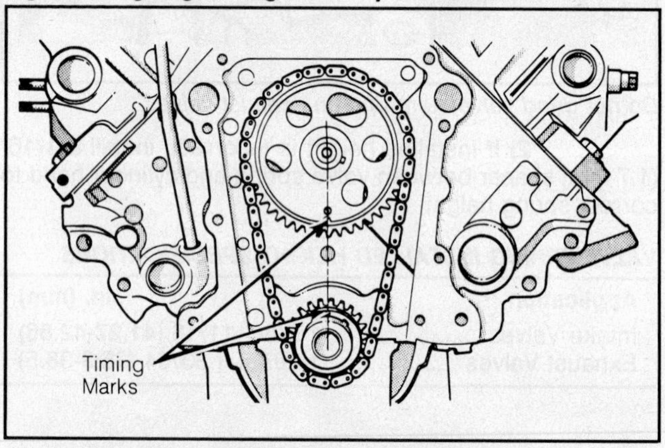

Align chain and sprockets on bench prior to installation.

3) With chain placed on sprockets, slide both sprockets evenly over their respective shafts. *See Fig. 10.* Use a straightedge to measure alignment of timing marks.

4) Install fuel pump eccentric, cup washer and camshaft sprocket bolt. Tighten bolt and check camshaft end play.

VALVE TIMING

CAUTION: Do not turn crankshaft further than indicated, as valve spring might bottom and result in serious valve train damage.

1) Rotate crankshaft until No. 6 exhaust valve is closing and No. 6 intake valve is opening.

2) Insert a 1/4" spacer between rocker arm and valve stem tip of No. 1 intake valve. Insertion of spacer should bleed down lifter, bottoming lifter plunger.

3) Install a dial indicator on No. 1 intake valve, so plunger contacts valve spring retainer as nearly perpendicular as possible. Zero dial indicator.

4) Rotate crankshaft clockwise until dial indicator shows .010" (.25 mm) of lift for 5.2L engines, or .034" (.86 mm) lift for 5.9L engines.

5) If valve timing is correct, the timing of the crankshaft pulley should read from 10° BTDC to 2° ATDC.

6) Inspect sprocket index marks, timing chain wear and accuracy of "TDC" mark on timing indicator, if reading is not within limits.

CAMSHAFT

NOTE: Whenever a new camshaft is installed, install new valve lifters.

5.2 & 5.9 LITER V8 (Cont.)

Removal

1) With engine removed from vehicle, remove intake manifold, front cover and timing chain. Remove rocker arm and shaft assemblies.

2) Label push rods and valve lifters for installation in original locations, then remove. Replace any lifter that exhibits a "dished" wear condition.

3) Remove distributor and lift out distributor/oil pump drive shaft. Remove camshaft thrust plate, noting location of oil tab.

4) Install a long bolt into front of camshaft to aid in removal of camshaft from engine. Remove camshaft, using care not to damage camshaft bearings.

Installation

1) Lubricate camshaft lobes and bearing journals. Insert camshaft to within 2" (50.8 mm) of its final position in block.

2) Install Camshaft Holder (C-3509) in distributor drive hole, and hold in position using distributor lock bolt. This prevents camshaft from contacting and possibly knocking out welch plug in rear of block.

3) Install thrust plate and chain oil tab. Ensure that top edge of tab is flat against thrust plate to provide oil for chain lubrication.

4) Install timing chain and sprockets. Install fuel pump eccentric, cup washer, and camshaft sprocket bolt. *See Fig. 11.*

5) Remove camshaft holding tool. Reverse removal procedure to complete installation.

Fig. 11: Exploded View of Camshaft Assembly

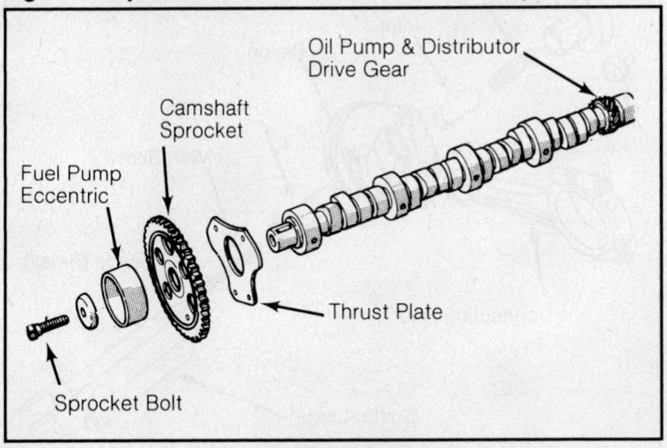

CAMSHAFT END PLAY

End play is taken by thrust plate behind camshaft sprocket. End play should be .002-.010" (.05-.25 mm). If end play is not within specifications, replace thrust plate.

CAMSHAFT BEARINGS

Removal

With engine completely disassembled, drive out rear cam bearing welch plug. Using camshaft bearing remover/installer, drive out bearings.

Installation

1) Using camshaft bearing remover/installer, install new bearings into place. Ensure that No. 2 bearing oil hole aligns with oil passage going to left cylinder head.

2) Ensure that No. 4 bearing oil hole aligns with oil passage going to right cylinder head. Replace camshaft welch plug at rear of engine. Be sure plug does not leak.

PISTONS, PINS & RINGS

OIL PAN

See OIL PAN REMOVAL at end of ENGINE section.

PISTON & ROD ASSEMBLY

Removal

1) Remove cylinder head and oil pan. Place piston at bottom of stroke and cover top of piston to collect cuttings. Remove ridge at top of cylinder bore using ridge reamer.

2) Inspect connecting rods and caps for cylinder identification and mark as necessary. Remove rod cap. Cover exposed rod cap bolts with rubber hose to protect crankshaft. Carefully push piston out top of cylinder bore and install rod caps on mating rods.

Installation

1) Compression ring gaps must be staggered so neither is in line with oil ring rail gap. Ensure identification marks on compression rings are facing upward.

2) Oil ring expander ends should be butted under notch (front) of piston. Oil ring rail gaps should be facing middle of engine (when installed), and spread 3" (76 mm) apart. *See Fig. 12.*

Fig. 12: Positioning Oil Rings for Installation

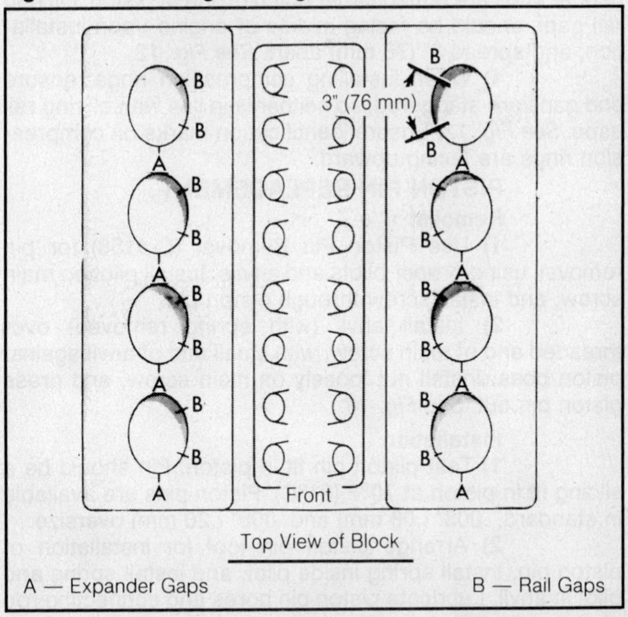

Do not allow ring gaps to change during installation.

3) Immerse piston and rings in clean engine oil and slide ring compressor over piston, and tighten. Do not allow position of rings to change.

4) Be sure connecting rod bolts are covered, to protect cylinder bore and crankshaft journal surfaces from being damaged during piston installation.

5) Rotate crankshaft so connecting rod journal is in center of cylinder bore. Position piston in cylinder bore. Notch on piston head must face front of engine, and larger connecting rod chamfer must face crankshaft fillet.

6) Tap piston into cylinder bore using hammer handle. Guide connecting rod into place on crankshaft journal. Install rod cap, and tighten.

5.2 & 5.9 LITER V8 (Cont.)

FITTING PISTONS

NOTE: **Make all measurements at 70°F (21°C).**

1) Check cylinder bore for taper or out-of-round, using a micrometer. Maximum allowable cylinder bore taper is .010" (.25 mm), and out-of-round must not exceed .005" (.13 mm).

2) If cylinder walls show excessive taper or out-of-round, or are badly worn, they will require reboring and honing for installation of new pistons and rings.

3) If cylinders are honed, wash thoroughly with scrub brush and soapy water, then rinse well. Oil bores after cleaning to prevent rust. Piston assemblies are available in standard and .020" (.51 mm) oversize.

4) With piston and cylinder bores dry and clean, measure piston diameter at top of skirt, 90° to piston pin axis. Measure cylinder bore halfway down cylinder and 90° to crankshaft centerline. Difference between measurements is piston-to-cylinder wall clearance.

FITTING RINGS

1) Measure ring end gap in cylinder bore with feeler gauge. Ring must be square in bore, about 2" (50 mm) from bottom of bore.

2) With ring lands clean, measure ring side clearance between ring and ring land with feeler gauge. Oil ring rails should be free in groove.

3) When installing oil rings, ensure ring expander ends are butted under notch (front) of piston. Oil ring rail gaps should be facing middle of engine upon installation, and spread 3" (76 mm) apart. *See Fig. 12.*

4) When installing compression rings, ensure end gaps are staggered, so neither is in line with oil ring rail gaps. *See Fig. 12.* Ensure identification marks on compression rings are facing upward.

PISTON PIN REPLACEMENT

Removal

1) Use Piston Pin Remover (C-4158) for pin removal, using proper pilots and anvils. Install pilot on main screw, and install screw through piston pin.

2) Install anvil (with spring removed) over threaded end of main screw, with small end of anvil against piston boss. Install nut loosely on main screw, and press piston pin out. *See Fig. 13.*

Installation

1) Test piston pin fit in piston. Pin should be a sliding fit in piston at 70°F (21°C). Piston pins are available in standard, .003" (.08 mm) and .008" (.20 mm) oversize.

2) Arrange piston pin tool for installation of piston pin. Install spring inside pilot, and install spring and pilot in anvil. Lubricate piston pin bores and connecting rod pin bore. Install piston pin over main screw. *See Fig. 14.*

3) Place piston (with notch up) and connecting rod over pilot, so pilot extends through piston pin bores. Assemble rods to pistons of the right cylinder bank (2, 4, 6 and 8) with indent on piston head opposite to larger chamfer on large bore end of connecting rod.

4) Assemble rods to pistons of the left cylinder bank (1, 3, 5 and 7) with indent on piston head on the same side as the large chamfer on large bore end of connecting rod.

5) Install main screw and piston pin in piston, and install nut on main screw to hold assembly together. Press piston pin in, until piston pin bottoms on the pilot.

Checking Pin Fit

Assemble piston pin tool as for piston pin removal. Secure butt end of main screw in vise. Attach a torque wrench to nut, and test torque to 15 ft. lbs. (20 N.m). If connecting rod moves downward on piston pin, replace connecting rod and retest.

Fig. 13: Removing Piston Pin

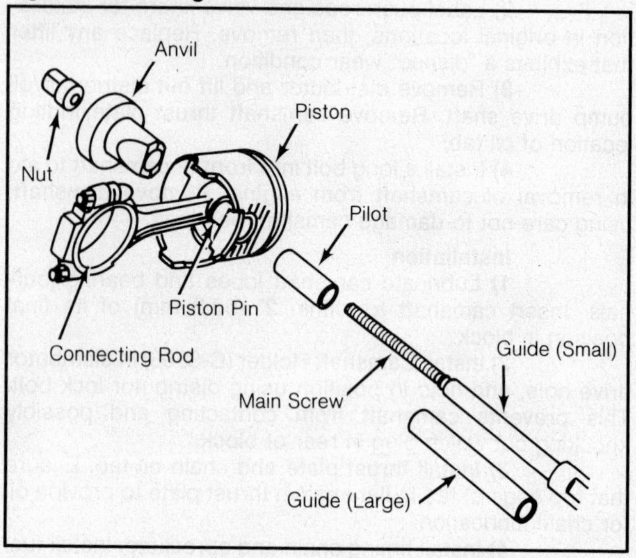

Fig. 14: Installing Piston Pin

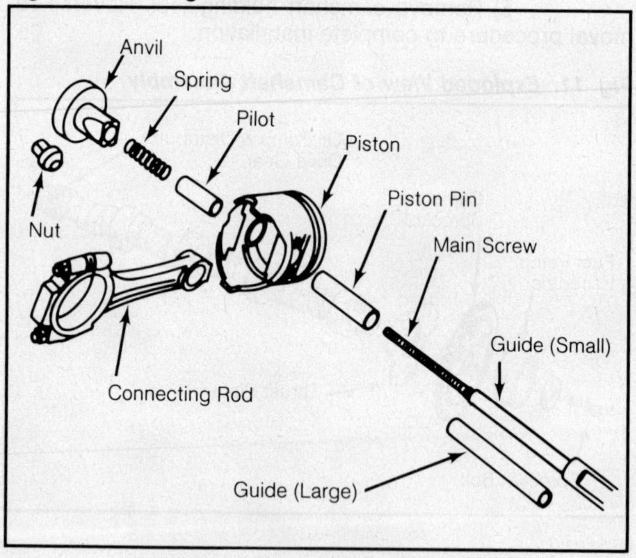

CRANKSHAFT & ROD BEARINGS

CONNECTING ROD BEARINGS

NOTE: **Use Plastigage method for checking bearing clearances. Remove oil film from surfaces to be checked.**

1) After ensuring rod caps are marked for cylinder identification, remove rod caps. Turn crankshaft until connecting rod to be checked starts moving toward the top of the engine.

2) Place Plastigage across width of bearing shell in cap, approximately 1/4" (6 mm) off center and away from oil holes. Tighten bearing cap. Do not rotate crankshaft.

5.2 & 5.9 LITER V8 (Cont.)

3) Remove bearing cap and compare width of flattened Plastigage with inch scale on package. Difference in readings between the ends indicates amount of taper present. Compare readings with specifications.

4) New bearings are available in standard, .001" (.03 mm), .002" (.05 mm), .003" (.08 mm), .010" (.25 mm) and .012" (.31 mm) undersize. Always install bearings in pairs. Do not use a new bearing half with an old bearing half.

5) Install connecting rod bearings so formed tang fits into machined groove in connecting rod. Install rod caps. "V" groove of bearing must match "V" groove of cap. Tighten nuts.

MAIN BEARINGS

1) Check main bearing clearances one at a time. To accurately determine clearance, weight of crankshaft must first be eliminated (when checking with engine installed). A .010" (.25 mm) minimum thickness cardboard shim (matchbook cover) should be used for this purpose.

2) Remove crankshaft main cap(s) on either side of bearing being checked. See MAIN BEARING CLEARANCE CHECK table. When checking clearance of No. 1 or No. 5 main bearings, remove only adjacent main cap.

3) Place a cardboard shim between the bearing shell(s) and cap(s) which were removed. Install these "shimmed" bearing cap(s) and tighten to 10-15 ft. lbs. (14-20 N.m).

MAIN BEARING CLEARANCE CHECK

When Checking	Shim
Number 1 Bearing	Number 2 Bearing
Number 2 Bearing	Number 1 & 3 Bearings
Number 3 Bearing	Number 2 & 4 Bearings
Number 4 Bearing	Number 3 & 5 Bearing
Number 5 Bearing	Number 4 Bearing

4) Measure clearance, using Plastigage method. Tighten main bearing cap bolts to 85 ft. lbs. (115 N.m).

5) New bearings are available in standard, .001" (.03 mm), .002" (.05 mm), .003" (.08 mm), .010" (.25 mm) and .012" (.31 mm) undersize. Do not use an old bearing half with a new bearing half.

6) Upper and lower bearings are not interchangeable. *See Fig. 15.* Lower bearings 1, 2 and 4 are interchangeable. Upper bearings 1, 2 and 4 are interchangeable.

7) Replace main bearings one at a time. To extract upper main bearing from cylinder block, insert Pin (C-3059) into oil hole of crankshaft journal. Rotate crankshaft clockwise, allowing pin to push upper bearing out of cylinder block.

8) When installing a new upper main bearing, slightly chamfer sharp edges from plain side of new bearing, then start bearing in place. Using pin, install upper bearing in reverse order of removal procedure.

CRANKSHAFT END PLAY

Check crankshaft end play. If not within specifications, replace thrust bearing (No. 3 main bearing).

REAR MAIN BEARING OIL SEAL

Split-type rubber seals may be installed without removing crankshaft. Rubber seals must be installed as pairs, and cannot be used with rope seals.

Fig. 15: Main Bearing Identification

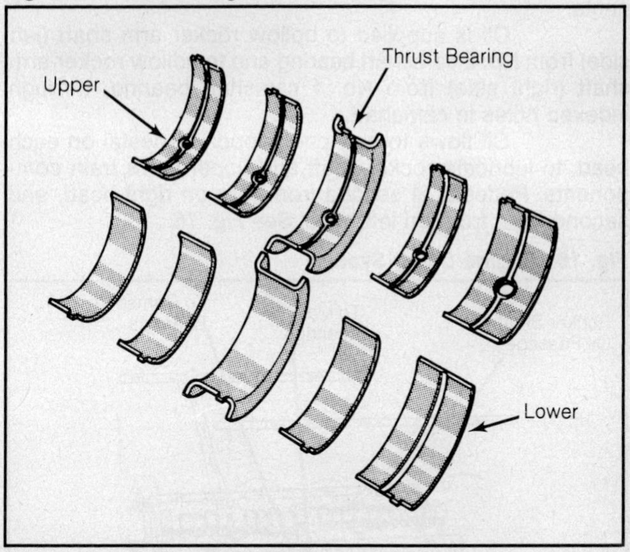

Upper (grooved) bearings and lower (plain) bearings are not interchangeable.

Removal

Remove oil pan, oil pump and rear main bearing cap. Remove upper seal by pressing on end of seal with small screwdriver, being careful not to damage crankshaft. Remove lower seal from main cap.

Installation

1) On 5.2L engines, insert cap seals into slots in bearing cap. Seal with Yellow paint goes in right side of cap (cap in installed position). Make sure seals are installed with narrow sealing edges up.

2) Also make sure that edges of cap seals line up exactly with shoulder in bearing cap, to prevent oil leakage. Install seal edge toward inside of shoulder, and pull outward on small end of seal until edge lines up with shoulder.

3) On all engines, lightly oil seal lips. With crankshaft surface clean and lightly oiled, rotate upper seal half into block with paint stripe toward rear. Use care not to cut or shave seal outer surface.

4) Place lower seal in bearing cap with paint stripe toward rear. On 5.9L engines, apply sealer on cap surface next to rear main oil seal ends. Install cap on engine block and tighten.

ENGINE OILING

CRANKCASE CAPACITY

Capacity of all engines is 5 quarts (4.7L). Add 1 quart (.95L) when replacing oil filter.

OIL FILTER

Replace at first oil change, and every other oil change thereafter.

NORMAL OIL PRESSURE

Normal oil pressure should be 30-80 psi (2.1-5.6 kg/cm^2) at 2000 RPM.

OIL PRESSURE REGULATOR VALVE

Located in oil pump. Not adjustable.

ENGINE OILING SYSTEM

System has a rotor-type oil pump and full-flow oil filter. Oil is forced by pump through a series of oil

5.2 & 5.9 LITER V8 (Cont.)

passages in engine to provide lubrication to engine components.

Oil is supplied to hollow rocker arm shaft (left side) from No. 2 camshaft bearing and to hollow rocker arm shaft (right side) from No. 4 camshaft bearing, through indexed holes in camshaft.

Oil flows to only one support pedestal on each head, to lubricate rocker shaft and upper valve train components. Pedestal is second from rear on right head, and second from front on left head. *See Fig. 16.*

Fig. 16: Engine Oiling System

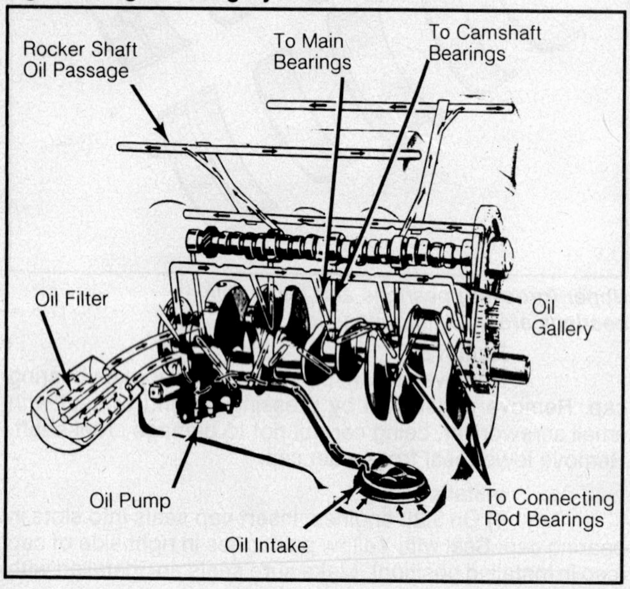

OIL PUMP

Removal

Remove oil pan. Remove bolts and oil pump from rear main bearing cap. Ensure oil pump and rear main bearing cap machined surfaces are clean and free from burrs.

Disassembly

1) Remove cotter pin, drill a 1/8" (3 mm) hole into relief valve retainer cap and insert a self-tapping sheet metal screw into cap. Clamp screw into vise and while supporting pump, remove cap by tapping pump body using soft hammer.

2) Discard retainer cap and remove spring and relief valve. Remove pump cover and discard oil seal ring. Remove inner rotor and shaft. Lift out outer rotor. *See Fig. 17.*

Inspection

1) Clean all parts thoroughly. Replace oil pump assembly if mating surface of pump cover is scratched or grooved.

2) Lay a straightedge across pump cover. Using a feeler gauge, measure cover wear. If measurement is not within specifications, replace pump assembly.

3) Measure thickness of outer and inner rotors. Measure outer rotor diameter. If measurements are not within specifications, replace rotors.

4) Slide outer rotor (chamfered end first) into pump body. Press rotor to one side and measure clearance between rotor and pump body. If measurement is not within specifications, replace pump assembly.

Fig. 17: Oil Pump Assembly

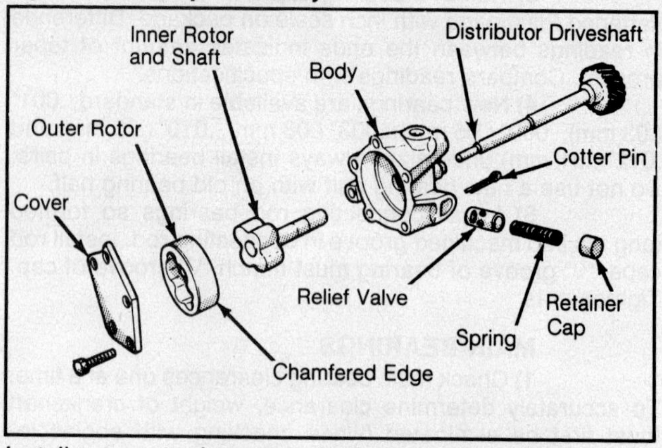

Install outer rotor into pump body with large chamfered edge inward.

5) With outer rotor installed in pump body, place inner rotor and shaft into pump body. Measure clearance between inner and outer rotors. If clearance is not within specifications, replace rotors.

6) With rotors installed in pump body, place a straightedge (between bolt holes) across pump face. Measure clearance between rotors and straightedge. If clearance is not within specifications, replace pump assembly.

7) Inspect oil pressure relief valve plunger for scoring and free operation in bore. Small marks may be removed with 400 grit wet/dry sandpaper.

8) Check free length of relief valve spring. Compress relief valve spring and check spring pressure. Pressure should be 16.2-17.2 lbs. (7.35-7.80 kg) at 1 11/32" (34.1 mm). Replace spring if it fails to meet specifications.

OIL PUMP SPECIFICATIONS

Application	In. (mm)
Clearance Over Rotors	.003 (.076) Max.
Inner & Outer Rotor Thickness	
5.2L Engine	.826 (20.98) Min.
5.9L Engine	.944 (23.98) Min.
Pump Cover Wear	.0014 (.035) Max.
Outer Rotor Diameter	2.47 (62.74) Min.
Outer Rotor-to-Pump Body	.013 (.33) Max.
Rotor Tip Clearance	.009 (.23) Max.
Spring Free Length	2 1/32 - 2 3/64 (51.6- 52.0)

Reassembly

Assemble pump, using new parts if necessary. Ensure that outer rotor is installed in pump body with large chamfered edge inward. Install oil seal rings between cover and pump body. Tighten oil pump cover bolts to 95 INCH Lbs. (11 N.m).

Installation

Prime oil pump. Reverse removal procedure to complete installation.

ENGINE COOLING

WATER PUMP

CAUTION: After removing fluid unit, do not place drive unit with shaft pointing downward. Silicone fluid from fluid unit may drain into fan drive bearing, causing lubricant failure.

5.2 & 5.9 LITER V8 (Cont.)

Removal

1) Drain cooling system. Remove radiator, if vehicle is equipped with A/C. Remove all drive belts. Remove fan, spacer (or fluid unit), pulley and bolts as an assembly.

2) If vehicle is not equipped with A/C, remove alternator bracket bolts, and position alternator out of way. On A/C models, remove alternator, adjusting bracket and power steering pump. Position components aside.

3) Remove heater and by-pass hoses. Remove A/C compressor pulley and field coil assembly, if used. Remove A/C compressor bracket, if used. Remove water pump.

Installation

Clean all gasket mating surfaces. Install water pump using new gasket. Reverse removal procedure to complete installation.

NOTE: **For further information on cooling system capacities and other cooling system components, see appropriate article in ENGINE COOLING at end of ENGINE section.**

TIGHTENING SPECIFICATIONS

Application	Ft. Lbs. (N.m)
A/C Compressor Bracket Bolts	50 (68)
Camshaft Sprocket Bolt	50 (68)
Connecting Rod Nuts	45 (61)
Cylinder Head Bolts	
Step 1	50 (68)
Step 2	105 (143)
Flywheel-to-Crankshaft Bolts	55 (75)
Intake Manifold Bolts	
Step 1	25 (34)
Step 2	40 (54)
Main Bearing Cap Bolts	85 (115)
Oil Pump Bolts	30 (41)
Vibration Damper Bolt	100 (136)
Water Pump Bolts	30 (41)
	INCH Lbs. (N.m)
Camshaft Thrust Plate	210 (24)
Exhaust Manifold	
Bolts	240 (27)
Nuts	180 (20)
Rocker Arm Shaft Bolts	200 (23)

ENGINE SPECIFICATIONS

GENERAL SPECIFICATIONS

Year	DISPLACEMENT		Fuel System	HP@RPM	Torque Ft. Lbs.@RPM	Compr. Ratio	BORE		STROKE	
	Cu. In.	Liters					In.	mm	In.	mm
1985	318	5.2	2-Bbl.	150@4000 [1]	255@2000 [2]	9.0:1	3.91	99.3	3.31	84.1
	360	5.9	4-Bbl.	175@4000 [3]	280@2000 [4]	8.5:1	4.00	101.6	3.58	90.9

[1] – California models: 145 at 3600 RPM.
[2] – California models: 250 at 1600 RPM.
[3] – For models of 8500 lbs. GVWR and over: 180 at 3600 RPM (Calif.: 175 at 4000 RPM.)
[4] – For models of 8500 lbs. GVWR and over: 270 at 2000 RPM (Calif.: 255 at 1600 RPM.)

VALVES

Engine Size & Valve	Head Diam. In. (mm)	Face Angle	Seat Angle	Seat Width In. (mm)	Stem Diameter In. (mm)	Stem Clearance In. (mm)	Valve Lift In. (mm)
5.2L							
Intake	1.780 (45.21)	44.5-45°	45-45.5°	.065-.085 (1.65-2.16)	.372-.373 (9.45-9.47)	.001-.003 (.02-.08)	.373 (9.47)
Exhaust	1.517 (38.53)	44.5-45°	45-45.5°	.080-.100 (2.03-2.54)	.371-.372 (9.42-9.45)	.002-.004 (.05-.10)	.400 (10.16)
5.9L							
Intake	1.880 (47.75)	44.5-45°	45-45.5°	.065-.085 (1.65-2.16)	.372-.373 (9.45-9.47)	.001-.003 (.02-.08)	.410 (10.41)
Exhaust	1.617 (41.07)	44.5-45°	45-45.5°	.080-.100 (2.03-2.54)	.371-.372 (9.42-9.45)	.002-.004 (.05-.10)	.410 (10.41)

Chrysler Corp. Engines

5.2 & 5.9 LITER V8 (Cont.)

ENGINE SPECIFICATIONS (Cont.)

PISTONS, PINS, RINGS

Engine	PISTONS Clearance In. (mm)	PINS Piston Fit In. (mm)	PINS Rod Fit In. (mm)	RINGS Ring No.	RINGS End Gap In. (mm)	RINGS Side Clearance In. (mm)
5.2L	.0005-.0015 (.013-.038)	.000-.0005 (.000-.038)	.0007-.0014 (.018-.035)	1 & 2	.010-.020 (.25-.51)	.0015-.0030 (.038-.076)
				3	.015-.055 (.38-1.40)	.0002-.0050 (.005-.127)
5.9L	.0005-.0015 (.013-.038)	.00025-.00075 (.0064-.0190)	.0007-.0014 (.018-.035)	1 & 2	.010-.020 (.25-.51)	.0015-.0030 (.038-.076)
				3	.015-.055 (.38-1.40)	.0002-.0050 (.005-.127)

CRANKSHAFT MAIN & CONNECTING ROD BEARINGS

Engine	MAIN BEARINGS Journal Diam. In. (mm)	MAIN BEARINGS Clearance In. (mm)	MAIN BEARINGS Thrust Bearing	MAIN BEARINGS Crankshaft End Play In. (mm)	CONNECTING ROD BEARINGS Journal Diam. In. (mm)	CONNECTING ROD BEARINGS Clearance In. (mm)	CONNECTING ROD BEARINGS Side Play In. (mm)
5.2L	2.4995-2.5005 (63.487-63.513)	.0005-.0020 [1] (.013-.051)	3	.002-.007 (.05-.18)	2.124-2.125 (53.95-53.98)	.0005-.0022 (.013-.056)	.006-.014 (.15-.36)
5.9L	2.8095-2.8105 (71.361-71.387)	.0005-.0020 [1] (.013-.051)	3	.002-.009 (.05-.23)	2.124-2.125 (53.95-53.98)	.0005-.0022 (.013-.056)	.006-.014 (.15-.36)

[1] – Desired clearance for No. 1 main bearing is .0005-.0015" (.013-.038 mm).

VALVE SPRINGS

Engine	Free Length In. (mm)	PRESSURE Lbs. @ In. (Kg @ mm) Valve Closed	PRESSURE Lbs. @ In. (Kg @ mm) Valve Open
5.2L			
Intake	2.00 (50.8)	78-88@1.69 (35-40@42.85)	170-184@1.31 (77-83@33.35)
Exhaust	1.81 (46.0)	80-90@1.20 (36-41@37.69)	180-194@1.06 (81-87@27.00)
5.9L			
Intake	2.00 (50.8)	78-88@1.69 (35-40@42.85)	170-184@1.31 (77-83@33.35)
Exhaust	1.81 (46.0)	80-90@1.48 (36-41@37.69)	181-197@1.06 (81-89@27.00)

CAMSHAFT

Engine	Journal Diam. In. (mm)	Clearance In. (mm)	Lobe Lift In. (mm)
5.2L & 5.9L [1]			
No.1	1.998-1.999 (50.75-50.77)	.001-.003 (.025-.076)	.....
No. 2	1.982-1.983 (50.34-50.37)		
No. 3	1.967-1.968 (49.96-49.99)		
No. 4	1.951-1.952 (49.56-49.58)		
No. 5	1.5605-1.5615 (39.64-39.66)		

[1] – End play is .002-.010" (.05-.15 mm).

ENGINE CODING

ENGINE IDENTIFICATION

Engine is identified by the 8th character of the Vehicle Identification Number (VIN). The VIN is stamped on a metal tag, attached to the upper left side of the instrument panel and is visible through the windshield. The VIN can also be found on the Safety Compliance Certification Label located on the door outside edge of the left door.

ENGINE IDENTIFICATION CODES

Engine	Code
2.0L 1-Bbl.	C
2.3L EFI	A

ENGINE REMOVAL

See Engine Removal at end of ENGINE section.

MANIFOLDS & CYLINDER HEAD

INTAKE MANIFOLD

Removal (2.0L)

1) Drain cooling system. Remove air cleaner. Disconnect accelerator cable. Disconnect and label all vacuum hoses. Remove hot water hose from manifold cover nipple fitting. Remove engine oil dipstick. Disconnect heat tube at EGR valve.

2) Disconnect fuel line at carburetor fuel filter. Remove engine oil dipstick tube retaining bolt from intake manifold. Disconnect and remove PCV valve from intake manifold and engine block.

3) Remove distributor cap and wires as an assembly. Remove plastic spark plug wire connector from valve cover. Remove intake manifold retaining bolts and remove intake manifold from vehicle.

Removal (2.3L)

1) Drain cooling system. Disconnect negative battery terminal. Remove fuel cap to relieve fuel tank pressure. Remove pressure from fuel system at the fuel pressure relief valve using EFI Pressure Gauge (T80L-9974-A). Pressure relief valve is located on fuel line in upper right hand corner of engine compartment.

NOTE: To access pressure relief valve, valve cap must be removed.

2) Disconnect electrical connectors at throttle position sensor, knock sensor, air charge temperature sensor and engine coolant temperature sensor. Disconnect and label vacuum hoses at vacuum tree. Remove throttle linkage shield.

3) Disconnect throttle linkage, cruise control and kickdown cable. Disconnect throttle cable from bracket and position aside. Disconnect air intake hose, air by-pass hose and crankcase vent hose. Disconnect PCV system. Disconnect coolant by-pass hose. Disconnect EGR tube from EGR valve at flange nut.

4) Disconnect fuel supply and return hoses at push-connect fittings. Remove engine oil dipstick bracket retaining bolt. Remove 4 upper intake manifold retaining nuts. Remove upper intake manifold and throttle body assembly.

5) Disconnect electrical connectors from injectors and set aside. Remove 2 fuel supply manifold retaining bolts. Carefully remove fuel supply manifold and injectors. Remove 4 bottom retaining bolts from lower manifold. Remove 4 upper retaining bolts from lower manifold. Remove lower manifold.

Installation (2.0L & 2.3L)

Clean all intake manifold gasket mating surfaces. Reinstall intake manifold on engine with new intake manifold gasket. Tighten all bolts in proper tightening sequence. *See Figs. 1 and 2*. To complete installation, reverse removal procedure.

Fig. 1: Intake Manifold Bolt Tightening Sequence

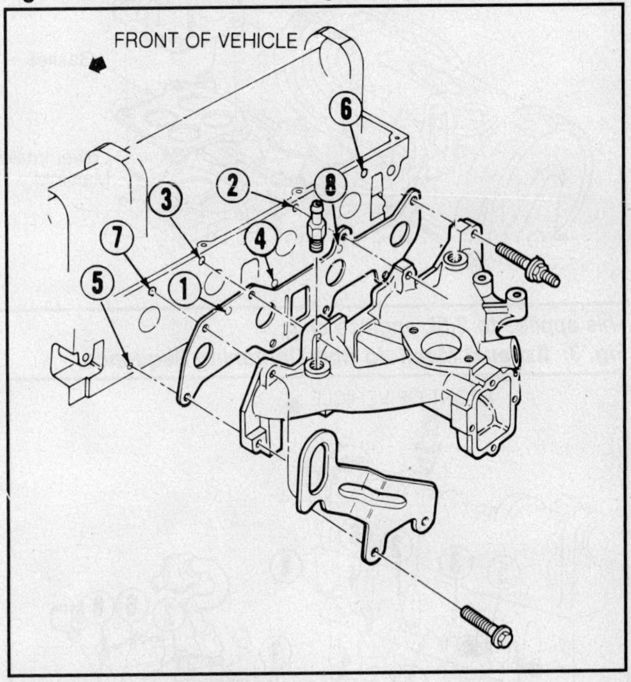

This applies to 2.0L engines only.

EXHAUST MANIFOLD

Removal

1) Remove air cleaner and duct assembly. Remove EGR line at exhaust manifold and loosen at EGR tube. Remove check valve at exhaust manifold. Remove hose from rear of by-pass valve.

2) Remove screw retaining heater hoses to valve cover. Remove 8 exhaust manifold-to-cylinder head attaching bolts. Remove exhaust pipe-to-exhaust manifold attaching bolts. Remove exhaust manifold.

Installation

Install exhaust manifold and tighten manifold-to-cylinder head attaching bolts to specification in proper sequence. *See Fig. 3*. Reverse removal procedure to install remaining components.

CYLINDER HEAD

Removal

1) Drain cooling system. Remove air cleaner assembly. Remove heater hose retaining screw from valve cover. Disconnect spark plug wires from spark plugs. Remove distributor cap and wires as an assembly. Remove sparks plugs and oil dipstick.

Ford Engines

2.0 & 2.3 LITER 4-CYLINDER (Cont.)

Fig. 2: Intake Manifold Bolt Tightening Sequence

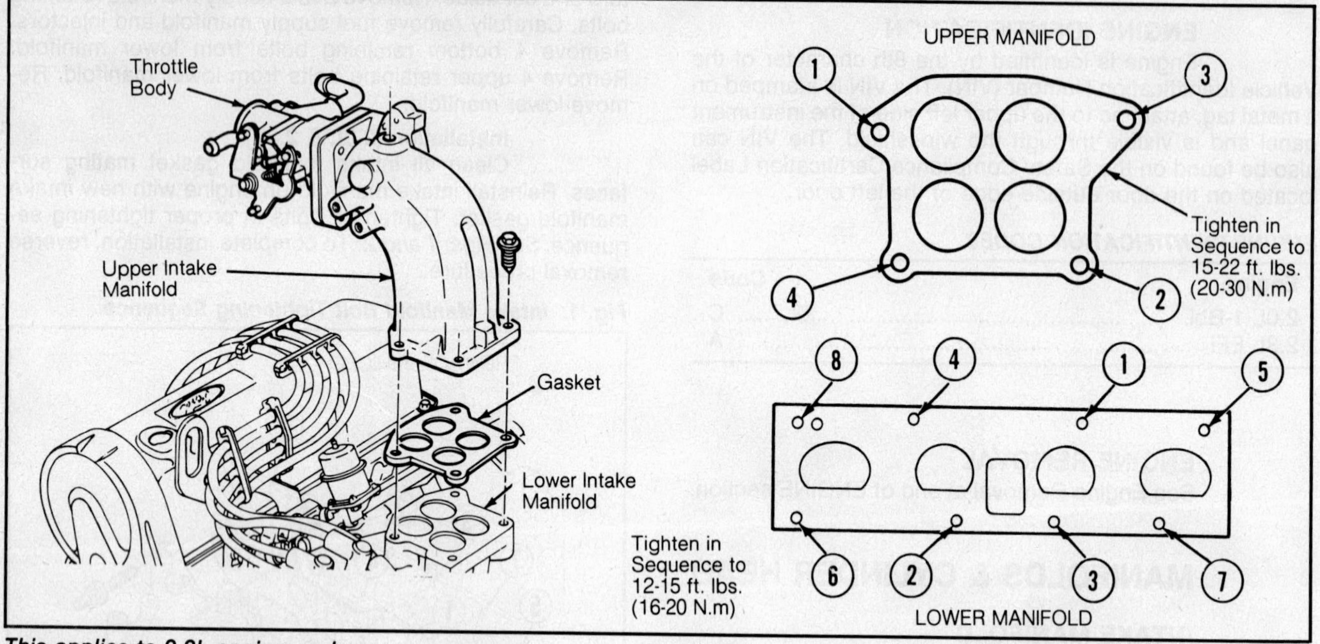

This applies to 2.3L engines only.

Fig. 3: Exhaust Manifold Bolt Tightening Sequence

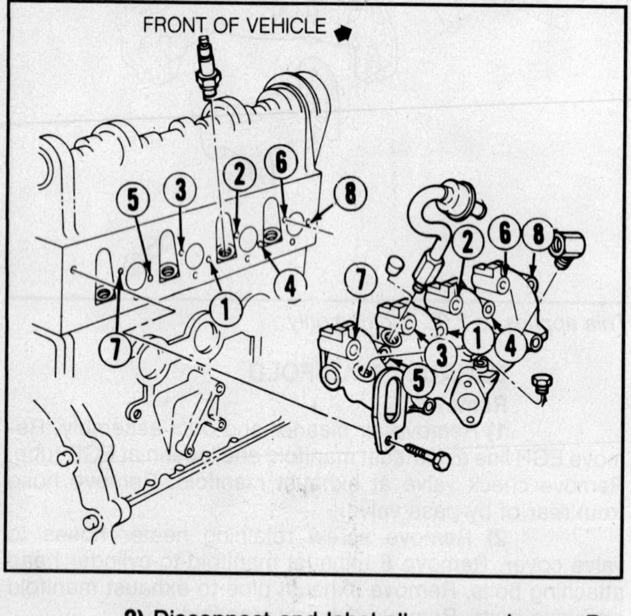

2) Disconnect and label all vacuum hoses. Remove valve cover retaining bolts and remove valve cover. Remove intake manifold as previously described. Remove alternator belt. Remove bolts attaching alternator bracket to cylinder head. Remove upper radiator hose.

3) Remove timing belt cover retaining bolts. Remove power steering pump bracket, if equipped. Loosen timing belt idler pulley retaining bolts. Position idler pulley in unloaded position and tighten retaining bolts. Remove timing belt from cam pulley and auxiliary pulley.

4) Remove heat stove from exhaust manifold. Remove 8 exhaust manifold-to-cylinder head attaching bolts. Remove timing belt idler pulley. Remove timing belt idler pulley spring from cylinder head. Disconnect oil pressure sending unit wire. Remove head bolts and cylinder head.

Installation

Clean all gasket mating surfaces. Position new cylinder head gasket on block. Reinstall cylinder head and tighten head bolts in proper sequence. *See Fig. 4*. Reverse removal procedure to install remaining components.

Fig. 4: Cylinder Head Bolt Tightening Sequence

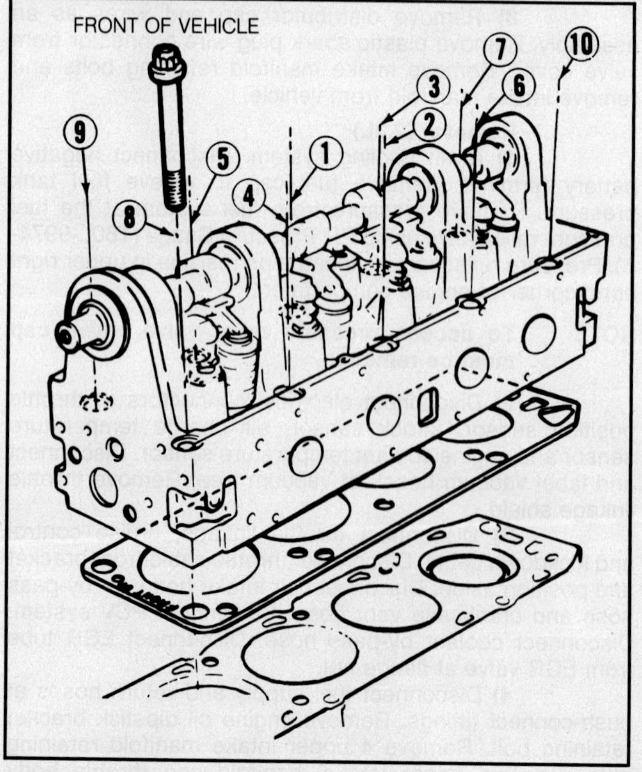

Ford Engines

2.0 & 2.3 LITER 4-CYLINDER (Cont.)

CAMSHAFT

ENGINE FRONT COVER

Removal

1) Loosen thermactor pump bolts and remove drive belt. Remove fan blade and water pump pulley attaching bolts. Remove fan and pulley. Loosen alternator retaining bolts and remove drive belt. Drain cooling system and remove upper radiator hose.

2) Remove crankshaft pulley bolt and pulley. Remove thermostat housing and gasket. Remove bolts attaching power steering pump to engine and position pump aside. Remove front cover attaching bolts and remove front cover.

Installation

Reverse removal procedure to install engine front cover and all other remaining components.

TIMING BELT

Removal

Align timing pointer with TDC mark on crankshaft pulley. Remove engine front cover. Release tension from timing belt by loosening timing belt tensioner bolts. Remove timing belt from gears.

Installation

Reverse removal procedures and align timing belt and gears as described in VALVE TIMING in this article.

VALVE TIMING

Checking Timing

1) Remove access plug from engine front cover. Set crankshaft at top dead center. Align timing mark (TDC) on crankshaft pulley with "TC" mark on engine front cover.

CAUTION: Always turn engine in direction of normal rotation. Backward rotation may cause timing belt to jump time.

2) Look through access hole in engine front cover to ensure timing mark on camshaft gear is lined up with pointer on inner timing belt cover. *See Fig. 5*.

3) Remove distributor cap and check that rotor is pointing at No. 1 spark plug wire terminal in distributor cap. Reinstall distributor cap and access plug.

Adjusting Timing

1) Remove engine front cover. Loosen timing belt tensioner adjustment screw. Retract tensioner and tighten adjusting screw to hold tensioner in retracted position. Remove crankshaft pulley and timing belt guide. Remove timing belt and inspect for wear or damage.

2) Replace belt if damaged or excessively worn. Align crankshaft gear and camshaft gear as described under Checking Timing procedure. Remove distributor cap and set rotor so that it points to No. 1 firing position by turning auxiliary shaft.

3) Install timing belt over crankshaft gear, auxiliary gear and camshaft gear, in that order. Loosen tensioner adjustment bolt to allow tensioner to move against timing belt. Remove spark plugs.

4) Rotate crankshaft 2 complete turns in normal rotation to remove slack from timing belt. Tighten tensioner pivot and adjustment bolts. Ensure that timing marks are still properly aligned.

5) Install crankshaft pulley and timing belt guide. Install engine front cover and spark plugs. Start engine and check ignition timing. Adjust ignition timing if necessary.

Fig. 5: Timing Belt Alignment Mark Locations

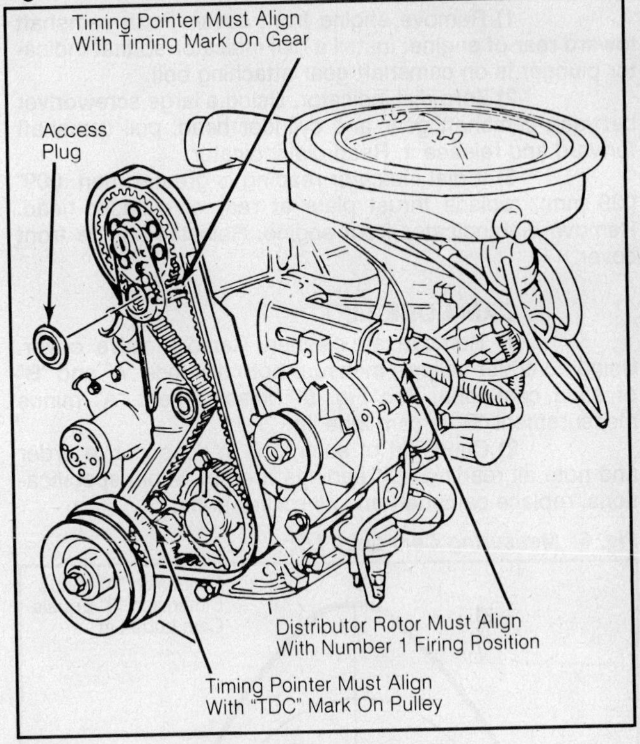

CAMSHAFT

Removal

1) Drain cooling system. Remove air cleaner assembly. Disconnect spark plug wires from spark plugs and valve cover and position aside. Disconnect and label all vacuum hoses. Remove valve cover bolts and valve cover.

2) Remove alternator retaining bolts and remove drive belt. Remove bolts that attach alternator bracket to cylinder head and position alternator aside. Remove upper radiator hose. Remove fan shroud retaining bolts and remove fan shroud. Remove timing belt cover.

3) Remove power steering belt, if equipped. Release tension from timing belt and remove timing belt. Using Valve Spring Compressor (T74P-6565-A), depress valve springs and remove rocker arms. Using Gear Puller (T74P-6256), remove camshaft gear from camshaft.

4) Using Seal Remover (T74P-6700-A), remove camshaft seal. Remove rear camshaft retainer. Raise vehicle on hoist. Remove right and left engine mount bolts and nuts. Place a transmission jack under engine and raise engine as high as possible.

5) Place wood blocks between engine mounts and chassis brackets. Remove transmission jack. Lower vehicle from hoist. Remove camshaft, using care not to damage camshaft journals or lobes.

Installation

1) Ensure that threaded plug is installed in rear of camshaft. Coat camshaft lobes with polyethylene grease. Lubricate camshaft journals with heavy oil before installation. Carefully slide camshaft through bearings. Install camshaft rear retainer.

2) Using Seal Installer (T74P-6150-A), install camshaft seal. Install camshaft gear. Use Gear Holder (T74P-6256-B) to hold camshaft gear while tightening bolt. Reverse removal procedures to complete camshaft installation.

Ford Engines

2.0 & 2.3 LITER 4-CYLINDER (Cont.)

CAMSHAFT END THRUST

1) Remove engine front cover. Push camshaft toward rear of engine. Install a dial indicator so that indicator plunger is on camshaft gear attaching bolt.

2) Zero dial indicator. Using a large screwdriver between camshaft gear and cylinder head, pull camshaft forward and release it. Read dial indicator.

3) If dial indicator reading is greater than .009" (.29 mm), replace thrust plate at rear of cylinder head. Remove dial indicator from engine. Reinstall engine front cover.

CAM LOBE LIFT

1) Remove air cleaner. Remove valve cover. Using a vernier caliper, measure both distance "A" and "B" of each cam lobe. *See Fig. 6*. Measurement "A" minus measurement "B" is cam lobe lift.

2) Check lift of each lobe in consecutive order and note all readings. If readings are not within specifications, replace camshaft and all rocker arms.

Fig. 6: Measuring Cam Lobe Lift

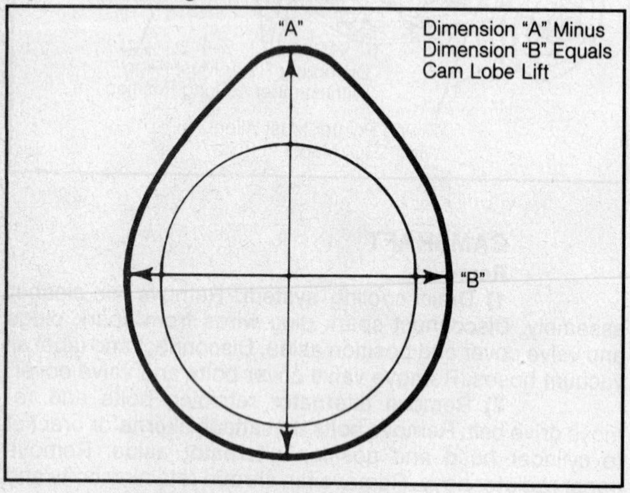

CAMSHAFT BEARINGS

Removal & Installation

When camshaft bearing replacement is necessary, do so using Camshaft Bearing Remover/Installer (T71P-6250-A). *See Fig. 7*.

Fig. 7: Removing & Installing Camshaft Bearings

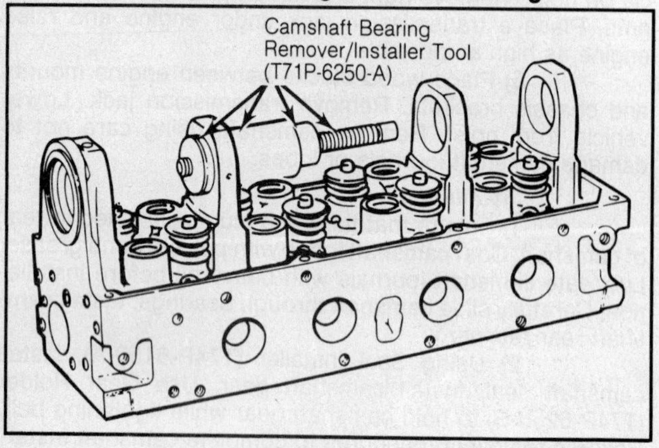

AUXILIARY SHAFT

Removal

1) Remove engine front cover. Release tension from timing belt. Remove fuel pump. Remove distributor assembly. Using Gear Puller (T74P-6256-B), remove gear from front of auxiliary shaft. Remove 2 bolts from auxiliary shaft retaining plate. Remove retaining plate.

2) Carefully slide auxiliary shaft from engine. Do not allow distributor drive gear or fuel pump lobe to contact bearing surfaces.

Installation

To install, reverse removal procedure.

VALVES

VALVE ARRANGEMENT

E-I-E-I-E-I-E-I (Front-to-rear).

VALVE STEM OIL SEALS

Valve stem oil seals are used on all valves. If seals are removed for any reason, new seals must be used on reassembly. For removal and installation procedures, see VALVE SPRINGS in this article.

VALVE SPRINGS

Removal

1) Remove air cleaner. Remove screw retaining heater hose to valve cover. Disconnect vacuum hoses as necessary. Disconnect spark plug wires from spark plugs and position aside. Remove valve cover from engine.

2) Using Valve Spring Compressor (T74P-6565-A), compress valve spring and remove rocker arm. Remove spark plug and place Air Line Adapter (6513-ABA) into spark plug hole. Apply 140 psi (9.8 kg/cm^2) to cylinder.

3) Again compress valve spring and remove retainer locks and spring retainer. Release pressure from valve spring and remove spring. Remove and discard valve stem oil seal.

Installation

1) Install new valve stem oil seal using Seal Installer (T73P-6571-A). Install and compress valve spring. With valve spring compressed, install spring retainer and retainer locks.

2) Apply polyethylene grease to all contact surfaces of rocker arm. Compress valve spring and install rocker arm.

3) Remove air pressure and air line adapter from spark plug hole and reinstall spark plug. Install all remaining components in reverse order of removal.

VALVE SPRING INSTALLED HEIGHT

1) Valve spring installed height should be measured with rocker arms removed. Measurement should be made from cylinder head spring pad to top of valve spring retainer.

VALVE SPRING INSTALLED HEIGHT SPECIFICATIONS

Application	Measurement In. (mm)
2.0L & 2.3L	1.49-1.55 (37.8-39.4)

2.0 & 2.3 LITER 4-CYLINDER (Cont.)

2) If height is not within specifications, install .030" (.76 mm) spacers between cylinder head spring pad and valve spring. Do not install more spacers than are necessary to obtain specified height.

VALVE GUIDE SERVICING

Always use reamers in proper sequence (smallest first). Reface valve seat after valve guide has been reamed. After reaming, use a scraper to break sharp corner at top inside diameter of valve guide bore. Valves with oversized stems are available with stems that are .003" (.08 mm), .015" (.38 mm) and .030" (.76 mm) oversize.

HYDRAULIC VALVE LIFTER

Service lifters only as complete assemblies. Disassemble lifters and thoroughly clean. DO NOT interchange parts between lifters. Reassemble lifters and test with hydraulic lifter test fluid and lifter leak-down tester. Leak-down rate on hydraulic lifters is 2-8 seconds at 1/8" (3.2 mm) travel.

Fig. 8: Exploded View of Hydraulic Lifter Assembly

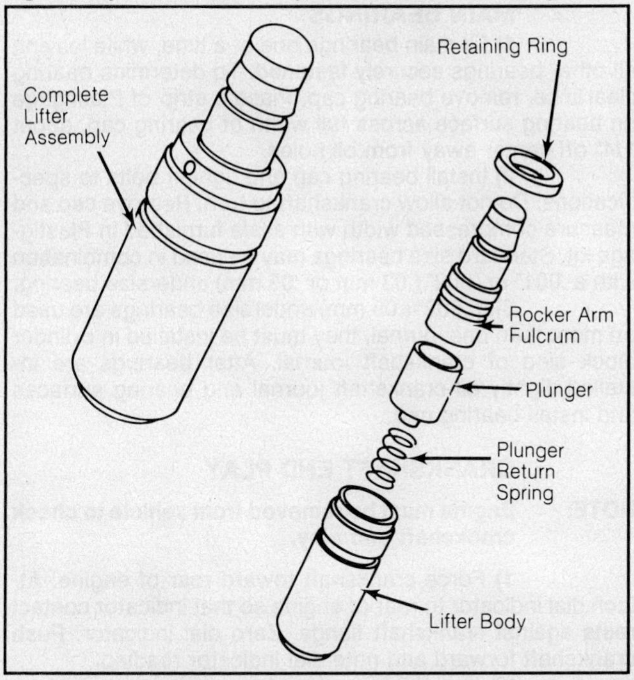

HYDRAULIC VALVE LIFTER ADJUSTMENT

Valve lifters are set at zero lash. No adjustment is necessary.

PISTONS, RINGS & PINS

OIL PAN

See OIL PAN REMOVAL at end of ENGINE section.

PISTON & ROD ASSEMBLY

Removal

Remove cylinder head. Remove oil pan retaining bolts and remove oil pan. Remove oil pump pick-up tube. Remove connecting rod cap and bearing. Push piston up through cylinder bore. Remove piston from cylinder bore.

Installation

1) Install bearing halves in rod and rod cap. Ensure ring gaps are properly positioned on piston. *See Fig. 9.* Install ring compressor on piston and install piston into block.

Fig. 9: Correct Spacing of Piston Ring Gaps

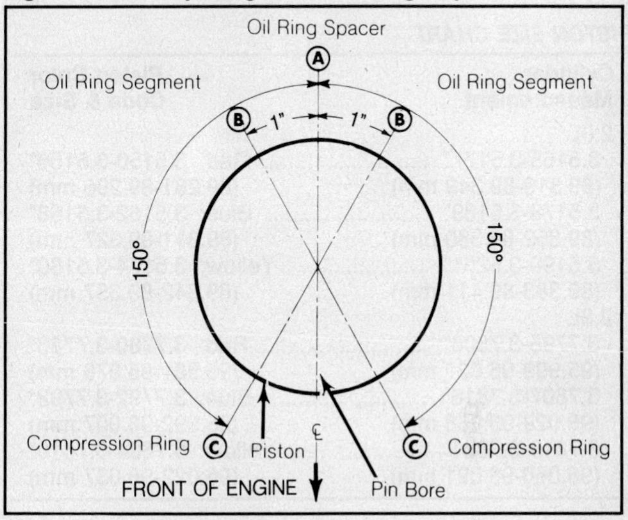

2) Guide piston rods over rod journals. Install rod caps and tighten nuts. Reverse removal procedure to complete installation of remaining components.

FITTING PISTONS

NOTE: Make all measurements with piston and block at normal room temperature (70°F, 21°C).

1) Measure piston skirt 90° to piston pin axis. Measure cylinder bore 90° to crankshaft centerline, at top, middle, and bottom of bore. Use these measurements to determine piston-to-cylinder bore clearance.

2) Measure cylinder bore 90° to crankshaft centerline at top of bore (below ring travel) and at bottom of bore (above ring travel). These measurements determine cylinder taper. Taper (difference between the 2 measurements) must not exceed .010" (.25 mm).

3) Measure cylinder bore at center of piston travel, 90° to crankshaft centerline. Measure bore at center of piston travel in line with crankshaft centerline. Out-of-round is the difference between the 2 measurements, and must not exceed .005" (.13 mm).

4) If taper or out-of-round are beyond limits, or cylinder walls are deeply scored, hone or bore cylinders for installation of new pistons. After cylinders have been honed or bored, measure cylinder diameter. Compare cylinder diameter measurements with those in PISTON SIZE CHART to obtain correct size piston.

FITTING RINGS

1) Select proper ring set for size of cylinder bore. Position ring in cylinder bore. Push ring down into bore to area where normal ring wear is not encountered. Use a piston to position ring so that it is square with cylinder wall.

2) Measure gap between ends of ring using feeler gauge. If ring gap is less than or greater than

2.0 & 2.3 LITER 4-CYLINDER (Cont.)

specified, a smaller or larger ring will have to be used. Check side clearance of compression rings with feeler gauge, of specified thickness, inserted between ring and its lower land on piston.

3) Feeler gauge should slide freely around entire circumference of piston without binding. If feeler gauge binds because of high spots on lower land of piston, piston should be replaced.

PISTON SIZE CHART

Cylinder Measurement	Piston Color Code & Size
2.0L	
3.5165-3.5177" (89.319-89.349 mm)	Red: 3.5150-3.5156" (89.281-89.296 mm)
3.5178-3.5189" (89.352-89.380 mm)	Blue: 3.5162-3.5168" (89.311-89.327 mm)
3.5190-3.5201" (89.383-89.411 mm)	Yellow: 3.5174-3.5180" (89.342-89.357 mm)
2.3L	
3.7795-3.7806" (95.999-96.027 mm)	Red: 3.7780-3.7786" (95.961-95.976 mm)
3.7807-3.7818" (96.029-96.058 mm)	Blue: 3.7792-3.7798" (95.992-96.007 mm)
3.7819-3.7831" (96.060-96.091 mm)	Yellow: 3.7804-3.7810" (96.022-96.037 mm)

PISTON PIN REPLACEMENT

Removal

Using an arbor press and Piston Pin Remover/Installer (T68P-6135-A), press piston pin from piston and connecting rod.

Installation

Apply a light coat of oil to all parts that are to be assembled. Position piston and connecting rod as shown in *Fig. 10*. Using arbor press and piston pin remover/installer, press piston pin through piston and connecting rod until centered in connecting rod.

Fig. 10: Correct Positioning of Piston and Connecting Rod for Installation of Piston Pin

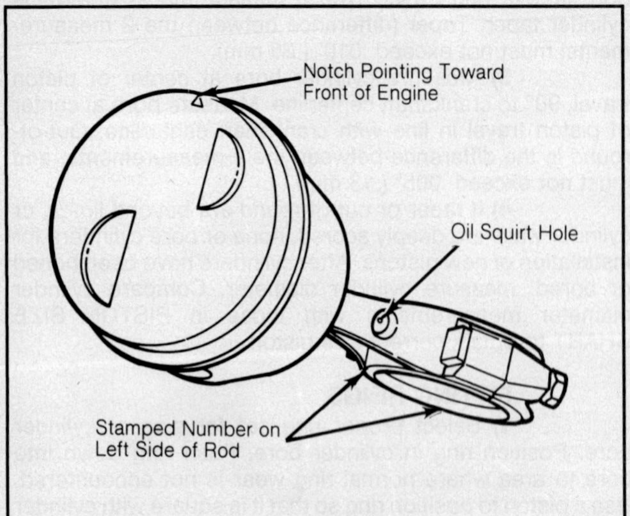

CRANKSHAFT & ROD BEARINGS

CONNECTING ROD BEARINGS

1) Fit rod bearings one at a time, while leaving all other bearings securely fastened. To determine bearing clearance, remove bearing cap. Place a strip of Plastigage on bearing surface across full width of bearing cap, about 1/4" off center away from oil holes.

2) Install bearing cap and tighten bolts to specifications. Do not allow crankshaft to turn. Remove cap and measure compressed width with scale furnished in Plastigage kit.

3) Standard size bearings may be used in combination with a .001" or .002" (.03 mm or .05 mm) undersize bearing. If .002" (.05 mm) undersize bearings are used on more than one journal, they must be installed on piston side of rod on crankshaft journal.

4) After bearings are installed, lightly oil crankshaft journal and bearing surfaces and install bearing cap.

MAIN BEARINGS

1) Fit main bearings one at a time, while leaving all other bearings securely fastened. To determine bearing clearance, remove bearing cap. Place a strip of Plastigage on bearing surface across full width of bearing cap, about 1/4" off center away from oil holes.

2) Install bearing cap and tighten bolts to specifications. Do not allow crankshaft to turn. Remove cap and measure compressed width with scale furnished in Plastigage kit. Standard size bearings may be used in combination with a .001" or .002" (.03 mm or .05 mm) undersize bearing.

3) If .002" (.05 mm) undersize bearings are used on more than one journal, they must be installed in cylinder block side of crankshaft journal. After bearings are installed, lightly oil crankshaft journal and bearing surfaces and install bearing cap.

CRANKSHAFT END PLAY

NOTE: **Engine must be removed from vehicle to check crankshaft end play.**

1) Force crankshaft toward rear of engine. Attach dial indicator to rear of engine so that indicator contact rests against crankshaft flange. Zero dial indicator. Push crankshaft forward and note dial indicator reading.

2) If end play exceeds specification, replace thrust bearing. If end play is less than specified, check for damaged or improperly aligned thrust bearing.

REAR MAIN BEARING OIL SEAL

NOTE: **Engine or transmission must be removed from vehicle to replace rear main bearing oil seal.**

Removal

Install 2 sheet metal screws into seal. Pull on screws until seal is removed from engine.

Installation

1) Position seal on Seal Installer (T82L-6701-A). Seal must be installed with spring side facing toward engine. *See Fig. 11*. Place seal installer and seal assembly on engine.

2) Install 2 bolts through seal installer into crankshaft. Alternately tighten bolts until seal is completely installed. Remove seal installer.

2.0 & 2.3 LITER 4-CYLINDER (Cont.)

Fig. 11: Installing Rear Main Bearing Oil Seal

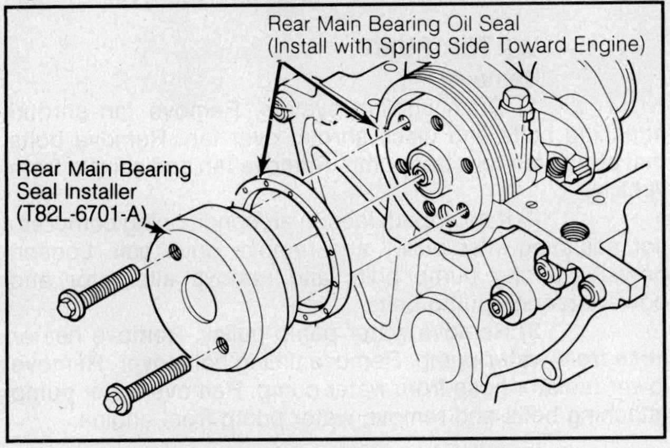

ENGINE OILING

CRANKCASE CAPACITY

Crankcase capacity is 4 quarts (3.8L) for 2.0L engine and 5 quarts (4.7L) for 2.3L engines. Add 1 quart (.9L) when oil filter is replaced.

OIL FILTER

Oil filter should be replaced every 12 months or 7500 miles, whichever occurs first.

NORMAL OIL PRESSURE

Normal oil pressure with engine at normal operating temperature and running at 2000 RPM should be 40-60 psi (2.8-4.2 kg/cm^2).

OIL PRESSURE REGULATOR VALVE

Valve is located in oil pump body and is not adjustable.

ENGINE OILING SYSTEM

System is pressure fed from a rotor-type oil pump. Oil flows through oil filter before entering main oil gallery. *See Fig. 12*.

OIL PUMP

Removal

Remove oil pan. Remove nut securing pick-up tube bracket to main bearing cap stud. Remove 2 bolts attaching oil pump to engine block. Remove oil pump assembly. Be careful not to drop oil pump drive shaft.

Disassembly

1) Remove 2 bolts attaching oil pick-up tube to oil pump. Remove pick-up tube and gasket. Remove pump cover attaching screw and remove cover. Remove inner rotor and shaft assembly. Remove outer rotor. Drill a small hole in pressure relief valve chamber cap. *See Fig. 13*.

2) Insert a small screw into cap and remove from pump housing. Remove pressure relief valve spring and plunger from pump housing.

Inspection

1) Clean all parts in solvent and dry thoroughly with compressed air. Ensure that all dirt or metal particles are removed from pressure relief valve chamber.

2) Check inside of pump housing, outer rotor and inner rotor for excessive wear or damage. Check mating surface of pump cover for wear. If pump cover mating surface is excessively worn, scored or grooved, replace pump assembly.

Fig. 12: Engine Oiling System

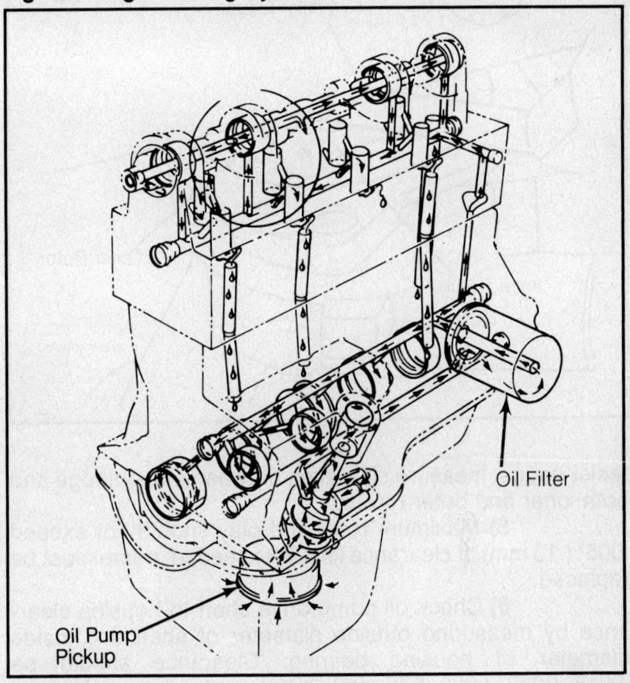

3) Measure rotor tip clearance. *See Fig. 14*. If rotor tip clearance exceeds specification, pump assembly must be replaced.

Fig. 13: Exploded View of Oil Pump Assembly

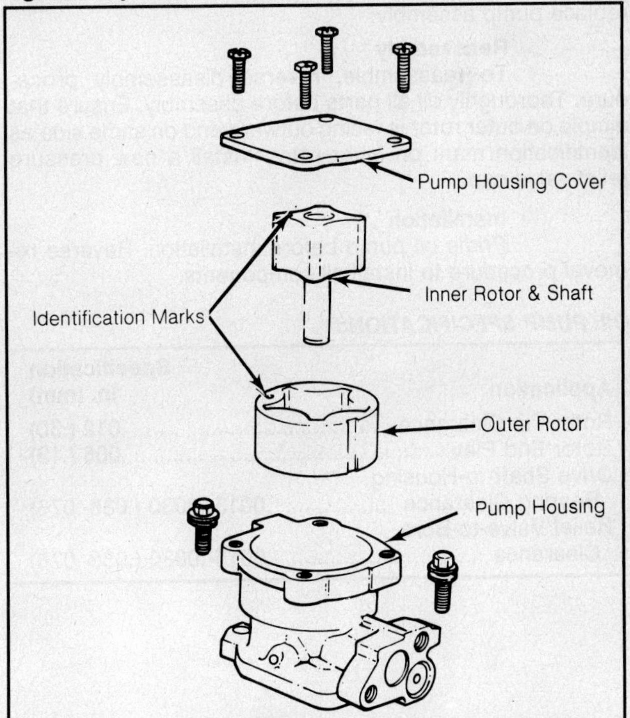

4) With rotor assembly installed in pump housing, place a straightedge across pump housing. Using a

Ford Engines

2.0 & 2.3 LITER 4-CYLINDER (Cont.)

Fig. 14: Checking Inner Rotor Tip Clearance

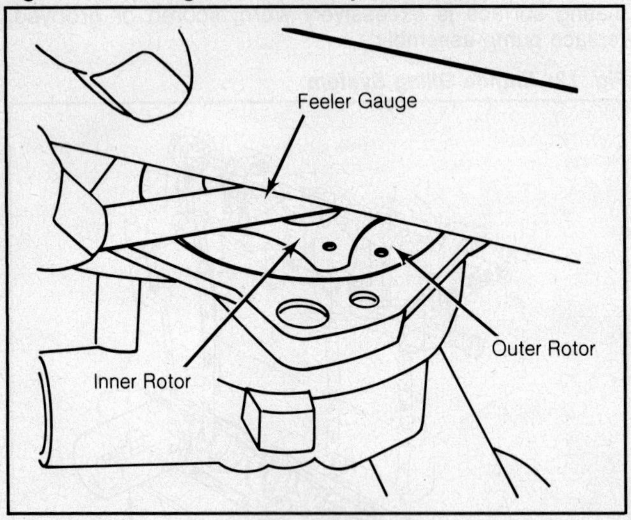

feeler gauge, measure clearance between straightedge and both inner and outer rotors.

5) Maximum rotor end play should not exceed .005" (.13 mm). If clearance limit is exceeded, pump must be replaced.

6) Check oil pump drive shaft-to-housing clearance by measuring outside diameter of shaft and inside diameter of housing bearing. Clearance should be .0015-.0030" (.038-.076 mm). If not, replace pump assembly.

7) Check pressure relief valve-to-bore clearance. Check tension of pressure relief valve spring. Spring tension should be 15.2-17.2 lbs. (6.9-7.8 kg) when spring is extended to 1.2" (30.4 mm). If spring tension is not correct, replace pump assembly.

Reassembly

To reassemble, reverse disassembly procedure. Thoroughly oil all parts before assembly. Ensure that dimple on outer rotor is facing outward and on same side as identification mark on inner rotor. Install a new pressure relief valve cap.

Installation

Prime oil pump before installation. Reverse removal procedure to install all components.

OIL PUMP SPECIFICATIONS

Application	Specification In. (mm)
Rotor Tip Clearance	.012 (.30)
Rotor End Play	.005 (.13)
Drive Shaft-to-Housing Bearing Clearance	.0015-.0030 (.038-.076)
Relief Valve-to-Bore Clearance	.0015-.0030 (.038-.076)

ENGINE COOLING

WATER PUMP

Removal

1) Drain cooling system. Remove fan shroud attaching bolts and place shroud over fan. Remove bolts that attach fan to water pump. Remove fan and shroud from vehicle.

2) If equipped, loosen air conditioning compressor adjusting idler pulley and remove drive belt. Loosen power steering pump bolts and remove alternator and power steering pump belts.

3) Remove water pump pulley. Remove heater hose from water pump. Remove timing belt cover. Remove lower radiator hose from water pump. Remove water pump attaching bolts and remove water pump from engine.

Installation

To install, reverse removal procedure. Make sure that gasket surfaces are clean. Apply Sealer (D8AZ-19554-A) to water pump bolts prior to installation.

NOTE: **For further information on cooling system capacities and other cooling system components, see appropriate article in ENGINE COOLING SYSTEMS at end of ENGINE section.**

TIGHTENING SPECIFICATIONS

Application	Ft. Lbs. (N.m)
Auxiliary Shaft Gear Bolt	28-40 (38-54)
Belt Tensioner	
Adjusting Bolt	14-21 (19-28)
Pivot Bolt	28-40 (38-54)
Camshaft Gear Bolt	50-71 (68-96)
Connecting Rod Cap	
1st Step	25-30 (34-41)
2nd Step	30-36 (41-49)
Cylinder Head	
1st Step	50-60 (68-81)
2nd Step	80-90 (108-122)
Exhaust Manifold	16-23 (22-31)
Flywheel-to-Crankshaft	56-64 (76-87)
Intake Manifold (2.0L)	14-21 (19-28)
Intake Manifold (2.3L)	
Lower Manifold	14-21 (19-28)
Upper Manifold	15-22 (20-30)
Main Bearing Cap	
1st Step	50-60 (68-81)
2nd Step	80-90 (108-122)
Oil Pump-to-Block	14-21 (19-28)
Water Pump	14-21 (19-28)
	INCH Lbs.
Auxiliary Shaft Thrust Plate	72-108 (8-12)
Camshaft Thrust Plate	72-108 (8-12)
Valve Cover	72-96 (8-11)

2.0 & 2.3 LITER 4-CYLINDER (Cont.)

ENGINE SPECIFICATIONS

GENERAL SPECIFICATIONS

Year	DISPLACEMENT Cu. In.	DISPLACEMENT Liters	Fuel System	HP@RPM	Torque Ft. Lbs.@RPM	Compr. Ratio	BORE In.	BORE mm	STROKE In.	STROKE mm
1985	122 140	2.0 2.3	1-Bbl. EFI	74@4000 90@4000	108@2600 130@1800	9.0:1 9.5:1	3.518 3.780	89.4 96.0	3.126 3.126	79.4 79.4

VALVES

Engine Size & Valve	Head Diam. In. (mm)	Face Angle	Seat Angle	Seat Width In. (mm)	Stem Diameter In. (mm)	Stem Clearance In. (mm)	Valve Lift In. (mm)
2.0L							
Intake	1.598-1.622 (40.59-41.19)	44°	45°	.060-.080 (1.52-2.03)	.3416-.3423 (8.677-8.694)	.0010-.0027 (.025-.069)	.390 (9.91)
Exhaust	1.370-1.390 (34.79-35.31)	44°	45°	.070-.090 (1.79-2.29)	.3411-.3418 (8.664-8.682)	.0015-.0032 (.038-.081)	.390 (9.91)
2.3L							
Intake	1.723-1.747 (43.76-44.37)	44°	45°	.060-.080 (1.52-2.03)	.3416-.3423 (8.677-8.694)	.0010-.0027 (.025-.069)	.400 (10.16)
Exhaust	1.490-1.510 (37.85-38.35)	44°	45°	.070-.090 (1.79-2.29)	.3411-.3418 (8.664-8.682)	.0015-.0032 (.038-.081)	.400 (10.16)

PISTONS, PINS, RINGS

Engine	PISTONS Clearance In. (mm)	PISTONS Piston Fit In. (mm)	PINS Rod Fit In. (mm)	RINGS Ring No.	RINGS End Gap In. (mm)	RINGS Side Clearance In. (mm)
2.0L & 2.3L	.0014-.0022 (.036-.056)	.0002-.0004 (.005-.010)	Interference Fit	1 & 2	.010-.020 (.25-.51)	.002-.004 (.05-.10)
				3	.015-.055 (.38-1.39)	Snug Fit

CRANKSHAFT MAIN & CONNECTING ROD BEARINGS

Engine	MAIN BEARINGS Journal Diam. In. (mm)	MAIN BEARINGS Clearance In. (mm)	MAIN BEARINGS Thrust Bearing	MAIN BEARINGS Crankshaft End Play In. (mm)	CONNECTING ROD BEARINGS Journal Diam. In. (mm)	CONNECTING ROD BEARINGS Clearance In. (mm)	CONNECTING ROD BEARINGS Side Play In. (mm)
2.0L & 2.3L	2.3982-2.3990 (60.914-60.935)	.0008-.0015 (.020-.038)	No. 3	.004-.008 (.10-.20)	2.0462-2.0472 (51.973-51.999)	.0008-.0015 (.020-.038)	.0035-.0105 (.089-.267)

VALVE SPRINGS

Engine	Free Length In. (mm)	PRESSURE Lbs. @ In. (Kg @ mm) Valve Closed	PRESSURE Lbs. @ In. (Kg @ mm) Valve Open
2.0L & 2.3L			
Intake	1.877 (47.68)	71-79@1.52 (32-36@38.6)	.....
Exhaust	1.877 (47.68)	71-79@1.52 (32-36@38.6)	.....

CAMSHAFT

Engine	Journal Diam. In. (mm)	Clearance In. (mm)	Lobe Lift In. (mm)
2.0L & 2.3L	1.7713-1.7720 (44.991-45.009)	.001-.003 (.025-.076)	.2381 [1] (6.047)

[1] – Lobe lift for 2.3L engine is .2437".

2.3 LITER 4-CYL. TURBO DIESEL

ENGINE CODING

ENGINE IDENTIFICATION

Engine is identified by the 8th character of the Vehicle Identification Number (VIN). The 10th character identifies the model year. The VIN is stamped on a metal tag, attached to the upper left side of the instrument panel and is visible through the windshield. The VIN can also be found on the Safety Compliance Certification Label located on the door outside edge of the left door.

ENGINE IDENTIFICATION CODE

Engine	Code
2.3L Turbo Diesel	E

ENGINE REMOVAL

See ENGINE REMOVAL at end of ENGINE section.

MANIFOLDS & CYLINDER HEAD

INTAKE MANIFOLD

Removal

1) Disconnect negative battery cables. Remove A/C compressor support bracket. Remove A/C compressor and position aside. Remove inlet fitting from intake manifold.

2) Remove turbo oil feed line at cylinder head and turbo housing. Remove oil line clamp bolt. Loosen bolts attaching turbo heat shield to exhaust manifold. Remove top bolt and position heat shield aside.

3) Remove wastegate actuator from turbo and mounting bracket. Remove top 2 actuator mounting bracket bolts. Loosen bottom bracket bolts and position bracket aside. Remove 5 remaining intake manifold bolts and 2 nuts. Remove intake manifold.

Installation

To install, reverse removal procedure.

EXHAUST MANIFOLD

Removal

1) Disconnect negative battery cables. Remove A/C compressor support bracket. Remove A/C compressor and position aside. Remove inlet fitting from intake manifold. Remove air inlet tube from air cleaner-to-turbo inlet.

2) Remove wastegate actuator from turbo and mounting bracket. Raise vehicle. Disconnect exhaust pipe at turbo exhaust fitting. Lower vehicle. Disconnect turbo oil feed line from cylinder head and turbo housing.

3) Remove exhaust manifold attaching nuts. Remove exhaust manifold and turbo as an assembly. Remove turbo from exhaust manifold, if necessary.

Installation

To install, reverse removal procedure.

CYLINDER HEAD

Removal

1) Disconnect negative battery cables. Mark location of hood hinges and remove hood. Drain cooling system. Disconnect breather hose from rocker cover. Remove heater hose clamp from rocker cover. Position hoses aside. Remove cooling fan and shroud.

2) Remove fan belts. Remove upper front timing cover. Loosen and remove camshaft/injection pump timing belt from camshaft sprocket. Remove turbo inlet hose from air cleaner and turbo. Raise vehicle. Disconnect exhaust pipe from turbo outlet. Lower vehicle.

3) Remove fuel conditioner and bracket and position aside. Disconnect and remove fuel lines between injection pump and nozzles. Cap all lines and fittings using Protective Cap Set (T85L-9395-A). Disconnect heater hose at left rear of cylinder head.

4) Remove A/C compressor and mounting bracket. Disconnect No. 2 and No. 3 glow plug electrical connectors. Disconnect coolant temperature switch lead. Remove intake and exhaust manifolds as previously described.

5) Remove rocker arm cover. Loosen cylinder head bolts in sequence, using a 10 mm hex head socket. *See Fig. 1.* Remove cylinder head and gasket.

Fig. 1: Cylinder Head Loosening Sequence

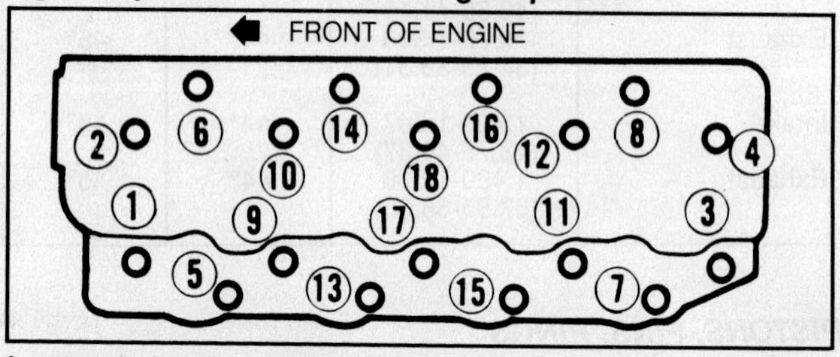

Loosen bolts using a 10 mm hex head socket.

Inspection

Check head for cracks, damage or water leaks. Check precombustion chambers for looseness. If any precombustion chamber is loose or head is cracked, replace head. Check cylinder head for warpage. Maximum allowable warpage is .008" (.20 mm). Replace head if warped beyond specification.

Installation

To install, reverse removal procedure. Ensure head gasket is installed with tapered edge to rear. Tighten cylinder head bolts to specification in sequence, using 2 step procedure. *See Fig. 2.* Ensure half-moon gasket is installed in rear of head.

Fig. 2: Cylinder Head Tightening Sequence

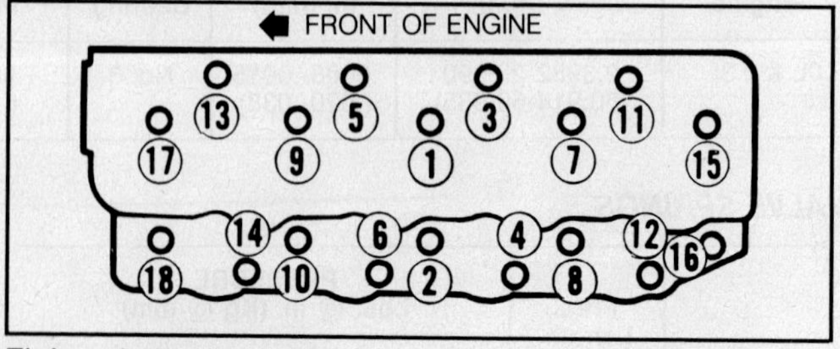

Tighten bolts to specification in 2 steps.

CAMSHAFT

TIMING BELTS

Removal

1) Disconnect negative battery cables. Remove fan belts. Remove 5 upper front timing belt cover retaining

2.3 LITER 4-CYL. TURBO DIESEL (Cont.)

bolts. Remove upper front cover. Remove cooling fan and shroud. Remove water pump pulley. Remove crankshaft pulley attaching bolt. Rotate crankshaft until No. 1 piston is at TDC on compression stroke.

2) Remove vibration damper using Damper Remover (T58P-6316-D). Remove 5 lower front timing belt cover attaching bolts and remove cover. Loosen timing belt tensioners and remove belts. Mark direction of rotation on timing belts before removal.

3) Remove timing belts. Check timing belts for missing teeth, cracking or excessive wear. Replace timing belt if necessary. Camshaft/injection pump timing belt must be removed to access silent shaft timing belt.

NOTE: **DO NOT loosen nut near timing scale unless removing silent shaft timing belt. This nut is for silent shaft timing belt tensioner. Loosening this nut may change silent shaft timing belt tension. See Fig. 3.**

Fig. 3: Silent Shaft Timing Belt Tensioner Nut

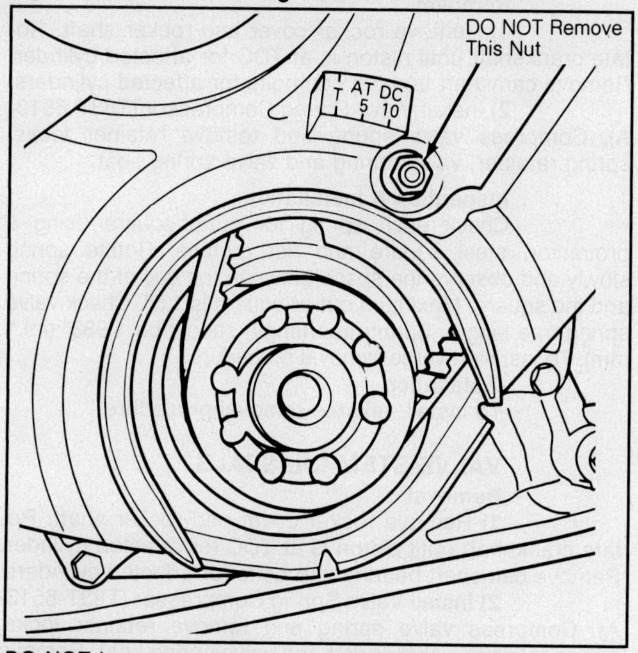

DO NOT loosen nut unless removing silent shaft timing belt.

Installation

1) Align crankshaft timing marks. Align left and right silent shaft timing marks. Install silent shaft timing belt. Ensure belt is installed for rotation in original direction. Align camshaft and injection pump timing marks. *See Fig. 4.*

2) Fabricate timing belt tensioner, using a pivot nut from rear brake adjuster and bar stock. *See Fig. 5.* Release tension on tensioner spring, using belt tensioner. Rotate tensioner toward water pump and tighten top bolt.

3) Install camshaft/injection pump timing belt. Ensure belt is installed to rotate in original rotation. Maintain tension on belt. Loosen top tensioner bolt to tension timing belt. Tighten tensioner hold-down bolts. To complete installation, reverse removal procedure.

FRONT OIL SEAL

Removal

1) Disconnect negative battery cables. Remove cooling fan and shroud. Remove fan belts. Remove crankshaft pulley, upper and lower timing belt covers and timing

Fig. 4: Timing Mark Alignment

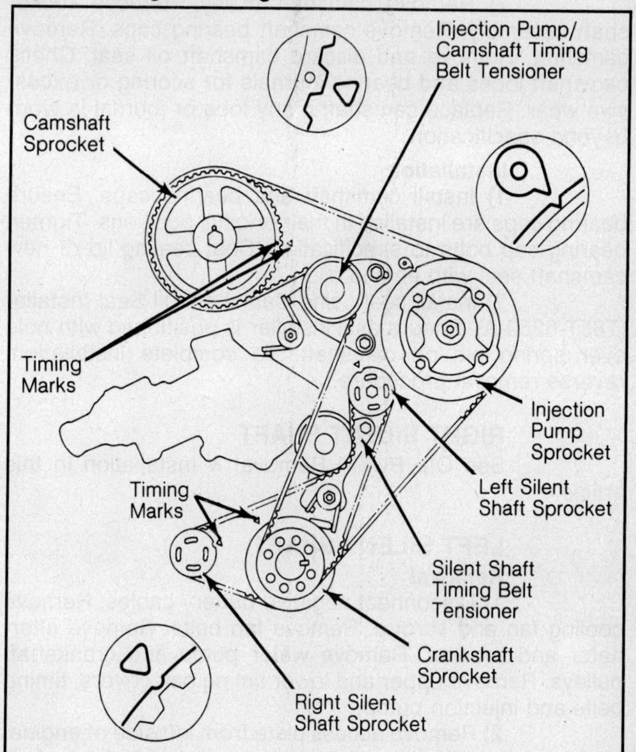

Fig. 5: Timing Belt Tensioner

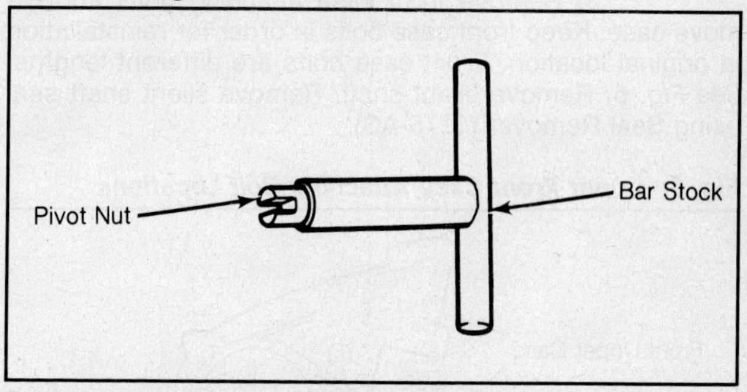

Fabricate tool from rear brake pivot nut and bar stock.

belts as previously described. Remove crankshaft sprockets and timing plate.

2) Carefully punch small hole in metal portion of seal. Insert Seal Remover (T77L-9533-B) and remove seal. Clean dirt and oil from lower case.

Installation

Apply a film of oil on inside and outside of new seal. Install seal using Seal Installer (T85T-6019-A). Remove seal installer. Install large crankshaft sprocket, timing plate and small timing sprocket. Install and adjust timing belts. To complete installation, reverse removal procedure.

CAMSHAFT

Removal

1) Disconnect negative battery cables. Remove rocker arm cover. Remove upper front timing belt cover. Rotate crankshaft until No. 1 piston is at TDC on compression stroke. Loosen camshaft/injection pump drive belt tensioner and remove timing belt.

2.3 LITER 4-CYL. TURBO DIESEL (Cont.)

2) Remove camshaft pulley. Remove rocker shaft assembly. Remove camshaft bearing caps. Remove camshaft. Remove and discard camshaft oil seal. Check camshaft lobes and bearing journals for scoring or excessive wear. Replace camshaft if any lobe or journal is worn beyond specification.

Installation

1) Install camshaft and bearing caps. Ensure bearing caps are installed in their original positions. Tighten bearing cap bolts to specification. Coat sealing lip of new camshaft seal with engine oil.

2) Install seal using Camshaft Oil Seal Installer (T85T-6250-A). Ensure esal installer is positioned with hole over spring pin on camshaft. To complete installation, reverse removal procedure.

RIGHT SILENT SHAFT

See OIL PUMP Removal & Installation in this article.

LEFT SILENT SHAFT

Removal

1) Disconnect negative battery cables. Remove cooling fan and shroud. Remove fan belts. Remove alternator and bracket. Remove water pump and crankshaft pulleys. Remove upper and lower timing belt covers, timing belts and injection pump.

2) Remove access plate from left side of engine. Insert socket extension into hole to prevent silent shaft rotation. Remove silent shaft-to-sprocket attaching bolt. Remove sprocket.

3) Remove front case attaching bolts and remove case. Keep front case bolts in order for reinstallation in original location. Front case bolts are different lengths. *See Fig. 6*. Remove silent shaft. Remove silent shaft seal using Seal Remover (1175-AC).

Fig. 6: Upper Front Case Attaching Bolt Locations

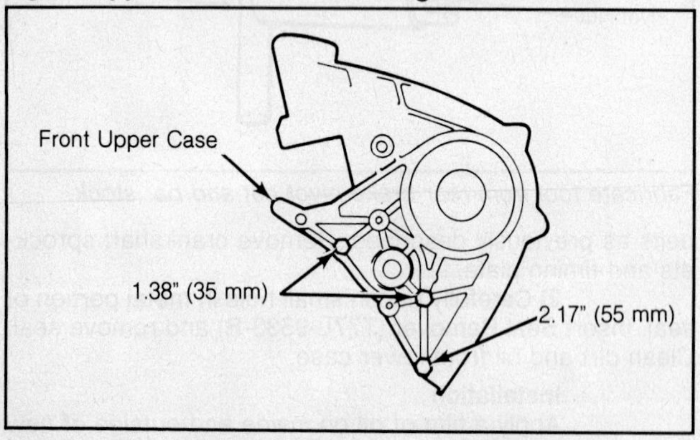

Install bolts in original locations as shown.

Installation

To install, reverse removal procedure and note the following: Install upper front case bolts in original locations. Ensure silent shaft sprocket is properly installed onto silent shaft.

SILENT SHAFT BEARINGS

Removal & Installation

Remove silent shafts. Install Silent Shaft Bearing Puller (T65L-6250-A). Tighten collet on remover. Rotate nut to remove bearing. Install new bearing on Silent Shaft Bearing Installer (T85T-6150-B) and Drive Handle (T80T-4000-W). Drive bearing into block until installer is seated.

VALVES

VALVE ARRANGEMENT

E-I-E-I-E-I-E-I (Front-to-rear).

ROCKER SHAFT ASSEMBLY

Removal & Installation

1) Remove rocker cover. Loosen rocker shaft attaching bolts 1 turn at a time, from front-to-rear. Remove rocker shaft.

2) Position rocker shaft on cylinder head. Ensure end of rocker shaft with single oil hole is toward front of engine and that rocker shaft is installed with oil holes facing down.

VALVE SPRINGS

Removal

1) Remove rocker cover and rocker shaft. Rotate crankshaft until piston is at TDC for affected cylinder. Remove camshaft bearing cap bolts for affected cylinders.

2) Install Valve Spring Compressor (T83T-6513-A). Compress valve spring and remove retainer locks, spring retainer, valve spring and valve spring seat.

Inspection & Installation

Check each spring for out-of-square using a protractor, steel square and flat surface. Rotate spring slowly and observe the space between top coil of the spring and the square. Maximum out-of-square is 1.5°. Check valve spring free length. Spring free length should be 1.933" (49.1 mm). To install, reverse removal procedure.

Installation

To install, reverse removal procedure.

VALVE STEM OIL SEALS

Removal

1) Remove rocker cover and rocker shaft. Rotate crankshaft until piston is at TDC for affected cylinder. Remove camshaft bearing cap bolts for affected cylinders.

2) Install Valve Spring Compressor (T83T-6513-A). Compress valve spring and remove retainer locks, spring retainer, valve spring and valve spring seat. Remove valve stem oil seals, using Seal Remover (T72J-6571) and slide hammer.

Installation

Install new oil seals, using Seal Installer (T85T-6571-A). To complete installation, reverse removal procedure. Adjust valves.

VALVE GUIDE SERVICING

1) Check valve guide-to-stem clearance using a dial indicator and Valve Guide Clearance Checker (6505-G). Move valve back-and-forth in guide. Observe dial indicator reading.

2) Divide reading by 2, the division factor of the tool. If valve stem-to-guide clearance is excessive, replace valve and/or valve guide. Valves with oversize stems are not available.

3) To replace valve guide, use Valve Guide Remover/Installer (T83T-6510-A). Drive old guide out toward combustion chamber side of head. Position new guide in rocker arm side of head. Using valve guide remover/installer, drive new guide into head until installer bottoms on cylinder head. Reface valve seat.

2.3 LITER 4-CYL. TURBO DIESEL (Cont.)

NOTE: Valve guides with oversize O.D. are available for use in heads with damaged valve guide bores. Ream valve guide bore using Reamer (T85T-6510-B) and install oversize guide.

VALVE CLEARANCE ADJUSTMENT

1) Run engine until it reaches normal operating temperature. Remover cover. Rotate crankshaft until No. 1 piston is at TDC on compression stroke. Check and adjust valve clearance for valves shown in VALVE CLEARANCE ADJUSTMENT chart.

2) Rotate crankshaft until No. 4 piston is at TDC on compression stroke. Check and adjust valve clearance for valves shown in VALVE CLEARANCE ADJUSTMENT chart.

VALVE CLEARANCE ADJUSTMENT

Cylinder At TDC	Check Int. Nos.	Check Exh. Nos.
No. 1	1, 2	1, 3
No. 4	3, 4	2, 4

PISTONS, PINS & RINGS

OIL PAN

See OIL PAN REMOVAL at end of ENGINE section.

PISTON & ROD ASSEMBLY

Removal

1) Remove cylinder head and oil pan. With piston placed at bottom of stroke, remove ridge from top of cylinder bore using ridge reamer. Mark right side of connecting rods and caps for cylinder identification.

2) Position piston to be removed at bottom of stroke. Remove rod cap and upper bearing from connecting rod. Using wooden hammer handle, push piston out top of cylinder bore. Install rod cap on mating rod.

Installation

1) Properly position rings on piston and install upper bearing in rod. *See Fig. 7.* Coat rod bearing surfaces, cylinder bore, piston and rings with engine oil. Install ring compressor over piston and rings.

2) Ensure position of rings does not change. Turn crankshaft to position journal at bottom of stroke. With arrow on top of piston toward front of engine, install piston and rod assembly into cylinder bore while guiding rod onto crankshaft journal.

3) Align rod bearing cap mark with connecting rod mark. Install and tighten connecting rod cap. Ensure crankshaft turns smoothly.

FITTING PISTONS

1) Measure cylinder bore at top, middle and bottom. Take measurements both in-line and 90° to crankshaft centerline. If wear is excessive, cylinders should be bored for installation of oversize piston.

2) Measure piston diameter 90° to piston pin. Subtract this figure from cylinder bore diameter to determine piston-to-cylinder wall clearance. Pistons are available in .010" (.25 mm), .020" (.50 mm), .030" (.75 mm) and .040" (1.00 mm) oversize.

Fig. 7: Correctly Spaced Piston Ring Gaps

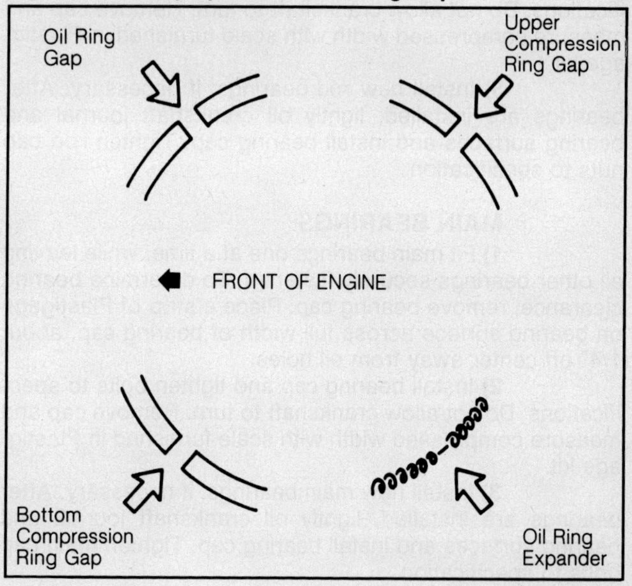

FITTING RINGS

1) Position ring into cylinder bore in which it is going to be used. If a new ring is being fitted, position ring into cylinder where normal ring wear is not encountered. If a used ring is being fitted, position ring in most worn part of cylinder liner.

2) Use head of a piston to position ring squarely in bore. Measure ring end gap with a feeler gauge. If ring gap is not within specifications, try another ring set.

3) Check compression ring side clearance with a feeler gauge inserted between ring and lower ring land. The feeler gauge should slide freely around entire ring circumference without binding.

4) Any piston wear that occurs will form a step at inner portion of lower land. If lower ring lands have high steps or ring side clearance is excessive, piston should be replaced.

NOTE: Top compression ring groove is constructed of a special cast iron ring carrier. Ring carrier is cast into piston to increase ring groove durability.

PISTON PINS

Piston pins are full-floating type. Pin is held in place by a snap ring on each end. Replace piston pins showing signs of fracture, etching or wear. Check piston pin fit in piston and rod. Check piston pin diameter and replace if not within specifications.

CRANKSHAFT & ROD BEARINGS

CONNECTING ROD BEARINGS

1) Fit rod bearings one at a time, while leaving all other bearings securely fastened. To determine bearing clearance, remove bearing cap. Place a strip of Plastigage on bearing surface across full width of bearing cap, about 1/4" off center away from oil holes.

2.3 LITER 4-CYL. TURBO DIESEL (Cont.)

2) Install bearing cap and tighten bolts to specifications. Do not allow crankshaft to turn. Remove cap and measure compressed width with scale furnished in Plastigage kit.

3) Install new rod bearings, if necessary. After bearings are installed, lightly oil crankshaft journal and bearing surfaces and install bearing cap. Tighten rod cap nuts to specification.

MAIN BEARINGS

1) Fit main bearings one at a time, while leaving all other bearings securely fastened. To determine bearing clearance, remove bearing cap. Place a strip of Plastigage on bearing surface across full width of bearing cap, about 1/4" off center away from oil holes.

2) Install bearing cap and tighten bolts to specifications. Do not allow crankshaft to turn. Remove cap and measure compressed width with scale furnished in Plastigage kit.

3) Install new main bearings, if necessary. After bearings are installed, lightly oil crankshaft journal and bearing surfaces and install bearing cap. Tighten main cap bolts to specification.

THRUST BEARING ALIGNMENT

1) Install all main bearing caps except thrust bearing (No. 3). Ensure bearing caps are installed in original positions. Tighten main bearing cap bolts to specification. Install thrust bearing cap with bolts finger tight.

2) Pry crankshaft forward against thrust surface of upper half of bearing. Hold crankshaft forward and pry thrust bearing cap to rear. This aligns both halves of bearing. Retain forward pressure on crankshaft. Tighten main cap bolts to specification.

3) Pry crankshaft toward rear of engine. Check crankshaft end play. Replace thrust bearing if end play is excessive. If end play is still excessive, replce crankshaft. If end play is less than specification, check thrust bearing for damaged thrust surface or contamination.

REAR MAIN BEARING OIL SEAL

Removal

1) Raise vehicle. Remove transmission and clutch assembly, if equipped. Remove flywheel. Drain engine oil. Loosen oil pan retaining bolts. Remove 2 oil pan-to-rear seal retainer bolts.

2) Remove 5 bolts attaching rear seal retainer to engine block. Remove rear seal retainer and gasket. Remove oil separator from rear seal retainer. Remove rear main bearing oil seal from retainer using punch.

Installation

1) Position seal retainer face down on an arbor press plate. Ensure bottom lip of retainer is positioned on plate with lip flange over edge of plate. Lubricate oil seal with engine oil. Press seal into retainer using Rear Seal Installer (T85T-6701-A).

2) Install oil separator in seal retainer with oil drain hole at bottom. Install oil seal retainer and tighten mounting bolts to specification. Install 2 oil pan bolts. Tighten all oil pan bolts to specification. To complete installation, reverse removal procedure.

ENGINE OILING

CRANKCASE CAPACITY

Crankcase capacity is 6.8 quarts (6.5L) including oil filter and cooler.

NORMAL OIL PRESSURE

Normal oil pressure should be 11.4 psi (.8 kg/cm^2) at idle with engine at operating temperature.

OIL PRESSURE REGULATOR VALVE

Oil pressure regulator valve is located in oil pump body. Valve is nonadjustable.

ENGINE OILING SYSTEM

The lubrication system is pressure fed by a crescent-type oil pump. Oil pump draws oil from pan through oil strainer and pick-up assembly. Oil is then pumped through oil cooler, when oil temperature is above 212°F (100°C). Oil by-passes oil cooler when oil temperature is below this point.

After oil passes the cooler it goes through oil filter and into main oil gallery. Oil then flows crankshaft, turbocharger, camshaft, silent shafts, rocker shaft and piston cooling jets.

OIL PUMP

Removal & Disassembly

1) Disconnect negative battery cables. Remove cooling fan and shroud. Remove water pump pulley, crankshaft pulley, upper and lower timing belt covers, timing belts and crankshaft sprockets.

2) Loosen oil pan bolts. Remove 6 front oil pan-to-front case bolts. Remove pipe plug in right side of engine block. Insert phillips head screwdriver into hole to prevent right side silent shaft from rotating. Remove silent shaft sprocket attaching nut. Remove sprocket.

Fig. 8: Exploded View of Oil Pump Assembly

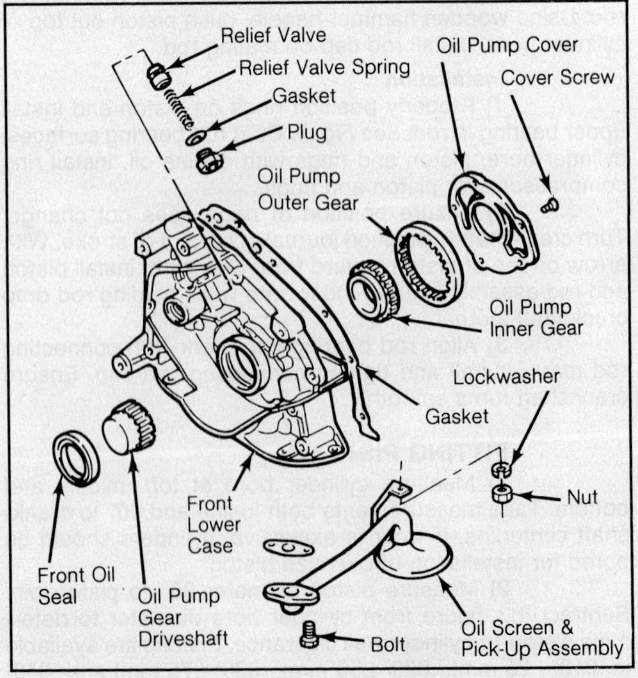

2.3 LITER 4-CYL. TURBO DIESEL (Cont.)

3) Remove front case-to-engine block attaching bolts. Remove front case and gasket. Remove silent shaft reverse rotation gear cover. Remove silent shaft and gears. Remove oil pump cover. Remove oil pump drive gear, inner rotor and outer rotor.

NOTE: Mark oil pump gears for reassembly reference before disassembling pump.

4) Remove silent shaft reverse rotation drive gear oil seal using Seal Remover (T58L-101-B). Remove crankshaft front oil seal.

Reassembly & Installation

1) Install silent shaft oil seal using a 21 mm socket. Install Seal Protector (T85T-6150-A) on drive gear before installation. Install silent shaft reverse rotation gears with marks aligned. Install oil pump gears in front housing with marks aligned.

2) Install oil pump cover and tighten to specification. Install silent shaft in reverse rotation drive gear and position front cover and new gasket on engine. Use care not to damage silent shaft bearing.

3) Install front cover bolts and tighten to specification. Ensure front cover bolts are installed in original locations. *See Fig. 9*. To complete installation, reverse removal procedure.

Fig. 9: Lower Front Cover Bolt Locations

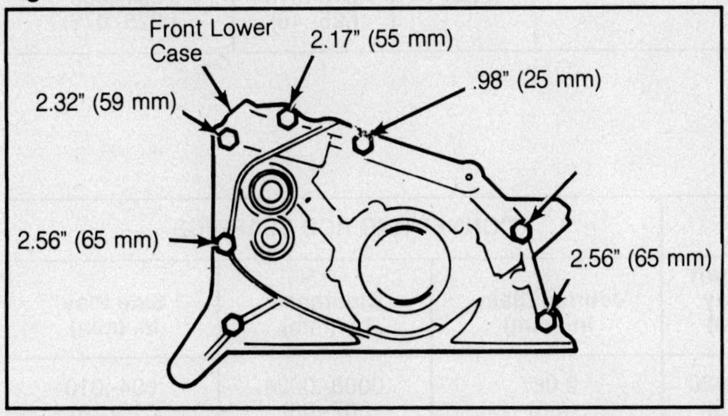

Install bolts in locations shown.

ENGINE COOLING

WATER PUMP

Removal

1) Disconnect negative battery cables. Remove cooling fan and shroud. Remove fan belts. Remove belt tensioner. Remove 4 water pump pulley attaching bolts. Remove water pump pulley. Remove A/C compressor support bracket.

2) Drain cooling system. Disconnect lower radiator hose from thermostat housing adapter. Remove thermostat housing, adapter and thermostat. Remove upper and lower timing belt covers. Remove 6 water pump attaching bolts and remove water pump.

Installation

Clean all gasket mating surfaces. Install new pump, with gasket, and tighten bolts. Install thermostat, housing and adapter using new gaskets. To complete installation, reverse removal procedure.

NOTE: For further information on cooling system capacities and other cooling system components, see appropriate article in ENGINE COOLING SYSTEMS section.

TIGHTENING SPECIFICATIONS

Application	Ft. Lbs. (N.m)
Camshaft Bearing Cap Bolts	14-15 (19-20)
Camshaft Sprocket Bolt	47-54 (64-73)
Connecting Rod Nuts	33-34 (45-47)
Crankshaft Pulley Bolts	123-137 (167-186)
Cylinder Head Bolts	
Cold	76-83 (103-112)
Hot	84-90 (113-122)
Exhaust Manifold Bolts/Nuts	11-14 (15-19)
Flywheel Bolts	94-101 (128-137)
Injection Pump Sprocket Nut	40-50 (54-68)
Intake Manifold Bolts/Nuts	11-14 (15-19)
Main Bearing Cap Bolts	55-61 (74-83)
Rocker Shaft Bolts	25-28 (34-39)
Rocker Arm Adjusting Nuts	9-13 (12-17)
Silent Shaft Sprocket Bolt	25-28 (34-39)
Timing Belt Tensioner Nut	16-21 (22-29)
	INCH Lbs.
Front Case Bolts	108-120 (12-14)
Oil Pan Bolts	54-66 (6-7)
Rocker Cover Bolts	48-60 (5-7)
Silent Shaft Chamber Cover Bolts	36-48 (4-5)

ENGINE SPECIFICATIONS

GENERAL SPECIFICATIONS

Year	DISPLACEMENT		Fuel System	HP@RPM	Torque Ft. Lbs.@RPM	Compr. Ratio	BORE		STROKE	
	Cu. In.	Liters					In.	mm	In.	mm
1985	143.2	2.3	Fuel Inj.	.....	.....	21.0	3.59	91.1	3.54	90

2.3 LITER 4-CYL. TURBO DIESEL (Cont.)

ENGINE SPECIFICATIONS (Cont.)

VALVES

Engine Size & Valve	Head Diam. In. (mm)	Face Angle	Seat Angle	Seat Width In. (mm)	Stem Diameter In. (mm)	Stem Clearance In. (mm)	Valve Lift In. (mm)
2.3L							
Intake	1.57 (40)	45°	45°	.....	.315 (8)	.0012-.0024 (.03-.06)	.....
Exhaust	1.34 (34)	45°	45°	.....	.315 (8)	.0020-.0035 (.05-.09)	.....

PISTONS, PINS, RINGS

Engine	PISTONS	PINS		RINGS		
	Clearance In. (mm)	Piston Fit In. (mm)	Rod Fit In. (mm)	Ring No.	End Gap In. (mm)	Side Clearance In. (mm)
2.3L	.0016-.0024 (.041-.061)	.0001-.0002 (.002-.005)	[1]	No. 1	.010-.016 (.25-.41)	.001-.002 (.025-.051)
				No. 2	.010-.016 (.25-.41)	.001-.003 (.025-.076)
				Oil	.010-.018 (.25-.46)	.001-.003 (.025-.076)

[1] – Piston pin is full-floating.

CRANKSHAFT MAIN & CONNECTING ROD BEARINGS

Engine	MAIN BEARINGS				CONNECTING ROD BEARINGS		
	Journal Diam. In. (mm)	Clearance In. (mm)	Thrust Bearing	Crankshaft End Play In. (mm)	Journal Diam. In. (mm)	Clearance In. (mm)	Side Play In. (mm)
2.3L	2.598 (66)	.0008-.0020 (.02-.05)	No. 3	.0008-.0020 (.02-.05)	2.087 (53)	.0008-.0024 (.02-.06)	.004-.010 (.10-.25)

VALVE SPRINGS

Engine	Free Length In. (mm)	PRESSURE Lbs. @ In. (Kg @ mm)	
		Valve Closed	Valve Open
2.3L	1.933 (49.1)	61@1.591 (27.7@40.4)	.....

CAMSHAFT

Engine	Journal Diam. In. (mm)	Clearance In. (mm)	Lobe Lift In. (mm)
2.3L	1.181 (30)	.002-.004 (.05-.10)	.....

ENGINE CODING

ENGINE IDENTIFICATION

Engine is identified by the 8th character of Vehicle Identification Number (VIN). The VIN is stamped on a metal plate visible through windshield on left upper side of instrument panel. VIN is also located on Safety Compliance Certification Label, attached to left door lock pillar.

ENGINE IDENTIFICATION CODES

Engine	Code
2.8L 2-Bbl.	S

ENGINE REMOVAL

See ENGINE REMOVAL at end of ENGINE section.

MANIFOLDS & CYLINDER HEAD

INTAKE MANIFOLD

Removal

1) Disconnect negative battery cable. Remove air cleaner assembly. Disconnect throttle cable from engine. Drain cooling system. Remove water hose from water outlet to radiator. Remove by-pass hose from intake manifold to thermostat housing rear cover.

2) Remove distributor cap and spark plug wires as an assembly. Disconnect vacuum hose and wiring harness from distributor. Observe and mark position of rotor and distributor housing for reassembly reference. Remove distributor hold-down bolt and distributor.

3) Remove valve covers. Remove fuel line and fuel filter. Remove intake manifold attaching bolts and nuts. Lightly tap intake manifold with plastic mallet to break gasket seal. Lift intake manifold from engine.

Installation

1) Remove all gasket material and sealant. Apply sealing compound to mating surfaces. Place intake manifold gasket in position. Ensure tab on right cylinder head gasket fits into cut-out on manifold gasket. Apply sealer to attaching bolt bosses on intake manifold.

2) Position manifold and install attaching bolts. Start each bolt at least 2 full turns by hand. Tighten bolts and nuts to specification in sequence. *See Fig. 1.* Reverse removal procedure to complete installation. Bleed cooling system and check ignition timing.

Fig. 1: Intake Manifold Bolt Tightening Sequence

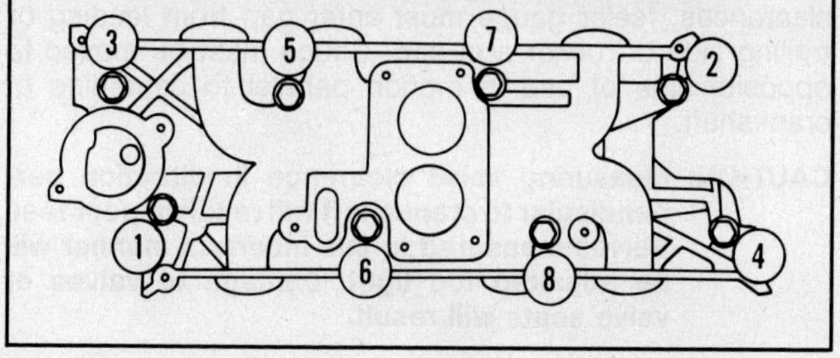

EXHAUST MANIFOLD

Removal

1) Remove air cleaner assembly. Remove nuts attaching shroud to left exhaust manifold. Remove nuts attaching exhaust pipe to exhaust manifold. Remove thermactor components as necessary to remove exhaust manifold(s).

2) Disconnect choke heat tubes at carburetor. Disconnect oxygen sensor wire at left exhaust manifold. Remove exhaust manifold attaching bolts. Remove exhaust manifold from cylinder head.

Installation

Use new exhaust pipe gasket. Reverse removal procedure to complete installation.

CYLINDER HEAD

Removal

1) Drain cooling system. Remove intake manifold as previously described. Remove valve covers and rocker arm shaft assemblies. Remove push rods and keep in order for installation in original positions.

2) Remove exhaust manifolds. Remove cylinder head attaching bolts. Remove cylinder heads from engine and discard head gaskets.

Installation

1) Position head gasket on engine block. Install cylinder head alignment studs into upper front and rear cylinder head bolt holes in engine block.

NOTE: **Cylinder head gaskets are marked with words "front" and "top" for correct installation positioning. Left and right head gaskets are not interchangeable.**

2) Position cylinder heads over alignment studs on engine block. Install cylinder head attaching bolts and remove alignment studs. Tighten all bolts in specified sequence. *See Fig. 2.*

3) Reverse removal procedure to complete installation of remaining components.

Fig. 2: Cylinder Head Bolt Tightening Sequence

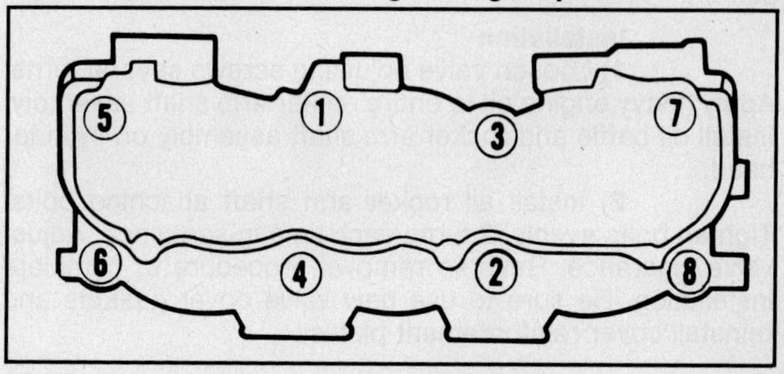

Use 3-step procedure to tighten head bolts.

VALVES

VALVE ARRANGEMENT

Right Side – I-E-I-E-E-I (Front-to-rear).
Left Side – I-E-E-I-E-I (Front-to-rear).

ROCKER ARM SHAFT ASSEMBLY

Removal

1) Remove air cleaner assembly. Remove spark plug wires. Remove PCV valve and hose. Remove carburetor choke air deflector plate. Remove valve cover bolts and washer. Ensure that washers are installed in their original positions.

2) Disconnect transmission fluid dipstick tube from valve cover. Disconnect kickdown linkage from carburetor, if equipped. Position thermactor air hose and wiring harness away from right valve cover. Remove engine oil fill cap.

3) Disconnect vacuum line from canister purge solenoid and canister-to-purge solenoid hose. If equipped with power brakes, disconnect brake booster hose. Lightly tap valve cover with plastic hammer to break seal.

4) Remove valve covers. Loosen rocker arm shaft attaching bolts 2 turns each time, in sequence, until all bolts are removed. Lift rocker arm shaft assembly with oil baffle from cylinder head.

Disassembly

Remove spring washer and roll pin from each end of rocker arm shaft. Slide rocker arms, springs and rocker arm shaft supports off shaft. Mark all parts for reassembly reference.

Fig. 3: Exploded View of Rocker Arm Shaft Assembly

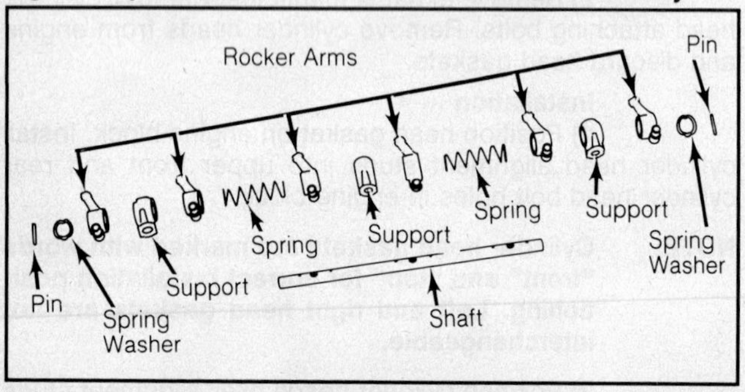

Notch in end face of shaft must point downward.

Reassembly

When rocker arm shaft is reassembled, oil holes in shaft must point downward. Notch on end face of shaft must point downward on both banks. Coat all parts with heavy engine oil and reassemble in reverse order of disassembly.

Installation

1) Loosen valve adjusting screws several turns. Apply heavy engine oil to entire rocker arm shaft assembly. Install oil baffle and rocker arm shaft assembly on cylinder head.

2) Install all rocker arm shaft attaching bolts. Tighten bolts evenly, 2 turns each time in sequence. Adjust valve clearance. Reverse removal procedure to complete installation. Be sure to use new valve cover gaskets and reinstall cover reinforcement plates.

VALVE SPRINGS AND/OR VALVE STEM OIL SEALS

Removal

1) Remove air cleaner. Remove valve cover and rocker arm shaft. Remove spark plug wire and spark plug from cylinder in which valve spring will be removed.

2) Remove both push rods from cylinder to be serviced. Install air line adapter in spark plug hole. Apply air pressure to cylinder.

CAUTION: Crankshaft may rotate until air pressure forces piston to bottom of stroke. Keep hands clear of belts and pulleys.

3) Using Valve Spring Compressor (T74P-6565-A and B), compress valve spring and remove spring retainer locks, spring retainer and spring. Remove valve stem oil seal.

Installation

Install new valve stem oil seal. Position spring over valve with tighter coils toward cylinder head. Compress spring and install retainer and locks. Reverse removal procedure to complete installation.

VALVE SPRING INSTALLED HEIGHT

1) Valve spring installed height should be measured with rocker arms removed. Measurement should be made from cylinder head spring pad to bottom side of valve spring retainer.

2) If height is not within specifications, install spacers between cylinder head spring pad and valve spring to obtain specified height. Do not install more spacers than necessary as stress will be placed upon valve springs and camshaft lobes.

VALVE SPRING INSTALLED HEIGHT SPECIFICATIONS

Application	Measurement In. (mm)
2.8L	1.578-1.609 (40.08-40.88)

VALVE GUIDE SERVICING

Always use reamers in proper sequence (smallest first). Reface valve seat after valve guide has been reamed. After reaming, use scraper to break sharp corner at top inside diameter of valve guide bore. Valves are available with .008" (.20 mm), .016" (.41 mm) and .032" (.81 mm) oversize stems.

VALVE CLEARANCE ADJUSTMENT

1) Engine must be cold for correct valve clearance adjustment. Remove valve covers. Turn engine until intake valve of No. 5 cylinder just starts to move into open position. Adjust both valves for No. 1 cylinder.

2) Intake valve clearance is correct when .014" (.36 mm) feeler gauge is snug or drags lightly while .015" (.38 mm) gauge is very tight. Exhaust valve clearance is correct when .016" (.41 mm) feeler gauge is snug or drags lightly while .017" (.43 mm) gauge is very tight.

3) To adjust valves in cylinder firing order (1-4-2-5-3-6), rotate engine so that intake valve is just opening on cylinders in order 5-3-6-1-4-2. Adjusting screws are self-locking type. Turn screw clockwise to reduce clearance or counterclockwise to increase clearance.

4) Use 1 feeler of each size to adjust clearances rather than stepped "go/no-go" gauge. When checking clearances, feeler gauge must enter gap from leading or trailing side of rocker arm pad. Gauge must be moved to opposite side of pad in motion parallel to centerline of crankshaft.

CAUTION: Measuring valve clearance in direction perpendicular to crankshaft will result in poor feel. Valves measured in this incorrect manner will be adjusted too tight. Damage to valves or valve seats will result.

5) Install valve covers with new gaskets. Start engine and check for oil and vacuum leaks.

VALVE CLEARANCE ADJUSTMENT

Application	In. (mm)
2.8L	
Intake	.014 (.36)
Exhaust	.016 (.41)

CAMSHAFT

ENGINE FRONT COVER

Removal

1) Remove oil pan. Drain cooling system and remove radiator. Remove air conditioning compressor and power steering bracket. Remove alternator, thermactor pump and remaining drive belts.

2) Remove fan. Remove water pump. Remove heater and radiator hoses. Remove drive pulley from crankshaft. Remove front cover retaining bolts. Lightly tap front cover with plastic hammer to break seal.

3) Remove front cover. If cover plate gasket needs replacement, remove 2 bolts and cover plate. Remove guide sleeves from front of block if necessary.

Installation

1) Apply sealing compound to engine block and back side of front cover plate. If removed, install guide sleeves with new sealing rings so that chamfered edge faces front cover. Place gasket and cover plate on engine, using 4 front cover bolts to align plate and gasket.

2) Install and tighten 2 cover plate-to-block bolts. Remove 4 front cover bolts. Apply sealing compound to front cover gasket. Place gasket on front cover. Place cover on engine and start front engine cover retaining bolts a few turns.

3) Center front cover with Front Cover Aligner (T74P-6019-A) in front cover seal. Tighten engine front cover attaching bolts. Reverse removal procedure to complete installation.

FRONT COVER OIL SEAL

Removal

Drain cooling system. Remove radiator, crankshaft pulley and water pump drive belt. Using Seal Remover (1175-AC) and slide hammer, remove front cover oil seal from engine front cover.

Installation

Coat new front cover oil seal with Lubriplate. Slide oil seal and Seal Installer (T74P-6700-A) onto crankshaft. Drive oil seal in until installer contacts front cover. Reverse removal procedure to complete installation.

TIMING GEARS

Removal

Drain cooling system and crankcase. Remove oil pan. Remove radiator. Remove water pump and engine front cover. Remove camshaft gear retaining bolt. Remove camshaft gear. Using gear puller and Shaft Protector (T71P-7137-H), remove crankshaft gear.

Installation

1) Align keyway in camshaft gear with key on camshaft. Slide gear onto camshaft and install camshaft gear retaining bolt. Ensure camshaft end play is correct.

2) Align keyway in crankshaft gear with key on crankshaft and timing marks on both gears. *See Fig. 4*. Slide gear onto crankshaft. Reverse removal procedure to complete installation.

Fig. 4: Aligning Timing Marks on Timing Gears

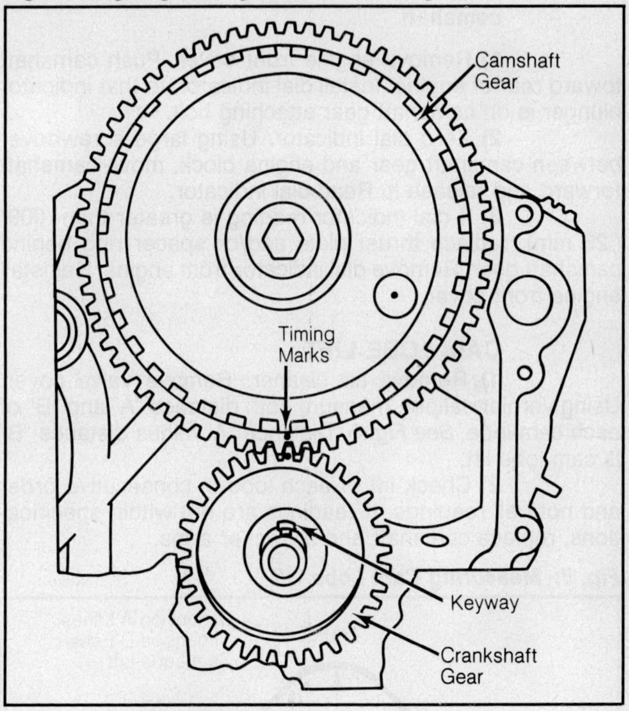

CAMSHAFT

Removal

1) Disconnect negative battery cable. Drain crankcase. Remove radiator. Remove fan, spacer, drive belt and pulley.

2) Remove spark plug wires from spark plugs. Remove distributor cap and wires as an assembly. Disconnect distributor wiring harness and vacuum hose. Remove distributor.

3) Remove alternator and thermactor pump. Remove fuel lines, fuel filter and carburetor. Remove intake manifold. Remove valve covers and rocker arm shaft assemblies.

4) Remove push rods and keep in order for reinstallation in original locations. Remove tappets from bores and keep in order for reinstallation in original location. Remove oil pan. Remove crankshaft damper.

5) Remove water pump and engine front cover as an assembly. Remove camshaft gear attaching bolt and washer. Slide gear off of camshaft. Remove camshaft thrust plate. Carefully slide camshaft out of engine.

Installation

1) Coat camshaft journals and tappets with heavy engine oil. Apply Lubriplate to camshaft lobes. Carefully install camshaft into engine block.

2) Install camshaft thrust plate so main oil gallery is covered. Tighten bolts. Check camshaft end play.

Ford Engines

2.8 LITER V6 (Cont.)

Align timing marks and install camshaft gear. Reverse removal procedure to install remaining components.

CAMSHAFT END PLAY

CAUTION: Prying against aluminum/nylon gear while valve train is placing load on camshaft may cause gear damage. When checking camshaft end play, back off valve lash adjusters or loosen rocker arm shaft to remove load from camshaft.

1) Remove engine front cover. Push camshaft toward rear of engine. Install dial indicator so that indicator plunger is on camshaft gear attaching bolt.

2) Zero dial indicator. Using large screwdriver between camshaft gear and engine block, move camshaft forward and release it. Read dial indicator.

3) If dial indicator reading is greater than .009" (.29 mm), replace thrust plate and/or spacer ring behind camshaft gear. Remove dial indicator from engine. Reinstall engine front cover.

CAM LOBE LIFT

1) Remove air cleaner. Remove valve cover. Using vernier caliper, measure both distance "A" and "B" of each cam lobe. *See Fig. 5*. Distance "A" minus distance "B" is cam lobe lift.

2) Check lift of each lobe in consecutive order and note all readings. If readings are not within specifications, replace camshaft and all rocker arms.

Fig. 5: Measuring Cam Lobe Lift

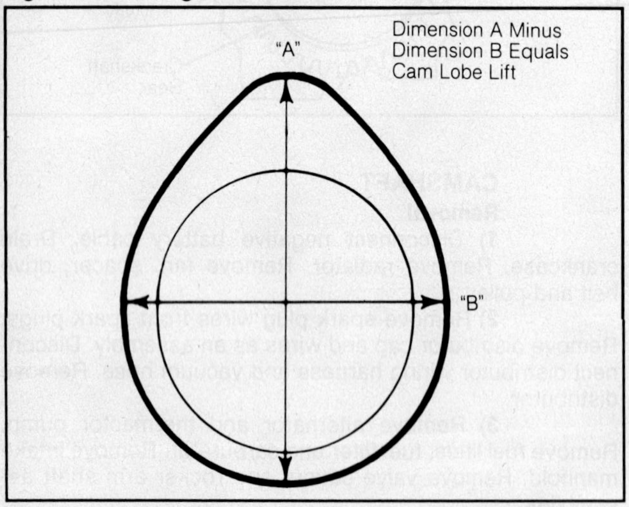

CAMSHAFT BEARINGS

Removal

1) Remove engine from vehicle and place on engine stand. Remove flywheel. Remove camshaft. Remove rear bearing bore plug.

2) Using Camshaft Bearing Remover/Installer (T71P-6250-A), remove camshaft bearings from engine block. Use Adapter Tube (T72C-6250) when removing front and rear bearings.

Installation

1) Install camshaft bearings in engine block using camshaft bearing remover/installer. When installing bearing, ensure that oil hole in bearing is aligned with oil hole in engine block.

2) Oil hole alignment of number 2 and 3 bearings can be checked by inserting piece of welding rod through engine block oil gallery and camshaft bearing. Reverse removal procedure to complete installation.

PISTONS, RINGS & PINS

OIL PAN

See OIL PAN REMOVAL at end of ENGINE section.

PISTON & ROD ASSEMBLY

Removal

1) Drain cooling system and crankcase. Remove intake manifold, cylinder heads, oil pan and oil pump.

2) Rotate crankshaft until piston to be removed is at bottom of stroke. Place cloth on top of piston to collect cuttings. Remove any ridges or deposits from upper end of cylinder bore.

3) Ensure that all connecting rods and rod caps are marked so that they can be installed in their original locations. Remove connecting rod nuts and cap.

4) Push piston out through top of engine block using hammer handle. Remove bearing inserts from connecting rod and cap.

Installation

1) Apply light engine oil to piston rings, piston and cylinder walls. Ensure that ring gaps are properly spaced around piston. Install piston ring compressor on piston. *See Fig. 6*.

Fig. 6: Correctly Spacing Piston Ring Gaps

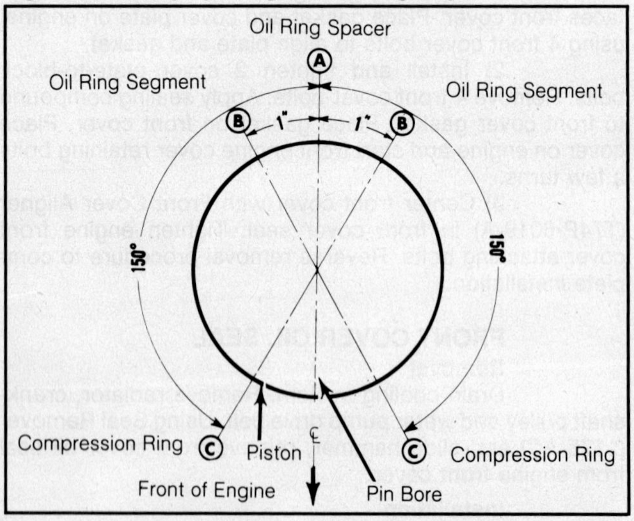

2) Using hammer handle, push piston into cylinder block until top of piston is just below top of cylinder block. Carefully guide connecting rod onto crankshaft journal. Indentation notch on head of piston faces front of engine.

NOTE: Ensure piston and rod assembly is returned to same cylinder from which it was removed.

3) Apply light coat of engine oil to journals and bearings. Install connecting rod cap and tighten nuts. Numbers on connecting rod and bearing cap must be on same side of assembled rod and face left side of engine.

2.8 LITER V6 (Cont.)

FITTING PISTONS

NOTE: **Make all measurements with piston and block at normal room temperature of 70°F (21°C).**

1) Measure piston skirt 90° to piston pin axis. Measure cylinder bore 90° to crankshaft centerline, at top, middle and bottom of bore. Use these measurements to determine piston-to-cylinder bore clearance.

2) Measure cylinder bore 90° to crankshaft centerline at top of bore (below ring travel) and at bottom of bore (above ring travel). These measurements determine cylinder taper. Taper (difference between 2 measurements) must not exceed .010" (.25 mm).

3) Measure cylinder bore at center of piston travel, 90° to crankshaft centerline. Measure bore at center of piston travel in-line with crankshaft centerline. Out-of-round is difference between 2 measurements, and must not exceed .005" (.13 mm).

4) If taper or out-of-round are beyond limits, or cylinder walls are deeply scored, hone or bore cylinders for installation of new pistons. After cylinders have been honed or bored, measure cylinder diameter. Select proper piston to obtain specified piston-to-cylinder bore clearance.

FITTING RINGS

1) Select proper ring set for size of cylinder bore. Position ring in cylinder bore in which it is going to be used.

2) Push ring down into bore to area where normal ring wear is not encountered. Use piston to position ring so that it is square with cylinder wall.

3) Measure gap between ends of ring using feeler gauge. If ring gap is either less or greater than specified, smaller or larger ring will have to be used.

4) Check side clearance of compression rings with feeler gauge inserted between ring and lower edge of ring land on piston. Feeler gauge should slide freely around entire circumference of piston without binding.

5) If feeler gauge binds because of high spots on lower land of piston, piston should be replaced.

PISTON PIN REPLACEMENT

Removal

Using an arbor press and Piston Pin Remover/Installer (T68P-6135-A and T72C-6135), press piston pin from piston and connecting rod.

Fig. 7: Correct Positioning of Piston and Connecting Rod

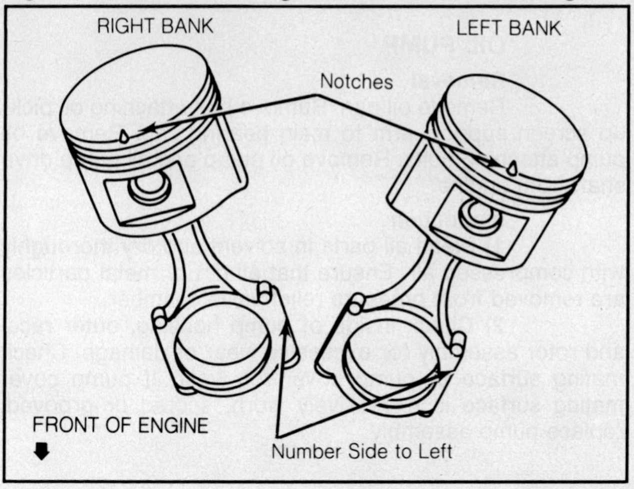

Installation

Apply light coat of oil to all parts that are to be assembled. Assemble piston and connecting rod. Using arbor press and piston pin remover/installer, press piston pin through piston and connecting rod until centered in connecting rod. *See Fig. 7.*

CRANKSHAFT & ROD BEARINGS

CONNECTING ROD BEARINGS

Removal

1) Drain crankcase. Remove oil pan and oil pump. Rotate crankshaft until connecting rod being worked on is at bottom of stroke. Mark cap and rod for reassembly if not already marked. Remove rod cap from rod. Remove bearing inserts.

2) Inspect bearings for wear or scuffing. Use Plastigage method to determine bearing wear and clearance. If standard bearings are being replaced with new bearings, try to obtain minimum specified clearance.

3) Bearings can be selectively fitted to obtain desired clearance. If standard bearing will not give proper clearance, try half of .001" (.03 mm) or .002" (.05 mm) undersize bearing in combination with half of standard bearing to obtain clearance.

Installation

1) Ensure bearing inserts and bearing bore of connecting rod are clean. Clean crankshaft journal. Install bearing inserts in connecting rod and cap. Ensure tang on bearing fits slot on rod.

2) Apply engine oil to bearing inserts and crankshaft journal. Pull rod down snugly to journal and install rod cap. Tighten rod nuts. Check side clearance between connecting rods on common journals.

3) Clean oil pump intake screen and prime oil pump. Turn pump shaft until oil comes out of outlet. Install oil pump and pan. Start engine and check for leaks.

MAIN BEARINGS

Removal

1) If rear main bearing is to be replaced, remove engine and place on stand. If rear main bearing is not to be replaced, remaining bearings can be replaced with engine in vehicle. Drain crankcase.

2) Remove oil pan and oil pump. Remove one bearing cap at a time, leaving others securely fastened. Insert Upper Bearing Remover/Installer (6331-E) in oil hole of journal. *See Fig. 8.*

3) Rotate crankshaft slowly in direction of normal operation and force upper bearing insert out of block. Ensure 4 thrust washers on No. 3 bearing are in good condition. Clean journals. Check journals and bearing inserts for wear or damage.

Installation

1) Coat new bearing with heavy engine oil. Place smooth end (without tang) of bearing insert over crankshaft on locking tang side of block. Partially install bearing insert.

2) Install upper bearing installer/remover in journal oil hole. Slowly rotate crankshaft in opposite direction of normal engine rotation. Stop when bearing tang is fully seated in block slot.

Ford Engines

2.8 LITER V6 (Cont.)

Fig. 8: Installation of Upper Main Bearing Remover/Installer

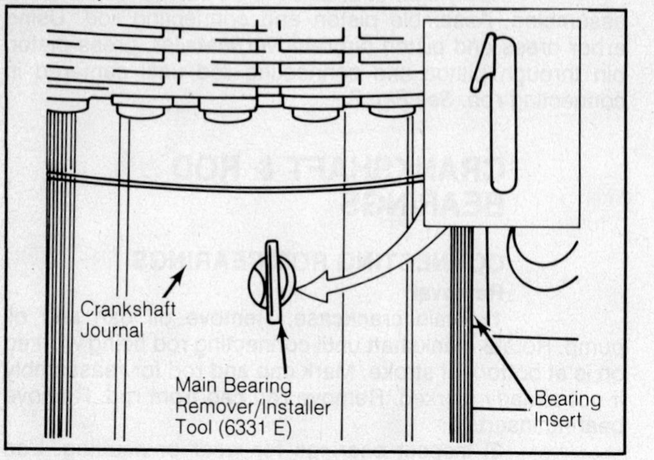

3) Remove bearing installer. Select fit lower bearing insert using Plastigage method. Coat bearing insert and journal with heavy engine oil. Install main bearing cap and tighten bolts.

4) When replacing rear main bearing, coat rear portion of bearing cap flats with sealer. Do not put sealer on flats where cap bolts come through. Replace rear main cap wedge seals at this time, 1 in cap groove and 1 in block front cover.

5) Install oil pump after priming. Install oil pan and fill crankcase. Check for leaks after engine is running.

THRUST BEARING ALIGNMENT

Loosen bolts on number 3 main bearing cap. Pry crankshaft toward front of engine. With prying pressure on crankshaft, tighten main bearing cap bolts.

REAR MAIN BEARING OIL SEAL

Removal

1) Remove transmission from vehicle. Remove pressure plate and clutch disc, if equipped. Remove flywheel, flywheel housing and rear plate.

2) Punch 2 holes in rear main bearing oil seal. Punch holes directly opposite of each other and just above bearing cap-to-block split. Install sheet metal screw in each hole.

3) Using 2 large screwdrivers, pry on both screws at same time until seal is removed from engine block. It may be necessary to use wood blocks as fulcrum points when prying seal out.

Installation

1) Coat outside diameter of oil seal with engine oil. Coat inside diameter of oil seal with lubriplate.

2) Using Seal Installer (T72C-6165), drive oil seal into engine block until seal is firmly seated. Reverse removal procedure to complete installation.

ENGINE OILING

CRANKCASE CAPACITY

Crankcase capacity is 4 quarts (3.8L). Add 1 quart (.9L) when oil filter is replaced.

OIL FILTER

Oil filter should be replaced every 7500 miles.

NORMAL OIL PRESSURE

Normal oil pressure with engine hot and running at 2000 RPM should be 40-60 psi (2.8-4.2 kg/cm^2).

OIL PRESSURE REGULATOR VALVE

Valve is located in oil pump body and is not adjustable.

ENGINE OILING SYSTEM

System is pressure fed from rotor-type oil pump. Oil flows through oil filter before entering main oil gallery. *See Fig. 9.*

Fig. 9: Engine Oiling System

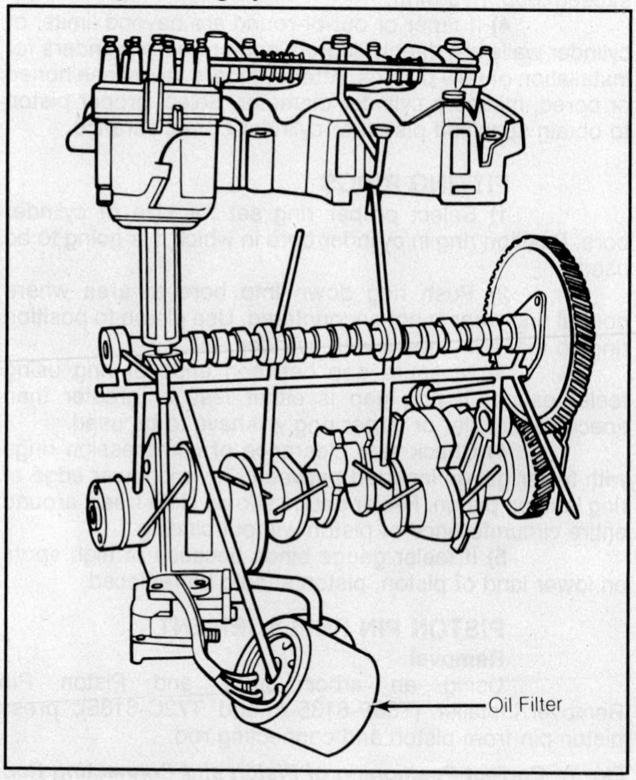

OIL PUMP

Removal

Remove oil pan. Remove bolt attaching oil pick-up screen support arm to main bearing cap. Remove oil pump attaching bolts. Remove oil pump and oil pump drive shaft from engine.

Inspection

1) Clean all parts in solvent and dry thoroughly with compressed air. Ensure that all dirt or metal particles are removed from pressure relief valve chamber.

2) Check inside of pump housing, outer race, and rotor assembly for excessive wear or damage. Check mating surface of pump cover for wear. If pump cover mating surface is excessively worn, scored or grooved, replace pump assembly.

Ford Engines

2.8 LITER V6 (Cont.)

Fig. 10: Checking Inner Rotor Tip Clearance

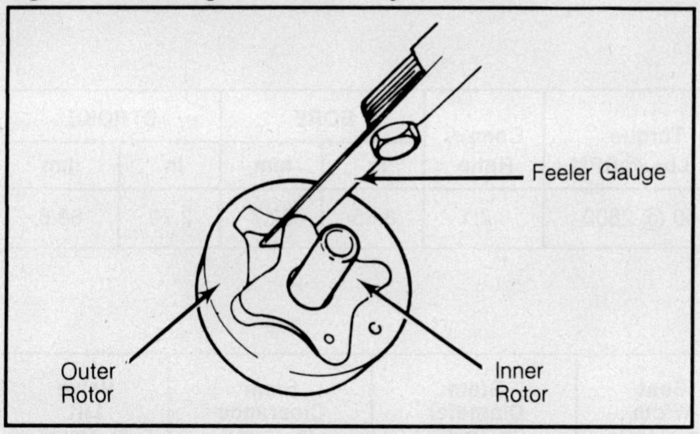

Place rotor assembly on flat surface when measuring.

3) Measure rotor tip clearance between inner and outer rotors. Remove rotor assembly from pump and place on flat surface. Feeler gauge must be inserted at least .5" (13 mm) into space between inner and outer rotors. *See Fig. 10*. If rotor tip clearance exceeds specification, pump assembly must be replaced.

Installation

Fill and prime oil pump with oil before installation. Rotate pump shaft to fill pump body with oil. Install pump drive shaft with pointed end up. Reverse removal procedure to install all components.

OIL PUMP SPECIFICATIONS

Application	Specification In. (mm)
Rotor Tip Clearance	.012 (.31)
Rotor End Play	.005 (.13)
Drive Shaft-to-Housing Bearing Clearance	.0015-.0030 (.038-.076)
Relief Valve-to-Bore Clearance	.0015-.0030 (.038-.076)

ENGINE COOLING

CAUTION: Do not operate engine with hood open until fan has been checked for cracks or separation.

WATER PUMP

Removal

1) Drain cooling system. Disconnect lower radiator hose and heater return hose from water inlet housing.

2) Remove fan and fan clutch assembly using Fan Clutch Holder and Nut Wrench (T83T-6312-A and B). *See Fig. 11*. Water pump hub and fan clutch nut have left-hand threads.

3) Loosen alternator mounting bolts and remove drive belt. On models with A/C, remove alternator and bracket. On all models, remove water pump pulley.

4) Remove water pump attaching bolts. Note different bolt lengths for reinstallation in correct location. Remove water pump assembly, water inlet housing and thermostat from front of engine.

Installation

To install, reverse removal procedure.

NOTE: For further information on cooling system capacities and other cooling system components, see appropriate article in ENGINE COOLING SYSTEMS at end of ENGINE section.

Fig. 11: Removing Fan & Fan Clutch Assembly

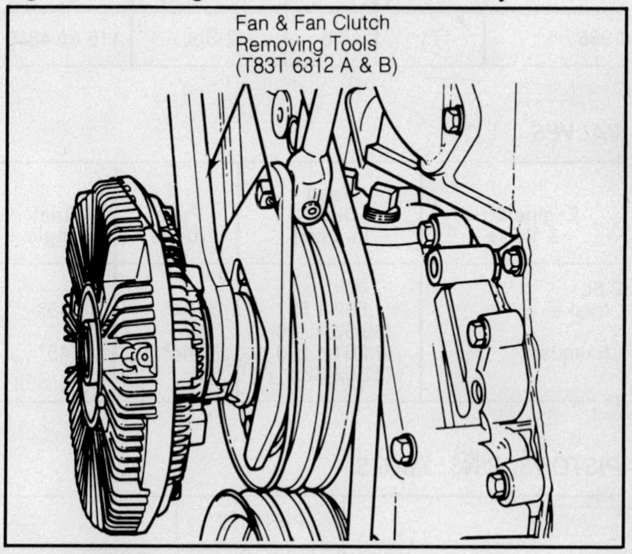

Fan clutch-to-pump hub nut has left-hand thread.

TIGHTENING SPECIFICATIONS

Application	Ft. Lbs. (N.m)
Camshaft Gear Bolt	30-36 (41-49)
Camshaft Thrust Plate	13-16 (18-22)
Connecting Rod Nut	19-24 (26-33)
Crankshaft Pulley-to-Crankshaft	85-96 (115-130)
Cylinder Head Bolt	
1st Step	29-40 (39-54)
2nd Step	40-51 (54-69)
3rd Step	70-85 (95-115)
Exhaust Manifold	20-30 (27-41)
Fan Clutch-to-Water Pump Hub [1]	15-25 (20-34)
Flywheel-to-Crankshaft	47-52 (64-71)
Front Cover-to-Engine Block	13-16 (18-22)
Main Bearing Cap Bolt	65-75 (88-102)
Rocker Arm Shaft Bolt	43-50 (58-68)
	INCH Lbs. (N.m)
Intake Manifold	
1st Step	36-72 (4-8)
2nd Step	72-132 (8-15)
3rd Step	132-180 (15-20)
4th Step	180-216 (20-24)
Oil Pump-to-Engine Block	72-120 (8-14)
Valve Cover	36-60 (4-7)
Water Pump	84-108 (10-12)

[1] – Left-hand thread.

Ford Engines

2.8 LITER V6 (Cont.)

ENGINE SPECIFICATIONS

GENERAL SPECIFICATIONS

Year	DISPLACEMENT Cu. In.	DISPLACEMENT Liters	Fuel System	HP@RPM	Torque Ft. Lbs.@RPM	Compr. Ratio	BORE In.	BORE mm	STROKE In.	STROKE mm
1985	171	2.8	2-Bbl.	115 @ 4800	150 @ 2600	8.7:1	3.65	92.7	2.70	68.6

VALVES

Engine Size & Valve	Head Diam. In. (mm)	Face Angle	Seat Angle	Seat Width In. (mm)	Stem Diameter In. (mm)	Stem Clearance In. (mm)	Valve Lift In. (mm)
2.8L							
Intake	1.562-1.577 (39.67-40.06)	44°	45°	.060-.079 (1.52-2.01)	.3159-.3167 (8.023-8.044)	.0008-.0025 (.020-.064)	.373 (9.47)
Exhaust	1.261-1.276 (32.02-32.41)	44°	45°	.060-.079 (1.52-2.01)	.3149-.3156 (7.998-8.016)	.0018-.0035 (.045-.089)	.373 (9.47)

PISTONS, PINS, RINGS

Engine	PISTONS Clearance In. (mm)	PINS Piston Fit In. (mm)	PINS Rod Fit In. (mm)	RINGS Ring No.	RINGS End Gap In. (mm)	RINGS Side Clearance In. (mm)
2.8L	.0011-.0019 (.028-.048)	.0003-.0006 (.008-.015)	Interference Fit	1 & 2	.015-.023 (.38-.58)	.0020-.0033 (.051-.084)
				3	.015-.055 (.38-1.39)	Snug Fit

CRANKSHAFT MAIN & CONNECTING ROD BEARINGS

Engine	MAIN BEARINGS Journal Diam. In. (mm)	MAIN BEARINGS Clearance In. (mm)	MAIN BEARINGS Thrust Bearing	MAIN BEARINGS Crankshaft End Play In. (mm)	CONNECTING ROD BEARINGS Journal Diam. In. (mm)	CONNECTING ROD BEARINGS Clearance In. (mm)	CONNECTING ROD BEARINGS Side Play In. (mm)
2.8L	2.2433-2.2441 (56.979-57.000)	.0008-.0015 (.020-.038)	No. 3	.004-.008 (.10-.20)	2.1252-2.1260 (53.980-54.000)	.0006-.0016 (.015-.040)	.004-.011 (.10-.28)

CAMSHAFT

Engine	Journal Diam. In. (mm)	Clearance In. (mm)	Lobe Lift In. (mm)
2.8L			
No.1	1.7285-1.7293 (43.904-43.924)	.0010-.0026 (.025-.066)	.2555 (6.49)
No. 2	1.7135-1.7143 (43.523-43.543)		
No. 3	1.6985-1.6992 (43.141-43.160)		
No. 4	1.6835-1.6842 (42.761-42.779)		

VALVE SPRINGS

Engine	Free Length In. (mm)	PRESSURE Lbs. @ In. (Kg @ mm) Valve Closed	PRESSURE Lbs. @ In. (Kg @ mm) Valve Open
2.8L	1.91 (48.5)	60-68@1.59 (27-31@40.4)	138-149@1.22 (63-68@31.0)

Ford Engines

4.9 LITER 6-CYLINDER

ENGINE CODING

ENGINE IDENTIFICATION

Engine is identified by the eighth character of Vehicle Identification Number (VIN). VIN is visible through windshield on left upper side of instrument panel. VIN is also located on Safety Compliance Certification Label, attached to left door lock pillar.

ENGINE IDENTIFICATION CODE

Engine	Code
4.9L 1-Bbl.	Y

ENGINE REMOVAL

See ENGINE REMOVAL at end of ENGINE section.

MANIFOLDS & CYLINDER HEAD

MANIFOLD ASSEMBLY

Removal

1) Remove air cleaner. Disconnect accelerator cable or rod at carburetor. Remove accelerator return spring. Remove kickdown rod return spring (vehicles with automatic transmission). Remove accelerator rod bellcrank assembly.

2) Label and disconnect all vacuum lines at carburetor. Disconnect fuel inlet line at carburetor. Disconnect carburetor feedback solenoid and choke electric assist connectors. Disconnect header pipe from exhaust manifold. Disconnect power brake vacuum line (if equipped).

3) Remove crankcase vent hose from intake manifold. Remove manifolds from cylinder head. Separate manifolds by removing nuts securing manifolds together. Discard all gaskets.

Installation

NOTE: DO NOT use combination intake/exhaust gasket if installing new exhaust manifold.

1) Clean mating surfaces of cylinder head and manifolds. If only one manifold is to be replaced, transfer tube fittings and install new studs. Lightly coat intake and exhaust manifold mating surfaces with graphite grease. Using new gasket, position exhaust manifold over studs of intake manifold.

2) Install lock washers, and tighten nuts finger tight. Coat manifold assembly and cylinder head mating surfaces lightly with graphite grease. Using new gasket, install and tighten intake manifold. Ensure gaskets have not become dislodged. Tighten nuts securing manifolds together. *See Fig. 1*.

3) Using new gaskets as required, install remaining components in reverse order of removal. Adjust linkage and carburetor.

CYLINDER HEAD

CAUTION: Do not pry between cylinder head and block when detaching head assembly, as gasket surface may be damaged.

Fig. 1: Intake & Exhaust Manifold Tightening Sequence

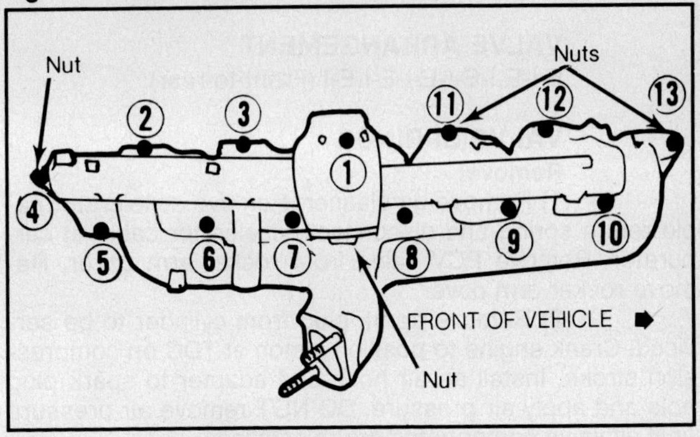

Tighten to 22-32 ft. lbs. (30-43 N.m).

Removal

1) Drain cooling system and remove air cleaner. Remove PCV valve and carburetor fuel inlet line. Disconnect vent hose at intake manifold. Label and remove all vacuum lines at carburetor.

2) Remove accelerator cable return spring and disconnect accelerator cable from carburetor. On vehicles with automatic transmission, disconnect kickdown rod at carburetor. Disconnect Electronic Engine Control (EEC) harness from all sensors, if equipped.

3) Disconnect upper radiator hose and heater hose at coolant outlet elbow. Remove coil bracket retaining bolt, and position coil to one side. Disconnect exhaust pipe from manifold. Remove rocker arm cover. Loosen rocker arm bolts, and rotate rocker arms to one side.

4) Identify push rods for reinstallation in original locations and remove. Disconnect spark plug wires at spark plugs. Remove cylinder head bolts and attach lifting eyes to cylinder head. Using engine hoist and lifting sling, raise cylinder head and manifold assembly from engine.

Installation

1) Clean all gasket mating surfaces. Check block and head gasket surfaces for warpage. Position new gasket over dowel pins on cylinder block. Install lifting eyes on cylinder head (in same locations as used to detach head assembly). Using lifting device, position cylinder head over block.

2) Carefully lower head assembly onto block. Ensure dowel pins properly engage in head. Remove hoist and lifting eyes. Coat threads of head bolts with engine oil and install. Tighten head bolts in sequence using 3 steps. *See Fig. 2*.

3) Lubricate push rod ends, rocker arm fulcrum seats and sockets with polyethylene grease and install. Reverse removal procedure to complete installation.

Fig. 2: Cylinder Head Tightening Sequence

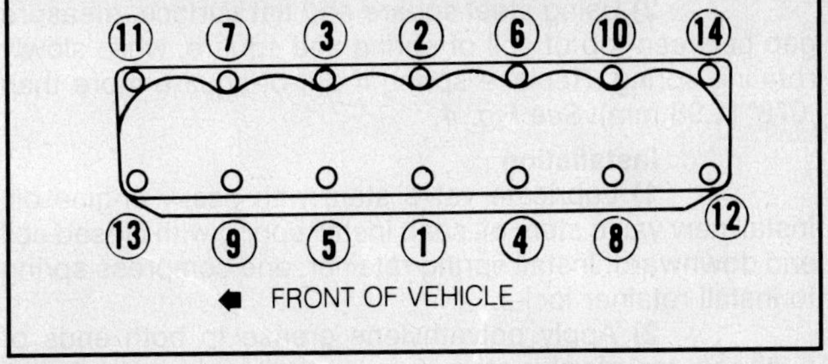

Tighten bolts in 3 steps.

4.9 LITER 6-CYLINDER (Cont.)

VALVES

VALVE ARRANGEMENT

E-I-E-I-E-I-E-I-E-I-E-I (Front-to-rear).

VALVE SPRINGS

Removal

1) Remove air cleaner. Remove accelerator cable return spring and disconnect accelerator cable at carburetor. Remove PCV valve from rocker arm cover. Remove rocker arm cover.

2) Remove spark plug from cylinder to be serviced. Crank engine to position piston at TDC on compression stroke. Install an air hose and adapter to spark plug hole and apply air pressure. DO NOT remove air pressure until all valve components are reinstalled.

3) Remove rocker arm bolt, fulcrum seat, rocker arm, fulcrum guide and push rod. Reinstall bolt. Using valve spring compressor, compress spring and remove retainer locks. Remove spring retainer, spring and oil seal.

Fig. 3: Valve Assembly for 4.9L Engine

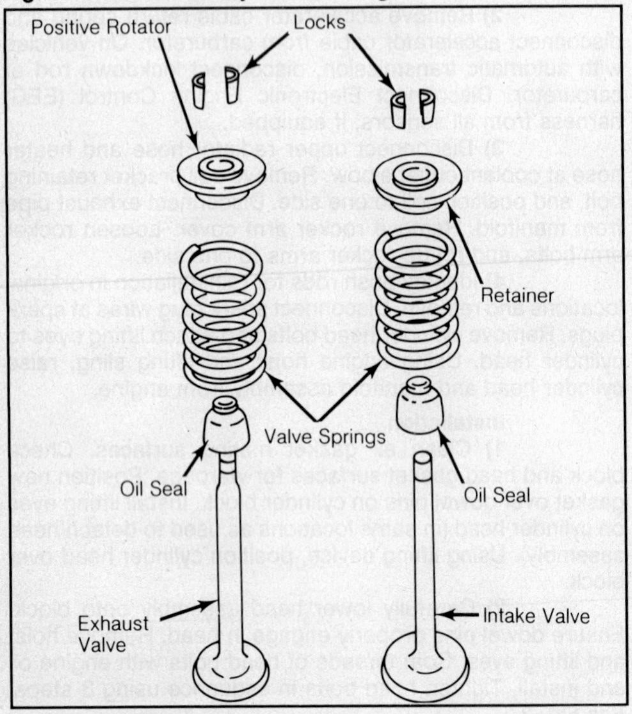

Install springs with tighter coils downward.

Inspection

1) Inspect valve stem for wear and binding in valve guide. Using valve spring tester, check valve spring tension. Replace springs that fail to meet specifications.

2) Using steel square and flat surface, measure gap between top of coil of spring and square, while slowly rotating spring. Replace spring if out-of-square more than .078" (1.98 mm). *See Fig. 4*.

Installation

1) Lubricate valve stem with heavy engine oil. Install new valve stem oil seal. Install spring with closed coil end downward. Install spring retainer, and compress spring to install retainer locks.

2) Apply polyethylene grease to both ends of push rod, top of valve stem, fulcrum seat and socket. Install push rod, rocker arm, fulcrum seat and bolt. Check valve

Fig. 4: Checking Valve Spring Squareness

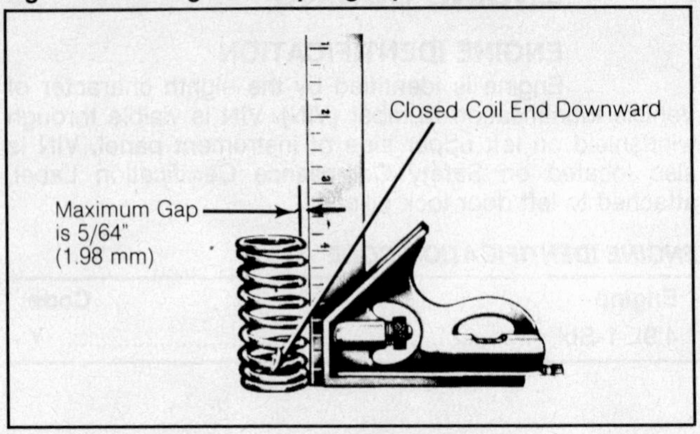

Measure gap while slowly rotating spring.

clearance. See VALVE CLEARANCE ADJUSTMENT in this article.

3) Remove air hose and adapter. Install spark plug. Reverse removal procedure to install remaining components.

VALVE SPRING INSTALLED HEIGHT

CAUTION: Do not install spacers unless necessary to meet specifications. Excessive use of spacers will overstress valve train.

1) Using dividers and scale, measure assembled height of valve spring from surface of cylinder head spring pad to underside of spring retainer. *See Fig. 5*.

Fig. 5: Checking Valve Spring Installed Height

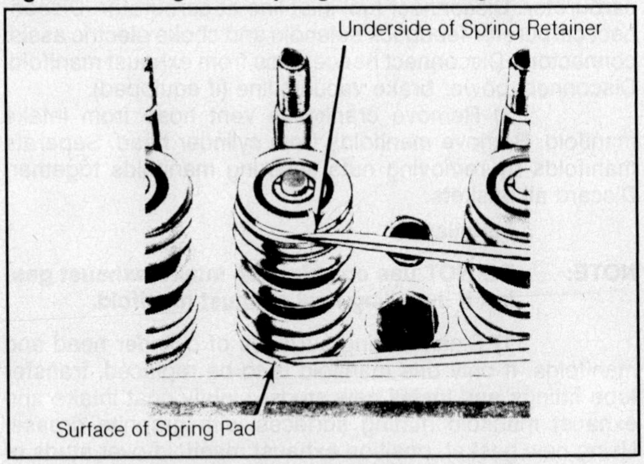

Do not install spacers unless necessary.

2) If spring height is excessive, install necessary .030" (.76 mm) spacer(s) between cylinder head spring pad and valve spring to correct height.

VALVE SPRING INSTALLED HEIGHT SPECIFICATIONS

Application	Specification In. (mm)
Intake	1.61-1.67" (40.89-42.42 mm)
Exhaust	1.44-1.50" (36.58-38.10 mm)

VALVE STEM OIL SEALS

Cup-type Teflon oil seals are used on valves. Install cupped side down over valve stem. Use procedure described in VALVE SPRINGS to replace seals.

4.9 LITER 6-CYLINDER (Cont.)

VALVE GUIDE SERVICING

When reaming valve guides, always use reamers in proper size sequence, from smallest to largest. Reface valve seats after reaming operation. Use scraper to break sharp corner at top of valve guide bore after reaming. *See Fig. 6.* Replacement valves are available in .003" (.08 mm), .015" (.38 mm) and .030" (.76 mm) oversize.

Fig. 6: Reaming Valve Guides

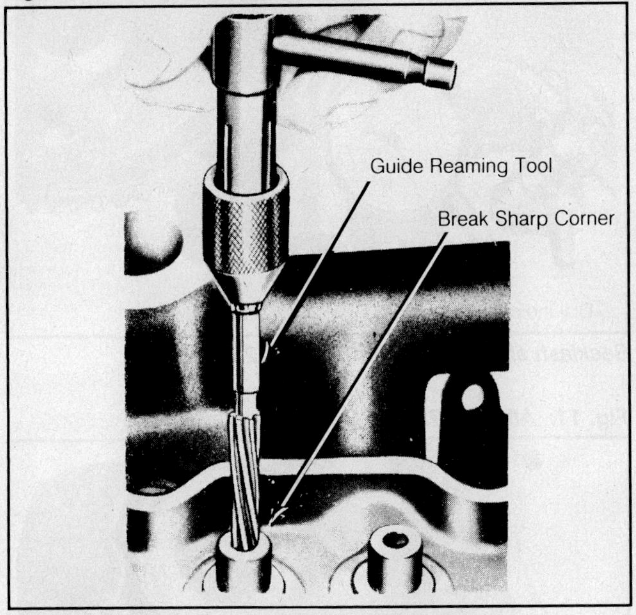

Always use reamers in proper size sequence.

HYDRAULIC VALVE LIFTERS

1) Lifters should be serviced as complete assemblies only. Lifters must be disassembled and cleaned prior to testing, and must be tested using hydraulic lifter testing fluid. Test cannot be performed with engine oil in lifters. Lifter components are select fit and are not interchangeable. *See Fig. 7.*

Fig. 7: Hydraulic Lifter Assembly

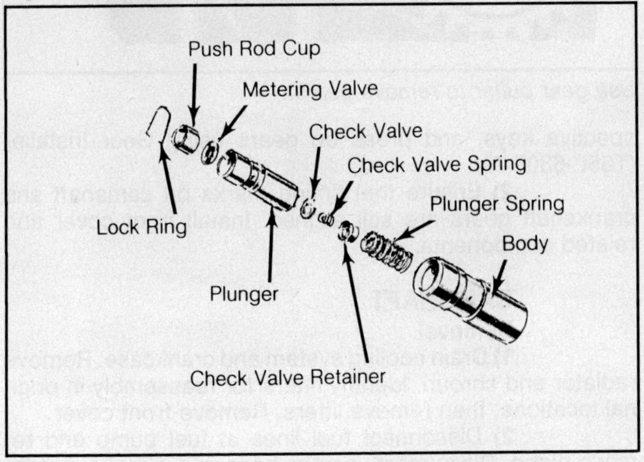

Do not interchange components between lifters.

2) Leak-down rate on all lifters is 10-50 seconds at 1/16" (1.6 mm) plunger travel, using lifter leak-down tester. Specification is for amount of time required for plunger to leak-down under 50 lb. load with testing fluid in lifter. Replace lifter assembly if range specified is exceeded.

VALVE CLEARANCE ADJUSTMENT

1) Positive stop rocker arm bolts are used to eliminate valve clearance adjustments. Valve stem-to-rocker arm clearance is measured with lifter collapsed. To obtain correct valve clearance after machine work is done, .060" (1.52 mm) undersize or .060" (1.52 mm) oversize push rod may be used.

2) With ignition switch in "OFF" position, use remote starter switch to turn crankshaft. Rotate crankshaft until No. 1 piston is at TDC of compression stroke. Mark timing mark on vibration damper with chalk, then make 2 additional chalk marks on vibration damper, spaced approximately 120° apart. *See Fig. 8.*

Fig. 8: Marking Vibration Damper for Valve Clearance Adjustment

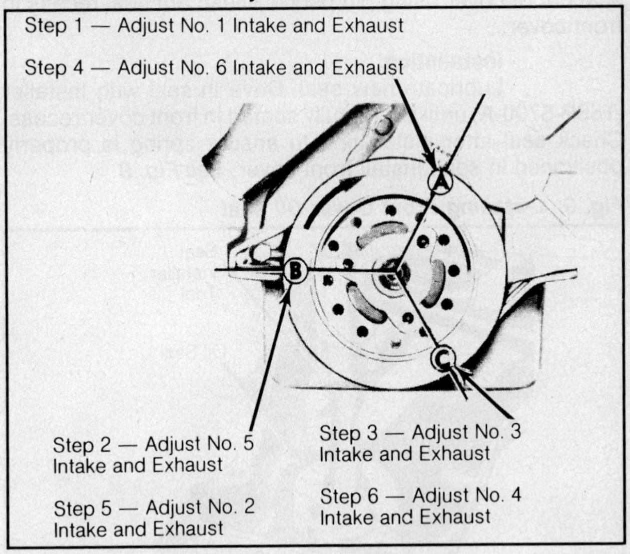

Space chalk marks approximately 120° apart.

3) Slowly collapse lifter plunger until completely bottomed, using Lifter Compressor (T70P-6513-A). While maintaining pressure on lifter, use feeler gauge to check clearance between rocker arm and valve stem tip. Desired clearance is .125-.175" (3.18-4.45 mm). Allowable range is .100-.200" (2.54-5.08 mm).

4) If clearance is less than specifications, install shorter push rod. If clearance is greater than specifications, install longer push rod. Rotate crankshaft 120° (in direction of normal rotation) to adjust next set of valves in firing order sequence. Firing order is 1-5-3-6-2-4. Repeat procedure for remaining valves.

CAMSHAFT

ENGINE FRONT COVER

Removal

1) Drain crankcase and cooling system. Remove radiator and shroud. Remove alternator adjusting arm bolt, and swing arm to side.

2) Remove fan, drive belts, spacer and pulleys. Remove vibration damper. Remove oil pan front bolts and front cover attaching bolts. Remove front cover and gasket.

Installation

1) Cut front oil pan seal flush with cylinder block/pan junction. Remove seal. Clean all gasket mating surfaces. Cut and fit new pan seal. Seal must fit flush with cylinder block/pan junction.

4.9 LITER 6-CYLINDER (Cont.)

2) Coat cylinder block and front cover gasket surfaces with oil resistant sealer. Install front cover gasket. Apply silicone sealer to junction of block and pan. Lubricate front cover oil seal.

3) Position front cover in place. Start front cover and pan attaching bolts. Slide Front Cover Aligner (T68P-6019-A) over crankshaft and into seal bore.

4) Install alternator adjusting arm. Tighten the oil pan bolts first, then tighten front cover bolts. Remove the aligner. Reverse removal procedure to complete installation.

FRONT COVER OIL SEAL

Removal

With front cover removed from engine, drive oil seal out of cover using pin punch. Clean out seal recess in front cover.

Installation

Lubricate new seal. Drive in seal with Installer (T68P-6700-A) until seal is fully seated in front cover recess. Check seal after installation to ensure spring is properly positioned in seal. Install front cover. *See Fig. 9.*

Fig. 9: Installing Front Cover Oil Seal

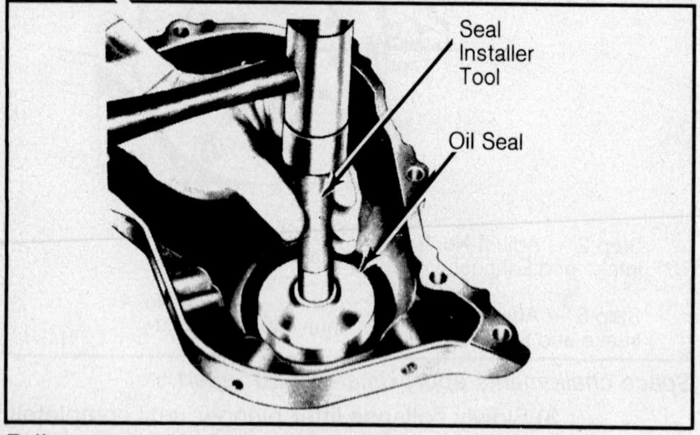

Fully seat seal in front cover recess.

TIMING GEARS

CAUTION: To avoid possible damage to valve train, never rotate camshaft or crankshaft unless timing gears are installed.

Checking Gear Backlash

1) Remove engine front cover. Make 6 chalk marks on camshaft gear, about 60° apart. Attach dial indicator to front of cylinder block. *See Fig. 10.*

Fig. 10: Checking Timing Gear Backlash

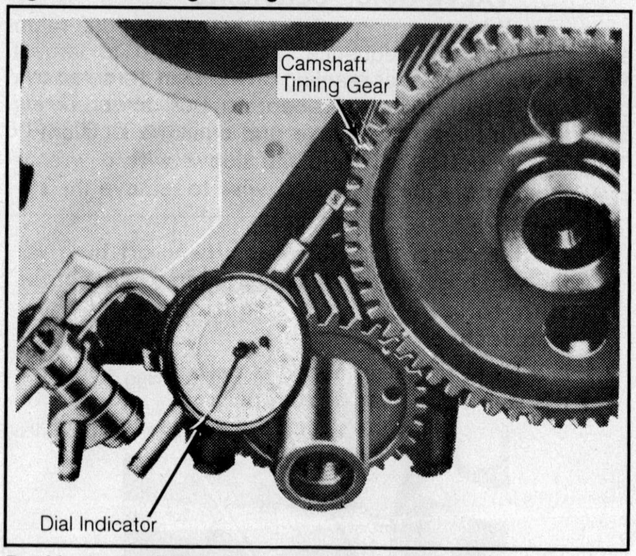

Backlash should be .004-.010 (.10-.25 mm).

2) Using dial indicator to measure amount of gear backlash, take measurements at each of 6 chalk marks on camshaft gear.

3) To obtain an accurate reading, hold gear firmly against block. Backlash should be .004-.010" (.10-.25 mm). If any reading is not within limits, replace timing gears as set.

Removal

Drain cooling system and crankcase. Remove engine front cover and oil slinger. Align camshaft and crankshaft gear timing marks. *See Fig. 11.* Use gear puller to remove camshaft and crankshaft gears.

Fig. 11: Aligning Timing Marks

Use gear puller to remove gears.

Installation

1) Ensure camshaft key spacer and thrust plate are correctly installed. Align both gear keyways with respective keys, and press on gears using Gear Installer (T65L-6306-A).

2) Ensure that timing marks on camshaft and crankshaft gears are still aligned. Install front cover and related components.

CAMSHAFT

Removal

1) Drain cooling system and crankcase. Remove radiator and shroud. Identify lifters for reassembly in original locations, then remove lifters. Remove front cover.

2) Disconnect fuel lines at fuel pump and remove pump. Disconnect vacuum hose and wires to distributor, and remove distributor.

3) Turn crankshaft to align gear timing marks. Remove camshaft thrust plate bolts, gear, key, thrust plate and spacer. Remove camshaft, taking care not to damage camshaft lobes or bearings.

4.9 LITER 6-CYLINDER (Cont.)

Installation

1) Coat camshaft lobes with polyethylene grease and coat journals with engine oil. Assemble key, spacer and thrust plate to camshaft. Align gear keyway with key and install gear.

2) Install the camshaft, gear and thrust plate as an assembly. With timing marks aligned, tighten thrust plate attaching bolts. Replace front cover oil seal. Reverse removal procedure to complete installation, using new gaskets.

Fig. 12: Camshaft Assembly

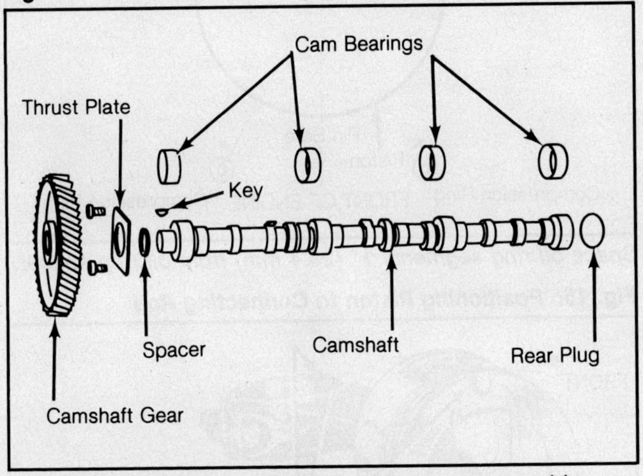

Install camshaft, gear and thrust plate as an assembly.

CAMSHAFT END PLAY

1) Remove engine front cover. Loosen rocker arms. Push camshaft rearward into engine. Install dial indicator with point positioned on camshaft gear retaining bolt. Zero dial indicator.

2) Place large screwdriver between camshaft gear and block. Pull camshaft forward and then release. Replace thrust plate if dial indicator reading is not within limits.

CAM LOBE LIFT

1) Remove rocker arm cover, rocker arm bolt, fulcrum seat and rocker arm. Ensure push rod end is in valve lifter socket. Install remote starter switch. Use dial indicator to check lobe lift in consecutive order.

2) Position dial indicator and cup-shaped adapter on end of push rod (in same plane as push rod movement). *See Fig. 13.*

3) Rotate crankshaft until lifter and push rod are at lowest position. Zero dial indicator. Rotate crankshaft slowly until push rod is in fully raised position. Record dial indicator reading and compare with specifications.

4) Maximum allowable lift loss is .005" (.127 mm). If lift on any lobe is below specifications, replace camshaft and valve lifters.

CAMSHAFT BEARINGS

Removal

1) Remove engine from vehicle and remove flywheel. Remove camshaft and rear cam bearing plug. Remove crankshaft.

2) Push pistons to top of cylinders. Using Camshaft Bearing Remover/Installer (T65L-6250-A), drive out camshaft bearings.

Fig. 13: Checking Camshaft Lobe Lift

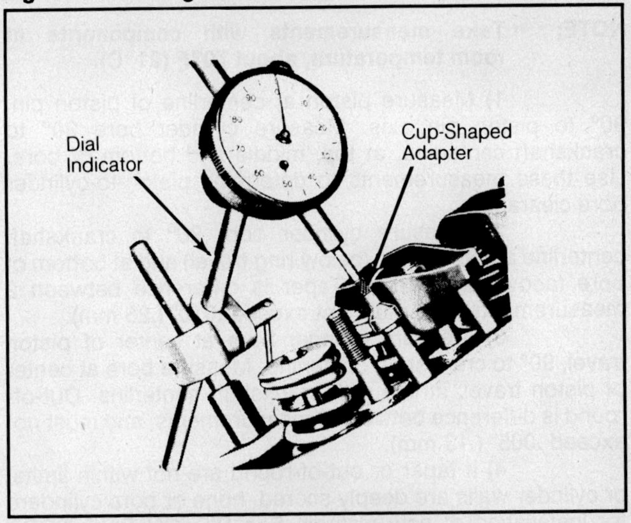

Ensure push rod is in valve lifter socket.

Installation

1) Using bearing installer, install new bearings. Ensure oil holes in bearings align with oil holes in cylinder block.

2) Install front bearing so distance of .020-.035" (.51-.64 mm) exists between front edge of bearing and face of cylinder block.

PISTONS, RINGS & PINS

OIL PAN

See OIL PAN REMOVAL at end of ENGINE section.

PISTON & ROD ASSEMBLY

Removal

1) Remove cylinder head, oil pan and oil pump. Turn crankshaft until piston to be removed is at bottom of stroke. Place cloth over piston to collect metal cuttings.

2) Using ridge reamer, remove ridge and deposits from upper end of cylinder bore. Never cut into ring travel area in excess of 1/32" when removing ridge. Ensure all connecting rod caps are marked for cylinder identification. Remove connecting rod cap.

3) Using wooden hammer handle, push connecting rod and piston out top of cylinder. Avoid damage to crankshaft journal or cylinder wall, when removing piston and rod.

Installation

1) Properly install piston rings. *See Fig. 14.* Oil piston, rings and cylinder wall with light engine oil. Install ring compressor on piston, ensuring ring location does not change.

2) Place rod journal at bottom of its stroke. Place piston into cylinder bore, with notch on top of piston toward front of engine. Tap piston into cylinder bore, using wooden hammer handle.

3) Carefully guide rod over crankshaft journal, until it seats on journal. Install and tighten rod cap. Check rod side play.

Ford Engines

4.9 LITER 6-CYLINDER (Cont.)

FITTING PISTONS

NOTE: Take measurements with components at room temperature, about 70°F (21°C).

1) Measure piston at centerline of piston pin, 90° to piston pin axis. Measure cylinder bore 90° to crankshaft centerline, at top, middle and bottom of bore. Use these measurements to determine piston-to-cylinder bore clearance.

2) Measure cylinder bore 90° to crankshaft centerline at top of bore (below ring travel) and at bottom of bore (above ring travel). Taper is difference between 2 measurements, and must not exceed .010" (.25 mm).

3) Measure cylinder bore at center of piston travel, 90° to crankshaft centerline. Measure bore at center of piston travel, in line with crankshaft centerline. Out-of-round is difference between 2 measurements, and must not exceed .005" (.13 mm).

4) If taper or out-of-round are not within limits, or cylinder walls are deeply scored, hone or bore cylinders for installation of new pistons. See PISTON SIZE CODE chart.

5) If bore diameter is in lower third of range, Red piston should be used. In middle third of range, Blue piston should be used. For upper third of range, Yellow or .003" (stamped on dome) piston should be used.

PISTON SIZE CODE

Size Code	Piston Diameter In. (mm)
Red	3.9982-3.9988 (101.554-101.570)
Blue	3.9994-4.0000 (101.585-101.600)
Yellow (.003")	4.0008-4.0014 (101.620-101.636)

FITTING RINGS

1) Position ring in cylinder bore at point where normal ring wear is not present. Exercise care not to damage ring or cylinder bore. Ring must be square in bore. Check ring end gap with feeler gauge.

2) Check side clearance of compression rings, with feeler gauge inserted between ring and its lower land. Feeler gauge should slide freely around entire circumference of piston without binding.

3) Properly install rings on piston. Space end gaps of oil ring segments 1" (25.4 mm) on either side of oil ring spacer end gap. *See Fig. 14.*

PISTON PIN REPLACEMENT

Removal

Use press and Pin Remover/Installer (T68P-6135-A) to remove piston pin from piston and connecting rod.

Installation

1) Lightly coat parts to be assembled with engine oil. Position piston and connecting rod as shown. *See Fig. 15.*

2) When properly assembled, notch on piston head will face toward front of engine, and bearing tang side of connecting rod will be positioned toward camshaft (left) side of engine.

3) Start piston pin in piston and connecting rod. Using press and Pin Remover/Installer (T68P-6135-A),

Fig. 14: Correctly Spaced Piston Rings

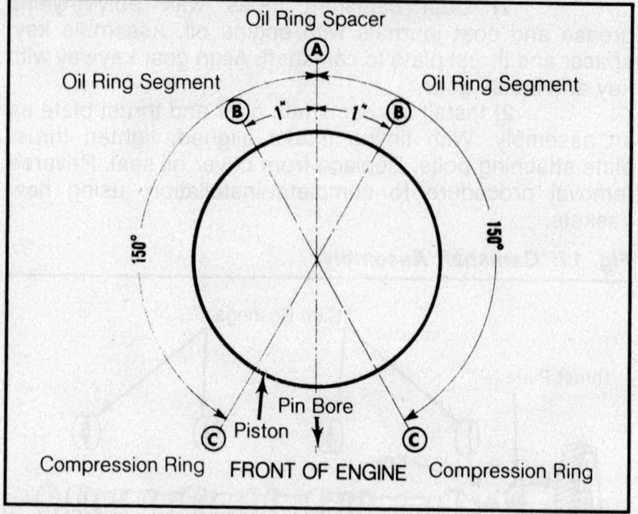

Space oil ring segments 1" (25.4 mm) from oil ring spacer.

Fig. 15: Positioning Piston to Connecting Rod

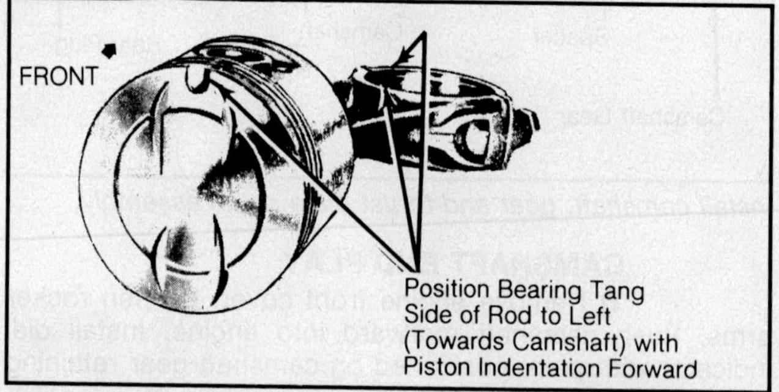

Press in piston pin until centered in connecting rod.

push piston pin through piston until pin is centered in connecting rod. Ensure piston floats freely throughout press operation.

CRANKSHAFT & ROD BEARINGS

CONNECTING ROD BEARINGS

NOTE: Use Plastigage method for checking bearing clearances. Perform following procedures with oil pan and oil pump removed. Remove oil film from surfaces to be checked.

1) Ensure rod caps are marked for cylinder identification. Place crankshaft journal of cylinder to be checked at bottom of its stroke. Remove rod cap.

2) Clean crankshaft and bearings. Measure clearance using Plastigage method. Standard bearing may be used in combination with .001" (.025 mm) or .002" (.051 mm) undersize bearing to obtain proper bearing clearance. Try to obtain minimum specified clearance.

3) Install upper bearing in rod and pull rod down until bearing seats fully on journal. Install other bearing in rod cap. Install cap and tighten. Check rod side clearance.

MAIN BEARINGS

1) Fit main bearings individually, leaving other bearings securely fastened. Ensure main bearing caps are marked for identification.

4.9 LITER 6-CYLINDER (Cont.)

2) Remove main bearing cap. Support crankshaft weight by placing jack under counterweight adjacent to bearing being checked.

3) Use Plastigage method to measure bearing clearance. Standard size bearings may be used in combination with .001" (.025 mm) or .002" (.051 mm) undersize bearing.

4) If .002" (.051 mm) undersize main bearings are used on more than one journal, install them on cylinder block side of crankshaft.

NOTE: To replace rear main bearing, engine must be removed from vehicle.

5) Replace each main bearing set individually. Loosen all main bearing caps until they are finger tight. This will make it easier to remove and install upper bearings. Remove bearing cap to which new bearings are to be installed.

6) Insert Upper Bearing Remover/Installer (6331-E) into crankshaft journal oil hole. Turn crankshaft in direction of normal rotation to push upper bearing out of block.

NOTE: Upper and lower bearing halves are not interchangeable. Upper half is drilled and grooved to provide entry of oil.

7) Lightly oil bearing and journal surfaces. Partially install plain end of upper bearing in place. Insert Upper Bearing Remover/Installer (6331-E) into journal oil hole.

8) Turn crankshaft slowly in opposite direction of normal rotation until bearing is seated. Remove bearing remover/installer. Install and tighten main bearing cap.

THRUST BEARING ALIGNMENT

1) Install thrust bearing cap after all other main caps have been tightened. Install thrust bearing cap bolts finger tight.

2) Pry crankshaft forward against thrust surface of upper half of bearing. Hold crankshaft forward and pry thrust bearing cap to rear. Tighten cap bolts, while holding forward pressure on crankshaft. *See Fig. 16.*

REAR MAIN BEARING OIL SEAL

NOTE: Seal may be replaced without removing crankshaft from engine.

Removal

1) Remove starter and transmission. Remove pressure plate and clutch disc (if equipped). Remove flywheel and engine rear cover plate. Using an awl, punch hole in oil seal metal surface between lip and block.

2) Screw threaded slide hammer end into hole and remove seal. Use care not to damage crankshaft oil seal surface. Clean oil seal recess in block and main bearing cap.

Installation

1) Inspect and clean crankshaft surface. Lightly coat crankshaft and new oil seal with engine oil. Start seal in place with lip facing forward. Use Seal Installer (T65P-6701-A) to drive in seal.

2) Keep installer straight in respect to centerline of crankshaft. Seal is properly installed when installer contacts cylinder block. Coat threads of flywheel bolts with oil resisting sealer. Reverse removal procedure to complete installation.

ENGINE OILING

Oil supply from pan is forced through lubrication system by rotor oil pump. Oil flows through full-flow oil filter, which routes oil into main oil gallery.

Oil gallery supplies oil to all internal engine bearings and lifters. Oil from lifters is forced through push rods to lubricate upper valve train area. Timing gears and chain are lubricated by splash method. *See Fig. 17.*

CRANKCASE CAPACITY

Crankcase capacity is 5 quarts (4.75L). Add 1 quart (.95L) when replacing oil filter.

OIL FILTER

Full-flow filter has an integral by-pass valve. Anti-drain back feature prevents reverse flow of oil when engine is shut down. Replace filter at first oil change, then every second oil change thereafter.

NORMAL OIL PRESSURE

Normal oil pressure is 40-60 psi (2.8-4.2 kg/cm^2) at 2000 RPM.

OIL PRESSURE REGULATOR VALVE

Oil pressure regulator valve is located in pump body, and is not adjustable.

Fig. 16: Aligning Thrust Bearing

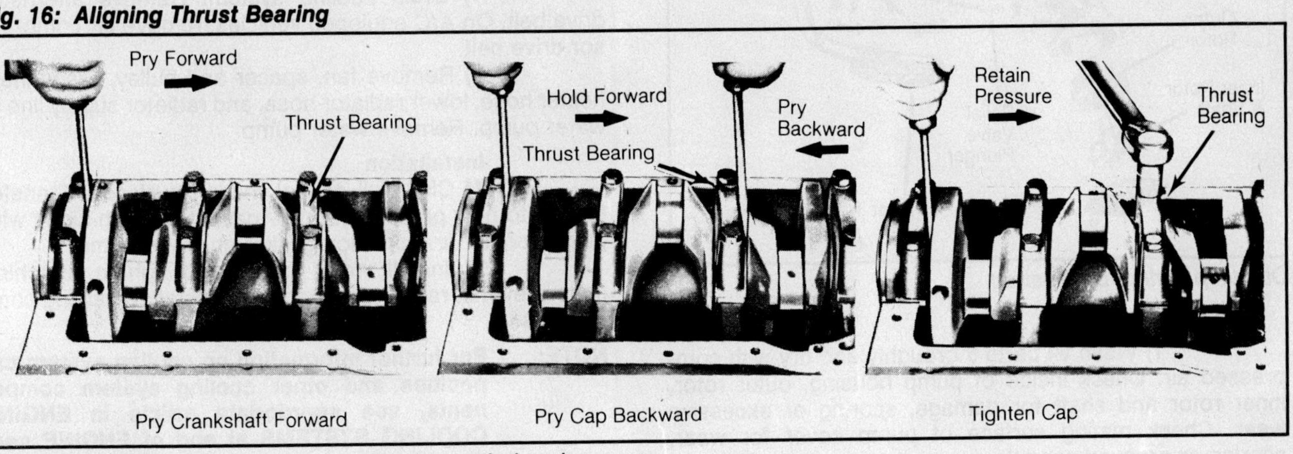

Align thrust bearing after tightening all other main bearing caps.

Ford Engines

4.9 LITER 6-CYLINDER (Cont.)

Fig. 17: Engine Oiling System

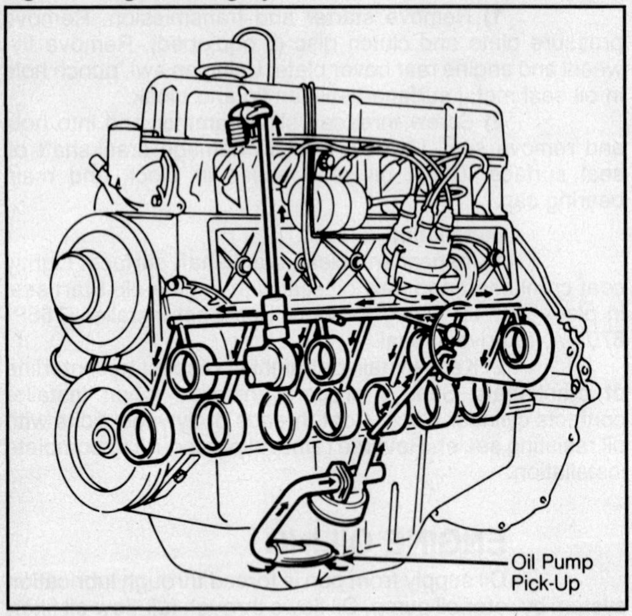

OIL PUMP

NOTE: **Pump cannot be repaired. Replace complete pump assembly if any part requires replacement.**

Removal

Remove oil pan. Remove nut securing oil pump inlet tube bracket to engine, and remove oil pump attaching bolts. Remove oil pump assembly.

Disassembly

1) Remove oil inlet tube. Remove cover attaching bolts and cover. Remove inner rotor and shaft and outer rotor.

2) Drill small hole into oil pressure relief valve cap. Insert self-threading sheet metal screw into cap, and pull cap from chamber. Remove spring and plunger. *See Fig. 18.*

Fig. 18: Oil Pump Assembly

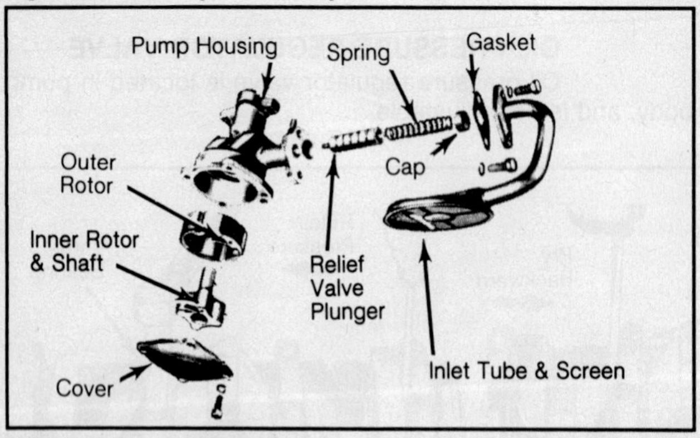

Oil pump cannot be repaired.

Inspection

1) Wash all parts thoroughly and dry with compressed air. Check inside of pump housing, outer rotor, inner rotor and shaft for damage, scoring or excessive wear. Check mating surface of pump cover for wear, scoring or grooved condition.

2) Remove rotor assembly from pump housing and place on flat surface. Using feeler gauge inserted to 1/2" minimum depth, measure inner to outer rotor tip clearance. Install rotor assembly in pump housing. Lay straightedge over rotor assembly and housing. Insert feeler gauge between straightedge and housing to measure rotor end play.

3) Measure outer rotor-to-housing clearance using feeler gauge. Measure shaft outside diameter and housing bearing inside diameter. Difference between readings is shaft-to-housing bearing clearance.

4) Relief valve spring should test to 20.6-22.6 lbs. (9-10 kg) at 2.49" (63.2 mm). Inspect relief valve spring for worn or collapsed condition.

5) Check relief valve plunger for scoring. Ensure plunger moves freely in bore. Check clearance between relief valve plunger and bore.

OIL PUMP SPECIFICATIONS

Application	Specification In. (mm)
Rotor Tip Clearance	.012 (.31) Max.
Rotor End Play	.004 (.10) Max.
Outer Rotor-to-Housing Clearance	.001-.013 (.03-.33)
Shaft-to-Housing Clearance	.0015-.0030 (.038-.076)
Relief Valve-to-Bore Clearance	.0015-.0030 (.038-.076)

Reassembly

Clean and oil parts thoroughly. Install relief valve plunger, spring and new cap. Stake cap into position. Reassemble remaining components in reverse order of disassembly, using new gasket for oil inlet tube.

Installation

Prime oil pump by filling inlet opening with oil and rotating pump shaft until oil emerges from outlet opening. Install and tighten oil pump to cylinder block.

ENGINE COOLING

WATER PUMP

Removal

1) Drain cooling system. Remove alternator drive belt. On A/C equipped vehicles, remove air compressor drive belt.

2) Remove fan, spacer and pulley. Disconnect heater hose, lower radiator hose, and radiator supply line at water pump. Remove water pump.

Installation

1) Clean all gasket mating surfaces. Transfer fittings to new pump. Coat new gasket on both sides with gasket sealer and position gasket on water pump.

2) Install water pump and tighten attaching bolts. Reverse removal procedure to install remaining components.

NOTE: **For further information on cooling system capacities and other cooling system components, see appropriate article in ENGINE COOLING SYSTEMS at end of ENGINE section.**

Ford Engines

4.9 LITER 6-CYLINDER (Cont.)

ENGINE SPECIFICATIONS

GENERAL SPECIFICATIONS

Year	DISPLACEMENT		Fuel System	HP@RPM	Torque Ft. Lbs.@RPM	Compr. Ratio	BORE		STROKE	
	Cu. In.	Liters					In.	mm	In.	mm
1985	300	4.9	1-Bbl.	120 @ 3200 [1]	245 @ 1600 [2]	8.4:1	4.00	101.6	3.98	101.1

[1] – Horsepower rating ranges from 118 HP at 3000 RPM to 125 HP at 3400 RPM, depending upon model application.
[2] – Torque rating ranges from 230 ft. lbs. at 2000 RPM to 258 ft. lbs. at 1400 RPM, depending upon model application.

VALVES

Engine Size & Valve	Head Diam. In. (mm)	Face Angle	Seat Angle	Seat Width In. (mm)	Stem Diameter In. (mm)	Stem Clearance In. (mm)	Valve Lift In. (mm)
4.9L							
Intake	1.769-1.793 (44.93-45.54)	44°	45°	.060-.080 (1.52-2.03)	.3416-.3423 (8.68-8.69)	.0010-.0027 (.025-.069)	.403 (10.24)
Exhaust	1.551-1.569 (39.40-39.85)	44°	45°	.070-.090 (1.78-2.29)	.3416-.3423 (8.68-8.69)	.0010-.0027 (.025-.069)	.403 (10.24)

PISTONS, PINS, RINGS

Engine	PISTONS	PINS		RINGS		
	Clearance In. (mm)	Piston Fit In. (mm)	Rod Fit In. (mm)	Ring No.	End Gap In. (mm)	Side Clearance In. (mm)
4.9L	.0010-.0018 (.025-.046)	.0003-.0005 (.008-.013)	Interference Fit	1	.010-.020 (.25-.51)	.0019-.0036 (.048-.091)
				2	.010-.020 (.25-.51)	.002-.004 (.05-.10)
				Oil	.015-.055 (.38-.1.40)	Snug Fit

CRANKSHAFT MAIN & CONNECTING ROD BEARINGS

Engine	MAIN BEARINGS				CONNECTING ROD BEARINGS		
	Journal Diam. In. (mm)	Clearance In. (mm)	Thrust Bearing	Crankshaft End Play In. (mm)	Journal Diam. In. (mm)	Clearance In. (mm)	Side Play In. (mm)
4.9L	2.3982-2.3990 (60.914-60.935)	.0008-.0015 (.020-.038)	No. 5	.004-.008 (.10-.20)	2.1228-2.1236 (53.919-53.939)	.0008-.0015 (.020-.038)	.006-.013 (.15-.33)

4.9 LITER 6-CYLINDER (Cont.)

ENGINE SPECIFICATIONS (Cont.)

VALVE SPRINGS

Engine	Free Length In. (mm)	PRESSURE Lbs. @ In. (Kg @ mm) Valve Closed	Valve Open
4.9L			
Intake	1.97 (50.0)	66-74@1.64 (30-34@41.7)	166-184@1.24 (75-83@31.5)
Exhaust	1.78 (45.2)	66-74@1.47 (30-34@37.3)	166-184@1.07 (75-83@27.2)

CAMSHAFT

Engine	Journal Diam. In. (mm)	Clearance In. (mm)	Lobe Lift In. (mm)
4.9L	2.017-2.018 [1] (51.23-51.26)	.001-.003 (.03-.08)	.247-.249 (6.27-6.32)

[1] – Camshaft end play is .001-.007" (.03-.18 mm).

TIGHTENING SPECIFICATIONS

Application	Ft. Lbs. (N.m)
Camshaft Thrust Plate Bolt	12-18 (17-24)
Connecting Rod Cap Nut	40-45 (54-61)
Cylinder Head Bolt	
Step 1	50-55 (67-75)
Step 2	60-65 (82-88)
Step 3	70-85 (94-115)
Flywheel-to-Crankshaft Bolt	75-85 (102-115)
Front Cover Bolt	12-18 (17-24)
Intake-to-Exhaust Manifold Nut	22-32 (30-43)
Main Bearing Cap Bolt	60-70 (81-95)
Manifolds-to-Cylinder Head Bolt	22-32 (30-43)
Oil Filter Adapter Bolt	40-50 (54-68)
Oil Pan Bolt	10-12 (14-17)
Oil Pump Attaching Bolt	10-15 (14-20)
Rocker Arm Bolt	17-23 (23-31)
Vibration Damper Bolt	130-150 (176-203)
Water Pump Bolt	12-18 (17-24)

Ford Engines

5.0 & 5.8 LITER V8

ENGINE CODING

ENGINE IDENTIFICATION

The eighth character of Vehicle Identification Number (VIN) identifies engine. The VIN is stamped on a metal tab attached to left upper side of instrument panel, near windshield. The VIN is also found on the Safety Compliance Certification Label on left door lock pillar.

ENGINE IDENTIFICATION CODES

Engine	Code
5.0L 2-Bbl.	F
5.0L EFI	N
5.8L 2-Bbl.	G
5.8L 4-Bbl.	H

ENGINE REMOVAL

See ENGINE REMOVAL at end of ENGINE section.

MANIFOLDS & CYLINDER HEAD

INTAKE MANIFOLD

Removal (Carbureted Models)

1) Drain cooling system. Remove air cleaner, intake duct assembly and crankcase ventilation hose. Disconnect accelerator cable, speed control linkage and transmission kickdown rod from carburetor. Remove accelerator cable bracket.

2) Disconnect electric choke and carburetor solenoid wires. Disconnect primary and secondary wires from coil. Disconnect spark plug wires from plugs. Remove distributor cap and wires as an assembly. Remove fuel line at carburetor. Disconnect fuel evaporation hoses.

3) Disconnect vacuum hoses at distributor and remove distributor. Disconnect upper radiator hose, by-pass hose and heater hose from intake manifold. Disconnect temperature sending unit wire. Remove intake manifold and carburetor as an assembly. Remove and discard gaskets and seals. Discard bolt sealing washers.

NOTE: **Install manifold promptly after applying RTV sealer, as sealer sets up in 15 minutes.**

Installation (Carbureted Models)

1) Clean all gasket mating surfaces. Apply 1/8" bead of RTV sealer at 4 corners of cylinder block seal mounting surface-to-cylinder head junction. Apply 1/16" bead of RTV sealer to top of seal ends, across full width of seal. Position manifold gaskets and seals on engine.

2) Install and tighten manifold, taking care not to misalign seals and gaskets. *See Fig. 1.* To complete installation, reverse removal procedure. Retighten manifold bolts after engine has reached normal operating temperature.

Removal (EFI Models)

1) Disconnect negative battery cable. Drain cooling system. Disconnect electrical connectors at air by-pass valve, throttle position sensor and EGR position sensor. Disconnect throttle linkage at throttle ball.

2) Disconnect automatic overdrive linkage from throttle body. Remove throttle bracket, with cables attached, from intake manifold. Disconnect and label all

Fig. 1: Intake Manifold Tightening Sequence

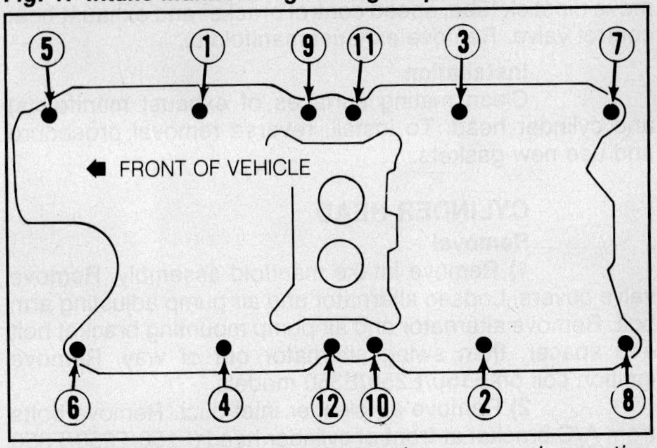

Retighten manifold after running engine to normal operating temperature.

vacuum lines. Disconnect PCV valve and hose from intake manifold.

3) Remove canister purge lines from throttle body. Disconnect EGR tube from EGR valve at flange nut. Remove upper intake manifold support bracket. Remove 6 upper intake manifold mounting bolts. Remove upper intake manifold.

4) Disconnect spark plug wires at spark plugs. Remove distributor cap and wires as an assembly. Mark distributor and rotor positions. Remove distributor. Disconnect electrical connections at engine coolant temperature (ECT) sensor, engine temperature sending unit, air charge temperature (ACT) sensor and knock sensor.

5) Disconnect injector wiring harness. Locate and note position of plated stud and O_2 ground wire for installation. Remove O_2 ground wire from intake manifold stud. Disconnect fuel supply and return lines from fuel rails. Remove upper radiator hose.

6) Remove heater and by-pass hoses. Remove air cleaner bracket. Remove coil and set aside. Remove intake manifold bolts and studs. Remove lower intake manifold.

NOTE: **Plated stud and ground wire must be installed in same position from which it was removed.**

Installation (EFI Models)

1) Clean all gasket mating surfaces. Apply 1/8" bead of RTV sealer at 4 corners of cylinder block seal mounting surface-to-cylinder head junction. Apply 1/16" bead of RTV sealer to top of seal ends, across full width of seal. Position lower intake manifold gaskets and seals on engine.

2) Install 2 locator pins in opposite corners. Install and tighten lower manifold, taking care not to misalign seals and gaskets. Remove locator pins. To complete installation, reverse removal procedure. Retighten manifold bolts after engine has reached normal operating temperature.

EXHAUST MANIFOLD

Removal

1) Remove air cleaner and intake duct assembly. Remove crankcase ventilation hose. Remove bolts attaching air cleaner inlet duct (E150/E250/E350). Disconnect exhaust pipe(s). If equipped, remove exhaust manifold heat shield.

5.0 & 5.8 LITER V8 (Cont.)

2) If removing left side exhaust manifold, remove dipstick tube, speed control bracket and exhaust heat control valve. Remove exhaust manifold(s).

Installation

Clean mating surfaces of exhaust manifold(s) and cylinder head. To install, reverse removal procedure and use new gaskets.

CYLINDER HEAD

Removal

1) Remove intake manifold assembly. Remove valve covers. Loosen alternator and air pump adjusting arm bolt. Remove alternator and air pump mounting bracket bolt and spacer, then swing alternator out of way. Remove ignition coil on E150/E250/E350 models.

2) Remove air cleaner inlet duct. Remove bolts from A/C bracket at front of cylinder head (F150/F250/F350 and Bronco). Remove oil dipstick and tube. Remove speed control bracket (if equipped). Disconnect muffler inlet pipe from exhaust manifolds.

3) Loosen rocker arm fulcrum bolts, and rotate rocker arms to one side. Remove push rods in sequence, for later installation in original locations. Remove thermactor air supply manifold, supply hose and pump valve as an assembly (E150/E250/E350).

4) Disconnect thermactor air supply hoses at check valves (F150/F250/F350 and Bronco). Remove cylinder head.

NOTE: **Do not apply sealer to head gasket.**

Installation

1) Clean all gasket mating surfaces. Check cylinder head and block for flatness. Position new cylinder head gasket over dowel pins on block surface.

2) Position cylinder head on block and install head bolts. Tighten 5.8L head bolts in 3 steps. Tighten 5.0L head bolts in 2 steps. *See Fig. 2.*

Fig. 2: Cylinder Head Tightening Sequence

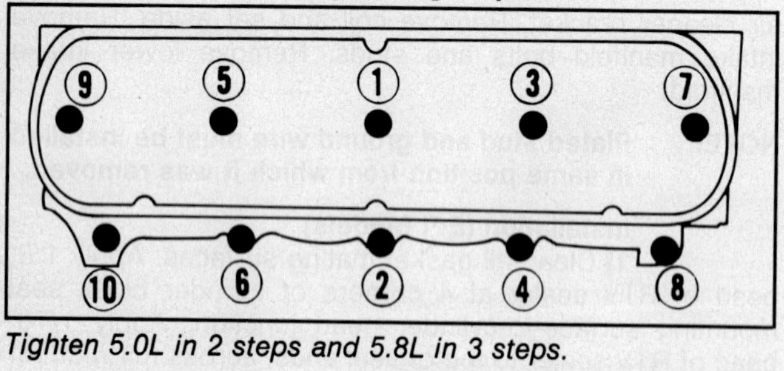

Tighten 5.0L in 2 steps and 5.8L in 3 steps.

3) Prior to their installation, lubricate push rod ends, valve stem tips, rocker arms and fulcrum seats with polyethelene grease. To complete installation, reverse removal procedure and use new gaskets.

VALVES

VALVE ARRANGEMENT

Right Bank – I-E-I-E-I-E-I-E (Front-to-rear).
Left Bank – E-I-E-I-E-I-E-I (Front-to-rear).

ROCKER ARM ASSEMBLY

Inspect fulcrum bolts, fulcrums, rocker arms and fulcrum guides for excessive wear. Replace worn parts. Coat rocker arm parts with polyethelene grease before installation. *See Fig. 3.*

Fig. 3: Rocker Arm Assembly

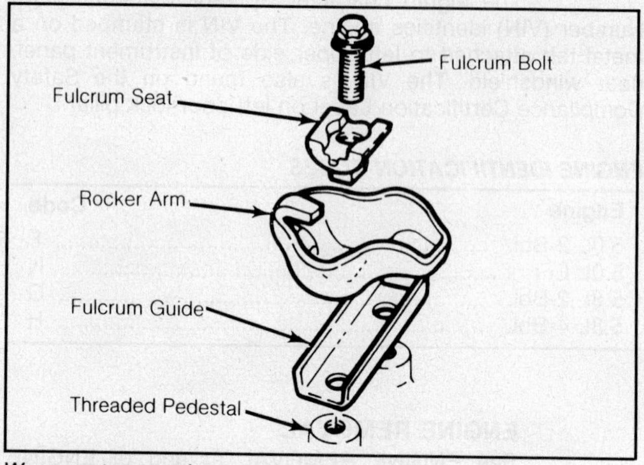

Worn parts must be replaced.

VALVE SPRINGS

Removal

1) Remove air cleaner and valve covers. Remove spark plug. Rotate crankshaft to bring piston to TDC on compression stroke. Remove rocker arm fulcrum bolt, fulcrum, rocker arm and push rod. Remove exhaust valve stem cap.

2) Install air hose and adapter into spark plug hole and apply air pressure to cylinder. Install fulcrum bolt for use with valve spring compressor. Compress valve spring and remove locks, retainer, sleeve and valve spring. Remove and discard oil seal. *See Fig. 4.*

NOTE: **Wrap rubber band or tape around valve stem end to prevent valve from falling into cylinder in case air pressure forces piston down.**

Fig. 4: Compressing Valve Spring

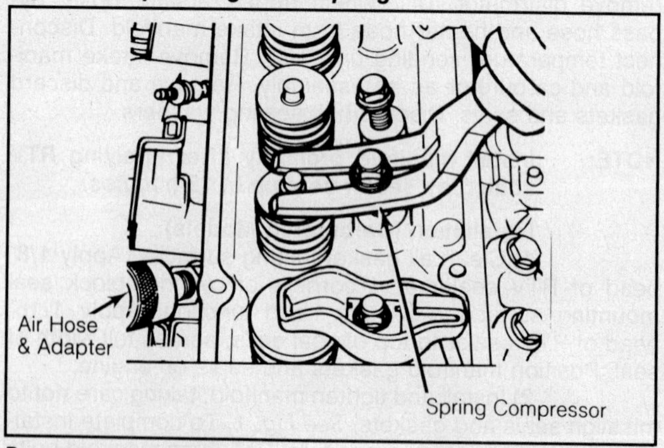

Do not remove air pressure from cylinder until valve components are reassembled.

Inspection

1) Inspect valve stem for wear and out-of-round. Check valve for binding in valve guide. Using valve spring tester, check springs for proper tension. Replace spring if tension is incorrect.

2) Inspect each spring for squareness using a steel square and flat surface. Replace spring if more than 5/64" (1.98 mm) out-of-square. *See Fig. 5.*

Fig. 5: Checking Valve Spring Squareness

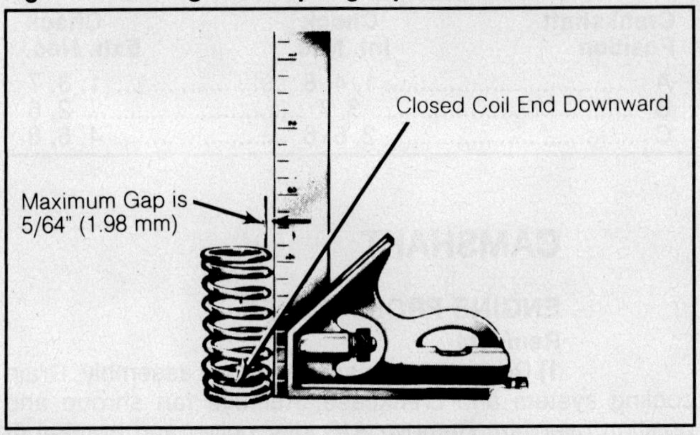

Measure gap between top of spring coil and square while slowly rotating spring.

Installation

1) Lubricate valve stem and install valve stem oil seal. Place spring in position over valve and install spring retainer and sleeve. Compress valve spring and install retainer locks. *See Fig. 6*. Remove valve spring compressor and fulcrum bolt.

Fig. 6: Exploded View of Valve Assemblies

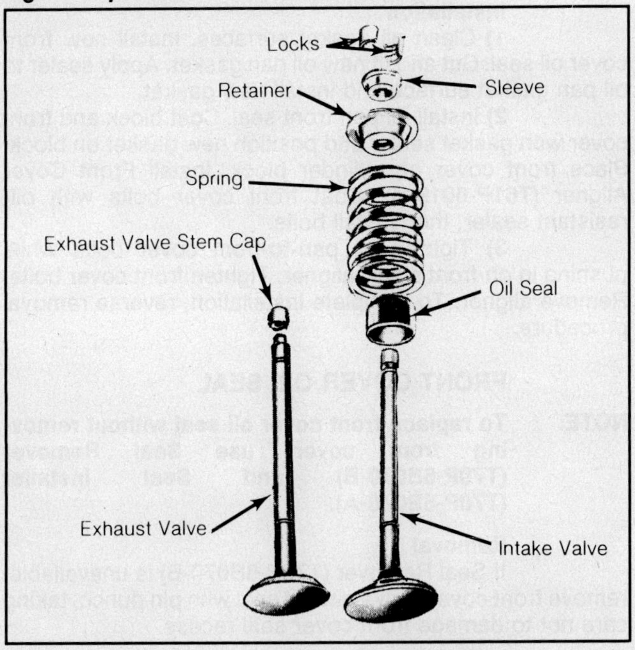

Lubricate valve components before assembly.

2) Apply polyethelene grease to push rod ends, valve stem tip, rocker arm and fulcrum before installation. Install valve stem caps on exhaust valves. Turn off air pressure and remove air hose and adapter. To complete installation, reverse removal procedure.

VALVE SPRING INSTALLED HEIGHT

CAUTION: Install spacers only if necessary. Excessive use of spacers will overstress the valve train.

1) Using dividers and a ruler, measure spring installed height from surface of cylinder head pad to underside of spring retainer. *See Fig. 7*.

2) If spring installed height is excessive, install .030" (.76 mm) spacer(s) between head and spring to bring spring installed height within limits.

Fig. 7: Checking Valve Spring Installed Height

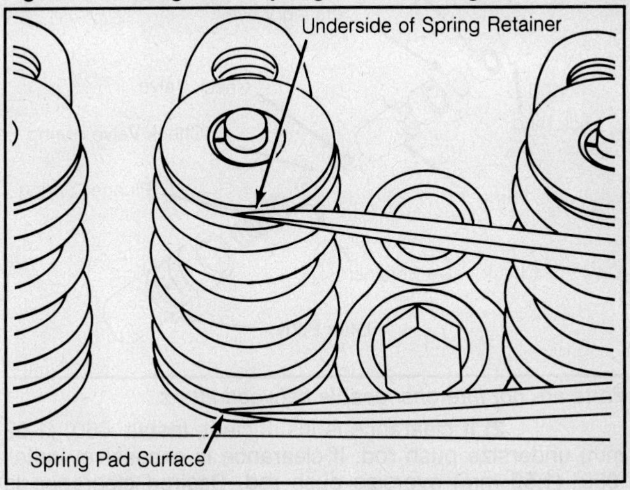

Install .030" (.76 mm) spacer(s) to correct spring height.

VALVE SPRING INSTALLED HEIGHT SPECIFICATIONS

Application	In. (mm)
5.0L	
Intake	1.672-1.703 (42.47-43.26)
Exhaust	1.578-1.609 (40.08-40.87)
5.8L	
Intake	1.766-1.797 (44.86-45.64)
Exhaust	1.578-1.609 (40.08-40.87)

VALVE STEM OIL SEALS

Cup-type oil seals are used on all valves. Lubricate valve stem with engine oil and install new valve stem seal with cup side down over valve guide. Use a 5/8" deep-well socket and mallet to drive oil seal onto valve stem.

VALVE GUIDE SERVICING

Always use reamers in proper sequence. Reface valve seat after valve guide is reamed. After reaming, use a scraper to break sharp corner at top inside diameter of valve guide bore. Oversize valves are available in .015" (.38 mm) and .030" (.76 mm).

HYDRAULIC VALVE LIFTERS

Service lifters as complete assemblies only. Lifter parts are select fit. DO NOT interchange parts between lifters. Disassemble lifters and clean thoroughly. Reassemble lifters and test with hydraulic lifter test fluid and lifter leak-down tester. Leak-down rate on hydraulic lifters is 10-50 seconds with .063" (1.60 mm) plunger travel. *See Fig. 8*.

VALVE CLEARANCE ADJUSTMENT

1) Slowly bleed down lifter plunger (until bottomed) using lifter compressor. With lifter plunger bottomed, use a feeler gauge to measure clearance between rocker arm and valve stem tip.

5.0 & 5.8 LITER V8 (Cont.)

Fig. 8: Hydraulic Lifter Assembly

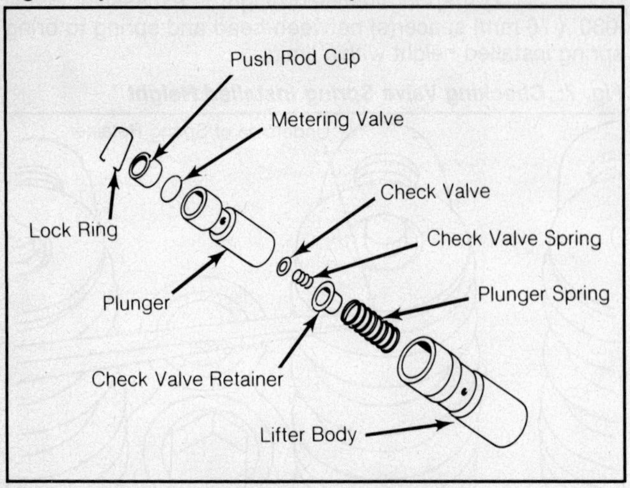

Parts are not interchangeable between lifters.

2) If clearance is insufficient, install .060" (1.52 mm) undersize push rod. If clearance is excessive, install .060" (1.52 mm) oversize push rod. Desired clearance is .125-.175" (3.18-4.45 mm).

3) Use a remote starter to rotate crankshaft with ignition off. Rotate crankshaft until No. 1 piston is at TDC on compression stroke. Using TDC timing mark on vibration damper for references "A" and "B". Rotate crankshaft 360° from mark "A" for reference mark "B". Make chalk mark "C" about 90° clockwise on vibration damper. *See Fig. 9.*

4) With crankshaft in positions as specified in VALVE CLEARANCE ADJUSTMENT tables, check valve clearance between rocker arm and valve stem tip.

Fig. 9: Marking Vibration Damper for Valve Clearance Adjustment

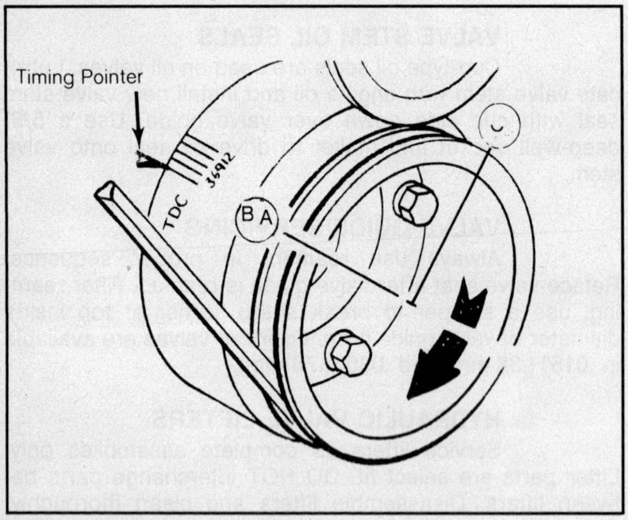

Space marks about 90° apart.

5.0L VALVE CLEARANCE ADJUSTMENT

Crankshaft Position	Check Int. Nos.	Check Exh. Nos.
A	1, 7, 8	1, 5, 4
B	5, 4	2, 6
C	2, 3, 6	7, 3, 8

5.8L VALVE CLEARANCE ADJUSTMENT

Crankshaft Position	Check Int. Nos.	Check Exh. Nos.
A	1, 4, 8	1, 3, 7
B	3, 7	2, 6
C	2, 5, 6	4, 5, 8

CAMSHAFT

ENGINE FRONT COVER

Removal

1) Remove air cleaner and duct assembly. Drain cooling system and crankcase. Remove fan shroud and position over fan. Remove A/C idler pulley and bracket (if equipped). Remove all hoses and brackets attached to water pump.

2) Remove radiator (E150/E250/E350). Remove all drive belts, fan, spacer, pulley and shroud. Remove crankshaft pulley and vibration damper. Remove fuel pump (except EFI).

3) Remove oil pan-to-front cover bolts. Remove front cover and water pump as an assembly. Cut oil pan gasket flush with cylinder block.

Installation

1) Clean all gasket surfaces. Install new front cover oil seal. Cut and fit new oil pan gasket. Apply sealer to oil pan gasket surface and install new gasket.

2) Install oil pan front seal. Coat block and front cover with gasket sealer and position new gasket on block. Place front cover on cylinder block. Install Front Cover Aligner (T61P-6019-B). Coat front cover bolts with oil-resistant sealer, then install bolts.

3) Tighten oil pan-to-front cover bolts while pushing in on front cover aligner. Tighten front cover bolts. Remove aligner. To complete installation, reverse removal procedure.

FRONT COVER OIL SEAL

NOTE: **To replace front cover oil seal without removing front cover, use Seal Remover (T70P-6B070-B) and Seal Installer (T70P-6B070-A).**

Removal

If Seal Remover (T70P-6B070-B) is unavailable, remove front cover. Drive out old seal with pin punch, taking care not to damage front cover seal recess.

Installation

Coat new seal with Lubriplate. Using seal installer, drive seal into front cover recess. Check that seal is fully seated and spring is properly positioned in seal. Install front cover.

TIMING CHAIN & SPROCKET

NOTE: **Perform following procedure with engine front cover removed.**

Checking Timing Chain Deflection

1) Turn crankshaft counterclockwise to take up slack on left side of timing chain. Establish a reference point on block and measure from this point to left side of chain. *See Fig. 10.*

5.0 & 5.8 LITER V8 (Cont.)

Fig. 10: Measuring Timing Chain Deflection

Maximum deflection is 1/2" (12.7 mm).

2) Rotate crankshaft clockwise to take up slack on right side of chain. Force left side of chain outward and measure distance between reference point and chain.

3) Deflection is difference between the 2 measurements. If deflection exceeds .50" (12.7 mm), replace timing chain and sprockets.

Removal

Rotate crankshaft until timing marks are aligned. *See Fig. 11.* Remove camshaft sprocket bolt, washers and fuel pump eccentric (except EFI). Remove both sprockets and timing chain as an assembly.

Installation

1) Position timing chain and sprockets with timing marks aligned and slide onto crankshaft and camshaft as an assembly.

2) Install fuel pump eccentric (except EFI), washers and camshaft sprocket bolt, and tighten bolt.

Fig. 11: Aligning Timing Marks

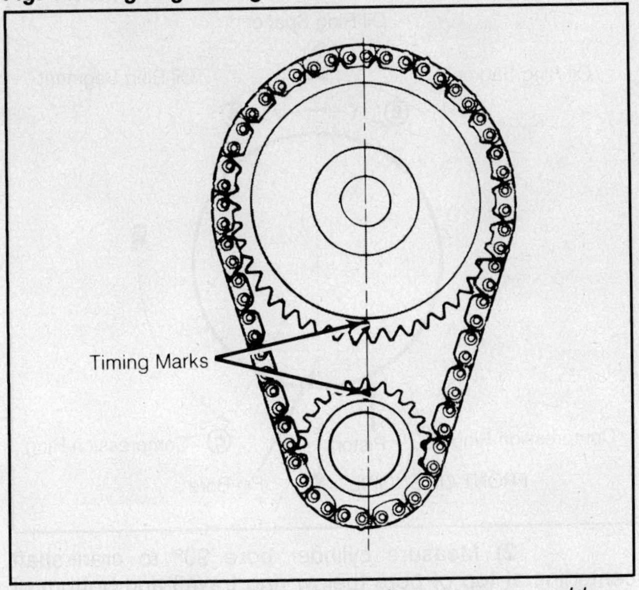

Remove and install chain and sprockets as an assembly.

Lubricate fuel pump eccentric, timing chain and sprockets with engine oil. Install front cover.

CAMSHAFT

Removal

1) Remove grille (E150/E250/E350). Drain cooling system and crankcase. Remove radiator, front cover, timing chain and sprockets. Remove intake manifold assembly.

2) Remove valve covers. Loosen rocker arm fulcrum bolts, and rotate rocker arms to one side. Remove push rods and valve lifters in sequence. Label for installation in their original locations.

3) Remove camshaft thrust plate and carefully pull camshaft out through front of engine. Use care to avoid damage to camshaft bearings and journals. *See Fig. 12.*

Fig. 12: Camshaft Assembly

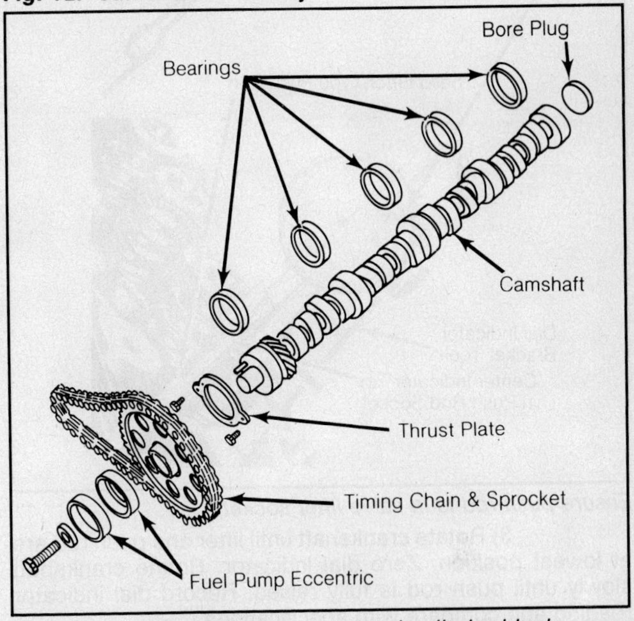

Install thrust plate with groove toward cylinder block.

Installation

1) Oil camshaft journals and apply polyethelene grease to lobes. Carefully slide camshaft into position. Coat camshaft thrust plate with engine oil, and install with groove toward cylinder block.

2) Lubricate lifters with engine oil and install. Lubricate rocker arms, fulcrum seats, valve stem tips and push rod ends with polyethelene grease before installing.

3) To complete installation, reverse removal procedure and use new gaskets. Check valve clearance.

CAMSHAFT END PLAY

CAUTION: Do not pry against camshaft sprocket without first relieving valve train load on camshaft.

1) Loosen rocker arm fulcrum bolts to relieve load on camshaft. Push camshaft toward rear of engine. Position dial indicator so pointer is on camshaft sprocket attaching bolt. Zero dial indicator.

2) Place a large screwdriver between camshaft sprocket and cylinder block. Pull camshaft forward and release. Camshaft end play should be .001-.007" (.03-.18 mm). If beyond limits, replace thrust plate.

CAM LOBE LIFT

1) Remove valve cover, fulcrum bolt, fulcrum seat, rocker arm and fulcrum guide. Ensure push rod end is in valve lifter socket. Install remote starter switch to rotate crankshaft.

2) Use a dial indicator to check lobe lift in consecutive order. Position dial indicator pointer (or cup-shaped adapter) on end of push rod (in same plane as push rod movement). *See Fig. 13.*

Fig. 13: Checking Camshaft Lobe Lift

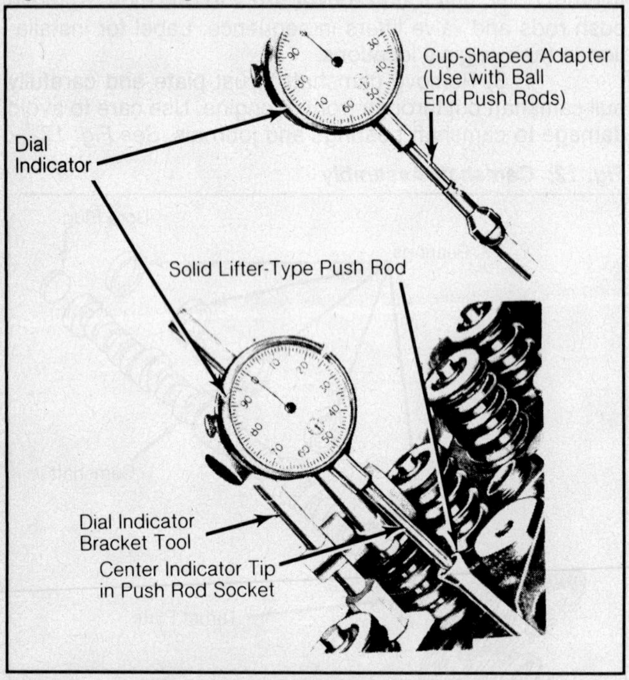

Ensure push rod is in valve lifter socket.

3) Rotate crankshaft until lifter and push rod are at lowest position. Zero dial indicator. Rotate crankshaft slowly until push rod is fully raised. Record dial indicator reading and compare with specifications.

4) Maximum allowable lift loss is .005" (.13 mm). If lift on any lobe is below specifications, replace camshaft and valve lifter(s) operating on worn lobe(s).

CAMSHAFT BEARINGS

NOTE: Camshaft bearings are not interchangeable from one bore to another.

Removal

1) Replace camshaft bearings with engine removed from vehicle. Remove camshaft, flywheel, crankshaft and rear bearing bore plug.

2) Push pistons to top of cylinders. Use camshaft bearing remover/installer, to remove camshaft bearings.

Installation

1) Using camshaft bearing remover/installer, install bearings into place. Ensure oil holes are properly aligned in each bore.

2) Install front bearing .005-.020" (.13-.51 mm) rearward of front face of cylinder block. Install new rear bearing bore plug.

PISTONS, RINGS & PINS

OIL PAN

See OIL PAN REMOVAL at end of ENGINE section.

PISTON & ROD ASSEMBLY

CAUTION: Never cut more than 1/32" (.79 mm) into ring travel area.

Removal

1) Remove cylinder head, oil pan and oil pump. Place piston at bottom of stroke and cover with a cloth to collect cuttings.

2) Use ridge reamer to remove any ridge or deposit on upper end of cylinder bore. Ensure connecting rods and caps are marked for cylinder identification.

3) Remove rod cap. Push piston and rod out top of cylinder bore. Use care not to damage crankshaft journal or cylinder wall. Install rod cap on mating rod.

Installation

1) Coat cylinder bore, piston and rings with engine oil. Ensure that ring gaps are properly spaced. *See Fig. 14*. Install a ring compressor on piston.

NOTE: Large chamfered side of rod bearing end must be positioned toward crankpin thrust face of crankshaft.

2) Install each piston and rod assembly in its respective bore, with arrow (or notch) on piston head facing front of engine. Guide connecting rod onto crankshaft journal until connecting rod bearing seats on crankshaft. Install and tighten rod caps.

FITTING PISTONS

NOTE: Take measurements with components at about 70°F (21°C).

1) Measure piston skirt 90° to piston pin axis. Measure cylinder bore 90° to crankshaft centerline, at top, middle and bottom of bore. Use measurements to determine piston-to-cylinder bore clearance.

Fig. 14: Correctly Spaced Piston Rings

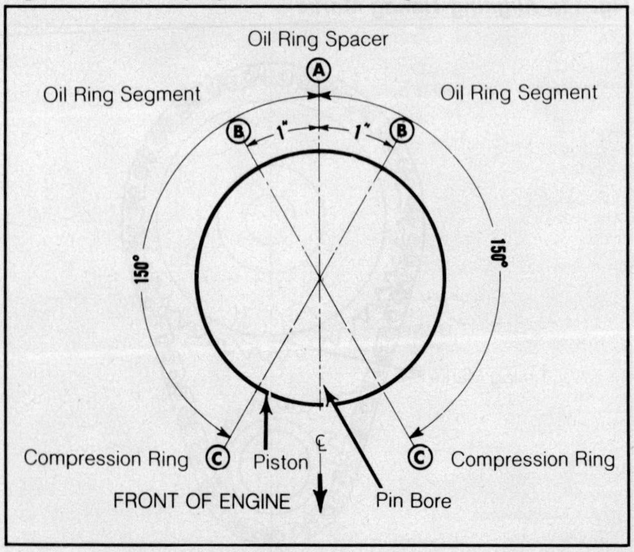

2) Measure cylinder bore 90° to crankshaft centerline at top of bore (below ring travel) and bottom of bore (above ring travel). Taper (difference between the 2 measurements) must not exceed .010" (.25 mm).

3) Measure cylinder bore at center of piston travel, 90° to crankshaft centerline. Measure bore at center of piston travel in line with crankshaft centerline. Out-of-round (difference between the 2 measurements) must not exceed .005" (.13 mm).

4) If taper or out-of-round are beyond limits, or cylinder walls are deeply scored, hone or bore cylinders for installation of new pistons. See PISTON SIZE CODES chart.

PISTON SIZE CODES

Size Code	Size In. (mm)
5.0L	
Red	3.9984-3.9990 (101.559-101.575)
Blue	3.9996-4.0002 (101.590-101.605)
.003" Oversize	4.0008-4.0014 (101.620-101.636)
5.8L	
Red	3.9978-3.9984 (101.544-101.559)
Blue	3.9990-3.9996 (101.575-101.590)
.003" Oversize	4.0002-4.0008 (101.605-101.620)

Fig. 15: Correct Positioning of Piston to Connecting Rod

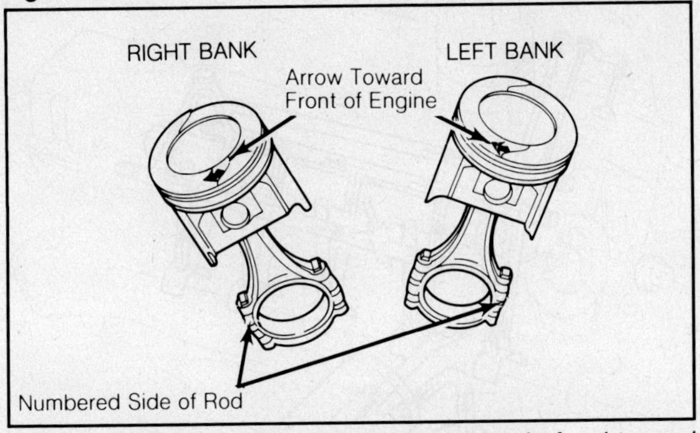

Position large chamfered side of bearing end of rod toward crankpin thrust face of crankshaft.

CRANKSHAFT & ROD BEARINGS

CONNECTING ROD BEARINGS

1) Ensure rod caps are marked for cylinder identification. Place crankshaft journal of cylinder to be checked at bottom of stroke and remove rod cap.

2) Use Plastigage method to check bearing clearances. To obtain proper bearing clearance, a standard bearing may be used in combination with a .001" (.025 mm) or .002" (.051 mm) undersize bearing.

3) Measure connecting rod side clearance after bearings and caps have been installed. *See Fig. 16.*

MAIN BEARINGS

1) Fit main bearings one at a time, leaving other bearings securely fastened. Ensure main bearing caps are marked for identification. Remove main bearing cap.

Fig. 16: Measuring Connecting Rod Side Clearance

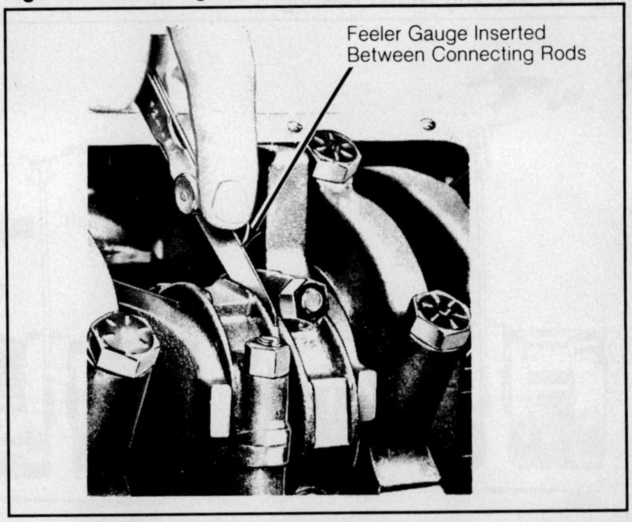

Side clearance is .010-.020" (.25-.51 mm).

2) Support crankshaft weight by placing a jack under counterweight adjacent to bearing being checked. Use Plastigage method to measure bearing clearances.

3) Standard size bearings may be used in combination with a .001" (.025 mm) or .002" (.051 mm) undersize bearing. If .002" (.051 mm) undersize main bearings are used on more than one journal, they must be installed in cylinder block side of crankshaft journal.

4) Replace main bearing sets one at a time, leaving other bearings securely fastened. Remove bearing cap. Insert Upper Bearing Remover/Installer (6331-E) into crankshaft journal oil hole. Turn crankshaft clockwise, allowing bearing remover/installer to push upper bearing out of cylinder block.

5) Lightly oil bearing and journal surfaces. Partially install plain end of upper bearing in place. Insert bearing remover/installer into journal oil hole. Turn crankshaft slowly counterclockwise until bearing is seated. Remove bearing remover/installer. Install and tighten main bearing cap.

THRUST BEARING ALIGNMENT

1) Install thrust bearing cap after all other main bearing caps have been tightened. Install thrust bearing cap bolts finger tight.

2) Pry crankshaft forward against thrust surface of upper half of bearing. Hold crankshaft forward and pry thrust bearing cap to rear. Tighten cap bolts while retaining forward pressure on crankshaft. *See Fig. 17.*

REAR MAIN BEARING OIL SEAL

Removal

1) Remove transmission. If equipped, remove clutch cover and clutch disc. Remove flywheel. Using a sharp awl, punch hole in seal metal surface between lip and cylinder block.

2) Screw threaded end of slide hammer into hole and extract seal. Use care not to damage crankshaft.

Installation

Lubricate seal lip and crankshaft with engine oil. Position seal on Seal Installer (T82L-6701-A) and install seal (with seal lip facing forward) until installer contacts block. Install remaining components in reverse order of removal procedure.

5.0 & 5.8 LITER V8 (Cont.)

Fig. 17: Aligning Thrust Bearing

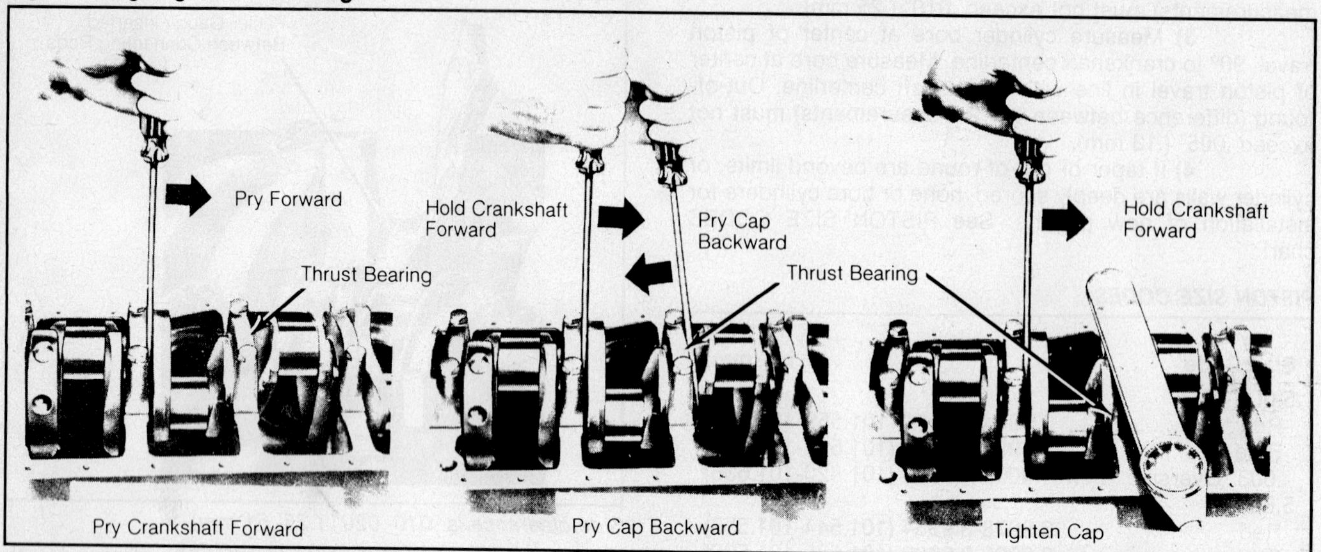

Align thrust bearing after all other bearings have been tightened.

ENGINE OILING

CRANKCASE CAPACITY

Crankcase capacity is 5 quarts (4.75L). Add 1 quart (.95L) when replacing oil filter.

OIL FILTER

Full-flow filter has an integral by-pass valve. Replace filter at first oil change, then every second oil change thereafter.

NORMAL OIL PRESSURE

Normal oil pressure should be 40-60 psi (2.8-4.2 kg/cm^2) at 2000 RPM.

OIL PRESSURE REGULATOR VALVE

Oil pressure regulator valve is located in pump body. Valve is nonadjustable.

ENGINE OILING SYSTEM

A rotor-type oil pump supplies oil through a full-flow oil filter before entering main oil gallery. Oil from main gallery enters main bearings and camshaft bearings. Oil passages then direct oil to various internal components. *See Fig. 18*.

OIL PUMP

Removal

Remove oil pan. Remove nut securing oil pump pick-up to engine. Remove oil pump attaching bolts and intermediate drive shaft. Remove oil pump assembly.

Disassembly

1) Remove oil pump pick-up. Remove cover attaching bolts and cover. Remove inner rotor, shaft and outer rotor. *See Fig. 19*.

2) Drill small hole into oil pressure relief valve cap. Insert self-threading sheet metal screw into cap and pull cap from chamber. Remove spring and plunger.

Fig. 18: Engine Oiling System

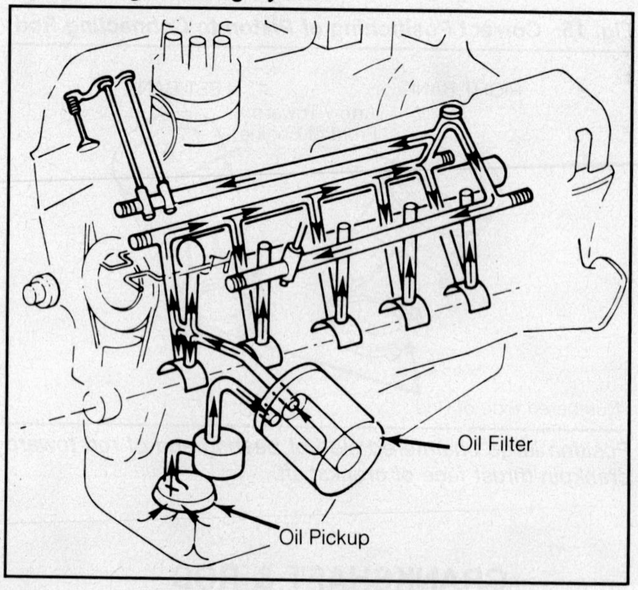

NOTE: If any part of oil pump needs replacing, replace complete pump.

Inspection

1) Wash all parts thoroughly and dry with compressed air. Check internal parts of pump for damage, scoring or excessive wear. Check pump cover for wear, scoring or grooves. Remove rotor assembly from pump housing. Using feeler gauge, measure inner-to-outer rotor tip clearance.

2) Install rotor assembly in pump housing. Lay a straightedge over rotor assembly and housing. Insert feeler gauge between straightedge and housing to measure rotor end play.

3) Measure outer rotor-to-housing clearance using feeler gauge. Measure shaft outside diameter and housing bearing inside diameter. Difference between readings is shaft-to-housing bearing clearance.

Fig. 19: Oil Pump Assembly

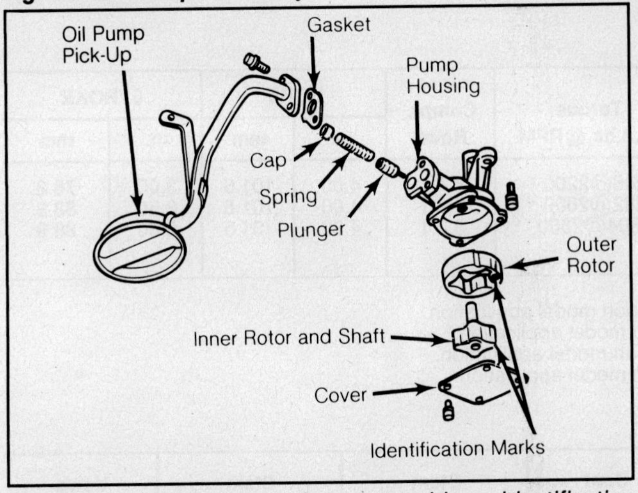

Dimple on outer rotor must face same side as identification mark on inner rotor.

4) Relief valve spring should test to 10.6-12.2 lbs. (5.0-5.5 kg) at 1.74" (44.2 mm) for 5.0L engines and 18.2-20.2 lbs. (8-9 kg) at 2.49" (63.3 mm) for 5.8L engines.

5) Inspect relief valve spring for worn or collapsed condition. Check relief valve plunger for scores and for free operation in bore. Check clearance between relief valve plunger and bore.

OIL PUMP SPECIFICATIONS

Application	Specification In. (mm)
Rotor Tip Clearance	.012 (.30) Max.
Rotor End Play	.004 (.10) Max.
Outer Rotor-to-Housing Clearance	.001-.013 (.03-.33)
Shaft-to-Housing Clearance	.0015-.0030 (.038-.076)
Relief Valve-to-Bore Clearance	.0015-.0030 (.038-.076)

Reassembly

Clean and oil all parts. Install relief valve plunger, spring and new cap. Stake cap into position. Install remaining components in reverse order of disassembly, using new gasket for oil pump pick-up.

Installation

1) Prime oil pump by filling inlet opening with engine oil, then rotate pump shaft until engine oil emerges from outlet opening.

2) Firmly seat intermediate shaft into distributor socket. Shaft stop should touch roof of crankcase. Position shaft stop as necessary.

3) Remove shaft and insert into oil pump. Install and tighten shaft and pump as an assembly. Install oil pan.

CAUTION: If pump and shaft do not readily seat, do not force into position. Realign drive shaft hex with distributor shaft socket and reinstall.

ENGINE COOLING

WATER PUMP

Removal

1) Drain cooling system. Remove air cleaner and duct assembly. Remove fan shroud and position over fan. Remove A/C idler pulley and bracket (if equipped).

2) Remove all hoses and brackets attached to water pump (including coil and bracket on EEC-equipped vehicles). Remove radiator (E150/E250/E350). Remove all drive belts, fan, spacer, pulley and shroud.

Installation

1) Clean all gasket mating surfaces. Transfer fittings to new pump (if required). Coat new gasket on both sides with gasket sealer and position on cylinder front cover.

2) Install water pump and tighten attaching bolts. To complete installation, reverse removal procedure.

NOTE: For further information on cooling system capacities and other cooling system components, see appropriate article in ENGINE COOLING SYSTEMS at end of ENGINE section.

TIGHTENING SPECIFICATIONS

Application	Ft. Lbs. (N.m)
Camshaft Thrust Plate Bolt	9-12 (12-16)
Camshaft Sprocket Bolt	40-45 (54-61)
Connecting Rod Cap Nut	
5.0L	19-24 (26-33)
5.8L	40-45 (54-61)
Cylinder Head Bolt	
5.0L	
Step 1	55-65 (75-88)
Step 2	65-72 (88-98)
5.8L	
Step 1	85 (115)
Step 2	95 (129)
Step 3	105-112 (142-152)
Exhaust Manifold Bolt	18-24 (24-33)
Flywheel-to-Crankshaft Bolt	75-85 (102-115)
Upper & Lower Intake Manifold Bolts & Studs	23-25 (31-34)
Main Bearing Cap Bolt	
5.0L	60-70 (81-95)
5.8L	95-105 (129-142)
Oil Pump-to-Cylinder Block Bolt	22-32 (30-43)
Rocker Arm Fulcrum Bolt	18-25 (24-34)
Vibration Damper Bolt	70-90 (95-122)

5.0 & 5.8 LITER (Cont.)

ENGINE SPECIFICATIONS

GENERAL SPECIFICATIONS

Year	DISPLACEMENT Cu. In.	DISPLACEMENT Liters	Fuel System	HP@RPM	Torque Ft. Lbs.@RPM	Compr. Ratio	BORE In.	BORE mm	STROKE In.	STROKE mm
1985	302	5.0	2-Bbl.	145@3400 [1]	248@2200 [2]	8.4:1	4.00	101.6	3.00	76.2
	351	5.8	2-Bbl.	150@3400 [3]	282@2000 [4]	8.3:1	4.00	101.6	3.50	88.9
	351	5.8	4-Bbl.	210@4000	304@2800	8.3:1	4.00	101.6	3.50	88.9

1 – Horsepower ratings of 150 HP at 3600 RPM available, depending upon model application.
2 – Torque rating of 249 ft. lbs. at 2600 RPM available, depending upon model application.
3 – Horsepower rating of 157 HP at 3400 RPM available, depending upon model application.
4 – Torque rating of 287 ft. lbs. at 1800 RPM available, depending upon model application.

VALVES

Engine Size & Valve	Head Diam. In. (mm)	Face Angle	Seat Angle	Seat Width In. (mm)	Stem Diameter In. (mm)	Stem Clearance In. (mm)	Valve Lift In. (mm)
5.0L							
Intake	1.690-1.694 (42.93-43.03)	44°	45°	.060-.080 (1.52-2.03)	.3416-.3423 (8.677-8.694)	.0010-.0027 (.025-.069)	.....
Exhaust	1.439-1.463 (36.55-37.16)	44°	45°	.060-.080 (1.52-2.03)	.3411-.3418 (8.664-8.682)	.0015-.0032 (.038-.081)	.....
5.8L							
Intake	1.770-1.794 (44.96-45.57)	44°	45°	.060-.080 (1.52-2.03)	.3416-.3423 (8.677-8.694)	.0010-.0027 (.025-.069)	.....
Exhaust	1.453-1.468 (36.91-37.29)	44°	45°	.060-.080 (1.52-2.03)	.3411-.3418 (8.664-8.682)	.0015-.0032 (.038-.081)	.....

PISTONS, PINS, RINGS

Engine	PISTONS Clearance In. (mm)	PINS Piston Fit In. (mm)	PINS Rod Fit In. (mm)	RINGS Ring No.	RINGS End Gap In. (mm)	RINGS Side Clearance In. (mm)
5.0L	.0018-.0026 (.046-.066)	.0002-.0004 (.005-.010)	Interference Fit	1 & 2	.010-.020 (.25-.51)	.002-.004 (.05-.10)
				3	.010-.035 (.25-.89)	Snug Fit
5.8L	.0018-.0026 (.046-.066)	.0003-.0005 (.008-.013)	Interference Fit	1 & 2	.010-.020 (.25-.51)	.002-.004 (.05-.10)
				3	.010-.035 (.25-.89)	Snug Fit

CRANKSHAFT MAIN & CONNECTING ROD BEARINGS

Engine	MAIN BEARINGS Journal Diam. In. (mm)	MAIN BEARINGS Clearance In. (mm)	MAIN BEARINGS Thrust Bearing	MAIN BEARINGS Crankshaft End Play In. (mm)	CONNECTING ROD BEARINGS Journal Diam. In. (mm)	CONNECTING ROD BEARINGS Clearance In. (mm)	CONNECTING ROD BEARINGS Side Play In. (mm)
5.0L	2.2482-2.2490 (57.104-57.125)	.0008-.0015 (.013-.038)	No. 3	.004-.008 (.10-.20)	2.1228-2.1236 (53.919-53.939)	.0008-.0015 (.020-.038)	.010-.020 (.25-.51)
5.8L	2.9994-3.0002 (76.185-76.205)	.0008-.0015 (.020-.038)	No. 3	.004-.008 (.10-.20)	2.3103-2.3111 (58.682-58.702)	.0008-.0015 (.020-.038)	.010-.020 (.25-.51)

5.0 & 5.8 LITER (Cont.)

ENGINE SPECIFICATIONS (Cont.)

VALVE SPRINGS

Engine	Free Length In. (mm)	PRESSURE Lbs. @ In. (Kg @ mm) Valve Closed	Valve Open
5.0L			
Intake	2.04 (51.8)	74-82@1.78 (34-37@45.2)	196-212@1.36 (89-96@34.5)
Exhaust	1.85 (47.0)	76-84@1.60 (35-38@40.6)	190-210@1.20 (86-95@30.5)
5.8L			
Intake	2.04 (51.8)	74-82@1.78 (34-37@45.2)	190-210@1.36 (86-95@30.5)
Exhaust	1.85 (47.0)	76-84@1.60 (35-38@40.6)	190-210@1.20 (86-95@30.5)

CAMSHAFT

Engine	Journal Diam. In. (mm)	Clearance In. (mm)	Lobe Lift In. (mm)
5.0L & 5.8L [1]			
No. 1	2.0805-2.0815 (52.845-52.870)	.001-.003 (.03-.08)	[2]
No. 2	2.0655-2.0665 (52.464-52.489)		[3]
No. 3	2.0505-2.0515 (52.083-52.108)		
No. 4	2.0355-2.0365 (51.702-51.727)		
No. 5	2.0205-2.0215 (51.321-51.346)		

[1] – End play is .001-.007" (.03-.18mm).
[2] – 5.0L Int. is .2375" (6.033 mm); Exh. is .2474" (6.284 mm).
[3] – 5.8L Int. & Exh. are .2600" (6.604 mm).

6.9 LITER V8 DIESEL

ENGINE CODING

ENGINE IDENTIFICATION

The eighth character of the Vehicle Identification Number (VIN) identifies the engine. The VIN is stamped on a metal tab attached to the instrument panel upper left side, near the windshield. The VIN is also on the Safety Compliance Certification Label on the left door lock pillar.

ENGINE IDENTIFICATION CODE

Application	Code
6.9L Diesel	I

ENGINE REMOVAL

See ENGINE REMOVAL at end of ENGINE section.

MANIFOLDS & CYLINDER HEAD

INTAKE MANIFOLD

Removal

1) Disconnect battery ground cables. Remove air cleaner. Install Intake Manifold Cover (T83T-9424-A). On E250/E350 models, disconnect fuel inlet and return lines from fuel filter. Remove filter and bracket as an assembly.

2) Remove engine oil filler neck. Remove bolts attaching injection pump to drive gear. Disconnect electrical connectors to injection pump. Disconnect accelerator cable and speed control cable from throttle lever, if equipped.

3) Remove accelerator cable bracket, with cables attached, from intake manifold and position aside. Cap all fuel lines and fittings. Remove fuel filter-to-injection pump fuel line and cap fittings.

4) Remove and cap injection pump inlet elbow and fitting adapter. Remove fuel return line on injection pump, rotate out of way and cap all fittings. Remove fuel injection lines from nozzles and cap lines and nozzles.

5) Using Injection Pump Mounting Wrench (T83T-9000-B), remove 3 nuts attaching injection pump to injection pump adapter. Remove injection pump with nozzle lines attached.

6) Remove fuel return hoses from No. 7 and 8 nozzles and fuel tank. Remove engine wiring harness from engine and engine harness ground cable from back of left cylinder head. Remove intake manifold bolts and manifold from cylinder head.

Installation

1) Install and tighten intake manifold. Install engine wiring harness on engine. Connect and tighten engine wiring harness ground wire to rear of left cylinder head.

2) Install new "O" ring on drive gear end of injection pump. Move injection pump into position. Position alignment dowel on injection pump into alignment hole on drive gear.

3) Install and tighten bolts attaching injection pump to drive gear. Install nuts attaching injection pump to adapter. Align scribe lines on injection pump flange and injection pump adapter and tighten nuts.

4) Remove caps from nozzles and fuel lines. Using Fuel Line Nut Wrench (T83T-9396-A), install and tighten fuel line nuts on nozzles. Connect fuel return line to injection pump and tighten.

5) Using solvent, clean old sealant from injection pump elbow threads and dry thoroughly. Apply a light coating of pipe sealant on elbow threads.

6) Install elbow in injection pump adapter and tighten to 72 INCH lbs. (8 N.m). If necessary, tighten more to align elbow with injection pump fuel inlet line, but do not exceed 360° rotation or 120 INCH lbs. (14 N.m).

7) To complete installation, reverse removal procedure. Apply a 1/8" bead of RTV sealant to injection pump adapter housing. Start engine and check for leaks.

Fig. 1: Intake Manifold Tightening Sequence

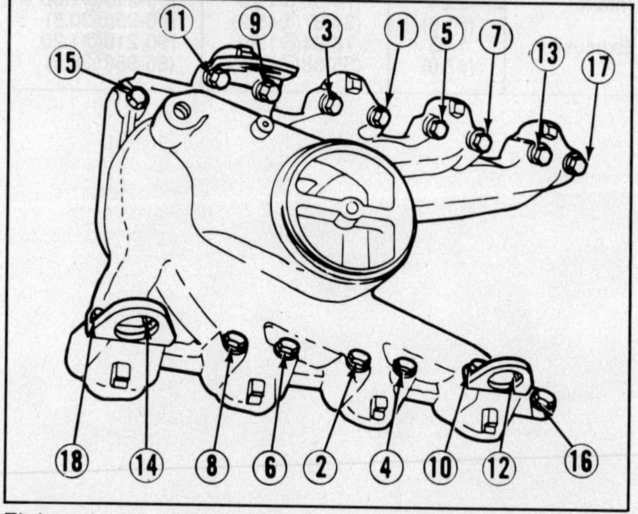

Tighten bolts progressively to 24 ft. lbs. (33 N.m)

EXHAUST MANIFOLDS

Removal

1) Disconnect battery ground cables. Raise vehicle. Disconnect exhaust pipes from manifolds. Bend tabs back on left exhaust manifold. Remove bolts and manifold.

2) Lower vehicle. On E250/E350 models, remove radiator fan shroud halves and dipsticks (with tubes) for engine and transmission. On all models, bend tabs back on right exhaust manifold. Remove bolts and manifold.

Installation

To install, reverse removal procedure.

CYLINDER HEADS

Removal

1) Disconnect battery ground cables. Drain cooling system. Remove overflow reservoir tube from the radiator neck and upper and lower radiator hoses from the radiator.

2) Remove screws holding fan shroud halves together and screws attaching shroud halves to the radiator. Remove shroud.

3) Using Fan Clutch Pulley Holder and Nut Wrench (T83T-6312-A and B), remove radiator fan and clutch assembly by turning nut clockwise (left-hand thread).

4) Disconnect alternator and fuel supply line heater wiring from alternator. Remove alternator adjusting bolt and pivot bolt and remove alternator. Remove vacuum pump.

5) Remove fuel filter inlet, outlet and return lines and cap lines and fittings with Protective Cap Set (T83T-

6395-A). Remove alternator and vacuum pump mounting bracket and fuel filter bracket with filter attached.

6) Remove heater hose from cylinder head. Remove injection pump and intake manifold. Remove crankcase depression regulator tube and grommet from valley pan.

7) Remove bolts attaching valley pan strap to front of engine block and remove strap. Remove valley pan drain plug and valley pan.

8) Raise vehicle. Disconnect exhaust pipes from exhaust manifolds. Remove bolt holding engine oil dipstick tube. Remove bolt attaching transmission oil dipstick tube to cylinder head.

9) Lower vehicle. Remove right side engine oil dipstick and dipstick tube. Remove valve cover attaching screws and remove covers. Remove valve rocker arm post mounting bolts. Remove valve rocker arms, posts and push rods in order and mark for reinstallation.

10) Clean exterior of each nozzle assembly, fuel inlet and fuel leak-off piping connections and surrounding area with clean fuel oil or solvent. Blow dry with compressed air. Remove fuel line retaining clamps from nozzle lines.

11) Disconnect nozzle fuel inlet (high pressure) and fuel leak-off tees from each assembly and position out of the way. Cover open ends of fuel inlet lines and nozzles.

12) Remove injection nozzles by turning counterclockwise. Carefully pull nozzle assembly with copper washer from engine and place in order for reinstallation. Cover nozzle assembly fuel inlet opening and nozzle tip with plastic cap. Remove glow plugs.

13) Remove cylinder head bolts. Attach lifting eyes to each end of cylinder head. Install sling to lifting eyes and carefully lift cylinder head out of engine compartment. Remove head gasket.

Fig. 2: Cylinder Head Tightening Sequence

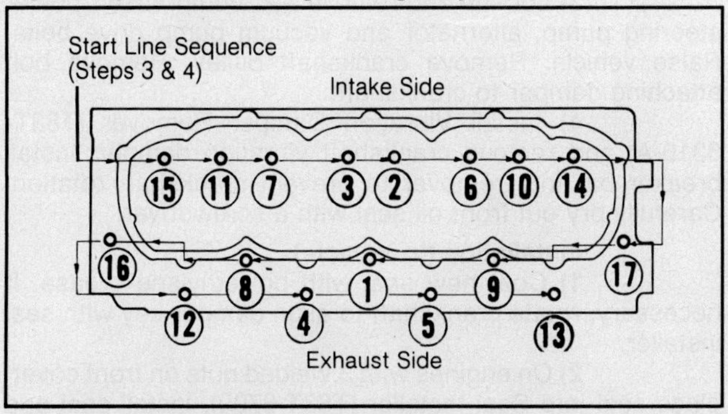

Tighten bolts in 4 steps to 80 ft. lbs. (108 N.m).

Installation

To install cylinder heads, reverse removal procedure and note the following: Ensure head gasket mating surfaces, cylinder head bolt threads and threads in block are clean. Head gasket requires no sealer. Apply 1/8" bead of RTV sealant to each end of cylinder block before installing valley cover.

VALVES

VALVE ARRANGEMENT

Left Bank – I-E-I-E-I-E-I-E (Front-to-rear).
Right Bank – E-I-E-I-E-I-E-I (Front-to-rear).

ROCKER ARM SHAFT ASSEMBLY

Removal & Installation

Remove valve cover attaching screws and remove covers. Remove valve rocker arm post mounting bolts. Remove valve rocker arms, posts and push rods in order and mark for reinstallation. To install, reverse removal procedure.

VALVE SPRINGS & OIL SEALS

Removal

With cylinder head removed, compress valve spring and remove valve keepers. *See Fig. 3*. Release spring compressor and remove retainer, spring, damper, seal and valve rotators.

Installation

To install valve springs, reverse removal procedure. Lubricate and install valve stem oil seal using Valve Stem Seal Replacer (T83T-6571-A).

Fig. 3: Removing Valve Spring

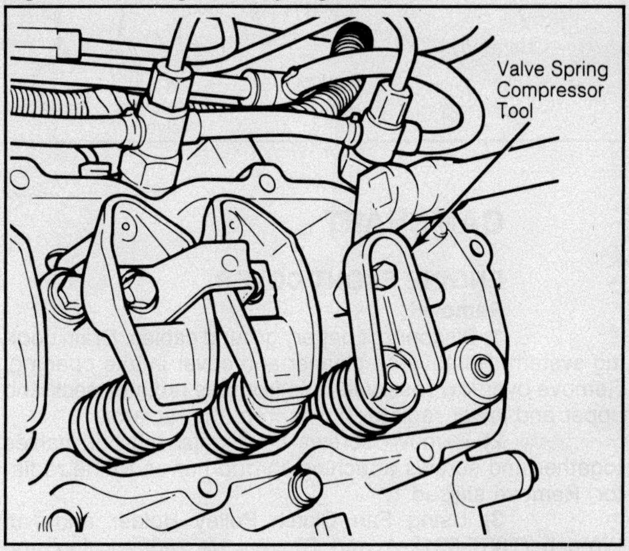

VALVE GUIDE SERVICING

If valve stem-to-guide clearance is excessive, insert sleeves are available. To install, drill out valve guide and ream drilled guide bore for insert sleeve. Chill valve guide in dry ice. Using arbor press, carefully press valve guide in cylinder head. Ream valve guide to proper size. Break sharp edge at top of guide using a scraper.

NOTE: **Reface valve seat after installing new valve guides.**

HYDRAULIC VALVE LIFTERS

NOTE: **Hydraulic roller lifters are used. Service lifters as complete assemblies only. Do not interchange parts between lifters.**

Removal

Keep lifters and push rods in order for installation in their original locations. Remove valve covers, rocker arm shafts and push rods. Remove lifter guide retainer. Remove lifters.

Disassembly

Using small screwdriver, remove plunger retainer. Remove push rod seat and metering valve. Remove plunger and plunger spring.

Ford Engines

6.9 LITER V8 DIESEL (Cont.)

Inspection

Clean all parts in clean solvent or diesel fuel. Check for nicks, burrs or scoring on parts. Ensure lifter roller operates smoothly and without excessive play.

Reassembly

Coat all parts with clean engine oil. Reverse disassembly procedure.

Installation

Lubricate lifters and bores with clean engine oil. Install lifters into their original position in block. Install lifter guides and guide. To complete installation, reverse removal procedure.

Fig. 4: Exploded View of Hydraulic Valve Lifter

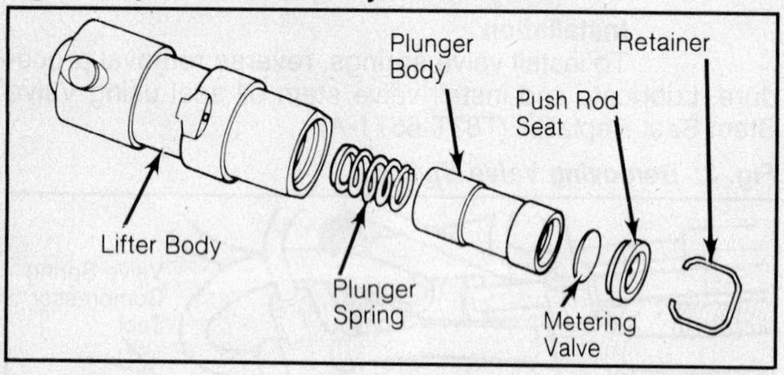

CAMSHAFT

ENGINE FRONT COVER

Removal

1) Disconnect battery ground cables. Drain cooling system. Remove air cleaner and cover intake opening. Remove overflow reservoir tube from the radiator neck and upper and lower radiator hoses from the radiator.

2) Remove screws holding fan shroud halves together and screws attaching shroud halves to the radiator. Remove shroud.

3) Using Fan Clutch Pulley Holder and Nut Wrench (T83T-6312-A and B), remove radiator fan and clutch assembly by turning nut clockwise (left-hand thread). Remove engine oil filler neck.

4) Remove bolts attaching injection pump to drive gear. Disconnect electrical connectors to injection pump. Disconnect accelerator cable and speed control cable from throttle lever, if equipped.

5) Remove accelerator cable bracket, with cables attached from intake manifold and position aside. Cap all fuel lines and fittings. Remove fuel filter-to-injection pump fuel line and cap fittings.

6) Remove and cap injection pump inlet elbow and fitting adapter. Remove fuel return line on injection pump, rotate out of the way and cap all fittings. Remove fuel injection lines from nozzles and cap lines and nozzles.

7) Using Injection Pump Mounting Wrench (T83T-9000-B), remove 3 nuts attaching injection pump to injection pump adapter. Lift injection pump, with nozzle lines attached, up and out of engine compartment.

8) Loosen power steering pump and A/C compressor and remove drive belts. Loosen vacuum pump and alternator and remove drive belts. Remove water pump pulley.

9) Disconnect heater hose from water pump. Remove heater hose fitting from water pump. Remove alternator adjusting arm and adjusting arm bracket.

10) Remove A/C compressor and position out of the way. Remove A/C compressor brackets. Remove power steering pump and bracket and position out of the way. Remove water pump attaching bolts and pump.

11) Raise vehicle. Remove crankshaft pulley. Remove bolt attaching damper to crankshaft. Install Vibration Damper Remover (T83T-6316-A) and remove vibration damper.

12) Remove ground cables at front of engine. Remove 5 bolts attaching front cover to engine block and oil pan. Lower vehicle. Remove bolts attaching engine front cover to engine block and remove cover.

Installation

Clean all sealing surfaces. Apply gasket sealer to engine block sealing surfaces. Install engine block gaskets. Apply 1/8" bead of RTV sealant on front of engine block and 1/4" bead on front of oil pan. To complete installation, reverse removal procedure.

FRONT COVER OIL SEAL

Removal (Out Of Vehicle)

Remove and support front cover. Using an arbor press, Drive Handle (T80T-4000-W) and a 3 1/4" diameter spacer, drive crankshaft seal out of front cover.

Installation (Out Of Vehicle)

Coat new front seal with polyethylene grease. Using Seal Installer (T83T-6700-A), a spacer and arbor press, install new seal.

Removal (In Vehicle)

1) Disconnect battery cables. Remove screws holding fan shroud halves together and screws attaching shroud halves to the radiator. Remove shroud.

2) Using Fan Clutch Puller and Nut Wrench (T83T-6312-A and B), remove radiator fan and clutch assembly by turning nut clockwise (left-hand thread).

3) Loosen and remove A/C compressor, power steering pump, alternator and vacuum pump drive belts. Raise vehicle. Remove crankshaft pulley. Remove bolt attaching damper to crankshaft.

4) Install Vibration Damper Remover (T83T-6316-A) and remove crankshaft vibration damper. Install breaker bar into remover to prevent crankshaft rotation. Carefully pry out front oil seal with a screwdriver.

Installation (In Vehicle)

1) Coat new seal with polyethylene grease. If necessary, rotate crankshaft to align damper key with seal installer.

2) On engines with 3 welded nuts on front cover, place seal into Seal Installer (T83T-6700). Install seal and installer over end of crankshaft and attach bridge to welded nuts. Draw seal into front cover by rotating center screw clockwise. When installer bottoms on front cover, seal is at proper depth.

3) On engines without 3 welded nuts on front cover, place seal into Seal Installer (T83T-6700). Install seal and installer over end of crankshaft and tighten nut against washer and installer.

4) On all engines, lubricate damper seal nose with engine oil and install crankshaft vibration damper using Damper Installer (T83T-6316-B). Apply RTV sealant to engine side of washer to prevent oil leakage past keyway.

5) Install and tighten bolt attaching vibration damper to crankshaft. Install and tighten crankshaft pulley. Lower vehicle. To complete installation, reverse removal procedure.

6.9 LITER V8 DIESEL (Cont.)

TIMING GEAR

Removal

Remove engine front cover. Remove camshaft allen screw. Install Gear Puller (T83T-6316-A) and remove gear.

Installation

To install, reverse removal procedure and adjust engine timing.

CAMSHAFT

Removal

1) Remove engine from vehicle and support on engine stand. Remove injection pump and adapter, intake manifold, hydraulic valve lifters and engine front cover.

2) Using flare nut wrench, loosen fuel pump threaded connections and retighten snugly. Do not remove lines at this time.

3) Loosen fuel pump mounting bolts 1-2 turns. Apply hand force to loosen fuel pump if gasket is stuck. Rotate engine by nudging starter until fuel pump cam lobe is at low position.

4) Disconnect fuel pump inlet, outlet and fuel return line. Remove fuel pump attaching bolts, remove pump and discard gasket.

5) Remove camshaft allen screw. Install Gear Puller (T83T-6316-A) and remove timing gear. Install Gear Puller (T77E-4220-B) and shaft protector and remove fuel pump cam and spacer.

6) Remove thrust plate attaching bolts and thrust plate. Using Camshaft Bearing Driver (T65L-6250-A) and Camshaft Adapter (Rotunda 014-00314), carefully remove camshaft by pulling toward front of engine.

Installation

Lubricate camshaft journals and lobes with engine oil. Coat camshaft lobes with polyethylene grease. Position camshaft to align timing marks on gears. To complete installation, reverse removal procedure.

CAMSHAFT END PLAY

1) Push camshaft toward rear of engine. Install dial indicator so indicator point is on camshaft sprocket attaching screw. Zero dial indicator.

2) Place a large screwdriver between camshaft sprocket and cylinder block. Pull camshaft forward and release. Camshaft end play should be .001-.009" (.03-.23 mm). If end play is excessive, replace thrust plate.

CAM LOBE LIFT

1) Remove fresh air inlet tube and air cleaner. Cover intake opening. Remove valve cover attaching screws and remove covers. Remove valve rocker arm post mounting bolts. Remove valve rocker arms and posts in order and mark for reinstallation.

2) Use a dial indicator to check lobe lift in consecutive order. Position dial indicator point (or cup-shaped adapter) on push rod end (in same plane as push rod movement. *See Fig. 5*.

3) Rotate crankshaft by hand until lifter and push rod are at lowest position. Zero dial indicator. Rotate crankshaft slowly until push rod is fully raised. Record dial indicator reading and compare with specifications.

4) Maximum allowable lift loss is .005" (.13 mm). If any lobe lift is below specification, replace camshaft and valve lifter operating on worn lobe(s).

Fig. 5: Checking Camshaft Lobe Lift

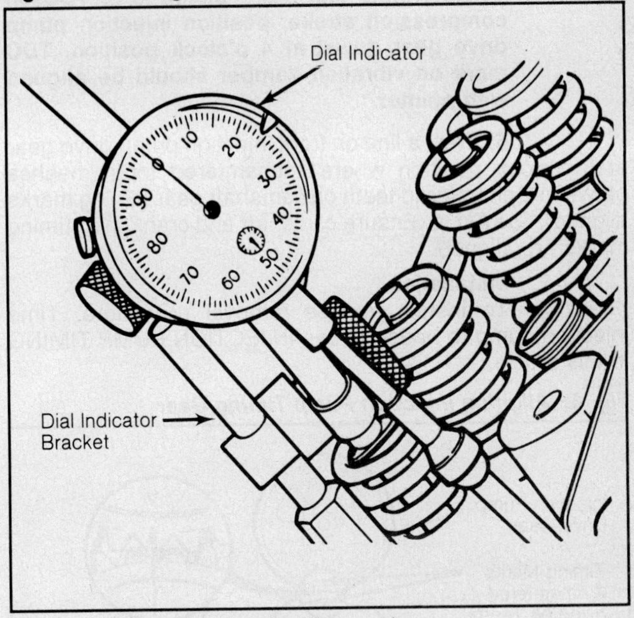

Ensure push rod is in valve lifter socket.

CAMSHAFT BEARINGS

NOTE: Camshaft bearings are not interchangeable from one bore to another.

Removal

Replace camshaft bearings with engine removed from vehicle. Remove camshaft, flywheel, crankshaft and rear bearing bore plug. Push pistons to top of cylinders. Remove camshaft bearings using camshaft bearing remover/installer.

Installation

1) Using camshaft bearing installer/remover, install bearings into place. Ensure oil holes are properly aligned with holes in block.

2) Install front bearing .040-.060" (1.02-1.52 mm) rearward of cylinder block front face. Check bearing installation with straightedge and feeler gauge. Install new rear bearing bore plug.

INJECTION PUMP TIMING GEAR

Removal

1) Disconnect negative battery cables. Remove air cleaner and install Intake Opening Cover (T83T-9424-A). Remove oil filler neck. Remove bolts attaching injection pump to drive gear.

2) Unplug electrical connectors to injection pump. Disconnect accelerator cable and speed control cable from throttle lever. Remove accelerator cable bracket, with cables attached, and position out of way.

3) Disconnect and cap fuel inlet and return lines from fuel filter. Remove fuel filter and bracket as an assembly. Remove injection pump fuel line and cap fittings. Remove fuel injection lines from nozzles. Cap lines and nozzles to prevent contamination.

4) Remove 3 nuts retaining injection pump to adapter. Remove injection pump. Remove injection pump adapter. DO NOT remove drive gear at this time. Remove glow plugs. Rotate crankshaft by hand so that No. 1 piston is at TDC on compression stroke.

Ford Engines

6.9 LITER V8 DIESEL (Cont.)

NOTE: To determine that No. 1 piston is at TDC on compression stroke, position injection pump drive gear dowel at 4 o'clock position. TDC mark on vibration damper should be aligned with pointer.

5) Draw a line on front injection pump drive gear at 6 o'clock position where 1 chamfered tooth meshes between 2 chamfered teeth on camshaft gear (timing marks aligned). *See Fig. 6*. Ensure camshaft and crankshaft timing marks are aligned.

Installation

To install, reverse removal procedure. Time injection pump to housing. See INJECTION PUMP TIMING in this article.

Fig. 6: Aligning Injection Pump Timing Gear

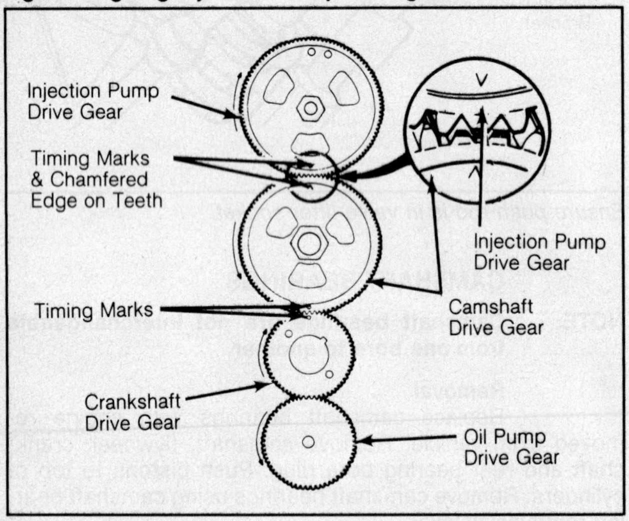

INJECTION PUMP TIMING

Loosen 3 nuts retaining injection pump to gear housing slightly to allow pump rotation. Align timing mark on pump with timing mark on housing. *See Fig. 7*.

Fig. 7: Injection Pump Timing Marks

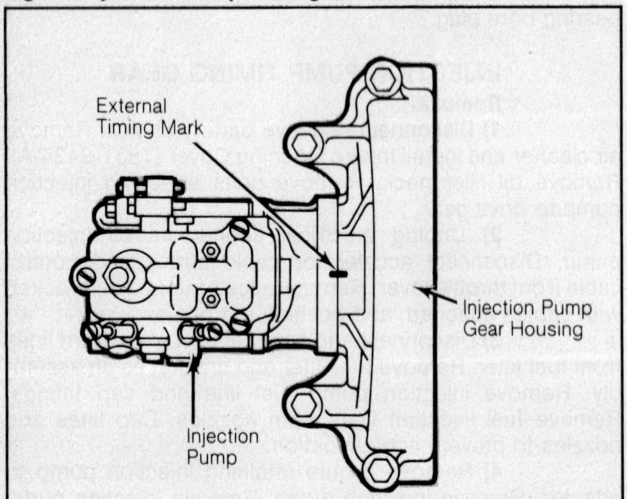

PISTONS, RINGS & PINS

OIL PAN

See OIL PAN REMOVAL at end of ENGINE section.

PISTON & ROD ASSEMBLY

Removal

1) With engine removed from vehicle, remove injection pump, intake manifold, cylinder heads, oil pan and oil pump. Place piston at bottom of stroke and cover with a cloth to collect cuttings.

2) Use ridge reamer to remove any ridge or deposit on cylinder bore upper end. Ensure connecting rods and caps are marked for cylinder identification.

CAUTION: Never cut more than 1/32" (.8 mm) into ring travel area.

3) Remove rod cap and install protective sleeves on rod bolts. Push piston and rod out top of cylinder bore. Use care not to damage crankshaft journal or cylinder wall. Install rod cap on mating rod.

Installation

1) Coat cylinder bore, piston and rings with engine oil. Ensure that ring gaps are properly spaced. *See Fig. 8*. Install a ring compressor on piston.

Fig. 8: Correct Spacing of Piston Rings

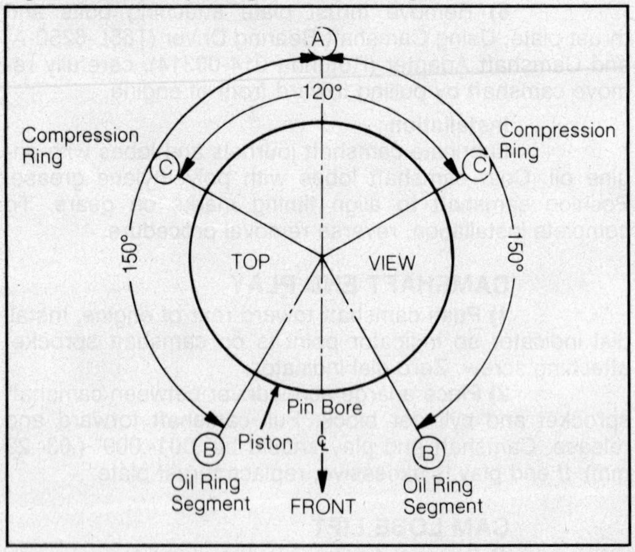

2) Install each piston and rod assembly in its respective bore, with arrow (or notch) on piston head facing toward camshaft.

NOTE: Large chamfer on connecting rod faces toward front of engine on right bank rods and toward rear of engine on left bank rods.

3) Guide connecting rod onto crankshaft journal until connecting rod bearing seats on crankshaft. Install and tighten rod caps.

4) Check bearing clearances using Plastigage method. Install oil pump and oil pan. To complete installation, reverse removal procedure.

6.9 LITER V8 DIESEL (Cont.)

FITTING PISTONS

NOTE: Take measurements with pistons and block at 70°F (21°C).

1) Measure piston skirt 90° to piston pin axis. Measure cylinder bore 90° to crankshaft centerline, at top, middle, and bottom of bore. Use these measurements to determine piston-to-cylinder bore clearance.

2) Measure cylinder bore 90° to crankshaft centerline at top of bore (below ring travel) and at bottom of bore (above ring travel). Taper (difference between the 2 measurements) must not exceed .005" (.13 mm).

3) Measure cylinder bore at center of piston travel, 90° to crankshaft centerline. Measure bore at center of piston travel in line with crankshaft centerline. Out-of-round (difference between the 2 measurements) must not exceed .002" (.05 mm).

4) If taper or out-of-round are excessive, or if cylinder walls are deeply scored, hone or bore cylinders for new pistons. Remove piston oil cooling jets before boring or honing engine block.

FITTING RINGS

1) Carefully position ring in cylinder bore where normal ring wear is not present. Ring must be square in bore. Check ring end gap with a feeler gauge.

2) Using a feeler gauge, check side clearance of compression rings. Feeler gauge should slide freely around entire circumference of piston without binding. If lower lands have high steps, replace piston.

PISTON PIN REPLACEMENT

Removal

Using arbor press and piston pin remover, press piston pin from piston and connecting rod.

Installation

1) Lightly coat all parts to be assembled with engine oil. Position piston to connecting rod.

2) Start piston pin in piston and connecting rod. Using arbor press and pin installer, press pin through piston and connecting rod until it is centered in connecting rod.

CRANKSHAFT & ROD BEARINGS

CONNECTING ROD BEARINGS

1) Ensure rod caps are marked for cylinder identification. Place crankshaft journal of cylinder to be checked at bottom of stroke and remove rod cap.

2) Place strip of Plastigage on bearing surface over full width of cap, about 1/4" (6 mm) off center and away from oil holes.

3) Install cap and tighten. Do not turn crankshaft. Remove cap and measure compressed width of Plastigage.

4) If necessary, regrind the crankshaft and install undersize bearings. Measure connecting rod side clearance after the bearings and caps have been installed. *See Fig. 9.*

MAIN BEARINGS

1) Fit main bearings one at a time, while leaving other bearings tightened. Ensure main bearing caps are marked for identification.

Fig. 9: Measuring Connecting Rod Side Clearance

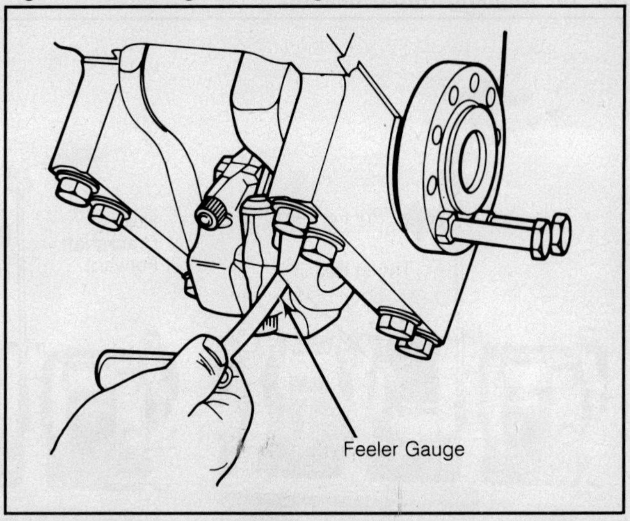

Side clearance is .008-.020" (.20-.51 mm).

2) Remove main bearing cap. Wipe oil from all contact surfaces such as crankshaft journal, bearing insert, bearing caps, etc.

3) Use Plastigage method to measure main bearing clearance. If necessary, regrind crankshaft and install undersize bearings.

THRUST BEARING ALIGNMENT

1) Install thrust bearing cap after all other main bearing caps have been tightened. Install thrust bearing cap bolts finger tight.

2) Pry crankshaft forward against thrust surface of upper half of bearing. Hold crankshaft forward and pry thrust bearing cap rearward. Tighten cap bolts while retaining forward pressure on crankshaft. *See Fig. 10.*

CRANKSHAFT END PLAY

1) Push crankshaft to rear of engine. Install dial indicator with pointer perpendicular to crankshaft flywheel flange. Zero indicator. Rotate crankshaft forward and note dial reading. End play should be .002-.009" (.05-.23 mm).

2) If end play is excessive, replace thrust bearing. If end play is less than .002" (.05 mm), realign thrust bearing or inspect thrust bearing faces for scratches or dirt.

REAR MAIN BEARING OIL SEAL

Removal

Remove transmission. If equipped, remove clutch cover and clutch disc. Remove flywheel. Remove and support rear cover. Using an arbor press and 4 1/8" diameter spacer, remove rear oil seal. *See Fig. 11.*

Installation

1) Clean rear cover and engine block gasket surfaces. Remove old RTV sealant from oil pan-to-rear cover sealing surface, clean with solvent and dry thoroughly.

2) Coat new rear crankshaft oil seal with polyethylene grease. Using an arbor press and rear crankshaft Seal Installer (T83T-6701-A), install new rear main bearing oil seal.

NOTE: Install seal from engine block side of rear cover, flush with seal bore inner surface.

Ford Engines

6.9 LITER V8 DIESEL (Cont.)

Fig. 10: Aligning Thrust Bearing

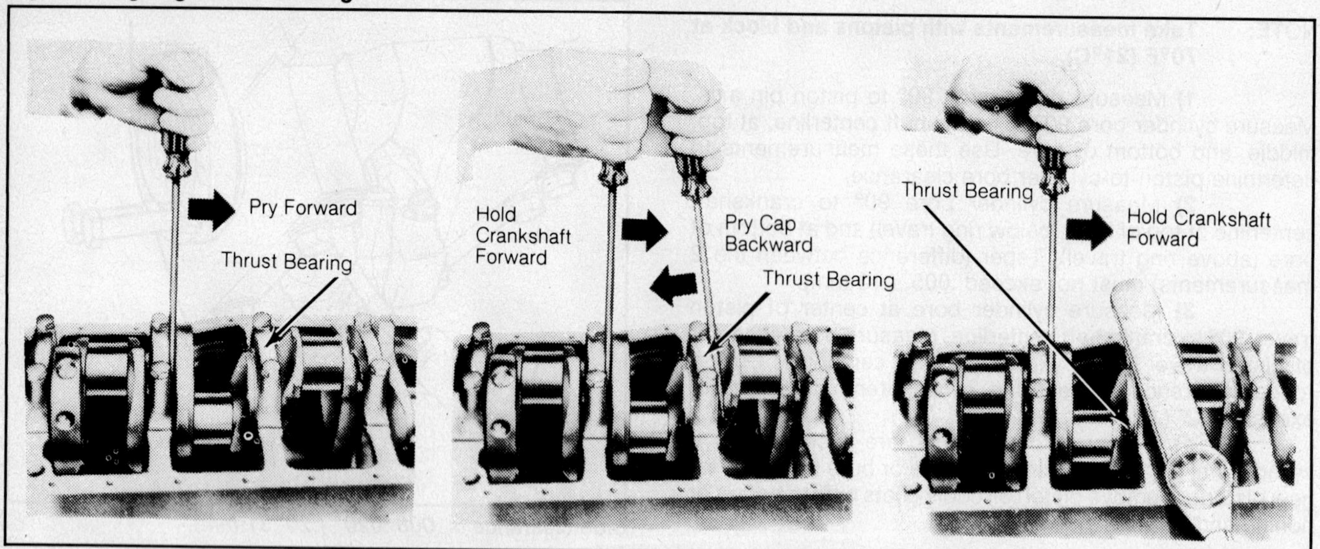

Align thrust bearing after all other bearings have been tightened.

Fig. 11: Rear Main Bearing Oil Seal Removal

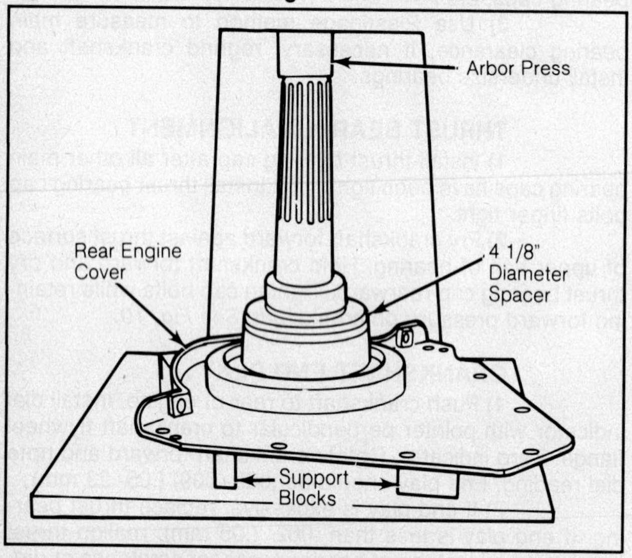

3) Install Rear Seal Pilot (T83T-6701-B) on crankshaft. Apply gasket sealant to engine block gasket surfaces. Install rear cover gasket to engine block.

4) Immediately before installing rear cover, apply a 1/4" bead of RTV sealant on oil pan sealing surface. Push rear cover into position on engine block, install bolts and tighten. To complete installation, reverse removal procedure.

ENGINE OILING

CRANKCASE CAPACITY

Crankcase capacity is 10 quarts (9.5L), including filter change.

OIL FILTER

Replace oil filter every 5,000 miles or 12 months, whichever comes first.

NORMAL OIL PRESSURE

Normal oil pressure should be 40-60 psi (2.81-4.22 kg/cm^2) at 2000 RPM.

OIL PRESSURE REGULATOR VALVE

Oil pressure regulator valve is located in oil pump body. Valve is nonadjustable.

ENGINE OILING SYSTEM

Full pressure lubrication through a full flow oil filter and oil cooler is supplied by a gear-type oil pump. Main oil gallery feeds oil through passages to camshaft and crankshaft. Valve lifter gallery feeds valve lifters, which feed rocker arms through hollow push rods.

OIL PUMP

Removal

Remove oil pan, oil pump and pick-up tube.

NOTE: **Do not disassemble oil pump. It is serviced as a complete assembly only.**

Installation

Remove old gasket material and clean mating surfaces of oil pan, oil pick-up tube, engine block and front and rear covers with solvent and dry thoroughly. Prime oil pump with engine oil. Rotate pump drive gear to distribute oil within pump body. Reverse removal procedure to install.

ENGINE COOLING

WATER PUMP

Removal

1) Disconnect battery cables. Drain cooling system. Remove overflow reservoir tube from the radiator neck and upper and lower radiator hoses from the radiator.

2) Remove screws holding fan shroud halves together and screws attaching shroud halves to the radiator. Remove shroud.

6.9 LITER V8 DIESEL (Cont.)

Fig. 12: Engine Oiling System

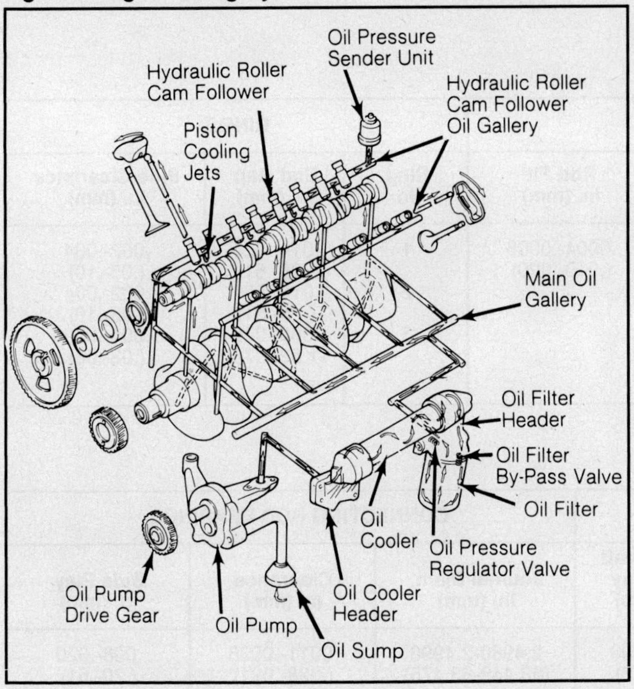

3) Using Fan Clutch Pulley Holder and Nut Wrench (T83T-6312-A and B), remove radiator fan and clutch assembly by turning nut clockwise (left-hand thread).

4) Loosen power steering pump, A/C compressor, vacuum pump and alternator and remove drive belts. Remove water pump pulley. Disconnect heater hose from water pump and remove fitting.

5) Remove alternator adjusting nut and bracket. Remove A/C compressor and move out of the way. Remove A/C compressor brackets. Remove power steering pump and bracket and move out of the way. Remove water pump.

Installation

Clean all gasket mating surfaces. Install fabricated dowel pins for water pump alignment. *See Fig. 13.* Coat 2 top and bottom bolts with RTV sealer. Using new gasket, install pump. To complete installation, reverse removal procedure.

NOTE: For further information on cooling system capacities and other cooling system components, see appropriate article in ENGINE COOLING SYSTEMS at end of ENGINE section.

Fig. 13: Water Pump & Front Cover Installation Dowels

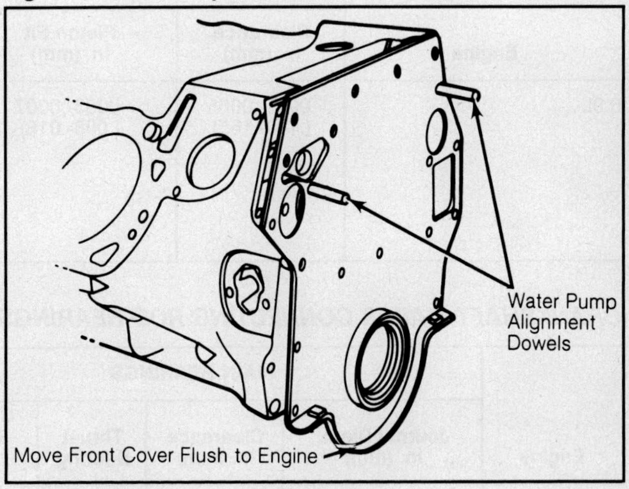

TIGHTENING SPECIFICATIONS

Application	Ft.Lbs. (N.m)
Camshaft Gear Screw	12-18 (17-24)
Connecting Rod Cap Bolts	[1] 48-54 (65-73)
Cylinder Head Bolts	[2] 80 (108)
Exhaust Manifold Bolts	35 (47)
Flywheel-to-Crankshaft Bolts	47 (64)
Injection Nozzle	35 (47)
Injection Pump Adapter Bolts	14 (19)
Injection Pump Outlet Fitting Nut	22 (30)
Intake Manifold Bolts	24 (33)
Main Bearing Cap Bolts	[3] 95 (129)
Vibration Damper-to-Crankshaft Bolt	90 (122)
Water Pump Cover Bolts	14 (19)

[1] – Tighten in 2 steps.
[2] – Tighten in 4 steps.
[3] – Tighten in 2 steps.

ENGINE SPECIFICATIONS

GENERAL SPECIFICATIONS

Year	DISPLACEMENT Cu. In.	DISPLACEMENT Liters	Fuel System	HP@RPM	Torque Ft. Lbs.@RPM	Compr. Ratio	BORE In.	BORE mm	STROKE In.	STROKE mm
1985	420	6.9	Diesel	170@3300	315@1400	20.7:1	4.00	101.6	4.18	106.2

VALVES

Engine Size & Valve	Head Diam. In. (mm)	Face Angle	Seat Angle	Seat Width In. (mm)	Stem Diameter In. (mm)	Stem Clearance In. (mm)	Valve Lift In. (mm)
6.9L							
Intake	.....	30°	30°	.065-.095 (1.65-2.41)	.3717-.3724 (9.441-9.459)	.0012-.0029 (.030-.074)	.....
Exhaust	.....	37.5°	37.5°	.065-.095 (1.65-2.41)	.3717-.3724 (9.441-9.459)	.0012-.0029 (.030-.074)	.....

Ford Engines

6.9 LITER V8 DIESEL (Cont.)

ENGINE SPECIFICATIONS (Cont.)

PISTONS, PINS, RINGS

Engine	PISTONS Clearance In. (mm)	PINS Piston Fit In. (mm)	PINS Rod Fit In. (mm)	RINGS Ring No.	RINGS End Gap In. (mm)	RINGS Side Clearance In. (mm)
6.9L	.0055-.0065 (.140-.165)	.0003-.0007 (.008-.018)	.0004-.0008 (.010-.020)	1	.014-.024 (.36-.61)	.002-.004 (.05-.10)
				2	.010-.024 (.25-.61)	.002-.004 (.05-.10)
				3	.060-.070 (1.52-1.78)	.001-.003 (.03-.08)

CRANKSHAFT MAIN & CONNECTING ROD BEARINGS

Engine	MAIN BEARINGS Journal Diam. In. (mm)	MAIN BEARINGS Clearance In. (mm)	MAIN BEARINGS Thrust Bearing	MAIN BEARINGS Crankshaft End Play In. (mm)	CONNECTING ROD BEARINGS Journal Diam. In. (mm)	CONNECTING ROD BEARINGS Clearance In. (mm)	CONNECTING ROD BEARINGS Side Play In. (mm)
6.9L	3.1228-3.1236 (79.319-79.339)	.0018-.0046 (.046-.117)	No. 3	.002-.009 (.05-.23)	2.4980-2.4990 (63.449-63.475)	.0011-.0036 (.028-.091)	.008-.020 (.20-.51)

VALVE SPRINGS

Engine	Free Length In. (mm)	PRESSURE Lbs. @ In. (Kg @ mm) Valve Closed	PRESSURE Lbs. @ In. (Kg @ mm) Valve Open
6.9L			
Intake	2.04 (51.8)	60 @ 1.80 (27 @ 45.7)	.....
Exhaust	2.04 (51.8)	60 @ 1.80 (27 @ 45.7)	.....

CAMSHAFT

Engine	Journal Diam. In. (mm)	Clearance In. (mm)	Lobe Lift In. (mm)
6.9L	2.0990-2.1000 (53.315-53.340)	.001-.005 (.03-.13)	.....

Ford Engines

7.5 LITER V8

ENGINE CODING

ENGINE IDENTIFICATION

The eighth character of the Vehicle Identification Number (VIN) identifies engine. VIN is near windshield on left upper side of instrument panel. The VIN number is also on the Safety Compliance Certification Label, attached to left door lock pillar.

ENGINE IDENTIFICATION CODE

Engine	Code
7.5L 4-Bbl.	L

ENGINE REMOVAL

See ENGINE REMOVAL at end of ENGINE section.

MANIFOLDS & CYLINDER HEAD

INTAKE MANIFOLD

Removal

1) Drain cooling system. Remove air cleaner and ducting. Disconnect coolant hoses at intake manifold and water pump and position them aside. Remove PCV valve and hose. Label and disconnect all vacuum hoses at carburetor, vacuum control valve and intake manifold.

2) Disconnect spark plug wires at spark plugs and remove wires from valve cover brackets. Disconnect high-tension lead at coil. Remove distributor cap and spark plug wires as an assembly.

3) Remove distributor with vacuum hoses attached. Disconnect accelerator linkage. If equipped, disconnect transmission kickdown linkage and speed control linkage bracket at carburetor.

4) Remove accelerator linkage attaching bolts. Position all linkages out of way. Disconnect fuel line at carburetor.

5) Label and disconnect all electrical wiring from intake manifold. Remove coil and bracket assembly. Remove intake manifold and carburetor as an assembly.

Installation

1) Clean all gasket surfaces. Apply 1/8" bead silicone sealer to 4 corners of cylinder block seal mounting surface. Install manifold gasket and front and rear seals. Apply 1/16" bead silicone sealer along full width of front and rear seal ends. *See Fig. 1.*

Fig. 1: Intake Manifold Sealer Application Points

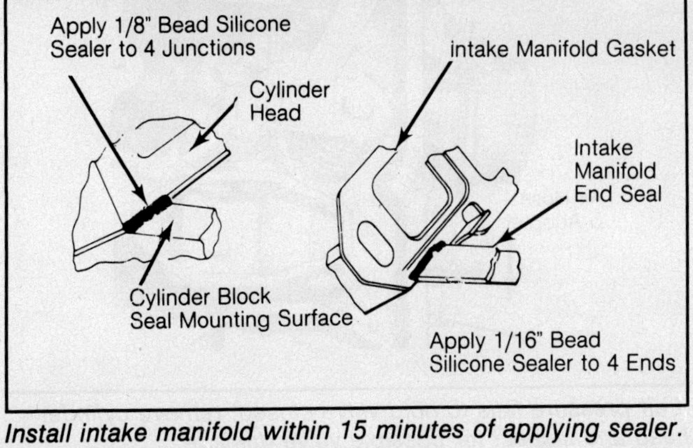

Install intake manifold within 15 minutes of applying sealer.

2) Position intake manifold over 4 studs in cylinder heads. Check for proper alignment of gaskets and seals before tightening. Tighten intake manifold, then repeat tightening sequence. *See Fig. 2.*

Fig. 2: Intake Manifold Tightening Sequence

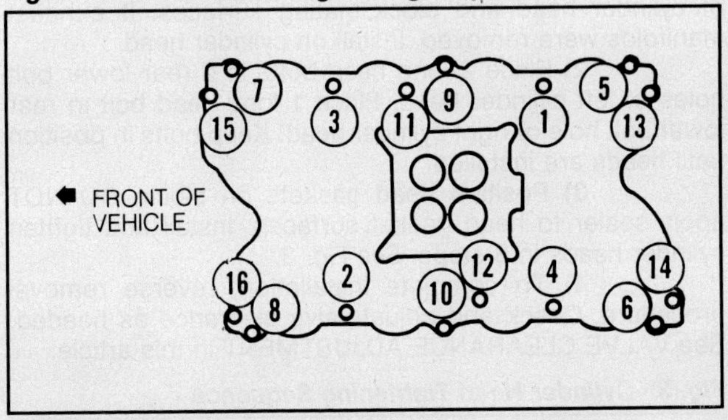

Tighten to 22-32 ft. lbs. (30-43 N.m), then repeat tightening sequence.

3) To complete installation, reverse removal procedure. Retighten intake manifold after engine has reached normal operating temperature.

EXHAUST MANIFOLD

Removal

If removing right exhaust manifold, remove air cleaner, ducting and heat shroud. Remove spark plug wires from spark plugs. Disconnect exhaust pipe from exhaust manifold. Remove attaching bolts, then remove manifold, lifting bracket and spark plug heat shields.

Installation

1) Clean mating surfaces of cylinder head and manifold. Clean mounting flange of manifold and exhaust pipe. Apply light film of graphite grease to manifold machined surface.

2) Position spark plug wire heat shields and exhaust manifold on cylinder head. Install attaching bolts and washers, starting at 4th bolt hole from front of each manifold. Position lifting bracket under bolts at 3rd exhaust port from front of engine.

3) On right exhaust manifold, install shoulder stud for air intake heat shroud at 1st and 6th bolt holes from front of manifold. Install shoulder stud for dipstick tube in 1st hole of left exhaust manifold. Tighten exhaust manifold. Using new gaskets, install and tighten exhaust pipes.

CYLINDER HEAD

Removal

1) Drain cooling system. Remove intake manifold. Disconnect exhaust pipes at manifolds. Loosen alternator attaching bolts and remove bolt attaching alternator bracket to right cylinder head.

2) If A/C equipped, loosen drive belt. Shut off compressor at service valves and remove valves and hoses from compressor. Remove A/C compressor support bracket attaching nuts from water pump. Remove and position compressor aside. Remove compressor upper mounting bracket from cylinder head.

3) If equipped, remove bolts attaching power steering reservoir bracket to left cylinder head. Position reservoir and bracket out of way. Remove valve covers. Remove rocker arm assemblies and push rods in sequence, so they can be installed in their original positions.

7.5 LITER V8 (Cont.)

4) Remove cylinder heads and exhaust manifolds as assemblies. Discard cylinder head gaskets. Remove exhaust manifolds.

Installation

1) Clean gasket mating surfaces. Check flatness of cylinder head and block mating surfaces. If exhaust manifolds were removed, install on cylinder head.

2) Place 2 long head bolts in 2 rear lower bolt holes of left cylinder head. Place 1 long head bolt in rear lower bolt hole of right cylinder head. Keep bolts in position until heads are installed.

3) Position head gaskets on block. DO NOT apply sealer to head gasket surfaces. Install and tighten cylinder heads in 3 steps. *See Fig. 3.*

4) To complete installation, reverse removal procedure. Check and adjust valve clearance as needed. See VALVE CLEARANCE ADJUSTMENT in this article.

Fig. 3: Cylinder Head Tightening Sequence

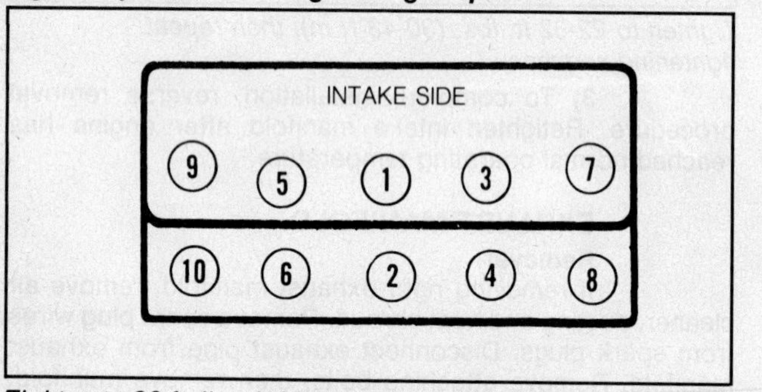

Tighten to 80 ft. lbs. (108 N.m), then to 110 ft. lbs. (149 N.m), and finally to 130-140 ft. lbs. (176-190 N.m).

VALVES

VALVE ARRANGEMENT

Right Bank – I-E-I-E-I-E-I-E (Front-to-rear).
Left Bank – E-I-E-I-E-I-E-I (Front-to-rear).

ROCKER ARM ASSEMBLY

1) Inspect all rocker arm components for excessive wear or damage and replace as necessary. Before installing rocker arm assembly, lubricate top of valve stem, fulcrum seat and socket area of rocker arm with polyethylene grease.

2) Ensure fulcrum seat base is inserted in its slot on cylinder head before tightening fulcrum bolt. *See Fig. 4.*

VALVE SPRINGS

Removal

1) Remove air cleaner and duct assembly. Remove valve cover and spark plug from cylinder to be serviced. Rotate crankshaft until piston is at TDC at end of compression stroke. Remove rocker arms and push rods from valves to be serviced.

2) Install an air hose with adapter into spark plug hole and turn on air supply. DO NOT remove air pressure on until valves are supported. Install rocker arm fulcrum bolt. Using a spring compressor, compress valve spring and remove retainer locks. Remove retainer, spring and oil seal. *See Fig. 5.*

Fig. 4: Rocker Arm Assembly

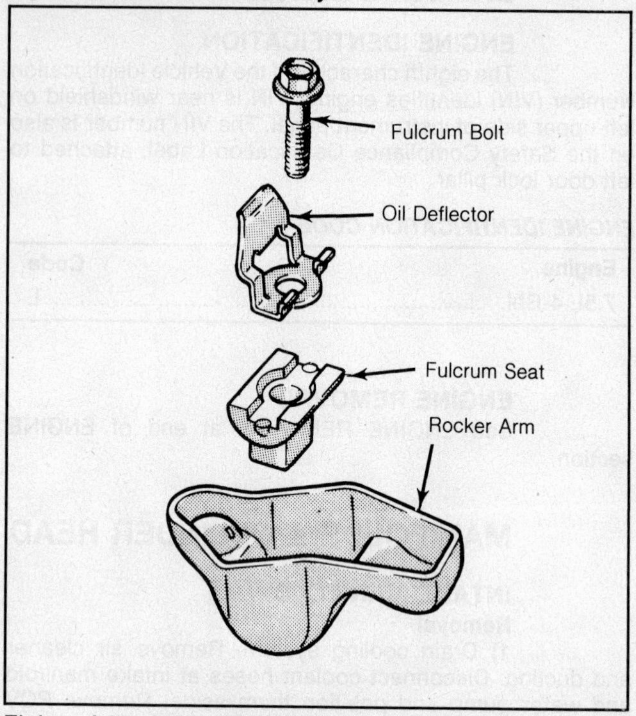

Tighten fulcrum bolt to 18-25 ft. lbs. (24-34 N.m).

Inspection

1) Wrap a rubber band or tape around end of valve stem. This will keep valve from falling into cylinder if air pressure forces piston downward. Turn off air supply.

2) Inspect valve stem for wear and out-of-round condition. Move valve up and down in guide and check for binding. Using valve spring tester, test springs for proper tension. Replace springs that fail to meet specifications.

3) Inspect each spring for squareness using a steel square and flat surface. Measure gap between top spring coil and square while slowly rotating spring. Replace spring if more than 5/64" out-of-square. *See Fig. 6.*

Fig. 5: Removing and Installing Valve Spring

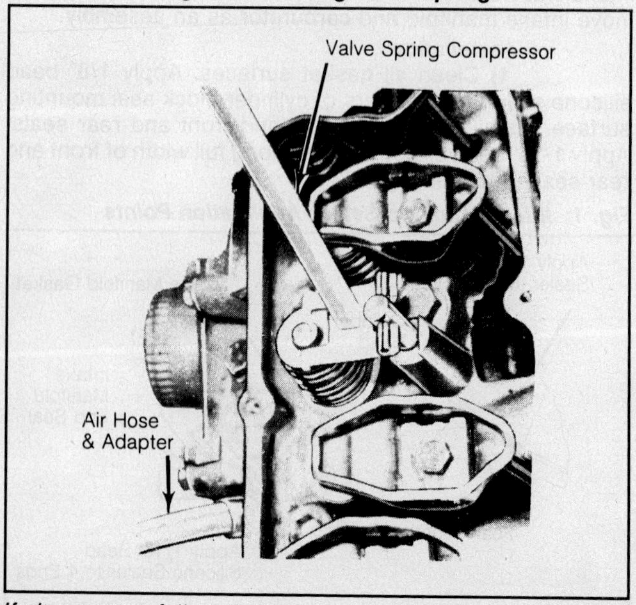

If air pressure fails to hold valve closed, remove cylinder head and inspect for possible valve damage.

Fig. 6: Checking Valve Spring Squareness

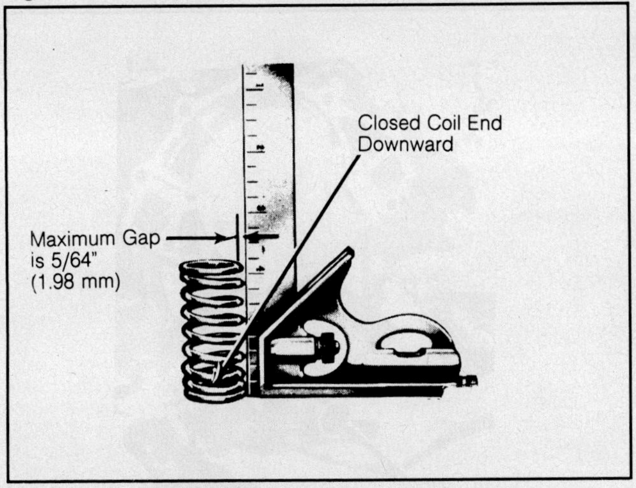

Measure gap while slowly rotating spring.

Installation

1) Hold valve closed and turn air pressure on again. Install new valve stem oil seals. Place spring in position over valve and position spring retainer in place. Compress valve spring and install retainer locks. *See Fig. 5.*

2) Apply polyethylene grease to push rod ends, valve stem tip, fulcrum seats and sockets. Install push rods and rocker arms. Turn off air pressure. Remove air hose and adapter. To complete installation, reverse removal procedure.

VALVE SPRING INSTALLED HEIGHT

CAUTION: Install spacers only if necessary. Excess use of spacers will stress valve train.

1) Using dividers and a scale, measure installed height of valve spring. Measure from surface of cylinder head spring pad to underside of spring retainer (or rotator). *See Fig. 7.*

2) If spring height is excessive, install .030" (.76 mm) spacer(s) between cylinder head spring pad and valve spring.

Fig. 7: Checking Installed Height of Valve Spring

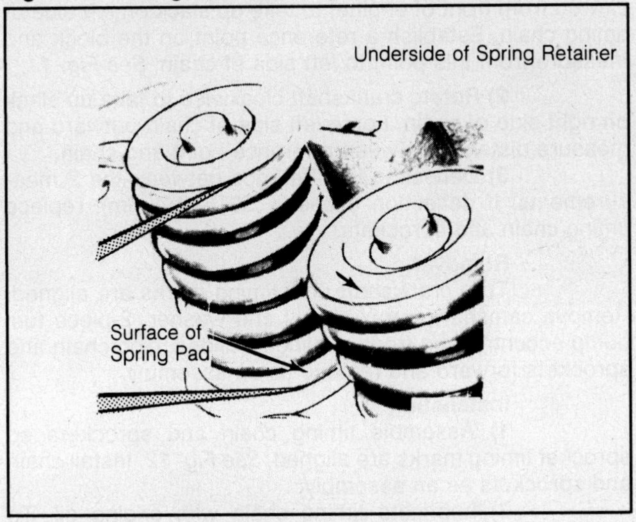

Do not install spacer(s) unless necessary.

VALVE SPRING INSTALLED HEIGHT

Application	In. (mm)
7.5L	1.797-1.828 (45.64-46.43)

VALVE STEM OIL SEALS

Umbrella-type oil seals are used on all valves. Lubricate valve stem with engine oil and install new seal with cup side down over valve guide. Use a 5/8" deep-well socket and light mallet to seat seal on valve stem.

VALVE GUIDE SERVICING

When reaming guides, always use reamers in proper sequence. Always reface valve seats and valves after valve guides are reamed. Replacement valves are available with standard, .015" (.38 mm), and .030 (.76 mm) oversize stems.

HYDRAULIC VALVE LIFTERS

1) Service lifters as assemblies only. Disassemble and clean lifters before testing. Test lifters with hydraulic lifter test fluid. DO NOT interchange parts between lifters. *See Fig. 8.*

Fig. 8: Hydraulic Valve Lifter Assembly

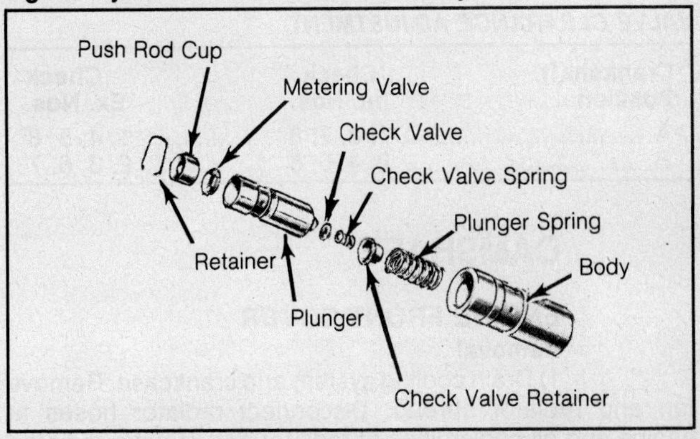

Parts are not interchangeable between lifters.

2) Leak-down rate on hydraulic lifters is 10-50 seconds, with 1/16" (1.6 mm) plunger travel under 50 lb. (23 kg) load. Replace lifter if it fails leak-down test, or is worn or damaged.

VALVE CLEARANCE ADJUSTMENT

1) Turn crankshaft to place No. 1 piston on TDC at end of compression stroke. Make chalk mark at points "A" and "B" on crankshaft pulley at TDC. *See Fig. 9.* Rotate crankshaft 360° for mark "B".

2) Using lifter bleed-down wrench, apply pressure to push rod end of rocker arm. Slowly bleed down lifter until lifter plunger is completely bottomed.

3) While holding lifter in this position, check clearance between rocker arm and valve stem tip with a feeler gauge. Desired collapsed lifter gap clearance is .100-.150" (2.54-3.81 mm), allowable clearance is .075-.175" (1.90-4.45).

4) If clearance is less than specified, install a .060" (1.52 mm) shorter push rod. If clearance is greater, install a .060" (1.52 mm) longer push rod.

Fig. 9: Crankshaft Positions for Valve Adjustment

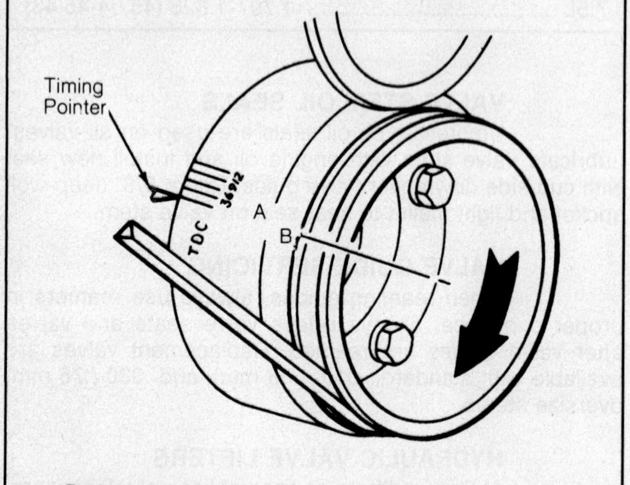

VALVE CLEARANCE ADJUSTMENT

Crankshaft Position	Check Int. Nos.	Check Ex. Nos.
A	1, 3, 7, 8	1, 4, 5, 8
B	2, 4, 5, 6	2, 3, 6, 7

CAMSHAFT

ENGINE FRONT COVER

Removal

1) Drain cooling system and crankcase. Remove fan and radiator shroud. Disconnect radiator hoses at engine and oil cooler lines at radiator and remove radiator.

2) Remove all drive belts and water pump pulley. Remove air pump. If equipped, remove A/C compressor support bracket from water pump. Disconnect heater hose from water pump and loosen by-pass hose clamp at pump.

3) Remove crankshaft pulley, vibration damper and Woodruff key from crankshaft. Disconnect and plug fuel line inlet at fuel pump and remove fuel pump. Remove bolts attaching front cover to cylinder block.

4) Remove front cover and water pump as an assembly. Using a knife, cut oil pan seal flush with cylinder block face. Discard front cover gasket and pan seal.

Installation

1) Coat gasket surface of oil pan with gasket sealer. Cut and position required section of a new seal on oil pan. Apply silicone sealer at block-to-pan junction. Apply gasket sealer to front cover and cylinder block gasket surfaces.

2) Position front cover on cylinder block. Install Front Cover Seal Aligner (T68P-6019-A) on crankshaft. *See Fig. 10*. Coat threads of cover bolts with oil-resistant sealer and install bolts.

3) While pushing in on aligner, tighten oil pan-to-cover bolts. Remove aligner and tighten front cover-to-cylinder block bolts. To complete installation, reverse removal procedure.

Fig. 10: Aligning Front Cover

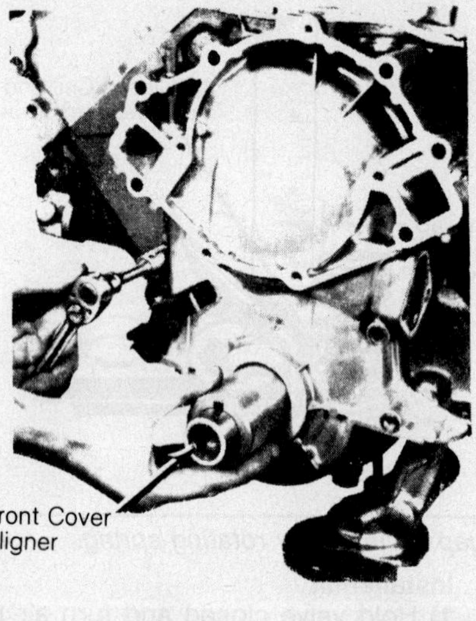

To install aligner, it may be necessary to force cover down against pan seal.

FRONT COVER OIL SEAL

Removal

With engine front cover removed, drive out old oil seal with pin punch. Clean seal recess in front cover.

Installation

Coat new seal with polyethylene grease and install seal using Seal Installer (T72J-177). Ensure seal spring remains in proper position.

TIMING CHAIN & SPROCKET

NOTE: Perform following procedures with engine front cover removed.

Checking Timing Chain Deflection

1) Rotate crankshaft counterclockwise (as viewed from front of engine) to take up slack on left side of timing chain. Establish a reference point on the block and measure from this point to left side of chain. *See Fig. 11*.

2) Rotate crankshaft clockwise to take up slack on right side of chain. Force left side of chain outward and measure distance between reference point and chain.

3) Deflection is difference between the 2 measurements. If deflection exceeds .50" (12.7 mm), replace timing chain and sprockets.

Removal

Turn crankshaft until timing marks are aligned. Remove camshaft sprocket bolt and washer, 2-piece fuel pump eccentric and front oil slinger. Slide timing chain and sprockets forward and remove as an assembly.

Installation

1) Assemble timing chain and sprockets so sprocket timing marks are aligned. *See Fig. 12*. Install chain and sprockets as an assembly.

2) Lubricate timing chain with engine oil. To complete installation, reverse removal procedure.

7.5 LITER V8 (Cont.)

Fig. 11: Measuring Timing Chain Deflection

Maximum deflection is 1/2" (12.7 mm).

CAMSHAFT

Removal

1) Remove radiator, front cover, timing chain and sprockets. Remove intake manifold and carburetor as an assembly. Remove valve covers.

2) Loosen all rocker arm bolts. Rotate rocker arms to one side. Remove push rods and valve lifters, keeping them in order for installation in original locations.

3) If equipped, remove A/C condenser and carefully secure condenser to left fender well. Remove grille. Remove camshaft thrust plate attaching bolts and remove camshaft, taking care not to damage camshaft bearings or journals.

Installation

1) Oil camshaft journals and apply polyethylene grease to cam lobes. Carefully slide camshaft into position. Install and tighten thrust plate.

2) Lubricate lifters with engine oil and install. Lubricate rocker arms, fulcrum seats, valve stem tips and push rods with polyethylene grease before installing.

3) To complete installation, reverse removal procedure. Use new gaskets where required. *See Fig. 13.*

CAMSHAFT END PLAY

CAUTION: Do not pry against camshaft sprocket without first relieving valve train load on camshaft.

1) Loosen rocker arm fulcrum bolts to relieve load on camshaft. Push camshaft toward rear of engine. Install dial indicator so that indicator point is on camshaft sprocket attaching bolt. Zero dial indicator.

2) Pull camshaft forward and release. Check dial indicator reading to obtain end play. If end play is excessive, replace camshaft thrust plate.

CAM LOBE LIFT

1) Remove valve cover. Remove fulcrum bolt, fulcrum seat and rocker arm. Ensure push rod end is in valve lifter socket.

2) Use a dial indicator to check lobe lift in consecutive order. Position dial indicator point (or cup-

Fig. 12: Aligning Timing Marks

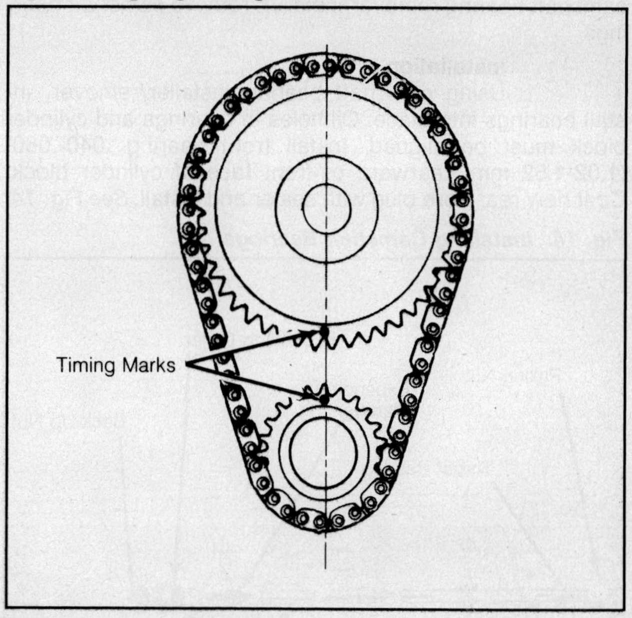

Remove and install chain and sprockets as an assembly.

Fig. 13: Camshaft Assembly

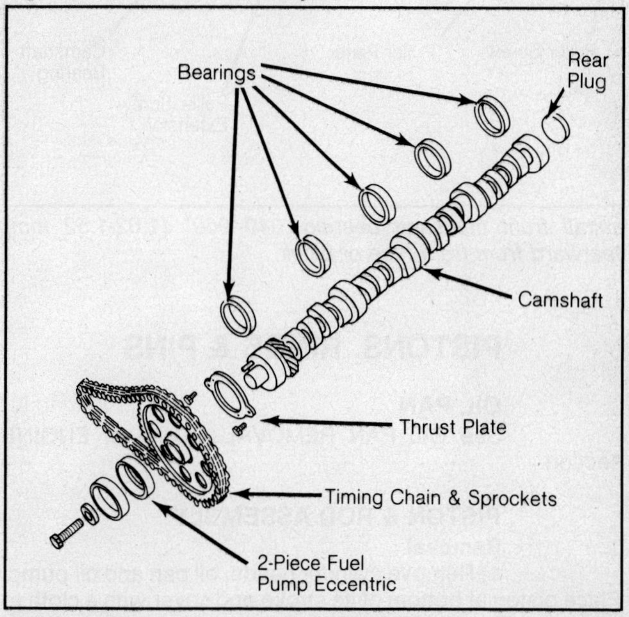

Tighten camshaft sprocket bolt to 40-45 ft. lbs. (54-61 N.m).

shaped adapter) on end of push rod (in same plane as push rod movement).

3) Turn crankshaft until lifter and push rod are at lowest position. Zero dial indicator. Turn crankshaft slowly until push rod is fully raised. Compare dial indicator reading with specifications.

4) Maximum allowable lobe wear is .005" (.13 mm). If lobe lift is insufficient, replace camshaft and valve lifter(s) operating on worn lobe(s).

CAMSHAFT BEARINGS

Removal

Remove engine from vehicle. Remove camshaft, flywheel and crankshaft. Push pistons to top of cylinders. Remove camshaft rear bearing bore plug. Using camshaft bearing remover/installer, remove camshaft bearings.

Installation

Using camshaft bearing installer/remover, install bearings into place. Oil holes in bearings and cylinder block must be aligned. Install front bearing .040-.060" (1.02-1.52 mm) rearward of front face of cylinder block. Coat new rear bore plug with sealer and install. *See Fig. 14*.

Fig. 14: Installing Camshaft Bearings

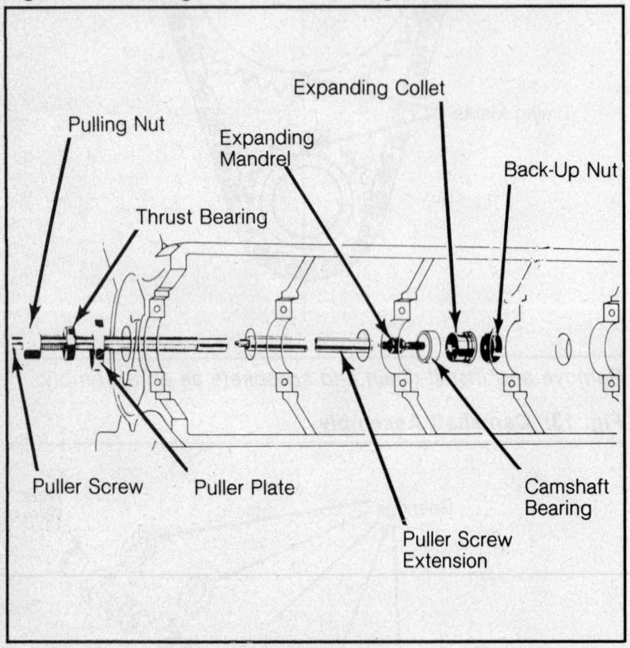

Install front camshaft bearing .040-.060" (1.02-1.52 mm) rearward from front face of block.

PISTONS, RINGS & PINS

OIL PAN

See OIL PAN REMOVAL at end of ENGINE section.

PISTON & ROD ASSEMBLY

Removal

1) Remove cylinder heads, oil pan and oil pump. Place piston at bottom of its stroke and cover with a cloth to collect metal cuttings. Use ridge reamer to remove ridge or deposits from upper end of cylinder bore.

NOTE: Never cut more than 1/32" (.79 mm) into ring travel area when removing ridge.

2) Ensure all connecting rods and caps are marked for cylinder identification. Remove rod cap. Push piston and rod out top of cylinder. Use care not to damage crankshaft journal or cylinder wall. Install rod cap on mating rod.

Installation

1) Coat cylinder bore, piston and rings with engine oil. Position ring gaps. *See Fig. 15*. Install ring compressor. Do not allow ring gaps to change.

Fig. 15: Correctly Spaced Ring Gaps

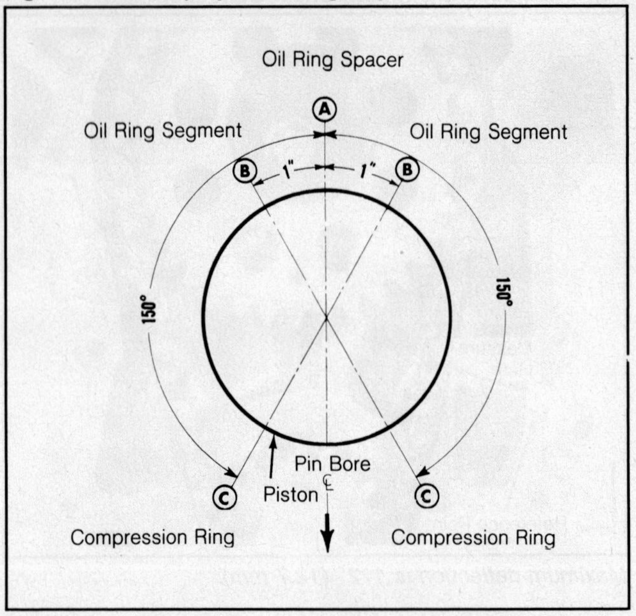

Space oil ring segments 1" (25 mm) from oil ring spacer.

2) Position crankshaft journal at bottom of stroke. Place piston into bore, with notch in piston head toward front of engine.

3) Carefully push piston into cylinder bore until slightly below top of cylinder, then push it downward until rod bearing seats on crankshaft journal. Install and tighten connecting rod cap. Check side clearance between connecting rods on each crankshaft journal. Install cylinder heads, oil pump and oil pan.

FITTING PISTONS

NOTE: Take measurements with piston and crankcase at about 70°F (21°C).

1) Measure piston at centerline of piston pin, 90° to piston pin axis. Measure cylinder bore 90° to crankshaft centerline, at top, middle and bottom of bore. Use measurements to determine piston-to-bore clearance.

2) Measure cylinder bore 90° to crankshaft centerline at top of bore (below ring travel) and at bottom of bore (above ring travel). Taper is the difference between the 2 measurements. Taper must not exceed .010" (.25 mm).

3) Measure cylinder bore at center of piston travel, 90° to crankshaft centerline. Measure bore at center of piston travel, in line with crankshaft centerline. Out-of-round (difference between the 2 measurements) must not exceed .005" (.13 mm).

4) If taper or out-of-round are not within limits, or cylinder walls are deeply scored, bore and hone cylinders for installation of new pistons. Check PISTON SIZE CODES table.

PISTON SIZE CODES

Code	Piston Size In. (mm)
Red	4.3585-4.3591 (110.706-110.721)
Blue	4.3597-4.3603 (110.736-110.752)
.003" Oversize	4.3609-4.3615 (110.767-110.782)

FITTING RINGS

1) Position ring squarely in cylinder bore at a point where normal ring wear is not present. Use care not to damage ring or cylinder bore. Check ring end gap with a feeler gauge.

2) Check side clearance of compression rings, by inserting feeler gauge between ring and its lower land. Feeler gauge should slide freely around entire circumference of piston without binding. If lower lands have high steps, replace piston.

PISTON PIN REPLACEMENT

Removal

Using an arbor press and piston pin remover/installer, press piston pin from piston and connecting rod. *See Fig. 16.*

Fig. 16: Removing and Installing Piston Pin

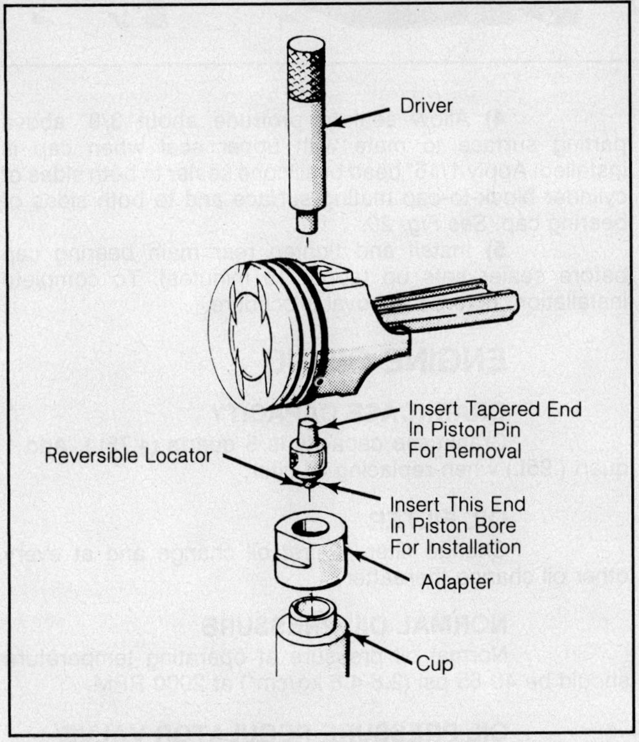

Install pin until end of pin is .063-.125" (1.59-3.18 mm) below chamfer of pin bore.

Installation

1) Apply light coat of engine oil to all parts to be assembled. Assemble piston to connecting rod with numbered side of rod toward outside of engine and notch in piston head positioned forward. *See Fig. 17.*

2) Start piston pin in piston and connecting rod. Using arbor press and pin remover/installer, press pin into piston and connecting rod until end of pin is .063-.125" (1.6-3.2 mm) below chamfer of piston pin bore.

CRANKSHAFT & ROD BEARINGS

CONNECTING ROD BEARINGS

1) Ensure rod caps are marked for cylinder identification. Place crankshaft journal of cylinder to be checked at bottom of stroke and remove rod cap. Using Plastigage method to measure rod bearing bearing clearance.

Fig. 17: Proper Piston to Connecting Rod Position

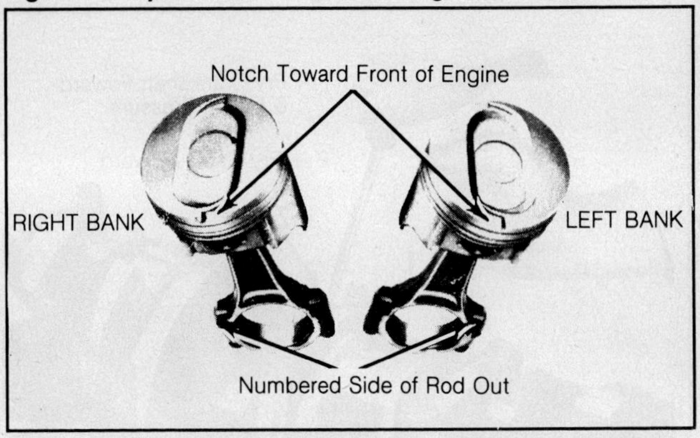

Position numbered side of rod toward outside of engine.

2) Standard bearings may be used with a .001" (.025 mm) or .002" (.051 mm) undersize bearing to obtain proper bearing clearance. With rod cap and bearing installed, check connecting rod side clearance between rod and crankshaft thrust face.

MAIN BEARINGS

1) Fit main bearings one at a time, leaving other bearings securely fastened. Ensure main bearing caps are marked for identification. Remove main bearing cap. Position jack under counterweight, next to bearing being checked.

2) Use Plastigage method to measure main bearing clearance. Standard size bearings may be used in combination with a .001" (.025 mm) or .002" (.051 mm) undersize bearings.

3) If .002" (.051 mm) undersize main bearings are used on more than one journal, bearings must be installed in cylinder block side of crankshaft journal.

4) Replace main bearing sets one at a time, leaving other bearings securely fastened. Remove bearing cap. Insert Upper Bearing Remover/Installer (6331E) into crankshaft journal oil hole. Turn crankshaft clockwise, rotating upper bearing out of block.

5) Lightly oil bearing and journal surfaces. Partially install plain end of upper bearing in place. Insert bearing remover/installer into journal oil hole. Turn crankshaft slowly counterclockwise until bearing is seated, then remove bearing remover/installer. Install and tighten main bearing cap.

THRUST BEARING ALIGNMENT

1) Install thrust bearing cap after all other main bearing caps have been tightened. Install thrust bearing cap bolts finger tight.

2) Pry crankshaft forward against thrust surface of upper half of bearing. Hold crankshaft forward and pry thrust bearing cap to rear. Tighten thrust bearing cap bolts while retaining forward pressure on crankshaft. *See Fig. 18.*

REAR MAIN BEARING OIL SEAL

Removal

1) Remove oil pan and oil pump (if required). Loosen all main bearing cap bolts to slightly lower crankshaft. Do not lower more than 1/32" (.79 mm). Remove rear

Ford Engines

7.5 LITER V8 (Cont.)

Fig. 18: Aligning Thrust Bearing

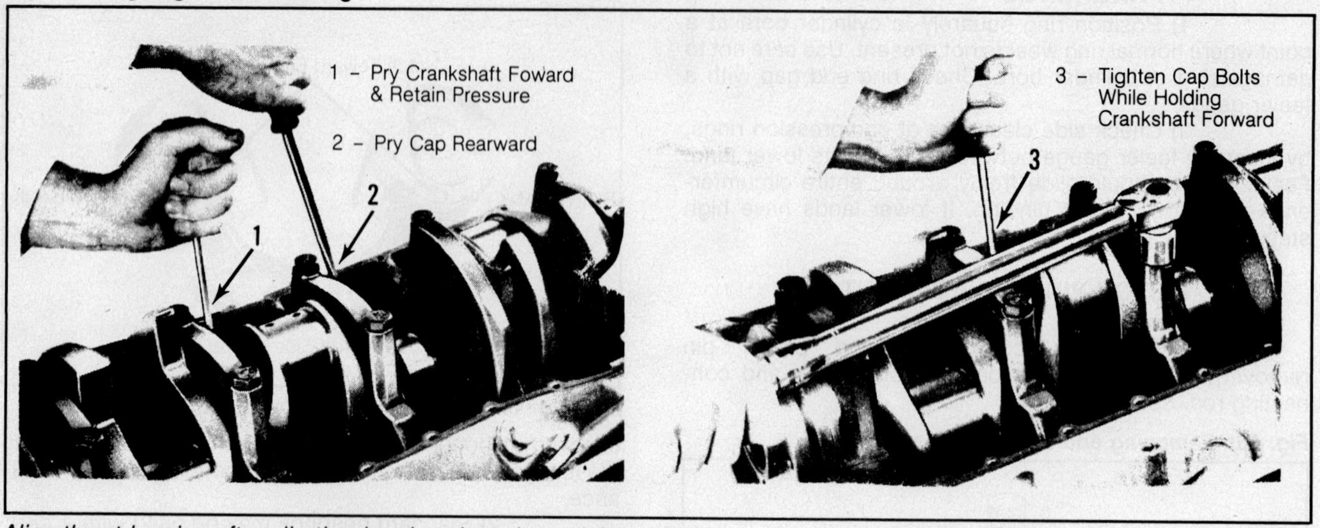

Align thrust bearing after all other bearings have been tightened.

main bearing cap and remove lower oil seal half. Use seal remover to remove upper seal.

2) If seal remover is not available, install a small metal screw in one end of the seal. Pull on screw to remove seal. Use care not to damage crankshaft seal surface. If equipped, remove oil seal retaining pin from bearing cap. Pin is not used with split-lip type seal.

Installation

1) Carefully clean oil seal grooves in bearing cap and block. Dip split-lip seal halves in engine oil. Carefully install upper seal into groove in cylinder block, with undercut side of seal toward front of engine.

NOTE: **Avoid damage to outside diameter of seal when installing in groove. Do not allow oil to get onto area where sealer will be applied.**

2) Rotate seal on crankshaft journal until about 3/8" of seal protrudes below parting surface. *See Fig. 19.*

3) Tighten all main bearing cap bolts except rear main. Install lower seal in rear main bearing cap with undercut side of seal toward front of engine.

Fig. 19: Installing Rear Main Bearing Oil Seal

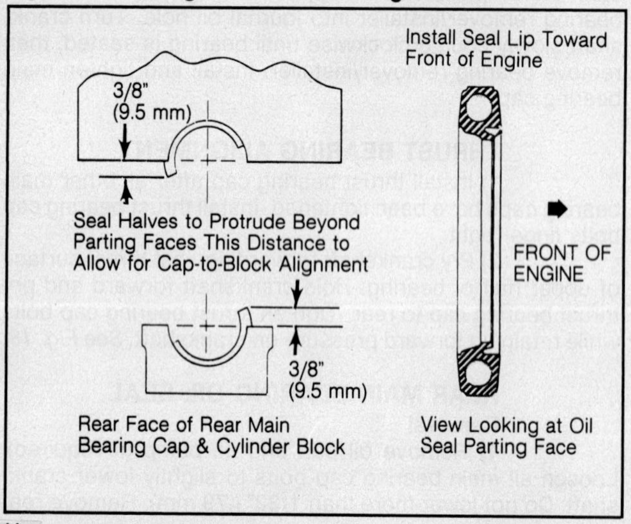

Use care not to damage crankshaft or new oil seal.

4) Allow seal to protrude about 3/8" above parting surface to mate with upper seal when cap is installed. Apply 1/16" bead of silicone sealer to both sides of cylinder block-to-cap mating surface and to both sides of bearing cap. *See Fig. 20.*

5) Install and tighten rear main bearing cap before sealer sets up (about 15 minutes). To complete installation, reverse removal procedure.

ENGINE OILING

CRANKCASE CAPACITY

Crankcase capacity is 5 quarts (4.75L). Add 1 quart (.95L) when replacing oil filter.

OIL FILTER

Change filter at first oil change and at every other oil change thereafter.

NORMAL OIL PRESSURE

Normal oil pressure at operating temperature should be 40-65 psi (2.8-4.6 kg/cm^2) at 2000 RPM.

OIL PRESSURE REGULATOR VALVE

Oil pressure regulator valve is located in pump body. Valve is non adjustable.

ENGINE OILING SYSTEM

Distributor-driven oil pump provides full-pressure lubrication to all camshaft and crankshaft bearings. Engine feeds oil through hydraulic valve lifters and hollow push rods to rocker arms and upper valve train area. Timing chain and sprockets are lubricated by drainage from No. 1 camshaft bearing. *See Fig. 21.*

OIL PUMP

NOTE: **If any part of oil pump needs replacing, replace entire pump.**

Removal

Raise engine at least 4" from engine mounts. Loosen oil pan attaching bolts and lower pan. Remove oil pump and oil inlet tube and lay assembly in pan. Remove pan with pump assembly.

7.5 LITER V8 (Cont.)

Fig. 20: Silicone Sealer Application Points

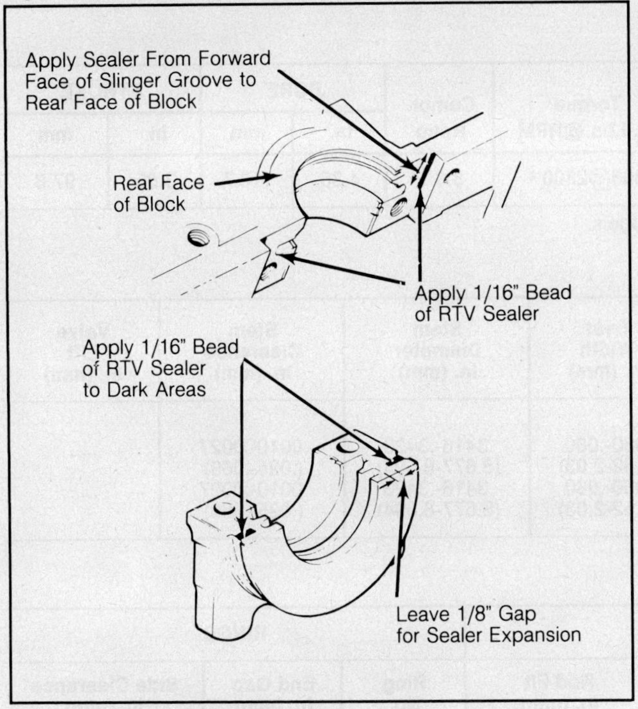

Do not allow sealer to contact lip of seal.

Disassembly

Remove oil inlet tube from pump. Remove pump cover. Remove inner rotor, shaft and outer rotor from oil pump. Drill small hole in oil pressure relief valve cap. Insert self-threading sheet metal screw into cap and pull cap from chamber. Remove spring and plunger.

Fig. 21: Engine Oiling System

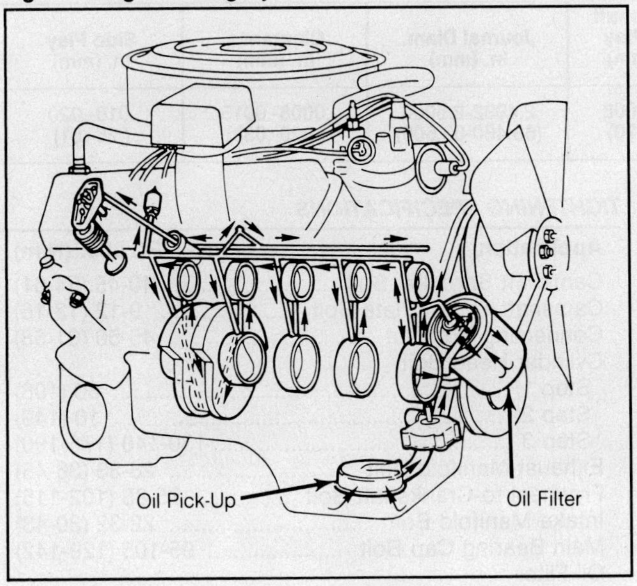

Inspection

1) Wash all parts thoroughly and dry with compressed air. Check pump housing, outer rotor, inner rotor, shaft and pump cover for damage, scoring or excessive wear. Remove rotor assembly from pump housing. Using feeler gauge, measure inner-to-outer rotor tip clearance.

2) Install rotor assembly in pump housing. Lay a straightedge over rotor assembly and housing. Insert feeler gauge between straightedge and housing to measure rotor end play. Using a feeler gauge, measure clearance between outer rotor and pump housing.

3) Measure shaft outside diameter and housing bearing inside diameter. Difference between readings is shaft-to-housing bearing clearance.

4) Relief valve spring should test to 20.6-22.6 lbs. (9-10 kg) at 2.49" (63.5 mm). Inspect relief valve spring for worn or collapsed condition. Check relief valve plunger for scores and free operation in bore. Check clearance between relief valve plunger and bore.

OIL PUMP SPECIFICATIONS

Application	In. (mm)
Rotor Tip Clearance	.012 (.30)
Rotor End Play	.004 (.10) Max.
Outer Rotor-to-Housing Clearance	.001-.013 (.03-.33)
Shaft-to-Housing Clearance	.0015-.0030 (.038-.076)
Relief Valve-to-Bore Clearance	.0015-.0030 (.038-.076)

Reassembly

Clean and oil all parts thoroughly. Install relief valve plunger, spring and new cap. Stake cap into position. To complete reassembly, reverse disassembly procedure.

Installation

Prime oil pump. To install oil pump, reverse removal procedure. Use new gaskets.

ENGINE COOLING

WATER PUMP

Removal

1) Drain cooling system. Remove fan shroud and fan. Loosen power steering pump attaching bolts. If A/C equipped, remove compressor top bracket. Remove A/C idler pulley and bracket assembly.

2) Remove all drive belts. Remove air pump, alternator and bracket, and power steering pump. Disconnect all hoses from water pump, and loosen by-pass hose clamp at pump. Remove remaining attaching bolts and remove water pump. Remove separator plate from water pump and discard gaskets.

Installation

To install, reverse removal procedure. Use new gaskets coated on both sides with water-resistant sealer.

NOTE: For further information on cooling system capacities and other cooling system components, see appropriate article in ENGINE COOLING SYSTEMS at end of ENGINE section.

Ford Engines

7.5 LITER V8 (Cont.)

ENGINE SPECIFICATIONS

GENERAL SPECIFICATIONS

Year	DISPLACEMENT Cu. In.	DISPLACEMENT Liters	Fuel System	HP@RPM	Torque Ft. Lbs.@RPM	Compr. Ratio	BORE In.	BORE mm	STROKE In.	STROKE mm
1985	460	7.5	4-Bbl.	226@4400 [1]	365@2800 [2]	8.0:1	4.36	110.7	3.85	97.8

[1] – 221@4200 for California models. [2] – 361@2600 for California models.

VALVES

Engine Size & Valve	Head Diam. In. (mm)	Face Angle	Seat Angle	Seat Width In. (mm)	Stem Diameter In. (mm)	Stem Clearance In. (mm)	Valve Lift In. (mm)
7.5L							
Intake	2.075-2.090 (52.70-53.09)	44°	45°	.060-.080 (1.52-2.03)	.3416-.3423 (8.677-8.694)	.0010-.0027 (.025-.069)	.....
Exhaust	1.646-1.661 (41.81-42.19)	44°	45°	.060-.080 (1.52-2.03)	.3416-.3423 (8.677-8.694)	.0010-.0027 (.025-.069)	.....

PISTONS, PINS, RINGS

Engine	PISTONS Clearance In. (mm)	PINS Piston Fit In. (mm)	PINS Rod Fit In. (mm)	RINGS Ring No.	RINGS End Gap In. (mm)	RINGS Side Clearance In. (mm)
7.5L	.0022-.0030 (.056-.076)	.0002-.0005 (.005-.013)	Interference Fit	1 & 2	.010-.020 (.25-.51)	.0025-.0045 (.064-.114)
				3	.010-.035 (.25-.89)	Snug

CRANKSHAFT MAIN & CONNECTING ROD BEARINGS

Engine	MAIN BEARINGS Journal Diam. In. (mm)	MAIN BEARINGS Clearance In. (mm)	MAIN BEARINGS Thrust Bearing	MAIN BEARINGS Crankshaft End Play In. (mm)	CONNECTING ROD BEARINGS Journal Diam. In. (mm)	CONNECTING ROD BEARINGS Clearance In. (mm)	CONNECTING ROD BEARINGS Side Play In. (mm)
7.5L	2.9994-3.0002 (76.185-76.205)	.0008-.0015 (.020-.038)	No. 3	.004-.008 (.10-.20)	2.4992-2.5000 (63.480-63.500)	.0008-.0015 (.020-.038)	.010-.020 (.25-.51)

CAMSHAFT

Engine	Journal Diam. In. (mm)	Clearance In. (mm)	Lobe Lift In. (mm)
7.5L [1]	2.1238-2.1248 (53.945-53.970)	.001-.003 (.03-.08)	.252 [2] (6.40) .278 [3] (7.06)

[1] – End play is .001-.006" (.05-.15 mm). [2] – Intake. [3] – Exhaust.

VALVE SPRINGS

Engine	Free Length In. (mm)	PRESSURE Lbs. @ In. (Kg @ mm) Valve Closed	PRESSURE Lbs. @ In. (Kg @ mm) Valve Open
7.5L Int. & Exh. [1]	2.06 (52.3)	76-84 @ 1.81 (34-38 @ 46.0)	218-240 @ 1.33 (99-109 @ 33.8)

[1] – Valve spring installed height is 1.797-1.828" (45.64-46.43 mm).

TIGHTENING SPECIFICATIONS

Application	Ft. Lbs. (N.m)
Camshaft Sprocket Bolt	40-45 (54-61)
Camshaft Thrust Plate Bolt	9-12 (12-16)
Connecting Rod Nut	45-50 (61-68)
Cylinder Head Bolt	
Step 1	80 (108)
Step 2	110 (149)
Step 3	130-140 (176-190)
Exhaust Manifold Bolt	28-33 (38-45)
Flywheel-to-Crankshaft Bolt	75-85 (102-115)
Intake Manifold Bolt	22-32 (30-43)
Main Bearing Cap Bolt	95-105 (129-142)
Oil Filter	
Adapter-to-Cylinder Block Bolt	40-50 (54-68)
Insert-to-Cylinder Block/Adapter Bolt	45-55 (61-75)
Oil Pump Attaching Bolt	22-32 (30-43)
Rocker Arm Fulcrum Bolt	18-25 (24-34)
Vibration Damper-to-Crankshaft Bolt	70-90 (95-122)

ENGINE CODE DESIGNATIONS

IDENTIFICATION CODING

General Motors engines may be identified by the 8th character of the Vehicle Identification Number (VIN) located on the left, upper side of the instrument panel. This number is visible through the windshield from outside the vehicle. An additional identification code will be found on the engine. This code can also be found on the under hood emission control decal. This information pertains to Chevrolet and GMC vehicles.

CHEVROLET & GMC

Engine	Code
1.9L 4-Cyl. (VIN A)	FZJ, FZK
2.2L 4-Cyl. (VIN S) [1]	UMU
2.5L 4-Cyl. (VIN E)	AAK, AAL, ABS, ABM
2.8L V6 (VIN B)	TAA, TAB, TAC, TAD TAF, TAH, TAJ, TAK TAM, TAR, TAS, TAT TAU, TAX, TAY, TAZ TBB, TBC, TBD, TBF TBH, TBN, TBP
4.3L V6 (VIN N)	TCA, TCB, TCC, TCD TCF, TNA, TNB, TND TNF, TNG, TNH, TNK TNL, TNM, TWA, TWB TWC, TWD, TWF, TWH
4.8L 6-Cyl. (VIN T)	TRA, TRC, TRD, TRF TRH, TRJ, TRM, TRN TRR, TRS, TRT, TRU
5.0L V8 (VIN F)	FDW, FFD
5.0L V8 (VIN H)	FCU, FCW, FCX, FCY FCZ, FFA, FFB, FFC TTA, TTB, TTF, TTH TTJ, TTP, TTR, TTS

[1] – Diesel engine.

CHEVROLET & GMC (Cont.)

Engine	Code
5.7L V8 (VIN K)	C7R, FLH, FLJ, FLK FLL, FLM, FLN, FLR FLS, FLT, FLW, FMK FML, FMM, FMR, FMS FMT, FNA, FNB, FNC FND, FNF, FNH, FNJ FNK, FNM, FNN, FNR FNS, FRS, FRT, FRU T8A, T8B, T8C
5.7L V8 (VIN L)	FMA, FMB, FMC, FMD FMF, FMH, FMJ, FMU FMW, THW, THZ
6.2L V8 (VIN C) [1]	DHB, DHC, DHD DHF, DHH, DHJ DHK, DHL, DHM DHN, DHP, DHW DHX, DHY
6.2L V8 (VIN J) [1]	DFN, DHS, DHT, DHZ DJB, DJC, DJF, DJH DJJ, DJK, DJM, DJN DJR, DJS, DJT, DJU DJW, DJX, DJZ
7.4L V8 (VIN W)	AKA, AKB, AKC, AKD AKF, AKH, AKJ, AKK AKM, AKN, AKR, TZA TZB, TZC, TZD, TZF TZG, TZH, TZJ, TZK TZL, TZM

[1] – Diesel engine.

General Motors Engines

1.9 LITER 4-CYLINDER

ENGINE CODING

ENGINE IDENTIFICATION

The eighth character of the Vehicle Identification Number (VIN) designates engine type. The VIN is located on a plate attached to the top left corner of the instrument panel. Engine identification number is stamped on a machined pad on left rear side of cylinder block, just above the oil pan.

ENGINE IDENTIFICATION CODE

Engine	Code
1.9L 2-Bbl.	A

ENGINE REMOVAL

See ENGINE REMOVAL at end of ENGINE section.

MANIFOLDS & CYLINDER HEAD

INTAKE MANIFOLD

Removal

1) Disconnect negative battery cable. Drain cooling system, including cylinder block. Remove air cleaner. Disconnect upper radiator hose and heater hoses from intake manifold, and position out of way.

2) Label and disconnect all vacuum hoses, ventilation hoses and electrical connectors at intake manifold, carburetor and distributor. Disconnect fuel inlet and return hoses from carburetor. Disconnect accelerator cable.

3) Detach oil dipstick tube bracket from intake manifold. Disconnect EGR pipe from EGR valve adapter. Remove 8 intake manifold bolts. Remove intake manifold and carburetor as an assembly.

Installation

1) Check manifold for cracks. Ensure manifold-to-head surface distortion does not exceed .016" (.4 mm). Resurface manifold if needed.

2) Clean all gasket surfaces. Using new gasket, install intake manifold and nuts. Tighten manifold nuts, working outward from the center. To complete installation, reverse removal procedure.

EXHAUST MANIFOLD

Removal

1) Disconnect battery negative cable. Raise vehicle and disconnect header pipe and EGR pipe from exhaust manifold. Lower vehicle. Remove air cleaner bolts and lift air cleaner to remove hot air hose.

2) If equipped, remove A/C compressor and power steering pump. Remove brackets. Remove 4 bolts holding heat shield to exhaust manifold. Remove heat shield. Remove exhaust manifold cover and manifold.

Installation

Check exhaust manifold for cracks or damage. Ensure head and manifold gasket surfaces are clean and have no nicks. To install, use a new gasket and reverse removal procedure. Tighten mounting nuts progressively, working outward from the center.

CYLINDER HEAD

Removal

1) Remove valve cover. Remove EGR pipe clamp bolt from rear of cylinder head. Raise vehicle and disconnect exhaust pipe at manifold. Lower vehicle and drain cooling system. Disconnect heater hoses from intake manifold and cylinder head.

2) If equipped, remove A/C compressor and power steering pump and position aside. Disconnect accelerator linkage and fuel hoses at carburetor. Disconnect all electrical connections, vacuum hoses and ventilation hoses at cylinder head, intake manifold, carburetor and distributor.

3) Rotate distributor until No. 4 piston is at TDC on end of compression stroke. Remove distributor cap and mark rotor-to-housing relationship. Disconnect spark plug wires at spark plugs, and remove distributor cap with spark plug wires attached. Remove distributor.

4) Remove fuel pump. Retract timing chain automatic adjuster shoe by depressing adjuster lock lever with a screwdriver and rotating clockwise (viewed from top of engine), while pushing in shoe. *See Fig. 1*. After locking automatic adjuster, ensure chain tension is released.

Fig. 1: Releasing Timing Chain Tension

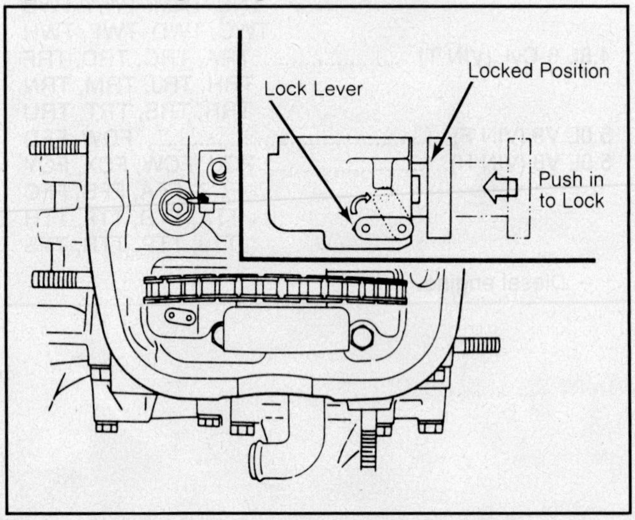

Depress automatic adjuster lock lever and rotate in direction indicated.

Fig. 2: Cylinder Head Tightening Sequence

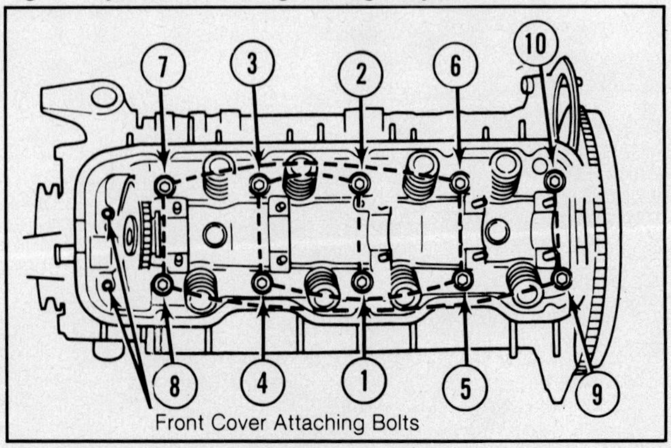

Tighten in progressive steps to 60 ft. lbs. (81 N.m), then tighten to 72 ft. lbs. (98 N.m).

1.9 LITER 4-CYLINDER (Cont.)

5) Remove timing sprocket bolt, and slide camshaft sprocket and fuel pump eccentric from camshaft. Keep sprocket on chain damper and tensioner. Do not remove chain from sprocket.

6) Disconnect air pump hose and check valve at air injection manifold. Remove cylinder head bolts progressively, in reverse of tightening sequence. Remove cylinder head with intake and exhaust manifolds attached.

Installation

Clean all gasket surfaces. Clean head bolt and block threads. Install new head gasket with "TOP" facing up. To complete installation, reverse removal procedure. Tighten head bolts in progressive steps. *See Fig. 2.* Adjust valves.

CAMSHAFT

ENGINE FRONT COVER

Removal

1) Remove cylinder head, as previously described. Remove oil pan and pick-up tube from oil pump. Remove all drive belts from crankshaft pulley, then remove vibration damper.

2) If equipped, remove A/C compressor or power steering pump and set aside. Remove distributor and engine front cover and discard cover gasket.

Installation

1) Clean all gasket mating surfaces. Install new gasket on cylinder block. Align oil pump gear punch mark with oil filter side of front cover. Align pump gear dowel pin center with pump cover alignment mark. *See Fig. 3.*

Fig. 3: Aligning Oil Pump for Front Cover Installation

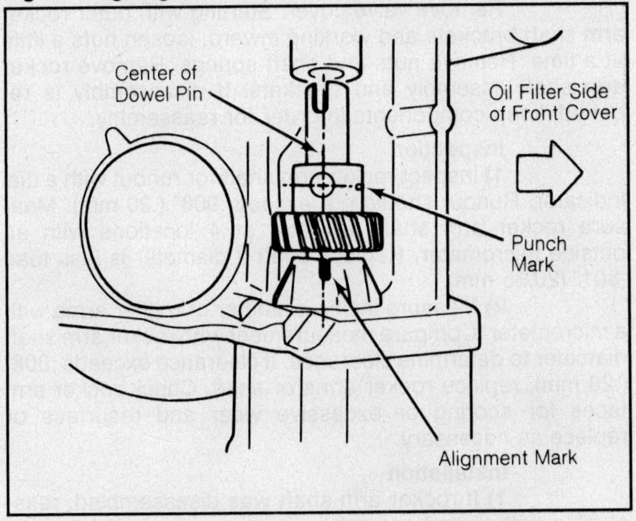

Engage oil pump gear with crankshaft pinion gear.

2) Turn crankshaft until No. 1 piston is at TDC. Engage pinion gear with oil pump gear on crankshaft and install front cover. Ensure oil pump drive gear punch mark faces rearward. Ensure pump shaft slotted end is parallel with front of cylinder block, and that offset is forward.

3) Install and tighten front cover bolts. To complete installation, reverse removal procedure.

FRONT COVER OIL SEAL

Removal

Disconnect negative battery cable. Drain cooling system and remove radiator. Remove engine fan. Remove drive belts from crankshaft pulley. Remove vibration damper. Carefully pry out front cover oil seal.

Installation

Install new seal using Seal Installer (J-26587). Lubricate seal lips with engine oil. To complete installation, reverse removal procedure.

TIMING CHAIN & SPROCKETS

Removal

1) Remove front cover, as previously described. Retract automatic timing chain adjuster shoe by depressing adjuster lock lever and rotating clockwise (viewed from top of engine), while pushing in shoe. *See Fig. 1.* After locking automatic adjuster, ensure chain tension is released.

2) Remove timing chain and sprockets. Use a gear puller to remove crankshaft sprocket and pinion gear, if removal is necessary.

Inspection

1) Check sprockets for wear and replace if necessary. Measure 40 links of timing chain (outside pin-to-outside pin), with 22 lbs. (10 kg) of force stretching chain. Replace chain if measurement exceeds 15.16" (385 mm).

2) Remove automatic chain adjuster, check rack teeth for wear and replace adjuster if teeth are worn. Remove chain tensioner "E" clip and remove tensioner.

3) Check chain tensioner and pivot pin for wear and replace as necessary. Inspect chain guide for wear or plugged lower oil jet. Clean or replace as necessary. Ensure jet oil port faces crankshaft.

Installation

1) To install chain tensioner, lubricate tensioner and place over pin. Put "E" clip on pin, then tap pin into engine block until clip just clears tensioner.

2) If removed, install crankshaft sprocket and pinion gear onto crankshaft with grooved side toward front cover. Install Woodruff key. Turn crankshaft until No. 1 piston is at TDC and Woodruff key faces up.

3) Install timing chain on crankshaft, aligning chain mark plate (facing front) with mark on crankshaft timing sprocket. Ensure side of chain with most links between mark plates is on chain guide side of engine. *See Fig. 4.*

NOTE: **Keep timing chain engaged with camshaft sprocket until sprocket is installed.**

4) Install camshaft sprocket so triangular timing mark aligns with chain mark plate. Install automatic chain adjuster and release lock (if removed). To complete installation, reverse removal procedure.

CAMSHAFT

Removal

1) Remove valve cover. Rotate crankshaft until No. 4 piston is at TDC on end of compression stroke. Remove distributor cap and mark rotor-to-housing position. Remove distributor and fuel pump.

2) Fully retract automatic timing chain adjuster shoe by depressing adjuster lock lever and rotating clockwise (viewed from top of engine), while pushing in shoe. *See*

Fig. 4: Aligning Timing Chain and Sprockets

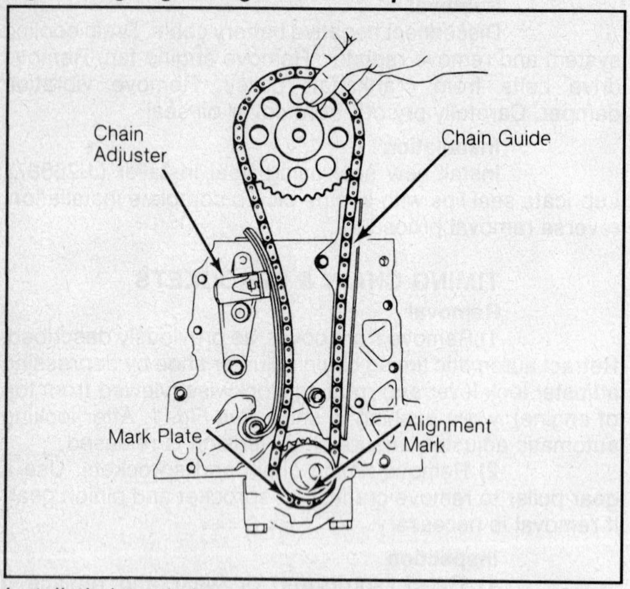

Install timing chain with most links between mark plates toward chain guide side (left side) of engine.

Fig. 1. Ensure chain tension is released after locking adjuster.

3) Remove camshaft sprocket and fuel pump eccentric from camshaft. Keep timing sprocket on chain damper and tensioner without removing chain from sprocket. Remove rocker arm shaft and bracket assembly. Remove camshaft.

Inspection

1) Inspect camshaft lobes and journals for wear. Using a micrometer, measure lobe height and journal diameter. If lobe height is less than 1.431" (36.35 mm), journal diameter is less than 1.33" (33.8 mm), or difference between journal diameter measurements is greater than .002" (.05 mm), replace camshaft.

2) Measure runout using a dial indicator. Replace camshaft if runout exceeds .004" (.10 mm). To check camshaft end play, position camshaft on cylinder head and attach dial indicator to front end of head. *See Fig. 5*.

3) Push camshaft rearward and zero dial indicator. Push camshaft forward to record maximum movement. If end play exceeds .008" (.20 mm), check for cylinder head and camshaft wear. Replace worn components.

Installation

1) Lubricate camshaft journals and mating bearing surfaces in cylinder head with engine oil. Position camshaft on cylinder head and install rocker arm shaft and bracket assembly. Ensure that No. 1 rocker arm shaft bracket mark is aligned with camshaft thrust flange mark, and that front cover TDC mark is aligned with crankshaft pulley groove.

2) Using care not to allow chain to separate from camshaft sprocket, assemble sprocket to camshaft. Install fuel pump eccentric and sprocket attaching bolt and washer.

3) Remove half-moon seal from front of cylinder head, then tighten camshaft sprocket bolt. Replace half-moon seal in cylinder head. Install distributor. Depress automatic adjuster shoe to release lock. Check timing chain tension. To complete installation, reverse removal procedure.

Fig. 5: Measuring Camshaft End Play

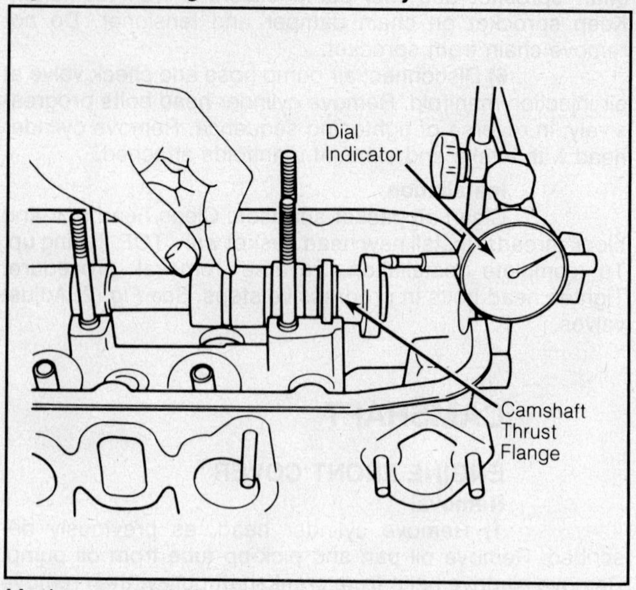

Maximum camshaft end play is .008" (.20 mm).

VALVES

VALVE ARRANGEMENT

Right Side – All intake.
Left Side – All exhaust.

ROCKER ARM SHAFT ASSEMBLY

Removal

Remove valve cover. Starting with outer rocker arm shaft brackets and working inward, loosen nuts a little at a time. Remove nuts and shaft springs. Remove rocker arm shaft assembly and brackets. If disassembly is required, keep components in order for reassembly.

Inspection

1) Inspect rocker arm shaft for runout with a dial indicator. Runout should not exceed .008" (.20 mm). Measure rocker arm shaft diameter at 4 locations with an outside micrometer. Replace shaft if diameter is less than .801" (20.35 mm).

2) Measure inside diameter of rocker arms with a micrometer. Compare measurement with rocker arm shaft diameter to determine clearance. If clearance exceeds .008" (.20 mm), replace rocker arms or shaft. Check rocker arm faces for scoring or excessive wear and resurface or replace as necessary.

Installation

1) If rocker arm shaft was disassembled, reassemble with cylinder number on upper face of brackets pointing toward front of engine. Install longer shafts on exhaust valve side of engine. Position shaft alignment marks toward front of engine.

2) Position mark on camshaft thrust flange upward, to align with mark on No. 1 bracket. *See Fig. 6*. Lubricate rocker arm shaft, rocker arms and valve stems with engine oil. Position rocker arm shaft assembly onto cylinder head.

3) Install rocker arm shaft springs and stud nuts. Hold outer edges of springs between adjustable wrench jaws while tightening nuts to prevent spring damage.

1.9 LITER 4-CYLINDER (Cont.)

Tighten stud nuts in progressive steps, working outward from center bracket. To complete installation, reverse removal procedure. Adjust valves.

Fig. 6: Installing Rocker Arm Shaft Assembly

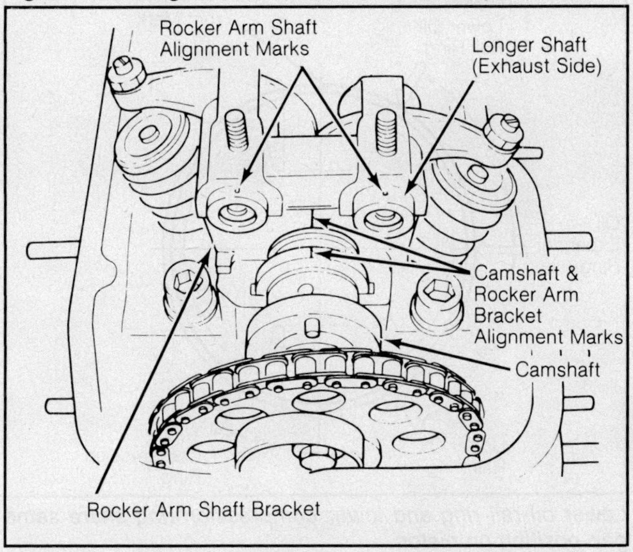

Tighten rocker arm shaft brackets to 16 ft. lbs. (22 N.m).

VALVE SPRINGS & OIL SEALS

Removal

1) Disconnect battery negative cable. Remove air cleaner and valve cover. Remove rocker arm shaft and bracket assembly, as previously described. Disconnect spark plug wire from cylinder to be serviced and remove spark plug.

2) Install an air hose and adapter to spark plug hole and apply air pressure. Using Valve Spring Compressor (J-26513), compress valve spring. *See Fig. 7*. Remove valve spring retainers, spring cap and inner and outer springs. Remove valve stem oil seal and lower spring seat.

NOTE: Do not remove air pressure from cylinder until valve spring components are reassembled.

Fig. 7: Compressing Valve Spring

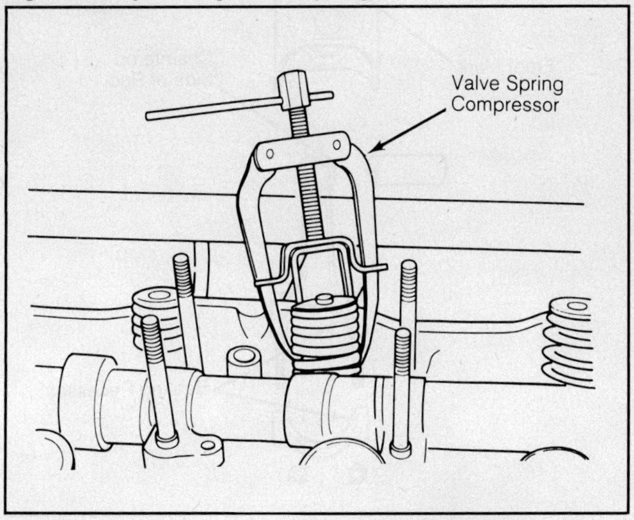

Do not remove air pressure until after reassembly.

Inspection

1) Using a flat surface and steel square, measure valve springs for out-of-round. Take measurement between top of spring and square while slowly rotating spring. Out-of-round must not exceed 5/64" (2 mm).

2) Measure inner and outer valve spring free length with a ruler. Check outer valve spring tension with a valve spring tester. Replace springs if free length or tension is incorrect.

VALVE SPRING TENSION

Valve Spring	Pressure Lbs. @ In. (kg @ mm)
Outer	51-60 @ 1.61 (23-27 @ 41.0)

Installation

1) Install lower spring seat. Lubricate valve stem and lower spring seat with engine oil. Lubricate new oil seal with engine oil and install over valve stem and onto valve guide. Ensure oil seal inside lip fits into valve guide groove. Install inner and outer springs and spring cap.

2) Using Spring Compressor (J-26513), compress springs and install retainers. Ensure retainers fully seat in valve stem groove. Relieve air pressure. To complete installation, reverse removal procedure.

VALVE GUIDE SERVICING

Replace valves and guides together. Replace intake valve and guide if valve stem diameter is less than .310" (7.88 mm). Replace exhaust valve and guide if valve stem diameter is less than .309" (7.85 mm).

Removal

Disassemble cylinder head. Insert Valve Guide Remover/Installer (J-26512) into valve guide from combustion chamber side of cylinder head. Drive valve guide out top of cylinder head.

Installation

Apply engine oil to outer surface of valve guide and position guide in bore. Using valve guide remover/installer, drive guide into cylinder head until remover/installer bottoms on head.

VALVE CLEARANCE ADJUSTMENT

1) Ensure rocker arm shaft brackets are properly tightened. Cold valve clearances are .006" (.15 mm) for intake valves, and .010" (.25 mm) for exhaust valves.

2) Turn crankshaft until No. 1 piston is at TDC on end of compression stroke. Adjust valves as listed in table. *See Fig. 8*. Turn crankshaft 1 revolution until No. 4 piston is at TDC on end of compression stroke and adjust remaining valves.

VALVE CLEARANCE ADJUSTMENT

Piston at TDC	Adjust Intake	Adjust Exhaust
No. 1	Nos. 1, 2	Nos. 1, 3
No. 4	Nos. 3, 4	Nos. 2, 4

1.9 LITER 4-CYLINDER (Cont.)

Fig. 8: Adjusting Valve Clearance

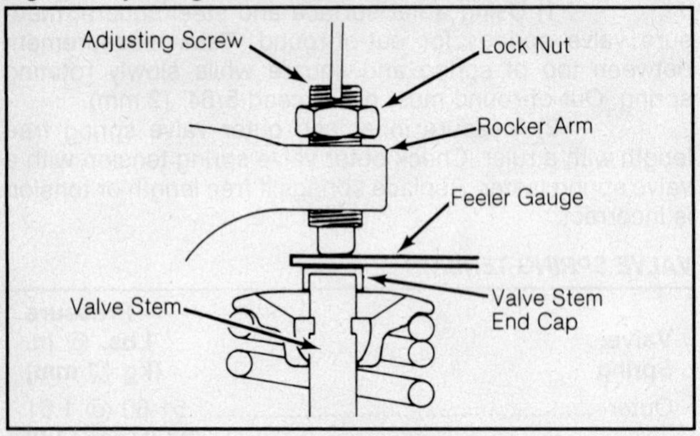

Cold valve clearances are .006" (.15 mm) for intake valves and .010" (.25 mm) for exhaust valves.

PISTONS, RINGS & PINS

OIL PAN

See OIL PAN REMOVAL at end of ENGINE section.

PISTON & ROD ASSEMBLY

Removal

1) Remove cylinder head and oil pan. With piston placed at bottom of stroke, remove ridge from top of cylinder bore using ridge reamer. Mark right side of connecting rods and caps for cylinder identification.

2) Position piston to be removed at bottom of stroke. Remove rod cap and upper bearing from connecting rod. Using wooden hammer handle, push piston out top of cylinder bore. Install rod cap on mating rod.

Installation

1) Properly position rings on piston and install upper bearing in rod. *See Fig. 9*. Coat rod bearing surfaces, cylinder bore, piston and rings with engine oil. Install ring compressor over piston and rings.

2) Ensure position of rings does not change. Turn crankshaft to position journal uppermost. With mark on piston head positioned toward front of engine, install piston and rod assembly into cylinder bore while guiding rod onto crankshaft journal.

3) Align rod bearing cap mark with connecting rod mark. Install and tighten connecting rod cap. Ensure crankshaft turns smoothly.

FITTING PISTONS

NOTE: Measurements should be taken at 70°F (21°C).

1) Measure diameter of piston (skirt) 90° to piston pin bore, at a point 1 9/16" (40 mm) below piston head. Measure cylinder bore diameter at bottom of bore (above ring travel), at a point where least wear can be measured.

2) The difference between the two measurements is piston-to-cylinder bore clearance. Using cylinder bore gauge, measure cylinder bore diameter 90° to crankshaft, then in line with crankshaft. Take measurements about 5/16" to 2 3/4" below upper face of cylinder block.

3) Rebore block if wear exceeds .008" (.2 mm). Replace block if bore diameter exceeds 3.460" (88.04 mm).

Cylinder bore original diameter is designated by a letter code stamped on cylinder block upper face.

Fig. 9: Desired Piston Ring Spacing

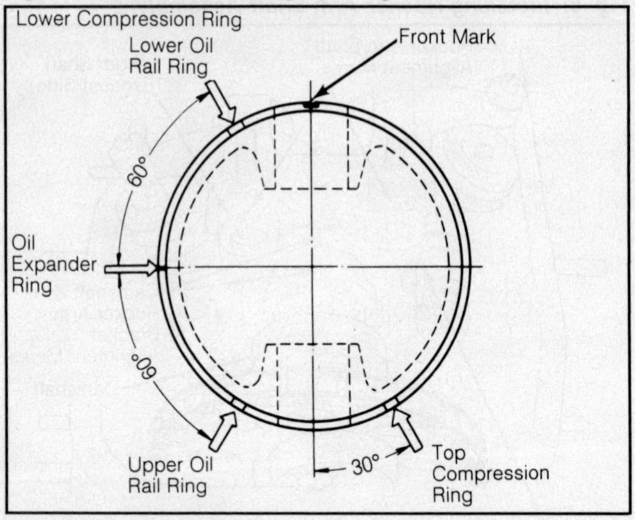

Lower oil rail ring and lower compression ring share same gap position on piston.

CYLINDER BORE CODES

Code	Cylinder Bore Diameter
"A"	3.4191-3.4194" (87.000-87.010 mm)
"B"	3.4195-3.4198" (87.011-87.020 mm)
"C"	3.4199-3.4202" (87.021-87.030 mm)
"D"	3.4203-3.4206" (87.031-87.040 mm)

FITTING RINGS

1) Position ring into cylinder bore at a point where bore diameter is smallest. Ring must be square in bore. Measure ring end gap with a feeler gauge.

Fig. 10: Piston-to-Connecting Rod Positioning

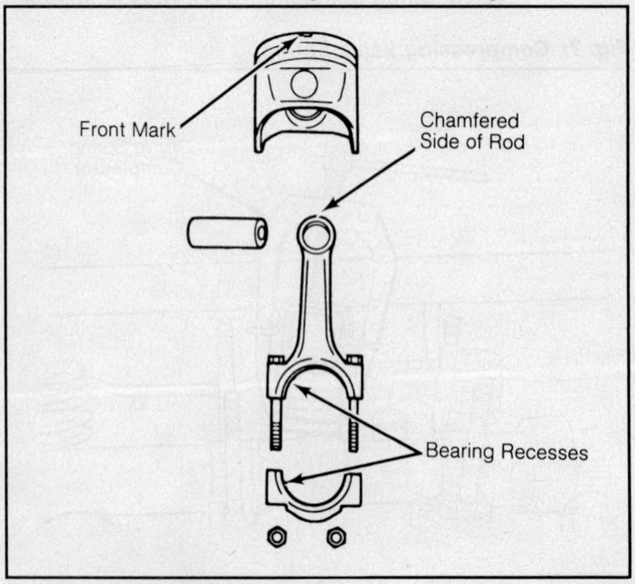

Note position of bearing recesses.

2) Using feeler gauge, measure side clearance between piston rings and ring land. Take measurements at several points around circumference of piston. Replace piston and rings if measurement exceeds specification, or if there is abnormal wear on piston rings or ring land.

PISTON PIN REPLACEMENT

Removal

Using arbor press and piston pin remover, press pin from piston and connecting rod.

Installation

Apply coat of engine oil to piston pin bores in piston and connecting rod. Assemble connecting rod to piston with chamfered side on rod's pin bore end on same side as front mark on piston head. *See Fig. 10.* Using arbor press and pin installer, press piston pin into piston and rod assembly.

CRANKSHAFT & ROD BEARINGS

CONNECTING ROD BEARINGS

1) Mark connecting rod and rod caps for cylinder identification. Place crankshaft journal of cylinder to be checked at bottom of stroke and remove rod cap.

2) Place a strip of Plastigage across journal surface, in line with crankshaft, about 1/4" off center and away from oil holes. Install cap and tighten to specification. Do not turn crankshaft.

3) Remove cap and measure width of compressed Plastigage. Replacement bearings are available in standard, .010" (.25 mm) and .020" (.50 mm) undersizes.

MAIN BEARINGS

1) Check main bearing clearances one at a time. Ensure main bearing caps are marked for identification. Use Plastigage method (as previously described) to measure main bearing clearance.

2) Install upper main bearings in cylinder block and position crankshaft in place. Install thrust washers on both sides of No. 3 journal, with oil grooves toward crankshaft counterweight. Pry crankshaft rearward and check thrust clearance with feeler gauge inserted between crankshaft and thrust washer.

3) Install main bearings and caps. Arrows on bearing caps must be positioned toward front of engine. Tighten bearing caps in progressive steps in the following sequence: No. 3, No. 4, No. 2, No. 5 and No. 1.

4) Replacement bearings are available in standard, .010" (.25 mm) and .020" (.50 mm) undersizes.

THRUST BEARING ALIGNMENT

Install bearings on cylinder block. Position crankshaft over bearings. Install thrust bearing in position on both sides of No. 3 journal. Pry crankshaft rearward. Using a feeler gauge, check clearance between crankshaft and thrust bearing. If clearance exceeds .012" (.30 mm), replace thrust bearings.

REAR MAIN BEARING OIL SEAL

Removal

Remove starter and position aside. Remove transmission. Remove clutch cover and pressure plate assembly. Remove flywheel and cover. Pry old seal out of retainer and discard seal.

Installation

Position new seal in retainer. Fill gap between lips of seal with grease and coat seal lips with engine oil. Place retainer on a flat surface and drive seal into place using Seal Installer (J-22928 A). To complete installation, reverse removal procedure.

ENGINE OILING

CRANKCASE CAPACITY

Crankcase capacity is 4 quarts (3.8L), with or without oil filter replacement.

NORMAL OIL PRESSURE

Normal oil pressure should be 30-40 psi (2.1-2.8 kg/cm^2) with engine at operating temperature at speeds of 35-40 MPH.

OIL PRESSURE REGULATOR VALVE

Oil pressure regulator valve is located in oil pump body. Valve is nonadjustable.

ENGINE OILING SYSTEM

Engine lubrication system is pressure circulation type with full-flow oil filter. Pump delivers oil to main gallery, where it is routed to crankshaft journals. Through oil passages in crankshaft, oil is fed to connecting rod journals, connecting rods, and then to piston pins.

A branched oil passage from No. 3 crankshaft journal routes oil to cylinder head and rocker arms. An oil well on upper face of cylinder head lubricates camshaft. Timing chain and sprockets are lubricated with oil feed from No. 1 crankshaft journal oil passage, and sprayed by oil jet on chain guide. Oil pump houses a relief valve.

OIL PUMP

Removal

Remove oil pan. Remove bolt attaching oil inlet pipe to engine. Remove oil pump from front cover.

Installation

Prime oil pump. Assemble pump and inlet tube to engine. Install and tighten attaching bolts.

ENGINE COOLING

WATER PUMP

Removal

Disconnect battery negative cable. Remove lower fan shroud and drain radiator. Remove A/C compressor, if equipped. Remove air pump and alternator mounting bolts. Pivot pump and generator toward engine and remove drive belts from water pump pulley and fan and air pump drive pulley. Remove fan, set plate and pulley. Remove water pump.

Installation

To install, reverse removal procedure. Adjust belt tensions. Fill system with coolant, start engine and check for coolant leaks.

NOTE: **For further information on cooling system capacities and other cooling system components, see appropriate article in ENGINE COOLING SYSTEMS at end of ENGINE section.**

1.9 LITER 4-CYLINDER (Cont.)

ENGINE SPECIFICATIONS

GENERAL SPECIFICATIONS

Year	DISPLACEMENT Cu. In.	DISPLACEMENT Liters	Fuel System	HP@RPM	Torque Ft. Lbs.@RPM	Compr. Ratio	BORE In.	BORE mm	STROKE In.	STROKE mm
1985	119	1.9	2-Bbl.	82 @ 4600	101 @ 3000	8.4:1	3.43	87	3.23	82

VALVES

Engine Size & Valve	Head Diam. In. (mm)	Face Angle	Seat Angle	Seat Width In. (mm)	Stem Diameter In. (mm)	Stem Clearance In. (mm)	Valve Lift In. (mm)
1.9L							
Int.	1.59 (40.4)	45°	45°	.....	.310 Min. (7.88 Min.)	.0009-.0022 (.023-.056)	.....
Exh.	1.34 (34.0)	45°	45°	.....	.309 Min. (7.85 Min.)	.0015-.0031 (.038-.078)	.....

PISTONS, PINS, RINGS

Engine	PISTONS Clearance In. (mm)	PINS Piston Fit In. (mm)	PINS Rod Fit In. (mm)	RINGS Ring No.	RINGS End Gap In. (mm)	RINGS Side Clearance In. (mm)
1.9L	.0018-.0026 (.045-.065)	[1]	Press Fit	1	.014-.020 (.35-.50)	.006 Max. (.15 Max.)
				2	.014-.020 (.35-.50)	.006 Max. (.15 Max.)
				3	.008-.035 (.20-.90)	.006 Max. (.15 Max.)

1 – Pin should press into piston with finger pressure.

CRANKSHAFT MAIN & CONNECTING ROD BEARINGS

Engine	MAIN BEARINGS Journal Diam. In. (mm)	MAIN BEARINGS Clearance In. (mm)	MAIN BEARINGS Thrust Bearing	MAIN BEARINGS Crankshaft End Play In. (mm)	CONNECTING ROD BEARINGS Journal Diam. In. (mm)	CONNECTING ROD BEARINGS Clearance In. (mm)	CONNECTING ROD BEARINGS Side Play In. (mm)
1.9L	2.2016-2.2022 (55.920-55.935)	.0008-.0025 (.021-.064)	No. 3	.012 Max. (.30 Max.)	1.9262-1.9268 (48.925-48.940)	.0007-.0025 (.018-.064)	.014 Max. (.35 Max.)

VALVE SPRINGS

Engine	Free Length In. (mm)	PRESSURE Lbs. @ In. (Kg @ mm) Valve Closed	PRESSURE Lbs. @ In. (Kg @ mm) Valve Open
1.9L			
Inner	.....	.....	.....
Outer	1.89 (48.1)	.....	.....

CAMSHAFT

Engine	Journal Diam. In. (mm)	Clearance In. (mm)	Lobe Lift In. (mm)
1.9L [1]	1.336-1.337 (33.94-33.96)	.0016-.0035 (.040-.090)	.....

1 – End play is .002-.006" (.05-.15 mm).

TIGHTENING SPECIFICATIONS

Application	Ft. Lbs. (N.m)
Camshaft Sprocket Bolt	58 (79)
Connecting Rod Cap Nuts	43 (58)
Cylinder Head Bolts	[1] 72 (98)
Engine Front Cover Bolts	18 (24)
Engine Rear Plate Bolts	36 (49)
Exhaust Manifold Nuts	16 (22)
Flywheel-to-Crankshaft Bolts	76 (103)
Intake Manifold Nuts	16 (22)
Main Bearing Cap Bolts	72 (98)
Rocker Shaft Bracket Bolts	16 (22)
Vibration Damper Bolt	87 (118)

1 – Tighten in progressive steps to 60 ft. lbs. (81 N.m), then tighten to 72 ft. lbs. (98 N.m).

General Motors Engines

2.2 LITER 4-CYLINDER DIESEL

ENGINE CODING

ENGINE IDENTIFICATION

Engine identification code is 8th character of Vehicle Identification Number (VIN). VIN is stamped on metal tab, located on top of instrument panel near lower left of windshield. Engine serial number is stamped on machined pad, located at left front of cylinder block.

ENGINE IDENTIFICATION CODE

Engine	Code
2.2L Diesel	S

ENGINE REMOVAL

See ENGINE REMOVAL at end of ENGINE section.

MANIFOLDS & CYLINDER HEAD

INTAKE & EXHAUST MANIFOLDS

Removal

1) Disconnect negative battery cable. Remove air cleaner. Remove PCV hose from valve cover and pipe. Disconnect heater pipe bracket. Disconnect all wiring and clips from intake manifold.

2) Disconnect exhaust pipe at manifold. Remove intake manifold bolts and exhaust manifold nuts. Remove intake and exhaust manifolds.

NOTE: **Either manifold may be removed separately but both must be removed in order to replace common intake and exhaust gasket.**

Installation

Clean gasket surfaces on both manifolds and on cylinder head. Ensure sealing surfaces are smooth and free from deep scoring or scratching. Install new common intake and exhaust manifold gasket. Install both manifolds and tighten evenly to avoid warping. Install remaining parts in reverse order of removal.

CYLINDER HEAD

Removal

1) Disconnect negative battery cable. Drain cooling system. Remove rocker arm shaft and push rods. Unbolt rocker arm bolts in reverse order of installation. *See Fig. 2.* Mark push rods for reassembly in same location. Disconnect upper radiator hose from engine. Remove heater tube.

2) Disconnect exhaust pipe at manifold. Remove vacuum pump. Unbolt A/C compressor from engine and place aside with hoses attached. Disconnect heater hose and bracket. Disconnect all electrical wiring to engine. Disconnect PCV hose from pipe and place to side.

3) Remove dipstick and unbolt dipstick tube bracket. Disconnect injection lines, plugging them to avoid contamination. Disconnect breather and oil jet pipes. Disconnect return hose. Remove cylinder head bolts in reverse order of installation. *See Fig. 1.* Remove cylinder head.

Installation

1) Clean gasket surfaces of both head and block. Clean out bolt hole threads in block. Clean threads of cylinder head bolts. Install new head gasket over dowel pins with "TOP" mark facing upward. Lightly oil cylinder head bolt threads and seating face.

2) Install cylinder head. Tighten bolts in sequence. *See Fig. 1.* Install push rods in original locations. Install and tighten the rocker arm shaft assembly in sequence. *See Fig. 2.* Reverse removal procedure to complete installation.

Fig. 1: Cylinder Head Tightening Sequence

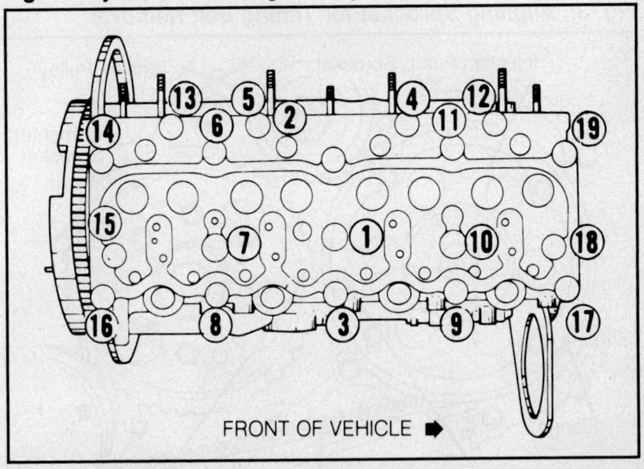

Reverse sequence for removal procedure.

Fig. 2: Rocker Arm Shaft Assembly Tightening Sequence

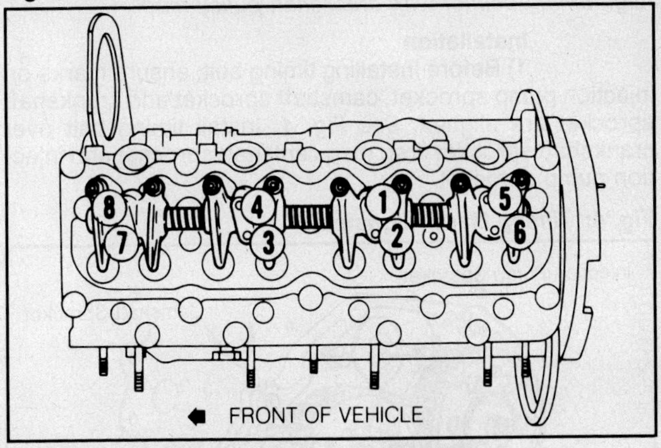

Loosening sequence is reverse of installation.

CAMSHAFT

TIMING BELT COVER

Removal

1) Disconnect negative battery cable. Remove power steering reservoir. Remove upper fan shroud and fan. Loosen drive belts and remove fan drive pulley. Remove upper timing belt cover.

2) Remove alternator belt. Align crankshaft pulley with timing indicator on TDC mark. Unbolt crankshaft pulley and remove. Remove lower belt cover.

Installation

To install, reverse removal procedure.

TIMING BELT

Removal

1) Disconnect negative battery cable. Align crank pulley with timing pointer. Remove crank pulley.

2.2 LITER 4-CYLINDER DIESEL (Cont.)

Remove upper and lower timing belt covers. Ensure injection pump sprocket and camshaft sprocket timing marks are aligned. *See Fig. 3.*

2) Remove injection pump sprocket flange bolts. When removing tension spring, do not distort spring with excess force. Remove nut of tension pulley. Remove tension pulley and tension center together. Remove timing belt. Ensure sprocket positions do not change.

Fig. 3: Aligning Sprocket for Timing Belt Removal

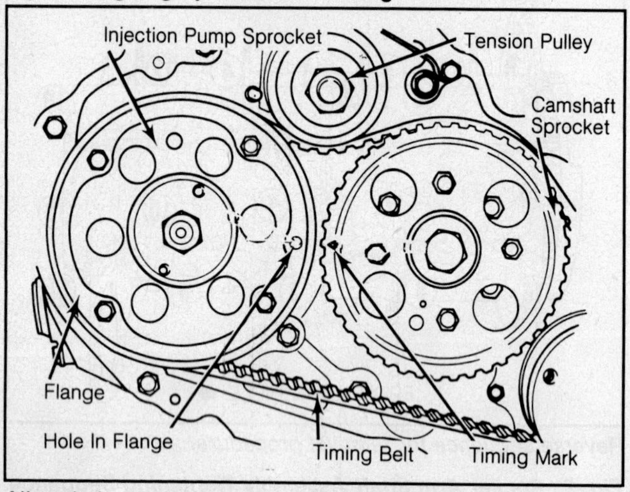

Align timing pointer with crankshaft pulley mark.

Installation

1) Before installing timing belt, ensure marks on injection pump sprocket, camshaft sprocket and crankshaft sprocket are aligned. *See Fig. 4.* Install timing belt over crankshaft sprocket first, then camshaft sprocket and injection pump sprocket.

Fig. 4: Timing Mark Alignment

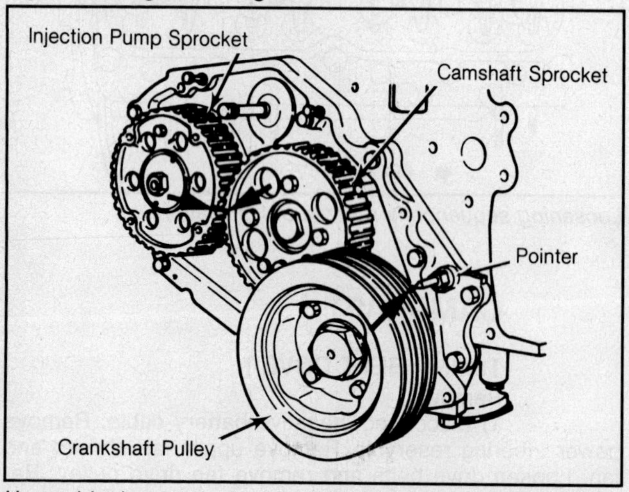

Heavy black arrows show points of timing mark alignment.

2) Install tension center and tension pulley. End of tension center must be in contact with 2 pins on timing belt housing. *See Fig. 5.* Hand tighten nut (tension pulley must slide freely). Install tension spring and tighten nut to 22-36 ft. lbs. (30-50 N.m).

3) Turn crankshaft 2 complete revolutions in direction of normal rotation to seat belt. Rotate crankshaft another 90° past TDC to settle injection pump. Loosen tension pulley nut completely to allow pulley to take up slack. Tighten nut to 78-95 ft. lbs. (106-129 N.m).

Fig. 5: Tension Wheel Installation

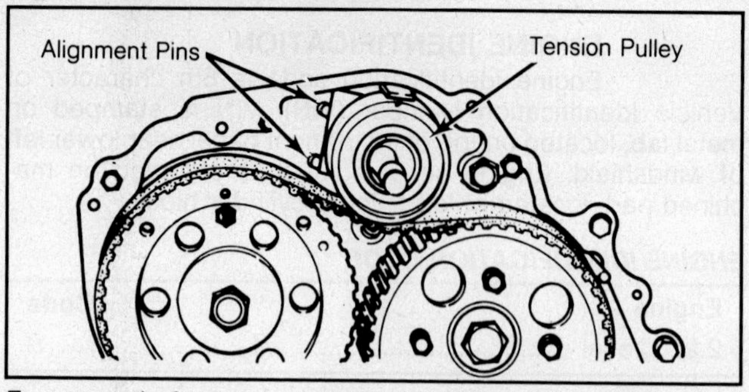

Ensure end of tension center is in contact with 2 pins.

4) Install and tighten injection pump sprocket flange. Ensure hole in flange lines up with timing mark on pump sprocket. *See Fig. 3.* Turn crankshaft 2 turns more, bringing No. 1 cylinder to TDC on compression stroke.

5) Check timing mark alignment. Check belt tension with Belt Tension Gauge (J-29771). Tension should be 33-55 lbs. (15-25 kg). Adjust valve clearance. Reverse removal procedure to complete installation.

VALVE TIMING

Refer to TIMING BELT INSTALLATION in this article to check valve timing.

INJECTION PUMP TIMING

1) Ensure notched lines on injection pump flange and injection pump front bracket are aligned. *See Fig. 6.* Rotate crankshaft until No. 1 cylinder is at TDC on compression stroke. Remove upper belt cover. Check belt tension.

Fig. 6: Injection Pump Alignment Marks

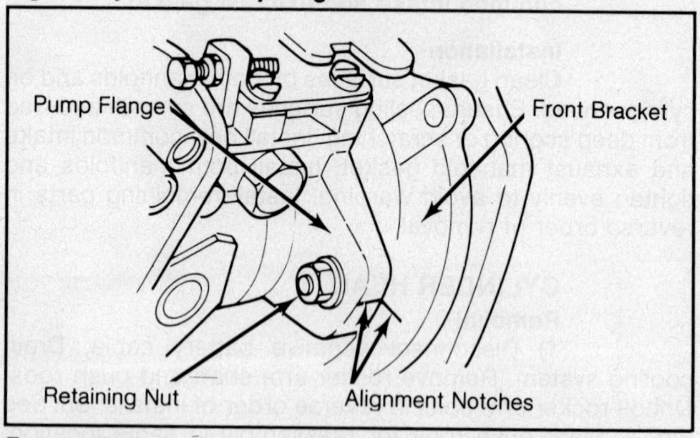

Ensure timing marks on pump and camshaft sprockets are also aligned.

2) Ensure timing marks on sprockets are aligned. *See Fig. 3.* Disconnect injection lines from pump and remove distributor head screw with washer. Install Dial Indicator (J-29763) with preload of approximately .04" (1 mm).

3) Slowly rotate crankshaft counterclockwise (reverse of normal rotation) until No. 1 cylinder is 45-60° BTDC (dial indicator needle should stop moving). Zero dial indicator. Turn crankshaft pulley slightly in both directions and check that dial needle does not move.

4) Turn crankshaft in normal direction of rotation (clockwise) until 15° BTDC timing mark is aligned with timing pointer. *See Fig. 7.* Dial indicator should read .02" (.5 mm). If indicator reading is not correct, hold crankshaft at 15° BTDC.

Fig. 7: Injection Pump Timing Adjustment

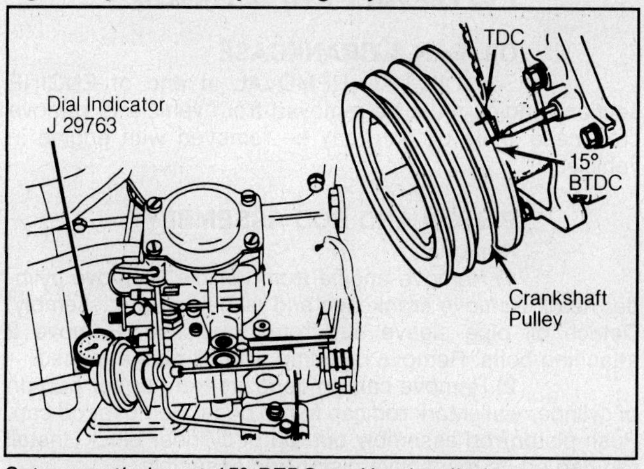

Set pump timing at 15° BTDC on No. 1 cylinder.

5) Loosen 2 retaining nuts at injection pump flange. Rotate pump body in relation to front bracket until dial indicator reads .02" (.5 mm). Tighten retaining nuts. Repeat timing check procedure and recheck reading.

CAMSHAFT

Removal

1) Remove engine from vehicle. Remove upper timing belt cover. Remove rocker arm shaft assembly and push rods, keeping push rods in order for reassembly. Align timing marks.

2) Lock injection pump sprocket to housing with 6 mm bolt threaded into housing through hole in sprocket. Remove crankshaft pulley. Remove lower timing belt housing. Remove injection pump sprocket flange. Remove tension spring and pulley with center.

3) Remove timing belt. Remove camshaft gear and hub. Remove camshaft oil seal retainer. Remove oil pump. Remove camshaft from engine. Avoid damaging camshaft bearings. Remove lifters.

Installation

Coat camshaft, lifters, and camshaft bearings with oil. Install lifters. Carefully install camshaft to avoid damage to bearings. Reverse removal procedure to complete installation.

CAMSHAFT BEARINGS

Remove and install bearings using Camshaft Bearing Remover/Installer (J-29764). Be sure to align oil holes in bearings with oil gallery openings in cylinder block.

CAMSHAFT OIL SEAL

Removal

Remove timing belt. Install 6 mm bolt through hole in camshaft sprocket and into threaded hole in housing to prevent turning of sprocket. Remove sprocket bolts and locating bolt. Remove sprocket with Puller (J-22888). Remove oil seal retainer. Remove oil seal.

Installation

Using seal installer, install oil seal into retainer until seated. Install remaining components in reverse order of removal.

CAMSHAFT END PLAY

1) Remove timing belt. Attach dial indicator to cylinder block with indicator point on camshaft sprocket center bolt. Push camshaft rearward and zero dial indicator. Use screwdriver to pry camshaft forward and record end play.

2) Maximum camshaft end play is .008" (.20 mm). If measured end play exceeds specification, either oil pump drive gear on camshaft or driven gear on pump is worn. Replace parts as necessary.

VALVES

VALVE ARRANGEMENT

E-I-I-E-E-I-I-E (Front-to-rear).

ROCKER ARM SHAFT ASSEMBLY

Removal

Remove valve cover. Starting with ends and working inward, remove rocker arm bracket attaching bolts. Remove rocker arm shaft assembly. If disassembly is necessary, keep parts in order.

Installation

To install, reverse removal procedure. Tighten attaching bolts evenly in sequence, commencing with inner bolts and working outward in circular pattern. *See Fig. 2.*

VALVE GUIDE SERVICING

Inspection

Use dial indicator to check valve stem-to-guide clearance. Position dial indicator point against valve stem about .40" (10 mm) above end of guide. Rock valve stem back and forth and measure clearance. If clearance exceeds .008" (.20 mm), replace valve and worn guide.

Removal

Working from combustion chamber (bottom) side of cylinder head, drive out old guide with Valve Guide Remover/Installer (J-26512).

Installation

Coat outer surface of guide with engine oil. Working from upper side of head, drive guide into head with Remover/Installer (J-26512). Top edge of valve guide should project from cylinder head .47" (12.0 mm). Always replace valve guide and valve as set.

VALVE STEM OIL SEALS

Removal

Remove rocker arm shaft assembly. Position piston of cylinder concerned to TDC. Using Spring Compressor (J-29760), compress spring and remove spring retainer locks. Release pressure and remove spring retainer and springs. Remove valve stem oil seal.

Installation

Apply engine oil to inner face of new oil seal and to valve stem. Install oil seal with projection on inner face of seal fitted to groove in guide. Install inner and outer springs with Green painted side (tighter coiled end) toward cylinder head. Using spring compressor, install remaining components in reverse order of removal.

VALVE SEAT INSERTS

Removal

To remove seat, arc-weld bead of metal around inner face of seat. Allow to cool few minutes. Using screwdrivers, pry out valve seat.

2.2 LITER 4-CYLINDER DIESEL (Cont.)

Installation

Using press, install new seat. Grind seat to correct width and angle. Lap valve into seat to complete installation.

VALVE SPRINGS

Removal & Installation

To remove and install valve springs, see VALVE STEM OIL SEALS in this article.

Inspection

1) Measure inner and outer valve spring free length. Test valve spring tension with valve spring tester. Replace springs that do not meet specification. Always replace inner and outer springs as set.

2) Using flat surface and steel square, check valve spring for squareness. Take measurement between top of spring and square, while slowly rotating spring. Inclination from perpendicular must not exceed .04" (1.0 mm). Replace inner and outer springs as set.

SWIRL CHAMBER REPLACEMENT

Removal

1) Measure chamber depth in head with straightedge and feeler gauge. If depth exceeds .0008" (.020 mm), chamber must be replaced. Use small diameter drift, .12-.20" (3-5 mm) to drive out old chamber.

2) Insert drift through injection nozzle hole until touching swirl chamber. Drive chamber out with hammer. Turn cylinder head over and drive heat shield out from bottom of injector hole with drift and hammer.

Installation

1) Install lock ball into groove in swirl chamber. Align lock ball in chamber with groove in cylinder head. Press chamber into head, using force of 9923-11,025 lbs. (4500-5000 kg).

2) Piece of scrap metal should be placed between press and chamber to prevent damage. Grind face of swirl chamber flush with face of cylinder head to complete installation.

3) Install heat shield into injector hole from top. Flanged side must face up. Use brass drift and hammer to tap lightly on flange of heat shield. Always use new heat shield.

VALVE CLEARANCE ADJUSTMENT

1) Tighten rocker arm shaft bracket bolts to 108-204 INCH lbs. (12-23 N.m) before adjusting valves. Cold valve clearance is .016" (.40 mm) for all valves. Hot valve clearance is .015" (.37 mm) for all valves.

2) Turn crankshaft until No. 1 piston is at TDC of compression stroke. Adjust valve clearance as listed in valve clearance setting sequence table. Turn crankshaft 1 revolution to place No. 4 piston at TDC of compression stroke and adjust remaining valves.

VALVE CLEARANCE SETTING SEQUENCE

Piston On TDC	Adjust Int. Nos.	Adjust Exh. Nos.
No. 1	1, 2, 3	1
No. 4	4	2, 3, 4

PISTONS, PINS & RINGS

OIL PAN & CRANKCASE

See OIL PAN REMOVAL at end of ENGINE section. Engine must be removed from vehicle to remove crankcase while oil pan may be removed with engine in vehicle.

PISTON AND ROD ASSEMBLY

Removal

1) Remove engine from vehicle. Remove cylinder head. Remove crankcase and oil pan as an assembly. Detach oil pipe sleeve nut from crankcase. Remove 2 attaching bolts. Remove oil pump with oil pipe attached.

2) Remove carbon deposits from upper portion of cylinder wall. Mark rod cap to rod body. Remove rod cap. Push piston/rod assembly out top of cylinder block. Install rod cap on its respective piston/rod assembly.

Installation

1) Lightly oil rings, piston and cylinder wall. Ensure ring gaps are properly spaced. *See Fig. 8.* Ensure bearing halves are properly seated in connecting rod and cap.

Fig. 8: Piston Ring Gap Locations

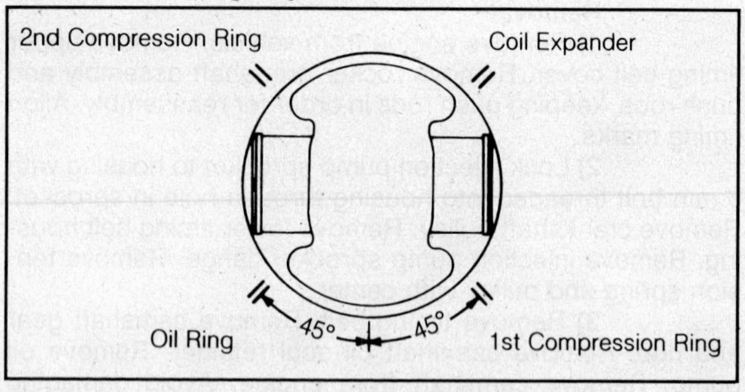

2) Install ring compressor and compress rings. Install piston in cylinder. Ensure mark on piston head points toward front of engine. Install and tighten rod cap. Reverse removal procedure to complete installation.

FITTING PISTONS

1) Measure cylinder bore diameter at points 5/8" and 4 1/2" below cylinder block deck surface. Take measurements both in line with and 90° to crankshaft centerline. If wear is excessive, cylinder should be bored for installation of oversize piston.

2) Measure piston diameter at right angle to piston pin. Subtract this figure from cylinder diameter to determine piston-to-cylinder wall clearance.

PISTON DIAMETER SPECIFICATIONS

Application	In. (mm)
Standard	3.4654-3.4670 (87.955-87.995)
1st Oversize	3.4851-3.4867 (88.455-88.495)
2nd Oversize	3.5048-3.5064 (88.955-88.995)

FITTING RINGS

1) Position rings into cylinder bore at point where bore diameter is smallest. Ring must be square in bore. Measure ring end gap with feeler gauge.

2.2 LITER 4-CYLINDER DIESEL (Cont.)

2) Using feeler gauge, check ring side clearance. Ensure rings turn freely in their ring grooves. When installing rings on piston, ensure gaps are correct. *See Fig. 8*. Ends of expander ring should be 180° from oil ring rail gap.

3) Install rings on piston in this order: expander ring, oil ring, 2nd compression ring, 1st compression ring. Manufacturing mark "N" on rings must be upward.

PISTON PIN REPLACEMENT

Removal

To remove pin, use snap ring pliers and remove snap rings from piston. Use brass rod to drive out pin. Piston pin bushings in small end of rod are replaceable.

Installation

1) Assemble rod to piston so arrow indicating front of piston head points to marked side of rod. Cylinder number marks will be on rod (on side with bearing tang) under combustion chamber side of piston head. *See Fig. 9*.

2) Coat pin with oil and install in piston and rod with finger pressure. Install snap rings to secure pin in place.

Fig. 9: Positioning Rod to Piston

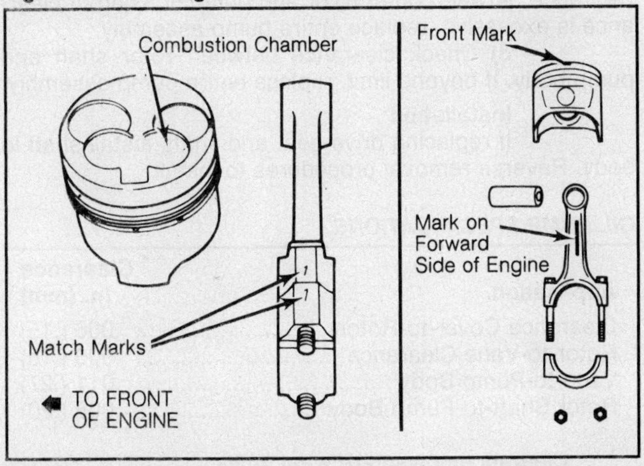

Note position of identification markings when installing rod to piston.

CRANKSHAFT & ROD BEARINGS

NOTE: To check bearing clearances, remove engine from vehicle. Following procedures are performed with oil pan removed, and oil film removed from surfaces to be checked.

CONNECTING ROD BEARINGS

1) Ensure rod caps are match marked to rods for cylinder identification, remove rod caps. Use Plastigage method to check for proper clearance.

2) If not within limits, install new bearings if crankpin is not worn beyond limits. Crankshaft bearing journals and rod bearing journals cannot be refinished or ground to undersize.

MAIN BEARINGS

1) Mark all bearing caps for assembly identification. Check clearances 1 at time. With all bearing caps (except one being checked) tightened, check clearances using Plastigage method.

2) If clearances are excessive, replace crankshaft and bearings. Taper must not exceed .0010" (.025 mm). Crankshaft journals and crankpins cannot be reground.

3) To check crankshaft runout, place "V" blocks under crankshaft at No. 1 and No. 5 journals. Zero dial indicator with tip on No. 3 journal. Slowly turn crankshaft at least 1 full revolution and record runout measured by idal indicator. If runout exceeds .0024" (.060 mm), replace crankshaft and bearings.

4) When installing thrust bearing (No. 3), oil grooved thrust faces must be turned outward toward crankshaft counterweights. Install arch gaskets on bearing caps 1 and 5 to seal caps to oil pan. Use liquid gasket sealer to hold gasket in place while installing caps. Gasket should not project more than .002" (.05 mm) from fitting face of cap. *See Fig. 10*.

5) Apply thin coat of silicone sealer to fitting face of bearing caps 1 and 5. *See Fig. 10*. Install all bearing caps with arrow pointing to front of engine. Ensure arch gasket protrusions fit properly, when installing bearing caps 1 and 5.

6) No. 2 and No. 4 bearing caps are identical. Install bearing cap with mark "A" on rear face in No. 2 position. Tighten caps in progressive steps, in sequence of 3, 4, 2, 5 and 1.

Fig. 10: Arch Gasket & Sealer Installation

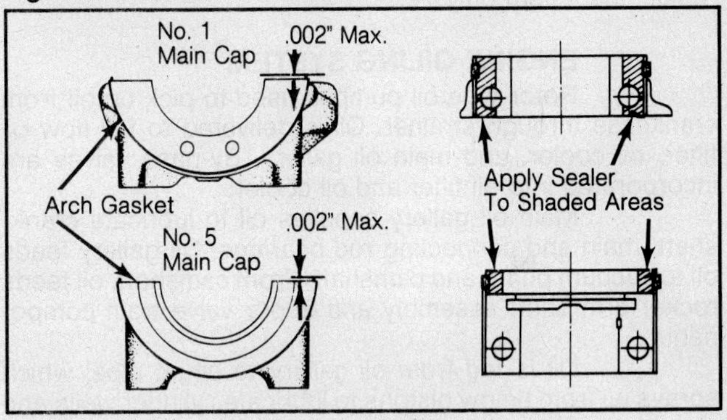

Install bearing caps before sealer sets up.

CRANKSHAFT END PLAY

Using feeler gauge, measure crankshaft end play between face of thrust bearing and thrust surface of crankshaft. Move crankshaft fully to one end of block. Measure clearance between crankshaft thrust face and thrust bearing. If clearance is greater than .012" (.30 mm), replace thrust bearings.

REAR MAIN BEARING OIL SEAL

Removal

Remove engine or transmission from vehicle. If equipped, remove clutch cover and disc. Remove flywheel. Remove rear oil seal.

Installation

Coat seal lip and outer edge of seal with engine oil. Using Seal Installer (J-29818), install new seal. Reverse removal procedure to install remaining components.

CRANKSHAFT FRONT OIL SEAL

Removal

Remove camshaft oil seal retainer. Hold crankshaft from turning and remove crankshaft pulley. Using

General Motors Engines

2.2 LITER 4-CYLINDER DIESEL (Cont.)

puller, remove crankshaft sprocket. Remove front oil seal dust cover, then remove oil seal.

Installation

Coat seal lip with engine oil. Use Seal Installer (J-24250) to install oil seal. Install remaining components in reverse order of removal.

ENGINE OILING

CRANKCASE CAPACITY

Crankcase capacity is 6.0 quarts (5.7L) with oil filter replacement and oil cooler installed.

OIL FILTER

Oil filter should be changed every 7,500 miles or 12 months in normal service. If vehicle is operated under severe conditions, oil filter should be changed every 3,000 miles or 3 months.

NORMAL OIL PRESSURE

Normal oil pressure for all models is 50-60 psi (3.5-4.5 kg/cm^2) at high engine speeds.

OIL PRESSURE REGULATOR VALVE

Oil pressure regulator valve is at junction of main engine oil gallery and oil jet pipe. Regulator valve is a replacement item only.

ENGINE OILING SYSTEM

Rotor-type oil pump is used to pick up oil from crankcase through strainer. Oil is delivered to full flow oil filter, oil cooler, and main oil gallery. By-pass valves are incorporated into oil filter and oil cooler.

Main oil gallery supplies oil to lubricate crankshaft, main and connecting rod bearings. Oil gallery feeds oil to vacuum pump and camshaft. From camshaft, oil feeds rocker arm shaft assembly and upper valve train components.

Oil is fed from oil gallery to oil jet pipe, which sprays oil from below pistons to lubricate cylinder walls and piston pins. Oil spray from oil jets also aids in piston cooling.

OIL PUMP

Removal

To remove, first drain crankcase and remove engine from vehicle. Disconnect PCV hose at crankcase. Remove dipstick tube and oil pan. Unbolt and remove crankcase. Remove oil pipe sleeve nut and 2 bolts holding pump in place. Remove oil pump.

Inspection

1) Disassemble oil pump and clean all parts thoroughly. Inspect for signs of unusual wear or damage. With rotor and vane installed in pump, lay straightedge over pump housing. Use feeler gauge to measure clearance between rotor, vane and pump cover (straightedge). If clearance is excessive, replace rotor and vane as set.

Fig. 11: Oil Pump Assembly

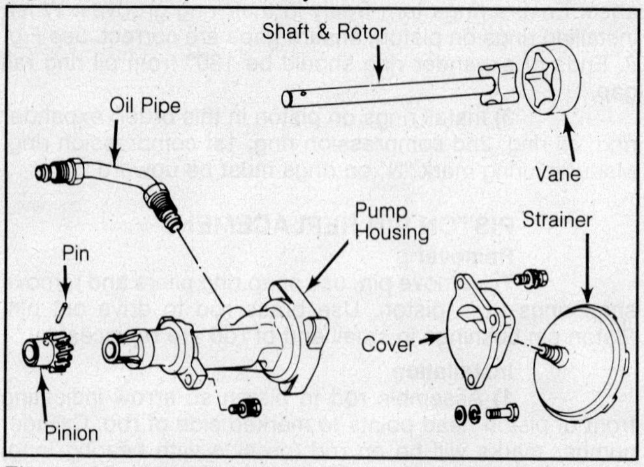

Thoroughly clean all parts prior to measuring clearances.

2) Using feeler gauge, measure clearance between rotor tip and vane. If clearance is beyond limit, replace rotor and vane as set. Using feeler gauge, measure clearance between outer rotor and pump housing. If clearance is excessive, replace entire pump assembly.

3) Check clearance between rotor shaft and pump body. If beyond limit, replace entire pump assembly.

Installation

If replacing drive gear and shaft, install shaft in body. Reverse removal procedures to install.

OIL PUMP SPECIFICATIONS

Application	[1] Clearance In. (mm)
Clearance Cover-to-Rotor	.006 (.15)
Rotor-to-Vane Clearance	.006 (.15)
Vane-to-Pump Body	.011 (.27)
Rotor Shaft-to-Pump Body	.008 (.20)

[1] – Clearances given are wear limits.

ENGINE COOLING

WATER PUMP

Removal

Drain cooling system and remove battery, fan, fan shroud and upper radiator hose. Remove drive belts and fan pulley. Remove water pump retaining bolts and remove pump.

Installation

Clean gasket mating surfaces. Using new gasket, install water pump in reverse order of removal.

NOTE: **For furthur information on cooling system capacities and other cooling system components, see appropriate article in ENGINE COOLING SYSTEMS at end of ENGINE section.**

General Motors Engines

2.2 LITER 4-CYLINDER DIESEL (Cont.)

ENGINE SPECIFICATIONS

GENERAL SPECIFICATIONS

Year	DISPLACEMENT		Fuel System	HP@RPM	Torque Ft. Lbs.@RPM	Compr. Ratio	BORE		STROKE	
	Cu. In.	Liters					In.	mm	In.	mm
1985	136.6	2.2	Fuel Inj.	62@4300	96@2200	21:1	3.46	88	3.62	92

VALVES

Engine Size & Valve	Head Diam. In. (mm)	Face Angle	Seat Angle	Seat Width In. (mm)	Stem Diameter In. (mm)	Stem Clearance In. (mm)	Valve Lift In. (mm)
2.2L							
Intake	.....	45°	45°	.047-.059 (1.20-1.50)	.310-.315 (7.88-8.00)	.0015-.0027 (.039-.068)	.....
Exhaust	.....	45°	45°	.047-.059 (1.20-1.50)	.309-.315 (7.85-8.00)	.0025-.0037 (.064-.093)	.....

CRANKSHAFT MAIN & CONNECTING ROD BEARINGS

Engine	MAIN BEARINGS				CONNECTING ROD BEARINGS		
	Journal Diam. In. (mm)	Clearance In. (mm)	Thrust Bearing	Crankshaft End Play In. (mm)	Journal Diam. In. (mm)	Clearance In. (mm)	Side Play In. (mm)
2.2L	2.3591-2.3594 (59.92-59.93)	.0011-.0033 (.029-.085)	No. 3	.0018 Max. (.300)	2.0835-2.0839 (52.92-52.93)	.0016-.0047 (.040-.120)	.....

PISTONS, PINS, RINGS

Engine	PISTONS	PINS		RINGS		
	Clearance In. (mm)	Piston Fit In. (mm)	Rod Fit In. (mm)	Ring No.	End Gap In. (mm)	Side Clearance In. (mm)
2.2L	.0062-.0070 (.157-.177)	.00008-.0005 (.002-.012)	.0003-.0007 (.008-.020)	No. 1	.008-.016 (.20-.40)	.0035-.0045 (.090-.115)
				No. 2	.008-.016 (.20-.40)	.002-.003 (.05-.07)
				Oil	.008-.016 (.20-.40)	.0024-.0045 (.060-.114)

VALVE SPRINGS

Engine	Free Length In. (mm)	PRESSURE Lbs. @ In. (Kg @ mm)	
		Valve Closed	Valve Open
2.2L			
Inner	1.89 (47.9)	12-14@1.46 [1] (5.5-6.3@37.0)	.....
Outer	1.86 (47.3)	43-49@1.54 [1] (19.7-22.2@39.0)	.....

[1] – Compressed height as measured in spring tension tester.

CAMSHAFT

Engine	Journal Diam. In. (mm)	Clearance In. (mm)	Lobe Lift In. (mm)
2.2L	1.87-1.89 (47.6-48.0)	.0047 Max. (.119)	.....

General Motors Engines

2.2 LITER 4-CYLINDER DIESEL (Cont.)

ENGINE SPECIFICATIONS (Cont.)

VALVE TIMING

Engine	INTAKE		EXHAUST	
	Open (BTDC)	Close (ABDC)	Open (BBDC)	Close (ATDC)
2.2L	16°	54°	56°	14

TIGHTENING SPECIFICATIONS

Application	Ft. Lbs. (N.m)
Cylinder Head Bolt	
Step 1	40-47 (54-64)
Step 2	
New Bolt	54-61 (73-83)
Used Bolt	61-69 (83-94)
Camshaft Sprocket Bolt	72-87 (97-118)
Connecting Rod Nut	58-65 (79-88)
Crankshaft Sprocket Bolt	124-151 (168-205)
Engine Rear Plate Bolt	55-67 (75-91)
Flywheel Bolt	65-72 (88-98)
Main Bearing Cap Bolt	116-130 (157-176)
Intake Manifold Bolt	10-17 (14-23)
Exhaust Manifold Nut	10-17 (14-23)
Injection Pump Timing Pulley Bolt	42-52 (57-71)
Oil Jet Pipe Bolt	24-27 (33-37)
Oil Jet Bolt	22 (30)
Oil Cooler Bolt	54-61 (73-83)
Rocker Arm Shaft Bolt	10-17 (14-23)
Tension Pulley Bolt	78-95 (106-129)

ENGINE CODING

ENGINE IDENTIFICATION

Engine may be identified by the 8th character of the Vehicle Identification Number (VIN). VIN is stamped on metal tag, attached to left side of dash, near windshield. Engine identification number is stamped on machined pad on left rear of engine block below cylinder head.

ENGINE IDENTIFICATION CODE

Engine	Code
2.5L TBI	E

ENGINE REMOVAL

See ENGINE REMOVAL at end of ENGINE section.

MANIFOLDS & CYLINDER HEAD

INTAKE MANIFOLD

Removal

1) Disconnect negative battery cable. Remove air cleaner. Unplug electrical connectors at intake manifold. Disconnect accelerator and throttle valve cables at bellcrank. Disconnect fuel and vacuum lines at throttle body and manifold. Drain cooling system.

2) Disconnect by-pass hose at intake manifold. Remove rear alternator adjusting bracket. Disconnect alternator brace and move aside. Disconnect cruise control cable. Disconnect and label all vacuum hoses.

3) Disconnect vacuum line hold-down at thermostat housing. Disconnect heater hose at intake manifold. Disconnect coil. Remove intake manifold.

Installation

To install, reverse removal procedure. Tighten bolts to specifications. *See Fig. 1*.

Fig. 1: Intake Manifold Tightening Sequence

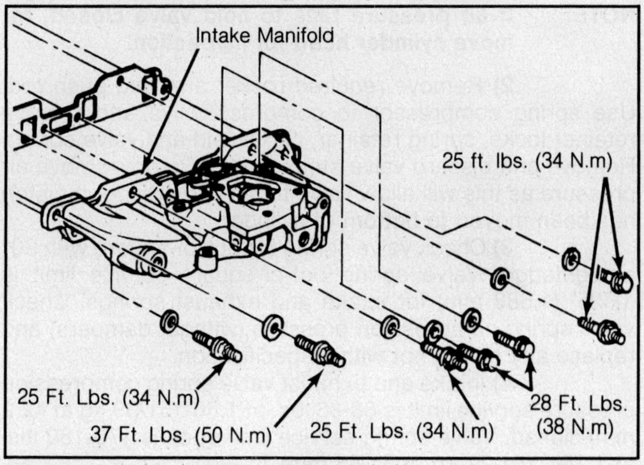

Tighten bolts to specifications shown.

EXHAUST MANIFOLD

Removal

1) Disconnect negative battery cable. Disconnect A/C belt. Remove A/C compressor and set aside. Remove rear A/C adjusting bracket. Raise vehicle. Disconnect exhaust pipe at manifold. Lower vehicle.

2) Remove air cleaner. Disconnect oxygen sensor wire. Remove exhaust manifold bolts. Remove exhaust manifold. *See Fig. 2*.

Installation

To install, reverse removal procedure.

Fig. 2: Exhaust Manifold Tightening Sequence

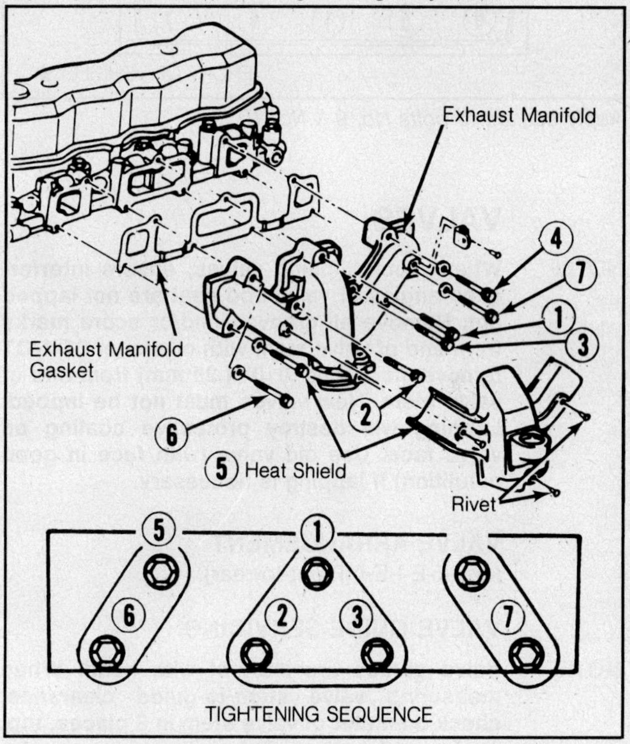

CYLINDER HEAD

Removal

1) Disconnect negative battery cable. Drain cooling system. Remove air cleaner. Remove A/C compressor and set aside. Disconnect PCV hose. Remove EGR valve. Disconnect spark plug wires at spark plugs. Disconnect vacuum line hold-down clamp at thermostat housing. Disconnect and label all vacuum hoses.

2) Remove valve cover. Unplug wires at throttle body. Disconnect accelerator, throttle valve and cruise control cables. Remove alternator brace. Disconnect by-pass hose at intake manifold. Remove A/C compressor bracket. Disconnect exhaust pipe at manifold.

3) Remove A/C refrigerant line hold-down clamp. Remove alternator. Disconnect upper radiator hose. Disconnect fuel line bracket at fuel filter. Remove oil dipstick tube. Disconnect fuel and vacuum lines near fuel filter. Remove head bolts. Disconnect wiring harness bracket at rear of head.

4) Disconnect coil bracket from head. Loosen rocker arms and rotate to one side. Remove push rods. Remove brace between intake manifold and block. Remove head with intake and exhaust manifolds attached. Remove intake and exhaust manifolds.

Installation

Clean all gasket surfaces on block, head and manifolds. Check cylinder head gasket surface for warpage. Clean head bolt threads and head bolt threads in block.

To install, reverse removal procedure. Tighten head bolts (in sequence) to specification. *See Fig. 3.*

Fig. 3: Cylinder Head Tightening Sequence

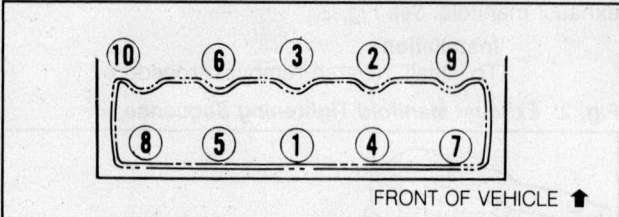

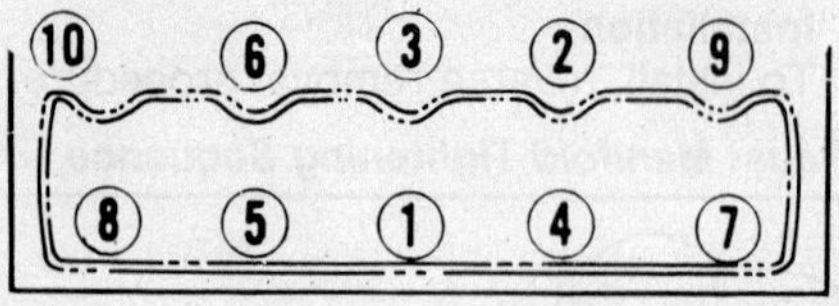

Apply sealant to bolts No. 9 & No. 10.

VALVES

NOTE: **When reconditioning valves, ensure interference angles of valve and seat are not lapped out. Remove all grooves and/or score marks from end of valve stem with oil stone. DO NOT remove more than .010" (.25 mm) from end of valve stem. New valves must not be lapped. Lapping will destroy protective coating on valve face. Use old valve (with face in good condition) if lapping is necessary.**

VALVE ARRANGEMENT

I-E-I-E-E-I-E-I (Front-to-rear).

VALVE GUIDE SERVICING

NOTE: **Valve guides are integral with head. When measuring valve stem-to-guide clearance, check diameter of valve stem in 3 places; top, center and bottom. Exhaust valves have tapered stems and are .001" (.025 mm) larger at top of stem than at valve head end.**

1) With cylinder head removed and disassembled, check valve stem-to-guide clearance. If clearance exceeds service limits, recondition valve guide. Service valves are available in standard, .003" and .005" oversize.

2) To check valve guide wear, insert valve with head positioned .079" away from valve seat. Attach dial gauge to cylinder head. Position gauge indicator against valve stem at right angle and just above guide. Move valve in guide and note guide wear shown on dial gauge.

3) Maximum dial gauge reading for intake valve-to-guide clearance is shown in table. Use Valve Guide Cleaner (J-8101) for cleaning guides. Use Valve Guide Reamers (J-5830-02) in sequence to ream guides for installation of valves with oversize stems.

4) Reface valve seat after valve guide is reamed. If valve seat face is reground, check margin width dimension. Check valve seats for proper angle and seat width. Measure valve seat runout. Valve seat runout should be within .002" (.05 mm) for intake and exhaust.

5) Intake valve seat width is .035-.075" (.89-1.91 mm). Exhaust valve seat width is .058-.097" (1.47-2.46 mm). Use scraper to break (lightly chamfer or bevel) sharp top inside edge of guide. After valve guide repair, inspect valve stem end for wear before installation. Valve stem end may be reconditioned by grinding.

VALVE STEM OIL SEALS

NOTE: **An "O" ring type seal is installed on lower groove of valve stem on all valves. A Teflon type oil seal is installed on guide of intake valves only, in addition to "O" ring type. A light coat of oil on stem will help prevent twisting of the "O" ring type seal during installation. If oversized valves are used, oversized valve stem oil seals will be needed.**

1) If valve or valve seat has not been damaged, valve springs, seals, cup shields and retainers may be replaced by holding affected valve against seat using air pressure.

2) Use Air Line Adapter (J-22794), installed in spark plug hole, to hold valves shut. A minimum of 140 psi (9.8 kg/cm^2) line pressure is required. If air pressure does not hold valve shut, valve is damaged or burnt and cylinder head must be removed for service.

NOTE: **If Air Line Adapter (J-22794) is not available, an adapter can be constructed by welding air hose fitting to body of spark plug with porcelain removed.**

3) After removing rocker arm, reinstall rocker arm bolt. Insert slotted end of spring compressor under rocker bolt head. Compress valve spring and remove valve retainer locks. Remove compressor, retainer, cup shield, spring and oil seal.

4) With valve in head, install plastic seal protector cap over end of valve stem. Lubricate protector cap and start stem seal carefully over cap. Push seal down until seal jacket touches top of valve guide. Remove plastic seal protector cap. Using Valve Seal Installer/Tester (J-22330), bottom seal on valve guide.

VALVE SPRINGS

Removal

1) Remove valve cover and spark plug on cylinder to be serviced. Ensure piston is at top of stroke with both valves closed. Install air line with adapter in spark plug hole. Apply minimum of 140 psi (9.8 kg/cm^2) line pressure.

NOTE: **If air pressure fails to hold valve closed, remove cylinder head for inspection.**

2) Remove required rocker arm and push rod. Use spring compressor to compress valve and remove retainer locks, spring retainer, cup shield and valve spring. Remove and discard valve stem seal(s). Do not remove air pressure as this will allow valve to fall into cylinder if piston has been moved to bottom of cylinder.

3) Check valve spring for out-of-square with 90° straightedge. Valve spring out-of-square service limit is .0625" (1.588 mm) for intake and exhaust springs. Check valve spring compression pressure (without dampers) and replace any spring not within specification.

4) Intake and exhaust valve spring compression pressure service limit is 68-86 lbs. at 1.66" (31-39 kg at 42.2 mm) closed. Valve spring service limit open is 170-180 lbs. at 1.254" (51-77 kg at 31.85 mm).

Installation

1) Lubricate valve stem with engine oil and install new valve stem seal. Place spring in position over valve and install cup shield and spring retainer. Compress valve spring and install locks. Check valve spring for proper installed height.

CAUTION: Install shim spacers only if necessary. Do not use more than 2 spacers, as this will over-stress springs and overload camshaft lobes.

2) Measure from top of valve seat to top of valve spring or oil shield. If excessive, install .063" valve spring seat shim. Ensure spring height with shim does not result in installed height under minimum specification.

3) Remove air pressure and adapter and install spark plugs. Apply polyethylene grease to ends of push rods and tip of valve stems. Install rocker arms and tighten.

VALVE SPRING INSTALLED HEIGHT

Installed height of valve spring should be 1.690" (42.93 mm). Measure spring height from surface of cylinder head pad to underside of spring retainer. If installed height exceeds specifications, install shim below spring to reduce height to specifications.

PUSH ROD SIDE COVER

Removal

1) Disconnect negative battery cable. Remove alternator and bracket. Remove brace between intake manifold and block. Drain cooling system. Disconnect lower radiator and heater hoses.

2) Remove oil pressure sending unit. Remove wiring harness brackets from side cover. Remove side cover nuts and side cover.

Installation

Clean gasket sealing surfaces. Apply a 3/16" thick, continuous bead of RTV to side cover. Install side cover and tighten bolts. To complete installation, reverse removal procedure.

Fig. 4: Exploded Veiw of Lifter Retainer Assembly

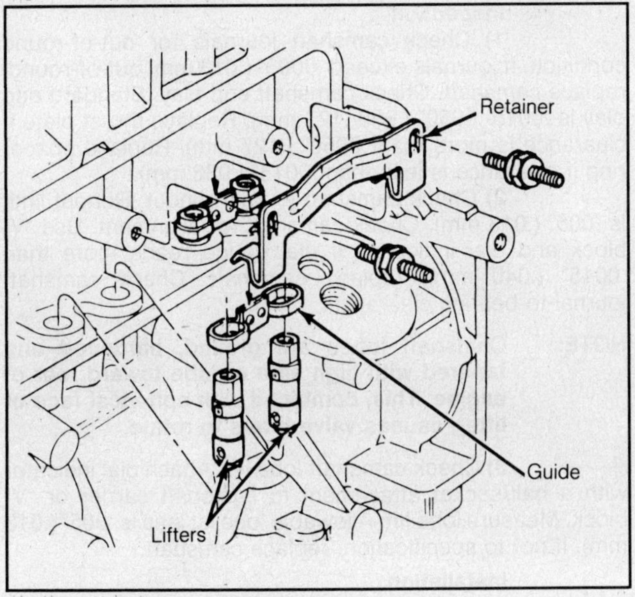

Lifter, guide and retainer shown.

HYDRAULIC ROLLER VALVE LIFTERS

NOTE: Before replacing hydraulic lifter for noisy operation, ensure noise is not caused by improper collapsed lifter gap, worn rocker arms, push rods or valve tips. If lifter assembly is stuck in bore, use Hydraulic Lifter Puller (J-3049) or magnet.

Removal & Installation

1) Remove valve cover, intake manifold and push rod cover. Loosen rocker arm and rotate for clearance from push rod. Remove push rod, lifter retainer and guide plates. Using lifter remover or magnet, remove lifters.

2) Clean and inspect, but do not mix components or positions. Parts are select-fit and not interchangeable. If lifter is sticking, disassemble and clean dirt, metal chips or varnish from components.

3) If lifter check valve is not functional, obstructions may be preventing closure when cam lobe is moving lifter, or check valve spring may be broken. *See Fig. 5.*

Fig. 5: Exploded View of Hydraulic Roller Tappet Assembly

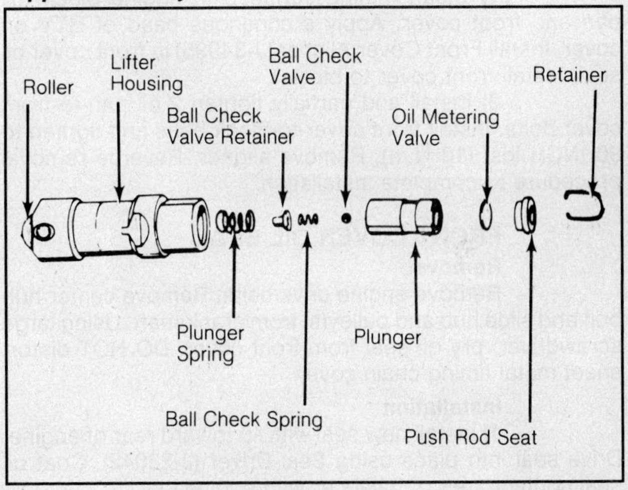

4) Clean or replace components as necessary. If plunger is not free in body of lifter, replace entire assembly. Plunger should drop to bottom of body by its own weight when assembled dry. Assemble lifter and check free operation by pressing down on cap.

NOTE: When performing leak-down test, use test fluid. Lifters cannot be checked with engine oil. New lifters already contain test fluid. If new lifter is installed, remove sealer coating from inside of new lifter and check leak-down rate. If old lifter is disassembled and cleaned, fill with test fluid before installing and testing.

5) Place lifter upright in Hydraulic Lifter Leak-Down Tester (J-5790-01) and check leak-down rate. Leak-down rate is 12-90 seconds measured at .0938" (2.38 mm) plunger travel, under 50 lb. (22 kg) load. Inspect lifter body for scuffing or wear and replace if worn. Inspect lifter roller-to-cam lobe contact area.

6) Surface face must be smooth with no pits or flat spots. Replace any lifter with flat spots or pits on surface. Inspect roller for freedom of movement and replace if binding or roughness is felt. Inspect related cam lobe for proper lobe lift. Replace camshaft (and lifters if necessary) if any lobe is worn beyond specification.

7) Check lifter-to-bore clearance. Standard clearance is .0025" (.064 mm). Standard diameter of lifter is .8420-.8427" (21.387-21.405 mm). Standard lifter bore diameter is .8435-.8445" (21.425-21.450 mm).

8) Coat lifter base with Molykote. When installing, ensure lifter is on base circle of camshaft. Tighten rocker arm bolt. Coat gasket surfaces with RTV sealer and install push rod cover and valve cover.

2.5 LITER 4-CYLINDER (Cont.)

CAMSHAFT

ENGINE FRONT COVER

Removal

1) Disconnect negative battery cable. Disconnect power steering reservior fan shroud. Remove upper fan shroud. Remove fan belts, fan and pulley. Remove alternator, brackets and brace.

2) Remove crankshaft pulley. Remove crankshaft hub bolt. Remove crankshaft hub. Disconnect lower radiator hose at water pump. Remove front cover bolts and front cover.

Installation

1) Clean mating surfaces of engine block, oil pan and front cover. Apply a continous bead of RTV on cover. Install Front Cover Aligner (J-34995) in front cover oil seal. Install front cover to block.

2) Install and partially tighten 2 oil pan-to-front cover bolts. Install front cover-to-block bolts and tighten to 90 INCH lbs. (10 N.m). Remove aligner. Reverse removal procedure to complete installation.

FRONT COVER OIL SEAL

Removal

Remove engine drive belts. Remove center hub bolt and slide hub and pulley(s) from crankshaft. Using large screwdriver, pry oil seal from front cover. DO NOT distort sheet metal timing chain cover.

Installation

1) Install new seal with lip toward rear of engine. Drive seal into place using Seal Driver (J-23042). Coat oil seal contact area of balancer with engine oil.

2) Position hub on crankshaft and slide into position until it bottoms against crankshaft gear. Install center bolt and tighten. Install pulley-to-hub bolts using sealing compound and tighten. Install belts and adjust tension. Reverse removal procedure to complete installation.

CAMSHAFT & TIMING GEAR

Removal

1) Remove engine from vehicle and install on engine stand. Remove valve cover. Loosen rocker arm bolts and pivot rocker arms aside. Remove push rods. Remove intake manifold. Remove push rod side cover and remove valve lifters. Remove distributor and fuel pump.

Fig. 6: Oil Pump Drive Shaft Assembly

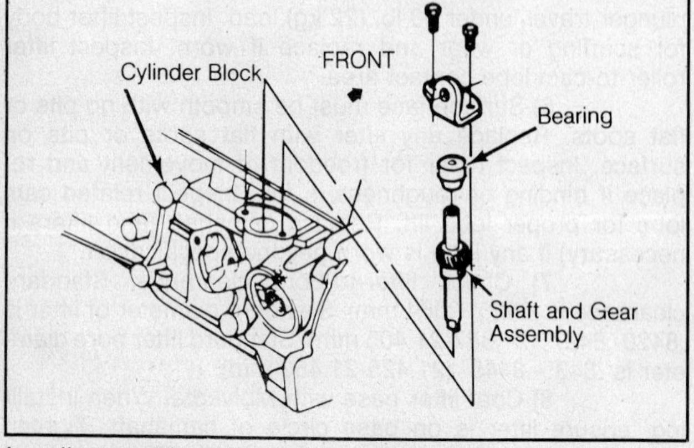

Install assembly while turning shaft to index with camshaft drive gear and position properly in oil pump body.

2) Remove alternator, lower alternator bracket and front engine mount bracket assembly. Remove oil pump drive shaft retainer plate bolts. Remove bushing and shaft assembly. Remove front pulley hub and timing gear cover. *See Fig. 6.*

3) Remove 2 camshaft thrust plate retaining bolts by working through holes in camshaft gear. *See Fig. 7.* Remove camshaft and gear assembly by pulling it through front of block. Use care not to damage camshaft bearings.

Fig. 7: Thrust Plate Bolt Removal

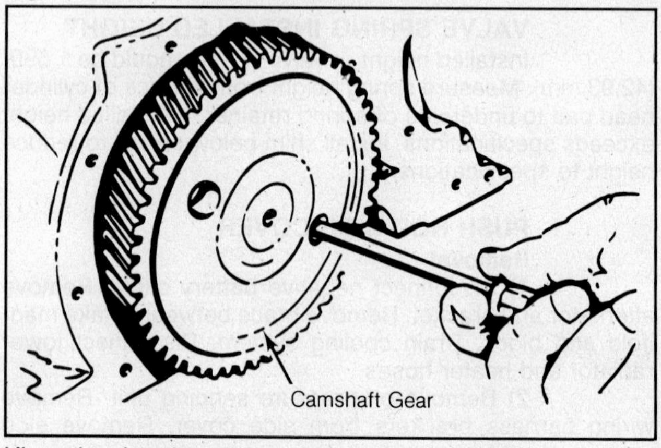

View showing thrust plate bolt access holes.

4) Use press plate and Adapter (J-971) on press to remove timing gear from camshaft. Place camshaft through opening in plates on table of press and press camshaft out of timing gear. Position thrust plate so that Woodruff key in camshaft does not damage thrust plate during removal.

Inspection

1) Check camshaft journals for out-of-round condition. If journals exceed .0005" (.013 mm) out-of-round, replace camshaft. Check camshaft end play. Standard end play is .0015-.0050" (.038-.127 mm). Replace thrust plate if clearance is more than .0050" (.127 mm). Replace spacer ring if clearance is less than .0015" (.038 mm).

2) Check camshaft journal runout. Runout limit is .005" (.013 mm). Check camshaft for alignment. Use "V" block and dial indicator. If dial gauge reads more than .0015" (.040 mm), replace camshaft. Check camshaft journal-to-bearing clearance.

NOTE: Camshaft lobes are ground, hardened and tapered with high side of lobe toward rear of engine. This, combined with spherical face of lifter, causes valve lifters to rotate.

3) Check camshaft lobe lift. Attach dial indicator with a ball/socket attachment to camshaft carrier or "V" block. Measure lobe lift. Allowable lobe lift loss is .005" (.013 mm). If not to specification, replace camshaft.

Installation

1) Support camshaft at back of front journal in arbor press using press plate adapters. Install gear spacer ring and thrust plate over end of camshaft. Install Woodruff key in shaft keyway.

2) Install camshaft gear and press it onto camshaft until it bottoms against gear ring spacer ring. Measure thrust plate end clearance. Clearance should be .0015-.0050" (.038-.127 mm). If less than .0015" (.138 mm), replace spacer ring. If more than .0050" (.127 mm), replace thrust plate.

3) Coat camshaft journals with engine oil and install camshaft in engine block. Be careful not to damage camshaft bearings. Align timing marks by rotating camshaft and crankshaft until timing marks on gear teeth line up.

4) Engine is now timed to No. 4 cylinder firing position. Install 2 camshaft thrust plate-to-block bolts and tighten. Install timing gear cover and new gasket. Line up hub keyway to crankshaft key, install hub and tighten center bolt.

5) Install lifters, push rods, push rod cover, oil pump shaft and gear assembly and fuel pump. To install distributor, turn crankshaft 360° to firing position of No. 1 cylinder (timing marks aligned on balancer and timing pad and valves closed).

6) Install distributor in original position and align shaft with rotor arm toward No. 1 plug contact. Pivot each rocker arm over push rod and tighten rocker arm bolt (with lifter on base circle of camshaft). To complete installation, reverse removal procedure.

CAMSHAFT BEARINGS

Removal

With engine, flywheel and camshaft removed, drive out expansion plug from rear camshaft bearing. Remove by driving out from inside. Using Camshaft Bearing Remover (J-21473-1), drive out front bearing toward rear of engine and rear bearing toward front. Install Camshaft Bearing Remover Extension (J-21054-1). Drive center bearing out toward rear of engine.

Installation

Install each bearing on installer and replace in block in reverse order of removal. Ensure oil hole in camshaft bearings and cylinder block line up. Install front camshaft bearing with bearing recessed about 1/8" into engine block. This uncovers oil hole to timing gear oil nozzle. Reverse removal procedure to complete installation.

PISTONS, PINS & RINGS

OIL PAN

See OIL PAN REMOVAL at end of ENGINE section.

PISTON & ROD ASSEMBLY

NOTE: **When removing ridge at top of cylinder bore, never cut into ring travel area more than .03125" (.794 mm). Before removing piston and connecting rod, ensure rod caps are marked to their related rods for proper reassembly. DO NOT damage crankshaft journals or cylinder wall during removal.**

Removal

1) With cylinder head and oil pan removed, inspect cylinder bores for ridges and/or deposits. Move piston to be removed to bottom of bore and cover with cloth to catch cuttings.

2) Remove ridge at top of cylinder bores (using ridge reamer) before removing pistons from block. Rotate crankshaft and inspect connecting rods and rod caps for cylinder identification. Mark them if necessary.

3) Remove rod cap and push each piston and rod assembly out top of cylinder bore. To protect crankshaft, place sleeve or rubber hose over rod bolts. Remove bearing inserts from rod and cap and inspect for size, wear and damage. Install rod caps on mating rods.

NOTE: **Notch on top of piston faces front of engine. Raised notch on rod should be opposite notch on piston top when installed.**

Installation

1) Check fit of new piston and/or rings in cylinder bore before assembling piston and pin to connecting rod. Check piston pin for clearance, etching or wear. Position piston so that notched side of rod is opposite notch on piston top. Press pistons onto rods.

2) New pistons must be installed in the cylinder for which they were fitted. Install used pistons in the cylinder from which they were removed. Oil piston rings and cylinder walls with light coat of oil.

3) Ensure ring gaps are properly spaced and install ring compressor on piston. Marked side of compression rings must be toward top of piston. *See Fig. 8*.

Fig. 8: Ring Gap Spacing & Piston-to-Rod Location

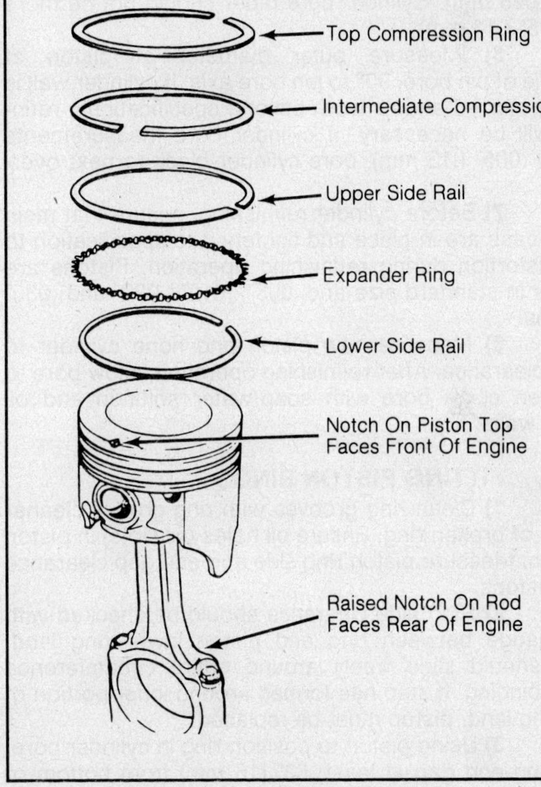

Mark on compression rings faces upward.

4) Install Connecting Rod Bolt Guide Set (J-6305-11) or rubber sleeves before installing piston and rod assembly in bore. Tap gently with wooden handle to insert piston/rod assembly into cylinder bore.

5) After bearings have been inserted, apply engine oil to journals and bearings. Ensure oil hole in bearing insert aligns with oil hole in connecting rod. Turn crankshaft throw to bottom of its stroke. Guide piston/rod assembly over crankshaft journal until rod bearing seats.

6) Remove rod bolt protectors. Match rod cap to rod and install. Tighten cap nuts in 2 steps. Repeat procedure for each piston assembly. After piston/rod assembly is installed, check side clearance of connecting rod on each crankshaft journal.

2.5 LITER 4-CYLINDER (Cont.)

FITTING PISTONS

1) Inspect pistons and replace any showing signs of excessive wear, wavy ring lands, or fractures. Replace piston if sponge-like or eroded surface is on edge of piston top (caused by detonation or pre-ignition).

2) If shiny surface on thrust side of piston is found, check for bent connecting rod. Replace piston and/or rod as necessary. Inspect connecting rods for signs of fracture and bearing bores for out-of-round and taper.

3) If bore exceeds recommended limits and/or rod is fractured, replace rod. Check pistons for fractures at ring lands, skirts and pin bosses. Check for scuffed, rough or scored skirts. Check piston-to-cylinder bore clearance by measuring piston and bore diameters.

4) Ensure piston and cylinder bore are clean, dry and at room temperature 70°F (21°C) during measurement. Measure diameter of cylinder bore at top, middle and bottom with gauge at right angle and parallel to centerline of engine.

5) Inspect cylinder walls for scoring, roughness or other signs of wear. Check bore for out-of-round and taper. Cylinder bore out-of-round should not be more than .0010" (.025 mm). Cylinder bore taper should not be more than .005" (.13 mm).

6) Measure outer diameter of piston at centerline of pin bore, 90° to pin bore axis. If cylinder wall is severely marred and/or worn beyond specifications, refinishing will be necessary. If cylinder bore measurements differ by .005" (.13 mm), bore cylinder block to next oversize.

7) Before cylinder refinishing, ensure that main bearing caps are in place and tightened to specification to avoid distortion during refinishing operation. Pistons are available in standard size and .005", .010", .020" and .030" oversizes.

8) Measure new piston and hone cylinder to correct clearance. After refinishing operation, allow bore to cool, then clean bore with soap/water solution and oil cylinder walls.

FITTING PISTON RINGS

1) Clean ring grooves with ring groove cleaner or piece of broken ring. Ensure oil holes (or slots) in piston are clean. Measure piston ring side and end gap clearance for all pistons.

2) Ring side clearance should be checked with feeler gauge between ring and piston lower ring land. Gauge should slide freely around entire circumference without binding. If step has formed around inner portion of lower ring land, piston must be replaced.

3) Using piston to position ring in cylinder bore, check ring end gap at least .63" (16 mm) from bottom of bore. Install rings on pistons with end gaps staggered at proper intervals. Ensure ring gap is not in line with thrust face of pin bore.

4) Ensure manufacturer's marks face up when rings are installed. Install oil ring expander first, followed by lower oil ring side rail and upper side rail. Do not use ring expander on side rails. When installing lower side rail, place one end between piston ring groove and expander.

5) Hold end firmly and press down portion to be installed until side rail is in position. Install upper side rail. Using ring expander, install intermediate and upper rings. Check that all components are within specifications.

6) If new piston rings are to be installed and no visible cross-hatch marks remain on cylinder walls, remove cylinder wall glaze using spring-type hone. After honing, clean bore and block with soap/water solution and oil cylinder walls.

FITTING PISTON PINS

NOTE: **When removing or installing piston pin, connecting rod should be in firm contact with body of pin installer.**

Removal

1) Remove bearing inserts from connecting rod and cap. Mark pistons, pins and inserts (if reusable) to assure assembly with same rod. Press piston pin from piston and connecting rod using Piston Support (J-24086) and Piston Pin Remover/Installer (J-24086-10).

2) Inspect and replace any piston pin showing signs of fracture, etching or wear. Check piston pin-to-rod bore fit. Check ID of connecting rod piston pin bore. If pin bore in rod is larger than specification, install .0010" (.025 mm) oversize piston pin.

3) Ensure proper fit by honing or reaming piston pin bore to light slip fit. Check table for proper specification. Standard piston pin diameter is .938-.942" (23.83-23.93 mm). Lubricate pin and small end of rod bore with engine oil.

Installation

1) Check piston-to-cylinder bore clearance before assembling piston and pin to connecting rod. Ensure oil hole in connecting rod aligns with oil hole in bearing and arrow or notch on top of piston is pointed toward front of engine.

2) Notch on rod big end near center of upper bearing insert must face rear of engine. Start piston pin in piston and connecting rod. Using guide bar and push rod, press pin through both piston and rod until pilot hub bottoms on support fixture and/or pin is centered in piston.

3) After pilot hub bottoms, DO NOT exceed 5000 lbs. (2275 kg) pressure with press. Ensure piston floats during pin installation operation.

CRANKSHAFT & ROD BEARINGS

NOTE: **Following procedures are with oil pan and cylinder head removed. Main and rod bearing size is indicated by letter stamped into bearing tang or actual bearing size stamped opposite of tang. Bearing marks are as follows: A = .0005", B = .0010", and C = .0015".**

CONNECTING ROD BEARINGS

1) Remove connecting rod bearing caps and mark rods and caps for proper installation. Inspect each bearing for peeling, melting, seizure or improper contact. Replace defective bearings. Use Plastigage method for bearing clearance check.

2) Measure outside diameter of crankshaft connecting rod bearing journals to determine if out-of-round or tapered. Journal out-of-round must not exceed .0005" (.013 mm) in a half turn. Journal runout (one turn) must not exceed .0005" (.013 mm). Journal taper must not exceed .0005" (.013 mm).

3) When checking connecting rod clearances, crankshaft does not have to be supported. Instead, turn crankshaft until connecting rod to be checked starts moving toward top of engine, thus unloading lower bearing.

4) Cut Plastigage to same length as width of rod bearing. Place in bearing cap, parallel with crankshaft (away from oil hole or groove). Install rod bearings and cap. Tighten in 2 steps to specifications. Always install caps with markings in original positions.

5) Do not turn crankshaft with Plastigage installed. Remove rod bearing cap from crankshaft and measure Plastigage at its widest part (using scale on Plastigage package). If clearance exceeds specifications, replace bearing.

NOTE: **If clearance cannot be brought within specifications with service bearings, grind crankshaft to next undersize. If already ground to maximum undersize, replace crankshaft.**

6) Selective fitting is required on each connecting rod. After inspection and/or replacement, coat bearing surfaces with heavy engine oil. Tighten connecting rod bearing caps in 2 steps.

NOTE: **Connecting rod bearing cap and rod identification numbers must remain on same side. Precision bearings are used in this engine and shimming is not acceptable for adjustment. Always replace bearings in pairs. Never use new bearing in combination with used bearing. Never file or grind connecting rods or caps when fitting bearings.**

7) Check for shiny surface on either side of piston pin boss, indicating bent connecting rod. Twisted rods may not create identifiable wear patterns, but will disturb the action of entire crankshaft assembly and may cause excessive oil consumption.

8) Check connecting rod side clearance with dial indicator contact point resting against rod cap. Pull cap toward front of engine and zero dial indicator. Push cap toward rear of engine and compare reading to specification. If excessive, replace connecting rod and cap.

9) If side clearance is less than specification, remove rod and cap. Check for scratches, burrs, nicks or dirt between crankshaft and rod. Dress minor imperfections with oil stone.

10) During assembly, ensure oil hole in bearing aligns with oil hole in connecting rod. Ensure bearing tangs are seated in appropriate slots in rod and cap. Ensure connecting rod bolt heads are properly seated in connecting rod.

MAIN BEARINGS

NOTE: **Selective fit main bearings are used in engine. DO NOT scrape gum or varnish deposits from bearings. Clean inserts and caps in solvent. DO NOT file or lap bearing caps or use shims to obtain proper bearing clearance.**

1) Inspect each bearing for peeling, melting, seizure or improper contact. Replace defective bearings. If copper-lead bearing base is visible but is not showing in more than 20% of total area, bearing is not excessively worn.

2) Measure outside diameter of crankshaft main bearing journals in at least 4 places to determine if out-of-round or tapered. Journal out-of-round must not exceed .0005" (.013 mm) in a half turn. Journal runout (one turn) must not exceed .0005" (.013 mm). Journal taper must not exceed .0005" (.013 mm).

NOTE: **Observe location of high spots on main bearings. If high spots are not in line, crankshaft may be bent and should be checked.**

3) To check main bearings, shim adjacent main bearings to bearing being check. Alternate method is to position jack under counterweight adjoining bearing being checked so weight of crankshaft will not compress Plastigage and provide an incorrect reading.

4) DO NOT position jack under crankshaft pulley. Crankshaft post damage will result. With all bearing caps (other than one being checked) tight, check clearances using Plastigage method.

NOTE: **If undersize bearings are used on more than one journal, position in cylinder block rather than bearing cap. Do not turn crankshaft with Plastigage installed.**

5) If standard and undersize bearing combination do not bring bearing clearance within specified limits, crankshaft will have to be refinished and undersized bearings installed. If journal will not clean up to maximum undersize bearing, replace crankshaft.

6) If journals are remachined, ensure same journal shoulder radius is reproduced. Too small a radius will result in fatigue failure of crankshaft. Too large a radius will result in bearing failure due to radial ride of bearing.

7) When journals are refinished, chamfer oil holes and polish journals with No. 320 grit polishing cloth and engine oil. After chamfer and polish operations, clean crankshaft thoroughly in solvent and blow out oil passages with compressed air.

8) When crankshaft main bearings are installed, ensure oil distributing grooves on bearings are installed on same side. Oil new upper bearing and insert plain (unnotched) end between crankshaft and notched side of block. Rotate bearing into place. Install main caps and tighten to specification.

THRUST BEARING ALIGNMENT

1) Check crankshaft end play with crankshaft bearing caps installed. Mount dial indicator to front of engine and locate probe on nose of crankshaft. Move crankshaft to rear of its travel. Zero dial indicator.

2) Move crankshaft forward and read end play on gauge. Replace No. 5 main thrust bearing (upper and lower) if not to specification. Standard crankshaft end play is .0035-.0085" (.089-.216 mm). Rotate crankshaft to ensure there is no excessive drag.

3) If end play is less than specification, inspect thrust bearing surfaces for scratches, burrs, nicks or dirt. Clean up minor imperfections with oil stone. Recheck end play.

CRANKSHAFT FLANGE RUNOUT

1) With engine removed and crankshaft installed, measure crankshaft flange runout. Mount dial indicator gauge plate flat against flange. Place dial indicator stem on lower left transmission mounting bolt boss (flat area around mounting bolt hole). Set indicator to zero. *See Fig. 9.*

2) Observe and record readings obtained on all mounting bolt hole bosses. Measurements should not vary

General Motors Engines

2.5 LITER 4-CYLINDER (Cont.)

more than .010" (.25 mm). If readings are more than specifications, remount dial gauge plate and recheck flange runout. If runout is excessive, replace crankshaft. Check threaded holes, clean and retap as necessary.

Fig. 9: Checking Crankshaft Flange Runout

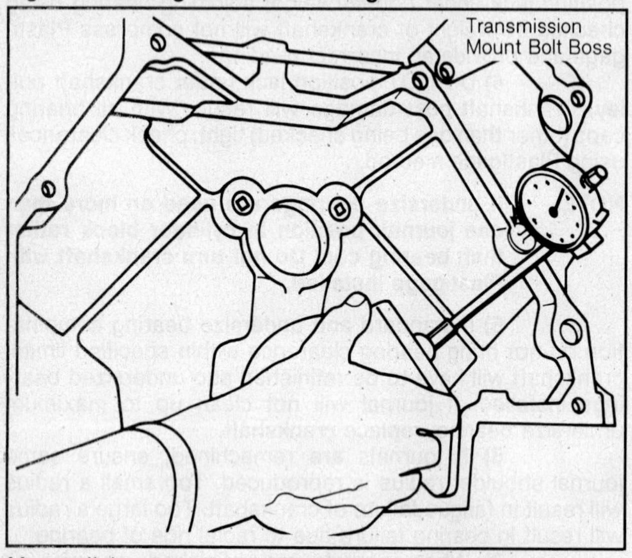

Mount dial gauge plate to flange and observe readings at each transmission mount bolt boss.

REAR MAIN BEARING OIL SEAL

NOTE: Rear main bearing oil seal can be removed and installed without removal of oil pan or crankshaft.

Removal

Remove transmission assembly. On manual transmission, remove pressure plate and clutch disc. Remove flywheel retaining bolts and flywheel. Remove rear main bearing oil seal by prying out with screwdriver. Take care not to scratch crankshaft or seal surface. Clean block-to-seal mating surface.

Installation

Coat outside surface of new seal with engine oil and install with lip toward engine. Ensure that seal is firmly in place. Install flywheel. On manual transmission, install pressure plate and clutch disc. Install transmission assembly.

ENGINE OILING

CRANKCASE CAPACITY

Crankcase capacity is 4 quarts (3.7L) with oil filter change; 3 quarts (2.8L) without filter change.

NORMAL OIL PRESSURE

Normal oil pressure is 36-41 psi (2.53-2.88 kg/cm^2) at 2000 RPM.

OIL PRESSURE REGULATOR VALVE

Oil pressure regulator valve is located in oil pump body. Valve is nonadjustable.

ENGINE OILING SYSTEM

Oil pump draws oil from pan, feeding it through the oil filter and into passage along right side of the block where it intersects lifter bosses. Oil is then routed to camshaft and crankshaft bearings through smaller drilled passages.

Oil is supplied to rocker arms through hydraulic lifters. By-pass valves are located in pick-up screen, oil filter mounting and oil pump. Oil returns to pan through return holes in head and block.

OIL PUMP

Removal & Disassembly

Remove oil pan. Remove 2 flange mounting bolts and nut from main bearing cap bolt. Remove oil pump and screen as an assembly. Do not disturb oil pick-up tube on screen or body. Disassemble pump and inspect for excessive wear or cracks. *See Fig. 10.*

Fig. 10: Exploded View of Oil Pump Assembly

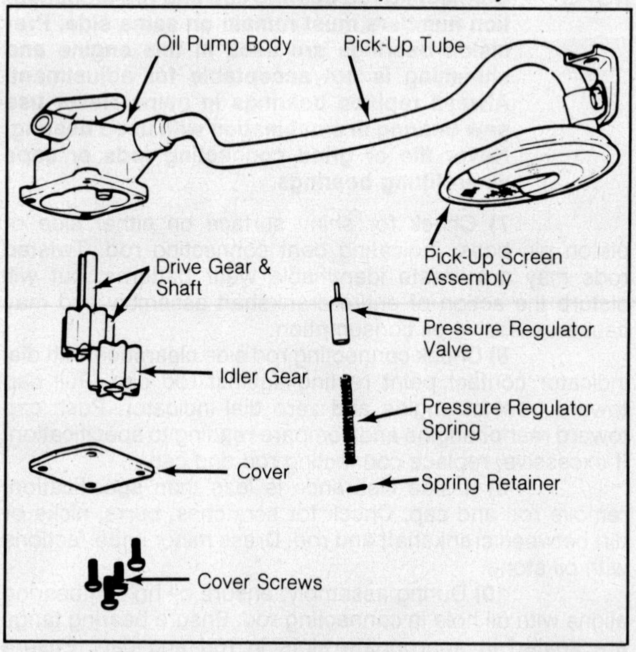

Reassembly & Installation

1) Install drive gear and shaft. Install idler gear with smooth side toward cover. Fill oil pump cavities with petroleum jelly to ensure immediate oil pressure. Install cover, tighten retaining bolts and ensure shaft turns freely. Install regulator valve plunger, spring, retainer and pin.

2) Align oil pump shaft to match with oil pump drive shaft tang. Install oil pump in block. Position flange over oil pump drive shaft lower bushing. No gasket is used. Tighten bolts. Pump should slide easily into place. Install oil pan with new gaskets and seals.

ENGINE COOLING

WATER PUMP

Removal

Disconnect negative battery cable. Drain engine coolant. Remove all accessory drive belts. Remove lower radiator hose at water pump. Remove water pump attaching bolts and remove water pump.

2.5 LITER 4-CYLINDER (Cont.)

Installation

If installing new pump, transfer pulley from old pump. Apply continuous bead of sealer to clean pump sealing surface. Install water pump while sealer is still wet and tighten attaching bolts. Install lower radiator hose and drive belts. Connect negative battery cable. Fill cooling system and check for leaks.

NOTE: For further information on cooling system capacities and other cooling system components, see appropriate article in ENGINE COOLING SYSTEMS section.

ENGINE SPECIFICATIONS

GENERAL SPECIFICATIONS

Year	DISPLACEMENT Cu. In.	DISPLACEMENT Liters	Fuel System	HP@RPM	Torque Ft. Lbs.@RPM	Compr. Ratio	BORE In.	BORE mm	STROKE In.	STROKE mm
1985	151	2.5	EFI	92@4400	134@2800	9.0:1	4.00	101.6	3.00	76.2

VALVES

Engine Size & Valve	Head Diam. In. (mm)	Face Angle	Seat Angle	Seat Width In. (mm)	Stem Diameter In. (mm)	Stem Clearance In. (mm)	Valve Lift In. (mm)
2.5L							
Intake	1.72 (43.7)	45°	46°	.035-.075 (.89-1.9)	.3418-.3425 (8.682-8.699)	.0010-.0027 (.025-.069)	.....
Exhaust	1.50 (38.1)	45°	46°	.058-.097 (1.47-2.46)	.3418-.3425 (8.682-8.699)	.0010-.0027 [1] (.025-.069)	.....

[1] – Measured at top of guide. Bottom is .0020-.0037" (.051-.094 mm).

PISTONS, PINS, RINGS

Engine	PISTONS Clearance In. (mm)	PINS Piston Fit In. (mm)	PINS Rod Fit In. (mm)	RINGS Ring No.	RINGS End Gap In. (mm)	RINGS Side Clearance In. (mm)
2.5L	.0014-.0022 [1] (.036-.056)	.0003-.0005 (.008-.013)	Press Fit	1	.010-.022 (.25-.56)	.0015-.0030 (.051-.076)
				2	.010-.020 (.25-.51)	.0010-.0030 (.025-.076)
				3	.015-.055 (.38-1.40)	.....

[1] – Top clearance shown, bottom clearance is .0020-.0037" (.051-.094 mm).

CRANKSHAFT MAIN & CONNECTING ROD BEARINGS

Engine	MAIN BEARINGS Journal Diam. In. (mm)	MAIN BEARINGS Clearance In. (mm)	MAIN BEARINGS Thrust Bearing	MAIN BEARINGS Crankshaft End Play In. (mm)	CONNECTING ROD BEARINGS Journal Diam. In. (mm)	CONNECTING ROD BEARINGS Clearance In. (mm)	CONNECTING ROD BEARINGS Side Play In. (mm)
2.5L	2.300 [1] (58.42)	.0005-.0022 (.013-.056)	No. 5	.0035-.0085 (.089-.216)	2.000 (50.80)	.0005-.0026 (.013-.066)	.006-.022 (.15-.56)

[1] – Maximum out-of-round permissible is .0005" (.013 mm).

2.5 LITER 4-CYLINDER (Cont.)

ENGINE SPECIFICATIONS (Cont.)

VALVE SPRINGS

Engine	Free Length In. (mm)	PRESSURE Lbs. @ In. (Kg @ mm)	
		Valve Closed	Valve Open
2.5L	2.08 52.8	78-86@1.66 (35-39@42.20)	122-180@1.25 (55-82@31.85)

CAMSHAFT

Engine	Journal Diam. In. (mm)	Clearance In. (mm)	Lobe Lift In. (mm)
2.5L	1.869 (47.473)	.0007-.0027 [1] (.018-.069)	.398 (10.312)

[1] – Camshaft end play is .0015-.0050" (.038-.127 mm).

TIGHTENING SPECIFICATIONS

Application	Ft. Lbs. (N.m)
Connecting Rod Nuts	32 (44)
Cylinder Head Bolt	[1] 92 (125)
EGR Valve-to-Manifold	10 (14)
Exhaust Manifold Bolt	44 (60)
Fan Bolt	18 (25)
Flywheel Bolt	44 (60)
Fuel Pump Bolt	18 (25)
Harmonic Balancer Bolt	160 (212)
Intake Manifold Bolt	29 (40)
Main Bearing Cap Bolt	70 (95)
Oil Pump Bolt	22 (30)
Oil Pump Cover Bolt	10 (14)
Oil Pump Drive Shaft Cover Plate	10 (14)
Rocker Arm Bolt	20 (27)
Throttle Body Bolt	15 (20)
Throttle Body Nut	15 (20)
Water Pump-to-Block Bolt	25 (34)
	INCH Lbs.
Camshaft Thrust Plate Bolt	84 (10)
Front Cover Bolt	84 (10)
Lifter Retainer Bolt	84 (10)
Oil Pan Bolt	75 (6)
Rocker Arm Cover Bolts	6 (8)

[1] – Cylinder head bolts No. 9 & 10 require thread sealer.

General Motors/Jeep Engines

2.8 LITER V6

ENGINE CODING

ENGINE IDENTIFICATION

The engine identification number is stamped on a machined pad on front of cylinder block, just rearward of engine front cover. The Vehicle Identification Number (VIN) is located on the left side of the dash panel at the base of the windshield.

On GM vehicles, the eighth character of the (VIN) denotes engine type. On Jeep vehicles, the fourth character of the (VIN) denotes engine type.

ENGINE IDENTIFICATION CODES

Engine	Code
2.8L 2-Bbl.	
GM	B
Jeep	W

ENGINE REMOVAL

See ENGINE REMOVAL at end of ENGINE section.

MANIFOLDS & CYLINDER HEADS

INTAKE MANIFOLD

Removal

1) Disconnect battery negative cable. Remove air cleaner. Drain cooling system. Label and disconnect all electrical connectors, vacuum hoses and emissions hoses at distributor, carburetor and intake manifold.

2) Disconnect fuel line at carburetor. Disconnect spark plug wires at spark plugs. Remove distributor cap and mark position of rotor. Remove distributor.

3) Remove all brackets attached to rocker arm covers, and remove covers. Remove upper radiator hose and heater hose from engine. Remove A/C drive belt and rotate compressor aside. Remove intake manifold and discard gaskets.

Installation

1) Clean all gasket mating surfaces. Apply 3/16" bead of silicone sealant to front and rear sealing ridges of cylinder block. Install new intake manifold side gaskets onto cylinder heads. Gaskets are stamped "Left Side" and "Right Side".

Fig. 1: Intake Manifold Gasket Modification

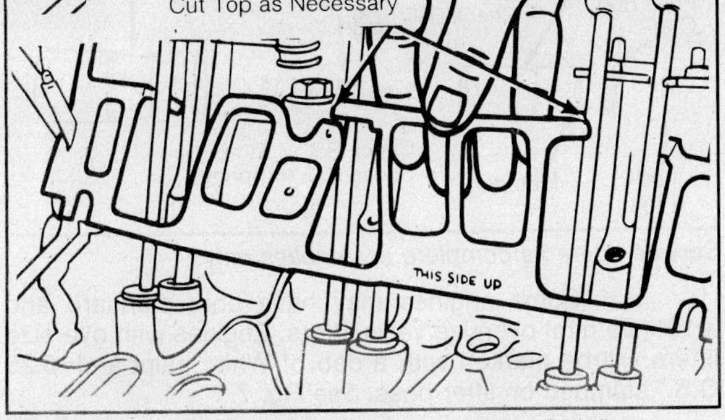

Gaskets are stamped "Left Side" and "Right Side".

2) Hold gaskets in place by extending silicone sealant bead 1/4" onto ends of side gaskets. New side gaskets will need to be cut to install behind push rods. *See Fig. 1.*

3) Install intake manifold. Ensure sealing areas between cylinder ridges and ends of manifold are completely sealed. Install and tighten manifold attaching bolts and nuts. *See Fig. 2.* To complete installation, reverse removal procedure.

Fig. 2: Intake Manifold Tightening Sequence

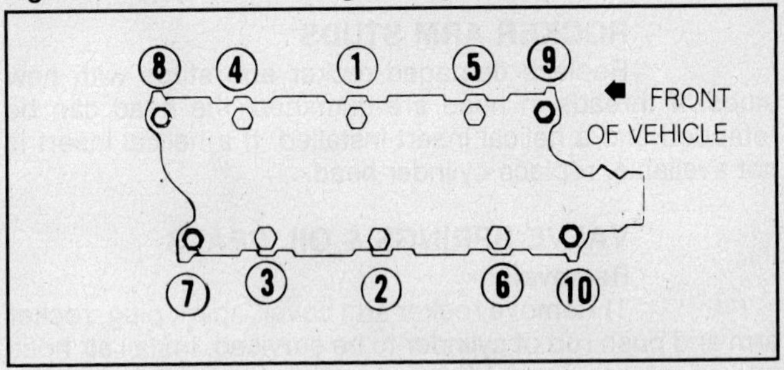

Tighten bolts and nuts to 13-25 ft. lbs. (18-34 N.m).

EXHAUST MANIFOLD

Removal

Disconnect negative battery cable. Raise vehicle and disconnect exhaust pipes. On left side, remove 4 rear manifold bolts and 1 nut. Lower vehicle. On both sides, disconnect air diverter valve, hoses and wires. Remove power steering bracket. Remove manifold bolts and manifold.

Installation

To install, clean manifold-to-head mating surfaces and reverse removal procedure.

CYLINDER HEADS

Removal

1) Remove intake manifold as previously described. Raise vehicle and disconnect exhaust pipes at manifolds. Drain coolant from block. Remove oil dipstick tube attachment. Lower vehicle and loosen rocker arm nuts and rotate rockers to side.

2) Remove push rods in sequence for reinstallation in original locations. Remove alternator, power steering pump, A/C compressor, and respective mounting brackets for these components. Position assemblies aside. Remove cylinder heads.

Installation

1) Clean all gasket mating surfaces. Clean head bolt and cylinder block threads. Head gaskets are marked "This Side Up". Properly install gaskets in place on cylinder block. Install cylinder heads. Apply sealant to head bolt threads and install bolts. Tighten bolts in sequence. *See Fig. 3.*

Fig. 3: Cylinder Head Tightening Sequence

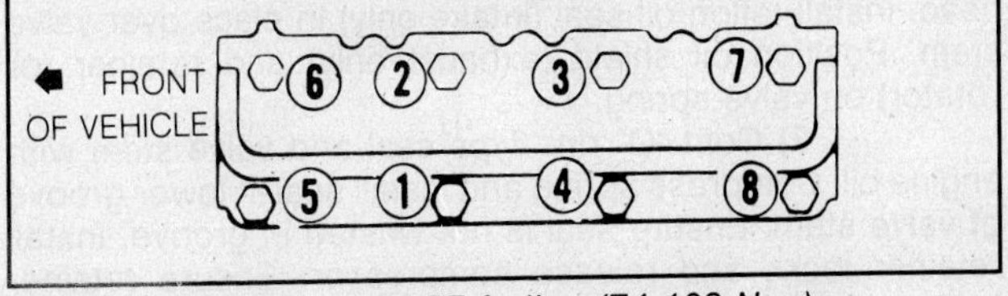

Tighten head bolts to 55-77 ft. lbs. (74-108 N.m).

2.8 LITER V6 (Cont.)

2) Coat rocker arm balls and rocker arm mating surfaces with assembly lubricant before installing. To complete installation, reverse removal procedure. Adjust valves.

VALVES

VALVE ARRANGEMENT

Left Bank – E-I-I-E-I-E (Front-to-rear).
Right Bank – E-I-E-I-I-E (Front-to-rear).

ROCKER ARM STUDS

Replace damaged rocker arm studs with new studs. If threads in head are damaged, the head can be retapped and a helical insert installed. If a helical insert is not available, replace cylinder head.

VALVE SPRINGS & OIL SEALS

Removal

1) Remove rocker arm cover, spark plug, rocker arm and push rod of cylinder to be serviced. Install air hose and adapter to spark plug hole and apply air pressure. Do not remove air pressure until components have been reassembled.

2) Using a valve spring compressor, compress valve spring and remove valve retainer locks and oil seal. Release compressor and remove retainer (or rotator), oil shield (exhaust only), and valve spring damper. On intake valves, remove teflon oil seal. *See Fig. 4.*

Fig. 4: Intake and Exhaust Valve Assemblies

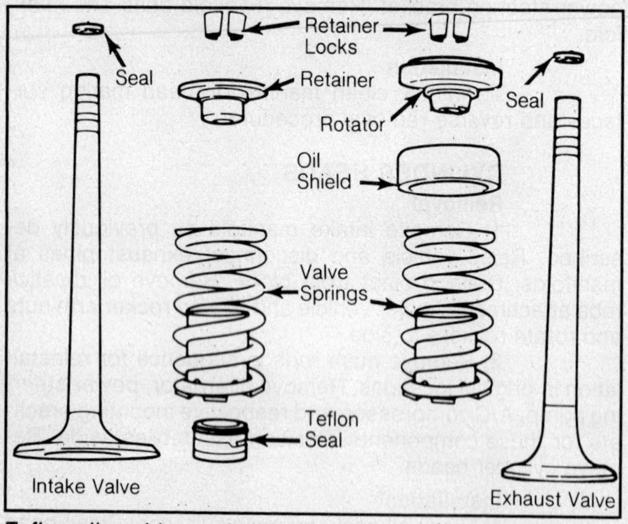

Teflon oil seal is used with "O" ring seal on intake valves.

Inspection

Using valve spring tester, check valve spring tension. Springs (without dampers) should test to within 10 lbs. of specification. Replace spring if not within limits.

Installation

1) Position valve spring and damper on cylinder head. Install teflon oil seal (intake only) in place over valve stem. Position oil shield (exhaust only) and retainer (or rotator) on valve spring.

2) Coat "O" ring type seal and valve stem with engine oil. Compress spring and install seal in lower groove of valve stem. Ensure seal is not twisted in groove. Install retainer locks and release compressor. Ensure retainer locks are properly seated in upper groove of valve stem.

VALVE SPRING INSTALLED HEIGHT

CAUTION: Never shim valve springs to a height less than specifications.

Installed height of valve springs should be 1.58" (40 mm). For intake valves, measure from top of spring damper tabs to bottom of retainer. For exhaust valves, measure from top of spring damper tabs to where top of valve spring contacts inside bottom of oil shield. If measurement exceeds specified height, install a .030" (.76 mm) shim at spring seat. *See Fig. 5.*

Fig. 5: Checking Valve Spring Installed Height

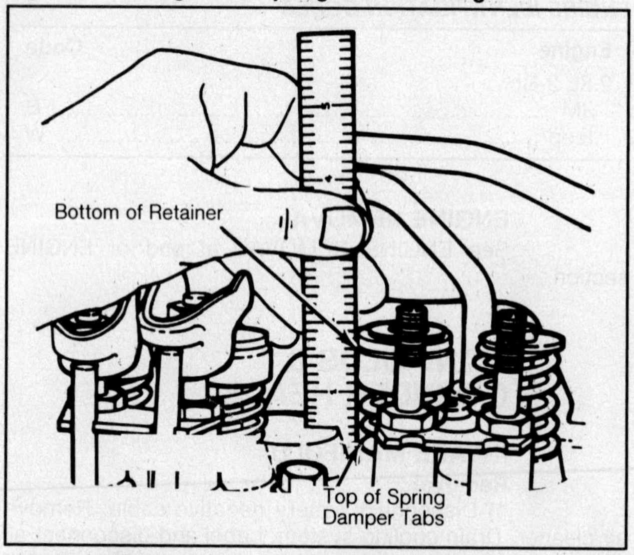

Installed height is 1.58" (40 mm). Never shim to a height less than specification.

VALVE GUIDE SERVICING

If valve stem-to-guide clearance exceeds specifications, ream valve guide to proper oversize. Valves are available with .0035" (.089 mm), .0155" (.394 mm) and .0305" (.775 mm) oversize stems.

HYDRAULIC VALVE LIFTERS

If lifters are removed, ensure they are installed in original locations. Service lifters as complete assemblies only. If lifters are disassembled for cleaning and inspection, they should be reassembled and tested in a lifter leak-down rate tester. *See Fig. 6.*

Fig. 6: Hydraulic Lifter Assembly

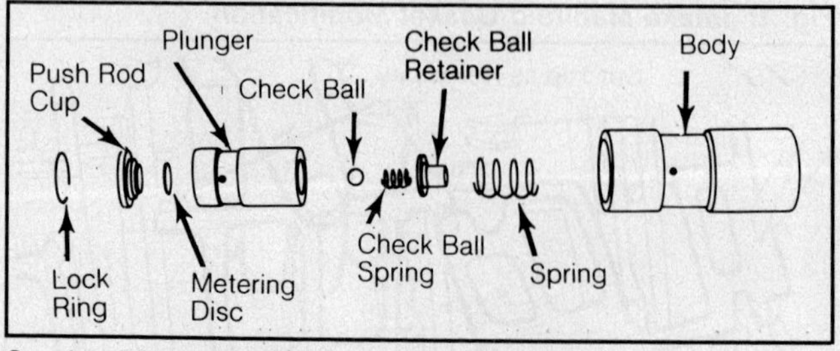

Service lifters as complete assemblies only.

Some engines may have both standard and .010" (.25 mm) oversize valve lifters. Engines with oversize lifters will be marked with a dab of White paint and "0.25 O.S." stamped on lifter boss. *See Fig. 7.*

2.8 LITER V6 (Cont.)

Fig. 7: Identifying Oversize Lifters

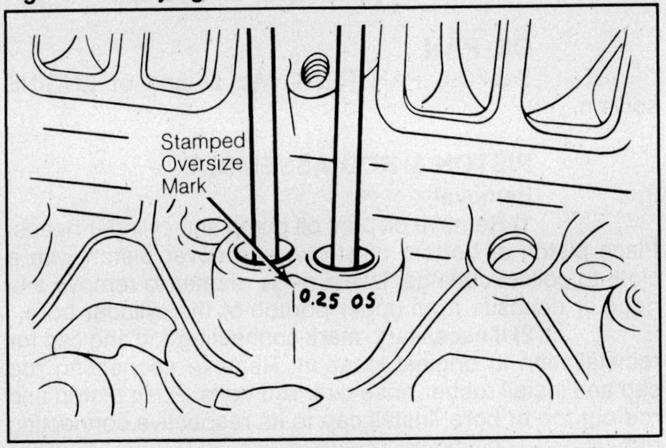

Lifter bosses are also marked with a dab of White paint.

VALVE CLEARANCE ADJUSTMENT

1) Adjust valves by backing off adjusting nut until lash (play) is felt at push rod. Then tighten nut until all lash is removed. Tighten adjusting nut an additional 1 1/2 turns. *See Fig. 8.*

2) Rotate crankshaft to bring No. 1 piston at TDC on end of compression stroke. Adjust valves as listed in table.

3) Rotate crankshaft 360° to bring No. 4 piston at TDC on end of compression stroke. Adjust remaining valves. Install rocker arm covers. Check timing and idle speed.

VALVE CLEARANCE ADJUSTMENT

Piston at TDC	Adjust Intake	Adjust Exhaust
No. 1	Nos. 1, 5, 6	Nos. 1, 2, 3
No. 4	Nos. 2, 3, 4	Nos. 4, 5, 6

Fig. 8: Valve Clearance Adjustment

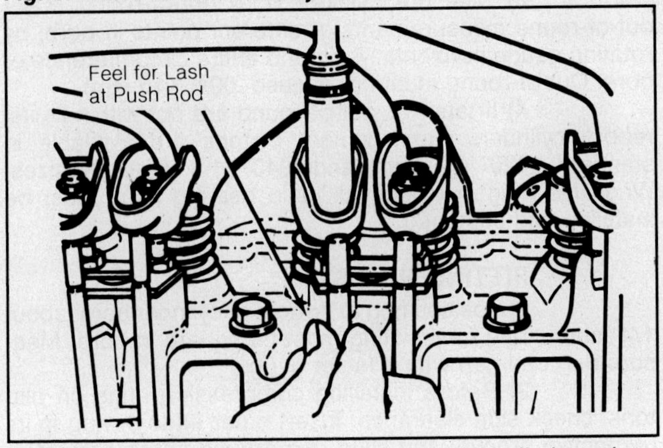

Tighten adjusting nut 11/2 turns after lash is eliminated.

CAMSHAFT

ENGINE FRONT COVER

Removal

Disconnect negative battery cable. Remove all drive belts, drain cooling system and remove water pump. If equipped, remove A/C compressor and mounting bracket. Remove vibration damper. Disconnect radiator lower hose at front cover and heater hose at water pump. Remove front cover.

Installation

1) Clean sealing surfaces thoroughly. Apply 3/32" bead of RTV sealant to front cover-to-block sealing surface. Apply 1/8" bead silicone sealant to bottom of front cover sealing surface. *See Fig. 9.*

2) Place front cover on engine and install stud bolt and 2 lower bolts. Coat water pump bolts with pipe thread sealant. Apply 3/32" bead RTV sealant to water pump sealing surface, and install water pump and attaching bolts. To complete installation, reverse removal procedure.

Fig. 9: Front Cover Sealant Application

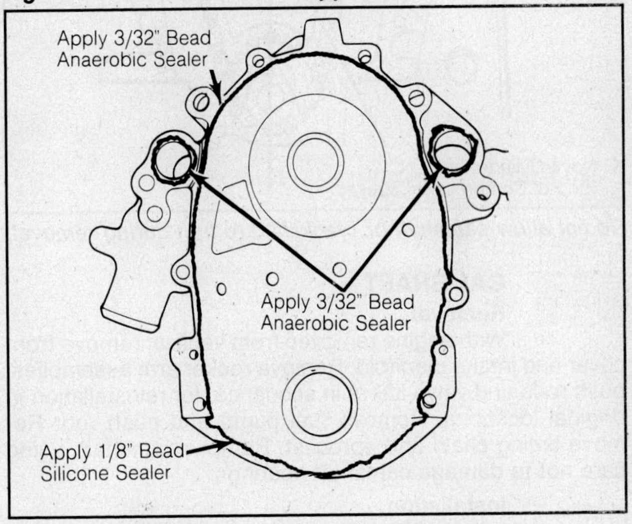

Install and tighten front cover and water pump before sealant sets up.

FRONT COVER OIL SEAL

Removal

Oil seal may be replaced with front cover installed. Remove vibration damper. Using large screwdriver, pry seal out of cover. Use care not to damage crankshaft sealing area or front cover.

Installation

Install new seal with open side of seal toward inside of front cover. Use Seal Installer (J-23042) to drive seal into position. Install vibration damper.

TIMING CHAIN

Removal

1) Remove front cover. Rotate crankshaft to position No. 4 piston at TDC on end of compression stroke. Timing marks on camshaft and crankshaft sprockets should be aligned. No. 1 piston will be at TDC on end of exhaust stroke. *See Fig. 10.*

2) Remove camshaft sprocket bolts, then remove sprocket and chain. Do not allow camshaft or crankshaft to turn.

Installation

Install timing chain and camshaft sprocket. Timing marks must be aligned. *See Fig. 10.* Use attaching bolts to draw sprocket onto camshaft and tighten bolts. Lubricate chain with engine oil. Install remaining components in reverse order of removal.

2.8 LITER V6 (Cont.)

Fig. 10: Aligning Timing Sprockets

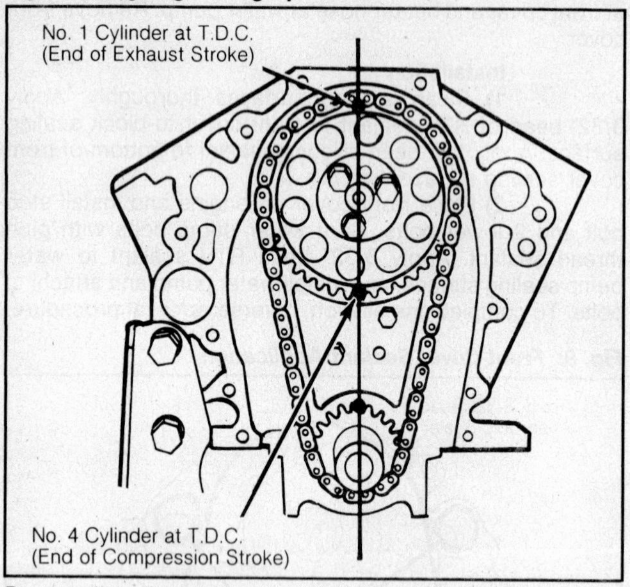

Do not allow camshaft or crankshaft to turn during removal.

CAMSHAFT

Removal

With engine removed from vehicle, remove front cover and intake manifold. Remove rocker arm assemblies, push rods and valve lifters in sequence, for reinstallation in original locations. Remove fuel pump and push rod. Remove timing chain and sprocket. Remove camshaft, using care not to damage camshaft bearings.

Installation

Lubricate journals with engine oil and apply assembly lubricant to camshaft lobes. Carefully install camshaft. Prior to installing rocker arm assemblies, coat rocker arm ball and mating rocker arm surface with assembly lubricant. To complete installation, reverse removal procedure.

CAM LOBE LIFT

1) Remove rocker arm assemblies. Mount dial indicator on rocker arm stud. Position dial indicator and ball socket adapter on push rod.

2) Slowly rotate engine clockwise until lifter is on base circle of camshaft. Zero dial indicator. Rotate engine until push rod is fully raised. Record lobe lift reading and compare with specifications. If not within limits, replace camshaft and lifters.

CAMSHAFT BEARINGS

Removal

Remove engine from vehicle. Remove camshaft. Ensure rod and main bearing caps are marked, and remove all caps. Push pistons to top of bores. Remove crankshaft. Remove camshaft rear cover from cylinder block. Using a camshaft bearing remover/installer remove camshaft bearings.

Installation

Using bearing remover/installer, install front and rear bearings first. These act as guides for the remover/installer and center the remaining bearings being pulled into place. Ensure bearing oil holes line up with oil gallery holes in block. To complete installation, reverse removal procedure.

PISTONS, RINGS & PINS

OIL PAN

See OIL PAN REMOVAL at end of ENGINE section.

PISTON & ROD ASSEMBLY

Removal

1) Remove oil pan, oil pump and cylinder heads. Place piston at bottom of stroke and cover piston with a cloth to collect cuttings. Use a ridge reamer to remove any ridge or deposits from upper portion of the cylinder bore.

2) If necessary, mark connecting rod and cap for reinstallation in original location. Remove connecting rod cap and install rubber hose over rod bolts. Push piston and rod out top of bore. Install cap to its respective connecting rod.

Installation

1) Install rings on piston, and position ring gaps. *See Fig. 11*. Apply a light coat of engine oil to piston, rings and cylinder bore. Using ring compressor, compress piston rings. Ensure ring gaps do not change during compressor installation.

2) Cover rod bolts with protective rubber hose. Install piston with notch (or machined hole) in piston head, toward front of engine. Rod bearing tang slot must be positioned away from camshaft. Remove rubber hose from rod bolts. With rod bearings installed, install and tighten rod caps.

FITTING PISTONS

1) Using telescopic gauge and micrometer, measure cylinder bore diameter. Measure piston diameter across piston skirt, at center of piston pin. Difference between 2 measurements is piston-to-cylinder clearance.

2) Using cylinder bore gauge, measure cylinder bore taper by working gauge up and down in bore. Difference between high and low readings is taper. Taper must not exceed .004" (.10 mm).

3) Measure cylinder bore out-of-round. Take out-of-round measurements at different points in bore, by rotating gauge horizontally, around entire circumference of bore. Out-of-round must not exceed .004" (.10 mm).

4) If taper or out-of-round are not within limits, rebore cylinders. Replacement pistons are available in standard, .020" (.50 mm) and .040" (1.0 mm) oversizes. When reboring cylinders, all main bearing caps must be installed and tightened.

FITTING RINGS

1) Position ring at bottom of cylinder bore, about 1/4" above ring travel. Ring must be square in bore. Measure ring end gap with a feeler gauge.

2) Before installing compression rings on pistons, check side clearance. Insert outer edge of ring in its respective groove, and slide ring around entire circumference of groove. The ring should slide freely in groove. If ring grooves have high steps on lower lands, piston must be replaced.

3) Check side clearance of compression rings, with feeler gauge inserted between ring and ring groove. Install and properly space rings on piston. Ensure oil ring spacer ends are butted, and not overlapped. Note that oil ring spacer anti-rotation tang is inserted into oil hole (or slot) of piston. *See Fig. 11*.

General Motors/Jeep Engines

2.8 LITER V6 (Cont.)

Fig. 11: Desired Ring Gap Locations

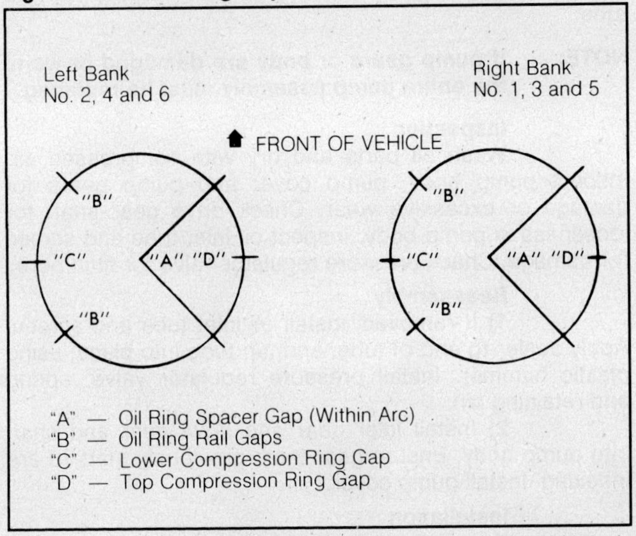

Insert oil ring spacer tang in piston oil hole (or slot). Hole is within arc of oil ring spacer gap "A".

PISTON PIN REPLACEMENT

Removal

Using an arbor press and piston pin remover/installer, press pin from piston and connecting rod.

Installation

Check clearance of pin in piston. Replace piston and pin assembly if not within limits. Lubricate piston and connecting rod pin bores. Assemble connecting rod to piston. Using piston pin remover/installer and an arbor press, press piston into place. Check piston for freedom of movement on pin.

CRANKSHAFT & ROD BEARINGS

NOTE: **This engine uses precision bearings, and shimming is not acceptable for adjustment. Never file or grind connecting rods or caps when fitting bearings.**

CONNECTING ROD BEARINGS

1) Remove rod cap and use Plastigage method to check bearing clearance. With crank pin and bearing clean, place Plastigage across full width of bearing, about 1/4" off center and away from oil holes. Install and tighten rod cap. Do not let crankshaft turn.

2) Remove rod cap and determine clearance by measuring width of compressed Plastigage at widest point. If clearance is excessive, select a new undersize bearing and remeasure clearance.

3) Clean crankshaft journal and bearing seat in rod and cap. Insert bearings in rod and cap, then coat bearings with engine oil. Pull piston and rod assembly down onto crankshaft. Install and tighten rod cap. After all rods are installed, check side play between rod cap and crank pin thrust face.

4) Replacement bearings are available in standard, .0005" (.013 mm) and .0010" (.026 mm) undersizes for use with standard size crankshaft.

MAIN BEARINGS

1) Use Plastigage method to check bearings. If engine is in vehicle, crankshaft must be supported at front and rear. Ensure that all bearing caps, other than the one being checked, are tightened to specifications. When checking No. 1 main bearing, remove all drive belts from crankshaft pulley.

2) Start with rear main bearing cap and work forward. New bearings are available in standard, .0006" (.016 mm) and .0012" (.032 mm) undersizes, for use with standard size crankshaft. Always replace both upper and lower bearing halves together.

3) Remove main bearings from cylinder block using bearing remover/installer. Insert remover/installer in crankshaft oil hole and rotate crankshaft clockwise. If remover/installer is unavailable, use a bent cotter pin.

4) Lubricate journal and bearing. Insert plain end of new bearing between crankshaft and notched side of block. Insert bearing remover/installer into crankshaft oil hole. Rotate crankshaft counterclockwise to install bearing into place.

5) Install lower bearing half into cap, then lubricate with engine oil. Install and tighten main bearing cap with arrow pointing toward front of engine.

THRUST BEARING ALIGNMENT

1) Ensure all main bearing caps, except No. 3, are installed and tightened. Tighten No. 3 thrust bearing cap bolts to 11 ft. lbs. (15 N.m).

2) Tap end of crankshaft rearward, then forward, to line up main bearing and crankshaft thrust surfaces. Tighten thrust bearing cap. Retighten all main bearing cap bolts, including thrust bearing. Rotate crankshaft to ensure there is no excessive drag.

CRANKSHAFT END PLAY

Check crankshaft end play after aligning thrust bearing. Pry crankshaft forward and insert feeler gauge between crankshaft counterweight and No. 3 main bearing cap forward face. End play should be .002-.008" (.06-.21 mm).

REAR MAIN BEARING OIL SEAL

1) Remove oil pan, oil pump and rear main bearing cap. Remove upper and lower rope seal, loosening Nos. 2 and 3 main bearing bolts if necessary. Clean seal channel.

Fig. 12: Cross Section of Rear Main Seal

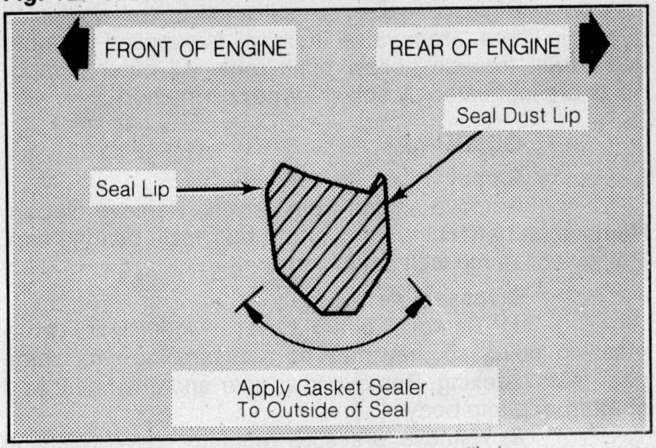

Install seal using shim stock to prevent seal damage.

2.8 LITER V6 (Cont.)

2) Apply a thin coat of gasket sealer to outside of rubber seal. Keep sealer off seal lips. Roll seal into position in cylinder block. Use a piece of shim stock to slip between seal and block to prevent seal damage. Turn crankshaft to ease installation. Seal lip must face front of engine and seal dust lip must face flywheel. *See Fig. 12.*

3) Apply gasket sealer to other half of seal and install in rear main bearing cap. Apply a 1/32" bead of anaerobic sealer to cap between rear main seal end and oil pan rear seal groove. Keep sealer off rear seal, bearing and drain slot. *See Fig. 13.*

Fig. 13: Applying Sealer to Rear Main Bearing Cap

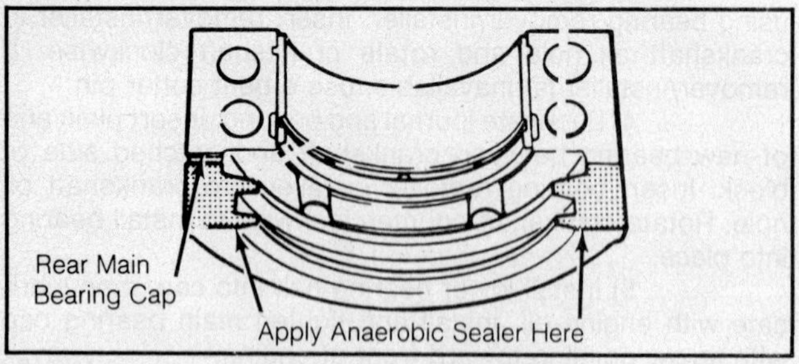

4) Apply light coat of engine oil to crankshaft surface at seal. Install rear main bearing cap. Tighten bearing cap bolts. Use Plastigage method to check bearings. Install oil pump and pan.

ENGINE OILING

CRANKCASE CAPACITY

4.5 quarts (4.2L) with filter replacement.

NORMAL OIL PRESSURE

Normal oil pressure is 30-50 psi (2.1-3.5 kg/cm²) at 35-40 MPH with engine at operating temperature.

OIL PRESSURE REGULATOR VALVE

Nonadjustable pressure regulator valve is located in oil pump body.

ENGINE OILING SYSTEM

The left main oil gallery (along upper left side of camshaft) supplies oil to the left bank hydraulic lifters. Left gallery directs oil to the camshaft bearings, crankshaft and right oil gallery.

Right oil gallery supplies oil to the right side hydraulic lifters. From valve lifters, oil is supplied to upper valve train through hollow push rods. All other components are lubricated by splash or nozzle method.

OIL PUMP

Removal

Remove engine from vehicle. Remove oil pan. Remove bolt attaching oil pump to rear main bearing cap. Remove oil pump with extension shaft.

Disassembly

1) Remove pump cover. Mark gears at a meshing point, so they may be reassembled with same gear teeth indexing. Remove idler gear and drive gear and shaft from pump body.

2) Remove pressure regulator valve retaining pin, valve and spring. Remove oil inlet tube from body, if it needs replacement. Do not remove screen on oil inlet tube.

NOTE: **If pump gears or body are damaged or worn, the entire pump assembly must be replaced.**

Inspection

Wash all parts and dry with compressed air. Inspect pump body, pump cover and pump gears for damage or excessive wear. Check drive gear shaft for looseness in pump body. Inspect oil inlet tube and screen for damage. Check pressure regulator valve for fit in bore.

Reassembly

1) If removed, install oil inlet tube and screen. Apply sealer to end of tube, and tap tube into place, using plastic hammer. Install pressure regulator valve, spring and retaining pin.

2) Install idler gear and drive gear and shaft into pump body. Ensure gear teeth previously marked are indexing. Install pump cover.

Installation

Prime oil pump. Assemble pump and extension shaft (with retainer) to rear main bearing cap. Ensure top end of hexagon extension shaft engages with hexagon socket of distributor drive gear. Install and tighten oil pump attaching bolt.

ENGINE COOLING

WATER PUMP

Removal

Disconnect battery negative cable. Drain cooling system. Remove heater hose from water pump. Remove water pump.

Installation

Apply 3/32" bead of anaerobic sealer to water pump sealing surface. Coat bolt threads with pipe thread sealer. Install and tighten water pump. Install remaining components in reverse order of removal.

NOTE: **For information on cooling system capacities and other cooling system components, see appropriate article in ENGINE COOLING SYSTEMS at end of ENGINE section.**

TIGHTENING SPECIFICATIONS

Application	Ft. Lbs. (N.m)
Camshaft Rear Cover Bolts	6-9 (8-12)
Camshaft Sprocket Bolts	15-20 (20-27)
Connecting Rod Cap Nuts	34-44 (46-60)
Crankshaft Pulley Bolts	20-30 (27-41)
Cylinder Head Bolts	55-77 (74-104)
Exhaust Manifold Bolts	20-30 (27-41)
Exhaust Manifold Studs	24-35 (32-47)
Flywheel-to-Crankshaft Bolts	45-59 (61-80)
Front Cover Bolts	13-22 (18-30)
Front Cover Studs	19-24 (26-33)
Intake Manifold Bolts	13-25 (18-34)
Main Bearing Cap Bolts	63-83 (85-112)
Oil Pump Attaching Bolt	26-35 (35-47)
Rocker Arm Studs	43-53 (58-72)
Water Pump	
6 mm Bolts	6-9 (8-12)
8 mm Bolts	13-18 (18-24)

General Motors/Jeep Engines

2.8 LITER V6 (Cont.)

ENGINE SPECIFICATIONS

GENERAL SPECIFICATIONS

Year	DISPLACEMENT		Fuel System	HP@RPM	Torque Ft. Lbs.@RPM	Compr. Ratio	BORE		STROKE	
	Cu. In.	Liters					In.	mm	In.	mm
1985	173	2.8	2-Bbl.	110@4800	145@2100	8.5:1	3.50	89.0	2.99	76.0

VALVES

Engine Size & Valve	Head Diam. In. (mm)	Face Angle	Seat Angle	Seat Width In. (mm)	Stem Diameter In. (mm)	Stem Clearance In. (mm)	Valve Lift In. (mm)
2.8L							
Intake	.....	45°	46°	.049-.059 (1.25-1.50)	.....	.0010-.0027 (.025-.069)	.....
Exhaust	.....	45°	46°	.063-.075 (1.60-1.90)	.....	.0010-.0027 (.025-.069)	.....

PISTONS, PINS, RINGS

Engine	PISTONS	PINS		RINGS		
	Clearance In. (mm)	Piston Fit In. (mm)	Rod Fit In. (mm)	Ring No.	End Gap In. (mm)	Side Clearance In. (mm)
2.8L	.0007-.0017 (.017-.043)	.0003-.0004 (.007-.009)	[1] .0007-.0020 (.019-.052)	1	.010-.020 (.25-.50)	.0012-.0027 (.030-.070)
				2	.010-.020 (.25-.50)	.0016-.0037 (.040-.095)
				3	.020-.055 (.51-1.40)	[2] .0078 (.199)

[1] – Interference fit.
[2] – Maximum clearance permitted.

CRANKSHAFT MAIN & CONNECTING ROD BEARINGS

Engine	MAIN BEARINGS				CONNECTING ROD BEARINGS		
	Journal Diam. In. (mm)	Clearance In. (mm)	Thrust Bearing	Crankshaft End Play In. (mm)	Journal Diam. In. (mm)	Clearance In. (mm)	Side Play In. (mm)
2.8L	[1] 2.493-2.494 (63.340-63.364)	.0016-.0031 (.041-.081)	No. 3	.002-.008 (.06-.21)	1.9983-1.9993 (50.758-50.784)	.0014-.0037 (.035-.095)	.006-.017 (.16-.44)

[1] – Except No. 3 journal. No. 3 journal diameter is 2.492-2.494" (63.32-63.35 mm).

VALVE SPRINGS

Engine	Free Length In. (mm)	PRESSURE Lbs. @ In. (Kg @ mm)	
		Valve Closed	Valve Open
2.8L	1.91 (48.50)	88@1.57 (39.91@40)	195@1.18 (88.45@30)

CAMSHAFT

Engine	Journal Diam. In. (mm)	Clearance In. (mm)	Lobe Lift In. (mm)
2.8L	1.867-1.870 (47.44-47.49)	.0010-.0040 (.025-.101)	[1] .231 (5.87) [2] .263 (6.67)

[1] – Intake.
[2] – Exhaust.

4.8 LITER 6-CYLINDER

ENGINE CODING

ENGINE IDENTIFICATION

Engine may be identified by the eighth character of the Vehicle Identification Number (VIN). VIN is stamped on metal tag, attached to left side of dash, near windshield. Engine identification number is also stamped on machined pad, at right hand side of cylinder block, to the rear of the distributor bore.

ENGINE IDENTIFICATION CODE

Engine	Code
4.8L 1-Bbl.	T

ENGINE REMOVAL

See ENGINE REMOVAL at end of ENGINE section.

MANIFOLDS & CYLINDER HEAD

INTAKE & EXHAUST MANIFOLD

Removal

1) Disconnect negative battery cable. Remove air cleaner. Disconnect both throttle controls at bellcrank, and remove throttle return spring. Disconnect fuel line and vacuum hoses at carburetor.

2) Disconnect crankcase vent hose at rocker arm cover. Remove vapor hose at vapor canister. Disconnect exhaust pipe at flange. Remove manifold assembly attaching bolts and clamps. Remove intake and exhaust manifold assembly.

Installation

Clean gasket surfaces. Place manifold in position with new gasket. Install and tighten clamps and bolts. Reverse removal procedure to complete installation.

CYLINDER HEAD

Removal

1) Drain cooling system and disconnect upper radiator hose at engine. Remove intake and exhaust manifold assembly. Remove rocker arm cover. Remove rocker arm assemblies and push rods. Keep in sequence for reinstallation in original locations.

2) Disconnect and label all wires and vacuum hoses that may interfere with head removal. If equipped, disconnect air injection hose at check valve. Remove cylinder head.

CAUTION: Do not apply gasket sealer to composition steel asbestos gaskets.

Fig. 1: Cylinder Head Tightening Sequence

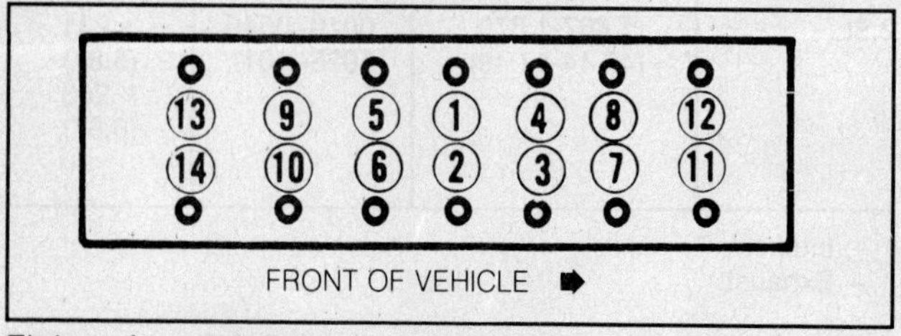

Tighten front left-hand head bolt to 85 ft. lbs. (115 N.m), and all others to 95 ft. lbs. (129 N.m).

Installation

1) Ensure gasket surfaces of cylinder head and block are clean, and all head bolt threads and threads in block are clean. Coat threads of head bolts with sealer.

2) To install cylinder head and remaining components, reverse removal procedure. Tighten head bolts in sequence. *See Fig. 1.* Lubricate rocker arm parts with Molykote. Adjust valves.

VALVES

VALVE ARRANGEMENT

E-I-I-E-E-I-I-E-E-I-I-E (Front-to-rear).

ROCKER ARM STUDS

Rocker arm studs that are loose in head or have damaged threads, can be replaced with oversize studs. Use Reamer (J-5715) for .003" (.08 mm) oversize replacement studs, and Reamer (J-6036) for .013" (.33 mm) oversize replacement studs.

Removal

Remove damaged stud using Stud Remover (J-5802 A). Install remover over stud. Tighten nut to extract stud from cylinder head.

Installation

Ream hole for oversize studs. Coat press-fit area of stud with hypoid axle grease. Drive rocker stud into place with Stud Driver (J-6880). When driver bottoms on head, stud is at correct height.

VALVE SPRINGS

Removal

1) Remove valve cover. Remove spark plug, rocker arm assembly and push rod of cylinder to be serviced. Install air hose and adapter in spark plug hole, and apply air pressure. Do not remove air pressure until all components have been reinstalled.

2) Use valve spring compressor to compress valve spring, and remove retainer locks. Release spring compressor and remove spring retainer or rotator, shield, spring, damper (if equipped), and oil seal. *See Fig. 2.*

Installation

Install damper, spring, shield and retainer. Use spring compressor to compress valve spring, and install new oil seal and retainer locks. Remove spring compressor. Remove air hose and adapter. Install remaining components in reverse order of removal.

Fig. 2: Exploded View of Valve Spring Assembly

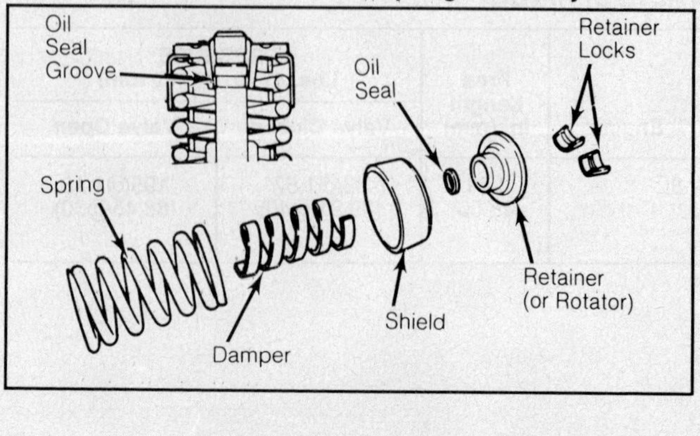

4.8 LITER 6-CYLINDER (Cont.)

VALVE SPRING INSTALLED HEIGHT

Measure valve spring installed height from spring seat (or top of shim), to top of spring (or valve shield). Installed height should be 1.63-1.69" (41.4-43.0 mm). If height exceeds specifications, install .063" (1.59 mm) thick shim under spring.

VALVE STEM OIL SEALS

"O" ring-type seals are used. Lightly coat seal with engine oil and install in lower groove of valve stem. Ensure seal is not twisted in groove.

VALVE GUIDE SERVICING

Valve guides are integral with cylinder head. If guide is worn, it must be reamed for installation of valves with oversize stems. Valves are available with .003" (.08 mm), .015" (.38 mm) and .030" (.76 mm) oversize stems. Use reamers in sequence when reaming valve guides.

HYDRAULIC VALVE LIFTERS

Disassemble and thoroughly clean lifters. Inspect all components for wear and damage. If any components are worn or damaged, complete lifter assembly must be replaced. If push rod seat or lifter body wear is noted, inspect mating engine components for wear. *See Fig. 3.*

Fig. 3: Cutaway View of Valve Lifter Assembly

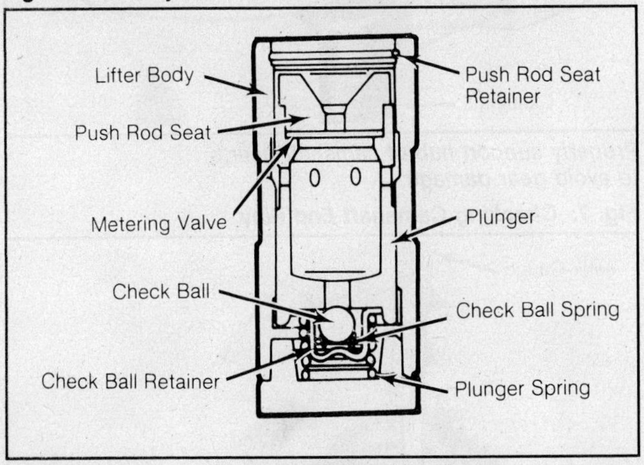

Replace lifters as complete assemblies; do not interchange parts between lifters.

VALVE CLEARANCE ADJUSTMENT

1) Remove distributor cap. Mark distributor housing at No. 1 and No. 6 rotor firing positions.

2) With distributor rotor in the positions designated in VALVE ADJUSTMENT table, adjust valves as follows: Loosen rocker arm adjusting nut until push rod lash (play) is felt. Tighten adjusting nut until all lash is removed. When lash has been removed, tighten adjusting nut 1 full turn to complete procedure.

VALVE CLEARANCE ADJUSTMENT

Rotor Position	Adjust Int. Nos.	Adjust Exh. Nos.
No. 1	1, 2, 4	1, 3, 5
No. 6	3, 5, 6	2, 4, 6

CAMSHAFT

ENGINE FRONT COVER

Removal

1) Drain cooling system and remove radiator. Remove drive belt(s), fan and pulley. Remove crankshaft pulley and vibration damper. Remove oil pan-to-front cover attaching bolts, then front cover-to-block attaching bolts.

2) Pull cover slightly forward to permit cutting of oil pan front seal. Cut oil pan seal flush with block at both sides of cover. Remove cover with attached portion of oil pan seal.

Installation

1) Clean all gasket mating surfaces. Cut tabs from new oil pan front seal. *See Fig. 4*. Install seal to front cover, pressing locating tips into holes in cover.

Fig. 4: Oil Pan Front Seal Modification

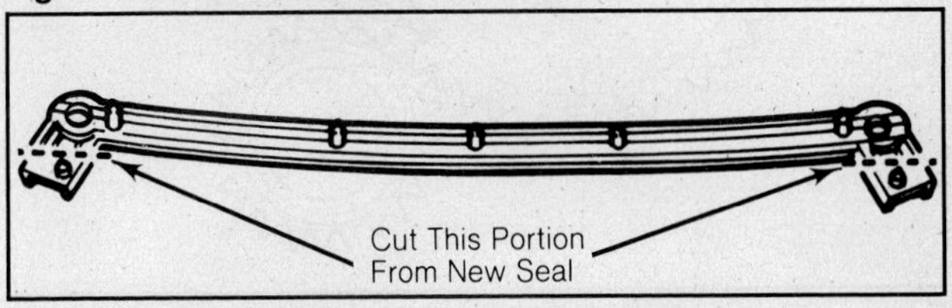

Use sharp instrument to ensure clean cut.

2) Coat front cover gasket with sealer, and position on cover. Apply 1/8" bead of RTV sealer to joint formed by oil pan and cylinder block. Install Oil Seal Aligner (J-23042) in front cover seal and install cover to cylinder block.

3) Install and partially tighten oil pan-to-cover bolts. Install front cover-to-cylinder block bolts. Remove aligner and tighten bolts. To install remaining components, reverse removal procedure.

FRONT COVER OIL SEAL

Removal (Front Cover Installed)

Remove vibration damper. Pry seal out of cover with screwdriver, using care not to damage cover seal surface.

Installation (Front Cover Installed)

Install new seal with open end toward inside of cover. Drive seal into place using Seal Driver (J-23042).

Removal (Front Cover Removed)

Pry seal out of cover with screwdriver, using care not to damage cover seal surface.

Installation (Front Cover Removed)

Install new seal with open end of seal toward inside of cover. Support cover at seal recess area. Using seal installer, drive seal into position.

CAMSHAFT

Removal

1) Remove engine from vehicle. Remove valve cover and loosen all rocker arm nuts. Rotate rocker arms to side and withdraw push rods in sequence, for reinstallation in original locations.

2) Remove valve lifter side cover and remove lifters. Remove front engine cover and fuel pump. Align crankshaft and camshaft timing gear marks. Remove camshaft thrust plate bolts through access holes in camshaft gear. Carefully remove camshaft.

4.8 LITER 6-CYLINDER (Cont.)

Installation

Coat camshaft lobes with Lubriplate. Reverse removal procedure to install camshaft. Ensure timing marks on gears are aligned. Take care to avoid damage to camshaft lobes or bearings. Install new valve lifters. Reassemble and install engine in vehicle. Change oil and oil filter. *See Fig. 5.*

Fig. 5: Timing Gear Mark Alignment

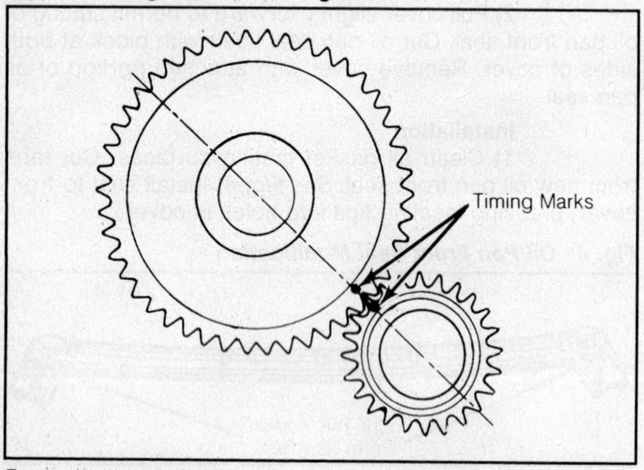

Remove camshaft thrust plate bolts through access holes in camshaft gear.

TIMING GEARS

Inspection

With engine front cover removed, check backlash between timing gear teeth. Backlash should be .004-.006" (.10-.15 mm) for new gears, and .004-.008" (.10-.20 mm) for used gears. Check crankshaft and camshaft gears for runout with dial indicator. Maximum camshaft gear runout is .004" (.10 mm). Maximum crankshaft gear runout is .003" (.08 mm).

Removal

Remove camshaft from engine. Position camshaft and gear on arbor press, and properly support hub of gear. Ensure thrust plate is positioned so Woodruff key in shaft will not be damaged when camshaft is pressed out of gear. Press camshaft from gear. *See Fig. 6.* Remove crankshaft gear from crankshaft, using Gear Puller (J-8105).

Installation

1) With crankshaft properly supported, use Hollow Driver (J-5590), to drive gear onto crankshaft.

2) To install camshaft gear, position camshaft in press with camshaft supported at back of front journal. Place gear spacer ring and thrust plate over camshaft and install Woodruff key in keyway. Press gear onto camshaft until it bottoms on gear spacer ring.

CAMSHAFT END PLAY

Check camshaft end play with feeler gauge. End play should be .001-.005" (.03-.13 mm). *See Fig. 7.*

CAM LOBE LIFT

1) With valve cover removed, remove rocker arm assemblies. Mount dial indicator on rocker arm stud. Position dial indicator and ball socket adapter on push rod. *See Fig. 8.*

2) Slowly rotate engine in direction of rotation until lifter is on base circle of camshaft. Zero dial indicator. Rotate engine until push rod is fully raised. Record lobe lift reading and compare with specifications. If not within limits, replace camshaft and lifters.

Fig. 6: Removing Camshaft from Gear

Properly support hub of camshaft gear, to avoid gear damage.

Fig. 7: Checking Camshaft End Play

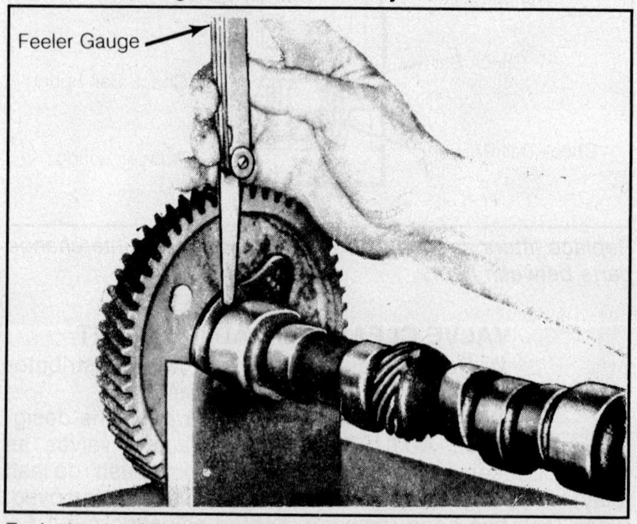

End play is .001-.005" (.03-.13 mm).

CAMSHAFT BEARINGS

Removal

With engine removed from vehicle, remove camshaft, oil pan and oil pump. Drive camshaft rear plug from block. Drive camshaft bearings from engine. Remove front and rear bearings after center bearings have been removed.

Fig. 8: Checking Camshaft Lobe Lift

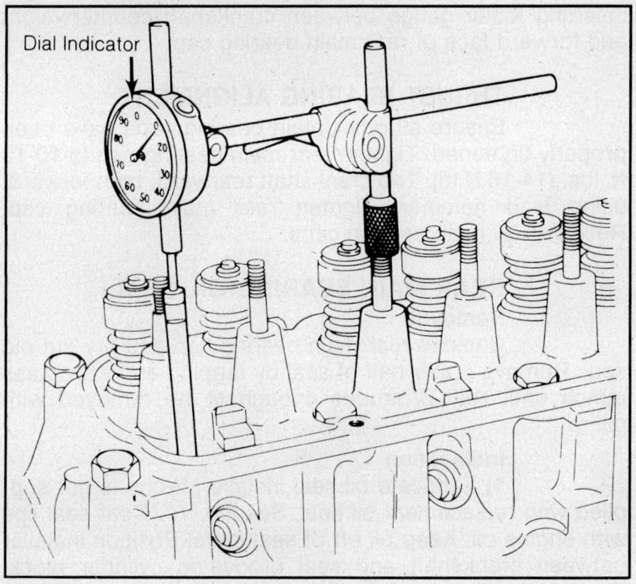

If readings are not within specifications, replace camshaft and lifters.

Installation

Install front and rear bearings first, to act as guide for pilot of installer, and to center remaining bearings being pulled into place. Oil holes in cam bearings must align with oil holes in block. Install new camshaft rear plug.

PISTON, PINS & RINGS

OIL PAN

See OIL PAN REMOVAL at end of ENGINE section.

PISTON & ROD ASSEMBLY

Removal

1) Remove oil pan, oil pump and cylinder head. Position piston at bottom of stroke, and cover with cloth to collect metal cuttings. Remove ridge at top of cylinder bore with ridge reamer.

2) If necessary, mark connecting rod for cylinder identification. Remove connecting rod cap nuts and cap, and cover rod bolts with rubber hose. Push piston and rod assembly out top of cylinder block.

Installation

1) Before installing piston and rod assembly, ensure ring gaps are properly spaced. *See Fig. 9.* Lightly coat pistons, rings and cylinder walls with engine oil. Install rod bearings in rod and cap, and lubricate with engine oil.

2) Compress piston rings with ring compressor. Do not allow position of rings to change. Cover connecting rod bolts with rubber hose. Install piston and rod assembly, with notch on top of piston facing front of engine. Install and tighten connecting rod cap.

FITTING PISTONS

1) Using telescopic gauge and micrometer, measure cylinder bore diameter 2 1/2" (64 mm) from top of bore. Measure piston diameter across piston skirt, at center line of piston pin. Difference between the two measurements is piston-to-cylinder bore clearance.

2) Using cylinder bore gauge, measure cylinder bore taper by working gauge up and down in bore. Measure cylinder bore out-of-round. Take measurements at different points in bore, by rotating gauge horizontally, around entire circumference of bore. Out-of-round must not exceed .002" (.05 mm).

3) Taper must not exceed .005" (.13 mm). If taper or out-of-round are not within limits, hone or bore cylinders for installation of new pistons.

FITTING RINGS

1) Position ring into cylinder bore about 1/4" above ring travel. Ring must be square in bore. Measure ring end gap with feeler gauge.

2) Before installing compression rings on pistons, check side clearance. Insert outer edge of ring in its respective groove, and slide ring around entire circumference of groove. Ring should slide freely in groove.

3) Check side clearance of compression rings, with feeler gauge inserted between ring and ring groove. Install rings with gaps properly positioned. Note that anti-rotation tang of oil ring spacer is inserted into oil hole (or slot) of piston. *See Fig. 9.*

Fig. 9: Desired Ring Gap Locations

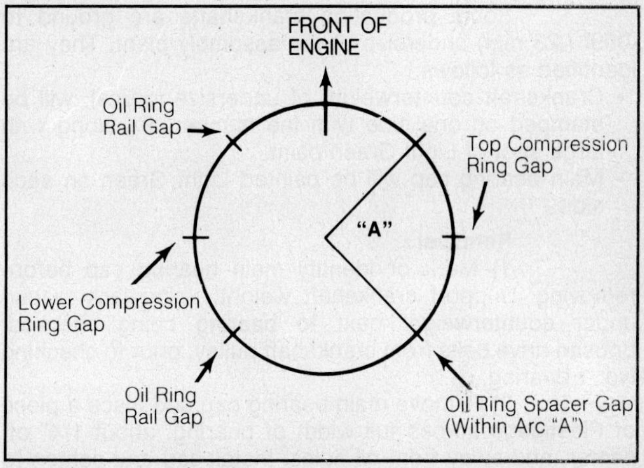

Insert tang of oil ring spacer in oil hole (or slot) of piston. Hole is located within arc of oil ring spacer gap "A".

PISTON PIN REPLACEMENT

Removal

Using arbor press and piston pin remover/installer, press piston pin from piston and connecting rod.

Installation

Check clearance of piston pin in piston, replace piston and pin assembly if not within limits. Lubricate piston pin holes in piston and connecting rod. Position connecting rod on piston and press in piston pin, using pin remover/installer and arbor press. Check piston for freedom of movement on piston pin.

CRANKSHAFT & ROD BEARINGS

NOTE: **Main and connecting rod bearings are precision insert type. Shims are not used for adjustment. During production, selective fitting of bearing inserts may be necessary to achieve**

4.8 LITER 6-CYLINDER (Cont.)

close tolerances. Therefore, half of a standard bearing insert and half of a .001" (.03 mm) undersize bearing insert may be found on the same journal. During repairs, always replace both inserts as a set.

CONNECTING ROD BEARINGS

1) Ensure rod caps are marked for cylinder identifcation. Remove rod cap and bearings. Inspect bearings for wear or damage and replace as necessary. Check crankshaft rod bearing journal for out-of-round or taper. Maximum crankshaft out-of-round or taper must not exceed .001" (.03 mm).

2) Check rod bearing clearance using Plastigage method. If clearance exceeds specifications, standard, .001" (.03 mm), or .002" (.05 mm) undersize bearings may be used in combination to produce correct clearance. If clearance is still excessive, crankshaft must be reconditioned.

3) Clean crankshaft journal and bearing surface in rod. Insert bearings in rod and cap, then lubricate bearing surfaces with oil. Pull piston and rod assembly down onto crankshaft. Install and tighten rod cap.

MAIN BEARINGS

Some production crankshafts are ground to .009" (.23 mm) undersize at the assembly plant. They are identified as follows:

- Crankshaft counterweight of undersize journal, will be stamped on one side with the number "9", along with large spot of Light Green paint.
- Main bearing cap will be painted Light Green on each side.

Removal

1) Mark or identify main bearing cap before removing. Support crankshaft weight, using jack placed under counterweight next to bearing being checked. Loosen drive belts from crankshaft pulley, prior to checking No. 1 bearing.

2) Remove main bearing cap and place a piece of Plastigage across full width of bearing, about 1/4" off center, and away from oil holes. Install cap and tighten to specifications. Do not allow crankshaft to turn.

3) Remove cap and measure width of Plastigage with scale furnished. Standard, .001" (.03 mm) or .002" (.05 mm) undersize bearing halves may be used in combination to obtain correct clearance. Always replace both upper and lower bearing halves.

4) With exception of rear main bearing, main bearings are removed from cylinder block using Bearing Remover/Installer (J-8080). Insert remover/installer in crankshaft oil hole and rotate crankshaft clockwise. If bearing remover/installer is not available, cotter pin may be bent, as necessary, to do the job.

5) To remove rear main bearing from block, partially drive out bearing with drift. Use pair of pliers, with jaws taped, to hold bearing thrust surface to oil slinger. Rotate crankshaft to remove bearing.

6) Lubricate journal and bearings. Insert plain end of new bearing between crankshaft and notched side of block. Insert bearing remover/installer into crankshaft oil hole, and rotate bearing into place. To install rear main bearing, use pliers (as used in removal), to aid in installation.

7) Install lower bearing half into cap. Install and tighten main bearing caps with arrows pointing toward front of engine. Align thrust bearing, then check crankshaft end play. Check end play by prying crankshaft forward, and inserting feeler gauge between crankshaft counterweight and forward face of rear main bearing cap.

THRUST BEARING ALIGNMENT

Ensure all other main bearing caps have been properly tightened. Tighten rear main bearing cap to 10-12 ft. lbs. (14-16 N.m). Tap crankshaft rearward, then forward, using lead hammer. Tighten rear main bearing cap. Retighten all main bearing caps.

REAR MAIN BEARING OIL SEAL

Removal

Remove rear main bearing cap and pry out old seal. Remove upper half of seal by tapping end with brass punch until seal protrudes enough to be removed with pliers.

Installation

1) Fabricate oil seal installer, if one is not supplied with replacement oil seal. *See Fig. 10.* Coat seal lips with engine oil. Keep oil off of seal ends. Position installer between crankshaft and seal groove in cylinder block. Position seal between tip of installer and crankshaft.

Fig. 10: Rear Main Oil Seal Installer

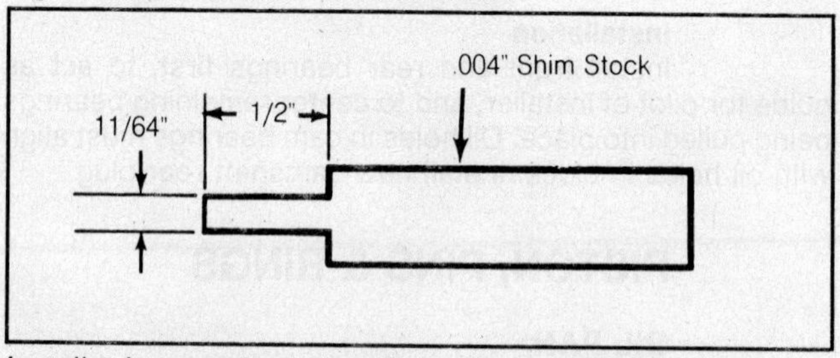

Installer is sometimes supplied with replacement oil seal.

2) Roll seal around crankshaft, using installer as "shoehorn" to protect seal from sharp corner of seal groove in cylinder block. Installer must remain in position until seal is positioned with both ends flush with block.

3) Install lower seal into bearing cap. Feed seal into cap using light pressure with thumb and finger. Apply sealer to cap-to-block mating surface of cylinder block, being careful to keep sealer off the seal split line. Install and tighten bearing cap.

ENGINE OILING

CRANKCASE CAPACITY

Crankcase capacity is 5 quarts (4.75L). Add 1 quart (.95L) when replacing oil filter.

OIL FILTER

Replace oil filter at every other oil change, or more often under severe conditions.

NORMAL OIL PRESSURE

Normal oil pressure with engine at operating temperature, should be 30-40 psi (2.1-2.8 kg/cm^2) at 2000 RPM.

OIL PRESSURE REGULATOR VALVE

Oil pressure regulator valve is located in pump body. Valve is nonadjustable.

4.8 LITER 6-CYLINDER (Cont.)

ENGINE OILING SYSTEM

Gear-type pump provides full pressure lubrication. Oil drawn through pick-up screen, is pressurized through pump and routed to oil filter. By-pass valve allows oil flow to main gallery in the event backpressure is encountered at filter.

Main gallery supplies oil to camshaft bearings, lifters and main bearings. Connecting rod bearings are supplied oil from crankshaft main bearings, through cross-drilled passages.

Oil passing through hollow push rods lubricates valve train. Oil drains back to crankcase through drain holes. Timing gears are lubricated through nozzle, which is fed from front camshaft bearing. *See Fig. 11.*

Fig. 11: Engine Oiling System

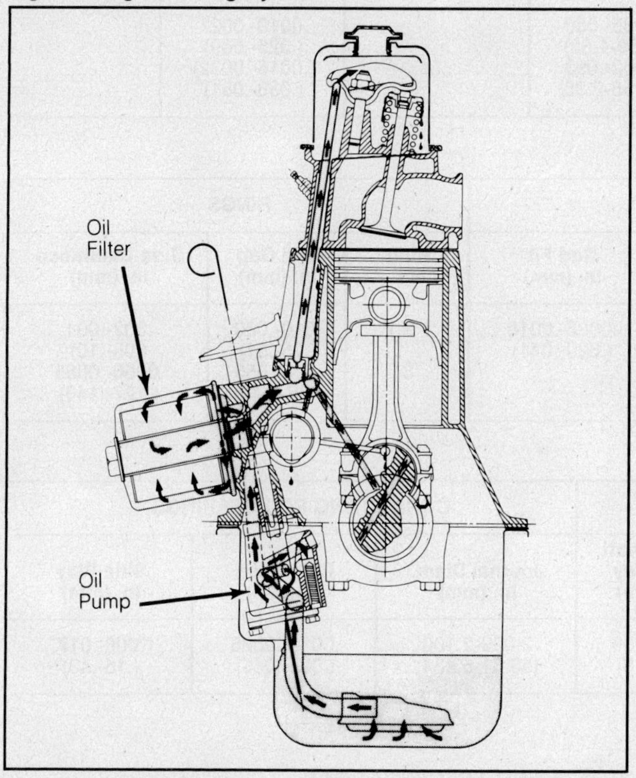

OIL PUMP

Removal

Remove oil pan. Remove oil inlet tube attaching bolt and oil pump attaching bolts. Remove oil pump and tube assembly.

Disassembly

Remove oil inlet tube assembly. Remove pump cover. Mark idler gear and drive gear at a meshing point, for later reassembly of gears in same meshing position. Remove idler gear and drive gear with shaft, from pump body. Remove pressure regulator valve retaining pin, then remove spring and valve.

NOTE: **If any part of oil pump requires replacement, entire pump assembly must be replaced.**

Inspection

1) Clean all parts. Inspect pump body and cover for cracks and excessive wear. Inspect pump gears for damage or excessive wear. Check drive gear shaft for looseness in pump body.

Fig. 12: Oil Pump Assembly

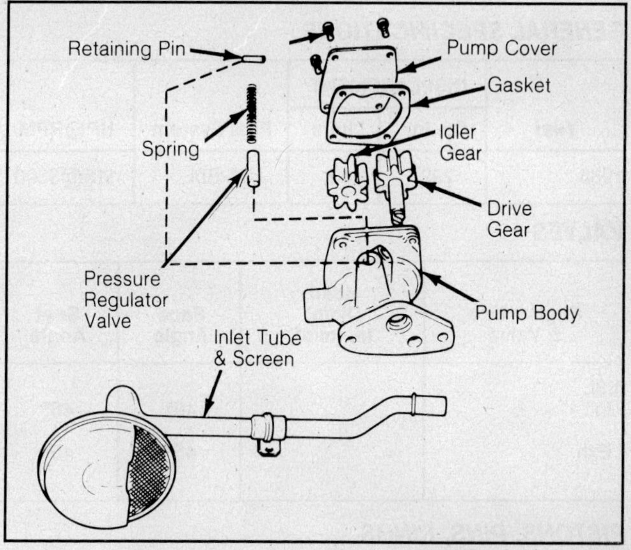

Be sure to mark gears at meshing point, prior to disassembly.

2) Inspect oil inlet tube assembly for damage. Check pressure regulator valve for fit in bore.

Reassembly

Install oil inlet tube assembly. Apply sealer to end of tube, and tap tube into place, using plastic hammer. Install idler gear into pump body with smooth side of gear toward cover opening. Reassemble remaining components in reverse order of disassembly.

Installation

Prime oil pump with engine oil prior to installation. Install oil pump and pick-up tube in reverse order of removal.

ENGINE COOLING

WATER PUMP

Removal

Disconnect negative battery cable. Drain cooling system. Remove drive belts, fan and pulley from water pump. Remove lower radiator hose and heater hose from water pump. If necessary, remove alternator adjusting bracket from water pump. Remove water pump.

Installation

Clean all gasket mating surfaces. Install components in reverse order of removal procedure, using new gasket.

NOTE: **For further information on cooling system capacities and other cooling system components, see appropriate article in ENGINE COOLING SYSTEMS at end of ENGINE section.**

General Motors Engines

4.8 LITER 6-CYLINDER (Cont.)

ENGINE SPECIFICATIONS

GENERAL SPECIFICATIONS

Year	DISPLACEMENT		Fuel System	HP@RPM	Torque Ft. Lbs.@RPM	Compr. Ratio	BORE		STROKE	
	Cu. In.	Liters					In.	mm	In.	mm
1985	292	4.8	1-Bbl.	115@3600	215@1600	8.0:1	3.88	98.5	4.12	104.7

VALVES

Engine Size & Valve	Head Diam. In. (mm)	Face Angle	Seat Angle	Seat Width In. (mm)	Stem Diameter In. (mm)	Stem Clearance In. (mm)	Valve Lift In. (mm)
4.8L							
Int.	.....	46°	46°	.035-.060 (.89-1.52)	.....	.0010-.0027 (.025-.069)	.....
Exh.	.....	46°	46°	.062-.093 (1.58-2.36)	.....	.0015-.0032) (.038-.081)	.....

PISTONS, PINS, RINGS

Engine	PISTONS	PINS		RINGS		
	Clearance In. (mm)	Piston Fit In. (mm)	Rod Fit In. (mm)	Ring No.	End Gap In. (mm)	Side Clearance In. (mm)
4.8L	.0026-.0036 (.066-.091)	.00015-.00025 (.0038-.0064)	.0008-.0016 (.020-.041)	1 & 2	.010-.020 (.25-.51)	.002-.004 (.05-.10)
				3	.015-.055 (.38-1.40)	.0050-.0055 (.127-.140)

CRANKSHAFT MAIN & CONNECTING ROD BEARINGS

Engine	MAIN BEARINGS				CONNECTING ROD BEARINGS		
	Journal Diam. In. (mm)	Clearance In. (mm)	Thrust Bearing	Crankshaft End Play In. (mm)	Journal Diam. In. (mm)	Clearance In. (mm)	Side Play In. (mm)
4.8L	2.2979-2.2994 (38.366-58.405)	[1] .0010-.0024 (.025-.061)	No. 7	.002-.006 (.05-.15)	2.099-2.100 (53.31-53.34)	.0010-.0026 (.025-.066)	.006-.017 (.15-.43)

[1] – Rear main bearing (No. 7) clearance is .0016-.0035" (.041-.89 mm).

VALVE SPRINGS

Engine	Free Length In. (mm)	PRESSURE Lbs. @ In. (Kg @ mm)	
		Valve Closed	Valve Open
4.8L	2.08 (52.8)	78-86@1.66 (35-39@42.2)	170-180@1.26 (77-81@32.0)

CAMSHAFT

Engine	Journal Diam. In. (mm)	Clearance In. (mm)	Lobe Lift In. (mm)
4.8L [1]	1.8677-1.8697 (47.440-47.490)	.....	.2315 (5.880)

[1] – End play is .003-.008" (.08-.20 mm).

TIGHTENING SPECIFICATIONS

Application	Ft. Lbs. (N.m)
Camshaft Thrust Plate Bolts	7 (9)
Connecting Rod Cap Nuts	40 (54)
Cylinder Head Bolts	[1] 95 (129)
Engine Front Cover Bolts	7 (9)
Exhaust Manifold Bolts	30 (41)
Flywheel-to-Crankshaft Bolts	110 (149)
Intake Manifold Bolts	40 (54)
Main Bearing Cap Bolts	65 (88)
Oil Pump Attaching Bolts	10 (13)
Vibration Damper Bolt	60 (81)
Water Pump Bolts	15 (20)

[1] – Tighten left-hand front bolt to 85 ft. lbs. (115 N.m).

General Motors Engines

4.3 LITER V6, 5.0 & 5.7 LITER V8

ENGINE CODING

ENGINE IDENTIFICATION

Engine identification number is stamped on a machined pad on front of cylinder block, immediately forward of right cylinder head. Engine can be identified by the eighth character of the Vehicle Identification Number (VIN). The VIN is located on a metal tag on the top left corner of the instrument panel, visible through the windshield.

ENGINE IDENTIFICATION CODES

Engine	Code
4.3L 4-Bbl.	N
5.0L 4-Bbl.	F
5.0L 4-Bbl.	H
5.7L 4-Bbl.	L
5.7L 4-Bbl.	M

ENGINE REMOVAL

See ENGINE REMOVAL at end of ENGINE section.

MANIFOLDS & CYLINDER HEAD

INTAKE MANIFOLD

Removal

1) Disconnect negative battery cable. Remove air cleaner. Drain cooling system. On van models, remove engine cover. On all models, remove air injection crossover hose.

2) Remove heater and radiator hoses. Remove alternator upper bracket. Label and disconnect necessary wires and hoses. Disconnect fuel line at carburetor. Disconnect carburetor linkage.

3) Remove spark plug wires. Remove distributor cap and mark position of rotor with chalk. Remove distributor. If equipped, remove A/C compressor and bracket. Remove brake vacuum pipe. Remove carburetor. Remove manifold bolts and intake manifold.

Installation

1) Clean all gasket mating surfaces. Apply 3/16" bead of silicone sealer at front and rear intake manifold mounting surface of cylinder block. Extend bead of sealer 1/2" up each cylinder head. *See Fig. 1.*

2) Install intake manifold gaskets on cylinder heads. Install manifold and tighten attaching bolts. *See Fig. 2.* Install distributor with rotor pointing to chalk mark. To complete installation, reverse removal procedure.

EXHAUST MANIFOLD

Removal

Remove heat stove tube. Remove spark plug heat shields. Disconnect exhaust pipe from manifold and wire aside. Remove end bolts, then remove center bolts and remove exhaust manifolds.

Installation

NOTE: If installing a new right manifold, carburetor heat stove must be transferred from old unit.

Clean all gasket mating surfaces. Install manifold and tighten attaching bolts. To complete installation, reverse removal procedure. Start engine and check for leaks.

Fig. 1: Silicone Sealer Application Points

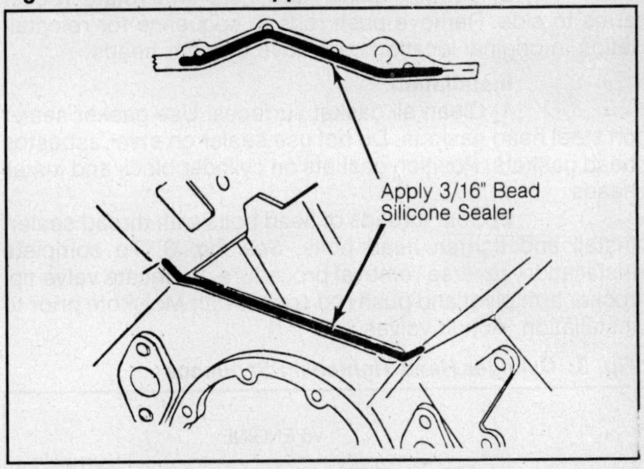

Install intake manifold before sealer sets up (10-15 minutes).

Fig. 2: Intake Manifold Tightening Sequence

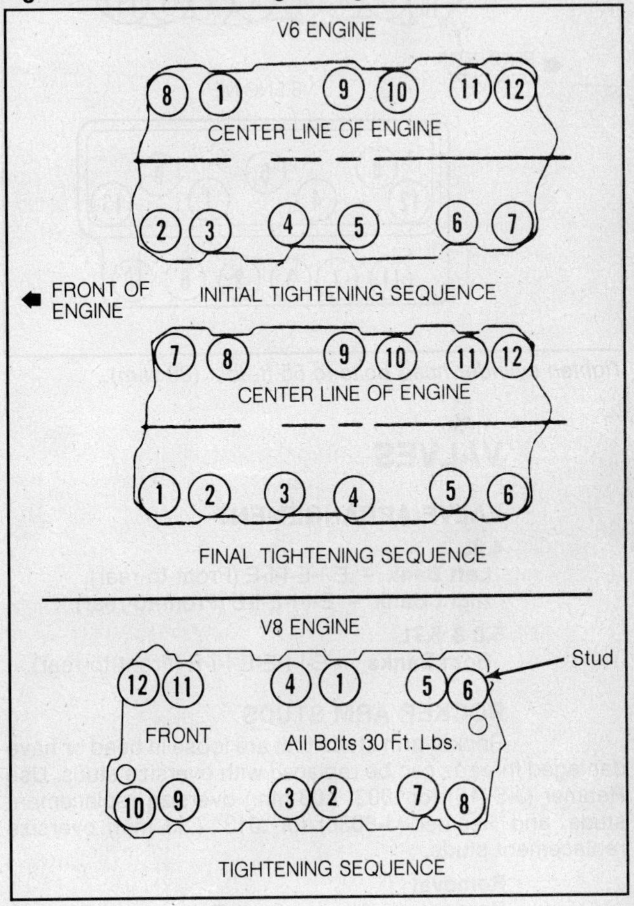

CYLINDER HEAD

Removal

1) Drain cooling system, including block. Remove intake and exhaust manifolds. Remove A/C compressor and bracket (if equipped). Remove alternator. Remove valve covers.

4.3 LITER V6, 5.0 & 5.7 LITER V8 (Cont.)

2) Loosen rocker arm nuts and rotate rocker arms to side. Remove push rods in sequence for reinstallation in original locations. Remove cylinder heads.

Installation

1) Clean all gasket surfaces. Use gasket sealer on steel head gaskets. Do not use sealer on steel/asbestos head gaskets. Position gaskets on cylinder block and install heads.

2) Coat threads of head bolts with thread sealer. Install and tighten head bolts. *See Fig. 3.* To complete installation, reverse removal procedure. Lubricate valve tip, rocker arm pivot and push rod socket with Molykote prior to installation. Adjust valves.

Fig. 3: Cylinder Head Tightening Sequence

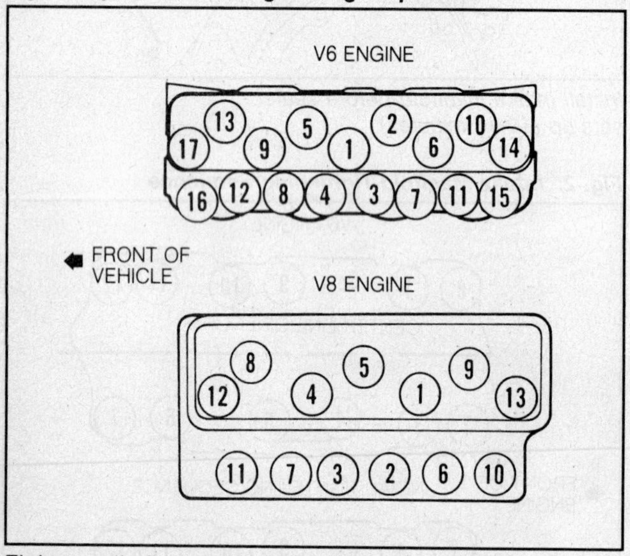

Tighten cylinder head bolts to 65 ft. lbs. (88 N.m).

VALVES

VALVE ARRANGEMENT

4.3L

Left Bank – E-I-E-I-I-E (Front-to-rear).
Right Bank – E-I-I-E-I-E (Front-to-rear).

5.0 & 5.7L

Both Banks – E-I-I-E-E-I-I-E (Front-to-rear).

ROCKER ARM STUDS

Rocker arm studs that are loose in head or have damaged threads can be replaced with oversize studs. Use Reamer (J-5715) for .003" (.08 mm) oversize replacement studs, and Reamer (J-6036) for .013" (.33 mm) oversize replacement studs.

Removal

Remove stud using Stud Remover (J-5802-1). Install remover over stud. Tighten nut on remover to extract stud from cylinder head.

Installation

Ream hole for oversize stud. Coat press-fit area of stud with hypoid axle grease. Drive stud into place with Stud Driver (J-6880). When driver bottoms out on head, stud is at correct height.

VALVE SPRINGS

Removal

1) With rocker arm cover removed, remove spark plug, rocker arm and push rod of cylinder to be serviced. Install air hose with adapter in spark plug hole, and turn on air supply. Do not remove air supply until all components are reinstalled.

2) Using valve spring compressor, compress valve spring and remove retainer locks. Release spring compressor and remove retainer, shield, spring, damper and oil seal. *See Fig. 4.*

Fig. 4: Valve Spring Assembly

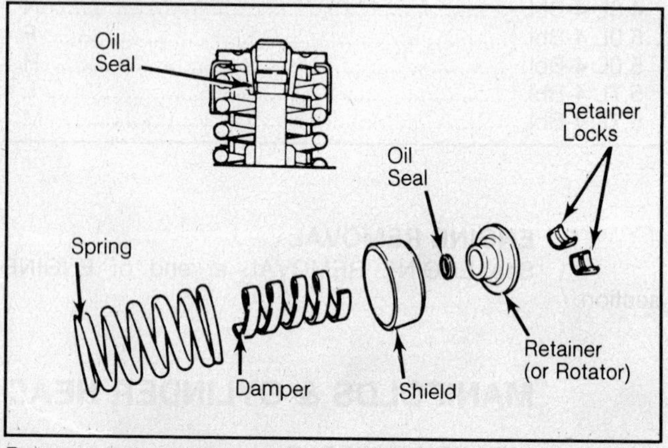

Rotators are used on exhaust valves.

Installation

Install damper, spring, shield and retainer. Using spring compressor, compress valve spring, and install new oil seal and retainer locks. Remove spring compressor. Remove air hose and adapter. Install remaining components in reverse order of removal.

VALVE SPRING INSTALLED HEIGHT

Measure installed height from spring seat (or top of shim), to top of spring shield. Installed height should be 1.687-1.750" (42.85-44.45 mm). If installed height exceeds specifications, install a .063" (1.60 mm) thick shim between spring seat and spring. Installed height should never be more than specified height.

VALVE STEM OIL SEALS

"O" ring type seal is used. Coat seal with engine oil and install in second groove of valve stem. Ensure seal is not twisted on valve stem.

VALVE GUIDE SERVICING

If valve stem-to-guide clearance is excessive, valves with oversize stems are available. Replacement valves are available with .003" (.08 mm), .015" (.38 mm) and .030" (.76 mm) oversize stems. Always use reamers in proper size sequence.

HYDRAULIC VALVE LIFTERS

1) Disassemble lifters and thoroughly clean. Inspect all components for wear and damage. If any components are worn or damaged, complete lifter assembly must be replaced.

2) If push rod seat or lifter body wear is noted, inspect mating engine components for wear. Prior to installing, lubricate bases of lifters with Molykote. *See Fig. 5.*

4.3 LITER V6, 5.0 & 5.7 LITER V8 (Cont.)

Fig. 5: Cutaway View of Valve Lifter Assembly

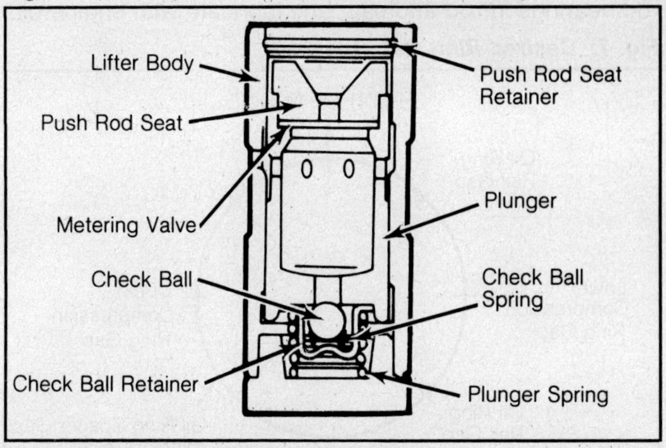

Replace lifters as complete assemblies; do not interchange parts between lifters.

VALVE CLEARANCE ADJUSTMENT

1) Rotate engine until No. 1 piston is on TDC at end of compression stroke. With piston in this position, adjust valves listed in appropriate VALVE CLEARANCE ADJUSTMENT table, using the following procedure:

2) Loosen rocker arm adjusting nut until play is felt in push rod. Tighten adjusting nut until play in push rod is removed. When play has been removed, tighten adjusting nut 1 full turn.

3) Rotate crankshaft 360° to bring No. 6 piston on TDC (No. 4 on 4.3L) at end of compression stroke. Adjust remaining valves listed in appropriate VALVE CLEARANCE ADJUSTMENT table.

4.3L VALVE CLEARANCE ADJUSTMENT

Piston at TDC	Adjust Intake	Adjust Exhaust
No. 1	Nos. 1, 2, 3	Nos. 1, 5, 6
No. 4	Nos. 4, 5, 6	Nos. 2, 3, 4

5.0 & 5.7L VALVE CLEARANCE ADJUSTMENT

Piston on TDC	Adjust Int. Nos.	Adjust Exh. Nos.
1	1, 2, 5, 7	1, 3, 4, 8
6	3, 4, 6, 8	2, 5, 6, 7

CAMSHAFT

ENGINE FRONT COVER

Removal

1) Disconnect negative battery cable at battery. Drain cooling system. If necessary, remove radiator shroud and position rearward, toward engine. Remove all accessory drive belts, fan and pulley.

2) Remove vibration damper. Remove all mounting brackets and coolant hoses attached to water pump. Remove water pump. Remove front cover and gasket.

Installation

1) Clean all gasket mating surfaces. Remove any excess oil pan gasket material extending beyond cylinder block. Apply a 1/8" bead silicone sealer to joint formed at oil pan and cylinder block.

2) Coat front cover gasket with gasket sealer and position on cover. Install cover-to-pan seal. Position cover on cylinder block. Loosely install cover-to-block upper attaching bolts. Tighten bolts alternately and evenly while pressing downward on cover, to allow dowels in block to enter holes in cover.

3) Install remaining cover bolts. Tighten all front cover bolts. Reverse removal procedure to install remaining components.

FRONT COVER OIL SEAL

Removal (Front Cover Installed)

Remove vibration damper. Pry seal out of cover with screwdriver, using care not to damage cover seal surface.

Installation (Front Cover Installed)

Install new seal with open end toward inside of cover. Drive seal into place using Seal Driver (J-23042).

Removal (Front Cover Removed)

Pry seal out of cover with screwdriver, using care not to damage cover seal surface.

Installation (Front Cover Removed)

Install new seal with open end of seal toward inside of cover. Support cover at seal recess area. Using seal installer, drive seal into position.

TIMING CHAIN

Removal

Remove engine front cover. Crank engine over until timing marks on camshaft and crankshaft sprockets are aligned. Remove camshaft sprocket and timing chain. If crankshaft sprocket replacement is necessary, use a gear puller to remove sprocket.

Installation

Use a hammer and hollow driver to install crankshaft sprocket onto crankshaft. Install camshaft sprocket and timing chain. Ensure timing marks on sprockets are aligned. Install and tighten sprocket bolts. *See Fig. 6.*

Fig. 6: Aligning Timing Sprocket Marks

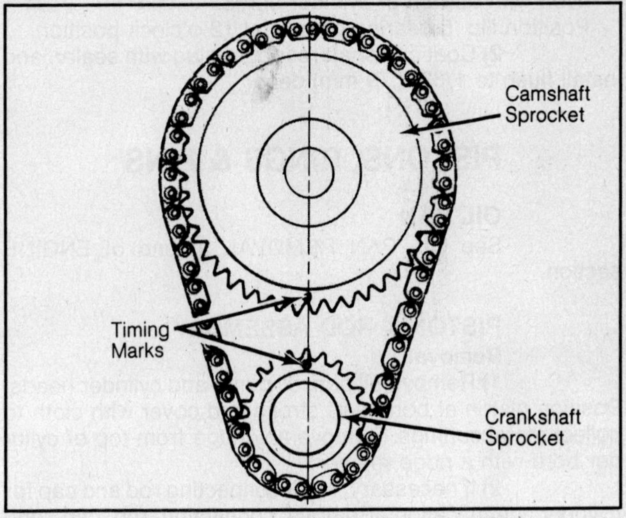

Tighten camshaft sprocket bolts to 20 ft. lbs. (27 N.m).

CAMSHAFT

Removal

Remove intake manifold, engine front cover and timing chain. Remove valve covers. Loosen all rocker arm

4.3 LITER V6, 5.0 & 5.7 LITER V8 (Cont.)

nuts and rotate rockers to one side. Remove push rods and lifters in sequence, for reinstallation in original locations. Remove radiator and grille. Remove fuel pump and push rod. Remove camshaft.

Installation

1) Coat camshaft lobes with Molykote, and journals with engine oil. Install camshaft. Temporarily place camshaft sprocket on camshaft and align timing marks. Install camshaft sprocket and chain. Tighten camshaft sprocket attaching bolts.

2) Lubricate timing chain with engine oil. When a new camshaft is installed, always install new lifters, and change oil and replace filter. Install remaining components. Adjust valves.

CAM LOBE LIFT

1) With valve cover removed, remove rocker arm assemblies. Mount dial indicator on rocker arm stud. Position dial indicator and ball socket adapter on push rod.

2) Slowly rotate engine in direction of rotation until lifter is on base circle of camshaft. Zero dial indicator. Rotate engine until push rod is fully raised. Record lobe lift reading and compare with specifications. If not within limits, replace camshaft and lifters.

CAMSHAFT BEARINGS

Removal

Remove engine from vehicle. Remove oil pan, oil pump, crankshaft and camshaft. Push pistons to top of cylinder bores. Remove rear bore plug. Using camshaft bearing remover/installer, remove camshaft bearings.

Installation

1) Bearings are installed using bearing remover/installer. Install front and rear camshaft bearings first, to act as guides for remover/installer pilot. Note the following prior to installing camshaft bearings:

- Position No. 1 bearing so that oil holes are equal distance from 6 o'clock position.
- Position oil holes of No. 2, 3 and 4 bearings at 5 o'clock position. Oil holes will be toward left side of engine and even with bottom of cylinder bores.
- Position No. 5 bearing oil hole at 12 o'clock position.

2) Coat camshaft rear bore plug with sealer, and install flush to 1/32" (.79 mm) deep.

PISTONS, RINGS & PINS

OIL PAN

See OIL PAN REMOVAL at end of ENGINE section.

PISTON & ROD ASSEMBLY

Removal

1) Remove oil pan, oil pump and cylinder heads. Position piston at bottom of stroke and cover with cloth to collect metal cuttings. Remove any ridge from top of cylinder bore with a ridge reamer.

2) If necessary, mark connecting rod and cap for cylinder identification. Remove connecting rod cap, and cover rod bolts with rubber hose. Push piston and rod assembly out top of cylinder bore.

Installation

1) Before installing piston and rod assembly, ensure ring gaps are properly spaced. *See Fig. 7.* Lightly coat pistons, rings and cylinder walls with engine oil. Install rod bearings in rod and cap, and lubricate with engine oil.

Fig. 7: Desired Ring Gap Spacing

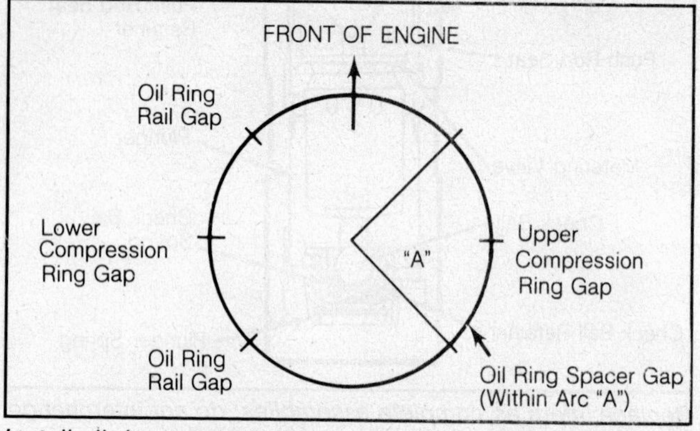

Install oil ring spacer in groove, and insert anti-rotation tang in drilled hole.

2) Compress piston rings with ring compressor. Do not allow ring position to change. Cover rod bolts with rubber hose. Install piston and rod assembly into cylinder bore, with bearing tang slots facing away from camshaft. Install and tighten rod cap.

FITTING PISTONS

1) Using telescopic gauge and micrometer, measure cylinder bore diameter at a point 2 1/2" from top of bore. Measure piston diameter across piston skirt, at centerline of piston pin. Difference between two measurements is piston-to-cylinder bore clearance.

2) Using cylinder bore gauge, measure cylinder bore taper by working gauge up and down in bore. Taper must not exceed .001" (.03 mm). To determine out-of-round, take measurements at different points in bore, by rotating bore gauge horizontally, around entire circumference of bore. Out-of-round must not exceed .002" (.05 mm).

3) If taper or out-of-round are not within limits, hone or bore cylinders for installation of new pistons.

PISTON DIAMETER SPECIFICATIONS

Bore Diameter	Piston Code	Piston Diameter
4.3L		
3.4990-3.4995	A	3.49775-3.49825
3.4995-3.5000	B	3.49825-3.49875
3.5000-3.5005	C	3.49875-3.49925
3.5005-3.5010	D	3.49925-3.49975
3.5090-3.5095 [1]	J	[1] 3.50775-3.50825
3.5095-3.5100 [1]	K	[1] 3.50825-3.50875
3.5100-3.5105 [1]	L	[1] 3.50875-3.50925
3.5105-3.5110 [1]	M	[1] 3.50925-3.50975
5.0L		
3.7990-3.7995	A	3.79775-3.79825
3.7995-3.8000	B	3.79825-3.79875
3.8000-3.8005 [2]	C	[2] 3.79875-3.79925
3.8005-3.8010 [2]	D	[2] 3.79925-3.79975
3.8090-3.8095 [1]	J	[1] 3.80775-3.80825
3.8095-3.8100 [1]	K	[1] 3.80825-3.80875
3.8010-3.8105 [1]	L	[1] 3.80875-3.80925
3.8105-3.8110 [1]	M	[1] 3.80925-3.80975

[1] – .010" oversize.
[2] – Standard high limit.

FITTING RINGS

1) Position ring in cylinder bore at a point about 1/4" above ring travel. Ring must be square in bore. Measure ring end gap with a feeler gauge. Check side clearance of compression rings prior to installing.

2) Check ring for binding in ring groove. To check for binding, insert outer edge of ring in its respective groove, and slide ring around entire circumference of piston groove. If binding occurs, check piston groove for high steps, or check ring for distortion.

PISTON PIN REPLACEMENT

Removal

Using an arbor press and piston pin remover/installer, press piston pin from piston and connecting rod.

Installation

Check clearance of piston pin in piston. Replace piston and pin if not within limits. Lubricate piston pin holes in piston and connecting rod with engine oil. Using pin remover/installer and arbor press, press piston pin into piston and connecting rod. Check piston for freedom of movement on piston pin.

CRANKSHAFT & ROD BEARINGS

NOTE: **Following procedures are performed with oil pan and oil pump removed. Remove oil film from surfaces to be checked.**

CONNECTING ROD BEARINGS

1) Ensure rod caps are marked for cylinder identification. Remove rod cap and bearings. Inspect bearings for wear or damage and replace as necessary.

2) Check crankshaft rod bearing journal for out-of-round or taper. Maximum crankshaft out-of-round or taper must not exceed .001" (.03 mm).

3) Check rod bearing clearance using the Plastigage method. If clearance exceeds specifications, standard, .001" (.03 mm) or .002" (.05 mm) undersize bearings may be used in combination to produce correct clearance. If clearance is still excessive, crankshaft must be reconditioned.

4) Clean crankshaft journal and bearing surface in rod. Insert bearings in rod and cap, then lubricate bearing surfaces with oil. Pull piston and rod assembly down onto crankshaft. Install and tighten rod cap.

CRANKSHAFT MAIN BEARINGS

NOTE: **Some production crankshafts are ground to .009" (.23 mm) undersize at the assembly plant. They are identified as follows: Crankshaft counterweight of undersize journal, will be stamped on one side with the number "9", along with a large spot of Light Green paint. Main bearing cap will be painted Light Green on each side.**

1) Measure main bearing clearances one at a time, while all other main caps are properly tightened. Mark or identify main bearing cap before removing. Support crankshaft weight, using a jack placed under counterweight next to the bearing being checked.

2) Start with rear main bearing (No. 5) and work forward. Also, remove drive belts from crankshaft pulley, prior to checking front (No. 1) bearing. Check main bearing clearance using Plastigage method. Install cap and tighten to specifications. Do not allow crankshaft to turn.

3) Remove cap and measure width of Plastigage with scale furnished. Standard, .001" (.03 mm) or .002" (.05 mm) undersize bearing halves may be used in combination to obtain correct clearance. Always replace both upper and lower bearing halves.

4) Upper main bearings are removed from cylinder block using Upper Main Bearing Remover/Installer (J-8080). Insert remover/installer in crankshaft oil hole and rotate crankshaft clockwise. If remover/installer is not available, a cotter pin may be bent, as necessary, to do the job.

5) Lubricate journal and bearings. Insert plain end of new bearing between crankshaft and notched side of block. Insert bearing remover/installer into crankshaft oil hole, and rotate bearing into place.

6) Install lower bearing half into cap. Install and tighten main bearing caps with arrows pointing toward front of engine. Check crankshaft end play after aligning thrust bearing. Check end play by prying crankshaft forward, and inserting feeler gauge between crankshaft counterweight and forward face of rear main bearing cap.

CRANKSHAFT END PLAY

1) Ensure all other main bearing caps have been properly tightened. Tighten rear main bearing cap to 10-12 ft. lbs. (14-16 N.m). Tap crankshaft rearward, then forward, using a lead hammer. Tighten rear main bearing cap. Retighten all main bearing caps.

2) Measure crankshaft end play with a feeler gauge. Pry crankshaft forward and measure clearance between front of rear main bearing and crankshaft thrust surface.

REAR MAIN BEARING OIL SEAL

Removal

Remove rear main bearing cap and pry out old seal. Remove upper half of seal by tapping end with brass punch until seal protrudes enough to be removed with pliers.

Installation

1) Fabricate an oil seal installer if not supplied with replacement oil seal. *See Fig. 8*. Coat seal lips with engine oil. Keep oil off of seal ends.

Fig. 8: Rear Main Oil Seal Installer

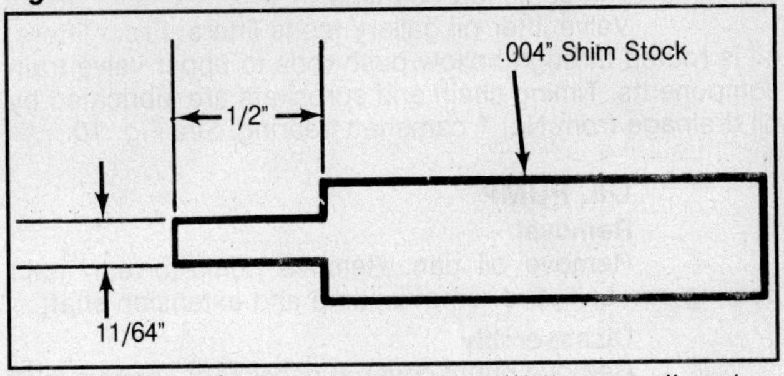

Installer is sometimes supplied with replacement oil seal.

2) Position installer between crankshaft and seal groove in cylinder block. Position seal between tip of installer and crankshaft, with oil seal lip toward front of engine. *See Fig. 9.*

General Motors Engines

4.3 LITER V6, 5.0 & 5.7 LITER V8 (Cont.)

Fig. 9: Rear Main Bearing Oil Seal Identification

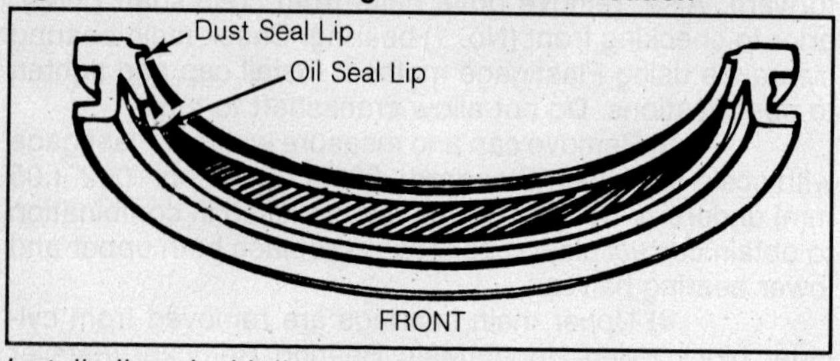

Install oil seal with lip towards front of engine.

3) Roll seal around crankshaft, using installer as a "shoehorn" to protect seal from sharp corner of seal groove in cylinder block. Leave installer in position, until both ends of seal are flush with block.

4) Install lower seal into bearing cap. Feed seal into cap using light pressure with thumb and finger. Apply sealer to cap-to-block mating surface of cylinder block, being careful to keep sealer off the seal split line. Install and tighten rear main bearing cap.

ENGINE OILING

CRANKCASE CAPACITY

Crankcase capacity is 4 quarts (3.8L). Add 1 quart (.95L) when replacing oil filter.

OIL FILTER

Replace oil filter at every other oil change, or more often under dusty or severe conditions.

NORMAL OIL PRESSURE

With engine at normal operating temperature, oil pressure should be 30-40 psi (2.1-2.8 kg/cm^2) at speeds of 35-40 MPH.

OIL PRESSURE REGULATOR VALVE

Oil pressure regulator valve is located in pump body. Valve is nonadjustable.

ENGINE OILING SYSTEM

Gear-type oil pump delivers full pressure lubrication to main oil gallery, through full-flow oil filter. Through drilled passages in block, main oil gallery feeds oil to all crankshaft and camshaft bearings.

Valve lifter oil gallery feeds lifters. From lifters, oil is routed through hollow push rods to upper valve train components. Timing chain and sprockets are lubricated by oil drainage from No. 1 camshaft bearing. *See Fig. 10.*

OIL PUMP

Removal

Remove oil pan. Remove pump-to-rear main bearing cap bolt, and remove pump and extension shaft.

Disassembly

Remove pump cover. If necessary, remove inlet tube and screen assembly. Mark gears at a meshing point, so they may be reassembled with same gear teeth indexing. Remove gears. *See Fig. 11.*

Fig. 10: Engine Oiling System

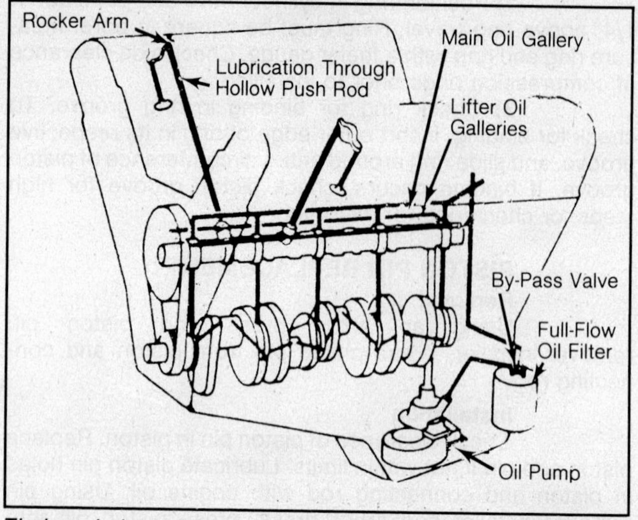

Timing chain and sprockets are lubricated by oil drainage from No. 1 camshaft bearing.

Fig. 11: Oil Pump Assembly

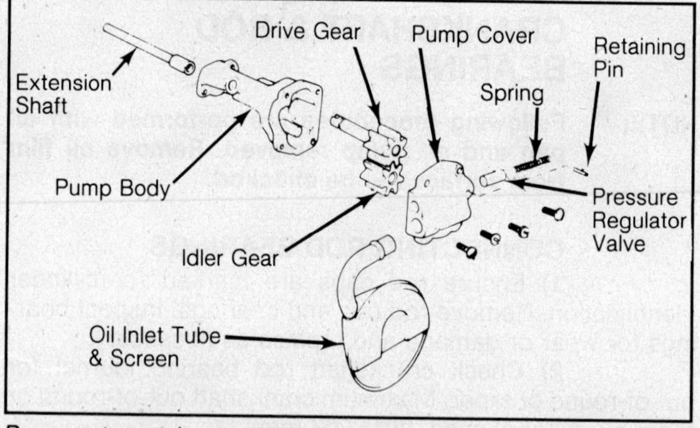

Be sure to mark gears at a meshing point, prior to disassembly of pump.

Inspection

1) Wash all parts and dry with compressed air. Inspect pump body and cover for cracks or excessive wear. Inspect pump gears for damage or excessive wear. If pump gears or body are damaged or worn, replace entire pump assembly.

2) Check drive gear shaft for looseness in pump body. Inspect oil inlet tube and screen assembly for damage. Check pressure regulator valve for fit in bore.

Reassembly

If removed, install oil inlet tube and screen assembly. Apply sealer to end of tube, and tap tube into place, using plastic hammer. Install pump gears into pump body, with marked gear teeth indexing. Idler gear must be installed with smooth side of gear toward cover opening. Reassemble remaining components in reverse order of disassembly.

Installation

Prime oil pump with engine oil. Assemble pump and extension shaft to engine. Ensure slot on top of extension shaft engages with drive tang on end of distributor shaft. Install and tighten attaching bolt. Install oil pan.

4.3 LITER V6, 5.0 & 5.7 LITER V8 (Cont.)

ENGINE COOLING

WATER PUMP

Removal

Disconnect negative battery cable at battery. Drain cooling system. Remove all drive belts, coolant hoses and mounting brackets attached to water pump. If necessary, remove fan shroud and position rearward toward engine. Remove fan and pulley. Remove water pump and gaskets.

Installation

Clean all gasket surfaces. Apply 1/8" bead silicone sealer to water pump gasket surfaces. Using new gaskets, install and tighten water pump. Install remaining components in reverse order of removal.

NOTE: **For further information on cooling system capacities and other cooling system components, see appropriate article in ENGINE COOLING SYSTEMS at end of ENGINE section.**

TIGHTENING SPECIFICATIONS

Application	Ft. Lbs. (N.m)
Camshaft Sprocket Bolts	20 (27)
Connecting Rod Nuts	45 (61)
Cylinder Head Bolts	65 (88)
Exhaust Manifold Bolts	20 (27)
Flywheel-to-Crankshaft Bolts	60 (81)
Intake Manifold Bolts	
4.3L	35 (47)
5.0 & 5.7L	30 (41)
Main Bearing Cap Bolts	70 (108)
Oil Pump Bolt	65 (88)
Vibration Damper Bolt	60 (81)
Water Pump Bolts	30 (41)

ENGINE SPECIFICATIONS

GENERAL SPECIFICATIONS

Year	DISPLACEMENT Cu. In.	DISPLACEMENT Liters	Fuel System	HP@RPM	Torque Ft. Lbs.@RPM	Compr. Ratio	BORE In.	BORE mm	STROKE In.	STROKE mm
1985										
VIN Code N	262	4.3	4-Bbl.	145@4000	225@2400	9.3:1	4.00	101.6	3.48	88.4
VIN Code F	305	5.0	4-Bbl.	155@4000	245@1600	8.6:1	3.74	95.0	3.48	88.4
VIN Code H	305	5.0	4-Bbl.	160@4400	235@2000	9.2:1	3.74	95.0	3.48	88.4
VIN Code L	350	5.7	4-Bbl.	165@3800	275@1600	8.2:1	4.00	101.6	3.48	88.4

VALVES

Engine Size & Valve	Head Diam. In. (mm)	Face Angle	Seat Angle	Seat Width In. (mm)	Stem Diameter In. (mm)	Stem Clearance In. (mm)	Valve Lift In. (mm)
4.3L							
Intake	.....	45°	46°	.031-.063 (.79-1.58)	.....	.0010-.0027 (.025-.069)	.....
Exhaust	.....	45°	46°	.063-.094 (1.58-2.38)	.....	.0010-.0027 (.025-.069)	.....
5.0L & 5.7L							
Intake	.....	45°	46°	.031-.063 (.79-1.58)	.....	.0010-.0027 (.025-.069)	.....
Exhaust	.....	45°	46°	.063-.094 (1.58-2.38)	.....	.0010-.0027 (.025-.069)	.....

PISTONS, PINS, RINGS

Engine	PISTONS Clearance In. (mm)	PINS Piston Fit In. (mm)	PINS Rod Fit In. (mm)	RINGS Ring No.	RINGS End Gap In. (mm)	RINGS Side Clearance In. (mm)
4.3L, 5.0L &5.7L	.0007-.0017 (.018-.043)	.00025-.00035 (.0064-.0089)	.0008-.0016 (.020-.041)	1	.010-.020 (.25-.51)	.0012-.0032 (.031-.081)
				2	.010-.025 (.25-.64)	.0012-.0032 (.031-.081)
				3	.015-.055 (.38-1.40)	.002-.007 (.05-.18)

4.3 LITER V6, 5.0 & 5.7 LITER V8 (Cont.)

ENGINE SPECIFICATIONS (Cont.)

CRANKSHAFT MAIN & CONNECTING ROD BEARINGS

Engine	MAIN BEARINGS Journal Diam. In. (mm)	MAIN BEARINGS Clearance In. (mm)	MAIN BEARINGS Thrust Bearing	MAIN BEARINGS Crankshaft End Play In. (mm)	CONNECTING ROD BEARINGS Journal Diam. In. (mm)	CONNECTING ROD BEARINGS Clearance In. (mm)	CONNECTING ROD BEARINGS Side Play In. (mm)
4.3L							
No. 1	2.4484-2.4493 (62.189-62.212)	.002-.008 (.05-.20)	No. 4	.002-.006 (.05-.15)	2.0988-2.0998 (53.310-53.335)	.0013-.0035 (.033-.089)	.008-.014 (.20-.36)
Nos. 2, 3 & 4	2.4481-2.4490 (62.182-62.205)	.001-.002 (.03-.05)					
5.0L & 5.7L							
No. 1	2.4484-2.4493 (62.189-62.212)	.002-.008 (.05-.20)	No. 5	.002-.006 (.05-.15)	2.0988-2.0998 (53.310-53.335)	.0013-.0035 (.033-.089)	.008-.014 (.20-.36)
Nos. 2, 3 & 4	2.4481-2.4490 (62.182-62.205)	.001-.002 (.03-.05)					
No. 5	2.4479-2.4488 (62.177-62.200)	.002-.003 (.05-.08)					

CAMSHAFT

Engine	Journal Diam. In. (mm)	Clearance In. (mm)	Lobe Lift In. (mm)
4.3L [1]	1.8682-1.8692 (47.452-47.478)	.....	[2] .357 (9.07) [3] .390 (9.91)
5.0L [1]	1.8682-1.8692 (47.452-47.478)	.....	[2] .2484 (6.309) [3] .2667 (6.774)
5.7L [1]	1.8682-1.8692 (47.452-47.478)	.....	[2] .2600 (6.604) [3] .2733 (6.942)

[1] – End play is .004-.012" (.10-.31 mm).
[2] – Intake.
[3] – Exhaust.

VALVE SPRINGS

Engine	Free Length In. (mm)	PRESSURE Lbs. @ In. (Kg @ mm) Valve Closed	PRESSURE Lbs. @ In. (Kg @ mm) Valve Open
4.3L, 5.0L & 5.7L			
Intake	2.03 (51.56)	76-84@1.70 (34-38@43.2)	194-206@125 (88-93@31.8)
Exhaust	2.03 (51.56)	76-84@170 (34-38@43.2)	194-206@1.25 (88-93@31.8)

6.2 LITER V8 DIESEL

ENGINE CODING

ENGINE IDENTIFICATION

Engine code number is suffix of engine identification number. Number is located on label on rear of left valve cover. The Vehicle Identification Number (VIN) is located on a metal plate on top left side of instrument panel, visible through windshield. Engine can be identified by the 8th character of the VIN.

ENGINE IDENTIFICATION CODE

Application	Code
6.2L Diesel (Light Duty)	C
6.2L Diesel (Heavy Duty)	J

ENGINE REMOVAL

See ENGINE REMOVAL at end of ENGINE section.

MANIFOLDS & CYLINDER HEADS

INTAKE MANIFOLD

Removal (Pickup)

1) Disconnect batteries. Remove air cleaner. Disconnect PCV hoses and secondary fuel filter lines. Remove secondary fuel filter and adapter. Loosen vacuum pump hold-down clamp and rotate pump to gain access to intake manifold bolt.

2) Remove EPR/EGR valve bracket and rear A/C bracket, if equipped. Remove intake manifold bolts and injection pipe clips. Retain bolts and studs in order for reinstallation in original position. Remove intake manifold from engine.

Installation

1) Clean all gasket surfaces. Install new manifold gasket. Open EGR passage in gasket if vehicle is equipped with EGR. Install intake manifold and tighten bolts in proper sequence.

2) Fill secondary fuel filter with clean fuel prior to installing filter. Reconnect fuel filter lines. Install bolts and studs in original positions. Reverse removal procedure to complete installation.

Removal (Van)

1) Disconnect batteries. Remove engine cover and air cleaner. Disconnect necessary wires and hoses and remove EGR/EPR switches. Remove crankcase depression regulator valve and disconnect hoses to valve.

2) Remove crankcase depression regulator valve hoses from intake manifold. Remove rear A/C compressor bracket, if equipped. Remove fuel filter-to-intake manifold bracket.

3) Remove vacuum pump. Place a rag or cover over hole to prevent foreign material from entering engine. Remove intake bolts and fuel line clips. Remove intake manifold.

Installation

Clean all gasket surfaces. Install new manifold gasket. Ensure EGR passage in gasket is opened if vehicle is equipped with EGR. Install intake manifold and tighten bolts in proper sequence. Reconnect fuel filter lines. Reverse removal procedure to complete installation.

Fig. 1: Intake Manifold Tightening Sequence

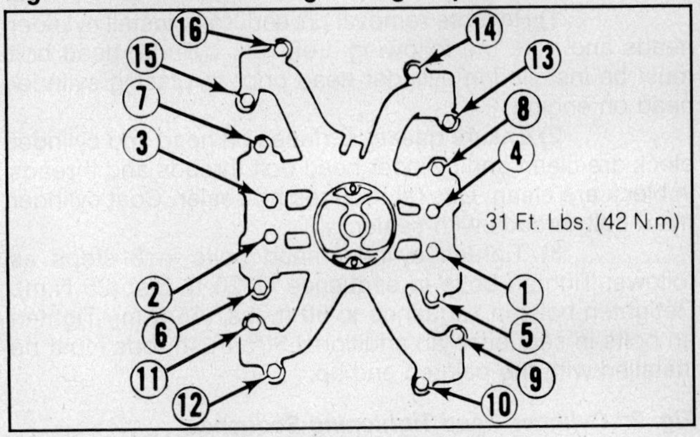

Tighten bolts gradually to 25-37 ft. lbs. (34-50 N.m).

EXHAUST MANIFOLD

Removal (Pickup - Right Side)

Disconnect batteries. Raise vehicle. Disconnect exhaust pipe from manifold flange. Lower vehicle. Disconnect glow plug wires. Remove air cleaner duct bracket. Remove glow plugs. Remove manifold bolts. Remove manifold.

Removal (Pickup - Left Side)

Disconnect batteries. Remove dipstick tube nut and tube. Disconnect glow plug wires and remove glow plugs. Remove manifold bolts. Raise vehicle. Disconnect exhaust pipe from manifold flange. Remove manifold from bottom.

Removal (Van - Right Side)

Disconnect batteries. Raise vehicle. Disconnect exhaust pipe from manifold flange. Lower vehicle. Disconnect glow plug wires. Remove manifold bolts. Remove manifold.

Removal (Van - Left Side)

Disconnect upper battery. Raise vehicle. Disconnect glow plug wires. Lower vehicle. Disconnect exhaust from manifold flange. Remove manifold bolts. Remove manifold.

Installation (All Models)

To install, reverse removal procedure.

CYLINDER HEADS

Removal (Pickup)

1) Remove intake manifold. Remove injection line clips from brackets. Disconnect injection lines from injector nozzles and cover nozzles. Remove injection lines at pump and mark for reassembly reference.

2) Remove fuel supply line from injection pump. Remove wiring harness and bracket from engine. Remove valve cover. Drain coolant. Remove dipstick tube. Disconnect ground wire from cowl at right side of engine.

3) Raise vehicle. Disconnect exhaust pipe from manifold. Lower vehicle. If equipped, remove A/C compressor from engine without disconnecting refrigerant lines and lay it on left side of engine compartment.

4) Remove alternator from engine and lay it on right side of engine compartment. Disconnect glow plug wires. Remove rocker arm assemblies and push rods. Note their positions to allow reinstallation in the same position.

5) Disconnect radiator, heater and by-pass hoses. Disconnect ground strap. Remove thermostat crossover/housing from cylinder head. Remove cylinder head bolts and cylinder head.

General Motors Engines

6.2 LITER V8 DIESEL (Cont.)

Installation

1) Reverse removal procedure to install cylinder heads and note the following: Left rear cylinder head bolt must be installed in cylinder head prior to placing cylinder head on engine.

2) Ensure gasket surfaces on head and cylinder block are clean and cylinder head bolt threads and threads in block are clean. Gasket requires no sealer. Coat cylinder head bolt threads with sealer.

3) Tighten cylinder head bolts in 3 steps as follows: Tighten bolts in sequence to 20 ft. lbs. (25 N.m). Retighten bolts in sequence to 50 ft. lbs. (65 N.m). Tighten an bolts in sequence an additional 90°. Push rods must be installed with the painted end up.

Fig. 2: Cylinder Head Tightening Sequence

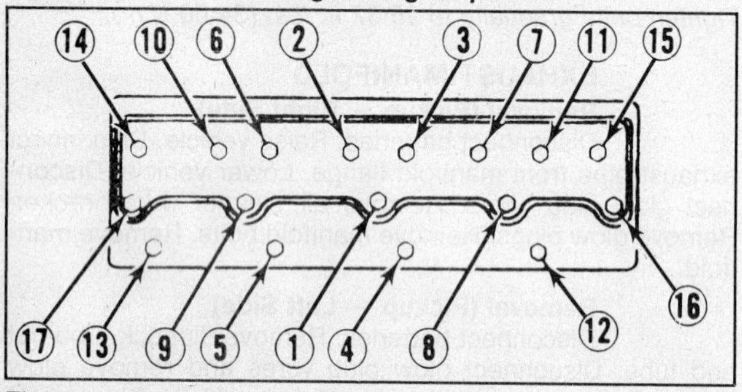

Tighten bolts in 3 steps.

Removal (Van)

1) Remove intake manifold. Install protective covers. Remove injection line clips from brackets. Raise vehicle. Disconnect injection lines from injector nozzles and cover nozzles.

2) Lower vehicle. Remove injection lines at pump and tag lines for reinstallation. If equipped with cruise control, remove transducer. If A/C equipped, remove upper fan shroud and A/C belt.

3) Raise vehicle. Disconnect exhaust pipes from manifolds. Remove left exhaust manifold. Remove power steering lower adjusting bolts. Disconnect glow plug wires and temperature switch. If A/C equipped, remove rear A/C brace from exhaust manifold. Disconnect glow plug wires.

4) Lower vehicle. If A/C equipped, discharge A/C system, disconnect A/C lines at compressor and remove compressor from brackets and remove compressor. Remove upper power steering attachment and move aside.

5) Loosen dipstick tube front bracket and remove from stud. Remove oil fill tube upper bracket. Disconnect T.V. cable. Remove glow plug controller and bracket. Remove glow plug relay.

6) Disconnect oil pressure switch and loom. Remove loom bracket and vacuum line clip bolt at head. Remove rocker cover bolts. Disconnect fuel return line bracket. Remove rocker cover.

7) Remove rocker arm assemblies and push rods. Note their positions to allow reinstallation in the same location. Drain cooling system. Remove air cleaner resonator and bracket. Remove transmission fill tube nut and position aside. Disconnect heater, radiator and by-pass hoses at crossover.

8) Remove alternator upper bracket, coolant crossover and cylinder head bolts. Disconnect transmission dipstick at rear of right head and remove tube. Remove cylinder head.

Installation

1) Reverse removal procedure to install cylinder heads and note the following: Left rear cylinder head bolt must be installed in cylinder head prior to placing cylinder head on engine.

2) Ensure gasket surfaces on head and cylinder block are clean and cylinder head bolt threads and threads in block are clean. Gasket requires no sealer. Coat cylinder head bolt threads with sealer. Tighten cylinder head bolts in sequence in 3 steps. Push rods must be installed with painted end up.

VALVES

VALVE ARRANGEMENT

Left Bank – I-E-I-E-I-E-I-E (Front-to-rear).
Right Bank – E-I-E-I-E-I-E-I (Front-to-rear).

ROCKER ARM SHAFT ASSEMBLY

Removal & Installation

Remove valve covers. Loosen rocker arm shaft bolts gradually and evenly to release valve spring pressure. Remove bolts and rocker arm shafts. To install, reverse removal procedure.

Fig. 3: Rocker Arm Shaft Mounting

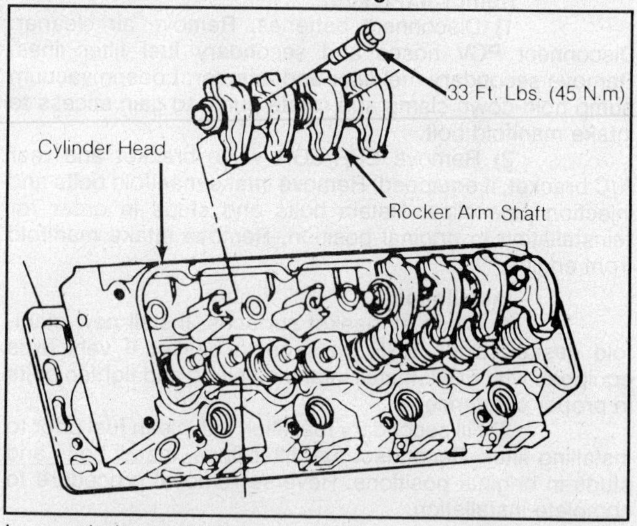

Loosen bolts gradually and evenly.

VALVE SPRINGS

Removal

With cylinder head removed, compress valve spring and remove valve keepers. Release spring compressor and remove retainer, spring, damper, seal and exhaust valve rotators.

Installation

To install valve springs, reverse removal procedure. Lubricate and install valve stem oil seal on valve stem before installing remaining components.

VALVE SPRING INSTALLED HEIGHT

Valve spring installed height is measured from top of shim at bottom of spring or spring seat to top of valve spring. If distance exceeds specified height, install a .063" (1.59 mm) thick shim. Installed height should never be more than .063" (1.59 mm) less than specified height.

VALVE SPRING INSTALLED HEIGHT

Application	Height In. (mm)
All	1.811 (46)

VALVE STEM OIL SEALS

An "O" ring type oil seal is installed on valve stem before valve spring is installed. See VALVE SPRINGS in this article.

VALVE GUIDE SERVICING

If valve stem-to-guide clearance is excessive, guides are removable and can be replaced, or valves with oversize stems are available. Use a Reamer (J-7049) to ream guides to correct size for oversize valve stems.

HYDRAULIC VALVE LIFTERS

NOTE: Hydraulic lifters used on the diesel engine are roller type. Lifters are serviced as complete assemblies only. Parts are not interchangeable between lifters.

Removal (Pickup)

Keep lifters and push rods in order for reinstallation. Remove valve covers, rocker arm shafts and push rods. Remove lifter guide clamps and guide plates. Remove lifters using Remover (J-29834).

Removal (Van)

Keep lifters and push rods in order for reinstallation. Remove cylinder heads, guide clamp and plate. Remove lifters.

Disassembly

With valve lifter removed from engine, remove retainer ring. Remove push rod seat and oil metering valve. Remove plunger and plunger spring. Remove check valve retainer from plunger and remove valve spring.

Inspection

Clean all parts in clean solvent or diesel fuel. Check for nicks, burrs or scoring on parts. Ensure lifter roller operates smoothly and without excessive play.

Reassembly

Coat all parts with clean engine oil, then reverse disassembly procedure.

Fig. 4: Exploded View of Hydraulic Valve Lifter

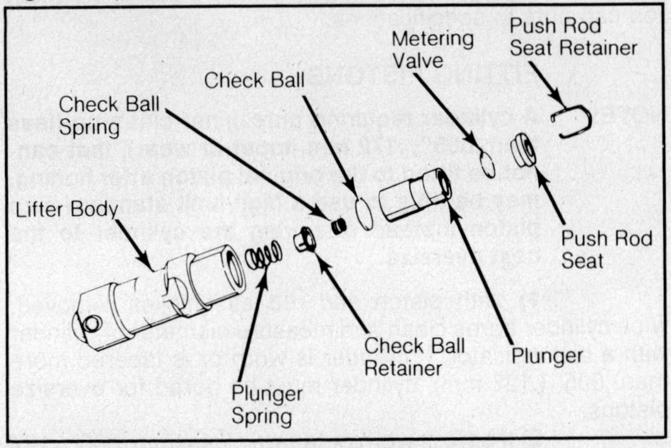

Always prime lifters with oil before installing.

Installation

Prime lifters by working plunger while lifter is submerged in clean kerosene or diesel fuel. Coat roller and bearings with assembly lube. Install lifters into their original position in block. Install lifter guide plate and clamp. Rotate crankshaft 2 full turns while checking to see that lifters are not binding against guide plates.

CAMSHAFT

ENGINE FRONT COVER

Removal

1) Drain coolant from engine. Disconnect negative battery cables. Remove fan belts, fan, fan shroud and pulley. Remove A/C hose bracket nuts. Remove oil fill tube. Remove alternator pivot bolt and drive belt. Remove alternator lower bracket.

2) Remove power steering belt and pump. Remove A/C compressor. Do not disconnect hoses or lines from either device. Support pump and compressor out of the way. Remove A/C compressor belt. Disconnect by-pass and lower radiator hose. Remove water pump bolts. Remove water pump plate and water pump.

3) Rotate engine and align marks on injection pump gear and camshaft gear. Scribe an alignment mark on injection pump flange and on front cover. Remove crankshaft pulley. Remove harmonic balancer using a puller.

4) Remove front cover-to-oil pan bolts. Remove fuel return line clips. Remove injection pump driven gear. Remove injection pump retaining nuts from front cover. Remove baffle and remaining front cover bolts. Remove front cover.

Installation

1) Clean sealing surfaces and apply a 3/32" bead of sealer to surface of cover that mates with engine and oil pan. Install front cover and baffle.

2) Install injection pump, aligning marks made during removal. Install injection pump drive gear. Align timing marks on pump gear and cam gear. To complete installation, reverse removal procedure.

FRONT COVER OIL SEAL

Removal & Installation (With Cover Removed)

Pry seal out of cover with a screwdriver. Install new seal with open end of seal toward inside of cover and drive into position. Support cover at seal area before driving in seal.

Removal & Installation (With Cover Installed)

With harmonic balancer removed, pry seal out of front cover. Install seal with open end of seal toward engine and drive into place with a Driver (J-22102) and hammer.

TIMING CHAIN & SPROCKETS

Removal

Remove front engine cover as previously outlined. Remove bolts securing camshaft gear. Remove injection pump drive gear. Remove cam sprocket, crank sprocket and timing chain.

Installation

Install camshaft sprocket, crankshaft sprocket and timing chain. Ensure timing marks on sprockets are aligned. Install and tighten sprocket bolts. Rotate crankshaft 360°. Install front cover as previously outlined. Align marks on injection pump gear and injection pump drive gear. Whenever the timing chain, sprockets or gears are replaced, it is necessary to retime the engine.

CAMSHAFT

Removal (Pickup)

1) Remove intake manifold, engine front cover and timing chain. Remove valve covers, rocker arms and push rods. Keep parts in order for reinstallation. Disconnect exhaust pipe from manifolds.

2) Remove cylinder heads with exhaust manifolds attached. Remove grille, A/C condenser and radiator if necessary. Remove vacuum pump. Remove lifters, guide plates and clamps. Keep parts in order for reinstallation. Remove fuel pump. Remove camshaft retainer plate and camshaft.

Installation

Lubricate camshaft journals and lobes with motor oil. If a new camshaft is being installed, coat camshaft lobes with Molykote. Position camshaft to align timing marks on sprockets. Install remaining components in reverse order of removal.

Fig. 5: Timing Chain Sprocket Alignment

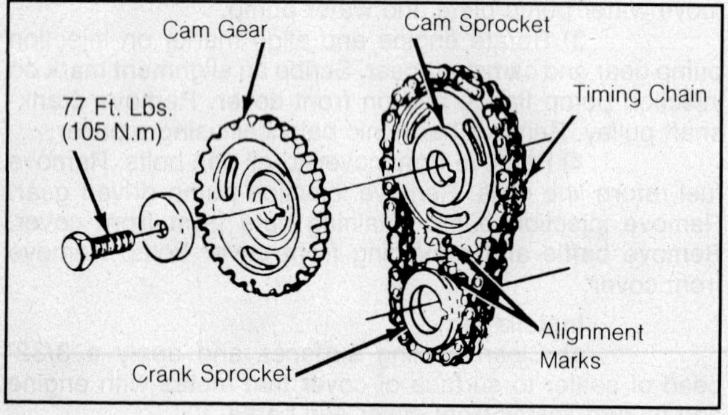

Removal (Van)

1) Disconnect batteries. Drain cooling system. Remove headlight bezels, grille and bumper. Remove lower valance panel, hood latch, coolant recovery bottle and upper tie bar. If A/C equipped, disconnect lines and remove condenser.

2) Disconnect low coolant wire and engine oil cooler lines at radiator. Disconnect automatic transmission cooler lines, if equipped. Disconnect upper and lower radiator hoses. Remove radiator and fan assembly.

3) Remove cylinder heads. Remove alternator lower bracket, water pump and crank pulleys. Using Damper Remover (J-23523) and Pilot (J-29788), remove torsional damper. Remove timing cover plate and water pump. Rotate crankshaft and align timing marks. Remove injection pump driven gear and inner baffle.

4) Align injection pump and front cover by scribing a line across pump flange and front cover. Remove front cover, fuel pump and lifters. Remove injection pump drive gear, timing chain and crankshaft gear. Remove camshaft retainer plate and camshaft.

Installation

Lubricate camshaft journals and lobes with motor oil. If a new camshaft is being installed, coat camshaft lobes with Molykote. Position camshaft to align timing marks on sprockets. Install remaining components in reverse order of removal.

CAM LOBE LIFT

With valve cover removed, remove rocker arm. Mount dial indicator on cylinder head. Position indicator stem on push rod with Adapter (J-8520). Rotate engine slowly until lifter is on heel of camshaft. Zero dial indicator. Rotate engine slowly until push rod is at fully raised position. Dial indicator will give total camshaft lobe lift. Lift should be within specifications.

CAMSHAFT BEARINGS

Use camshaft bearing Remover/Installer (J-6098) to remove bearings. Install front and rear bearings first by driving toward center of cylinder block. Align oil holes in front 4 bearings with oil holes in bearing bore in block. Position rear camshaft bearing oil hole at or near the 6 o'clock position. Install new rear cam bore plug flush with block, using sealer

PISTONS, RINGS & PINS

OIL PAN

See OIL PAN REMOVAL at end of ENGINE section.

PISTON & ROD ASSEMBLY

Removal

1) Remove oil pan, oil pump and cylinder heads. Remove ridge at top of cylinder bore with a ridge reamer. Check connecting rod and cap for identification marks or numbers and identify if necessary.

NOTE: **Each piston is fitted to its individual cylinder and should be marked for that cylinder.**

2) Remove connecting rod cap nuts and rod cap. Cover rod bolts with hose to protect crankshaft journals. Push piston and rod assembly up and out of cylinder block. It will be necessary to rotate crankshaft to various positions to facilitate removing piston and rod assemblies.

NOTE: **When cleaning pistons, DO NOT wire brush any part of piston assembly.**

Installation

1) Before installing piston and rod assembly, position ring gaps. *See Fig. 6.* Place connecting rod in bore with bearing tang slots facing away from camshaft.

2) Lubricate rod bearings, cylinder bore and crankshaft journal. Compress piston rings and push piston and rod assembly into position. Install rod cap and tighten rod cap nuts to specifications.

FITTING PISTONS

NOTE: **A cylinder requiring only minor clean-up (less than .005", .172 mm, taper or wear), that cannot be fitted to the original piston after honing, may be able to use a high-limit standard size piston instead of boring the cylinder to the next oversize.**

1) With piston and rod assemblies removed, wipe cylinder bores clean and measure diameter of cylinder with a dial indicator. If cylinder is worn or is tapered more than .005" (.127 mm), cylinder must be bored for oversize pistons.

2) If bore is worn or tapered less than .005" (.127 mm), cylinder can be cleaned and honed. If cylinders are bored, various oversize pistons are available.

Fig. 6: Piston Ring Gap Positioning

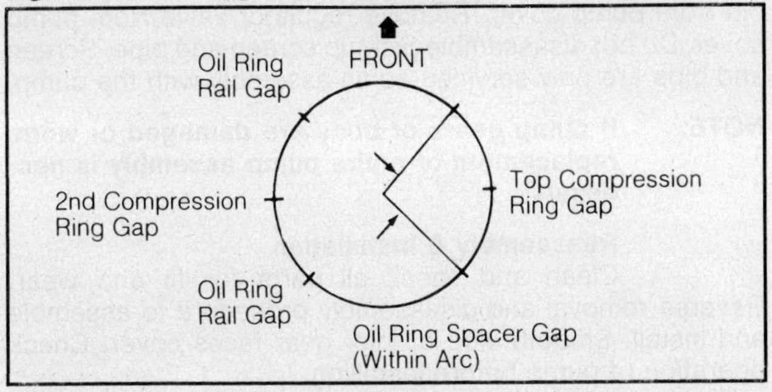

Stagger ring gaps to minimize compression loss.

3) To check fit of rings in cylinder bore, insert ring in cylinder bore and push ring into bore 1/4" with head of piston and measure ring end gap with a feeler gauge.

4) Before installing rings on pistons, ensure ring grooves are clean of carbon and inspect grooves for nicks or burrs. Install rings with gaps staggered. *See Fig. 6*.

PISTON PIN REPLACEMENT

Removal

With piston and rod assembly removed from engine, remove piston pin retaining rings. Slide pin out of piston and connecting rod.

Installation

Check clearance of pin in piston. If clearance exceeds specifications, piston and pin must be replaced. Lubricate piston pin and install into piston and rod. Secure pin with retaining rings. Rotate retaining rings in their grooves to ensure that they are completely seated. Check piston for freedom of movement on piston pin.

CRANKSHAFT & ROD BEARINGS

CONNECTING ROD BEARINGS

NOTE: Following procedures are performed with oil pan and oil pump removed.

1) Mark or identify rod cap to rod before removing rod cap nuts. With rod nuts removed, remove rod cap and bearing. Cover rod bolts with hose to protect crankshaft. Push up on piston and rod assembly and remove bearing from rod. Inspect bearings for wear or damage and replace as necessary.

2) Check crankshaft rod bearing journal for out-of-round or taper conditions. If crankshaft is out-of-round or is tapered more than .001" (.03 mm), crankshaft must be removed and ground for undersize bearings. Check crankshaft clearance using the Plastigage method.

3) If clearance exceeds specifications, a .001" (.03 mm) or .002" (.05 mm) undersize bearing may be installed to obtain correct clearance. If clearance is still excessive, crankshaft must be removed and ground for undersize bearings. Connecting rod bearings are available in .010" (.25 mm) and .020" (.51 mm) undersize.

4) To install bearings, clean crankshaft journal and bearing surface in rod. Insert bearing in rod and cap. Lubricate journal and pull piston and rod assembly down, aligning bearing on journal. Install rod cap noting identification marks and tighten rod nuts evenly.

CRANKSHAFT MAIN BEARINGS

1) Main bearings are selective fit by manufacturer during production. A standard size bearing may be used in combination with a .001" (.03 mm) undersize bearing to obtain correct clearance. This combination will decrease clearance .0005" (.013 mm).

2) Main bearings may be removed and replaced with crankshaft still installed in engine. Mark or identify main bearing caps to cylinder block before removing caps. Remove bearings from cylinder block.

3) Crankshaft clearance, taper or out-of-round conditions can be checked using the Plastigage method. If clearance exceeds specifications, a .001" (.03 mm) or .002" (.05 mm) undersize bearing may be installed to obtain correct clearance. Both bearings must be replaced on any journal not within specifications.

4) If correct clearance cannot be obtained or if journal is tapered or is out-of-round more than .0002" (.005 mm), crankshaft must be removed and ground for undersize bearings. To install bearings, ensure crankshaft journal and bearing surface in cap and block are clean.

5) Lubricate journal and install bearing cap. If bearings were removed with crankshaft still installed, use bearing remover/installer inserted in crankshaft oil hole to install upper bearing. Install main cap noting identification marks and tighten main bearing bolts evenly and to specifications.

CRANKSHAFT END PLAY

Pry crankshaft forward as far as possible and check crankshaft end play with a feeler gauge inserted between front of No. 3 main bearing and crankshaft. Replace thrust bearing if end play is not to specification.

Fig. 7: Checking Crankshaft End Play

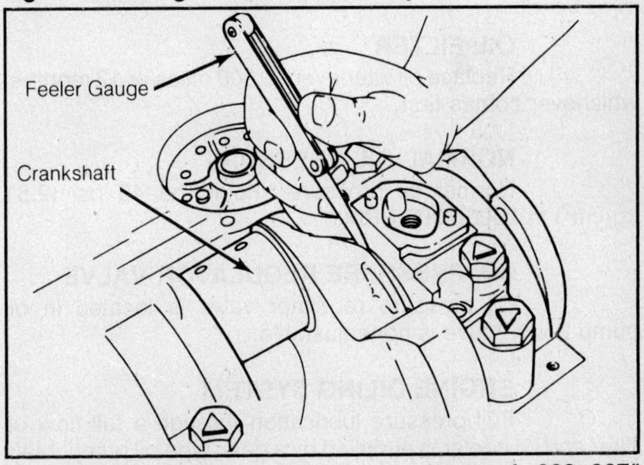

Use a feeler gauge to check for maximum of .002-.007" (.05-.18 mm) end play.

REAR MAIN BEARING OIL SEAL

To perform in-vehicle repair on rear main seal, General Motors recommends packing 1 piece of old main seal (lower half) into each side of block seal groove using Installers (J-29114-2, J-33154-2 and J-33154-1) along with old upper half of the seal.

After packing extra seal material into block, the excess is trimmed and then bottom half of seal is replaced with new material. However, if replacement of complete seal is desired, it can be done using Seal Kit (K-D Tools 492 or S & G Tools 31700) and the following procedure:

6.2 LITER V8 DIESEL (Cont.)

Removal & Installation

1) With oil pan removed, remove rear main bearing cap. Loosen all main cap bolts slightly. Thread screw of remover into upper half of rear main seal. Withdraw upper half of seal from block.

2) Feed steel mesh cable through upper rear main seal groove until it comes out on opposite side of crankshaft. Install a guide funnel over cable end. Lubricate new upper rear main seal and insert it in gripping end of mesh cable.

3) Pull on opposite end of mesh cable and guide new seal into groove. Remove installer from end of seal. Apply Loctite 496 to rear main cap seal groove and install seal. Seat seal in groove and trim end of seal flush with bearing cap.

4) Place a piece of Plastigage on rear main journal. Install rear main cap and tighten all main bearing caps to specifications. Remove rear main cap and check Plastigage for bearing clearance.

5) If out of specification, check ends of seal for frayed ends or excess material that may be preventing main cap from seating properly. Clean Plastigage from journal and bearing.

6) Apply a thin film of Anaerobic Sealant (No. 1052357) to surface of cap that mates with block. Keep sealant off bearing and seal. Apply a light coat of engine oil to surface of crankshaft that rides on seal. Install rear main bearing cap and tighten to specifications.

ENGINE OILING

CRANKCASE CAPACITY

Crankcase capacity is 7 quarts (6.6L) including filter change.

OIL FILTER

Replace oil filter every 5,000 miles or 12 months, whichever comes first.

NORMAL OIL PRESSURE

Normal oil pressure should be 40 psi (2.81 kg/cm^2) at 2000-3000 RPM.

OIL PRESSURE REGULATOR VALVE

Oil pressure regulator valve is located in oil pump body. Valve is nonadjustable.

ENGINE OILING SYSTEM

Full pressure lubrication through a full flow oil filter and oil cooler is supplied by a gear-type oil pump. Main oil gallery feeds oil through drilled passages to camshaft and crankshaft to lubricate bearings. Valve lifter gallery feeds the valve lifters, which feed the rocker arms through hollow push rods.

OIL PUMP

Removal

Remove oil pan. Remove pump-to-rear main bearing cap bolt. Remove oil pump and extension shaft.

Disassembly

1) Remove pump cover attaching screws and pump cover. Mark gears so they may be reassembled with same tooth indexing. Remove idler gear, drive gear and shaft from pump housing.

2) Remove pressure regulator valve retaining pin from pump cover. Remove regulator valve from pump cover. Do not disassemble pick-up screen and pipe. Screen and pipe are only serviced as an assembly with the pump.

NOTE: If pump gears or body are damaged or worn, replacement of entire pump assembly is necessary.

Reassembly & Installation

Clean and check all parts for fit and wear. Reverse removal and disassembly procedure to assemble and install. Smooth side of idler gear faces cover. Check operation of pump before installing.

NOTE: Bottom of screen must be parallel with bottom of pan.

ENGINE COOLING

WATER PUMP

Removal

1) Disconnect batteries. Remove fan and fan shroud. Drain radiator. If A/C equipped, remove A/C hose bracket nuts. Remove oil fill tube. Remove alternator pivot bolt, belt and lower bracket.

2) Remove power steering belt. Remove power steering pump and position aside. Remove A/C belt, if equipped. Disconnect by-pass hose and lower radiator hose. Remove water pump bolts, plate and pump.

Installation

Apply anaerobic sealant (No. 1052357) to sealing surface of plate so that sealer is wet to touch when bolts are tightened. Reverse removal procedure to complete installation.

NOTE: For further information on cooling system capacities and other cooling system components, see appropriate article in ENGINE COOLING SYSTEMS at end of ENGINE section.

TIGHTENING SPECIFICATIONS

Application	Ft. Lbs. (N.m)
Camshaft Sprocket Bolt	66-81 (90-110)
Connecting Rod Nuts	44-52 (60-70)
Crankshaft Balancer Bolt	140-162 (190-220)
Cylinder Head Bolts	
Step 1	20 (25)
Step 2	[1] 50 (65)
Exhaust Manifold Bolts	18-33 (25-45)
Front Cover Bolts	25-37 (34-50)
Injection Nozzle	44-60 (60-80)
Injection Pump Attaching Bolts	25-37 (34-50)
Injection Pump Driven Gear Bolt	13-20 (18-27)
Intake Manifold Bolts	25-37 (34-50)
Main Bearing Cap Bolts	
Inner	105-117 (143-158)
Outer	94-105 (128-143)
Oil Pump Attaching Bolts	59-74 (80-100)
Rocker Arm Shaft Bolts	41 (55)
Thermostat Housing Bolts	25-37 (34-50)
Water Pump Attaching Bolts	25-37 (34-50)
Water Pump Cover Bolts	15-20 (20-27)
Vacuum Pump Retaining Bolts	25-37 (34-50)

[1] – Then tighten an additional 90°.

6.2 LITER V8 DIESEL (Cont.)

ENGINE SPECIFICATIONS

GENERAL SPECIFICATIONS

Year	DISPLACEMENT Cu. In.	DISPLACEMENT Liters	Fuel System	HP@RPM	Torque Ft. Lbs.@RPM	Compr. Ratio	BORE In.	BORE mm	STROKE In.	STROKE mm
1985										
Light Duty	378	6.2	Diesel	130@3600	240@2000	21.3:1	3.98	101	3.82	97
Heavy Duty	378	6.2	Diesel	135@3600	240@2000	21.3:1	3.98	101	3.82	97

CRANKSHAFT MAIN & CONNECTING ROD BEARINGS

Engine	MAIN BEARINGS Journal Diam. In. (mm)	MAIN BEARINGS Clearance In. (mm)	MAIN BEARINGS Thrust Bearing	MAIN BEARINGS Crankshaft End Play In. (mm)	CONNECTING ROD BEARINGS Journal Diam. In. (mm)	CONNECTING ROD BEARINGS Clearance In. (mm)	CONNECTING ROD BEARINGS Side Play In. (mm)
6.2L	[1] 2.9494-2.9504 (74.917-74.941) [2] 2.9492-2.9502 (74.912-74.936)	[1] .0018-.033 (.046-.083) [2] .0022-.0037 (.055-.093)	No. 3	.0039-.0098 (.10-.25)	2.398-2.399 (60.913-60.939)	.0018-.0039 (.046-.099)	.0248-.0067 (.63-.17)

[1] – Journals 1, 2, 3, 4. [2] – Journal 5.

PISTONS, PINS, RINGS

Engine	PISTONS Clearance In. (mm)	PINS Piston Fit In. (mm)	PINS Rod Fit In. (mm)	RINGS Ring No.	RINGS End Gap In. (mm)	RINGS Side Clearance In. (mm)
6.2L	.004-.005 (.102-.138)	.0004-.0006 (.0101-.0153)	.0003-.0012 (.0081-.0309)	1	.012-.022 (.30-.55)	.003-.007 (.076-.178)
				2	.030-.039 (.75-1.0)	.002-.003 (.040-.076)
				3	.010-.020 (.25-.51)	.002-.004 (.040-.096)

VALVES

Engine Size & Valve	Head Diam. In. (mm)	Face Angle	Seat Angle	Seat Width In. (mm)	Stem Diameter In. (mm)	Stem Clearance In. (mm)	Valve Lift In. (mm)
6.2L							
Int.	.....	45°	46°	.035-.060 (.89-1.53)	.....	.001-.003 (.026-.076)	.421 (10.7)
Exh.	.....	45°	46°	.062-.093 (1.57-2.36)	.....	.001-.003 (.026-.076)	.421 (10.7)

VALVE SPRINGS

Engine	Free Length In. (mm)	PRESSURE Lbs. @ In. (Kg @ mm) Valve Closed	PRESSURE Lbs. @ In. (Kg @ mm) Valve Open
6.2L	.....	80@1.81 (36@46)	230@1.39 (105@35)

CAMSHAFT

Engine	Journal Diam. In. (mm)	Clearance In. (mm)	Lobe Lift In. (mm)
6.2L	[1] 2.166-2.164 (55.025-54.975) [2] 2.008-2.006 (51.025-50.975)	.001-.004 (.026-.010)	.2808 (7.133)

[1] – Journals 1, 2, 3 & 4. [2] – Journal 5.

General Motors Engines

7.4 LITER V8

ENGINE CODING

ENGINE IDENTIFICATION

Engine code number is suffix of engine identification number. Number is located on pad at front top center of engine block forward of intake manifold. The Vehicle Identification Number (VIN) is located on a metal plate on top leftside of instrument panel, visible through windshield. Engine can be identified by the 8th character of the VIN.

ENGINE IDENTIFICATION CODE

Application	Code
7.4L 4-Bbl.	W

ENGINE REMOVAL

See ENGINE REMOVAL at end of ENGINE section.

MANIFOLDS & CYLINDER HEAD

INTAKE MANIFOLD

Removal

1) Drain cooling system and remove air cleaner. Disconnect negative battery cable. Disconnect upper radiator hose and heater hose at manifold. Disconnect water pump by-pass hose. Disconnect PCV hose at valve cover.

2) Disconnect accelerator linkage and fuel inlet line at carburetor. Disconnect vacuum line at distributor. Remove distributor cap and mark rotor position. Remove distributor.

3) Remove air cleaner bracket, accelerator return spring bracket and accelerator bellcrank. If A/C equipped, remove compressor and bracket with lines attached. Hang compressor to side.

4) Remove upper alternator mounting bracket. Remove intake manifold bolts and pry manifold loose. Remove manifold with carburetor attached and discard all gaskets.

Installation

Clean all gasket surfaces and install gaskets on cylinder heads. Install new end seals on cylinder block. Install manifold. Tighten bolts in sequence. *See Fig. 1.* Install distributor. Ensure rotor is aligned with mark made during removal. Reverse removal procedure to complete installation.

Fig. 1: Intake Manifold Tightening Sequence

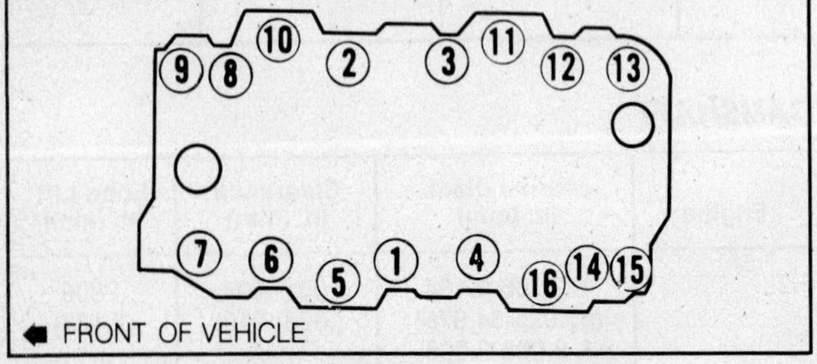

Tighten bolts gradually to 30 ft. lbs. (41 N.m).

EXHAUST MANIFOLD

Removal

Remove air cleaner and heat stove pipe. Remove spark plugs. Disconnect exhaust pipe from manifold. Wire exhaust pipe aside. Remove bolts, starting at end and moving to center of manifold. Remove manifold.

Installation

Clean surfaces. Install manifold and tighten bolts. Connect exhaust pipe to manifold. Install spark plugs and tighten. Install air cleaner.

CYLINDER HEAD

Removal

1) Drain cooling system. Remove intake manifold. Remove alternator lower mounting bolt and position alternator aside. If A/C equipped, remove compressor and forward bracket. Hang compressor to side with hoses attached.

2) Remove spark plugs. Disconnect exhaust pipes at manifolds and remove manifolds. Disconnect PCV hose from valve covers. Remove valve covers. Loosen rocker arm nuts and pivot rocker arms aside.

3) Remove push rods. Mark push rods to ensure reassembly in original positions. Remove all cylinder head bolts. Loosen cylinder head from block. Remove cylinder head and gasket.

Installation

1) Reverse removal procedure to install cylinder heads. Clean gasket sealing surfaces on head and cylinder block. Ensure cylinder head bolt threads and bolt holes in block are clean.

2) If cylinder head gasket is steel type, coat both sides with sealer. Composition asbestos/steel gasket requires no sealer. Place cylinder head gasket over dowels with bead facing up. Coat cylinder head bolt threads with sealer. Tighten cylinder head bolts in sequence. *See Fig. 2.*

3) Install exhaust manifolds and connect exhaust pipes. Install intake manifold. Install valve train assembly. Adjust valves. See VALVE CLEARANCE ADJUSTMENT. Install remaining parts in reverse of disassembly.

Fig. 2: Cylinder Head Tightening Sequence

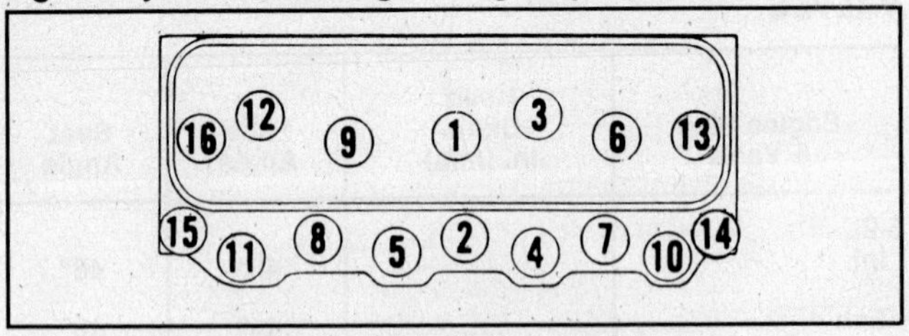

Tighten bolts gradually to 80 ft. lbs. (108 N.m).

VALVES

VALVE ARRANGEMENT

E-I-E-I-E-I-E-I (Left Bank, front-to-rear).
I-E-I-E-I-E-I-E (Right Bank, front-to-rear).

ROCKER ARM STUDS

Push rod guides are attached to cylinder head by rocker arm studs. Replace as necessary and tighten studs. Coat threads on cylinder head end of stud with sealer.

VALVE SPRINGS

Removal

With cylinder head removed, compress valve spring and remove valve keepers. Release spring compressor. Remove retainer, seal, damper, spring and valve rotator (exhaust valves).

Installation

To install valve springs, reverse removal procedure. Lubricate and install valve stem oil seal on valve stem before installing remaining components.

VALVE SPRING INSTALLED HEIGHT

Valve spring installed height is measured from top of shim or spring seat to top of valve spring or valve spring shield. If distance exceeds specified height, install .063" (1.6 mm) thick shim. Installed height should never be more than .063" (1.6 mm) less than specified height.

VALVE SPRING INSTALLED HEIGHT SPECIFICATIONS

Application	In. (mm)
7.4L	1.797" (45.60)

Fig. 3: Exploded View of Valve Spring Assembly

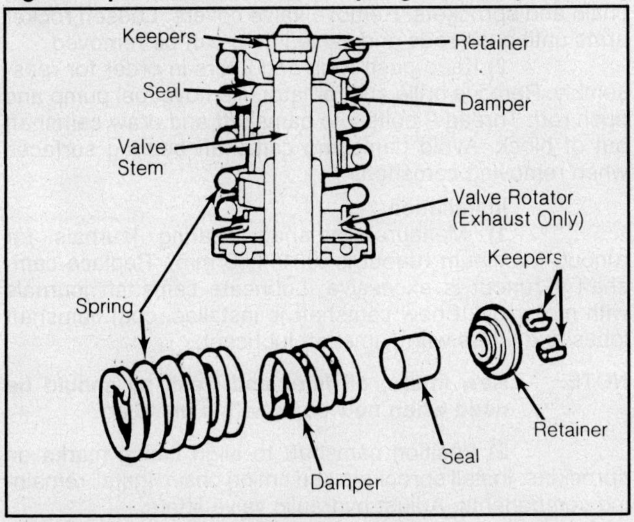

Exhaust valves use a rotator.

VALVE STEM OIL SEALS

Coat valve stem oil seal with oil and install on valve stem before valve spring is installed. *See Fig. 3.*

VALVE GUIDE SERVICING

If valve stem-to-guide clearance is excessive, valves with oversize stems are available. Use Reamer Set (J-7049) to ream guides to correct size for oversize valve stems.

HYDRAULIC VALVE LIFTERS

Removal

Remove intake manifold. Remove rocker arm assembly and push rods. Keep parts in order for reassembly. Remove lifters using magnet. Keep lifters in order for reassembly in same position.

Disassembly

Depress plunger in lifter using push rod. Pry out seat retainer. Remove push rod seat and metering valve. Remove plunger, ball check valve assembly and plunger spring from lifter body. Pry ball retainer from plunger. Remove check ball and spring.

Reassembly

1) Clean and inspect components. If any parts are worn or damaged, complete lifter must be replaced. If lifter body is galled, check lifter bore in block. If bottom of lifter is scored or worn, inspect camshaft lobe.

2) If push rod seat is worn, check push rod. If new camshaft and/or lifters are installed, always use EP lube additive for break-in of new parts. Lifter foot must be convex for proper lifter rotation to occur.

3) Position check ball on small hole in bottom of plunger. Insert check ball spring on seat in ball retainer. Put retainer over ball so that spring presses on ball. Press retainer into position in plunger carefully.

Fig. 4: Cutaway View of Hydraulic Valve Lifter

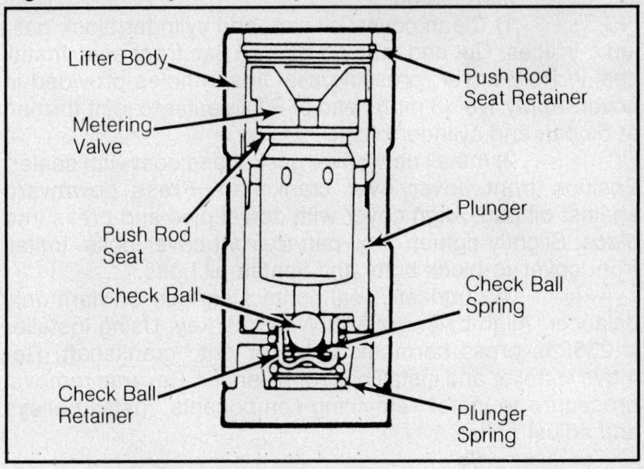

If any parts are worn, complete lifter must be replaced.

4) Put plunger spring over ball retainer. Slide lifter body over spring and plunger. Ensure oil feed holes in plunger and lifter body are aligned. Fill assembly with SAE 10 oil and depress plunger until it feels solid. Do not force or pump plunger.

5) With plunger depressed, insert 1/16" (1.6 mm) punch through both oil holes in plunger assembly and lifter body. This will hold plunger down against lifter spring tension. Release plunger and refill assembly with SAE 10 oil.

6) Install metering valve and push rod seat. Install push rod seat retainer. Depress push rod seat and remove punch holding plunger. Coat lifter face with camshaft lubricant and install.

7) Install intake and exhaust manifolds. Set valve clearance. Install remaining parts in reverse of disassembly. Start engine and check timing.

VALVE CLEARANCE ADJUSTMENT

1) Rotate engine until timing marks are aligned and No. 1 cylinder is at TDC. Back off rocker arm adjusting nut on No. 1 intake and exhaust rocker arm until play in push rod is detected.

2) Tighten rocker arm nut until play in push rod is eliminated, then tighten adjusting nut one additional turn.

7.4 LITER V8 (Cont.)

With engine at No. 1 firing position, adjust intake valves 1, 2, 5 and 7 and exhaust valves 1, 3, 4 and 8.

3) Rotate engine 360° to No. 6 firing position and follow same procedure for adjusting valves. With engine at No. 6 TDC, adjust intake valves 3, 4, 6 and 8 and exhaust valves, 2, 5, 6 and 7.

CAMSHAFT

ENGINE FRONT COVER

Removal

1) Remove fan belts, fan and pulley. Remove alternator. Remove radiator shroud and water pump. Remove accessory drive pulley and harmonic balancer retaining bolt. Remove harmonic balancer using puller.

2) Remove cover retaining screws and pull cover forward slightly. Using sharp knife, cut oil pan front seal flush with cylinder block. Remove cover and gasket.

Installation

1) Clean cover, oil pan, and cylinder block gasket surfaces. Cut end tabs off new oil pan front seal. Install seal in front cover, pressing seal tips in holes provided in cover. Apply 1/8" (3 mm) bead of RTV sealer to joint formed at oil pan and cylinder block.

2) Install new cover gasket and coat with sealer. Position front cover over crankshaft. Press downward against oil pan. Align cover with dowel pins and press into place. Slightly tighten 2 oil pan-to-front cover bolts. Install front cover-to-block bolts and tighten all bolts.

3) Lubricate seal contact surface on harmonic balancer. Align balancer with Woodruff key. Using Installer (J-23523), press harmonic balancer onto crankshaft. Remove installer and install bolt for balancer. Reverse removal procedure to install remaining components. Install pulleys and adjust belts.

FRONT COVER OIL SEAL

Removal & Installation (Front Cover Removed)

Pry seal out of cover from front. Install new seal with open end of seal facing toward inside of cover. Support cover at seal area before driving in seal. Install seal.

Removal & Installation (Front Cover Installed)

With harmonic balancer removed, pry seal out of front cover. Insert seal with open end of seal facing toward engine. Install seal using Driver (J-22102) and hammer. Be careful with surface of crankshaft.

TIMING CHAIN & SPROCKET

Removal

Remove front engine cover. Rotate engine until timing marks on camshaft and crankshaft sprockets are aligned. Remove bolts securing camshaft sprocket to camshaft. Remove sprocket with timing chain. Dislodge sprocket with light blow of plastic hammer.

Installation

Install timing chain on camshaft sprocket. Align timing mark on camshaft sprocket with crankshaft sprocket. *See Fig. 5*. Align dowel in end of camshaft with hole in camshaft sprocket. Install camshaft sprocket and bolts. Tighten sprocket bolts evenly to draw camshaft sprocket onto camshaft. Lubricate timing chain with engine oil. Install front cover.

Fig. 5: Timing Chain Sprocket Alignment

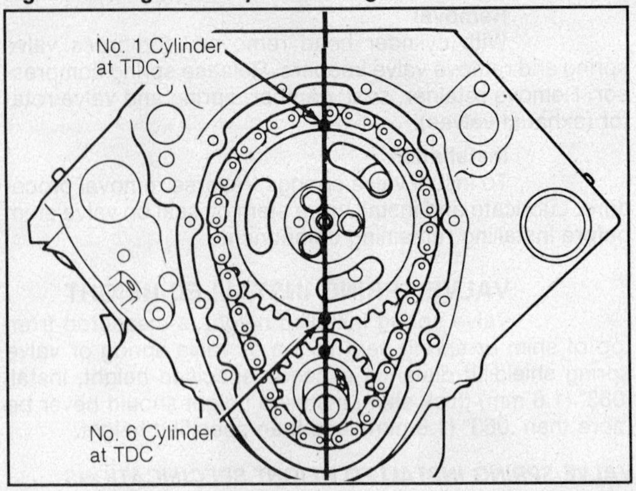

Rotate engine until timing marks on camshaft and crankshaft are aligned.

CAMSHAFT

Removal

1) Remove intake manifold, front cover, timing chain and sprockets. Remove valve covers. Loosen rocker arms until push rods and valve lifters can be removed.

2) Keep push rods and lifters in order for reassembly. Remove grille and radiator. Remove fuel pump and push rod. Thread 2 bolts into camshaft and draw camshaft out of block. Avoid damaging camshaft bearing surfaces when removing camshaft.

Installation

1) Measure camshaft bearing journals for runout. Maximum runout is .001" (.03 mm). Replace camshaft if runout is excessive. Lubricate camshaft journals with motor oil. If new camshaft is installed, coat camshaft lobes and lifters with camshaft lubricant.

NOTE: New lifters, oil filter and fresh oil should be used when new camshaft is installed.

2) Position camshaft to align timing marks on sprockets. Install sprockets and timing chain. Install remaining components. Adjust hydraulic valve lifters.

CAM LOBE LIFT

1) With valve cover removed, remove rocker arm. Mount dial indicator on cylinder head. Position indicator stem on push rod with Ball Socket Adapter (J-8520). Ensure push rod is in lifter socket.

2) Rotate engine slowly until lifter is on heel of camshaft and set dial indicator to zero. Rotate engine slowly until push rod is at fully raised position. Dial indicator will give total camshaft lobe lift.

CAMSHAFT BEARINGS

Removal

1) Camshaft and crankshaft must be removed to replace camshaft bearings. Fasten connecting rods against sides of block so there is no interference when replacing camshaft bearings. Use tape or hose to cover connecting rod bolts for protection of crankshaft journals.

2) When crankshaft and camshaft have been removed, drive camshaft rear plug from block. Index pilot of

7.4 LITER V8 (Cont.)

Bearing Remover (J-6098) in front camshaft bearing and install puller screw through pilot.

3) Mount remover with shoulder toward bearing. Ensure enough threads are engaged in remover. Using 2 wrenches, hold puller screw while turning nut. When bearing is free from block, remove driver and bearing from puller screw.

4) Remove remaining bearings (except front and rear) in same fashion. Pilot of remover has to be indexed in rear bearing in order to remove rear intermediate bearing. Mount remover on driver handle and remove front and rear camshaft bearings. Drive bearings toward center of block to remove.

Installation

1) Using installer mounted on driver, install front and rear bearings first by driving toward center of cylinder block. Front and rear bearings will act as guides for pilot and center remaining bearings as they are pulled into place.

2) Index pilot in front camshaft bearing and install puller screw with nut and thrust washer run to end of threads. Index new bearing in bore with oil hole of No. 1 through No. 4 bearings aligned with holes in bore of block.

3) No. 5 bearing must be positioned with oil hole at or near 6 o'clock. This is because of bore configuration for No. 5 bearing. It will be necessary to index pilot in rear bearing to install rear intermediate bearing.

4) After bearings have been installed, remove installer and ensure that oil holes are correctly aligned. Coat new rear plug with sealer and install in block. Plug depth may be flush or recessed up to depth of .031" (.80 mm).

PISTONS, RINGS & PINS

OIL PAN

See OIL PAN REMOVAL at end of ENGINE section.

PISTON & ROD ASSEMBLY

Removal

1) Drain engine oil. Remove oil pan, oil pump and cylinder heads. Rotate crankshaft until piston to be removed is at bottom of stroke. Cover piston with rag to catch any metal shavings. Remove any ridge at top of cylinder bore with ridge reamer.

2) Remove connecting rod cap nuts and rod cap. If bearings will be reused, mark them for installation in original rod and cap. Push piston and rod assembly up and out of cylinder block. Repeat procedure to remove all piston and rod assemblies.

NOTE: When cleaning pistons, do not wire brush any part of piston assembly.

Installation

1) Ensure cylinder bore is clean. Use mild detergent and hot water or light honing if necessary to clean cylinder walls. Wipe bore with light engine oil and clean dry cloth. Clean crankshaft journal and bearing surface in rod.

2) Position ring gaps properly. *See Fig. 6*. Lubricate and install bearing inserts in rod and cap. Lightly lubricate journals, piston and cylinder bore. Compress rings with Ring Compressor (J-8037). Bearing tang slots face away from camshaft.

3) Place connecting rod and piston assembly in respective bore. Tap piston and rod assembly down. Align bearing on journal carefully to avoid damage to journal surface. Match identification marks and install rod cap. Tighten rod nuts evenly.

FITTING PISTONS

1) With piston and rod assemblies removed, wipe cylinder bores clean. Measure diameter of cylinder with cylinder bore gauge or inside micrometer. If cylinder is tapered more than .005" (.127 mm), cylinder must be bored for oversize piston.

2) If bore is worn or tapered less than .005" (.127 mm), cylinder can be cleaned and honed and .001" (.025 mm) oversize piston may be installed. If cylinders are bored, various oversize pistons are available.

FITTING RINGS

1) To check fit of rings in cylinder bore, insert ring in bore and push ring into bore .25" (6.5 mm) with head of piston. Measure ring end gap with feeler gauge.

Fig. 6: Piston Ring Gap Positioning

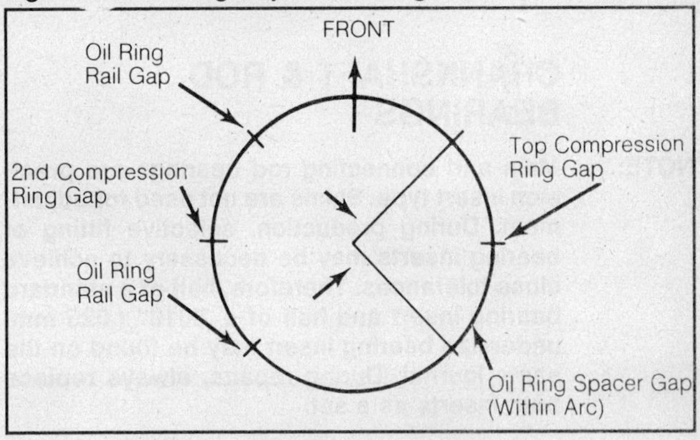

Stagger ring gaps to minimize compression loss.

Fig. 7: Piston Pin Removal & Installation

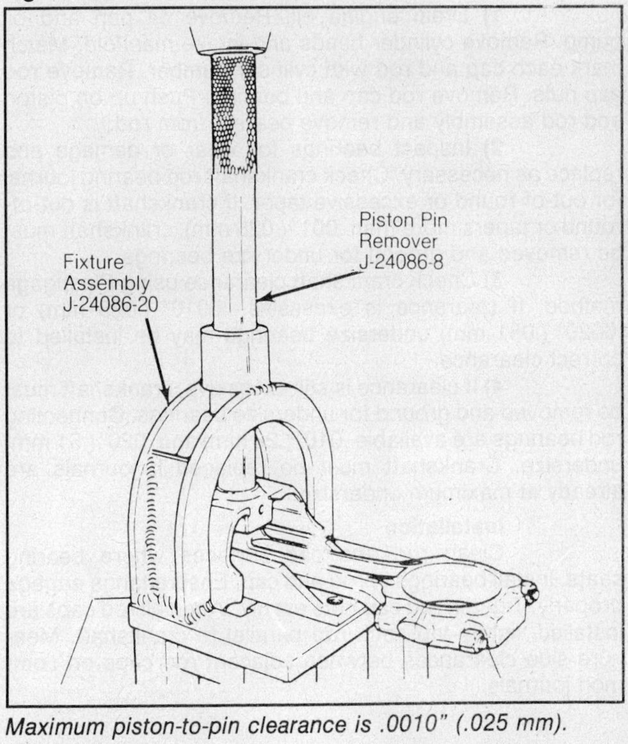

Maximum piston-to-pin clearance is .0010" (.025 mm).

General Motors Engines

7.4 LITER V8 (Cont.)

2) Ensure ring grooves are clear of carbon and inspect grooves for nicks or burrs. Install rings with gaps staggered. All compression rings are marked on upper side. Ensure that rings move freely in grooves after installation.

PISTON PIN REPLACEMENT

Removal

With piston and rod assembly removed, remove piston pin using Remover and Installer (J-24086-8 & J-24086-20) on a press. Separate piston from connecting rod.

Installation

1) Check clearance of pin in piston. If clearance exceeds wear limit of .001" (.0254 mm), piston and pin must be replaced. Position piston and rod so that valve notch in top of piston faces opposite side from bearing tang slots in connecting rod.

2) Lubricate piston pin and press in place using installer and arbor press. Do not exceed 5000 psi (352 kg/cm^2). Note that pin-to-rod fit is interference fit. Check piston for freedom of movement on piston pin.

CRANKSHAFT & ROD BEARINGS

NOTE: **Main and connecting rod bearings are precision insert type. Shims are not used for adjustment. During production, selective fitting of bearing inserts may be necessary to achieve close tolerances. Therefore, half of a standard bearing insert and half of a .0010" (.025 mm) undersize bearing insert may be found on the same journal. During repairs, always replace both inserts as a set.**

CONNECTING ROD BEARINGS

Removal

1) Drain engine oil. Remove oil pan and oil pump. Remove cylinder heads and intake manifold. Match mark each cap and rod with cylinder number. Remove rod cap nuts. Remove rod cap and bearing. Push up on piston and rod assembly and remove bearing from rod.

2) Inspect bearings for wear or damage and replace as necessary. Check crankshaft rod bearing journal for out-of-round or excessive taper. If crankshaft is out-of-round or tapers more than .001" (.025 mm), crankshaft must be removed and ground for undersize bearings.

3) Check crankshaft clearance using Plastigage method. If clearance is excessive, .0010" (.025 mm) or .0020" (.051 mm) undersize bearings may be installed to correct clearance.

4) If clearance is still excessive, crankshaft must be removed and ground for undersize bearings. Connecting rod bearings are available .010" (.26 mm) and .020" (.51 mm) undersize. Crankshaft must be replaced if journals are already at maximum undersize.

Installation

Clean rod and cap surfaces where bearing seats. Install bearings in rod and cap. Ensure tangs engage properly. Tighten rod cap nuts evenly. When all rod caps are installed, lightly tap each rod parallel to crankshaft. Measure side clearances between adjacent rod caps on common journals.

MAIN BEARINGS

1) Drain oil. Remove oil pan and oil pump. Main bearings may be removed and installed without removing crankshaft from engine. Remove spark plugs if changing bearings without removing crankshaft. Number and index main bearing caps to cylinder block before removing caps.

2) Use Plastigage method to measure main bearing wear. Remove main bearing caps 1 at a time for measurement. Accessory drive belts must be loosened when measuring No. 1 (front) main bearing. Incorrect reading could be caused by tension of belts on snout of crankshaft.

3) Remove bearing caps. Insert main bearing remover (or bent cotter pin) in crankshaft oil hole. Rotate crankshaft clockwise as viewed from front of engine. Roll upper bearing out of block.

4) Oil new upper bearing and insert plain end (without tang) between crankshaft and side of block with locating notch. Rotate bearing into place and take remover out of crankshaft oiling hole. Oil new lower bearing and install in cap.

5) Install main bearing cap with arrow pointing toward front of engine. Ensure cap is installed in same location from which it was removed. Tighten all main bearing caps except rear main bearing cap to 110 ft. lbs. (149 N.m).

6) Tighten rear main bearing cap to 10-12 ft. lbs. (14-16 N.m). Tap crankshaft rearward and then forward in bearings. This will cause rear main bearing and crankshaft thrust surfaces to line up. Now tighten all main bearing caps to 110 ft. lbs. (149 N.m).

THRUST BEARING END PLAY

Pry crankshaft forward as far as possible and check end play with feeler gauge inserted between front of rear main bearing and crankshaft. Replace rear main bearing if end play is excessive. *See Fig. 8.*

Fig. 8: Checking Crankshaft End Play

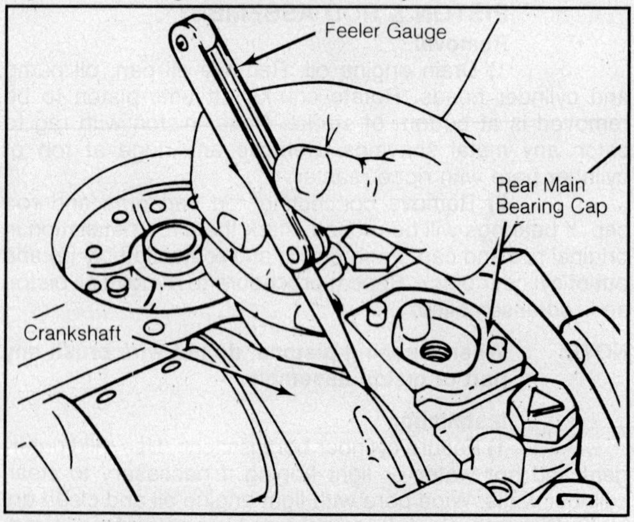

End play should not exceed .006-.010" (.15-.25 mm).

REAR MAIN BEARING OIL SEAL

Removal

Remove rear main bearing cap. Pry out lower half of old oil seal. To remove upper half of old seal, tap one end with brass pin punch until other end of seal protrudes enough to be removed with pliers.

Installation

1) Fabricate installer from shim stock. *See Fig. 9.* Clean any old sealant or dirt from bearing cap and crankshaft with nonabrasive cleaner. Coat seal lips and seal bead of upper seal with motor oil.

2) Keep mating ends of seal half dry of oil. Position installer tip between crankshaft and seal seat in cylinder block. Position seal between tip of installer and crankshaft with seal bead contacting tip.

3) Ensure oil sealing lip points toward front of engine. Installer must remain in position until seal is positioned with both ends flush with block.

Fig. 9: Rear Main Seal Installer

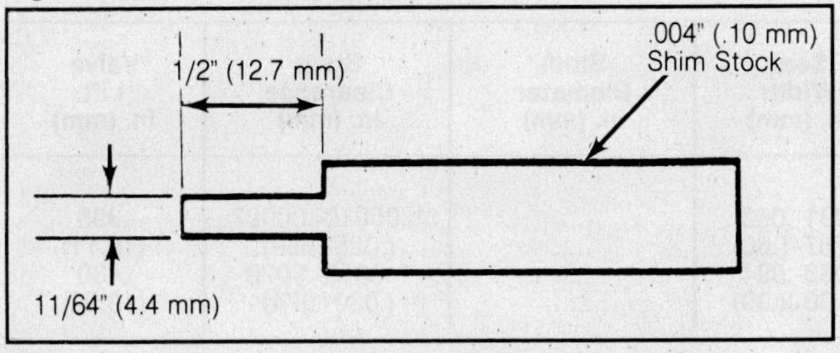

Use seal installer like a "shoehorn" to help install and protect seal.

4) Roll seal around crankshaft, using installer as "shoehorn" to protect seal bead from sharp corner of seat surface in cylinder case. Ensure oil seal lip is positioned toward front of engine.

5) Remove installer, taking care not to remove seal. Install lower half of seal in bearing cap, using installer as "shoehorn" again. Feed seal into cap using light pressure with thumb and finger.

6) Install bearing cap with sealant applied to case-to-cap face. Do not allow sealant to get on split line of seal. Tighten rear main bearing cap to 10-12 ft. lbs. (14-16 N.m). Tap end of crankshaft rearward and then forward with a lead hammer to line up thrust surfaces. Tighten rear main bearing cap to 110 ft. lbs. (149 N.m).

Fig. 10: Rear Main Oil Seal

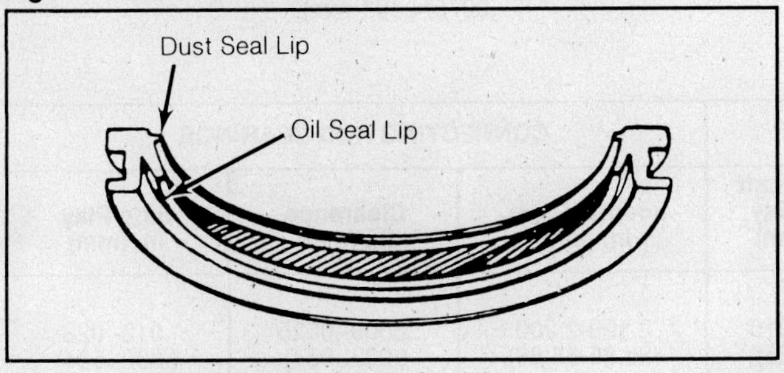

Oil seal lip faces toward front of engine.

ENGINE OILING

CRANKCASE CAPACITY

Crankcase capacity is 6 quarts (5.7L). Add 1 quart (.95L) with filter change.

OIL FILTER

Replace every other oil change or more often under dusty conditions.

NORMAL OIL PRESSURE

Normal oil pressure should be 40 psi (2.8 kg/cm^2) at 2000 RPM.

OIL PRESSURE REGULATOR VALVE

Oil pressure regulator valve is located in oil pump body. Valve is nonadjustable.

ENGINE OILING SYSTEM

Engine oiling is provided by pressure lubrication through full-flow oil filter which is supplied by gear-type oil pump. Main oil gallery feeds oil through drilled passages to camshaft and crankshaft to lubricate bearings. Valve lifter gallery feeds valve lifters, which feed rocker arms through hollow push rods.

OIL PUMP

Removal & Disassembly

1) Drain oil and remove oil pan. Remove pump-to-rear main cap bolt and remove pump and extension shaft. Remove pump cover attaching screws and pump cover.

2) Remove pressure regulator from pump cover. Mark gears so they may be reassembled with same teeth indexing. Remove idler gear, drive gear, and shaft from pump body.

3) Remove pressure regulator valve retaining pin, pressure regulator valve, washer and spring. Examine pick-up screen and pipe. If screen or pipe are damaged, pump must be replaced as assembly. Screen and pipe assembly are welded to pump body.

Reassembly & Installation

Check operation of oil pump. Check all parts for fit and wear. If pump gears or body are damaged or worn, replacement of entire pump assembly is necessary. Reverse removal and disassembly procedure to assemble and install.

ENGINE COOLING

WATER PUMP

Removal

1) Disconnect negative battery ground cable. Drain cooling system and remove accessory drive belts. Remove fan hub attaching bolts. Remove fan and pulley.

2) Remove bolts attaching upper and lower alternator braces to water pump and swing brace aside. Remove lower radiator hose, heater hose and by-pass hose from water pump. Remove water pump attaching bolts and water pump.

Installation

1) Transfer heater and by-pass hose fittings to new water pump. Clean all gasket mating surfaces. Apply silicone to gasket surfaces. Reverse removal procedure to complete installation.

2) Fill cooling system and start engine. Run engine with radiator cap off until thermostat opens (upper radiator hose gets hot). Top radiator up until coolant level reaches bottom of filler neck with engine idling. Install radiator cap. Ensure arrows line up with overflow tube.

NOTE: **For further information on cooling system capacities and other cooling system components, see appropriate article in ENGINE COOLING SYSTEMS at end of ENGINE section.**

7.4 LITER V8 (Cont.)

ENGINE SPECIFICATIONS

GENERAL SPECIFICATIONS

Year	DISPLACEMENT		Fuel System	HP@RPM	Torque Ft. Lbs.@RPM	Compr. Ratio	BORE		STROKE	
	Cu. In.	Liters					In.	mm	In.	mm
1985	454	7.4	4-Bbl.	230@3800	360@2800	7.9:1	4.30	109.2	4.00	101.6

VALVES

Engine Size & Valve	Head Diam. In. (mm)	Face Angle	Seat Angle	Seat Width In. (mm)	Stem Diameter In. (mm)	Stem Clearance In. (mm)	Valve Lift In. (mm)
7.4L							
Intake	.....	45°	46°	.031-.063 (.787-1.60)	....	[1] .00010-.00027 (.025-.069)	.398 (10.11)
Exhaust	....	45°	46°	.063-.094 (1.60-2.39)	....	[2] .0012-.0029 (.030-.074)	.430 (10.92)

[1] – Wear limit .0037" (.094 mm). [2] – Wear limit .0049" (.125 mm).

PISTONS, PINS, RINGS

Engine	PISTONS	PINS		RINGS		
	Clearance In. (mm)	Piston Fit In. (mm)	Rod Fit In. (mm)	Ring No.	End Gap In. (mm)	Side Clearance In. (mm)
7.4L	[1] .003-.004 (.076-.102)	[2] .00025-.00035 (.006-.009)	[3] .0013-.0021 (.033-.053)	1	[4] .010-.020 (.25-.51)	[5] .0017-.0032 (.043-.081)
				2	[4] .010-.020 (.25-.51)	[5] .0017-.0032 (.043-.081)
				3	[6] .015-.055 (.38-1.40)	[7] .0050-.0065 (.127-.165)

[1] – Wear limit .0050" (.127 mm).
[2] – Wear limit .001" (.03 mm).
[3] – Interference fit.
[4] – Wear limit .030" (.76 mm).
[5] – Wear limit .0042" (.107 mm).
[6] – .065" (1.65 mm).
[7] – .0075" (.191 mm).

CRANKSHAFT MAIN & CONNECTING ROD BEARINGS

Engine	MAIN BEARINGS				CONNECTING ROD BEARINGS		
	Journal Diam. In. (mm)	Clearance In. (mm)	Thrust Bearing	Crankshaft End Play In. (mm)	Journal Diam. In. (mm)	Clearance In. (mm)	Side Play In. (mm)
7.4L	[1] 2.7481-2.7490 (69.80-69.83) [2] 2.7476-2.7486 (69.79-69.81)	[1] .0013-.0025 (.033-.064) [2] .0024-.0040 (.061-.102)	No. 5	.006-.010 (.15-.25)	2.199-2.200 (55.85-55.88)	.0009-.0025 (.023-.064)	.013-.023 (.330-.584)

[1] – Journal No. 1, 2, 3 & 4.
[2] – Journal No. 5.

7.4 LITER V8 (Cont.)

ENGINE SPECIFICATIONS (Cont.)

VALVE SPRINGS

Engine	Free Length In. (mm)	PRESSURE Lbs. @ In. (Kg @ mm)	
		Valve Closed	Valve Open
7.4L	2.12 (53.9)	84-96@1.80 (38-44@45.7)	210-230@1.40 (95-104@35.6)

CAMSHAFT

Engine	Journal Diam. In. (mm)	Clearance In. (mm)	Lobe Lift In. (mm)
7.4L			
Intake	1.9482-1.9492	.....	.2323-.2363
	(49.484-49.510)	.....	(5.90-6.00)
Exhaust	1.9482-1.9492	.....	.2510-.2550
	(49.484-49.510)	.....	(6.38-6.48)

TIGHTENING SPECIFICATIONS

Application	Ft. Lbs. (N.m)
Camshaft Sprocket Bolt	20 (27)
Connecting Rod Cap Nuts	50 (68)
Cylinder Head Bolts	80 (108)
Exhaust Manifold Bolts	20 (27)
Flywheel Bolts	65 (88)
Harmonic Balancer Bolt	85 (115)
Intake Manifold Bolts	30 (41)
Main Bearing Cap Bolts	110 (149)
Oil Pump Bolts	65 (88)
Rocker Arm Stud	50 (68)
Water Pump Bolts	30 (41)

Jeep Engines

2.1 LITER TURBO DIESEL

ENGINE CODING

ENGINE IDENTIFICATION

Engine may be identified from the Vehicle Identification Number (VIN). VIN is located on the dash panel at the base of the windshield. The 4th character identifies the engine and the 10th character establishes the model year. Additionally, an engine identification plate is attached to the right side of the cylinder block.

ENGINE IDENTIFICATION CODE

Application	Code
2.1L Turbo Diesel	F

ENGINE REMOVAL

See ENGINE REMOVAL at end of ENGINE section.

MANIFOLDS & CYLINDER HEAD

INTAKE & EXHAUST MANIFOLDS

Removal

1) Disconnect negative battery cable. Drain cooling system, including engine block. Disconnect turbocharger oil supply and return lines at turbocharger. Remove exhaust manifold-to-turbo attaching bolts and turbo.

2) Disconnect and plug injector lines. Disconnect and plug injection pump lines. Carefully remove fuel lines. Disconnect exhaust pipe at manifold. Remove pre-intake and intake/exhaust manifolds. Clean gasket mating surfaces on cylinder head and block.

Installation

To install, reverse removal procedure.

Fig. 1: Intake & Exhaust Manifold Assembly

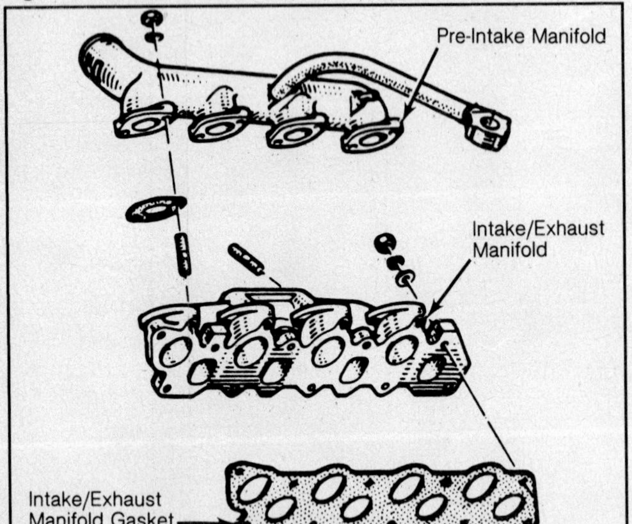

CYLINDER HEAD

Removal

1) Disconnect negative battery cable. Drain cooling system, including engine block. Remove fan belt(s) and accessories. Disconnect turbocharger oil supply and return lines at turbocharger. Remove exhaust manifold-to-turbo attaching bolts and turbo.

2) Remove valve cover. Remove plug from left side of engine block. Rotate crankshaft into position and insert TDC Rod (Mot. 861) into TDC slot in crankshaft counterweight. Ensure that rod is not inserted into crankshaft counterweight balance hole and that crankshaft will not rotate. *See Fig. 2.*

Fig. 2: Installing TDC Rod Into Crankshaft

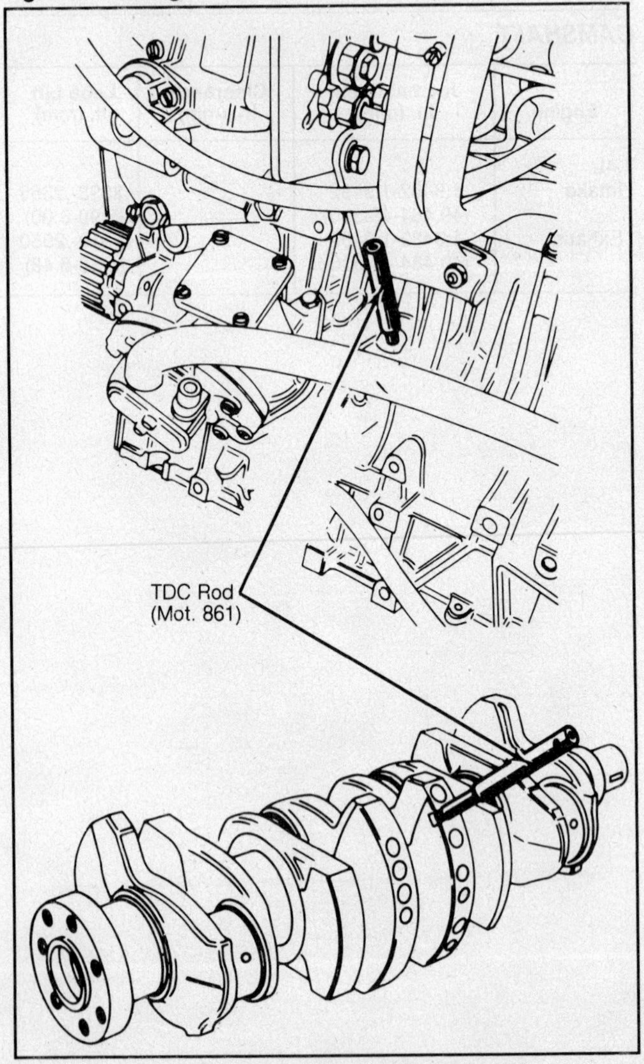

Ensure rod is inserted into TDC slot in crankshaft.

3) Remove fan and pulley. Remove timing belt cover. Install Sprocket Holder (Mot. 854) and remove camshaft sprocket retaining bolt. Remove sprocket holder. Loosen timing belt tensioner bolts and position tensioner away from belt. Tighten tensioner bolts. Remove timing belt.

4) Disconnect and plug injector lines. Disconnect and plug injection pump lines. Carefully remove fuel lines. Remove all hoses from injection pump. Remove injection pump and brackets as an assembly.

5) Loosen and remove cylinder head retaining bolts except pivot bolt. *See Fig. 3.* Loosen pivot bolt, but DO NOT remove at this time. Tap cylinder head with a wood block and hammer to loosen head gasket. Remove pivot bolt from cylinder head.

2.1 LITER TURBO DIESEL (Cont.)

CAUTION: DO NOT lift cylinder head away from block until head gasket is completely loosened from cylinder liners. Damage to cylinder liner seals could result.

Fig. 3: Cylinder Head Pivot Bolt

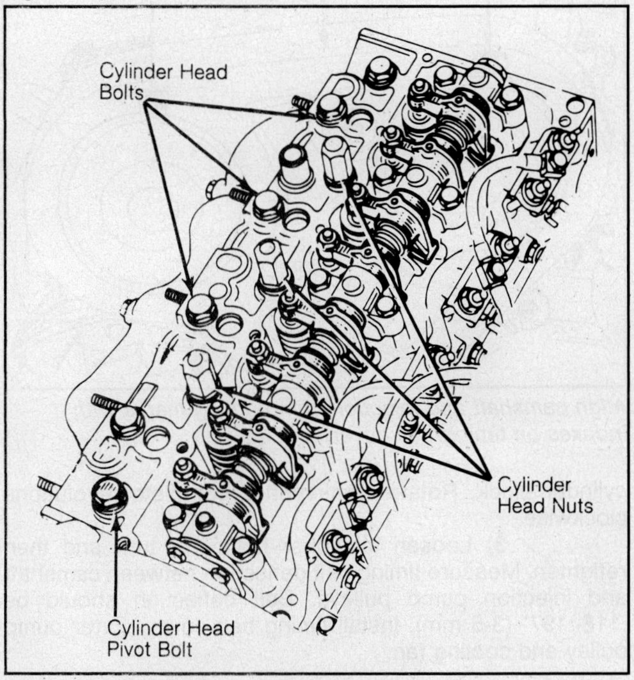

Remove all head bolts except pivot bolt.

6) Remove rocker arm shaft and retaining bolts from head. Remove cylinder head and gasket. Install Cylinder Liner Clamps (Mot. 521-01) on cylinder block. Remove pre-intake and intake/exhaust manifolds from cylinder head.

7) Measure and record valve recess in cylinder head below head gasket surface for all valves. Valve recess should be .031-.045" (.80-1.15 mm).

Installation

NOTE: Check piston protrusion mesurement and select proper thickness head gasket before installing cylinder head. See PISTON PROTRUSION MEASUREMENT section in this article.

1) Install pre-intake and intake/exhaust manifolds. Install head gasket and cylinder head on block. Tighten cylinder head bolts in sequence using the following procedure.

2) Tighten all head bolts to 22 ft.lbs. (30 N.m). Tighten all head bolts to 37 ft. lbs. (50 N.m). Tighten all head bolts to 70-77 ft. lbs. (95-105 N.m). Then retighten all head bolts to 70-77 ft. lbs. (95-105 N.m).

3) Cylinder head bolts must be retightened after engine has reached operating temperature. Run engine for at least 20 minutes. Allow engine to cool for at least 2 1/2 hours.

4) Loosen each head bolt (in sequence) 1/2 turn and retighten bolts to 70-77 ft. lbs. (95-105 N.m). Retighten all bolts (in sequence) to 70-77 ft. lbs. (95-105 N.m).

PISTON PROTRUSION MEASUREMENT

1) Piston protrusion measurement is necessary to determine the thickness of replacement cylinder head gasket if major components (crankshaft, connecting rods or pistons) have been replaced.

2) Rotate crankshaft clockwise 1 revolution and position No. 1 piston near TDC. Place Thrust Plate (Mot. 252-01) on top of piston. Insert Dial Indicator (Mot. LM) in Gauge Block (Mot. 251-01). Tighten screw clamp and place assembly on 1 side of thrust plate. *See Fig. 4.*

Fig. 4: Measuring Piston Protrusion

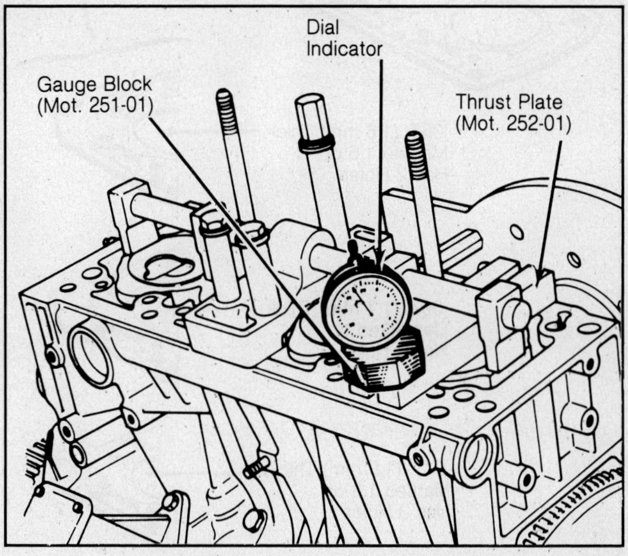

3) Zero dial indicator with pointer located on cylinder block face. Place dial indicator pointer on piston crown. Rotate the crankshaft clockwise until piston is at TDC. Repeat procedure with dial indicator on opposite side of thrust plate.

4) Record dial indicator readings. Calculate the average of the 2 readings. Check piston protrusion for remaining cylinders. Use the reading from the piston with the largest protrusion to determine cylinder head gasket thickness.

5) If the largest average piston protrusion is less than .038" (.96 mm), use .063" (1.6 mm) thick head gasket (marked 1.6 or has 2 holes). If largest protrusion is .038-.041" (.96-1.04 mm), use .067" (1.7 mm) thick head gasket (unmarked or has 1 hole).

6) If largest protrusion is greater than .041" (1.04 mm), use .071" (1.8 mm) thick head gasket (marked 1.8 or has 3 holes). *See Fig. 5.*

PISTON-TO-CYLINDER HEAD CLEARANCE

1) Piston-to-cylinder head clearance must be greater than .023" (.6 mm). Check clearance between valve, when seated, and piston using the following procedure. Rotate crankshaft clockwise until piston being checked is near TDC.

2) Compress valve spring using Valve Spring Compressor (Mot. 382) and remove valve locks and spring. Push down on valve stem and ensure piston is near TDC. Attach Bracket (Rou. 541) to an adjacent rocker shaft bearing pedestal with a bearing hold-down bolt.

3) Attach dial indicator to bracket and align indicator at top of valve stem. With valve resting on piston crown, rotate crankshaft to position piston at TDC. Zero dial indicator. Lift valve up into its seat and observe dial indicator reading.

2.1 LITER TURBO DIESEL (Cont.)

Fig. 5: Cylinder Head Gasket Markings

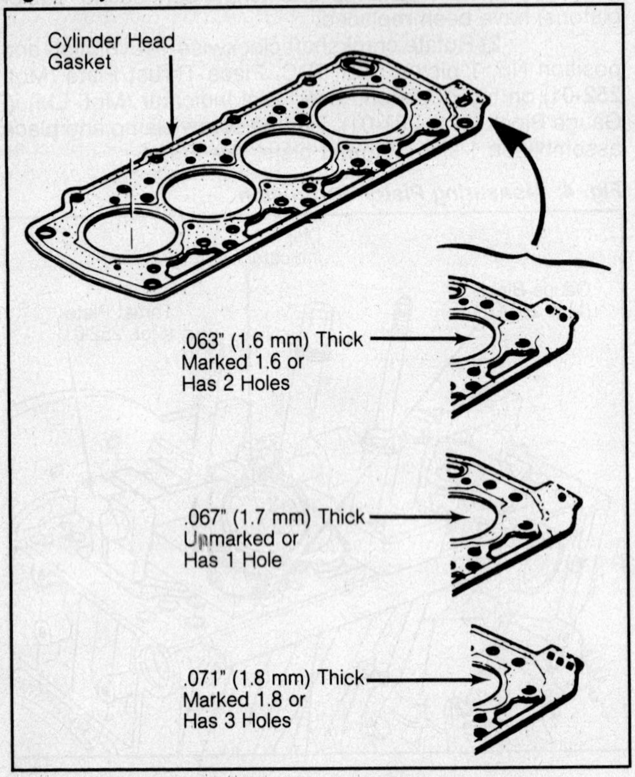

Use appropriate thickness head gasket.

4) Calculate piston-to-cylinder head clearance using the following procedure. Subtract the valve recess dimension from the valve travel distance. Result should be greater than .023" (.6 mm). Reinstall valve spring and retainer. Compress valve spring and install locks.

CAMSHAFT

TIMING BELT

Removal

1) Disconnect negative battery cable. Rotate crankshaft to bring No. 1 piston to TDC on compression stroke. Remove plug on left side of block. Insert TDC Rod (Mot. 861) through hole and into TDC slot in crankshaft counterweight.

2) Ensure crankshaft will not rotate. Remove cooling fan and water pump pulley. Remove timing belt cover. Loosen timing belt tensioner bolts. Position tensioner away from timing belt. Tighten tensioner bolts. Remove timing belt.

Installation

NOTE: There should be 19 teeth between camshaft sprocket and injection pump timing marks.

1) Install timing belt on gears. Temporarily install timing belt cover. Position camshaft and injection pump pulley timing marks at 12 o'clock position. Ensure crankshaft, camshaft and injection pump timing marks are properly aligned. Remove timing belt cover. *See Fig. 6.*

2) Loosen timing belt tensioner bolts 1/2 turn. Allow tensioner to adjust belt tension. Tighten tensioner bolts. Remove TDC Rod (Mot. 861) and install plug in cylinder block. Rotate crankshaft 2 complete revolutions clockwise.

Fig. 6: Aligning Camshaft and Injection Pump Timing Marks

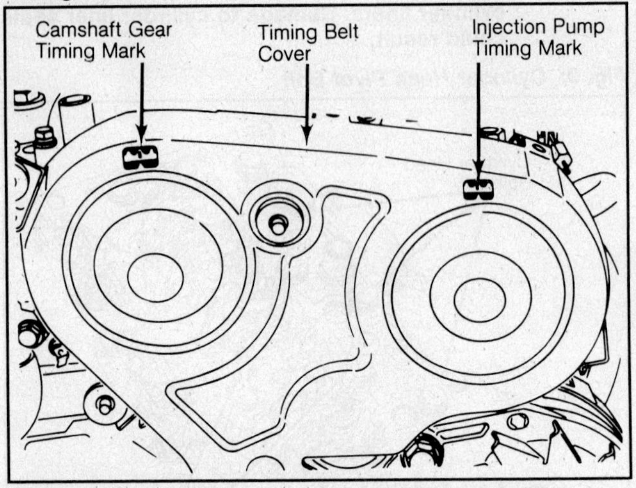

Align camshaft and injection pump timing marks with indexes on timing belt cover.

3) Loosen tensioner bolts 1/2 turn and then retighten. Measure timing belt deflection between camshaft and injection pump pulleys. Belt deflection should be .118-.197" (3-5 mm). Install timing belt cover, water pump pulley and cooling fan.

ROCKER ARM SHAFT ASSEMBLY

Removal & Disassembly

1) Remove rocker arm cover. Remove rocker shaft assembly retaining bolts. Remove rocker shaft assembly. Clean gasket mating surfaces. Remove camshaft thrust thrust plate.

2) Remove rocker shaft end plug and filter. Remove No. 1 rocker shaft bearing. Remove set bolt on No. 5 bearing. Remove springs, rocker arms and remaining rocker shaft bearings. Keep all parts in order for installation in original locations.

Reassembly & Installation

1) Install No. 5 bearing on rocker shaft. Install set bolt in bearing so that rocker shaft oil holes face downward. Install rocker arms, springs and bearings in original positions. Ensure intermediate shaft bearing offset is installed toward rear of engine.

2) Replace rocker shaft oil filter. Tighten rocker arm shaft end nut to 15 ft. lbs. (20 N.m). DO NOT overtighten. Install camshaft thrust plate. Position rocker arm shaft assembly on cylinder head.

3) Ensure camshaft thrust plate is in camshaft groove. Ensure rocker shaft bearing locating dowels are properly positioned. Tighten rocker shaft bearing bolts to specification. Install rocker arm cover.

CAMSHAFT

Removal

1) Remove rocker arm shaft assembly and timing belt as previously described. Install Sprocket Holder (Mot. 854) and remove camshaft sprocket bolt. Remove camshaft sprocket using Puller (B. Vi. 28-01).

2) Remove camshaft oil seal by prying it out gently with a small screwdriver. Remove camshaft.

Installation

1) Install camshaft. Install rocker shaft assembly. Install camshaft oil seal using Seal Installer (Mot. 791-01). Measure camshaft end play. End play should be .002-.006" (.05-.15 mm). Install camshaft sprocket and retaining bolt.

2) Install Camshaft Sprocket Holder (Mot. 855) and tighten camshaft sprocket retaining bolt to 37 ft. lbs. (50 N.m). Rotate camshaft sprocket to align timing mark at 12 o'clock position.

INTERMEDIATE SHAFT

Removal

Remove vacuum pump and oil pump drive gear. Hold intermediate shaft sprocket using Sprocket Holder (Mot. 855) and loosen sprocket retaining bolt. Remove sprocket retaining bolt and sprocket. Remove intermediate shaft cover and clamp. Remove intermediate shaft.

Installation

1) Install intermediate shaft and clamp. Install intermediate shaft gasket and cover. Apply Loctite 242 to cover retaining bolt threads. Loosely install cover retaining bolt and nut.

2) Install intermediate shaft oil seal and align cover using Seal Installer/Aligner (Mot. 790). If intermediate shaft oil seal contact surface is grooved from original seal, insert a .04" (1 mm) washer between seal and installer. This will install the seal further inward on the shaft.

3) Install intermediate shaft sprocket with wider offset toward cylinder block. Hold sprocket and tighten retaining bolt to 37 ft. lbs. (50 N.m). Install oil pump drive gear and vacuum pump.

4) Clearance between intermediate shaft cover and timing belt tensioner must be adjusted to prevent lateral movement of the timing belt when the belt is tightened. Correct clearance is .004" (.1 mm). Adjust clearance by turning adjusting screw. Tighten lock nut. *See Fig. 7.*

Fig. 7: Adjusting Intermediate Shaft Cover-to-Timing Belt Tensioner Clearance

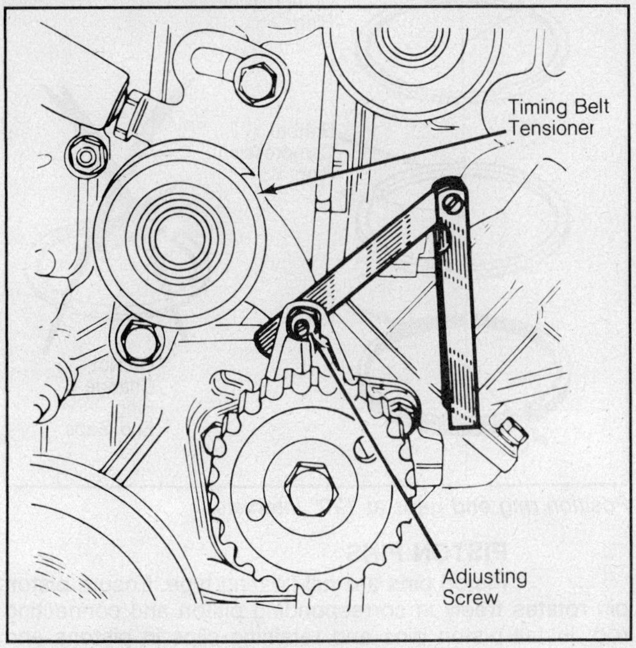

Correct clearance is .004" (.1 mm).

FRONT OIL SEAL

Removal

1) Remove timing belt as previously described. Remove crankshaft pulley retaining bolt, washer and pulley. Position Sprocket Remover (B. Vi. 28-01) and Shaft End Protector (Rou. 15-01) with jaws inserted behind washer.

2) Force washer and sprocket forward until washer stops at Woodruff key. Remove sprocket remover and reposition remover jaws between sprocket and washer. Remove sprocket. Remove Woodruff key and washer. Remove front oil seal from No. 5 main cap.

Installation

Install front oil seal using Seal Installer (Mot. 789). Install washer, Woodruff key and crankshaft sprocket. Ensure washer is installed with chamfered side toward cylinder block. Chamfered edge of sprocket bore faces washer. To complete installation, reverse removal procedure.

VALVES

VALVE ARRANGEMENT

I-E-I-E-I-E-I-E (Front-to-rear).

VALVE SPRINGS AND/OR VALVE STEM OIL SEALS

Removal

1) Remove cylinder head. Remove rocker arm shaft assembly. Remove camshaft. Compress valve springs using Valve Spring Compressor (Mot. 382). Remove valve locks.

2) Remove valve spring compressor. Remove valve spring retainer, spring, washer and oil seal. Remove valves from head.

Installation

Install new valve stem oil seal. Install washer and valve spring. Compress valve spring and install retainer and valve locks. Remove spring compressor. To complete installation, reverse removal procedure.

VALVE SPRING INSTALLED HEIGHT

Using a valve spring tester, place valve spring under a load of 51.7 lbs. (23.5 kg). Spring height should be 1.547" (39.3 mm). Under a load of 134.9 lbs. (61.2 kg), height should be 1.173" (29.8 mm). Spring free length should be 1.779" (45.2 mm).

PRECOMBUSTION CHAMBERS

Removal

1) Remove cylinder head. Remove injectors and holders from head. Mark injectors for reassembly reference. Remove copper washers and heat shields.

2) Plug injector fittings to prevent contamination. Remove precombustion chambers using a drift, inserted through injector bores.

Installation

1) Precombustion chambers are available in 2 sizes. Measure diameter of precombustion chamber bore for proper replacement chamber. Press chambers into cylinder head.

2) Measure chamber protrusions from cylinder head gasket surface using Gauge Block (Mot. 251-01), Thrust Plate (Mot. 252-01) and Dial Indicator (Mot. LM).

Jeep Engines

2.1 LITER TURBO DIESEL (Cont.)

Precombustion chamber protrusion should be .0003-.0015" (.01-.04 mm).

VALVE CLEARANCE ADJUSTMENT

NOTE: **No. 1 cylinder is at rear of engine. Ensure adjusting screw is aligned with valve stem when screw is tightened. Valve stem may be bent if valve stem and adjusting screw are not aligned.**

Rotate crankshaft clockwise until No. 1 cylinder exhaust valve is wide open. Adjust valves as shown in VALVE CLEARANCE ADJUSTMENT table. Intake valve clearance should be .008" (.20 mm). Exhaust valve clearance should be .010" (.25 mm).

VALVE CLEARANCE ADJUSTMENT

Exhaust Valve Open	Adjust Intake	Adjust Exhaust
No. 1	No. 3	No. 4
No. 3	No. 4	No. 2
No. 4	No. 2	No. 1
No. 2	No. 1	No. 3

CYLINDER LINERS, PISTONS, PINS & RINGS

OIL PAN

See OIL PAN REMOVAL at end of ENGINE section.

CYLINDER LINER, PISTON & ROD ASSEMBLY

NOTE: **Each cylinder liner and piston are a matched set. Mark each liner and piston for reassembly reference. If a replacement liner and piston kit is installed, dissolve protective coating with mineral spirits. DO NOT scrape coating from liner or piston.**

Removal

1) Remove cylinder head and oil pan. Remove piston skirt cooling oil jet assembly-to-oil pump pipe and oil pump. Mark connecting rods and caps for reassembly reference. Remove connecting rod bolts, caps and bearings. Remove Cylinder Liner Clamps (Mot. 521-01), if installed.

2) Remove connecting rod, piston and cylinder liner as an assembly. Thoroughly clean cylinder liner-to-block contact surfaces. Remove piston and rod assemblies from liners. Remove "O" ring and plastic ring from each liner.

Installation

1) Install new "O" ring and plastic ring on liner. Install liners in their original positions. Install dial indicator on Gauge Block (Mot. 251-01) and tighten screw clamp. Place Thrust Plate (Mot. 252-01) across each cylinder liner, in turn, and secure tightly with Retainer (Mot. 853).

2) Tighten retainer bolts gradually and alternately to 37 ft. lbs. (50 N.m). This assures each cylinder liner will be in firm contact with block. Measure cylinder liner protrusion. Cylinder liner protrusion should be .0019-.0047" (.05-.12 mm).

3) If cylinder liner protrusion is not within specification, install replacement liner and measure liner protrusion to determine if cylinder block or liner is defective.

4) With all cylinder liner protrusions within specification, arrange them so that the difference in protrusion between any 2 adjacent liners does not exceed .0016" (.04 mm). Arrange cylinder liners so that protrusions are stepped down from No. 1 cylinder to No. 4 cylinder or from No. 4 cylinder to No. 1 cylinder.

5) When correct cylinder liner protrusion arrangement has been obtained, match each piston and rod assembly to its original liner. Re-mark each piston and rod assembly according to its new position in cylinder block.

6) Lubricate pistons, rings and cylinder liners. Install piston and rod assembl'es into their matched cylinder liner. Machined side of connecting rod must be parallel to flat on side of cylinder liner. Cylinder number marks must face intermediate shaft side of block when installed in liner.

NOTE: **Ensure cylinder liners are installed correctly in block, otherwise cut-outs for piston skirt cooling oil jets will not be in correct position.**

FITTING PISTONS

Pistons and cylinder liners are matched set. DO NOT mix piston and cylinder liner sets. If piston or cylinder liner is defective, a new piston and cylinder liner matched set must be installed. Ensure combustion chamber in each piston crown faces toward intermediate shaft side of block.

FITTING RINGS

Piston rings are pre-gapped and existing gaps should not be changed. Position ring gaps on pistons at 120° intervals. *See Fig. 8.*

Fig. 8: Piston Ring Gap Locations

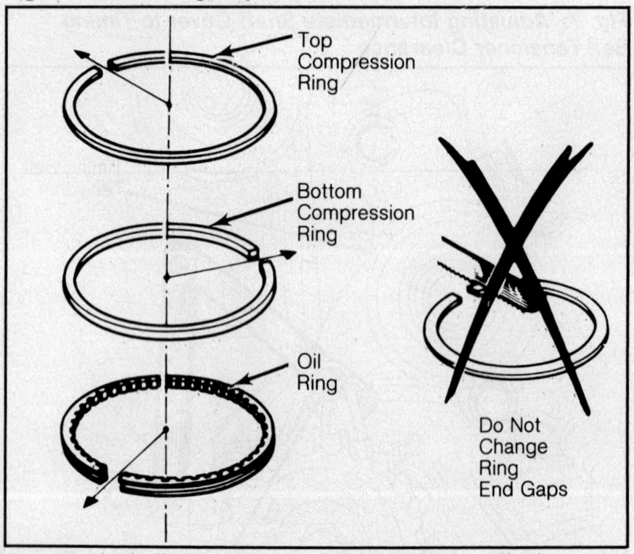

Position ring end gaps at 120° intervals.

PISTON PINS

Piston pins are full-floating type. Ensure piston pin rotates freely in corresponding piston and connecting rod. Install piston pins and retaining clips in pistons and connecting rods.

2.1 LITER TURBO DIESEL (Cont.)

CRANKSHAFT & ROD BEARINGS

CONNECTING ROD BEARINGS

1) Ensure rod caps are marked for cylinder identifcation. Remove rod cap and bearings. Inspect bearings for wear or damage and replace as necessary. Check crankshaft rod bearing journal for out-of-round or taper.

2) Check rod bearing clearance using Plastigage method. If clearance exceeds specifications, crankshaft must be reconditioned or replaced. Clean crankshaft journal and bearing surface in rod.

3) Insert bearings in rod and cap, then lubricate bearing surfaces with oil. Pull piston and rod assembly down onto crankshaft. Install and tighten rod cap.

MAIN BEARINGS

1) Ensure main caps are marked for reassembly reference. Remove main caps. Inspect bearings for wear or damage and replace as necessary. Check main bearing journals for out-of-round or taper.

2) Check main bearing clearance using Plastigage method. If clearance exceeds specifications, crankshaft must be reconditioned or replaced. Clean crankshaft journals and main bearing bores in block. Thoroughly clean sealer from sides of No. 1 and No. 5 main bearing caps.

3) Install bearings in block. Lubricate bearings and install crankshaft. Install main caps. Measure distance between block and sides of No. 1 and No. 5 main bearing caps. If distance is .197" (5 mm) or less, use .201" (5.1 mm) thick side seal.

4) If distance is more than .197" (5 mm), use .212" (5.4 mm) thick side seal. Install side seals in bearing caps with grooves facing out. Each side seal should protrude about .008" (.2 mm) from edge of cap. Lubricate side seals with engine oil.

5) Position a strip of foil on each side of bearing cap and install seal. Remove foil strip. Tighten main cap bolts to 65-72 ft. lbs. (87.5-97.5 N.m).

CRANKSHAFT END PLAY

1) Install dial indicator at rear main bearing so that dial indicator pointer rests against crankshaft flange. Push crankshaft forward and zero dial indicator. Push crankshaft rearward and measure end play.

2) Crankshaft end play should be .001-.005" (.05-.15 mm). If end play is incorrect, remove No. 2 main cap and install new thrust washers.

REAR MAIN BEARING OIL SEAL

1) With engine removed from vehicle, remove rear main bearing oil seal. Clean block and main bearing cap. Install rear main bearing oil seal using Oil Seal Installer (Mot. 788).

2) If rear main bearing oil seal contact surface is grooved from original seal, install a .06" (1.5 mm) thick spacer between installer and replacement oil seal. This will install seal further inward on crankshaft.

ENGINE OILING

CRANKCASE CAPACITY

Crankcase capacity is 5.8 quarts (5.5L) without filter change. Add .5 quart (.5L) when changing oil filter.

NORMAL OIL PRESSURE

Normal oil pressure is 11.6 psi (.8 kg/cm^2) at idle and 43.5 psi (3.1 kg/cm^2) at 3000 RPM.

OIL PRESSURE REGULATOR VALVE

Oil pressure regulator valve is located in oil pump body. Valve is nonadjustable.

ENGINE OILING SYSTEM

Gear-type oil pump delivers full pressure to piston skirt cooling oil jets and to main oil gallery, through full-flow oil filter and oil cooler (when oil temperature exceeds 212°F). Main gallery feeds crankshaft bearings, rocker shaft, camshaft and intermediate shaft bearings and turbocharger.

OIL PUMP

Removal

Remove oil pan. Remove piston skirt cooling oil jet assembly-to-oil pump pipe. Remove oil pump retaining bolts and oil pump. Ensure locating dowels are installed in oil pump. Remove oil pump drive shaft.

Disassembly

Remove pressure relief valve assembly from oil pump housing. Remove oil pump cover. Mark gears for reassembly reference. Remove drive and driven gears.

Reassembly

1) Install gears into housing with assembly marks aligned. Measure oil pump gear-to-housing clearance. Clearance should be .001-.0047" (.05-.12 mm). Measure gear end clearance with a straightedge and feeler gauge.

2) End clearance should be .0007-.0039" (.02-.10 mm). Replace gears that are not within specifications. Install pump cover and pressure relief valve assembly. Prime oil pump.

Installation

Install oil pump. Ensure locating dowels are in place. Tighten retaining bolts to 30-33 ft. lbs. (60-65 N.m). Install piston skirt cooling oil jet assmbly-to-oil pump pipe. Install oil pan. Ensure oil pan is flush with rear edge of block. This will prevent damage to oil pan when transmission is installed.

ENGINE COOLING

WATER PUMP

Removal

Disconnect negative battery cable. Drain cooling system. Remove fan belts. Remove fan and water pump pulley. Remove timing belt cover. Remove heater hose from pump. Retain timing belt tensioner plunger using long strap. Remove water pump, inlet housing and gasket from block. *See Fig. 9.*

Installation

Replace gasket located between water pump body and plate. Attach inlet housing to water pump body. To complete installation, reverse removal procedure.

NOTE: **For further information on cooling system capacities and other cooling system components, see appropriate article in ENGINE COOLING SYSTEMS at end of ENGINE section.**

Jeep Engines

2.1 LITER TURBO DIESEL (Cont.)

Fig. 9: Retaining Timing Belt Tensioner Plunger

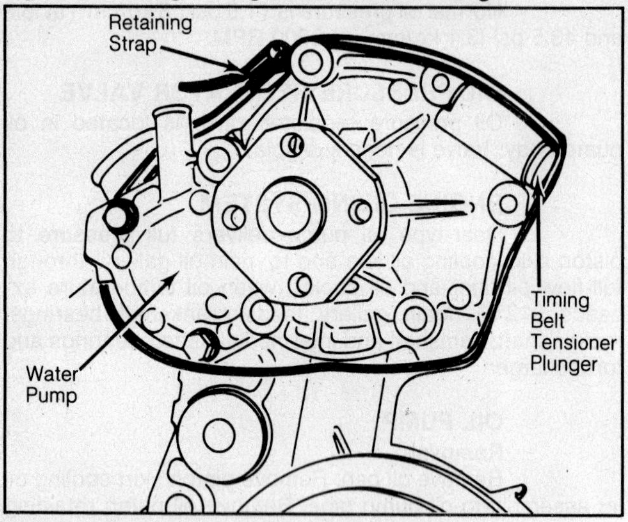

Install retaining strap as shown.

TIGHTENING SPECIFICATIONS

Application	Ft. Lbs. (N.m)
Camshaft Sprocket Bolt	37 (50)
Connecting Rod Bolts	48 (65)
Converter Drive Plate Bolts	52 (70)
Cylinder Head Bolts	
Step 1	22 (30)
Step 2	37 (50)
Step 3	70-77 (95-105)
Step 4	70-77 (95-105)
Flywheel Bolts	44 (60)
Intermediate Shaft Sprocket Bolt	37 (50)
Main Bearing Cap Bolts	69 (92.5)
Oil Jet Tube Assembly	
Lower Bolts	18 (25)
Upper Bolts	7 (10)
Oil Pump Bolts	33 (43)
Rocker Arm Shaft Bolts	20 (27)
Rocker Arm Shaft Plug	15 (20)
Vibration Damper Bolt	96 (130)

ENGINE SPECIFICATIONS

GENERAL SPECIFICATIONS

Year	DISPLACEMENT Cu. In.	DISPLACEMENT Liters	Fuel System	HP@RPM	Torque Ft. Lbs.@RPM	Compr. Ratio	BORE In.	BORE mm	STROKE In.	STROKE mm
1985	126	2.1	Fuel Inj.	85@3750	132@2750	21.5:1	3.385	86	3.503	89

VALVES

Engine Size & Valve	Head Diam. In. (mm)	Face Angle	Seat Angle	Seat Width In. (mm)	Stem Diameter In. (mm)	Stem Clearance In. (mm)	Valve Lift In. (mm)
2.1L							
Intake	1.582 (40.2)	45°	45°	.063-.075 (1.6-1.9)	.314 (8)	.0015-.0050 (.038-.127)	.....
Exhaust	1.307 (33.2)	45°	45°	.063-.075 (1.6-1.9)	.314 (8)	.0015-.0050 (.038-.127)	.....

PISTONS, PINS, RINGS

Engine	PISTONS Clearance In. (mm)	PINS Piston Fit In. (mm)	PINS Rod Fit In. (mm)	RINGS Ring No.	RINGS End Gap In. (mm)	RINGS Side Clearance In. (mm)
2.1L	1	1	Press Fit	No. 1	1	.006 (.15)
				No. 2	1	.006 (.15)
				Oil	1	.006 (.15)

1 – Piston, pin and liner are matched set and clearance is set at factory.

2.1 LITER TURBO DIESEL (Cont.)

ENGINE SPECIFICATIONS (Cont.)

CRANKSHAFT MAIN & CONNECTING ROD BEARINGS

Engine	MAIN BEARINGS				CONNECTING ROD BEARINGS		
	Journal Diam. In. (mm)	Clearance In. (mm)	Thrust Bearing	Crankshaft End Play In. (mm)	Journal Diam. In. (mm)	Clearance In. (mm)	Side Play In. (mm)
2.1L	2.475 (62.88)	.0015-.003 (.038-.076)	No. 2 [1]	.0055-.0090 (.14-.23)	2.216 (56.29)	.0015-.003 (.038-.076)	.012-.019 (.31-.50)

[1] – Crankshaft journals are numbered 1-4, with No. 1 at rear of engine.

VALVE SPRINGS

Engine	Free Length In. (mm)	PRESSURE Lbs. @ In. (Kg @ mm)	
		Valve Closed	Valve Open
2.1L	1.779 (45.2)	51.7@1.547 (23.45@39.3)	134.9@1.173 (61.19@29.8)

Jeep Engines

2.5 LITER 4-CYLINDER

ENGINE CODING

ENGINE IDENTIFICATION

The Vehicle Identification Number (VIN) is located on the upper left side of dash, visible through windshield. The 4th character of the VIN identifies the engine size. The 10th character identifies the model year.

Engine identification code is stamped on a machined surface on right side of cylinder block, between No. 3 and No. 4 cylinders. The letter portion of the code identifies engine displacement, carburetor type, and compression ratio. In addition, engines built for sale in Georgia and Tennessee have a non-repeating number stamped on right side of engine above build date code.

ENGINE REMOVAL

See ENGINE REMOVAL at end of ENGINE section.

ENGINE IDENTIFICATION CODE

Engine	Code
2.5L 1-Bbl.	U

SPECIAL ENGINE MARKS

Some engines are produced at factory with oversize or undersize components. These engines are identified by a letter code stamped on a boss between ignition coil and distributor. Letters are decoded as follows:

- "B" indicates all cylinder bores .010" (.25 mm) oversize.
- "C" indicates all camshaft bearing bores .010" (.25 mm) oversize.
- "M" indicates all main bearing journals .010" (.25 mm) undersize.
- "P" indicates all connecting rod journals .010" (.25 mm) undersize.

MANIFOLDS & CYLINDER HEAD

INTAKE & EXHAUST MANIFOLDS

Removal

1) Disconnect negative battery cable. Remove air cleaner, EGR pipe and PCV hose. Drain cooling system. Disconnect fuel line, vacuum lines and electrical connections.

CAUTION: Disconnect negative battery cable before disconnecting fuel line to prevent possible fire hazard.

2) Disconnect throttle linkage, downshift linkage, and cruise control (if equipped). Remove carburetor and carburetor spacer. Remove bellcrank and throttle linkage brackets and move to one side. Remove heater hoses at intake manifold.

3) Remove A/C compressor, if equipped. Raise vehicle and disconnect exhaust pipe. Remove power steering pump and bracket and set aside. Remove manifold to cylinder head bolts and remove manifolds. Disconnect O_2 sensor lead.

Installation

Clean gasket surfaces on manifolds and cylinder head. Install manifolds and gasket on cylinder head. Start all bolts and finger tighten. Tighten manifold-to-cylinder head bolts in sequence. *See Fig. 1.* Reverse removal procedure to complete installation.

Fig. 1: Intake & Exhaust Manifold Tightening Sequence

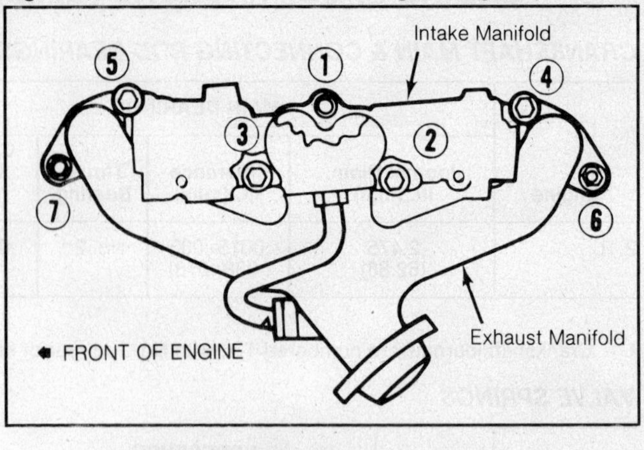

CYLINDER HEAD

Removal

1) Disconnect negative battery cable. Drain cooling system and remove air cleaner. Remove intake and exhaust manifolds as previously outlined.

2) Remove A/C compressor and power steering pump. Disconnect and label all hoses and electrical connections at cylinder head. Disconnect spark plug wires and remove spark plugs. Remove rocker arm cover nuts.

3) Cut RTV sealant with a putty knife or razor blade. Do not pry rocker arm cover up until seal has been completely cut. Alternately loosen cap screws at each bridge and pivot assembly 1 turn at a time.

4) Remove rocker arm assemblies and all push rods. Keep in order for reassembly in original position. Remove cylinder head bolts and remove cylinder head. Place head on 2 blocks of wood to prevent damage to valves.

Installation

1) Ensure gasket surfaces are clean of foreign matter and free of nicks. Clean carbon from combustion chambers and tops of pistons. Apply an even coat of head gasket sealant to both sides of gasket. Install new gasket in position with the word "TOP" up.

2) Carefully install cylinder head and tighten all bolts in sequence (except No. 8) to 85 ft. lbs. (115 N.m). Apply sealing compound to threads of cylinder head bolt No. 8 and tighten to 75 ft. lbs. (102 N.m). *See Fig. 2.*

NOTE: Ensure all cylinder head bolt threads are clean. If the threads are dirty, correct torque cannot be achieved.

Fig. 2: Cylinder Head Tightening Sequence

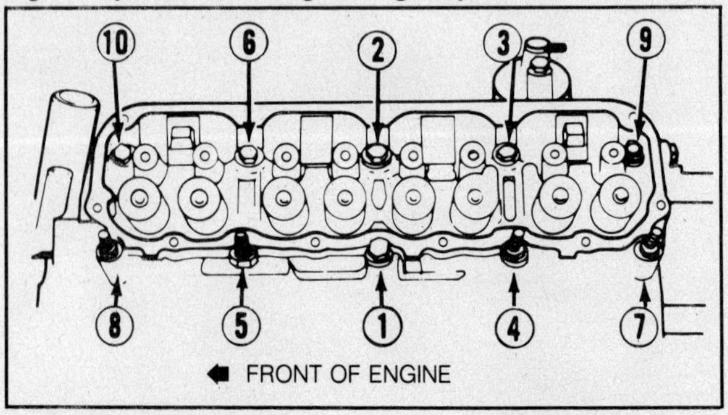

3) Reverse removal procedure for remaining components. When installing rocker arm cover, use RTV sealant between cover and head.

VALVES

VALVE ARRANGEMENT

E-I-I-E-E-I-I-E (Front-to-rear).

VALVE GUIDE SERVICING

Valve guides are an integral part of the cylinder head. If valve guide-to-stem clearance is excessive, guides should be reamed and new oversize valves should be installed.

VALVE STEM OIL SEALS

Cup-type oil seals are used on all valve stems and should be replaced whenever valve spring is removed or valve service is performed.

VALVE SPRINGS

Removal

1) Remove rocker arm cover. Alternately loosen each cap screw 1 turn at a time to avoid damaging bridge. Remove bridge and pivot assembly and spark plug on cylinder to be serviced.

2) Install air hose adapter to spark plug hole and apply a minimum 90 psi (6.33 kg/cm^2) air pressure. Using spring compressor, compress valve spring and remove valve locks. Remove compressor, retainer, cup shield, spring and oil seal.

Installation

To install, reverse removal procedure.

VALVE SPRING INSTALLED HEIGHT

Valve spring installed height is 1.625" (41.3 mm). Test valve spring tension with tester. Springs should be compressed to 1.20" (30.5 mm) without internal damper springs. Proper spring tension is 205-220 lbs. (93-100 kg) at installed height of 1.20" (30.5 mm).

Fig. 3: Exploded View Of Hydraulic Valve Lifter Assembly

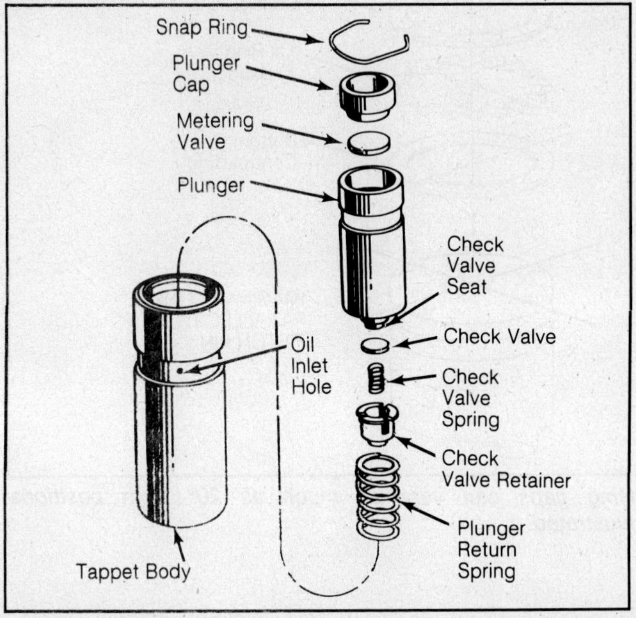

HYDRAULIC VALVE LIFTERS

Valve lifters are serviced as complete units. Parts are not interchangeable between lifters. If lifter shows signs of wear or is noisy, it should be replaced. Check camshaft mating surface for wear. Replace parts as necessary. *See Fig. 3.*

CAMSHAFT

ENGINE FRONT COVER

Removal

1) Disconnect negative battery cable. Loosen belts and remove fan and shroud. Remove alternator and A/C compressor bracket, if equipped. Remove bolts and separate belt pulley from vibration damper. Remove retaining bolt and washer.

2) Remove vibration damper using Puller (J-21719). Remove oil pan-to-timing gear cover and cover-to-engine block screws. Pull cover slightly forward enough to permit cutting of oil pan front seal.

3) Using a sharp knife, cut oil pan front seal flush with cylinder block at both sides of cover. Remove cover and attached portion of oil pan front seal. Remove cover gasket.

Installation

1) Clean mating surfaces of engine block and front cover. Replace front section of oil pan seal removed with similiar section from new seal. Coat seal with gasket sealer and place in position. Apply sealant to joint of oil pan and cylinder block.

2) Install Front Cover Aligner (J-22248) in front cover seal. Install front cover-to-block. Install and partially tighten oil pan-to-front cover screws. Install cover-to-block screws, tighten all screws. Remove front cover aligner. Reverse removal procedure to complete installation.

FRONT COVER OIL SEAL

Removal & Installation

1) Remove oil seal from front cover, using care not to damage front cover. Position new seal with lip toward rear of engine. Drive seal into cover using Installer (J-22248).

2) Lightly coat oil seal contact area of balancer with engine oil. Position balancer on crankshaft and tap it onto the crankshaft until it bottoms. Install center bolt and tighten. Reverse removal procedure to complete installation.

CAMSHAFT & TIMING GEAR

NOTE: **Support camshaft when removing to prevent damaging camshaft bearings.**

Removal

1) Drain cooling system. Remove engine front cover. Disconnect oil cooler lines (if equipped) and remove radiator. If equipped with A/C, remove condenser and compressor.

2) Remove valve tappets. Remove distributor with ignition wires and fuel pump. Pull chain tensioner block toward tensioner lever to compress spring. Hold block and turn tensioner lever to lock (up) position. See *Fig. 4*.

3) Remove camshaft sprocket bolt, oil slinger, camshaft sprockets and timing chain. Remove camshaft by pulling out through front of block.

Jeep Engines

2.5 LITER 4-CYLINDER (Cont.)

Fig. 4: Location of Timing Chain Tensioner Lock

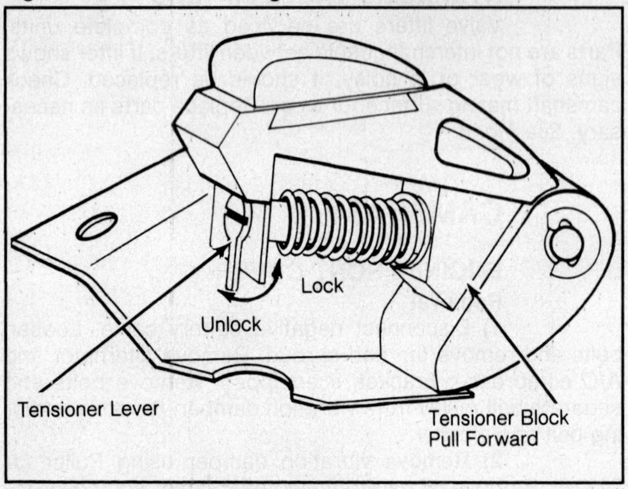

Installation

1) Coat camshaft journals with engine oil and install camshaft in engine block being careful not to damage camshaft bearings. Align timing marks by rotating camshaft and crankshaft until valve timing marks on sprockets line up. *See Fig. 5.*

2) Turn tensioner lever to the unlock (down) position. Ensure tensioner is released before installing timing chain cover. Reverse removal procedure to complete installation.

Fig. 5: Aligning Sprocket Timing Marks

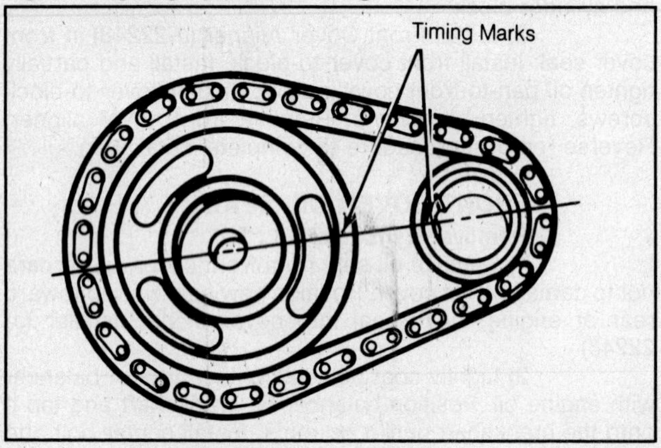

CAMSHAFT BEARINGS

Removal

Engine must be removed to replace camshaft bearings. Remove rear camshaft bearing plug and camshaft. Remove camshaft bearings with a standard bearing remover made for stepped camshaft bearings.

Installation

Ensure oil holes in bearings are aligned with oil galleries in block. Install bearings with a screw-type installer that provides steady pressure. Do not use a driver-type installer. It is not necessary to line-bore bearings after installation.

PISTONS, PINS & RINGS

OIL PAN

See OIL PAN REMOVAL at end of ENGINE section.

PISTON & ROD ASSEMBLY

NOTE: **New pistons must be installed in same cylinders for which they were fitted. Install used pistons in same cylinders from which they were removed.**

Removal

1) With cylinder head and oil pan removed, use a ridge reamer to remove any ridge or deposits from upper end of cylinder bore. Piston should be at bottom of stroke and covered with a cloth to collect cuttings.

2) Check connecting rod and piston for proper identification and mark if necessary. Remove bearing cap and cover rod bolts with rubber hose to prevent damage to crankshaft and cylinder walls. Remove piston and rod assembly through top of cylinder block.

Installation

1) Before installing rings on piston, ensure that correct size rings have been selected by measuring ring gap. Place ring in block at lower end of travel area and ensure that ring is level. Using feeler gauge, measure ring gap.

2) After installing rings on piston, measure ring side clearance, using feeler gauge. Position ring gaps as shown in *Fig. 6*.

3) Install rubber hose on connecting rod bolts. Using piston ring compressor, insert rod and piston assembly into cylinder so that arrows on top of piston face toward front of engine.

4) From beneath engine, position connecting rod with upper bearing insert into place against journal. Remove rubber tubing and install lower bearing insert and cap. Tighten cap nuts. Reverse removal procedure to complete installation.

Fig. 6: Piston Ring Gap Positions

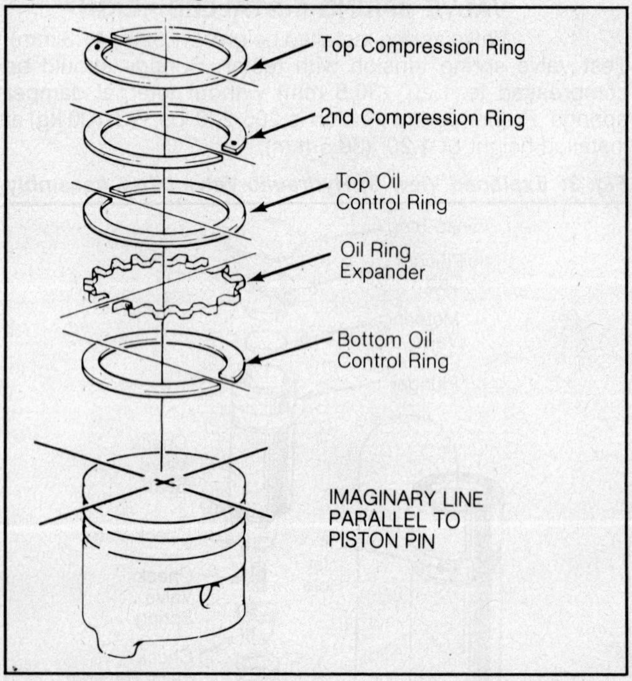

Ring gaps can vary as much as 20° from positions illustrated.

2.5 LITER 4-CYLINDER (Cont.)

NOTE: Arrows on top of piston face front of engine; oil squirt holes in rod face camshaft when installed.

FITTING PISTONS

Measure cylinder bore 2.25" (57.2 mm) from top of bore. Measure piston diameter at a point perpendicular to center of piston pin. Pistons are available in standard, .010" (.25 mm), .020" (.51 mm) and .030" (.76 mm) oversize. Selective fitting of each piston is required. Once proper piston has been selected, mark piston with cylinder number in which it was fitted.

NOTE: Manufacturer recommends using an expanding-type hone to true cylinder bore and remove glaze. Do not use more than 10 strokes per cylinder (1 stroke is 1 down-and-up motion).

PISTON PIN REPLACEMENT

NOTE: Piston and pin must be at standard room temperature when determining if the fit is correct. The pin must gravity-fall from the piston. Never reuse piston pin after it has been installed and removed from a connecting rod.

Removal

Position piston on Support (J-21872-1), with Pin Pilot (J-21872-2) and Driver (J-21872-3) on an arbor press. Apply force to press piston pin completely out of piston.

Installation

1) Insert Pilot (J-21872-2) through piston and connecting rod. Place assembly on Support (J-21872-1). Insert piston pin through the upper piston pin bore and into connecting rod pin bore.

2) Position Driver (J-21782-3) inside pin. Using arbor press, press pin through connecting rod and piston bores until pilot indexes with mark on support. Remove piston and connecting rod. Pin should be centered in rod ± .0312" (.792 mm).

NOTE: Piston pin installation requires a 2000 lb. (906 kg) press fit. If little effort is required to install in connecting rod, it must be replaced.

CRANKSHAFT & ROD BEARINGS

NOTE: All bearings are select fit to their respective journal to obtain specified operating clearance between bearing and journal. In production, select fit is obtained by using multiple sized, color-coded bearing inserts. The color codes are on the edge of bearing insert.

CONNECTING ROD BEARINGS

1) Remove oil pan and oil pump. Turn crankshaft and rod to be serviced to bottom of stroke. Remove bearing cap and lower shell.

2) Push piston and rod assembly up far enough to remove upper bearing shell. Check clearances using Plastigage method and replace bearings as necessary. Bearings are available in standard, .001" (.025 mm), .002" (.051 mm) and .010" (.25 mm) undersize.

3) Rod journal is identified during production by a paint mark on the adjacent counterweight toward the flanged end (rear) of the crankshaft.

NOTE: Never use a pair of bearing inserts with more than a .001" difference in size. All odd size bearing inserts must be on bottom (rod cap) side.

4) Rotate crankshaft after installation of new bearing to ensure crankshaft is not binding. Reverse removal procedure to complete assembly.

MAIN BEARINGS

NOTE: When removing crankshaft on engine equipped with automatic transmission, mark torque converter and converter drive plate before removal for installation reference. Install in same position. When replacing crankshaft components, note that service replacement dampers, crankshafts, flywheels, torque converters and clutch components are balanced individually and may be replaced without balancing complete assembly.

1) When required, upper and lower bearing inserts of different sizes may be used as a pair. Do not use a new bearing with an old bearing.

2) Remove oil pan, oil pump and spark plugs. Remove cap on bearing requiring replacement and remove lower bearing insert from cap. Rotate crankshaft so that upper bearing insert will rotate in the direction of its locking tab. This will roll upper bearing insert out of block.

3) Check clearances using Plastigage method and replace bearings as necessary. Bearings are available in standard, .001" (.025 mm), .002" (.051 mm) and .010" (.25 mm) undersize.

4) Main bearing journal size is identified in production by a paint mark on the adjacent journal toward the flanged end (rear) of the crankshaft, except the rear main journal. This mark is on the crankshaft rear flange.

NOTE: If different sized bearing inserts are fitted to the journal, the odd size inserts must all be on top (cylinder block) or bottom (main bearing cap). Never use a pair of bearing inserts with more than a .001" difference in size.

5) With new bearings lightly oiled and installed, rotate crankshaft to check for excessive drag. When reinstalling rear bearing cap. Apply a thin bead of Loctite 515 or equivalent, to 1/2 of each cap-to-block mating surface.

CRANKSHAFT END PLAY

1) Using a feeler gauge, measure crankshaft end play at front end of thrust bearing. Number 2 bearing is thrust bearing. If not within specifications, replace thrust bearing.

2) When replacing thrust bearing, pry crankshaft fore and aft to align faces of thrust bearing before final tightening.

REAR MAIN BEARING OIL SEAL

NOTE: Main bearing oil seal is a one-piece unit that can be removed and replaced without removal of oil pan or crankshaft.

2.5 LITER 4-CYLINDER (Cont.)

Removal

Remove transmission, clutch housing and flywheel, or converter drive plate. Remove rear main bearing oil seal by prying it out with a screwdriver, taking care not to scratch crankshaft.

Installation

1) With lip of seal facing toward front of engine, center seal over end of crankshaft. With soft hammer, tap seal into groove until it seats.

2) Take care to prevent seal from binding on crankshaft and not seating properly. Install converter drive plate or flywheel, clutch assembly, clutch housing and transmission.

ENGINE OILING

CRANKCASE CAPACITY

Crankcase capacity is 5 quarts (4.7 L) with oil filter change.

NORMAL OIL PRESSURE

Normal oil pressure should be 37-75 psi (2.6-5.3 kg/cm²) at 2000 RPM.

OIL PRESSURE REGULATOR VALVE

Oil pressure regulator valve is located in oil pump body. Valve is nonadjustable.

ENGINE OILING SYSTEM

Engine lubrication is accomplished through a gear-type pump which picks up oil from oil pan sump. Oil is pumped through full-flow oil filter and into an oil passage which runs along right side of block and intersects lifter bores. Oil is then routed to camshaft and crankshaft bearings through smaller drilled passages.

Oil is supplied to rocker arms through hydraulic lifters which feed oil up push rod tubes to rocker arms. By-pass valves are located in oil filter mounting and oil pump to allow for any clogged or restricted conditions.

Many internal parts have no direct oil feed and rely on gravity or splash oiling from other direct feed components. Oil returns to oil sump through oil return holes in cylinder head and block.

OIL PUMP

NOTE: **Oil pump is located in oil sump. Oil pan must be removed for access. See OIL PAN REMOVAL at end of ENGINE section.**

Removal

Remove 2 bolts and remove pump and screen as an assembly. Do not disturb oil pick-up pipe on screen or body.

NOTE: **If oil pump pick-up is moved in pump body, a new replacement tube and strainer must be installed to maintain an airtight seal.**

Installation

Disassemble pump and inspect for wear or damage. Check gear end clearance with feeler gauge. Clearance should be .002-.004" (.05-.10 mm). *See Fig. 7.* Check gear-to-body clearance with feeler gauge. Clearance should be between .004-.008" (.10-.20 mm). Replace pump as a unit if parts are defective. *See Fig. 8.*

Fig. 7: Checking Oil Pump End Clearance with Feeler Gauge

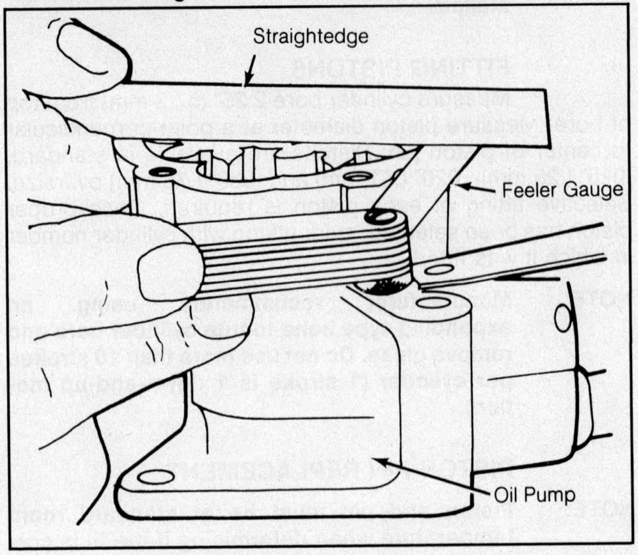

Fig. 8: Exploded View of Engine Oil Pump Assembly

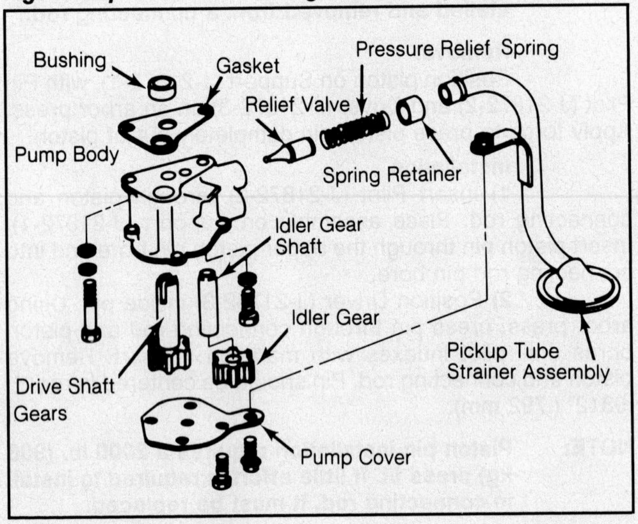

ENGINE COOLING

WATER PUMP

Removal

1) Drain cooling system. Disconnect fan shroud from radiator. Remove drive belts. Remove fan retaining bolts and remove shroud, fan pulley and fan assembly.

2) Disconnect lower radiator hose at water pump. Disconnect heater hoses from water pump. Remove water pump retaining bolts and remove water pump.

Installation

Clean all gasket surfaces. Drive belts must be positioned on fan pulley when fan assembly and pulley are installed. To complete installation, reverse removal procedure. Check for leaks.

NOTE: **For further information on cooling system capacities and other cooling system components, see appropriate article in ENGINE COOLING SYSTEMS at end of ENGINE section.**

Jeep Engines

2.5 LITER 4-CYLINDER (Cont.)

ENGINE SPECIFICATIONS

GENERAL SPECIFICATIONS

Year	DISPLACEMENT		Fuel System	HP@RPM	Torque Ft. Lbs.@RPM	Compr. Ratio	BORE		STROKE	
	Cu. In.	Liters					In.	mm	In.	mm
1985	150	2.5	1-Bbl.	.....	.....	9.2:1	3.88	98.5	3.19	81.0

VALVES

Engine Size & Valve	Head Diam. In. (mm)	Face Angle	Seat Angle	Seat Width In. (mm)	Stem Diameter In. (mm)	Stem Clearance In. (mm)	Valve Lift In. (mm)
2.5L							
Int.	1.91 (48.4)	44°	44.5°	.040-.060 (1.02-1.52)	.311-.312 (7.89-7.98)	.001-.003 (.02-.07)	.424 (10.7)
Exh.	1.50 (38.0)	44°	44.5°	.040-.060 (1.02-1.52)	.311-.312 (7.89-7.98)	.001-.003 (.02-.07)	.424 (10.7)

PISTONS, PINS, RINGS

Engine	PISTONS	PINS		RINGS		
	Clearance In. (mm)	Piston Fit In. (mm)	Rod Fit In. (mm)	Ring No.	End Gap In. (mm)	Side Clearance In. (mm)
2.5L	.0012-.0013 (.030-.033)	.0003-.0005 (.008-.013)	Press Fit	1	.010-.020 (.25-.51)	.0017-.003 (.043-.08)
				2	.010-.020 (.25-.51)	.0017-.003 (.043-.08)
				3	.010-.025 (.25-.64)	.001-.008 (.03-.20)

CRANKSHAFT MAIN & CONNECTING ROD BEARINGS

Engine	MAIN BEARINGS				CONNECTING ROD BEARINGS		
	Journal Diam. In. (mm)	Clearance In. (mm)	Thrust Bearing	Crankshaft End Play In. (mm)	Journal Diam. In. (mm)	Clearance In. (mm)	Side Play In. (mm)
2.5L	2.4996 (63.489)	.001-.0025 (.03-.06)	No. 5	.0015-.0065 (.038-.165)	2.0934 (53.17)	.00015-.002 (.044-.05)	.017 (.35)

VALVE SPRINGS

Engine	Free Length In. (mm)	PRESSURE Lbs. @ In. (Kg @ mm)	
		Valve Closed	Valve Open
2.5L	1.82 (46.2)	66-74@1.63 (30-34@41.4)	200-220@1.20 (91-100@30.5)

CAMSHAFT

Engine	Journal Diam. In. (mm)	Clearance In. (mm)	Lobe Lift In. (mm)
2.5L			
No. 1	2.029 (51.54)	.0001-.0003 (.025-.076)	.265 (6.73)
No. 2	2.019 (51.28)		
No. 3	2.009 (51.03)		
No. 4	2.000 (50.80)		

TIGHTENING SPECIFICATIONS

Application	Ft. Lbs. (N.m)
Camshaft Sprocket Bolts	80 (108)
Connecting Rod Cap Nuts	33 (45)
Cylinder Head Bolts	85 (115)
Exhaust Manifold Bolts & Nuts	23 (31)
Flywheel-to-Crankshaft Bolts	[1] 50 (68)
Intake Manifold Bolts	23 (31)
Main Bearing Cap Bolts	80 (108)
Oil Pump Attaching Bolts	
Short	10 (14)
Long	17 (23)
Rocker Arm Bolts	19 (26)
Vibration Damper Bolt	[2] 80 (108)
Water Pump Bolts	13 (18)

[1] – Tighten an additional 60° turn after torque value is reached.

[2] – With bolt cleaned and threads lubricated with oil.

4.2 LITER 6-CYLINDER

ENGINE CODING

ENGINE IDENTIFICATION

Vehicle Identification Number (VIN) is located on top left side of dash, visible through windshield. The 4th character identifies engine size and the 10th character identifies the model year.

Engine identification code is stamped on a machined surface on right side of cylinder block, between No. 2 and No. 3 cylinders. The letter portion of the code identifies engine displacement, carburetor type and compression ratio.

ENGINE IDENTIFICATION CODE

Engine	Code
4.2L 2-Bbl.	C

ENGINE REMOVAL

See ENGINE REMOVAL at end of ENGINE section.

SPECIAL ENGINE MARKS

Some engines are produced at factory with oversize or undersize components. These engines are identified by a letter code stamped on a boss between ignition coil and distributor. Letters are decoded as follows:

- "B" indicates all cylinder bores .010" (.25 mm) oversize.
- "C" indicates all camshaft bearing bores .010" (.25 mm) oversize.
- "M" indicates all main bearing journals .010" (.25 mm) undersize.
- "P" indicates all connecting rod journals .010" (.25 mm) undersize.

MANIFOLDS & CYLINDER HEAD

INTAKE & EXHAUST MANIFOLDS

Removal

1) Remove air cleaner. Disconnect fuel line at carburetor. Label and disconnect all vacuum hoses, ventilation hoses and electrical connectors at carburetor.

2) Disconnect throttle cable at bellcrank. If equipped, disconnect throttle valve rod. Disconnect PCV hose and heater wire from manifold. Drain radiator and disconnect coolant hoses from intake manifold.

3) Disconnect vacuum hoses from ported vacuum switch (CTO valve) and EGR valve. Disconnect EGR tube fittings from intake and exhaust manifolds. Disconnect vacuum hose at diverter valve.

4) Disconnect air injection hoses at air pump and air injection manifold check valve, and remove with diverter valve attached. Remove air pump. If equipped, remove power steering pump (with hoses attached) and position aside.

5) If A/C equipped, remove drive belt idler pulley. Disconnect exhaust pipe from manifold. Remove oxygen sensor, if equipped. Remove manifolds.

Installation

1) Clean mating surfaces of manifolds and cylinder head. Position exhaust manifold to cylinder head and install alignment sleeves over end studs. Exhaust manifold does not use a manifold-to-cylinder head gasket. Tighten bolts1 and 2, then remove alignment sleeves.

Fig. 1: Intake & Exhaust Manifold Tightening Sequence

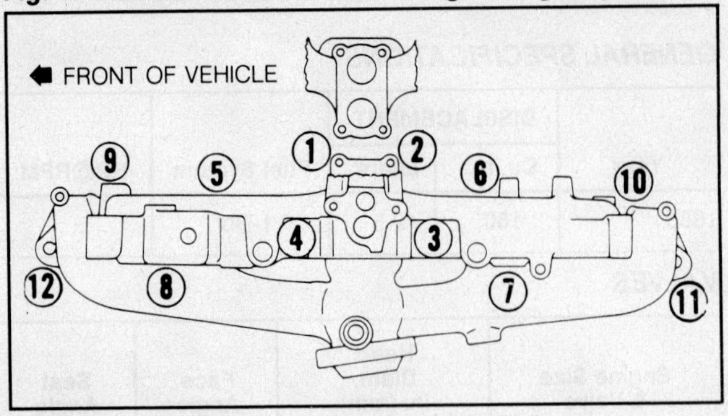

Tighten manifold bolts to 23 ft. lbs. (31 N.m).

2) Loosely connect EGR tube to intake manifold. Install intake manifold gasket and intake manifold. Loosely connect EGR tube to exhaust manifold. Tighten intake manifold bolts 3 and 4. Install remaining nuts and bolts. Tighten manifold bolts in sequence. *See Fig. 1.*

3) Tighten EGR tube fittings. Install remaining components in reverse order of removal. Start engine and inspect for coolant and vacuum leaks.

CYLINDER HEAD

NOTE: Rocker arm cover is made of molded plastic. Use care when removing and installing to prevent damage to cover.

Removal

1) Drain cooling system and disconnect radiator hose at thermostat housing. Remove air cleaner and rocker arm cover. Remove rocker arm bolts, loosening bolts 1 turn at a time. Remove bridge and pivot assembly.

2) Remove rocker arms and push rods in order, for reinstallation in original locations. Disconnect power steering pump (if equipped), air pump and brackets, and position aside.

3) Remove intake and exhaust manifold assembly from cylinder head. If A/C equipped, remove drive belt idler bracket from cylinder head. Remove alternator bracket-to-head mounting bolt. Remove A/C compressor from mounting bracket and position aside.

4) Remove spark plugs and disconnect temperature sending unit wire. Disconnect negative battery cable. Remove ignition coil and bracket. Remove cylinder head and discard gasket.

Installation

Clean all gasket mating surfaces. Apply an even coat of sealing compound to both sides of cylinder head gasket, and position on block with word "TOP" facing up. Install and tighten cylinder head. *See Fig. 2.* Reverse removal procedure to complete installation.

Fig. 2: Cylinder Head Tightening Sequence

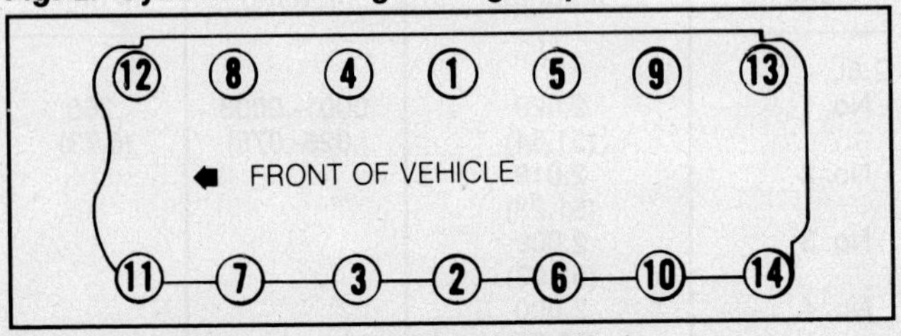

Tighten head bolts to 85 ft. lbs. (115 N.m).

4.2 LITER 6-CYLINDER (Cont.)

VALVES

VALVE ARRANGEMENT

E-I-I-E-I-E-E-I-E-I-I-E (Front-to-rear).

ROCKER ARM ASSEMBLY

Both intake and exhaust rocker arms for each cylinder pivot on a bridge and pivot assembly. *See Fig. 3.* The bridge and pivot assembly maintains correct rocker arm-to-valve tip alignment. When removing rocker arm assemblies, always keep parts in order for reinstallation in original locations.

Fig. 3: Rocker Arm Assembly

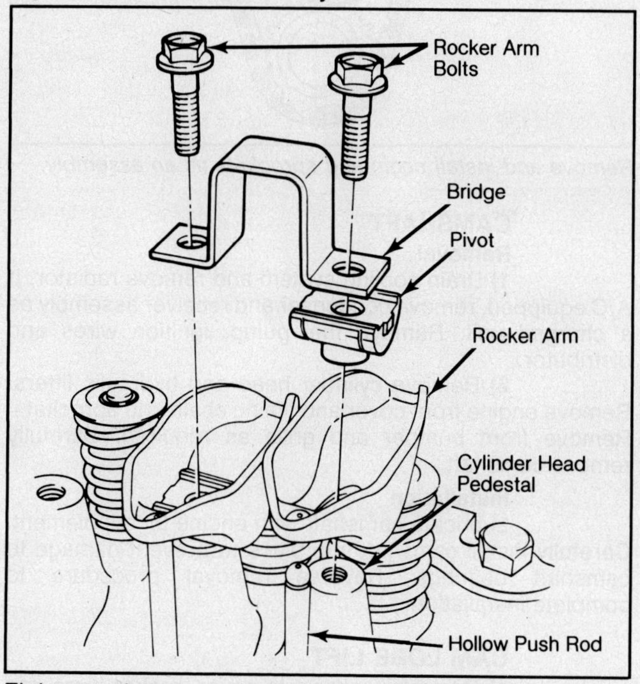

Tighten rocker arm bolts to 19 ft. lbs. (26 N.m).

VALVE SPRINGS

Although normal service is performed with cylinder head removed, it is possible to replace seals, locks, retainers or broken springs with cylinder head installed.

NOTE: On A/C equipped vehicles, a flexible air hose adapter must be used when servicing No. 1 cylinder.

Removal

1) Remove rocker arm cover. Remove bridge and pivot assemblies, rocker arm and push rod of valve to be serviced. Remove spark plug and install 14 mm (thread size) air adapter in spark plug hole.

2) Connect an air hose and maintain a constant pressure of at least 90 psi (6.3 kg/cm²). Using Valve Spring Compressor (J-2534-1), compress valve spring and remove locks. Remove valve spring retainer, valve spring and oil seal.

Inspection

Using valve spring tester, check valve springs for proper tension. Measure free length of valve springs. Replace springs that are not within specification.

Installation

1) Use a 7/16" deep-well socket and light hammer to gently tap valve stem seal into place on valve stem. Ensure sharp edges of valve lock groove do not damage oil seal during installation. Install valve spring and retainer. Compress spring with valve spring compressor, and install locks.

2) Tap each valve spring from side-to-side to ensure spring is seated properly. Turn off air supply and remove air hose and adapter. Install remaining components in reverse order of removal.

VALVE STEM OIL SEALS

Nylon valve stem oil seals are used on all valves to keep engine oil from entering combustion chambers through valve guides. Replace oil seals if deteriorated, or when valve service is performed. Replacement seals are available for valves with oversize stems

VALVE GUIDE SERVICING

1) Valve guides are integral with cylinder head and are not replaceable. Replacement valves are available in .003" (.08 mm), .015" (.13 mm) and .030" (.76 mm) oversize stems.

2) To check stem-to-guide clearance, clean valve guide bore with solvent and a rifle brush. Use a ball gauge and micrometer to measure guide wear. Take measurements of guide crosswise and lengthwise to head, inserting ball gauge 3/8" into guide bore from top of head.

3) If either measurement exceeds .003" (.08 mm), ream valve guide for installation of valve with oversize stem. Always ream valve guides in progressive steps, using reamers in sequence to obtain desired size.

HYDRAULIC VALVE LIFTERS

1) Service lifters as complete assemblies only. Parts are not interchangeable between lifters. Inspect lifter body for signs of scuffing. Inspect base of lifter for concave wear. If concave wear is present, replacement of camshaft and lifters is necessary.

2) Disassemble and clean lifters, then reassemble. *See Fig. 4.* Using lifter leak-down rate tester and lifter test fluid, test lifter leak-down rate.

3) Compress lifter plunger and record time required for tester needle to align with .125" mark on scale. Leak-down rate should be 20-110 seconds.

4) Replace lifters that fail test. Do not prime lifters with engine oil prior to installation. Lifters will fill with oil within 3-8 minutes of engine operation.

Fig. 4: Hydraulic Lifter Assembly

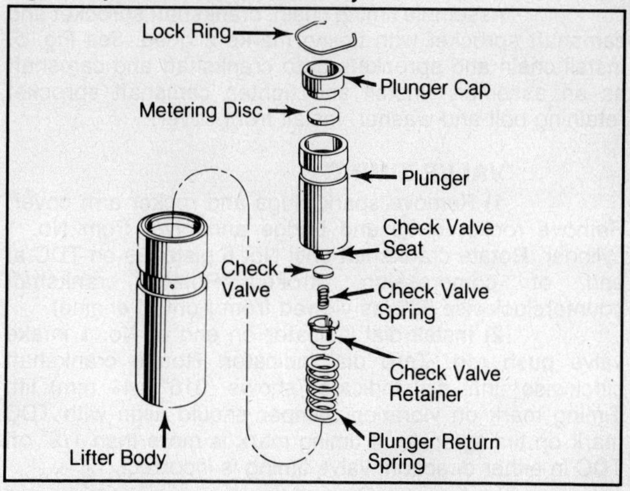

Do not interchange parts between lifters.

4.2 LITER 6-CYLINDER (Cont.)

CAMSHAFT

ENGINE FRONT COVER

Removal

1) Remove drive belt(s), fan and spacer from water pump. Remove crankshaft pulley and vibration damper. Remove oil pan-to-cover bolts and front cover-to-cylinder block bolts. Remove front cover and gasket.

2) Cut oil pan gasket end tabs flush with front face of cylinder block and remove tabs. Clean all gasket mating surfaces.

Installation

1) Apply gasket sealer to both sides of new front cover gasket and fit gasket to block. Cut end tabs from new oil pan gasket and fit onto oil pan. Cement these pieces to oil pan.

2) Install oil pan seal on lower end of front cover. Heavily coat end tabs of oil pan seal with non-hardening sealing compound.

3) Position front cover to engine. Place Front Cover Aligner (J-22248) into front cover. Install cover attaching bolts. Tighten all bolts and remove aligner. Reverse removal procedure to complete installation.

FRONT COVER OIL SEAL

Removal

Remove drive belt(s). Remove crankshaft pulley and vibration damper. Use Seal Remover (J-9256) to remove oil seal.

Installation

1) Position new oil seal onto Seal Installer (J-22248), with seal lip facing outward. Apply light coat of sealer to outside diameter of seal case.

2) Install Draw Screw (J-9163) into seal installer. Tighten nut on draw screw assembly to press seal into cover until it bottoms. Apply light film of engine oil to seal lip and install remaining components in reverse order of removal.

TIMING CHAIN & SPROCKETS

Removal

Remove engine front cover. Rotate crankshaft to align timing marks on camshaft and crankshaft sprockets. Remove camshaft and crankshaft sprockets and timing chain as an assembly.

Installation

Assemble timing chain, crankshaft sprocket and camshaft sprocket with timing marks aligned. *See Fig. 5.* Install chain and sprockets onto crankshaft and camshaft as an assembly. Install and tighten camshaft sprocket retaining bolt and washer. Install front cover.

VALVE TIMING

1) Remove spark plugs and rocker arm cover. Remove rocker arms and bridge and pivot from No. 1 cylinder. Rotate crankshaft until No. 6 piston is on TDC at end of compression stroke. Rotate crankshaft counterclockwise 90° (as viewed from front of engine).

2) Install dial indicator on end of No. 1 intake valve push rod. Zero dial indicator. Rotate crankshaft clockwise until dial indicator shows .016" (.41 mm) lift. Timing mark on vibration damper should align with TDC mark on timing scale. If timing mark is more than 1/2" off TDC in either direction, valve timing is incorrect.

Fig. 5: Timing Chain Sprocket Alignment

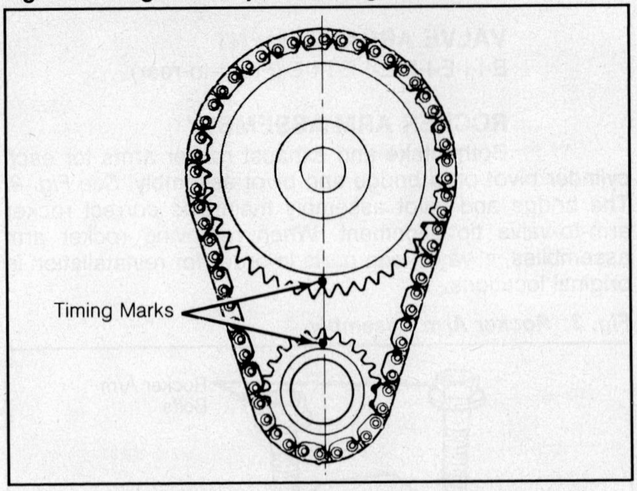

Remove and install chain and sprockets as an assembly.

CAMSHAFT

Removal

1) Drain cooling system and remove radiator. If A/C equipped, remove condenser and receiver assembly as a charged unit. Remove fuel pump, ignition wires and distributor.

2) Remove cylinder head and hydraulic lifters. Remove engine front cover and timing chain and sprockets. Remove front bumper and grille as required. Carefully remove camshaft.

Installation

Lubricate camshaft with engine oil supplement. Carefully install camshaft into place to prevent damage to camshaft bearings. Reverse removal procedure to complete installation.

CAM LOBE LIFT

1) Remove rocker arm cover, rocker arms and bridge and pivot assembly. Remove spark plugs.

2) Using mounting fixture, attach dial indicator to cylinder head so indicator point rests on top of push rod. Dial indicator point must be in same plane as push rod vertical movement.

3) Rotate crankshaft slowly until valve lifter is on base circle of cam lobe. In this position, push rod will be at its lowest point. Zero dial indicator.

4) Rotate engine until push rod is in fully raised position and record reading. Compare recorded lobe lift with specifications. If less than specifications, replace camshaft. Check remaining cam lobes in same manner.

CAMSHAFT BEARINGS

Remove engine from vehicle to install camshaft bearings. To provide steady pressure when installing bearings, use a screw-type camshaft bearing installer. Do not use a driver-type bearing installer. Ensure oil holes in bearings are aligned with oil holes in block.

PISTONS, RINGS & PINS

OIL PAN

See OIL PAN REMOVAL at end of ENGINE section.

4.2 LITER 6-CYLINDER (Cont.)

PISTON & ROD ASSEMBLY

Removal

1) Remove cylinder head and oil pan. Position piston at bottom of stroke and cover with a cloth to collect metal cuttings. Using a ridge reamer, remove any ridge or deposits on upper end of cylinder bore.

2) If necessary, mark connecting rods and caps for cylinder identification. Remove connecting rod bearing cap and bearings.

3) Install pieces of rubber hose over connecting rod bolts to protect cylinder walls and crankshaft. Push piston and rod assembly out top of cylinder block and install rod cap on mating rod.

Installation

1) Lightly coat pistons, rings, and cylinder walls with engine oil. Properly position rings on piston. *See Fig. 6*. Using ring compressor, compress rings on piston. Ensure position of rings does not change.

2) Install upper bearing into rod, and cover rod bolts with protective rubber hose. Position piston in bore with arrow on piston head pointing toward front of engine.

3) Install piston and rod assembly into its respective bore, while guiding connecting rod onto crankshaft journal. Install and tighten rod cap.

FITTING PISTONS

1) Measure each cylinder bore with an inside micrometer, approximately 2 5/16" below top of cylinder bore. Using a micrometer, measure piston 90° to piston pin at centerline of pin. Difference between 2 measurements is piston-to-cylinder bore clearance.

2) Using bore gauge or inside micrometer, measure cylinder bore 90° to crankshaft at top of bore, and also at bottom of bore. Taper is the difference between the 2 measurements.

3) Turn bore gauge or inside micrometer 120° and measure at top and bottom of bore. Turn gauge or micrometer another 120° and repeat measurement. Difference between the 2 measurements is out-of-round.

4) If out-of-round or taper exceed .001" (.025 mm), bore and hone cylinder for installation of oversize piston.

FITTING RINGS

1) Measure ring side clearance with feeler gauge fitted between ring land and ring. Rotate ring in groove around entire circumference of piston. Ring must not bind in groove.

2) Push ring down into bore, near bottom of ring travel. Ring must be square in bore. Measure ring end gap with feeler gauge.

3) Install rings on piston with markings (indicating top of ring) pointing up. *See Fig. 6*. Install upper and lower rings with gaps positioned 180° apart.

PISTON PIN REPLACEMENT

Removal

Using piston pin remover/installer and an arbor press, press piston pin out of piston and rod assembly. Discard piston pin.

Inspection

To check replacement piston pin for fit, position piston so pin bore is in a vertical position. At room temperature, replacement pin should slide completely through pin bore without using force. If pin jams in bore, replace piston.

Fig. 6: Ring Gap Positions & Markings

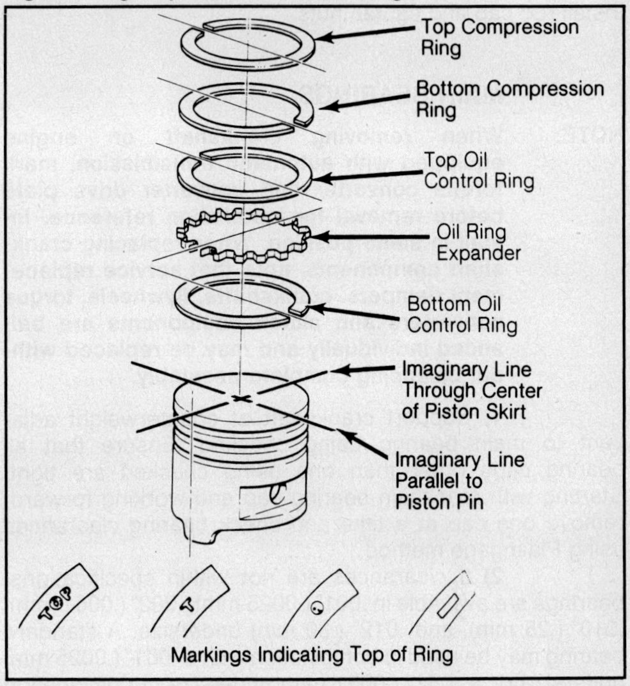

Ring gaps can vary as much as 20° from positions illustrated.

Installation

1) Assemble connecting rod to piston. When properly assembled, arrow on piston head will point toward front of engine, and oil hole in connecting rod will face camshaft side of engine. Use piston pin remover/installer and arbor press to press pin through connecting rod and piston.

2) Pin should be centered in connecting rod. The piston pin requires a 2000 lb. (907 kg) press fit. If little effort is required to install pin in connecting rod, or if rod moves on pin, replace connecting rod.

CRANKSHAFT & ROD BEARINGS

NOTE: **Main and rod bearings in production are identified by color-coded paint marks, which are located on bearing inserts. When replacing bearing inserts, all odd size inserts must be either all on top (in cylinder block) or all on bottom (in main or rod caps).**

CONNECTING ROD BEARINGS

1) After ensuring rod caps are marked for cylinder identification, remove rod caps. Use Plastigage method to check for proper bearing clearance. If not within specification, new bearings must be installed. New bearings are available in .001" (.0025 mm), .002" (.0051 mm), .010" (.25 mm) and .012" (.30 mm) undersize.

2) Selective fitting is required on each connecting rod. A standard bearing may be used in combination with .001" (.0025 mm) undersize or .002" (.0051 mm) undersize in combination with .001" (.0025 mm) undersize. Never use a pair of inserts that differ more than one

4.2 LITER 6-CYLINDER (Cont.)

bearing size as a pair. Coat bearing surfaces with oil, install rod cap and tighten nuts.

MAIN BEARINGS

NOTE: **When removing crankshaft on engine equipped with automatic transmission, mark torque converter and converter drive plate before removal for installation reference. Install in same position. When replacing crankshaft components, note that service replacement dampers, crankshafts, flywheels, torque converters and clutch components are balanced individually and may be replaced without balancing complete assembly.**

1) Support crankshaft at counterweight adjacent to main bearing being checked. Ensure that all bearing caps other than one being checked are tight. Starting with rear main bearing cap and working forward, remove one cap at a time and check bearing clearances using Plastigage method.

2) If clearances are not within specifications, bearings are avaliable in .001" (.0025 mm), .002" (.0051 mm), .010" (.25 mm), and .012" (.30 mm) undersize. A standard bearing may be used in combination with a .001" (.0025 mm) undersize or a .002" (.0051 mm) undersize in combination with a .001" (.0025 mm) undersize.

3) Remove all upper bearings by inserting fabricated cotter pin in oil hole of crankshaft journal and rotating crankshaft clockwise to roll bearing from engine. *See Fig. 7.*

Fig. 7: Upper Main Bearing Remover/Installer

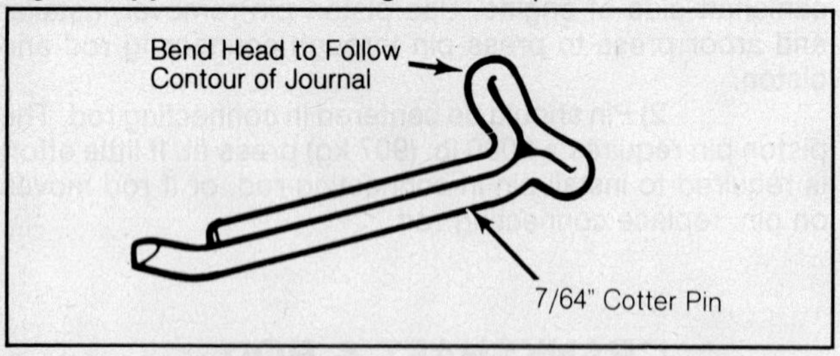

Fabricate from 7/64" cotter pin.

4) If clearance exceeds specification using pair of .002" (.0051 mm) undersize bearing inserts, measure crankshaft journal diameter with micrometer. If journal diameter is correct, crankshaft bore in cylinder block may be misaligned, which requires cylinder block replacement or machining to true bore.

5) If diameter for journals 1 through 5 is less than 2.4981" (63.452 mm) or diameter for journal 6 is less than 2.4975" (63.437 mm), replace crankshaft or grind down to accept appropriate undersize bearing insert.

6) To install, oil new bearing and rotate crankshaft so upper bearing will rotate in direction of locating tang. Install bearing cap with lower bearing and tighten bolts.

CRANKSHAFT END PLAY

1) Crankshaft end play is controlled at No. 3 main bearing, which is flanged for this purpose. Attach dial indicator to cylinder block adjacent to No. 3 main bearing.

2) Move crankshaft forward and position dial indicator push rod on face of crankshaft counterweight. Zero dial indicator. Move shaft fore and aft. Note dial indicator pointer. Crankshaft end play is .0015"-.0065" (.038-.165 mm), desired range is .0020"-.0025" (.015-.064 mm).

3) If end play is not within specifications, inspect thrust faces for wear. If no wear is apparent, install new thrust bearing and remeasure end play. If end play is still not within specifications, replace crankshaft.

4) When replacing thrust bearing, crankshaft should be moved back and forth to align thrust faces of bearings before final tightening.

REAR MAIN BEARING OIL SEAL

Removal

Remove oil pan and rear main bearing cap. Loosen remaining main bearing cap bolts. Using a brass drift, tap upper seal around crankshaft until seal protrudes enough to permit removal with pliers. Remove lower seal from bearing cap.

Installation

1) Clean crankshaft seal surface. Lightly coat lips of new seal halves with engine oil and their outer surfaces with liquid soap. *See Fig. 8.* Install upper seal into block with lip facing toward front of engine.

2) Install lower seal into bearing cap with lip facing front. Ensure seal is firmly seated in bearing cap recess. Apply silicone sealer to chamfered edges of bearing cap and to both sides of seal ends. *See Fig. 8.* Install rear main bearing cap. Tighten all main bearing cap bolts.

Fig. 8: Rear Main Bearing Oil Seal Installation

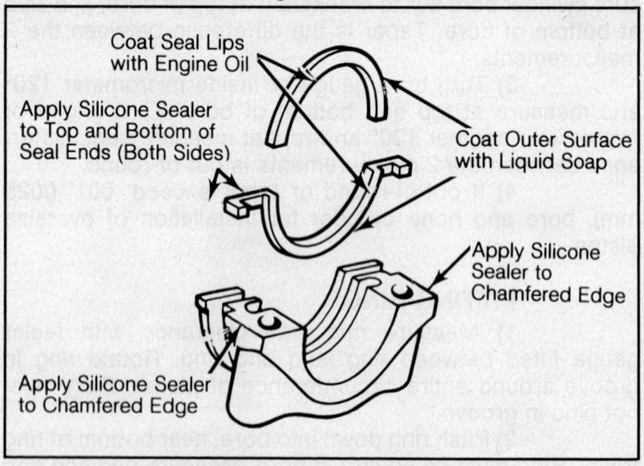

Do not apply sealer to cylinder block mating surface.

ENGINE OILING

CRANKCASE CAPACITY

Crankcase capacity is 5 quarts (4.8L). Add 1 quart (.95L) when replacing oil filter.

OIL FILTER

CAUTION: **Always use short (4.25") oil filter on 6-cylinder CJ vehicles. Longer (5.44") oil filter may contact engine mount or frame rail and puncture, causing possible engine damage.**

4.2 LITER 6-CYLINDER (Cont.)

Replace every 7500 miles or 7 1/2 months, whichever comes first. Filter is full-flow type mounted on right side of crankcase.

NORMAL OIL PRESSURE

Normal oil pressure should be 37-75 psi (2.6-5.3 kg/cm^2) maximum above 1600 RPM. Minimum oil pressure should be 13 psi (.9 kg/cm^2) at 600 RPM.

OIL PRESSURE REGULATOR VALVE

Oil pressure regulator valve is located in pump body. Valve is nonadjustable.

ENGINE OILING SYSTEM

Oil under pressure is forced from gear-type oil pump to a full-flow oil filter. A by-pass valve is located in oil filter mounting base.

Oil flows from filter to main oil gallery. Branched passages from main oil gallery direct oil to upper main bearings. Internally drilled passages in crankshaft route oil to connecting rod journals.

Oil flows through each connecting rod, which disperses oil flow through a squirt hole in the rod. This dispersed oil lubricates camshaft lobes, distributor drive gear, cylinder walls and piston pins.

Lifters receive oil directly from main gallery, which is directed through hollow push rods to lubricate upper valve train area. Passages from main gallery lubricate camshaft bearings. Front camshaft bearing directs oil through camshaft sprocket, which slings oil to lubricate timing chain. *See Fig. 9.*

Fig. 9: Engine Oiling System

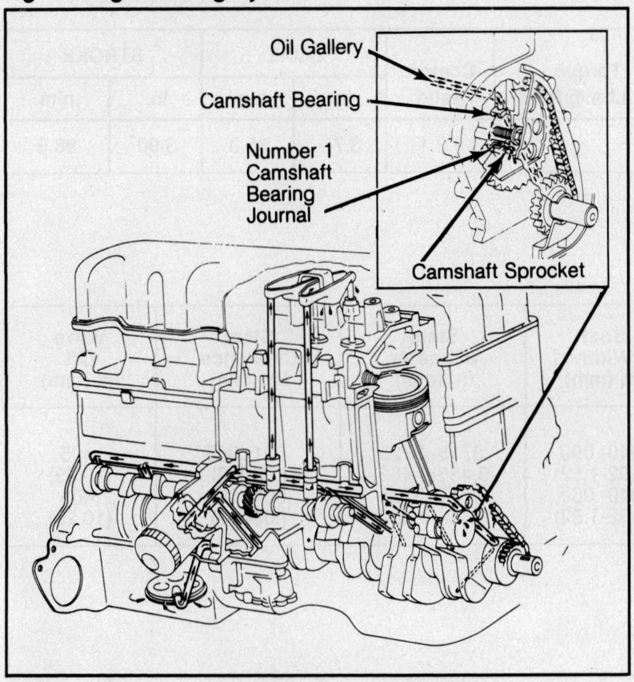

Check that sludge build-up has not clogged oil filter and opened by-pass valve.

OIL PUMP

Removal & Disassembly

Drain crankcase and remove oil pan. Remove oil pump. Do not disturb position of oil inlet tube in pump body. If tube position is moved within pump body, a new tube and screen assembly must be installed to ensure an airtight seal. Remove pump cover.

Inspection

1) Place straightedge across gears in pump body. Using feeler gauge, measure gear end clearance between pump body and straightedge. If gear end clearance is excessive, replace oil pump assembly.

2) Using feeler gauge, measure gear-to-body clearance by inserting feeler gauge between a gear tooth and pump body wall. Take measurement directly opposite the point of gear mesh. Rotate gears and measure each tooth in this manner. Replace both gears and idler shaft if not within limits.

3) If oil pressure relief valve inspection is necessary, oil inlet tube and screen assembly must be removed and replaced with a new unit. Remove cotter pin, spring retainer, spring and relief valve from pump body. Check valve and bore for sticking condition and wear, and replace as necessary.

Reassembly & Installation

1) If removed, install oil pressure relief valve, spring, retainer and cotter pin. *See Fig. 10.* Apply light film of non-hardening sealing compound around end of tube and drive tube into pump body. Ensure tube support bracket is aligned with bolt hole in pump body.

Fig. 10: Oil Pump and Filter Assembly

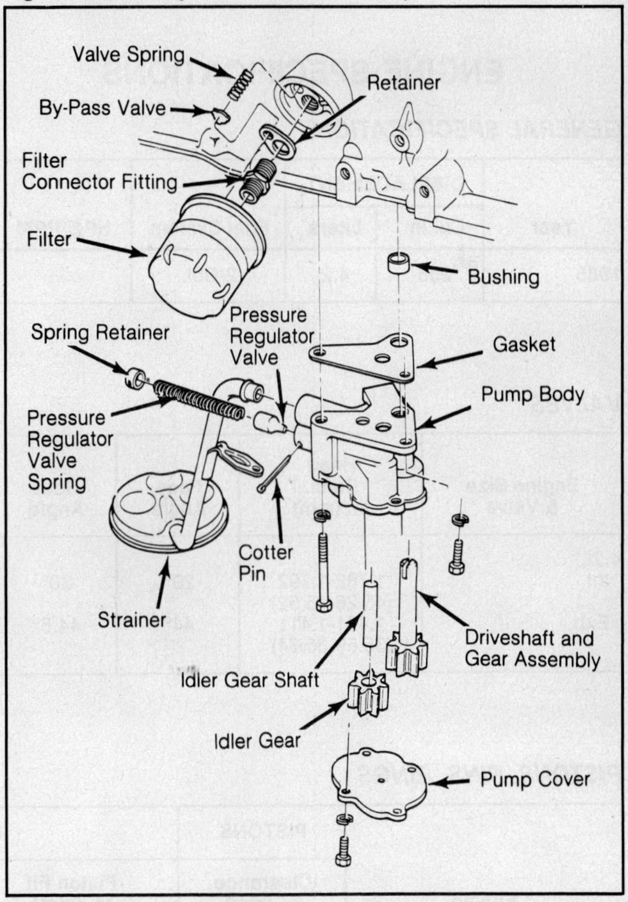

Oil inlet tube and strainer assembly must be replaced if moved within pump body.

2) Install idler shaft, idler gear and drive gear into pump body. Prime pump by filling pump cavity with

Jeep Engines

4.2 LITER 6-CYLINDER (Cont.)

petroleum jelly. Do not use grease. Apply sealer around perimeter of pump cover. Install and tighten pump cover. Using new gasket, install and tighten oil pump. Install oil pan and refill crankcase.

OIL PUMP SPECIFICATIONS

Application	Specification In. (mm)
Gear-to-Body Clearance	.0005-.0025 (.013-.063)
Gear End Clearance	.004-.008 (.10-.20)

ENGINE COOLING

WATER PUMP

Removal

Drain cooling system. Disconnect radiator and heater hoses from pump. Remove drive belts from pump pulley. If equipped, remove fan shroud from radiator. If necessary, rotate fan shroud 1/2 turn to facilitate water pump removal. Remove water pump and discard gasket.

Installation

Clean all gasket mating surfaces. Using new gasket, install and tighten water pump. Reverse removal procedure to complete installation.

NOTE: For further information on cooling system capacities and other cooling system components, see appropriate article in ENGINE COOLING SYSTEMS at end of ENGINE section.

TIGHTENING SPECIFICATIONS

Application	Ft. Lbs. (N.m)
Camshaft Sprocket Bolts	80 (108)
Connecting Rod Cap Nuts	33 (45)
Cylinder Head Bolts	85 (115)
Engine Front Cover Bolts	16 (22)
Exhaust Manifold Bolts & Nuts	23 (31)
Flywheel-to-Crankshaft Bolts	105 (142)
Intake Manifold Bolts	23 (31)
Main Bearing Cap Bolts	80 (108)
Oil Pump Cover Bolts	6 (8)
Oil Pump Attaching Bolts	
Short	10 (14)
Long	17 (23)
Rocker Arm Bolts	19 (26)
Vibration Damper Bolt	80 (108)
Water Pump Bolts	13 (18)

ENGINE SPECIFICATIONS

GENERAL SPECIFICATIONS

Year	DISPLACEMENT		Fuel System	HP@RPM	Torque	Compr.	BORE		STROKE	
	Cu. In.	Liters			Ft. Lbs.@RPM	Ratio	In.	mm	In.	mm
1985	258	4.2	2-Bbl.	.....	.....	9.2:1	3.75	95.3	3.90	98.9

VALVES

Engine Size & Valve	Head Diam. In. (mm)	Face Angle	Seat Angle	Seat Width In. (mm)	Stem Diameter In. (mm)	Stem Clearance In. (mm)	Valve Lift In. (mm)
4.2L							
Int.	1.782-1.792 (45.26-45.52)	29°	30°	.040-.060 (1.02-1.52)	.3715-.3725 (9.436-9.462)	.001-.003 (.03-.08)	.405 (10.29)
Exh.	1.401-1.411 (35.59-35.84)	44°	44.5°	.040-.060 (1.02-1.52)	.3715-.3725 (9.436-9.462)	.001-.003 (.03-.08)	.405 (10.29)

PISTONS, PINS, RINGS

Engine	PISTONS	PINS		RINGS		
	Clearance In. (mm)	Piston Fit In. (mm)	Rod Fit In. (mm)	Ring No.	End Gap In. (mm)	Side Clearance In. (mm)
4.2L	.0009-.0017 (.023-.043)	.0003-.0005 (.008-.013)	Press Fit	1 & 2	.010-.020 (.25-.51)	.0017-.0032 (.043-.081)
				3	.010-.025 (.25-.64)	.001-.008 (.03-.20)

4.2 LITER 6-CYLINDER (Cont.)

ENGINE SPECIFICATIONS (Cont.)

CRANKSHAFT MAIN & CONNECTING ROD BEARINGS

Engine	MAIN BEARINGS				CONNECTING ROD BEARINGS		
	Journal Diam. In. (mm)	Clearance In. (mm)	Thrust Bearing	Crankshaft End Play In. (mm)	Journal Diam. In. (mm)	Clearance In. (mm)	Side Play In. (mm)
4.2L	2.4996-2.5001 (63.489-63.502)	.0010-.0025 (.025-.064)	No. 3	.0015-.0065 (.038-.165)	2.0934-2.0955 (53.172-53.226)	.001-.003 (.03-.08)	.010-.019 (.25-.48)

CAMSHAFT

Engine	Journal Diam. In. (mm)	Clearance In. (mm)	Lobe Lift In. (mm)
4.2L			
No. 1	2.029-2.030 (51.54-51.56)	.001-.003 (.03-.08)	.253 (6.43)
No. 2	2.019-2.020 (51.28-51-31)	.001-.003 (.03-.08)	.253 (6.43)
No. 3	2.009-2.010 (51.03-51.05)	.001-.003 (.03-.08)	.253 (6.43)
No. 4	1.999-2.000 (50.77-50.80)	.001-.003 (.03-.08)	.253 (6.43)

VALVE SPRINGS

Engine	Free Length In. (mm)	PRESSURE Lbs. @ In. (Kg @ mm)	
		Valve Closed	Valve Open
4.2L	1.99 (50.5)	64-72@1.79 (29-33@45.5)	188-202@1.41 (85-92@35.8)

6.0 LITER V8

ENGINE CODING

ENGINE IDENTIFICATION

The Vehicle Identification Number (VIN) is located on upper left side of dash, visible through windshield. The 4th character identifies the engine size. The 10th character identifies the model year.

Engine code number is located on a plate attached to front of right rocker cover. Letter portion of code identifies engine displacement, carburetor type and compression ratio.

ENGINE IDENTIFICATION CODE

Engine	Code
6.0L 2-Bbl.	N

SPECIAL ENGINE MARKINGS

Some engines are produced at factory with oversize or undersize components. These engines are identified by a letter code stamped adjacent to engine code number on right valve cover. Letters are decoded as follows:

- "B" indicates all cylinder bores .010" (.25 mm) oversize.
- "C" indicates all camshaft bearing bores .010" (.25 mm) oversize.
- "P" indicates all connecting rod bearings .010" (.25 mm) undersize.
- "M" indicates all main bearing journals .010" (.25 mm) undersize.
- "PM" indicates all connecting rod and main bearings .010" (.25 mm) undersize.

ENGINE REMOVAL

See ENGINE REMOVAL at end of ENGINE section.

MANIFOLDS & CYLINDER HEAD

INTAKE MANIFOLD

Removal

1) Disconnect negative battery cable. Drain cooling system. Remove air cleaner. Disconnect spark plug wires from spark plugs and position wires and plastic separators away from intake manifold area.

2) Disconnect upper radiator hose, by-pass and heater hoses from intake manifold. Disconnect primary and secondary ignition wires from coil. Remove coil and bracket.

3) Label and disconnect all electrical connectors, ventilation hoses and vacuum hoses from intake manifold, carburetor and distributor. Disconnect fuel line from carburetor. Disconnect throttle linkages from carburetor and intake manifold, and position aside.

4) Disconnect air pump hoses from air pump and injection manifolds. Position hoses and diverter valve aside. Remove carburetor. Remove intake manifold. Discard gasket and seals.

Installation

1) Clean all gasket mating surfaces. Coat both sides of new gaskets with non-hardening sealer. Position gaskets onto cylinder heads. Install new end seals. Apply non-hardening sealer to seal ends.

2) Install and tighten intake manifold. Install remaining components in reverse order of removal.

EXHAUST MANIFOLD

Removal

1) Disconnect spark plug wires. Disconnect air injection hose at air injection manifold. Disconnect exhaust pipe at exhaust manifold.

2) Remove exhaust manifold retaining screws. Separate exhaust manifold from cylinder head. Remove air injection manifold, fittings and washers.

Installation

Clean all gasket mating surfaces. Install air injection manifold on exhaust manifold. Install and tighten exhaust manifold. To complete installation, reverse removal procedure.

CYLINDER HEAD

Removal

1) Disconnect negative battery cable. Drain cooling system and cylinder block. Remove air cleaner and rocker arm covers. Alternately loosen rocker arm bolts 1 turn at a time to avoid damage to bridges. Remove rocker arm assemblies and push rods.

2) Keep rocker arm assemblies and push rods in order for reinstallation in original locations. Remove spark plugs. Remove intake and exhaust manifolds. Loosen all drive belts. If A/C equipped, remove A/C compressor mounting bracket.

3) Disconnect alternator support brace from cylinder head. Remove air pump and power steering pump and their respective mounting brackets, and position aside. Remove cylinder heads and discard gaskets.

Installation

1) Clean threads of head bolts and threads in cylinder block. Clean all gasket mating surfaces. Apply an even coat of sealer to both sides of head gaskets. Position gasket on block with stamped word "TOP" facing upward.

2) Install and tighten cylinder head. *See Fig. 1.* To complete installation, reverse removal procedure. It is not necessary to retighten head bolts after engine has been operated.

Fig. 1: Cylinder Head Tightening Sequence

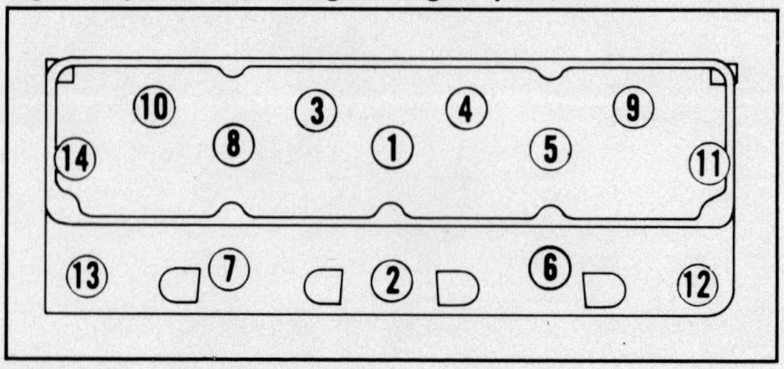

Tighten head bolts to 110 ft. lbs. (149 N.m).

VALVES

VALVE ARRANGEMENT

Both Banks – E-I-I-E-E-I-I-E (Front-to-rear).

ROCKER ARM ASSEMBLY

Both intake and exhaust rocker arms for each cylinder pivot on a bridge and pivot assembly. *See Fig. 2.*

The bridge and pivot assembly maintains correct rocker arm-to-valve tip alignment. When removing rocker arm assemblies, always keep parts in order for reinstallation in original locations.

Fig. 2: Rocker Arm Assembly

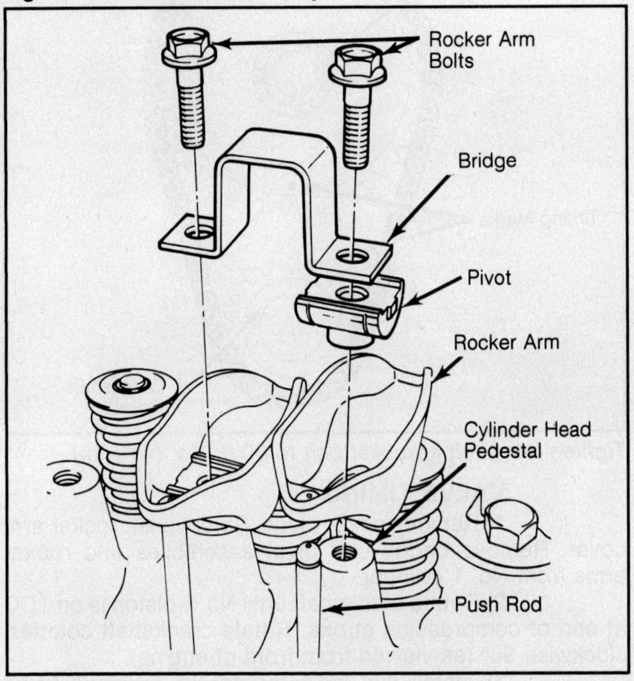

Tighten rocker arm bolts to 19 ft. lbs. (25 N.m).

VALVE SPRINGS

Although normal service is performed with cylinder head removed, it is possible to replace seals, locks, retainers or broken springs with cylinder head installed.

Removal

1) Remove air cleaner. Remove rocker arm cover. Remove bridge and pivot assemblies, rocker arm, and push rod of valve to be serviced.

2) Remove spark plug and install 14 mm (thread size) air hose adapter into spark plug hole. Connect an air hose to adapter and maintain constant air pressure of at least 90 psi (6.3 kg/cm^2).

3) Using Valve Spring Compressor (J-22534), compress valve spring and remove locks. Remove valve spring retainer, valve spring and oil seal.

Inspection

Using valve spring tester, check valve springs for proper tension. Measure free length of valve springs. Replace springs that fail specification.

Installation

1) Use a 7/16" deep-well socket and light hammer to gently tap valve stem seal into place on valve stem. Ensure sharp edges of valve lock groove do not damage oil seal during installation. Install valve spring with closed-coil end down, then install retainer.

2) Compress spring with valve spring compressor, and install locks. Tap each valve spring from side to side to ensure spring is seated properly. Turn off air supply and remove air hose and adapter. To complete installation, reverse removal procedure.

VALVE STEM OIL SEALS

Nylon valve stem seals are used on all valves. Replace seals whenever they become deteriorated, or valve service is performed. Use a 7/16" deep-well socket and light mallet to seat valve seals onto stems. Ensure sharp edges of valve lock groove do not damage seal during installation.

VALVE GUIDE SERVICING

Valve guides are integral with cylinder head and are not replaceable. Replacement valves are available with .003" (.08 mm), .015" (.38 mm) and .030" (.76 mm) oversize stems.

1) Clean valve guide bore with solvent and a rifle brush. Use a ball gauge and micrometer to measure guide wear. Take measurements of guide crosswise and lengthwise to head, inserting ball gauge 3/8" into guide bore from top of head.

2) Difference between the two measurements is guide bore out-of-round. Ream valve guides if out-of-round measurement exceeds .0025" (.06 mm).

3) If guide measures more than .003" (.08 mm) larger than guide bore diameter specifications, ream valve guide for installation of valve with oversize stem.

4) Always ream valve guides in progressive steps, using reamers in sequence to obtain desired size.

HYDRAULIC VALVE LIFTERS

1) Service lifters as complete assemblies only. Parts are not interchangeable between lifters. Inspect lifter body for signs of scuffing. Inspect base of lifter for concave wear. If concave wear is present, replacement of camshaft and lifters is necessary.

2) Disassemble, clean and reassemble lifters. *See Fig. 3*. Using lifter leak-down rate tester and lifter test fluid, test lifter leak-down. Compress lifter plunger and record time required for tester needle to align with .125" mark on scale. Leak-down rate should be 20-110 seconds.

3) Replace lifters that fail test. Do not attempt to prime lifters with engine oil prior to installation. Lifters will fill with oil within 3-8 minutes of engine operation. Discard lifters not within specifications.

Fig. 3: Hydraulic Valve Lifter Assembly

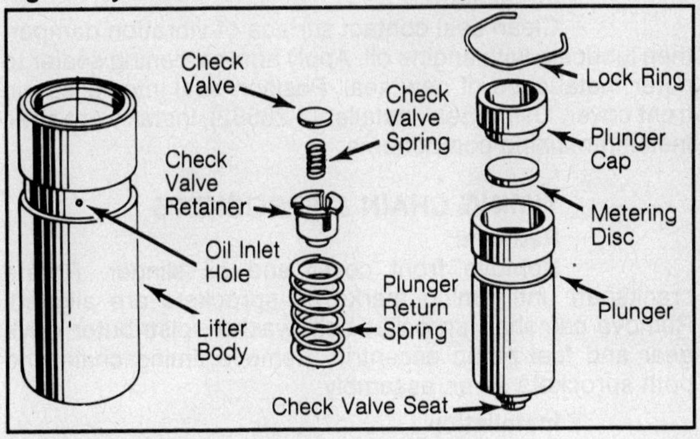

Do not interchange parts between lifters.

CAMSHAFT

ENGINE FRONT COVER

Removal

1) Drain radiator and cylinder block. Disconnect radiator hoses, heater hose and by-pass hose from manifold and water pump. Remove all drive belts. Remove fan and hub assembly. If A/C equipped, remove compressor and bracket from engine and position aside. Do not disconnect A/C hoses.

2) Remove alternator and mounting bracket. Remove idler pulley. If equipped, remove power steering pump and bracket assembly. Remove air pump and mounting bracket as an assembly, with hoses attached. Remove fuel pump and distributor. Remove crankshaft damper pulley and vibration damper.

3) Remove front oil pan bolts. Remove bolts attaching front cover-to-cylinder block, noting their lengths and locations for reinstallation in same positions. Remove front cover. Remove front cover lower locating dowel pin from cylinder block.

Installation

1) Use a sharp knife to cut both sides of oil pan gasket flush with engine block. Using cut pieces as a template, cut and fit replacement gasket pieces from new gasket. Clean all gasket mating surfaces. Install new front oil pan seal to bottom of front cover.

2) Align tabs of replacement oil pan gasket pieces with oil pan seal on front cover and cement into place on bottom of front cover. Apply non-hardening sealer to both sides of front cover gasket and install on front cover. Apply non-hardening sealer to oil pan-to-cylinder block junctions.

3) Place front cover in position on cylinder block and install front oil pan bolts. Tighten bolts slowly and evenly until cover aligns with upper locating dowel pin. Insert lower locating dowel pin through appropriate hole in front cover, and drive pin into cylinder block.

4) Install and tighten remaining front cover bolts. To complete installation, reverse removal procedure. Fill cooling system. Start engine and inspect for oil and coolant leaks.

FRONT COVER OIL SEAL

Removal

Loosen all drive belts. Remove crankshaft pulley and vibration damper. Use Oil Seal Remover (J-9256) to remove oil seal.

Installation

Clean seal contact surface of vibration damper, then lubricate with engine oil. Apply non-hardening sealer to outer metal case of new seal. Position seal into recess in front cover. Using Seal Installer (J-26562), install front seal. Install remaining components.

TIMING CHAIN & SPROCKETS

Removal

Remove front cover and oil slinger. Rotate crankshaft until timing marks on sprockets are aligned. Remove camshaft sprocket bolt, washer, distributor drive gear and fuel pump eccentric. Remove timing chain and both sprockets as an assembly.

Installation

1) Assemble timing chain over camshaft and crankshaft sprockets with timing marks on sprockets aligned. *See Fig. 4*. Install chain and sprockets as an assembly. Ensure timing marks on sprockets are aligned.

2) Install remaining components while noting the following: Fuel pump eccentric must be installed with stamped word "REAR" facing camshaft. Camshaft washer fits into recess in distributor drive gear.

Fig. 4: Timing Chain & Sprocket Alignment

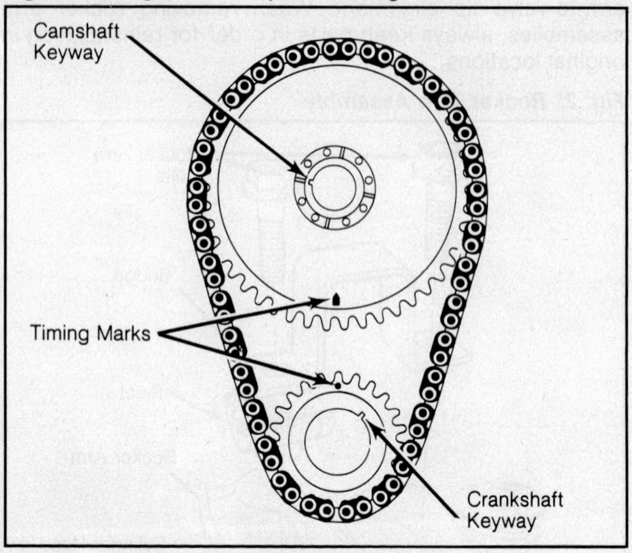

Tighten camshaft sprocket bolt to 30 ft. lbs. (41 N.m).

VALVE TIMING

1) Remove spark plugs. Remove left rocker arm cover. Remove bridge and pivot assemblies and rocker arms from No. 1 cylinder.

2) Rotate crankshaft until No. 6 piston is on TDC at end of compression stroke. Rotate crankshaft counterclockwise 90° (as viewed from front of engine).

3) Install dial indicator on No. 1 intake valve push rod end. Use rubber hose to secure indicator point to end of push rod. Dial indicator point must be in same plane as push rod vertical movement. Zero dial indicator.

4) Slowly rotate crankshaft in direction of normal rotation until dial indicator shows .020" (.51 mm) lift. Timing mark on vibration damper should align with TDC mark on timing scale. If timing mark is off more than 1/2" in either direction, valve timing is incorrect.

CAMSHAFT

Removal

1) Drain radiator and cylinder block. Remove radiator. If A/C equipped, remove condenser and receiver assembly as a charged unit. Remove rocker arm covers. Remove bridge and pivot assemblies, rocker arms and push rods in order, for reinstallation in original locations.

2) Remove intake manifold. Remove valve lifters in order for reinstallation in original locations. Remove front cover. Rotate crankshaft to align timing marks on camshaft and crankshaft sprockets.

3) Remove timing chain and sprockets as an assembly. Remove hood latch support bracket. Remove front bumper or grille (as required). Remove camshaft.

Installation

To install camshaft, reverse removal procedure while noting the following: Heavily coat camshaft and lifters with an engine oil supplement prior to installation. Fuel pump eccentric must be installed with stamped word "REAR" facing camshaft sprocket. Camshaft washer fits into recess in distributor drive gear. *See Fig. 5*.

CAM LOBE LIFT

1) Remove rocker arm covers and spark plugs. Remove bridge and pivot assemblies and rocker arms in order, for reinstallation in original locations.

Fig. 5: Camshaft Assembly

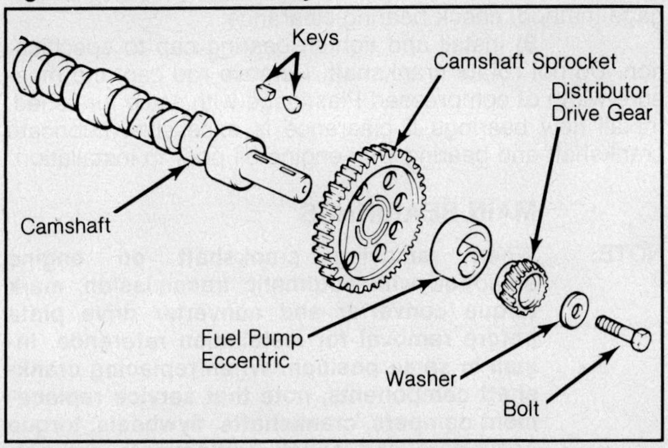

Fuel pump eccentric must be installed with stamped word "REAR" facing camshaft sprocket.

2) Using mounting fixture, attach dial indicator to cylinder head so indicator point rests on top of push rod. Use a piece of rubber hose to secure indicator point to end of push rod. Dial indicator point must be in same plane as push rod vertical movement. *See Fig. 6*.

3) Rotate crankshaft slowly until valve lifter is on base circle of cam lobe. In this position, push rod will be at its lowest travel. Zero dial indicator.

4) Rotate engine until push rod is in fully raised position and record reading. Correct lobe lift is .260-.270" (6.60-6.86 mm). If less than specifications, replace camshaft and lifters. Check remaining cam lobes in same manner.

Fig. 6: Dial Indicator Installation for Checking Cam Lobe Lift & Valve Timing

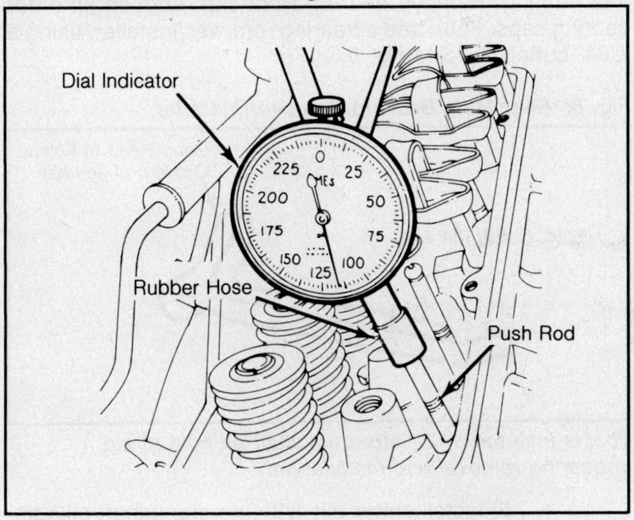

Correct cam lobe lift is .260-.270" (6.60-6.86 mm).

CAMSHAFT BEARINGS

Remove engine from vehicle to install camshaft bearings. Use screw-type Camshaft Bearing Remover/Installer (J-21054-1) and proper adapters, to replace camshaft bearings. Do not use a driver-type bearing remover/installer. Ensure oil holes in bearings are aligned with oil holes in block.

PISTONS, RINGS & PINS

OIL PAN

See OIL PAN REMOVAL at end of ENGINE section.

PISTON & ROD ASSEMBLY

Removal

1) Remove cylinder heads and oil pan. Position piston at bottom of stroke and cover with a cloth to collect metal cuttings. Using a ridge reamer, remove any ridge or deposits on upper end of cylinder bore.

2) If necessary, mark connecting rods and caps for cylinder identification. Remove connecting rod bearing cap and bearings.

3) Install pieces of rubber hose over connecting rod bolts to protect cylinder walls and crankshaft. Push piston and rod assembly out top of cylinder block and install rod cap on mating rod.

Installation

1) Lightly coat piston, rings and cylinder wall with engine oil. Properly position rings on piston. *See Fig. 7.* Using ring compressor, compress rings on piston. Ensure position of rings does not change.

2) Install upper bearing into rod, and cover rod bolts with protective rubber hose. Position piston in bore with notches on piston head pointing toward front of engine.

3) Install piston and rod assembly into its respective bore, while guiding connecting rod onto crankshaft journal. Install and tighten rod cap.

Fig. 7: Ring Gap Positions & Markings

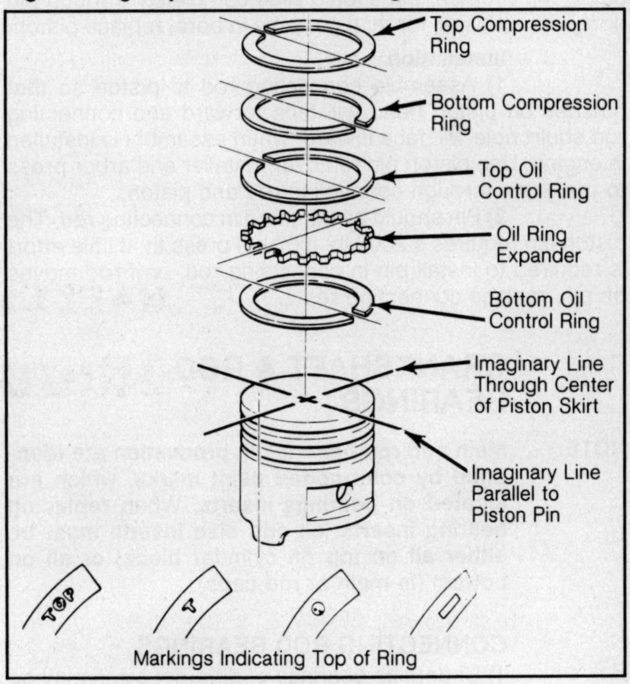

Ring gaps can vary as much as 20° from positions illustrated.

FITTING PISTONS

1) Measure each cylinder bore approximately 2 5/16" below top of cylinder bore. Measure each piston 90° to piston pin at centerline of pin. Difference between the two measurements is piston-to-cylinder bore clearance.

6.0 LITER V8 (Cont.)

2) Using bore gauge or inside micrometer, measure cylinder bore 90° to crankshaft at top of bore, and also at bottom of bore. Taper is the difference between the two measurements.

3) Turn measuring tool 120° and measure at top and bottom of bore. Turn tool another 120° and repeat measurement. Difference between the two measurements is out-of-round.

4) If out-of-round exceeds .003" (.08 mm), or taper exceeds .005" (.13 mm), bore and hone cylinder for installation of oversize piston.

FITTING RINGS

1) Measure ring side clearance with feeler gauge fitted between ring land and ring. Measure clearance while rotating ring in groove. Ring must not bind in groove.

2) Measure end gap of each compression ring in cylinder bore. Push a ring down into bore, near bottom of ring travel. Ring must be square in bore. Measure ring end gap with feeler gauge.

3) Install rings on piston. *See Fig. 7*. Install upper and lower rings with gaps positioned 180° apart. Ensure ring markings (indicating top of ring), point upward.

PISTON PIN REPLACEMENT

Removal

Using piston pin remover/installer and an arbor press, press piston pin out of piston and rod assembly. Discard piston pin.

Inspection

To check replacement piston pin for fit, position piston so pin bore is in a vertical position. At room temperature, replacement pin should slide completely through pin bore without using force. If pin jams in bore, replace piston.

Installation

1) Assemble connecting rod to piston so that notches on piston head will face forward and connecting rod squirt hole will face inward, when assembly is installed in engine. Use piston pin remover/installer and arbor press to press pin through connecting rod and piston.

2) Pin should be centered in connecting rod. The piston pin requires a 2000 lb. (907 kg) press fit. If little effort is required to install pin in connecting rod, or if rod moves on pin, replace connecting rod.

CRANKSHAFT & ROD BEARINGS

NOTE: **Main and rod bearings in production are identified by color-coded paint marks, which are located on bearings inserts. When replacing bearing inserts, all odd size inserts must be either all on top (in cylinder block) or all on bottom (in main or rod caps).**

CONNECTING ROD BEARINGS

1) Undersize bearings of different sizes may be used in combination to achieve desired clearance. Never use a pair of bearings on same journal that differ more than .001" (.03 mm) in size. Rod journal size is identified by a color-coded paint mark on adjacent counterweight, toward rear of crankshaft.

2) Rotate crankshaft to position connecting rod at bottom of stroke. Ensure rod cap is marked for cylinder identification. Remove connecting rod cap. Using Plastigage method, check bearing clearance.

3) Install and tighten bearing cap to specification. Do not rotate crankshaft. Remove rod cap and measure width of compressed Plastigage with scale furnished. Install new bearings if clearance is excessive. Lubricate crankshaft and bearing with engine oil prior to installation.

MAIN BEARINNGS

NOTE: **When removing crankshaft on engine equipped with automatic transmission, mark torque converter and converter drive plate before removal for installation reference. Install in same position. When replacing crankshaft components, note that service replacement dampers, crankshafts, flywheels, torque converters and clutch components are balanced individually and may be replaced without balancing complete assembly.**

1) Check main bearing clearances one at a time. Use Plastigage method to check main bearing clearances, tightening caps to specification.

2) When required, undersize bearings of different sizes may be used in combination to obtain correct bearing clearance. Using this method, ensure that all odd-sized bearings are installed on same side of crankshaft. Never use a pair of bearings that differ more than .001" (.03 mm) in size.

3) Main bearing caps are numbered 1 to 5 (front-to-rear). Main journal size (except rear main) is identified in production by a color-coded paint mark on adjacent counterweight toward rear of crankshaft. Rear main journal has a paint mark on the crankshaft rear flange.

4) To replace main bearings, remove main cap and bearing. Remove bearing from cap. Loosen all other bearing caps. Fabricate a bearing remover/installer, using a 7/64" cotter pin. *See Fig. 8*.

Fig. 8: Rear Main Bearing Remover/Installer

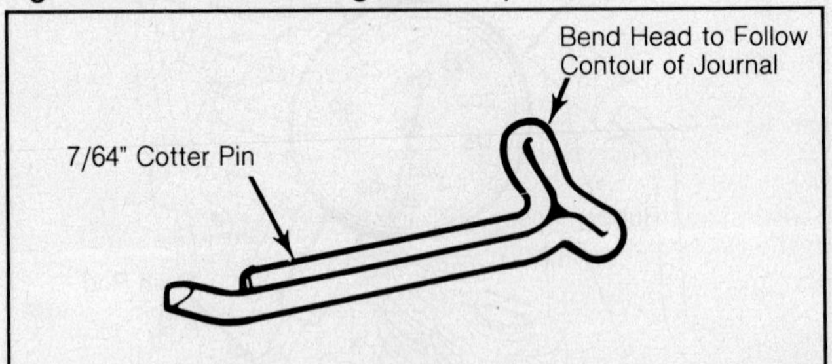

Tool is inserted 1/2" into crankshaft oil hole to aid in bearing removal and installation.

5) Install cotter pin 1/2" into crankshaft oil hole. Rotate crankshaft in direction of bearing tang slot in block to force bearing out of block.

6) Apply a light film of oil to new upper bearing. Start plain end of bearing into bearing tang side of block. Use cotter pin tool to push upper main bearing into place, by rotating crankshaft in opposite direction of removal.

7) Install remaining bearings using same procedure. Install lower bearings into caps. Install and tighten main caps with arrows pointing toward front of engine.

CRANKSHAFT END PLAY

1) Crankshaft end play is controlled at No. 3 main bearing, which is flanged for this purpose. Attach dial indicator to cylinder block adjacent to No. 3 main bearing.

2) Move crankshaft forward and position dial indicator push rod on face of crankshaft counterweight and set dial pointer to zero. Move shaft fore and aft. Note dial indicator pointer. Crankshaft end play is .003"-.008" (.08-.20 mm).

3) If end play is not within specifications, inspect thrust faces for wear. If no wear is apparent, install new thrust bearing and remeasure end play. If end play is still not within specifications, replace crankshaft.

4) When replacing thrust bearing, crankshaft should be moved back and forth to align thrust faces of bearings before final tightening.

REAR MAIN BEARING OIL SEAL

Removal

Remove oil pan and rear main bearing cap. Loosen remaining main bearing cap bolts. Using a brass drift, tap upper seal around crankshaft until seal protrudes enough to permit removal with pliers. Remove lower seal from bearing cap.

Installation

1) Clean crankshaft seal surface. Lightly coat lips of new seal halves with engine oil and outer surface of seal case with liquid soap. *See Fig. 9*. Install upper seal into block with lip facing toward front of engine.

2) Install lower seal into bearing cap with lip facing front. Ensure seal is firmly seated in bearing cap recess. Apply silicone sealer to chamfered edges of bearing cap and to both sides of seal ends. *See Fig. 9*. Install rear main bearing cap. Tighten all main bearing cap bolts.

Fig. 9: Rear Main Bearing Oil Seal Installation

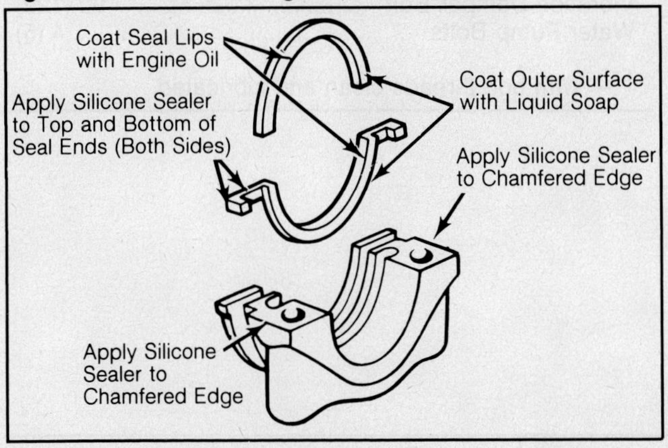

Do not apply sealer to cylinder block mating surface.

ENGINE OILING

CRANKCASE CAPACITY

Crankcase capacity is 4 quarts (3.8L). Add 1 quart (.95L) when replacing oil filter.

OIL FILTER

Replace filter every 7500 miles or 7 1/2 months, whichever comes first. Filter is full-flow type, mounted on engine front cover.

NORMAL OIL PRESSURE

Normal oil pressure should be 37-75 psi (2.6-5.3 kg/cm^2) maximum above 1600 RPM. Minimum oil pressure should be 13 psi (.9 kg/cm^2) at 600 RPM.

OIL PRESSURE REGULATOR VALVE

Oil pressure regulator valve is located in oil pump body. Valve is nonadjustable.

ENGINE OILING SYSTEM

Oil is forced from a gear-type oil pump to a full-flow oil filter. Oil is directed to right main oil gallery through a passage that extends internally up left front side of cylinder block. A passage that intersects with right main oil gallery directs oil to left main oil gallery.

Right and left main oil galleries directly lubricate lifters. Passages extend down from right oil gallery to lubricate camshaft and crankshaft bearings.

Crankshaft is internally drilled to provide oil to connecting rod bearings and journals. A squirt hole in each connecting rod cap disperses oil to cylinder walls, pistons and piston pins, with each rotation of crankshaft.

Oil routed from front camshaft bearing passes through camshaft sprocket to lubricate timing chain components. Oil from lifters is directed through hollow push rods to lubricate upper valve train area.

Fig. 10: Engine Oiling System

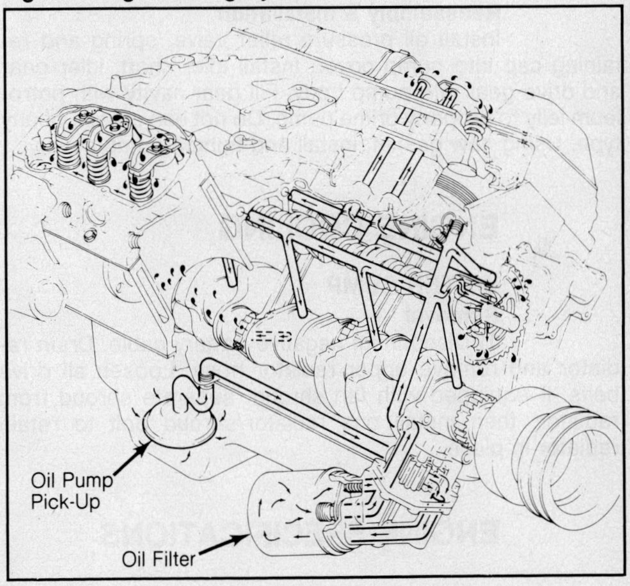

OIL PUMP

Removal & Disassembly

Remove retaining bolts and separate oil pump cover, gasket and oil filter as an assembly from pump body (engine front cover). Slide drive gear, idler gear and idler shaft out of pump body. Unscrew oil pressure relief valve cap and remove spring and plunger from pump cover. Thoroughly clean all parts.

Inspection

1) Plastigage method (preferred) or feeler gauge method (alternate) can be used to measure gear end clearance. Using either method, ensure pump gears are up into pump body as far as possible, to accurately determine clearance.

6.0 LITER V8 (Cont.)

2) Using Plastigage method, place strip of Plastigage across full width of each gear. Install pump cover and gasket and tighten to specification. Remove pump cover and measure width of compressed Plastigage with scale furnished.

3) Using feeler gauge method, place straightedge across gears and pump body. Insert feeler gauge between straightedge and pump body to measure clearance.

4) With gears installed in pump body, insert feeler gauge between gear tooth and inner wall of pump body, directly opposite point of gear mesh. Rotate gears and measure clearance between each gear tooth and pump body in same manner.

5) Check relief valve plunger for wear or binding in pump cover. If wear is apparent or binding occurs, replace pump cover and relief valve plunger.

OIL PUMP SPECIFICATIONS

Application	Specification In. (mm)
Gear End Clearance	
Plastigage Method	.002-.008 (.05-.20)
Feeler Gauge Method	.004-.008 (.10-.20)
Gear-to-Body Clearance	.0005-.0025 (.013-.064)

Reassembly & Installation

Install oil pressure relief valve, spring and retaining cap into pump cover. Install idler shaft, idler gear and drive gear into pump body. Fill gear cavity with petroleum jelly to properly prime pump. Do not use grease of any type. Using new gasket, install and tighten pump cover.

ENGINE COOLING

WATER PUMP

Removal

1) Disconnect negative battery cable. Drain radiator and remove upper radiator hose. Loosen all drive belts. If equipped with fan shroud, separate shroud from radiator, then install one radiator/shroud bolt to retain radiator in place.

2) Remove fan and hub from water pump. Remove fan and shroud from engine compartment. If A/C equipped, remove mounting stud from water pump that compressor bracket is secured to. Remove alternator and bracket and position aside.

3) If power steering equipped, remove front half of power steering bracket from water pump mounting stud. Disconnect all coolant hoses from water pump. Remove water pump and discard gasket.

Installation

Clean all gasket mating surfaces. Check front cover cavity for corrosion. Using new gasket, install and tighten water pump. To complete installation, reverse removal procedure.

NOTE: **For further information on cooling system capacities and other cooling system components, see appropriate article in ENGINE COOLING SYSTEMS at end of ENGINE section.**

TIGHTENING SPECIFICATIONS

Application	Ft. Lbs. (N.m)
Camshaft Sprocket Bolt	30 (41)
Connecting Rod Cap Nuts	33 (45)
Cylinder Head Bolts	110 (149)
Engine Front Cover Bolts	25 (34)
Exhaust Manifold	
2 Center Bolts	25 (34)
4 Outer Bolts	15 (20)
Flywheel-to-Crankshaft Bolts	105 (142)
Intake Manifold Bolts	43 (58)
Main Bearing Cap Bolts	100 (136)
Oil Pump Cover Bolts	5 (7)
Rocker Arm Bolts	19 (26)
Vibration Damper Bolt	[1] 90 (122)
Water Pump Bolts	4 (5)

[1] – With bolt threads clean and lubricated.

ENGINE SPECIFICATIONS

GENERAL SPECIFICATIONS

Year	DISPLACEMENT		Fuel System	HP@RPM	Torque Ft. Lbs.@RPM	Compr. Ratio	BORE		STROKE	
	Cu. In.	Liters					In.	mm	In.	mm
1985	360	6.0	2-Bbl.	.....	.....	8.25:1	4.08	103.6	3.44	87.4

6.0 LITER V8 (Cont.)

ENGINE SPECIFICATIONS (Cont.)

VALVES

Engine Size & Valve	Head Diam. In. (mm)	Face Angle	Seat Angle	Seat Width In. (mm)	Stem Diameter In. (mm)	Stem Clearance In. (mm)	Valve Lift In. (mm)
6.0L							
Intake	2.02-2.03 (51.3-51.6)	29°	30°	.040-.060 (1.02-1.52)	.3715-.3725 (9.44-9.46)	.001-.003 (.03-.08)	.....
Exhaust	1.68-1.69 (42.6-42.8)	44°	45°	.040-.060 (1.02-1.52)	.3715-.3725 (9.44-9.46)	.001-.003 (.03-.08)	.....

CRANKSHAFT MAIN & CONNECTING ROD BEARINGS

Engine	MAIN BEARINGS Journal Diam. In. (mm)	MAIN BEARINGS Clearance In. (mm)	MAIN BEARINGS Thrust Bearing	MAIN BEARINGS Crankshaft End Play In. (mm)	CONNECTING ROD BEARINGS Journal Diam. In. (mm)	CONNECTING ROD BEARINGS Clearance In. (mm)	CONNECTING ROD BEARINGS Side Play In. (mm)
6.0L							
No. 1, 2, 3, 4	2.7474-2.7489 (69.78-69.82)	.001-.003 (.03-.08)	No. 3	.003-.008 (.08-.20)	2.0934-2.0955 (53.17-53.27)	.001-.003 (.03-.08)	.006-.018 (.15-.46)
No. 5	2.7464-2.7479 (69.76-69.80)	.002-.004 (.05-.10)					

PISTONS, PINS, RINGS

Engine	PISTONS Clearance In. (mm)	PINS Piston Fit In. (mm)	PINS Rod Fit In. (mm)	RINGS Ring No.	RINGS End Gap In. (mm)	RINGS Side Clearance In. (mm)
6.0L	.0012-.0020 (.030-.051)	.0003-.0005 (.008-.013)	Press Fit	1	.010-.020 (.25-.51)	.0015-.0030 (.038-.076)
				2	.010-.020 (.25-.51)	.0015-.0035 (.038-.089)
				3	.015-.045 (.38-1.14)	.000-.007 (.00-.18)

VALVE SPRINGS

Engine	Free Length In. (mm)	PRESSURE Lbs. @ In. (Kg @ mm) Valve Closed	PRESSURE Lbs. @ In. (Kg @ mm) Valve Open
6.0L	1.99 (50.5)	64-72@1.79 (29-33@45.5)	202-220@1.36 (92-100@34.5)

CAMSHAFT

Engine	Journal Diam. In. (mm)	Clearance In. (mm)	Lobe Lift In. (mm)
6.0L			
No. 1	2.1195-2.1205 (53.835-53.861)	.001-.003 (.03-.08)	.266 (6.76)
No. 2	2.0895-2.0905 (53.073-53.099)	.001-.003 (.03-.08)	.266 (6.76)
No. 3	2.0595-2.0605 (52.311-52.337)	.001-.003 (.03-.08)	.266 (6.76)
No. 4	2.0295-2.0305 (51.549-51.575)	.001-.003 (.03-.08)	.266 (6.76)
No. 5	1.9995-2.0005 (50.787-50.815)	.001-.003 (.03-.08)	.266 (6.76)

Oil Pan Removal

CHRYSLER CORP.

4-CYLINDER ENGINES

2.2L

Drain engine oil. Remove oil pan bolts. Remove oil pan and clean all mating surfaces. When installing, use new end gaskets. Form rail gaskets with 1/8" diameter bead of RTV (PN-4318025).

2.6L

Drain engine oil. Remove oil pan bolts. Clean pan rail and dispose of gasket. Clean pan thoroughly. Use new gasket when installing pan.

6-CYLINDER ENGINES

3.7L

1) Disconnect battery ground cable. Remove engine oil dipstick. Raise vehicle and support with safety stands. Drain engine oil.

2) Remove engine-to-transmission strut. Remove torque converter inspection cover plate (if equipped with automatic transmission). Remove oil pan retaining bolts and oil pan.

3) When installing, apply 1/8" diameter drop of RTV at 4 corners of rubber seal and cork gasket.

V8 ENGINES

5.2L & 5.9L

1) Disconnect battery ground cable. Remove engine oil dipstick. Raise vehicle and support with safety stands. Drain engine oil.

2) Remove exhaust crossover pipe. Remove left engine-to-transmission support strut. Remove oil pan retaining bolts and oil pan.

3) When installing, apply drop of RTV sealer to corners of rubber seal and cork gasket. On 5.9L engines, ensure notches on side gaskets align with notches located at flywheel end on engine block.

FORD

4-CYLINDER ENGINES

2.0L & 2.3L

NOTE: **On vehicles with manual transmissions, oil pan is removed to rear. On models with automatic transmissions, oil pan is removed to front.**

1) Disconnect negative battery cable. Remove air cleaner assembly. Remove engine oil dipstick and tube. Remove engine mount retaining nuts. If equipped, disconnect oil cooler lines at radiator.

2) Remove fan shroud. On models with automatic transmission, remove radiator attaching bolts. Raise and support radiator by wiring it to hood.

3) On all vehicles, raise vehicle on hoist. Drain engine oil. Remove starter. Disconnect tube from exhaust manifold to intake pipe bracket at thermactor check valve.

4) Remove transmission mount nuts. On vehicles with automatic transmission, remove bellcrank from converter housing. Disconnect oil cooler lines from retainer on engine block. Remove front crossmember.

5) On vehicles with manual transmissions, disconnect right front lower shock absorber mount. On all vehicles, position jack under engine and raise engine. Place 2 1/2" high block of wood under engine for support. Remove jack.

6) On vehicles with automatic transmissions, place jack under transmission and raise slightly.

7) On all vehicles, remove oil pan retaining bolts and lower pan to chassis. Remove oil pump drive and pick-up tube assembly. Remove oil pan from vehicle. Clean oil pan gasket surface. Clean exterior of oil pump and pick-up tube screen.

2.3L TURBO DIESEL

1) Disconnect negative battery cables. Remove engine oil dipstick. Remove cooling fan and shroud. Drain cooling system and remove radiator. Remove alternator belt. Remove A/C condenser mounting bolts. Support condenser up and out of way.

2) Raise vehicle. Drain engine oil. Remove front crossmember. Remove stabilizer bar brackets. Lower stabilizer bar. Disconnect power steering hoses at pump. Remove power steering hose hold-down clamp and position hose aside.

3) Remove motor mount nuts. Raise engine and support with blocks between mounts and crossmember. Remove oil pan bolts and lower pan. Remove 2 bolts and 1 nut holding oil pump pick-up tube. Lower pick-up tube into oil pan.

4) Rotate crankshaft until main bearing throws are parallel to bottom of engine. This provides clearance to remove oil pan. Remove oil pan through the front by raising it up between engine and radiator support. Then lower it out through bottom.

6-CYLINDER ENGINES

4.9L

Bronco & Pickup Models

1) Disconnect negative battery cable. Drain engine oil and cooling system. Remove radiator. On California Pickup models, disconnect hoses to air by-pass/air control valve. Remove valve from rear of engine.

2) On all models, raise vehicle. Remove starter. Remove front engine mount nuts. Raise front of engine with jack and wood block. Place 1" blocks of wood under engine mounts.

3) Lower engine onto blocks and remove transmission jack. Remove oil pan bolts and lower pan to crossmember. Remove oil pump and inlet tube bolts. Lower assembly into bottom of pan. Remove oil pan.

Van Models

1) Disconnect negative battery cable. Remove engine cover, air cleaner and carburetor. On models with A/C, discharge system and remove compressor. Drain cooling system.

2) Remove EGR valve. On E250 (Heavy Duty models) and E350 models, remove thermactor check valve after disconnecting hose. On all models, remove upper radiator hose. Remove fan shroud.

3) On models with automatic transmission, remove filler tube. On all models, disconnect exhaust pipe at manifold. Raise vehicle. Disconnect and plug fuel pump inlet line. Remove alternator heat shield and front engine mount nuts.

4) Disconnect lower radiator hose and transmission cooler lines. Remove power steering return line clip located in front of crossmember. Remove starter and engine oil dipstick tube. Raise engine and place 3" blocks under engine mounts.

5) Lower engine. Remove oil pan bolts. Remove oil pump pick-up and screen. Remove oil pan. Clean pan and block gasket surfaces.

V6 ENGINES

2.8L

Aerostar Models

Disconnect negative battery cable. Remove starter. Remove front motor mount bolts. Raise vehicle. Drain engine oil. Raise engine and support with blocks between crossmember and mounts. Remove oil pan.

Bronco II & Ranger Models

1) Disconnect negative battery cable. Remove air cleaner assembly. Remove fan shroud and position over fan. Remove distributor cap and position away from firewall. Remove distributor from engine.

2) Remove front engine mount attaching nuts. Remove engine dipstick tube. Raise vehicle. Drain engine oil. On models with automatic transmissions, remove fill tube from pan and plug hole. On all models, remove oil filter.

3) Disconnect exhaust pipes at manifolds. Disconnect oil cooler bracket and lower cooler. Remove starter. Disconnect front stabilizer bar and position forward. Place jack under engine and raise engine as far as possible.

4) Place wood blocks between engine mounts and frame. Lower engine and remove jack. Remove oil pan attaching bolts and lower pan.

V8 ENGINES

5.0L & 5.8L

Bronco & Pickup Models

1) Disconnect negative battery cable. Remove engine oil dipstick (only on pan entry models). Remove fan shroud and position over fan. Disconnect engine mounts at chassis brackets.

2) On automatic transmission models, disconnect oil cooler line at left side of radiator. Raise engine and place wood blocks under engine supports.

3) Disconnect exhaust pipes at manifolds. Drain engine oil. Remove oil pan bolts. Lower oil pan onto crossmember. Remove 2 bolts holding oil pump pick-up to oil pump.

4) Remove nut attaching oil pick-up to No. 3 main bearing cap stud. Lower pick-up and screen assembly into oil pan. Remove oil pan.

Van Models

1) Disconnect negative battery cable. Remove engine cover. Remove air cleaner and drain cooling system.

2) If equipped with A/C and/or power steering, remove compressor and/or power steering pump with hoses attached and position out of way. Disconnect upper radiator hose. Remove fan shroud bolts.

3) Remove oil filler tube. Remove dipstick-to-exhaust manifold bolt. Raise vehicle. Remove splash shield under alternator. Disconnect lower radiator hose.

4) If equipped, disconnect automatic transmission cooler lines at radiator. Remove engine mount nuts. Disconnect fuel line at fuel pump. Drain crankcase and remove dipstick tube from oil pan. Disconnect exhaust pipes at manifolds.

5) If equipped, remove automatic transmission dipstick and tube. Disconnect shift linkage rods from transmission. Remove center drive shaft support.

6) Remove drive shaft from transmission. Place transmission jack with wood block under oil pan and raise engine. Insert wood blocks between engine and mounts to support engine.

NOTE: **Engine and transmission assembly will pivot around rear engine mount. Engine must remain centered in engine compartment to obtain required lift of 4", which is measured from front mounts.**

7) Remove oil pan attaching bolts and lower oil pan. Remove oil pump and pick-up tube bolts (except 5.8L engine in E150/350 models). Remove nut attaching pick-up tube to No. 3 bearing cap stud and lay tube in oil pan. Remove oil pan.

7.5L

1) Disconnect negative battery cable. Remove engine cover. Disconnect air intake tube and remove air cleaner assembly. Drain cooling system. Disconnect throttle and transmission linkage from carburetor. Disconnect power brake vacuum line from engine.

2) Disconnect fuel line, choke lines, and air cleaner adapter from carburetor. Disconnect radiator hoses. Disconnect automatic transmission and engine oil cooler lines from radiator. Remove fan, fan shroud and radiator.

3) Remove power steering pump and position aside with hoses connected. Remove engine oil dipstick tube and front engine mount attaching bolts. Remove oil filler tube and bracket. If equipped, remove A/C hoses or rotate them downward at rear of compressor to clear dashboard.

4) Raise vehicle. Drain crankcase and remove oil filter. Remove exhaust pipes at manifolds. Disconnect manual and kickdown linkages from transmission. Remove drive shaft and coupling shaft assembly.

5) Remove transmission dipstick tube assembly. Remove engine oil dipstick and tube from oil pan. Position jack with wood block under oil pan and raise engine until transmission touches floor board.

NOTE: **Engine and transmission will pivot around rear engine mount. Engine must remain centered in engine compartment to achieve required lift of 4" at front mounts.**

6) Insert wood blocks between engine and mounts to support engine. Remove oil pan bolts and lower oil pan onto crossmember. Remove oil pump and pick-up assembly and place in oil pan. Remove oil pan to rear.

Oil Pan Removal

FORD (Cont.)

6.9L DIESEL

1) Disconnect ground cables from both batteries. Remove engine oil dipstick. Remove transmission oil dipstick. Remove air cleaner and cover intake opening.

NOTE: **Fan and clutch assembly are held on with left-hand threaded nut.**

2) Remove fan and fan clutch assembly with Removers (T83T-6312-A and B). Drain cooling system. Remove lower radiator hose. Disconnect and plug power steering return hose at pump. Disconnect all wiring from alternator. Raise vehicle.

3) Disconnect and plug automatic transmission cooler lines at radiator. Disconnect and plug fuel pump inlet line. Drain engine oil and remove oil filter. Remove transmission dipstick tube. Disconnect exhaust pipes at both manifolds and at muffler flange. Remove pipes.

4) Remove upper exhaust pipe stud from right exhaust manifold. Remove engine mount nuts. Lower vehicle. Attach lifting brackets to front of engine on E250/350 models. Attach lifting sling to eyes on intake manifold on F250/350.

5) On all models, raise engine until transmission housing contacts body. Place wood blocks between engine mounts and frame. Use 2 3/4" block on left side and 2" block on right side.

6) Lower engine onto blocks. Raise vehicle. Remove flywheel inspection plate. Position fuel pump inlet line at back of crossmember No. 1. Ensure automatic transmission cooler lines are out of way.

7) Remove oil pan attaching bolts and allow oil pan to drop. Remove oil pump and oil pump pick-up from engine and place in oil pan (on F250/350 models). Remove oil pan from vehicle, turning crankshaft to clear counterweights if necessary. On E250/350 models, oil pump can be removed after pan is removed.

GENERAL MOTORS

4-CYLINDER ENGINES

1.9L

1) Disconnect negative battery cable. Drain engine oil. Remove engine. Remove oil pan attaching hardware. Remove oil level gauge guide tube from intake manifold and oil pan. Remove oil pan.

2) When installing, apply thin coat of sealer to each end of gasket and at seams of rear main and front cover. Align holes of gasket on block and install oil pan.

2.5L

Astro & Safari Models

1) Disconnect negative battery cable. Raise vehicle. Drain engine oil. Remove strut rods. Disconnect exhaust pipe at exhaust manifold. Remove torque converter cover.

2) Disconnect starter brace at block. Remove starter. Disconnect transmission oil cooler lines at oil pan. Remove oil pan. When installing, apply thin coat of sealer to entire oil pan sealing flange. Align holes of gasket on block and install oil pan.

2WD Models

1) Disconnect negative battery cable. Raise vehicle. Drain engine oil. Remove strut rods. Disconnect exhaust pipe at exhaust manifold. Remove torque converter cover.

2) Disconnect starter brace at block. Remove starter. Disconnect transmission oil cooler lines at oil pan. Remove oil pan. When installing, apply thin coat of sealer to entire oil pan sealing flange. Align holes of gasket on block and install oil pan.

4WD Models

1) Disconnect negative battery cable. Disconnect power steering reservior at fan shroud. Remove dipstick. Raise vehicle and drain engine oil. Disconnect brake line clips at crossmember.

2) Remove crossmember. Disconnect transmission cooler lines at flywheel cover. Disconnect exhaust pipe at exhaust manifold. Disconnect catalytic converter hanger. Remove flywheel cover.

3) Remove drive shaft splash shield. Mark position of idler arm for reinstallation in original position. Disconnect idler arm. Remove steering gear bolts. Pull steering gear and linkage forward.

4) Disconnect front differential housing at mounts and move forward. Remove starter. Loosen starter-to-block brace bolt. Disconnect front drive shaft at pinion. Remove motor mount through bolts. Raise engine. Remove oil pan.

5) When installing, apply thin coat of sealer to entire oil pan sealing flange. Align holes of gasket on block and install oil pan.

2.2L DIESEL

Disconnect negative battery cable. Raise vehicle and drain engine oil. Remove oil pan bolts. Remove oil pan. Clean mating surfaces on pan and crankcase. To install, use new gasket and install oil pan.

6-CYLINDER ENGINES

4.8L

Van Models

1) Disconnect negative battery cable and remove engine cover. Remove air cleaner and studs. Remove fan shroud. Remove radiator upper supports. Raise vehicle.

2) On manual transmission models, disconnect clutch cross shaft from left front mount bracket. Remove transmission-to-bellhousing upper bolt. Remove transmission rear mount bolts and install two 7/16" X 3" bolts. Raise transmission using jack and install 2" block between mount and crossmember.

3) On all models, remove starter and drain engine oil. Unhook positive battery cable from oil pan studs. Remove engine mount through bolts. Raise engine and insert wooden blocks between engine mounts and crossmember brackets.

4) Remove lower bellhousing cover. Remove oil pan attaching bolts and remove oil pan. Clean all gasket mating surfaces.

5) When installing, apply thin coat of sealer to entire oil pan sealing flange. Align holes of gasket on block and install oil pan.

All Other Models

1) Disconnect negative battery cable. Raise vehicle and drain engine oil. Remove starter and lower bellhousing cover.

2) Remove engine mount through bolts. Raise front of engine, reinstall through bolts, and lower engine. Remove oil pan bolts and oil pan. Clean gasket mating surfaces.

3) When installing, apply thin coat of sealer to entire oil pan sealing flange. Align holes of gasket on block and install oil pan.

V6 ENGINES

2.8L

2WD Models

1) Disconnect negative battery cable. Drain engine oil. Remove engine. Remove oil pan attaching hardware. Remove oil pan. Clean all gasket mating surfaces.

2) When installing, apply thin coat of sealer to entire oil pan sealing flange. Align holes of gasket on block and install oil pan.

4WD Models

1) Disconnect battery. Remove dipstick. Raise vehicle. Remove drive belt splash, front axle and transfer case shields. Disconnect brake lines at crossmember. Remove No. 2 crossmember.

2) On automatic transmission models, remove converter hanger bolts. Disconnect exhaust pipes at manifold and slide exhaust rearward. On all models, disconnect front propeller shaft at drive pinion.

3) Disconnect engine braces at flywheel cover and loosen braces at block. Remove flywheel cover. Remove starter bolts and lay starter aside. Disconnect steering shock absorber at frame bracket. Remove steering gear bolts.

4) Mark position of idler arm location for reinstallation, then remove attaching bolts. Pull steering gear and linkage forward. Remove front differential housing mounting bolts and move housing forward.

5) Remove motor mount through bolts. Drain oil. Remove oil pan bolts. Raise engine. Remove oil pan. Clean all gasket mating surfaces.

6) When installing, apply 1/8" bead of sealer on entire oil pan sealing flange. Align holes of gasket on block and install oil pan.

4.3L

Astro & Safari Models

1) Disconnect negative battery cable. Raise vehicle. Drain engine oil. Disconnect exhaust pipes at manifolds. Remove engine strut rods at inspection cover.

2) Remove inspection cover. Remove starter and set aside. Remove engine mount trim bolts. Remove oil pan. Clean all gasket mating surfaces.

3) When installing, apply 1/8" bead of sealer on entire oil pan sealing flange. Align holes of gasket on block and install oil pan.

All Other Models

1) Disconnect negative battery cable. Raise vehicle. Drain engine oil. Disconnect exhaust crossover pipe at manifolds. Remove engine strut rods at inspection cover. On 4WD pickup models with automatic transmission, remove strut rods at motor mounts.

2) Remove inspection cover. Remove starter and set aside. Remove engine mount trim bolts. Remove oil pan. Clean all gasket mating surfaces.

3) When installing, apply 1/8" bead of sealer on entire oil pan sealing flange. Align holes of gasket on block and install oil pan.

V8 ENGINES

5.0 & 5.7L

1) Raise vehicle. Drain engine oil. Remove exhaust crossover pipe. On models with automatic transmission, remove converter inspection cover.

2) On 4WD pickup models with automatic transmission, remove strut rods at engine mounts. On all models, remove oil pan bolts and oil pan. Clean all gasket mating surfaces. When installing, apply 1/8" bead of sealer on entire oil pan sealing flange. Align holes of gasket on block and install oil pan.

7.4L

1) Disconnect negative battery cable. Loosen fan shroud. Remove air cleaner and distributor cap. Raise vehicle and drain oil. On manual transmission models, remove starter.

2) On all models, remove lower bellhousing cover. Remove oil filter. On models equipped with oil pressure gauge, remove oil pressure line from block.

NOTE: **Pressure line is removed to prevent damage when engine is lifted.**

3) On all models, remove front engine mount through bolts. Raise engine and remove oil pan bolts. Remove oil pan and clean all gasket surfaces. When installing, apply 1/8" bead of sealer on entire oil pan sealing flange. Align holes of gasket on block and install oil pan.

6.2L DIESEL

Van Models

1) Disconnect negative battery cable. Remove engine cover, engine oil and transmission oil dipsticks. Disconnect engine dipstick tube at left rocker cover.

2) Disconnect transmission dipstick at bellhousing and pull from transmission. Disconnect T.V. cable at injection pump rod and at transmission dipstick tube.

3) Remove upper bellhousing bolt and vacuum pump. Raise vehicle. Remove propeller shaft. Disconnect speedometer cable at transmission.

4) Disconnect torque converter clutch connector, shift linkage and ATF cooler lines at transmission. Remove flex plate inspection cover and flex plate-to-torque converter bolts.

5) Support transmission. Remove transmission mount-to-crossmember nut and remove crossmember. Remove bellhousing-to-cylinder case bolts.

6) Remove transmission and flex plate. Remove dipstick tube from engine oil pan. Drain crankcase. Disconnect engine oil cooler lines at cylinder case. Remove starter.

7) Disconnect battery and cooler line clips. Remove oil pan bolts. Lower pan from block. Remove oil pump-to-main cap bolt, disconnect pump drive shaft and let assembly fall in pan. Remove oil pan. Clean all gasket mating surfaces.

Oil Pan Removal

GENERAL MOTORS (Cont.)

8) When installing, apply 1/8" bead of sealer on entire oil pan sealing flange. Install dipstick tube in pan before fully seating oil pan. Install oil pump. Align holes of gasket on block and install oil pan.

NOTE: **It may be necessary to rotate crankshaft so that forward throw and No. 1 and 2 journals are up, giving front of pan clearance.**

All Other Models

1) Disconnect negative battery cables. Raise vehicle and drain engine oil. Remove transmission dust cover. Remove oil pan bolts. Remove left engine mount through bolt.

2) Raise engine and remove oil pan. Clean mating surfaces of oil and old gasket. When installing, apply 1/32" bead of sealer on entire oil pan sealing flange. Sealer must be wet to touch when bolts are tightened.

JEEP

4-CYLINDER ENGINES

2.5L

1) Disconnect negative battery cable. Lock steering wheel (CJ7 and Scrambler models). Raise vehicle and drain oil. Lower exhaust pipe after disconnecting exhaust pipe from manifold and hanger from catalytic converter (Cherokee and Wagoneer models).

2) Remove starter. Remove converter/flywheel housing cover. Remove oil pan bolts and oil pan (slide to rear on CJ7 and Scrambler models). Clean block and pan mating surfaces completely. Apply RTV sealer to tab ends of front pan seal and to gasket contact points of seal ends. Coat inside curved surface of rear seal with soap.

2.1L TURBO DIESEL

Remove engine from vehicle. Drain engine oil. Remove engine oil dipstick and tube. Remove oil pan bolts and pan. Clean block and pan mating surfaces completely. Apply RTV sealer to gasket.

NOTE: **Ensure oil pan is installed flush to rear of block. Otherwise, oil pan may be damaged when transmission is installed.**

6-CYLINDER ENGINES

4.2L

1) Disconnect negative battery cable. Lock steering wheel. Raise vehicle and drain oil. Remove starter.

2) Remove converter/flywheel housing cover. Remove oil pan bolts. Slide oil pan to rear to remove. Use RTV on all end tabs when installing. Coat inside curved surface of rear seal with soap.

V6 ENGINES

2.8L

1) Disconnect negative battery cable. Disconnect right exhaust pipe from manifold. Raise and support vehicle. Drain oil. Disconnect left exhaust pipe at manifold. Remove starter motor.

2) Remove converter/flywheel housing cover. Disconnect exhaust pipe at catalytic converter flange. Lower exhaust pipe and rest "Y" portion on upper control arms of axle. Remove oil pan bolts. Remove oil pan.

3) Clean RTV from pan and block mating surfaces. Use new rear pan seal for installation. Use 1/8" diameter bead of RTV on entire pan sealing flange.

V8 ENGINES

6.0L

1) Disconnect negative battery cable. Drain engine oil. Remove starter. Remove oil pan bolts. Remove oil pan and end seals. Clean mating surface of pan and block.

2) When installing, apply RTV to end tabs of front and rear seals. Coat inside curved surface of rear seal with soap. Apply RTV to pan contacting surface of front and rear seals. Put RTV on gasket ends.

CHRYSLER CORP.

4-CYLINDER ENGINES

ALL MODELS

1) Disconnect battery ground. Scribe hood hinge location on hood for reassembly. Remove hood. Drain cooling system. Remove cooling system hoses from radiator and engine.

2) Remove radiator with shroud and fan assembly. Remove air cleaner with hoses. If equipped, unbolt A/C compressor and place to side with hoses attached. If equipped, unbolt power steering pump and place pump to side with hoses attached.

3) Remove oil filter. Disconnect wiring at engine, carburetor, and alternator. Disconnect accelerator cable. Remove fuel line and heater hoses. Remove alternator. Remove transmission lower case cover.

4) Disconnect exhaust pipe at manifold. Remove starter. Disconnect clutch cable on models with manual transmission. On models with automatic transmission, index flex plate to torque converter. Remove bolts holding converter to plate.

5) Attach "C" clamp to bottom front edge of torque converter housing to keep converter in place. Attach transmission holding device. Attach lifting hoist to engine. Remove right inner splash shield.

CAUTION: If insulator is to be removed, be sure to mark its position on side rail. Insulator must be installed in same position. Be sure clutch cable is disconnected before removing bolts from transmission case to engine.

6) Disconnect engine-to-chassis ground strap. Remove right side engine mount screw. Remove transmission case-to-cylinder block bolts. Remove front engine mount bolt. On models with manual transmission, remove stabilizing strut from suspension crossmember.

7) On 2.2L engines, remove insulator through bolt of left mount from inside fenderwell. Insulator bracket-to-transmission bolts may be removed instead of through bolt. Lift and remove engine from vehicle.

6-CYLINDER ENGINES

VAN & WAGON MODELS

1) Disconnect battery ground. Remove oil dipstick. Raise vehicle and remove air pump tube from exhaust pipe. Remove exhaust pipe. Remove inspection cover from transmission and drain crankcase. Remove engine-to-transmission strut.

2) Remove oil pan (turn crankshaft to clear front of oil pan if necessary). Turn oil pick-up tube upward to avoid damaging it. Remove flex plate-to-torque converter bolts. Remove lower transmission bellhousing bolts. Remove right motor mount nut.

3) Lower vehicle and drain cooling system. Remove engine cover, carburetor air cleaner and carburetor. If equipped with A/C, discharge system. Disconnect and plug A/C hoses. Remove fan shroud, windshield washer and overflow reservoirs. Remove front bumper, grille and support brace. Disconnect radiator hoses. Remove radiator and support as an assembly.

4) Remove steering pump bracket bolts and set pump aside with hoses attached. Remove air pump. Disconnect throttle linkage. Remove all hoses, electrical connections, and lines to coil, alternator, and other engine accessories. Remove alternator with brackets, fan blade, pulley and drive belts. Disconnect and cap flexible fuel pump line.

5) Remove starter and set aside. Remove distributor cap, spark plug wires and left engine mount nut. Attach lifting fixture to engine. Support transmission securely. Remove remaining transmission housing bolts and remove engine from front of vehicle.

ALL OTHER MODELS

1) Disconnect battery ground. Scribe hood hinges for reinstallation and remove hood. Drain cooling system and remove battery. Remove radiator, heater hoses and radiator. Set fan shroud aside and discharge air conditioning system (if equipped). Remove air cleaner, vacuum lines, distributor cap and wiring.

2) Remove carburetor, linkage, starter wiring and oil pressure wire. Remove starter, alternator, charcoal canister and horns. Remove A/C and power steering hoses (if equipped). Remove exhaust pipe at manifold. Remove transmission housing and inspection plate bolts. Attach "C" clamp to front of housing to prevent torque converter from coming out.

3) Index mark converter to flex plate for reassembly. Remove torque converter flex plate bolts. Support transmission securely. Disconnect flex plate from torque converter. Install engine lifting fixture and attach chain. Remove engine front mount bolts and remove engine from vehicle.

V8 ENGINES

VAN & WAGON MODELS

1) Disconnect battery ground. Remove oil dipstick. Raise vehicle and remove exhaust crossover pipe. Remove inspection cover from transmission. Drain engine oil and remove engine-to-transmission strut. Remove oil pan (rotate crankshaft to clear front of pan if necessary). Remove oil pump and pick-up tube.

2) Remove flex plate-to-torque converter bolts. Remove starter and set aside. Remove lower transmission housing bolts and engine mount nuts. Lower vehicle and drain cooling system. Remove engine cover and discharge A/C system. Disconnect and plug condenser lines. Remove front bumper, grille and support brace.

3) Remove air cleaner and carburetor. Disconnect radiator hoses and remove condenser, radiator and support as an assembly. Remove A/C compressor bracket bolts and set compressor aside. Remove air pump.

4) Remove power steering pump and set aside with hoses attached. Disconnect throttle linkage, heater and vacuum hoses and all electrical connections to coil, alternator and other engine accessories.

5) Remove alternator, fan blade (or fluid fan unit), pulley and all drive belts. Disconnect and cap flexible line at fuel pump. Remove left exhaust manifold heat shield, spark plug wires and distributor cap.

6) Attach lifting fixture to intake manifold. Support transmission securely in level position. Remove upper transmission housing bolts. Use lifting device to remove engine from front of vehicle.

CHRYSLER CORP. (Cont.)

TIGHTENING SPECIFICATIONS

Application	Ft. Lbs. (N.m)
Engine Mounts	
4-Cylinder	
Front	40 (54)
Left (Bolt to Transmission)	40 (54)
Right (Through Bolt)	70 (95)
Strut (Through Bolt)	40 (54)
All Other Models	
Front	75 (102)
Flex Plate-to-Converter	
4-Cylinder	40 (54)
All Other Models	23 (31)
Flex Plate-to-Crankshaft	
4-Cylinder	
A-413 Transaxle	65 (88)
A-470 Transaxle	100 (136)
All Other Models	55 (75)
Flywheel-to-Crankshaft	
4-Cylinder (2.2L Only)	65 (88)
All Other Models	55 (75)
Transmission-to-Engine	
4-Cylinder	70 (95)
All Other Models	
3/8"-16	30 (41)
7/16"-14	50 (68)

ALL OTHER MODELS

1) Scribe hood hinges for reassembly and remove hood. Drain cooling system and remove battery and air cleaner. Remove coolant hoses and radiator. Discharge A/C system (if equipped). Remove vacuum lines, distributor cap and wiring. Remove carburetor, linkage, starter wires and oil pressure wire.

2) Remove and cap A/C hoses and power steering hoses (if equipped). Remove starter, alternator, charcoal canister, and horns. Remove exhaust crossover pipe at manifold. Remove transmission housing bolts and inspection plate. Attach "C" clamp to front of transmission torque converter housing to prevent converter from falling.

3) Index mark converter to flex plate for reassembly. Remove flex plate bolts. Support transmission securely in level position. Disconnect flex plate from torque converter. Install engine lifting fixture and remove engine front mounts. Remove engine from engine compartment.

FORD

4-CYLINDER ENGINES

2.0L & 2.3L
Aerostar Models

NOTE: **Engine may be removed with or without transmission attached.**

1) Disconnect negative battery cable. Drain cooling system. Disconnect air cleaner outlet tube and idle speed control hose. Remove upper and lower radiator hoses. Disconnect heater hoses. Disconnect lower intake manifold hose from tee fitting in heater hose.

2) Remove fan shroud. Disconnect 2 electrical connectors at alternator. Remove throttle linkage shield. Disconnect accelerator cable and cruise control cable (if equipped) from throttle body. Unbolt cables from bracket and position cables out of way.

3) Discharge A/C system, if equipped. Remove suction and discharge hoses from compressor. Unplug A/C compressor electical connector. Unplug ignition coil electrical connector. Unplug Thick Film Ignition (TFI) module electrical connector. Disconnect knock sensor. Label and disconnect all vacuum hoses.

4) Disconnect hose and electrical connector from EGR valve. Remove engine cover. Disconnect throttle position sensor and oil pressure sending unit. Disconnect and plug fuel supply and return hoses. Disconnect fuel injection wiring harness, air charge temperature sensor and coolant temperature sensor. Disconnect engine ground strap.

5) If equipped with manual transmission, position shifter in Neutral. Remove shift lever-to-floor retaining bolts. Remove shift lever-to-transmission retaining bolts. Remove shift lever. Raise vehicle.

6) Disconnect transmission oil cooler lines at radiator, if equipped. Disconnect power steering pressure switch electrical connector, if equipped. Position front wheels in straight ahead position. Remove intermediate steering column shaft-to-steering gear retaining bolt. Disconnect steering column from steering gear.

7) Disconnect O_2 sensor wire. Disconnect exhaust pipe from manifold. Remove exhaust pipe and catalytic converter. Remove speedometer and/or tachometer cable from transmission. On manual transmissions, disconnect back-up light switch and shift indicator sender at transmission. Remove lock pin retaining hydraulic hose to slave cylinder in clutch housing. Remove and plug hose.

8) On automatic transmissions, disconnect neutral safety switch. Disconnect throttle and kickdown cable. Remove drive shaft. Remove both front wheel and tire assemblies. Disconnect stabiizer bar from lower control arm. Disconnect brake lines at frame bracket.

9) Support lower control arm and disconnect upper control arm from spindle at upper ball joint. Place safety chains around lower control arms and upper spring seats. Remove transmission crossmember. Remove transmission. Position Removal Table (109-0002) under crossmember and engine assembly.

10) Lower vehicle until crossmember rests on table. Place wood blocks under front crossmember and rear of engine (or transmission, if installed) to keep assembly level. Install safety chains around crossmember and table.

11) With engine and crossmember securely supported on table, remove 3 engine and crossmember-to-frame retaining bolts from each side of vehicle. Raise body from engine and crossmember assembly. Disconnect and plug power steering hoses from pump.

12) Remove motor mount nuts. Remove engine from crossmember. Remove transmission, if not previously removed.

Bronco II & Ranger Models

1) Disconnect and remove battery. Drain cooling system. Remove air cleaner and duct assembly. On 2.3L engines, disconnect air cleaner outlet tube at throttle body, idle speed control hose and heat riser tube.

2) Mark location of hood hinges and remove hood. Disconnect upper and lower radiator hoses from engine. Remove radiator shroud attaching screws. Remove upper radiator supports. Remove cooling fan and fan shroud. Remove radiator. Remove oil fill cap. Disconnect primary wire at coil.

3) Disconnect wires from oil pressure sending unit and water temperature sending unit. Disconnect wires from alternator and starter. Disconnect accelerator cable and kickdown rod from carburetor, if equipped. If equipped, remove A/C compressor from bracket and position aside with hoses attached.

4) Disconnect power brake vacuum hose. Disconnect chassis fuel line from fuel pump. On 2.3L engines, disconnect 2 push connect fittings at engine fuel rail. Disconnect heater hoses from engine. Remove engine mount nuts.

5) Raise vehicle. Drain crankcase. Remove starter motor. Disconnect exhaust pipe from manifold. Remove dust cover from transmission. On vehicles with manual transmissions, remove lower bellhousing-to-engine bolts and clutch slave cylinder.

6) On vehicles with automatic transmissions, remove flex plate-to-converter bolts and bellhousing lower attaching bolts. On all vehicles, lower vehicle. Support transmission with jack. Remove upper bellhousing-to-engine bolts. Attach an engine lifting device to engine. Lift engine out of vehicle.

2.3L TURBO DIESEL

Bronco II & Ranger Models

1) Mark location of hood hinges and remove hood. Disconnect battery ground cables from both batteries and from engine. Remove cables from vehicle. Drain cooling system. Remove crankcase breather hose from valve cover.

2) Disconnect air intake hose between air cleaner and turbocharger. Cap turbo inlet using Protective Cap Set (T85T-9395-A). Remove A/C compressor and set aside. Disconnect heater hoses. Disconnect upper and lower radiator hoses from engine.

3) Remove cooling fan. Remove radiator shroud attaching screws. Remove upper radiator supports. Remove radiator and shroud assembly. Disconnect electrical connector at fuel conditioner. Disconnect and plug fuel lines at fuel conditioner. Disconnect fuel return line at injection pump.

4) Disconnect vacuum lines at vacuum pump. Remove coolant overflow hose from filler neck. Disconnect accelerator and speed control cable (if equipped) at injection pump. Disconnect engine wiring harness from chassis harness at bottom of injector pump. Disconnect coolant temperature sensor and glow plug buss bar.

5) Remove starter. Raise vehicle. Remove right side wheel and tire assembly. Remove right side inner fender panel. Disconnect oil pressure switch wire. Disconnect oil cooler lines at oil filter adapter. Loosen engine mount nuts. Disconnect exhaust pipe from turbo outlet pipe.

6) Disconnect power steering hoses at pump. Disconnect clutch servo hydraulic line at clutch housing and position aside. Remove engine mount bolts. Remove transmission mounting bolts (except top 2). Lower vehicle. Attach lifting device to engine brackets. Remove top 2 transmission mounting bolts. Remove engine from vehicle.

V6 ENGINES

2.8L

Aerostar Models

NOTE: **Engine may be removed with or without transmission attached.**

1) Disconnect negative battery cable. Drain cooling system. Remove air cleaner and intake duct assembly. Remove upper and lower radiator hoses. Remove fan shroud. Disconnect Manifold Absolute Pressure (MAP) sensor. Disconnect A/C compressor electrical connectors. Remove A/C belt.

2) Remove A/C compressor and set aside. Remove engine cover. Disconnect accelerator and kickdown cables at carburetor. Label and disconnect all engine electrical connectors. Route engine harness out of engine compartment. Label and disconnect all vacuum hoses.

3) Disconnect speed control cable, if equipped. Remove air control valve-to-catalytic converter hose. Disconnect distributor electrical connector for Thick Film Ignition (TFI). Disconnect brake booster vacuum hose.

4) If equipped with manual transmission, position shifter in Neutral. Remove shift lever-to-floor retaining bolts. Remove shift lever-to-transmission retaining bolts. Remove shift lever. Raise vehicle. Remove heater hoses from bracket underneath engine at front of crossmember.

5) Disconnect transmission oil cooler lines at radiator, if equipped. Position front wheels in straight ahead position. Remove intermediate steering column shaft-to-steering gear retaining bolt. Disconnect steering column from steering gear. Disconnect oil pressure sending unit wire from beneath fuel pump.

6) Disconnect and plug fuel lines at fuel pump. Disconnect engine ground strap. Disconnect starter cable and ground cable from starter. Route cables away from crossmember. If equipped with manual transmission, remove lock pin retaining hydraulic hose to slave cylinder in clutch housing. Remove and plug hose.

7) Disconnect O_2 sensor wire from left side exhaust manifold. Disconnect knock sensor lead from engine above starter. Disconnect exhaust pipes from manifolds. Disconnect thermactor air tube at check valve. Disconnect and remove exhaust pipe and catalytic converter. Remove speedometer cable from transmission.

8) On manual transmissions, disconnect back-up light switch and shift indicator sender at transmission.

Engine Removal

FORD (Cont.)

On automatic transmissions, disconnect neutral safety switch. Disconnect throttle and kickdown cable. Remove drive shaft. Remove both front wheel and tire assemblies.

9) Disconnect stabiizer bar from lower control arm. Disconnect brake lines at frame bracket. Support lower control arm and disconnect upper control arm from spindle at upper ball joint. Place safety chains around lower control arms and upper spring seats.

10) Remove transmission crossmember. Remove transmission. Position Removal Table (109-0002) under crossmember and engine assembly. Lower vehicle until crossmember rests on table. Place wood blocks under front crossmember and rear of engine (or transmission, if installed) to keep assembly level.

11) Install safety chains around crossmember and table. With engine and crossmember securely supported on table, remove 3 engine and crossmember-to-frame retaining bolts from each side of vehicle. Raise body from engine and crossmember assembly. Ensure all wiring and hoses are disconnected before raising vehicle.

12) Disconnect and plug power steering hoses from pump. Remove motor mount nuts. Remove engine from crossmember. Remove transmission, if not previously removed.

Bronco II & Ranger Models

1) Disconnect or remove all thermactor components that may interfere with engine removal. Disconnect battery ground cable. Drain cooling system. Remove hood. Remove air cleaner and intake duct assembly. Disconnect upper and lower radiator hoses.

2) Remove fan shroud bolts and position shroud over fan. Remove radiator and shroud. Disconnect alternator ground wire from engine block. Remove alternator from engine and position aside. If equipped, remove A/C compressor and power steering pump and position aside with hoses attached.

3) Disconnect heater hoses from engine. Remove engine ground wires. Disconnect and plug fuel tank line at fuel pump. Disconnect throttle cable linkage at carburetor and intake manifold. Disconnect primary wire from coil.

4) Remove power brake vacuum hose from engine. Disconnect wiring from oil pressure and engine coolant temperature sending units. Raise vehicle. Disconnect exhaust pipes from manifolds. Remove starter. Remove front engine mount nuts or through bolts.

5) On vehicles with automatic transmissions, remove converter inspection cover and disconnect flex plate from converter. Remove kickdown rod. Remove bellhousing-to-engine bolts. Remove adapter plate-to-converter housing bolt.

6) On vehicles with manual transmissions, remove clutch linkage. On all vehicles, lower vehicle. Attach lifting device to brackets at exhaust manifolds. Support transmission. Remove engine from vehicle.

6-CYLINDER ENGINES

4.9L

Bronco & Pickup Models

1) Disconnect battery cables. Drain cooling system and crankcase. Mark hood hinge position and remove hood. Remove air cleaner assembly. Remove A/C compressor and condenser, if equipped. Disconnect heater hoses from engine.

2) Disconnect flexible fuel line at fuel pump. Remove radiator. Remove cooling fan, viscous drive, belt and water pump pulley. Disconnect accelerator cable at carburetor and remove retracting spring. If equipped, disconnect power brake vacuum hose from engine.

3) On models with automatic transmission, disconnect kickdown rod at bellcrank assembly. Disconnect exhaust pipe from manifold. Disconnect body ground strap and battery ground cable from engine. Disconnect engine wiring harness from coil and all sending units. Disconnect all EEC-IV sensors, if equipped.

4) Remove alternator mounting bolts and position alternator aside with wires attached. If equipped, remove power steering pump from mounting brackets and position aside with lines attached.

5) If equipped with air compressor, bleed air system and disconnect 2 pressure lines from compressor. Raise vehicle. Remove starter and automatic transmission fluid filler tube bracket (if equipped). Remove engine rear plate upper right bolt.

6) On vehicles with manual transmission, remove all bellhousing lower retaining bolts. Disconnect clutch retracting spring. On vehicles with automatic transmission, remove converter housing access cover and flex plate-to-converter nuts. Secure converter assembly in housing.

7) Remove automatic transmission cooler lines from clip at engine. Remove converter housing-to-engine lower retaining bolts. On all vehicles, remove insulator-to-intermediate support bracket nut from each front engine support. Lower vehicle and support transmission with floor jack.

8) Remove remaining bellhousing-to-engine bolts. Attach lifting device to engine. Raise engine slightly and carefully pull from transmission. Remove engine from vehicle.

Van Models

1) Remove engine cover. Drain cooling system. Remove air cleaner assembly. Disconnect battery. Remove front bumper. Remove grille and lower gravel deflector as assembly. Disconnect radiator hoses. Disconnect transmission oil cooler lines at radiator.

2) Remove radiator and shroud. Disconnect heater hoses from engine. Disconnect alternator and position aside. Remove power steering pump drive belt. Remove power steering pump and bracket from engine. Disconnect and plug fuel line at fuel pump.

3) Disconnect distributor, EEC-IV sensors and sending unit wires from engine. Disconnect brake booster hose from engine. Disconnect accelerator cable and remove bracket from engine. Disconnect automatic transmission kickdown at bellcrank. Remove exhaust manifold heat deflector and exhaust pipe-to-manifold nuts.

4) Disconnect both ends of transmission vacuum line at intake manifold and junction. Remove upper transmission-to-engine bolts. Remove automatic transmission dipstick tube support at intake manifold. Raise vehicle. Drain crankcase and remove oil filter.

5) Disconnect starter wiring and remove starter. Remove flywheel inspection cover. Remove flex plate-to-flywheel nuts. Remove front engine mount nuts. Remove remaining transmission-to-engine bolts. Lower vehicle from hoist. Attach lifting device to engine. Remove engine from vehicle.

FORD (Cont.)

V8 ENGINES

5.0L, 5.8L & 7.5L

Bronco & Pickup Models

1) Drain cooling system and crankcase. Mark hood hinges and remove hood. Disconnect battery and remove ground cables from cylinder block. Remove air cleaner and intake duct assembly with crankcase ventilation and carbon canister hoses attached. Disconnect radiator hoses.

2) Disconnect automatic transmission cooler lines (if equipped). If equipped with A/C, discharge system, remove condenser and disconnect hoses at compressor. Remove fan shroud, radiator, fan spacer and pulley. Remove alternator attaching bolts and position alternator aside.

3) Disconnect oil pressure sending unit wire. Disconnect and plug flexible fuel line at fuel tank line. Disconnect vacuum lines, carbon canister hose, heater hoses and electrical wiring from engine. Disconnect primary wire at coil. On 5.0L EFI models, disconnect chassis fuel line quick disconnect fittings at fuel rail.

4) Disconnect accelerator cable, transmission shift rod and speed control linkages and retracting spring from carburetor/throttle body. Disconnect power brake booster vacuum hose, if equipped. Remove bellhousing-to-engine upper bolts. Raise front of vehicle. Remove starter.

5) Disconnect exhaust pipes (and exhaust heat control valve, if equipped) from manifolds. Disconnect engine mounts from brackets on frame. If equipped with automatic transmission, remove converter inspection plate and flex plate-to-converter attaching bolts.

6) Remove remaining bellhousing-to-engine bolts. Lower vehicle and support transmission. Attach lifting device to engine. Carefully raise engine and separate it from transmission. Lift engine from vehicle taking care not to damage rear cover plate.

Van Models

1) Remove engine cover. Disconnect battery. Drain cooling system. Remove grille assembly with gravel deflector. Remove upper grille support bracket. Remove hood lock support and condenser upper mounting brackets (if equipped). Discharge A/C system.

2) Remove condenser and disconnect lines at compressor. Remove accelerator cable bracket. Disconnect radiator hoses from radiator. Disconnect heater hoses from engine. If equipped, disconnect automatic transmission cooler lines at radiator. Remove fan shroud and fan assembly. Remove radiator.

3) Pivot alternator inward and disconnect wiring. Remove air cleaner assembly. Remove air cleaner, air duct, valve assembly, and exhaust manifold shroud. Remove flex tube from exhaust manifold stove. Disconnect throttle cable from carburetor and remove cable bracket.

4) If equipped with automatic transmission, remove transmission shift rod. Disconnect fuel and choke lines. Remove carburetor and spacer plate. Disconnect all vacuum hoses from engine. Raise vehicle. Drain crankcase and remove oil filter. Disconnect exhaust pipes from manifolds.

5) Disconnect transmission filler tube from right cylinder head. Remove engine mount attaching bolts and nuts. Remove starter.

NOTE: **On 7.5L engines, right-hand mount through bolt is inserted from front of vehicle only. Left-hand mount through bolt is inserted from rear only.**

6) On vehicles with manual transmission, remove bellhousing-to-engine bolts. On vehicles with automatic transmission, remove converter inspection cover bolts. Remove flex plate-to-converter nuts. Remove bolts attaching adapter plate to converter housing. Remove converter housing-to-engine bolts.

7) On all vehicles, remove ground strap from engine block. Lower vehicle. Support transmission with floor jack. If equipped, remove power steering pump drive belt and front bracket. Disconnect engine wire loom and position aside.

8) Install Lifting Bracket (T75T-6000-A) to intake manifold. Remove upper bellhousing-to-engine bolts. Attach lifting device to engine. Carefully move engine foward and remove from vehicle.

6.9L DIESEL

1) Disconnect negative battery cables from both batteries. Mark hood hinges and remove hood. Drain cooling system. Remove air cleaner and intake duct assembly. Cover intake opening. Remove fan shroud halves. Remove fan and fan clutch assembly.

NOTE: **Fan and clutch assembly secured with left-hand threads.**

2) Disconnect upper and lower radiator hoses from radiator. Disconnect automatic transmissoin cooler lines from radiator. Remove radiator. If equipped, remove A/C compressor drive belt. Remove A/C compressor and position on upper radiator support with lines attached.

3) Remove power steering pump drive belt. Remove power steering pump and position aside with hoses attached. Disconnect fuel supply line heater and alternator wiring. Disconnect all sending unit wires from engine. Disconnect accelerator cable from injection pump.

4) Remove accelerator bracket from engine and position aside with accelerator cable. If equipped, remove transmission kickdown rod from injection pump. Disconnect main wiring harness connector from right side of engine. Disconnect engine ground strap from rear of engine.

5) Disconnect fuel return hose from left rear of engine. Remove vacuum supply hose from pump. Remove upper transmission-to-engine bolts. Disconnect heater hoses from engine. Raise vehicle.

6) Disconnect both battery ground cables at engine. Disconnect and plug fuel supply line at fuel supply pump. Remove starter. Disconnect exhaust pipes from manifolds. Remove engine mount-to-engine nuts. Remove flywheel inspection plate.

7) Remove flex plate-to-converter bolts. Lower vehicle. Support transmission with floor jack. Remove 4 lower transmission-to-engine bolts. Attach lifting device to engine. Lift engine to clear No. 1 crossmember. Pull engine forward, rotate 45° to left, and carefully lift engine from vehicle.

FORD (Cont.)

TIGHTENING SPECIFICATIONS

Application	Ft. Lbs. (N.m)
4-Cylinder	
2.0L & 2.3L	
Bellhousing-to-Engine	28-38 (38-51)
Engine Mount-to-Crossmember	71-94 (97-127)
Engine Mount-to-Bracket	65-85 (88-115)
Flex Plate-to-Converter	27-49 (37-66)
Rear Mount-to-Crossmember	71-94 (97-127)
Rear Mount-to-Transmission	60-80 (82-108)
2.3L Turbo Diesel	
Bellhousing-to-Engine	23-34 (31-46)
Crossmember-to-Frame	187-260 (254-352)
Flywheel-to-Crankshaft	54-64 (73-87)
Front Mount-to-Crossmember	45-65 (61-81)
Front Mount-to-Engine Bracket	45-60 (61-82)
Rear Mount-to-Cross Member	71-94 (97-127)
Rear Mount-to-Transmission	60-80 (82-108)
6-Cylinder	
Bellhousing-to-Engine	40-50 (54-68)
Front Mount-to-Chassis Support	
E150/350	60-80 (81-108)
F150/350 & Bronco	54-74 (73-100)
Front Mount-to-Engine	
E150/350	50-70 (68-95)
F150/350 & Bronco	60-80 (81-108)
Flex Plate-to-Converter	20-34 (27-46)
Rear Mount-to-Crossmember	
E150/350	50-70 (68-94)
F150/250 & Bronco	50-70 (68-94)
F350	30-50 (41-68)
Rear Mount-to-Transmission	
E150/350	50-70 (68-94)
F150/350 & Bronco	60-80 (81-108)
V6	
Bellhousing-to-Engine	28-38 (38-52)
Front Mount-to-Chassis	71-94 (96-127)
Front Mount-to-Engine Bracket	65-85 (88-115)
Flex Plate-to-Converter	20-34 (27-46)
Rear Mount-to-Crossmember	65-85 (88-115)
Rear Mount-to-Transmission	60-80 (81-108)

Application	Ft. Lbs. (N.m)
V8	
5.0L & 5.8L	
Bellhousing-to-Engine	40-50 (54-68)
Front Mount-to-Chassis	55-70 (75-95)
Front Mount-to-Engine	60-70 (81-95)
Flex Plate-to-Converter	20-34 (27-46)
Rear Mount-to-Crossmember	
2WD Models	50-70 (68-94)
4WD Models	30-50 (41-68)
Rear Mount-to-Transmission	
E150/350	50-70 (68-94)
F150/350 & Bronco	60-80 (81-108)
6.9L Diesel	
Bellhousing-to-Engine	50-65 (68-88)
Fan Clutch-to-Water Pump [1]	30 (41)
Front Mount-to-Chassis	54-74 (73-100)
Front Mount-to-Engine	65-85 (88-115)
Flex Plate-to-Converter	20-34 (27-46)
Rear Mount-to-Crossmember	
2WD Models	50-70 (68-95)
4WD Models	30-50 (41-68)
Rear Mount-to-Transmission	60-70 (81-95)
7.5L	
Bellhousing-to-Engine	40-50 (54-68)
Front Mount-to-Chassis	
E250/350	50-70 (68-95)
F250/350	54-74 (73-100)
Front Mount Through Bolt	40-58 (54-79)
Flex Plate-to-Converter	20-34 (27-46)
Rear Mount-to-Crossmember	50-70 (68-95)
Rear Mount-to-Transmission	50-60 (68-81)

[1] – Left-hand thread.

GENERAL MOTORS

4-CYLINDER ENGINES

1.9L

1) Open hood, mark position of hood hinges and remove hood. Disconnect negative battery cable and raise vehicle. Remove rear transmission mount nuts. Support transmission and remove crossmember at frame. Remove top transmission bolts and reinstall crossmember. Remove transmission support.

2) Remove engine-to-transmission bolts. Remove torque converter cover. Disconnect exhaust at manifold. Disconnect starter leads and remove motor mount bolts. Disconnect fuel lines and automatic transmission cooler lines. Lower vehicle and drain coolant.

3) Disconnect necessary wires and hoses from alternator, carburetor and other accessories. If equipped, remove power steering pump and A/C compressor and lay aside.

4) Loosen alternator and disconnect front heater hose. Remove upper fan shroud, radiator and heater hoses, fan assembly and transmission oil cooler lines. Remove radiator assembly.

5) Disconnect accelerator cable, spring and detent cable from carburetor. Using floor jack, support transmission. Install lifting device and remove engine from vehicle.

2.5L

Astro & Safari Models

1) Disconnect negative battery cable. Drain cooling system. Remove engine cover. Remove headlight bezel and grille. Remove radiator lower close-out panel. Remove radiator support brace. Remove lower tie bar and cross brace. Remove hood latch mechanism.

2) Remove upper core support. Remove upper and lower radiator hoses. Remove radiator filler panels.

Remove radiator and fan shroud as an assembly. Disconnect engine wiring harness at bulkhead connector. Disconnect wiring harness at ECM and pull through bulkhead.

3) Disconnect heater hoses at heater core. Remove accelerator cable. Disconnect ground cable at cylinder head. Disconnect canister purge hose. Remove air cleaner. Raise vehicle. Disconnect exhaust pipe at manifold. Disconnect wiring harness at transmission and frame.

4) Disconnect and remove starter. Remove flywheel inspection cover. Disconnect and plug fuel lines. Remove motor mount through bolts. Remove bellhousing bolts. Lower vehicle. Remove oil filler neck. Remove thermostat outlet. Install engine lifting device. Support transmission. Remove engine.

2WD Models

1) Disconnect negative battery cable. Remove hood. Disconnect power steering reservoir at fan shroud. Remove upper fan shroud and fan. Drain cooling system. Remove upper and lower radiator hoses. Remove radiator overflow hose. Disconnect transmission oil cooler lines at radiator.

2) Remove radiator. Remove A/C compressor and power steering pump and set aside. Remove air cleaner. Disconnect fuel line bracket at filter. Disconnect and plug fuel lines. Label and disconnect all vacuum hoses. Disconnect accelerator, cruise control and throttle valve cables. Remove heater hoses.

3) Disconnect O_2 sensor wire. Label and disconnect all electrical connectors on engine. Raise vehicle. Remove strut rods. Disconnect exhaust pipe at exhaust manifold. Remove flywheel cover. Remove drive belt splash shield, if equipped. Remove starter. Remove flex plate-to-converter bolts.

4) Remove 2 outer air dam bolts (left side). Remove lower fan shroud. Remove left side body mounting bolts. Install jack stands. Raise left side of body and support with block of wood. Remove upper transmission mounting bolts. Lower body.

5) Remove remaining transmission mounting bolts. Remove motor mount through bolts. Lower vehicle. Support transmission. Lift engine and remove ground wire and wire loom bracket at rear of cylinder head. Remove engine.

4WD Models

1) Disconnect negative battery cable. Remove hood. Disconnect power steering reservoir at fan shroud. Remove upper fan shroud and fan. Drain cooling system. Remove upper and lower radiator hoses. Remove radiator overflow hose. Disconnect transmission oil cooler lines at radiator.

2) Remove radiator. Remove A/C compressor and power steering pump and set aside. Remove air cleaner. Disconnect fuel line bracket at filter. Disconnect and plug fuel lines. Label and disconnect all vacuum hoses. Disconnect accelerator, cruise control and throttle valve cables. Remove heater hoses.

3) Disconnect O_2 sensor wire. Label and disconnect all electrical connectors on engine. Raise vehicle. Remove clips holding brake line to crossmember. Remove crossmember. Disconnect transmission cooler lines at flywheel cover. Disconnect propeller shaft at front axle.

4) Disconnect exhaust pipe at exhaust manifold. Remove flywheel cover. Remove drive belt splash shield, if equipped. Remove starter. Remove flex plate-to-converter bolts.

5) Remove 2 outer air dam bolts (left side). Remove lower fan shroud. Remove left side body mounting bolts. Install jack stands. Raise left side of body and support with block of wood. Remove upper transmission mounting bolts. Lower body.

6) Remove remaining transmission mounting bolts. Remove motor mount through bolts. Lower vehicle. Support transmission. Lift engine and remove ground wire and wire loom bracket at rear of cylinder head. Remove engine.

2.2L DIESEL

1) Disconnect battery. Disconnect exhaust pipe at manifold. Remove radiator hoses and drain cooling system. Remove power steering reservoir and upper fan shroud. Remove radiator and fan. Remove lower fan shroud.

2) Disconnect heater hoses at engine. Disconnect PCV at valve cover and remove air cleaner. Discharge A/C system and disconnect hoses from A/C compressor. Remove power steering pump from bracket and place aside with hoses connected. Disconnect accelerator cable.

3) Disconnect all wiring, vacuum hoses, and fuel lines at engine. Remove rear air cleaner bracket. Remove starter. Remove hood. Remove shifter boot and shifter. Raise vehicle. Remove right motor mount through bolt. Disconnect lower clutch cable. Disconnect clutch bellcrank at frame.

4) Disconnect back-up light wiring and speedometer cable at transmission. Remove propeller shaft. Remove transmission mount nut and support transmission. Remove crossmember and transmission-to-bellhousing bolts. Remove transmission. Remove bellhousing.

5) Lower vehicle. Disconnect upper clutch cable and remove bellcrank. Attach lifting equipment to engine. Remove left motor mount through bolt. Disconnect battery ground at block. Raise engine and remove from vehicle.

V6 ENGINES

2.8L

2WD Models

1) Disconnect battery. Remove hood. Drain cooling system. Disconnect upper and lower radiator hoses and overflow hose. Remove upper fan shroud and disconnect automatic transmission cooler lines, if equipped. Remove radiator and fan. Disconnect heater hoses.

2) Remove air cleaner. Disconnect ground wires and cables, main feed wires and any necessary wiring at firewall. Label and disconnect all vacuum hoses at engine. Disconnect throttle and cruise control cables. Remove distributor cap. Raise vehicle.

3) Disconnect exhaust pipe at converter and both manifolds. Remove strut rods and flywheel cover at bellhousing. Remove torque converter bolts. Remove converter hanger at exhaust pipe and rear shield. Remove lower fan shroud. Disconnect fuel lines at pump.

4) Remove 2 outer air dam bolts. Remove left body mount bolts and install jack stands. Raise body and remove bellhousing bolts. Lower body and remove motor mount through bolts. Remove jack stands. Lower vehicle.

GENERAL MOTORS (Cont.)

5) If equipped, disconnect A/C compressor and power steering pump from engine and set aside. Attach lifting equipment to engine. Support transmission and remove engine from vehicle.

4WD Models With Automatic Transmission

1) Disconnect battery and underhood light. Remove hood. Raise vehicle. On Blazer models, remove body mounts. On chassis cab models, loosen and remove 2 front body mounts. On all models, remove front air dam end bolts.

2) Raise body above frame and remove top transmission-to-engine bolts. Lower body to frame. Remove remaining transmission-to-engine bolts. Unbolt and remove No. 2 crossmember. Disconnect exhaust pipe at manifolds. Disconnect converter hanger.

3) Disconnect front propeller shaft at differential. Remove bellhousing cover. Unclip automatic transmission cooler lines at engine. Remove motor mount bolts. Remove flex plate-to-converter bolts. Remove front splash shield and lower fan shroud. Lower vehicle.

4) Drain cooling system. Remove upper fan shroud and radiator hoses. Disconnect automatic transmission cooler lines at radiator. Remove radiator. Remove fan and air cleaner. If equipped, remove A/C compresser and power steering pump and set aside with hoses attached.

5) Disconnect fuel lines at pump. Disconnect vacuum and emission hoses from engine. Disconnect accelerator, throttle valve, and cruise control cables (as equipped). Disconnect engine wiring harness at firewall.

6) Disconnect any remaining wiring from engine. Disconnect heater hoses at engine. Support transmission securely. Attach lifting device to engine. Remove engine from vehicle.

4WD Models With Manual Transmission

1) Disconnect battery and underhood light. Remove hood. Remove air cleaner. Drain cooling system and remove upper fan shroud. Disconnect radiator hoses and remove radiator. Remove fan and clutch.

2) If equipped, remove A/C compresser and power steering pump and set aside with hoses attached. Disconnect fuel lines at pump. Remove vacuum hoses and heater hoses at engine. Disconnect accelerator and cruise control cables. Disconnect engine wiring harness, main feed wire, and ground strap at firewall.

3) Remove lower fan shroud. Disconnect battery ground at engine. Remove distributor cap and diverter valve. Remove shifter boot and console cover. Remove transfer case shifter, transmission shifter, and transmission shift lever. Raise vehicle.

4) Remove front and rear skid plates. Remove front splash shield. Drain transfer case and transmission. Remove rear propeller shaft. Disconnect speedometer cable. Disconnect front propeller shaft at transfer case. Disconnect shift linkage and vacuum hoses at transfer case.

5) Disconnect parking brake cable. Remove rear mount and converter bracket. Support transfer case. Unbolt transfer case and remove it from vehicle. Remove crossmember. Disconnect back-up light wiring and clip. Unbolt slave cylinder and hang to side.

6) Remove clutch release bearing. Remove flywheel inspection cover. Remove 3 left side body mounting bolts. Raise left side of body. Install block of wood to hold body up. Remove bellhousing.

7) Disconnect exhaust at manifolds and converter. Disconnect clutch cross shaft at frame. Remove starter. Remove motor mount bolts. Lower vehicle. Attach lifting device and remove engine.

4.3L

Astro & Safari Models

1) Disconnect negative battery cable. Drain cooling system. Raise vehicle. Disconnect exhaust pipe at exhaust manifolds. Disconnect strut rods at flywheel inspection cover. Remove torque converter bolts. Disconnect and remove starter. Remove oil filter.

2) Disconnect harness at transmission and frame. Disconnect and plug fuel lines. Disconnect lower transmission and engine oil cooler lines at radiator. Remove lower fan shroud bolts. Remove motor mount through bolts. Remove bellhousing bolts. Lower vehicle. Remove headlight bezels and grille.

3) Remove radiator lower close-out panel. Remove radiator support brace. Remove core support cross brace. Remove lower tie bar. Remove hood latch mechanism. Disconnect master cylinder and set aside. Remove upper fan shroud. Remove upper core support. Remove upper and lower radiator hoses.

4) Disconnect upper transmission and engine oil cooler lines. Remove radiator. Discharge A/C system. Remove radiator filler panels. Remove engine cover. Remove brace at rear of A/C compressor. Disconnect A/C hose at accumulator. Remove A/C compressor and bracket. Remove power steering pump.

5) Label and disconnect necessary vacuum hoses. Disconnect wiring harness at bulkhead. Remove right kick panel. Disconnect wiring harness at ESC module and push through bulkhead. Remove distributor cap. Remove A/C accumulator. Disconnect fuel line at carburetor.

6) Disconnect and remove diverter valve. Remove transmission dipstick tube. Disconnect heater hoses at heater core. Remove horn. Remove air injection check valves. Install engine lifting device. Support transmission. Remove engine.

Van Models

1) Disconnect battery and drain cooling system. Remove glove box and engine cover. Remove outside air duct. Remove power steering reservoir bracket. Disconnect hood release cable. Remove upper fan shroud bolts. Disconnect overflow hoses. Disconnect transmission oil cooler lines at radiator.

2) Disconnect upper and lower radiator hoses. Remove radiator. Remove upper fan shroud, fan and pulley. Remove air cleaner. Remove cruise control servo. Remove brake booster vacuum hose at carburetor. Disconnect accelerator and throttle valve cables. Disconnect fuel line and vacuum hoses at caburetor.

3) Remove carburetor. Remove distributor cap. Disconnect air injection hoses at diverter valve. Remove diverter valve. Remove heater hoses. Disconnect PCV valve. Label and disconnect remaining vacuum hoses. Label and disconnect engine electrical harness. Discharge A/C system.

4) Remove A/C compressor brace and compressor. Remove upper half of dipsick tube. Remove oil filler and transmission dipstick tubes. Disconnect accelarator cable at dipstick. Disconnect and plug fuel lines at fuel pump. Remove power steering pump. Remove A/C idler pulley.

5) Remove headlight bezels and grille. Remove upper radiator support. Remove lower fan shroud. Remove lower filler panel and hood latch support. Disconnect A/C lines at condenser. Remove condenser. Raise vehicle. Drain engine oil. Disconnect exhaust pipe at exhaust manifolds.

6) Disconnect strut rods at flywheel inspection cover. Remove fywheel inspection cover. Remove starter. Remove torque converter mounting bolts. Remove bellhousing bolts. Remove motor mount through bolts. Lower vehicle. Support transmission. Install lifting device and remove engine.

6-CYLINDER ENGINES

4.8L

1) Disconnect battery. Remove air cleaner and drain cooling system. Disconnect accelerator cable and detent cable (automatic transmission) from throttle lever. Disconnect wiring from engine.

2) Remove radiator hoses from radiator and heater hoses from engine. Remove radiator, fan and water pump pulley. Disconnect fuel line from fuel pump. Remove hood. Raise vehicle.

3) Remove starter, flywheel or converter inspection cover, and exhaust pipe from manifold. If equipped with automatic transmission, remove converter-to-flex plate bolts. Remove engine mount bolts. On 4WD models, remove strut rods at motor mounts.

4) On all models, remove bellhousing retaining bolts and support transmission with chain. Lower vehicle and attach lifting device. Remove engine.

V8 ENGINES

5.0 & 5.7L

Van Models

1) Disconnect battery cables and drain cooling system. Remove coolant reservoir, grille, upper radiator support and lower grille valance. Disconnect automatic transmission cooler lines (if equipped) and radiator hoses. If equipped with A/C, discharge system and remove condenser and vacuum reservoir.

2) Remove washer jar with bracket, radiator brackets, radiator and shroud. Remove engine cover. Remove air cleaner, air stove pipe and accelerator cable from carburetor. If equipped with power steering, remove pump and lay aside.

3) Disconnect wiring from firewall connection and remove carburetor. Remove thermostat housing, oil fill pipe and disconnect heater hoses. If equipped with cruise control, remove servo, transducer and bracket.

4) Raise vehicle. Disconnect exhaust pipe at manifold. Remove propeller shaft and plug extension housing. Disconnect shift linkage. Disconnect fuel line from pump. Disconnect speedometer cable. Remove transmission mount bolts and engine mount bracket-to-frame bolts.

5) Drain crankcase. Remove engine mount through bolts. Raise engine slightly and remove engine mounts. Block up engine with wooden block between oil pan and crossmember. Lower vehicle and install lifting device. Remove engine and transmission as assembly.

All Other Models

1) Disconnect battery cables and drain cooling system. Remove hood, air cleaner, accessory drive belts, fan and water pump pulley. Disconnect all hoses, lines, linkage and wiring from engine. If equipped with A/C, remove compressor and lay aside.

2) Disconnect transmission oil cooler lines (if equipped) and remove radiator with shroud. If equipped with power steering, remove pump and lay aside. Disconnect fuel line from fuel pump.

3) Raise vehicle and drain crankcase. On 4WD models with automatic transmission, remove strut rods at motor mounts. On all models, disconnect crossover pipe from exhaust manifold.

4) Remove flywheel or converter inspection cover. Remove starter and wiring along right pan rail. Remove fuel gauge wiring. If equipped with automatic transmission, remove converter-to-flex plate attaching bolts.

5) Support transmission and remove bellhousing-to-engine bolts. Remove lower engine mount bracket-to-frame bolts. Lower vehicle and attach lifting device. Remove engine.

7.4L

1) Remove hood. Disconnect battery. Remove air cleaner. Drain cooling system. Disconnect radiator and heater hoses. Remove radiator and fan shroud. Disconnect all hoses, lines, linkage and wiring from engine.

2) Remove power steering pump and A/C compressor, if equipped. Raise vehicle. Drain crankcase. Disconnect exhaust pipe at manifold and torque converter bracket at transmission rear mount. Remove starter.

3) Remove bellhousing cover. Remove flex plate-to-converter attaching bolts. Remove motor mount through bolts and bellhousing-to-engine bolts.

4) Lower vehicle. Using floor jack, raise transmission. Attach lifting device and raise engine. Remove motor mount-to-engine brackets. Remove engine.

6.2L DIESEL

Van Models

1) Disconnect batteries. Remove headlight bezels, grille, bumper and lower grille valance. Remove hood latch, washer jar, upper fan shroud and tie bar, and engine cover. If equipped with A/C, discharge system, disconnect condenser lines and remove condenser.

2) Disconnect low coolant wire. Drain cooling system. Disconnect engine oil and automatic transmission cooler lines, and both radiator hoses at radiator. Remove radiator and fan assembly. Scribe or paint mark on front cover and injection pump flange and remove fuel injection pump.

3) Raise vehicle. Disconnect exhaust pipe at manifold. Remove inspection cover, flex plate-to-converter bolts, and motor mount through bolts. Disconnect block heater at element and ground wire-to-block. Remove bellhousing-to-engine bolts. Remove starter.

4) Lower vehicle. If equipped with cruise control, remove transducer. If equipped with A/C, remove rear brace, disconnect lines at compressor, and remove brackets and compressor. If equipped with power steering, remove pump and position aside. Remove oil fill tube upper bracket and glow plug relay.

5) Disconnect oil pressure sender and loom. Remove air cleaner resonator and bracket. Remove

Engine Removal

GENERAL MOTORS (Cont.)

transmission fill tube nut. Disconnect heater, radiator and by-pass hoses at crossover. Remove alternator upper bracket and coolant crossover. Disconnect fuel lines at fuel pump. Install lifting device. Remove engine.

All Other Models

1) Disconnect batteries. Raise vehicle. Remove inspection cover. Disconnect torque converter and exhaust pipe. Remove starter. Remove bellhousing bolts and left and right motor mount bolts.

2) Disconnect block heaters. Remove wire harness, automatic transmission cooler lines and front battery cable clamp at oil pan. Disconnect fuel return and oil cooler lines at engine. Remove lower fan shroud bolts. Lower vehicle. Remove hood and drain cooling system.

3) Remove air cleaner with resonator and primary filter from cowl. Disconnect ground cable at alternator bracket, alternator wires and clips. Disconnect TPS, EGR/EPR and fuel cut-off at injection pump. Remove harness from clips at rocker covers and disconnect glow plugs.

4) Disconnect EGR/EPR solenoids, glow plug controller, temperature sender and move harness aside. Disconnect left side ground strap. Remove fan, upper radiator hoses at engine, and fan shroud. Remove power steering pump and belt. Remove power steering reservoir and position aside.

5) Disconnect vacuum at cruise servo and accelerator cable at injection pump. Disconnect heater hose and lower radiator hose at engine. Disconnect oil cooler lines, heater hose and overflow at radiator.

6) Disconnect automatic transmission cooler lines. Remove upper radiator cover, radiator and detent cable. Support transmission and remove engine.

TIGHTENING SPECIFICATIONS

Application	Ft. Lbs. (N.m)
4-Cylinder	
1.9L & 2.0L	
Bellhousing-to-Engine	55 (75)
Flex Plate-to-Converter	35 (47)
Front Mount-to-Engine	29-39 (39-53)
Front Mount-to-Bracket	29-39 (39-53)
Rear Mount-to-Crossmember	25 (34)
Rear Mount-to-Transmission	35 (47)
2.2L Diesel [1]	
6-Cylinder	
4.8L	
Bellhousing-to-Engine	35 (47)
Flex Plate-to-Converter	35 (47)
Front Mount Through Bolt	75 (102)
Rear Mount-to-Crossmember	45 (61)
Rear Mount-to-Transmission	35 (47)
V6	
2.8L	
Bellhousing-to-Engine	55 (75)
Front Mount-to-Chassis	35-48 (47-65)
Front Mount-to-Engine Bracket	53-66 (72-89)
Flex Plate-to-Converter	35 (47)
Rear Mount-to-Crossmember	25 (34)
Rear Mount-to-Transmission	35 (47)

Application	Ft. Lbs. (N.m)
4.3L	
Bellhousing-to-Engine	30 (41)
Front Mount Through Bolt	74 (100)
Front Mount-to-Chassis	35 (47)
Front Mount-to-Engine Bracket	35 (47)
Flex Plate-to-Converter	35 (47)
Rear Mount-to-Adapter	24 (32)
Rear Mount Adapter-to-Crossmember	45 (61)
Rear Mount-to-Transmission	44 (60)
V8	
All Models	
Bellhousing-to-Engine	30 (41)
Front Mount-to-Chassis	35 (47)
Front Mount-to-Engine	37 (50)
Front Mount Through Bolt	85 (115)
Flex Plate-to-Converter	35 (47)
Rear Mount-to-Crossmember	40 (54)
Rear Mount-to-Transmission	35 (47)

[1] – No specifications available at this time.

JEEP

4-CYLINDER ENGINES

2.5L

1) Disconnect negative battery cable. Drain cooling system. Remove lower radiator hose. Remove air cleaner. Detach engine compartment light from hood. Mark hinge locations and remove hood. Remove fan shroud. If equipped, disconnect automatic transmission cooler lines from radiator.

2) Remove upper radiator hose and coolant recovery hose. Remove radiator and A/C condenser (if equipped). Remove fan assembly. Hold fan pulley to water pump flange using 5/16" X 1/2" SAE capscrew. Disconnect heater hoses. Disconnect throttle linkages, cruise control cable (if equipped) and TV rod.

3) Disconnect wires from starter and CEC System wiring harness connector. Disconnect fuel pipe from fuel pump. Disconnect fuel return hose at fuel filter. If equipped, disconnect hoses from A/C compressor and power steering pump. Drain power steering pump reservoir. Cap all fittings and hose ends.

4) Remove vacuum check valve from brake booster, if equipped. Tag and remove all wiring and vacuum lines connected to engine or accessories. Raise and support vehicle. Remove starter. Disconnect exhaust pipe from manifold.

5) Remove converter/flywheel housing cover. Remove engine mount nuts at bracket side. On automatic transmission models, index mark flex plate and torque converter. Remove flex plate-to-converter bolts.

JEEP (Cont.)

6) Remove upper and loosen lower bellhousing-to-engine bolts. Attach lifting equipment to engine. Raise engine off front mounts. Place support under bellhousing. Remove remaining bellhousing-to-engine bolts. Lift engine out of engine compartment.

NOTE: **Installation of engine may be easier if engine mount pads are removed from engine brackets while aligning engine and transmission.**

2.1L TURBO DIESEL

1) Disconnect negative battery cable. Remove skid plate. Drain cooling system. Remove air cleaner. Mark hinge locations and remove hood. If A/C equipped, front-seat the service valves and remove them from compressor. Remove upper and lower radiator hoses. Remove "E" clip from bottom of radiator.

2) Raise vehicle. Disconnect automatic transmission oil cooler lines. Remove splash shield from oil pan. Lower vehicle. Remove fan shroud and fan. Remove radiator/condenser assembly. Remove intercooler. Remove exhaust shield from manifold. Disconnect oil hoses at remote oil filter adapter. Remove oil filter.

3) Label and disconnect all vacuum hoses and electrical connectors. Disconnect and plug fuel inlet and return lines. Disconnect accelerator cable. Raise vehicle. Disconnect and drain power steering hoses at power steering pump. Disconnet exhaust pipe at exhaust manifold.

4) Remove left motor mount through bolt retaining nut (automatic transmission only). Remove motor mount cushion retaining bolts. Support engine and remove left motor mount. Remove starter.

5) On automatic transmission models, mark and remove converter-to-drive plate bolts through starter opening. Reinstall left motor mount and cushion through bolt. Remove engine support.

6) On all models, remove transmission-to-engine retaining bolts. Lower vehicle. Remove power steering reservior and set aside. Remove oil separator and disconnect hoses. Remove heater hoses. Remove top transmission-to-engine bolt.

7) Remove reference pressure regulator from dash panel. Connect engine lifting device and support transmission. Remove engine.

6-CYLINDER ENGINES

4.2L

1) Disconnect battery cables and remove battery. Drain cooling system. Disconnect engine compartment light from hood. Mark hinge location for installation reference and remove hood. Remove air cleaner. Disconnect and plug front fuel line at pump and fuel return line at frame.

2) Disconnect heater hoses at heater. Label and disconnect all wiring, lines, linkage and hoses at engine. Remove vacuum switch assembly bracket from cylinder head cover. Disconnect both radiator hoses and automatic transmission cooler lines (if equipped) at radiator. Remove radiator and shroud.

3) Remove fan and spacer. Use 5/16" X 1/2" SAE bolt to hold fan pulley to water pump flange. Remove starter and disconnect engine ground strap. Remove engine mount-to-bracket nuts. Disconnect exhaust pipe at manifold.

4) On models with A/C, discharge system. Disconnect and plug hoses and ports at compressor. Remove power brake vacuum check valve, if equipped. On models with power steering, disconnect hoses at steering gear. Drain reservoir and plug open fittings. Remove bracket bolt for automatic transmission filler tube, if equipped.

5) Lift and support vehicle. On models with automatic transmission, remove converter housing cover. Index mark converter and flex plate for reassembly. Remove flex plate-to-converter bolts, rotating crankshaft to access each bolt. Remove oil pan bolts which hold automatic transmission cooler lines. Remove exhaust pipe support brace at converter housing (CJ7 and Scrambler models).

6) On manual transmission models, remove flywheel housing cover. Remove inner support bolts for clutch release arm. Disconnect springs and remove clutch release arm. Remove outer bracket retainer for release lever rod. On all models, remove upper and loosen lower bellhousing bolts.

7) Lower vehicle. Support transmission. If A/C equipped, remove idler pulley and mounting bracket. Attach lifting equipment to engine. Raising engine off front mounts, place support under transmission. Remove lower bellhousing bolts. Lift engine from compartment while pulling forward.

V6 ENGINES

2.8L

1) Disconnect battery cables. Remove air cleaner. Mark hinge location and remove hood. Drain cooling system. Remove upper and lower radiator hoses, and coolant recovery hoses from radiator. Remove fan shroud. Disconnect automatic transmission cooler pipe fittings at radiator.

2) Discharge A/C system, if equipped. Remove radiator and condenser (if A/C equipped). Remove fan assembly. Remove heater hoses. Disconnect throttle linkage. Unhook cruise control cable and TV cable, if equipped. Remove power brake booster vacuum hose.

3) Tag and disconnect all wiring and vacuum hoses to engine. Disconnect power steering pump assembly and place aside with hoses attached. Disconnect fuel pipe fittings at fuel pump. Disconnect A/C hoses at compressor. Raise vehicle.

4) Disconnect exhaust pipes at manifold and catalytic converter and place aside. Remove the converter/flywheel housing cover. Disconnect flex plate from torque converter. Remove wiring at starter motor. Remove bellhousing-to-engine bolts.

5) Lower vehicle and support transmission. Remove air pump with hoses attached and place aside. Attach lifting equipment to engine. Remove engine mount through bolts. Disconnect ground strap from rear of left cylinder head. Lift engine and remove from vehicle.

Engine Removal

JEEP (Cont.)

V8 ENGINES

6.0L

1) Disconnect cables and remove battery. Drain cooling system. Mark hinge location and remove hood. Remove air cleaner, radiator hoses and heater hoses. Disconnect automatic transmission cooler lines at radiator and at engine bracket. Remove radiator shroud.

2) Remove radiator. Remove cooling fan assembly. If equipped, drain power steering reservoir and disconnect hoses. On models with A/C, drain system and remove service valves from compressor. Remove Cruise Command vacuum servo cable from carburetor linkage.

3) Disconnect wiring harness from engine and place aside. Remove fuel lines at tubing on frame. Disconnect transmission filler tube bracket from right cylinder head. Do not remove tube from transmission case. Disconnect power brake booster vacuum hose.

4) Disconnect vacuum hose for heater doors at intake manifold. Remove both engine mount-to-frame nuts. Use lifting device to support engine. Remove upper bellhousing-to-engine bolts. Disconnect exhaust pipe at manifolds and support bracket.

5) Remove starter. Support transmission using floor jack. Remove converter housing cover. Index mark assembled position of converter and flex plate. Remove flex plate-to-converter bolts. Remove lower TV and inner manual linkage support.

6) Disconnect TV rod at lower end of bellcrank. Remove remaining bolts securing transmission. Raise engine and pull forward to remove from vehicle. Be careful to avoid damage to power brake unit.

TIGHTENING SPECIFICATIONS

Application	Ft. Lbs. (N.m)
4-Cylinder Engine	
Clutch Housing-to-Block Bolts	55 (75)
Flex Plate-to-Converter	26 (35)
Flywheel Bolts	[1] 50 (68)
Front Support Bracket-to-Block	45 (61)
Front Support Cushion-to-Crossmember	33 (45)
Rear Support Bracket-to-Transmission	33 (45)
Rear Support Cushion-to-Bracket	30 (41)
6-Cylinder Engine	
Automatic Transmission-to-Block	28 (38)
Clutch Housing-to-Block	
Top	27 (37)
Bottom	43 (58)
Flex Plate-to-Converter	22 (30)
Flex Plate/Flywheel-to-Crankshaft	105 (142)
Front Support Bracket-to-Block	45 (61)
Front Support Cushion-to-Crossmember	37 (50)
Rear Support Bracket-to-Transmission	33 (45)
Rear support Cushion-to-Bracket	30 (41)

Application	Ft. Lbs. (N.m)
V6 Engine	
Engine Mounting Bracket	70-92 (95-125)
Flex Plate-to-Converter	25-35 (34-47)
Starter-to-Block	25-30 (34-40)
Transmission-to-Block	48-63 (65-85)
V8 Engine	
Automatic Transmission-to-Block	28 (38)
Clutch Housing-to-Block	30 (41)
Flex Plate-to-Converter	22 (30)
Flex Plate/Flywheel-to-Crankshaft	105 (142)
Front Support Bracket-to-Block	35 (47)
Front Support Bracket-to-Crossmember	37 (50)
Rear Support Bracket-to-Transmission	33 (45)
Rear Support Cushion-to-Crossmember	18 (24)
Starter-to-Bellhousing	18 (24)

[1] – Tighten an additional 60°.

GENERAL COOLING SYSTEM SERVICING

DESCRIPTION

Basic liquid cooling systems consist of radiator, water pump, thermostat, cooling fan, pressure cap, heater, and various connecting hoses and cooling passages in block and cylinder head. Many vehicles use clutching fan, which may incorporate thermostatic control, or flexible blade fan, or both, to reduce noise and power requirements at high engine speeds.

Some models use thermoswitch located in radiator tank to activate electric cooling fan(s). This system is usually found on vehicles with transversely mounted engines. Due to exhaust emission control, some vehicles use thermostatic vacuum switch to advance ignition timing in case of overheating.

As most new models require use of permanent, year round (ethylene glycol) type anti-freeze, coolant recovery systems are being used more commonly to prevent coolant loss. Requirements for antifreeze have changed due to materials used in engine manufacture.

MAINTENANCE

DRAINING

Remove radiator cap and open heater control valve to maximum heat position. Open drain petcocks or remove plugs in bottom of radiator and in engine block. In-line engines usually have 1 plug or petcock, while V-engines will have 1 for each bank of cylinders.

CLEANING

Good cleaning compound will remove most rust and scale. Follow manufacturer's instructions in use of cleaner. If considerable rust and scale have to be removed, flushing will be necessary. Clean radiator cooling fins by blowing out with compressed air from back to front of radiator.

NOTE: **Some models use plastic or aluminum components in radiators. Ensure proper cleaning solution is used.**

FLUSHING

1) Back flushing is very effective procedure for removing rust and scale from cooling system. Radiator, engine and heater core should be flushed separately for best results.

2) To flush radiator, connect flushing gun to water outlet of radiator and disconnect water inlet hose. Use hose, connected to radiator inlet, to prevent flooding engine. Use air in short bursts only, as clogged radiator could be easily damaged. Continue flushing until water runs clear.

3) To flush engine, remove thermostat and reinstall housing. Connect flushing gun to water outlet of engine. Disconnect heater hoses from engine. Flush using short air bursts until water runs clean. Flush heater core as described for radiator. Ensure heater control valve is set to maximum heat position before flushing heater.

REFILLING

Engine should be running while refilling cooling system to prevent air from being trapped in engine block. After system is full, continue running engine until thermostat is open. Recheck coolant level. Do not overfill system. Refer to appropriate COOLANT CAPACITY table in ENGINE COOLANT SPECIFICATIONS article in this section.

TESTING

THERMOSTAT

1) Visually inspect thermostat for corrosion and proper sealing. If satisfactory, suspend thermostat and thermometer in container of water. Do not allow either thermostat or thermometer to touch bottom of container as concentration of heat could cause an incorrect reading.

2) Heat water until thermostat just begins to open. Note temperature at which thermostat begins to open. Compare to specification in table. See ENGINE COOLANT SPECIFICATIONS article in this section. Replace thermostat if it does not open.

Fig. 1: Testing Thermostat

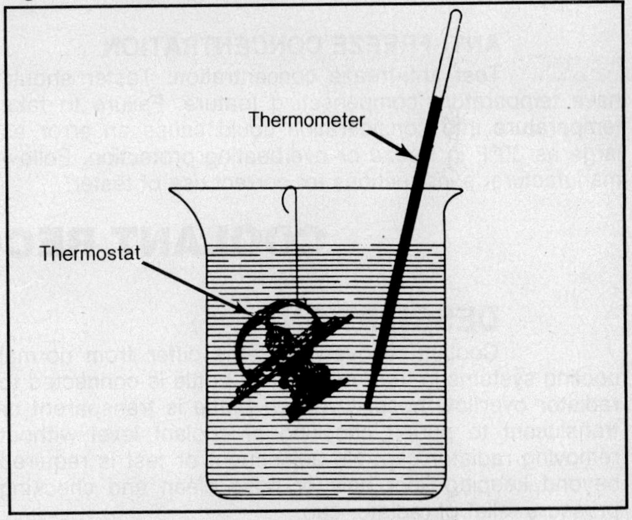

Thermostat should open as water is heated.

PRESSURE TESTING

Pressure tester is used to test both radiator cap and complete cooling system. Test as follows, or follow tool manufacturer's instructions.

Radiator Cap

Visually inspect radiator cap. Dip cap in water and connect to tester. Pump tester to bring pressure to upper limit of cap specification. Pressure cap specifications are given in ENGINE COOLANT SPECIFICATIONS article in this section. If cap fails to hold pressure within specified range, replace cap.

Cooling System

1) With engine stopped, wipe radiator filler neck seat clean. Fill radiator to correct level. Attach cooling system tester to radiator and pump until pressure is at upper level of radiator rating. If pressure drops, inspect for external leaks. If no external leaks are evident, start engine and run with tester attached.

NOTE: **Pressure may build up quickly. Release any pressure above limit of pressure cap specifications or cooling system damage may result.**

2) Extremely rapid build-up of pressure may indicate combustion leak into cooling system. Check for water at tailpipe. Excessive water could indicate faulty head gasket, cracked block or cylinder head near exhaust ports.

GENERAL COOLING SYSTEM SERVICING (Cont.)

Remove oil dipstick and check for water droplets in oil. If water is evident, serious internal leak is indicated.

Fig. 2: Testing Radiator Pressure Cap

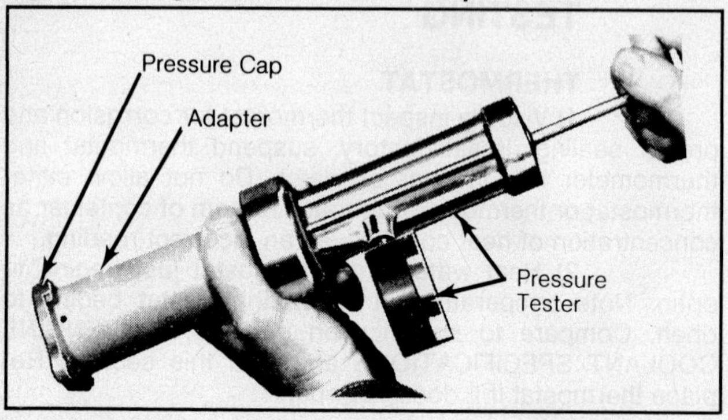

Attach cap to tester and apply correct pressure.

Fig. 3: Pressure Testing Cooling System

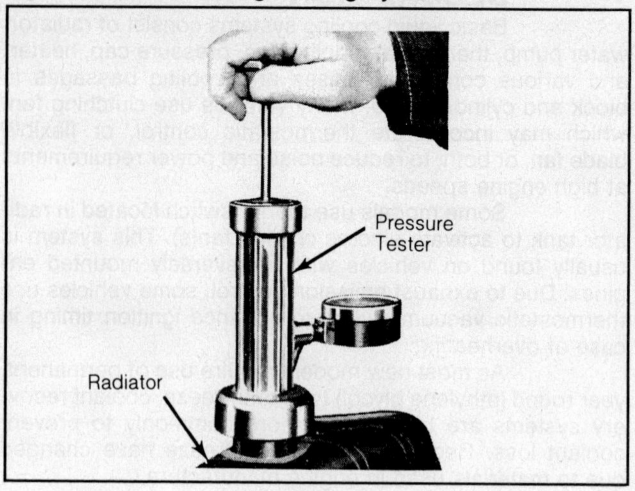

ANTI-FREEZE CONCENTRATION

Test anti-freeze concentration. Tester should have temperature compensating feature. Failure to take temperature into consideration could cause an error as large as 30°F in freeze or overheating protection. Follow manufacturer's instructions for correct use of tester.

COOLANT RECOVERY SYSTEMS

DESCRIPTION

Coolant recovery systems differ from normal cooling systems in that an overflow bottle is connected to radiator overflow hose. Overflow bottle is transparent or translucent to permit checking of coolant level without removing radiator cap. No adjustment or test is required beyond keeping vent hole or hose clean and checking pressure relief of radiator cap.

OPERATION

As coolant temperature rises and pressure in system exceeds pressure relief valve of radiator cap, excess coolant flows into overflow bottle. As engine cools and coolant contracts, vacuum is formed in system, drawing coolant, stored in overflow bottle, back into radiator. In properly maintained cooling system, only coolant loss will be through evaporation.

Fig. 1: Coolant Recovery System

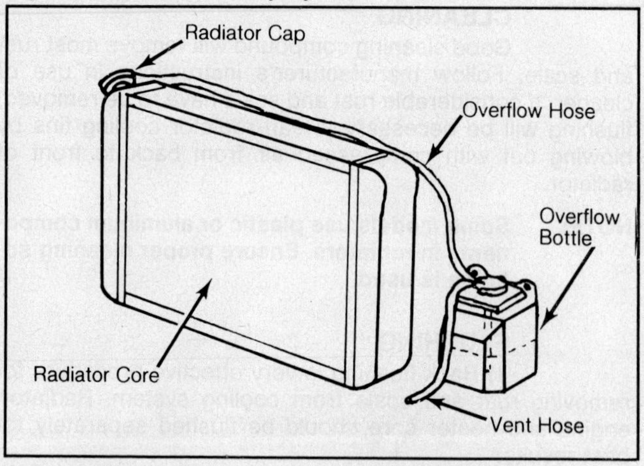

System should minimize loss of coolant.

RADIATOR CAPS

DESCRIPTION

Radiator cap consists of pressure valve and vacuum valve. Cap has several different functions: preventing coolant loss when vehicle is in motion; preventing impurities from entering cooling system to minimize corrosion; allowing atmospheric pressure to eliminate vacuum that occurs in system during engine cooling period; and raising coolant boiling point approximately 3°F (1.6°C) per psi increase by maintaining constant cooling system pressure. See ENGINE COOLANT SPECIFICATIONS article in this section for manufacturer's radiator cap specifications.

Fig. 1: Radiator Cap Operation

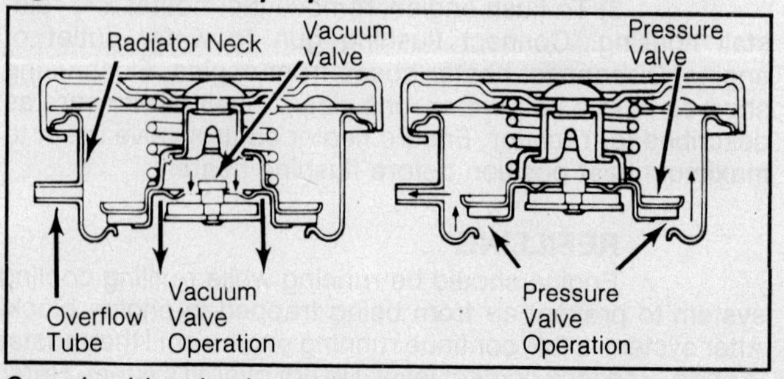

Cap should maintain constant pressure in cooling system.

THERMOSTATICALLY CONTROLLED ELECTRIC FANS

Chrysler Corp. FWD

DESCRIPTION

On 2.2L engines, fan control is accomplished by on-board computer. Coolant temperature is sensed by the coolant temperature sensor located on thermostat housing. This sensor has 2 thermister sensors, 1 of which is for the electric cooling fan.

Computer controls cooling fan so that fan will not run during engine cranking. Fan will run continuously while A/C compressor clutch is engaged. On non-air conditioned vehicles or with A/C off, cooling fan will run at vehicle speeds above 40 MPH only if coolant temperature is above 230°F (110°C). Fan will turn off when coolant temperature drops below 220°F (104°C).

On 2.6L engines, cooling fan switch is mounted in lower radiator tank. The switch is normally open and closes when coolant temperature reaches 200°F (93°C). Cooling fan relay is located on left inner fender panel.

Fan will not operate while ignition is turned off, except California and/or High Altitude vehicles. These vehicles have 10 minute after-run feature when radiator air discharge temperature is above 100°F (38°C).

TESTING

NOTE: Testing procedures not available for cooling fan relay at time of publication.

COOLANT TEMPERATURE SENSOR

Disconnect wiring connector at sensor. Connect ohmmeter to sensor terminals. With engine/sensor temperature at 200°F (93°C), ohmmeter reading should be 700-800 ohms. With engine/sensor at room temperature, about 70°F (21°C), ohmmeter reading should be 5000-6000 ohms. Replace sensor if not within specifications.

COOLING FAN SWITCH

If cooling fan turns on when coolant temperature reaches 200°F (93°C) and off when coolant temperature drops to 170°F (73°C), switch is operating normally.

Install jumper wire in female connector. This simulates a closed fan switch at any temperature. If fan does not operate with ignition switch "ON", check cooling fan, fuses and wiring.

To check switch calibration, remove switch from radiator. Immerse switch into a circulation oil bath heated to 212°F (100°C). Switch should be closed. Use a continuity light to determine if switch is closed. Lower temperature to 170°F (73°C) and ensure switch opens. Replace switch if defective.

NOTE: When immersing switch in oil bath, DO NOT immerse electrical terminals.

COOLING FAN MOTOR

If fan motor is not operating properly, disconnect fan motor wiring connector. Install jumper wire between fan motor and 12-volt battery. If fan runs, motor is okay. Test relays, switches, fuses and wiring.

VARIABLE SPEED COOLING FANS

FAN DRIVE WITH THERMOSTATIC CONTROL

DESCRIPTION

This unit consists of thermostatically controlled fluid fan drive (torque control clutch). Thermal control drive is silicone filled coupling connecting fan to fan pulley. Drive is operated by control valve. Control valve is governed by temperature sensitive bimetal coil or strip. Control valve maintains flow of silicone through drive.

During periods of operation when radiator discharge air temperature is low, fan drive limits fan speed. High radiator discharge air temperature causes bimetal to allow greater flow of silicone to enter drive. This increases drag between driven member and driving member, resulting in higher fan speed and increased cooling.

TESTING

1) When engine overheating or insufficient cooling by air conditioning occur, fan drive and thermostatic control must be tested. Start with cool engine to ensure complete fan drive disengagement. Cover radiator grille sufficiently to induce high engine temperature.

2) Start engine. Operate at 2000 RPM and turn on air conditioning, if equipped. Fan noise will increase when fan drive engages. It will take 5-10 minutes for fan to become engaged. While operating engine under these conditions, observe temperature light to prevent overheating. If hot light comes on, remove cover from radiator grille.

3) As soon as drive engages, remove radiator grille cover and turn air conditioning off to assist in engine cooling. After several minutes fan drive should disengage. This can be determined by reduction in fan speed and noise. If fan drive fails to function as described, it should be replaced.

4) Fan drive should also be replaced if shaft seal is leaking fluid. If noise or roughness can be felt while turning by hand, replace drive. Frozen unit must be replaced. Blade tip rock of more than 1/4" front-to-rear indicates worn drive unit which should be replaced.

Fig. 1: Thermal Control Fan Drive Unit

Rotation speed will vary with engine temperature.

FAN DRIVE WITHOUT THERMOSTATIC CONTROL

DESCRIPTION

This unit is same as thermostatically controlled fan drive except it is not controlled by bimetallic (temperature sensitive) coil. Fan drive allows fan to be driven in normal manner at low speeds while higher engine speed limits rotational speed of fan to predetermined rate. Silicone in drive housing provides more positive drive at lower speeds and allows greater slippage between driven member and driving member at higher engine speeds.

TESTING

In case of engine overheating during low speed or idle operation, increase engine speed to approximately 1000 RPM in Neutral. If condition is not corrected by increasing engine speed, replace fan drive unit with unit that is known to be operating properly and test by operating vehicle under same conditions. Replace unit assembly if trouble is corrected with test unit. All units are non-adjustable. Replace unit if damaged or operating improperly.

FLEX-BLADE FAN

DESCRIPTION

This unit is fixed blade assembly designed to flex blades as engine RPM increases. As RPM increases, blade pitch decreases, saving power and decreasing noise level. No adjustment or test is required beyond keeping fan belt adjusted to proper tension and ensuring that unit is not damaged.

Fig. 2: Flex-Blade Fan

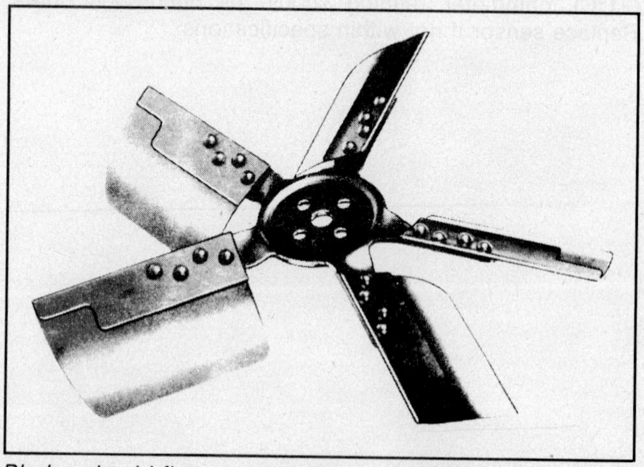

Blades should flex as engine RPM increases.

Engine Cooling Systems

ENGINE COOLANT SPECIFICATIONS

CHRYSLER CORP.

THERMOSTAT

Pellet type thermostat is located in water outlet elbow. On 2.2L, 3.7L, 5.2L, and 5.9L engines, opening temperature is 195°F (91°C). Thermostat should be fully open at 219°F (105°C) on these engines. On 2.6L California models, thermostat opening starts at 180°F (83°C) and is fully open at 205°F (97°C). On all other 2.6L engines, opening starts at 190°F (89°C) and is fully open at 215°F (103°C).

PRESSURE CAP

All models use 14-18 psi (1.0-1.2 kg/cm^2) pressure cap which should be tested in that range. Center of cap is equipped with vent valve which allows small flow through cap when temperature is below boiling point. Valve closes when boiling point is reached. Valve also opens when coolant is cooling and contracting, permitting liquid to return to radiator from coolant reserve tank.

WATER PUMP

Pump is serviced only as an assembly. When replacing water pump, be sure correct pump is used. Pump impeller must be compatible with pulley system drive ratio. It is possible to replace pump without discharging air conditioning system. When replacing water pump because of bearing or shaft failure, carefully inspect fan for cracks, loose blades or rivets caused by excessive vibration. Replace fan if any damage observed.

MAINTENANCE

Inspect cooling system every 12 months or 15,000 miles. Drain and flush cooling system at 36 months or 52,000 miles, and every 24 months or 30,000 miles thereafter. Maintain coolant mixture of 50% ethylene glycol type anti-freeze and 50% water year-round. Coolant must have silicate inhibitors.

CHRYSLER COOLANT CAPACITY

Application	Quarts (L)
2.2L	8.5 (8.0)
2.6L	9.5 (9.0)
3.7L	
D & W100/350 & Ramcharger	13 (12.3)
B150/250	[2] 14 (13.2)
5.2L	
D & W100/350 & Ramcharger	17 (16.1)
B150/250	[1 2] 16 (15.1)
B350	[1 2] 16 (15.1)
5.9L	
D & W100/350 & Ramcharger	15.5 (14.7)
B150/250	[2 3] 14.5 (13.7)
B350	[2 3] 17 (16.1)

1 – Add 2 qts. (1.9L) for A/C or Max. Cool.
2 – Add 1 qt. (.9L) for aux. heat.
3 – Add 1 qt. (.9L) for A/C, 2 qts. (1.9L) for Max. Cool.

FORD

CAUTION: Do not stand in line with or near radiator fan when engine is running until fan has been checked for damage or loose parts. Never repair fan if damaged. Fan must be replaced as assembly.

THERMOSTAT

Thermostat, located in water outlet elbow, has an opening temperature of 192°F (89°C) on 4-cylinder and V8 engines, 197°F (92°C) on 6-cylinder engines and 180°F (82°C) on V8 diesel engines.

PRESSURE CAP

All models use 13 psi (.9 kg/cm^2) pressure cap which should be tested at 10-14 psi (.7-1.0 kg/cm^2).

WATER PUMP

If wear or damage exists, water pump unit replacement is recommended. Do not attempt to overhaul or repair pump.

MAINTENANCE

Vehicle maintenance schedule "B" or (B) is on glovebox and engine Emission Control Information Decal. Check coolant condition annually. Drain, clean, flush and refill system if dirt or rust impairs cooling ability. Hoses and clamps should be inspected every 3 years or 50,000 miles, whichever occurs first.

FORD COOLANT CAPACITY

Application	Quarts (L)
2.0L & 2.3L Engines	
Aerostar	
Auto. Trans.	7.6 (7.2)
Man. Trans.	6.8 (6.4)
All Other Models	
With A/C	7.2 (6.8)
Without A/C	6.5 (6.2)
2.3L Turbo Diesel	
Standard Cooling	12.0 (11.4)
Extra Cooling or A/C	13 (12.3)
Super Cooling or A/C	10.7 (10.1)
2.8L Engines	
Aerostar	8.0 (7.6)
All Others	
With A/C	7.8 (7.4)
Without A/C	7.2 (6.8)
4.9L Engines	
F150/350 & Bronco	
Auto. Trans.	14.0 (13.2)
Man. Trans.	13.0 (12.3)
E150/350 [1]	
With Heater	16.0 (15.1)
With Heater & A/C	18.5 (17.5)

1 – Add 1.8 qts. (1.7L) for auxiliary heater.

ENGINE COOLANT SPECIFICATIONS (Cont.)

FORD COOLANT CAPACITY (Cont.)

Application	Quarts (L)
5.0L Engines	
F150/350 & Bronco	
Standard or Extra Cooling	13.0 (12.2)
Super Cooling or A/C	14.0 (13.2)
E150/350	
Standard Cooling	15.0 (14.2)
Extra Cooling	17.5 (16.6)
Super Cooling or A/C	18.5 (17.5)
5.8L Engines	
F150/350 & Bronco	
Standard or Extra Cooling	15.0 (14.2)
Super Cooling or A/C	16.0 (15.1)
E150/350 [1]	
Standard or Extra Cooling	20.0 (18.9)
Super Cooling or A/C	21.0 (20.0)
6.9L Diesel	31.0 (29.3)
7.5L Engines	
F250/350	
Man. Trans. & Extra Cooling	16.5 (15.6)
All Other Options	17.5 (16.6)
E250/350	[1] 28.0 (26.5)

[1] – Add 1.8 qts. (1.7L) for auxiliary heater.

GENERAL MOTORS

THERMOSTAT

All models use thermostat that starts to open at 195°F (91°C), and is fully open at 222°F (106°C).

PRESSURE CAP

All models use 15 psi (1.0 kg/cm^2) pressure cap which should be tested at 14-17 psi (.9-1.2 kg/cm^2).

WATER PUMP

Water pump is serviced only as an assembly.

MAINTENANCE

Inspect cooling system every 12 months or 15,000 miles. Drain and flush cooling system every 24 months or 30,000 miles. Maintain coolant level with 50% mixture of ethylene glycol based anti-freeze and low mineral content water in all seasons.

JEEP

THERMOSTAT

Thermostat, located in water outlet elbow, is pellet type with an opening temperature of 192-198°F (89-92°C). Thermostat should be fully open at 218°F (103°C) on all engines.

PRESSURE CAP

All models use 12-15 psi (.8-1.0 kg/cm^2) pressure cap. Cap should hold in specified range of pressure for 30 seconds or more.

WATER PUMP

Water pump impeller is pressed on rear of pump shaft and bearing assembly. Pump is serviced as assembly only. Engines with serpentine (single) drive belt use reverse rotating water pump and viscous (Tempatrol) fan drive assembly. Components have "REVERSE" stamped on cover of drive and inner side of fan. Water pump has "REV" cast into body.

MAINTENANCE

At 12,500 miles or 12 months, change engine coolant. Thereafter, change engine coolant at start of winter. Maintain coolant level with 50% mixture of ethylene glycol based anti-freeze and low mineral content water year-around.

GENERAL MOTORS COOLANT CAPACITY

Application	Quarts (L)
All Models	
1.9L	9.5 (9.0)
2.2L Diesel	
Std.	11.5 (11.0)
Heavy Duty or A/C	12.0 (11.5)
2.5L	10.0 (9.5)
2.8L	12.0 (11.5)
4.3L	
Astro/Safari Models	13.5 (12.8)
"C" & "K" Models	10.9 (10.3)
"G" Models	11.1 (10.5)
4.8L	
"P" Models	13.8 (13.1)
All Other Models	15.5 (14.7)
5.0L & 5.7L	
"P" Models	15.5 (14.6)
"G" Models	17.0 (16.0)
All Other Models	
With A/C	18.0 (17.0)
Without A/C	17.5 (16.6)
6.2L Diesel	
"C" & "K" Models	25.0 (23.7)
"G" Models	
VIN C	24 (22.7)
VIN J	25.6 (24.2)
"P" Models	
Forward Control Chassis	25 (23.7)
Motor Home Chassis	24.7 (23.4)
7.4L	
"C" & "K" Models	
With A/C	24.5 (23.2)
Without A/C	23.0 (21.8)
"P" Models	22.5 (21.3)

JEEP COOLANT CAPACITY

Application	Quarts (L)
Cherokee & Wagoneer	
2.1L Turbo Diesel	9 (8.5)
2.5L Engines [1]	10.0 (9.5)
2.8L Engines [1]	12.0 (11.4)
CJ7 & Scrambler	
2.5L & 4.2L Engines	
Standard	11.0 (10.4)
With A/C or Heavy Duty	14.0 (13.2)
Grand Wagoneer & Truck	
4.2L Engines [2]	10.5 (9.9)
6.0L Engines [2]	14.0 (13.2)

[1] – Includes 2.3 qts. (2.17L) for coolant recovery bottle.
[2] – Includes 1 qt. (.9L) for heater.

SECTION 8

CLUTCHES

CONTENTS

NOTE: **ALSO SEE GENERAL INDEX.**

IMPORTANT: **Because of the many model names used by vehicle manufacturers, accurate identification of models is important. See Model Identification at the front of this publication.**

Clutches

CLUTCH TROUBLE SHOOTING

CONDITION	POSSIBLE CAUSE	CORRECTION
Chattering or Grabbing	Incorrect lever adjustment	See adjustment in CLUTCHES
	Oil, grease or glaze on facings	Disassemble and clean or replace
	Loose "U" joint flange	See DRIVE AXLES
	Worn input shaft spline	See CLUTCHES
	Binding pressure plate	See CLUTCHES
	Binding release lever	See CLUTCHES
	Binding disc hub	See Removal in CLUTCHES
	Unequal pressure plate contact	Replace worn/misaligned components
	Loose/bent clutch disc	See Removal & Installation in CLUTCHES
	Incorrect transmission alignment	See Removal in MANUAL TRANSMISSION
	Worn pressure plate, disc or flywheel	See Removal & Installation in CLUTCHES
	Broken or weak pressure springs	Replace pressure plate
	Sticking clutch pedal	See General Servicing in CLUTCHES
	Incorrect disc facing	Replace and match components
	Engine loose in chassis	Tighten all mounting bolts
Spinning	Dry or worn bushings	Lubricate and replace worn parts
	Misaligned clutch housing	See Removal in MANUAL TRANSMISSION
	Bent or distorted clutch disc	Replace and match components
	Excessive pedal free play	See Adjustment in CLUTCHES
Dragging	Oil or grease on facings	Clean and replace if necessary
	Incorrect lever or pedal adjustment	See Adjustment in CLUTCHES
	Dust or dirt on clutch	See General Servicing in CLUTHCES
	Worn or broken facings	Replace worn/damaged components
	Bent clutch disc or pressure plate	Replace and match components
	Clutch disc hub binding on shaft	See General Servicing in CLUTCHES
	Binding pilot bushing	See Gereral Servicing in CLUTCHES
	Sticking release bearing sleeve	See CLUTCHES
Rattling	Weak or broken release lever spring	Replace spring and check alignment
	Damaged pressure plate	Replace and match components
	Broken clutch return spring	Replace spring
	Worn splines on disc or input shaft	Replace disc and/or input shaft
	Worn clutch release bearing	Replace spring and check alignment
	Dry or worn pilot bushing	Lubricate or replace bushing
	Unequal release lever contact	Align or replace lever
	Incorrect pedal free play	See Adjustment in CLUTCHES
	Warped clutch disc	Replace and match components
Slipping	Pressure springs worn or broken	Replace damaged components
	Oily, greasy or worn clutch facings,	Clean or replace components
	Incorrect clutch alignment	See CLUTCHES
	Warped clutch disc or pressure plate	Replace and match damaged components
	Binding release levers or clutch pedal	See General Servicing in CLUTCHES
Squeaking	Worn or damaged release bearing	Replace worn/damaged parts
	Dry or worn pilot/release bearing	Lubricate or replace if necessary
	Pilot bearing turning in crankshaft	See Removal in CLUTCHES
	Worn input shaft bearing	Replace bearing and seal
	Incorrect transmission alignment	See Removal in MANUAL TRANSMISSION
	Dry clutch fork between pivot	See General Servicing in CLUTCHES
Heavy and/or Stiff Pedal	Sticking release bearing sleeve	See General Servicing in CLUTCHES
	Dry or binding pedal hub	Lubricate and align components
	Floor mat interference with pedal	Lay mat flat in proper area
	Dry or binding ball/fork pivots	Lubricate and align components
Grinding	Dry release bearing	See General Servicing in CLUTCHES
	Dry or worn pilot bearing	Lubricate or replace bearing
	Worn input shaft bearing	Replace bearing
Whirring	Incorrect pedal free play	See Adjustment in CLUTCHES
	Incorrect transmission alignment	See Removal in MANUAL TRANSMISSION

Clutches

CHRYSLER CORP.

DESCRIPTION

Clutches used on all Chrysler Corp. vehicles are dry, single disc design. Adjustment for wear is not provided in clutch itself.

On FWD models, clutch release cable is self-adjusting. Prelubricated clutch bearing is constant running type. No external adjustments can be made.

On RWD models, clutch pedal linkage is adjustable to maintain pedal free play. Clutch linkage on all models is mechanical type.

Fig. 1: Exploded View of Clutch Assembly

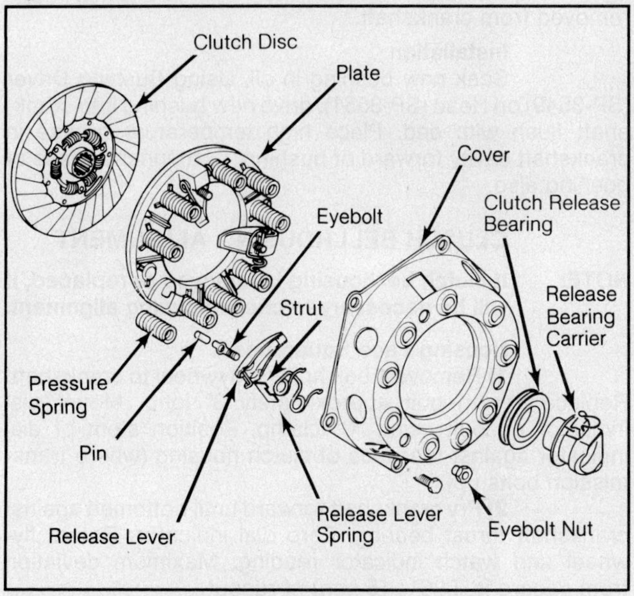

Mark clutch cover position before disassembly.

REMOVAL & INSTALLATION

TRANSAXLE

Removal (A-460 & A-525)

1) Disconnect battery ground strap. Support engine at No. 4 cylinder exhaust manifold bolt with lifting hook attached to support fixture. Remove upper bellhousing bolts. Disconnect gearshift operating lever from selector shaft. Remove both front wheels and tires. Disconnect clutch linkage. *See Fig. 2.*

2) Remove left front splash shield. Remove both drive axles. See FRONT WHEEL DRIVE AXLE SHAFTS article in DRIVE AXLE Section. Remove engine anti-rotational link. Remove speedometer drive assembly from extension housing. Remove starter.

3) Remove clutch cover. Remove engine mount bracket from front crossmember. Remove front mount through bolt and bellhousing bolts. Position jack under transaxle. Remove left engine mount from transaxle and engine. Remove lower bellhousing bolts. Lower transaxle from vehicle.

Installation

Use new nut to hold operating lever to selector shaft. Make 2 locating pins from either studs with screwdriver slots cut in end or bolts with heads cut off and slots cut in end of bolt. Use locating pins in place of 2 top bolts that hold transaxle to engine to align transaxle. Reverse removal procedure to install transmission.

Fig. 2: FWD Clutch Release Self-Adjusting Linkage

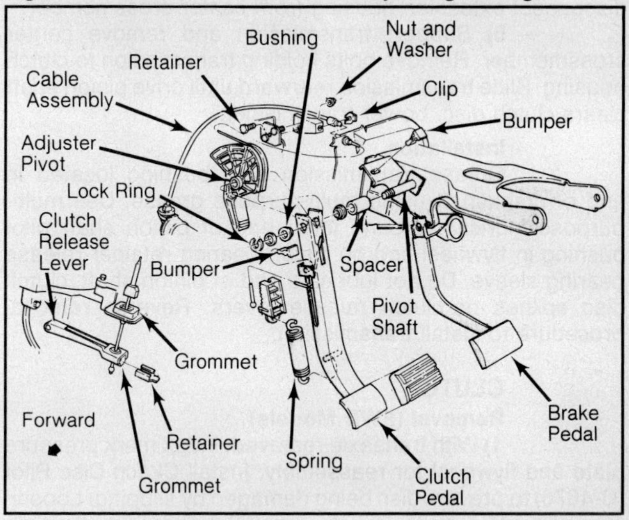

No adjustment is provided.

TRANSMISSION

Removal (NP 435)

1) Disconnect negative battery cable from battery. Remove retaining screws from floor pan boot and slide up and off shift lever.

2) Remove shift lever retainer by pressing down, rotating retainer counterclockwise and releasing retainer. Remove 4 bolts attaching skid plate to underside of frame.

3) Remove 5 bolts attaching front of skid plate to transmission crossmember. Remove skid plate. Disconnect speedometer cable.

4) Disconnect front and rear propeller shafts and secure out of the way. Disconnect shift rods at transfer case. Support transfer case with jack.

5) Remove bolts holding extension to transfer case. Move transfer case rearward and disengage front input spline. Lower transfer case from vehicle. Disconnect back-up light switch.

6) Install engine support over frame rails. Be sure support ends are against underside of oil pan flange. Support transmission and remove center crossmember.

7) Remove transmission to clutch housing bolts. Slide transmission rearward until drive pinion shaft clears clutch disc. Remove transmission.

Installation

Grease transmission pilot bushing located in end of crankshaft using multi-purpose grease. Do not lubricate end of pinion shaft, clutch disc splines or clutch release levers. Reverse removal procedure to install transmission.

Removal (4-Speed Overdrive)

1) Disconnect negative cable from battery. Remove retaining screws from floor pan boot and slide up and off shift lever. Remove shift lever.

2) Remove retaining clips, washers and control rods from shift unit levers. Remove 2 bolts and washers securing shift unit to mounting plate on extension housing and remove unit.

3) Drain transmission fluid. Mark propeller shaft position for reinstallation and disconnect at rear universal joint. Pull shaft yoke out of transmission extension housing.

4) Disconnect speedometer cable and back-up light switch. Install engine support. Be sure support ends are against underside of oil pan flange. Raise engine and disconnect extension housing from center crossmember.

5) Support transmission and remove center crossmember. Remove bolts holding transmission to clutch housing. Slide transmission rearward until drive pinion shaft clears clutch disc. Lower transmission.

Installation

Grease transmission pilot bushing located in end of crankshaft using multi-purpose grease. Use multi-purpose lubricant around inner end of pinion shaft pilot bushing in flywheel and on pinion bearing retainer release bearing sleeve. Do not lubricate end of pinion shaft, clutch disc splines or clutch release levers. Reverse removal procedure to install transmission.

CLUTCH

Removal (FWD Models)

1) With transaxle removed, index mark pressure plate and flywheel for reassembly. Install Clutch Disc Pilot (C-4676) to prevent disc being damaged by slipping. Loosen pressure plate bolts in sequence, 2 turns each time, to avoid warping plate.

2) Remove inner "E" clip from clutch bearing shaft. Slide shaft out of transaxle housing, noting large shaft bushing by "E" clip and small bushing by clutch bearing fork. Slide clutch release bearing and fork off input shaft seal retainer. Do not immerse prelubricated release bearing in solvent.

Installation

1) Reverse removal procedure to install release bearing, bearing fork, and bearing shaft. Make sure bushings are in correct location. Check that flywheel runout is less than .003" (.08 mm) for one full revolution. Clutch disc should be replaced if worn to within .015" (.38 mm) of rivet heads.

2) Clean all parts, making sure that no oil or heat damage has occurred. Mount disc and pressure plate on flywheel. Make sure that dowels and index marks are aligned on flywheel and pressure plate. Use clutch pilot to keep disc in line with center of crankshaft.

3) Keep pressure on pilot while tightening bolts on pressure plate enough to hold disc in place. Tighten pressure plate bolts slowly, in sequence, until all are seated. Tighten bolts to specification and remove pilot. Install transmission.

Removal (RWD Models)

1) With transmission and transfer case (if equipped) removed, remove clutch housing pan. Disconnect clutch fork return spring. Remove fork rod spring washer from pin and remove fork rod, adjusting nut, washer and insulator.

2) Remove clutch fork and release bearing (if not removed with transmission). Mark position of clutch cover on flywheel for reassembly. Remove clutch cover bolts by loosening 1 or 2 turns at a time until all bolts are removed. Remove clutch cover and disc from flywheel.

Installation

1) Ensure flywheel surface is clean. Install clutch cover and disc with pilot. Ensure cover is in original position on flywheel.

2) Tighten cover bolts a few turns at a time, alternately and evenly. Lubricate bearing sleeve cavity with grease.

3) Apply thin grease coat to release fork pads, clutch fork fingers and pivot contact area. Reverse removal procedure and install transmission.

PILOT BUSHING

NOTE: **Pilot bushing is not used with transaxles.**

Removal

Thread Bushing Puller (SP-3631) into bushing about 3-4 turns. Put Puller Cup (SP-3633) over threaded shaft. Run Puller Nut (SP-1191) down puller until nut rests against cup. Hold puller and turn puller nut until bushing is removed from crankshaft.

Installation

Soak new bushing in oil. Using Bushing Driver (SP-3549) on Head (SP-3551), drive new bushing into crankshaft flush with end. Place high temperature grease in crankshaft cavity forward of bushing. Coat inner surface of bushing also.

CLUTCH BELLHOUSING ALIGNMENT

NOTE: **If clutch bellhousing is removed or replaced, it will be necessary to check housing alignment.**

Housing Face Squareness

1) Remove 1 bolt holding flywheel to crankshaft. Replace it with bolt approximately 3" long. Mount dial indicator on bolt using "C" clamp. Position stem of dial indicator against rear face of clutch housing (where transmission bolts up).

2) Pry crankshaft forward until bottomed against crankshaft thrust bearing. Zero dial indicator. Rotate flywheel and watch indicator reading. Maximum deviation from square is .006" (.15 mm) of runout.

3) If runout is excessive, loosen housing bolts and insert shim between clutch housing and block at point of lowest reading. Remeasure housing face squareness. If housing face is square within specification, proceed to measure housing bore runout.

Housing Bore Runout

1) Position tip of dial indicator to inside of pilot bore of clutch housing. Zero dial indicator. Rotate flywheel and watch indicator reading. Bore runout should not exceed .008" (.20 mm). If runout is greater, install offset dowels.

2) Select dowels from sizes listed. Dowels must be used in pairs of same size. See OFFSET DOWEL SELECTION chart. Remove clutch housing and original dowels from rear face of engine block. Install offset dowels with slots parallel and aligned in direction of maximum runout.

3) Dowels must be seated in block up to shoulder of offset. Install clutch housing and tighten bolts. Remount dial indicator and check bore runout. Minor adjustment can be made by turning dowel with screwdriver until runout is correct.

OFFSET DOWEL SELECTION

Runout In. (mm)	Offset Dowel In. (mm)
.009-.020 (.23-.51)	.007 (.18)
.022-.034 (.56-.86)	.014 (.36)
.036-.050 (.91-1.27)	.021 (.53)

CHRYSLER CORP. (Cont.)

ADJUSTMENTS

CLUTCH LINKAGE

NOTE: On models with transaxles, no adjustments are possible. Self-adjusting clutch cable, when correctly installed, completely releases clutch through constant running clutch bearing.

All RWD Models

Adjust clutch fork push rod to obtain 3/32" (2.4 mm) free play at end of clutch fork. Free play will provide correct pedal free play of approximately 1" (25 mm).

TIGHTENING SPECIFICATIONS

Application	Ft. Lbs. (N.m)
FWD	
Bellhousing-to-Engine	70 (95)
Clutch Cover-to-Flywheel Bolts	21 (29)
Flywheel-to-Crankshaft	65 (88)
RWD	
Clutch Cover-to-Flywheel Bolts	
5/16"	17 (23)
3/8"	30 (41)
Clutch Fork Pivot Bolts	17 (23)
Housing-to-Engine Block Bolts	
7/16"	50 (68)
3/8"	30 (41)
Transmission-to-Clutch Housing	50 (68)
Transmission-to-Flywheel Bolts	55 (75)

Clutches

FORD – HYDRAULIC

DESCRIPTION

Hydraulic clutch control consists of hydraulic master cylinder, slave cylinder, reservoir and connecting linkages. Clutch disc and pressure plate are single disc type. Clutch release bearing or bearing arm is activated by hydraulic pressure. Pilot bearing (roller needle type) is mounted in flywheel and requires no lubrication unless clutch assembly is serviced. No adjustment of clutch linkage or pedal position is required.

CAUTION: On all models, disconnect master cylinder push rod if slave cylinder is to be disconnected from release lever or bearing. Permanent damage to slave cylinder will occur if master cylinder is activated with slave cylinder disconnected.

REMOVAL & INSTALLATION

TRANSMISSION

Removal (Aerostar Models)

1) Disconnect negative battery cable. Put transmission in Neutral. Lift boot assembly after removing 4 bolts holding boot to floorboards. Unbolt and remove shift lever assembly, with boot and knob, from transmission remote shift rail adapter.

2) Raise and support vehicle securely. Disconnect starter wiring and remove starter. Remove clip holding Red supply tube to clutch slave cylinder. Disconnect tube from slave cylinder and plug openings to avoid contamination. Remove all wiring from senders (back-up, shift indicator and Neutral switch) on transmission.

3) Disconnect speedometer cable or wire (electronic speedometer) from fitting on transmission. Mark propeller shaft and rear axle flange for reassembly and balance references. Remove propeller shaft. Cap end of transmission extension housing to avoid spilling oil.

4) Remove nuts holding insulator to crossmember. Loosen nuts holding front insulators to crossmember brackets. Place jack under transmission. Secure transmission to jack with safety chain. Raise transmission slightly and remove crossmember.

5) Unbolt clutch bellhousing from engine block. Move transmission backward until bellhousing clears dowel pins in rear of engine block. If transmission is to be out of vehicle for very long, support rear of engine so that engine does not hang on front mounts.

Installation

NOTE: Use only special washers to avoid corrosion where steel contacts aluminum.

1) If removed, place clutch slave cylinder over transmission input shaft. Tower section of cylinder must face transmission. Tabs on slave cylinder align with slots in rear face of bellhousing. Position bellhousing over tabs and tighten nuts holding bellhousing to transmission.

2) Secure transmission on jack and lift into position. Make sure clutch housing indexes with dowel pins on rear of engine block. Tighten bolts holding bellhousing to engine. Install insulator on transmission, if removed, and tighten bolts. Install crossmember and partially tighten nuts.

3) Lower transmission so studs of insulator are in holes of crossmember. Tighten nuts holding insulator to crossmember. Tighten nuts holding front insulators to frame brackets. Tighten nuts holding transmission crossmember to frame. Remove cap from transmission housing and install propeller shaft, making sure to align reference marks.

4) Reconnect speedometer cable or wire. Connect remaining wiring to transmission switches. Install Red supply tube in slave cylinder and attach clip holding tube and fitting to cylinder. Install starter and connect wiring. Make sure transmission oil level is correct. Install shift lever and shifter boot. Connect battery and bleed hydraulic clutch system.

Removal (Bronco II & Ranger Models)

1) Place transmission in Neutral. Remove boot retainer screws. Remove bolts holding retainer cover to gearshift lever retainer. Disconnect clutch master cylinder push rod from clutch pedal.

2) Remove gearshift lever assembly by pulling shim and bushing straight up and away from gearshift lever retainer. Cover shift tower opening in extension housing.

3) Disconnect clutch hydraulic system master cylinder push rod from clutch pedal. Disconnect negative battery cable. Raise and support vehicle. Disconnect driveshaft at rear axle drive flange.

4) Pull driveshaft rearward and disconnect from transmission. Install plug in extension housing. Remove clutch housing dust shield and slave cylinder and secure aside.

5) Remove speedometer cable from extension housing. Disconnect starter motor and back-up light switch. Place jack under engine and wood block under oil pan. On 4WD vehicles, remove transfer case. Remove starter motor. Place transmission jack under transmission.

6) Remove bolts, lockwashers and flat washers attaching transmission to rear engine plate. Remove transmission mount and bolts holding damper to crossmember.

7) Remove crossmember. Lower engine jack. Remove clutch housing from locating dowels. Slide transmission rearward until input shaft spline clears clutch disc. Remove transmission from vehicle.

Installation

To install transmission, reverse removal procedure. Be sure to align splines on input shaft with splines in clutch disc.

Removal ("E" Series With 3-Speed)

1) Raise and support vehicle. Drain transmission fluid. Disconnect propeller shaft from flange at transmission. Secure propeller shaft out of the way.

2) Disconnect speedometer cable from extension housing. Disconnect gear shift rods from transmission shift levers. Position jack under transmission.

3) Raise transmission. Remove 4 bolts holding transmission extension housing insulator and retainer to extension housing. Remove 4 bolts holding transmissionto flywheel housing. Install engine support bar on frame. Remove transmission.

Installation

To install transmission, reverse removal procedure. Splines on input shaft and splines in clutch disc must be aligned. Move transmission forward on guide pins until input shaft pilot enters bearing or bushing in crankshaft. If front bearing retainer binds, work release bearing lever until hub slides onto front bearing retainer.

Removal ("E" Series With 4-Speed Overdrive)

1) Place wood block under clutch pedal to prevent clutch depression. Raise and support vehicle. Mark

FORD – HYDRAULIC (Cont.)

propeller shaft position for reinstallation. Disconnect propeller shaft from rear universal joint flange.

2) Slide propeller shaft off transmission output shaft. Insert extension housing seal installer into extension housing. Disconnect speedometer cable from extension housing.

3) Remove retaining clips, flat washers and spring washers. Secure shift rods to shift levers. Remove bolts holding shift control to transmission extension housing. Remove nuts holding shift control to transmission case.

4) Remove rear transmission support bolts connecting crossmember support to transmission extension housing. Support transmission using a jack. Raise transmission to remove weight from No. 3 crossmember.

5) Remove No. 3 crossmember bolts and remove crossmember. Raise engine enough to remove weight from crossmember. Remove retaining bolts and remove crossmember.

6) Remove bolts holding transmission to flywheel housing. Move transmission rearward until input shaft clears flywheel housing. Remove transmission.

Installation

To install transmission, reverse removal procedure. Install guide pins in flywheel housing lower mounting bolt holes. Move transmission on guide pins until input shaft splines enter clutch hub splines and case is against flywheel housing.

Removal (2WD "F" Series)

1) Remove floor mat and body floor pan cover. Remove gearshift lever shift ball and boot as an assembly. Remove weather pad.

2) Raise and support vehicle. Position transmission jack under transmission and disconnect speedometer cable. Disconnect back-up light switch at rear of gearshift housing cover.

3) Disconnect propeller shaft and clutch linkage from transmission and wire aside. Remove transmission attaching bolts. Move transmission rearward until input shaft clears clutch housing. Lower transmission.

Installation

To install transmission, reverse removal procedure. Install guide studs in clutch housing and raise transmission until input shaft splines are aligned with clutch disc splines. Clutch release bearing and hub must be properly positioned in release lever fork.

Removal (4WD "F" Series)

1) From inside vehicle, remove floor mat. Remove screws holding access cover to floor pan. Place shift lever in Reverse and remove shift lever cover. Remove insulator and dust cover.

2) From transfer case and transmission, remove shift lever, shift ball and boot as assemblies. Raise and support vehicle. Drain transmission. Disconnect front and rear propeller shafts from transfer case and wire aside.

3) Remove retainer ring holding shift link in place and remove shift link from transfer case. Remove speedometer cable.

4) Place jack under transfer case. Disconnect transfer case from transmission and remove transfer case. Remove rear support bracket from transmission. Place jack under transmission and remove rear support bracket and brace. Undo bolts holding transmission to bellhousing and remove transmission.

Installation

To install transmission, reverse removal procedure. Install 2 guide studs in bellhousing top holes to guide transmission into position.

PRESSURE PLATE & CLUTCH DISC

Removal

Remove transmission. Mark pressure plate and flywheel for reassembly reference. Loosen bolts holding pressure plate to flywheel evenly until springs are expanded. Remove pressure plate and clutch disc from flywheel.

Installation

1) Clean pressure plate and flywheel surface with commercial alcohol base solvent. Place clutch disc on flywheel. Align disc center with pilot bearing using old input shaft or clutch pilot.

2) Place pressure plate on flywheel and align marks made during disassembly. Tighten bolts evenly in clockwise rotation. Tighten every other bolt for first 3 bolts, then skip 2 to 4th bolt, then every other bolt until all 6 bolts are tightened to specification.

3) Remove clutch disc pilot. To complete installation, reverse remaining removal procedure.

CLUTCH RELEASE BEARING

Removal (Aerostar, Bronco II & Ranger Models)

Remove clutch slave cylinder from bellhousing. Bend back 4 plastic retainers on bearing carrier. Remove bearing from carrier.

Installation

Using multipurpose grease (Ford Part No. C1AZ-19590-B or ESA-M1C75-B), fill annular groove of release bearing. Coat inside diameter of bearing with thin film of lubricant. Push release bearing into carrier. Make sure bearing is aligned with 4 retainers of carrier. Install slave cylinder in bellhousing.

Fig. 1: Aerostar, Bronco II & Ranger Clutch Release Bearing

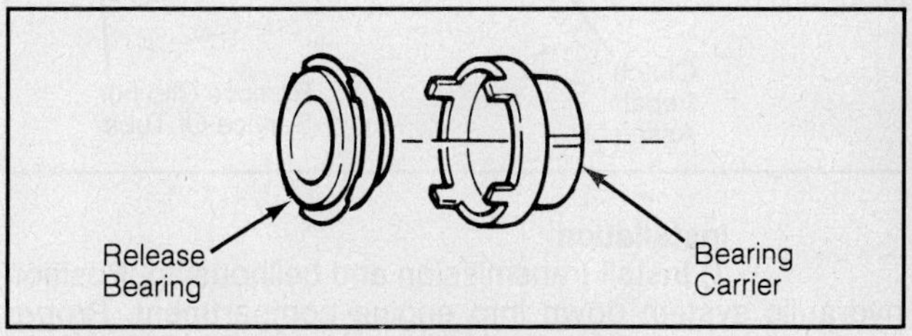

Align bearing with retainer tangs on carrier.

Removal (All Other Models)

Remove transmission. Remove clutch release lever from stud in bellhousing. Remove release bearing and hub from lever. Check bearing for any roughness and replace if necessary. Check bore of bearing hub for burrs or scoring that could bind on input shaft retainer.

Installation

1) Before installing bearing, fill annular groove with multipurpose lithium base grease. Lightly coat inside diameter of release bearing. Lubricate fingers and fulcrum point of release lever.

2) DO NOT use grease on pivot assembly of van models. Position release lever on pivot stud in bellhousing.

Clutches

FORD – HYDRAULIC (Cont.)

CLUTCH PILOT BEARING

Removal

Remove transmission, pressure plate and clutch disc. Use Impact Slide Hammer (T59L-100-B) and Puller Jaw (T58L-101-A) to remove pilot bearing.

Installation

Coat pilot bore in crankshaft with multipurpose lithium base grease. Do not use too much grease as it could contaminate clutch disc. Using bearing driver, install bearing in crankshaft with seal facing out toward transmission. Install clutch disc, pressure plate and transmission.

NOTE: **Use care when installing transmission so that input shaft does not damage pilot bearing.**

CLUTCH HYDRAULIC SYSTEM

Removal (Aerostar, Bronco II & Ranger Models)

1) Remove lock pin and disconnect master cylinder push rod from clutch pedal. Remove bolts holding master cylinder to firewall. Remove bolts holding reservoir to access cover of cowl.

2 Remove master cylinder from opening in firewall. Remove hydraulic system assembly upward from engine compartment. Remove transmission and bellhousing. Remove slave cylinder from bellhousing.

Fig. 2: Aerostar, Bronco II & Ranger Hydraulic Clutch System

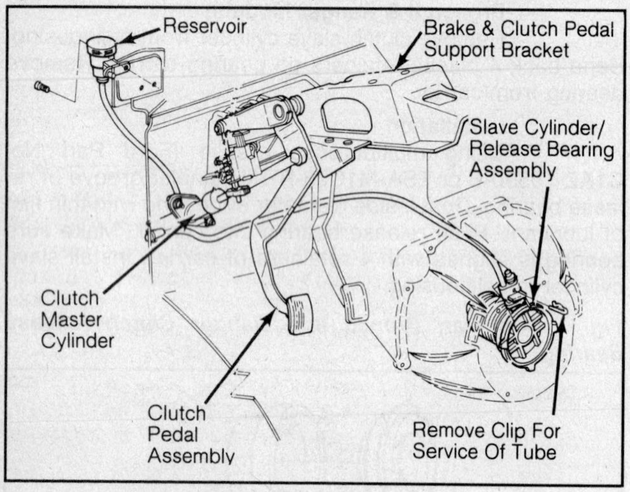

Installation

1) Install transmission and bellhousing. Position hydraulic system down into engine compartment. Proper routing for tube from master cylinder to slave cylinder is above brake tubes and below steering column shaft. On 2.8L vehicles, tube MUST lie on top of clutch housing.

2) Insert master cylinder push rod through opening in firewall. Attach master cylinder to firewall. Install fluid reservoir on access cover. Apply light film of SAE 30 oil to push rod bushing.

3) Install bushing and push rod on clutch pedal. Install lock pin. Check clutch reservoir and top up if necessary. Depress clutch pedal 10 times to check proper release and smooth operation.

Removal ("E" & "F" Series)

1) Remove cotter pin holding push rod to clutch pedal lever inside cab. Disconnect push rod and remove bushing. Remove 2 nuts holding clutch reservoir and mas-

Fig. 3: Aerostar, Bronco II and Ranger Clutch Slave Cylinder

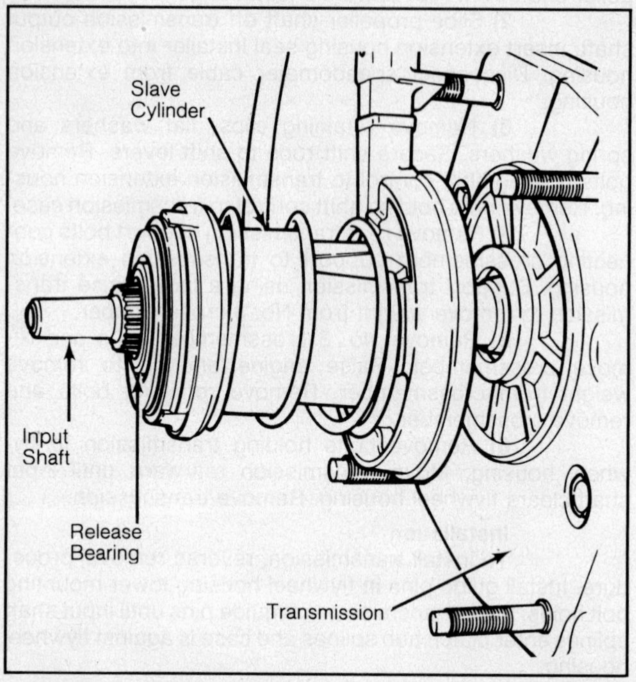

ter cylinder assembly to firewall. Remove clutch reservoir and master cylinder assembly from firewall in engine compartment.

2) Note correct routing of clutch tubing to slave cylinder. Lift 2 retaining tabs of slave cylinder retainer bracket. Unhook tabs from bellhousing. Slide slave cylinder

Fig. 4: Pickup & Van Hydraulic Clutch System

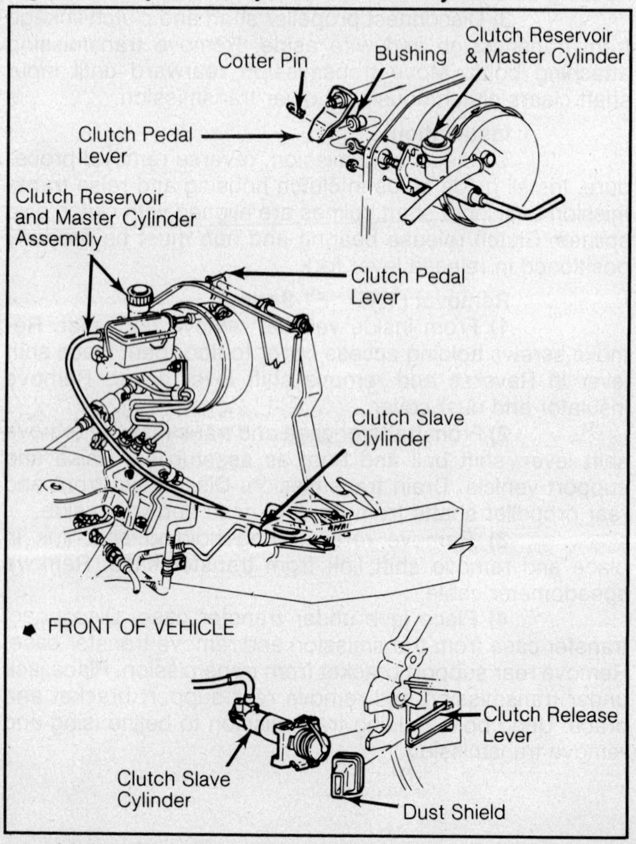

outward to remove. Disengage push rod from release lever while removing slave cylinder. Remove system from vehicle.

Installation

1) Position clutch fluid reservoir and master cylinder on firewall and tighten 2 nuts from inside cab. Route clutch tubing and slave cylinder to bellhousing. Be sure nylon tubing is kept away from possible exhaust heat.

2) Move slave cylinder push rod into cylinder. Engage push rod in release lever. Slide slave cylinder into bellhousing lugs. Seat cylinder in recess of lugs. Apply light film of SAE 30 engine oil to master cylinder push rod bushing.

3) From inside vehicle, install bushing on clutch lever pedal. Connect clutch master cylinder push rod to clutch pedal lever and install cotter pin. Check that reservoir fluid level is up to step. DO NOT overfill. Depress clutch pedal at least 10 times to verify proper operation.

NOTE: Slave cylinders in new systems come with shipping strap which positions rod and also provides rod bearing insert. First use of pedal after system is installed will break strap and allow normal operation of system.

HYDRAULIC SYSTEM BLEEDING

1) Clean area around reservoir cap of any dirt or grease. Fill reservoir to top with approved brake fluid (DOT 3 Specification). Run hose from bleeder screw to container to avoid having brake fluid get into bellhousing. Loosen bleed screw and keep fluid level in reservoir to step.

2) Fluid and bubbles will flow from tube attached to slave cylinder bleed screw. When stream of fluid is solid (no air bubbles visible), close bleed screw. Make sure fluid in reservoir is level with step. Put diaphragm and cap on reservoir.

3) Place light load on clutch pedal and open bleed screw. Maintain pressure until pedal reaches floor. Close bleed screw while keeping pedal fully depressed. DO NOT allow pedal to return before bleed screw is fully tightened. Top up reservoir to step.

4) Check Red supply tube for air bubbles while clutch pedal is being operated slowly. If air is apparent, tap on tube so that air will rise to master cylinder and then go into reservoir. System should now be fully bled and working properly.

5) Test system by starting vehicle, depressing clutch and putting shift lever into reverse position. No grating or grinding noise should be heard or felt with clutch pedal within .50" (12.7 mm) of floor. If noise is heard, check for air in system. Repeat bleeding procedure if air is evident.clutch reservoir and top up if necessary. Depress clutch pedal 10 times to check proper release and smooth operation.

CLUTCH PEDAL

Removal (Aerostar Models)

Disconnect push rod from clutch pedal. Disconnect clutch/starter interlock switch from pedal. Remove retainer clip from pedal shaft. Remove pedal and shaft assembly from bracket. Remove bushings from bracket.

NOTE: When clutch pedal and shaft assembly are removed from bracket, brake pedal, bushings and spring washer will fall out of bracket.

Installation

1) Check bushings and shaft for wear or damage. Replace parts as necessary. Lubricate bushings with light film of SAE 30 oil. Insert 2 outer bushings in bracket. Put brake pedal, inner bushings and spring washer into bracket. Slide clutch pedal shaft through bracket.

2) Put retainer clip on pedal shaft. Connect clutch/starter interlock switch to clutch pedal. Connect push rod to pedal. Check and adjust clip on interlock switch if necessary.

Removal (All Other Models)

Disconnect pedal return spring from pedal and bracket. Unhook barbed end of clutch/starter interlock switch from pedal. Remove clutch pedal after removing retaining nut on end of shaft. Remove bushing from pedal shaft.

Fig. 5: Aerostar Clutch & Brake Pedal Assembly

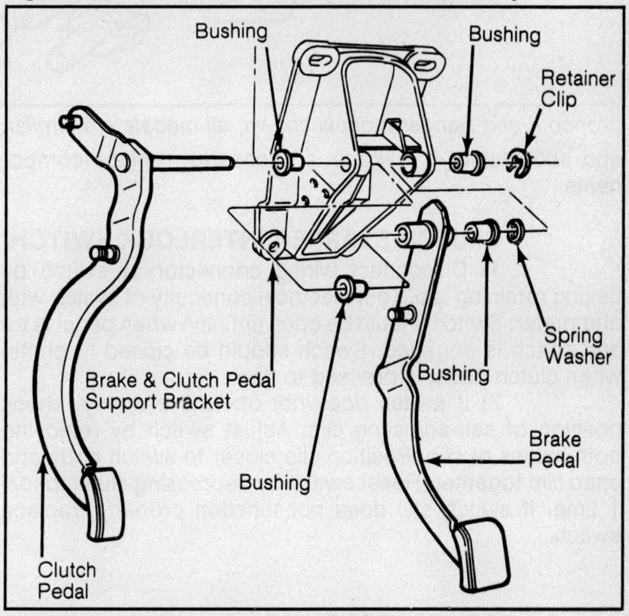

Brake pedal rides on clutch pedal shaft.

Installation

Install bushing on shaft. Place pedal on shaft and tighten nut. Install return spring. Make sure spring is hooked to pedal and bracket securely. Insert barbed end of interlock switch rod into bracket. Check and adjust switch action if necessary.

TESTING

CLUTCH PEDAL TRAVEL

"E" & "F" Series

1) Measure travel of clutch slave cylinder push rod. With clutch pedal pushed fully to floor, slave cylinder push rod should extend at least .69" (17.5 mm) on models with 4.9L, 5.0L and 5.8L engines. On models with 6.9L and 7.5L engines, push rod should extend at least .53" (13.5 mm) against clutch lever head.

2) On all models, system is functioning properly if push rod travel meets or exceeds limit. If slave cylinder does not have acceptable travel, check reservoir fluid level. If reservoir requires fluid, check hydraulic system for leakage.

3) Remove rubber boots from cylinder and check for leakage past cylinders. Slight moisture is normal

Clutches

FORD – HYDRAULIC (Cont.)

Fig. 6: Clutch/Starter Interlock Switch

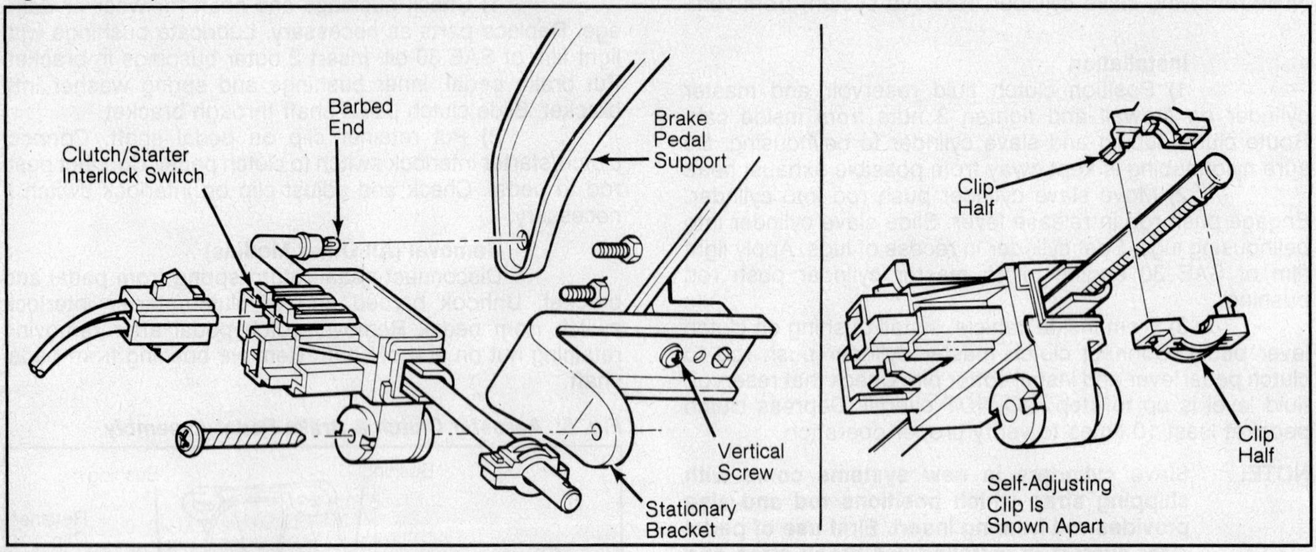

Bronco II and Ranger models shown; all models are similar.

and acceptable. If leakage is excessive, replace components.

CLUTCH/STARTER INTERLOCK SWITCH

1) Disconnect wiring connector at switch by flexing retaining tab. Test electrical continuity of switch with ohmmeter. Switch should be open (infinity) when pedal is up and clutch is engaged. Switch should be closed (0 ohms) when clutch pedal is pressed to floor.

2) If switch does not operate properly, check position of self-adjusting clip. Adjust switch by removing both halves of clip. Position clip closer to switch body and snap clip together. Reset switch by depressing clutch pedal 1 time. If switch still does not function properly, replace switch.

ADJUSTMENTS

CLUTCH BELLHOUSING ALIGNMENT

NOTE: If clutch bellhousing is removed or replaced, it will be necessary to check housing alignment.

Whenever bellhousing is removed from engine or replaced, alignment must be checked to prevent excessive transmission wear, drive train vibration, clutch pilot or release bearing noises or transmission jumping out of gear.

1) With transmission and bellhousing removed, check for nicks and burrs and remove paint and other foreign material from bellhousing faces and bore surfaces, rear of engine block and rear engine plate. Make sure locating dowels are tight and in good condition.

2) Mount bellhousing and rear engine plate on engine block. Tighten bolts holding bellhousing to block to specification. Install Expanding Collet Post (T75L-6392-A) into clutch disc with dial indicator base post attached to collet post. *See Fig. 7.*

3) Tighten nut on end of collet post until split collet expands and locks into clutch disc hub. Collet post must show no movement as erratic readings would result. Mount dial indicator on base post using universal bracket and short Support Bar (T75L-4201-B).

Fig. 7: Alignment Tool Post Assembly Installed

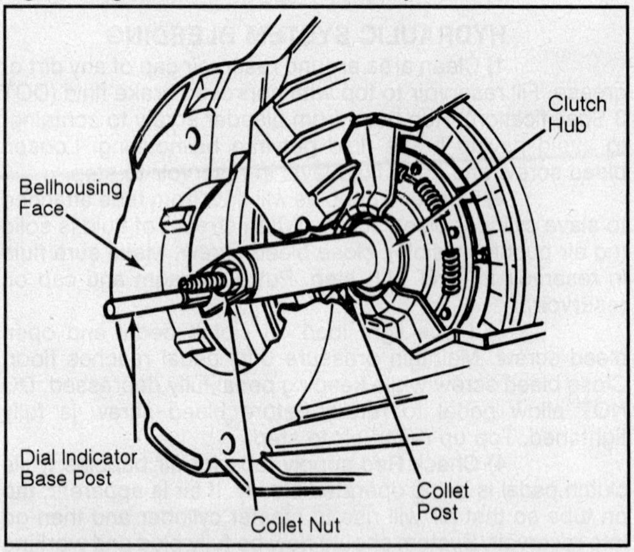

Make sure collet post cannot move in clutch hub.

4) Position dial indicator so tip rests against rear face of bellhousing at right angle. *See Fig. 8.* Push crankshaft to rear to eliminate end play. Zero dial indicator. While pushing crankshaft toward rear, rotate crankshaft through 360° revolution.

5) Check that dial indicator has returned to zero when starting point is reached. If reading is not zero, end play or loose collet post have affected reading. Note maximum and minimum readings of dial indicator during 1 revolution to determine face runout. Repeat measurement for accuracy and verification.

6) Attach lever adapter to dial indicator. Place rubber band as shown to preload dial indicator and to provide constant light pressure of lever tip against bellhousing bore inner circumference. DO NOT make rubber band too tight. *See Fig. 9.* Zero dial indicator.

7) Rotate crankshaft through 360°. Record maximum variation of indicator. Repeat procedure again to verify reading. If face runout exceeds .010" (.25 mm) and/or bore runout exceeds .015" (.38 mm), bellhousing alignment

FORD – HYDRAULIC (Cont.)

Fig. 8: Tool Setup For Measuring Face Runout

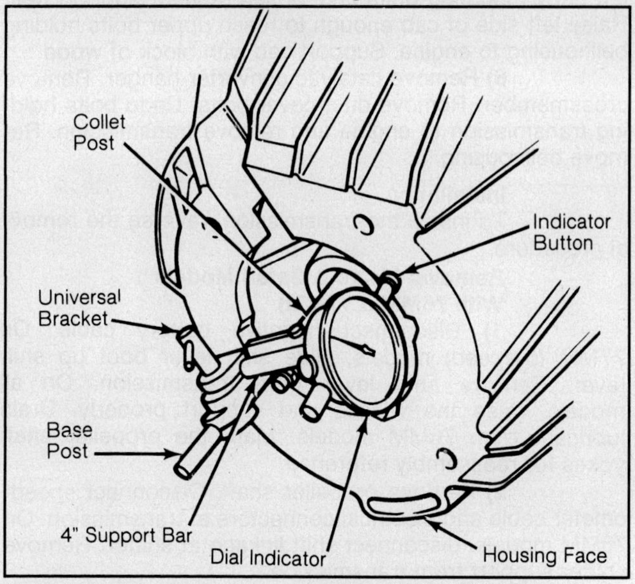

Limit for bellhousing face runout is .010" (.25 mm).

Fig. 9: Tool Setup For Measuring Bore Runout

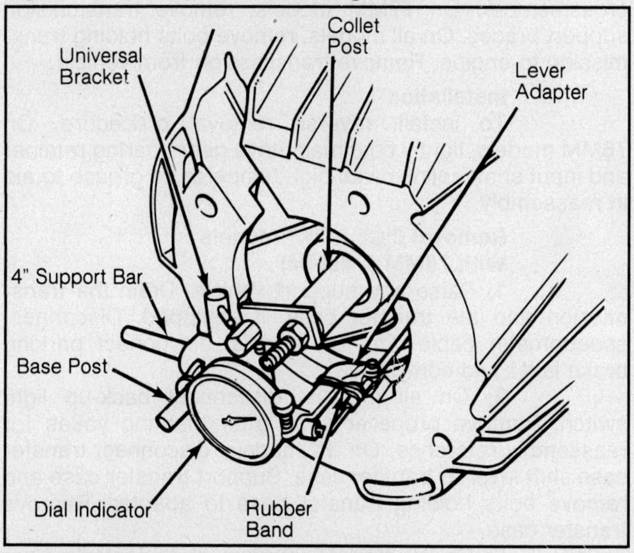

Limit for bore runout is .015" (.38 mm).

must be corrected. Shims may be used to correct face runout. *See Fig. 10.*

8) Shim required must be half of largest negative dial indicator reading. Shim should be installed between bellhousing and engine block at point of largest negative reading. Repeat measurements. If both bore and face runouts are out of limits, shim bellhousing until face runout is correct.

9) Check bore runout again. If bore runout is still excessive, shim bellhousing to limit of face runout. If bore runout is still excessive, bellhousing must be replaced.

Fig. 10: Bellhousing Alignment Shim

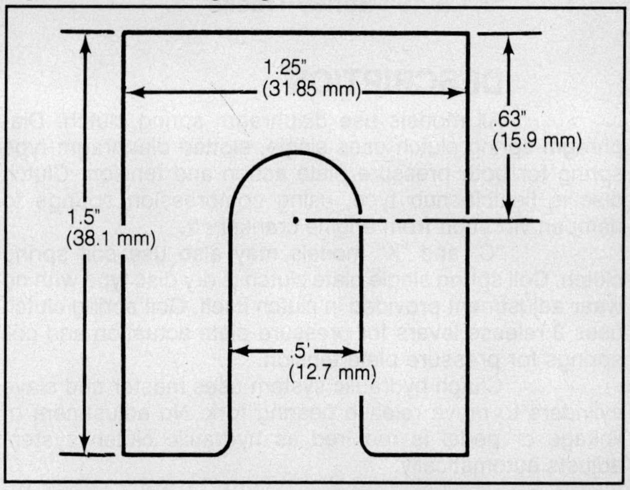

Thickness is half of maximum negative dial indicator reading.

TIGHTENING SPECIFICATIONS

Application	Ft. Lbs. (N.m)
Bellhousing-to-Engine Bolt	
4.9L, 5.0L & 5.8L Engines	40-50 (54-68)
6.9L Diesel & 7.5L Engines	35-50 (47-68)
All Other Engines	28-38 (38-51)
Insulator-to-Crossmember Nut	
Aerostar, Bronco II & Ranger	71-94 (96-127)
All Other Models	50-70 (68-95)
Insulator-to-Transmission Bolt	60-80 (81-108)
Pressure Plate-to-Flywheel Bolt	
4.9L, 5.0L & 5.8L Engines	20-29 (27-39)
6.9L Diesel & 7.5L Engines	15-20 (21-27)
All Other Engines	15-24 (20-33)
Master Cylinder-to-Firewall Bolt	15-20 (21-27)
Slave Cylinder-to-Clutch Housing	15-20 (21-27)
Starter-to-Bellhousing Bolt	15-20 (21-27)
Transmission-to-Bellhousing Nut	
Aerostar, Bronco II & Ranger	30-40 (41-54)
All Other Models	35-50 (47-68)

Clutches

GENERAL MOTORS – HYDRAULIC

Astro, Safari, "C", "K" & "S" Series Trucks

DESCRIPTION

All models use diaphragm spring clutch. Diaphragm spring clutch uses single, slotted diaphragm type spring for both pressure plate action and tension. Clutch disc is flexible hub type, using compression springs to dampen vibration from engine crankshaft.

"C" and "K" models may also use coil spring clutch. Coil spring single plate clutch is dry disc type with no wear adjustment provided in clutch itself. Coil spring clutch uses 3 release levers for pressure plate actuation and coil springs for pressure plate tension.

Clutch hydraulic system uses master and slave cylinders to move release bearing fork. No adjustment of linkage or pedal is required as hydraulic clutch system adjusts automatically.

TESTING & DIAGNOSIS

CLUTCH RELEASE

1) Start engine and put brakes on. Depress clutch pedal until it is about 1/2" (12.7 mm) from floor mat. Shift back and forth between 1st and Reverse. If shifts are smooth, clutch is working properly. If shifts are not smooth, clutch is not releasing fully.

2) Check pedal bushings for sticking or excessive wear. Check clutch fork is properly installed on ball stud in bellhousing. Fork can pull off ball stud if not properly lubricated. Check slave cylinder and pedal travel. Measure slave cylinder travel at clutch fork.

3) Slave cylinder should have minimum travel of .624" (15.85 mm) on "S" models with 1.9L or 2.2L engines. On Astro, Safari and "S" models with 2.5L or 2.8L engines, minimum travel should be .832" (21.13 mm) for slave cylinder. Clutch pedal should have about 6" (152.4 mm) of travel for these models.

4) On "C" and "K" models, slave cylinder should have minimum of 1.0" (25.4 mm) when pedal is fully depressed. Clutch pedal should have about 8.3" (210.8 mm) of travel for these models.

REMOVAL & INSTALLATION

TRANSMISSION

Removal ("S" Models With 77MM & 77.5MM)

1) Disconnect negative battery cable. Remove shift lever boot screws and slide boot off shift lever. Remove shift lever bolts at transmission.

2) On 77MM transmissions, shift transmission into Neutral and remove shift lever. On 77.5MM transmissions, remove upper starter retaining nut. Disconnect electrical connection and clip at shift tower.

3) On all models, raise vehicle. Remove propeller shaft. On models with 77.5MM transmission, disconnect exhaust pipe at manifold.

4) On all models, disconnect speedometer cable and electrical connector at transmission. Disconnect clutch slave cylinder from transmission. Support transmission. Remove transmission mounting bolts.

5) Remove lower starter mounting bolt. Remove left body mounting bolts and loosen radiator support bolt. Raise left side of cab enough to reach upper bolts holding bellhousing to engine. Support cab with block of wood.

6) Remove catalytic converter hanger. Remove crossmember. Remove dust cover bolts. Undo bolts holding transmission to engine and remove transmission. Remove bellhousing.

Installation

To install the transmission, reverse the removal procedure.

Removal (Astro & Safari Models With 76MM & 77MM)

1) Disconnect negative battery cable. On 77MM (5-speed) models, slide shift lever boot up shift lever. Remove shift lever from transmission. On all models, raise the vehicle and support properly. Drain lubricant from 76MM models. Mark the propeller shaft yokes for reassembly reference.

2) Remove propeller shaft. Disconnect speedometer cable and electrical connectors at transmission. On 76MM models, disconnect shift linkage at shifter. Remove shifter support from transmission.

3) On all models, support transmission and remove bolts holding mount to transmission. Remove crossmember. On 77MM models, remove transmission support braces. On all models, remove bolts holding transmission to engine. Remove transmission from vehicle.

Installation

To install, reverse removal procedure. On 76MM models, lightly coat main drive gear bearing retainer and input shaft splines with high temperature grease to aid in reassembly.

Removal ("C" & "K" Models With 76MM & 89MM)

1) Raise and support vehicle. Drain the transmission and the transfer case, if equipped. Disconnect speedometer cable. On "C" models, disconnect parking brake lever and controls.

2) On all models, disconnect back-up light switch. Remove propeller shaft after marking yokes for reassembly reference. On "K" models, disconnect transfer case shift lever at transfer case. Support transfer case and remove bolts holding transfer case to adapter. Remove transfer case.

3) On all models, remove shift controls from transmission. Support transmission and remove crossmember. Remove bolts holding transmission to clutch housing. Move transmission rearward to free from engine. Remove transmission.

Installation

Apply light coat of grease to main drive gear bearing retainer and splined part of transmission main drive gear shaft. Align main drive gearshaft with clutch disc hub by rotating transmission companion flange or output yoke. To complete installation, reverse removal procedure.

Removal ("C" & "K" Models With 117MM)

1) Remove transmission shift lever boot retainer screws. Slide boot and retainer off lever. Remove shift lever by pushing down and turning collar counterclockwise.

2) Raise and support vehicle. Drain transmission and disconnect speedometer cable. Disconnect front propeller shaft universal joint at yoke and secure aside.

3) If equipped, support transfer case and remove bolts holding transfer case to adapter. Remove transfer case.

4) Disconnect exhaust pipes at exhaust manifold. Remove bolts holding transmission mount to crossmember. Support transmission. Remove bolts holding crossmember to frame and remove crossmember.

5) Remove upper bolts holding transmission to clutch housing and install guide pins. Remove remaining bolts holding transmission to clutch housing. Slide transmission rearward until drive gear clears clutch assembly. Remove transmission.

Installation

Apply grease to the main drive gear bearing retainer and splined part of the transmission main drive gear shaft. To complete transmission installation, reverse removal procedure.

PRESSURE PLATE & CLUTCH DISC

Removal (Astro, Safari & "S" Models)

1) Remove transmission and bellhousing. Slide clutch fork from ball stud, which is threaded into housing. Install Clutch Pilot (J 33169 or J 33034) in clutch disc during removal.

2) Letter "X" should be painted in White or etched on clutch cover and flywheel. Mark flywheel and clutch cover for reassembly if "X" is not evident.

3) Loosen bolts holding clutch on flywheel 1 or 2 turns each time until clutch plate spring tension is released. Remove clutch pilot, clutch cover and disc.

Installation

1) Support clutch disc and pressure plate on flywheel with clutch pilot. Damper springs of disc face transmission. Flywheel side of disc is marked.

2) Make sure index marks on pressure plate and flywheel are aligned. Tighten bolts evenly in sequence to avoid distortion. Remove pilot. Lubricate ball stud and fork fingers with high temperature grease, such as graphite.

3) Lubricate O.D. groove and completely pack I.D. recess of release bearing. Reverse removal procedure, making sure clutch hub and pilot bearing are properly aligned.

Removal ("C" & "K" Models)

1) With transmission removed, remove slave cylinder from bellhousing. Remove bellhousing. Pry clutch fork until it pops off from ball pivot. Remove release bearing from clutch fork. Mark position of clutch cover on flywheel for reassembly.

2) Install Clutch Pilot (J-5824) or used clutch drive gear to support clutch assembly during removal. Loosen clutch cover bolts 1 or 2 turns at a time until clutch plate spring tension is released.

3) On models with coil spring clutch, place spacers between clutch levers and cover to keep levers depressed as clutch is removed. Spacers should be about 3/8" (9.5 mm) in thickness. Mark flywheel side of disc for reassembly reference. Remove used clutch drive gear and remove clutch cover and disc.

Installation

Lubricate clutch fork ball seat and recess in release bearing. Reverse removal procedure, making sure clutch hub and pilot bearing are aligned. Bleed hydraulic systme if necessary.

CLUTCH PILOT BEARING

Removal & Installation (1.9L & 2.2L Engines)

Remove flywheel. Remove pilot bearing using small slide hammer. Install pilot bearing with Bearing Driver (J-8092 and J-26516-A).

Fig. 1: "S" Model Clutch Pedal Assembly

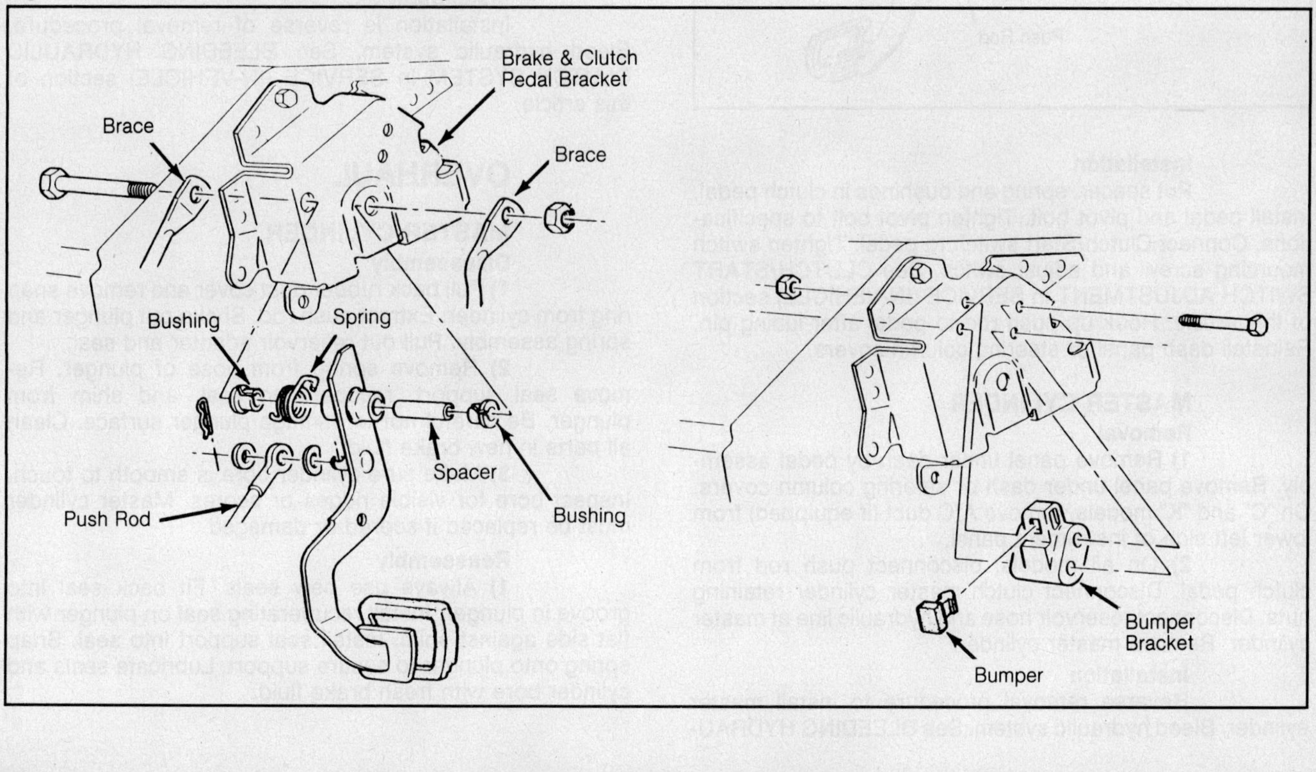

GENERAL MOTORS - HYDRAULIC (Cont.)

Removal & Installation
(6.2L Diesel Engine)

This bearing is Torrington design which is sealed and requires no lubrication. To remove bearing from crankshaft, use Bearing Puller (J-23907). To install, place bearing on pilot of Bearing Driver (J-34140). Drive bearing into crankshaft until driver bottoms out.

Removal & Installation
(All Other Engines)

Place threaded end of Pilot Bearing Remover (J-1448) and remove bearing. Install bearing using Bearing Driver (J-1552). Put some drops of machine oil into clutch pilot bearing.

CLUTCH PEDAL ASSEMBLY

Removal

Disconnect negative battery cable. Remove panel under dash or steering column covers. On "C" and "K" models, remove A/C duct (if equipped) from lower left side of instrument panel. On all models, disconnect clutch/start switch from pedal and bracket. Disconnect push rod. Remove pivot bolt and clutch pedal assembly. Remove bushings, spacer and spring from pedal assembly.

Fig. 2: Astro & Safari Clutch Pedal Assembly

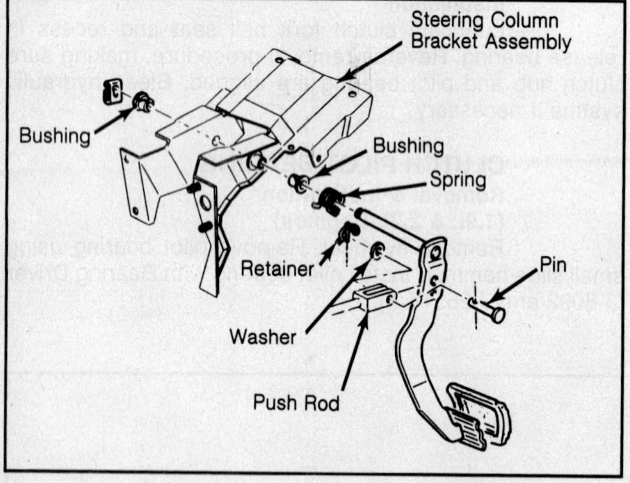

Installation

Put spacer, spring and bushings in clutch pedal. Install pedal and pivot bolt. Tighten pivot bolt to specifications. Connect Clutch/Start switch to pedal. Tighten switch mounting screw and adjust switch. See CLUTCH/START SWITCH ADJUSTMENT in SERVICE (IN-VEHICLE) section of this article. Hook up push rod to pedal after lubing pin. Reinstall dash panel or steering column covers.

MASTER CYLINDER

Removal

1) Remove panel under dash by pedal assembly. Remove panel under dash or steering column covers. On "C" and "K" models, remove A/C duct (if equipped) from lower left side of instrument panel.

2) On all models, disconnect push rod from clutch pedal. Disconnect clutch master cylinder retaining nuts. Disconnect reservoir hose and hydraulic line at master cylinder. Remove master cylinder.

Installation

Reverse removal procedure to install master cylinder. Bleed hydraulic system. See BLEEDING HYDRAULIC CLUTCH SYSTEM in SERVICE (IN-VEHICLE) section of this article.

Fig. 3: "C" & "K" Model Clutch Pedal Assembly

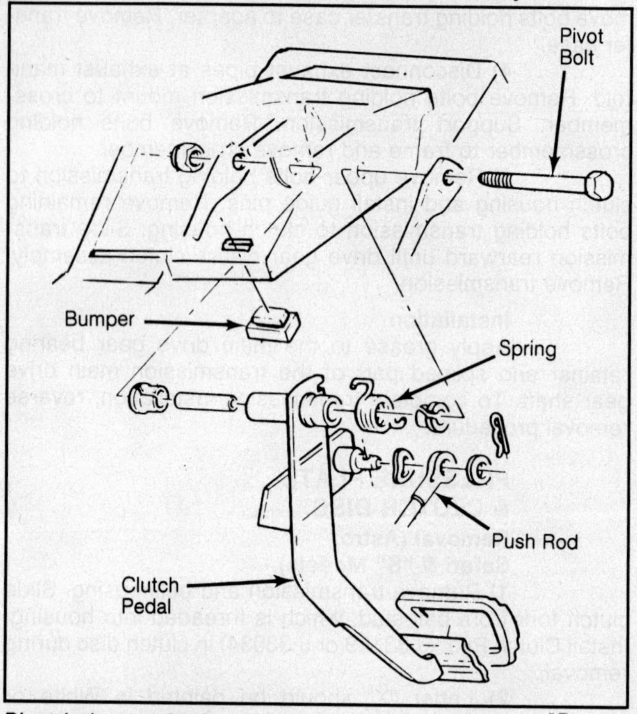

Pivot bolt must be installed as shown.

SLAVE CYLINDER

Removal

Raise vehicle. Disconnect and cap hydraulic line at slave cylinder. Remove slave cylinder and remove from vehicle.

Installation

Installation is reverse of removal procedure. Bleed hydraulic system. See BLEEDING HYDRAULIC CLUTCH SYSTEM in SERVICE (IN-VEHICLE) section of this article.

OVERHAUL

MASTER CYLINDER

Disassembly

1) Pull back rubber dust cover and remove snap ring from cylinder. Extract push rod. Shake out plunger and spring assembly. Pull out reservoir adapter and seal.

2) Remove spring from nose of plunger. Remove seal support, recuperation seal, and shim from plunger. Be careful not to damage plunger surface. Clean all parts in new brake fluid.

3) Make sure cylinder bore is smooth to touch. Inspect bore for visible ridges or scores. Master cylinder must be replaced if scored or damaged.

Reassembly

1) Always use new seals. Fit back seal into groove in plunger. Install recuperating seal on plunger with flat side against shim. Install seal support into seal. Snap spring onto plunger to secure support. Lubricate seals and cylinder bore with fresh brake fluid.

GENERAL MOTORS – HYDRAULIC (Cont.)

Fig. 4: Exploded View of Clutch Master Cylinder

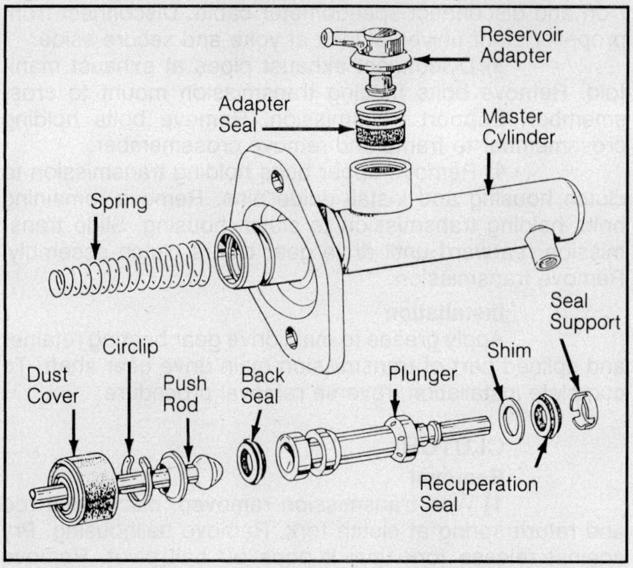

Reservoir mounts on cylinder in Astro and Safari models.

2) Carefully install plunger assembly into bore of cylinder. Depress plunger with push rod and seat snap ring in groove. Install rubber dust boot after lightly greasing inside of boot. Put reservoir adapter seal into master cylinder and press adapter into seal.

SLAVE CYLINDER

Disassembly

1) Remove push rod and rubber dust cover. Remove retaining snap ring. Shake plunger and spring assembly out of cylinder. Carefully remove seal from plunger. Do not damage plunger surface.

2) Clean all hard parts in new brake fluid. Inspect cylinder bore for ridges or scratches. Bore must be smooth to touch. Replace cylinder if bore does not pass inspection.

Reassembly

1) Use only new seals. Place seal in groove on plunger. Lubricate bore and seal with new brake fluid. Slide spring and plunger assembly into cylinder bore. *See Fig. 5.*

Fig. 5: Exploded View of Clutch Slave Cylinder

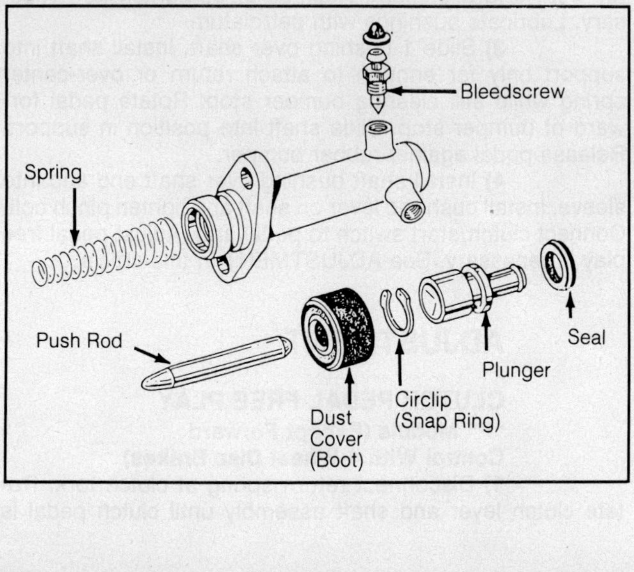

2) Depress plunger far enough to install snap ring in groove. Grease inside of dust boot and install boot. Install push rod in cylinder boot.

SERVICE (IN-VEHICLE)

BLEEDING HYDRAULIC CLUTCH SYSTEM

1) Fill master cylinder with new brake fluid (DOT 3). Raise vehicle. Disconnect slave cylinder from bellhousing, leaving line attached. Hold slave cylinder at angle of 45° with bleeder at highest point.

2) Fully depress clutch pedal and open bleeder. Close bleeder and release pedal. Repeat sequence until all air is removed from system. Make sure master cylinder reservoir stays full during bleeding process.

ADJUSTING CLUTCH/START SWITCH

NOTE: **DO NOT adjust clutch/start switch before carpets or floor mats are in place or switch will not work correctly.**

Position slider on switch shaft at opposite end from switch. Depress clutch pedal to floor mat or carpet. Move slider along switch shaft so that switch button is fully depressed.

TIGHTENING SPECIFICATIONS

Application	Ft. Lbs. (N.m)
Astro & Safari	
Bellhousing-to-Engine	48-62 (65-84)
Crossmember-to-Mount	35 (47)
Crossmember-to-Frame	35 (47)
Flywheel-to-Crankshaft	
4-Cyl.	60-75 (81-102)
V6	55-75 (75-102)
Pressure Plate-to-Flywheel	
4-Cyl.	15-22 (20-30)
V6	55-75 (75-102)
Transmission-to-Mount	35 (47)
"S" Models	
Bellhousing-to-Engine	
4-Cylinder	37 (50)
V6	55 (75)
Crossmember-to-Mount	25 (34)
Crossmember-to-Frame	25 (34)
Flywheel-to-Crankshaft	
1.9L & 2.2L	70 (95)
2.5L & 2.8L	50 (68)
Pressure Plate-to-Flywheel	20 (27)
Transmission-to-Mount	35 (47)
"C" & "K" Models	
Bellhousing-to-Engine	30 (41)
Crossmember-to-Mount	40 (54)
Crossmember-to-Frame	55 (75)
Pressure Plate-to-Flywheel	30 (41)
Transmission-to-Bellhousing	75 (102)
Transmission-to-Mount	40 (54)

Clutches

GENERAL MOTORS – MECHANICAL

Chevrolet, GMC Vans & "P" Series Trucks

DESCRIPTION

These vehicles use 2 types of clutches, either coil spring design or diaphragm spring design. Mechanical linkage is used to actuate clutch.

Coil spring single plate clutch is dry-disc type with no wear adjustment provided in clutch itself. Coil spring clutch uses 3 release levers for pressure plate actuation and coil springs for pressure plate tension.

Diaphragm spring clutch uses single, slotted diaphragm type spring for both pressure plate action and tension.

TESTING & DIAGNOSIS

CLUTCH RELEASE

1) Start engine and apply brakes. Depress clutch pedal until it is about 1/2" (12.7 mm) from floor mat. Shift back and forth between 1st and Reverse. If shifts are smooth, clutch is working properly. If shifts are not smooth, clutch is not releasing fully.

2) Check pedal bushings for sticking or excessive wear. Check clutch release fork is properly installed on ball stud in bellhousing. Fork can pull off ball stud if not properly lubricated. Check cross shaft levers and support bracket for bends, cracks or damage.

3) Check condition of engine mounts, as worn mounts allow engine to move and cause binding in linkage at cross shaft. Make sure that ball studs, both mount brackets and cross shaft all have some clearance between one another.

4) Make sure there is some clearance between spring fingers of release fork and front bearing retainer of transmission. If there is no clearance, fork may be installed on stud incorrectly. Worn clutch disc will also cause lack of clearance.

REMOVAL & INSTALLATION

TRANSMISSION

Removal (76MM & 89MM)

1) Raise and support vehicle. Drain transmission. Disconnect speedometer cable. Disconnect parking brake lever and controls. Disconnect back-up light switch. Disconnect propeller shaft.

2) Remove shift controls from transmission. Support transmission with jack and remove crossmember. Remove bolts holding transmission to clutch housing. Move transmission rearward until input shaft clears clutch assembly. Remove transmission.

Installation

Apply light coat of grease to main drive gear bearing retainer and splined part of transmission main drive gear shaft. Align main drive gear shaft with clutch disc hub by rotating transmission companion flange or output yoke. To complete installation, reverse removal procedure.

Removal (117MM)

1) Remove transmission shift lever boot retainer screws. Slide boot and retainer off lever. Remove shift lever by pushing down and turning collar counterclockwise.

2) Raise and support vehicle. Drain transmission and disconnect speedometer cable. Disconnect front propeller shaft universal joint at yoke and secure aside.

3) Disconnect exhaust pipes at exhaust manifold. Remove bolts holding transmission mount to crossmember. Support transmission. Remove bolts holding crossmember to frame and remove crossmember.

4) Remove upper bolts holding transmission to clutch housing and install guide pins. Remove remaining bolts holding transmission to clutch housing. Slide transmission rearward until drive gear clears clutch assembly. Remove transmission.

Installation

Apply grease to main drive gear bearing retainer and splined part of transmission main drive gear shaft. To complete installation, reverse removal procedure.

CLUTCH

Removal

1) With transmission removed, disconnect rod and return spring at clutch fork. Remove bellhousing. Pry against release fork until it pops off ball pivot. Remove release bearing from clutch fork. Mark position of clutch cover on flywheel for reassembly.

2) Install used clutch drive gear to support clutch assembly during removal. Loosen clutch cover bolts 1 or 2 turns at time until clutch plate spring tension is released. Remove used clutch drive gear and remove clutch cover and disc.

Installation

Lubricate clutch fork ball seat and recess in release bearing. Reverse removal procedure, making sure clutch hub and pilot bearing are aligned.

CLUTCH PEDAL ASSEMBLY

Removal

1) Apply parking brake. Disconnect clutch/start switch from pedal arm. Unbolt and remove push rod lever at pedal shaft. Slide clutch pedal and shaft assembly far enough to clear pedal stop. Insert dummy shaft through support and brake pedal assembly to hold components in place.

2) Let return or over-center spring pull pedal up enough to unhook spring. Remove pedal and shaft assembly from support bracket. Check pedal bushings and shaft for wear and alignment. Replace or straighten as necessary. Lubricate bushings with petrolatum.

3) Slide 1 bushing over shaft. Install shaft into support only far enough to attach return or over-center spring while still clearing bumper stop. Rotate pedal forward of bumper stop. Slide shaft into position in support. Release pedal against rubber bumper.

4) Install shaft bushing over shaft end and into sleeve. Install push rod lever on shaft and tighten pinch bolt. Connect clutch/start switch to pedal arm. Adjust pedal free play if necessary. See ADJUSTMENT in this article.

ADJUSTMENT

CLUTCH PEDAL FREE PLAY

"P" Models (Except Forward Control With 4-Wheel Disc Brakes)

1) Disconnect return spring at clutch fork. Rotate clutch lever and shaft assembly until clutch pedal is

GENERAL MOTORS – MECHANICAL (Cont.)

seated against rubber pedal stop. Force clutch fork push rod rearward until release bearing just contacts clutch release levers.

2) Loosen clutch swivel lock nut. Adjust rod length until swivel can be easily inserted in gauge hole. *See Fig. 1.* Increase push rod length until all lash is removed. Remove swivel from gauge hole and insert it in lower hole on lever.

Fig. 1: "P" Model Free Play Adjustment

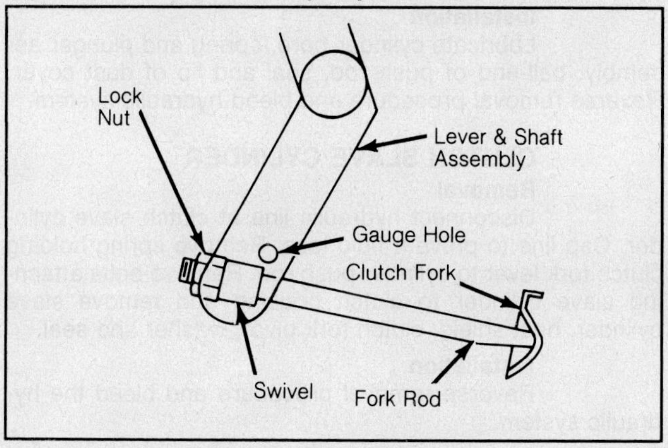

This does not apply to forward control models with 4-wheel disc brakes.

3) Secure swivel with 2 washers and cotter pin. Tighten lock nut, making sure that rod length does not change. Install return spring and check pedal free play. Free play should be 1.25-1.50" (31-37 mm).

"P" Models (Forward Control With 4-Wheel Disc Brakes)

1) Disconnect fork return spring. Loosen lock nut "G" at swivel. Move push rod against fork to eliminate clearance between release bearing and clutch fingers. Rotate shaft lever until pedal touches rubber bumper on bracket.

2) Rotate fork rod until there is .25-.31" (6.4-7.9 mm) clearance between shoulder on rod and fork adjustment nut. *See Fig. 2.* Tighten lock nut "G" against swivel. Install return spring.

3) Check free play clearance at pedal. Free play should be 1.38-1.63" (35-41 mm). Readjust if necessary.

Van Models

1) Disconnect return spring at clutch fork. Loosen clutch fork swivel nut "A" about 1/2" (12.7 mm). Hold push rod against fork until clutch release bearing contacts clutch fingers.

Fig. 2: "P" Model Free Play Adjustment

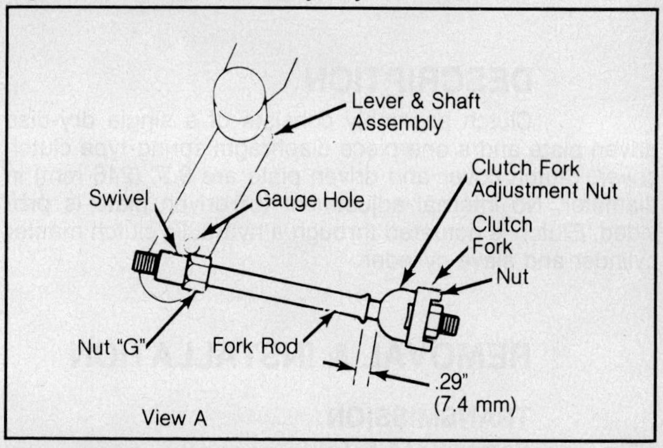

This applies to forward control models with 4-wheel disc brakes.

2) Rotate push rod adjusting nut "B" until .25" (6.4 mm) clearance between nut "B" and swivel is obtained. *See Fig. 3.* Connect return spring and tighten nut "A" until swivel locks against nut "B". Check that pedal free play is about 1.25-1.50" (31-37 mm). Readjust if necessary.

Fig. 3: Van Free Play Adjustment

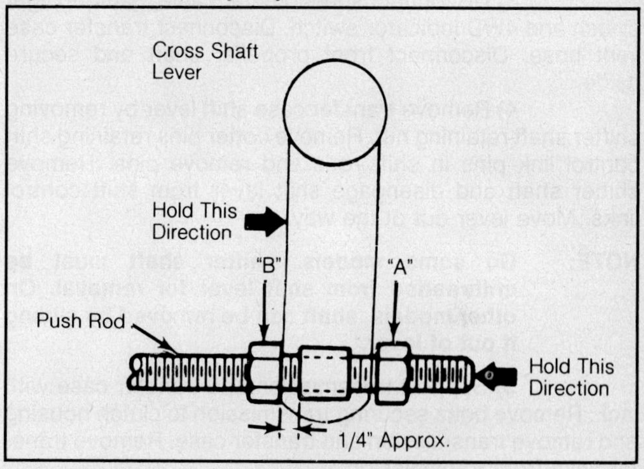

Turn adjusting nut "B" to change clearance.

TIGHTENING SPECIFICATIONS

Application	Ft. Lbs. (N.m)
Bellhousing-to-Engine Bolts	30 (41)
Pressure Plate-to-Flywheel Bolts	30 (41)
Transmission-to-Bellhousing Bolts	75 (102)

Clutches

JEEP – HYDRAULIC

4-Cyl. CJ7, Scrambler

DESCRIPTION

Clutch assembly consists of a single dry-disc driven plate and a one-piece diaphragm spring-type clutch cover. Clutch cover and driven plate are 9.7" (246 mm) in diameter. No internal adjustment for driven plate is provided. Clutch is actuated through a hydraulic clutch master cylinder and slave cylinder.

REMOVAL & INSTALLATION

TRANSMISSION

Removal (T4 & T5)

1) Remove screws attaching shift lever boot to floorpan. Slide boot over lever. Remove shift lever and lever housing from transmission. Raise vehicle and support with safety stands.

2) Disconnect rear propeller shaft from transfer case and secure out of the way. Place a jack under clutch housing to support engine. Remove rear crossmember from frame.

3) Disconnect speedometer cable, back-up light switch and 4WD indicator switch. Disconnect transfer case vent hose. Disconnect front propeller shaft and secure aside.

4) Remove transfer case shift lever by removing shifter shaft retaining nut. Remove cotter pins retaining shift control link pins in shift rods and remove pins. Remove shifter shaft and disengage shift lever from shift control links. Move lever out of the way.

NOTE: **On some models, shifter shaft must be unthreaded from shift lever for removal. On other models, shaft can be removed by sliding it out of lever.**

5) Support transmission and transfer case with jack. Remove bolts securing transmission to clutch housing and remove transmission and transfer case. Remove transfer case from transmission.

Installation

To install, reverse removal procedure.

CLUTCH

Removal

1) With transmission, transfer case and release bearing removed, remove clutch housing. Mark position of clutch cover on flywheel for reassembly.

2) Loosen clutch cover bolts 1 or 2 turns at a time until clutch cover spring tension is released. Remove cover bolts and remove clutch cover and disc.

Installation

1) Check all components for wear or damage and replace as necessary. Using clutch alignment tool, align clutch disc and loosely install clutch cover. Be sure marks made during removal are aligned.

2) To avoid warping clutch cover, tighten each cover bolt a few turns at a time. Reverse removal procedure to complete installation.

CLUTCH MASTER CYLINDER

Removal

1) Disconnect hydraulic line at clutch master cylinder. Plug line and cylinder opening to prevent dirt from entering. Remove cotter pin and washer holding cylinder push rod on clutch pedal.

2) Slide push rod off pedal pivot. Remove nuts attaching clutch master cylinder to mounting studs on dash panel and remove cylinder.

Installation

Lubricate cylinder bore, spring and plunger assembly, ball-end of push rod, seal and lip of dust cover. Reverse removal procedure and bleed hydraulic system.

CLUTCH SLAVE CYLINDER

Removal

Disconnect hydraulic line at clutch slave cylinder. Cap line to prevent fluid loss. Remove spring holding clutch fork lever to cylinder push rod. Remove bolts attaching slave cylinder to clutch housing and remove slave cylinder, heat shield, clutch fork pivot, washer and seal.

Installation

Reverse removal procedure and bleed the hydraulic system.

OVERHAUL

CLUTCH MASTER CYLINDER

Disassembly

1) Remove reservoir cap and rubber cover. Remove push rod dust cover and discard dust cover. Remove snap ring holding push rod in cylinder bore and discard snap ring.

2) Remove push rod, retaining washer and seal as an assembly. Discard push rod seal. Remove plunger, valve spring and valve stem assembly from cylinder bore by tapping cylinder body on wood block.

3) Compress valve spring slightly. Pry tab of valve stem retainer upward to release retainer, spring and stem assembly from plunger. Remove seal from plunger and discard. Remove spring retainer and valve stem from valve spring.

NOTE: **Retainer tab is located in rectangular slot in side of stem retainer.**

4) Remove valve stem from retainer. Remove spring washer and stem tip seal from end of valve stem. Discard stem tip seal and spring washer. Clean parts with brake fluid or brake cleaning solvent. Inspect cylinder bore for wear, nicks or scores. Replace if necessary.

Reassembly

1) Lubricate cylinder bore with brake fluid. Make sure lip of plunger seal faces stem end of plunger. Install stem tip seal so seal shoulder fits in undercut at end of valve stem.

2) End of valve stem should pass through stem retainer and seat in small bore in end of plunger. Bend retainer tab downward to lock stem and retainer on plunger. Reverse disassembly procedure to complete assembly.

JEEP – HYDRAULIC (Cont.)

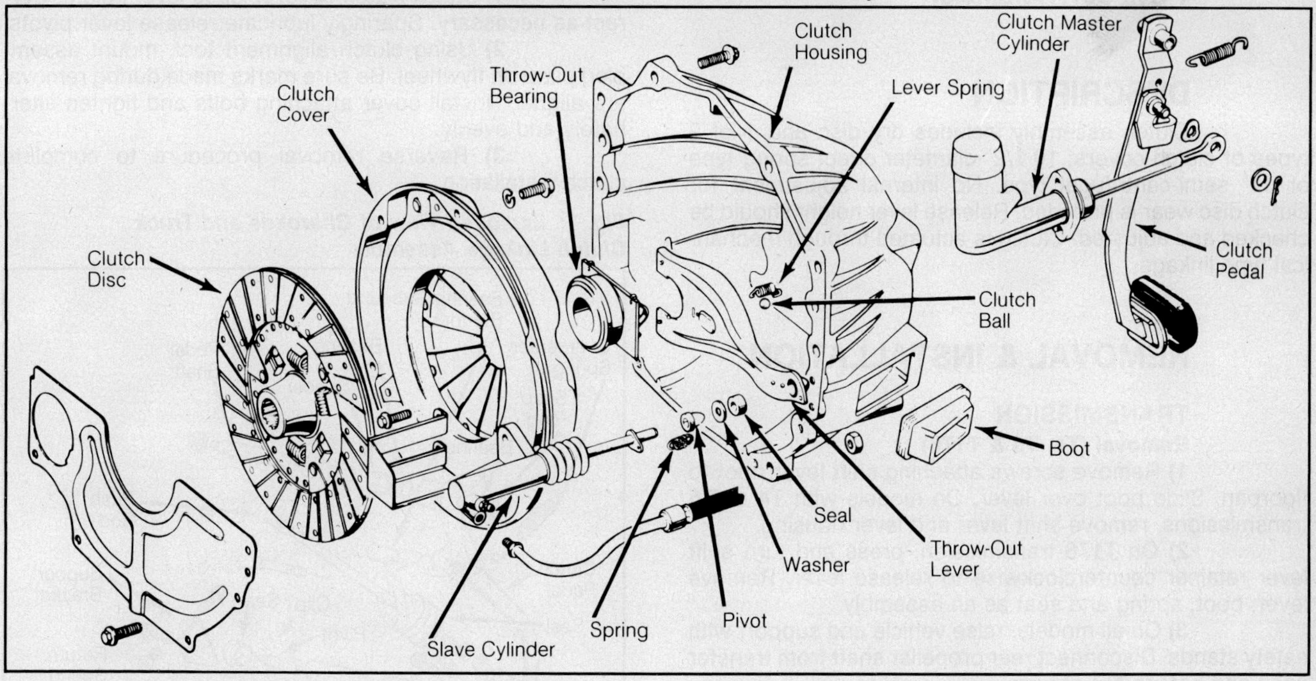

Fig. 1: Exploded View of 4-Cylinder CJ7 & Scrambler Hydraulic Clutch Assembly

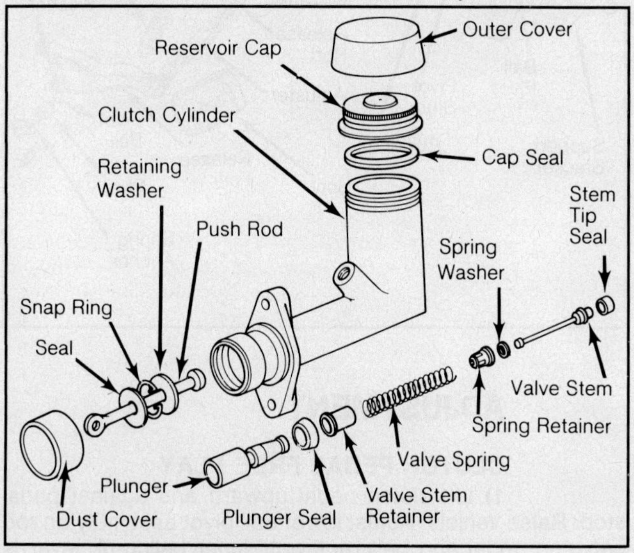

Fig. 2: Exploded View Of Clutch Master Cylinder

Clean parts in brake fluid only.

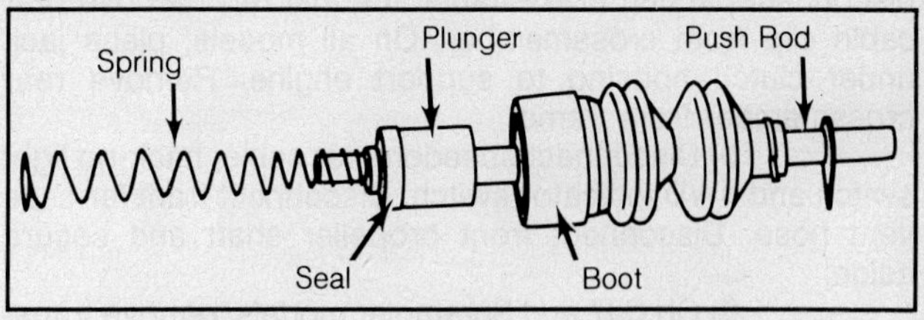

Fig. 3: Exploded View Of Clutch Slave Cylinder

CLUTCH SLAVE CYLINDER

Disassembly

1) Clean cylinder exterior. Remove dust boot from cylinder. Remove cylinder push rod, plunger and spring as an assembly. Remove spring seal from plunger.

2) Remove snap ring holding push rod in plunger. Remove push rod and boot. Remove boot from push rod. Clean parts with brake fluid or brake cleaning solvent. Inspect cylinder bore for wear, nicks or scores. Replace if necessary.

Reassembly

Reverse disassembly procedure. Lubricate cylinder bore and seal with brake fluid before reassembly.

HYDRAULIC SYSTEM BLEEDING

1) Make sure clutch master cylinder is full of brake fluid (SAE J 1703, DOT 3). Compress slave cylinder plunger by pushing release lever as far forward as possible.

2) Attach rubber hose to bleeder screw. Immerse other end of hose in glass container 1/2 full of brake fluid. Loosen bleeder screw and hold release lever forward. Depress and hold clutch pedal to end of its travel.

3) Tighten bleeder screw and release pedal. Repeat bleeding operation until fluid entering container is free of bubbles. Do not allow reservoir to run out of fluid during bleeding. Refill clutch master cylinder to level mark on reservoir.

TIGHTENING SPECIFICATIONS

Application	Ft. Lbs. (N.m)
Bellhousing-to-Engine Bolts	54 (73)
Crossmember Bolts	34-40 (46-54)
Flywheel-to-Crankshaft Bolts	[1] 65 (73)
Pressure Plate-to-Flywheel Bolts	23 (31)
Transmission-to-Bellhousing Bolts	54 (73)

[1] – Plus additional 60° turn after reaching torque specification.

JEEP – MECHANICAL

All Models, Except
4-Cyl. CJ7, Scrambler

DESCRIPTION

Clutch assembly includes dry disc and 1 of 2 types of clutch covers; 10 1/2" diameter direct spring type or 11" semi-centrifugal type. No internal adjustment for clutch disc wear is provided. Release lever height should be checked and adjusted. Clutch is actuated through mechanical type linkage.

REMOVAL & INSTALLATION

TRANSMISSION

Removal (T4, T5 & T176)

1) Remove screws attaching shift lever boot to floorpan. Slide boot over lever. On models with T4 or T5 transmissions, remove shift lever and lever housing.

2) On T176 transmission, press and turn shift lever retainer counterclockwise to release lever. Remove lever, boot, spring and seat as an assembly.

3) On all models, raise vehicle and support with safety stands. Disconnect rear propeller shaft from transfer case and secure out of way.

4) On Cherokee, Truck and Wagoneer models, disconnect parking brake cable at equalizer. Remove rear cable clip from crossmember. On all models, place jack under clutch housing to support engine. Remove rear crossmember from frame.

5) Disconnect speedometer cable, back-up light switch and 4WD indicator switch. Disconnect transfer case vent hose. Disconnect front propeller shaft and secure aside.

6) On CJ7 and Scrambler models, remove transfer case shift lever by removing shifter shaft retaining nut. Remove cotter pins holding shift control link pins in shift rods and remove pins. Remove shifter shaft and disengage shift lever from shift control links. Move lever out of way.

NOTE: On some models, shifter shaft must be unthreaded from shift lever for removal. On other models, shaft can be removed by sliding it out of lever.

7) On Cherokee, Truck and Wagoneer models, remove cotter pin and washers connecting link to shift lever. Disconnect link from shift lever. On all models, support transmission and transfer case with jack.

8) Remove bolts securing transmission to clutch housing and remove transmission and transfer case. Remove transfer case from transmission.

Installation

To install, reverse removal procedure.

CLUTCH

Removal

1) With transmission removed, remove starter motor, release bearing and clutch housing. Mark position of clutch cover on flywheel for reassembly.

2) Loosen each clutch cover bolt 1 or 2 turns at a time to relieve spring tension on cover. Remove clutch cover and driven plate from flywheel.

Installation

1) Check clutch cover release lever height. Correct as necessary. Sparingly lubricate release lever pivots.

2) Using clutch alignment tool, mount assembled plate on flywheel. Be sure marks made during removal are aligned. Install cover attaching bolts and tighten alternately and evenly.

3) Reverse removal procedure to complete clutch installation.

Fig. 1: Exploded View of Cherokee and Truck Clutch Linkage Assembly

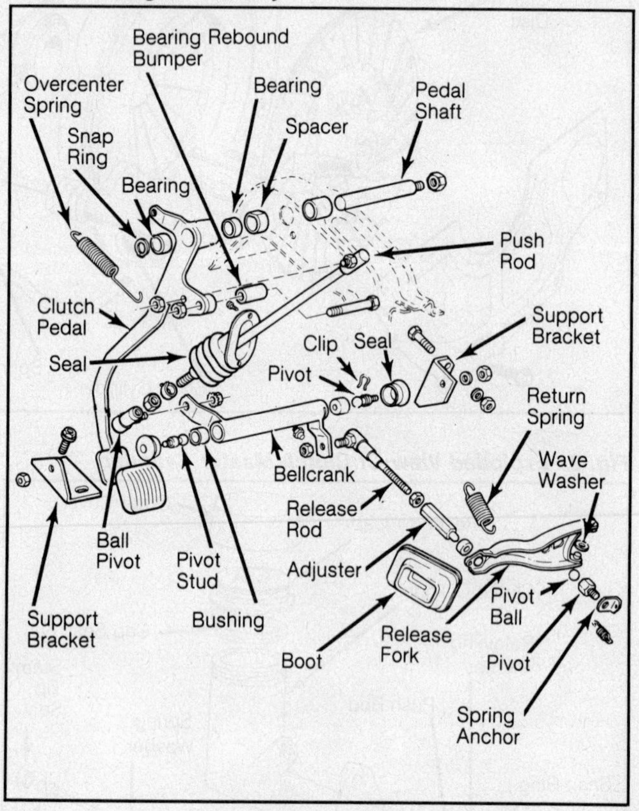

ADJUSTMENT

CLUTCH PEDAL FREE PLAY

1) Lift clutch pedal upward and against pedal stop. Raise vehicle. Adjust lower ball pivot assembly on rod between pedal and bellcrank until inner bellcrank lever is parallel with front face of clutch housing.

3) Loosen release rod adjuster lock nut. Turn release rod adjuster to obtain specified pedal free play.

CLUTCH PEDAL FREE PLAY

Application	Inches (mm)
6-Cylinder Models	1.00-1.25 (25.4-31.7)
V8 Models	.38-.63 (9.6-16.0)

CLUTCH RELEASE LEVER

1) Position gauge plate (J-1048) on flywheel. Position clutch cover over gauge plate with release fingers aligned with machined lands on plate. Gauge plate hub should be centered between release levers. Attach cover to flywheel.

JEEP – MECHANICAL (Cont.)

2) Tighten cover screws in rotation, 1 or 2 turns at a time. Set each release lever by depressing 2 or 3 times. Measure height of each lever in relation to gauge hub using Lever Height Gauge (J-23330).

3) Turn adjusting lever nuts until all 3 levers are at specified height. Work levers up and down and recheck measurements.

CLUTCH LEVER RELEASE HEIGHT

Application	Inches (mm)
6-Cylinder Models	2.04-2.16 (51.8-68.6)
V8 Models	.19 (4.7)

Fig. 2: Measuring Clutch Release Lever Height

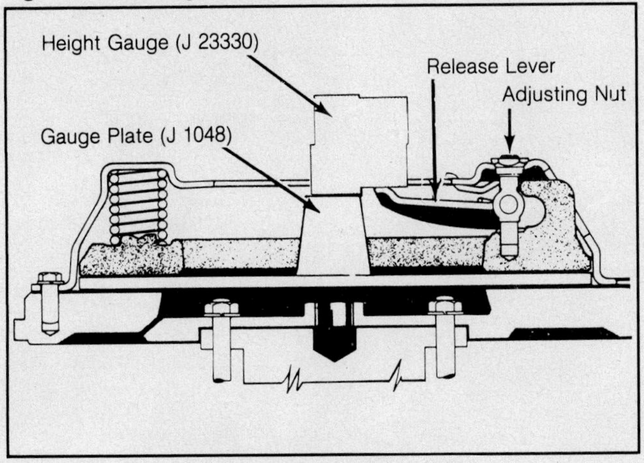

Turn nuts until levers are at specified height.

TIGHTENING SPECIFICATIONS

Application	Ft. Lbs. (N.m)
Bellhousing-to-Engine Bolt	
6-Cyl. (Top)	35 (47)
6-Cyl. (Bottom)	45 (61)
V8	30 (41)
Crossmember Bolts	34-70 (47-54)
Pressure Plate-to-Flywheel Bolts	40 (54)
Transmission-to-Bellhousing Bolts	54 (73)

SECTION 9

DRIVE AXLES

CONTENTS

NOTE: ALSO SEE GENERAL INDEX.

IMPORTANT: Because of the many model names used by vehicle manufacturers, accurate identification of models is important. See Model Identification at the front of this publication.

Drive Axles

TROUBLE SHOOTING

CONDITION	POSSIBLE CAUSE	CORRECTION
General Knocking or Clunking	Excessive differential side gear clearance	See Overhaul in DRIVE AXLES
	Worn rear axle pinion shaft	See Overhaul in DRIVE AXLES
	Worn case or differential cross shaft in case	See Overhaul in DRIVE AXLES
	Excessive end play of axle shafts-to-differential cross shaft	See Overhaul in DRIVE AXLES
	Gear teeth mutilitated	See Overhaul in DRIVE AXLES
	Improper axle shaft spline fit	See Overhaul in DRIVE AXLES
	Total axle backlash too great	See Overhaul in DRIVE AXLES
	Incorrect driveline angle	See Adjustment in PROPELLER SHAFT ALIGNMENT
Clunking During Initial Engagement	Excessive differential side gear clearance	See Overhaul in DRIVE AXLES
	Excessive ring and pinion backlash	See Overhaul in DRIVE AXLES
	Worn or loose pinion shaft	See Overhaul in DRIVE AXLES
	Worn or damaged inboard joint	See Overhaul in DRIVE AXLES
Gear Howl or Whine	Improper pinion depth	See Overhaul in DRIVE AXLES
	Improper ring gear backlash adjustment	See Overhaul in DRIVE AXLES
	Improper ring gear runout	See Overhaul in DRIVE AXLES
	Impropr bearing preload	See Overhaul in DRIVE AXLES
	Excessive pinion bearing wear	See Overhaul in DRIVE AXLES
Clicking or Chatter on Turns	Wrong lubricant in differential	Drain and refill differential
	Clutch plates worn	See Overhaul in POSITIVE TRACTION DIFFERENTIALS
	Worn or damaged outboard joints	See Overhaul in DRIVE AXLES
	Differential side gears or pinion worn	See Overhaul in DRIVE AXLES
Knock or Click Approximately Every Second Revolution	Flat spot on rear wheel bearing	See Overhaul in DRIVE AXLES
Grunt Noise on Stops	Lack of lubricant in propeller shaft slip yoke	See UNIVERSAL JOINTS
Groan in Forward or Reverse	Wrong lubricant in differential	Replace lubricant
Knock in Drive Line in High Gear at 10 MPH	Worn or damaged universal joints	See UNIVERSAL JOINTS
	Side gear hub counterbore in differential worn oversize	See Overhaul in DRIVE AXLES
Ping, Snap or Click in Drive Line	Loose upper or lower control arm bushing bolts	See Replacement in FRONT SUSPENSION
	Loose companion flange	See Overhaul in DRIVE AXLES
Scraping Noise	Slinger, companion flange or end yoke rubbing on rear axle carrier	See Overhaul in DRIVE AXLES
Car Will Not Move	Broken axle shaft	See Overhaul in DRIVE AXLES
	Broken pinion stem	See Overhaul in DRIVE AXLES
	Broken welds	See Overhaul in DRIVE AXLES
	Axle lock up	See Overhaul in DRIVE AXLES
	Broken gear teeth	See Overhaul in DRIVE AXLES
	Broken wheel bearing	See Overhaul in DRIVE AXLES
Axle Backlash	Excessive ring and pinion clearance	See Overhaul in DRIVE AXLES
	Loose fitting differential pinion shaft	See Overhaul in DRIVE AXLES
	Excessive side gear-to-case clearance	See Overhaul in DRIVE AXLES
Leakage at Differential or Driveshaft	Rough outside surface on splined yoke	See Overhaul in DRIVE AXLES
	Drive pinion seal or nut	See Overhaul in DRIVE AXLES
	Axle cover gasket, or axle shaft seal	See Overhaul in DRIVE AXLES
	Bad welds or improper axle vent hose	See Overhaul in DRIVE AXLES
	Case porosity	Apply heat resistant silicone sealer to case

TROUBLE SHOOTING (Cont.)

CONDITION	POSSIBLE CAUSE	CORRECTION
Roughness, Shudder or Vibration Upon Heavy Acceleration	Double cardan joint ball seats worn, and ball set spring may be broken	See UNIVERSAL JOINTS
	Excessive joint angle	See Propeller Shaft Alignment in DRIVE AXLES
	Sticking inboard joint assembly	See UNIVERSAL JOINTS
	Worn or damaged inboard or outboard joints	See UNIVERSAL JOINTS
Roughness, Vibration or Body Boom Experienced at Any Speed	Rough rear wheel bearings	See Overhaul in DRIVE AXLES
	Unbalanced or damaged propeller shaft	Check and/or balance propeller shaft
	Unbalanced or damaged tires	Check and/or balance tires
	Worn or damaged universal joints	See UNIVERSAL JOINTS
	Bent of damaged drive shaft, or undercoating on drive shaft	Check drive shaft balance
	Tight universal joints	Lubricate or replace as necessary
	Burrs or gouges on companion flange	Resurface or replace flange
	Drive shaft or companion shaft runout too great	Repair or replace as necessary
	Excessive looseness at slip yoke spline	See Overhaul in DRIVE AXLES

GEAR TOOTH CONTACT PATTERNS

INSPECTION

PRELIMINARY INSPECTION

Wipe lubricant from internal parts. Rotate gears, and inspect for wear or damage. Mount dial indicator to housing, and check backlash at several points around ring gear. Backlash must be within specifications at all points. If no defects are found, check gear tooth contact pattern.

GEAR TOOTH CONTACT PATTERN

NOTE: **Drive pattern should be well centered on ring gear teeth. Coast pattern should be centered, but may be slightly toward toe of ring gear teeth.**

1) Paint ring gear teeth with marking compound. Wrap cloth or rope around drive pinion flange to act as brake. Rotate ring gear until clear tooth contact pattern is obtained.

2) Contact pattern will indicate whether correct pinion bearing mounting shim has been installed and if drive gear backlash has been set properly. Backlash between drive gear and pinion must be maintained within specified limits, until correct tooth pattern is obtained.

ADJUSTMENTS

GEAR BACKLASH & PINION SHIM CHANGES

NOTE: **Backlash is adjusted by either shifting shims from 1 side of differential case to other or by turning adjusting nuts on which differential side bearings ride. Changing pinion shims changes distance from face of pinion to centerline of ring gear.**

1) With no change in backlash, moving pinion further from ring gear moves drive pattern toward heel and top of tooth, and moves coast pattern toward toe and top of tooth.

2) With no change in backlash, moving pinion closer to ring gear moves drive pattern toward toe and bottom of tooth, and moves coast pattern toward heel and bottom of tooth.

3) With no change in pinion shim thickness, an increase in backlash moves ring gear further from pinion. Drive pattern moves toward heel and top of tooth, and coast pattern moves toward heel and top of tooth.

4) With no change in pinion shim thickness, decrease in backlash moves ring gear closer to pinion gear. Drive pattern moves toward toe and bottom of tooth, and coast pattern moves toward toe and bottom of tooth.

Fig. 1: Drive Axle Gear Tooth Pattern

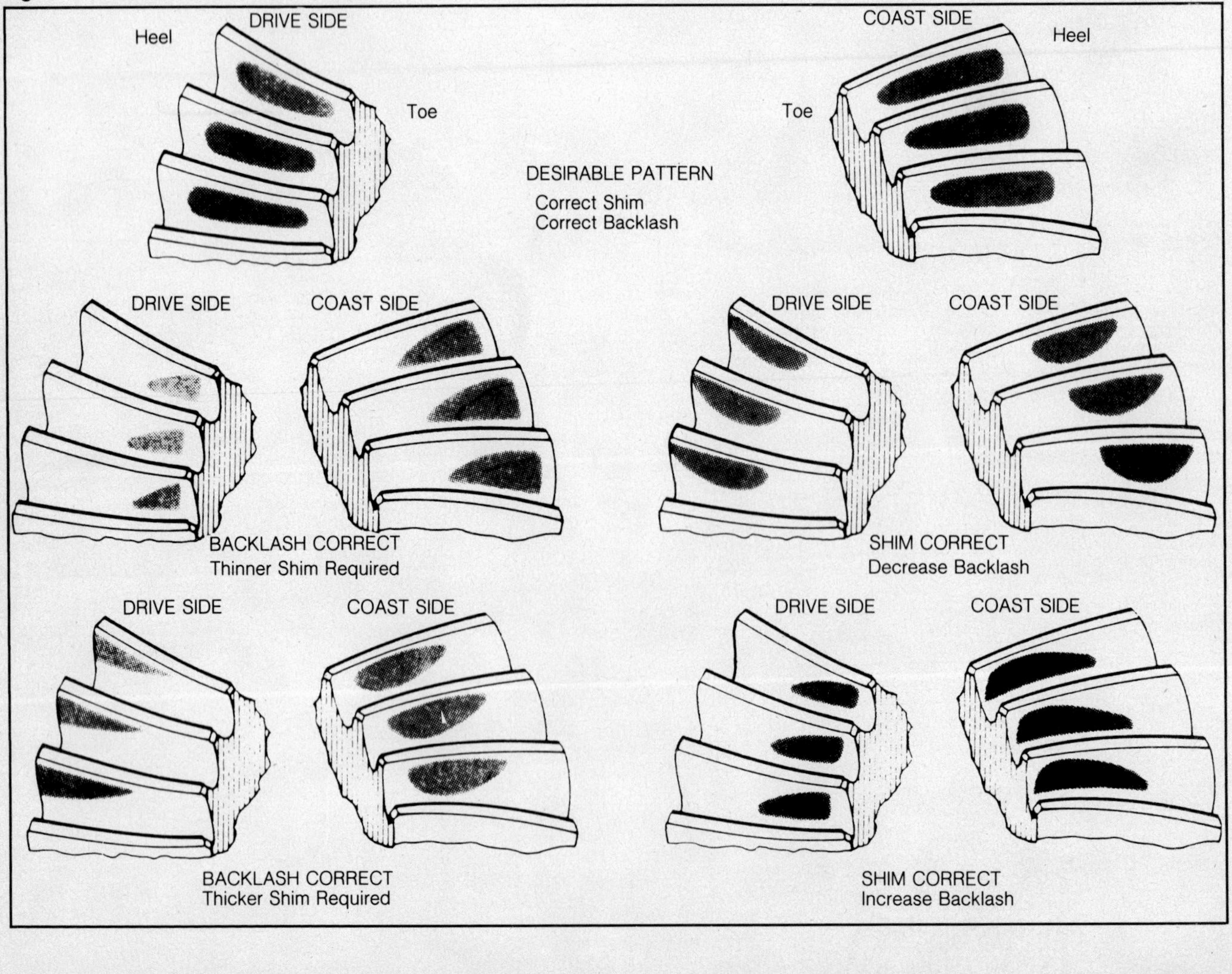

AXLE RATIO IDENTIFICATION

CHRYSLER CORP.

A metal tag is attached to one of the rear axle housing cover bolts. Tag gives number of teeth for ring gear and pinion gear. To obtain gear ratio, divide larger number by smaller number.

FORD

Axle ratio code is stamped on Vehicle Certification Plate located on rear face of left door on all models. First 2 digits of code identifies ratio and capacity of rear axle.

Third digit of code identifies ratio and capacity of front axle. Rear axles have a tag bolted to drive axle that contains drive axle ratio. Code designations are as follows:

FORD AXLE RATIO IDENTIFICATION

Code	Ratio
Conventional Rear Differentials	
17	2.47:1
81	2.73:1
14	3.00:1
31	3.07:1
18, 38, 72, 82	3.08:1
13 [1], 23 [1], 42, 74, 84	3.45:1
16	3.50:1
G3, 23, 33, 43, 53, 63, 73	3.54:1
F9, 19, 26, 29, 39, 49, 69	3.55:1
14 [1], 24 [1], 24, 27, 34, 44, 86, 96	3.73:1
18 [1]	3.80:1
G2, 12 [1], 22, 25, 32, 35, 42, 45, 47, 52, 62, 65, 72, 87	4.10:1
13	4.11:1
65	4.56:1
Limited Slip Rear Differentials	
H4	3.00:1
H8	3.08:1
F5	3.45:1(Ranger)
H6	3.50:1
B3, C3, D3, E3	3.54:1
B6, B9, C9, H9	3.55:1
B7, D4, E4	3.73:1
B2, B5, C2, C5, D2, D5, D7, E2, F5, 22	4.10:1
Locking Rear Differentials	
F4	3.45:1
F3	3.54:1
A4, B4, F6, K6, 44	3.73:1
A2, F7	4.10:1
H3	4.11:1
Conventional Front Differentials	
E57A-AFA	3.45:1
E5TA-MA, E5TA-RA, E5TA-SA, E5TA-XA	3.54:1
E57A-AGA	3.73:1
E5TA-NA, E5TA-TA	4.09:1
E5TA-YA, E5TA-ZA, E57A-DB	4:10:1
Limited Slip Front Differentials	
E5TA-PA	3.54:1
E5TA-UA, E5TA-ACA	4.09:1
E57A-EB	4.10:1

[1] – Applies to Aerostar only.

GENERAL MOTORS

Identification code for rear axles is stamped on rear surface of right rear axle tube. Identification code for front axles is stamped on top rear of left axle tube. On Dana built front axles, axle ratio code is on tape stripe around right front axle tube.

GENERAL MOTORS "C", "G", "K" & "P" SERIES AXLE RATIO IDENTIFICATION

Code	Ratio
Conventional Rear Differentials	
BB3, BRA, BRD, BR3, BX3, CK3, CN3	2.73:1
BC3, BSA, BSC, BSD, BS3, BY3, CR3	3.08:1
GGF, GGK, GMA, GMG	3.21:1
BDC, BDB, BDD, BDF, HBG	3.23:1
BBC, BBD, BBJ, BBK, BBN, BBR, BD3, BT3, BZ3, CA3, CX3, HMR	3.42:1
BCY, BCW, BCX, BFA, BFK, BFN, BFU, BFW, BF3, BU3, CY3, GDF, GGG, GGL, GGP, GGY, GHB, GLH, GMB, GMH, GMP, GMW, HBB,HBN	3.73:1
BCZ, BHK, GDL, GGH, GGM, GGZ, GHC, GHM, GHR, GLJ, GLP, GLS, GLU, GMD, GMK, GMS, HBD	4.10:1
BKC, BKN, GDC, GGJ, GGN, GHA, GHD, GHN, GHS, GLL, GLR, GLT, GLW, GMM, GMT, HBJ	4.56:1
BKT	4.88:1
BNB, GHU	5.13:1
TSA	5.29:1
TTA	5.83:1
Locking Rear Differentials	
BH3, BRF, BRH, CC3, CJ3, CS3, CU3	2.73:1
AZ3, BJ3, BRB, BSB, BSF, BSH, CD3, CT3, CW3	3.08:1
HBH	3.23:1
BA3, BBA, BBF, BBH, BBM, BBS, BBT, BK3, CF3, CZ3, HMS	3.42:1
BDA, BFC, BFD, BFF, BFH, BFJ, BFM, BFR, BFX, BFY, BM3, DA3, GDG, GGU, GHF, GHJ, GLK, GMC, GMJ, GMR, GMX, HBC, HPB	3.73:1
BJA, BJB, BJD, GDK, GGR, GGW, GHG, GHK, GLM, GLX, GMF, GML, HBF	4.10:1
BKD, GDD, GGT, GGX, GHH, GHL, GHP, GHT, GLN, GLY, GMN, GMU, HBK	4.56:1
Front Differentials	
HAN	2.73:1
HAP	3.08:1
HAU, MKB	3.23:1
HAR, HAW, MHC	3.42:1
HAS, HAT, MBC, TBA, TBB	3.73:1
GBB, MCD, TCA, TCB	4.10:1
TDA, TDB	4.56:1

AXLE RATIO IDENTIFICATION (Cont.)

GENERAL MOTORS ASTRO, SAFARI & "S" SERIES AXLE RATIO IDENTIFICATION

Code	Ratio
Conventional Rear Differentials	
FAA	2.56:1
FCA, FCB	2.73:1
FFA, FFB, GNH, GNM, GNX	3.08:1
FMA, FMB, GNJ, GNN, GNT, GNY, GPB	3.42:1
FRA, FRB, GNK, GNP, GNU, GNZ, GPC, GPG	3.73:1
FSA, FSD, GNL, GNR, GNW, GPA, GPD, GPH	4.11:1
Locking Rear Differentials	
FBA	2.56:1
GNS	3.08:1
GPF	3.42:1
Front Differentials	
GBD	3.42:1
GBF	3.73:1
GBG	4.11:1

JEEP

On CJ7 and Scrambler models, the front axle code number is cast into bottom surface of housing. On all other models the front axle code number is cast into upper surface of reinforcing rib at left side of axle housing. A gear ratio tag is attached to left side of axle housing cover on front axles.

On all models except "J20" truck models, rear axle ratio code letter is located on axle housing tube boss, adjacent to dowel hole. On "J20" truck models, rear axle model number is cast into boss on lower right side of axle housing, adjacent to housing cover.

JEEP AXLE RATIO IDENTIFICATION

Code	Ratio
Conventional Differentials	
D	2.73:1
B	3.31:1
A	3.54:1
H	3.73:1
C	4.10:1
S	[1] 3.73:1
T	[1] 3.31:1
Locking Differentials	
DD	2.73:1
CC	3.31:1
AA	3.54:1
HH	3.73:1
CC	4.10:1
SS	[1] 3.73:1
TT	[1] 3.31:1

[1] – Applies to Cherokee/Wagoneer models only.

CHRYSLER CORP. 8 3/8" & 9 1/4" RING GEAR

Pickup, RWD Van

DESCRIPTION

Axle assembly is hypoid gear type with an integral carrier housing. It is used on light duty vehicles with semi-floating axles. Pinion bearing preload adjustment is made with collapsible spacer. Differential bearing preload adjustment is made with adjusting nuts on which bearing races seat Removable housing cover permits inspection and minor servicing of differential without removal from vehicle. Service procedures are same for both size assemblies, except for some tightening specifications and special tool numbers.

AXLE RATIO & IDENTIFICATION

Small metal tag attached to rear axle housing cover bolt identifies axle ratio. Chrysler Corp. also uses Spicer (Dana) axles for some applications. To distinguish these models from Chrysler Corp. models, refer to SPICER (DANA) axle articles in this section.

REMOVAL & INSTALLATION

AXLE SHAFTS & BEARINGS

Removal

1) Raise vehicle and remove wheel, tire and brake drum. Loosen housing cover attaching bolts to drain lubricant. Remove housing cover. Remove pinion shaft lock screw and differential pinion shaft.

2) Force axle shaft toward center of vehicle. Remove "C" washer lock from groove in axle shaft. Pull axle shaft out of housing, using care not to damage roller bearing. Remove oil seal from housing bore.

3) To remove axle shaft bearing from axle housing, use Bearing Puller (C-4167). Attach slide hammer to puller and remove axle shaft bearing and inspect. If either axle or bearing show any signs of brinnelling, spalling or pitting, discard component.

4) Dents caused by axle shaft splines should be polished smooth, or rubber on outside diameter of seal will be torn and seal leakage will result. Inspect both axle and bearing. If either show signs of excessive wear, discard bearing.

NOTE: **Always install new axle shaft oil seal.**

Installation

1) Clean all parts thoroughly. Install axle shaft bearing squarely into housing bore. Making sure bearing is bottomed against shoulder in bore. Lubricate and install oil seal in housing bore.

2) Slide axle shaft into place being careful not to damage oil seal. Install "C" washer lock into groove in axle shaft. Pull outward on axle shaft so that "C" washer lock seats in counterbore of differential side gear.

3) Install differential pinion shaft through case and pinions. Aligning hole in shaft with lock screw hole in case. Install pinion shaft lock screw and tighten securely. Install housing cover and identification tag.

PINION FLANGE & SEAL

Removal

1) Raise vehicle, mark propeller shaft universal joint, drive pinion flange and pinion stem for reassembly. Disconnect propeller shaft and tie out of way. Remove rear wheels and brake drums to prevent false preload reading.

2) Using torque wrench calibrated in INCH lbs., measure and record pinion bearing preload. Remove drive pinion nut and pull off flange using puller. Pry out oil seal, taking care not to damage machined surface.

Installation

1) Install new pinion oil seal squarely into bore in housing until seal flange seats against housing flange face. Position pinion flange on pinion stem, making sure marks are aligned. Install pinion washer (convex side out) and nut. Tighten nut to specifications and rotate pinion through several revolutions to be sure bearing rollers are properly seated.

NOTE: **Outside diameter of seal is precoated with special sealer. No additional sealing compound is required.**

2) Measure pinion bearing preload. Continue tightening pinion nut until preload is same as that noted before disassembly. Preload should NEVER be more than 10 INCH lbs. (1.1 N.m) over original setting.

CAUTION: **Under NO circumstances should pinion nut be backed off to lessen preload. If desired preload is exceeded, new collapsible spacer must be installed, and nut retightened until proper preload is obtained.**

AXLE ASSEMBLY

Removal & Installation

1) Raise vehicle and block brake pedal in position. Remove wheels, tires and brake drums. Disconnect brake lines at wheel cylinders and cap to prevent fluid loss. Disconnect parking brake cables.

2) Mark propeller shaft universal joint, drive pinion flange and pinion stem for reassembly. Disconnect propeller shaft and tie out of way. Remove shock absorbers and rear spring "U" bolts. Remove rear axle assembly. To install, reverse removal procedure.

OVERHAUL

DISASSEMBLY

NOTE: **It is not necessary to remove complete rear axle assembly to overhaul differential.**

1) Remove wheels and brake drums. Mark propeller shaft and universal joint for reassembly, remove propeller shaft and tie out of way. Drain lubricant and remove housing cover. Measure and record axle shaft end play.

2) Insert feeler gauge between each end of axle shaft and pinion shaft. Record maximum thickness that can be inserted in each side. If end play is less than .005" (.13 mm), measure side gear clearance.

3) Using 2 feeler gauges of equal thickness, insert 1 gauge above and 1 gauge below side gear hub next to thrust surface. If clearance is more than .012" (.30 mm),

CHRYSLER CORP. 8 3/8" & 9 1/4" RING GEAR (Cont.)

Fig. 1: Exploded View of Chrysler Corp. 8 3/8" Drive Axle Assembly

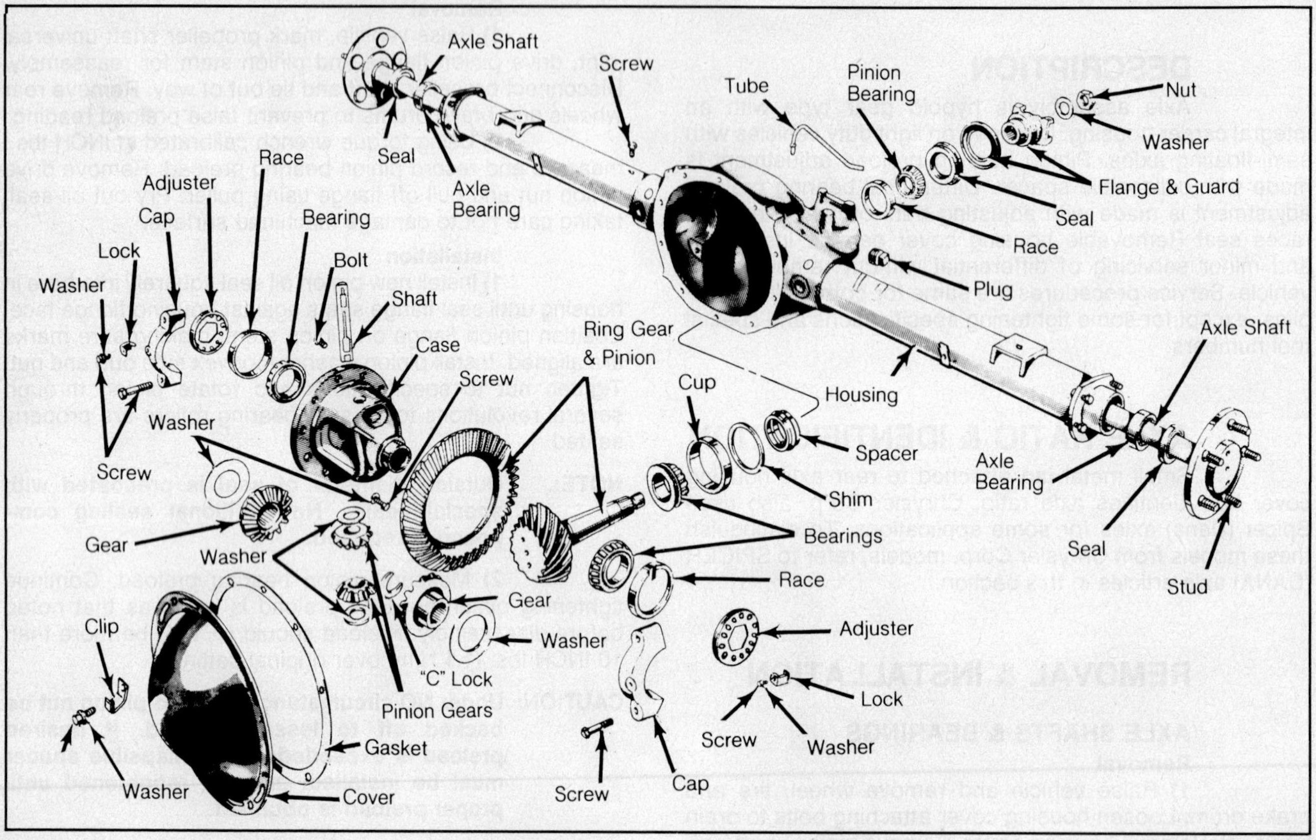

replace side gear. Remove axle shafts as previously described.

4) Measure and record differential side play, ring gear runout and pinion bearing preload. Mark differential gear and case at point of maximum runout. There should be no side play and ring gear runout should not exceed .005" (.13 mm).

5) If ring gear runout exceeded .005" (.13 mm), differential case flange runout must be checked. Using Hex Adjuster (C-4164), tighten adjusters until all case side play is eliminated.

6) Mount dial indicator to housing and place indicator stem on ring gear flange of differential case. Rotate case several times, checking reading on dial indicator. If reading varies more than .005" (.13 mm), replace differential case.

7) Remove drive pinion flange and seal as previously described. Mark side bearing caps and axle housing for reassembly. Remove adjuster locks, loosen but do not remove bearing caps. Insert hex adjuster through axle tube and loosen hex adjuster on each side.

8) Remove bearing caps, adjusters and differential case assembly. Be sure to keep all bearing races and adjusters with their respective bearings. Using soft drift punch and hammer, drive pinion shaft out of housing.

NOTE: Bearings, races, collapsible spacer and shim(s) must be replaced after driving out pinion.

9) Drive bearing races out of housing using hammer and soft drift punch. Remove shim(s) from behind rear race and record thickness. Remove bearing cones from pinion shaft using Puller and Adapter (C-293-PA and C-293-42).

10) Mount differential case assembly in soft-jawed vise. Remove and discard ring gear bolts (left-hand thread). Using soft-faced hammer, drive ring gear off differential case.

NOTE: Do not remove ring gear from differential case unless case or gear set is replaced.

CLEANING & INSPECTION

1) Clean all components in cleaning solvent. Inspect all machined surfaces for smoothness or raised edges, and polish or flatten as required.

2) Inspect all bearings and races for wear or pitting and replace as set. Inspect all gear teeth for wear or chipping and replace as matched set only. Inspect all splined components for wear or damage and replace as required.

REASSEMBLY & ADJUSTMENT

Case Assembly

1) Install thrust washers on differential side gears and position gears in differential case. Place thrust washers on differential pinion gears and position gears in case so that they are 180° apart when they are in mesh with side gears.

2) Rotate side gears until holes in pinion gears are in alignment with pinion shaft holes in case. Install differential pinion shaft. Make sure hole in pinion shaft is aligned with lock screw hole in case.

CHRYSLER CORP. 8 3/8" & 9 1/4" RING GEAR (Cont.)

Fig. 2: Relieving Chamfer Edge On Ring Gear

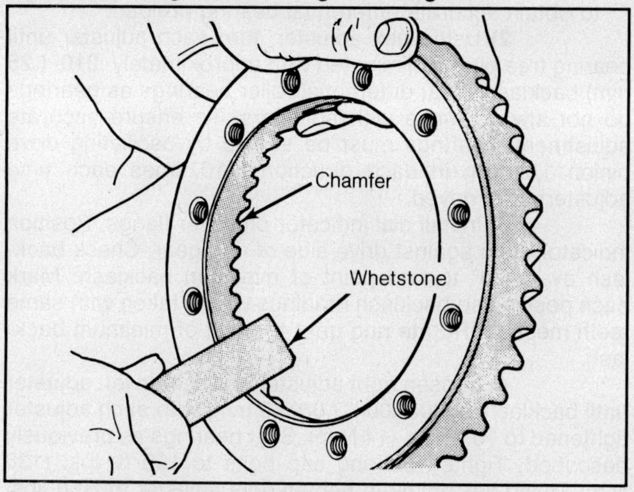

Surfaces of ring gear and case flange must be smooth.

3) Make sure contact surface of ring gear and case flange is clean and free of all nicks and burrs. Using fine whetstone, relieve any sharp edge of chamfer on inside diameter of ring gear. Relieving chamfer insures that no burrs will become imbedded between case flange and ring gear causing ring gear distortion. *See Fig. 2.*

Fig. 3: Installing Ring Gear on Differential Case

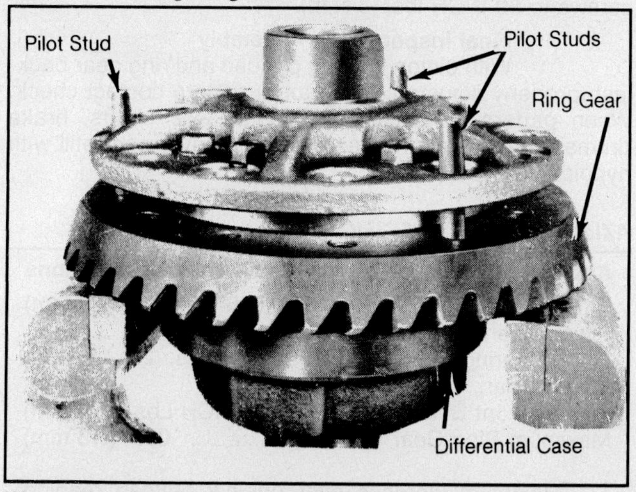

Warm ring gear to install on differential case.

4) Heat ring gear using heat lamp, hot oil or water. Temperature of ring gear must not exceed 300°F (149° C). Do not use torch to heat ring gear. Install 3 equally spaced pilot studs on ring gear. Place heated ring gear on jaws of vise and install case using new left-hand threaded bolts. *See Fig. 3.*

5) Tighten ring gear-to-case bolts alternately and evenly to specifications. Install side bearings on case using Bearing Installer and Driver (C-4340 and C-4171 for 8 3/8" ring gear. C-4213 and C-4171 for 9 1/4" ring gear). Lubricate assembly with hypoid gear lubricant.

Drive Pinion Depth

1) Install both drive pinion bearing races into axle housing bores. Assemble Pinion Locating Spacer (SP-6030) over body of Main Stem (SP-5385) followed by rear pinion bearing. Insert assembly into axle carrier from rear.

NOTE: **Tool numbers used apply to 8 3/8" ring gear axles. For equivalent tool numbers for 9 1/4" ring gear axles, see EQUIVALENT TOOL NUMBER chart.**

2) On 8 3/8" assembly, hold spacer and main stem assembly in position and install front pinion bearing over Spacer (SP-5382) and position over main stem of tool. On 9 1/4" assembly, position spacer and main stem assembly in housing. Install front pinion bearing and Washer (SP-6022).

3) Procedure from this point is same for both assemblies, except for tool numbers. Position Compression Sleeve (SP-3194B), Centralizing Washer (SP-534), and Main Screw Nut (SP-3193) on main stem. Hold compression sleeve with Companion Flange Wrench (C-3281) and tighten nut. Allow tool to rotate as nut is being tightened to prevent damaging bearings and races. *See Fig. 4.*

Fig. 4: Seating Pinion Bearing Races

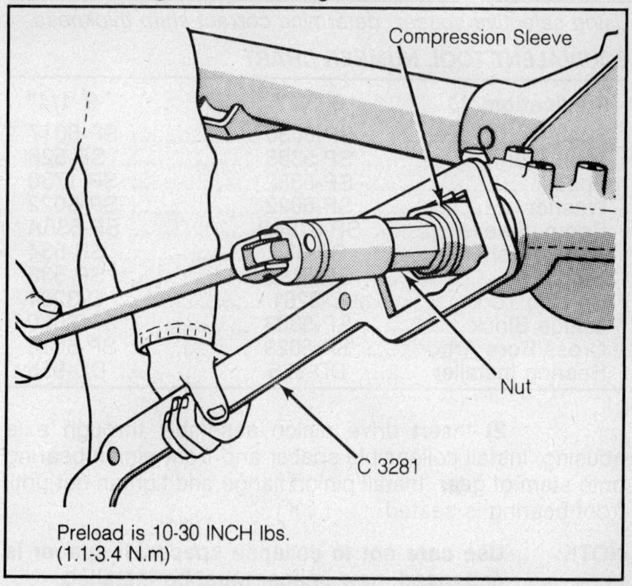

Rotate tool while tightening pinion nut.

4) Loosen tool nut, then retighten to obtain pinion bearing preload of 10-30 INCH lbs. (1.3-3.4 N.m). Rotate tool after tightening to properly seat pinion bearings. Install Gauge Block (SP-5383) on main tool and tighten screw.

5) Position Cross Bore Arbor (SP-6029) in housing side bearing seats and center arbor in bore. Position bearing caps on carrier pedestals and insert .002" (.051 mm) spacer between arbor and each cap. Install cap bolts and tighten to 10 ft. lbs. (14 N.m).

6) Use feeler gauge to determine proper thickness of shims that will fit snugly between arbor and gauge block. This fit must be snug but not excessively tight.

7) To select correct shim pack, read markings on end of pinion head. When marking is minus, add that amount of thickness to feeler gauge thickness to obtain thickness of correct shim pack. When marking is plus, subtract that amount of thickness. Remove all tools and rear pinion bearing race from housing. *See Fig. 5.*

Pinion Bearing Preload

1) Place selected shim in pinion shaft bore and reinstall rear pinion bearing cup. Lubricate rear pinion bearing and press into position on drive pinion stem.

CHRYSLER CORP. 8 3/8" & 9 1/4" RING GEAR (Cont.)

Fig. 5: Measuring Shim Pack Thickness

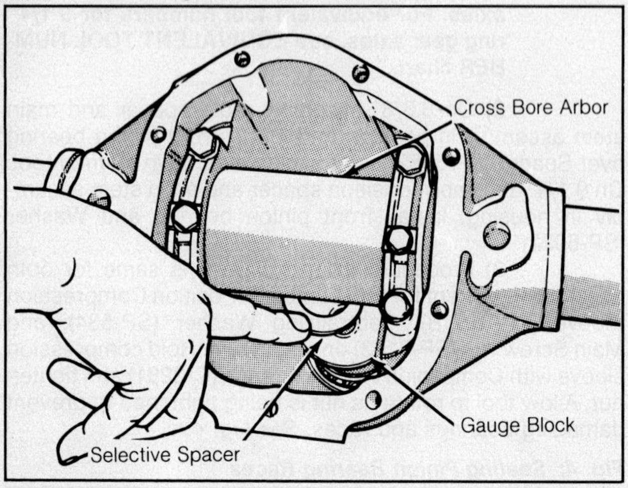

Using selective spacer, determine correct shim thickness.

EQUIVALENT TOOL NUMBER CHART

Application	8 3/8"	9 1/4"
Spacer	SP-6030	SP-6017
Main Stem	SP-5385	SP-526
Spacer	SP-5382	SP-1730
Washer	SP-6022	SP-6022
Comp. Sleeve	SP-3194B	SP-535A
Cent. Washer	SP-534	SP-534
Nut	SP-3193	SP-533
Holding Tool	C-3281	C-3281
Gauge Block	SP-5383	SP-6020
Cross Bore Arbor	SP-6029	SP-6018
Bearing Installer	DD-955	DD-955

2) Insert drive pinion assembly through axle housing. Install collapsible spacer and front pinion bearing onto stem of gear. Install pinion flange and tighten nut until front bearing is seated.

NOTE: Use care not to collapse spacer. If spacer is collapsed, new spacer must be installed.

3) With front bearing fully seated, remove pinion flange. Install new pinion oil seal into housing so flange of seal is fully seated against housing flange face.

4) Install pinion flange, Belleville washer (convex side out) and nut on pinion stem. While rotating pinion assembly (to insure proper bearing seating), tighten pinion flange nut until all end play is removed.

5) Tighten pinion nut to specified torque and measure pinion bearing preload by rotating pinion through several revolutions with INCH lb. torque wrench. Continue tightening pinion flange nut in small increments until correct bearing preload is obtained. Do not back off nut to lessen bearing preload. If desired preload is exceeded, new collapsible spacer must be installed and nut retightened until proper preload is obtained.

Backlash & Side Bearing Preload

1) Two precautions must be observed when checking and adjusting ring gear backlash and differential bearing preload.

- Index gears so same teeth are meshed during all backlash measurements. Permissible backlash variation is .003" (.08 mm). For example, if backlash at minimum point is .006" (.15 mm) and backlash at maximum point is .009" (.23 mm), variation is correct.
- It is also important to maintain specified adjuster torque to obtain accurate differential bearing preload.

2) Using hex adjuster, turn each adjuster until bearing free play is eliminated with approximately .010" (.25 mm) backlash. Seat differential roller bearings as bearings do not always move with adjusters. To ensure accurate adjustment, bearings must be seated by oscillating drive pinion 1/2 turn in each direction 5-10 times each time adjusters are moved.

3) Install dial indicator on cover flange. Position indicator stem against drive side of ring gear. Check backlash every 90° to find point of minimum backlash. Mark each position so backlash readings will be taken with same teeth meshed. Rotate ring gear to point of minimum backlash.

4) Loosen right adjuster and tighten left adjuster until backlash is .003-.004" (.08-.10 mm) with each adjuster tightened to 10 ft. lbs. (14 N.m). Seat bearings as previously described. Tighten bearing cap bolts to 100 ft. lbs. (136 N.m). Using hex adjuster, tighten right adjuster to 70 ft. lbs. (95 N.m). Seat bearings and continue to tighten right adjuster until torque remains constant at 70 ft. lbs. (95 N.m).

5) Check backlash again with indicator. If backlash is not between .006-.008" (.15-.20 mm), increase torque on right adjuster and seat bearings. Continue this operation until backlash is .006-.008" (.15-.20 mm). Tighten left adjuster to 70 ft. lbs. (95 N.m) and seat bearings. With adjustments completed, install adjuster locks. Make sure lock teeth are engaged in adjuster threads. Tighten lock screws to 90 INCH lbs. (8 N.m).

Final Inspection & Assembly

With pinion bearing preload and ring gear backlash properly adjusted, make tooth pattern contact check. When pattern is satisfactory, install axle shafts, brake drums, wheels and tires, axle housing cover and refill with hypoid gear lubricant.

AXLE ASSEMBLY SPECIFICATIONS

Application	Specifications
Ring Gear Backlash	.006-.008" (.15-.20 mm)
Pinion Bearing Preload	
New Bearings	20-35 INCH Lbs. (2.3-4.0 N.m)
Used Rear,	
New Front Bearing	[1] 10 INCH Lbs. (1.1 N.m)
Maximum Ring Gear Runout	.005" (.13 mm)

[1] – Maximum increase over original preload reading before disassembly.

TIGHTENING SPECIFICATIONS

Application	Ft. Lbs. (N.m)
Ring Gear-to-Diff. Case Bolts [1]	
8 3/8" Ring Gear	55 (75)
9 1/4" Ring Gear	70 (95)
Drive Pinion Nut (Minimum)	210 (286)
Side Bearing Cap Bolts	
8 3/8" Ring Gear	55 (75)
9 1/4" Ring Gear	100 (136)
	INCH Lbs. (N.m)
Bearing Adjuster Lock Bolts	90 (8)

[1] – Left-hand threaded bolts.

FORD 7 1/2" RING GEAR

Aerostar, Bronco II & Ranger

DESCRIPTION

The rear axle is a hypoid design ring and pinion gear encased in an integral cast iron housing. A one-piece differential case contains a conventional two-pinion differential assembly. Semi-floating axle shafts are retained by "C" washer locks at splined end of shafts.

AXLE RATIO & IDENTIFICATION

A metal tag stamped with axle model, date of manufacture, ratio, ring gear diameter and assembly plant is attached to rear cover.

Fig. 1: Rear Axle Identification Tag

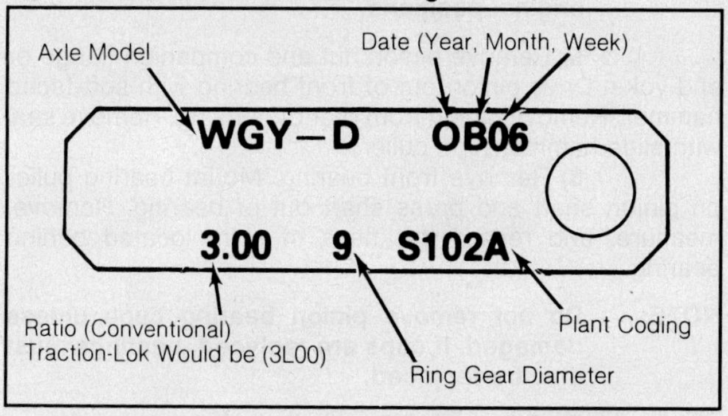

Use information on tag to order replacement parts.

REMOVAL & INSTALLATION

AXLE SHAFTS & BEARINGS

Removal

1) Raise vehicle and support with safety stands. Remove wheel assemblies and brake drums. Remove housing cover and drain lubricant.

2) For all axle ratios except 3.73:1 and 4.10:1, remove differential pinion shaft lock bolt and pinion shaft. Push axle toward center and remove "C" locks.

3) On 3.73:1 and 4.10:1 ratio axles, rotate pinion shaft so it faces side gear to provide clearance for "C" lock removal. Remove pinion shaft lock bolt. Place hand behind differential case and push out pinion shaft until step on shaft contacts ring gear. Remove "C" locks from shafts.

4) On all axles, remove axles, being careful not to cut axle seal. Using a slide hammer and puller, remove bearing and seal as a unit.

Installation

1) Lubricate bearing with rear axle lubricant and install bearings with a driver. Install seal. If seal becomes cocked during installation, remove it and replace it with a new one.

NOTE: **On 3.73:1 and 4.10:1 ratio axles, ensure pinion shaft step contacts ring gear before inserting axle in housing.**

2) Insert axle in housing with care to avoid damage to oil seal. Start splines into side gear and push axle firmly until button end of axle shaft can be seen in case. Install "C" locks, then push shafts outward to seat locks in counterbore of differential side gears.

Fig. 2: Ford 7 1/2" Integral Housing Axle Assembly

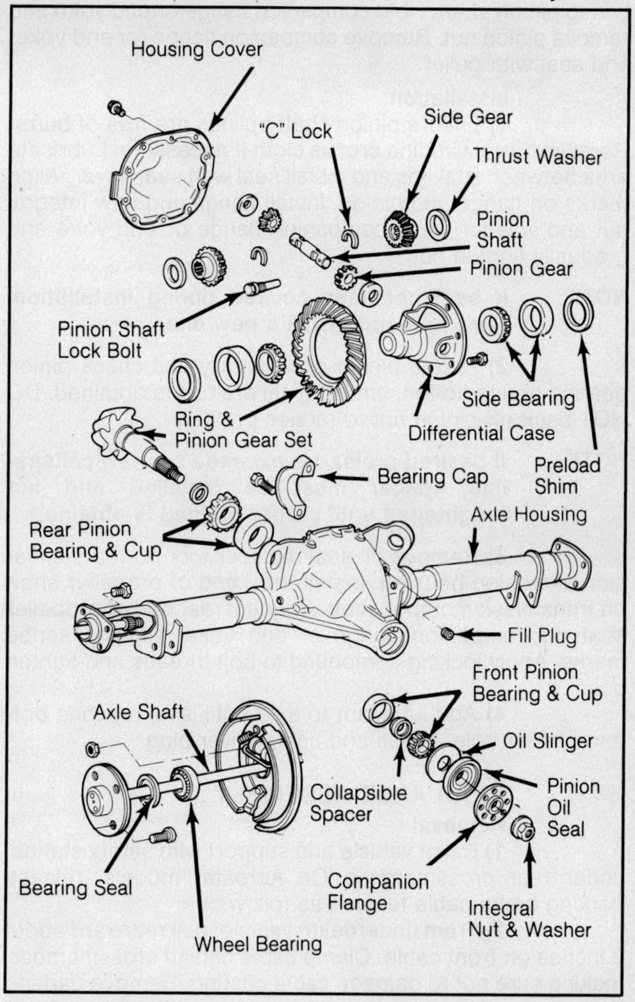

Aerostar uses axle end yoke instead of companion flange.

3) Position pinion shaft through case and pinion gears, aligning shaft hole with lock screw hole. Install and tighten lock bolt.

4) Clean gasket mounting surfaces and apply silicone sealant in a 1/8" to 3/16" bead on face of carrier housing. Install housing cover and add lubricant until level reaches bottom of filler hole. Install filler plug.

NOTE: **No gasket other than silicone seal is used. Cover assembly must be installed within 15 minutes of sealant application.**

PINION FLANGE & OIL SEAL

NOTE: **Pinion flange and oil seal replacement affects bearing preload. Preload must be carefully reset during reassembly.**

Removal

1) Raise vehicle and support with safety stands. Remove wheel assemblies and brake drums. Scribe alignment marks on companion flange (or end yoke) and propeller shaft for installation reference. Remove propeller shaft.

2) Install oil seal replacer tool in transmission extension housing to prevent oil leakage. Using an INCH lb. torque wrench, measure and record torque required to rotate pinion through several revolutions.

FORD 7 1/2" RING GEAR (Cont.)

3) Mark companion flange or end yoke in relation to pinion shaft. Hold companion flange or end yoke and remove pinion nut. Remove companion flange (or end yoke) and seal with puller.

Installation

1) Ensure pinion shaft splines are free of burrs. Remove burrs with fine crocus cloth if necessary. Lubricate area between seal lips and install seal with seal driver. Align marks on flange and pinion. Install flange and new integral nut and washer. Hold companion flange or end yoke and gradually tighten nut.

NOTE: **If seal becomes cocked during installation, remove it and install a new one.**

2) Rotate pinion occasionally and check pinion bearing preload often, until original preload is obtained. DO NOT back off pinion nut to reduce preload.

NOTE: **If desired preload is exceeded, a new collapsible spacer must be installed and nut retightened until proper preload is obtained.**

3) Remove oil seal replacer tool from transmission extension housing. Install front end of propeller shaft on transmission output shaft. Connect rear end of propeller shaft to companion flange or end yoke, aligning scribe marks. Apply locking compound to bolt threads and tighten bolts.

4) Add lubricant to axle until level reaches bottom of filler hole. Install and tighten filler plug.

REAR AXLE ASSEMBLY

Removal

1) Raise vehicle and support with safety stands, under rear crossmember. On Aerostar models, release parking brake cable tension as follows:

2) From underneath vehicle, pull rearward about 2 inches on front cable. Clamp cable behind crossmember, making sure not to damage cable coating. Remove parking brake cables from equalizer. Compress tabs on retainers and pull cables through rear crossmember.

3) On all models, remove housing cover and drain lubricant. Remove axle shafts as previously described.

4) Remove brake backing plates and wire plates out of way to frame. Mark and disconnect propeller shaft at companion flange or end yoke.

5) Disconnect axle vent from housing (at brake junction block on some models). Disconnect brake line from housing clips. Disconnect upper arms and shock absorbers from housing.

6) Lower housing on jack until coil springs can be removed. Disconnect lower arms from housing and remove axle housing.

Installation

To install, reverse removal procedure. Apply locking compound to threads holding axle vent and brake block (if used) to axle housing.

OVERHAUL

DISASSEMBLY

NOTE: **Differential case and drive pinion may be serviced in vehicle.**

1) Raise vehicle and support with safety stands under rear frame crossmember. Remove housing cover and drain lubricant.

2) Mount a dial indicator, measure, and record ring gear backlash and runout. Remove rear wheel assemblies and brake drums. Remove "C" locks and axle shafts as previously described.

3) Place alignment marks on propeller shaft, yoke and companion flange for reassembly reference. Remove propeller shaft. Mark 1 differential bearing cap for reassembly reference and note arrow position.

4) Loosen bearing cap bolts and bearing caps. Pry differential case, bearing cups, and shims out until loose in bearing caps. Remove bearing caps and differential.

NOTE: **Bearing cups and caps must be installed in original positions.**

5) Remove pinion nut and companion flange or end yoke. Drive pinion out of front bearing with soft-faced hammer. Remove pinion from rear of housing. Remove seal with slide hammer type puller.

6) Remove front bearing. Mount bearing puller on pinion shaft and press shaft out of bearing. Remove, measure, and record thickness of shim located behind bearing.

NOTE: **Do not remove pinion bearing cups unless damaged. If cups are replaced, bearings must also be replaced.**

7) Remove differential side bearings with a puller. Mark differential case and ring gear for reassembly reference. Remove and discard ring gear mounting bolts.

8) Press or tap off ring gear. Drive out pinion shaft lock pin and shaft with a punch. Remove pinion gears, side gears and thrust washers.

NOTE: **If a 3.73:1 or 4.10:1 ratio ring gear is removed, make sure pinion shaft is installed before installing ring gear.**

CLEANING & INSPECTION

Clean all parts thoroughly in cleaning solvent. Examine pinion and ring gear teeth for scoring, excessive wear, nicks and chipping. Check bearing cups for deep scores, galling or spalling. Check carrier bearings for pitting, scoring and roller ends for stepping. If any components show damage, wear or scoring replace components.

When replacing ring gear and pinion, note original factory shim thickness to adjust for variations in both carrier casting and original gear set dimension. Variations are marked on pinion gear head and ring gear.

NOTE: **Ring and pinion gear set must be replaced in matched sets.**

REASSEMBLY

1) Lubricate all parts with rear axle lubricant. Place side gears and thrust washers into case. Place pinion gears and thrust washers exactly opposite each other in case openings, and in mesh with side gears.

2) Install ring gear with new mounting bolts. If bolts are covered with Green coating over 1/2" of threaded area, install and tighten bolts. If new bolts do not have green coating, apply small amount of locking compound to bolt threads and tighten bolts.

FORD 7 1/2" RING GEAR (Cont.)

NOTE: Ring gear bolts should not be reused.

ADJUSTMENT

1) If new components have been installed, proper gear set assembly must be checked using a Rear Axle Pinion Depth Gauge (T79P 4020) to determine correct pinion shim.

2) If bearing cups have been replaced, new cone and roller assemblies should be installed. Cups must be seated in bores so a .0015" (.038 mm) feeler gauge will not fit between cup and bottom of bore.

3) Rear pinion bearing must be pressed on so it is firmly seated against spacer shim and pinion gear.

Pinion Depth

1) Assemble depth gauge and install aligning adapter, gauge disc .89" (23 mm), and gauge block screw. Place rear pinion bearing over aligning disc and into bearing cup of carrier housing.

2) Install front pinion bearing into front bearing cup. Place tool handle onto screw and hand tighten. *See Fig. 3.* Make sure pinion depth measuring tool is properly installed and tightened.

Fig. 3: Installation of Pinion Depth Measuring Tools

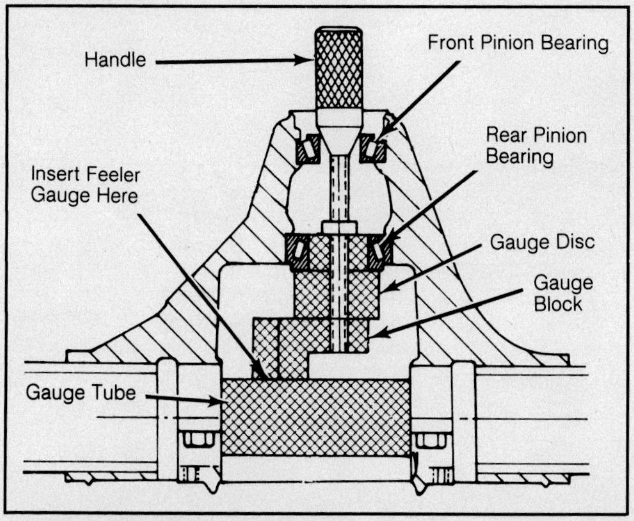

Check tool for proper installation.

3) Apply a light film of oil to pinion bearings. Rotate gauge block several times to seat bearings. Rotational torque on gauge block assembly should be 20 INCH lbs. (2.25 N.m) with new bearings.

4) Final position of gauge block should be 45° above axle shaft centerline. Clean differential bearing bores thoroughly and install gauge tube. Tighten bearing cap bolts.

5) Using flat pinion shims as a gauge for shim selection, hold gauge block in proper position and measure clearance between gauge block and tube.

6) Correct shim selection is accomplished when a slight drag is felt as shim is drawn between gauge block and tube.

Pinion Bearing Preload

1) Place pre-selected shim on pinion shaft. Press bearing onto shaft until bearing and shim are firmly seated against shoulder of shaft. Install new collapsible spacer on pinion shaft.

2) Lubricate bearings with axle lubricant. Install front pinion bearing in housing. Install new pinion oil seal. Insert companion flange or end yoke into seal and hold firmly in place.

3) From rear of carrier housing, insert pinion shaft into flange. Start a new pinion nut on pinion shaft and gradually tighten pinion nut (hold flange).

4) Check bearing preload often. As soon as preload is measured, turn pinion shaft in both directions several times to seat bearings.

5) Tighten pinion nut and continue to measure pinion bearing preload until specified pinion torque is obtained. If bearing preload is exceeded before torque specification is reached, replace collapsible spacer.

6) Install new pinion nut and repeat procedures. Do not loosen pinion nut to reduce pinion bearing preload.

Differential Bearing Preload & Ring Gear Backlash

1) With pinion depth set and pinion installed, place differential case and gear assembly with bearings and cups into carrier.

2) Install a .265" (6.7 mm) shim on left (ring gear side) side of differential. Install left bearing cap finger tight.

3) Choose largest shim that will fit with a slight drag and install it on right (pinion gear side) side of differential. Install right bearing cap and tighten all cap bolts to specification.

4) Rotate gear assembly to ensure free operation. Check ring and pinion backlash. If backlash is less than specified, add .020" (.51 mm) to shim size on right side and subtract .020" (.51 mm) from shim size on left side.

5) If backlash is still not within specifications, increase or decrease shim size where necessary to correct reading. *See Fig. 4.*

Fig. 4: Backlash Adjustment

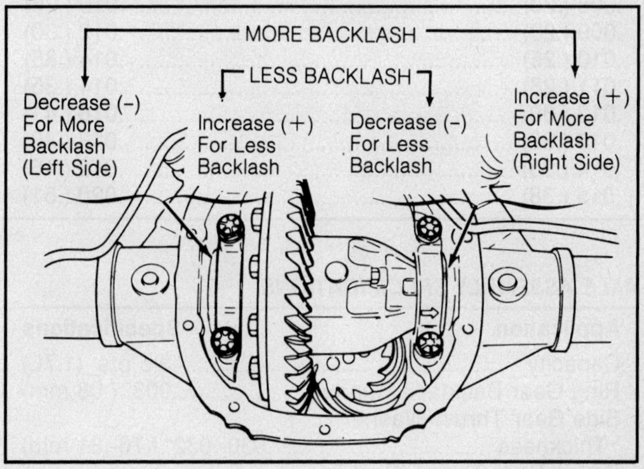

6) Retighten bearing cap bolts and rotate gear assembly several times. Recheck backlash and correct as necessary. Increase both left and right shim sizes .006" (.15 mm) and reinstall for correct preload.

7) Make sure shims are seated and gear assembly turns freely. Using marking compound, check gear tooth contact pattern.

FINAL ASSEMBLY

1) Clean differential case housing lip and apply a continuous bead of silicone sealant. Install cover and tighten bolts. Install backing plates and propeller shaft, and tighten bolts.

Drive Axles

FORD 7 1/2" RING GEAR (Cont.)

2) Install wheel bearings, seals, brake drums, and wheel assemblies. Fill axle with lubricant. Adjust brakes if required.

Fig. 5: Measuring Ring Gear Backlash

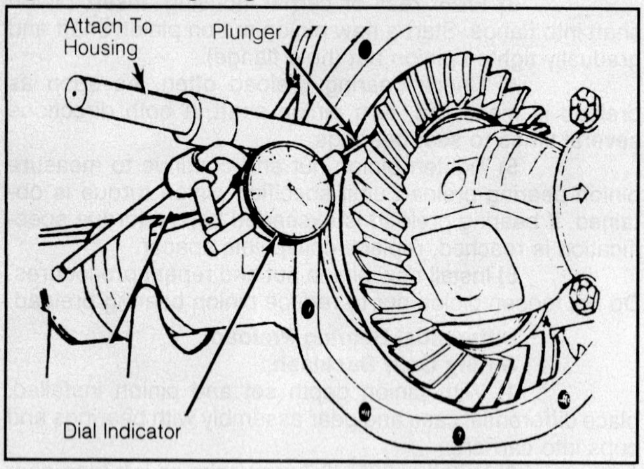

BACKLASH-TO-SHIM THICKNESS CONVERSION

Required Change In Backlash In. (mm)	Change In Shim Thickness In. (mm)
.001 (.025)	.002 (.051)
.002 (.051)	.002 (.051)
.003 (.076)	.004 (.10)
.004 (.10)	.006 (.15)
.005 (.13)	.006 (.15)
.006 (.15)	.008 (.20)
.007 (.18)	.010 (.25)
.008 (.20)	.010 (.25)
.009 (.23)	.012 (.30)
.010 (.25)	.014 (.35)
.011 (.28)	.014 (.35)
.012 (.30)	.016 (.41)
.013 (.33)	.018 (.46)
.014 (.35)	.018 (.46)
.015 (.38)	.020 (.51)

AXLE ASSEMBLY SPECIFICATIONS

Application	Specifications
Capacity	3.5 pts. (1.7L)
Ring Gear Backface Runout	.003" (.08 mm)
Side Gear Thrust Washer Thickness	.030-.032" (.76-.81 mm)
Pinion Gear Thrust Washer Thickness	.030-.032" (76-81 mm)
Nominal Pinion Shim Thickness	.030" (.76 mm)
Ring Gear Backlash	.008-.015" (.20-38 mm)
Maximum Backlash Variation Between Teeth	.004" (10 mm)
	INCH Lbs. (N.m)
Pinion Bearing Preload	
Original Bearings (With Oil Seal)	8-14 (.9-1.6)
New Bearings	16-29 (1.8-3.2)

TIGHTENING SPECIFICATIONS

Application	Ft. Lbs. (N.m)
Bearing Cap Bolts	70-85 (95-115)
Pinion Shaft Lock Bolt	15-30 (20-40)
Ring Gear Bolts	70-85 (95-115)
Rear Cover Bolts	25-35 (34-47)
Pinion Nut	170 (230)

FORD 8.8" & 10.25" RING GEAR

Bronco, E250/350, F150/250, Ranger

DESCRIPTION

The rear axle is a hypoid design ring and pinion gear encased in an integral cast iron housing. A one-piece differential case contains a conventional two-pinion differential assembly. Semi-floating axle shafts are retained by "C" washer locks at splined end of shafts.

A full-floating, 10.25" ring gear axle, with brake drums mounted outside of the hubs, was introduced mid-year. Full-floating shafts are retained by bolts attached to the hub, which rides on 2 bearings at the outer end of the axle tube.

AXLE RATIO & IDENTIFICATION

A metal tag stamped with axle model, date of manufacture, ratio, ring gear diameter and assembly plant is attached to rear cover.

Fig. 1: Rear Axle Identification Tag

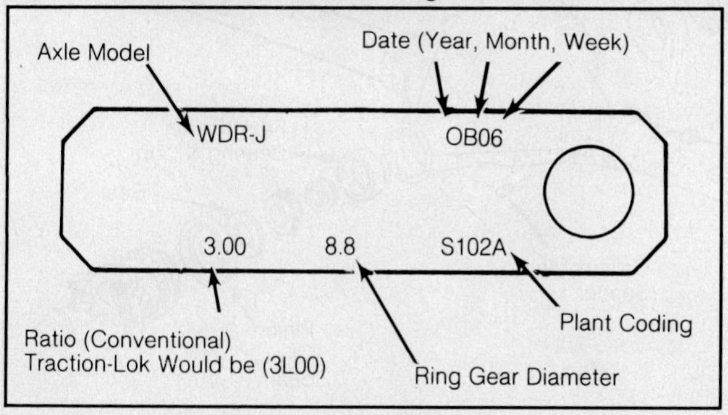

Use information on tag to order replacement parts.

REMOVAL & INSTALLATION

AXLE SHAFTS & BEARINGS

Removal (Semi-Floating)

1) Raise vehicle and support with safety stands. Remove wheel assemblies and brake drums. Remove housing cover and drain lubricant.

2) Remove differential pinion shaft lock bolt and pinion shaft. Push axle shaft toward center and remove "C" locks.

3) Remove axle shaft, being careful not to cut axle seal. Using a slide hammer and puller, remove bearing and seal as a unit.

Installation

1) Lubricate bearing with rear axle lubricant and install bearing with a driver. Install seal. If seal becomes cocked during installation, remove it and replace it with a new one.

2) Insert axle in housing with care to avoid damage to oil seal. Install "C" locks and push shafts outward to seat locks in counterbore of differential side gears.

3) Replace pinion gears and washers (if removed). Turn gear assembly to align pinion gear and thrust washer bores with pinion shaft holes on case. Install pinion shaft and lock bolt. Clean gasket mating surfaces and apply silicone sealant in a 1/8" to 3/16" bead on face of carrier housing and install housing cover.

NOTE: **No gasket other than silicone seal is used. Cover assembly must be installed within 15 minutes of sealant application.**

Removal (Full-Floating)

1) Set parking brake and loosen 8 axle shaft attaching bolts. Raise vehicle to working height, keeping axle parallel to floor. Release parking brake and back off rear brake adjustment if necessary.

2) Remove wheel and brake drum. Discard push-on drum retainer nuts. Remove axle shaft bolts and axle shaft.

NOTE: **Left side hub nut is left-hand thread.**

3) Install Hub Wrench (T85T-4252-AH) so its drive tangs engage 4 slots in hub nut. Remove hub nut. Hub nut will rachet during removal.

4) Install Step Plate Adapter (D80L-630-7) and remove hub using a puller. Do not drop outer hub bearing.

5) Place hub in soft-jawed vise. Remove hub seal and inner bearing. Reposition hub in vise and remove inner bearing cup with brass drift. Reposition hub in vise and remove outer bearing cup with a brass drift.

Installation

1) Holding Driver Handle (T80T-4000-W) and Bearing Cup Replacer (T75T-1225-A) straight, install outer and then inner bearing cups. Place hub inner bearing in cup.

2) Install oil seal using Hub Oil Seal Installer (T85T-1175-AH), making sure the words "OIL SIDE" face toward hub inner bearing. Strike tool handle until hub seal seats fully.

NOTE: **Install new seal if seal misaligns during or after installation.**

3) Clean spindle thoroughly, then coat it with axle lubricant. Pack hub bearing race and roller assembly using lithium base lubricant and a bearing packing tool.

4) With the outer bearing acting as a pilot, push hub and outer bearing on spindle. Install hub nut on spindle and tighten clockwise for right-hand thread, counterclockwise for left-hand thread.

NOTE: **Make sure hub nut tab is in keyway before thread engagement.**

5) Install Hub Wrench (T85T-4252-AH) on spindle. Tighten hub nut to 55-65 ft. lbs. (75-88 N.m) while rotating hub occasionally. Hub nut will ratchet as it is tightened. After tightening nut, rachet back 5 notches on hub nut.

6) Inspect axle shaft "O" ring and replace if necessary. Install axle shaft. Coat axle shaft retaining bolt threads with Loctite. Install and tighten axle shaft bolts until they seat. DO NOT tighten axle shaft bolts to specifications at this time.

7) Install brake drum and wheel. Loosen filler plug and check lubricant level. Add lubricant if necessary. Install filler plug. Lower vehicle and make brake adjustments if necessary. Tighten wheel lug nuts to 125-155 ft. lbs. (170-210 N.m). Tighten axle shaft retaining bolts to 60-80 ft. lbs. (81-108).

PINION FLANGE & OIL SEAL

NOTE: **Pinion flange and oil seal replacement affects bearing preload. Preload must be carefully reset during reassembly.**

Drive Axles

FORD 8.8" & 10.25" RING GEAR (Cont.)

Fig. 2: Ford 8.8" & Early 10.25" Integral Housing Axle Assembly

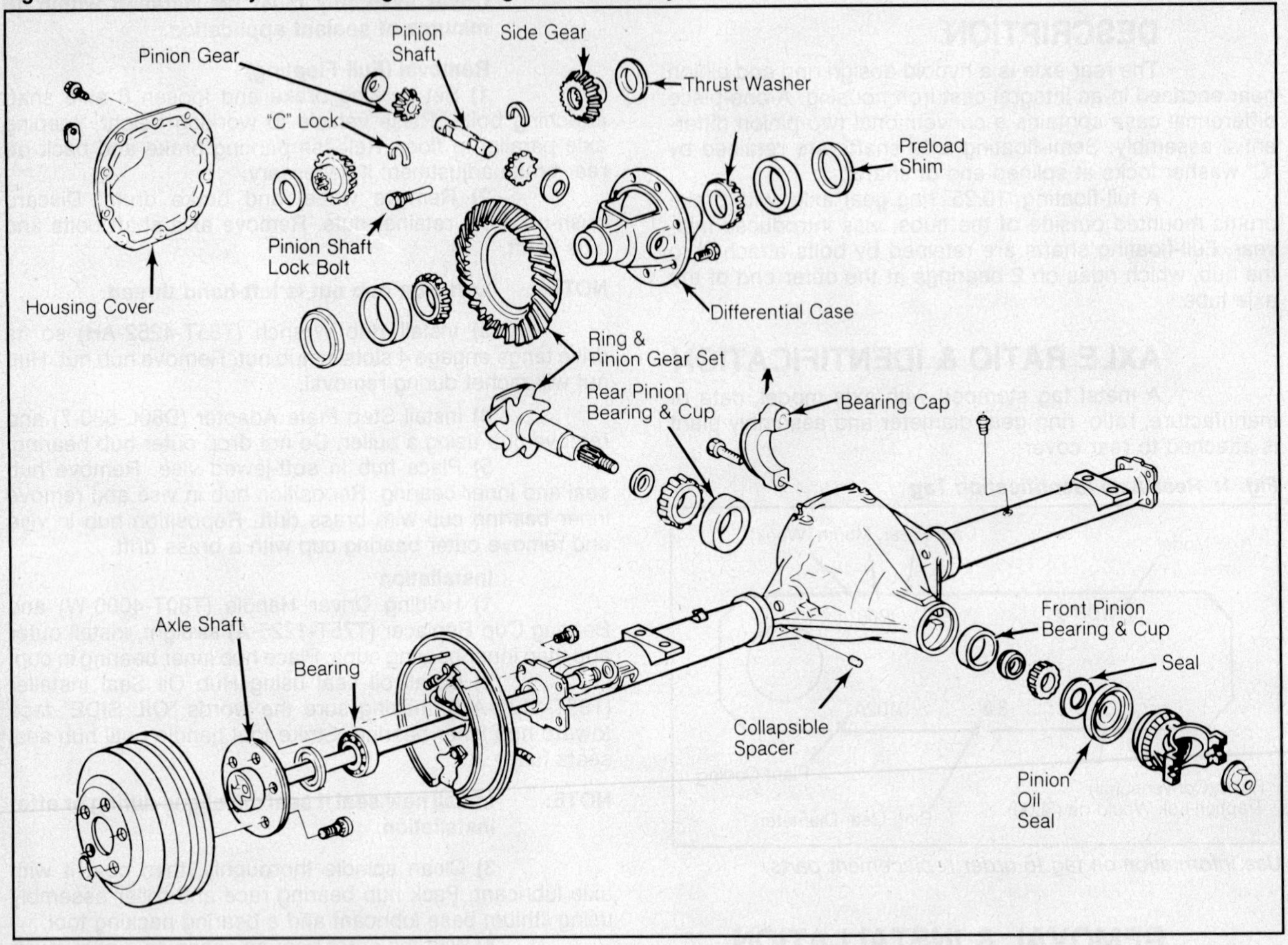

Fig. 3: Full-Floating 10.25" Axle Hub Components

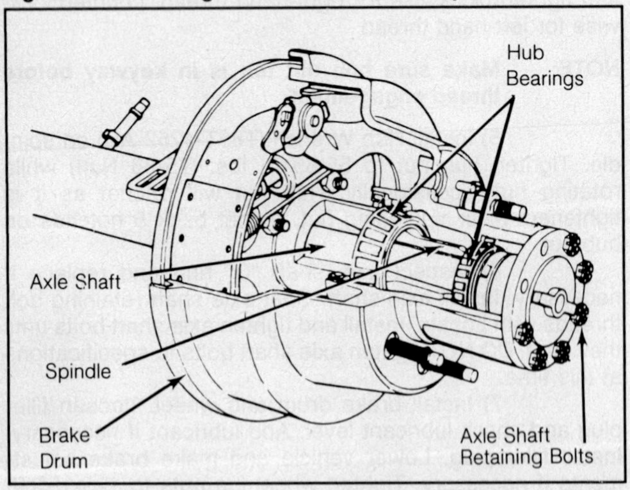

Fig. 4: Hub Wrench Tool

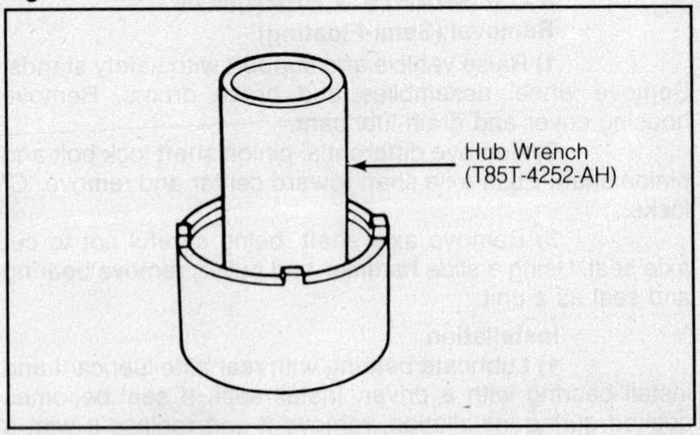

Removal

1) Raise vehicle and support with safety stands. Remove wheel assemblies and brake drums. Scribe alignment marks on companion flange and propeller shaft for installation reference. Remove propeller shaft.

2) Using an INCH lb. torque wrench, measure and record torque required to rotate pinion through several revolutions.

3) Mark companion flange in relation to pinion shaft. Hold companion flange and remove pinion nut. Remove companion flange and seal with puller.

Installation

1) Install seal. Align marks on flange and pinion. Install flange and new integral nut and washer. Hold companion flange and gradually tighten nut.

2) Rotate pinion occasionally and check pinion bearing preload often, until original preload is obtained. DO NOT loosen pinion nut to decrease pinion bearing preload.

FORD 8.8" & 10.25" RING GEAR (Cont.)

Fig. 5: Installing Hub Outer Bearing Cup

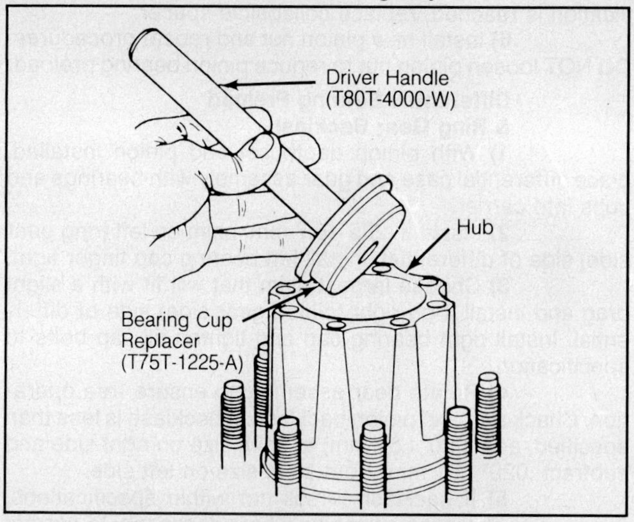

NOTE: **If desired preload is exceeded, a new collapsible spacer must be installed and nut retightened until proper preload is obtained.**

REAR AXLE ASSEMBLY

Removal

1) Raise vehicle and support with safety stands under rear crossmember. Remove housing cover and drain lubricant. Remove axle shafts as previously described.

2) Remove brake backing plates and wire plates to frame. Mark and disconnect propeller shaft at companion flange.

3) Disconnect axle vent from housing (at brake junction block on some models). Disconnect brake line from housing clips. Disconnect upper arms and shock absorbers from housing.

4) Lower housing on jack until coil springs can be removed. Disconnect lower arms from housing and remove axle housing.

Installation

To install, reverse removal procedure. Apply locking compound to threads holding axle vent and brake block (if used) to axle housing.

OVERHAUL

DISASSEMBLY

NOTE: **Differential case and drive pinion may be serviced in vehicle.**

1) Raise vehicle and support with safety stands, under rear frame crossmember. Remove housing cover and drain lubricant.

2) Mount a dial indicator, measure, and record ring gear backlash and runout. Remove rear wheel assemblies and brake drums. Remove axle shafts as previously described.

3) Place alignment marks on propeller shaft, yoke and companion flange for reassembly reference. Remove propeller shaft. Mark 1 differential bearing cap for reassembly reference and note arrow position.

4) Loosen bearing cap bolts and bearing caps. Pry differential case, bearing cups, and shims out until loose in bearing caps. Remove bearing caps and differential.

NOTE: **Bearing cups and caps must be installed in original positions.**

5) Remove pinion nut and companion flange. Drive pinion out of front bearing using soft-faced hammer. Remove pinion from rear of housing. Remove seal using slide hammer.

6) Remove front bearing. Mount bearing puller on pinion shaft and press shaft out of bearing. Remove, measure, and record thickness of shim located behind bearing.

NOTE: **Do not remove pinion bearing cups unless damaged. If cups are replaced, bearings must also be replaced.**

7) Remove differential side bearings with a puller. Mark differential case and ring gear for reassembly reference. Remove and discard ring gear mounting bolts.

8) Press or tap off ring gear. Drive out pinion shaft lock pin and shaft with a punch. Remove pinion gears, side gears and thrust washers.

CLEANING & INSPECTION

1) Clean all parts thoroughly in cleaning solvent. Examine pinion and ring gear teeth for scoring, excessive wear, nicks and chipping. Check bearing cups for deep scores, galling or spalling. Check carrier bearings for pitting, scoring and roller ends for stepping. If any components show damage, wear or scoring replace components.

2) When replacing ring gear and pinion, note original factory shim thickness to adjust for variations in both carrier casting and original gear set dimension. Variations are marked on pinion gear head and ring gear.

NOTE: **Ring and pinion gear set must be replaced in matched sets.**

REASSEMBLY

1) Lubricate all parts with rear axle lubricant. Place side gears and thrust washers into case. Place pinion gears and thrust washers exactly opposite each other in case openings, in mesh with side gears.

2) Install ring gear with new mounting bolts. If bolts are covered with Green coating over 1/2" of threaded area, install and tighten bolts. If new bolts do not have Green coating, apply small amount of locking compound to bolt threads and tighten bolts.

NOTE: **Ring gear bolts should not be reused.**

ADJUSTMENT

1) If new components have been installed, proper gear set assembly must be checked using Rear Axle Pinion Depth Gauge Kit (T79P-4020-A) to determine correct pinion shim.

2) If bearing cups have been replaced, new cone and roller assemblies should be installed. Cups must be seated in bores so a .0015" (.038 mm) feeler gauge will not fit between cup and bottom of bore.

3) Rear pinion bearing must be pressed on so it is firmly seated against spacer shim and pinion gear.

Pinion Depth

1) Assemble depth gauge and install aligning adapter, gauge disc .89" (23 mm), and gauge block screw.

Drive Axles

FORD 8.8" & 10.25" RING GEAR (Cont.)

Place rear pinion bearing over aligning disc and into bearing cup of carrier housing.

2) Install front pinion bearing into front bearing cup. Place tool handle onto screw and hand tighten. *See Fig. 6.* Make sure pinion depth measuring tool is properly installed and tightened.

Fig. 6: Installation of Pinion Depth Measuring Tools

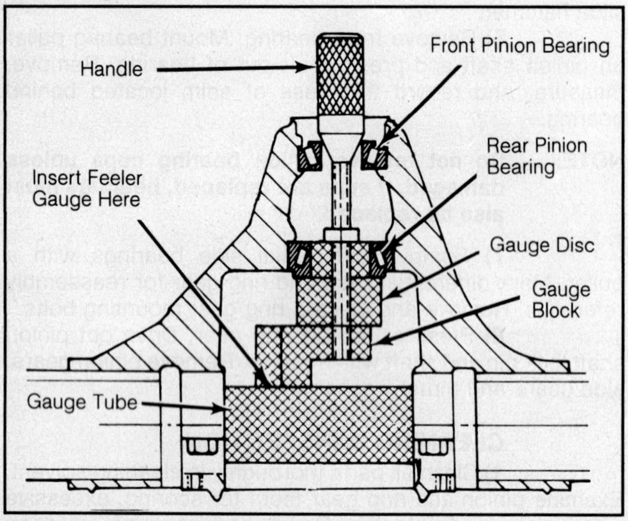

Check tool for proper installation.

3) Apply a light film of oil to pinion bearings. Rotate gauge block several times to seat bearings. Rotational torque on gauge block assembly should be 20 INCH lbs. (2.25 N.m) with new bearings.

4) Final position of gauge block should be 45° above axle shaft centerline. Clean differential bearing bores thoroughly and install gauge tube. Tighten bearing cap bolts.

5) Using flat pinion shims as a gauge for shim selection, hold gauge block in proper position and measure clearance between gauge block and tube.

6) Correct shim selection is accomplished when a slight drag is felt as shim is drawn between gauge block and tube.

Pinion Bearing Preload

1) Place pre-selected shim on pinion shaft. Press bearing onto shaft until bearing and shim are firmly seated against shoulder of shaft. Install new collapsible spacer on pinion shaft.

2) Lubricate bearings with axle lubricant. Install front pinion bearing in housing. Install new pinion oil seal. Insert companion flange into seal and hold firmly in place.

3) From rear of carrier housing, insert pinion shaft into flange. Start a new pinion nut on pinion shaft and gradually tighten pinion nut (hold flange).

4) Check bearing preload often. As soon as preload is measured, turn pinion shaft in both directions several times to seat bearings.

5) Tighten pinion nut and continue to measure pinion bearing preload until specified pinion torque is obtained. If bearing preload is exceeded before torque specification is reached, replace collapsible spacer.

6) Install new pinion nut and repeat procedures. DO NOT loosen pinion nut to reduce pinion bearing preload.

Differential Bearing Preload & Ring Gear Backlash

1) With pinion depth set and pinion installed, place differential case and gear assembly with bearings and cups into carrier.

2) Install a .265" (6.7 mm) shim on left (ring gear side) side of differential. Install left bearing cap finger tight.

3) Choose largest shim that will fit with a slight drag and install it on right (pinion gear side) side of differential. Install right bearing cap and tighten all cap bolts to specification.

4) Rotate gear assembly to ensure free operation. Check ring and pinion backlash. If backlash is less than specified, add .020" (.51 mm) to shim size on right side and subtract .020" (.51 mm) from shim size on left side.

5) If backlash is still not within specifications, increase or decrease shim size where necessary to correct reading. *See Fig. 7.*

Fig. 7: Backlash Adjustment

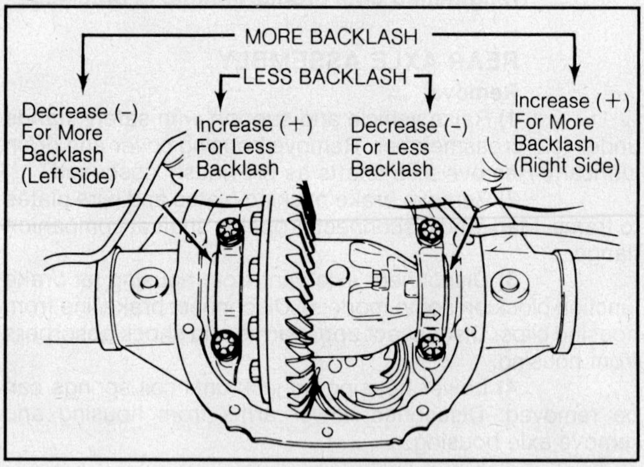

6) Retighten bearing cap bolts and rotate gear assembly several times. Recheck backlash and correct as necessary. Increase both left and right shim sizes .006" (.15 mm) and reinstall for correct preload.

7) Make sure shims are seated and gear assembly turns freely. Using marking compound, check gear tooth contact pattern.

FINAL ASSEMBLY

1) Clean differential case housing lip and apply a continuous bead of silicone sealant. Install cover and tighten bolts. Install backing plates and propeller shaft, and tighten bolts.

2) Install wheel bearings, seals, brake drums, and wheel assemblies. Fill axle with lubricant. Adjust brakes if required.

FORD 8.8" & 10.25" RING GEAR (Cont.)

BACKLASH-TO-SHIM THICKNESS CONVERSION

Required Change In Backlash In. (mm)	Change In Shim Thickness In. (mm)
.001 (.025)	.002 (.051)
.002 (.051)	.002 (.051)
.003 (.076)	.004 (.10)
.004 (.10)	.006 (.15)
.005 (.13)	.006 (.15)
.006 (.15)	.008 (.20)
.007 (.18)	.010 (.25)
.008 (.20)	.010 (.25)
.009 (.23)	.012 (.30)
.010 (.25)	.014 (.35)
.011 (.28)	.014 (.35)
.012 (.30)	.016 (.41)
.013 (.33)	.018 (.46)
.014 (.35)	.018 (.46)
.015 (.38)	.020 (.51)

Fig. 8: Measuring Ring Gear Backlash

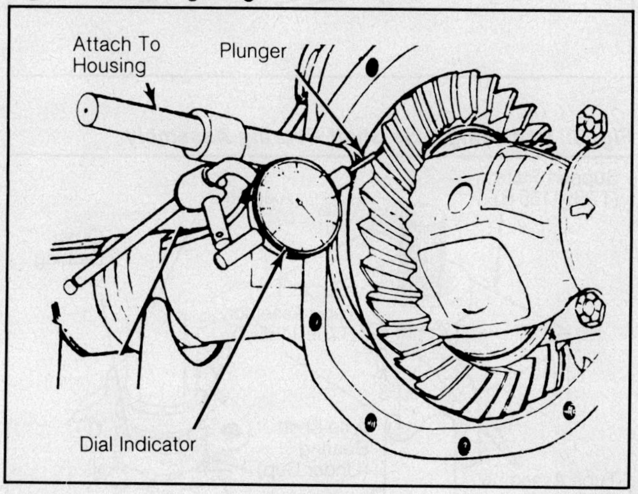

AXLE ASSEMBLY SPECIFICATIONS

Application	Specifications
Capacity	5.5 pts. (2.6L)
Ring Gear Backface Runout	.004" (1 mm)
Side Gear Thrust Washer Thickness	.030-.032" (.76-.81 mm)
Pinion Gear Thrust Washer Thickness	.030-.032" (.76-.81 mm)
Nominal Pinion Shim Thickness	.030" (.76 mm)
Ring Gear Backlash	.008-.015" (.20-38 mm)
Maximum Backlash Variation Between Teeth	.004" (1 mm)
Pinion Bearing Preload	
Original Bearings (With Oil Seal)	8-14 INCH lbs. (.9-1.6 N.m)
New Bearings	16-29 INCH lbs. (1.8-3.2 N.m)

TIGHTENING SPECIFICATIONS

Application	Ft. Lbs. (N.m)
Axle Shaft Bolts (Full-Floating)	60-80 (81-108)
Bearing Cap Bolts	
8.8"	70-85 (95-115)
10.25"	80-95 (109-129)
Hub Nut (Full-Floating)	[1] 55-60 (75-88)
Pinion Shaft Lock Bolt	15-30 (20-40)
Ring Gear Bolts	
8.8"	70-85 (95-115)
10.25"	100-120 (136-163)
Rear Cover Bolts	25-35 (34-47)
Pinion Nut (Minimum)	160 (217)

[1] – Before racheting back 5 notches.

Drive Axles

FORD 9" RING GEAR

Bronco, E150

DESCRIPTION

The axle is a banjo housing with removable carrier. Drive pinion is straddle-mounted and pinion depth is adjusted by shims. Ring gear and differential case are mounted on the removable carrier.

Preload on side bearings is set by adjusting nuts on which bearing cups rest. The removable carrier and lack of a rear cover plate help distinguish this unit from Dana (Spicer) units. It is used with semi-floating axles in all applications. Ring gear diameter is 9.0" (228.6 mm).

AXLE RATIO & IDENTIFICATION

Axle ratio and model identification numbers may be found on the metal tag, attached to axle by 1 carrier bolt. Other information on tag includes date code, ring gear diameter and assembly plant code. The information on this tag must be used to order replacement parts.

Fig. 1: Ford Drive Axle Identification Tag

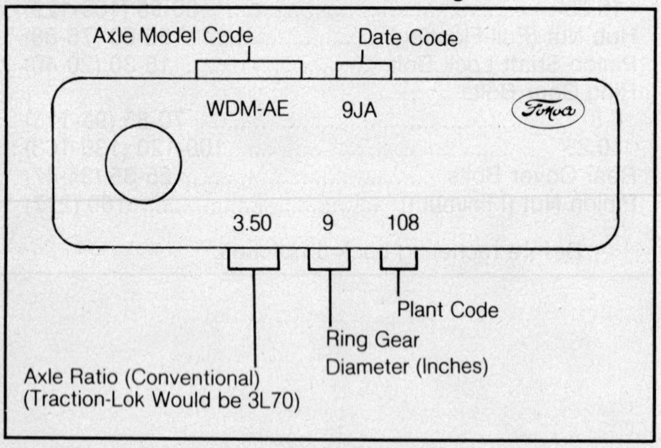

Use information on tag to order replacement parts.

REMOVAL & INSTALLATION

AXLE SHAFTS, BEARINGS & SEALS

Removal

1) Remove wheel assembly and brake drum. Working through axle shaft flange hole, remove nuts securing wheel bearing retainer plate.

2) Carefully remove axle shaft from housing using slide hammer and Axle Shaft Puller Adapter (T66L-4234-A). Remove bearing cup from axle housing using slide hammer and Bearing Cup Puller (T77F-1102-A).

3) Remove brake backing plate and wire it to frame rail. If replacing wheel bearing or seal, first remove inner retainer ring. DO NOT use heat to remove retainer ring; use the following procedure:

4) Drill a 1/4-1/2" (6-12 mm) hole about 3/8" (9.5 mm) into bearing retainer ring. *See Fig. 2.* DO NOT drill through retainer ring into axle shaft.

5) Split retainer ring with chisel positioned across drilled hole. Remove bearing cup from housing and place it over bearing.

6) Place Collet and Support Plate (T75L-1165-A, B or C) over bearing. Place axle shaft in press. Press off bearing and seal. *See Fig. 3.*

NOTE: If collet is not used, bearing must be replaced.

Fig. 2: Drilling Axle Bearing Retainer Ring

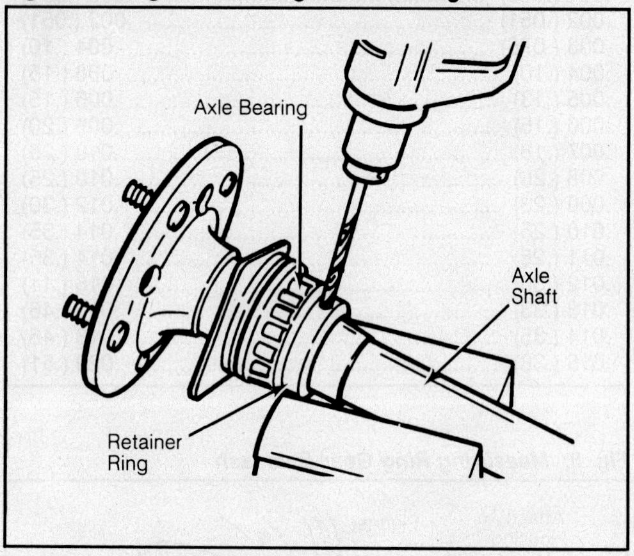

Fig. 3: Removing Axle Shaft Bearing Assembly

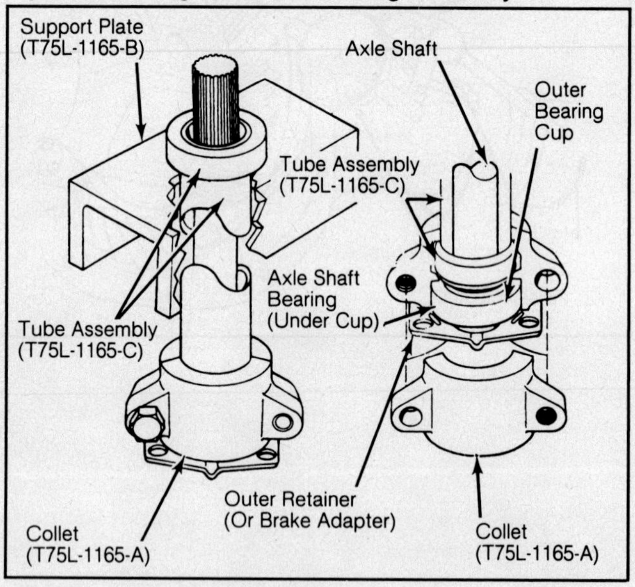

Installation

1) Install outer retainer plate (if removed), making sure it is not installed backward. Place new, lubricated seal and bearing on axle shaft, making sure cup rib ring faces axle flange.

2) Press tapered bearing and seal onto axle shaft using Support Plate and Adapter (T75L-1165-DA). Apply enough pressure to seat bearing against axle shoulder.

3) Position new bearing retainer on shaft, then press it into position firmly against bearing. Apply lubricant to outer diameter of cup and seal. Install brake backing plate and attaching bolts.

FORD 9" RING GEAR (Cont.)

Fig. 4: Exploded View of Ford Separate Housing Drive Axle

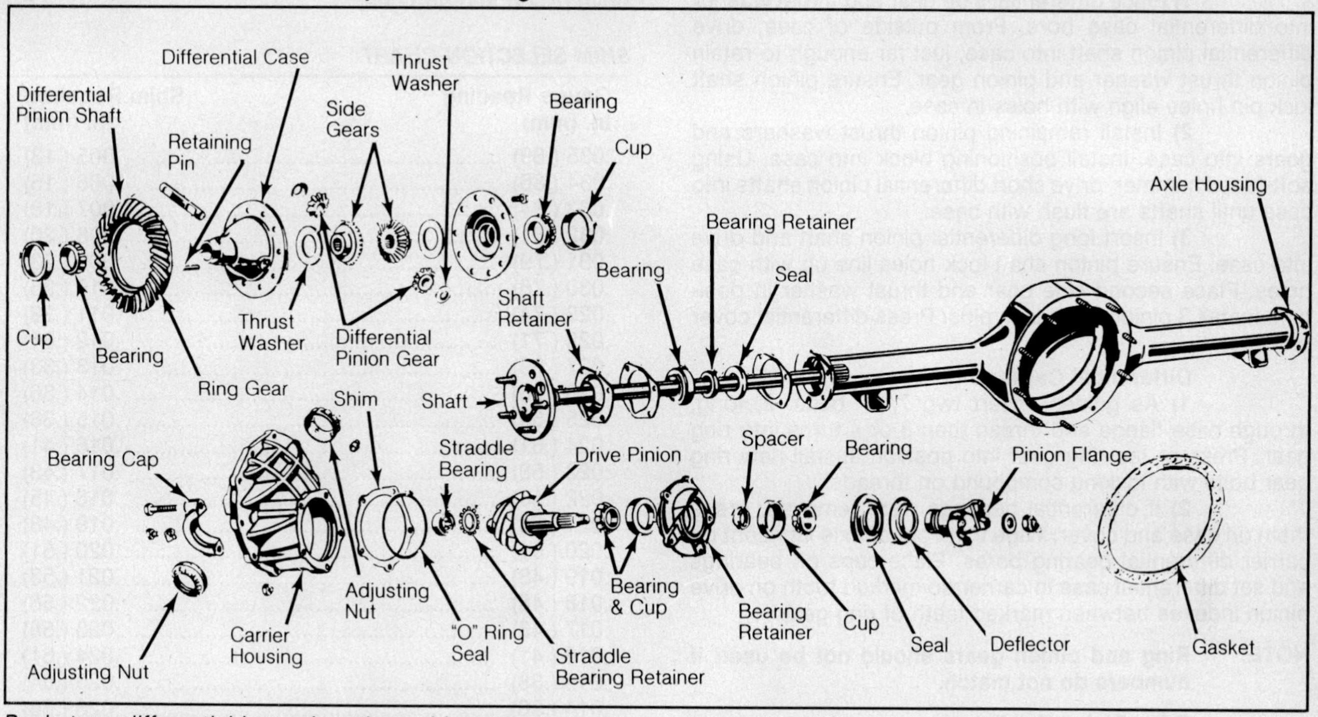

Banjo type differential is used on these drive axles.

4) Before sliding axle shaft into housing, ensure outer seal is fully mounted on bearing. Carefully slide axle shaft into housing. Start axle splines into side gear and push shaft in until bearing bottoms in housing.

5) Install bearing retainer plate and attaching nuts. Install brake drum and wheel assembly.

PINION FLANGE & SEAL

Removal

1) Mark propeller shaft end yoke and pinion flange for reassembly reference. Disconnect propeller shaft and tie it out of way. Hold cups on "U" joint spider with tape. Scribe marks on pinion shaft and pinion flange for reassembly reference.

2) Measure and record pinion bearing preload. While holding companion flange, remove pinion nut and washer. Remove companion flange using puller. Remove oil seal with slide hammer and seal remover.

Installation

1) Press new oil seal into bore in bearing retainer, and seal outer edge with oil resistant sealer. If seal becomes cocked during installation, remove it and install a new one. Install pinion flange, washer and new nut. Tighten pinion shaft nut slowly, while rotating pinion flange to ensure proper seating of pinion bearings.

2) Continue tightening nut, taking frequent preload readings. If recorded preload reading was less than specification, tighten to specifications. If recorded reading was more than specification, tighten to original reading.

3) Install drive shaft. DO NOT back off pinion nut to lessen preload. If backed off, a new spacer must be installed.

DIFFERENTIAL CARRIER

Removal & Installation

Remove both axle shafts. Mark propeller shaft end yoke and pinion flange for reassembly reference. Remove propeller shaft. Drain rear axle lubricant. Remove carrier attaching bolts and differential carrier. To install carrier, reverse removal procedure.

OVERHAUL

DISASSEMBLY

1) Mark differential bearing caps and mating bearing supports for reassembly reference. Remove adjusting nut locks, bearing caps and adjusting nuts. Lift differential case from carrier. Remove differential side bearings from case.

2) Mark differential case, cover and ring gear for reassembly. Separate differential cover from case. Remove side gear thrust washer and side gear. Using a drift, drive out 3 differential pinion shaft lock pins.

3) Using a brass drift, drive out long differential pinion shaft retaining pin. With brass drift inside case, drive out 2 short differential pinion shafts. Remove positioning block, differential pinions and thrust washers from case. Remove side gear and thrust washer from case.

4) Place a protective sleeve on pinion pilot bearing surface. Press drive pinion shaft out of pinion retainer. Then press pinion shaft out of pinion rear bearing race. Remove pilot bearing and bearing retainer using a driver.

NOTE: **Do not remove drive pinion bearing cups from retainer unless cups are worn or damaged, or if race and rollers are damaged.**

5) To remove drive pinion bearing cups, use Bearing Cup Puller (T77F-1102-A or D78P-125-B).

REASSEMBLY & ADJUSTMENT

NOTE: **Lubricate all parts with gear lubricant during assembly.**

FORD 9" RING GEAR (Cont.)

Differential Case

1) Place differential side gear and thrust washer into differential case bore. From outside of case, drive differential pinion shaft into case, just far enough to retain pinion thrust washer and pinion gear. Ensure pinion shaft lock pin holes align with holes in case.

2) Install remaining pinion thrust washers and gears into case. Install positioning block into case. Using soft-faced hammer, drive short differential pinion shafts into case until shafts are flush with case.

3) Insert long differential pinion shaft and drive into case. Ensure pinion shaft lock holes line up with case holes. Place second side gear and thrust washer in position. Install 3 pinion shaft lock pins. Press differential cover on case.

Differential Carrier

1) As guides, insert two 7/16" bolts, 2" long, through case flange and thread then 3 or 4 turns into ring gear. Press or tap ring gear into position. Install new ring gear bolts with locking compound on threads.

2) If differential bearings were removed, press them on case and cover. Wipe thin coat of axle lubricant on carrier differential bearing bores. Place cups on bearings and set differential case in carrier so marked tooth on drive pinion indexes between marked teeth of ring gear.

NOTE: **Ring and pinion gears should not be used if numbers do not match.**

Drive Pinion Depth

1) Press new pinion bearing cups into pinion retainer housing until fully seated, making sure a .0015" (.038 mm) feeler gauge cannot be inserted between bearing cup and bottom of bore.

2) Install new straddle bearing and retainer (with concave side up) in carrier. Fully seat bearing and retainer. Press rear pinion bearing onto pinion shaft.

3) Determine pinion shim thickness by performing the following steps:

- If same ring and pinion gears are being reused, install original shim pack.
- If new ring and pinion gears are being installed, use "nominal" thickness shim, and make tooth contact pattern to see if additional shims are required.

4) Adjust pinion depth using Rear Axle Pinion Depth Gauge (T79P-4020-A) as follows:

- Assemble aligning adapter and gauge disc over threaded shaft.
- Install gauge block on threaded shaft, and tighten securely.
- Insert gauge assembly and new rear pinion bearing into pinion bearing retainer assembly.
- Install front pinion bearing. Install handle on tool assembly with tapered end in front pinion bearing.

5) Install pinion bearing retainer and gauge assembly into carrier (without a pinion shim). Tighten retainer assembly mounting bolts to 30-45 ft. lbs. (41-61 N.m). Rotate gauge block so it rests against pilot boss. Install gauge tube in differential bearing bore. Install and tighten bearing cap and bolts. *See Fig. 5.*

6) Using a feeler gauge, select the thickest blade that will enter between gauge block and gauge tube. *See Fig. 5.* Insert feeler blade directly along top of gauge block to insure a correct reading. The fit should provide a slight drag.

7) Select correct shim to be inserted, by comparing feeler gauge thickness with shim requirement in SHIM SELECTION CHART. Remove assembly and install drive pinion and ring gear.

SHIM SELECTION CHART

Gauge Reading In. (mm)	Shim Required In. (mm)
.035 (.89)	.005 (.13)
.034 (.86)	.006 (.15)
.033 (.84)	.007 (.18)
.032 (.81)	.008 (.20)
.031 (.79)	.009 (.23)
.030 (.76)	.010 (.25)
.029 (.74)	.011 (.28)
.028 (.71)	.012 (.31)
.027 (.69)	.013 (.33)
.026 (.66)	.014 (.36)
.025 (.64)	.015 (.38)
.024 (.61)	.016 (.41)
.023 (.58)	.017 (.43)
.022 (.56)	.018 (.45)
.021 (.53)	.019 (.48)
.020 (.51)	.020 (.51)
.019 (.48)	.021 (.53)
.018 (.46)	.022 (.56)
.017 (.43)	.023 (.58)
.016 (.41)	.024 (.61)
.015 (.38)	.025 (.64)
.014 (.36)	.026 (.66)
.013 (.33)	.027 (.69)
.012 (.31)	.028 (.71)
.011 (.28)	.029 (.74)
.010 (.25)	.030 (.76)
.009 (.23)	.031 (.79)
.008 (.20)	.032 (.81)
.007 (.18)	.033 (.84)
.006 (.15)	.034 (.86)
.005 (.13)	.035 (.89)
.004 (.10)	.036 (.91)
.003 (.08)	.037 (.94)
.002 (.05)	.038 (.97)

Pinion Bearing Preload
(With Collapsible Preload Spacer)

1) Place new preload spacer on drive pinion shaft. Install front pinion bearing and bearing retainer. Press bearing into position, being careful not to crush spacer. Install "O" ring in groove in bearing retainer. Place selected pinion depth shim on carrier housing. Install pinion assembly and tighten bolts.

2) Install pinion flange, washer and nut. Tighten pinion flange nut to 175 ft. lbs. (238 N.m). Check pinion bearing preload.

3) Continue to tighten pinion flange nut until proper preload is obtained. Do not exceed 175 ft. lbs. (238 N.m) at this time. Do not back off nut to obtain preload. If torque on pinion shaft is less than 175 ft lbs. (238 N.m) after preload is set, a new collapsible spacer must be installed.

Backlash & Side Bearing Preload

1) With cups on differential side bearings, and differential case in carrier, slide assembly along bores until a slight amount of backlash is felt between gear teeth. Set adjusting nuts in bores so nuts just contact bearing cups. Each nut should be engaging approximately the same number of threads.

FORD 9" RING GEAR (Cont.)

Fig. 5: Measuring Ford Pinion Depth With Gauge

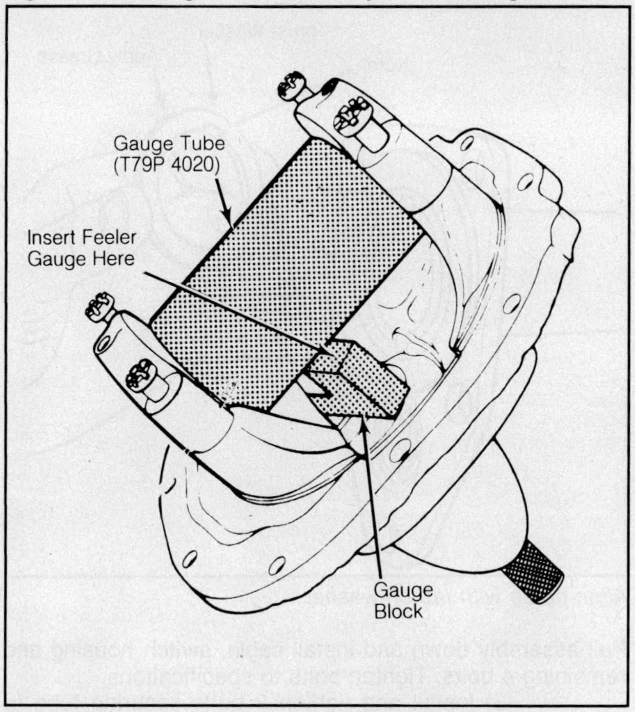

Using feeler gauge, measure pinion depth.

2) Carefully position bearing caps on carrier, install bearing cap bolts, and tighten to specifications. Make sure adjusting nuts turn freely as bolts are tightened. If not, remove caps and inspect for damaged threads. Loosen cap bolts and retorque to 25 ft. lbs. (34 N.m).

3) Loosen right adjusting nut until it is away from cup. Tighten left nut until ring gear is just forced into pinion with no backlash. Make sure right nut is still loose. Install dial indicator. *See Fig. 6.*

Fig. 6: Adjusting Side Bearing Preload

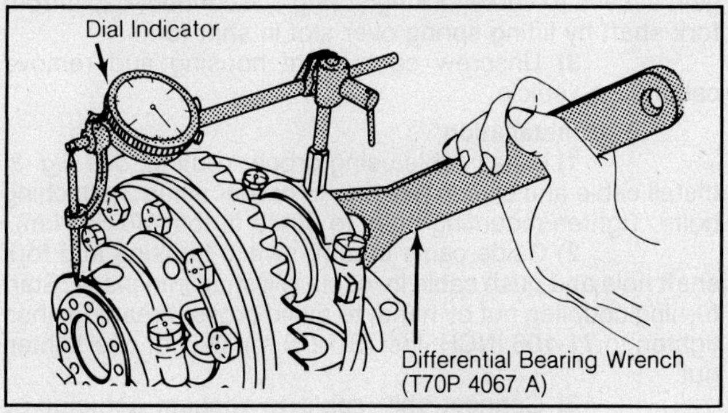

Loosen right adjusting nut, and tighten left side.

4) Tighten right nut until it first contacts bearing cup. Continue tightening until side bearing preload (case spread) is correct. Turn pinion gear several times in each direction to seat bearings and make sure no binding is evident.

5) Tighten bearing cap bolts to specifications. Install a dial indicator on carrier, so contact tip of indicator bears against face of gear tooth on outer diameter of ring gear.

6) Measure backlash at several locations on ring gear. If backlash measurements vary more than .004" (.10 mm), there is excessive runout in gear or mounting.

7) If backlash is not correct, loosen 1 adjusting nut and tighten opposite nut an equal amount. This will move ring gear into adjustment. After this procedure, always check case spread specifications.

8) When side bearing preload and ring gear backlash are correctly set, perform gear tooth pattern check, and install carrier into axle housing.

NOTE: **When moving adjusting nuts, final movement should always be made in a tightening direction. If nut must be loosened 1 notch, loosen 2 notches and then tighten 1 notch.**

AXLE ASSEMBLY SPECIFICATIONS

Application	Specifications
In. (mm)	
Ring Gear Backlash	.008-.015 (.20-.38)
Ring Gear Runout (Max.)	.004 (.10)
Backlash Variation (Max.)	.004 (.10)
Side Bearing Preload (Case Spread)	
New Bearings	.008-.012 (.20-.30)
Used Bearings	.005-.008 (.13-.20)
Side Gear Thrust	
Washer Thickness	.030-.032 (.76-.81)
Pinion Gear Thrust	
Washer Thickness	.030-.033 (.76-84)
Nominal Pinion Shim Thickness	.015 (.38)
	INCH Lbs. (N.m)
Pinion Bearing Preload (Rotating Torque)	
Collapsible Spacer	
New Bearings	8-14 (1.0-1.5)
Used Bearings	16-29 (1.8-3.3)

TIGHTENING SPECIFICATIONS

Application	Ft. Lbs. (N.m)
Side Bearing Cap Bolts	70-85 (95-115)
Ring Gear Bolts	70-85 (95-115)
Pinion Flange Nut	
Collapsible Spacer (Min.)	175 (238)
Pinion Bearing	
Retainer-to-Carrier	30-45 (41-60)
Carrier-to-Housing	25-40 (34-54)
Adjusting Nut Lock Bolts	12-25 (17-33)
Bearing Retainer Plate Bolt	20-40 (28-54)

GENERAL MOTORS "S" SERIES FRONT AXLE

"S" Series 4WD

DESCRIPTION

Chevrolet "S" series 4WD models use an independent front drive axle with an automatic engagement system. This system consists of a transfer case with a synchronized input shaft, and a front axle unit with central locking clutch and vacuum operated cable shift control.

The axle is a hypoid gear type with a split housing design. Drive axles are used with constant velocity (CV) joints. The inner CV joints use a "Tri-Pot" design, and outer CV joints are a "Double Offset" design.

To engage 4WD, transfer case is shifted into "4 HIGH" or "4 LOW", at which time front axle will automatically engage. A synchronizer in the transfer case allows shifting from 2WD to 4WD while vehicle is moving. However, shifting into or out of "4 LOW" or "NEUTRAL" must be made with vehicle stopped while pressing shift lever button.

AXLE RATIO & IDENTIFICATION

To determine drive axle ratio, see DRIVE AXLE RATIO IDENTIFICATION article in this section.

REMOVAL & INSTALLATION

For removal, installation and overhaul of drive axles, see FRONT WHEEL DRIVE AXLE SHAFTS article in this section.

TUBE & SHAFT ASSEMBLY

Removal

1) Disconnect battery ground cable. Remove shift cable from vacuum actuator by disengaging lock spring. Then push in actuator diaphragm to release cable.

2) Unlock steering wheel. Raise vehicle and place safety stands under frame. Remove front wheels, engine drive belt shield and front axle skid plate (if equipped).

3) Place a support under right lower control arm and disconnect right upper ball joint. Remove support so control arm can hang free. Disconnect right drive axle shaft from differential output shaft. Keep axle from turning by inserting a drift through opening on top of brake caliper into a vane of brake rotor.

4) Remove 4WD indicator light connection from switch. Remove 3 bolts securing cable and switch housing. Pull housing away to gain access to cable locking spring. Do not unscrew cable coupling nut unless cable is being replaced. See SHIFT CABLE Removal in this article.

5) Disconnect shift cable from shift fork shaft by lifting spring over slot in shift fork. Remove 2 bolts securing tube bracket to frame bracket and remove remaining 2 bolts securing tube assembly to carrier.

6) Remove tube assembly by working around drive axle. Do not allow sleeve, thrust washers, connector and output shaft to fall out of carrier while removing tube.

Installation

1) Install sleeve, thrust washers, connector and output shaft in carrier. Apply Loctite 514 on axle tube to differential surface. Be sure to install thrust washer with notch aligned with tab on washer. *See Fig. 1.*

2) Install tube and shaft assembly to differential and install 1 bolt at 1 o'clock position but do not tighten it.

Fig. 1: Installing Axle Tube Thrust Washer

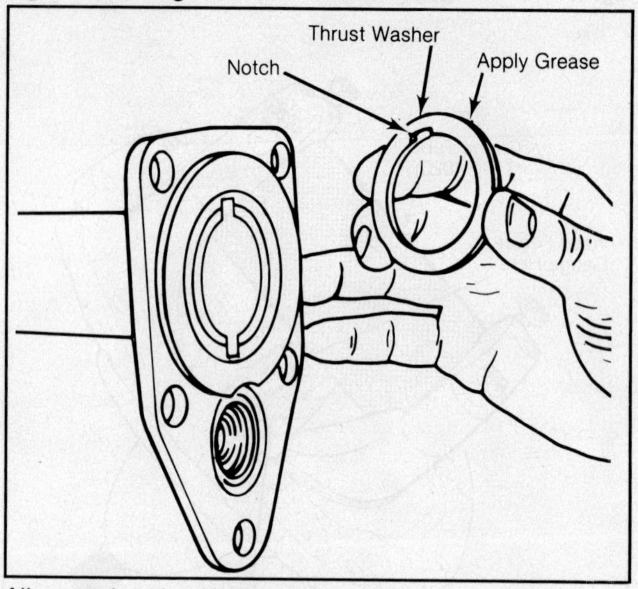

Align notch with tab on washer

Pull assembly down and install cable, switch housing and remaining 4 bolts. Tighten bolts to specifications.

3) Install and tighten 2 bolts securing tube to frame. Check shift unit operation. To complete installation, reverse removal procedure.

SHIFT CABLE

Removal

1) Disengage shift cable from vacuum actuator by disengaging locking spring, then, push actuator diaphragm in to release cable. Squeeze 2 locking fingers of cable with pliers, then pull cable out of bracket hole. *See Fig. 3.*

2) Raise vehicle and remove 3 bolts securing cable and switch housing to carrier. Pull housing away to gain access to cable locking spring. Disconnect cable from fork shaft by lifting spring over slot in shift fork.

3) Unscrew cable from housing and remove cable from vehicle.

Installation

1) Install cable using proper routing. *See Fig. 3.* Install cable and switch housing to carrier using 3 attaching bolts. Tighten mounting bolts to 30-40 ft. lbs. (40-55 N.m).

2) Guide cable though switch housing into fork shaft hole and push cable in, cable will snap into place. Start turning coupling nut by hand, to avoid cross threading, then tighten to 71-106 INCH. lbs. (8-12 N.m). Do not overtighten nut.

3) Connect shift cable to vacuum actuator by pressing cable into bracket hole. Cable and housing will snap into place. Check cable operation.

FRONT AXLE ASSEMBLY

Removal

1) Raise vehicle and place safety stands on frame. Remove wheels. Remove brake calipers and flexible hoses at brackets. Using ball joint puller, disconnect tie rods at steering knuckles.

2) Remove shock lower bolts and push shocks out of way. Remove bolts attaching drive axle to axle tube. Remove axle shaft cotter pin, nut and washer.

GENERAL MOTORS "S" SERIES FRONT AXLE (Cont.)

Fig. 2: Chevrolet 4WD "S" Series Front Axle Assembly

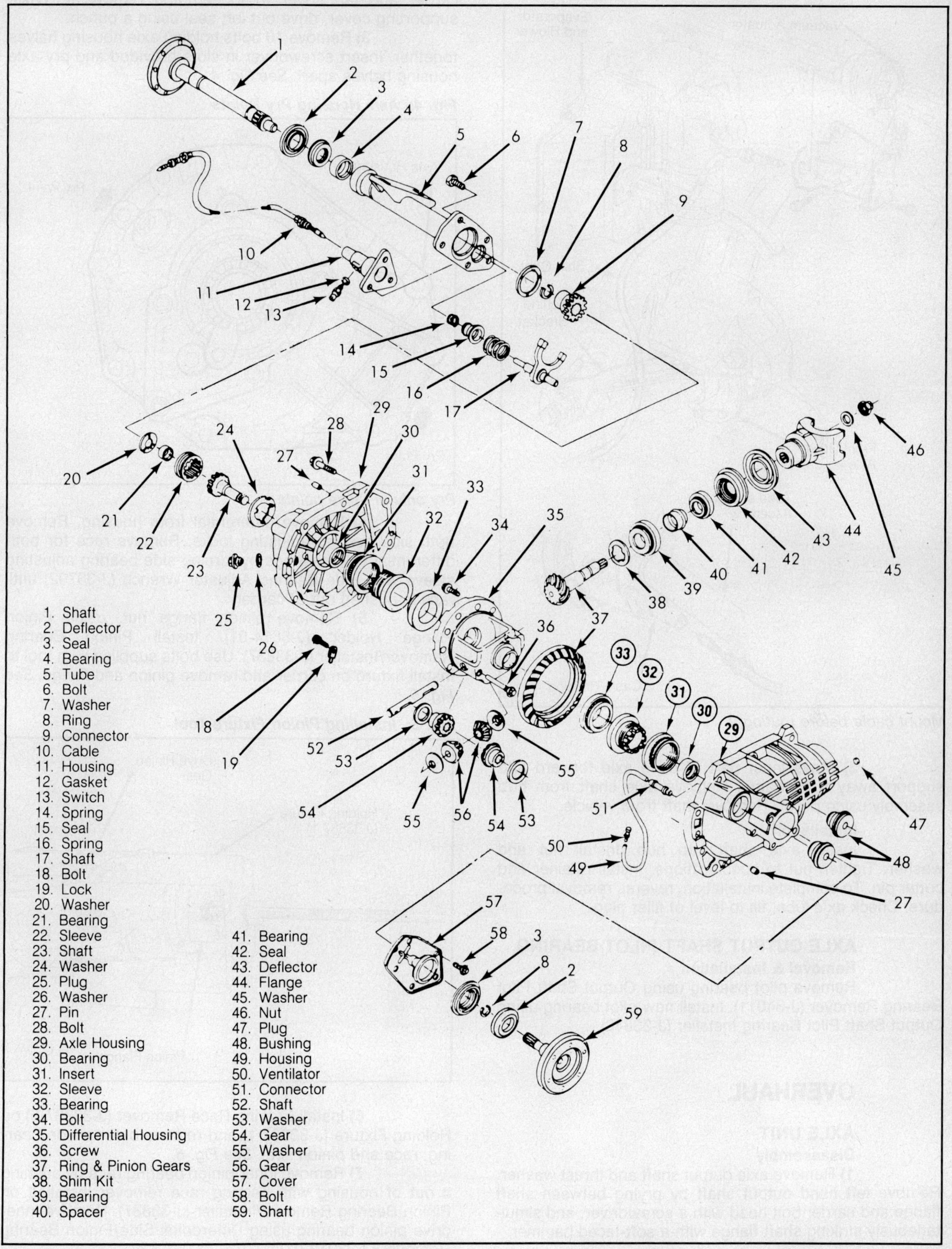

1. Shaft
2. Deflector
3. Seal
4. Bearing
5. Tube
6. Bolt
7. Washer
8. Ring
9. Connector
10. Cable
11. Housing
12. Gasket
13. Switch
14. Spring
15. Seal
16. Spring
17. Shaft
18. Bolt
19. Lock
20. Washer
21. Bearing
22. Sleeve
23. Shaft
24. Washer
25. Plug
26. Washer
27. Pin
28. Bolt
29. Axle Housing
30. Bearing
31. Insert
32. Sleeve
33. Bearing
34. Bolt
35. Differential Housing
36. Screw
37. Ring & Pinion Gears
38. Shim Kit
39. Bearing
40. Spacer
41. Bearing
42. Seal
43. Deflector
44. Flange
45. Washer
46. Nut
47. Plug
48. Bushing
49. Housing
50. Ventilator
51. Connector
52. Shaft
53. Washer
54. Gear
55. Washer
56. Gear
57. Cover
58. Bolt
59. Shaft

GENERAL MOTORS "S" SERIES FRONT AXLE (Cont.)

Fig. 3: Routing Front Axle Shift Cable

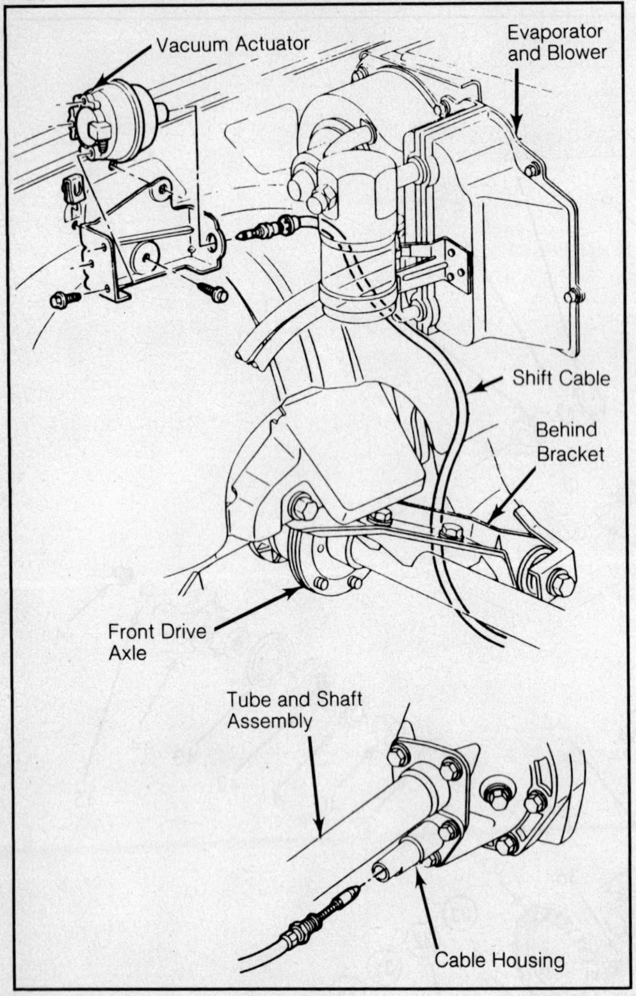

Mount cable before routing it.

3) Move inner part of drive axle forward and support away from frame. Remove axle shaft from hub assembly using puller. Remove shaft from vehicle.

Installation

Install axle shaft into hub. Install nut and washer. Tighten nut to specifications. Install retainer and cotter pin. To complete installation, reverse removal procedure. Check axle lube, fill to level of filler plug.

AXLE OUTPUT SHAFT PILOT BEARING

Removal & Installation

Remove pilot bearing using Output Shaft Pilot Bearing Remover (J-34011). Install new pilot bearing using Output Shaft Pilot Bearing Installer (J-33842).

OVERHAUL

AXLE UNIT

Disassembly

1) Remove axle output shaft and thrust washer. Remove left hand output shaft by prying between shaft flange and carrier bolt head with a screwdriver, and simultaneously striking shaft flange with a soft-faced hammer.

2) Remove 6 bolts securing left side cover-to-carrier and tap cover to loosen and remove it. While supporting cover, drive out left seal using a punch.

3) Remove 10 bolts holding axle housing halves together. Insert screwdriver in slots provided and pry axle housing halves apart. *See Fig. 4.*

Fig. 4: Axle Housing Pry Points

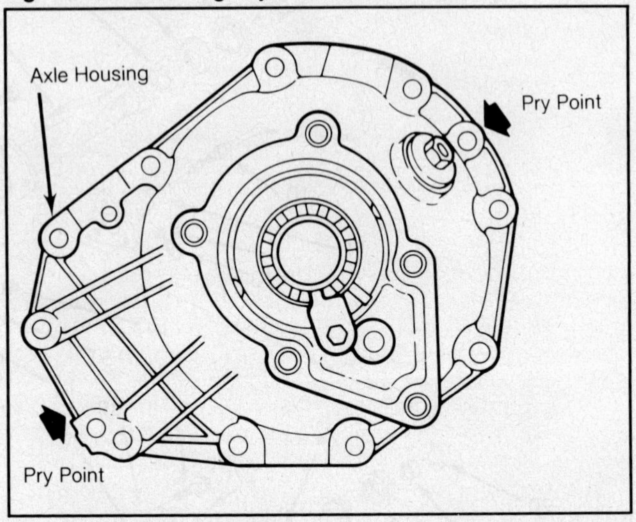

Pry only at these points.

4) Remove differential from housing. Remove both side bearing adjusting locks. Remove race for both differential side bearings by turning side bearing adjusting sleeve with Side Bearing Adjuster Wrench (J-33792) until race is pushed out of carrier.

5) Remove pinion flange nut, using Pinion Flange Holder (J-8614-01). Install Pinion Bearing Remover/Installer (J-33837). Use bolts supplied with tool to install fixture on carrier and remove pinion and flange. *See Fig. 5.*

Fig. 5: Installing Pinion Fixture Tool

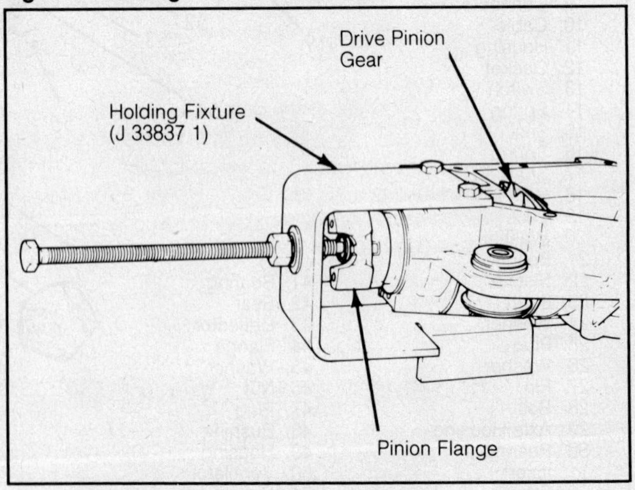

6) Install Bearing Race Remover (J-33837-6) on Holding Fixture (J-33837-1) and remove outer pinion bearing, race and pinion seal. *See Fig. 6.*

7) Remove inner pinion bearing race by pushing it out of housing with bearing race remover installed on Pinion Bearing Remover/Installer (J-33837). Remove inner drive pinion bearing using Differential Side/Pinion Bearing Remover (J-22912-01).

GENERAL MOTORS "S" SERIES FRONT AXLE (Cont.)

Fig. 6: Removing Pinion Bearing Race

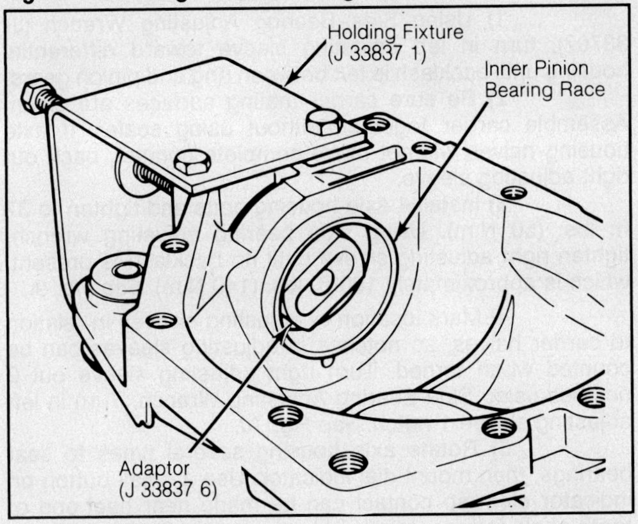

Cleaning & Inspection

1) Clean all parts in cleaning solvent. Inspect all bearings, bearing cups, races and rollers for scoring, chipping or excessive wear. Inspect axle shaft and side gear splines for excessive wear.

2) Inspect ring gear and pinion for scoring, cracking or chipping. Inspect differential case, pinion side gears, thrust washers and pinion shaft for cracks, scoring, galling or excessive wear.

Reassembly

1) Lubricate outer pinion and inner bearing races and install using Holding Fixture (J-33837-1) and Bearing Race Installer (J-33837-4) until races are seated in housing. Lubricate inner and outer bearings, then set pinion depth. See ADJUSTMENTS in this article.

2) Install inner pinion bearing on shaft using Pinion Bearing Installer (J-33785). Install new collapsible spacer on pinion shaft and position assembly in carrier. Lubricate outer pinion bearing and install in housing. *See Fig. 7.*

Fig. 7: Install Inner Bearing Race

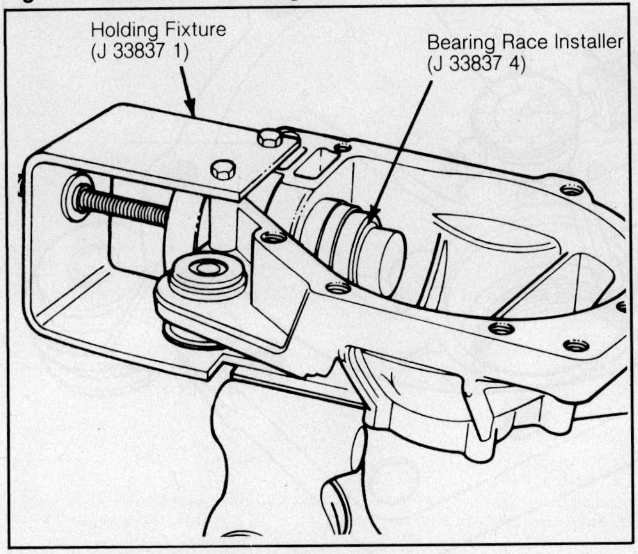

Make sure races are properly seated.

3) Lubricate pinion bearing seal with axle lube and install seal using Pinion Seal Installer (J-33782). Install pinion flange, washer and nut.

4) Install Flange Holder (J-8614-01) on pinion flange and hold flange while tightening pinion flange nut. Tighten nut until no end play is detectable. When no end play is detectable, preload specifications are being approached. No further tightening should be attempted until bearing preload has been checked.

NOTE: After preload has been checked, final tightening should be done very carefully. If preload was 5 INCH lbs. (.6 N.m), any additional tightening of pinion nut can add many additional INCH lbs. of torque. Check preload after each slight amount of tightening.

5) Rotate pinion several times to ensure bearings have been seated. Set final preload to 15-25 INCH lbs. (1.7-2.8 N.m).

6) Assemble output shaft bearings and adjusting sleeves into inserts in carrier and tighten finger tight. Install differential side bearing race into housing using Differential Side Bearing Race Installer (J-23423-A).

7) Using new output shaft bearings and adjusting sleeve inserts. Press output shaft bearings into adjusting sleeves from inner side of sleeves, using Output Shaft Bearing Installer (J-33788).

8) Install adjusting sleeve and bearing into insert and tighten finger tight. Press entire assembly into axle housing using Differential Side Bearing Race Installer (J-23423-A).

9) Install differential into housing and set backlash adjustment to specification. See ADJUSTMENTS in this article.

10) Install left differential housing seal. Support housing to prevent distorting or bending of housing. Apply gasket sealer to housing surface and install housing cover. Tighten nuts to specifications.

DIFFERENTIAL HOUSING

Disassembly

1) Remove side bearings using Differential Side/Pinion Bearing Remover (J-22912-01). Remove pinions, side gears and thrust washers from housing. Mark side gears and housing so they can be installed in their original location.

2) If ring gear is to be replaced and is tight on housing after removing (right-hand thread) bolts, drive off ring gear using a brass drift and hammer. Do not pry between ring gear and housing.

Reassembly

1) Lubricate all parts with axle lubricant. Place side gear thrust washers over side gear hubs and install side gears in housing. If using original parts, install in original positions.

2) Position a pinion (with washer) between side gears and rotate gears until pinion is directly opposite from opening in housing. Place other pinion between side gears so pinion shaft holes align. Rotate gears to make sure holes in pinions will line up with holes in housing.

3) If holes line up, rotate pinions back toward opening just enough to permit sliding in pinion thrust washers. Install 2 new bolts into opposite sides of ring gear, then install ring gear on housing. Tighten ring gear bolts.

GENERAL MOTORS "S" SERIES FRONT AXLE (Cont.)

ADJUSTMENTS

DRIVE PINION DEPTH

NOTE: **All "S" 4WD truck front wheel drive pinions are "nominal" or "zero" pinions and are not marked. Shim thickness will equal dial indicator gauge reading.**

1) Lubricate inner and outer pinion bearings liberally with axle lubricant.

2) Hold pinion bearings in position and install Pinion Shim Setting Gauge (J-33838). With gauge installed, preload inner and outer pinion bearing to 15-25 INCH lbs. (1.7-2.8 N.m) by tightening mounting bolt while holding end of gauge shaft with a wrench.

3) Using dial indicator, set reading to "0", then position dial indicator on pinion shim setting gauge. Push dial indicator downward until needle rotates approximately 3 turns clockwise. Tighten dial indicator in this position. *See Fig. 8.*

4) Set button of Pinion Shim Setting Gauge on differential bearing bore. Rotate gauge slowly back and forth until dial indicator reads lowest point of bore. Set dial indicator to "0". Repeat rocking action of gauge to verify "0" setting.

5) After "0" setting is obtained and verified, move gauge button out of differential side bearing bore. Record dial indicator reading. Use a shim that is exactly the same size as indicator reading.

6) Remove dial indicator and gauge from carrier. Position correct shim on drive pinion. Install drive pinion.

RING GEAR BACKLASH

1) Using Side Bearing Adjusting Wrench (J-33792), turn in left adjusting sleeve toward differential housing until backlash is felt between ring and pinion gears.

2) Be sure carrier mating surfaces are clean. Assemble carrier together without using sealer. If axle housing halves will not make complete contact, back out right adjusting sleeve.

3) Install 4 axle housing bolts and tighten to 37 ft. lbs. (50 N.m). Using side bearing adjusting wrench, tighten right adjusting sleeve until no backlash is present, which is approximately 100 ft. lbs. (140 N.m). *See Fig. 9.*

4) Mark location of adjusting sleeves in relation to carrier halves, so notches in adjusting sleeves can be counted when turned. Turn right adjusting sleeve out 2 notches using Side Bearing Adjusting Wrench. Turn in left adjusting sleeve 1 notch. *See Fig. 10.*

5) Rotate axle housing several times to seat bearings, then mount dial indicator. Use a small button on indicator stem so contact can be made near heel end of tooth angle for accurate backlash reading. Set backlash to specifications.

6) If backlash is not within specifications, readjust adjusting sleeves as necessary. Do not install adjusting sleeve locks at this time.

7) Mark right adjusting sleeve so it can be repositioned in same location and loosen sleeve to releave right side bearing to differential housing contact. Remove 4 axle housing bolts, and axle housing half. Apply Loctite 514 on 1 axle housing surface.

Fig. 8: Setting Pinion Shim Gauge

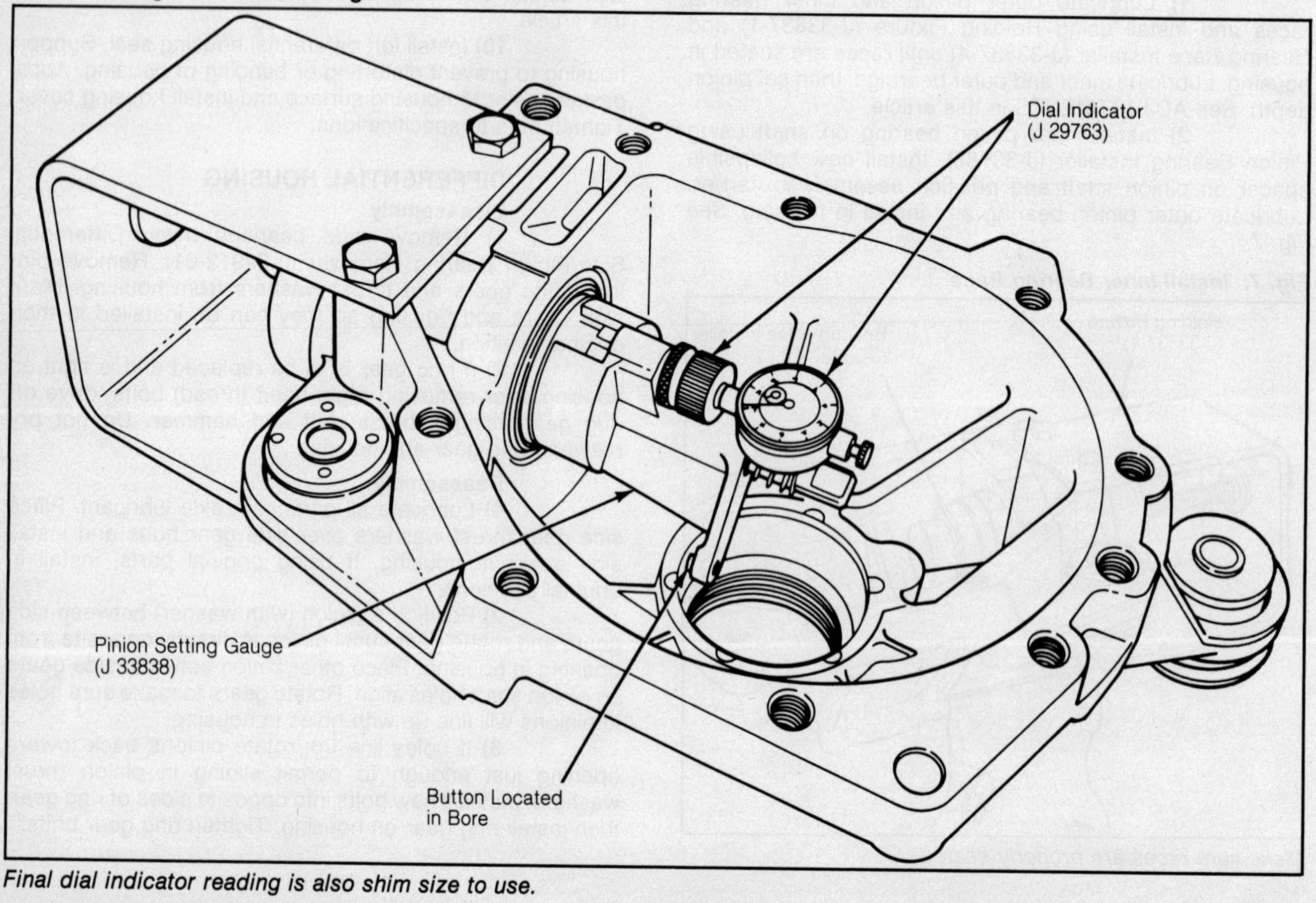

Final dial indicator reading is also shim size to use.

GENERAL MOTORS "S" SERIES FRONT AXLE (Cont.)

Fig. 9: Position of Bolts in Axle Housing

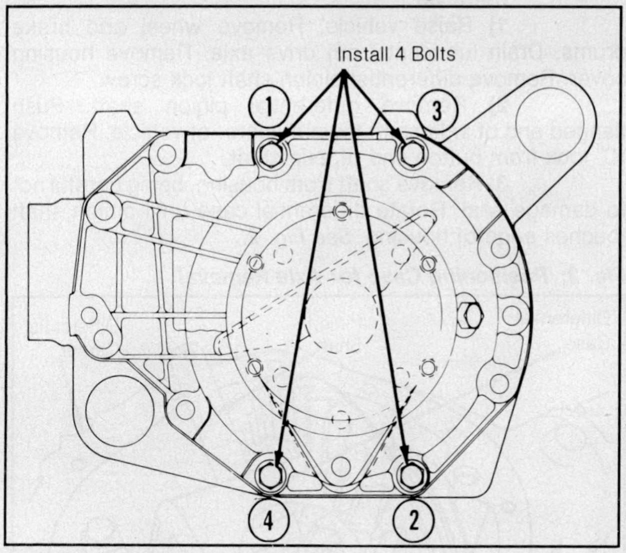

Tighten bolts to 37 ft. lbs. (50 N.m).

8) Reinstall axle housing halves and install 10 attaching bolts and tighten to specification. Reposition right adjusting sleeve in previous marked position and install both adjusting sleeve locks.

9) Perform gear tooth contact pattern check. See DRIVE AXLE GEAR TOOTH PATTERNS article in this section.

Fig. 10: Marking Adjusting Sleeve Location

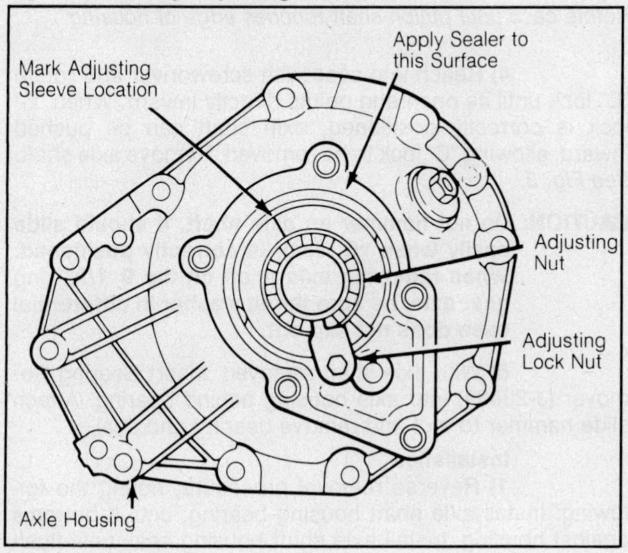

Always mark location of adjusting sleeves.

AXLE ASSEMBLY SPECIFICATIONS

Application	Specifications
Ring Gear Backlash Runout	.003" (.08 mm)
Ring Gear Backlash	.003-.010" (.08-.25 mm)
	INCH Lbs. (N.m)
Pinion Bearing Preload	15-25 (1.7-2.8)

TIGHTENING SPECIFICATIONS

Application	Ft. Lbs. (N.m)
Axle Housing	30-40 (40-55)
Axle Housing to Frame	60-74 (80-100)
Cable Switch Housing	30-40 (40-55)
Drive Axle to Output Flange	53-63 (72-85)
Ring Gear Attaching Bolts	52-66 (70-90)

GENERAL MOTORS 7 1/2", 8 1/2" & 9 1/2" RING GEARS

Chevrolet & GMC
Astro, Safari, C, K, G20: Rear Axle
K10/20: Front Axle

NOTE: **General Motors 8 1/2" ring gear drive axle is used as the front drive axle on K10/20 models. For removal and installation instructions, see articles on Locking Hubs and 4-Wheel Drive Steering Knuckles. These models may also be equipped with a Dana (Spicer) front drive axle. See appropriate article in this section.**

DESCRIPTION

Axle assembly is hypoid gear type with integral carrier housing. It is used on Light Duty emission vehicles with semi-floating and full-floating axles. Pinion bearing preload is made with a collapsible spacer. Differential side bearing preload adjustment and drive pinion depth adjustment are made by shims.

A removable housing cover permits inspection and minor servicing of differential without removing axle from vehicle. Service procedures are the same for all assemblies, except for tightening specifications and special tool numbers.

AXLE RATIO & IDENTIFICATION

General Motors uses several types of axles. The 7 1/2", 8 1/2" and 9 1/2" axles can be distinguished from others by the configuration of their housing covers and by the number of attaching bolts. To determine drive axle ratio, see DRIVE AXLE RATIO IDENTIFICATION article in this section.

Fig. 1: General Motors 7 1/2", 8 1/2" & 9 1/2" Ring Gear Housing Cover Gaskets

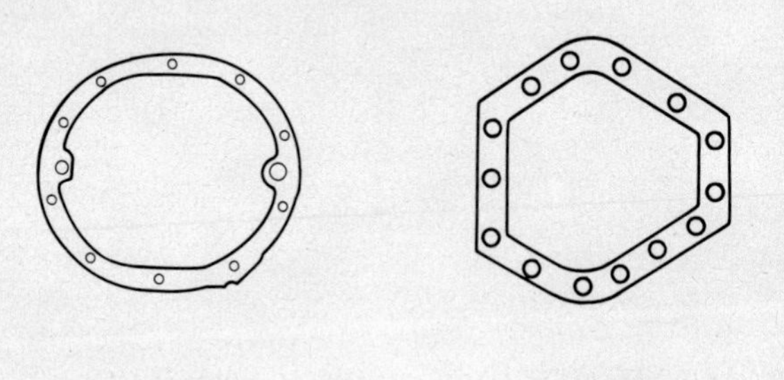

Illustration is for identification.

REMOVAL & INSTALLATION

AXLE SHAFTS & BEARINGS

NOTE: **For front axle shaft and bearing removal, see articles on Spicer (Dana) Full-Floating Axles or 4-Wheel Drive Steering Knuckles in this section.**

Semi-Floating
Removal

1) Raise vehicle. Remove wheel and brake drums. Drain lubricant from drive axle. Remove housing cover. Remove differential pinion shaft lock screw.

2) Remove differential pinion shaft. Push flanged end of axle shaft toward center of vehicle. Remove "C" lock from button end of axle shaft.

3) Remove shaft from housing, being careful not to damage seal. Rotate differential case until pinion shaft touches edge of housing. *See Fig. 2.*

Fig. 2: Positioning Case for Axle Removal

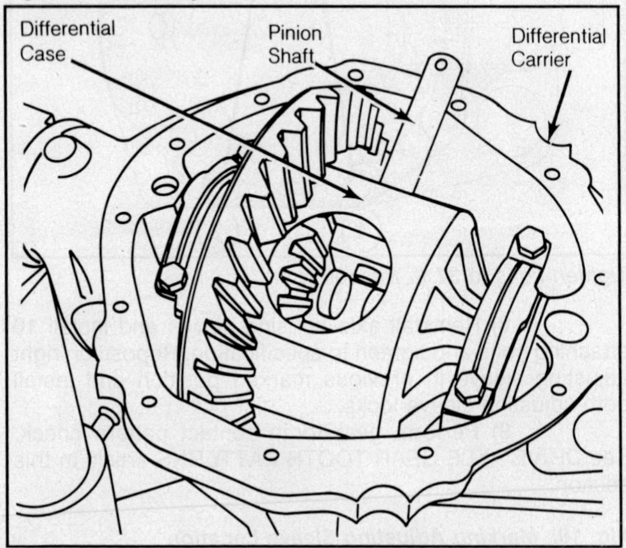

Rotate case until pinion shaft touches edge of housing.

4) Reach into case with screwdriver and rotate "C" lock until its open end points directly inward. When "C" lock is correctly positioned, axle shaft can be pushed inward, allowing "C" lock to be removed. Remove axle shaft. *See Fig. 3.*

CAUTION: **Do not hammer on axle shaft. It should slide easily when "C" lock is correctly positioned. When removing axle shaft on the 9 1/2" ring gear axle, be sure thrust washer in differential case does not slip out.**

5) With axle shaft removed, insert Bearing Remover (J-23689) into axle housing behind bearing. Attach slide hammer to tool and remove bearing and seal.

Installation

1) Reverse removal procedure, noting the following: Install axle shaft housing bearing, until it bottoms against housing. Install axle shaft housing seal, until flush with outer edge of axle tube.

2) After installing axle shaft and "C" lock, pull axle shaft outward so "C" lock seats in side gear counterbore. *See Fig. 3.*

Full-Floating
Removal

1) Remove bolts attaching axle shaft flange to wheel hub. Tap on flange with soft-faced hammer to loosen shaft. Grip rib on end of flange with locking pliers and twist to start shaft removal.

2) Remove shaft from axle tube. Thoroughly clean axle shaft flange and end of wheel hub.

GENERAL MOTORS 7 1/2", 8 1/2" & 9 1/2" RING GEARS (Cont.)

Fig. 3: Correct Positioning of "C" Lock for Removal

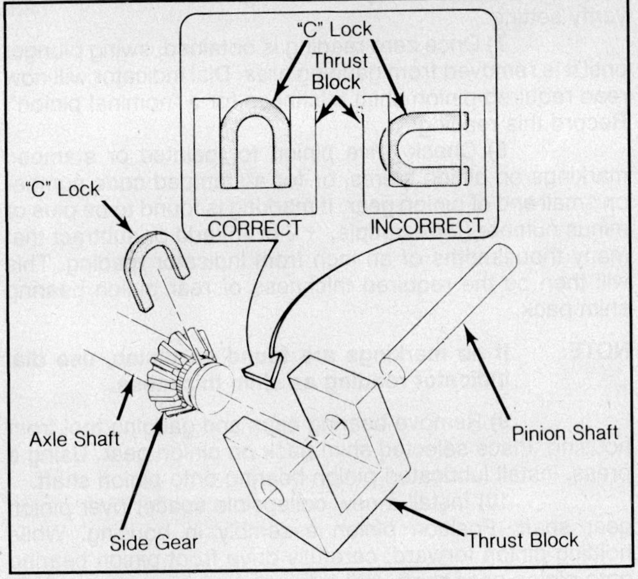

When "C" lock is correctly positioned, axle shaft can be pushed inward.

Installation

1) Use a new gasket or apply silicone sealant over axle shaft. Position axle shaft in housing so shaft splines enter differential side gear.

2) Position axle shaft so holes align and install flange-to-hub attaching bolts. Tighten bolts.

PINION FLANGE & SEAL

Removal

1) Raise vehicle and allow axle to hang free. Disconnect universal joint and tie propeller shaft out of the way.

2) Rotate pinion shaft through several revolutions, using an INCH lb. torque wrench. Note and record pinion bearing preload. Mark relationship of pinion flange and shaft for reassembly.

3) Count number of threads on pinion shaft. Hold yoke with Companion Flange Holder (J-8614-11) and remove self-locking nut. Remove yoke using a puller. Pry seal from housing.

Installation

1) Inspect pinion flange oil seal surface, drive splines, ears and bearing contact surface. Replace pinion flange if necessary.

2) Pack seal lip cavity with lithium base extreme pressure lubricant. Place seal in bore. Using Gauge Plate (J-22804-1) and Seal Driver (J-21057), drive seal into place. Make sure seal is square in carrier. Pack cavity between end of pinion splines and pinion flange with a non-hardening sealer.

3) Using Companion Flange Holder (J-8614-11), install flange on pinion shaft. Install washer and nut in original position, taking note of scribe marks and number of exposed threads. Measure pinion preload. Tighten nut in small increments, until preload exceeds original figure by 1-5 INCH lbs. (.1-.6 N.m). Install propeller shaft and lower vehicle.

CAUTION: Do not hammer flange onto pinion shaft, as ring gear and pinion will be damaged.

AXLE ASSEMBLY

Removal

1) Raise vehicle. Raise axle until tension is released from springs and shock absorbers. Disconnect propeller shaft from flange. Tie propeller shaft out of way.

2) Disconnect shock absorbers at lower mounts. Disconnect vent hose from vent connector. Disconnect and plug brake hose at connector on axle housing.

3) Remove rear brake drums. Disconnect parking brake cable at actuating levers and at flange plate. Remove "U" bolt nuts, washers, spacers and clamp plates. Lower axle assembly and remove from vehicle.

Installation

To install axle assembly, reverse removal procedure. Bleed brake system.

OVERHAUL

DISASSEMBLY

NOTE: Check and record ring gear backlash and pinion bearing preload before disassembly.

1) Remove lock screws retaining pinion shaft and remove pinion shaft. Remove axle shafts, and roll out differential pinions and thrust washers. Mark pinions and thrust washers for reassembly. Remove side gears and thrust washers. Mark side gears and thrust washers for reassembly.

2) Mark differential bearing caps and housing for reassembly. Loosen bearing cap bolts, and tap bearing cap surfaces to loosen caps. Using pry bar inserted in differential carrier, pry against housing to remove carrier.

NOTE: Be careful, as carrier bearings are preloaded. Carrier will fall free after being pried past a certain point.

3) After removing carrier, place bearing cups with appropriate shims. Install bearing caps onto housing in their original position before removal. Using Differential Side Bearing Remover (J-22888 & J-8107-2 for 7 1/2" ring gears, J-8107-4 for 8 1/2" & J-8107-3 for 9 1/2" ring gear), remove differential side bearings.

NOTE: Ring gear bolts on 7 1/2" axles have left-hand threads.

4) Remove ring gear bolts. Tap ring gear off carrier using a soft drift and hammer. Using an INCH lb. torque wrench, check torque required to rotate drive pinion. If no preload reading is obtained, check for looseness of pinion assembly. Looseness indicates pinion bearings should be replaced.

5) Install Companion Flange Holder (J-8614-11) on flange with holder notches toward flange. Remove pinion nut and washer, and remove flange. Install pinion nut halfway on pinion. Install differential cover using 2 bolts. Tap end of pinion, using soft drift and large hammer to remove pinion.

NOTE: Do not damage pinion bearings when removing pinion from differential housing.

6) Remove differential cover and pinion assembly. Remove pinion oil seal and front bearing from housing. Inspect bearings and bearing cups, and replace them as required. Discard oil seal, pinion nut and collapsible spacer.

GENERAL MOTORS 7 1/2", 8 1/2" & 9 1/2" RING GEARS (Cont.)

CLEANING & INSPECTION

1) Clean all parts in cleaning solvent. Inspect all bearings, bearing cups, races and rollers for scoring, chipping or excessive wear. Inspect axle shaft and side gear splines for excessive wear.

2) Inspect ring gear and pinion for scoring, cracking or chipping. Inspect differential case, pinion side gears, thrust washers and pinion shaft for cracks, scoring, galling or excessive wear.

REASSEMBLY & ADJUSTMENT

Case Assembly

Using guide pins if necessary, install ring gear squarely onto case. Tighten ring gear bolts evenly and alternately. Install side gears, differential pinions and thrust washers into case. Install differential pinion shaft and lock screw. Tighten lock screw finger tight.

Drive Pinion Depth & Bearing Preload

1) Drive pinion rear bearing shim thickness must be determined whenever a new axle housing, ring and pinion set, or pinion bearings are installed. Shim pack thickness is determined by using Pinion Setting Gauge Set (J-21777).

2) If removed, install pinion bearing cups into housing. Place lubricated pinion bearings into cups. Position Gauge Plate (J-23597-11 for 7 1/2"; J-21777-29 for 8 1/2"; or J-21777-85 for 9 1/2" ring gear) and rear pinion bearing pilot on preloaded stud.

3) Install through rear pinion bearing, front pinion bearings and Front Pinion Bearing Pilot (J-21777-42). Install hex nut until snug. Rotate bearings to insure proper seating. Hold preload stud stationary with a wrench on flats. Tighten hex nut until 20 INCH lbs. (2.2 N.m) are required to rotate bearings. *See Fig. 4.*

Fig. 4: Sectional View of Pinion Setting Gauge Set

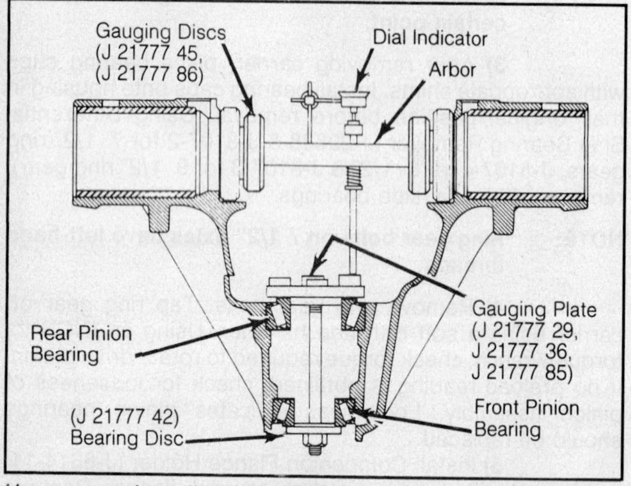

Use appropriate discs and plates with each differential.

4) Mount Side Bearing Gauging Discs (J-21777-45) on ends of arbor. Place arbor into carrier making sure discs are properly seated. Install side bearing caps and bolts. Tighten bolts to avoid movement.

5) Position dial indicator on mounting post of arbor, with contact button resting on top surface of plunger. Preload dial indicator 1/2 revolution, then tighten in this position.

6) Place plunger onto gauging area of gauge plate. Rock plunger rod slowly back and forth across gauging area until dial indicator reads greatest deflection. Set indicator to zero. Repeat rocking action several times to verify setting.

7) Once zero reading is obtained, swing plunger until it is removed from gauging area. Dial indicator will now read required pinion shim thickness for a "nominal pinion". Record this reading.

8) Check drive pinion for painted or stamped markings on pinion stems, or for a stamped code number on small end of pinion gear. If marking is found to be plus or minus number (for example, +2 or -5) add or subtract that many thousandths of an inch from indicator reading. This will then be the required thickness of rear pinion bearing shim pack.

NOTE: **If no markings are found on pinion, use dial indicator reading as shim thickness.**

9) Remove bearing caps and gauging tool from housing. Place selected shim pack on pinion gear. Using a press, install lubricated pinion bearing onto pinion shaft.

10) Install a new collapsible spacer over pinion gear shaft. Position pinion assembly in housing. While holding pinion forward, carefully drive front pinion bearing onto pinion gear shaft until a few threads are exposed.

11) Install seal, pinion flange, washer and nut. Tighten until all end play is removed. Rotate pinion several times to seat bearings. Check preload using an INCH lb. torque wrench.

12) Continue tightening nut, and checking preload until specified preload is obtained. Do not back off nut to lessen preload. If preload is exceeded, a new collapsible spacer must be installed, and nut must be retightened until proper preload is obtained.

Side Bearing Preload

1) Lubricate bearings, and place differential assembly into position in housing. Hold in place by hand.

2) Install Bearing Strap (J-22779-6) on left bearing. Tighten bolts evenly to a snug fit. Install right bearing cap. Tighten bolts to a snug fit.

3) Position ring gear tight against pinion, so backlash is .000-.001" (0-.025 mm). Insert Gauge Tool (J-22779) between left bearing cup and carrier housing.

4) While moving tool up and down, tighten adjusting nut until a slight drag is felt. Tighten lock bolt on side of tool.

5) Install .170" (4.32 mm) adjustment spacer and shim between right bearing and carrier. Insert a feeler gauge, thick enough to create a slight drag, between shim and carrier.

6) To determine correct side bearing shim thickness, measure thickness of adjusted gauging tool. Record measurement. Add together dimensions of shim, spacer and feeler gauge. Record measurement.

7) Subtract .010" (.25 mm) from ring gear (left) side measurement and add .010" (.25 mm) to opposite (right) side measurement. This allows for correct backlash adjustment.

8) To obtain correct preload, add .004" (10 mm) to both measurements. The total is the correct shim pack thickness for each side.

Example:

Ring Gear Side (Left) Shim Pack
.250" (Gauging Tool Measurement) -
-.010" (Backlash Adjustment)

GENERAL MOTORS 7 1/2", 8 1/2" & 9 1/2" RING GEARS (Cont.)

+.004" (Bearing Preload)
=.244" (Ring Gear Side Shim Pack)

Opposite Ring Gear Side (Right) Shim Pack
.265" (Combined Measurement Total)
+.010" (Backlash Adjustment)
+.004" (Bearing Preload)
=.279" (Opposite Ring Gear Side Shim Pack)

9) Install ring gear side shim first. Wedge opposite side shim between bearing cup and spacer. Install shim so chamfered side is against spacer.

NOTE: If shim is not chamfered enough and scrapes spacer when it is installed, file or grind chamfer before installation.

10) It may be necessary to partially remove differential when right side shim is installed. Tap shim into place with a soft-faced hammer. Tighten bearing cap bolts to specifications.

Backlash & Final Assembly

1) Check backlash at 4 locations around ring gear, using a dial indicator mounted to axle housing. Variation should not exceed .001" (.025 mm). If backlash is incorrect, adjust side bearing shims as necessary.

CAUTION: Total shim pack thickness must not be changed. If a shim is removed from one side, the same thickness shim must be added to the other side.

2) After adjustment is completed, make a tooth contact pattern test, and make any necessary corrections. Install axle shafts and housing cover.

AXLE ASSEMBLY SPECIFICATIONS

Application	Specifications In. (mm)
Ring Gear Backlash	.005-.008 (.13-.20)
Side Bearing Preload	.008 (.20)
	INCH Lbs. (N.m)
Pinion Bearing Preload	
7 1/2" Ring Gear	
Used Bearings	8-12 (1.0-1.4)
New Bearings	24-32 (2.7-3.6)
8 1/2" Ring Gear	
Used Bearings	5-10 (.6-1.13)
New Bearings	15-30 (1.7-3.4)
9 1/2" Ring Gear	
Used Bearings	5-15 (.6-1.7)
New Bearings	20-25 (2.3-2.8)

TIGHTENING SPECIFICATIONS

Application	Ft. Lbs. (N.m)
Differential Bearing Adjusting Lock	
9 1/2" Ring Gear	20 (27)
Ring Gear-to-Differential Case	
7 1/2" Ring Gear	[1] 90 (120)
8 1/2" Ring Gear	80 (109)
9 1/2" Ring Gear	110 (150)
Side Bearing Cap	
8 1/2" Ring Gear	55 (75)
9 1/2" Ring Gear	65 (88)

[1] - Left-hand thread. Use new bolts.

Fig. 5: Exploded View of General Motors 8 1/2" & 9 1/2" Ring Gear Axle Assembly

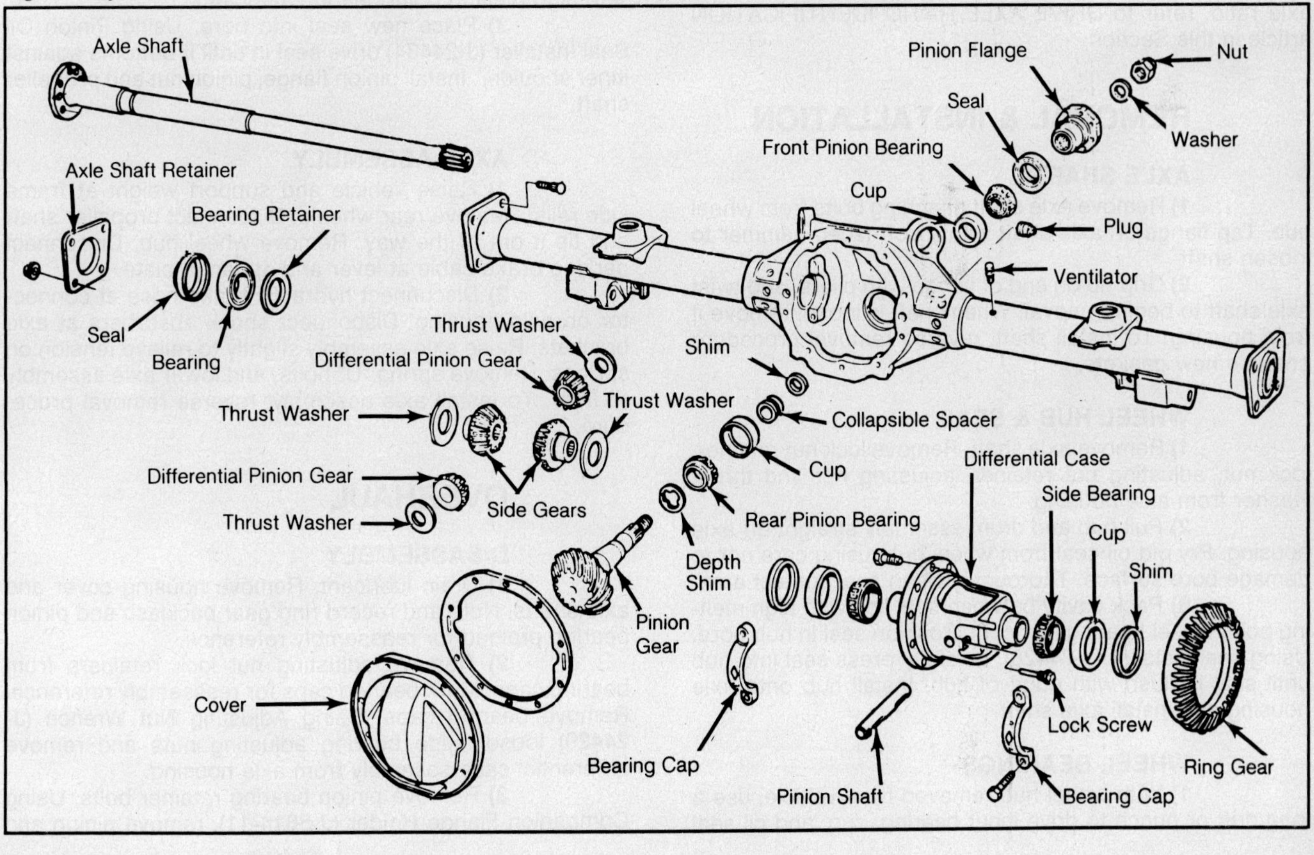

GENERAL MOTORS 10 1/2" RING GEAR

Chevrolet & GMC, Rear Axle C20/30 Models, G30 Models, K20/30 Models, P20/30 Models

NOTE: Vehicle series numbers used in this article have been abbreviated for common reference to Chevrolet and GMC models. Chevrolet models use numerical designations as listed; GMC models are identified as follows: 10 = 1500; 20 = 2500; 30 = 3500.

NOTE: The 10 1/2" ring gear is not used on vehicles with dual rear wheels. Some models may use Spicer (Dana) axles. See appropriate articles in this section.

DESCRIPTION

The axle assembly is the hypoid gear type with integral carrier housing. It is used with full floating axles.

The drive pinion bearing preload adjustment is made with a collapsible spacer. The differential side bearing preload adjustment and the drive pinion depth adjustment are made by side bearing adjusting nuts.

A removable 14-bolt housing cover permits inspection and minor servicing of differential without removal from vehicle.

AXLE RATIO & IDENTIFICATION

General Motors uses several types of axles in its vehicles. The 10 1/2" ring gear axle can be distinguished from the others by the configuration of its housing cover and by the number of attaching bolts. To determine drive axle ratio, refer to DRIVE AXLE RATIO IDENTIFICATION article in this Section.

REMOVAL & INSTALLATION

AXLE SHAFTS

1) Remove axle shaft attaching bolts from wheel hub. Tap flange on axle shaft with a soft-faced hammer to loosen shaft.

2) Grip rib on end of flange with pliers, and twist axle shaft to begin removal. When shaft is loose, remove it from housing. To install shaft, reverse removal procedure and use new gaskets.

WHEEL HUB & SEAL

1) Remove axle shaft. Remove lock nut retainer, lock nut, adjusting nut retainer, adjusting nut and thrust washer from axle housing.

2) Pull hub and drum assembly straight off axle housing. Pry old oil seal from wheel hub, using care not to damage bore surface. Thoroughly clean seal contact area.

3) Pack cavity between seal lips with high melting point wheel bearing lubricant. Position seal in hub bore. Using seal installer (J-24428), carefully press seal into hub until seal is flush with edge of hub. Install hub onto axle housing and install axle shaft.

WHEEL BEARINGS

1) With wheel hub removed from vehicle, use a long drift or punch to drive inner bearing, cup, and oil seal from hub. Remove outer bearing retaining ring. Drive outer bearing out of hub, using Outer Wheel Bearing Cup Tool (J-24426).

CAUTION: Inner bearing cup and outer bearing retaining ring must be removed before attempting to remove outer bearing cup.

2) Place outer bearing assembly into hub. Using Outer Wheel Bearing Cup Installer (J-8608), drive bearing past retaining ring groove in hub.

NOTE: Be sure chamfer of bearing cup installer (J-8608) does not contact bearing cup.

3) Install outer bearing retaining ring, and drive outer bearing cup back against ring until seated. Place inner bearing cup into hub.

4) Using Inner Wheel Bearing Cup Installer (J-24427), drive cup into hub until seated against shoulder. Install new oil seal with Wheel Hub Oil Seal Installer (J-24428). Place hub assembly onto axle housing.

5) Using Wheel Bearing Nut Wrench (J-2222-02) install adjusting nut, and tighten it to 50 ft. lbs. (70 N.m) while rotating hub assembly. Make sure bearing cones are seated and in contact with spindle shoulder. Back off nut until loose.

PINION FLANGE & SEAL

1) Disconnect propeller shaft, and tie it out of the way. For reassembly reference, scribe a line down pinion stem and pinion flange.

2) Using Companion Flange Holder (J-8614-11) remove pinion nut and pull pinion flange from stem. Pry oil seal from bore, using care not to damage machined surfaces. Clean area thoroughly. Pack cavity between seal lips with high melting point bearing lubricant.

3) Place new seal into bore. Using Pinion Oil Seal Installer (J-24434) drive seal in until it bottoms against inner shoulder. Install pinion flange, pinion nut and propeller shaft.

AXLE ASSEMBLY

1) Raise vehicle and support weight at frame side rails. Remove rear wheels. Disconnect propeller shaft and tie it out of the way. Remove wheel hub. Disconnect parking brake cable at lever and at flange plate.

2) Disconnect hydraulic brake hose at connector on axle housing. Disconnect shock absorbers at axle brackets. Raise axle assembly slightly to relieve tension on springs. Remove spring "U" bolts, and lower axle assembly to floor. To install axle assembly, reverse removal procedure.

OVERHAUL

DISASSEMBLY

1) Drain lubricant. Remove housing cover and axle shafts. Note and record ring gear backlash and pinion bearing preload for reassembly reference.

2) Remove adjusting nut lock retainers from bearing caps. Mark bearing caps for reassembly reference. Remove bearing caps. Using Adjusting Nut Wrench (J-24429) loosen side bearing adjusting nuts and remove differential case assembly from axle housing.

3) Remove pinion bearing retainer bolts. Using Companion Flange Holder (J-8614-11), remove pinion and

GENERAL MOTORS 10 1/2" RING GEAR (Cont.)

Fig. 1: Removing Pinion Nut

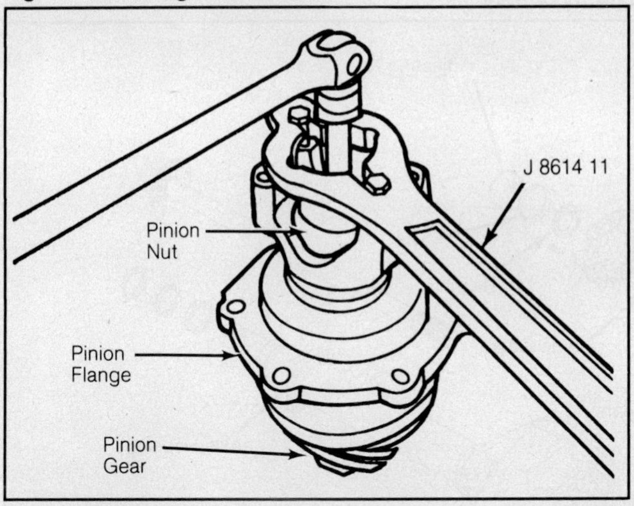

Discard pinion nut

bearing retainer assembly. *See Fig. 1.* Note and record number and thickness of shims removed. Using Companion Flange Holder Set (J-8614-3, J-8614-2 and J-8614-11), remove pinion flange and press pinion gear out of bearing retainer. *See Fig. 2.*

4) Press rear pinion bearing from gear. Drive front and rear pinion bearing cups and pinion oil seal from bearing retainer. Drive pinion straddle bearing from axle housing.

5) Mark differential case halves for reassembly reference. Remove ring gear bolts and ring gear. Split case halves. Remove side gears, differential spider, differential pinion gears and thrust washers.

Fig. 2: Removing Pinion Flange

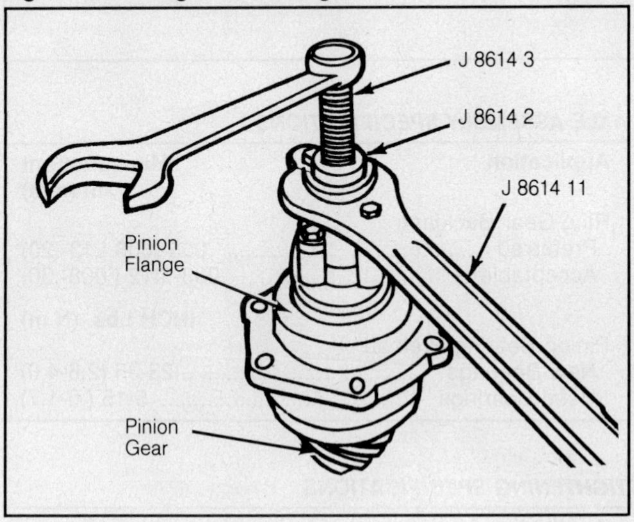

CLEANING & INSPECTION

1) Clean all parts in cleaning solvent. Inspect all bearings, bearing cups, races and rollers for scoring, chipping or excessive wear. Inspect axle shaft and side gear splines for excessive wear.

2) Inspect ring gear and pinion for scoring, cracking or chipping. Inspect differential case, pinion side gears, thrust washers and pinion shaft for cracks, scoring, galling or excessive wear.

REASSEMBLY & ADJUSTMENT

Case Assembly

1) Lubricate differential pinion gears, side gears and thrust washers with hypoid gear oil. Place pinion gears and thrust washers on differential spider. Install side gears and spider assembly into left half of differential case.

2) Assemble both halves of case, making sure alignment marks on both halves are together. Install 2 guide pins in ring gear, directly opposite each other.

3) Start guide pins through holes in case flange, and tap ring gear lightly with soft-faced hammer until ring gear attaching bolts can be started. Tighten bolts evenly until ring gear is flush with case flange. Remove guide pins and tighten all ring gear bolts alternately and evenly.

Pinion Depth & Bearing Preload

1) With pinion bearing retainer mounted in vise, install pinion gear and bearing assembly into retainer. Place pinion flange on gear stem. Install new pinion nut, and tighten nut in small increments until specified pinion bearing preload is obtained.

2) If original ring and pinion gears are to be reinstalled, use new pinion shims of same number and thickness as those removed.

3) If new gears are to be installed, compare pinion depth code number of new pinion gear with that of original pinion gear. From these 2 codes, determine correction factor by referring to Pinion Depth Code chart.

4) Combine correction factor with thickness of new shim pack. Place new shim pack onto carrier housing, and install pinion bearing retainer assembly. Tighten retainer bolts in a crosswise sequence.

Backlash & Final Assembly

1) Place lubricated bearing cups onto differential side bearings and place differential assembly into carrier. Install bearing caps in their original positions, and tighten cap bolts until just snug.

2) Loosen right side bearing adjusting nut, and tighten left side adjusting nut until zero backlash is obtained. Back off left adjusting nut 2 slots to a locking position.

3) Tighten right adjusting nut until case is in firm contact with left adjusting nut. Loosen right adjusting nut until it is free of bearing. Retighten nut until it just contacts bearing. Tighten right adjusting nut additional 2 slots (used bearings) or 3 slots (new bearings) to properly preload differential side bearings.

4) Using a dial indicator, measure ring gear backlash in at least 4 locations around ring gear. Adjust to specifications by moving adjusting nuts in or out as necessary. If 1 adjusting nut is loosened, the other nut must be tightened an equal amount to maintain side bearing preload.

5) With backlash adjustment complete, install adjusting nut lock fingers into slots in nuts, and attach fingers to bearing caps. Tighten bearing cap bolts, and perform gear tooth contact pattern check. Install axle housing cover.

Drive Axles

GENERAL MOTORS 10 1/2" RING GEAR (Cont.)

Fig. 3: Exploded View of Chevrolet & GMC 10 1/2" Ring Gear Axle Assembly

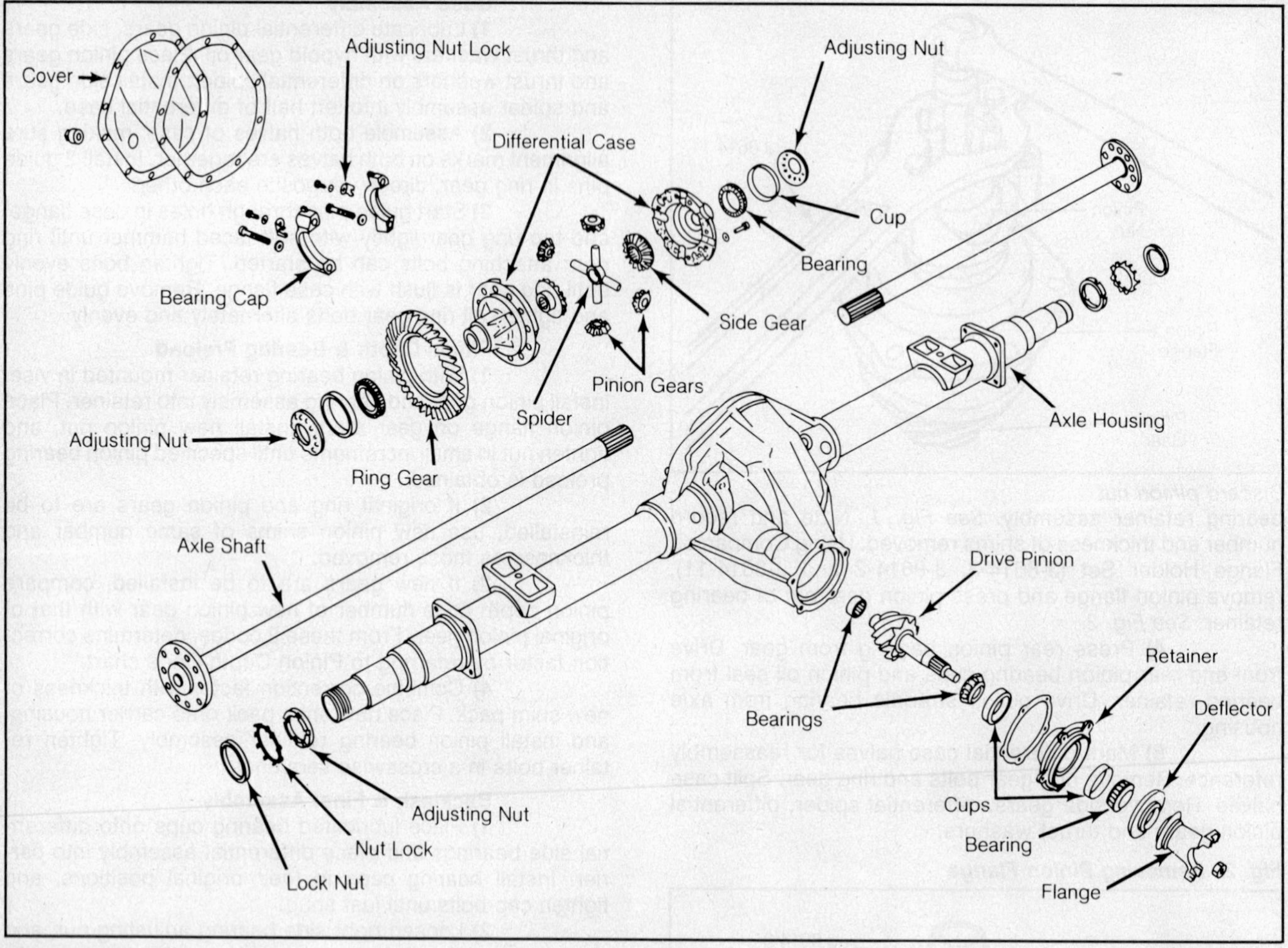

PINION DEPTH CODES

Original Code	Service Code	Correction In. (mm)
+2	+2	0 (0)
+2	+1	-.001 (-.025)
+2	0	-.002 (-.005)
+2	-1	-.003 (-.008)
+2	-2	-.004 (-.10)
+1	+2	+.001 (+.025)
+1	+1	0 (0)
+1	0	-.001 (-.025)
+1	-1	-.002 (-.005)
+1	-2	-.003 (-.008)
0	+2	+.002 (+.005)
0	+1	+.001 (+.025)
0	0	0 (0)
0	-1	-.001 (-.025)
0	-2	-.002 (-.005)
-1	+2	+.003 (+.008)
-1	+1	+.002 (+.005)
-1	0	+.001 (+.025)
-1	-1	0 (0)
-1	-2	-.001 (-.025)
-2	+2	+.004 (+.10)
-2	+1	+.003 (+.008)
-2	0	+.002 (+.005)
-2	-1	+.001 (+.025)
-2	-2	0 (0)

AXLE ASSEMBLY SPECIFICATIONS

Application	Measurement In. (mm)
Ring Gear Backlash	
Preferred	.005-.008 (.13-.20)
Acceptable	.003-.012 (.008-.30)
	INCH Lbs. (N.m)
Pinion Bearing Preload	
New Bearings	23-35 (2.6-4.0)
Used Bearings	5-15 (.6-1.7)

TIGHTENING SPECIFICATIONS

Application	Torque Ft. Lbs. (N.m)
Ring Gear	120 (163)
Side Bearing Cap	135 (184)
Drive Pinion Nut	[1]
Differential Bearing Adjusting Lock	20 (27)
Pinion Bearing Retainer	65 (84)

[1] – Tighten as necessary to obtain correct preload. Tighten to approximately 350 Ft. Lbs. (476 N.m).

JEEP 7 9/16" RING GEAR

Cherokee & Wagoneer (Rear)

DESCRIPTION

The rear axle housings consists of a cast iron center section and 2 steel axle tubes which are pressed into the center section. The ring and pinion gears and differential are contained within the axle housing. The conventional differential drives semi-floating tapered axle shafts.

AXLE RATIO & IDENTIFICATION

Code letters are used to identify the size and gear ratio of Jeep 7 9/16" axle. Code letters are stamped on right-hand axle tube boss of each rear axle center section. For axle ratios, see AXLE RATIO IDENTIFICATION article in this section.

REMOVAL & INSTALLATION

AXLE SHAFTS & BEARINGS

Removal

1) Remove rear wheel and drum. Disconnect parking brake cable at equalizer and brake line at wheel cylinder. Remove brake support plate assembly.

2) Using a puller, remove axle shaft from axle tube. Mount axle shaft in a vise. Drill a 1/4" (6 mm) hole 3/4 of the through retaining ring. Be careful not to drill into axle shaft.

3) Chisel a deep groove in retaining ring and remove ring. Remove bearing from axle shaft using arbor press. Remove seal. *See Fig. 2.*

Installation

1) Pack bearing with wheel bearing grease. Coat inner axle shaft seal with axle grease and outer portion of seal with gasket sealant.

2) Using Bearing Installer tool (J 22912 01). Press axle shaft bearing and retainer ring on axle shaft togather. Be sure bearing and retainer ring are properly seated against axle shaft shoulder. Install axle.

REAR YOKE & PINION OIL SEAL

Removal

1) Raise and support vehicle. Remove wheels and brake drums. Remove propeller shaft, marking parts for reassembly reference. Use an INCH lb. torque wrench to rotate pinion several revolutions. Record torque required to turn drive pinion.

2) Hold yoke from turning and remove pinion nut. Mark drive pinion shaft and yoke for reassembly reference. Remove yoke using pullers. Using a seal puller, remove pinion oil seal.

Fig. 1: Jeep 7 9/16" Rear Axle Assembly

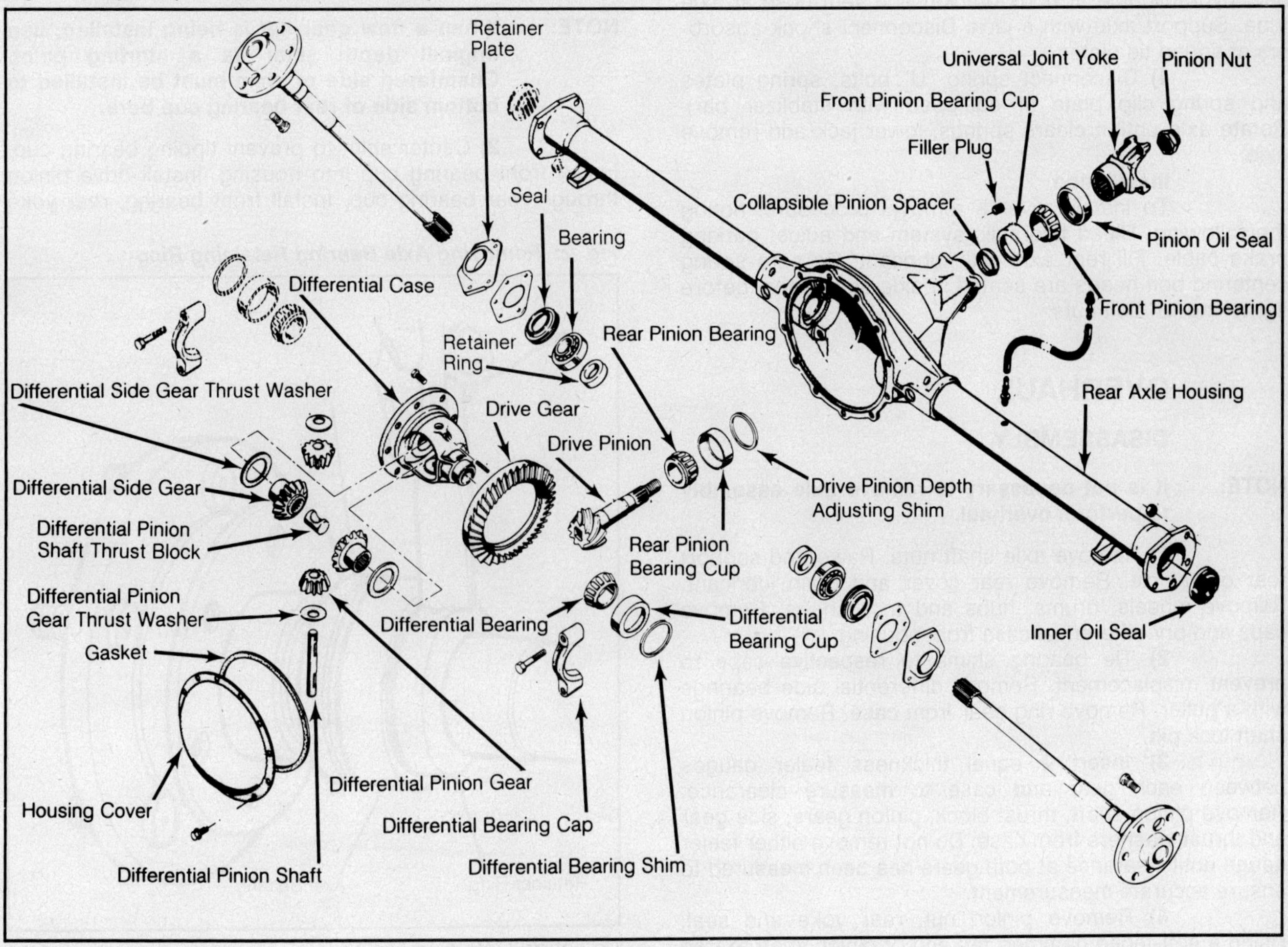

JEEP 7 9/16" RING GEAR (Cont.)

Installation

1) Coat new seal with rear axle lubricant, and install seal. Install rear yoke, aligining marks made at disassembly. Install NEW pinion nut and tighten just enough to remove end play.

2) Using an INCH lb. torque wrench, check torque required to turn pinion. Refer to torque reading recorded during disassembly and add 5 INCH lbs. (.6 N.m) torque for correct amount of preload. Tighten pinion slightly and recheck preload. Repeat procedure until desired preload is obtained.

CAUTION: Do not overtighten pinion nut. If desired preload is exceeded, a new collapsible pinion spacer sleeve must be installed and drive pinion preload reset.

REAR AXLE ASSEMBLY

Removal

1) Remove cotter pins and axle shaft nuts. Raise and support vehicle. Remove wheels, brake drum retaining screws and brake drums. Disconnect hydraulic lines from wheel cylinders. Remove support plates.

2) Remove axle shaft with puller. Remove axle cover, drain lubricant and reinstall cover. Disconnect parking brake cables at equalizer. Mark propeller shaft and axle yoke for reassembly reference. Remove propeller shaft.

3) Remove stabilizer bar (if equipped). Disconnect hydraulic line at body bracket and vent hose at axle tube. Support axle with a jack. Disconnect shock absorbers at spring tie plates.

4) Disconnect spring "U" bolts, spring plates and spring clip plate (if equipped with stablizer bar). Rotate axle until it clears springs, lower jack and remove axle.

Installation

To install, reverse removal procedure, noting the following; Bleed hydraulic system and adjust parking brake cable. Fill rear axle with lubricant. Be sure spring centering bolt heads are seated in axle spring seat before tightening "U" bolt nuts.

OVERHAUL

DISASSEMBLY

NOTE: It is not necessary to remove axle assembly to perform overhaul.

1) Remove axle shaft nuts. Raise and support rear of vehicle. Remove rear cover and drain lubricant. Remove wheels, drums, hubs and axle shafts. Remove caps and pry differential case from housing.

2) Tie bearing shims to respective caps to prevent misplacement. Remove differential side bearings with a puller. Remove ring gear from case. Remove pinion shaft lock pin.

3) Insert 2 equal thickness feeler gauges between each gear and case to measure clearance. Remove pinion shaft, thrust block, pinion gears, side gear and thrust washers from case. Do not remove either feeler gauge until clearance at both gears has been measured to ensure accurate measurement.

4) Remove pinion nut, rear yoke and seal. Using a soft-faced hammer, tap end of pinion shaft to free front bearing cone from shaft. Remove bearing from differential.

5) Remove drive pinion and rear bearing from housing. Discard collapsible spacer. Drive out front and rear bearing cups. Keep pinion depth shims (located behind rear bearing cup) for reassembly.

CLEANING & INSPECTION

1) Clean all components in solvent. Allow bearings to air dry. Inspect all machined surfaces for smoothness or raised edges. Inspect all bearings and cups for wear or pitting and replace as necessary. Inspect all gear teeth for wear or chipping and replace as necessary.

2) Check axle housing alignment. Place 2 straightedges across tube flanges and measure distance between flange ends. If straightedges are parallel within 3/32" (2 mm) at a distance of 11" (279 mm) from tube centerline, axle housing is serviceable.

3) Pinion shaft should be a press fit to a .010" (.25 mm) loose fit in case. Clearance of differential side gear in case bore should not exceed .007" (.18 mm).

REASSEMBLY

Drive Pinion

1) Press rear bearing on pinion stem with large diameter of roller cage toward gear. Clean housing bearing bores. Place shim in rear bearing bore and install rear bearing cup.

NOTE: When a new gear set is being installed, use original depth shim as a starting point. Chamfered side of shim must be installed to bottom side of rear bearing cup bore.

2) Center shim to prevent tipping bearing cup. Install front bearing cup into housing. Install drive pinion through rear bearing cup. Install front bearing, rear yoke

Fig. 2: Removing Axle Bearing Retaining Ring

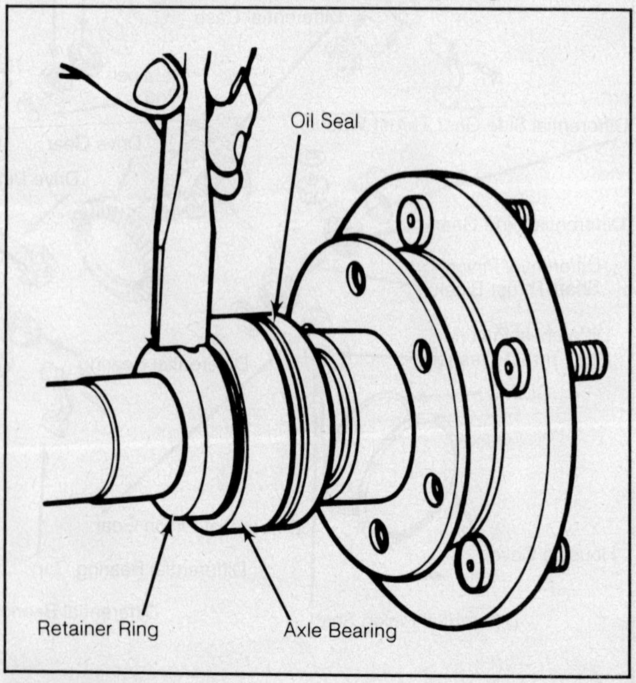

Do not drill into axle shaft.

JEEP 7 9/16" RING GEAR (Cont.)

and original pinion. Tighten nut to remove bearing end play only.

NOTE: **A new nut and collapsible spacer are not installed at this time as the pinion will be removed after a depth measurement.**

Differential Case

1) Install differential side bearings onto case with bearing driver and installer. Install thrust washers on differential gears with oil pocket toward gear. Install gears into bores in differential case.

2) Install thrust washers behind differential pinion gears. Mesh gears with differential gear so holes in gears are opposite and in line with each other. Roll gears around until pinion gear holes are aligned with shaft holes in case.

3) Measure any existing clearance between differential side gears and case, using 2 feeler gauges on opposite side of 1 gear. Clearance should not exceed .007" (.18 mm).

4) If measured side gear-to-case clearance at disassembly was more than .007" (.18 mm) and thrust surfaces of case are not worn, replace thrust washers and recheck clearance. If clearance is still more than .007" (.18 mm), replace side gears as a set. Install lock pin.

ADJUSTMENT

DRIVE PINION DEPTH

1) Observe numbers painted on drive pinion and ring gear. First number on pinion must match number on ring gear. Second number on pinion is pinion depth variance. If number is preceded by a plus sign, add that number to standard pinion depth. If number is preceded by a minus sign, subtract that from standard pinion depth.

2) If numbers do not match, gear set is not a matched set and should not be used. Some factory installed sets may have .01" (.25 mm) or .02" (.50 mm) machined off the pinion end face.

3) Identifying numbers will appear as +23, number 2 indicating that .02" (.50 mm) was removed from the end face and number 3 is pinion depth variance. If marked +16, the number 1 indicates that .010" (.25 mm) was removed from the end face and the number 6 is the pinion depth variance. These gear sets are exclusively factory installed.

Fig. 3: Pinion Depth and Preload Shim Location

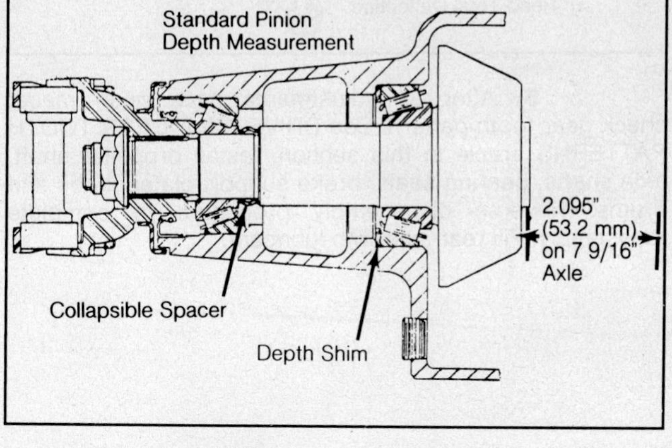

4) Standard pinion depth on 7 9/16" axle is 2.095" (53.2 mm). Result of addition or subtraction of shims will be desired pinion depth. Record this measurement for future reference.

5) Mount pinion setting gauge and discs on axle. Install gauge assembly with discs fully seated in housing bores. Install bearing cap and tighten bolts.

6) Position gauge block against end of drive pinion with clamp bar and screw. Loosen thumbscrew in end of gauge block and allow spring loaded plunger to contact arbor. Tighten thumbscrew, taking care not to disturb position of plunger.

7) Remove gauge block and measure distance from end of anvil to top of plunger head, using a 2-3" micrometer. Record this measured pinion depth for future reference.

8) Remove gauging tools, drive pinion and rear bearing cup. Remove drive pinion depth shim and record thickness. Add shim thickness to measured pinion depth. From this total subtract desired pinion depth.

9) The result represents correct shim thickness to be installed. Install correct thickness shim in rear bearing bore and install rear bearing cup. *See Fig. 3.*

NOTE: **Replacement gears marked with more than .009" (.23 mm) variance should not be used during overhaul.**

10) The Pinion Variance Chart will help determine the appropriate starter shim thickness when installing NEW gear sets. Note pinion variance numbers on new and old gear. Follow old pinion marking line across to new pinion marking column.

11) The number in the box indicates the change in shim thickness from original. For example, old pinion marked −3 and new pinion marked +2. Intersecting box shows −.005" (.13 mm) to be subtracted from original shim thickness. The starter shim thickness must not be used as a final shim setting. An actual pinion depth measurement must be made and final shim thickness adjusted as necessary.

DRIVE PINION BEARING PRELOAD

1) Install collapsible spacer and front bearing on drive pinion. Install oil seal rear yoke and nut. Tighten pinion nut only enough to remove bearing end play.

2) Gradually tighten nut to collapse spacer and to preload bearings. Using an INCH lb. torque wrench, measure torque required to turn drive pinion. If preload torque is less than desired, tighten pinion nut slightly and recheck preload. Continue procedure until correct preload is obtained.

CAUTION: **Do not overtighten pinion nut. If preload torque is exceeded, replace collapsible spacer and repeat operation.**

DIFFERENTIAL BEARING END PLAY

1) Place bearing cup over each differental bearing. Install differential case assembly (without drive gear) in axle housing. Install a shim on each side between bearing cup and housing. Use .142" (3.6 mm) shims.

2) Install bearing caps and tighten bolts finger tight. Mount dial indicator to housing so that button of indicator touches drive gear face of differential case. Using 2 screwdrivers, pry between shims and housing.

JEEP 7 9/16" RING GEAR (Cont.)

Fig. 4: Drive Pinion Depth Measurement

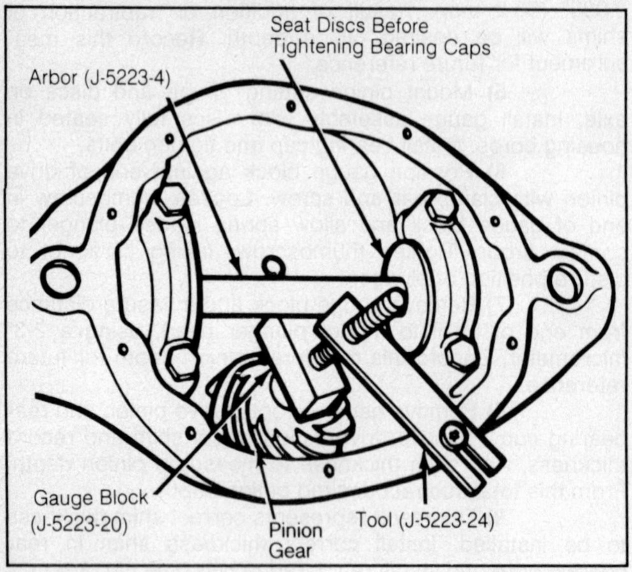

Pry assembly to 1 side, zero dial indicator, then pry assembly to opposite side. Read and record indicator reading.

3) Amount read on indicator is shim thickness to be added to arrive at a no preload and no end play condition. Shims are available in thicknesses of .142" (3.6 mm) to .174" (4.4 mm) in .002" (.05 mm) increments.

4) When all side play is eliminated, check drive gear face of case for runout. Runout should not exceed .002" (.05 mm). Remove case from housing, and retain shims used to eliminate side play. *See Fig. 5.*

Fig. 5: Differential Bearing Side Play and Runout Measurement

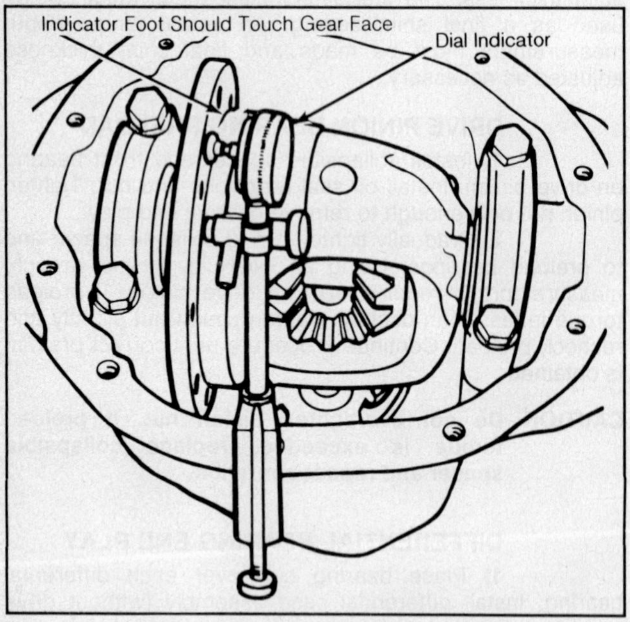

BACKLASH ADJUSTMENT

1) Install differential assembly (with drive gear) in housing using shims selected to remove side play. Tighten bearing cap bolts evenly.

2) Attach a dial indicator to housing so that button of indicator contacts drive side of a tooth of drive gear, and at a right angle to it. Rock drive gear and note movement on dial indicator.

3) Backlash should be .005-.009" (.13-.23 mm) with .008" (.20 mm) desired. To increase backlash, install thinner shim on drive gear side and a thicker shim on opposite side. To decrease backlash, reverse placement of shims. DO NOT change total shim thickness; alter positions only.

DIFFERENTIAL BEARING PRELOAD

1) Differential bearings are preloaded by increasing each shim thickness by .004" (.10 mm). Install differential bearing shims in axle housing bearing bore.

2) Assemble bearing cups on bearings (cups should completely cover rollers). Position differential so that bearings just start in axle housing bearing bores. Keep assembly square in housing and push in as far as possible.

3) Using a soft hammer, tap outer edge of bearing cups until seated in housing.

4) Install bearing caps, aligning marks made at disassembly. Install and tighten bolts. Preloading differential bearings may change backlash setting. Therefore, recheck backlash and correct if necessary. *See Fig. 6.*

Fig. 6: Differential Gear Backlash Check

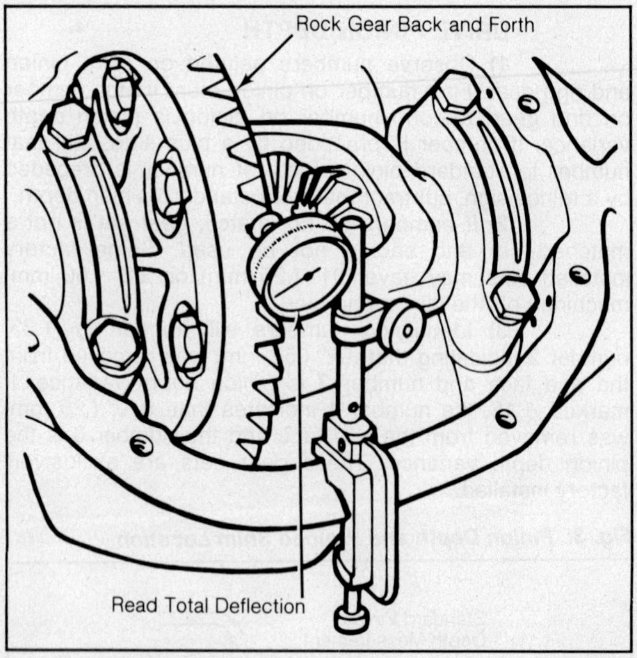

5) After all adjustments have been made, check gear tooth pattern. See DRIVE AXLE GEAR TOOTH PATTERNS article in this section. Install propeller shaft, axle shafts, bearing seals, brake support plates, hubs and drums. Reverse disassembly procedure to complete reassembly. Fill rear axle with lubricant.

JEEP 7 9/16" RING GEAR (Cont.)

AXLE ASSEMBLY SPECIFICATIONS

Application	Specification
Pinion Bearing Preload	15-25 INCH lbs. (2.3 N.m)
Differential Bearing Preload	.008" (.20 mm)
Ring/Pinion Backlash	.005-.009" (.13-.23 mm)
Case Flange Runout	.002" Max. (.05 mm)
Gear-to-Case Clearance	.007" Max. (.17 mm)
Capacity	3.0 pts. (1.4L)

TIGHTENING SPECIFICATIONS

Application	Ft. Lbs. (N.m)
Housing Cover	15 (20)
Brake Support Plate	32 (44)
Differential Bearing Cap	57 (78)
Drive Gear-to-Case	52 (71)
Universal Joint Bolts	15 (20)
Wheel Lug Nuts	75 (102)

PINION DEPTH SHIM ADJUSTMENT CHART (INCHES)

Old Pinion Marking	New Pinion Marking								
	-4	-3	-2	-1	0	+1	+2	+3	+4
+4	+0.008	+0.007	+0.006	+0.005	+0.004	+0.003	+0.002	+0.001	0
+3	+0.007	+0.006	+0.005	+0.004	+0.003	+0.002	+0.001	0	-0.001
+2	+0.006	+0.005	+0.004	+0.003	+0.002	+0.001	0	-0.001	-0.002
+1	+0.005	+0.004	+0.003	+0.002	+0.001	0	-0.001	-0.002	-0.003
0	+0.004	+0.003	+0.002	+0.002	0	-0.001	-0.002	-0.003	-0.004
-1	+0.003	+0.002	+0.001	0	-0.001	-0.002	-0.003	-0.004	-0.005
-2	+0.00	+0.00	0	-0.001	-0.002	-0.003	-0.004	-0.005	-0.006
-3	+0.001	0	-0.001	-0.002	-0.003	-0.004	-0.005	-0.006	-0.007
-4	0	-0.001	-0.002	-0.003	-0.004	-0.005	-0.006	-0.007	-0.008

JEEP 8 7/8" RING GEAR

CJ7, J10, Scrambler & Grand Wagoneer; Rear Axle

DESCRIPTION

The Jeep 8 7/8" ring gear axle assembly is a hypoid gear type with integral carrier housing. This semi-floating axle is used as the rear drive axle on CJ7, J10, Scrambler and Grand Wagoneer models. The axle is equipped with tapered axle shafts.

Pinion bearing preload is adjusted by varying shim thickness. A removable housing cover allows access to differential for inspection or minor servicing, without removing axle assembly.

AXLE RATIO & IDENTIFICATION

This Jeep axle assembly has a 10 bolt cover. Some Jeep models use a Spicer (Dana) axle. Refer to SPICER (DANA) SEMI-FLOATING or FULL-FLOATING articles in this section, for correct identification. To determine drive axle ratio, refer to DRIVE AXLE RATIO IDENTIFICATION article in this section.

REMOVAL & INSTALLATION

AXLE HUB

Removal (CJ & Scrambler Models)

1) Remove dust cap, nut and washer. Raise vehicle and remove tire and wheel. Remove brake drum retaining screws, and remove drum. Using puller (J 25109 01), remove hub.

2) Inspect hub for loose or damaged wheel studs. Check keyway and tapered center bore for wear or cracks. Replace hub if necessary.

CAUTION: Do not use a knockout or slide hammer-type puller to remove hub. This type of puller may damage axle assembly.

Installation of Original Hub (CJ & Scrambler Models)

1) Align axle key and hub keyway. Slide hub onto axle shaft as far as possible. Install nut and washer. Install drum retaining screws, wheel and tire.

2) Lower vehicle and tighten nut to 250 ft. lbs. (340 N.m). Tighten nut to align cotter key hole, do not back nut off.

NOTE: Installation procedures for a new hub and an old hub will differ. If axle shaft is replaced, hub must also be replaced, however, a new hub can be installed on an old axle shaft.

Installation of New Hub (CJ & Scrambler Models)

1) Align axle key and hub keyway. Slide hub onto axle shaft as far as possible. Install 2 lubricated thrust washers and axle shaft nut. Install drum retaining screws, wheel and tire. Lower vehicle. *See Fig. 1.*

2) Tighten axle shaft nut until distance from outer hub face to end of axle is 1 5/16". Pressing hub on to this dimension is necessary to form hub serrations correctly.

3) Remove axle shaft nut and 1 washer. Install nut, and tighten to 250 ft. lbs. (340 N.m). Tighten nut to align cotter key hole. Do not back off nut.

Fig. 1: Jeep Hub Installation Measurement

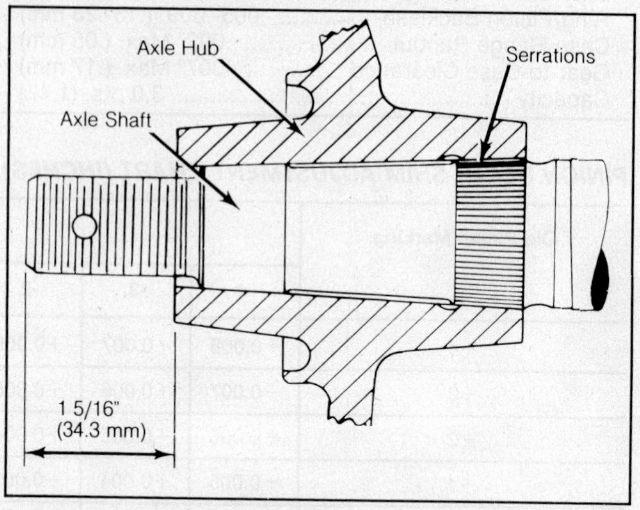

Tighten axle shaft nut until distance from outer hub face to end of axle is corrected as shown.

AXLE SHAFTS & BEARINGS

Removal (CJ & Scrambler Models)

1) Remove axle hub as previously outlined. Disconnect parking brake cable at equalizer, and brake line at wheel cylinder. Remove backing plate, oil seal, and shims from axle shaft.

2) Using puller (J 2498), remove axle shaft. Remove and discard inner seal. Bearing cone is press fit on axle shaft, and must be removed using an arbor press and mandrel.

Installation (CJ & Scrambler Models)

1) Press new axle bearing onto shaft, with small diameter of cone towards outer end of shaft. Coat inner axle shaft seal with a light coat of oil. Coat outer surface of metal retainer with non-hardening sealer.

NOTE: Tapered axle shaft bearings have no provision for lubrication, and should be packed with a good wheel bearing lubricant before installation.

2) Install inner seal in axle housing using an installer (J 21788). Place axle shaft in housing, and align splined end with differential gears. Install outer bearing cup. Coat backing plate with sealer at mounting area.

3) Install original shims, oil seal assembly, and backing plate. Tighten backing plate bolts to 35 ft. lbs. (47 N.m). Oil seal and retainer are located on outside of backing plate.

4) If left axle was removed, end play must be adjusted. To adjust end play, remove left axle hub, if not previously removed. Strike ends of both axles with a lead hammer to seat bearings.

5) Attach axle shaft end play tool (J 2092) and a dial indicator to left axle. Move axles back and forth to measure end play. End play should be .004-.008" (.10-.20 mm) with .006" (.15 mm) recommended.

JEEP 8 7/8" RING GEAR (Cont.)

6) Add shims to increase end play; remove shims to decrease end play. Install hub and drum, as previously outlined. Adjust brakes, and bleed brake hydraulic system.

Fig. 2: Removing Bearing Retaining Ring from J10 & Grand Wagoneer Models

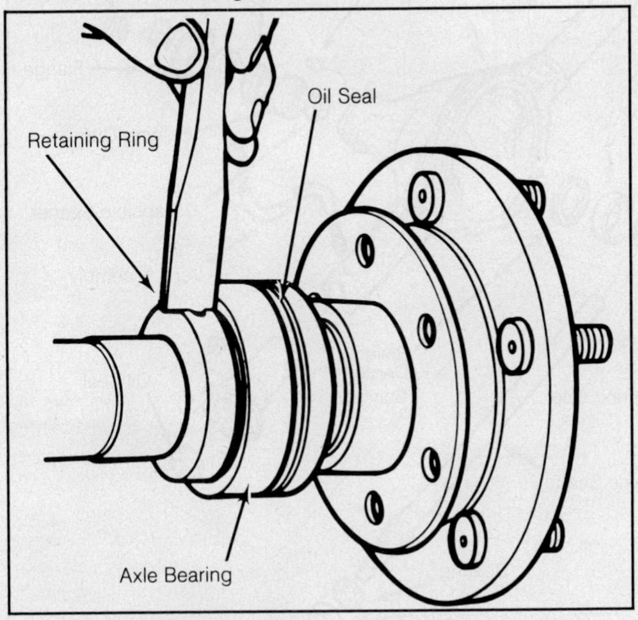

Drill retaining ring part way through, and cut with chisel.

Removal (All Other Models)

1) Raise and support vehicle, and remove rear wheels. Remove brake drum. Remove nuts and lock washers attaching support plate and retainer to axle tube flange.

2) Install slide hammer and adapter tool (J 2619 01 & J 21579) on axle flange, and remove axle shaft. Remove and discard oil seal from axle housing, and wipe seal bore in housing clean.

3) Mount axle shaft in vise. Drill a 1/4" (6 mm) hole in retaining ring approximately 3/4" way through ring thickness, making sure not to let drill contact axle shaft. *See Fig. 2.*

4) Position chisel over drilled hole in retaining ring and cut ring. Remove ring from axle shaft. Cut through oil seal using hacksaw and remove seal and retainer plate, making sure not to damage seal contact surface.

5) Remove axle shaft bearing using arbor press and mandrels.

CAUTION: Do not use a torch to remove axle shaft retaining ring or bearing.

Installation (All Other Models)

1) Install retainer plate on axle shaft. Pack wheel bearing lubricant in oil seal cavity and between oil seal lips. Install seal on axle shaft with outer face of seal facing axle flange.

2) Pack new axle bearing with wheel bearing lubricant. Install bearing on axle shaft, making sure bearing cup rib ring is facing axle flange.

3) Install bearing retainer ring. Press axle shaft bearing and retaining ring on axle shaft simultaneously. Make sure both are seated properly against axle shaft shoulder.

4) Install new oil seal in axle housing using an installer (J 21788). Install axle shaft through support plate. Coat outside diameter of bearing cup with wheel bearing lubricant before installing in bearing bore.

5) Tap flanged end of axle shaft lightly, using soft mallet to position axle shaft bearing in bearing bore of housing. Install axle shaft retainer and brake support plate to axle tube flange.

6) Install attaching lock washers and nuts. Tighten to 35 ft. lbs. (47 N.m). Install brake drums and rear wheels. Lower vehicle.

PINION FLANGE & SEAL

Removal

1) Raise and support vehicle. Remove both rear wheels and brake drums. Disconnect propeller shaft from flange. Mark propeller shaft position with flange. Connect an INCH lb. torque wrench to flange nut. Rotate several times, and measure torque required to turn pinion.

2) Record reading for assembly. Hold flange and remove nut. Mark position of flange on drive pinion. Discard pinion nut. Using a puller, remove flange. If surface is damaged or grooved, replace flange. Pry out old seal and discard.

Installation

1) Coat seal lip with axle lubricant before installing. Install seal using Seal Installer tool (J 22661). Align drive pinion shaft and flange marks, and install flange on drive pinion.

2) Tighten replacement nut only enough to remove end play. Check torque required to turn drive pinion. Refer to reading recorded during flange removal.

3) Tighten nut enough to exceed recorded reading by 5 INCH lbs. (.6 N.m). Repeat these steps until desired torque is obtained. Install propeller shaft aligning marks. Install brake drums and wheels.

CAUTION: Do not loosen and retighten nut. Do not over-tighten nut. If correct torque is exceeded, a new collapsible spacer must be installed, and drive pinion preload must be reset.

AXLE ASSEMBLY

Removal

1) Raise and support vehicle forward of rear springs. Remove wheels with tires. Mark propeller shaft position with flange, and disconnect propeller shaft. Disconnect shock absorbers and brake line at "T" fitting.

2) Plug open ends of brake lines to prevent dirt from entering system. Disconnect parking brake cable at equalizer. Support axle housing with a floor jack. Remove "U" bolts at spring.

3) If vehicle has springs mounted below axles, disconnect shackle bolts and lower spring from axle. Slide axle housing out from under vehicle.

Installation

1) To install axle assembly, reverse removal procedure. On CJ7 and Scrambler models, be sure spring centering bolt heads are seated in axle spring seat locating holes before tightening "U" bolt.

2) Bleed brake hydraulic system and check axle lubricant level.

JEEP 8 7/8" RING GEAR (Cont.)

Fig. 3: Exploded View of CJ & Scrambler Drive Axle Assembly

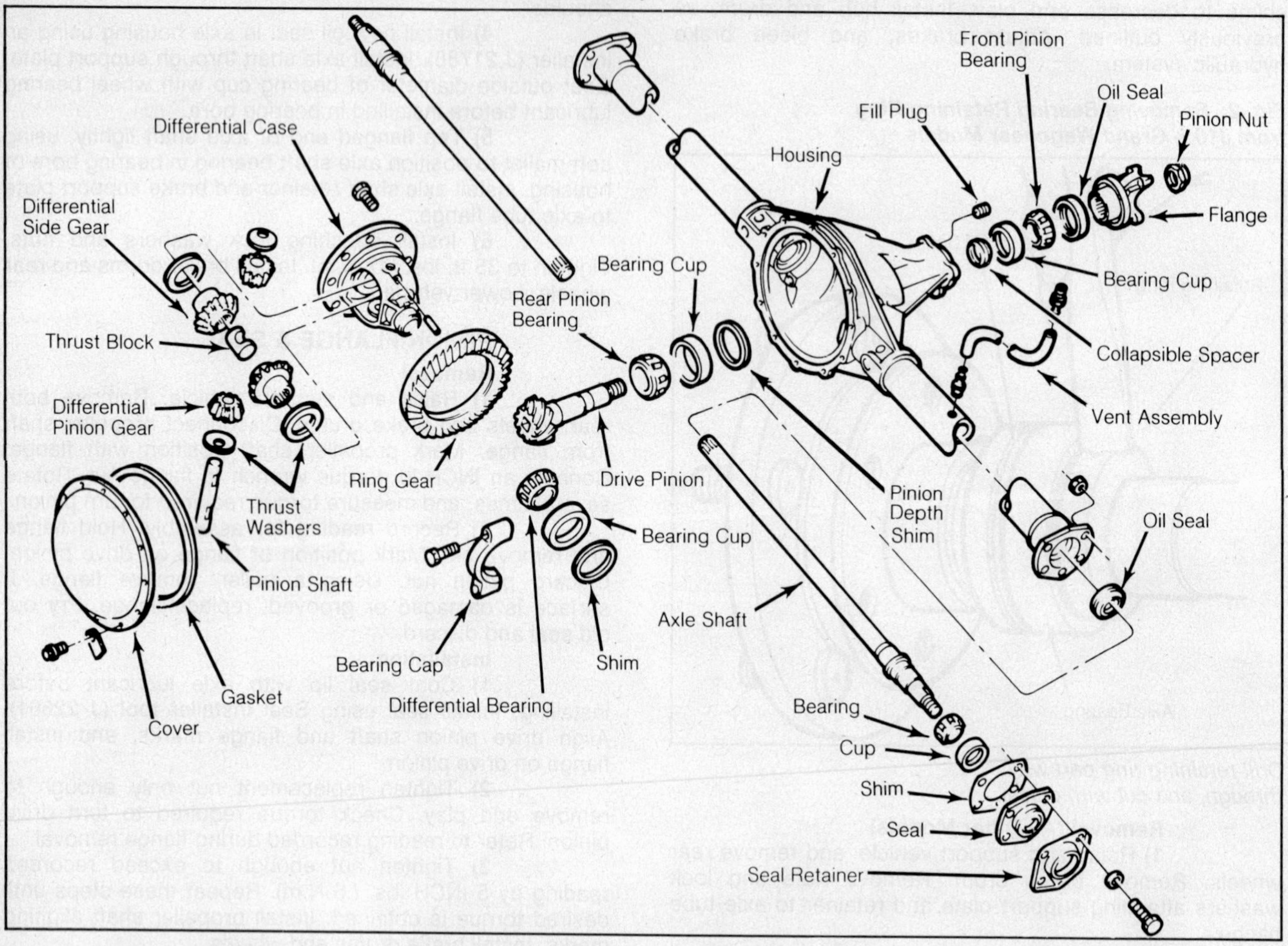

OVERHAUL

DISASSEMBLY

NOTE: It is not necessary to remove complete axle assembly from vehicle for overhaul.

1) Remove axle shaft dust caps and retaining nuts. Raise and support vehicle. Remove axle housing cover, and drain lubricant. Remove axle hubs as previously outlined. Mark differential side bearing caps with a center punch for reassembly.

2) Loosen bearing cap bolts, until they are retained by just a few threads. This will prevent differential from falling out. Pry differential loose in housing. Remove bearing caps and differential.

3) Secure bearing shims to their respective bearing caps and cups. *See Fig. 3.* Use puller (J 2497 01) to remove side bearings from differential. Make sure puller pulls against bearing cone and not bearing cage or rollers.

4) Remove ring gear retaining bolts, and tap ring gear off differential using a brass hammer. Drive out pinion shaft lock pin, using a 3/16" drift punch. Drive out pinion shaft using a punch. With shaft removed, withdraw thrust block.

5) Roll pinion gears around on side gears until they can be removed. Remove side gears and thrust washers. *See Fig. 4.* With propeller shaft removed, hold flange and remove retaining nut. Remove flange using a puller.

Fig. 4: Removal of Jeep Pinion Shaft Lock Pin

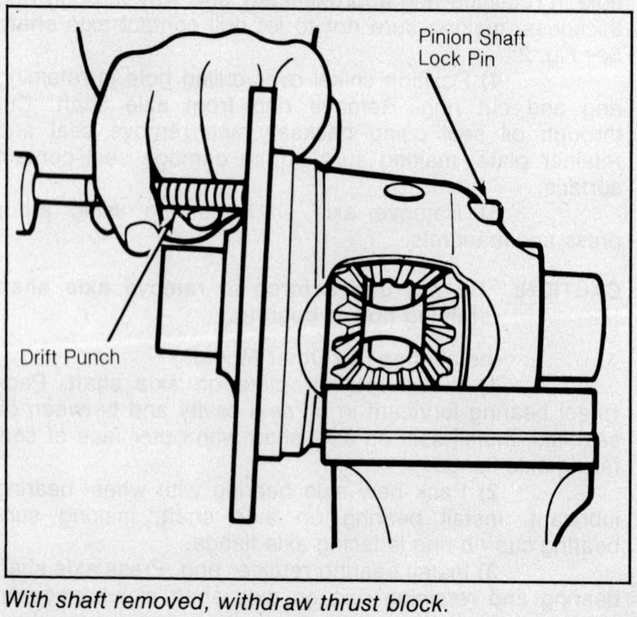

With shaft removed, withdraw thrust block.

JEEP 8 7/8" RING GEAR (Cont.)

6) Install housing cover with 2 bolts. Remove pinion seal. Strike end of drive pinion with a soft mallet. This will unseat front bearing cone from gear. Remove bearing cone. Remove and discard collapsible spacer. Remove housing cover, drive pinion, and rear bearing.

7) Remove front and rear bearing cups using a slide hammer and adapter. Pinion depth shims are behind rear bearing cone. Secure shims to cone for reassembly reference.

CLEANING & INSPECTION

1) Clean all components in solvent. Allow bearings to air dry. Inspect all machined surfaces for smoothness or raised edges. Inspect all bearings and cups for wear or pitting and replace as necessary. Inspect all gear teeth for wear or chipping and replace as necessary.

2) Check axle housing alignment. Place 2 straightedges across tube flanges and measure distance between flange ends. If straightedges are parallel within 3/32" (2 mm) at a distance of 11" (279 mm) from tube centerline, axle housing is serviceable.

REASSEMBLY & ADJUSTMENT

Drive Pinion Installation & Depth Adjustment

1) Pinion gear depth is distance from end face of pinion to the axle shaft centerline. This dimension is controlled by shims installed between pinion gear bearing and axle housing. *See Fig. 5.*

2) There are 2 numbers painted on pinion gear and 1 number painted on ring gear. The first number on pinion gear and number on ring gear identify both as a matched set.

NOTE: **Ring and pinion gears should not be used if numbers do not match, or if replacement gear sets are marked .009" or more.**

Fig. 5: Standard Setting Dimension & Pinion Depth Shim Location

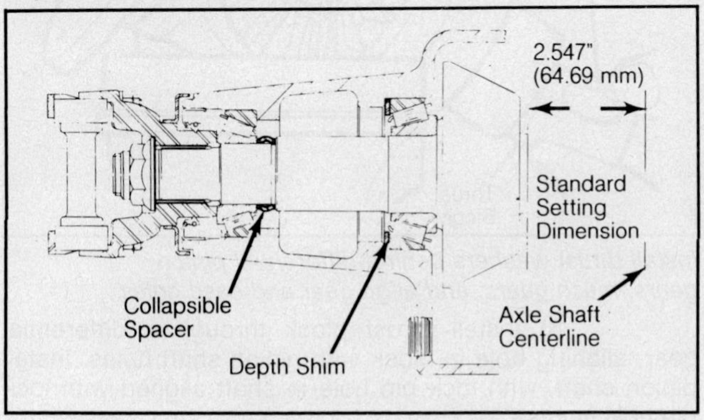

Pinion gear depth is the distance from end face of pinion to the axle shaft centerline.

3) Second number on pinion gear represents pinion depth variance. This indicates (in thousandths of an inch) the amount that the ring and pinion gear varied from standard setting to obtain the correct gear tooth contact pattern.

EXAMPLE:

- Standard pinion depth is 2.547" (64.69 mm). If pinion gear is marked "2", the set varied from the standard setting by .002" (.05 mm). This means that a .002" (.05 mm) thinner shim will be required than for a gear set marked "0".
- Some factory-installed sets may have .010" (.25 mm) or .020" (.51 mm) machined off pinion gear end face. Identifying numbers will appear differently.

EXAMPLE:

- If gear is machined .010" (.25 mm), the identifying number will appear as +16. The "1" indicates that .010" (.25 mm) was removed from end face; and the "6" indicates that pinion depth variance is .006" (.15 mm). A gear machined .020" (.51 mm) would be identified in the same manner, only a "2" will be used rather than a "1". The marking would then be +26.

4) To determine a starting shim thickness to measure pinion depth and determine the correct shim thickness, measure thickness of shim removed during disassembly. Note pinion depth variance on old and new pinion gears.

5) Using Pinion Depth Variance Chart, determine amount to be added or subtracted from original shim thickness to determine starting shim thickness.

EXAMPLE:

- If the old pinion is marked -3 and the new pinion is marked +2, the chart indicates -.005". This means that .005" (.13 mm) would be reduced from original shim thickness to determine starting shim.

NOTE: **Do not use starting shim thickness as final shim thickness.**

6) Install rear bearing on pinion gear. Make sure large diameter of bearing cage faces gear end of pinion. Make sure bearing is fully pressed against rear face of gear.

7) Make sure pinion gear bearing bores in housings are clean. Install shim in rear bearing cup bore. If shim is chamfered, make sure chamfered side faces bottom of bore.

8) Install front and rear bearing cups, using mandrels and drivers. Install pinion gear in position in housing.

9) Install front bearing, rear universal joint yoke, and original pinion nut. Tighten pinion nut only enough to remove all end play.

NOTE: **Do not install new pinion nut or collapsible spacer at this time. These will be installed when pinion bearing preload is adjusted.**

10) Note pinion depth variance marked on pinion gear. Add or subtract this from standard pinion depth. This is correct pinion depth. Record this figure.

11) Assemble pinion depth measuring gauge arbor tool (J 5223 4) and centering discs (J 5223 23). With discs fully seated, install gauge assembly in differential bearing cup bores. Install bearing caps, and tighten bolts securely.

12) Position gauge block (J 5223 20) on end face of pinion. Make sure anvil end of gauge block is seated on gear, and that gauge block plunger is under arbor tool.

13) Attach gauge block clamp (J 5223 14) and bolt (J 5223 24) to housing cover bolt. Tighten clamp bolt

JEEP 8 7/8" RING GEAR (Cont.)

down against gauge block to prevent block from moving. *See. Fig. 6.*

14) Loosen gauge block thumb screws, and allow gauge block plunger to contact arbor tool. Now tighten thumb screw securing plunger in position. Remove clamp and then gauge block.

15) Using a 2 to 3-inch micrometer, measure distance from end of anvil on gauge block to end of plunger. This represents measured pinion depth. Record this measurement.

16) Remove bearing caps. Remove arbor and disc assembly. Remove pinion gear, bearing cup, and depth shim from axle.

17) Measure thickness of starting shim. Add this to measurement obtained in step **15)**. From this total, subtract desired pinion depth measurement obtained in step **10)**. The result is the shim thickness required to obtain correct pinion depth.

EXAMPLE:

Standard Pinion Depth	2.547" (64.69 mm)
Pinion Depth Variance	+ .007" (.18 mm)
Desired Pinion Depth	=2.554" (64.87 mm)

Measured Pinion Depth	2.550" (64.77 mm)
Starting Shim Thickness	+.098" (2.49 mm)
Total Measured Pinion Depth	=2.648" (67.26 mm)

Total Measured Pinion Depth	2.648" (67.26 mm)
Desired Pinion Depth	-2.554" (64.87 mm)
Correct Shim Thickness	=.094" (2.39 mm)

Fig. 6: Measuring Pinion Depth

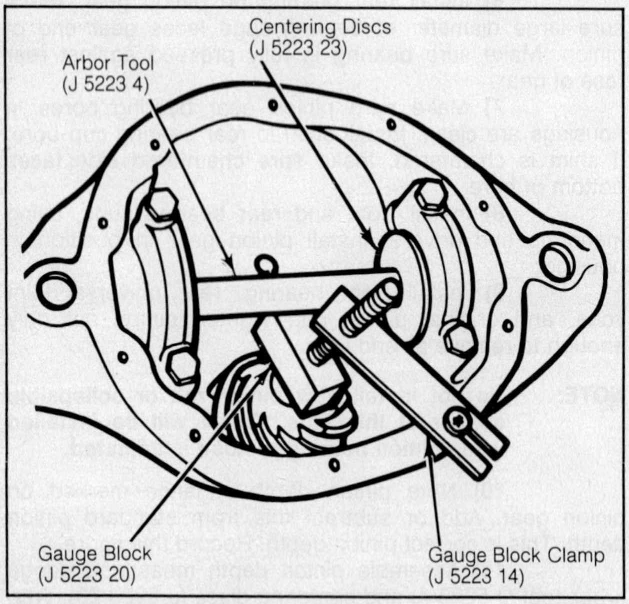

Tighten clamp down against gauge block to prevent block from moving.

Drive Pinion Bearing Preload

1) Install correct pinion gear depth shim(s) in housing bore. Install pinion gear and rear bearing. See PINION DEPTH SHIM ADJUSTMENT chart.

2) Install new collapsible spacer and front bearing in housing. Install pinion oil seal using installer (J 22661). Install universal joint yoke and a new retaining nut. Tighten nut finger tight.

3) Now hold yoke and tighten nut. While tightening, rotate pinion to make sure bearings seat evenly.

4) Using an INCH Lb. torque wrench, measure torque required to turn pinion. If pinion bearing preload is not to specification, continue tightening yoke retaining nut until correct preload is obtained.

CAUTION: Do not exceed specified torque. If torque is exceeded, a new collapsible spacer must be installed, and preload must be reset. Do not loosen nut to reduce torque.

Assembling Differential Carrier

1) Install differential bearing onto case. Install thrust washers on differential gears (oil pocket side toward gear). Install gears into bore in differential case. Install thrust washers behind differential pinion gears.

2) Mesh gears with differential gears, so holes are opposite and in line with each other. Roll gears around, until differential pinion gear holes are aligned with shaft holes in case. *See Fig. 7.*

Fig. 7: Installing Pinion Shaft and Thrust Block

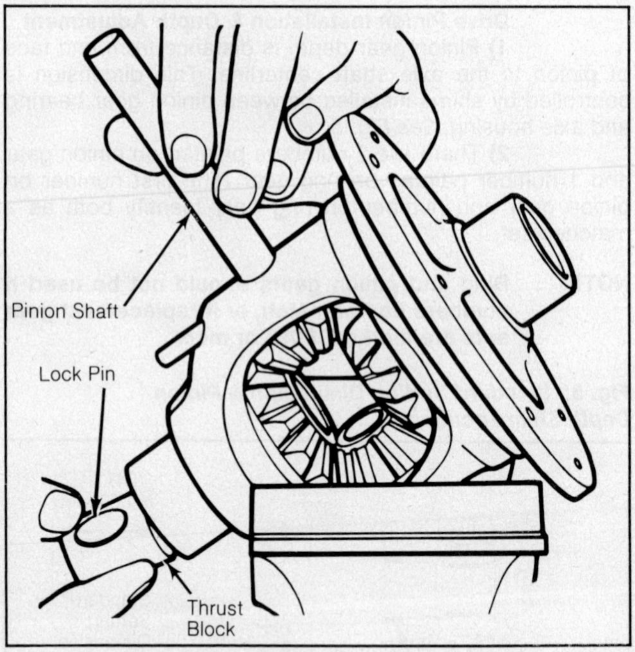

Install thrust washers behind differential pinion gears, mesh gears, and align gear and case holes

3) Install thrust block through a differential gear, aligning hole in block with pinion shaft holes. Install pinion shaft, with lock pin hole in shaft aligned with lock pin hole in case.

4) Measure any existing clearance between differential gears and case, using 2 feeler gauges on opposite sides of 1 gear. Clearance should be zero.

Adjusting Differential Bearings

1) Place bearing cup over each differential bearing. Install differential case assembly in axle housing. As a starting point, install an .080" (2.03 mm) shim on each side. Install bearing caps, and tighten bolts finger tight. Mount a dial indicator to housing so that plunger contacts ring gear mounting flange on differential.

2) Using 2 screwdrivers, pry between shims and housing. Pry assembly to one side, zero indicator. Pry

JEEP 8 7/8" RING GEAR (Cont.)

assembly to opposite side and read indicator. Do not read or zero indicator while prying. The amount read on indicator is the amount of shim to be added to arrive at a no preload and no end play condition.

3) Shims are available in thicknesses ranging from .080" to .110" (2.03 to 2.79 mm) in .002" (.05 mm) increments. With all side play eliminated, check ring gear mounting flange for runout. Runout should not exceed .002" (.05 mm). Remove differential case from housing, and retain shims used to eliminate side play.

Ring Gear Installation

Place ring gear on differential housing case, and install retaining bolts. Two bolts installed in opposite holes may be used to pull ring gear into place. Tighten bolts to specifications.

Backlash Adjustment

1) Install differential assembly in housing, using shim selected to remove side play. Tighten bearing cap screws to 87 ft. lbs. (118 N.m). Attach a dial indicator to housing, so that indicator plunger contacts drive side of a tooth on ring gear and is at a right angle (90°) to it.

2) Rock ring gear, and note movement on dial indicator. Backlash should be .005-.009" (.13-.23 mm), with .008" (.20 mm) desired. To increase backlash, install a thinner shim on ring gear side. To decrease backlash, reverse procedure, however, do not change total thickness of shims.

Differential Bearing Preload

1) Differential bearings are preloaded by increasing each shim thickness by .004" (.10 mm). Install differential bearing shim in axle housing bearing bores. Assemble bearing cups on bearings (cups should completely cover rollers). Position differential so that bearings just start in axle housing bearing bores. Keep assembly square in housing and push in as far as possible.

2) Using a soft hammer, tap outer edge of bearing cups until seated in housing. Do not distort shim by hammering them into housing. Install bearing caps, aligning scribe marks made at disassembly. Install and tighten bolts. Preloading differential bearings may change backlash setting, therefore recheck backlash and correct as necessary.

3) After all adjustments have been made, make a gear tooth pattern check to insure correct assembly. To complete reassembly, reverse disassembly procedures. Fill rear axle with lubricant.

AXLE ASSEMBLY SPECIFICATIONS

Application	In. (mm)
Axle Shaft End Play	.004-.008 (.10-.20)
Differential Bearing Preload (Shims)	.008 (.20)
Ring Gear Backlash	.005-.009 (.13-.23)
Pinion Gear Depth (Std. Setting)	2.547 (64.69)
	INCH Lbs. (N.m)
Pinion Bearing Preload	17-25 (1.9-2.8)

TIGHTENING SPECIFICATIONS

Application	Ft. Lbs. (N.m)
Differential Bearing Cap Bolts	87 (118)
Ring Gear Bolts	105 143)
Backing Plate Bolts	32 (44)
Rear Wheel Hub-to-Axle Nut	[1] 250 (340)
"U" Joint Bolt Clamp	16 (22)

[1] – CJ & Scrambler, 250 (340 N.m) Minimum.

PINION DEPTH SHIM ADJUSTMENT CHART (INCHES)

Old Pinion Marking	New Pinion Marking								
	-4	-3	-2	-1	0	+1	+2	+3	+4
+4	+0.008	+0.007	+0.006	+0.005	+0.004	+0.003	+0.002	+0.001	0
+3	+0.007	+0.006	+0.005	+0.004	+0.003	+0.002	+0.001	0	-0.001
+2	+0.006	+0.005	+0.004	+0.003	+0.002	+0.001	0	-0.001	-0.002
+1	+0.005	+0.004	+0.003	+0.002	+0.001	0	-0.001	-0.002	-0.003
0	+0.004	+0.003	+0.002	+0.002	0	-0.001	-0.002	-0.003	-0.004
-1	+0.003	+0.002	+0.001	0	-0.001	-0.002	-0.003	-0.004	-0.005
-2	+0.00	+0.00	0	-0.001	-0.002	-0.003	-0.004	-0.005	-0.006
-3	+0.001	0	-0.001	-0.002	-0.003	-0.004	-0.005	-0.006	-0.007
-4	0	-0.001	-0.002	-0.003	-0.004	-0.005	-0.006	-0.007	-0.008

ROCKWELL 12" RING GEAR

Chevrolet & GMC "P" Series Rear Axle

DESCRIPTION

The Rockwell drive axle uses a heavy duty hypoid drive pinion and ring gear. The differential and gear assembly are mounted on tapered roller bearings.

The straddle-mounted pinion has 2 tapered roller bearings in front of the pinion teeth to carry forward and reverse thrust loads. The 3rd bearing is behind the pinion teeth to carry radial load.

The preload on the differential side bearings is set by adjusting nuts on which bearing races rest. The differential has a 2-piece case and 4 differential pinion gears.

AXLE RATIO & IDENTIFICATION

The 12" ring gear drive axle assembly is the only one used on General Motors vehicles that has a removable carrier. To determine axle ratio, refer to DRIVE AXLE RATIO IDENTIFICATION in this section.

REMOVAL & INSTALLATION

AXLE SHAFT

Removal & Installation

Remove dust cap, and install Adapter (J-8117) in tapped hole on shaft flange. Using slide hammer on adapter, remove axle shaft. To install, reverse removal procedure, using new gaskets.

WHEEL HUB & SEAL

Removal

1) Remove axle shaft. Remove lock nut retainer, lock nut, adjusting nut retainer, adjusting nut and thrust washer from axle housing.

2) Pull hub and drum assembly straight off axle housing. Pry old oil seal from wheel hub, using care not to damage bore surface. Thoroughly clean seal contact surface area.

Installation

1) Pack cavity between seal lips with high melting point wheel bearing lubricant. Position seal in hub bore.

2) Using Seal Installer (J-24428), carefully press seal into hub until seal is flush with edge of hub. Install hub onto axle housing, and install axle shaft.

HUB BEARINGS

Removal

1) With wheel hub removed from vehicle, use long drift or punch to drive inner bearing, race and oil seal from hub.

2) Remove outer bearing retaining ring. Drive outer bearing out of hub, using Bearing Race Remover (J-24426).

CAUTION: Inner bearing race and outer bearing retaining ring must be removed before attempting to remove outer bearing race.

Installation

1) Place outer bearing assembly into hub. Using Bearing Race Installer (J-8608), drive bearing past retaining ring groove in hub. Be sure chamfer of bearing race installer does not contact bearing race.

2) Install outer bearing retaining ring, and drive race into hub until seated. Place inner bearing race into hub. Using Bearing Race Driver (J-24427), drive race into hub until seated against shoulder.

3) Install new oil seal with Oil Seal Installer (J-24428). Place hub assembly onto axle housing. Install adjusting nut, and adjust rear wheel bearing.

PINION FLANGE & SEAL

Removal

1) Disconnect propeller shaft and tie out of the way. Scribe a line down pinion nut, pinion stem and pinion flange for reassembly reference. Remove pinion nut and pull pinion flange from stem. *See Fig. 1.* Remove front bearing retainer from carrier.

Fig. 1: Removing Pinion Flange From Rockwell 12" Axle

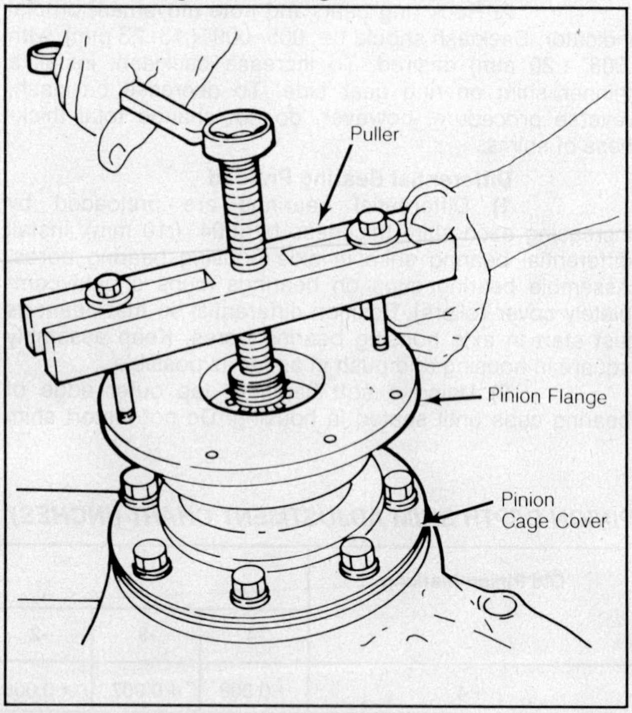

Do not use hammer to drive off flange.

2) Remove bolts holding oil seal retainer to carrier. Remove retainer and pry out oil seal from bore, using care not to damage machined surface.

Installation

Lubricate cavity between seal lips with bearing lubricant. Install a new pinion oil seal into bore, using Driver (J-22281). Be sure seal bottoms against shoulder in bore. Install bearing retainer to carrier. Install pinion flange, pinion nut and propeller shaft.

DIFFERENTIAL CARRIER

Removal & Installation

1) Drain differential. Remove axle shaft from drive unit and housing. Disconnect universal at pinion shaft. Remove carrier to housing stud nuts and washers. Loosen 2 top nuts and leave on studs to prevent carrier from falling out.

ROCKWELL 12" RING GEAR (Cont.)

Fig. 2: Exploded View of Rockwell 12" Axle Assembly

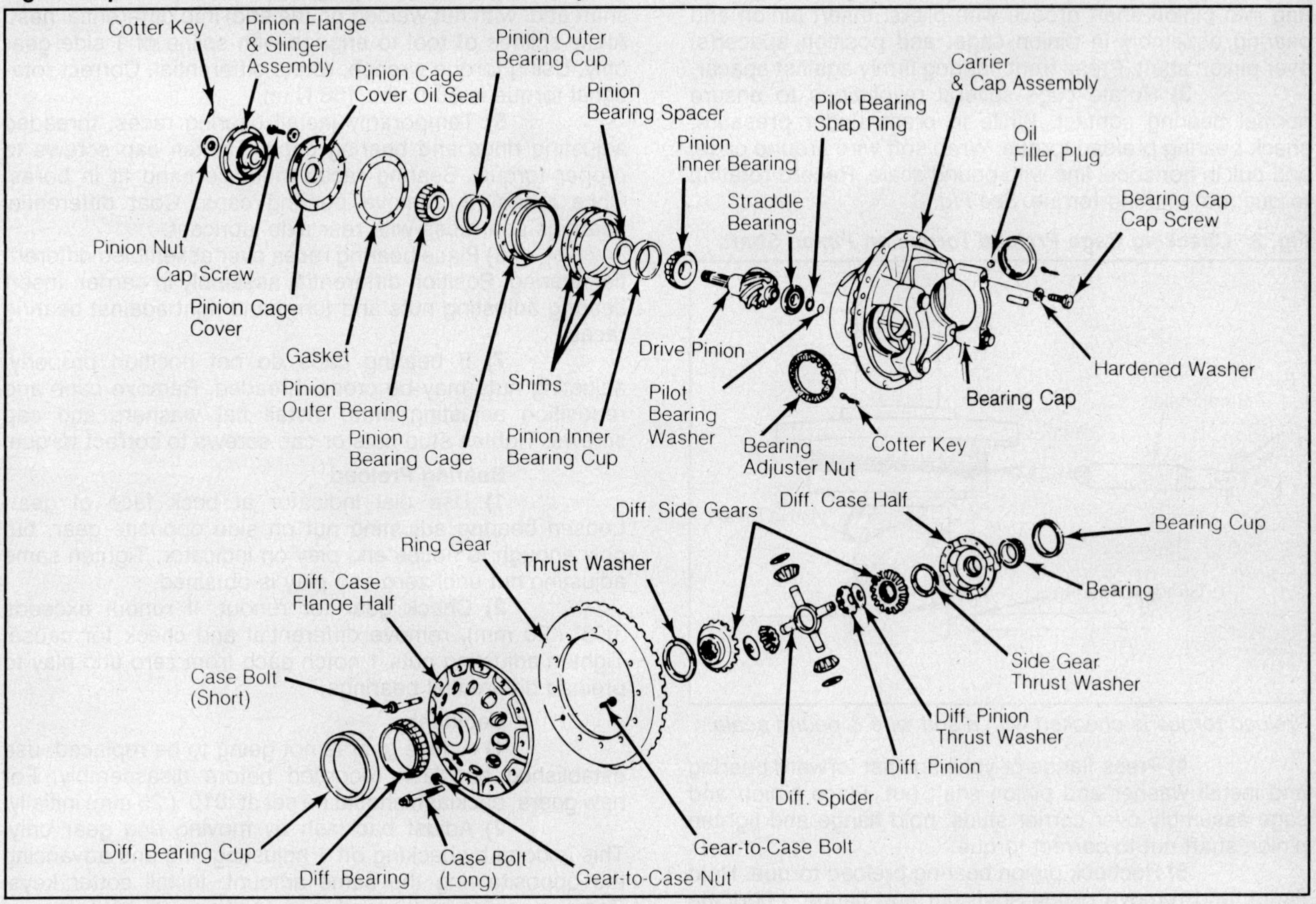

2) Break carrier loose from axle housing with soft mallet. Remove top nuts and washers, and work carrier free. Use a roller jack to safely remove carrier from housing. To install, reverse removal procedure.

OVERHAUL

DISASSEMBLY

NOTE: Check and record ring gear backlash and pinion bearing preload before disassembly.

Case & Gear Assembly

1) With carrier in holding fixture, loosen jam nuts and back off thrust adjusting screw. Center punch 1 differential carrier leg and bearing cap to identify for reassembly.

2) Remove differential adjusting nut locks and bearing cap bolts. Mark bearing caps and carrier for reassembly. Remove adjusting nuts and bearing caps. Remove differential and ring gear assembly from carrier.

3) Mark differential case halves for reassembly. Remove bolts and separate case halves. Remove spider, pinions, side gears, and thrust washers. If necessary, remove rivets and separate gear and case.

Pinion & Cage Assembly

Hold flange and remove pinion nut and washer. Remove flange with puller. Remove pinion cage capscrews. Remove bearing cover and seal assembly. Remove drive pinion bearing cage. Wire shim pack together and save for reassembly reference.

CLEANING & INSPECTION

1) Clean all parts in cleaning solvent. Inspect all bearings, bearing races, races and rollers for scoring, chipping or excessive wear. Inspect axle shaft and side gear splines for excessive wear.

2) Inspect ring gear and pinion for scoring, cracking or chipping. Inspect differential case, pinion side gears, thrust washers and pinion shaft for cracks, scoring, galling or excessive wear.

REASSEMBLY & ADJUSTMENT

Selecting Pinion Cage Shim Pack

To accurately install a new pinion and cage assembly into carrier, mathematically calculate the proper pinion cage shim pack thickness:

Example:

Original Pack Thickness	.030"
Original Variation Number (+2)	-.002"
Standard Pack Thickness	.028"
New Variation Number (+5)	+.005"
New Pack Thickness	.033"

Pinion & Cage

1) If new races are to be used, press firmly against pinion bearing cage shoulders. Lubricate bearings and races. Press rear thrust and radial bearings firmly against pinion shoulders with a sleeve that will bear only on inner race.

ROCKWELL 12" RING GEAR (Cont.)

2) Install radial bearing lock ring, and squeeze ring into pinion shaft groove with pliers. Insert pinion and bearing assembly in pinion cage, and position spacer(s) over pinion shaft. Press front bearing firmly against spacer.

3) Rotate cage several revolutions to ensure normal bearing contact. While in press under pressure, check bearing preload torque. Wrap soft wire around cage, and pull in horizonal line with pound scale. Record rotating torque, not starting torque. *See Fig. 3.*

Fig. 3: Checking Cage Preload Torque on Pinion Shaft.

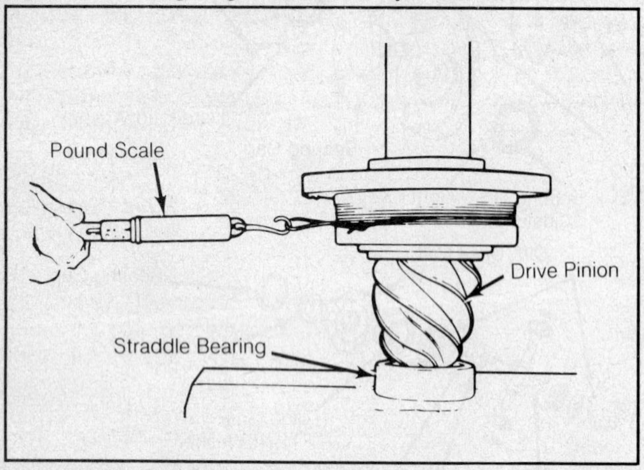

Preload torque is checked with a soft wire & pound scale.

4) Press flange or yoke against forward bearing and install washer and pinion shaft nut. Place pinion and cage assembly over carrier studs, hold flange and tighten pinion shaft nut to correct torque.

5) Recheck pinion bearing preload torque. Hold flange and remove pinion shaft nut and flange. Lubricate pinion shaft oil seal, and cover outer edge of seal body with a non-hardening sealing compound. Press seal against cover shoulder with seal driver.

6) Install new gasket and bearing cover. Press flange against forward bearing, and install washer and pinion shaft nut. Tighten nut to correct specifications.

Differential & Ring Gear

Heat ring gear to 180°F (82°C) for 10 minutes before assembling to differential. Do not press or drive ring gear onto case. New differential case and ring gear bolts should be used in place of rivets (if required).

Differential Pinion & Side Gear

1) Position thrust washer and side gear in ring gear and case half assembly. Place spider with pinions and thrust washers in position. Install components, side gear and thrust washer.

2) Align mating marks, position component case half and draw assembly together with 4 bolts. Check assembly for free rotation of differential gears. Correct if necessary.

3) Install remaining bolts and tighten to specifications. If bearings are to be replaced, press them onto differential case halves squarely. Place differential in vise.

4) Insert checking tool (made from splined axle shaft end, with nut welded on the end) into differential nest. Allow splines of tool to engage with spline of 1 side gear only. Using torque wrench, rotate differential. Correct rotational torque is 50 ft. lbs. (68 N.m).

5) Temporarily install bearing races, threaded adjusting rings and bearing caps. Tighten cap screws to proper torque. Bearing races must be hand fit in bores. Once races fit, remove bearing caps. Coat differential bearings and races with rear axle lubricant.

6) Place bearing races over assembled differential bearing. Position differential assembly in carrier. Insert bearing adjusting nuts and turn hand tight against bearing races.

7) If bearing caps do not position properly, adjusting nuts may be cross threaded. Remove caps and reposition adjusting nuts. Install flat washers and cap screws. Tighten stud nuts or cap screws to correct torque.

Bearing Preload

1) Use dial indicator at back face of gear. Loosen bearing adjusting nut on side opposite gear, but only enough to notice end play on indicator. Tighten same adjusting nut until zero end play is obtained.

2) Check gear for runout. If runout exceeds .008" (.20 mm), remove differential and check for cause. Tighten adjusting nuts 1 notch each from zero end play to preload differential bearings.

Backlash

1) If drive gear is not going to be replaced, use established backlash recorded before disassembly. For new gears, backlash should be set at .010" (.25 mm) initially.

2) Adjust backlash by moving ring gear only. This is done by backing off 1 adjusting ring and advancing the opposite ring the same amount. Install cotter keys. Remove carrier from stand, and position with back face of hypoid (spiral bevel) gear upward.

3) Remove adjusting screw and lock nut. Install thrust screw and lock nut, and tighten thrust screw sufficiently to locate thrust block firmly against back face of hypoid gear.

4) To secure correct adjustment of .010-.015" (.25-.38 mm) clearance, loosen adjusting screw (thrust screw) 1/4 turn and lock securely with nut. Recheck to ensure minimum clearance of .010" (.25 mm) during full rotation of bevel gear.

TIGHTENING SPECIFICATIONS

Application	Ft. Lbs. (N.m)
Pinion Bearing Cage Bolts	
Grade 5	25-35 (34-47)
Grade 7	30-40 (41-54)
Grade 8	35-50 (47-68)
Pinion Shaft Nut	300-400 (407-542)
Thrust Screw Jam Nut	150-190 (203-257)
Adjusting Ring Lock	20-30 (27-41)
Bearing Cap Bolts	115-140 (156-190)
Ring Gear-to-Case Bolts	85-115 (115-156)
Diff. Case Capscrews	60-75 (81-102)

SPICER (DANA) IFS AXLE

Ford Front Axles

DESCRIPTION

Independent Front Suspension (IFS) front axle is of integral carrier housing, hypoid gear type. Centerline of drive pinion is mounted above centerline of ring gear. Drive pinion and ring gear bearing settings are all adjusted by shims.

Model 28-IFS is used on Bronco II and 4WD Ranger models. Models 44-IFS, 44-IFS-HD and 50-IFS are used on all other 4WD models. Model 44-IFS is used on vehicles with front coil springs. Models 44-IFS-HD and 50-IFS are used on vehicles with leaf springs.

AXLE RATIO & IDENTIFICATION

Metal identification tag, stamped with gear ratio and part number, is secured to housing by 2 carrier bolts. If axle is equipped with limited slip differential, tag will have letters "LS" in part number. Axle model can be determined by measuring diameter of ring gear. See AXLE MODEL IDENTIFICATION table. To determine drive axle ratio, refer to DRIVE AXLE RATIO IDENTIFICATION in this section.

AXLE MODEL IDENTIFICATION

Model	Ring Gear Diameter
28	7.50"
44	8.50"
50	9.25"

REMOVAL & INSTALLATION

NOTE: For removal and installation instructions, see appropriate articles on LOCKING HUBS and 4-WHEEL DRIVE STEERING KNUCKLES in this section.

HUBS & BEARINGS

Removal

1) Raise vehicle and support securely. Remove wheels and tires. Remove manual or locking hub assemblies. Remove caliper with brake line attached and secure to frame with wire. Do not hang caliper with any tension on brake hose.

2) On Model 28-IFS axle with manual locking hubs, remove snap ring, axle shaft spacer, needle thrust bearing and bearing thrust washer from spindle. Remove outer bearing lock nut with 4-Prong Spindle Nut Spanner (T83T-1197-A). Remove lock nut washer and inner bearing adjusting nut.

3) On Model 28-IFS axle with automatic locking hubs, remove snap ring, axle shaft spacer, needle thrust bearing and bearing spacer. Carefully pull plastic cam assembly from bearing adjusting nut. Remove thrust washer and needle thrust bearing from adjusting nut. Remove adjusting nut with 2 3/8" Hex Socket (T70T-4252-B).

NOTE: Before removing adjusting nut, make sure that any part of locking key from cam assembly is removed from spindle keyway. Failure to clear keyway will result in thread damage on spindle. If locking key has broken off plastic cam assembly, discard complete cam assembly. Replace cam assembly with Ford Service Kit (1A053).

4) On Model 44 and 50 axles, remove hub bearing lock nut, lock ring and adjusting nut. Use Front Hub Bearing Spanner (T59T-1197-B on F150, F250 and Bronco models; D78T-1197-A on F350 and F250 HD models) to remove nuts.

5) On all models, remove hub and rotor. Outer bearing will slide of with hub. Remove grease seal and inner bearing. If bearings require replacement, remove races from hub with Internal Puller (D80L-943-A on Model 28; T77F-1102-A on Models 44 and 50) and attached Slide Hammer (T50T-100-A). Bearing races may also be removed with drift and hammer.

Installation & Adjustment (Hub Bearings On Model 28 With Manual Locking Hubs)

1) If bearings are replaced, drive new races into hub. Lubricate bearings with lithium base multipurpose wheel bearing grease. Install inner bearing and seal into hub. Install hub on spindle. Install outer bearing and adjusting nut. Tighten adjusting nut to 35 ft. lbs. (47 N.m) while turning hub back and forth to seat bearings.

2) Spin hub and back off adjusting nut 90°. Install lock washer on spindle. Mount lock washer over pin on adjusting nut, turning nut slightly if necessary to align pin. Install and tighten outer lock nut to 150 ft. lbs. (203 N.m) using 4-prong spanner.

3) Install bearing thrust spacer, needle thrust bearing and axle shaft spacer. Install snap ring on axle shaft. Install manual hub assembly. Install retaining washers, wheel and tire. Check that end play of hub bearings is .001-.003" (.03-.08 mm).

Installation & Adjustment (Hub Bearings On Model 28 With Automatic Locking Hubs)

1) If bearings are replaced, drive new races into hub. Lubricate bearings with lithium base multipurpose wheel bearing grease. Install inner bearing and seal into hub. Install hub on spindle. Install outer bearing and adjusting nut. Tighten adjusting nut to 35 ft. lbs. (47 N.m) while turning hub back and forth to seat bearings.

2) Spin hub and back off adjusting nut 90°. Retighten adjusting nut with torque wrench to 16 INCH lbs. (1.8 N.m). Align nearest hole in adjusting nut with center of spindle keyway. Install lock nut needle bearing and thrust washer. Press plastic cam assembly onto adjusting nut with locking key of cam in keyway of spindle.

3) Install bearing thrust washer, needle thrust bearing and axle shaft spacer. Clip snap ring onto axle shaft. Install automatic locking hub assembly with 3 legs of hub assembly inserted into 3 pockets of cam assembly. Install retaining washers, wheel and tire. Check that end play of hub on spindle is .001-.003" (.03-.08 mm).

Installation & Adjustment (Hub Bearings On Model 44)

1) If bearings are replaced, drive new races into hub. Lubricate bearings with lithium base multipurpose wheel bearing grease. Install inner bearing and seal into hub. Install hub on spindle. Install outer bearing and adjusting nut. Tighten adjusting nut to 50 ft. lbs. (68 N.m) while turning hub back and forth to seat bearings.

2) Back off adjusting nut by about 45°. Install lock washer, turning adjusting nut slightly to align hole in washer with nut. Install and tighten lock nut to 150 ft. lbs.

SPICER (DANA) IFS AXLE (Cont.)

(203 N.m). End play of hub assembly should be .00-.006" (.0-.15 mm).

Installation & Adjustment
(Hub Bearings On Model 50)

1) If bearings are replaced, drive new races into hub. Install inner bearing and seal into hub. Install hub on spindle. Install outer bearing and adjusting nut.

2) Tighten adjusting nut to 50 ft. lbs. (68 N.m) while turning hub back and forth to seat bearings. Back off adjusting nut and retighten to 31-39 ft. lbs. (42-53 N.m). Rotate hub and back off adjusting nut 135-150°. Put lock washer and lock nut on spindle.

3) Tighten lock nut to 65 ft. lbs. (88 N.m). Bend 1 tang of lock washer over adjusting nut and 1 tang over lock nut. Check that end play of hub asssembly is .001-.009" (.02-.25 mm).

SPINDLES & AXLE SHAFTS

Removal

1) Raise vehicle and support with safety stands. If equipped with locking hub assemblies, see removal and installation procedures in LOCKING HUBS and 4-WHEEL DRIVE STEERING KNUCKLES articles in this section.

2) Remove wheel and tire. Remove brake caliper assembly and tie to frame without any tension on brake hose. Remove hub and rotor. Unbolt spindle from knuckle studs. It may be necessary to tap spindle with soft mallet to break it loose.

3) Remove splash shield. On left side, remove axle shaft and joint assembly by pulling assembly through steering knuckle. On right side, remove keystone clamps holding rubber boot onto right axle shaft and stub shaft. Slide rubber boot onto stub shaft.

4) Pull right axle shaft and joint assembly from splined stub shaft. Clamp spindle on second step in soft-jawed vise. Remove grease seal and needle bearing from spindle, using slide hammer and Seal Remover (1175-AC). Using hammer, drive oil seal off axle shaft.

Installation

1) Clean spindle bearing bores thoroughly. Place bearing into bore with manufacturer's identification facing outward. Drive bearing into spindle using Spindle Bearing Driver (T83T-3123-A on Bronco II and Ranger models; T80T-4000-S on F150, F250 and Bronco models; T80T-4000-R on F350 models) and Driver Handle (T80T-4000-W).

2) Place grease seal in bore with lip facing away from spindle. Drive seal into bore, using driver handle and spindle bearing replacer on Bronco II and Ranger models. Use driver handle and Seal Replacer (T80T-4000-T) to install grease seal on all other models. Coat seal lip and axle shaft splines with multipurpose grease.

3) Slide left axle shaft and joint assembly through knuckle. Make sure shaft splines engage properly inside differential carrier. Install new axle shaft seal on right axle if removed. On right side stub shaft, install rubber boot with new keystone clamps. Install right axle shaft and joint assembly.

4) Make sure that wide male spline on axle shaft is aligned with wide tooth space in stub shaft slip yoke. Make sure splines fully engage. Slide rubber boot over assembly junction. Crimp clamps with Keystone Clamp Pliers (T63P-9171-A).

5) Install splash shield and spindle onto knuckle. Tighten spindle retaining nuts to 35-45 ft. lbs. (47-61 N.m). Install hub and rotor. Adjust hub bearings. Install wheel and tire.

STUB SHAFT & SLIP YOKE, CARRIER & BEARING

Removal

1) Disconnect propeller shaft and tie to side out of way. Remove both spindles and axle shaft assemblies. Support carrier and remove bolts holding carrier to support arm. Separate carrier from support arm and drain lubricant.

2) Remove carrier from vehicle. Install carrier in Holding Fixture (T57L-500-B) using Adapters (T83T-3010-A). Rotate slip yoke and stub shaft until open side of snap ring on inner end of stub shaft can be reached.

3) Remove snap ring. Remove stub shaft and slip yoke from carrier assembly. Remove oil seal and caged needle bearings together, using slide hammer and Collet (D80L-100-A).

Installation

1) Make sure bearing bore is clean and has no nicks. Place needle bearing on Needle Bearing Installer (T83T-1244-A on Model 28; T80T-4000-H on all other models). Bearing manufacturer's name and part number should face toward tool when installed in carrier bore.

2) Bearing installer is designed to stop on carrier housing when bearing has reached proper depth. Coat lip of seal with multipurpose grease. Drive seal into carrier. Install slip yoke and stub shaft so that groove on shaft is visible inside differential case.

3) Install snap ring. DO NOT tap on center of snap ring as ring will be damaged. Clean all RTV, oil and dirt from carrier and support arm. Apply continuous bead of RTV 1/4-3/8" (6.35-9.53 mm) wide on carrier. Bead should not pass over or outside holes.

NOTE: Carrier must be installed on support arm within 5 minutes after applying RTV sealant.

4) Using jack, install carrier on support arm with guide pins to align carrier. Install and tighten bolts in either clockwise or counterclockwise rotation to 40-50 ft. lbs. (54-68 N.m). On Model 28, install and tighten shear bolt holding carrier to left axle arm to 75-95 ft. lbs. (102-129 N.m).

5) Install both spindles, left and right axle shaft assemblies and propeller shaft. Let RTV cure for 1 hour before filling assembly with hypoid gear lubricant.

AXLE PIVOT BUSHING

Removal

Remove axle as described in AXLE ASSEMBLY. Install Forcing Screw (T78P-5638-A1), Bushing Remover (T80T-5638-A2 on Model 28; T80T-5638-A1 on Models 44 and 50) and Receiver Cup (T78P-5638-A4 on Model 28; T78P-5638-A3 on Models 44 and 50) on pivot bushing. Turn forcing screw to remove pivot bushing.

Installation

1) Place new pivot bushing in axle housing. Using Receiver Cup (T78P-5638-A4 on Model 28; T78P-5638-A2 on Models 44 and 50), forcing screw and Bushing Replacer (T82T-3006-A1 on Model 28; T80T-5638-A2 on Models 44 and 50), install bushing.

2) Bushings must be flared to prevent movement after installation. Use forcing screw, receiver cup and Flaring Flange (T83T-3006-A) to flare bushing lip. Install axle assembly.

SPICER (DANA) IFS AXLE (Cont.)

Fig. 1: Exploded View Of Spicer (Dana) Model 28-IFS Front Drive Axle

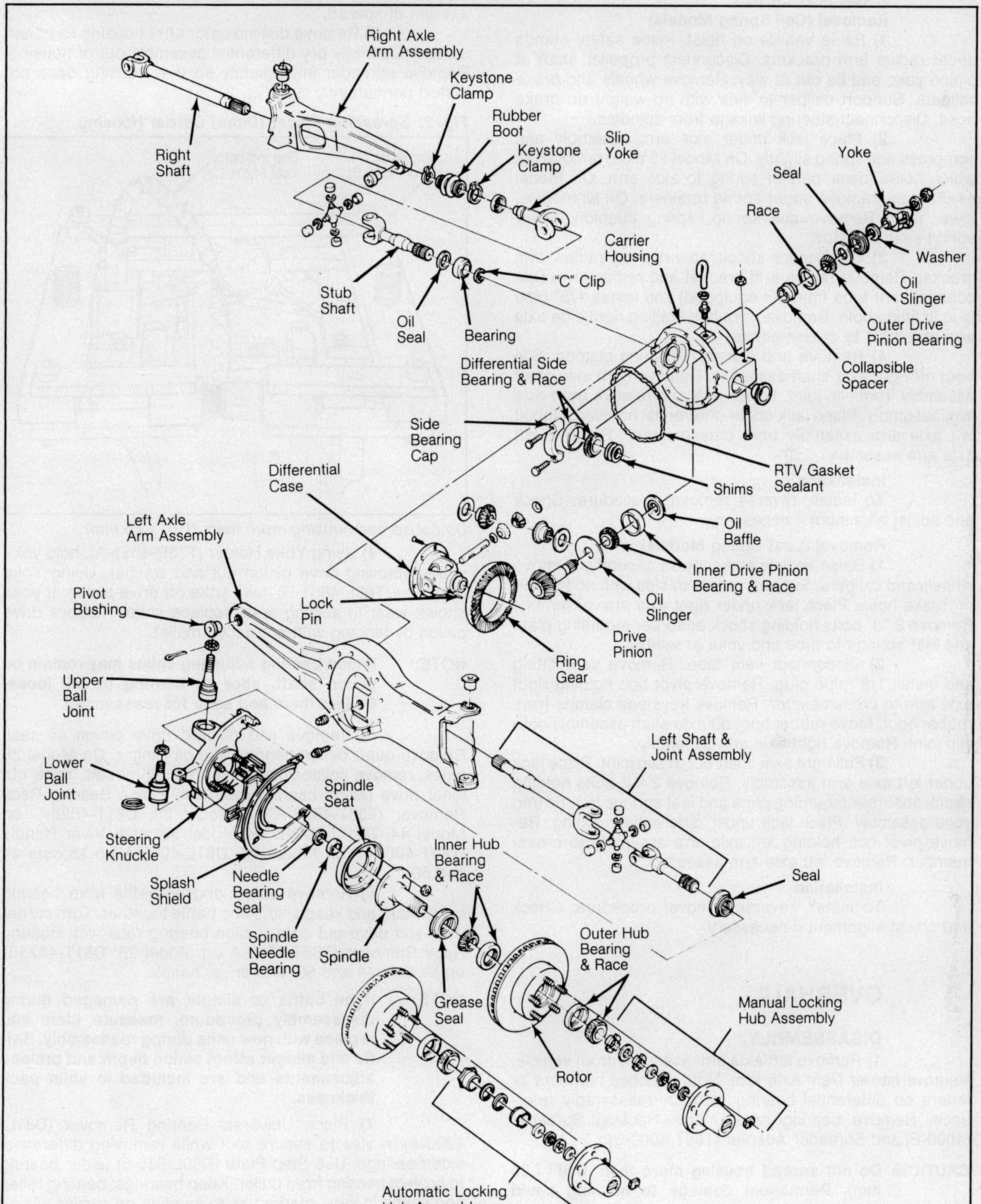

Models 44 and 50 use shims instead of collapsible spacer for drive pinion preload setting.

SPICER (DANA) IFS AXLE (Cont.)

AXLE ASSEMBLY

Removal (Coil Spring Models)

1) Raise vehicle on hoist. Place safety stands under radius arm brackets. Disconnect propeller shaft at pinion yoke and tie out of way. Remove wheels and brake calipers. Support caliper to side with no weight on brake hose. Disconnect steering linkage from spindles.

2) Place jack under axle arm assembly and compress coil spring slightly. On Model 28 axle, remove nut which holds lower part of spring to axle arm. On Model 44-IFS axle, remove upper spring retainers. On all models, lower jack. Remove coil spring, spring cushion, lower spring seat and stud.

3) Disconnect shock absorber at radius arm bracket. Remove radius arm bracket and radius arm. Disconnect vent tube fitting (if equipped) and install 1/8" pipe plug in fitting hole. Remove pivot bolt holding right side axle arm assembly to crossmember.

4) Remove and discard keystone clamps. Slip boot off right axle shaft assembly. Remove right axle shaft assembly from slip joint. Lower jack and remove right axle arm assembly. Place jack under differential housing. Unbolt left axle arm assembly from crossmember. Remove left axle arm assembly.

Installation

To install, reverse removal procedure. Check and adjust alignment if necessary.

Removal (Leaf Spring Models)

1) Raise vehicle and support securely. Remove wheels and calipers. Support caliper to side with no tension on brake hose. Place jack under right axle arm assembly. Remove 2 "U" bolts holding shock absorber mounting plate and leaf springs to tube and yoke assembly.

2) Disconnect vent tube. Remove vent fitting and install 1/8" pipe plug. Remove pivot bolt holding right axle arm to crossmember. Remove keystone clamps from rubber boot. Move rubber boot off axle shaft assembly onto slip joint. Remove right axle arm assembly.

3) Pull right axle shaft out of slip joint. Place jack under left axle arm assembly. Remove 2 "U" bolts holding shock absorber mounting plate and leaf springs to tube and yoke assembly. Place jack under differential housing. Remove pivot bolt holding left axle arm assembly to crossmember. Remove left axle arm assembly.

Installation

To install, reverse removal procedure. Check and adjust alignment if necessary.

OVERHAUL

DISASSEMBLY

1) Remove left axle arm assembly from vehicle. Remove carrier from axle arm. Note matched numbers or letters on differential bearing caps for reassembly reference. Remove bearing caps. Install Housing Spreader (4000-E) and Spreader Adapter (T80T-4000-B).

CAUTION: Do not spread housing more than .010" (.25 mm). Permanent damage to housing could result.

2) Rotate slip yoke and shaft assembly so open side of snap ring on shaft is exposed. Remove snap ring from shaft. Remove slip yoke and shaft assembly from carrier. Mount dial indicator on axle housing to measure amount of spread.

3) Remove dial indicator after housing has been spread. Carefully pry differential assembly out of housing. Remove spreader immediately so that housing does not distort permanently. *See Fig. 2.*

Fig. 2: Spreading Spicer (Dana) Carrier Housing

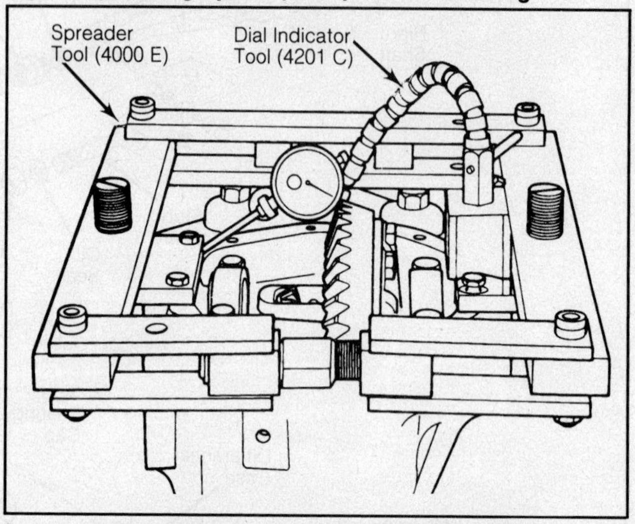

Do not spread housing more than .010" (.25 mm).

4) Using Yoke Holder (T78P-4851-A), hold yoke while removing drive pinion nut and washer. Using Yoke Remover (T65L-4851-B), take yoke off drive pinion. If yoke shows wear in sealing area, replace yoke. Remove drive pinion by tapping with soft-faced mallet.

NOTE: Pinion bearing adjusting shims may remain on pinion shaft, stick to bearing or fall loose. Collect them and save for reassembly.

5) Remove and discard drive pinion oil seal. Remove outer pinion bearing and oil slinger. On Model 28 axles, remove collapsible spacer. On all models, drive out inner drive pinion bearing race with Pinion Bearing Race Remover (T83T-4628-A on Model 28; D81T-4628-C on Model 44; D81T-4628-D on Model 50) and Driver Handle (T80T-4000-W on Model 28; D81L-4000-A on Models 44 and 50).

6) Remove shims and oil baffle from bearing bore. Mark and keep shims and baffle together. Turn carrier over and drive out outer pinion bearing race with Bearing Race Remover (T83T-4628-A on Model 28; D81T-4628-D on Models 44 and 50) and driver handle.

NOTE: If oil baffle or slinger are damaged during disassembly procedure, measure them and replace with new units during reassembly. Baffle and slinger affect pinion depth and preload adjustments and are included in shim pack thickness.

7) Place Universal Bearing Remover (D81L-4220-A) in vise to secure tool while removing differential side bearings. Use Step Plate (D80L-630-5) under bearing to protect bearing from puller. Keep bearings, bearing races and shims in sets, marked as to location on carrier.

8) Place differential case in vise with rags underneath to protect ring gear. Remove and discard ring gear bolts. Tap ring gear with soft-faced mallet to remove it from case. Drive out pinion shaft lock pin with drift. Drive out pinion shaft with drift.

Drive Axles

SPICER (DANA) IFS AXLE (Cont.)

9) Rotate side gears until pinion gears are aligned with case opening. Remove pinion gears and spherical washers. Remove side gears with thrust washers.

CLEANING & INSPECTION

1) Clean all components in solvent. Allow bearings to air dry. Inspect all machined surfaces for smoothness or raised edges. Inspect all gear teeth for wear or chipping and replace as necessary.

2) Check all bearings and races for nicks, roller end wear, grooves or any damage. Replace as needed. Replace all bearings if axle has high mileage. Check pinion yoke for wear in sealing area. Replace if worn.

3) Check differential pinion shaft, pinion gears, side gears and thrust washers for wear or damage. Replace all defective parts. Pinion gears must be replaced as sets.

REASSEMBLY & ADJUSTMENT

Precautions

1) When reassembling and adjusting ring and pinion assembly, pinion depth, pinion bearing preload, side bearing preload and backlash between ring and pinion must be adjusted.

2) If only pinion shaft and ring gear are to be replaced and carrier housing can be reused, compare pinion depth adjustment numbers etched in faces of old and new pinion heads. Using PINION DEPTH SHIM ADJUSTMENT chart, correct shims can be selected for new pinion shaft depth adjustment.

NOTE: **In order to use PINION DEPTH SHIM ADJUSTMENT chart procedure, old pinion shaft shim pack dimensions MUST be determined accurately. If original pinion shaft shim pack dimension cannot be determined accurately, Pinion Depth Gauge Set (T80T-4020-A) must be used to properly determine pinion depth setting. Depth gauge set must also be used if new carrier housing is to be used.**

3) The pinion depth adjustment number is determined by manufacturer at time of assembly. Number

PINION DEPTH SHIM ADJUSTMENT CHART (INCHES)

Old Pinion Marking	New Pinion Marking								
	-4	-3	-2	-1	0	+1	+2	+3	+4
+4	+0.008	+0.007	+0.006	+0.005	+0.004	+0.003	+0.002	+0.001	0
+3	+0.007	+0.006	+0.005	+0.004	+0.003	+0.002	+0.001	0	-0.001
+2	+0.006	+0.005	+0.004	+0.003	+0.002	+0.001	0	-0.001	-0.002
+1	+0.005	+0.004	+0.003	+0.002	+0.001	0	-0.001	-0.002	-0.003
0	+0.004	+0.003	+0.002	+0.001	0	-0.001	-0.002	-0.003	-0.004
-1	+0.003	+0.002	+0.001	0	-0.001	-0.002	-0.003	-0.004	-0.005
-2	+0.002	+0.001	0	-0.001	-0.002	-0.003	-0.004	-0.005	-0.006
-3	+0.001	0	-0.001	-0.002	-0.003	-0.004	-0.005	-0.006	-0.007
-4	0	-0.001	-0.002	-0.003	-0.004	-0.005	-0.006	-0.007	-0.008

PINION DEPTH SHIM ADJUSTMENT CHART (MILLIMETERS)

Old Pinion Marking	New Pinion Marking								
	-10	-8	-5	-3	0	+3	+5	+8	+10
+10	+0.20	+0.18	+0.15	+0.13	+0.10	+0.08	+0.05	+0.03	0
+8	+0.18	+0.15	+0.13	+0.10	+0.08	+0.05	+0.03	0	-0.03
+5	+0.15	+0.13	+0.10	+0.08	+0.05	+0.03	0	-0.03	-0.05
+3	+0.13	+0.10	+0.08	+0.05	+0.03	0	-0.03	-0.05	-0.08
0	+0.10	+0.08	+0.05	+0.03	0	-0.03	-0.05	-0.08	-0.10
-3	+0.08	+0.05	+0.03	0	-0.03	-0.05	-0.08	-0.10	-0.13
-5	+0.05	+0.03	0	-0.03	-0.05	-0.08	-0.10	-0.13	-0.15
-8	+0.03	0	-0.03	-0.05	-0.08	-0.10	-0.13	-0.15	-0.18
-10	0	-0.03	-0.05	-0.08	-0.10	-0.13	-0.15	-0.18	-0.20

SPICER (DANA) IFS AXLE (Cont.)

represents distance that best running position of pinion shaft deviates from "nominal" or standard distance between pinion gear face and centerline of axle. "Nominal" distance is measured from centerline of ring gear to face of gear on drive pinion shaft.

4) Pinions marked with "0" run at "nominal" or standard distance. "Nominal" distance for Model 28 axle is 2.228" (56.59 mm). On Model 44 axles, "nominal" distance is 2.625" (66.68 mm). On Model 50 axles, "nominal" distance is 2.810" (71.37 mm).

5) Pinion Depth Gauge Set (T80T-4020-A) allows shim pack adjustments to be made without having to remove and replace differential bearings when setting up shim packs. *See Fig. 3.*

Fig. 3: Pinion Depth Gauge Set (T80T-4020-A)

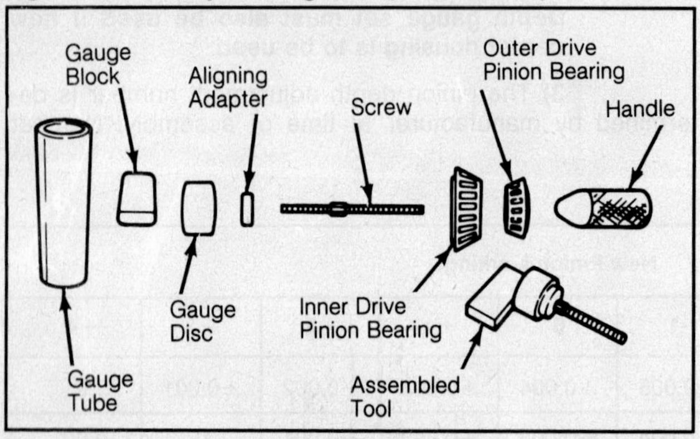

See table for correct tool application for axle model being repaired.

Differential Case

1) Place differential case in vise. Use multipurpose grease to lubricate side gears, pinion gears and all thrust washers. Install in case. Rotate side gears until holes in pinion gears and washers line up with holes in case.

2) Install differential pinion shaft. Inspect ring gear and case for burrs and nicks. Install ring gear and tighten bolts evenly to 50-60 ft. lbs. (68-81 N.m). Install Master Differential Bearings (T83T-4222-A on Model 28; D81T-4222-B on Model 44; D81T-4222-C on Model 50) on case. Install case in housing without shims.

Fig. 4: Measuring Differential Case End Play

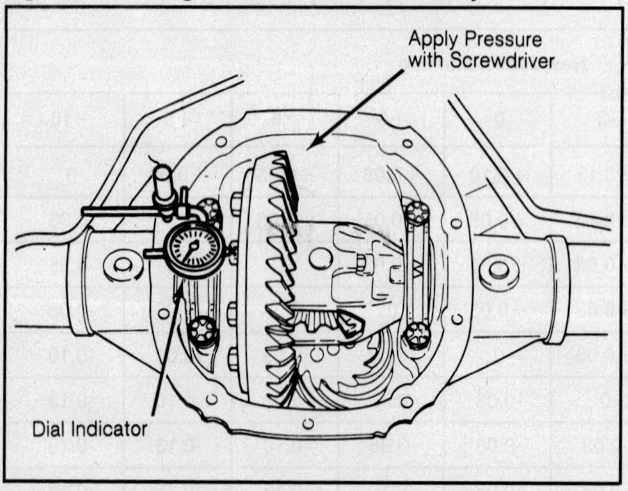

Check end play without shims installed on case.

3) Install side bearing caps. Mount dial indicator with minimum travel of .20" (5.1 mm) with indicator tip at 90° to flat surface on head of ring gear bolt. Measure and record amount of end play of differential case by moving it back and forth with screwdriver. *See Fig. 4.*

4) This measurement is total differential case end play. It will be used later to determine proper shim pack dimension. Remove case from housing. Leave master bearings on case at this time.

Drive Pinion Bearing Race Installation

1) Place inner and outer pinion bearing races in bores of carrier. Place Inner Race Installer (T71P-4616-A on Model 28; T80T-4000-D on Models 44 and 50) on inner bearing race. *See Fig. 5.*

2) Place Outer Race Installer (T71P-4616-A on Model 28; T80T-4000-E on Models 44 and 50) on outer bearing race. Install Forcing Screw (T75T-1176-A) through bearings. Tighten screw until bearing races are seated in carrier bore.

Fig. 5: Pinion Bearing Race Installer

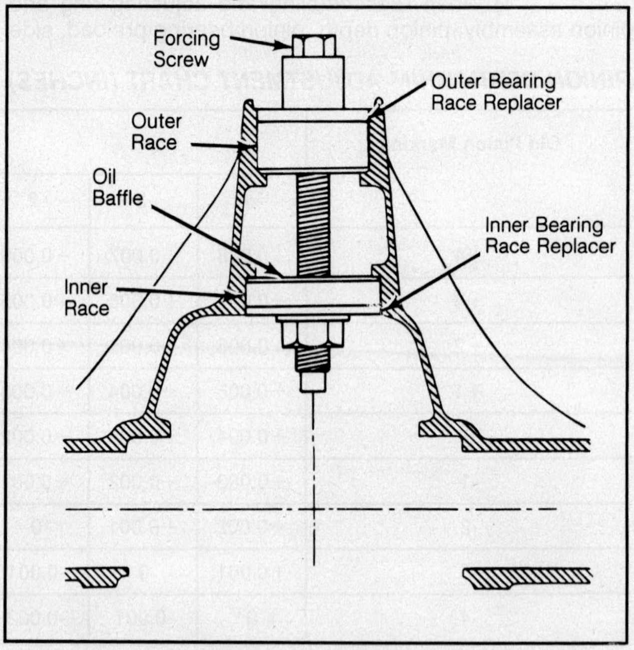

Install both pinion bearing races in carrier at same time.

Drive Pinion Depth

NOTE: **Tools in Pinion Depth Gauge Set (T80T-4020-A) must be checked before each use for nicks or damage. See PINION DEPTH GAUGE TOOL APPLICATION table for correct tool usage on particular axle. Any high spots on tools MUST be removed with medium India oilstone to ensure accurate readings.**

1) Put new inner drive pinion bearing on aligning adapter and assemble using gauge disc. *See Fig. 3.* Put outer pinion bearing (new or good used) into race. Put depth gauge assembly into housing with screw extending through outer bearing.

2) Thread handle onto screw finger tight. Using 3/8" torque wrench in square drive on handle, tighten handle until preload on bearings is 20-40 INCH lbs. (2.26-4.52 N.m). Center gauge tube in side bearing bore. Install side bearing caps and tighten bolts to 35-40 ft. lbs (47-54 N.m) on Model 28 axles and 80-90 ft. lbs. (108-122 N.m) on all other models.

SPICER (DANA) IFS AXLE (Cont.)

3) Place gauge block on top of face of drive pinion underneath gauge tube. Determine clearance between gauge block and gauge tube using feeler gauge. Correct feeler gauge will give feeling of slight drag as gauge strip passes between tube and block.

CAUTION: Make sure all tools are clean as incorrect readings could result if gauge tools have dirt or grit on them.

4) Thickness of correct feeler gauge is thickness of selective oil slinger (Model 28) or shim pack (Models 44 and 50) that is to be installed under inner bearing race, if drive pinion has NO markings on it. If drive pinion has plus (+) marking on face, subtract that number from thickness dimension. If drive pinion has minus (-) marking on face, add that number to thickness dimension.

NOTE: New inner pinion bearing used during depth measurement procedure MUST be used during final assembly for drive pinion depth to be correct. New oil slinger and/or baffle (if used) are to be measured as part of shim pack.

5) Remove inner pinion bearing race and install shim pack with oil baffle (if used) in carrier bearing bore. Reinstall inner bearing race in carrier. Press inner drive pinion bearing and oil slinger (if used) on drive pinion, using Axle Bearing/Seal Plate (T75-1165-B), Pinion Bearing Replacer (T57L-4621-B on Model 28; T53T-4621-B on Model 44; T70P-4625 on Model 50) and press.

PINION DEPTH GAUGE TOOL APPLICATION

Tool Name	Tool Number
Aligning Adapter	
Model 28	T76P-4020-A1
Models 44 & 50	T75P-4020-A2
Final Check Gauge Block	
Model 28	T83T-4020-F58
Model 44	D81T-4020-F52
Model 50	D81T-4020-F53
Gauge Block	
Model 28	T76P-4020-A10
Models 44 & 50	T80T-4020-F42
Gauge Disc	
Model 28	T83T-4020-F57
Model 44	D80T-4020-F44
Model 50	T80T-4020-F40
Gauge Tube	
Model 28	T76P-4020-A7
Model 44	D80T-4020-F47
Model 50	T80T-4020-F41
Handle	
All Models	T76P-4020-A11
Screw	
Model 28	T76P-4020-A9
Models 44 & 50	T80T-4020-F43

Drive Pinion Bearing Preload & Final Depth Check (Model 28)

1) Install drive pinion in carrier. Install outer bearing and oil slinger. Install pinion yoke, washer, deflector, oil slinger and NEW nut on pinion shaft. Use Yoke Installer (T83T-4851-A) and Yoke Holder (T78P-4851-A) to seat yoke. Tighten pinion yoke nut until rotational torque necessary to turn pinion is 10 INCH lbs. (1.1 N.m).

2) Install gauge tube in carrier bore. Install side bearing caps and tighten bolts to 35-40 ft. lbs. (47-54 N.m). Place final check gauge block on top of drive pinion face under gauge tube. Hold gauge block with thumb to keep it level. Measure distance between gauge tube and final check gauge block with feeler gauge. *See Fig. 6.*

3) Check reading of feeler gauge when slight drag is felt as gauge is pulled between gauge tube and gauge block. Correct reading should be .020" (.50 mm) greater than pinion depth adjustment figure etched in face of drive pinion with tolerance of .002" (.05 mm).

4) Drive pinion with "+2" etching should give reading of .022" (.55 mm) with tolerance of .002" (.05 mm). Acceptable reading would be .020-.024" (.50-.60 mm). If reading is too low, replace oil slinger under inner drive pinion bearing race with thinner oil slinger. If reading is too high, replace oil slinger with thicker one.

5) When drive pinion depth is correct, remove pinion yoke with holder and yoke remover. Remove outer bearing. Install NEW collapsible spacer. Reinstall outer bearing. Coat pinion yoke oil seal with hypoid gear oil. Install seal using Oil Seal Replacer (T71T-3010-R).

6) Make sure spring behind lip of seal does not jump out while seal is being installed. If spring does jump out, remove and replace seal. Install drive pinion yoke and tighten nut to 175 ft. lbs. (237 N.m). Measure drive pinion rotational torque. If preload is correct, rotational torque should be 15-35 INCH lbs. (1.7-4.0 N.m).

7) If rotational torque reading is too low, tighten pinion nut in small increments until reading is correct. DO NOT tighten drive pinion nut to more than 225 ft. lbs. (305 N.m).

8) If rotational torque reading is too high, collapsible spacer has been compressed too far. Remove and replace spacer. Repeat check of rotational torque.

CAUTION: Always use NEW collapsible spacer when reassembling drive pinion. NEVER tighten pinion yoke nut over 225 ft. lbs. (305 N.m) as collapsible spacer will be compressed too far.

Drive Pinion Bearing Preload & Final Depth Check (Models 44 & 50)

1) Measure original preload shim pack and replace with new shims of equal thickness. Install drive pinion in carrier housing. Install new preload shim pack on pinion shaft. Install outer bearing and oil slinger. Install drive pinion yoke with washer, deflector, slinger and NEW nut, using Yoke Installer (T80T-4000-G).

2) Tighten pinion yoke nut to 200-220 ft. lbs. (271-298 N.m). Using torque wrench, check rotational torque necessary to turn drive pinion. Torque reading should be 20-40 INCH lbs. (2.26-4.52 N.m) if preload is correct. If preload reading is too low, remove preload shims from drive pinion. If preload reading is too high, add preload shims to drive pinion.

3) Install gauge tube. Install side bearing caps and tighten bolts to 80-90 ft. lbs. (108-122 N.m). Place final check gauge block on top of drive pinion face under gauge tube. Hold gauge block with thumb to keep it level. Measure distance between gauge tube and gauge block with feeler gauge. *See Fig. 6.*

4) Check reading of feeler gauge when slight drag is felt as gauge is pulled between gauge tube and gauge block. Correct reading should be .020" (.50 mm) greater than pinion depth adjustment figure etched in face of drive pinion with tolerance of .002" (.05 mm).

SPICER (DANA) IFS AXLE (Cont.)

Fig. 6: Final Pinion Depth Check

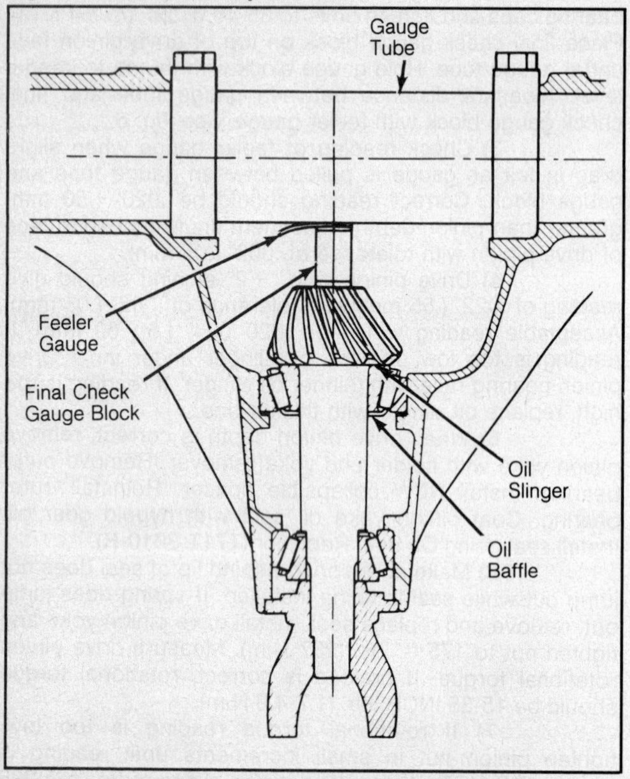

Hold thumb on gauge block to keep block level.

5) Drive pinion with "+2" etching should give reading of .022" (.55 mm) with tolerance of .002" (.05 mm). Acceptable reading would be .020-.024" (.50-.60 mm). If reading is too low, remove shims from underneath inner drive pinion bearing race. If reading is too high, add shims underneath inner drive pinion bearing race.

6) When final drive pinion depth check is correct, remove pinion yoke with holder and yoke remover. Coat pinion yoke oil seal with hypoid gear oil. Install seal using Oil Seal Replacer (T80T-4000-C).

7) Make sure spring behind lip of seal does not jump out while seal is being installed. If spring does jump out, remove and replace seal. Install drive pinion yoke and tighten nut to 200-220 ft. lbs. (271-298 N.m).

Ring & Pinion Gear Backlash (Model 28)

1) With drive pinion depth and preload adjustments properly made, install differential case into housing. Differential master bearings should still be on case. Force differential case away from drive pinion gear so that case is fully seated in cross bores of carrier.

2) Set dial indicator so that tip is against head of ring gear bolt at 90° to bolt. Rock ring gear so that teeth of ring gear mesh fully with drive pinion gear teeth. Force ring gear teeth against drive pinion gear teeth and zero dial indicator. Force ring gear and case away from drive pinion gear. Repeat this procedure until same reading is obtained each time.

3) This reading, less .006" (.15 mm), is thickness of shim pack that must go under differential side bearing on ring gear side of case. Remove case from carrier. Remove master bearings from case. Place correct shim pack on ring gear hub of case. Place side bearing on hub of case. Drive bearing onto case using Side Bearing Replacer (T80T-4000-J).

4) To determine shim pack thickness that goes under side bearing on opposite side of case from ring gear, subtract reading obtained in step **2)** from total case end play determined earlier. Add .003" (.08 mm) to figure determined for shim pack thickness on side opposite ring gear.

5) Place required thickness shim pack on hub of case opposite ring gear. Place Step Plate (D80L-630-5) on ring gear side bearing to protect bearing. Drive remaining side bearing onto case with side bearing replacer. Install side bearing races on side bearings.

6) Install housing spreader and dial indicator on carrier. Spread case to maximum of .015" (.37 mm) for installation procedure. Install differential case in carrier. Use soft-faced hammer to ensure that case seats fully in carrier bore. Use care to avoid damaging teeth of ring and pinion gears.

7) If partial or non-hunting/partial ring and pinion gear set is being used, line up mating marks on gears. Remove spreader and dial indicator. Install side bearing caps, making sure that letters stamped on caps match letters stamped on housing. Tighten cap bolts to 35-40 ft. lbs. (47-54 N.m).

8) Check ring and pinion gear backlash in 3 places equally spaced around ring gear. Backlash range is .004-.010" (.10-.25 mm) with allowable maximum variation of .003" (.08 mm).

9) If backlash figure is too high, ring gear must be moved closer to drive pinion gear. If backlash figure is too low, ring gear must be moved away from drive pinion gear. To change backlash readings, move shims from 1 side of differential case to other. Total thickness of end play shim packs must not change.

10) When backlash adjustment is completed, check tooth contact pattern. See GEAR TOOTH CONTACT PATTERNS in this section. Pattern should be correct if assembly and adjustments have been done properly.

11) When backlash is correct, apply bead of RTV to mating surfaces of carrier mounting face support arm. Bead should be 1/8-1/4" (3.2-6.4 mm) high and 1/4-1/2" (6.4-12.7 mm) wide. Install carrier on left axle arm assembly, using 2 guide pins and being careful not to smear sealant.

12) Tighten carrier bolts to 40-50 ft. lbs. (54-68 N.m). Tighten any bolt and then tighten bolt directly opposite. Tighten remaining bolts in clockwise or counterclockwise pattern.

13) Install and tighten carrier shear bolt and nut to 75-95 ft. lbs. (102-129 N.m). Allow 1 hour curing time for sealant. Fill assembly with hypoid lubricant.

Ring & Pinion Gear Backlash (Models 44 & 50)

1) With drive pinion depth and preload adjustments properly made, install differential case into housing. Differential master bearings should still be on case. Make sure case is fully seated in carrier bores. Set dial indicator so that tip is against head of ring gear bolt at 90° to bolt.

2) Rock ring gear so that teeth of ring gear mesh fully with drive pinion gear teeth. Force ring gear teeth against drive pinion gear teeth and zero dial indicator. Force ring gear and case away from drive pinion gear. Repeat this procedure until same reading is obtained each time.

3) This reading is thickness of shim pack that must go under differential side bearing on ring gear side of case. Remove dial indicator. Remove differential case from housing. Remove master bearings from differential case. Place shim pack of correct thickness on ring gear hub.

SPICER (DANA) IFS AXLE (Cont.)

4) Drive side bearing onto case using Side Bearing Installer (T80T-4000-J). Subtract thickness of shim pack installed on ring gear side of case from total differential case end play determined earlier.

5) Add .010" (.26 mm) for preload to figure determined for remaining end play. Result is thickness of shim pack that is to be installed on hub of differential case opposite ring gear (drive pinion side of case).

6) Place shim pack on case hub and drive side bearing onto case using side bearing installer. Support case with Step Plate (D80L-630-5) to protect side bearing already installed on ring gear side of case.

7) Install housing spreader and dial indicator on carrier housing. Set tip of dial indicator at same point used when case was removed from housing during disassembly procedure. Spread housing maximum of .010" (.25 mm) as damage could occur if housing is spread further. Remove dial indicator.

8) Place side bearing races on side bearings. Install case in carrier housing. Use soft-faced hammer to seat case assembly in carrier bore. Use care to avoid damaging teeth of ring and drive pinion gears. If partial or non-hunting/partial ring and pinion gear set is being used, line up mating marks on gears. Remove spreader and dial indicator.

9) Install side bearing caps, making sure that letters stamped on caps match letters stamped on housing. Tighten cap bolts to 80-90 ft. lbs. (108-122 N.m). Check ring and pinion gear backlash in 3 places equally spaced around ring gear. Backlash range is .005-.009" (.13-.23 mm) with allowable maximum variation of .003" (.08 mm).

Fig. 7: Drive Pinion & Ring Gear Tooth Contact

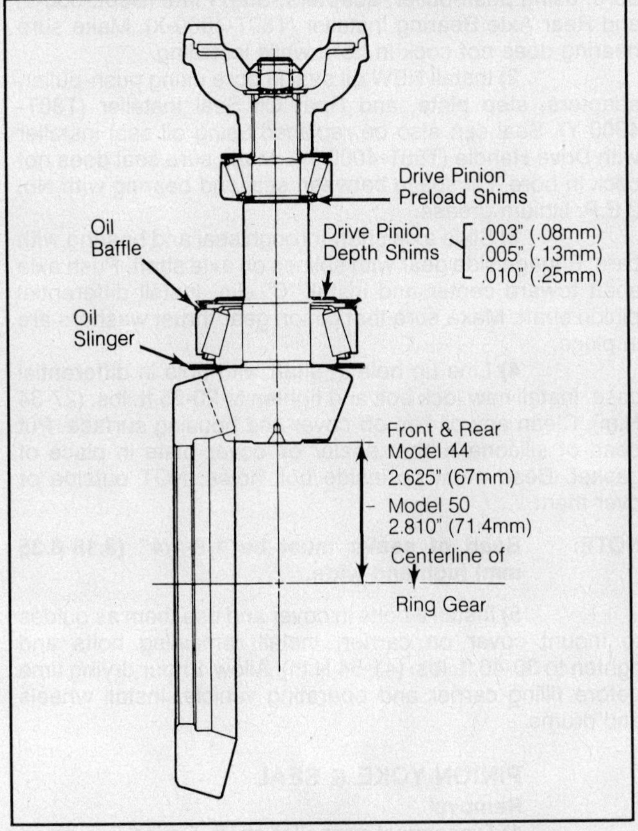

Preload settings do not affect drive pinion depth setting.

10) If backlash figure is too high, ring gear must be moved closer to drive pinion gear. If backlash figure is too low, ring gear must be moved away from drive pinion gear. To change backlash readings, move shims from 1 side of differential case to other. Total thickness of end play shim packs must not change.

11) When backlash adjustment is completed, check tooth contact pattern. See GEAR TOOTH CONTACT PATTERNS in this section. Pattern should be correct if assembly and adjustments have been done properly.

12) When backlash is correct, apply bead of RTV to mating surfaces of carrier mounting face support arm. Bead should be 1/8-1/4" (3.2-6.4 mm) high and 1/4-1/2" (6.4-12.7 mm) wide. Install carrier on left axle arm assembly, using 2 guide pins and being careful not to smear sealant.

13) Use new carrier bolts with adhesive-treated threads or clean old bolts and apply locking compound. Tighten carrier bolts to 30-40 ft. lbs. (41-54 N.m). Install and tighten support arm tab bolts on side of carrier to 85-100 ft. lbs. (115-136 N.m). Allow 1 hour curing time for sealant. Fill assembly with hypoid lubricant.

AXLE ASSEMBLY SPECIFICATIONS

Application	In. (mm)
Axle Shaft End Play	Non-Adjustable
Ring Gear-to-Pinion Backlash	
Model 28	.004-.010 (.10-.25)
Models 44 & 50	.005-.009 (.13-.23)
"Nominal" Pinion Gear Depth	
Model 28 (7.50" R.G.)	2.228" (56.52 mm)
Model 44 (8.50" R.G.)	2.625" (66.68 mm)
Model 50 (9.25" R.G.)	2.810" (71.37 mm)
	INCH Lbs. (N.m)
Drive Pinion Bearing Preload	
Model 28	15-35 (1.7-4.0)
Models 44 & 50	20-40 (2.3-4.5)

TIGHTENING SPECIFICATIONS

Application	Ft. Lbs. (N.m)
Axle Pivot Bolt	120-150 (163-203)
Pinion Shaft Yoke Nut	
Model 28	175-225 (237-305)
Models 44 & 50	200-220 (271-298)
Ring Gear-to-Case Bolt	50-60 (68-81)
Side Bearing Cap Bolt	
Model 28	35-40 (48-54)
Models 44 & 50	80-90 (108-122)

SPICER (DANA) SEMI-FLOATING AXLES

Ford Light Duty E & F250 Rear Axles

DESCRIPTION

Axle assembly is hypoid gear type with integral carrier housing. Drive pinion depth, pinion bearing preload, side bearing preload and ring gear backlash are all set or adjusted with shims.

Term "semi-floating" refers to drive axle configurations in which axle shafts support vehicle load. Axle shaft rides in axle bearing which is pressed into outer end of axle housing.

AXLE RATIO & IDENTIFICATION

Spicer (Dana) drive axles have removable rear cover plates. Cover plate is unique in shape, which allows positive identification of Spicer (Dana) drive axles on any vehicle. *See Fig. 1.*

Metal identification tag can be found attached to carrier housing by 2 cover bolts. Tag lists gear ratio and part numbers. Tag also tells if limited slip is used. Models used by Ford are 60-3 and 60-5 versions.

Fig. 1: Spicer (Dana) Housing Cover Gasket

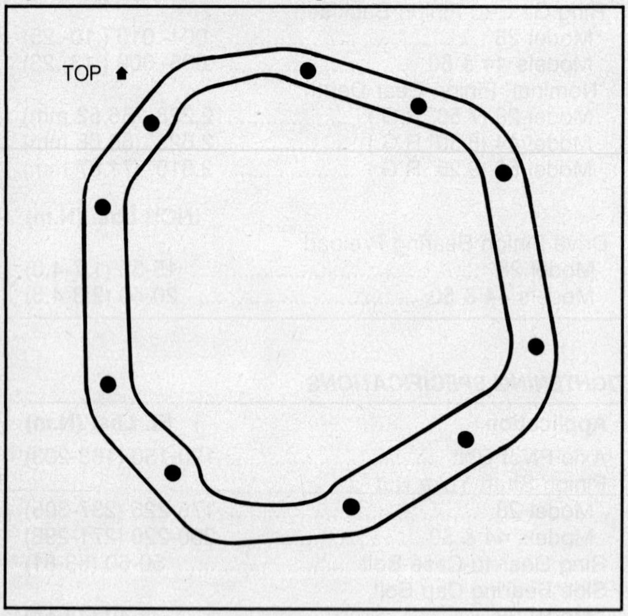

Gasket shape aids in identification.

REMOVAL & INSTALLATION

AXLE SHAFTS & BEARINGS

Removal

1) Raise vehicle and support securely. Remove wheels and brake drums. Remove cover plate to drain lubricant. Remove and discard differential pinion shaft screw.

2) Unit is equipped with 2 types of lock bolts. One has threads that are coated with locking compound. This type has 5/32" hexagram socket head and must be discarded after removal. The other type uses torque prevailing threads and has 12-point drive head.

NOTE: Lock bolts treated with locking compound must NEVER be reused. Lock bolts with torque prevailing threads may be used through 4 removal and installation procedures. If number of uses is unknown, replace lock bolt.

3) Remove differential pinion shaft. Push flanged end of axle shaft toward center of vehicle. Remove "C" clip from inner end of axle shaft. Pull axle shaft out of housing tube. Be careful to avoid damage to seals at ends of tube.

NOTE: DO NOT rotate differential side gears when removing axle shafts. Side gears turning cause pinion gears and thrust washers to turn in case and fall out of opening in case.

4) Pry oil seal out of end of axle tube and discard seal. Using Push-Puller (T81P-1104-C), Adapters (T81P-1104-B for coarse threads or D81T-1104-A for fine threads) and Rear Wheel Bearing Remover (T81T-1225-A), remove bearing from bore of axle housing.

CAUTION: Wear safety glasses when removing bearing from housing as bearing could explode or shatter under pressure.

5) Make sure bearing bore has no nicks or burrs. Polish bore with emery cloth. Clean bore with metal cleaning solvent. Any burrs or flaking in bore could cause premature failure of new bearing.

Installation

1) Coat bearing with axle lubricant to aid in installation and prevent scoring in bore. Install bearing in bore, using push-puller, adapters, Step Plate (D80L-630-1) and Rear Axle Bearing Installer (T80T-4000-X). Make sure bearing does not cock in bore while installing.

2) Install NEW oil seal in bore using push-puller, adapters, step plate, and Rear Oil Seal Installer (T80T-4000-Y). Seal can also be replaced using oil seal installer with Drive Handle (T80T-4000-W). Make sure seal does not cock in bore. Fill space between seal and bearing with No. 2 E.P. lithium grease.

3) Slide axle shaft through seal and bearing with care. Engage side gear with splines on axle shaft. Push axle shaft toward center and install "C" clip. Install differential pinion shaft. Make sure that pinion gear thrust washers are in place.

4) Line up hole in shaft with hole in differential case. Install new lock bolt and tighten to 20-25 ft. lbs. (27-34 N.m). Clean any oil film off cover and housing surface. Put bead of silicone rubber sealer on cover plate in place of gasket. Bead must go inside bolt holes, NOT outside or over them.

NOTE: Bead of sealer must be 1/8-1/4" (3.18-6.35 mm) high and wide.

5) Install 2 bolts in cover and use them as guides to mount cover on carrier. Install remaining bolts and tighten to 30-40 ft. lbs. (41-54 N.m). Allow 1 hour drying time before filling carrier and operating vehicle. Install wheels and drums.

PINION YOKE & SEAL

Removal

1) Disconnect propeller shaft. Scribe line down pinion shaft, yoke and nut for reassembly reference. Re-

SPICER (DANA) SEMI-FLOATING AXLES (Cont.)

move pinion nut, using Flange Holder (T57T-4851-B) to keep flange from turning.

2) Use Flange Remover (T65L-4851-B) to remove pinion flange from carrier. If area of flange that seal contacts is worn, replace flange. Pry seal out of housing. Avoid damaging machined bore.

Installation

1) Lubricate cavity between seal lips with high melting point lubricant. Drive seal into bore, making sure that seal bottoms against shoulder. Align flange with scribe marks made during disassembly.

2) Place flange on shaft and draw it down with pinion nut. Tighten pinion nut to specifications. Failure to tighten pinion nut to full specifications could result in damage to flange or pinion shaft. Install propeller shaft.

AXLE ASSEMBLY

Removal

1) Raise vehicle and support securely. Support axle assembly to take weight off suspension. Disconnect drive shaft at pinion flange and tie out of way. Remove hub and drum assembly.

2) Disconnect vent tube (if equipped). Disconnect parking brake cable(s) and service brake hydraulic lines. Disconnect shock absorbers at axle brackets. Disconnect springs and remove axle.

Installation

Reverse removal procedure. Do not fully tighten shock absorbers until weight of vehicle is on suspension. Bleed hydraulic system. Adjust parking brake before moving vehicle.

OVERHAUL

DISASSEMBLY

NOTE: **Axle housing does not need to be removed for overhaul. However, it is suggested that entire axle unit be removed from vehicle and held securely in stand or rack.**

1) Remove housing cover. Pull axle shafts far enough out of housing so carrier can clear ends of shafts. After shafts are removed, install pinion shaft with old lock bolt finger tightened. This procedure will keep pinion gears and thrust washers from rotating and dropping out of case.

2) If side bearing caps are not marked with letters, mark them for reassembly reference on correct side. Loosen side bearing cap bolts and install Axle Housing Spreader (4000-E) on housing. Mount dial indicator on axle housing to measure amount of spread.

CAUTION: **Do not spread housing more than .015" (.38 mm). Permanent damage to housing could result.**

3) Remove dial indicator after housing has been spread. Remove bearing cap bolts. Carefully pry differential assembly out of housing. Remove spreader tool immediately, so that housing does not take set.

4) Place Universal Bearing Remover (D81L-4220-A) in vise to secure tool while removing differential side bearings. Keep bearings, bearing races and shims in sets, marked as to location on carrier. Place differential case in vise with rags underneath to protect ring gear.

Fig. 2: Spreading Spicer (Dana) Carrier Housing

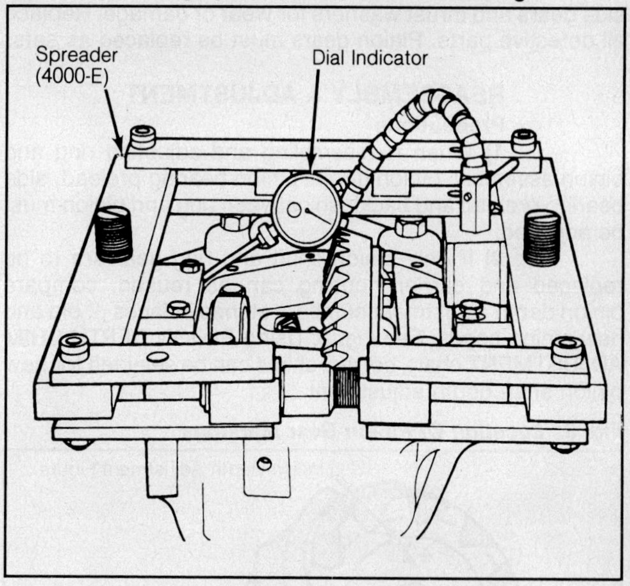

Do not leave spreader tension on housing as damage will result.

5) Remove and discard ring gear bolts. Tap ring gear with soft-faced mallet to remove it from case. Remove pinion shaft lock bolt with 12-point socket. Remove slip fitted pinion shaft. Rotate side gears until pinion gears are aligned with case opening.

6) Remove pinion gears and spherical washers. Remove side gears with thrust washers. Rotate nose of carrier to horizontal position. Hold flange with Pinion Flange Holder (T57T-4851-B) and remove pinion nut and washer. Using Flange Puller (T65L-4851-B), remove pinion yoke. Using soft-faced hammer, tap pinion shaft out of housing.

NOTE: **Pinion bearing adjusting shims may remain on pinion shaft, stick to bearing or fall loose. Collect them and save for reassembly.**

7) Remove pinion seal with Bearing Race Puller (T77F-1102-A) and slide hammer. Discard seal. Remove bearing and outer oil slinger. Turn nose of carrier housing downward. Remove outer pinion bearing race with Bearing Race Driver (D81T-4628-D) and Driver Handle (D81L-4000-A). Be careful not to damage carrier bore.

8) Remove inner bearing race with Bearing Race Driver (D81T-4628-A) and driver handle. Remove shims and baffle (if used) from race bore in carrier. Pull inner pinion bearing from drive pinion shaft with universal bearing remover.

NOTE: **Both oil slinger and baffle (if used) are part of shim pack and must be reused or replaced during reassembly procedure.**

CLEANING & INSPECTION

1) Clean all components in solvent. Allow bearings to air dry. Inspect all machined surfaces for smoothness or raised edges. Inspect all bearings and races for wear or pitting and replace as necessary. Inspect all gear teeth for wear or chipping and replace as necessary.

2) Check all bearings and races for nicks, roller end wear, grooves or any damage. Replace as needed. Replace all bearings if axle has high mileage. Check pinion flange for wear in sealing area. Replace if worn.

3) Check differential pinion shaft, pinion gears, side gears and thrust washers for wear or damage. Replace all defective parts. Pinion gears must be replaced as sets.

REASSEMBLY & ADJUSTMENT

Precautions

1) When reassembling and adjusting ring and pinion assembly, pinion depth, pinion bearing preload, side bearing preload and backlash between ring and pinion must be adjusted.

2) If only pinion shaft and ring gear are to be replaced and carrier housing can be reused, compare pinion depth adjustment numbers etched in faces of old and new pinion heads. *See Fig. 3.* Using PINION DEPTH SHIM ADJUSTMENT chart, correct shims can be selected for new pinion shaft depth adjustment.

Fig. 3: Location Of Pinion Gear Markings

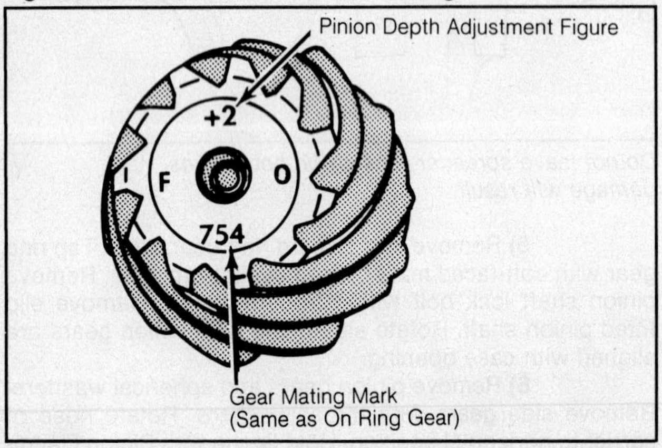

Gear mating numbers on ring and pinion gears must match.

NOTE: In order to use PINION DEPTH SHIM ADJUSTMENT chart procedure, old pinion shaft shim pack dimensions MUST be determined accurately. If original pinion shaft shim pack dimension cannot be determined accurately, Pinion Depth Gauge Set (T80T-4020-A) must be used to properly determine pinion depth setting. Depth gauge set must also be used if new carrier housing is to be used.

3) The pinion depth adjustment number is determined by manufacturer at time of assembly. Number represents distance that best running position of pinion shaft deviates from "nominal" or standard distance between pinion gear face and centerline of axle. "Nominal" distance for Model 60 axle is 3.125" (79.38 mm).

4) Pinion Depth Gauge Set (T80T-4020-A) allows shim pack adjustments to be made without having to remove and replace differential bearings when setting up shim packs. *See Fig. 4.*

Differential Case

1) Place differential case in vise. Use multipurpose grease to lubricate side gears, pinion gears and all thrust washers. Install in case. Rotate side gears until holes in pinion gears and washers line up with holes in case.

2) Install differential pinion shaft. Install new lock bolt finger tight. Inspect ring gear and case for burrs and nicks. Install ring gear and tighten bolts evenly to 100-120 ft. lbs. (136-163 N.m). Install Master Differential Bearings (D81T-4222-D) on case. Install case in housing without shims.

Fig. 4: Pinion Depth Gauge Set (T80T-4020-A)

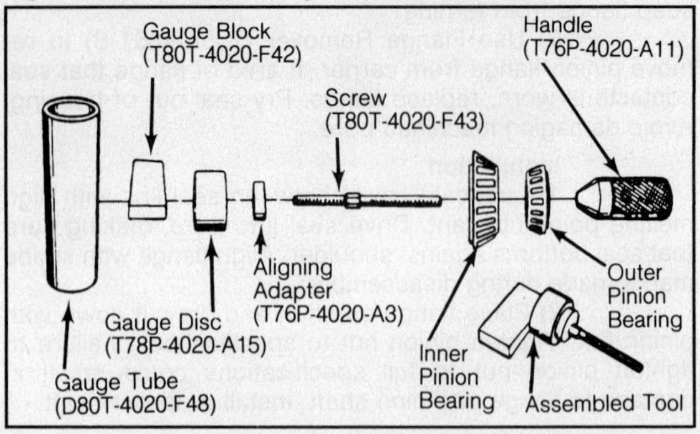

These tools are to be used on Model 60 axles only.

3) Install side bearing caps. Mount dial indicator with minimum travel of .20" (5.1 mm) with indicator tip at 90° to back of differential flange. Measure and record amount of end play of differential case by moving it back and forth with screwdriver. *See Fig. 5.*

Fig. 5: Measuring Differential Case End Play

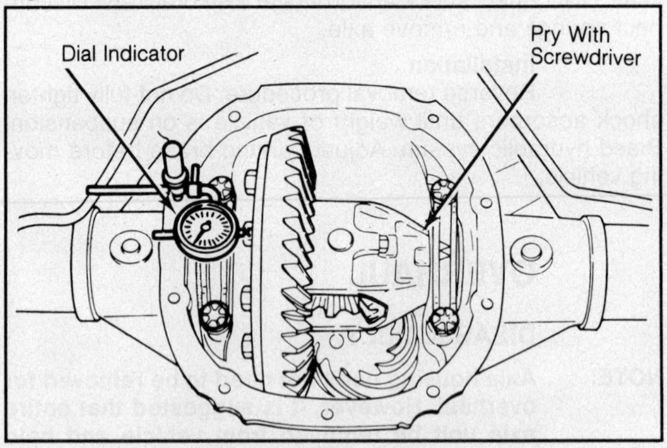

Check end play without shims installed on case.

4) This measurement is total differential case end play. It will be used later to determine proper shim pack dimension. Remove case from housing. Leave master bearings on case at this time.

Drive Pinion Bearing Race Installation

1) Place inner and outer pinion bearing races in bores of carrier. Place Inner Race Installer (T56T-4616-B2) on inner bearing race. Place Outer Race Installer (T56T-4616-B1) on outer bearing race.

2) Install Threaded Drawbar (T75T-1176) through bearings. Tighten drawbar until bearing races are seated in carrier bore.

Drive Pinion Depth

NOTE: Pinion depth gauge tools must be checked before each use for nicks or damage. Any high spots on tools MUST be removed with medium India oilstone to ensure accurate readings.

1) Put new inner drive pinion bearing on Aligning Adapter (T76P-4020-A3) and assemble with Pinion Depth Gauge Set (T80T-4020-A), using Gauge Disc (T78P-4020-A15). *See Fig. 4.* Put outer pinion bearing (new or good

SPICER (DANA) SEMI-FLOATING AXLES (Cont.)

PINION DEPTH SHIM ADJUSTMENT CHART (INCHES)

Old Pinion Marking	New Pinion Marking								
	-4	-3	-2	-1	0	+1	+2	+3	+4
+4	+0.008	+0.007	+0.006	+0.005	+0.004	+0.003	+0.002	+0.001	0
+3	+0.007	+0.006	+0.005	+0.004	+0.003	+0.002	+0.001	0	-0.001
+2	+0.006	+0.005	+0.004	+0.003	+0.002	+0.001	0	-0.001	-0.002
+1	+0.005	+0.004	+0.003	+0.002	+0.001	0	-0.001	-0.002	-0.003
0	+0.004	+0.003	+0.002	+0.001	0	-0.001	-0.002	-0.003	-0.004
-1	+0.003	+0.002	+0.001	0	-0.001	-0.002	-0.003	-0.004	-0.005
-2	+0.002	+0.001	0	-0.001	-0.002	-0.003	-0.004	-0.005	-0.006
-3	+0.001	0	-0.001	-0.002	-0.003	-0.004	-0.005	-0.006	-0.007
-4	0	-0.001	-0.002	-0.003	-0.004	-0.005	-0.006	-0.007	-0.008

PINION DEPTH SHIM ADJUSTMENT CHART (MILLIMETERS)

Old Pinion Marking	New Pinion Marking								
	-10	-8	-5	-3	0	+3	+5	+8	+10
+10	+0.20	+0.18	+0.15	+0.13	+0.10	+0.08	+0.05	+0.03	0
+8	+0.18	+0.15	+0.13	+0.10	+0.08	+0.05	+0.03	0	-0.03
+5	+0.15	+0.13	+0.10	+0.08	+0.05	+0.03	0	-0.03	-0.05
+3	+0.13	+0.10	+0.08	+0.05	+0.03	0	-0.03	-0.05	-0.08
0	+0.10	+0.08	+0.05	+0.03	0	-0.03	-0.05	-0.08	-0.10
-3	+0.08	+0.05	+0.03	0	-0.03	-0.05	-0.08	-0.10	-0.13
-5	+0.05	+0.03	0	-0.03	-0.05	-0.08	-0.10	-0.13	-0.15
-8	+0.03	0	-0.03	-0.05	-0.08	-0.10	-0.13	-0.15	-0.18
-10	0	-0.03	-0.05	-0.08	-0.10	-0.13	-0.15	-0.18	-0.20

used) into race. Put gauge assembly into housing with Screw (T80T-4020-F43) extending through outer bearing.

2) Thread Handle (T76P-4020-A11) onto screw finger tight. Using 3/8" torque wrench in square drive on handle, tighten handle until preload on bearings is 20-40 INCH lbs. (2.26-4.52 N.m). Center Gauge Tube (D80T-4020-F48) in side bearing bore. Install side bearing caps and tighten bolts to 80-90 ft. lbs. (108-122 N.m).

3) Place Gauge Block (T80T-4020-F42) on top of face of drive pinion underneath gauge tube. Determine clearance between gauge block and gauge tube using feeler gauge. Correct feeler gauge will give feeling of slight drag as gauge strip passes between tube and block.

CAUTION: Make sure all tools are clean as incorrect readings could result if gauge tools have dirt or grit on them.

4) Thickness of correct feeler gauge is thickness of shim pack that is to be installed under inner bearing race, if drive pinion has NO markings on it. If drive pinion has plus (+) marking on face, subtract that number from thickness dimension. If drive pinion has minus (-) marking on face, add that number to thickness dimension.

NOTE: New inner pinion bearing used during depth measurement procedure MUST be used during final assembly for drive pinion depth to be correct. New oil slinger and/or baffle (if used) are to be measured as part of shim pack.

5) Remove inner pinion bearing race and install shim pack with baffle (if used) in carrier bearing bore. Reinstall inner bearing race in carrier. Press inner drive pinion bearing and oil slinger (if used) on drive pinion, using Axle Bearing/Seal Plate (T75-1165-B), Axle Bearing/Seal Replacer (T75-1165-DA) and press.

Drive Axles

SPICER (DANA) SEMI-FLOATING AXLES (Cont.)

Fig. 6: Pinion Bearing Race Installer

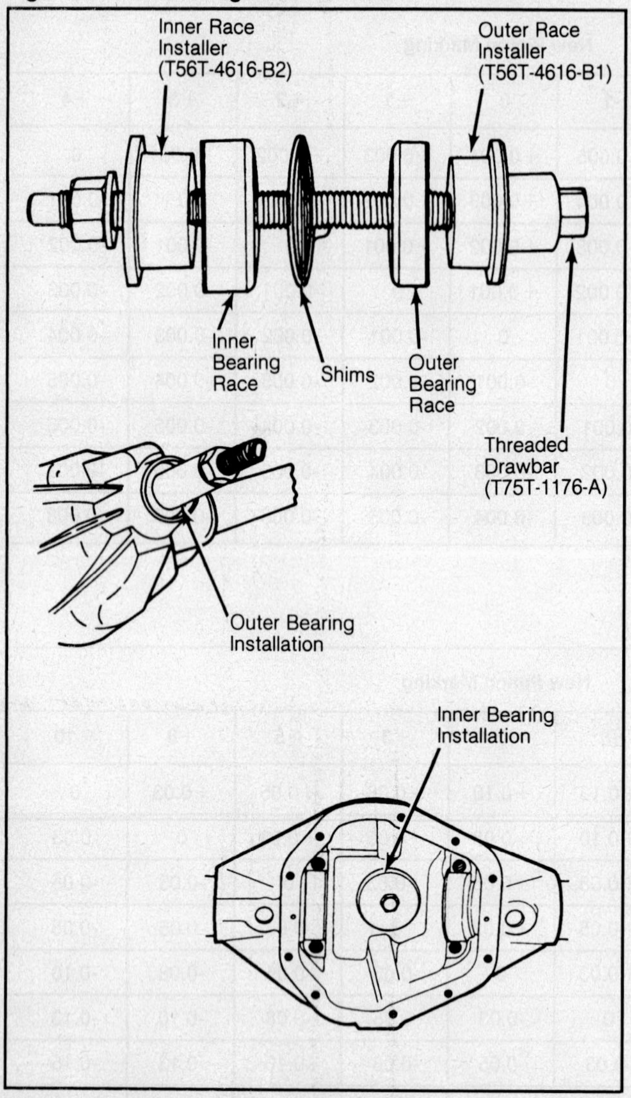

Install both pinion bearing races in carrier at same time.

Drive Pinion Bearing Preload & Final Depth Check

1) Install preload shims and slinger (if used) on drive pinion. Install drive pinion in carrier housing. Install outer drive pinion bearing using press, axle bearing/seal plate and axle bearing/seal installer. Install drive pinion flange with washer and NEW nut. Tighten nut to 240-300 ft. lbs. (325-407 N.m).

2) Using torque wrench, check rotational torque necessary to turn drive pinion. Torque reading should be 20-40 INCH lbs. (2.26-4.52 N.m) if preload is correct. If preload reading is too low, remove preload shims from drive pinion. If preload reading is too high, add preload shims to drive pinion.

3) Install gauge tube. Install side bearing caps and tighten bolts to 80-90 ft. lbs. (108-122 N.m). Place Final Check Gauge Block (D81T-4020-F54) on top of drive pinion face under gauge tube. Hold gauge block with thumb to keep it level. Measure distance between gauge tube and gauge block with feeler gauge.

4) Check reading of feeler gauge when slight drag is felt as gauge is pulled between gauge tube and gauge block. Correct reading should be .020" (.05 mm) greater than pinion depth adjustment figure etched in face of drive pinion with tolerance of .002" (.05 mm).

Fig. 7: Final Pinion Depth Check

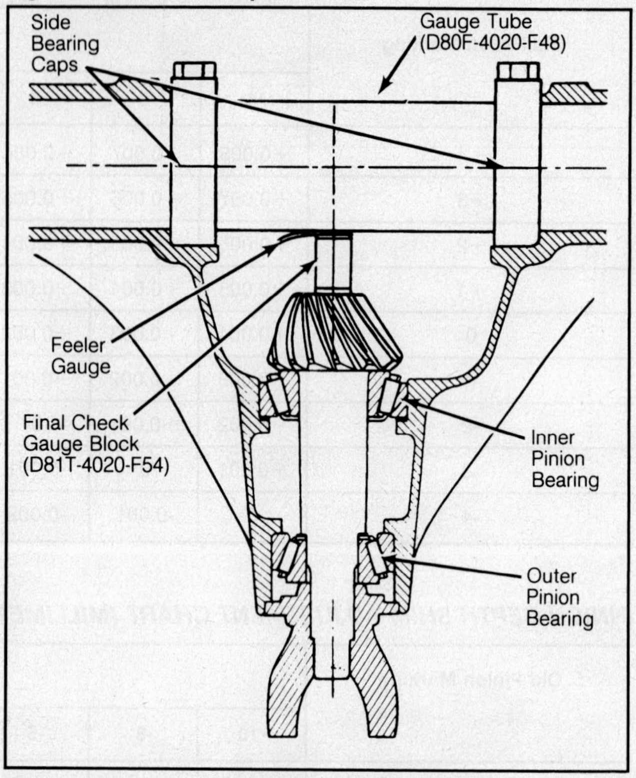

Hold gauge block with thumb to keep it level.

5) Drive pinion with "-2" etching should give reading of .018" (.46 mm) with tolerance of .002" (.05 mm). Acceptable reading would be .016-.020" (.41-.51 mm). If reading is too low, remove shims from underneath inner drive pinion bearing race. If reading is too high, add shims underneath inner drive pinion bearing race.

6) When final drive pinion depth check is correct, remove pinion flange with holder and flange remover. Coat pinion flange oil seal with multipurpose grease. Install seal using Oil Seal Replacer (T56T-4676-B).

7) Make sure spring behind lip of seal does not jump out while seal is being installed. If spring does jump out, remove and replace seal. Install drive pinion flange and tighten nut to 250-270 ft. lbs. (339-366 N.m).

Ring & Pinion Gear Backlash

1) With drive pinion depth and preload adjustments properly made, install differential case into housing. Differential master bearings should still be on case. Set dial indicator so that tip is against back of ring gear at 90° to gear.

2) Rock ring gear so that teeth of ring gear mesh fully with drive pinion gear teeth. Force ring gear teeth against drive pinion gear teeth and zero dial indicator. Force ring gear and case away from drive pinion gear. Repeat this procedure until same reading is obtained each time.

3) This reading is thickness of shim pack that must go under differential side bearing on ring gear side of case. Remove dial indicator. Remove differential case from housing. Remove master bearings from differential case. Place shim pack of correct thickness on ring gear hub.

SPICER (DANA) SEMI-FLOATING AXLES (Cont.)

4) Drive side bearing onto case using Side Bearing Installer (D81T-4221-A). Support case on opposite side with Step Plate (D80L-630-7) while installing side bearing. Subtract thickness of shim pack installed on ring gear side of case from total differential case end play determined earlier.

5) Add .015" (.36 mm) for preload to figure determined for remaining end play. Result is thickness of shim pack that is to be installed on hub of differential case opposite ring gear (drive pinion side of case).

6) Place shim pack on case hub and drive side bearing onto case using side bearing installer. Support case with step plate to protect side bearing already installed on ring gear side of case.

7) Install housing spreader and dial indicator on carrier housing. Set tip of dial indicator at same point used when case was removed from housing during disassembly procedure. Spread housing maximum of .015" (.38 mm) as damage could occur if housing is spread further. Remove dial indicator.

8) Place side bearing races on side bearings. Install case in carrier housing. Use soft-faced hammer to seat case assembly in carrier bore. Use care to avoid damaging teeth of ring and drive pinion gears. Remove spreader from housing.

9) Install side bearing caps, making sure that letters stamped on caps match letters stamped on housing. Tighten cap bolts to 80-90 ft. lbs. (108-122 N.m). Check ring and pinion gear backlash in 3 places equally spaced around ring gear. Backlash range is .005-.009" (.13-.23 mm) with allowable maximum variation of .002" (.05 mm).

10) If backlash figure is too high, ring gear must be moved closer to drive pinion gear. If backlash figure is too low, ring gear must be moved away from drive pinion gear. To change backlash readings, move shims from 1 side of differential case to other.

11) When backlash adjustment is completed, check tooth contact pattern. See GEAR TOOTH CONTACT PATTERNS in this section. Pattern should be correct if assembly and adjustments have been done properly.

12) When backlash is correct, install axle shafts. Install and tighten NEW differential pinion shaft lock bolt to 20-25 ft. lbs. (27-34 N.m). Install cover with new gasket. Tighten cover bolts to 30-40 ft. lbs. (41-54 N.m). Fill assembly with hypoid lubricant.

Fig. 8: Differential Shim Placement

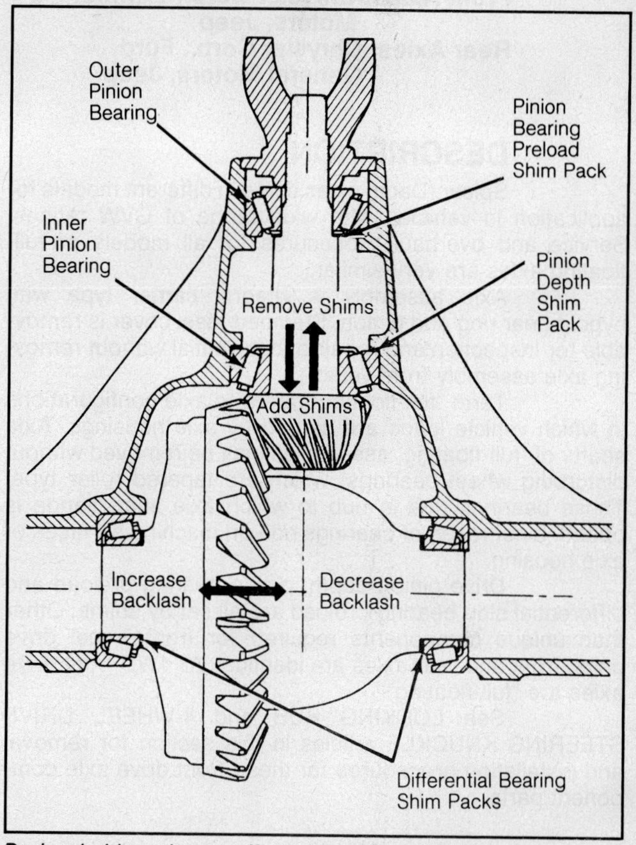

Preload shims do not affect drive pinion depth setting.

AXLE ASSEMBLY SPECIFICATIONS

Application	In. (mm)
Axle Shaft End Play	Non-Adjustable
Ring Gear Backlash	.005-.009 (.12-.15)
Differential Bearing Preload	.015 (.38)
	INCH Lbs. (N.m)
Pinion Bearing Preload	
New Bearings	20-40 (2-5)
Used Bearings	10-20 (1-2)

TIGHTENING SPECIFICATIONS

Application	Ft. Lbs. (N.m)
Differential Pinion Shaft Lock Pin	20-25 (27-34)
Drive Pinion Flange Nut	250-270 (339-366)
Differential Side Bearing Cap Bolt	80-90 (108-122)
Ring Gear-to-Case Bolt	100-120 (136-163)

Drive Axles

SPICER (DANA) FULL-FLOATING AXLES

Front Axles: Chrysler Corp., General Motors, Jeep
Rear Axles: Chrysler Corp., Ford, General Motors, Jeep

DESCRIPTION

Spicer (Dana) axles come in different models for application in vehicles with wide range of GVW ratings. Service and overhaul procedures for all models of full-floating axles are very similar.

Axle assembly is integral carrier type with hypoid gear ring and pinion. Stamped steel cover is removable for inspection and repair of differential without removing axle assembly from vehicle.

Term "full-floating" refers to axle configurations in which vehicle loads are carried by axle housings. Axle shafts of "full-floating" assemblies may be removed without disturbing wheel bearings, which are tapered roller type. These bearings ride in hub to which axle shaft flange is bolted. Inner races of bearings ride on machine surfaces of axle housing.

Drive pinion depth, pinion bearing preload and differential side bearing preload are all set by shims. Other than unique components required for front wheel drive units, front and rear axles are identical. All 4WD front drive axles are "full-floating".

See LOCKING HUB and 4-WHEEL DRIVE STEERING KNUCKLE articles in this section for removal and installation procedures for these front drive axle component parts.

AXLE RATIO & IDENTIFICATION

Steel cover plate has unique shape which allows positive identification of Spicer (Dana) axles on any model vehicle. Axle model can also be determined by measuring diameter of ring gear. See MODEL IDENTIFICATION table.

Metal tag, stamped with gear ratio, part numbers and limited slip identification, is held to housing by cover bolt. To determine drive axle ratio, refer to MODEL IDENTIFICATION BY RING GEAR SIZE table.

Fig. 1: Spicer (Dana) Housing Cover Gasket

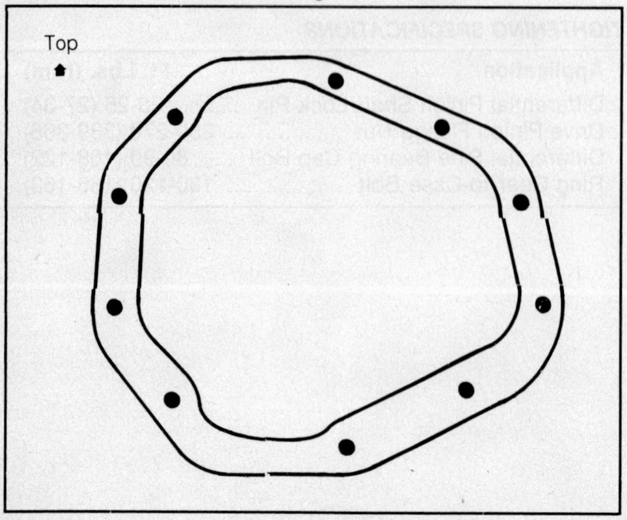

Illustration for identification purposes.

MODEL IDENTIFICATION BY RING GEAR SIZE

Model	Ring Gear Diameter
30	7.12"
44	8.50"
60	9.75"
61	9.75"
70	10.50"

REMOVAL & INSTALLATION

NOTE: **These axle models are used by several vehicle manufacturers. Tool numbers called out for procedures specific to make of vehicle will be tool number as used by individual vehicle manufacturer. Tool numbers called out for general procedures, such as OVERHAUL and PINION FLANGE & SEAL, will be tool number as used by Spicer (Dana). These tools are available from Miller Special Tools, which uses same numbering system as Spicer (Dana) does.**

HUBS & BEARINGS

NOTE: **Although hub bearings are lubricated by flow of axle oil, all manufacturers require that hub bearings be packed with high temperature, multipurpose grease before installation. This is to prevent damage that might be done to dry bearings before axle oil reached bearings.**

Removal (Front & Rear)

1) Raise vehicle and support securely. Remove wheels. Remove axle shaft or hub driving gear. On front axles, bend back ears on nut retainer. Remove outer lock nut and locking ring. On rear axles, pry locking pin or wedge out from adjusting nut. DO NOT move adjusting nut before locking wedge is removed.

2) On all axles, remove bearing adjusting nut, thrust washer (if equipped) and outer hub (wheel) bearing. Remove hub with inner bearing and seal. Drive inner bearing and seal out of hub with brass drift. Avoid damage to bearing cage.

3) Clean and inspect bearings and races. If bearings need replacement, drive outer races from hub with brass drift.

Installation & Adjustment (Chrysler Corp. Front Hubs)

1) If new bearings are to be used, drive outer races into hub. Make sure races bottom out in hub. Install inner bearing and seal. Install hub on spindle. Install outer bearing and adjusting nut.

2) Tighten adjusting nut to 50 ft. lbs. (68 N.m). Loosen adjusting nut and retighten to 30-40 ft. lbs. (41-54 N.m) while rotating hub assembly. Back off nut 135-150°. Position retaining washer on pin of adjusting nut. *See Fig. 3.*

3) Turn adjusting nut slightly to line up pin and hole if necessary. Install and tighten lock nut to 50 ft. lbs. (68 N.m). Check end play which should be .001-.010" (.03-.25 mm).

Installation & Adjustment (Chrysler Corp. Rear Hubs)

1) If bearings are replaced, drive new races into hub. Install inner bearing and seal into hub. Install hub on spindle. Install outer bearing and adjusting nut. Tighten

SPICER (DANA) FULL-FLOATING AXLES (Cont.)

Fig. 2: Exploded View Of Spicer (Dana) Full-Floating Axle Assembly

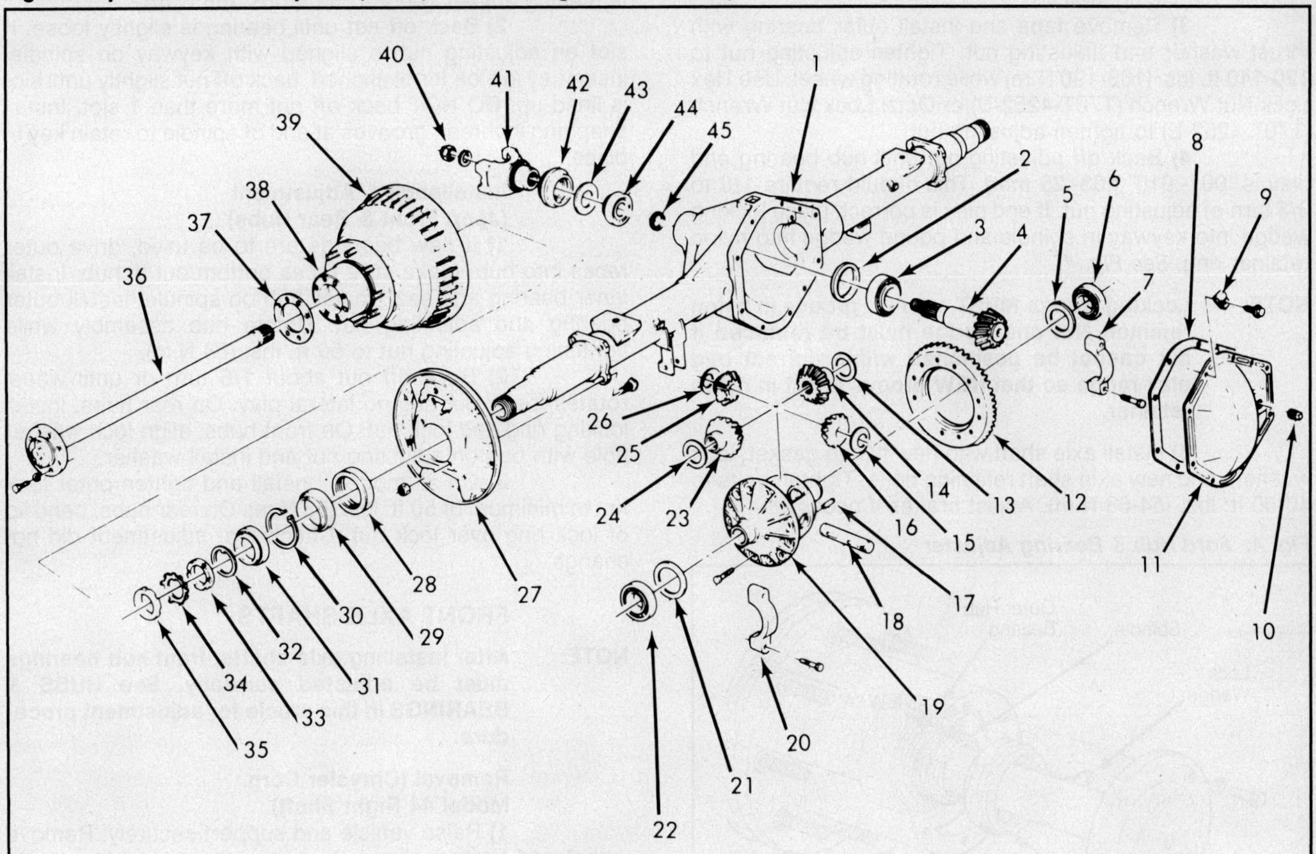

Fig. 1

1. Carrier Housing
2. Shim Pack
3. Inner Pinion Bearing
4. Drive Pinion
5. Shim Pack
6. Side Bearing
7. Bearing Cap
8. Cover Gasket
9. Clip
10. Plug
11. Cover
12. Ring Gear
13. Thrust Washer
14. Side Gear
15. Thrust Washer
16. Pinion Gear
17. Lock Pin
18. Pinion Shaft
19. Differential Case
20. Bearing Cap
21. Shim Pack
22. Side Bearing
23. Side Gear
24. Thrust Washer
25. Pinion Gear
26. Thrust Washer
27. Backing Plate
28. Seal
29. Inner Hub Bearing
30. Snap Ring
31. Outer Hub Bearing
32. Adjusting Washer
33. Adjusting Nut
34. Lock Washer
35. Lock Nut
36. Axle Shaft
37. Axle Flange Gasket
38. Hub
39. Brake Drum
40. Flange Nut
41. Pinion Flange
42. Pinion Seal
43. Slinger
44. Outer Pinion Bearing
45. Shim Pack

Assembly shown has 1-piece differential case.

Fig. 3: Chrysler Corp. Adjusting Nuts & Retainer Washer

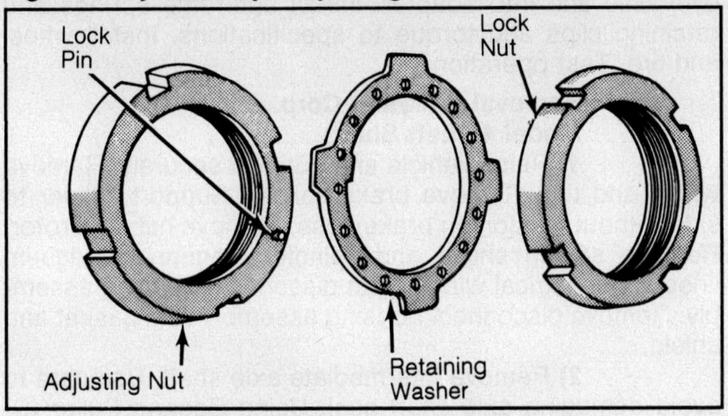

Hole in retainer must fit over pin on adjusting nut.

adjusting nut to 120-140 ft. lbs. (163-190 N.m) while rotating wheel.

2) Back off adjusting nut 1/3 turn (120°) to obtain end play of .001-.008" (.03-.20 mm). Drive nut lock (taper wedge) into spindle keyway. Install axle shaft with new gasket.

Installation & Adjustment (Ford Rear Hubs)

1) If bearings are replaced, press new outer races into hub with Bearing Race Replacer (T75T-1225-A and T75T-1225-B). Make sure bearing race is seated correctly. Feeler gauge .0015" (.038 mm) thick should NOT fit between shoulder in hub and bearing race.

2) Pack bearings with multipurpose, lithium base grease. Place inner bearing in hub and install new inner seal with bearing race replacer. Tape over threads on

SPICER (DANA) FULL-FLOATING AXLES (Cont.)

end of spindle. Slide hub assembly over spindle, using care to avoid damaging seal lips.

3) Remove tape and install outer bearing with thrust washer and adjusting nut. Tighten adjusting nut to 120-140 ft. lbs. (163-190 N.m) while rotating wheel. Use Hex Lock Nut Wrench (T70T-4252-D) or Octal Lock Nut Wrench (T70T-4252-E) to tighten adjusting nut.

4) Back off adjusting nut until hub bearing end play is .001-.010" (.03-.25 mm). This should require 1/8 to 3/8 turn of adjusting nut. If end play is correct, place locking wedge into keyway in spindle and pound wedge into nylon retainer ring. *See Fig. 4.*

NOTE: Locking wedge MUST cut new groove in nylon retainer. Nut and wedge must be replaced if nut cannot be positioned within correct end play range so that NEW groove is cut in nylon retainer.

5) Install axle shaft with new flange gasket, lock washers and new axle shaft retaining bolts. Tighten bolts to 40-50 ft. lbs. (54-68 N.m). Adjust brakes if necessary.

Fig. 4: Ford Hub & Bearing Adjuster

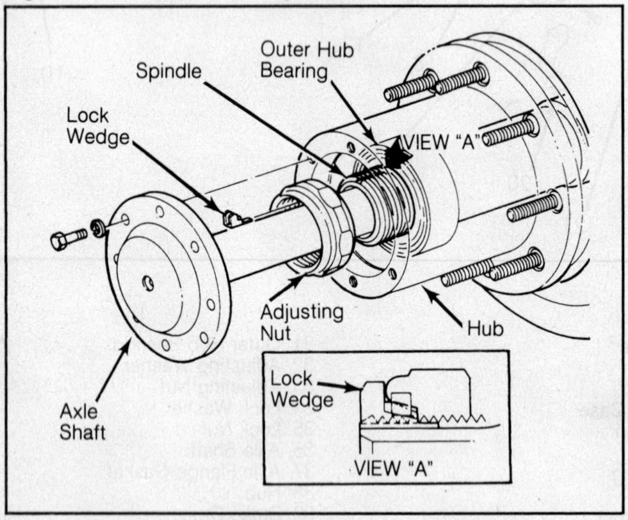

Wedge MUST cut new groove in nylon retainer.

Installation & Adjustment (General Motors Front Hubs)

1) If new bearings are to be used, drive outer races into hub. Make sure races bottom out in hub. Pack bearings with multipurpose greqase. Install inner bearing and seal. Install hub on spindle. Install outer bearing and adjusting nut.

2) Tighten adjusting nut to 50 ft. lbs. (68 N.m) while rotating hub. Back off nut and retighten to 35 ft. lbs. (47 N.m) while hub is rotating. Back off adjusting nut 3/8 turn maximum. Slide retainer washer onto spindle with tang in keyway on spindle.

3) Line up pin on adjusting nut with hole in retainer washer. Install and tighten lock nut to 160-205 ft. lbs. (217-278 N.m). Hub assembly end play should be .001-.010" (.03-.25 mm).

Installation & Adjustment (General Motors Rear Hubs)

1) If new bearings are to be used, drive outer races into hub. Make sure races bottom out in hub. Install inner bearing and seal. Install hub on spindle. Install outer bearing and adjusting nut. Rotate hub assembly while tightening adjusting nut to 50 ft. lbs. (68 N.m).

2) Back off nut until bearing is slightly loose. If slot on adjusting nut is aligned with keyway on spindle, insert key in slot. If not aligned, back off nut slightly until slot is lined up. DO NOT back off nut more than 1 slot. Install snap ring in thread grooves at end of spindle to retain key in place.

Installation & Adjustment (Jeep Front & Rear Hubs)

1) If new bearings are to be used, drive outer races into hub. Make sure races bottom out in hub. Install inner bearing and seal. Install hub on spindle. Install outer bearing and adjusting nut. Rotate hub assembly while tightening adjusting nut to 50 ft. lbs. (68 N.m).

2) Back off nut about 1/6 turn or until wheel rotates freely but has no lateral play. On rear hubs, install locking ring and lock nut. On front hubs, align lock washer hole with peg on adjusting nut and install washer.

3) On all models, install and tighten outer lock nut to minimum of 50 ft. lbs. (68 N.m). On rear hubs, bend lip of lock ring over lock nut. Check that adjustment did not change.

FRONT AXLE SHAFTS

NOTE: After installing axle shafts, front hub bearings must be adjusted correctly. See HUBS & BEARINGS in this article for adjustment procedure.

Removal (Chrysler Corp. Model 44 Right Shaft)

1) Raise vehicle and support securely. Remove wheel and brake caliper. Support caliper to side without tension on brake hose. If equipped with locking hubs, see removal and installation procedures in LOCKING HUBS and 4-WHEEL DRIVE STEERING KNUCKLES articles in this section.

2) Remove hub and brake rotor. Remove 6 nuts holding splash shield and spindle to knuckle. Remove splash shield and spindle. Remove caliper adapter from knuckle. Remove axle shaft assembly carefully. Remove seal and stone shield from axle shaft.

Installation

1) Install lip seal on axle shaft stone shield with lip toward axle spline. Carefully insert axle shaft into housing so as not to damage differential seal at side gears. Install spindle and brake splash shield. Tighten 6 nuts to specifications.

2) Install rotor and hub. Install brake adapter. Install inboard brake shoe on adapter. Slowly slide caliper over disc and into adapter. Install anti-rattle springs and retaining clips and torque to specifications. Install wheel and tire. Test operation.

Removal (Chrysler Corp. Model 44 Left Shaft)

1) Raise vehicle and support securely. Remove wheel and tire. Remove brake caliper. Support caliper to side without tension on brake hose. Remove hub and rotor. Remove splash shield and spindle. Disconnect vacuum lines and electrical wiring from disconnect housing assembly. Remove disconnect housing assembly with gasket and shield.

2) Remove intermediate axle shaft. Use care to avoid damaging axle shaft seal. Using Bearing Puller (D-

SPICER (DANA) FULL-FLOATING AXLES (Cont.)

330), remove needle bearing from intermediate axle shaft. Remove shift collar from housing. Remove differential cover and drain lubricant. Push inner axle shaft toward center of vehicle. Remove "C" lock from shaft.

3) Use Puller Handle (D-354-4) and Adapter (D-354-3) to remove inner axle shaft. Using puller handle with Crow Foot Pry (D-354-1) and Puller (C-637), remove bearing from inner axle shaft. Remove outer axle shaft bearing and seal from housing with Puller (C-637).

Installation

1) Using puller handle, Bearing Driver (D-354-2) and Installer (C-367), put bearing on inner axle shaft. Install inner axle shaft using puller handle and adapter. Install "C" lock on axle shaft. Install shift collar on splined end of inner shaft.

2) Install axle shaft bearing and seal in housing with Driver (D-360) and Handle (C-4171). Install needle bearing in intermediate shaft using Driver (D-328) and handle. Install intermediate shaft, using care to avoid damage to seal. Install disconnect housing assembly, making sure that shift fork rides in groove of shift collar.

3) Install remaining parts in reverse of removal procedure. When installing cover, use 1/16-3/32" bead of Mopar Silicone Rubber Sealant (4318025) around bolt circle of cover. Cover must be installed within 20 minutes of sealant application. Fill with lubricant and test operation.

Removal (Chrysler Corp. Model 60 Axle)

1) Block brake pedal up. Raise vehicle and support securely. Remove wheel and tire. If equipped with locking hubs, see removal and installation procedures in LOCKING HUBS and 4-WHEEL DRIVE STEERING KNUCKLES articles in this section.

2) Remove brake caliper and secure to side. Do not let caliper hang from brake line. Remove hub and rotor, using care to avoid damaging spindle threads. Remove inner brake pad from adapter. Remove rotor splash shield, brake adapter and spindle. Remove spindle from steering knuckle. Slide out inner and outer axle shaft with bronze spacer, seal and oil slinger.

Installation

1) Slide axle shaft into position. Place bronze spacer on axle shaft with chamfer side facing toward "U" joint. Install spindle, brake adapter and brake splash shield.

2) Install inner shoe on adapter. Install hub and rotor assembly on spindle. Install brake caliper, wheel and tire. Lower vehicle.

Removal (General Motors)

1) Raise vehicle and support securely. Remove wheel and tire. Remove brake caliper. If equipped with locking hubs, see removal and installation procedures in LOCKING HUBS and 4-WHEEL DRIVE STEERING KNUCKLES articles in this section.

2) Remove hub and rotor. Remove spindle. Carefully pull axle shaft assembly through hole in steering knuckle.

Installation

Install axle shaft assembly in housing. Care must be taken not to damage seal. Install thrust washer with chamfered end toward slinger on axle. Install spindle using new nuts and tighten to 65 ft. lbs. (88 N.m). Position hub and rotor assembly on spindle. Complete reassembly by reversing removal procedure.

Removal (Jeep)

1) Raise vehicle and position on safety stands. Remove wheel and tire. If equipped with locking hubs, see removal and installation procedures in LOCKING HUBS and 4-WHEEL DRIVE STEERING KNUCKLES articles in this section.

2) Remove disc brake caliper. Remove hub and brake rotor. Remove axle spindle. Remove axle shaft and universal joint assembly.

Installation

1) Make sure all components are clean. Make sure drive flange bolt and bolt hole threads are clean. Install axle shaft assembly taking care not to damage seal in axle housing. Install spindle and spindle bearing.

2) Install disc brake caliper and splash shield. Install disc brake rotor on spindle. Install hub assembly. Install disc brake caliper. Install wheel assembly and lower vehicle.

REAR AXLE SHAFTS

Removal

Remove flange nuts from hub studs. Using heavy hammer, rap sharply on center of axle flange to loosen tapered dowels. Remove dowels. Rap center of flange again to cause flange and axle assembly to spring away from hub. Remove axle without using prying devices which might damage axle flange and hub mating surfaces.

Installation

Clean mating surface of hub and axle flange. Install new gasket on face of hub. Insert axle shaft in housing and slide in until shaft splines engage with differential side gears. Tighten bolts holding axle shaft flange to hub.

PINION FLANGE & SEAL

NOTE: **Front and rear differentials are same, except for oil slinger on front differential pinion shaft. Pinion seal can be serviced with axle assembly installed in vehicle.**

Removal

1) Raise vehicle and support securely. Disconnect propeller shaft at drive axle end and tie to side rail of frame. Mount Flange Holder Wrench (C-3281) to keep flange from turning while removing pinion nut. Four notches on wrench should face flange. Discard nut.

2) Remove flange using Flange Puller (C-452). Remove oil seal from carrier bore using Pinion Seal Puller (C-748). Use care to avoid damage to machine surfaces. Clean seal contact area thoroughly.

Installation

CAUTION: **DO NOT try to drive flange on with hammer. Damage to ring and pinion gears will result.**

1) Lubricate cavity between seal lips with lithium base high pressure lubricant. Place seal in bore. Drive seal into carrier with Seal Installer (W-147-D on Model 44; C-3719-A with C-4735 on Model 60; C-359 on Model 70).

2) Place flange on end of pinion shaft. Press flange on pinion shaft, using flange holder and Flange Installer (C-496 on Model 44; C-3718 on Models 60 and 70). Leave flange holder in place and install pinion nut with washer. Tighten pinion nut to 200-220 ft. lbs. (271-298 N.m) on Models 44 and 70. On Model 60, tighten pinion nut to 240-300 ft. lbs. (325-407 N.m).

CAUTION: **Failure to tighten pinion nut to specification will result in flange or pinion shaft failure.**

SPICER (DANA) FULL-FLOATING AXLES (Cont.)

AXLE ASSEMBLY

Removal

1) Raise vehicle on hoist and support axle assembly to take weight off springs. Disconnect drive shaft at pinion flange and tie out of way. Remove hub and brake assemblies.

2) Disconnect vent tube, if equipped. Disconnect parking brake cable(s) and service brake hydraulic lines. Disconnect shock absorbers at axle brackets. Disconnect springs and remove axle.

Installation

Reverse removal procedure. Do not fully tighten shock absorber nut until vehicle weight is on suspension. Bleed hydraulic lines and adjust parking brake before moving vehicle.

OVERHAUL

DISASSEMBLY

1) Drain lubricant. Remove axle shafts and housing cover. If no side play is found in the differential case assembly, mount dial indicator on pilot stud with tip against back of ring gear. Measure runout of ring gear, marking ring gear and case at point of maximum.

2) If runout total exceeds .006" (.15 mm), ring gear could be loose or case could be damaged. Using .003" (.08 mm) feeler gauge, measure clearance between side bearing cap and outer race of side bearing. If feeler gauge can be forced between cap and race, bearing race may have been turning in carrier.

3) If race has been turning, carrier could be damaged. Observe identifying letters stamped into bearing caps and face of carrier sealing surface. Left-side letters are horizontal and right-side letters are vertical. Use these matched letters for reassembly reference.

4) Be sure that side bearing caps and differential carrier are marked so that caps may be reinstalled in their original positions. Remove side bearing caps. Use Housing Spreader (W-129-A on Model 44; D-167 on Models 60 and 70) to spread differential housing to .015" (.38 mm).

CAUTION: Do not spread housing more than .020" (.51 mm). Permanent damage to housing could result.

5) Mount dial indicator on pilot stud on left side of housing. Place tip against opposite side of case to measure spread. Mark point where indicator tip is placed for reassembly reference. When case is spread, remove dial indicator. *See Fig. 5.*

6) Carefully pry differential case out of housing. Remove spreader immediately to prevent possibility of carrier taking set. On models with side bearing shims between carrier and side bearing outer race, record sizes and positions of shims. Be careful not to damage machined surfaces of housing.

7) Put case in soft-jawed vise and remove ring gear bolts. DISCARD bolts. Tap ring gear loose with soft mallet. If ring gear runout measured earlier exceeded .006" (.15 mm), repeat runout measurement of case without ring gear. Total runout of case should not exceed .003" (.08 mm).

8) Using Flange Holder Wrench (C-3281) to hold flange in place, remove drive pinion nut and washer. Using holder wrench and Flange Puller (C-452), remove drive

Fig. 5: Correct Procedure for Spreading Housing

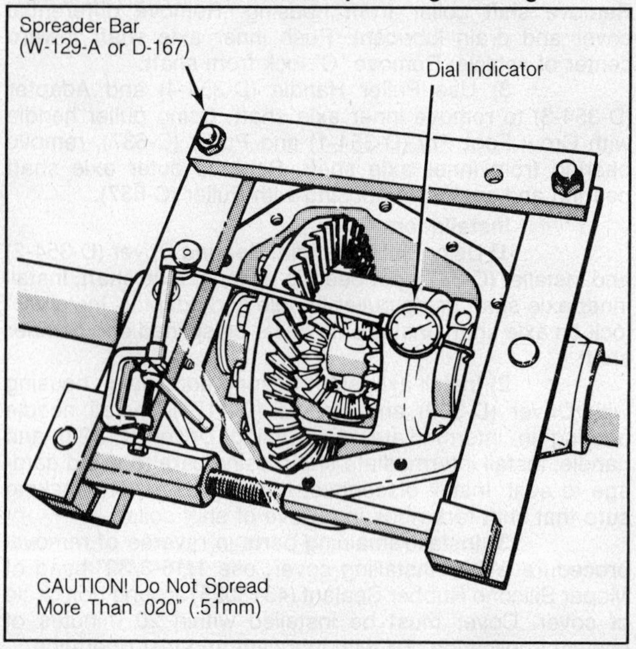

Do not leave tension on carrier housing or damage will result.

pinion flange. Using Pinion Seal Puller (C0748), remove pinion oil seal. Remove slinger, gasket, outer pinion bearing and preload shim pack.

9) Remove drive pinion with inner bearing. Remove inner and outer pinion bearing races. Remove and note thickness of shim pack behind inner bearing race. Remove inner pinion bearing from pinion shaft using Puller Press (DD-914-P) with Adapter Ring (DD-914-9) and Pinion Bearing Puller Plates (C-293-39 on Model 44; DD-914-37 on Model 60; DD-914-95 on Model 70).

NOTE: Pinion bearing adjusting shims may remain on pinion shaft, stick to bearing or fall loose. Collect and save them for reassembly.

10) Remove side bearings with Bearing Puller (C-293-PA), Extension Plug (C-293-3 on Model 44; DD-914-7 on Models 60 and 70) and Puller Plates (C-293-18 on Model 44; DD-914-62 on Models 60 and 70). Record shim thickness and location for reassembly reference.

11) If differential case is 1-piece unit, drive out lock pin holding differential pinion shaft to case. Remove differential pinion shaft, gears and thrust washers (1 for each gear).

12) If differential case is 2-piece unit, mark both differential case halves to aid reassembly in correct position. Remove bolts holding case halves together. Tap on top half of case to break it loose from lower half. Remove top half of case. Remove pinion gear spider, pinion gears, side gears and all thrust washers.

INSPECTION

Gears & Bearings

1) Use cleaning solvent to rinse gears and bearings. Check large end of bearing rollers where wear, if there is any, is most evident. Check pinion and flange splines for excessive wear. Make sure ring gear teeth are in good condition.

2) Check differential case for cracks, scoring of side gears, thrust washers and pinion thrust faces. Check fit

SPICER (DANA) FULL-FLOATING AXLES (Cont.)

of side gears to case and to axle shaft splines. Look at pinion shaft and spacer for scoring or excessive wear.

REASSEMBLY & ADJUSTMENT

Precautions

1) When reassembling and adjusting ring and pinion assembly, pinion depth, pinion bearing preload, side bearing preload and backlash between ring and pinion must be adjusted.

2) If only pinion shaft and ring gear are to be replaced and carrier housing can be reused, compare pinion depth adjustment numbers etched in faces of old and new pinion heads. *See Fig. 6.* Using PINION DEPTH SHIM ADJUSTMENT chart, correct shims can be selected for new pinion shaft depth adjustment.

Fig. 6: Location Of Pinion Gear Markings Showing Depth Adjustment Figures

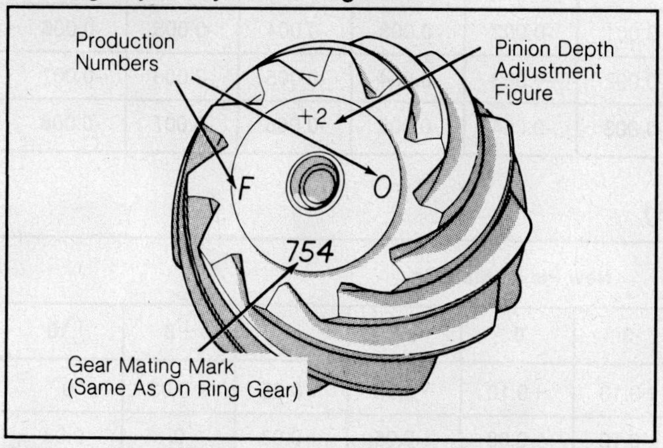

Gear mating numbers on new ring and pinion gears must match.

NOTE: **In order to use PINION DEPTH SHIM ADJUSTMENT chart procedure, old pinion shaft shim pack dimensions MUST be determined accurately. If original pinion shaft shim pack dimension cannot be determined accurately, Pinion Depth Gauge Set (D-271) must be used to properly determine pinion depth setting. Depth gauge set must also be used if new carrier housing is to be used.**

3) The pinion depth adjustment number is determined by manufacturer at time of assembly. Number represents distance that best running position of pinion shaft deviates from "nominal" or standard distance between pinion gear face and centerline of axle. *See Fig. 7.*

4) Pinion Depth Gauge Set (D-271) allows shim pack adjustments to be made without having to remove and replace differential bearings when setting up shim packs. *See Fig. 8.*.

Case Assembly (1-Piece)

1) Place differential case in holding fixture or vise. Lubricate all parts with gear oil. Place side gears and new thrust washers in case. Place differential pinions and new thrust washers in case. Rotate side gears until holes in pinion gears and washers line up with holes in case.

NOTE: **If new differential side and pinion gears are used with new washers, grar backlash should be correct due to close machine tolerances. If old gears and/or washers are used, gear backlash must be checked.**

2) Install differential pinion shaft. Install lock pin after aligning hole in shaft with hole in case. Peen edge of hole to keep pin in place. Inspect ring gear and case for any burrs or nicks. Install ring gear and tighten NEW ring gear bolts evenly in alternating pattern to 100-115 ft. lbs. (136-156 N.m).

3) Install Master Bearings (D-117) onto case. Install differential case in carrier. Install and tighten side bearing caps finger tight over master bearings. Caps must be in same location as marked during disassembly. Mount dial indicator on carrier with indicator tip against back of ring gear.

4) Pry case assembly to 1 side of carrier. Zero dial indicator and pry case in opposite direction. *See Fig. 9.* Record reading. This indicates thickness of shim pack necessary to eliminate clearance between case and side bearing races.

5) Actual placement of shim pack and necessary preload will be calculated after drive pinion is installed and pinion depth has been determined. Remove dial indicator. Remove bearing caps and differential case from carrier.

Case Assembly (2-Piece)

1) Lubricate all parts with gear oil. Install pinion gears with new washers on cross shaft. Install side gears and new washers with pinion gears and cross shaft into half of case that is flanged.

NOTE: **If new differential side and pinion gears are used with new washers, grar backlash should be correct due to close machine tolerances. If old gears and/or washers are used, gear backlash must be checked.**

2) Put top half of case on bottom half. Align scribe marks made before disassembly. Tighten all bolts finger tight. Tighten bolts alternately to 65-70 ft. lbs. (88-95 N.m). Mount ring gear on case. Install ring gear bolts finger tight, then tighten alternately to 100-110 ft. lbs. (136-149 N.m).

3) Install Master Bearings (D-117) onto case. Install differential case in carrier. Install and tighten side bearing caps finger tight over master bearings. Caps must be in same location as marked during disassembly. Mount dial indicator on carrier with indicator tip against back of ring gear.

4) Pry case assembly to 1 side of carrier. Zero dial indicator and pry case in opposite direction. *See Fig. 9.* Record reading. This indicates thickness of shim pack necessary to eliminate clearance between case and side bearing races.

5) Actual placement of shim pack and necessary preload will be calculated after drive pinion is installed and pinion depth has been determined. Remove dial indicator. Remove bearing caps and differential case from carrier.

Pinion Depth

NOTE: **If original ring and pinion is to be used, measure old shim packs and make up packs of same dimensions with new shims. Baffles are considered part of shim pack.**

1) Depth Gauge Set (D-271) is used to determine pinion depth. Place Master Pinion Block (D-139 on Model 44; D-120 on Model 60; D-137 on Model 70) in pinion bore of carrier. Put Arbor Discs (D-115-4-44 on Model 44; D-116-2 on Models 60 and 70) on Arbor (D-115-3). Install arbor in carrier with discs riding in bearing bore.

SPICER (DANA) FULL-FLOATING AXLES (Cont.)

PINION DEPTH SHIM ADJUSTMENT CHART (INCHES)

Old Pinion Marking	New Pinion Marking								
	-4	-3	-2	-1	0	+1	+2	+3	+4
+4	+0.008	+0.007	+0.006	+0.005	+0.004	+0.003	+0.002	+0.001	0
+3	+0.007	+0.006	+0.005	+0.004	+0.003	+0.002	+0.001	0	-0.001
+2	+0.006	+0.005	+0.004	+0.003	+0.002	+0.001	0	-0.001	-0.002
+1	+0.005	+0.004	+0.003	+0.002	+0.001	0	-0.001	-0.002	-0.003
0	+0.004	+0.003	+0.002	+0.001	0	-0.001	-0.002	-0.003	-0.004
-1	+0.003	+0.002	+0.001	0	-0.001	-0.002	-0.003	-0.004	-0.005
-2	+0.002	+0.001	0	-0.001	-0.002	-0.003	-0.004	-0.005	-0.006
-3	+0.001	0	-0.001	-0.002	-0.003	-0.004	-0.005	-0.006	-0.007
-4	0	-0.001	-0.002	-0.003	-0.004	-0.005	-0.006	-0.007	-0.008

PINION DEPTH SHIM ADJUSTMENT CHART (MILLIMETERS)

Old Pinion Marking	New Pinion Marking								
	-10	-8	-5	-3	0	+3	+5	+8	+10
+10	+0.20	+0.18	+0.15	+0.13	+0.10	+0.08	+0.05	+0.03	0
+8	+0.18	+0.15	+0.13	+0.10	+0.08	+0.05	+0.03	0	-0.03
+5	+0.15	+0.13	+0.10	+0.08	+0.05	+0.03	0	-0.03	-0.05
+3	+0.13	+0.10	+0.08	+0.05	+0.03	0	-0.03	-0.05	-0.08
0	+0.10	+0.08	+0.05	+0.03	0	-0.03	-0.05	-0.08	-0.10
-3	+0.08	+0.05	+0.03	0	-0.03	-0.05	-0.08	-0.10	-0.13
-5	+0.05	+0.03	0	-0.03	-0.05	-0.08	-0.10	-0.13	-0.15
-8	+0.03	0	-0.03	-0.05	-0.08	-0.10	-0.13	-0.15	-0.18
-10	0	-0.03	-0.05	-0.08	-0.10	-0.13	-0.15	-0.18	-0.20

2) Put Pinion Height Block (D-115-1-44 on Model 44; D-116-1 on Models 60 and 70) on top of master pinion block with side against arbor. Place Scooter Block (115-2) with Dial Indicator (D-106-5) on small step of pinion height block. Zero dial indicator with scooter block flat on pinion height block.

3) Move scooter block so that dial indicator tip touches arbor. Move block back and forth (perpendicular to arbor) to get highest reading. This reading, plus or minus value etched on pinion head, is thickness of shim pack necessary for pinion bearing.

4) Measure shims seperately with micrometer. If baffle is used, its thickness must be included in shim pack. This is also true if slinger is used between inner bearing and head of pinion shaft. Place pinion height shim pack in carrier bore for inner bearing race. Drive bearing race into carrier, making sure cup is fully seated.

Pinion Bearing Preload

1) Drive outer pinion bearing into carrier housing. Press inner pinion bearing onto pinion shaft using Press Tube (C-3095-A). Make sure that bearing seats fully. Insert pinion shaft into carrier. Install outer bearing, slinger (if equipped), flange, washer and nut.

NOTE: Pinion preload shims and oil seal should NOT be installed at this time.

2) Using INCH lb. torque wrench, tighten pinion nut until 10 INCH. lbs. (1.13 N.m) rotational torque is required to move pinion shaft. Recheck pinion depth with arbor and discs at this time. Place pinion height block on face of pinion shaft.

3) Place dial indicator on small step of height block for Model 60 axles. Place dial indicator on high step of block for Model 70 axles. Zero dial indicator and move it

SPICER (DANA) FULL-FLOATING AXLES (Cont.)

Fig. 7: Pinion Setting Standard Dimension

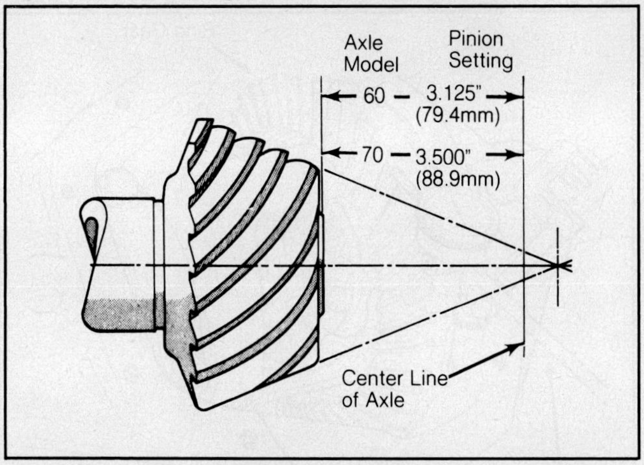

These are "nominal" distances from center of ring gear to face of pinion shaft; deviations are noted on pinion face.

Fig. 8: Pinion Depth Gauge Set (D-271)

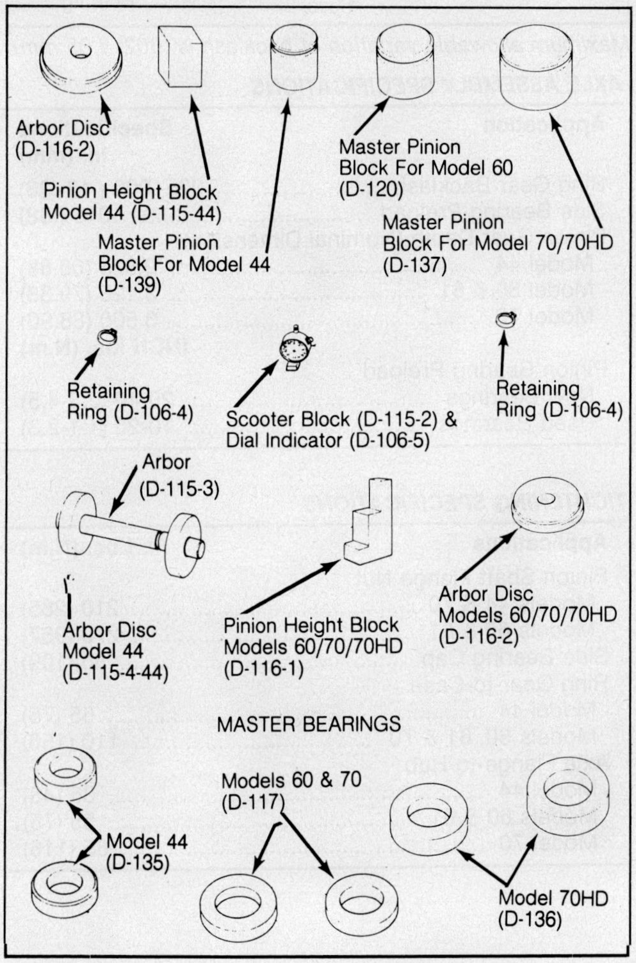

This set can be used on Models 44, 60/61 and 70.

across arbor to get highest reading. If reading is within .002" (.05 mm) of etching on pinion face, pinion depth is correct.

NOTE: **If pinion depth is not with .002" (.05 mm) of etched number on face of pinion, shim pack under inner bearing race must be changed before proceeding with differential settings.**

Fig. 9: Measuring Differential Case End Play

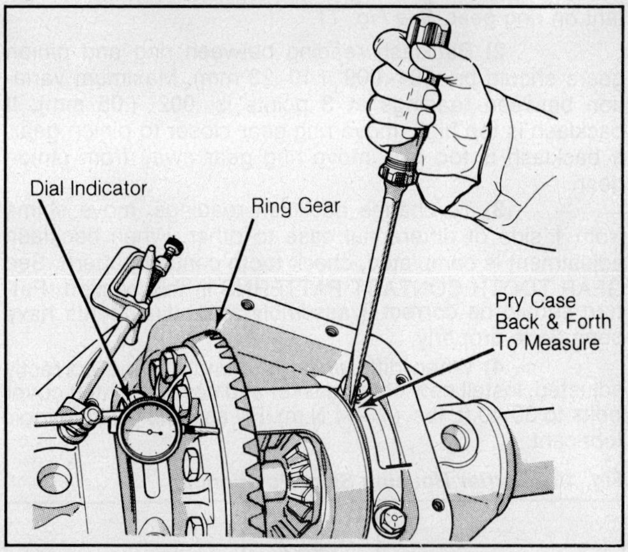

Use Master Bearings (D-117) for measurement.

4) Remove pinion nut, washer, flange, slinger and outer bearing. Place preload shims (removed during disassembly) on pinion. Installl bearing and slinger. After lightly coating lips with gear oil, install pinion seal in carrier housing. Install flange, washer and NEW pinion nut. Tighten nut to 240-300 ft. lbs. (325-407 N.m).

5) Using INCH lb. torque wrench, measure preload (rotational torque) of pinion shaft. Rotational torque required to keep pinion shaft turning freely and smoothly should be 20-40 INCH lbs. (2.3-4.5 N.m). If preload needs increasing, remove some shims and check again. To decrease preload, add some shims and recheck. *See Fig. 10.*

Differential Bearing Preload

1) Install differential case in housing with master bearings on case. Set up dial indicator in same position as when case end play was checked. *See Fig. 9.* Press ring gear towards pinion head while rocking ring gear so teeth mesh fully. Zero dial indicator while holding ring gear into pinion gear.

2) Press differential case (ring gear) away from pinion gear. Repeat until dial indicator gives same reading each time. This figure is shim pack thickness necessary between case and side bearing on ring gear side. Remove dial indicator and differential from carrier. Remove master bearings from case.

3) Put calculated shim pack on hub of case at ring gear side. Place side bearing on hub. Using Bearing Installer (C-4025A) and Handle (C-4171) to drive bearing onto case until it is seated. Take remaining shim pack as determined from case end play measurement and install pack on opposite side of case from ring gear.

4) Add .015" (.38 mm) thickness to shim pack opposite ring gear to provide side bearing preload. Drive side bearing onto case with installer and handle. Install spreader and dial indicator on carrier housing. Spread housing .015" (.38 mm). Put side bearing races onto side bearings. Install differential case into carrier.

Ring & Pinion Backlash

1) Install side bearing caps, making sure that reference marks made on caps and carrier match. Tighten cap bolts to 80-90 ft. lbs. (108-122 N.m). Check backlash

SPICER (DANA) FULL-FLOATING AXLES (Cont.)

between ring and pinion gears at 3 points spaced equidistant on ring gear. *See Fig. 11.*

2) Backlash reading between ring and pinion gears should be .004-.009" (.10-.23 mm). Maximum variation between readings at 3 points is .002" (.05 mm). If backlash is too high, move ring gear closer to pinion gear. If backlash is too low, move ring gear away from pinion gear.

3) To change backlash readings, move shims from 1 side of differential case to other. When backlash adjustment is completed, check tooth contact pattern. See GEAR TOOTH CONTACT PATTERNS in this section. Pattern should be correct if assembly and adjustments have been done properly.

4) When differential is complete and correctly adjusted, install new cover gasket and cover. Tighten cover bolts to 30-40 ft. lbs. (41-54 N.m). Fill assembly with hypoid lubricant.

Fig. 10: Carrier Housing Shim Positioning

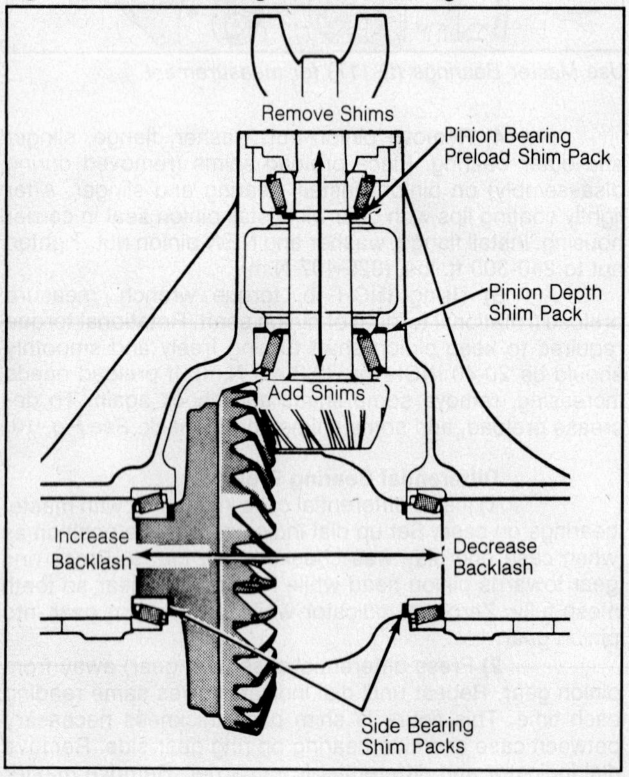

Fig. 11: Measuring Backlash Between Ring & Pinion Gears

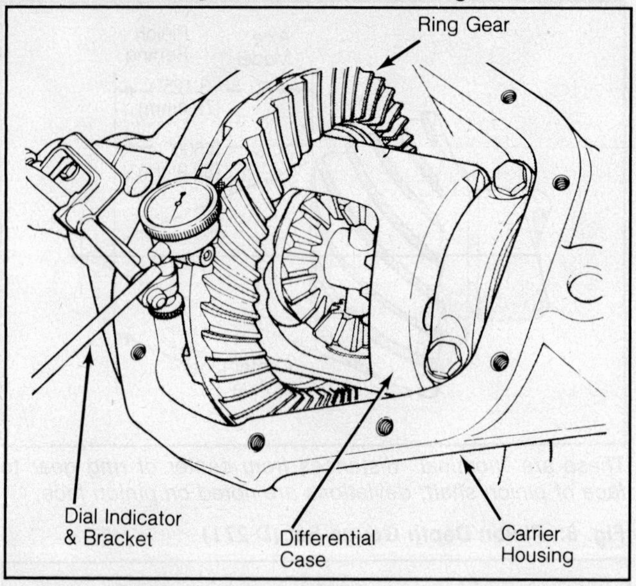

Maximum allowable variation of backlash is .002" (.05 mm).

AXLE ASSEMBLY SPECIFICATIONS

Application	Specifications In. (mm)
Ring Gear Backlash	.005-.009 (.13-.23)
Side Bearing Preload	.015 (.38)
Pinion Gear Depth (Nominal Dimension)	
Model 44	2.625 (66.68)
Model 60 & 61	3.125 (79.38)
Model 70	3.500 (88.90)
	INCH lbs. (N.m)
Pinion Bearing Preload	
New Bearings	20-40 (2.3-4.5)
Used Bearings	10-20 (1.1-2.3)

TIGHTENING SPECIFICATIONS

Applications	Ft. Lbs. (N.m)
Pinion Shaft Flange Nut	
Models 44 & 70	210 (285)
Models 60 & 61	270 (367)
Side Bearing Cap	80 (109)
Ring Gear-to-Case	
Model 44	55 (75)
Models 60, 61 & 70	110 (150)
Axle Flange-to-Hub	
Model 44	35 (48)
Models 60 & 61	55 (75)
Model 70	85 (116)

CHRYSLER CORP. SURE-GRIP 9 1/4" RING GEAR

Pickup, RWD Van

DESCRIPTION

The cone clutch Sure-Grip is a limited slip type differential. It is similar in operation to conventional type differentials, except for helix-grooved clutch cones that clutch side gears to differential case. These grooves assure maximum lubrication of clutch surface during operation.

Clutch cones and side gears are spring preloaded by 2 thrust plates and 4 coil spring. During torque application to axle, initial spring preloading of the clutch cones is increased by the gear separating forces between side gears and differential pinions.

This progressively increases internal resistance (friction) in differential. This differential is not positive or locking type unit, and will release before excessive driving force can be applied to 1 wheel.

AXLE RATIO & IDENTIFICATION

Sure-Grip differential is optional on Chrysler axles with 9 1/4" ring gear. See CHRYSLER CORP. 8 3/8" & 9 1/4" RING GEAR in this section.

LUBRICATION

Use multi-purpose gear lubricant (MIL-L-2105-B/API GL-5). Four ounces of Mopar Hypoid Gear Oil Additive Friction Modifier (4318060) MUST be used with every fluid change.

TESTING ON VEHICLE

1) Raise rear wheels off ground. Shut engine off. Place shift lever in "P" on models with A/T. Place shift lever in Low on models with M/T. Grip tread of tire and attempt to rotate wheel.

2) If rotation is extremely difficult or impossible, differential is performing correctly. If either wheel turns relatively easily or continuously, differential is not performing correctly and should be replaced.

REMOVAL & INSTALLATION

The same procedure is used to remove and install Sure-Grip differential as standard differential. See CHRYSLER CORP. 8 3/8" & 9 1/4" RING GEAR in this section.

CAUTION: During removal and installation of axle shafts, do not rotate one axle shaft unless both are in position. Rotation of one axle shaft without the other in place may result in misalignment of 2 spline segments with which axle shaft splines engage. This would necessitate difficult re-alignment procedures when shaft is reinstalled.

OVERHAUL

Sure-Grip differential is serviced as an assembly. Under NO circumstances should Sure-Grip differential be disassembled, reassembled and installed in vehicle.

Fig. 1: Sectional View of Chrysler Corp. Sure-Grip Differential Assembly

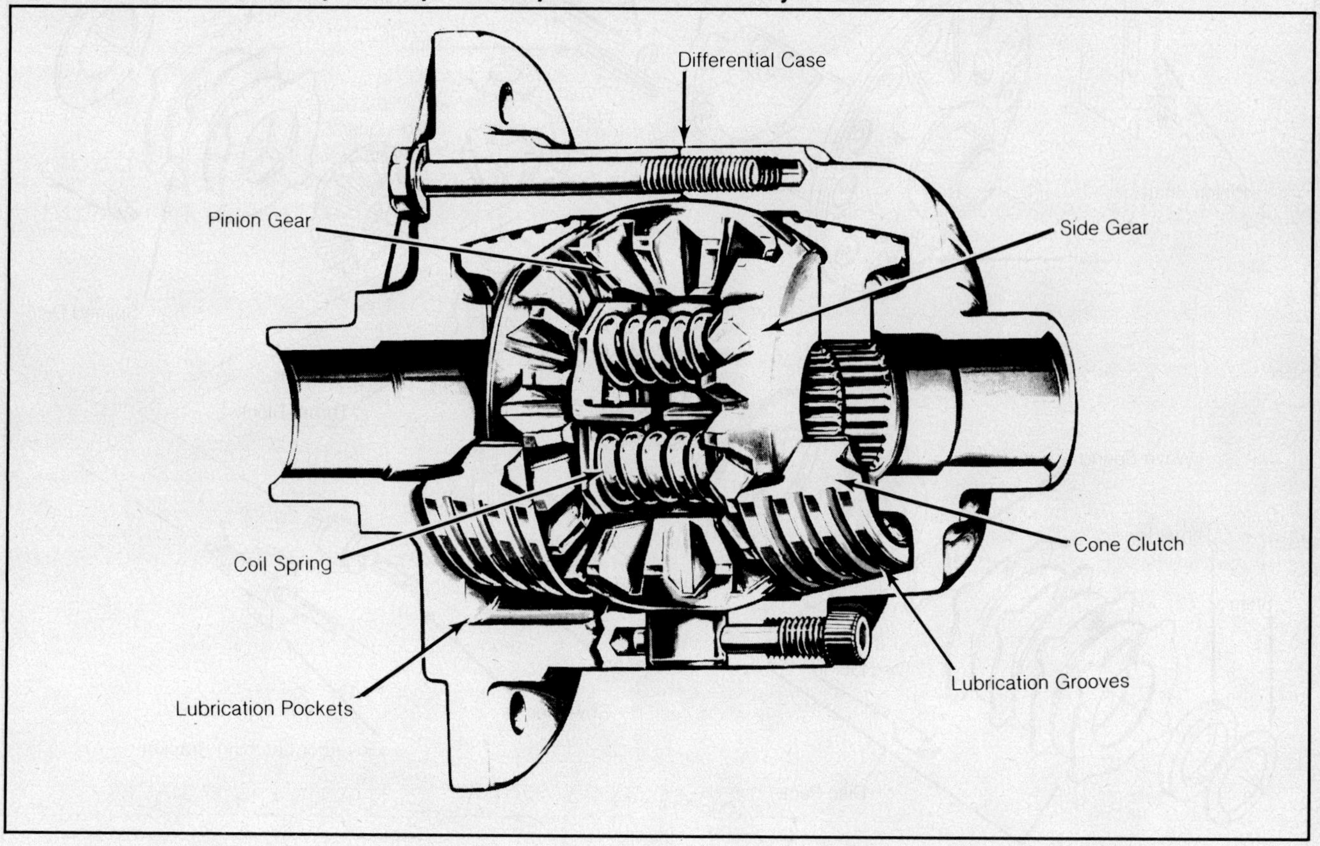

Positive Traction Differentials

EATON (ONE-PIECE CASE) LOCKING DIFFERENTIAL

Chevrolet, GMC C/K/G10/S
Front & Rear Axles

DESCRIPTION

The Eaton 1-piece case locking differential is a 2 pinion type, with a clutch disc pack behind each side gear.

The unit also utilizes a speed-sensitive device, which automatically locks both rear wheels if either wheel should spin excessively during slow vehicle operation.

AXLE RATIO & IDENTIFICATION

See GENERAL MOTORS 7 1/2", 8 1/2", & 9 1/2" RING GEAR article and DRIVE AXLE RATIO IDENTIFICATION article in this section.

LUBRICATION

Check lubricant level every 7500 miles or 6 months. Drain and refill every 15,000 miles. Use standard differential lubricant. Do not use Positraction lubricant.

TESTING ON VEHICLE

1) Raise vehicle so that both rear wheels can be rotated freely by hand. With 1 wheel held stationary, rotate other wheel approximately ½ turn every second.

2) Wheel should rotate freely. If both wheels turn, or try to turn, differential is defective. Raise vehicle as high as possible.

3) Have assistant in vehicle start the engine, and allow it to idle at 600-800 RPM. If equipped with automatic transmission, place transmission in drive, and apply brakes.

4) If equipped with manual transmission, depress clutch, and place transmission in first gear. Pull on 1 parking brake cable from under vehicle to lock 1 rear wheel.

5) With engine idling, slowly release brakes on automatic transmission models, or slowly release clutch on manual transmission models. Locked rear wheel should remain stationary, and free wheel should rotate slowly.

6) As free wheel speed increases, the differential should lock, causing both wheels to rotate or stop. If equipped with manual transmission, engine may stall.

Fig. 1: Exploded View of Eaton One-Piece Case Locking Differential

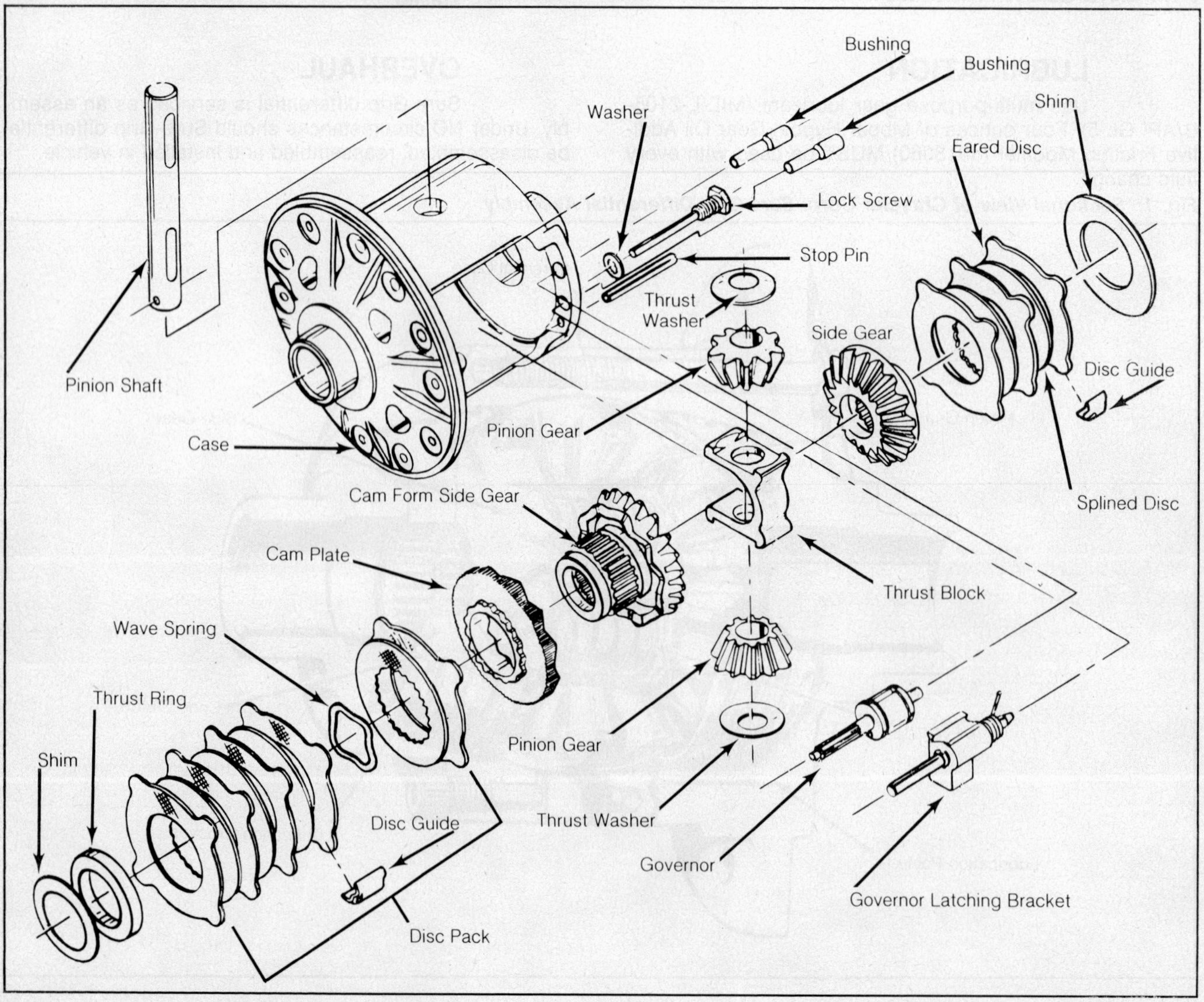

EATON (ONE-PIECE CASE) LOCKING DIFFERENTIAL (Cont.)

7) It may be necessary to accelerate to 10 MPH to lock differential. If speed increases beyond 20 MPH without locking differential, unit is defective. Lock opposite wheel and repeat test.

REMOVAL & INSTALLATION

Same procedure is used to remove and install locking differential as conventional differential. See GENERAL MOTORS 7 1/2", 8 1/2", & 9 1/2" RING GEAR article in this section.

OVERHAUL

DISASSEMBLY

Differential

1) With differential removed from housing, remove ring gear and side bearings. Note or mark position of latching bracket and governor assembly for reassembly.

2) Using puller, remove latching bracket spring, while pulling out governor assembly bushing. Remove stop pin by driving through case with drift punch.

3) Remove pinion shaft lock screw, and remove pinion shaft. Roll pinion gears out of case. Remove reaction block and pinion thrust washers. Remove cam gears, disc packs, and disc pack guide clips on both sides.

4) If cam gear or clutch discs must be replaced, cam gear assembly must be disassembled as follows.

Cam Gear Assembly

1) Measure and record overall length of gear assembly. Measure from face of gear to backside of thrust ring, and include shim. This dimension will be required for reassembly if thrust ring is replaced.

2) If thrust ring is replaced, check thrust ring bore in case for wear. If bore is scored excessively, replace complete differential.

3) Position gear with hub end up. Compress disc pack, and place a bearing removal mandrel (J-22912), between thrust ring and top disc. Beveled side of tool should be toward thrust ring.

4) Position cam gear and tool in a press, with tool supported on both sides. Place a 1½ - 1¾" plug on gear hub. Press against plug with press to remove thrust ring. Make sure all components are kept in correct order.

INSPECTION

1) Clean all parts in solvent. Inspect all bearings and gear teeth for chipping or wear. Replace as necessary. Inspect clutch plates and discs for signs of wear or overheating.

2) If reaction block or flange shims must be replaced, measure thickness of original components, and replace with components of identical size.

REASSEMBLY

Cam Gear Assembly

1) Place cam gear on bench with hub end up. Place cam plate on gear so that cam form on plate is against cam form on gear. Position on cam plate 2 eared discs, 1 splined disc and 1 wave spring, alternately in that order.

2) Position on gear hub, 2 splined discs and 3 eared discs alternately, starting and ending with an eared disc. Place cam gear in a press with hub end up . Install thrust ring on gear hub with press.

3) Make sure thrust ring is square with hub. Press thrust ring on until it is flush with shoulder. When installing ring, press down on disc to make sure splined disc does not wedge between thrust ring and gear shoulder.

4) When unit is assembled, check for correct disc sequence. Make sure that the first splined disc (large spline) is correctly located on cam plate.

Differential

1) Install disc pack guide clips on disc ears of cam gear disc pack. Use grease to retain clips on ears. Install cam gear assembly, with original shim in flange end of case.

2) If a new thrust ring has been installed on cam gear, it may be necessary to reshim. Measure overall length of cam gear assembly, including shim. Compare this measurement with 1 previously recorded.

3) If measurement variation is more than .003" (.08 mm) either way, install a new shim that will obtain a reading within .003" (.08 mm) of original measurement. Place an axle shaft in vise in a vertical position.

4) Mount differential case over end of axle shaft, engaging spline of side gear with shaft. Grease 2 pinion gear thrust washers, and locate them in their proper positions.

5) Assemble on to bell end gear hub, 2 splined discs and 3 eared discs alternately. Begin and end with an eared disc. Install 4 small clutch pack guide clips on ears of bell end clutch pack, using grease for retention.

6) Install in case with original shims. Original shim must be used to maintain correct clearance specification. Install 1 pinion gear through small opening in case, while inserting other pinion gear and reaction block through larger opening in case.

7) Rotate both pinion gears and reaction block 90° so that open side of reaction block is toward small opening in case. Make sure both pinion gears and thrust washers remain in correct position.

8) Install pinion shaft and lock screw. Place governor assembly and latching bracket into case. Place straight end of latching bracket spring over and to outside of engagement shaft.

9) This will preload the latching bracket against governor assembly. The latching bracket bushing has a tapered hole, and the governor assembly bushing has a straight hole.

10) Press bushing and ¼" stop pin into case. Install governor bushing in case, making sure shaft end play is between .004-.020" (.10-.51 mm). Press latching bracket bushing into case so end play is removed.

11) Press stop pin flush with case, install ring gear and side bearings on differential.

EATON (TWO-PIECE CASE) LOCKING DIFFERENTIAL

Chevrolet, GMC
C20/30, G/K/P30 Rear Axle

DESCRIPTION

The Eaton 2-piece locking differential is a 3 pinion type. With clutch disc packs behind both side gears. Unit also utilizes a speed-sensitive device which automatically locks both rear wheels if either wheel should spin excessively during slow vehicle operation.

AXLE RATIO & IDENTIFICATION

See GENERAL MOTORS 10 1/2" RING GEAR article and Drive Axle Ratio identification in this section.

LUBRICATION

Check lubricant level every 7500 miles or 6 months. Drain and refill every 15,000 miles. Use standard differential lubricant. Do not use Positraction lubricant.

Fig. 1: Exploded View of Eaton Two-Piece Case Locking Differential

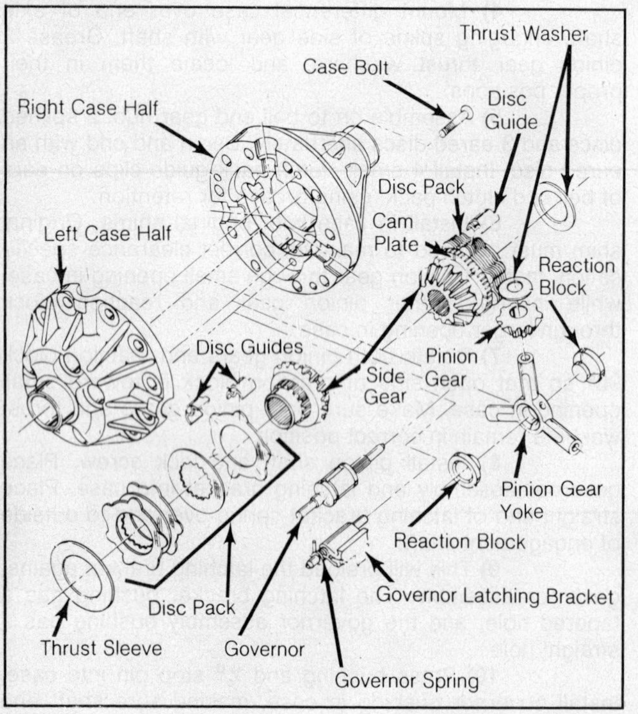

TESTING ON VEHICLE

1) Raise vehicle so that rear wheels can be rotated freely by hand. With 1 wheel held stationary, rotate the other wheel approximately 1/2 turn every second. Wheel should rotate freely.

2) If both wheels turn, or try to turn, differential is defective. Raise vehicle as high as possible. Leave 1 technician in vehicle. Start engine and allow to idle at 600-800 RPM.

3) If equipped with automatic transmission, place transmission in drive and apply brakes. If equipped with manual transmission, depress clutch and place transmission in low gear.

4) Pull on 1 parking brake cable from under vehicle to lock 1 rear wheel. With engine idling, slowly release brakes on automatic transmission models and slowly release clutch on manual transmission models.

5) Locked rear wheel should remain stationary and free wheel should rotate slowly. As free wheel speed increases, differential should lock, causing both wheels to rotate or stop. If equipped with a manual transmission, engine may stall.

6) It may be necessary to accelerate to 10 MPH to lock differential. If speed increases beyond 20 MPH without locking differential, unit is defective. Lock opposite wheel and repeat test.

REMOVAL & INSTALLATION

The same procedure is used to remove and install locking differential as conventional differential. See GENERAL MOTORS 10 1/2" RING GEAR article in this section.

OVERHAUL

DISASSEMBLY

Differential

1) With differential removed from housing, remove ring gear and side bearings. Remove 3 screws from front face of ring gear flange. Place differential on right side case half.

2) Using a screwdriver, gently pry case halves apart at yoke hole locations. Remove left side case half. Hold thumb against inside of gear hub when separating case halves. This will prevent side gear from falling out.

3) If governor and latching bracket are only components being replaced, proceed to step **8)** in Reassembly procedures. To further disassemble, pry under pinion gear yoke to remove from case half.

NOTE: **If cam gear or clutch disc must be replaced, cam gear assembly must be disassembled as follows:**

Cam Gear Assembly

1) Measure and record overall length of gear assembly. Measure from face of gear to back side of thrust ring and include shim. This dimension will be required for reassembly if thrust ring is replaced.

NOTE: **Thrust ring should be replaced only if it is absolutely necessary.**

2) If thrust ring is replaced, check thrust ring bore in case for wear. If bore is scored excessively, replace complete differential. Position gear with hub end up.

3) Compress disc pack and place bearing removal tool (J-22912) between thrust ring and tap disc. Beveled side of tool should be toward thrust ring. Position cam gear and tool in press with tool supported on both sides.

4) Place a 1 1/2"-1 3/4" plug on gear hub. Press against plug with a press to remove thrust ring. Make sure all components are in correct order.

EATON (TWO-PIECE CASE) LOCKING DIFFERENTIAL (Cont.)

INSPECTION

Clean all components in solvent. Inspect all bearings and gear teeth for chipping or wear. Replace as necessary. Inspect clutch plates and discs for signs of wear or overheating. If reaction blocks or flanges must be replaced, measure thickness of original components and replace with components of comparable size.

REASSEMBLY

NOTE: If cam gear assembly was disassembled, reassemble as follows:

Cam Gear Assembly

1) Place gear on bench with hub end up. Place cam plate on gear so that cam form on plate is against cam form on gear. Install 2 eared discs on cam plate, 1 splined disc and 1 wave spring alternately in that order.

2) Install on gear hub, 4 eared disc and 3 splined discs alternately, starting and ending with an eared disc. Place cam gear in a press with hub end up. Install thrust ring on gear hub with press.

3) Make sure thrust ring is square with hub. Press thrust ring on until it is flush with shoulder. When installing ring, press down on disc to make sure splined disc does not wedge between thrust ring and gear shoulder.

4) When unit is assembled, check for correct disc sequence. Make sure that the first splined disc (large spline) is correctly located on cam plate.

Differential

1) Install disc pack guide clips on disc ears of cam gear disc pack. Use grease to retain clips in ears. Install cam gear assembly and original shim in right case half.

2) If a new thrust ring was installed on cam gear, it may be necessary to reshim. Measure overall length of cam gear assembly, including shim. Compare this measurement with one previously recorded.

3) If measurement variation is more than .003" (.08 mm) either way, install a new shim that will obtain a reading within .003" (.08 mm) of original measurement.

4) Position right reaction block on gear face with buttonside of block facing up. Replace reaction block only if it is absolutely necessary. If a new block is being installed, measure face-to-face thickness of old block and obtain a new block of same thickness.

5) Install pinion gears and thrust washers on pinion yoke. Place yoke in correct position in housing. Make sure center of yoke is correctly positioned over reaction block button.

6) Tap on yoke lightly to correctly seat it in position. Position left reaction block on yoke with flange end up. Replace block only if it is absolutely necessary.

7) If a new block is being installed, measure face-to-face thickness of old block and obtain a new block of same thickness. The right and left reaction blocks are not necessarily the same thickness. If blocks are broken or it is impossible to measure thickness, complete differential must be replaced.

8) Install governor and latching bracket assemblies in correct position. Place straight end of latching bracket spring over and to outside of governor shaft. This will preload latching bracket against governor assembly.

9) Install original 3 eared discs and 2 splined discs on left side gear alternately, starting and ending with an eared disc.

10) Original disc must be used to maintain correct operating clearance in differential. Install 6 disc pack guide clips. Use grease to retain clips in place.

11) Install original shim in left case half. Remove disc pack from side gear and place in position in case half. Make sure guides are in correct position.

12) Install side gear in case, rotating gear to engage splines with splines on discs. Hold thumb on right case half. Make sure governor and latching bracket assembly holes are aligned in case halves. Install 3 screws.

13) Place 1 axle shaft in a vise in a vertical position. Install differential on axle shaft, making sure splines on axle are engaged in splines in side gear. Slowly rotate differential.

14) This can be easily done by inserting a short shaft or punch in a pinion yoke hole and pulling on shaft. Differential should turn smoothly without locking up or binding.

15) Differential will lock up if turned rapidly. Differential is now ready to be installed in housing.

Positive Traction Differentials

FORD TRACTION-LOK – 7 1/2" RING GEAR

Aerostar, Bronco II & Ranger

DESCRIPTION

Limited slip differential employs 2 sets of multiple disc clutches to control differential action. Side gear mounting distance is controlled by 7 plates each side; 3 steel, 4 friction and maximum of 2 steels shims selectively fit to control side gear position.

Plates are stacked on side gear hubs and housed in differential case. Also located in differential case is "S" shaped, 1-piece, preload spring between side gears. Spring applies initial force to clutch packs.

AXLE RATIO & IDENTIFICATION

To determine the drive axle ratio, refer to DRIVE AXLE RATIO IDENTIFICATION in this section.

LUBRICATION

Check lubricant level every 5000 miles or 5 months. Manufacturer recommends no specific drain and refill interval. Use only Ford Hypoid Gear Lubricant EOAZ-19580-A (ESP-M2C154-A).

TESTING ON VEHICLE

Raise 1 wheel and leave opposite wheel firmly on ground. Install Traction-Lok Torque Adapter (T59L 4204 A) on wheel mounting studs. Use torque wrench with minimum capacity of 200 ft. lbs. (271 N.m). With transmission in "N", note torque required to keep wheel rotating through several revolutions. Torque should be at least 20 ft. lbs. (27 N.m) while turning wheel. Wheel should turn smoothly without slipping or binding.

REMOVAL & INSTALLATION

NOTE: **In-vehicle adjustments are possible without removing differential case from axle housing.**

Removal & Installation

This differential is removed and installed using same procedure as conventional differential. See FORD 7 1/2" RING GEAR article in this section.

SERVICE (IN-VEHICLE)

CLUTCH PACKS

Removal

1) Raise vehicle. Remove rear wheels and brake drums. Remove cover from axle housing and drain lubricant. Working through cover opening, remove pinion shaft lock bolt and pinion shaft.

2) Push axle shafts inward until "C" locks at button end of shafts are clear of side gear recess. Remove "C" locks. Pull axle shafts out of housing.

NOTE: **Use care to avoid damaging axle seals when removing axle shafts. Shafts must be completely removed from axle housing.**

3) Using drift, drive "S" shaped preload spring half-way out of differential housing. Rotate differential housing 180°. Hold "S" shaped preload spring with pair of

Fig. 1: Exploded View of Aerostar, Bronco II & Ranger Traction-Lok Differential

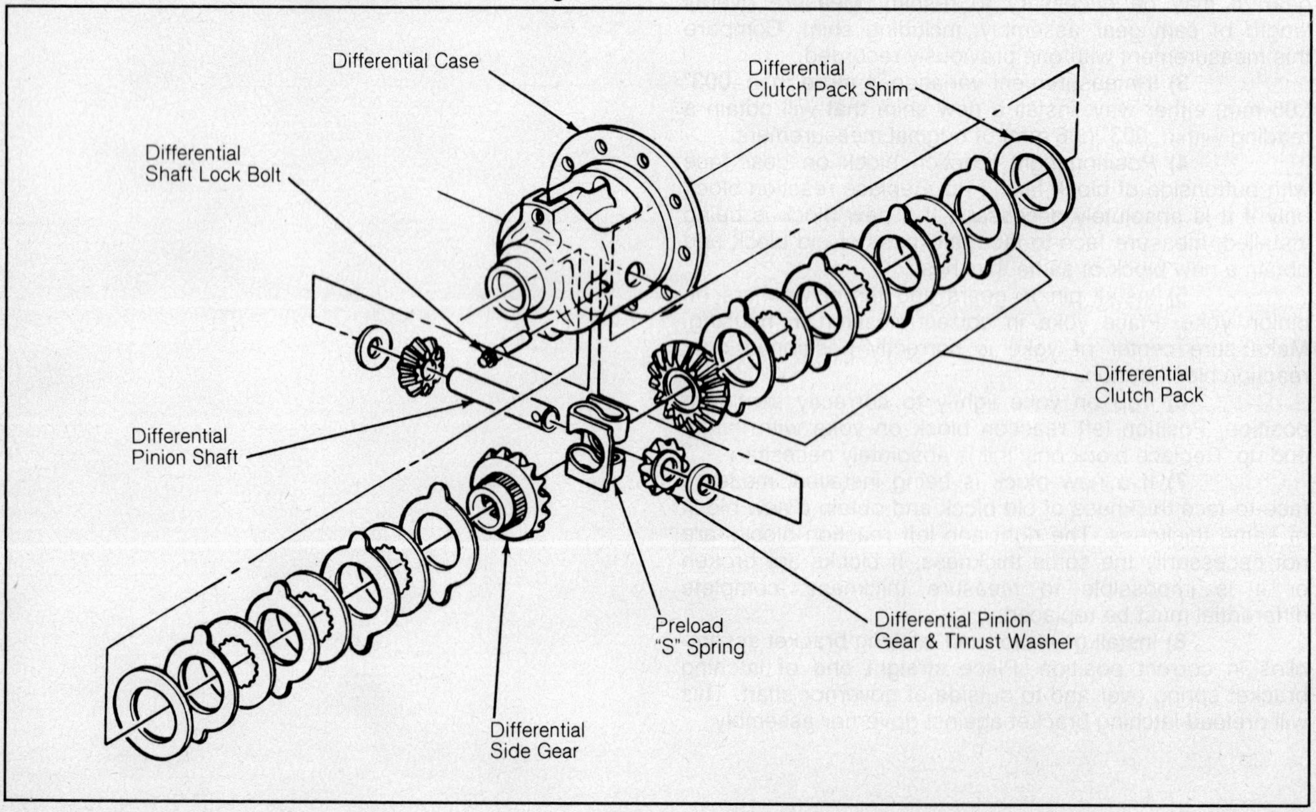

FORD TRACTION-LOK – 7 1/2" RING GEAR (Cont.)

pliers and tap spring until it is removed from differential. *See Fig. 2.*

Fig. 2: Removing Clutch Pack Preload Spring

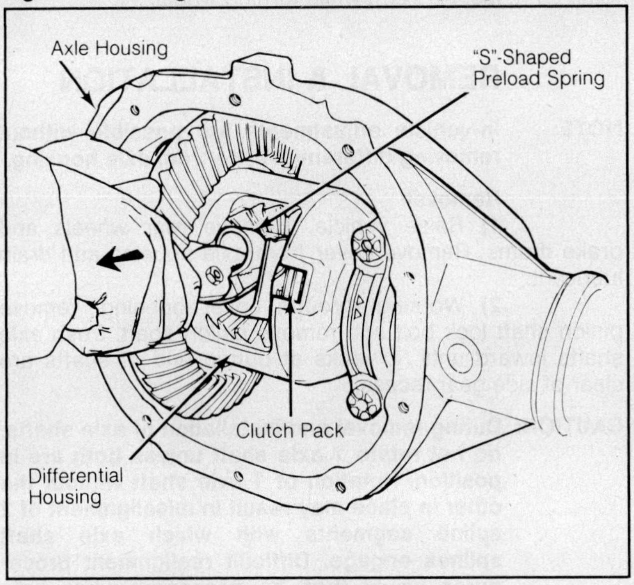

Use care when removing preload spring due to spring tension.

4) Using Pinion Rotator (T84P 4205 A) with 12" extension, rotate pinion gears until gears can be removed from differential. Remove left and right side gear and clutch pack with shim. Tag gears and clutch packs as left and right side.

5) Inspect clutch packs for wear and replace parts as necessary. Do not use any cleaning solvent on clutch plate surfaces. Wipe clean only. Install Differential Clutch Gauge (T84P 4946 A) on each of side gear clutch packs without shim.

6) Tighten to 60 INCH lbs. (6.7 N.m). Using feeler gauge, select thickest blade that will enter between clutch gauge and clutch pack. *See Fig. 3.* This reading will be thickness of new shim. Do not mix clutches or shims.

Installation

1) Lubricate friction plates with correct hypoid gear lubricant before reassembly. Install left side gear, clutch pack and new shim into cavity in differential housing. Repeat on right side.

2) Place pinion gears and thrust washers 180° apart on side gears. Install pinion gear rotator with 12" extension. Rotate tool until pinion gears are aligned with pinion shaft hole. Remove tool from differential housing.

3) Using soft-faced hammer, drive "S" shaped preload spring into position. Make sure spring is undamaged. Install axle shafts and "C" locks. Push axle shaft as far outboard as possible. Install pinion shaft and lock bolt.

NOTE: Tighten lock bolt using Stud and Bearing Mount EOAZ-19554-B (ESE-M4G167-A) only.

4) Install rear drums and wheels. Perform operational torque check to make sure unit is set up correctly. Using Silicone Rubber D6AZ-19562-B (ESB-M4G92A and ESE-M4G195-A), install rear cover assembly and tighten bolts. Fill axle assembly with lubricant to bottom of fill hole with unit in operating position.

Fig. 3: Measuring Clutch Pack Shim Size

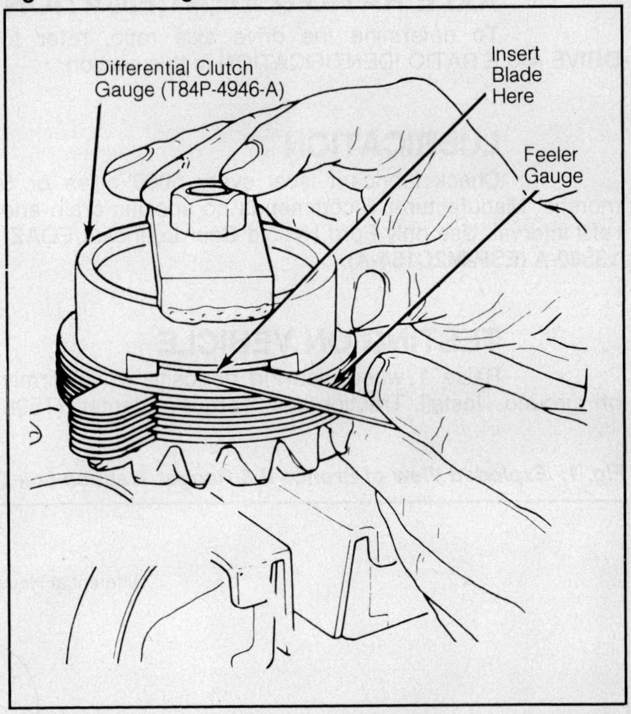

Lubricate friction plates before reassembly.

TIGHTENING SPECIFICATIONS

Application	Ft. Lbs. (N.m)
Pinion Shaft Lock Bolt	15-30 (20-41)
Rear Cover Assembly Bolt	25-35 (34-47)

Positive Traction Differentials

FORD TRACTION-LOK – 8.8" RING GEAR

All Models With 8.8" Ring Gear

DESCRIPTION

The limited slip differential employs 2 sets of multiple disc clutches to control differential action. Side gear mounting distance is controlled by 7 plates each side; 4 steel, 3 friction, and 1 steel shim by select size to control side gear position.

Also located in differential case, between side gears, is a 1-piece preload spring, which applies an initial force to clutch packs.

AXLE RATIO & IDENTIFICATION

To determine the drive axle ratio, refer to DRIVE AXLE RATIO IDENTIFICATION in this section.

LUBRICATION

Check lubricant level every 5000 miles or 5 months. Manufacturer recommends no specific drain and refill interval. Use only Ford Hypoid Gear Lubricant EOAZ-19580-A (ESP-M2C154-A).

TESTING ON VEHICLE

Raise 1 wheel, leaving opposite wheel firmly on ground. Install Traction-Lok Torque Adapter (T59L 4204 A) and torque wrench to wheel mounting studs. With transmission in "N", note torque required to keep wheel rotating through several revolutions. Torque should be at least 30 ft. lbs. (41 N.m) while turning wheel.

REMOVAL & INSTALLATION

NOTE: In-vehicle adjustments are possible without removing differential case from axle housing.

Removal

1) Raise vehicle. Remove rear wheels and brake drums. Remove cover from axle housing and drain lubricant.

2) Working through cover opening, remove pinion shaft lock bolt and remove pinion shaft. Push axle shafts inward until "C"-locks at button end of shafts are clear of side gear recess.

CAUTION: During removal and installation of axle shafts, do not rotate 1 axle shaft unless both are in position. Rotation of 1 axle shaft without the other in place may result in misalignment of 2 spline segments with which axle shaft splines engage. Difficult realignment procedures would then be necessary when axle shaft is reinstalled.

Fig. 1: Exploded View of Bronco II & Ranger Traction-Lok Differential

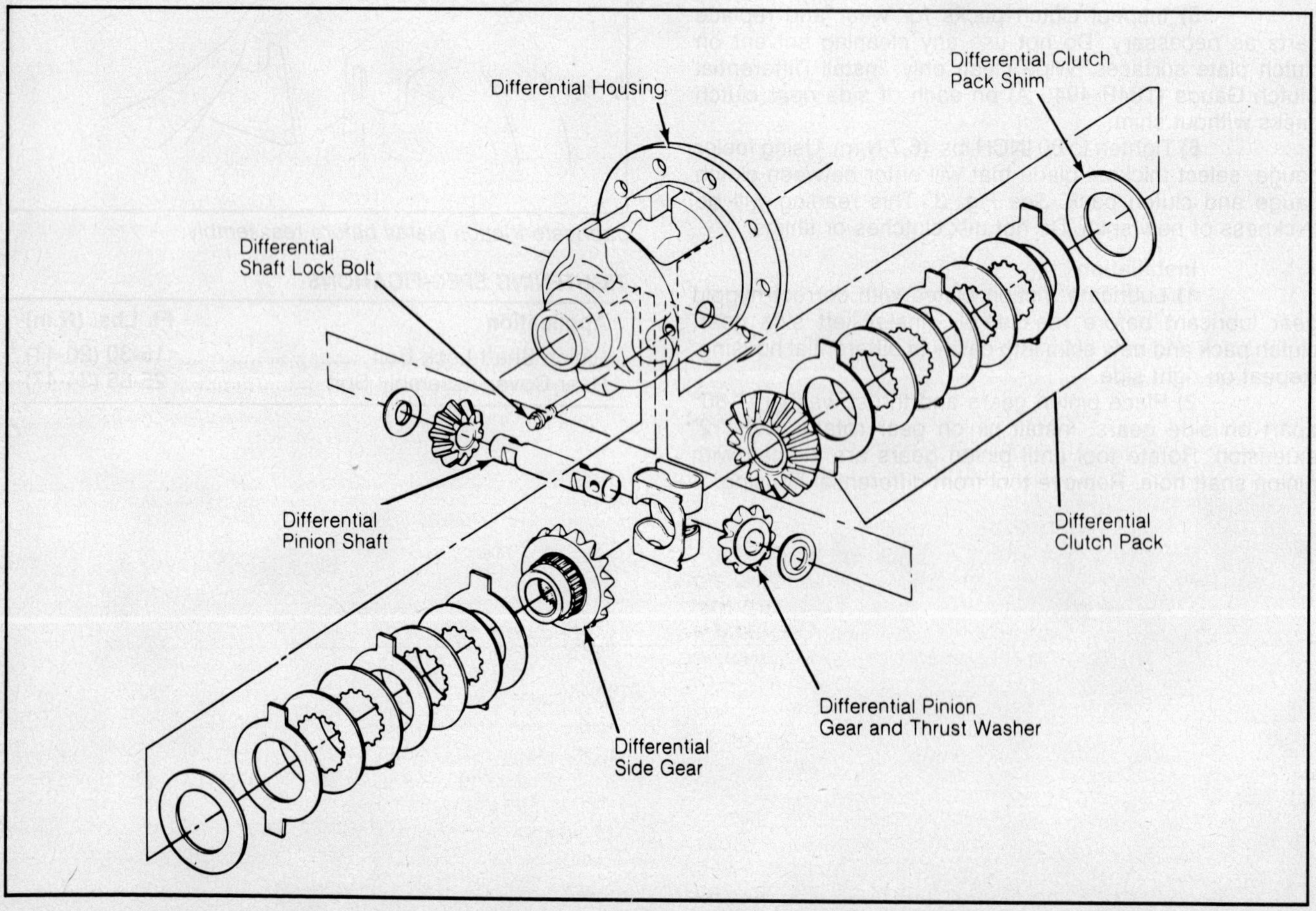

FORD TRACTION-LOK – 8.8" RING GEAR (Cont.)

3) With a suitable drift, drive "S"-shape preload spring half-way out of differential housing. Rotate differential housing 180°. Hold "S"-shaped preload spring with a pair of pliers and tap spring until it is removed from differential. *See Fig. 2.*

4) Using pinion rotator tool (T84P 4205 A) with a 12" extension, rotate pinion gears until gears can be removed from differential. Remove right and left side gear and clutch pack with shim and tag them "right and left side".

Fig. 2: Removing Clutch Pack Preload Spring

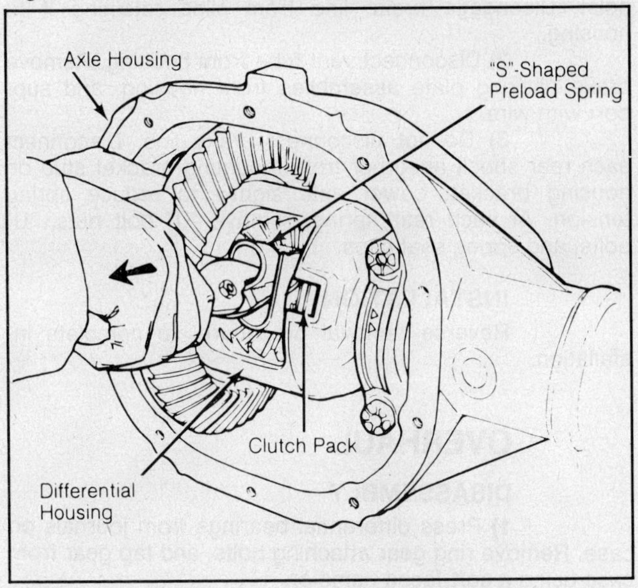

Use care when removing preload spring due to spring tension.

5) Inspect clutch packs for wear and replace parts as necessary. Do not use any cleaning solvent on clutch packs, wipe clean only.

6) Install clutch pack shim gauge (T84P 4946 A) on each of side gear clutch packs without shim. Tighten to 60 INCH lbs. (6.7 N.m). Using feeler gauge, select thickest blade that will enter between tool and clutch pack. This reading will be thickness of new shim. Do not mix clutches or shims.

Installation

1) Install left side-gear, clutch pack and new shim into cavity in differential housing. Repeat this step for right side.

2) Place pinion gears and thrust washers 180° apart on side gears. Install pinion gear rotator (T84P 4205 A). Rotate tool until pinion gears are alignedf with pinion shaft hole. remove tool from differential housing.

3) Hold "S"-shaped preload sprinng up to differential housing window and with a soft-faced hammer, hammer spring into position.

4) To complete installation, reverse removal procedures.

OVERHAUL

The Bronco II and Ranger Traction-Lok differential is serviced as an assembly only. Under no circumstances should differential be disassembled, reassembled, and installed in vehicle.

Positive Traction Differentials

FORD TRACTION-LOK – 9" RING GEAR

E150 Models

DESCRIPTION

Traction-Lok positive traction differential uses a multiple disc clutch to control differential action. Side gear mounting shims, friction discs, composite plate, clutch hub and guides are housed in differential cover.

Located in differential case, between side gears, is a 1-piece preload plate, block assembly, and 4 calibrated preload springs which apply an initial force to clutch pack.

Additional clutch capacity is derived from side gear thrust loads. Traction-Lok differential can have either 2 or 4 differential pinion gears.

AXLE RATIO & IDENTIFICATION

To determine the drive axle ratio, refer to DRIVE AXLE RATIO IDENTIFICATION in this section.

LUBRICATION

Check level of lubricant every 5,000 miles or 5 months. Manufacturer recommends no specific drain and refill interval. Use only Ford Hypoid Gear Lubricant.

TESTING ON VEHICLE

Raise 1 wheel, leaving opposite wheel firmly on ground. Install adapter and torque wrench to wheel mounting studs. With transmission in "N", note torque required to keep wheel rotating through several revolutions. Torque should be at least 40 ft. lbs. (54 N.m). Disregard initial starting torque.

REMOVAL & INSTALLATION

REMOVAL

1) Position safety stands under rear frame members, and support housing with either a floor jack or hoist. Disengage brake line from clips retaining it to housing.

2) Disconnect vent tube from housing. Remove brake backing plate assemblies from housing, and support with wire.

3) Do not disconnect brake line. Disconnect each rear shock absorber from mounting bracket stud on housing bracket. Lower axle sightly to reduce spring tension. At each rear spring, remove "U" bolt nuts, "U" bolts, and spring seat caps.

INSTALLATION

Reverse removal procedure, to complete installation.

OVERHAUL

DISASSEMBLY

1) Press differential bearings from journals on case. Remove ring gear attaching bolts, and tap gear from case using a soft-faced hammer.

2) Place differential assembly in press to load case halves so preload of springs is overcome, approximately 1000 lbs. (4455 N).

Fig. 1: Exploded View of Typical Ford Traction-Lok Differential Assembly

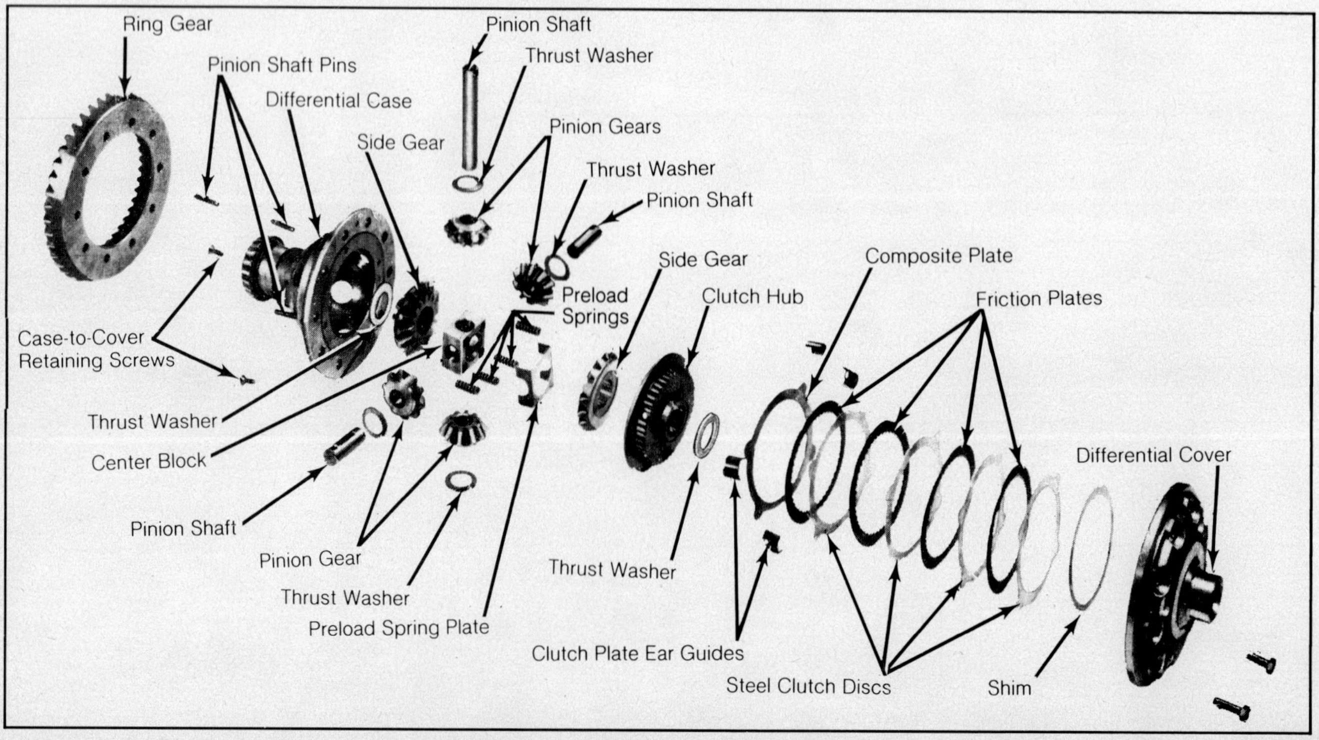

FORD TRACTION-LOK – 9" RING GEAR (Cont.)

3) If press is not available, two 7/16" bolts and nuts can be used in ring gear mounting holes (1 on each side) to compress case halves and overcome preload tension.

4) With case under pressure, loosen 2 case-to-cover retaining screws until 1 or 2 threads of each remain engaged. Release pressure, tap on cover to spring it loose. Remove 2 screws.

5) With cover facing down, lift off case. Remove preload spring plate and 4 preload springs. From cover, remove side gear, 4 clutch plate ear guides, clutch hub, friction plates, steel clutch discs and shims.

6) Using a drift, drive out pinion shaft lock pins from case. Drive long pinion shaft from case, working from end opposite lock pin hole. Remove 2 short pinion shafts, working from center outward.

7) Lift out thrust block, remove pinion gears, thrust washers, side gear and side gear thrust washer.

INSPECTION

1) Inspect clutch plates for unevenness or wear. Dog-eared plates must be free of burrs, nicks or scratches. Inspect internally splined clutch plates for condition of bond, bonding material, and wear.

2) Replace bonded plates if thickness is less than .085" (2.16 mm), or if plates are badly worn. Inspect all thrust surfaces and hubs for wear.

REASSEMBLY

1) Lubricate all parts with hypoid gear lubricant prior to assembly. Mount differential case in soft-jawed vise and place a side gear thrust washer and a side gear into counterbore in case.

2) Install pinion thrust washers, and place pinion gears on side gear, aligning holes in washers and ears with holes in case. Install center block so holes in block are aligned with holes in pinion gears and case.

3) Using a brass drift, drive pinion shafts into position from outside of case, making sure lock pin holes in shafts are aligned with corresponding holes in case.

4) Install shaft lock pins, making sure pinion and side gears move freely. Place 4 preload springs in holes provided in center block. Position preload plate over springs, making sure springs are properly seated.

Fig. 2: Sectional View of Center Block Installation

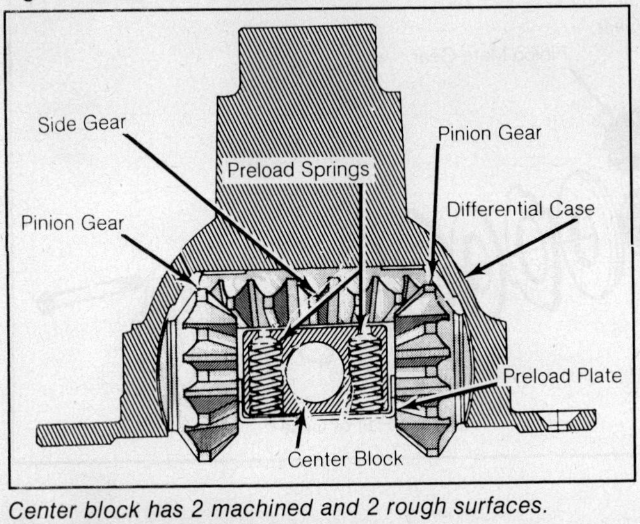

Center block has 2 machined and 2 rough surfaces.

5) Preload plate straddles center block over its narrower, or machined, width. Center block has 2 machined sides and 2 rough sides. Long shaft is driven through rough side, and short shaft is driven through machined side.

6) Mount differential cover in soft-jawed vise. Insert shim(s) of .050" (1.27 mm) total thickness in cover cavity. Install composite plate on back side of clutch hub, with friction material against hub.

7) Install friction plates and steel discs alternately onto hub, beginnning with friction plate and ending with steel disc. When new plates are used, soak in hypoid gear lubricant for 30 minutes before installation.

8) Place clutch hub with clutch plate into clutch gear cavities in differential cover, making sure splines on last friction plate are engaged on hub. Using a 5/8" x 2 1/2" bolt, compress clutch pack, and place shim template tool (T68P-4946-A) in clutch hub.

9) Some clearance should be observed between shim tool and cover-to-case mating surface. Using a feeler gauge, measure clearance. Refer to shim pack thickness chart to determine correct amount of shims to subtract from .050" (1.27 mm) shim pack originally installed.

Fig. 3: Sectional View of Clutch Pack Installation

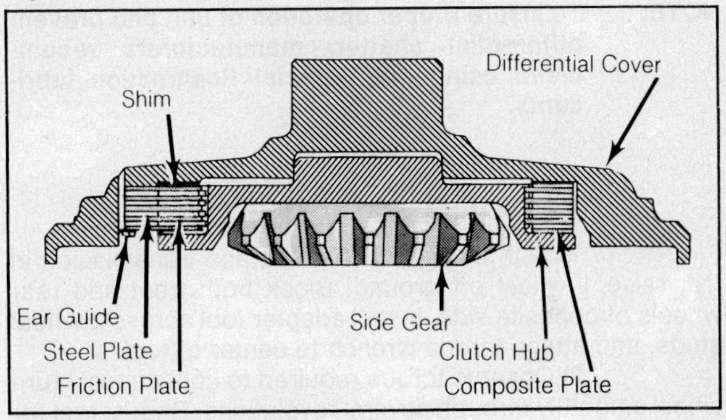

Shown with all clutch plates installed.

SHIM PACK THICKNESS

Gauge Reading	Correction	Total Shims
.001-.002"	None	.050"
.003-.007"	.005"	.045"
.008-.012"	.010"	.040"
.013-.017"	.015"	.035"
.018-.022"	.020"	.030"
.023-.027"	.025"	.025"
.028-.032"	.030"	.020"
.033-.037"	.035"	.015"
.038-.042"	.040"	.010"
.043-.047"	.045"	.005"
.048-.050"	.050"	None

10) Install selected shim in cover cavity, and install internal components as before. In order to correctly select proper shim, template tool must be used. Install 4 steel clutch ear guides and side gear.

11) Place both assemblies in press, force both halves together, and install cover-to-case screws. Install ring gear and ring gear attaching bolts. Tighten to 70-85 ft. lbs. (95-116 N.m).

Positive Traction Differentials

SPICER (DANA) POWER-LOK

Ford Motor Co.
Front and Rear Axles

DESCRIPTION

Power-Lok differential uses clutch packs that are preloaded by Belleville spring plates to provide limited slip action.

Torque in the axle causes the pinion shafts to move up ramps on the differential case to increase preload on clutch packs. This varies the amount of torque directed to each wheel, and causes the wheel with the greatest traction to receive the greatest torque.

Power-Lok is used on Spicer (Dana) axles that have a 2-piece differential case and 4 differential pinion gears.

AXLE RATIO & IDENTIFICATION

To determine axle ratio, refer to DRIVE AXLE RATIO IDENTIFICATION in this section.

LUBRICATION

NOTE: **To insure proper operation of unit and prevent differential chatter, manufacturers recommend using only special Positraction lubricants.**

TESTING ON VEHICLE

1) With engine not running and transmission in "N", raise 1 wheel off ground. Block both front and rear wheels of opposite side. Install adapter tool across 2 wheel studs, and attach torque wrench to center of tool.

2) Observe torque required to continuously turn wheel smoothly through several revolutions. Repeat test for opposite side. If differential is operating properly, torque should be 40-200 ft. lbs. (54-272 N.m). Disregard breakaway torque. Use rotating torque only.

REMOVAL & INSTALLATION

See SPICER (DANA) SEMI-FLOATING or FULL-FLOATING AXLE article in this section.

OVERHAUL

DISASSEMBLY

1) During disassembly, note and record relationship of all parts to each other, especially clutch disc and plates.

2) Mark case halves, pinion mate shafts, and their corresponding ramps. Mark differential spiders for reassembly reference. For front axle shaft and bearing removal, see SPICER (DANA) FULL-FLOATING AXLES or 4-WHEEL DRIVE STEERING KNUCKLES in this section.

3) Clamp differential assembly in a soft-jawed vise. Loosen, but do not remove case attaching bolts. Place differential assembly on bench with ring half of case down.

4) Remove case attaching bolts and cover half of case. Remove pinion mate gear, side gear ring and clutch pack. Keep parts with cover half of case for reassembly reference.

5) On model 70 differentials, remove corresponding parts from drive gear half of case. On all models, clean parts thoroughly.

INSPECTION

1) Inspect plates, discs, clutch rings, side gears, pinion mate gears, pinion mate shafts and spacer block for damage or wear.

2) Any part showing extreme wear or scoring should be replaced. The pinion mate shafts are unlike the shafts of a conventional differential, and therefore are not locked to differential case.

REASSEMBLY

NOTE: **During reaasembly, keep all parts clean and lubricate them with limited slip gear lubricant before installation.**

Fig. 1: Exploded View of Spicer (Dana) Power-Lok Differential Assembly

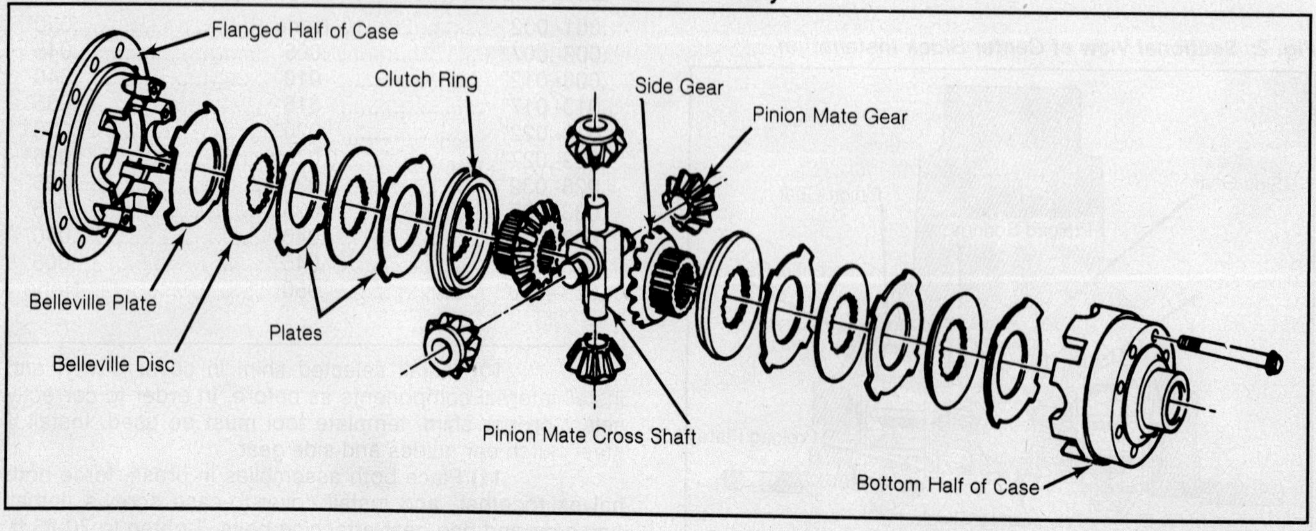

Positive Traction Differentials

SPICER (DANA) POWER-LOK (Cont.)

NOTE: All front axles have 3 friction surfaces; rear axles have 5 friction surfaces.

1) Replace plates and disc in exactly the same order as they were removed. *See Fig. 1.* Apply proper lubricant on each part. With plates and disc now assembled to clutch ring, line up ears of plates so they will enter easily into ring gear case half.

2) Turn case half upside down and install side gear in side gear ring. Place mate shaft and pinions on side gear ring. Align mate shaft and case markings.

3) Install cover half mate shaft and pinions. Align point markings. Place side gear on pinions and place side gear ring on side gear and pinions.

4) Assemble clutch pack on side gear. *See Fig. 2.* Align clutch plate lugs and install all parts in case.

5) Place cover half of case over assembly and align case marks. Lubricate bolt threads and turn each bolt a few threads. Using both axle shafts, align splines of side gear and side gear ring on both sides of case.

6) With axle shafts in position, tighten case bolts evenly and alternately to 65-70 ft. lbs. (88-95 N.m). If bolt heads have "180" stamped on them, tighten case bolts to 90-110 ft. lbs. (122-150 N.m).

7) Remove axle shafts. If assembly has been properly assembled, each pinion mate cross shaft should be tight on its ramp. If there is clearance between cross shaft and ramp, it should not be more than .010" (.25 mm), and should be equal at all 4 cross shaft ends.

Fig. 2: Disc and Plate Arrangement for One Side of Power-Lok Differential

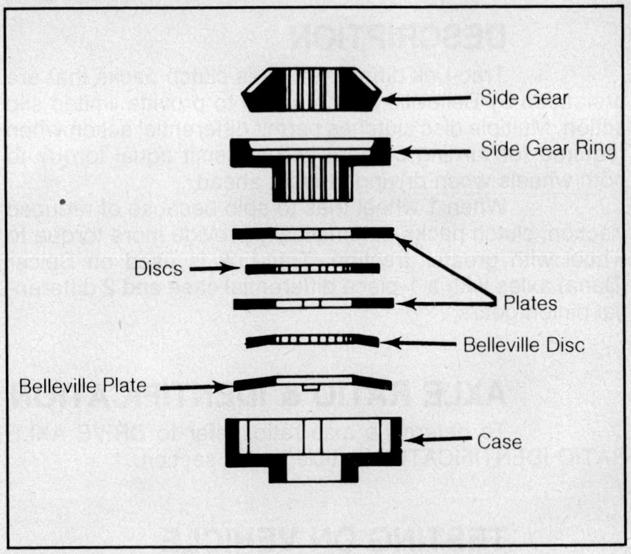

Apply lubricant on each part, and line up ears of plates for assembly.

Positive Traction Differentials

SPICER (DANA) TRAC-LOK

Chrysler Corp., Jeep

DESCRIPTION

Trac-Lok differential uses clutch packs that are preloaded by Belleville spring plates to provide limited slip action. Multiple disc clutches permit differential action when required for turning corners and transmit equal torque to both wheels when driving straight ahead.

When 1 wheel tries to spin because of reduced traction, clutch packs automatically provide more torque to wheel with greater traction. Trac-Lok is used on Spicer (Dana) axles with a 1-piece differential case and 2 differential pinion gears.

AXLE RATIO & IDENTIFICATION

To determine axle ratio, refer to DRIVE AXLE RATIO IDENTIFICATION article in this section.

TESTING ON VEHICLE

1) With engine off and transmission in Neutral, raise 1 wheel off ground and block both front and rear wheels of opposite side. Install adapter tool across 2 wheel studs and attach torque wrench to center of tool.

2) Observe torque required to continuously turn wheel smoothly through several revolutions. Repeat test for opposite side. If differential is operating properly, torque should be 40-200 ft. lbs. (54-272 N.m).

NOTE: Disregard breakaway torque. Use rotating torque only.

REMOVAL & INSTALLATION

See SPICER (DANA) SEMI-FLOATING or FULL-FLOATING article in this section.

OVERHAUL

Trac-Lok differential is serviced as an assembly only. DO NOT disassemble or reassemble Sure-Grip differential in vehicle.

DISASSEMBLY

During disassembly, note and record relationship of all parts to each other (especially clutch disc and plates). Mark case halves, pinion mate shafts and their corresponding ramps and differential spiders for reassembly reference.

NOTE: For front axle shaft and bearing removal, see articles on Spicer (Dana) Full-Floating Axles or 4-Wheel Drive Steering Knuckles in this section.

1) With axle assembly removed from vehicle and axles pulled out from housing, remove cover plate screws and cover. Remove differential bearing caps.

Fig. 1: Exploded View of Spicer (Dana) Trac-Lok Differential Assembly

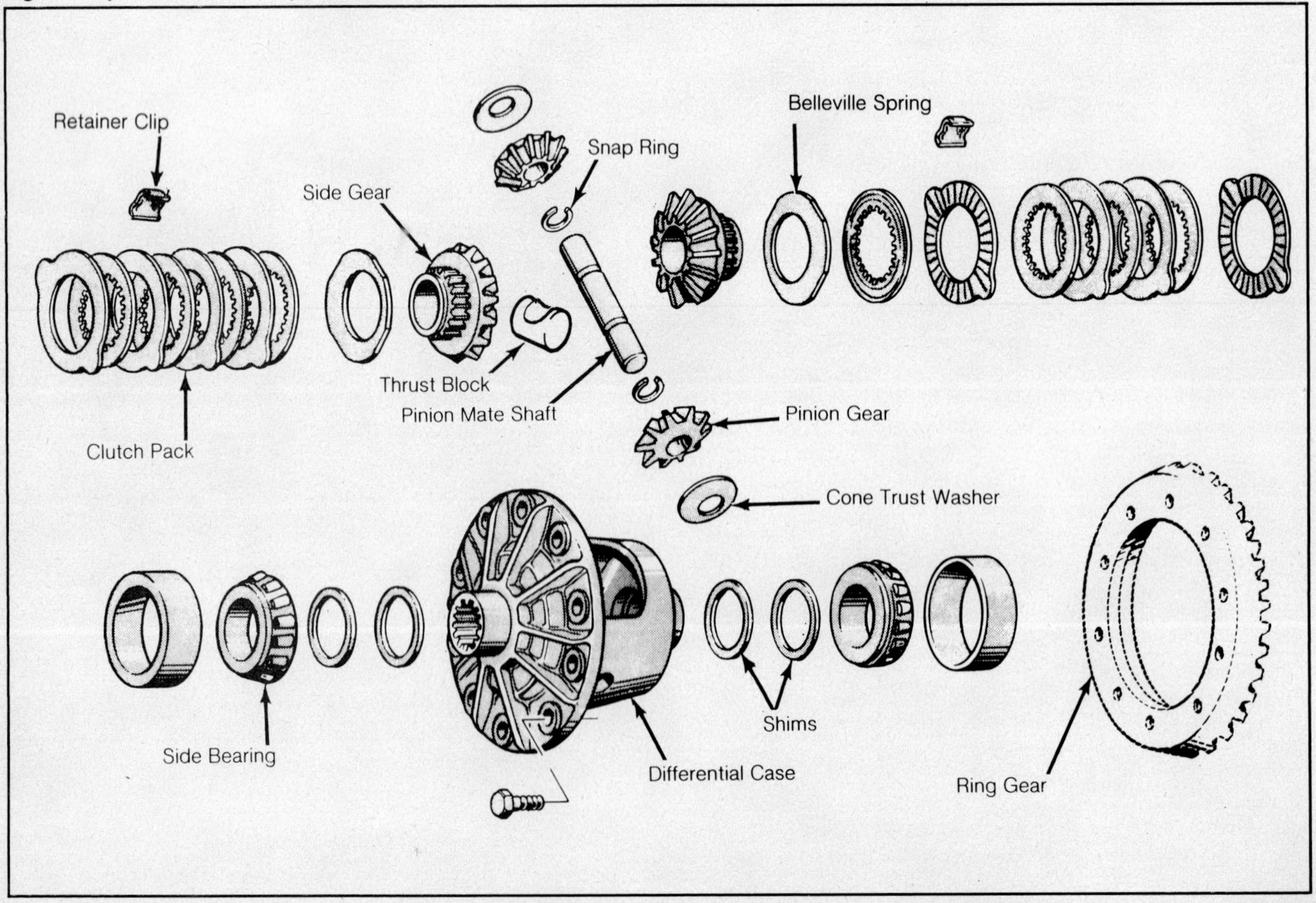

Positive Traction Differentials

SPICER (DANA) TRAC-LOK (Cont.)

Fig. 2: View Showing Typical Clutch Pack Arrangement

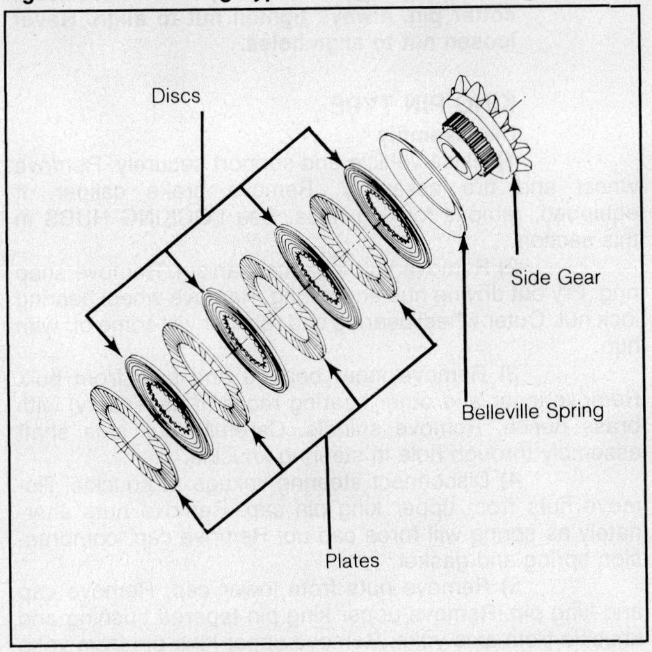

Not all combinations shown.

2) Note letters stamped on bearing caps for reassembly in proper location. Mount speader and dial indicator to housing. Spread housing to .020" (.51 mm). DO NOT spread it any wider.

3) Remove differential using 2 pry bars. Mark differential bearing cups for reassembly. Place axle in a vise, with splined end pointing up 2 3/4" (70 mm) above vise. Assemble differential to axle shaft with ring gear screws facing up.

4) Place shop towels under ring gear to protect it during removal. Remove and discard ring gear bolts. Remove ring gear from case using a rawhide mallet. Using 2 screwdrivers, remove snap rings from pinion mate shaft.

5) Remove pinion mate shaft using a brass drift. With differential on axle shaft, remove cross pin and spacer block (if equipped) using a drift. Place shop towels over vise jaws to protect gear teeth. On model 60 Track-Lok, pinion mate shaft is retained by a single lock pin. Drive lock pin from case using a 3/16" drift.

6) Gear Rotating Tool (J-23781) is required to perform the following steps. The tool consists of 3 parts; gear rotating tool, forcing screw and step plate. Install step plate in lower differential side gear.

7) Position pawl end of gear rotating tool on step plate. Lubricate forcing screw and center hole in stop plate before using. Insert forcing screw through top of case and thread into gear rotating tool.

8) Thread forcing screw so it becomes centered in stop plate. Tighten screw until differential side gears move away from pinion gears. This relieves load between gears allowing pinions some freedom of movement.

9) Use shim stock of .030" (.76 mm) thickness to remove spherical washers. Loosen forcing screw and retighten until a very slight movement of pinions is detected. Insert gear rotating pawl between 2 differential side gear teeth and roll pinion gears out of case.

NOTE: When rotating differential gear, adjust forcing screw until required load is applied to allow differential gears to rotate freely.

10) Retain top differential side gear and clutch pack in case by holding bottom of rotating tool while removing forcing screw. Remove rotating tool, stop plate, top differential gear and clutch pack from case.

11) Remove case from axle shaft. Invert case and remove remaining side gear and clutch pack. Remove retaining clips from both clutch packs and separate clutch plates and discs.

NOTE: Keep parts in same order as they were removed so they can be installed in their original positions.

INSPECTION

Clean and dry all parts. Inspect plates, discs and clips for excessive wear or scoring. Inspect gears for extreme wear, cracks or chips. Inspect case for scoring, wear or metal pickup on machined surfaces.

NOTE: If any 1 member of either clutch pack should be replaced, complete clutch pack for both sides should be replaced. If any 1 gear requires replacement, all differential gears and thrust washers should be replaced.

REASSEMBLY

NOTE: Lubricate all parts with positive traction lubricant before reassembly.

1) Reassemble Belleville spring plate, disc and plates to differential side gears in same position as originally assembled. Install retaining clips to ears of plates, making sure clips are fully seated.

2) Install clutch packs and differential side gears into case. Mount case assembly onto axle shaft, held in vise. While holding gears in place by hand, assemble gear rotating tool the same way as during disassembly.

3) Position differential pinion gears in place so holes in gears align with holes in case. Slightly tighten forcing screws.

NOTE: On models with single lock pin through case, make sure hole in shaft aligns with hole in case.

4) Install pinion gear thrust washers using small screwdriver to guide washers into position. Remove forcing screw, rotating tool and stop plate. Position thrust block between side gears and install differential pinion mate shaft.

5) Be sure snap ring grooves of shaft are exposed enough to install snap rings. On model 60 Trac-Lok, align shaft, shaft retaining pin bore and case pin bore. Tap shaft into position and install retaining pin.

6) If case is mounted in a vise with machined side of ring gear flange facing upward, use a 5/16" diameter punch to install retaining pin. Seat pin until punch bottoms in case bore.

7) If case is mounted in a vise, place machined side of ring gear flange downward. Wrap a length of tape around a 3/16" diameter punch approximately 1 3/4" from end of punch. Install retaining pin until edge of tape is flush with pin bore.

8) Remove case from axle shaft. Install ring gear on case, using all new ring gear bolts. Align ring gear and case bolt holes. Install ring gear bolts finger tight only.

9) Remount case on axle shaft, and tighten bolts evenly to specified torque. Install Trac-Loc differential assembly in axle housing. To complete differential and axle assembly, follow service procedures previously outlined for conventional axles.

4-Wheel Drive Steering Knuckles

ALL MANUFACTURERS

DESCRIPTION

Open type steering knuckles are used on all models. Open type knuckles provide sharper turning angle, which will decrease vehicle turning radius. All steering knuckles used on light duty trucks are mechanically similar.

Total vehicle weight is carried by axle housing and steering knuckle. Axle shafts are free floating. Depending upon vehicle model, steering knuckles can be attached to axle housing by either ball joints or roller bearings and king (pivot) pins.

OVERHAUL

BALL JOINT TYPE

Disassembly

1) Raise vehicle and support securely. Remove wheels. Remove brake caliper and rotor. If equipped, remove locking hubs. See LOCKING HUBS in this section.

2) Disconnect tie rod end from steering knuckle. Remove spindle nuts and lightly tap spindle with soft face hammer to free it from steering knuckle. Pull out axle shaft assembly. On General Motors "S" series, remove hub and bearing assembly.

3) Remove ball joint cotter keys and nuts. Break ball joints loose from steering knuckle. On Chrysler Corp. vehicles, lower ball joint does not need to be disconnected. Remove nuts holding lower knuckle to knuckle arm and separate components.

4) Clean all components with solvent and blow them dry with compressed air. Inspect all parts for burrs, chips, wear, flat spots or cracks. Replace all damaged or worn parts.

Reassembly

To reassemble, reverse disassembly procedure. Torque all fittings to specifications.

NOTE: When aligning upper ball joint nut to install cotter pin, always tighten nut to align. Never loosen nut to align holes.

KING PIN TYPE

Disassembly

1) Raise vehicle and support securely. Remove wheel and tire assembly. Remove brake caliper. If equipped, remove locking hubs. See LOCKING HUBS in this section.

2) Remove hub lock mechanism. Remove snap ring. Pry out driving hub and spring. Remove wheel bearing lock nut. Outer wheel bearing and retainer will come off with hub.

3) Remove inner bearing and seal from hub. Remove inner and outer bearing races (if necessary) with brass punch. Remove spindle. Carefully pull axle shaft assembly through hole in steering knuckle.

4) Disconnect steering linkage at knuckle. Remove nuts from upper king pin cap. Remove nuts alternately as spring will force cap up. Remove cap, compression spring and gasket.

5) Remove nuts from lower cap. Remove cap and king pin. Remove upper king pin tapered bushing and knuckle from axle yoke. Remove upper king pin from yoke using puller.

6) Using punch, drive out lower king pin bearing, bearing race, grease retainer and seal. Drive out from top to bottom.

Reassembly

1) Install new grease retainer and bearing race in bottom of yoke. Fill grease retainer with lubricant. Grease bearing and install in race. Install new lower king pin oil seal.

2) Care must be taken not to distort seal as it is driven into place. It will protrude slightly from surface of yoke. Using socket, install upper king pin. Installation torque is 500-600 ft. lbs. (680-816 N.m).

Fig. 1: Exploded View of Ball Joint Type Steering Knuckle Assembly

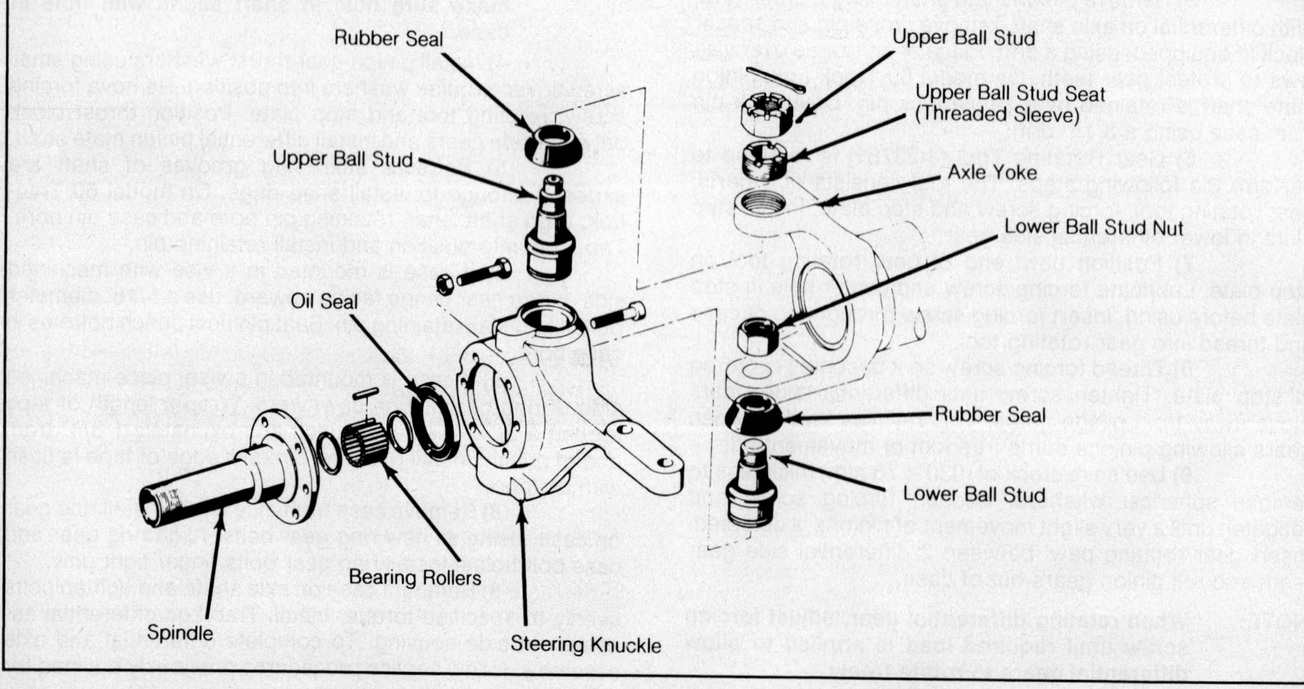

4-Wheel Drive Steering Knuckles

ALL MANUFACTURERS (Cont.)

3) Position felt seal on king pin. Install steering knuckle and tapered bushing on king pin. Install lower bearing cap and king pin. Tighten bolts alternately and evenly to specifications.

4) Install compression spring on upper king pin bushing. Install bearing cap using new gasket. Tighten nuts alternately and evenly to specifications.

ADJUSTMENT

BALL JOINTS

General Motors K10/20

1) Raise vehicle and support securely. Disconnect tie rod at steering knuckle. Connect spring tension gauge to tie rod hole in steering knuckle. Place steering knuckle in straight ahead position.

2) Measure force required to pull steering knuckle to right after initial breakaway. Pull should not exceed 25 ft. lbs. (34 N.m). If pull required is excessive, remove upper ball joint stud nut. Loosen adjusting sleeve as required.

Jeep

1) Raise vehicle and remove front wheels. Disconnect steering damper and connecting rod. Remove cotter pin from right side tie rod retaining nut. Rotate steering knuckles through complete arc several times.

2) Place torque wrench on right side tie rod retaining nut. Torque to turn knuckles through complete arc should not be more than 25 ft. lbs. (34 N.m).

3) If turning effort is excessive, disconnect tie rod ends at knuckles. Measure turning effort of right and left side knuckles. Individual turning effort should not be more than 10 ft. lbs. (14 N.m).

4) If individual turning effort is more than specified, replace upper ball joint split ring seat. If turning effort is more than 10 ft. lbs. (14 N.m) after split ring seat replacement, ball joints will have to be replaced.

TURNING ANGLE

1) Turning angle stop screws are located at rear of steering knuckle, just above axle centerline. To adjust, loosen lock nut on turning angle stop screw. Ford Motor Co. vehicles are nonadjustable.

2) Using turntable to measure angle, adjust stop screw to obtain specified angle. Tighten lock nut without changing setting.

TURNING ANGLE ADJUSTMENT

Application	Left Wheel	Right Wheel
Chrysler Corp.		
W150	37°	[1] 29°
W250	35°	[1] 29°
W350	34°	29°
Ford [2]		
F150 & Bronco	[3] 36°	[3] 36°
F250	33.4°	33.4°
F350	30.3°	30.3°
Bronco II & Ranger	[4]	[4]
General Motors	[4]	[4]
Jeep		
CJ7 & Scrambler	30-31°	30-31°
Cherokee & Wagoneer	32-33°	32-33°
All Others	36-37°	36-37°

1 – On models with 8.00 X 16.5 tires. On models with 7.00 RX 15tires and models with 10 RX 15 tires and manual steering, angle should be 27°. On models with 8.75 X 16.5 tires, angle should be 26°. On all models with power steering and on models with 9.50 X 16.5 or 7.50 X 16 tires, angle should be 24°.

2 – Angle stops are not adjustable. Parts must be repiaced if angle is incorrect.

3 – Angle should be 34° on models with 10 X 15 tires.

4 – Information not available from manufacturer.

TIGHTENING SPECIFICATIONS

Application	Ft. Lbs.(N.m)
Ball Joint Type	
Lower Ball Joint Nut	
Chrysler Corp.	80 (108)
Ford	95-110 (129-149)
General Motors	
"S" Series	83 (112)
All Others	70 (95)
Upper Ball Joint Nut	
Chrysler Corp.	100 (136)
Ford	85-100 (115-137)
General Motors	
"S" Series	50 (68)
All Others	100 (136)
Jeep	100 (136)
Upper Ball Joint Split Retaining Seat	
Chrysler Corp.	40 (54)
General Motors	50 (70)
Jeep	50 (68)
King Pin Type	
Chrysler Corp. & General Motors	
Drag Link-to-Steering Knuckle	60 (82)
King Pin Cap Bolts	70-90 (95-122)
Tie Rod-to-Steering Knuckle	45 (61)
Upper King Pin	500-600 (678-813)

Front Wheel Drive Axle Shafts

CHRYSLER CORP. FWD

Caravan, Mini Ram Van, Voyager

DESCRIPTION

Power from transaxle is transmitted to drive wheels by 2 axle shafts of unequal length. Both shafts use tripod type CV joints on inner end and Rzeppa type CV joints on outer end. Tripod joints are splined to transaxle while Rzeppa joint has stub axle splined to hub. Drive axle assemblies are of 2 different types, either G.K.N. or Citroen. *See Fig. 2.*

REMOVAL & INSTALLATION

SPEEDOMETER PINION GEAR

NOTE: **Speedometer pinion gear is located in extension housing on right side of transaxle. Pinion must be removed before removing right axle shaft assembly.**

Fig. 1: Speedometer Pinion and Adapter

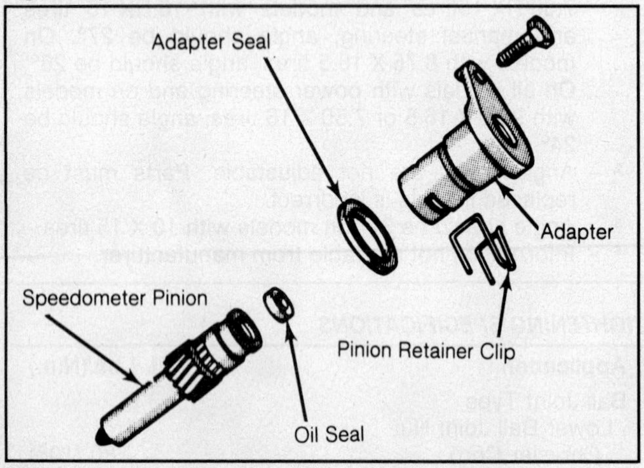

Remove pinion before removing right axle shaft.

Fig. 2: Chrysler Corp. Axle Shaft Identification

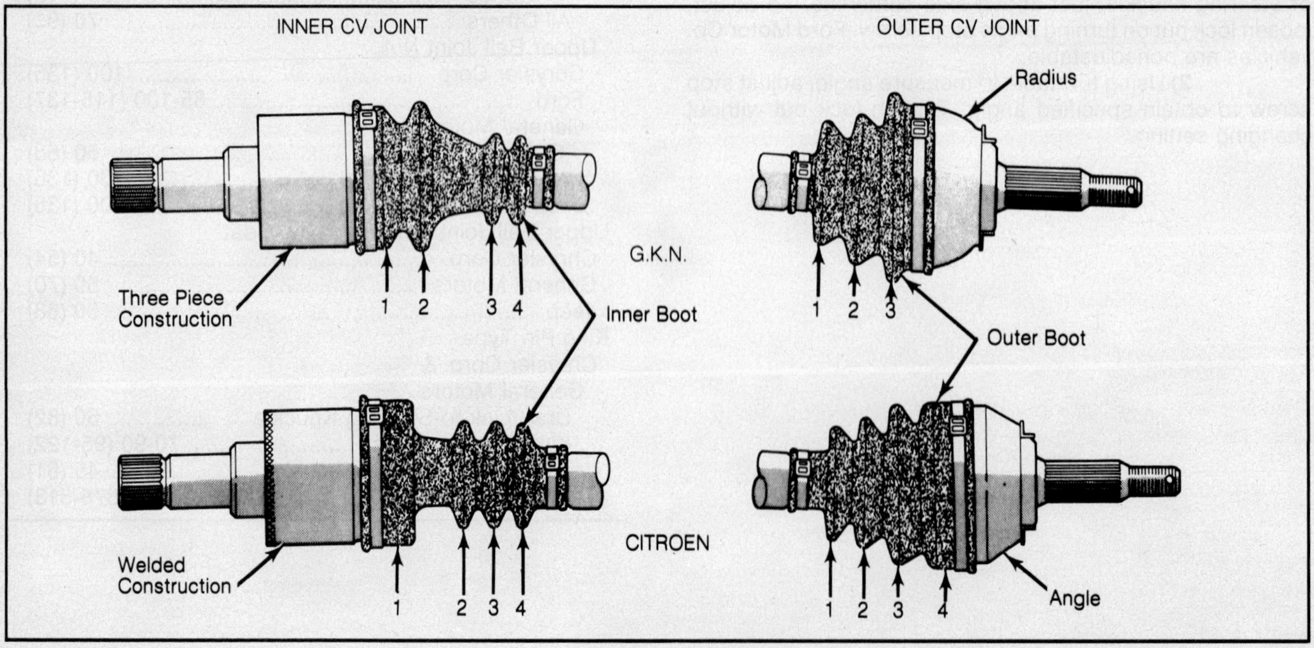

Removal

1) Remove clamp retaining bolt which holds pinion assembly into extension housing. Leaving cable connected, gently remove adapter and pinion from housing. Remove retainer clip from adapter and pull speedometer pinion out of adapter. *See Fig. 1.*

2) Check cable housing for transmission oil. If found, replace speedometer pinion and seal assembly. If oil is found between cable and adapter, replace small "O" ring on cable.

Installation

Make sure adapter and transmission housing area are clean. Speedometer pinion could become misaligned by even small amount of dirt. Pinion gear damage would result. Install and tighten retaining bolt.

AXLE SHAFTS

CAUTION: **Whenever steering knuckle and outer CV are separated, knuckle seal and wear sleeve on CV must be cleaned with solvent and relubricated before reassembly. Do not allow solvent to contact CV boot. Cover seal contact area of wear sleeve with 1/4" bead of multipurpose grease. Fill in lip-to-housing cavity of seal and lightly coat entire seal face and lip with multipurpose grease.**

Removal

1) Remove cotter key and hub nut lock from end of axle shaft. Loosen hub and lug nuts. Raise vehicle. Remove hub nut and wheel. Remove lower ball joint clamping bolt at steering knuckle. Pry against knuckle and control arm to separate ball joint from knuckle.

2) Separate outer CV joint from hub by holding CV joint and pushing out on knuckle assembly. Do not pry on CV joint. Support drive axle shaft at CV joints. Pull out on inner CV joint, holding inner joint at housing.

CAUTION: **Outer CV joint stub axle holds hub and bearing assembly together when installed. If vehicle must be moved, install bolt through hub assembly so assembly cannot loosen.**

CHRYSLER CORP. FWD (Cont.)

Fig. 3: Exploded View of Axle Shaft Assembly

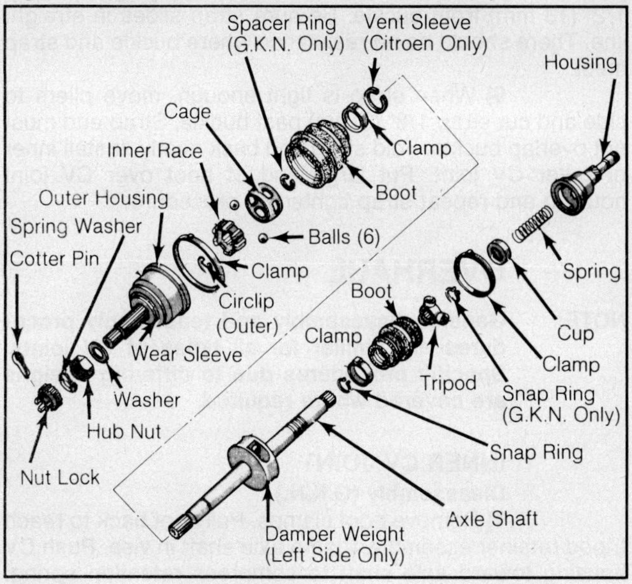

Installation

1) Hold inner CV at housing and guide splines into transaxle or intermediate shaft assembly. Push knuckle assembly outward and install outer CV stub axle. Reinstall knuckle on lower ball joint. Use original bolt or same grade as original for clamping ball joint to arm. Tighten clamping bolt to 70 ft. lbs. (95 N.m).

2) If inner CV boot appears twisted or distorted, vent it by inserting blunt rod between boot and shaft. If boot is held by rubber clamp, leave clamped. If held by metal clamp, clamp must be removed and replaced with new clamp after venting operation is complete. Use correct clamp and clamping procedure as described in CV boot installation in this article.

3) Install speedometer pinion. Fill differential. Install hub nut and tighten to 180 ft. lbs. (243 N.m). Install lock, spring washer, and new cotter pin. Wrap opened ends of cotter pin tightly around nut lock. Install wheel and tighten lug nuts to 95 ft. lbs. (129 N.m).

CV BOOTS

CAUTION: When using Clamping Pliers (C 4124) on G.K.N. boots, use care to avoid cutting bridge of clamp or damaging boot.

Removal (All)

Remove drive axle from vehicle. Remove clamps holding boot to CV joint and shaft. Remove CV joint from axle shaft. Use procedures described in drive axle overhaul and CV disassembly in this article. Remove boot from axle shaft.

Installation (G.K.N.)

1) Several different types of clamps are used on G.K.N. boots. Metal ladder type is most common. On inner CV joints, small rubber clamp may be used to hold small end of boot to axle shaft. Large metal spring clamp may be used to hold large end of boot to inner CV housing. *See Fig. 4.*

2) If equipped, slide small rubber clamp onto axle shaft. Slide inner CV boot onto shaft and position correctly. Right inner boot lip should line up with locating mark on axle shaft. Small end of left inner boot and both outer boots should fit in groove on axle shaft. *See Fig. 5.*

Fig. 4: CV Boot Clamps

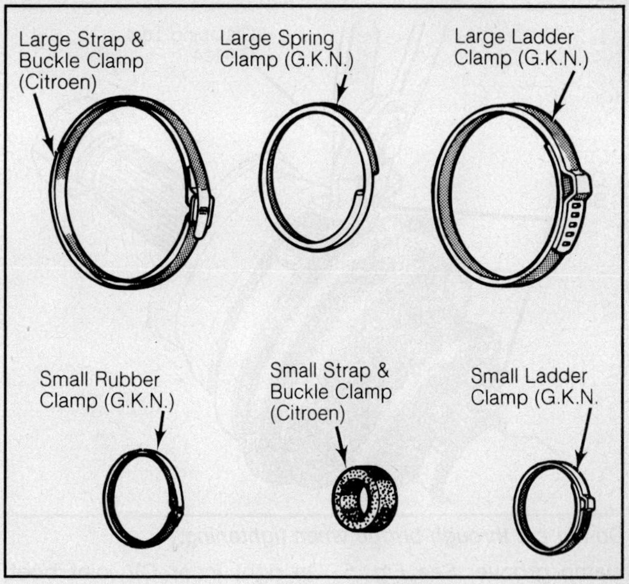

Citroen clamps may be found on G.K.N. type joints.

Fig. 5: CV Joint Boot Placement

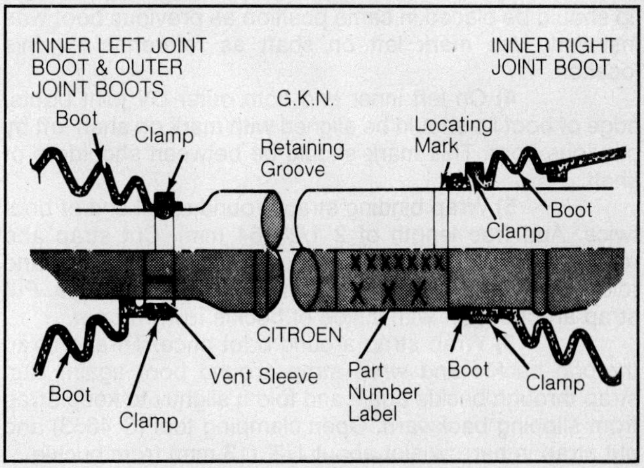

Use prior boot location if markings unclear.

3) Fasten small end of boot either by placing rubber clamp over groove in boot or by fitting metal clamp in groove on boot. Make sure boot is properly located and locate metal clamp tangs in slots. Make clamp as tight as possible by hand.

4) Close bridge of metal clamp with Clamp Pliers (C 4124). *See Fig. 6.* Install correct CV joint as described in CV assembly procedure in this article. Fit large end of boot in groove on housing or over retaining shoulder. Make sure boot does not get twisted.

5) Install metal spring clamp or metal ladder clamp in groove on boot. Locate ladder clamp tangs in slots, making clamp as tight as possible by hand. Close bridge with tool (C 4124) and squeeze tightly.

Installation (Citroen)

1) Citroen type CV joint boot uses 2-piece clamp consisting of strap and buckle. *See Fig. 4.* Clamp installing tool (C 4653) is used to tighten and cut strap clamps. *See Fig. 7.*

2) Slide small end of boot onto axle shaft. If installing outer CV joint boot, place vent sleeve under boot

Fig. 6: Installing Ladder Clamps on G.K.N. CV Boots

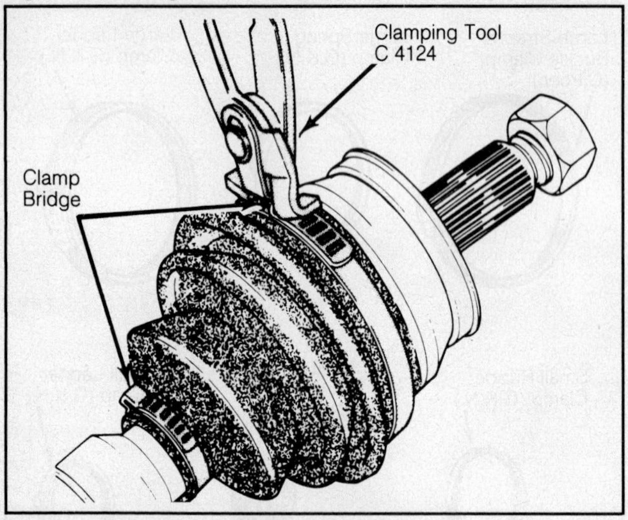

Do not cut through bridge when tightening.

clamp groove. *See Fig. 5.* On right inner CV joint boot, position face of boot lip in line with edge of part number label that is closest to CV joint.

3) If part number label is missing, edge of boot lip should be placed in same position as previous boot was installed. Use mark left on shaft as reference for this location.

4) On left inner and both outer CV joint boots, edge of boot lip should be aligned with mark on shaft left by previous boot. This mark should be between shoulders of shaft.

5) Wrap binding strap around small end of boot twice. Add free length of 2 1/2" (64 mm). Cut strap and remove from boot. Pass end of strap through buckle and fold it back about 1 1/8" (29 mm) on inside of buckle. Put strap around boot with inside of buckle toward boot.

6) Wrap strap around boot once. Thread strap through buckle and wrap strap around boot again. Run strap through buckle again and fold it slightly to keep strap from slipping backward. Open clamping tool (C 4653) and put strap in narrow slot about 1/2" (13 mm) from buckle.

7) Hold strap with one hand. Push clamping pliers forward and slightly upward. Fit hook of tool into eye of buckle. Tighten strap by closing handles of pliers. Rotate handle end of tool down while slowly releasing pressure on handles. Allow handles to open as end of pliers is rotated.

8) Open pliers completely and remove from strap and buckle. If strap is not tight, repeat tightening procedure once or twice, if necessary. Always grasp strap 1/2" (13 mm) from buckle. Be sure strap slides in straight line. There should be no resistance where buckle and strap meet.

Fig. 7: Installing Strap on Citroen CV Boots

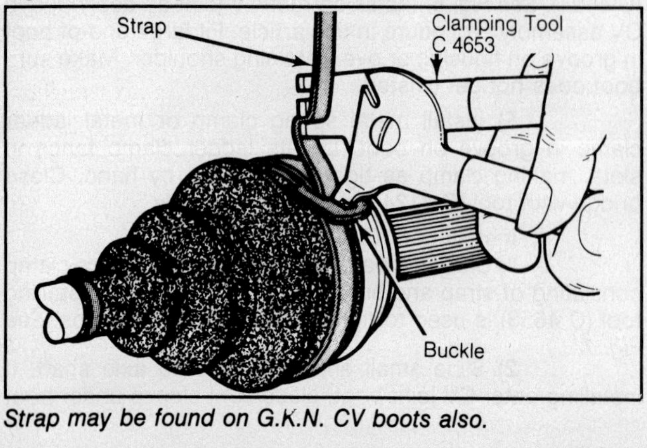

Strap may be found on G.K.N. CV boots also.

9) When strap is tight enough, move pliers to side and cut strap 1/8" (3 mm) past buckle. Strap end must not overlap buckle. Fold strap end back neatly. Install inner or outer CV joint. Put large end of boot over CV joint housing and repeat strap tightening procedure.

OVERHAUL

NOTE: **General disassembly and reassembly procedures are similar for all types of CV joints. Specific procedures due to differing designs are covered where required.**

INNER CV JOINT

Disassembly (G.K.N.)

1) Remove boot clamps. Pull boot back to reach tripod retainer assembly. Clamp axle shaft in vise. Push CV housing toward axle shaft to compress retention spring. Bend retaining tabs (part of housing) back with pliers while spring is compressed.

2) Support housing in horizontal plane while retention spring pressure forces housing off tripod. Remove outer snap ring from axle shaft groove. Remove tripod by hand. Use brass punch to tap tripod body if necessary.

Disassembly (Citroen)

1) Remove boot clamps and pull boot back. Tripod retainer ring (no tabs) is rolled into groove in outer housing. Spread retainer ring out at each tripod roller, using chisel or small pry. Retention spring will push housing from tripod.

NOTE: **Hold tripod rollers in place on trunion studs while removing housing. Secure rollers in place with tape when out of housing. Rollers and needle bearings could fall if not held in place.**

2) Retainer ring can also be cut out from housing. Do not damage housing or groove when cutting ring. New rings come with boot kit.

Inspection (All)

Clean grease from assembly. Check housing races and tripod components for wear or pitting. Inspect spring, spring cup, and rounded end of axle shaft. Replace parts if worn, galled, or pitted.

Reassembly (G.K.N.)

1) Install new axle boot on axle shaft. Slide tripod onto axle shaft, chamfered side first. Flat side of tripod should be next to retaining ring groove. Using grease found in boot kit, put 2 of 3 packets provided into boot. Third packet goes into CV housing.

2) Position retention spring in housing spring pocket. Install spring cup onto exposed end of spring. Lubricate concave surface of spring cup with grease.

NOTE: **Make sure that spring stays centered in housing spring pocket as tripod seats in spring cup.**

3) Install housing over tripod and bend retaining tabs into original position. Make sure tabs can hold tripod in housing. Place boot over retaining groove in housing. Clamp boot in position.

Reassembly (Citroen)

1) Fasten new boot to shaft. Install inner snap ring. Slide tripod onto shaft. Both sides are identical, so either side can go onto shaft first. Install outer snap ring in groove on shaft, locking tripod in position.

2) Using grease provided in boot kit, place 2/3 of 1 packet into boot. Rest of grease goes into housing. Position spring in housing spring pocket with spring cup in place over exposed end of spring. Lightly grease concave surface of spring cup.

NOTE: Make sure that spring stays centered in housing spring pocket as tripod seats in spring cup.

3) Remove tape holding tripod rollers and needle bearings in place on tripod studs. Hold rollers and needle bearings while installing tripod into housing. Roll edge of new retaining ring into machined groove in housing. Use hammer and dull punch to roll ring.

4) Hold retaining collar in place with 2 "C" clamps while rolling retainer ring into groove. Make sure retaining collar will hold tripod in housing. Position boot over retaining groove in housing. Clamp boot in place.

OUTER CV JOINT

Disassembly (All)

1) Remove and discard boot clamps. Wipe away grease so CV joint body edge is visible. Hold axle shaft in soft jaws of vise. Support joint body. Using soft hammer, give top of CV joint body sharp blow to break joint loose from internal circlip in groove at end of shaft.

2) Wear sleeve on outer CV housing is wipe surface for hub bearing seal. If sleeve is bent or damaged, pry wear sleeve away from machined ledge of CV joint. Remove and discard circlip from shaft groove. New circlip comes with replacement boot kit. *See Fig. 8.*

Fig. 8: Exploded View of Outer CV Joint

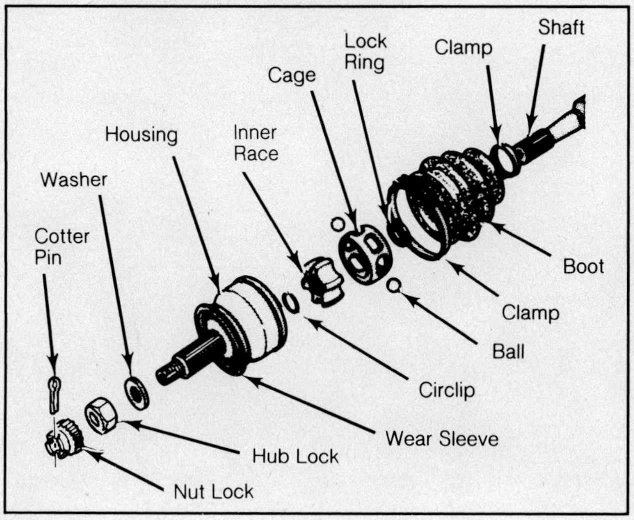

3) Remove heavy spacer ring from inner groove of G.K.N. type axle ONLY if shaft is damaged. If joint was operating properly, replace only the boots. If joint was noisy or badly worn, replace complete joint. Manufacturer recommends boot replacement whenever joint is replaced.

4) Wipe grease off outer CV joint and index mark inner race (cross), cage, and housing with dab of paint. Position joint vertically in vise, using soft jaws to clamp on splined shaft. Press down on 1 side of inner race to tilt cage and remove ball from opposite side. Repeat until all 6 balls are out.

CAUTION: Do not hit cage when using hammer and drift to loosen CV joint.

5) If joint is very tight, use brass drift and hammer to tap inner race and remove balls. Tilt cage and inner race assembly to vertical. Place 2 opposing, elongated cage windows in area between ball grooves in outer race. Citroen type joints alternate 2 short and 1 long cage window while G.K.N. type joints alternate long and short windows or have all identical cage windows.

6) Remove inner race and cage assembly by pulling upward away from the housing. Turn inner race 90° to cage. Align elongated cage window with one of spherical lands on race. Raise land to cage window and remove inner race by swinging it out of cage.

Inspection (All)

Check grease for contamination. Wash all parts in solvent and dry with compressed air. Inspect races for excessive wear and scoring. Check splined shaft and nut threads for damage. Check 6 balls for pitting, cracks, scoring, and wear. Inspect cage for excessive wear on spherical surfaces, surface ripples on cage window, cracks, or chipping. Inspect inner race (cross) for excessive wear or scoring of ball races.

NOTE: Any defects found justify replacing CV assembly as unit. Some polishing is normal, especially in ball races and in cage spheres. Replace polished parts only if they cause noise and vibration.

Reassembly (All)

1) Position new wear sleeve on joint housing machined ledge. Assemble installing tool (C 4698) and install wear sleeve. Lightly oil all components before reassembly. Align parts according to paint markings.

2) Insert 1 inner race (cross) into cage window and feed race into cage. Pivot inner race to fully assemble cage and race. Align opposing elongated cage windows with housing land. Feed cage assembly into housing. Pivot cage 90° to complete installation.

3) On properly assembled G.K.N. units, counterbore of inner race should face outward from joint. On properly assembled Citroen models, inner race and cage chamfers will face outward from joint. On all models, apply lubricant to ball races from packet in boot kit. *See Fig. 9.*

4) Distribute grease equally between all sides of ball grooves. Each joint uses one packet. Insert balls into raceways by tilting cage and inner race assembly. Fasten boot to shaft. Insert new circlip from shaft groove kit.

5) Position outer joint on splined end of axle shaft. Put hub nut on stub axle. Engage splines and tap sharply with mallet. Check that circlip is properly seated by trying to pull joint off shaft. Install large end of boot over joint housing making sure that boot is not twisted. Attach boot to housing.

Front Wheel Drive Axle Shafts

CHRYSLER CORP. FWD (Cont.)

Fig. 9: Cutaway Views of Outer CV Joints

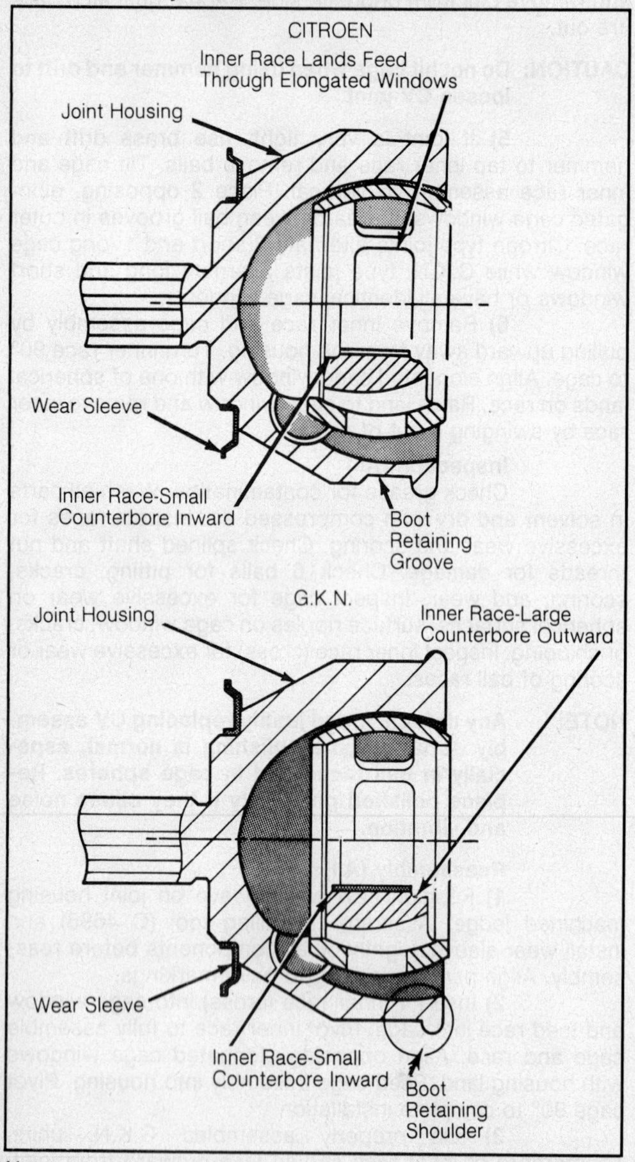

Note correct cage and inner race installation.

TIGHTENING SPECIFICATIONS

Application	Ft. Lbs. (N.m)
Axle Hub Nut	180 (244)
Ball Joint Clamp Nut	70 (95)
Wheel Lug Nut	95 (129)

Front Wheel Drive Axle Shafts

GENERAL MOTORS "S" SERIES 4WD TRUCKS

DESCRIPTION

Chevrolet and GMC "S" series 4WD models use an independent front drive axle which incorporates constant velocity (CV) joints. The inner CV joints uses a "Tri-Pot" design, and outer CV joints are a "Double Offset" design.

The inner CV joint is completely flexible, plus it has capability of in and out movement. The outer CV joint is also flexible, but cannot move in and out.

REMOVAL & INSTALLATION

AXLE SHAFTS

Removal & Installation

1) Raise and support vehicle on safety stands. Remove wheel and brake caliper and flex hoses at brackets. Remove tie rods at steering knuckle using Puller (J-24319). Remove shock lower bolts and push shocks out of way.

2) Remove drive axle-to-axle tube bolts. Remove axle shaft cotter pin, nut and washer. Position inner part of drive axle forward and support away from frame. Remove shaft from hub using Puller (J-28733). Remove axle shaft from vehicle.

3) Install axle shaft into hub. Tighten nut and washer to specifications. Install retainer, and install cotter pin. To complete installation, reverse the remaining removal procedure.

Fig. 2: Removing Front Drive Axle

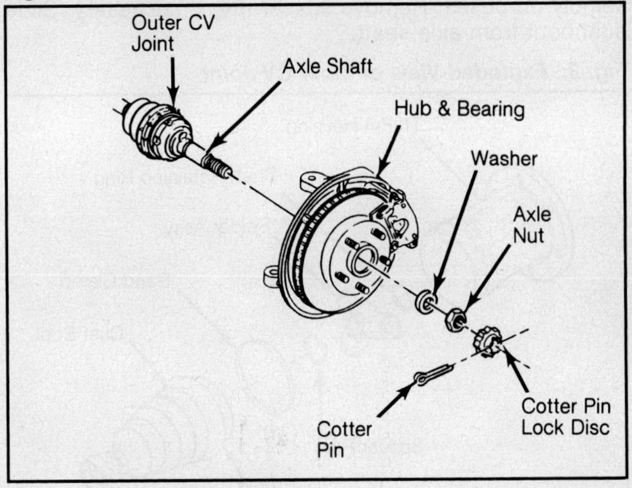

OVERHAUL

DISASSEMBLY

Inner CV Joint

1) Using side cutter pliers, cut dust boot band clamps. Pull boot from tri-pot housing and separate tri-pot housing from spider assembly. Wrap tape around spider assembly to retain needle bearings.

2) Using snap ring pliers, remove axle shaft retaining ring and separate spider assembly from axle

Fig. 1: Exploded View of Chevrolet & GMC "S" Series Drive Axle

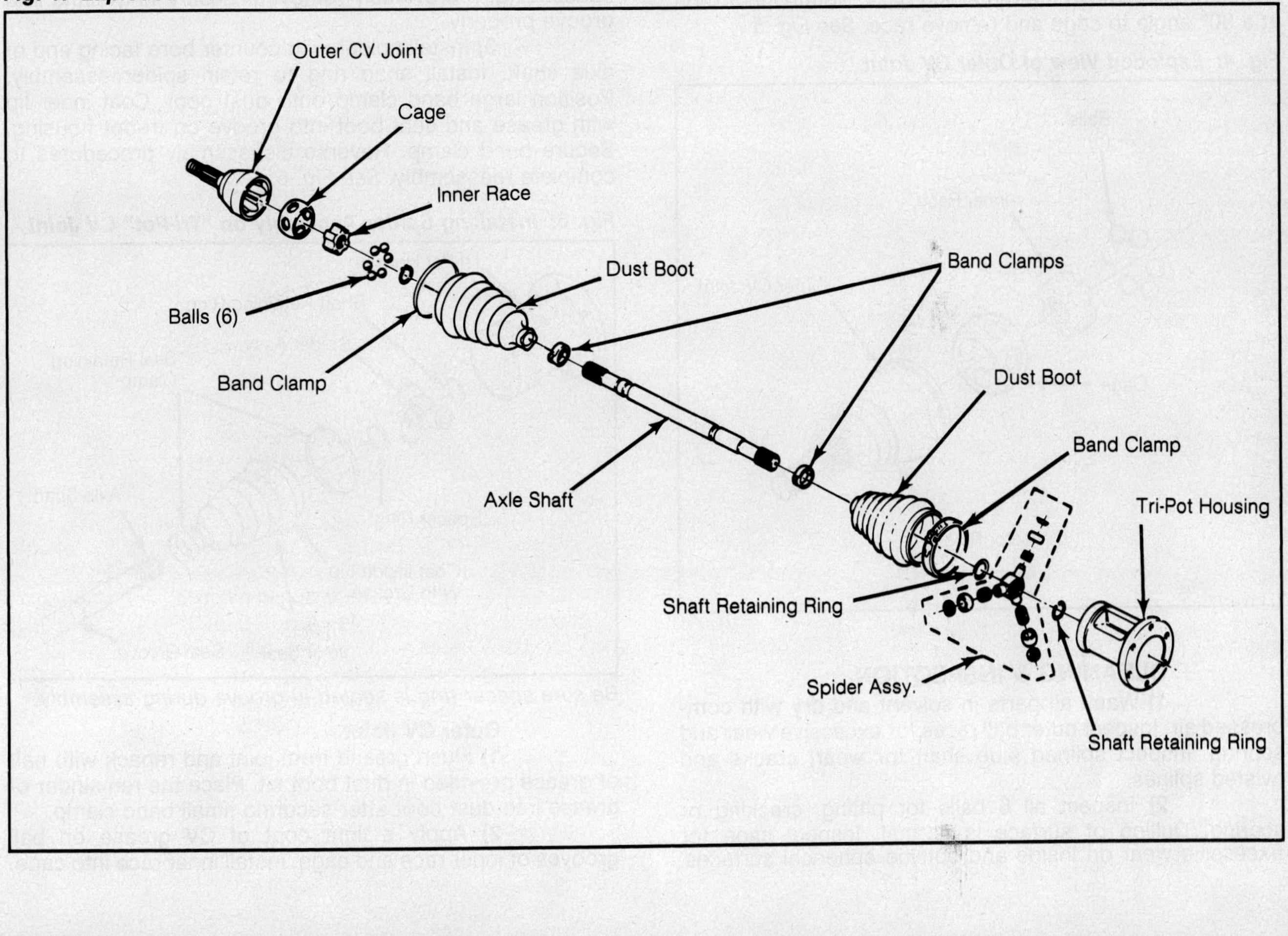

GENERAL MOTORS "S" SERIES 4WD TRUCKS (Cont.)

shaft. Note position of counter bore of spider for reassembly purposes. Remove spacer ring if necessary. Slide dust boot from axle shaft.

Fig. 3: Exploded View of Inner CV Joint

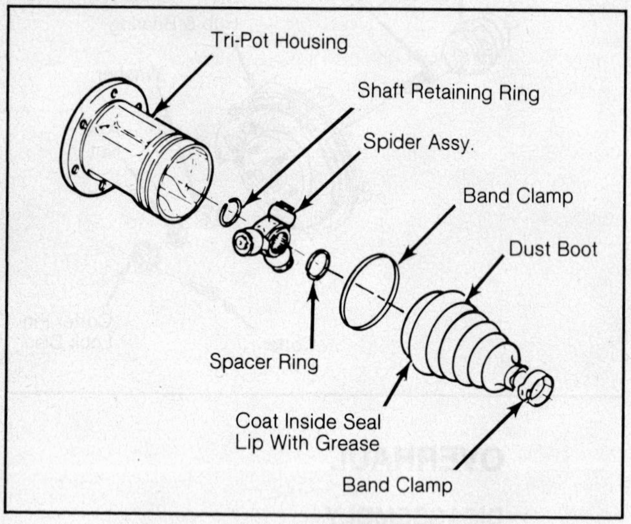

Outer CV Joint

1) Using side cutter pliers, cut dust boot clamps. Pull boot back from CV joint. Using Snap Ring Pliers (J-8059), spread retaining ring ears apart and pull axle shaft out of CV cage.

2) Using a brass drift and hammer, gently tap on cage until its tilted enough to remove the first ball. Repeat procedure to remove the remaining balls. Rotate inner race at a 90° angle to cage and remove race. *See Fig. 5*

Fig. 4: Exploded View of Outer CV Joint

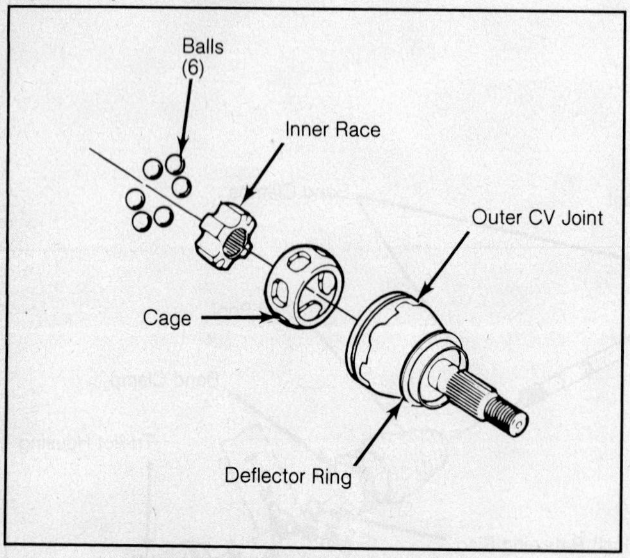

CLEANING & INSPECTION

1) Wash all parts in solvent and dry with compressed air. Inspect outer ball races for excessive wear and scoring. Inspect splined stub shaft for wear, cracks and twisted splines.

2) Inspect all 6 balls for pitting, cracking or scoring. Dulling of surface is normal. Inspect cage for excessive wear on inside and outside spherical surfaces.

Fig. 5: Removing Outer CV Joint Cage

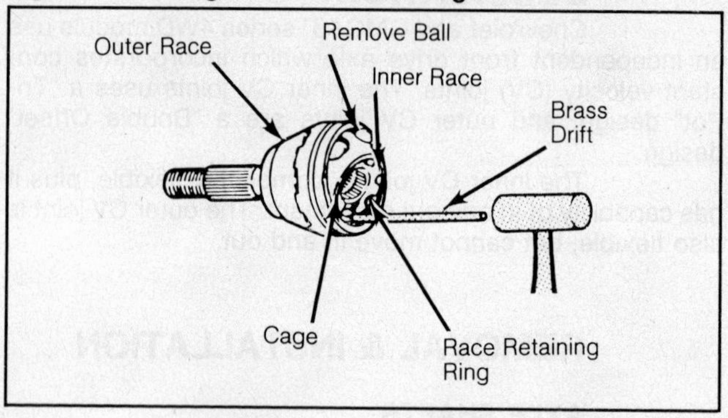

Look for heavy brinelling of cage windows and for cracks or chips.

3) Inspect inner race for excessive wear or scoring. If any damage is found, replace entire CV joint assembly. Polished areas in races and on cage spheres are normal and do not require joint replacement.

REASSEMBLY

Inner CV Joint

1) Flush grease from tri-pot housing. Repack housing using half of grease supplied in dust boot kit. Place the remainder of grease into dust boot after securing small band clamp.

2) Position small band clamp to dust boot. Slide boot onto axle shaft. Ensure boot seats into groove on axle shaft and secure clamp using side cutter pliers. Install spacer ring, if previously removed. Ensure ring seats into groove properly.

3) Install spider with counter bore facing end of axle shaft. Install snap ring to retain spider assembly. Position large band clamp onto dust boot. Coat inner lip with grease and seat boot into groove on tri-pot housing. Secure band clamp. Reverse disassembly procedures to complete reassembly. *See Fig. 6.*

Fig. 6: Installing Spider Assembly on "Tri-Pot" CV Joint

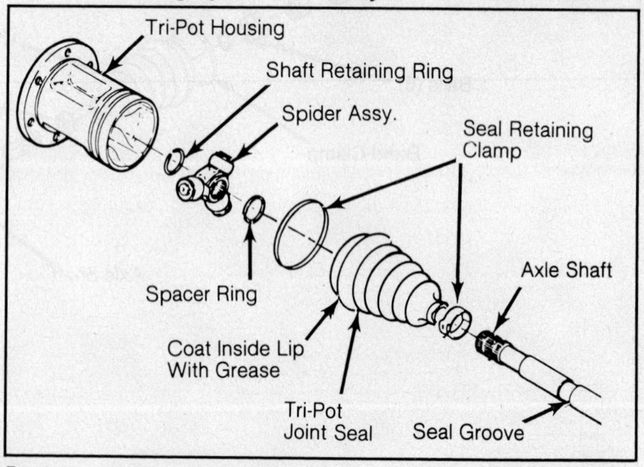

Be sure spacer ring is seated in groove during assembly.

Outer CV Joint

1) Flush grease from joint and repack with half of grease provided in dust boot kit. Place the remainder of grease into dust boot after securing small band clamp.

2) Apply a light coat of CV grease on ball grooves of inner race and cage. Install inner race into cage.

GENERAL MOTORS "S" SERIES 4WD TRUCKS (Cont.)

Pivot cage at a 90° angle to center line of outer race with cage windows aligned with lands of outer race.

NOTE: **Ensure retaining ring side of inner race faces axle shaft.**

3) Install ball bearings one at a time into outer CV joint as cage is tilted and rotated. After balls are installed into cage, pivot cage and inner race into installed position.

4) Position band clamp onto boot and slide boot onto axle shaft. Secure clamp using side cutter pliers. Coat inside lip (large diameter end of seal with CV grease. Slide large band camp onto dust boot.

5) Install snap ring onto axle shaft, and slide CV joint onto axle shaft until snap ring seats in groove. *See Fig. 7.* Slide dust boot toward joint until dust boot is in groove in axle shaft. Secure large band clamp. Reverse remaining disassembly procedure.

Fig. 7: Installing Outer CV Joint to Axle Shaft

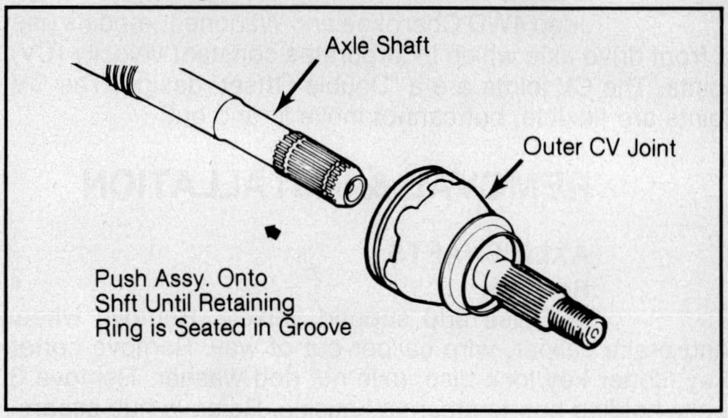
Axle Shaft
Outer CV Joint
Push Assy. Onto
Shft Until Retaining
Ring is Seated in Groove

TIGHTENING SPECIFICATIONS

Application	Ft. Lbs. (N.m)
Drive Axle Nut-to-Hub and Bearing	174 (235)
Drive axle Flange to Differential Flange	63 (85)
Hub-to-Knuckle Assembly	77 (105)
Wheel Lug Nuts	75 (102)

Front Wheel Drive Axle Shafts

JEEP 4WD CHEROKEE & WAGONEER

DESCRIPTION

Jeep 4WD Cherokee and Wagoneer models use a front drive axle which incorporates constant velocity (CV) joints. The CV joints are a "Double Offset" design. The CV joints are flexible, but cannot move in and out.

REMOVAL & INSTALLATION

AXLE SHAFTS

Removal

1) Raise and support vehicle. Remove wheel and brake caliper, wire caliper out of way. Remove cotter key, cotter key lock disc, axle nut and washer. Remove 3 bolts holding hub to steering knuckle. Remove hub assembly and splash shield from steering knuckle.

2) On left side, remove axle shaft. On right side, disconnect vacuum harness from shift motor. Remove shift motor from axle housing and remove axle shaft.

Installation

To install axle shaft, reverse removal procedure, noting the following. On right side, ensure shift collar is in position on intermediate shaft and that axle shaft is fully engaged over end of intermediate shaft. Install shift motor with fork engaged with collar.

OVERHAUL

DISASSEMBLY

1) Cut and remove both outer boot clamps. Slide boot off outer CV joint.

2) Using a block of wood seated on inner race, tap joint from shaft. If shaft is clamped in a vise, be sure to use protective vise jaws.

3) Tap outer CV cage with a brass punch until cage is tilted out far enough to remove first ball bearing. Remove remaining ball bearings in same manner.

4) Rotate outer CV joint cage outward until it is at a 90° angle to installed position. Align 2 oblong holes in outer joint cage with slots in interior wall of spindle housing and remove cage and inner race.

5) Remove inner race from cage by aligning shoulder between race grooves with inside of oblong cage holes. Rotate inner race out of cage using larger of 2 openings in cage.

6) Remove retaining ring and spacer ring from shaft and remove outer boot.

CLEANING & INSPECTION

1) Wash all parts in solvent and dry with compressed air. Inspect outer ball races for excessive wear and scoring. Inspect splined stub shaft for wear, cracks and twisted splines.

2) Inspect all 6 balls for pitting, cracking or scoring. Dulling of surface is normal. Inspect cage for excessive wear on inside and outside spherical surfaces. Look for heavy brinelling of cage windows and for cracks or chips.

3) Inspect inner race for excessive wear or scoring. If any damage is found, replace entire CV joint assembly. Polished areas in races and on cage spheres are normal and do not require joint replacement.

REASSEMBLY

1) Apply a light coat of CV grease on ball grooves of inner and outer races. Install inner race into cage using a rotating action opposite of removal. Inner race snap ring should face axle side.

2) Be sure ball bearing retaining ring is installed on inner race side facing small end of cage. Align windows of cage with outer racelands, and pivot cage with inner race into tilted position (opposite of removal).

3) Install ball bearings one at a time into outer CV joint as cage is tilted and rotated. After balls are installed into cage, pivot cage and inner race into installed position.

4) Slide new seal clamp for small end of boot seal, boot seal and seal retainer onto axle shaft. Coat inside lip (large diameter end of seal with CV grease. Slide seal retainer on end of seal.

5) Spread ears of bearing race snap ring, and slide CV joint onto axle shaft until snap ring seats in groove. Pack joint with approximately 1/2 of grease provided in seal kit. Apply remaining grease inside seal.

6) Slide seal toward joint until small end of seal is in groove in axle shaft. Position small clamp over small end of seal and into groove and tighten.

TIGHTENING SPECIFICATIONS

Application	Ft. Lbs. (N.m)
Axle Shift Motor Bolts	8 (11)
Drive Axle Nut-to-Hub and Bearing	175 (237)
Hub-to-Knuckle Assembly	75 (101)
Wheel Lug Nuts	75 (101)

Fig. 1: Exploded View of Jeep Cherokee & Wagoneer Drive Axle

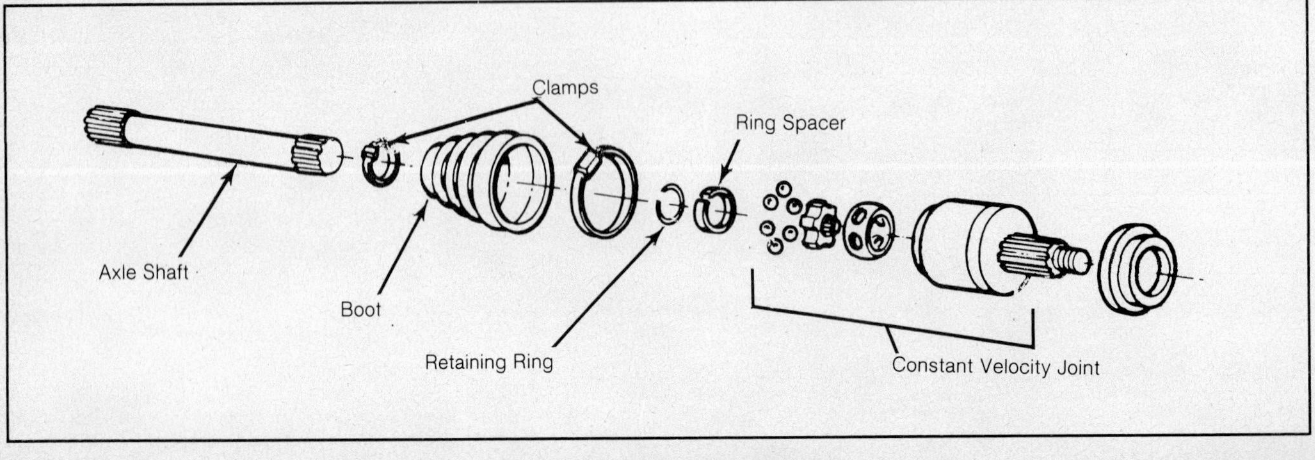

CHRYSLER CORP. DUALMATIC LOCKING HUB

DESCRIPTION

Locking hubs provide a means of engagement and disengagement of wheels on front drive axles. When locking hubs are engaged, full power is transmitted to both front wheels. When hubs are disengaged, front wheels are free to turn. Axle shafts and differential remain idle.

Engagement is accomplished through the action of gears within the hub. With hub in engaged position, the inner clutch gear locks with the outer clutch and engages the axle shaft with wheel hub.

REMOVAL & INSTALLATION

Removal

1) Turn shift knob to "Engage" position. Apply pressure to face of shift knob, remove 3 screws spaced 120° apart and nearest to flange. With an outward pull, remove shift knob from mounting base.

2) Remove snap ring from axle shaft. Remove cap screws and lockwashers from mounting base flange. Separate and remove locking hub assembly from rotor hub. Remove and discard gasket.

Inspection

Wash parts in mineral spirits and blow dry with compressed air. Examine splines shift knob, cam, sliding gear, drive shaft gear, and mounting base for damage.

Installation

1) Lubricate parts lightly with multi-purpose lubricant. Position new gasket and locking hub onto rotor hub. Install attaching cap screws and lock washers. Tighten to 30-40 ft. lbs. (41-54 N.m). Install axle shaft snap ring.

2) Position shift knob on mounting base. Align splines by pushing inward on shift knob and turning it clockwise to lock it in position. Install and tighten 3 shift knob retaining screws.

Fig. 1: Exploded View of Chrysler Corp. Dualmatic Locking Hub

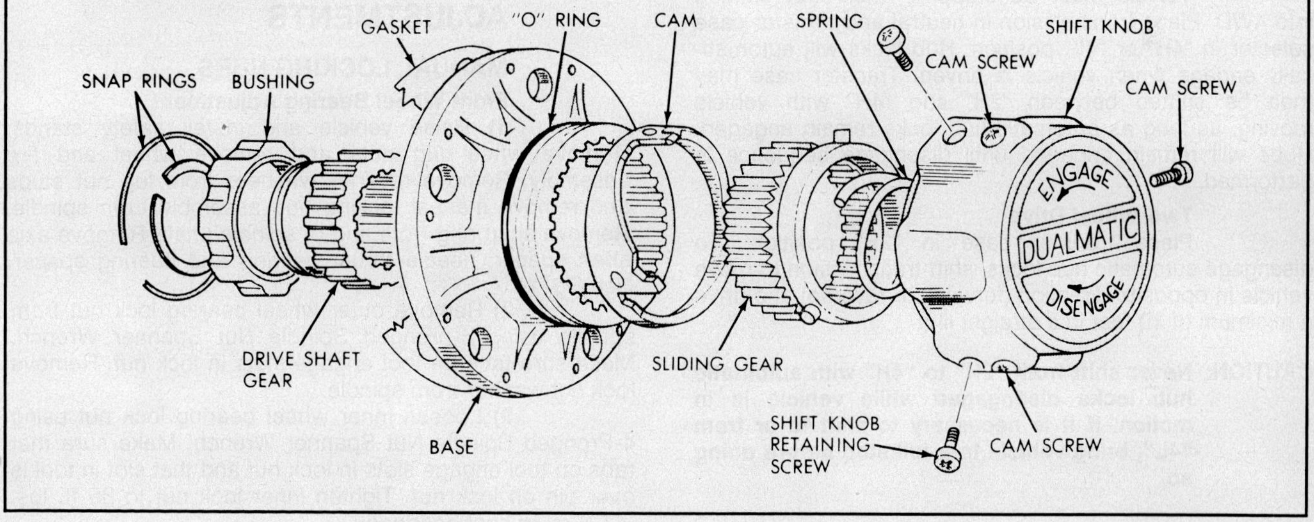

Locking Hubs

FORD BRONCO II & RANGER

Bronco II & Ranger 4WD

DESCRIPTION

The hub locks on Ranger 4WD and Bronco II vehicles, either automatically or manually actuate front driving axle. When actuated, hub lock body assembly locks hub and wheel and tire assembly to front driving axle axleshaft.

When released, front driving axle axleshaft is disengaged from hub body assembly and hub and tire and wheel assembly rotate freely on spindle.Two tapered opposed roller bearings allow hub and wheel and tire assembly to rotate on spindle. A seal is installed behind inner bearing to prevent wheel bearing lubricant from contaminating brake caliper and rotor surfaces.

OPERATION

AUTOMATIC LOCKING HUBS

Four-Wheel Drive

Vehicle must be stopped when first shifting into 4WD. Place transmission in neutral and transfer case selector in "4H" or "4L" position. Hub locks will automatically engage when vehicle is driven. Transfer case may then be shifted between "2H" and "4H" with vehicle moving, as long as automatic hub locks remain engaged. Hubs will remain engaged until disengage sequence is performed.

Two-Wheel Drive

Place transfer case in "2H" position. To disengage automatic hub locks, shift transmission to move vehicle in opposite direction (forward or reverse) and drive a minimum of 10 feet in a straight line.

CAUTION: **Never shift from "2H" to "4H" with automatic hub locks disengaged while vehicle is in motion. If it is necessary to shift to or from "4L", bring vehicle to a full stop before doing so.**

MANUAL LOCKING HUBS

Two-Wheel Drive

Shift transfer case to "2H" position and turn hub lock selector knob counter clockwise to "Free" position.

Four-Wheel Drive

Lock both hubs by turning selector knob clockwise to "Lock" position. If hub teeth do not engage with knob in this position, a slight movement of wheel in either direction will complete lock.

If vehicle is stopped, place transmission in neutral and select transfer case shift position. If vehicle is moving, transfer case may be shifted between "2H" and "4H" only, providing that hub locks are in "Lock" position. Shifting to or from "4L" position requres that vehicle be fully stopped and transmission be in neutral.

CAUTION: **Both hubs must be set in same function to avoid excess front differential wear on non-traction-lok front axles or steering pull on traction-lok front axles.**

ADJUSTMENTS

MANUAL LOCKING HUBS

Front Wheel Bearing Adjustment

1) Raise vehicle and install safety stands. Remove wheel lug nuts and remove wheel and tire assembly. Remove retainer washers from lug nut studs and remove manual locking hub assembly from spindle. Remove snap ring from end of spindle shaft. Remove axle shaft spacer, needle thrust bearing and bearing spacer. *See Fig. 1.*

2) Remove outer wheel bearing lock nut from spindle using 4-pronged Spindle Nut Spanner Wrench. Make sure tabs on tool engage slots in lock nut. Remove lock nut washer from spindle.

3) Loosen inner wheel bearing lock nut using 4-Pronged Spindle Nut Spanner Wrench. Make sure that tabs on tool engage slots in lock nut and that slot in tool is over pin on lock nut. Tighten inner lock nut to 35 ft. lbs. (47 N.m) to seat bearings.

Fig. 1: Exploded View of Manual Locking Hub Assembly

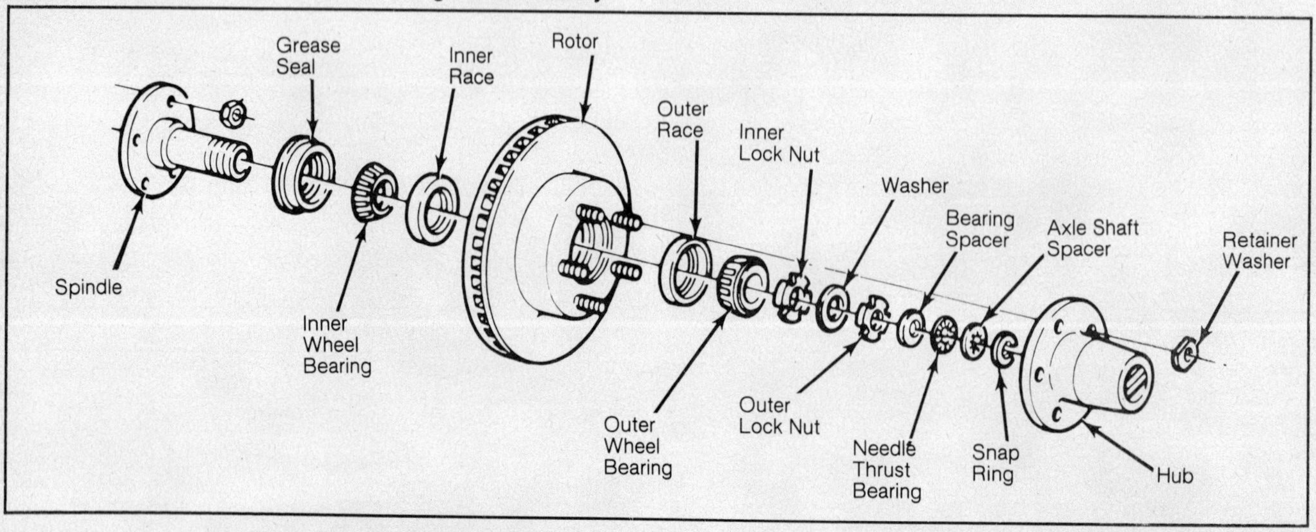

FORD BRONCO II & RANGER (Cont.)

4) Spin rotor and back off inner lock nut 1/4 turn. Install lock washer on spindle. It may be necessary to turn inner lock nut slightly so pin on lock nut aligns with closest hole in lock washer.

5) Install outer wheel bearing lock nut using Four Pronged Spindle Nut Spanner Wrench. Tighten lock nut to 150 ft. lbs. (203 N.m). Install bearing thrust spacer, needle thrust bearing and axle shaft spacer. Clip snap ring onto end of spindle.

6) Install manual hub assembly over spindle. Install retainer washers. Install wheel and tire assembly. Install and tightn lug nuts. Check end placy of wheel and tir assembly on spindle. End play should be .001-.003" (.02-.08 mm).

AUTOMATIC LOCKING HUBS

Front Wheel Bearing Adjustment

1) Raise vehicle and install safety stands. Remove wheel lug nuts and remove wheel and tire assembly. Remove retainer washers from lug nut studs and remove automatic locking hub assembly from spindle.

2) Remove snap ring from end of spindle shaft. Remove axle shaft spacer, needle thrust bearing and bearing spacer. Being careful not to damage plastic moving cam, pull cam assembly off wheel bearing adjusting nut and remove thrust washer and needle thrust bearing from adjusting nut.

CAUTION: To prevent damage to spindle threads, look into spindle keyway under adjusting nut hole and remove any portion of locking key that has been separated from cam assembly before removing adjusting nut. If this condition exists, do not re-use. Discard entire cam assembly and replace with Service Kit (1A053).

3) Loosen wheel bearing adjusting nut from spindle using a 2-3/8" hex socket. Whilerotating hub and rotor assembly, tighten wheel bearing adjusting nut to 35 ft. lbs. (47 N.m) to seat bearings, then back off nut 1/4 turn.

4) Retighten adjusting nut to 16 INCH lbs. (1.8 N.m) using a torque wrench. Align closest hole in wheel bearing adjusting nut with center of spindle keyway slot. Advance nut to next hole if required.

CAUTION: Extreme care must be taken when aligning spindle nut adjustment hole with center of spindle keyway slot to prevent damage to cam assembly locking key.

5) Install locknut needle bearing and thrust washer in order of removal and push or press cam assembly onto locknut by lining up key in fixed cam with spindle keyway. Install bearing thrust washer, needle thrust bearing and axle shaft spacer.

6) Clip snap ring onto end of spindle. Install automatic locking hub assembly over spindle by lining up 3 legs on hub assembly with 3 pockets in cam assembly. Install retainer washers. Install wheel and tire assembly. Install and tighten lug nuts. Final end play of wheel on spindle should be .001-.003" (.02-.08 mm).

REMOVAL & INSTALLATION

MANUAL LOCKING HUBS

Removal

1) Raise vehicle and install safety stands. Remove wheel lug nuts and remove wheel and tire assembly. Remove retainer washers from lug nut studs and remove manual locking hub assembly. To remove internal hub lock assembly from outer body assembly, remove outer lock ring seated in hub body groove. Internal assembly, spring and clutch gear will now slide out of hub body. DO NOT remove screw from plastic dial. Rebuild hub assembly in reverse order of disassembly.

Installation

Install manual locking hub assembly over spindle and place retainer washers on lug nut studs. Install wheel and tire assembly. Install lug nuts and tighten.

AUTOMATIC LOCKING HUBS

Removal & Installation

To remove and install automatic locking hubs, use AUTOMATIC LOCKING HUBS – FRONT WHEEL BEARING ADJUSTMENT procedure in this article.

Fig. 2: Exploded View of Automatic Locking Hub Assembly

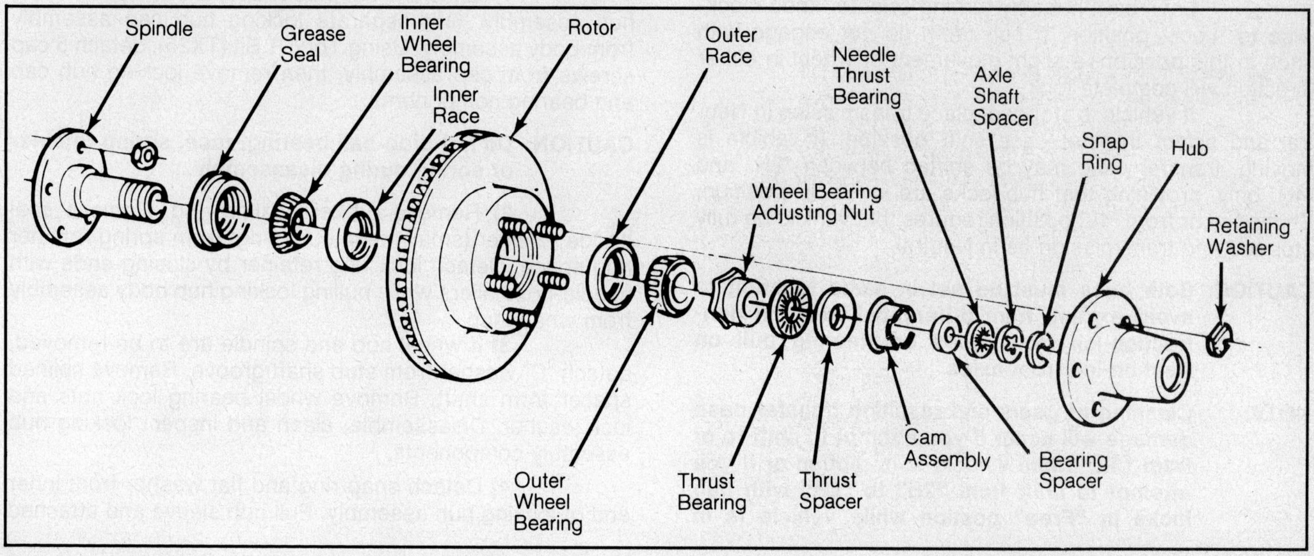

Locking Hubs

FORD – EXCEPT BRONCO II & RANGER

Bronco & "F" Series Pickup

DESCRIPTION

The hub locks on Bronco and F-150/350 4WD vehicles, either automatically or manually actuate front driving axle. When actuated, hub lock body assembly locks hub and wheel and tire assembly to front driving axle axleshaft.

When released, front driving axle axleshaft is disengaged from hub body assembly and hub and tire and wheel assembly rotate freely on spindle. Two tapered opposed roller bearings allow hub and wheel and tire assembly to rotate on spindle. A hub seal is installed behind inner bearing to prevent wheel bearing lubricant from contaminating brake caliper and rotor surfaces.

OPERATION

AUTOMATIC LOCKING HUBS

Four-Wheel Drive

Vehicle must be stopped when first shifting into 4WD. Place transmission in Neutral and transfer case selector in "4H" or "4L" position. Hub locks will automatically engage when vehicle is driven. Transfer case may then be shifted between "2H" and "4H" with vehicle moving, as long as automatic hub locks remain engaged. Hubs will remain engaged until disengage sequence is performed.

Two-Wheel Drive

Place transfer case in "2H" position. To disengage automatic hub locks, shift transmission to move vehicle in opposite direction (forward or reverse) and drive a minimum of 10 feet in a straight line.

CAUTION: **Never shift from "2H" to "4H" with automatic hub locks disengaged while vehicle is in motion. If it is necessary to shift to or from "4L", bring vehicle to a full stop before doing so.**

MANUAL LOCKING HUBS

Two-Wheel Drive

Shift transfer case to "2H" position and turn hub lock selector knob counter clockwise to "Free" position.

Four-Wheel Drive

Lock both hubs by turning selector knob clockwise to "Lock" position. If hub teeth do not engage with knob in this position, a slight movement of wheel in either direction will complete lock.

If vehicle is stopped, place transmission in Neutral and select transfer case shift position. If vehicle is moving, transfer case may be shifted between "2H" and "4H" only, providing that hub locks are in "Lock" position. Shifting to or from "4L" position requres that vehicle be fully stopped and transmission be in Neutral.

CAUTION: **Both hubs must be set in same function to avoid excess front differential wear on non-traction-lok front axles or steering pull on traction-lok front axles.**

NOTE: **Clashing of gears and resulting transfer case damage will occur if you attempt to shift to or from "4L" while vehicle is in motion or if you attempt to shift from "2H" to "4H" with hub locks in "Free" postion while vehicle is in motion. If it is necessary to shift to or from "4L", bring vehicle to a full stop before doing so.**

ADJUSTMENTS

FRONT WHEEL BEARING ADJUSTMENT

Bronco, F150/250

1) Raise vehicle and install safety stands. Remove hub lock assembly as outlined in REMOVAL & INSTALLATION. Tighten bearing inner adjusting nut to 50 ft. lbs. (68 N.m) while rotating wheel back and forth to seat bearing. Back off adjusting nut approximately 45°.

2) Assemble lock washer by turning inner lock nut to nearest hole in lock washer. To lock, install outer lock nut and tighten to 150 ft. lbs. (203 N.m). Final end play of hub on spindle should be .000-.006" (.00-.15 mm). Install automatic hubs. Remove safety stands and lower vehicle.

F250 (Heavy Duty) & F350

1) Raise and support vehicle on safety stands. Remove manual or automatic hub lock assembly. See REMOVAL & INSTALLATION. Using Front Wheel Bearing Spanner (D78T-1197-A) and a torque wrench, tighten inner adjusting nut to 50 ft. lbs. (68 N.m).

2) Back-off inner adjusting nut, then retighten to 31-39 ft. lbs. (41-54 N.m). While rotating hub, back-off adjusting nut 135° to 150°. Assemble outer lock nut and new lock washer, then tighten nut to 65 ft. lbs. (88 N.m).

3) Bend 1 ear of lock washer over the inner nut and the other ear of the lock washer over the outer nut. Install a dial indicator and check hub end play. Final end play of hub on spindle should be .001-.009" (.02-.25 mm).

4) If end play is beyond limits, remove hub and bearing assembly and inspect components for excessive wear or damage. Replace hub and/or bearing assemblies as necessary, then reinstall components. Install hub lock assembly. Remove safety stands and lower vehicle.

REMOVAL & INSTALLATION

AUTOMATIC LOCKING HUB

Removal

1) Raise and support vehicle. To remove locking hub assembly, first separate locking hub cap assembly from body assembly. Using Torx-R Bit (TX25), detach 5 cap screws from cap assembly, then remove locking hub cap and bearing components.

CAUTION: **Do not drop ball bearing, race, spring retainer or spring during disassembly.**

2) Remove rubber sealing ring. Remove seal bridge retainer (small metal stamping) from spring retainer ring space. Detach lock ring retainer by closing ends with needle-nose pliers while pulling locking hub body assembly from wheel hub.

3) If wheel hub and spindle are to be removed, detach "C" washer from stub shaft groove. Remove splined spacer from shaft. Remove wheel bearing lock nuts and lock washer. Disassemble, clean and inspect locking hub assembly components.

4) Detach snap ring and flat washer from inner end of locking hub assembly. Pull hub sleeve and attached

FORD – EXCEPT BRONCO II & RANGER (Cont.)

Fig. 1: Exploded View of Automatic Locking Hub Assy.

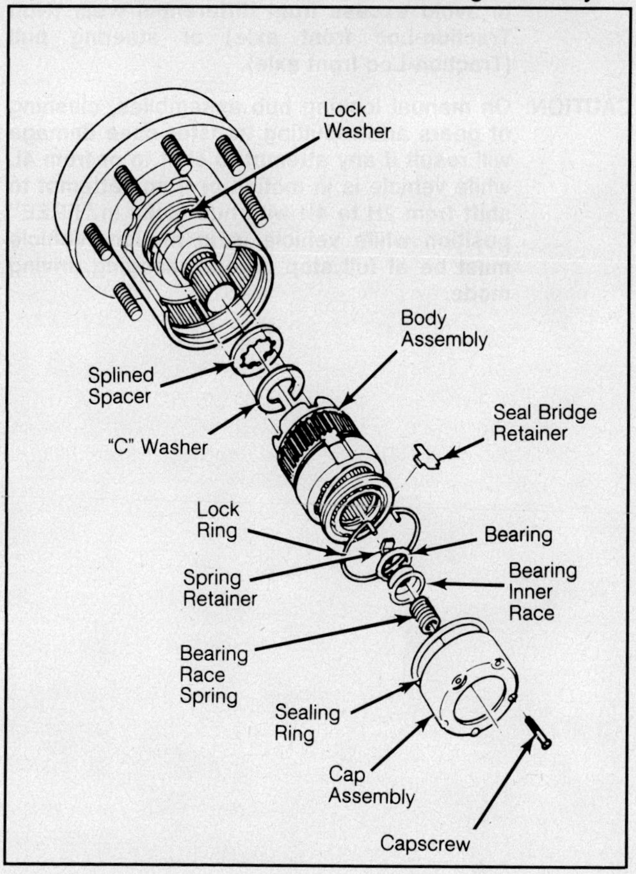

parts out of drag sleeve, then cock drag sleeve to unlock tangs of brake band. Remove drag sleeve assembly.

CAUTION: Do not remove brake band from drag sleeve.

5) Wash drag sleeve/brake band assembly in clean solvent and thoroughly blow dry. Lubricate brake band/drag sleeve assembly with lubricant meeting specification ESL-M1C93A (Darmex Spec. DX-123-LT). Work lubricant over spring and area of drag sleeve under spring.

6) Dip locking hub body assembly (except cap assembly and brake band/drag sleeve assembly) in Dexron II ATF and permit to drip dry for a few minutes before proceeding with assembly.

Inspection

Wash locking hub cap bearing, race and retainer in clean solvent, then inspect for excessive wear or damage. Replace components as needed. Thoroughly blow dry parts with compressed air. Do not spin bearings with air or damage can result. Repack bearing with lithium grease, then properly position bearing assembly in race. *See Fig. 2.*

Installation

1) To install locking hub components, first assemble 1 of 2 brake band tangs on each side of outer cage (plastic), which is located in window of inner cage (steel). It is necessary to cock these parts to engage tangs in this position as the drag sleeve is positioned against cam follower face. Install washer and snap ring.

2) If removed, install wheel bearing inner adjusting nut and lock washer. Tighten outer lock nut to 150 ft. lbs. (203 N.m). Install splined spacer and "C" washer onto axle shaft.

Fig. 2: Positioning Locking Hub Cap Bearing, Race & Spring Retainer

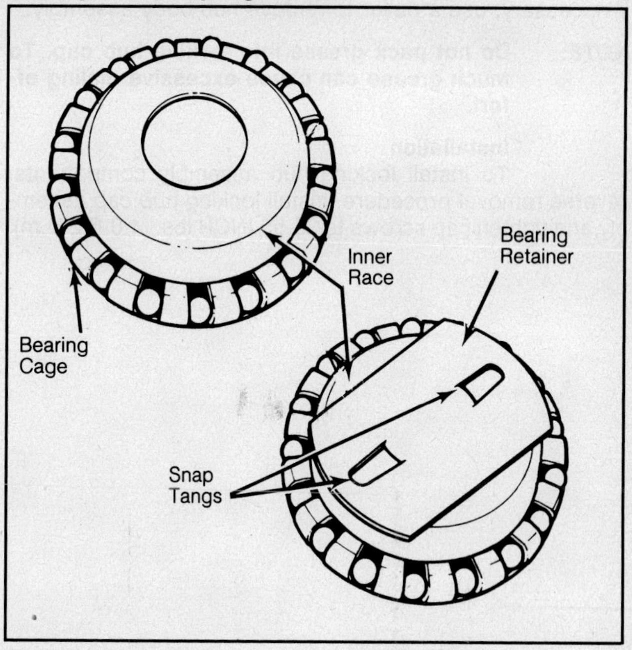

Position inner race into bearing assembly, then install bearing retainer as shown.

NOTE: Remove excess grease from hub lock and hub splines before installation.

3) Start locking hub assembly into hub. Ensure large tangs are lined up with lock washer and outside diameter and inside diameter splines are in line with hub and axle shaft splines.

4) Install retainer ring by closing ring ends with needle-nose pliers and, at the same time, push locking hub assembly into hub. Install seal bridge retainer (narrow end first).

5) Install rubber seal over locking hub. Install locking hub cap assembly. Ensure ball bearing, race, spring and retainer are in proper position. Tighten Torx-R bit screws to 40-50 INCH lbs. (4.5-5.6 N.m) following tightening sequence (tighten 1, skip 1, etc.) until complete.

MANUAL LOCKING HUB

Removal

1) To remove locking hub, first separate locking hub cap assembly from hub body assembly by removing 6 Allen head cap screws from cap assembly, then slip components apart. Detach snap ring (retainer ring) from end of axle shaft.

Fig. 3: Exploded View of Manual Locking Hub Assy.

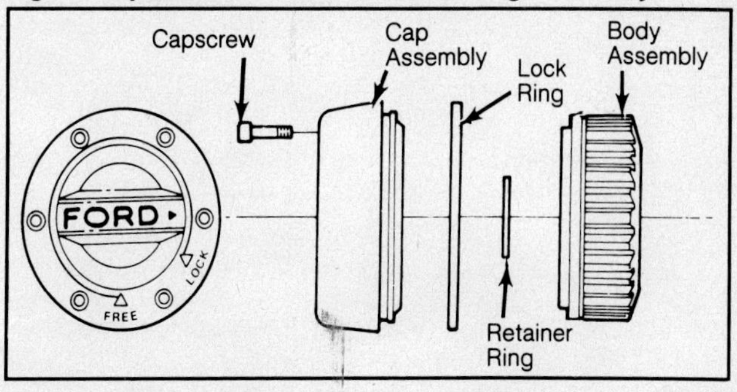

Locking Hubs

FORD – EXCEPT BRONCO II & RANGER (Cont.)

2) Remove lock ring (seated in groove of wheel hub). *See Fig. 3*. Slide hub body assembly out of wheel hub. If necessary, use a puller to remove hub body assembly.

NOTE: Do not pack grease into locking hub cap. To much grease can cause excessive dialing effort.

Installation

To install locking hub assembly components, reverse removal procedure. Install locking hub cap assembly and tighten cap screws to 35-55 INCH lbs. (4.0-6.2 N.m).

CAUTION: Ensure both hubs are set in the same function to avoid excess front differential wear (Non Traction-Loc front axle) or steering pull (Traction-Loc front axle).

CAUTION: On manual locking hub assemblies, clashing of gears and resulting transfer case damage will result if any attempt to shift to or from 4L while vehicle is in motion or if any attempt to shift from 2H to 4H with hub locks in "FREE" position while vehicle is in motion. Vehicle must be at full stop before changing driving mode.

Locking Hubs

GENERAL MOTORS AUTOMATIC TYPE

DESCRIPTION

The automatic locking hub automatically engages to lock and disengages to unlock the front axle shaft to (or from) the front hub. Shifting the transfer case into 4WD immediately engages automatic locking hubs.

Hubs remain engaged even during coasting or downhill operation. Automatic locking hubs disengage when the transfer case is shifted into 2-wheel drive, and when vehicle is slowly moved rearward several feet.

REMOVAL & INSTALLATION

REMOVAL

1) Remove 5 cap screws and cover to outer clutch housing. Remove bearing race spring assembly. Remove sealing ring and seal bridge retainer. Remove bearing components.

2) Squeeze tangs of wire retaining ring together with needle nose pliers. Pull remaining components of automatic hub from wheel. *See Fig. 1.*

INSTALLATION

New Hub

1) Make sure drag sleeve retainer washer is in position between wheel bearing adjusting nut and lock nut. Torque wheel bearing adjusting nut to 50 ft. lbs. (60 N.m) to seat bearings, then back off nut and tighten to 35 ft. lbs. (47 N.m) while rotating hub. Finally, back off nut a maximum of 3/8 turn.

Fig. 2: Drag Sleeve Retainer Washer

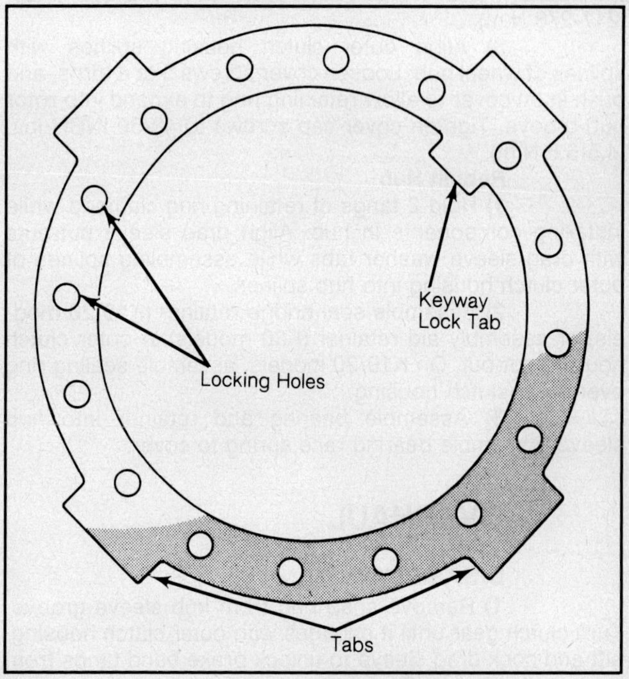

Fig. 1: Exploded View of General Motors Automatic Locking Hubs

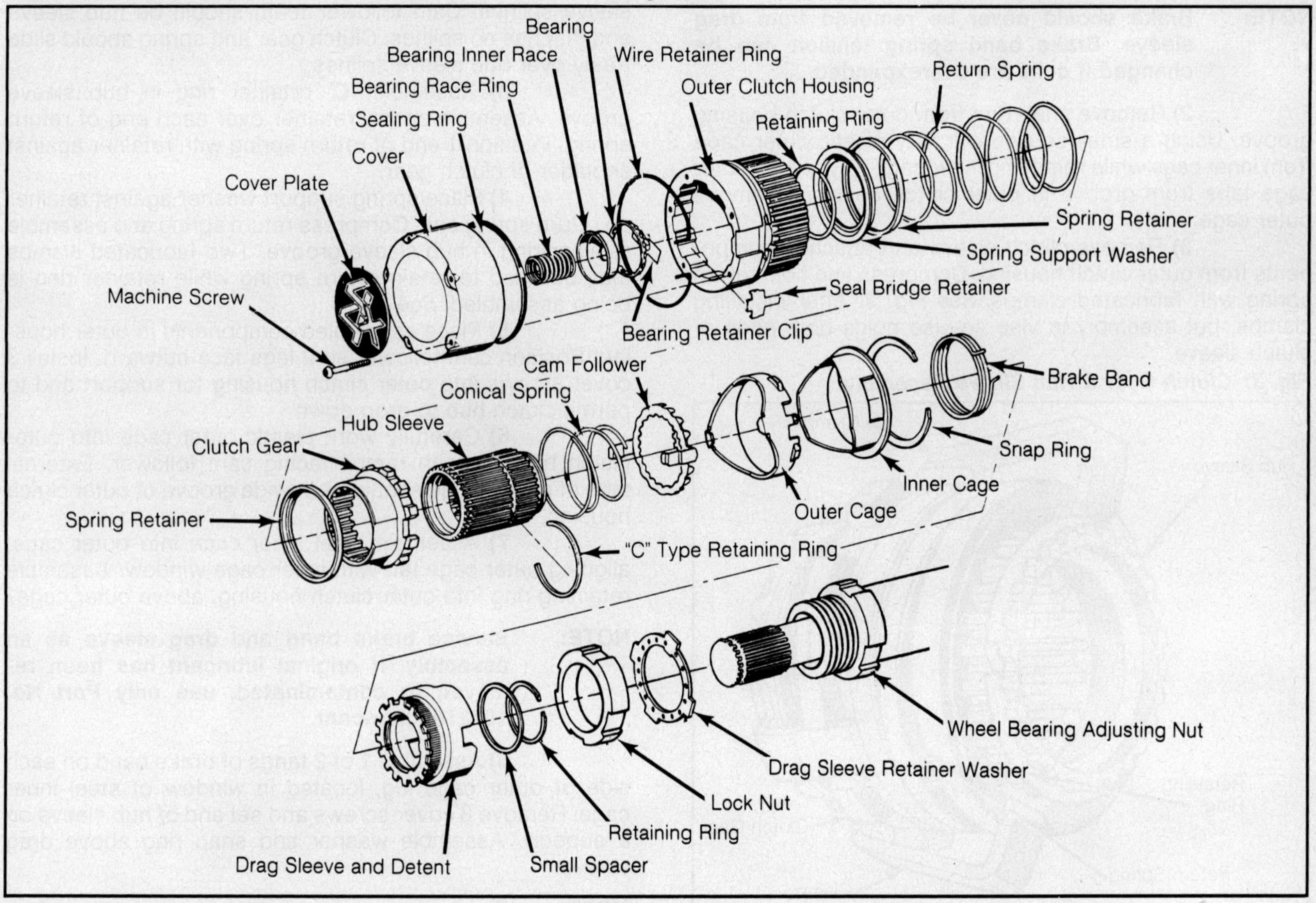

All other models are similar.

2) Assemble drag sleeve retainer washer (with tab in keyway) over axle shaft, against bearing adjustment nut. *See Fig. 2.* Adjustment nut pin must pass through 1 of the washer holes. Tighten outer lock nut to 160-205 ft. lbs. (217-278 N.m).

3) Align outer clutch housing splines with splines of wheel hub. Loosen cover screws 3 or 4 turns, and push in on cover to allow retaining ring to expand into rotor hub groove. Tighten cover cap screws to 40-50 INCH lbs. (4.5-5.6 N.m).

Rebuilt Hub

1) Hold 2 tangs of retaining ring clamped while installing components in hub. Align drag sleeve cut-outs with drag sleeve washer tabs while assembling splines of outer clutch housing into hub splines.

2) Assemble seal bridge retainer (K10/20 models) or assembly aid retainer (K30 models) in outer clutch housing cut-out. On K10/20 models, assemble sealing ring over outer clutch housing.

3) Assemble bearing and retainer into hub sleeve. Assemble bearing race spring to cover.

OVERHAUL

DISASSEMBLY

1) Remove snap ring from hub sleeve groove. Turn clutch gear until it engages with outer clutch housing. Lift and cock drag sleeve to unlock brake band tangs from inner cage window. Remove drag sleeve and brake assembly.

NOTE: **Brake should never be removed from drag sleeve. Brake band spring tension can be changed if coils are overexpanded.**

2) Remove snap ring from outer clutch housing groove. Using a small screwdriver, pry plastic outer cage from inner cage while removing inner cage. Pry plastic outer cage tabs from groove in outer clutch housing. Remove outer cage.

3) Remove clutch sleeve and attached components from outer clutch housing. Compress and hold return spring with fabricated clamps. *See Fig. 3.* After installing clamps, put assembly in vise so vise holds both ends of clutch sleeve.

Fig. 3: Clutch Gear & Hub Sleeve Assembly

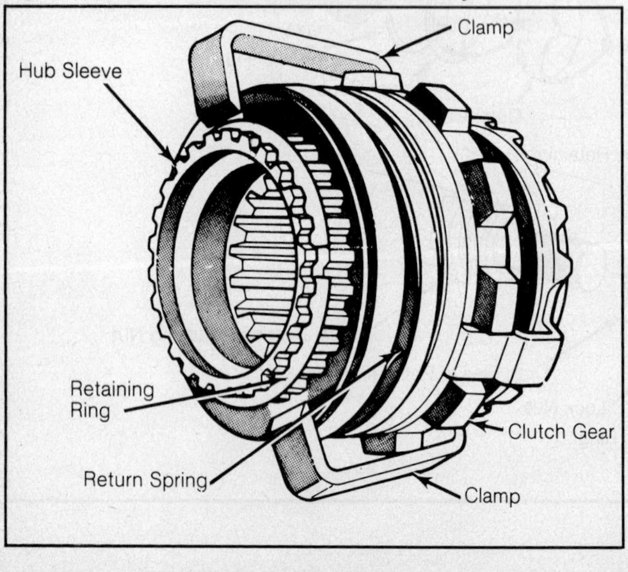

4) Remove retaining ring. Remove clamps holding return spring. Slowly open vise. Remove retainer seat, spring and spring support washers from hub sleeve.

5) Remove "C" retaining ring from clutch sleeve by positioning assembly so "C" ring ends align with cam follower legs and removing "C" ring through follower legs.

6) Remove conical spring from between cam follower and clutch gear. Separate cam follower from clutch gear.

CLEANING & INSPECTION

1) Wash all parts with cleaning solvent and blow them dry.

2) Check cover for cracks or porous condition. Check seats of cover screws for pitting, or a tapered, countersunk condition.

3) Check brake band for distortion or wear. Inspect teeth on clutch gear and cam follower for wear and broken teeth.

4) Check drag sleeve and drag sleeve retainer washer for cracks or wear. Check plastic outer cage for cracks and excessive wear on lugs.

5) Replace any components that warrant replacement. Dip all parts except bearing and race assembly, brake band, and drag sleeve assembly in ATF.

REASSEMBLY

1) Snap cam follower tangs over clutch gear flats. Compress conical spring and slide it into position with large end of spring against clutch gear.

2) Position clutch gear assembly over hub sleeve splines. Cam follower teeth should be hub sleeve end that has no splines. Clutch gear and spring should slide freely over hub sleeve splines.

3) Assemble "C" retainer ring in hub sleeve groove. Assemble spring retainer over each end of return spring. Position 1 end of return spring with retainer against shoulder of clutch gear.

4) Place spring support washer against retainer on return spring end. Compress return spring and assemble retainer ring in hub sleeve groove. Two fabricated clamps may be used to retain return spring while retainer ring is being assembled. *See Fig. 3.*

5) Place assembled components in outer housing. Position cam follower so 2 legs face outward. Install 3 cover screws into outer clutch housing for support and to permit clutch hub to drop down.

6) Carefully work plastic outer cage into outer clutch housing with ramps facing cam follower. External tabs of plastic cage should be in wide groove of outer clutch housing.

7) Assemble steel inner cage into outer cage, aligning outer cage tab with inner cage window. Assemble retaining ring into outer clutch housing, above outer cage.

NOTE: **Service brake band and drag sleeve as an assembly. If original lubricant has been removed or contaminated, use only Part No. 1052750 lubricant.**

8) Assemble 1 of 2 tangs of brake band on each side of outer cage lug, located in window of steel inner cage. Remove 3 cover screws and set end of hub sleeve on a support. Assemble washer and snap ring above drag sleeve.

NOTE: **The following steps may be completed as hub is installed in vehicle.**

GENERAL MOTORS AUTOMATIC TYPE (Cont.)

9) Assemble wire retaining ring in outer clutch housing (unsplined end) groove. Retainer ring tangs should point away from clutch housing splined end.

10) Hold wire retainer tangs together and assemble seal bridge retainer (K10/20 models) or assembly aid retainer (K30 models) over tangs. On K10/20 models, assemble "O" ring in outer clutch housing groove and over seal bridge.

11) Lubricate bearing with light wheel bearing grease and install bearing over inner race. Steel balls should be visible when bearing is properly installed.

12) Snap bearing retainer clip into outer race hole. Assemble bearing and retainer assembly in hub sleeve end. Assemble seal ring over outer clutch housing. Assemble bearing race spring into cover bore. Assemble cover and spring. Align cover holes with outer clutch housing holes and install 5 cap screws.

13) On K10/20 models, assemble "O" ring over seal bridge retainer to prevent it from jumping out of position. "O" ring may be left on, but is optional.

14) Hub sleeve and attached parts should turn freely after unit has been completely assembled. Loosen 5 cover cap screws to install hub in vehicle.

Locking Hubs

WARN SELECTIVE MANUAL TYPE

Jeep

DESCRIPTION

Locking hubs provide a means of engagement of front wheels on vehicles with front drive axle. When hub is engaged, full power is transmitted to both front wheels. When hubs are disengaged, front wheels are free to turn, but axle shafts and differential will remain idle.

Engagement is accomplished through action of gears within hub. With hub in engaged position, clutch body and hub body of hub assembly act as one piece to connect axle shaft to wheel hub. All Warn Selective Manual Hubs function similarly, regardless of differing external appearances.

IDENTIFICATION

All Warn Hubs employ brass control knobs to engage and disengage locking mechanism. Model number of hub is stamped into recess of control knob. See WARN SELECTIVE MANUAL TYPE HUBS table.

Warn Selective Manual Type Hubs

Application	Model No.
Jeep	
"CJ" & Scrambler	M243
All Other Models	M247

REMOVAL & INSTALLATION

NOTE: **Model M243 and M247 front drive hubs are serviced as either a complete assembly or subassembly, such as the hub body or clutch assembly only. Do not attempt to disassemble these units. If the entire hub or a subassembly has malfunctioned, replace the hub assembly or the defective subassembly as a unit only.**

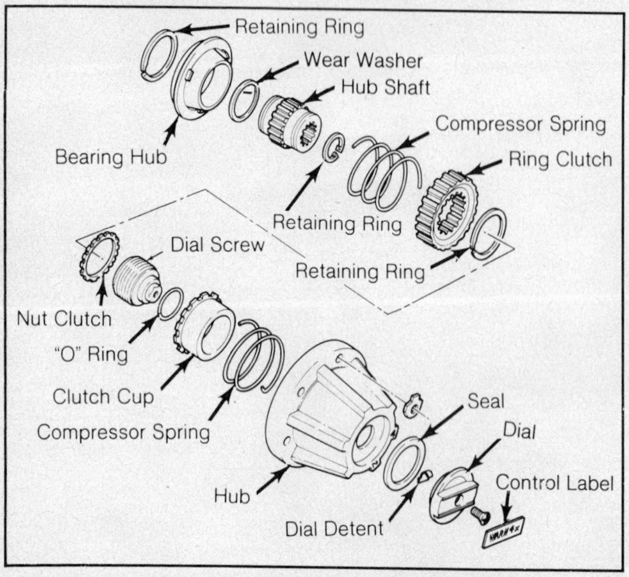

Fig. 1: Exploded View of Warn Hub Model M243

REMOVAL

Models M243 & M247

1) Remove bolts and tabbed lock washers (if equipped), attaching hub body to axle hub. Retain bolts and washers.

2) Remove retaining ring from axle shaft. Remove hub clutch and bearing assembly.

3) Clean hub components in solvent. Dry components, using compressed air or clean shop towel, or air dry.

4) Be sure old lubricant, dirt, water, or other foreign materials are flushed out.

CAUTION: **Do not turn hub control dial, until hub has been installed. The hub clutch nut and cup can be damaged severely, if dial is rotated while hub is off vehicle.**

INSTALLATION

Models M243 & M247

1) Lubricate hub components with all-purpose chassis lubricant. Apply light coat of lubricant only. Do not pack hub with lubricant.

2) On model M243, install hub clutch, bearing assembly, and retaining ring on axle shaft. Position new gasket on hub body, and install hub body and gasket.

3) On model M247, install hub clutch assembly and small retaining ring on axle shaft. Install large retaining ring in axle hub. Install new "O" ring if hub body is being replaced.

4) Align bolt holes in axle and hub body. Install bolts and tabbed lock washers (if equipped). Tighten bolts to 30 ft. lbs. (41 N.m), on model M243 and 30 INCH lbs. (3.4 N.m) on model M247.

5) Raise vehicle front end. Turn hub control dials to position "2" and rotate wheels. Wheels should rotate freely. If wheels drag, check hub installation. Also, be sure control dials fully engaged in 4x4 position.

Fig. 2: Exploded View of Warn Hub Model M247

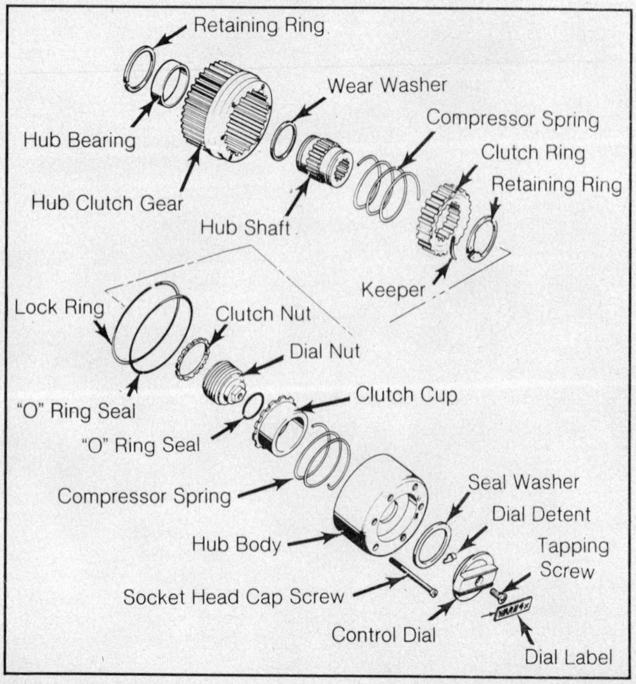

Locking Hubs

WARN SELECTIVE MANUAL TYPE (Cont.)

Fig. 3 Warn Hub Model M243 Clutch & Bearing Assembly

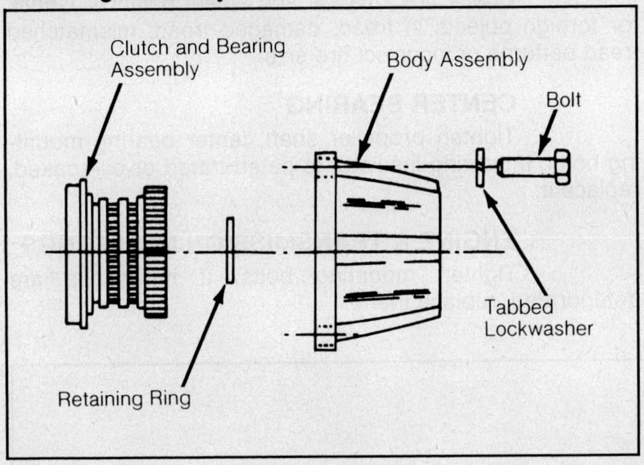

Fig. 4: Warn Hub Model 247 Clutch Assembly

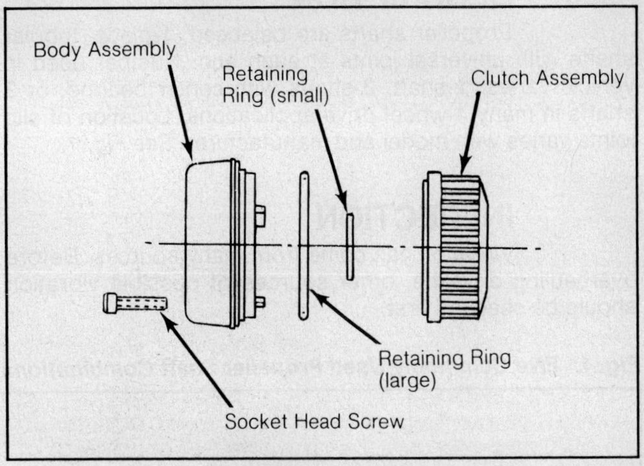

Propeller Shafts

PROPELLER SHAFT ALIGNMENT

DESCRIPTION

Propeller shafts are balanced, 1-piece, tubular shafts with universal joints at each end. Number used in vehicle varies: 1 shaft, 2 shafts with center bearing, or 3 shafts in many 4-wheel drive applications. Location of slip joints varies with model and manufacturer. *See Fig. 1.*

INSPECTION

Vibration can come from many sources. Before overhauling driveline, other sources of possible vibration should be checked first.

TIRES AND WHEELS

Check tire inflation and wheel balance. Check for foreign objects in tread, damaged tread, mismatched tread patterns or incorrect tire size.

CENTER BEARING

Tighten propeller shaft center bearing mounting bolts. If bearing insulator is deteriorated or oil-soaked, replace it.

ENGINE & TRANSMISSION MOUNTINGS

Tighten mounting bolts. If mountings are deteriorated, replace them.

Fig. 1: Five Commonly Used Propeller Shaft Combinations

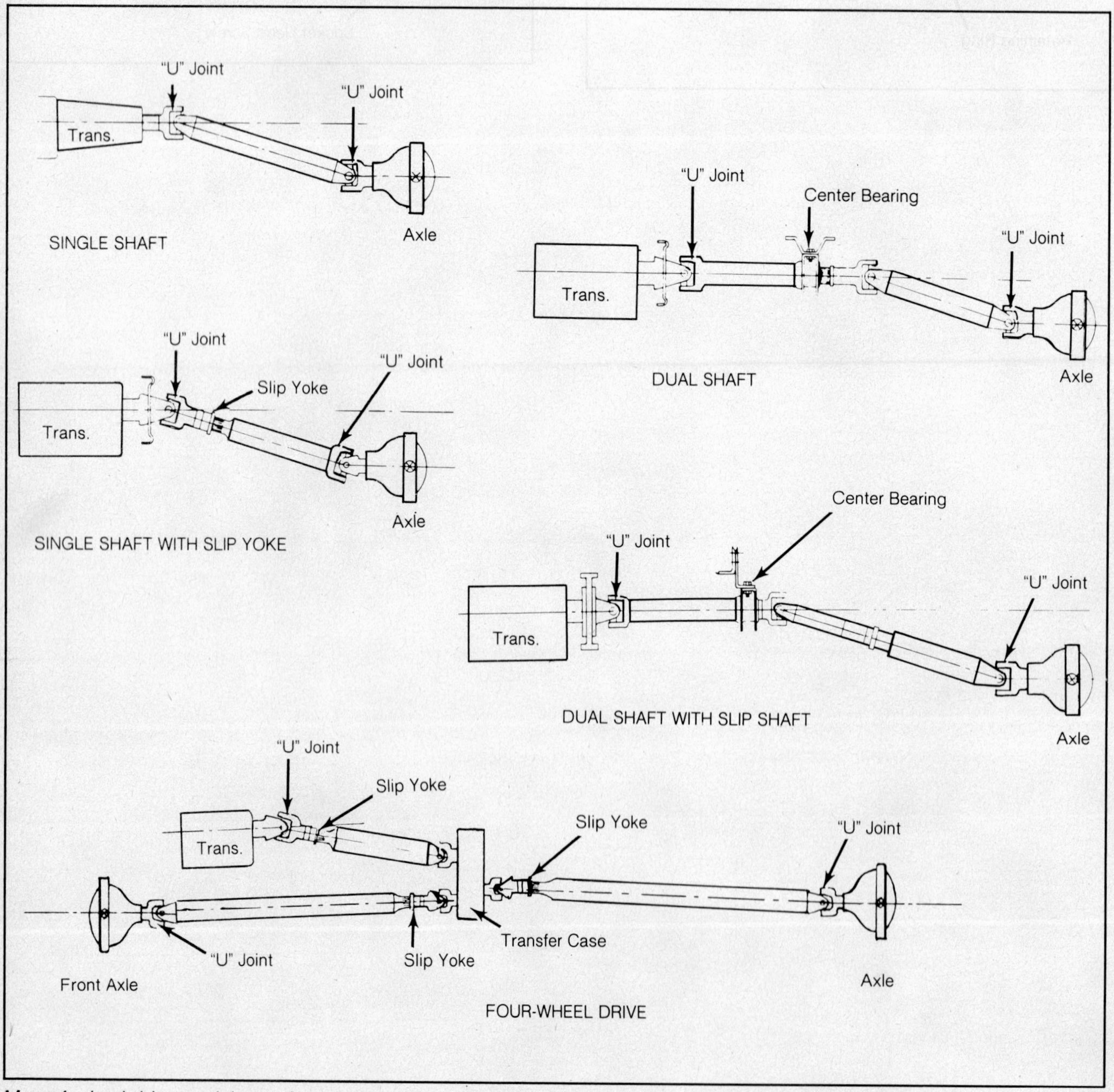

Many 4-wheel drive models use 3 propeller shafts.

PROPELLER SHAFT ALIGNMENT (Cont.)

PROPELLER SHAFT

Check propeller shaft for damage or dents that could effect balance. Check for undercoating adhering to shafts. If present, clean shafts thoroughly.

UNIVERSAL JOINTS

Check for foreign material stuck in joints. Check for loose bolts and worn bearings.

ADJUSTMENTS

PROPELLER SHAFT PHASING

2-Piece Shafts

1) All General Motors models with 32 splines use keys on spline and slip joint, which can only mate in correct position. On most models with 2-piece shafts, proper phasing is accomplished by keys on spline and slip joint.

2) On models with 2-piece shafts, rotate transmission yoke until trunnion is in horizontal plane. Install front propeller shaft with "U" joint trunnion in vertical plane. Connect bearing support to crossmember.

3) Make sure that front face of bearing support is perpendicular (90°) to centerline of propeller shaft. Install rear propeller shaft with "U" joint trunnion of slip joint in vertical plane.

4) Set differential pinion yoke trunnion in vertical plane. Connect rear propeller shaft to pinion yoke. If 2-piece shaft is correctly installed, centerline of trunnions at each end of individual shafts will be parallel. *See Fig. 2.*

1-Piece Shafts

Check that flanges on either end of propeller shaft are in same plane. Often there are arrows on slip joint and propeller shaft to aid in alignment. *See Fig. 3.* If flanges are not in same plane, disassemble universal joint and align.

Fig. 3: Slip Joint Alignment Arrows

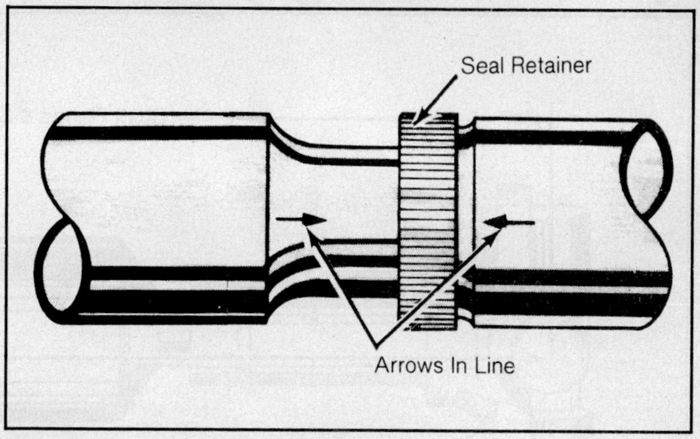

Align arrows for proper shaft phasing.

PROPELLER SHAFT BALANCE

1) Propeller shaft imbalance may often be cured by disconnecting shaft and rotating it 180° in relation to other components. Test by raising rear wheels off ground, and turning shaft with engine.

CAUTION: Do not run engine with transmission engaged for prolonged periods, as overheating of engine or transmission may occur.

2) On most models, balancing may be done by marking shaft in 4 positions, 90° apart. Place marks approximately 6" forward of weld, at rear end of shaft. Number marks 1 through 4.

3) Place screw-type hose clamp in No. 1 position, and rotate shaft with engine. If there is little or no change, move clamp to No. 2 position, and repeat test.

4) Continue procedure until vibration is at lowest level. If no difference is noted with clamp moved to all 4 positions, vibrations may not be propeller shaft imbalance.

Fig. 2: Phase Alignment Of 2-Piece Propeller Shafts

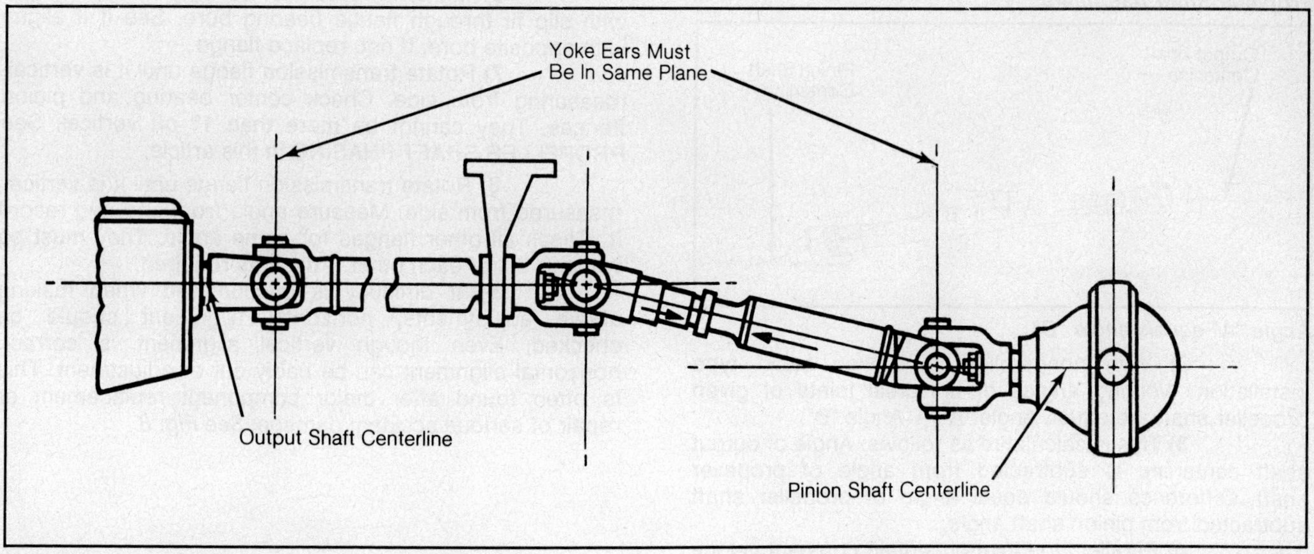

Trunnion yoke ears on each shaft must be parallel.

PROPELLER SHAFT ALIGNMENT (Cont.)

Fig. 4: Propeller Shaft Phase Alignment

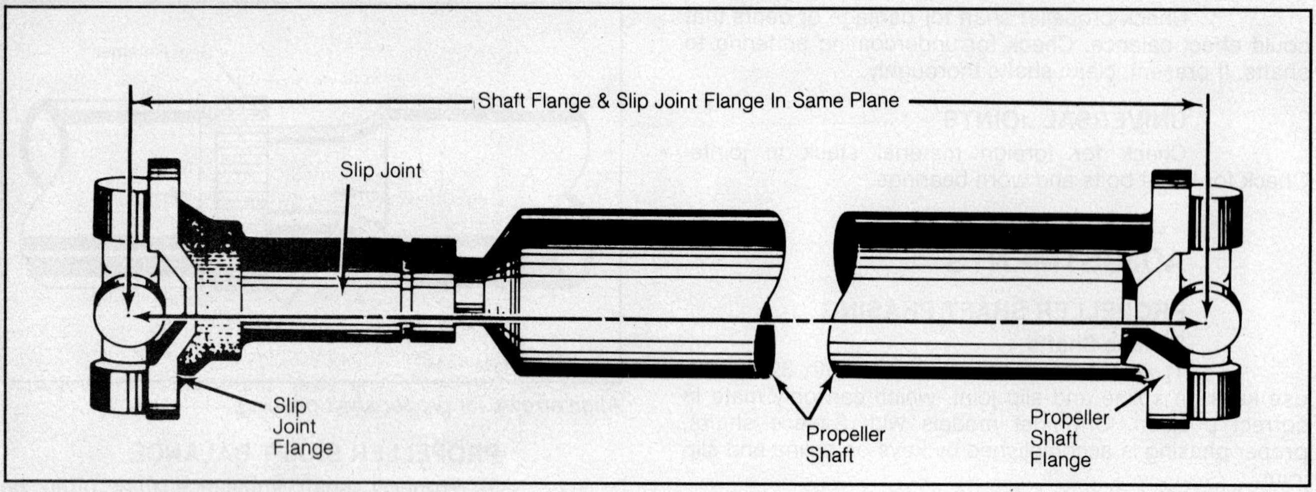

Align propeller shaft and slip joint trunnions in same plane.

5) If vibration is lessened but not completely gone, place 2 clamps at that point, and run test again. Combined weight of clamps in 1 position may worsen vibration. If so, rotate clamps 1/2" (12.7 mm) apart, above and below best position, and repeat test.

6) Continue to rotate clamps as necessary, until vibration is at lowest point. When point is reached where vibration has been eliminated, bend end of clamp so it will not loosen. If vibration level is still unacceptable, repeat procedure at front end of propeller shaft.

FLANGE ALIGNMENT & RUNOUT

1) All flanges must be perpendicular in both vertical and horizontal planes to engine crankshaft. Only exception is "broken back" type driveline, which has flanges that are not perpendicular in vertical plane. *See Fig. 5.*

Fig. 5: Typical "Broken Back" Type Propeller Shaft Alignment

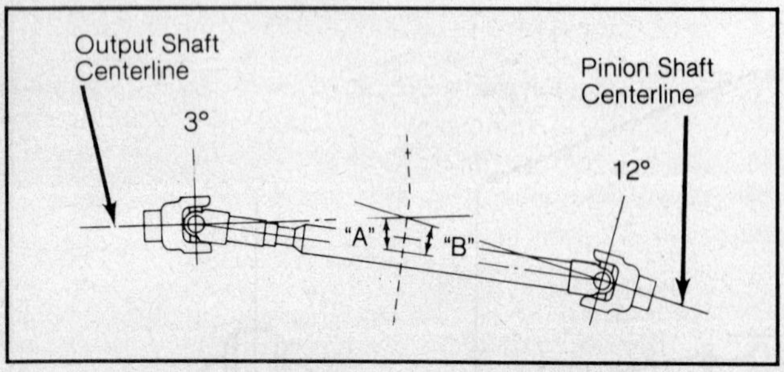

Angle "A" equals angle "B".

2) With nonparallel or "broken back" type installation, working angles of universal joints of given propeller shaft are equal. Angle "A" = Angle "B".

3) This is calculated as follows: Angle of output shaft centerline is subtracted from angle of propeller shaft. Difference should equal angle of propeller shaft subtracted from pinion shaft angle.

4) Parallel type joints maintain constant velocity between output shaft and pinion shaft. Vibration is minimized and component life maximized when universal joints are parallel.

Fig. 6: Aligning 1-Piece Propeller Shaft

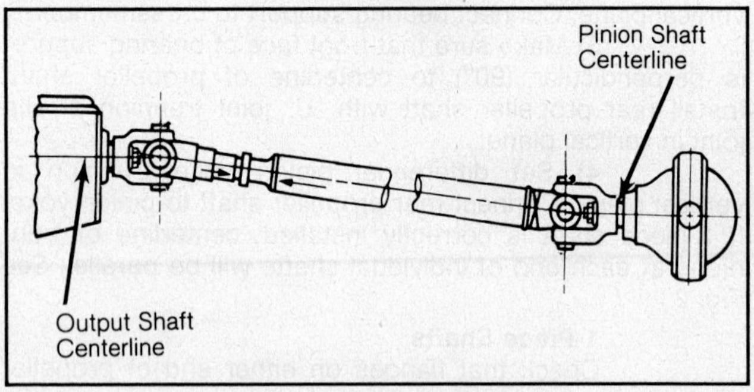

Yokes must be parallel.

5) Using dial indicator, measure runout of transmission flange, center bearing flange and pinion flange. If runout exceeds .003-.005" (.08-.13 mm), replace flange.

6) If dial indicator cannot be used, push rod with slip fit through flange bearing bore. See if it aligns with opposite bore. If not, replace flange.

7) Rotate transmission flange until it is vertical, measuring from side. Check center bearing and pinion flanges. They cannot be more than 1° off vertical. See PROPELLER SHAFT PHASING in this article.

8) Rotate transmission flange until it is vertical, measured from side. Measure angle from end and record it. Check all other flanges for same angle. They must be within 0°30' of each other. Adjust as required.

9) If difficulty is encountered when making above adjustments, horizontal alignment should be checked. Even though vertical alignment is correct, horizontal alignment can be badly out of adjustment. This is often found after major component replacement or repair of serious accident damage. *See Fig. 8.*

PROPELLER SHAFT ALIGNMENT (Cont.)

Fig. 7: Vertical Alignment of Propeller Shaft

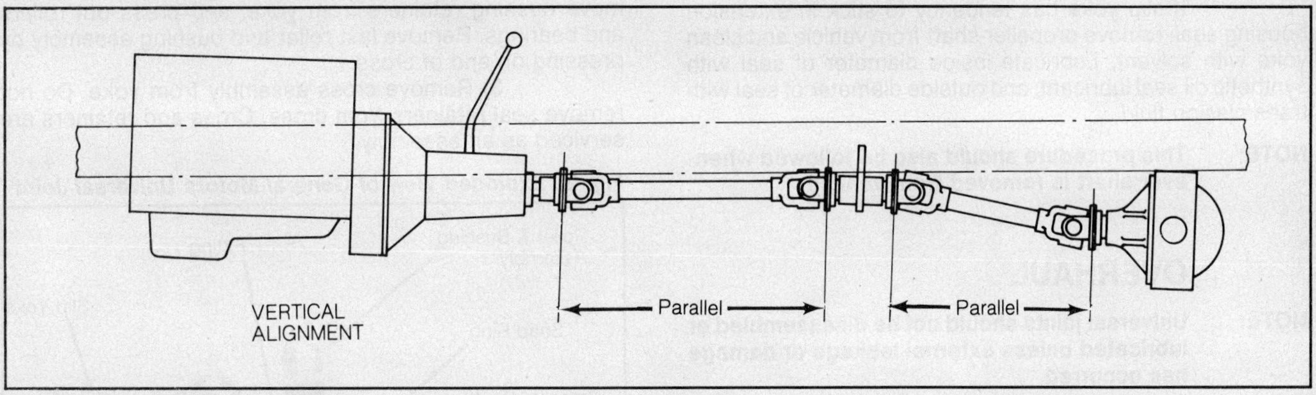

Pairs of flanges should be parallel.

Fig. 8: Horizontal Alignment of Propeller Shaft

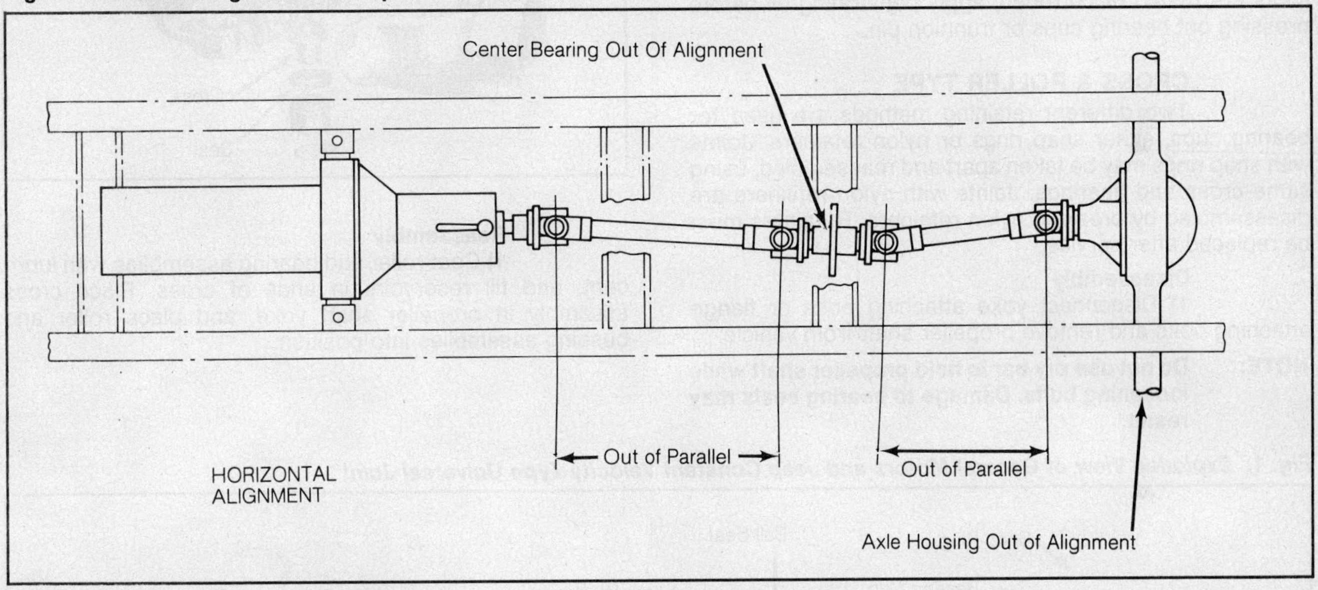

Plane of trunnions should be parallel.

Fig. 9: Checking Horizontal Alignment

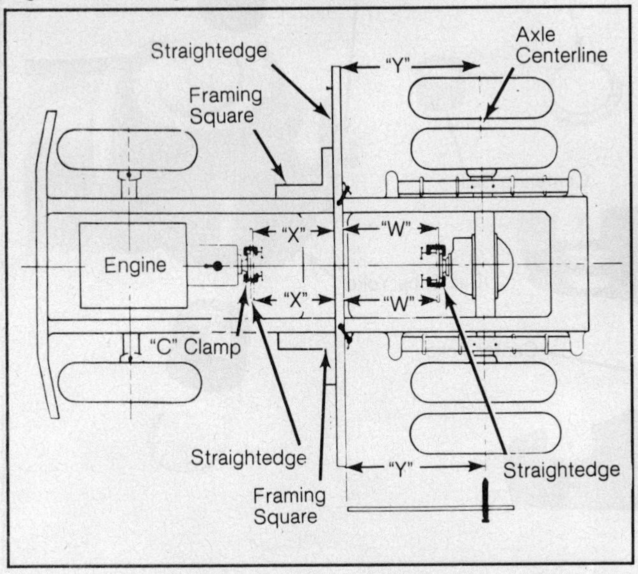

Measure at 6 points shown using straightedges and framing squares.

10) To make horizontal alignment checks, set up straightedges. *See Fig. 9.* Set transmission output flange horizontal and clamp straightedge to flange in horizontal plane. Repeat procedure with drive pinion flange. Make sure that flanges are horizontal by checking angle of straightedge with spirit level.

11) Clamp straightedge that is 12" longer than width of rear wheel track at 90° to frame side rails. Use large framing squares to align straightedge with side rails.

12) Measure distance "X" at each side. If both measurements are not within 1/16" (1.6 mm) of each other, transmission flange is misaligned horizontally.

13) Measure distance "Y" (edge of straightedge to axle shaft centerline) at each side. If 2 dimensions are not within 1/8" (3.2 mm) of each other, axle housing is misaligned.

14) Measure distance "W" at each side. If both measurements are not within 1/16" (1.6 mm) of each other, pinion flange is misaligned horizontally.

UNIVERSAL JOINTS

MAINTENANCE

If slip yoke has tendency to stick in extension housing seal, remove propeller shaft from vehicle and clean yoke with solvent. Lubricate inside diameter of seal with synthetic oil seal lubricant, and outside diameter of seal with transmission fluid.

NOTE: This procedure should also be followed whenever shaft is removed from vehicle.

OVERHAUL

NOTE: Universal joints should not be disassembled or lubricated unless external leakage or damage has occurred.

Before disassembly, scribe alignment marks on yoke and shaft to allow reassembly in original position. If joints are rusted or corroded, apply penetrating oil before pressing out bearing cups or trunnion pin.

CROSS & ROLLER TYPE

Two different retaining methods are used for bearing cups, either snap rings or nylon retainers. Joints with snap rings may be taken apart and reassembled, using same cross and bearings. Joints with nylon retainers are disassembled by breaking nylon retainers. Retainers must be replaced after service.

Disassembly

1) Disconnect yoke attaching bolts or flange attaching bolts and remove propeller shaft from vehicle.

NOTE: Do not use pry bar to hold propeller shaft while loosening bolts. Damage to bearing seals may result.

2) Remove retaining strap (if equipped). Remove bushing retainers from yoke, and press out rollers and bearings. Remove last roller and bushing assembly by pressing on end of cross.

3) Remove cross assembly from yoke. Do not remove seal retainers from cross. Cross and retainers are serviced as an assembly.

Fig. 2: Exploded View of General Motors Universal Joint

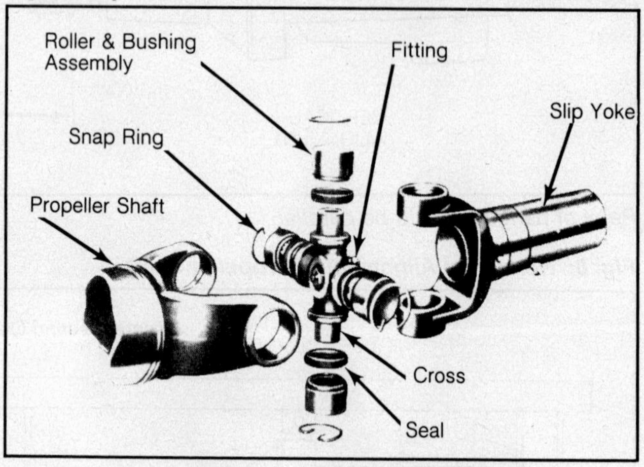

Reassembly

1) Coat roller and bearing assemblies with lubricant, and fill reservoirs in ends of cross. Place cross assembly in propeller shaft yoke, and place roller and bushing assemblies into position.

Fig. 1: Exploded View of General Motors and Jeep Constant Velocity Type Universal Joint

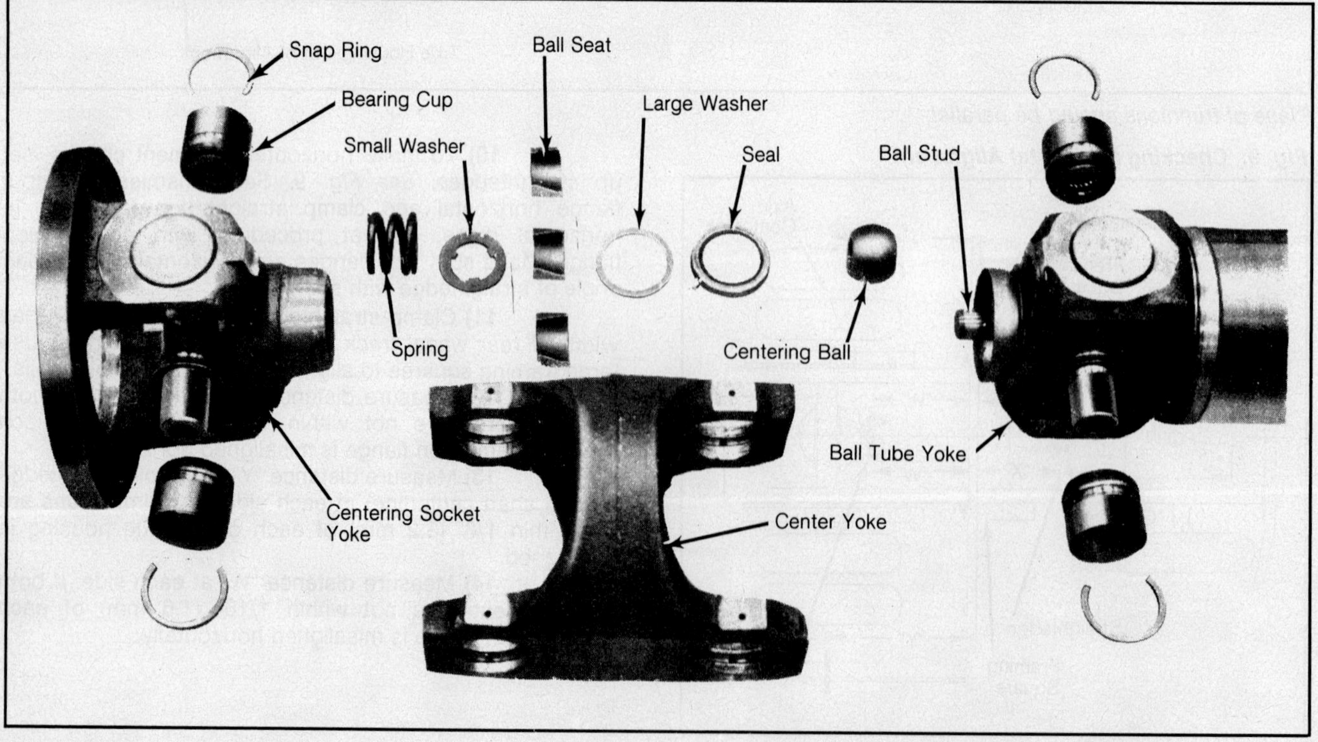

UNIVERSAL JOINTS (Cont.)

2) Press both bushing assemblies into yoke until retainers can be installed, being careful to keep cross aligned in center of bushings.

3) Install retainers, then repeat procedure for remaining bushings. Install strap (if equipped). Install propeller shaft in vehicle, aligning scribe marks.

CONSTANT VELOCITY TYPE

NOTE: **To prevent damage to constant velocity joints, center ball when removing propeller shaft assembly. When handling shaft after removal, support shafts on both sides of constant velocity joint if shaft is being moved horizontally. Do not allow 1 end to hang free or 1 shaft to bend at sharp angle. After removal, shaft may be carried vertically without damage.**

Disassembly (General Motors & Jeep)

1) Disconnect yoke attaching bolts and flange attaching bolts, and remove propeller shaft from vehicle. Mark joint so that center yoke, end yoke, and crosses will be installed in original positions.

2) Pry out all snap rings and press bearing out enough to allow bearing end to be clamped in vise. Tap on yoke until it is free of bearing.

3) Repeat procedure for remaining bearings. Remove remaining parts from center yoke assembly.

Reassembly

1) Pack all bearings with proper grease, and assemble center yoke components in reverse order of disassembly.

2) Using arbor press or vise, press 2 opposing bearings into position at same time until all bearings are installed. Be sure crosses and yokes remain aligned during this process.

3) Check for free movement of joint. If bind exists, seat bearings by sharply rapping yokes with brass hammer. Never hammer on bearings.

4) Install propeller shaft in vehicle, making sure marks made during disassembly are aligned.

Disassembly (Ford)

1) With propeller shaft removed from vehicle, position assembly in vise. Mark position of crosses, center yoke, and center socket in relationship with stud yoke welded to propeller shaft tube.

NOTE: **To obtain correct clearance, crosses must be installed on bosses in original positions.**

2) Remove snap rings in front of center yoke. Using "C" clamp, tighten screw until bearing protrudes 3/8" (10 mm).

3) Remove propeller shaft from vise. Tighten protruding part of bearing in vise. Rap against center yoke

Fig. 3: Exploded View of Ford Constant Velocity Type Universal Joint

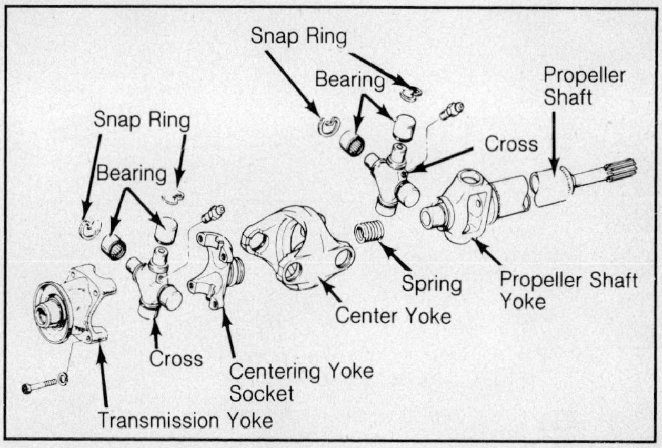

with hammer until bearing is free of yoke. Remove all bearings from cross in this manner.

4) Remove cross from center yoke. Remove centering socket from stud, and remove rubber seal from centering ball stud.

5) Remove snap rings from center and drive shaft yokes. Install "C" clamp tool, and tighten screws until bearing is pressing outward and center yoke contacts slinger ring. Do not press beyond this point or slinger will be damaged.

6) Clamp exposed end of bearing in vise and hammer on center yoke until bearing is free. Press against cross with "C" clamp to remove remaining bearing.

7) Remove center yoke from cross, and remove cross from propeller shaft using same procedure.

Reassembly

1) Clean all components in cleaning solvent. Place cross in propeller shaft yoke. Make sure cross bosses are installed in original position.

NOTE: **If repair kit is being installed, bosses will be lubrication plugs.**

2) Press in bearings, and install snap rings. Fill socket relief and coat ball with proper grease. Position center yoke over cross. Press in bearings and install snap rings.

3) Install new seal on centering ball stud. Place centering socket over stud. Place front cross in yoke. Make sure cross bosses (or lubrication plugs) are installed in original position.

4) Place cross loosely on center stop. Press first set of bearings into center yoke, then install second set. Install snap rings. Apply pressure to center yoke socket, and install remaining bearing cup. If replacement kit is used, remove plugs, and lubricate "U" joints. Reinstall plugs.

SECTION 10

BRAKES

CONTENTS

NOTE: **ALSO SEE GENERAL INDEX.**

IMPORTANT: Because of the many model names used by vehicle manufacturers, accurate identification of models is important. See Model Identification at the front of this publication.

Brakes

BRAKE SYSTEM TROUBLE SHOOTING

CONDITION	POSSIBLE CAUSE	CORRECTION
Brakes Pull Left or Right	Incorrect tire pressure	Inflate tires to proper pressure
	Front end out of alignment	See WHEEL ALIGNMENT
	Mismatched tires	Check tires sizes
	Restricted brake lines or hoses	Check hose routing
	Loose or malfunctioning caliper	See DISC BRAKES
	Bent shoe or oily linings	See DRUM BRAKES
	Malfunctioning rear brakes	See DRUM or DISC BRAKES
	Loose suspension parts	See SUSPENSION
Noises Without Brakes Applied	Front linings worn out	Replace linings
	Dust or oil on drums or rotors	See DRUM or DISC BRAKES
Noises with Brakes Applied	Insulator on outboard shoe damaged	See DISC BRAKES
	Incorrect pads or linings	Replace pads or linings
Brake Rough, Chatters or Pulsates	Excessive lateral runout	Check rotor runout
	Parallelism not to specifications	Reface or replace rotor
	Wheel bearings not adjusted	See SUSPENSION
	Rear drums out-of-round	Reface or replace drums
	Disc pad reversed, steel against rotor	Remove and reinstall pad
Excessive Pedal Effort	Malfunctioning power unit	See POWER BRAKES
	Partial system failure	Check fluid and pipes
	Worn disc pad or lining	Replace pad or lining
	Caliper piston stuck or sluggish	See DISC BRAKES
	Master cylinder piston stuck	See MASTER CYLINDERS
	Brake fade due to incorrect pads or linings	Replace pads or linings
	Linings or pads glazed	Replace pads or linings
	Worn drums	Reface or replace drums
Excessive Pedal Travel	Partial brake system failure	Check fluid and pipes
	Insufficient fluid in master cylinder	See MASTER CYLINDERS
	Air trapped in system	See BLEEDING
	Rear brakes not adjusted	See Adjustment in DRUM BRAKES
	Bent shoe or lining	See DRUM BRAKES
	Plugged master cylinder cap	See MASTER CYLINDER
	Improper brake fluid	Replace brake fluid
Pedal Travel Decreasing	Compensating port plugged	See MASTER CYLINDERS
	Swollen cup in master cylinder	See MASTER CYLINDERS
	Master cylinder piston not returning	See MASTER CYLINDERS
	Weak shoe retracting springs	See DRUM BRAKES
	Wheel cylinder piston sticking	See DRUM BRAKES
Dragging Brakes	Master cylinder pistons not returning	See MASTER CYLINDERS
	Restricted brake lines or hoses	Check line routing
	Incorrect parking brake adjustment	See DRUM BRAKES
	Parking brake cables frozen	See DRUM BRAKES
	Incorrect installation of inboard disc pad	Remove and replace correctly
	Power booster output rod too long	See POWER BRAKE UNITS
	Brake pedal not returning freely	See DISC or DRUM BRAKES
Brakes Grab or Uneven Braking Action	Malfunction of combination valve	See CONTROL VALVES
	Malfunction of power brake unit	See POWER BRAKE UNITS
	Binding brake pedal	See DISC or DRUM BRAKES
Pulsation or Roughness	Uneven pad wear caused by caliper	See DISC BRAKES
	Uneven rotor wear	See DISC BRAKES
	Drums out-of-round	Reface or replace drums

Brake System Applications

CHRYSLER CORP.

BRAKE SYSTEM APPLICATIONS

Application	Type	Make & Design	Master Cylinder	Power Unit
All FWD Models				
Front	Disc	Chrysler – Sliding Caliper	Chrysler	Bendix – Single Diaphragm
Rear	Drum	Chrysler – Single Anchor	Dual Piston	
All RWD Models				
Front	Disc	[1] Chrysler – Sliding Caliper	[2] Chrysler	[3] Bendix – Dual Diaphragm
Rear	Drum	[4] Chrysler – Single Anchor	Dual Piston	

[1] – Bendix sliding caliper type is used on W250 with Spicer 60 front axle and W350 models.
[2] – Bendix dual piston master cylinder is used on W250 with Spicer 60 front axle, W350 and D350 models.
[3] – Bendix single diaphragm is used on B150, B250, and B-350 models with 3600 lb. front axle. B350 with 4000 lb. front axle uses a transversely mounted Bendix dual diaphragm. B350 school bus with 3600 lb. front axle uses a Bendix Hydro-Boost power unit.
[4] – Bendix single anchor is used on D250 with Spicer 60 rear axle, W250, D350 with Spicer 60 Heavy Duty rear axle, and on W350 models.

FORD

BRAKE SYSTEM APPLICATIONS

Application	Type	Make & Design	Master Cylinder	Power Unit
Aerostar, Bronco II & Ranger				
Front	Disc	Bendix – Sliding Caliper	[1] Ford	Bendix – Single Diaphragm
Rear	Drum	Bendix – Single Anchor	Dual Piston	
All Other Models				
Front	Disc	[2] Dayton – Sliding Caliper	Ford	[3] Bendix – Single Diaphragm
Rear	Drum	Bendix – Single Anchor	Dual Piston	

[1] – Aerostar master cylinder uses a see-through reservoir, Bronco II and Ranger use a cast iron master cylinder.
[2] – Light duty single piston caliper. F250 above 6900 GVWR, E250/E350, F350 2WD/4WD, and F250 4WD model trucks are equipped with Dayton or Kelsey-Hayes H.D. dual piston sliding caliper.
[3] – E250/350, F250 H.D., and F350 (except 4WD crew cab) use Bendix dual diaphragm booster.

Brake System Applications

GENERAL MOTORS

BRAKE SYSTEM APPLICATIONS

[1] Application	Type	Make & Design	[2] Master Cylinder	Power Unit
Astro/Safari, "S"10/15				
Front	Disc	Delco – Floating Caliper	Delco –	[6] Delco Dual Diaphragm
Rear	Drum	Delco – Single Anchor	Quick Take-Up	
"C", "G" & "K"10 (Gas)				
Front	Disc	Delco – Floating Caliper	Delco –	[3] Bendix or Delco Single Diaphragm
Rear	Drum	Delco – Single Anchor	Dual Piston	
"C" & "K"10, "G"20, "P"20 (Diesel)				
Front	Disc	[4] Delco – Floating Caliper	Delco –	Bendix Hydro-Boost
Rear	Drum	Delco – Single Anchor	Dual Piston	
"C", "G" & "K"20, "G"30, "P"20 (Gas)				
Front	Disc	Bendix or Delco – Floating Caliper	Delco –	Delco Dual Diaphragm
Rear	Drum	Delco – Single Anchor	Dual Piston	
"C" & "K"30 (Gas & Diesel), "G"30 (Diesel)				
Front	Disc	[5] Bendix – Sliding Caliper	Bendix – Mini	Bendix Hydro-Boost
Rear	Drum	Delco – Single Anchor		
"P"30 Motor Home & Forward Control (Over 12,000 lb. GVW)				
Front	Disc	Bendix – Sliding Caliper	Bendix – Mini	Bendix Hydro-Boost
Rear	Disc	Bendix – Sliding Caliper		

[1] – Vehicle series numbers used in this chart are abbreviated for common reference to Chevrolet and GMC models.
[2] – All models with Low-Drag calipers use Delco Quick Take-Up master cylinder.
[3] – Suburban, "K"10, and heavy duty power brake models use Delco Dual Diaphragm power unit.
[4] – Models over 8500 GVW use Bendix Sliding Caliper and Bendix Mini master cylinder.
[5] – "G"/"P"30 models with gasoline engines under 8600 GVW use Bendix or Delco Floating Caliper with Delco Dual Piston master cylinder and Delco Dual Diaphragm power unit .
[6] – "S" models with 4100 GVW or 1000 payload capacity use Delco Single Diaphragm power unit.

JEEP

BRAKE SYSTEM APPLICATIONS

Application	Type	Make & Design	Master Cylinder	Power Unit
Grand Wagoneer & Truck				
Front	Disc	Delco – Floating Caliper	Delco	[2] Delco – Single Diaphragm
Rear	Drum	[1] Delco – Single Anchor	Quick Take-Up	
All Other Models				
Front	Disc	Delco – Floating Caliper	Delco	Delco – Single Diaphragm
Rear	Drum	[3] Bendix – Single Anchor	Dual Piston	

[1] – Lever type adjuster.
[2] – J20 truck uses Delco tandem diaphragm.
[3] – Cable type adjuster.

HYDRAULIC BRAKE BLEEDING

DESCRIPTION

Hydraulic system bleeding is necessary any time air has been introduced into system. Bleed brakes at all 4 wheels if master cylinder lines have been disconnected or master cylinder has run dry. Bleed brakes with pressure bleeding equipment or by manually pumping brake pedal while using bleeder tubes.

NOTE: **Hydro-Boost bleeding procedure is different than hydraulic brake bleeding. See BENDIX HYDRO-BOOST article in this section.**

HYDRAULIC CONTROL VALVES

When pressure bleeding disc brake equipped vehicles, metering section of hydraulic control valve must be deactivated before bleeding to permit fluid to flow to front brakes.

Use pressure bleeding override tool when applicable (Chrysler Corp. C-4121 and General Motors J-23709). If tool is not available, hold valve open by hand. DO NOT use "C" clamp or other non-yeilding device to hold valve open.

PRESSURE TANK BLEEDING

1) Clean master cylinder cap and surrounding area. Remove cap. With pressure tank at least 1/2 full, connect to master cylinder with adapters. Attach bleeder hose to first bleeder valve to be serviced. See BLEEDING SEQUENCE table.

2) Place other end of hose in clean glass jar partially filled with clean brake fluid so end of hose is submerged in fluid. Open release valve on pressure bleeder. Follow equipment manufacturer's pressure instructions unless noted below.

3) Unscrew bleeder valve 3/4-1 turn, noting fluid flow. When fluid flowing from cylinder to jar is free of bubbles, close bleeder valve securely. Bleed remaining cylinders in correct sequence and in same manner. Remove tool from control valve.

PRESSURE BLEEDER SETTINGS

Application	psi (kg/cm^2)
Chrysler Corp.	35 (2.5)
Ford	10-30 (.7-2.0)
General Motors	20-25 (1.4-1.8)
Jeep	15-20 (1.1-1.4)

MANUAL BLEEDING

NOTE: **When bleeding disc brakes, air may tend to cling to caliper walls. Lightly tap caliper, while bleeding, to aid in removal of air.**

1) Fill master cylinder. Install bleeder hose to first bleeder valve to be serviced. See BLEEDING SEQUENCE table. Submerge other end of hose in clean glass jar partially filled with clean brake fluid.

2) Open bleeder valve 3/4-1 turn. Depress brake pedal slowly through full travel. Close bleeder valve and release pedal. Repeat procedure until flow of fluid shows no signs of air bubbles.

Fig. 1: Wheel Cylinder Bleeding Procedure

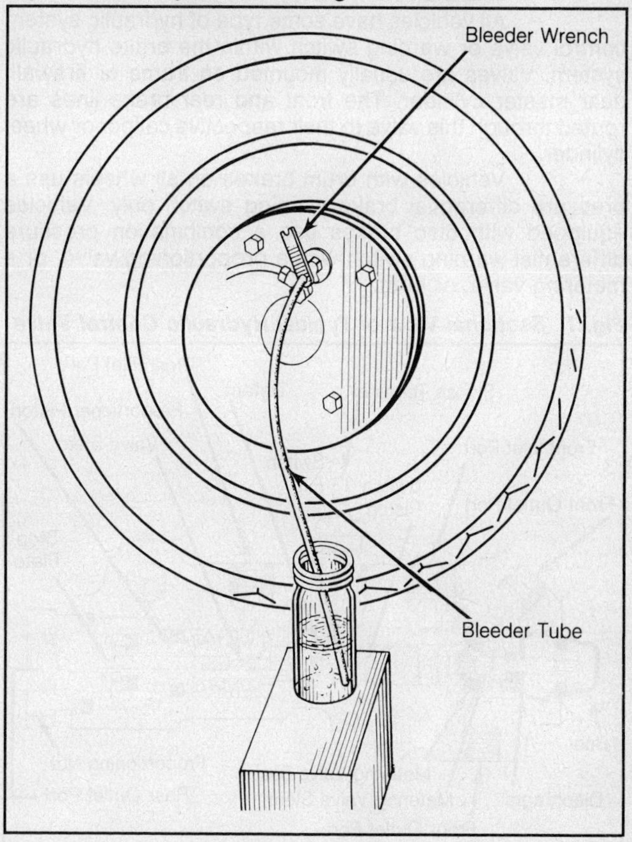

When bleeding brake system manually, ensure bleeder valve is closed when brake pedal is released.

BLEEDING SEQUENCE

Before bleeding system, exhaust all vacuum from power unit by depressing brake pedal several times. Bleed master cylinder if equipped with bleeder screws. Bleed slave cylinder on vehicles equipped with remote mount power assist units. Bleed wheel cylinders and calipers in sequence. See BLEEDING SEQUENCE table.

BLEEDING SEQUENCE

Application	Sequence
Chrysler Corp.	RR, LR, RF, LF
Ford	RR, LR, RF, LF
General Motors	RR, LR, RF, LF
Jeep	RR, LR, RF, LF

BRAKE FLUID SPECIFICATION

Application	Fluid Type
Chrysler Corp.	DOT 3
Ford	DOT 3
General Motors	DOT 3
Jeep	DOT 3 or 4

HYDRAULIC SYSTEM CONTROL VALVES

DESCRIPTION

All vehicles have some type of hydraulic system control valve or warning switch within the brake hydraulic system. Valves are usually mounted on frame or firewall, near master cylinder. The front and rear brake lines are routed through this valve to their respective caliper or wheel cylinder.

Vehicles with drum brakes on all wheels use a pressure differential brake warning switch only. Vehicles equipped with disc brakes use a combination pressure differential warning switch with a proportioning valve, or a metering valve, or both.

Fig. 1: Sectional View of Typical Hydraulic Control Valve

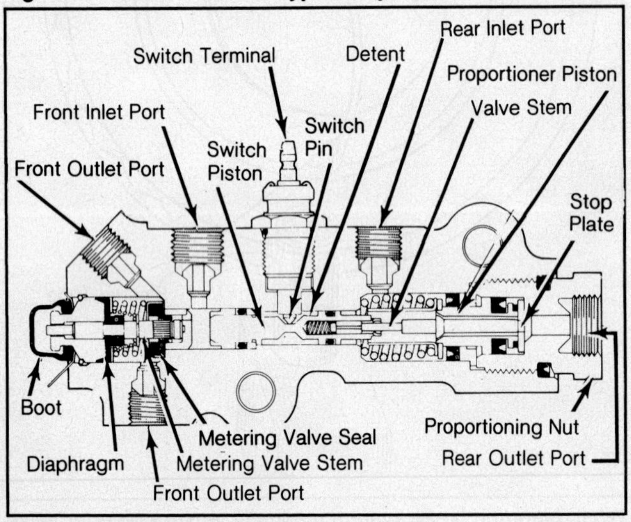

OPERATION

HEIGHT SENSING PROPORTIONING VALVE

All Chrysler Corp. FWD vans and wagons, and General Motors 30 series pickups use a height sensing proportioning valve that responds to changes in vehicle height. This valve automatically provides optimum front-to-rear brake balance, regardless of vehicle load.

The valve controls pressure to rear brakes by sensing vehicle load conditions through relative movement between rear axle and body. As vehicle load increases (resulting in decreased vehicle height), higher brake line pressure to rear brakes is allowed.

CAUTION: The use of aftermarket equipment (such as load leveling kits, air shocks, etc.), or making modifications that change the distance between axle and frame, will provide a false reading to brake proportioning valve. These modifications may result in unsatisfactory brake performance, which in turn could result in an accident and possible personal injury.

PRESSURE DIFFERENTIAL BRAKE WARNING SWITCH

This switch is used to warn vehicle operator that one of the hydraulic systems has failed. When hydraulic pressure is equal in both front and rear systems, switch piston remains centered and does not contact terminal in switch.

If brake system fails, hydraulic pressure moves piston toward failed side. Shoulder of piston then contacts switch terminal to provide ground for brake warning light.

PROPORTIONING VALVE

Valve operates by restricting, at a given ratio, hydraulic pressure to rear brakes when system hydraulic pressure reaches a certain point. This improves front-to-rear brake balance at high speed braking, when a percentage of rear weight is transfered to front wheels.

Valve reduces rear brake pressure, and delays rear wheel skid. On light brake application, valve allows full hydraulic pressure to rear brakes.

METERING VALVE

This valve holds off pressure to front disc brakes to allow rear drum brake shoes to overcome return spring pressure and make contact with rear drums. This prevents locking front brakes on slippery or icy surfaces under light braking conditions. Valve has no effect on front brake pressure during hard braking conditions.

TESTING

BRAKE WARNING LIGHT SYSTEM

Electrical Circuit

Disconnect wire from switch terminal and ground wire to chassis. Turn ignition switch on. Warning light should come on. If lamp does not light, bulb or wiring circuit is defective. Replace bulb or repair wiring as necessary. If lamp lights, turn off ignition and connect wire.

Warning Light Switch

1) Attach a bleeder hose to bleeder screw at either rear brake. Immerse other end of hose in container with brake fluid. Turn ignition on. Open bleeder screw while pressure is being applied to brake pedal. Warning lamp should light. Close bleeder screw before pressure is released from pedal.

2) Reapply brake pedal using moderate to heavy pressure. Light should go out. Repeat test on front brake system. System should function in same manner. Turn ignition off.

3) If lamp does not light on either system, but does light when electrical circuit is tested, the warning light switch portion of valve is defective.

HEIGHT SENSING PROPORTIONING VALVE

Chrysler Corp.

1) Disconnect external spring at proportioning valve end. Install gauge and "T" of Height Sensing Proportioning Valve Test Set (C-4007-a) in line of either master cylinder port to brake control valve assembly.

2) Install gauge and "T" of test set to either rear brake outlet port, between proportioning valve and rear brake line. Bleed rear brake system.

3) Have an assistant depress brake pedal. While holding pressure, note reading on inlet and outlet gauges. Inlet pressure should be 500 psi (35 kg/cm^2).

4) Oulet pressure should be 100-200 psi (7-14 kg/cm^2). If pressures are not as indicated, replace height sensing proportioning valve. If pressures are okay, adjust external spring and road test vehicle.

HYDRAULIC SYSTEM CONTROL VALVES (Cont.)

SERVICING

All hydraulic system switches and valves are nonadjustable and non-serviceable. If any part of hydraulic control valve is found to be defective, replace entire unit.

RESETTING SWITCH

After failed side of system has been repaired, applying brake pedal with moderate force will hydraulically center piston and turn off brake warning light.

REMOVAL & INSTALLATION

CONTROL VALVE

Removal

Disconnect brake warning light connection at switch. Disconnect all brake hydraulic lines at valve. Cover brake lines to prevent dirt from entering system. Remove valve mounting bolts. Remove valve from vehicle.

Installation

To install, reverse removal procedures. Bleed brake system. Center brake warning light switch piston. See RESETTING SWITCH in this article.

HEIGHT SENSING PROPORTIONING VALVE

Chrysler Corp.

1) Disconnect spring and brake lines from valve. Remove 2 screws securing valve and remove valve. Install new valve and bleed rear brake system.

2) Raise vehicle on hoist and allow rear suspension to hang free. Leave wheels and tires on vehicle. Ensure that shock absorbers are fully extended. Loosen adjustment lever fasteners. *See Fig. 2.*

3) Push valve lever toward valve until lever bottoms out on valve body and hold there. Rotate adjustment lever away from valve until all free play has been removed from actuator spring. Do not stretch spring. Tighten fasteners to 150 INCH Lbs. (17 N.m).

Fig. 2: Chrysler Corp. Height Sensing Proportioning Valve Installation

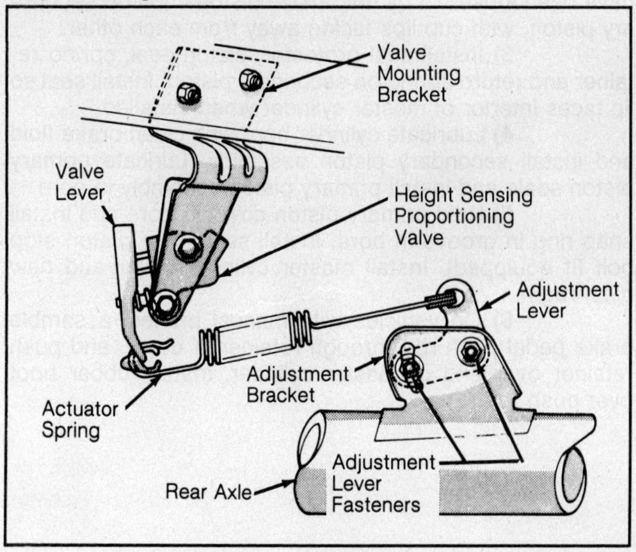

General Motors

1) Raise vehicle. Allow rear axle to hang free (no load condition), with wheels removed. Clean valve exterior to prevent dirt from entering hydraulic system. Disconnect brake lines from valve. Remove nut from shaft and remove lever. Remove 2 screws securing valve and remove valve.

2) To install valve, place valve on mounting bracket and tighten screws. Before installing lever assembly on valve shaft, ensure that all valve brackets, fasteners and links are securely attached.

3) If a new valve is being installed, install lever assembly on valve shaft by pushing plastic bushing and clip over serrations on valve shaft. If original valve is being installed, it must be adjusted. See ADJUSTMENTS in this article.

4) Install nut on shaft and tighten. Connect brake lines to valve. Bleed brake system. Lower vehicle and test brakes.

ADJUSTMENTS

HEIGHT SENSING PROPORTIONING VALVE

1) Raise vehicle. Allow rear axle to hang free (no load condition), with wheels on. Remove nut from valve shaft and remove lever assembly. *See Fig. 3.*

2) Rotate valve shaft to permit installation of adjustment gauge. Center hole of adjustment gauge must seat on "D" shape of valve shaft and gauge tang must seat in valve mounting hole. *See Fig. 3.*

3) Install lever on valve shaft by pushing plastic bushing and clip assembly over serrations on valve shaft using a "C" clamp or pliers. When properly installed, serrations on valve shaft fully engage plastic bushing.

NOTE: **Do not drive lever assembly on valve shaft by using nut as proper valve setting may be disturbed.**

4) Install nut and tighten to 70-98 INCH Lbs. (8-11 N.m). Break tang on adjustment gauge to allow valve assembly to rotate freely. Lower vehicle and test brakes.

Fig. 3: General Motors Height Sensing Proportioning Valve Adjustment

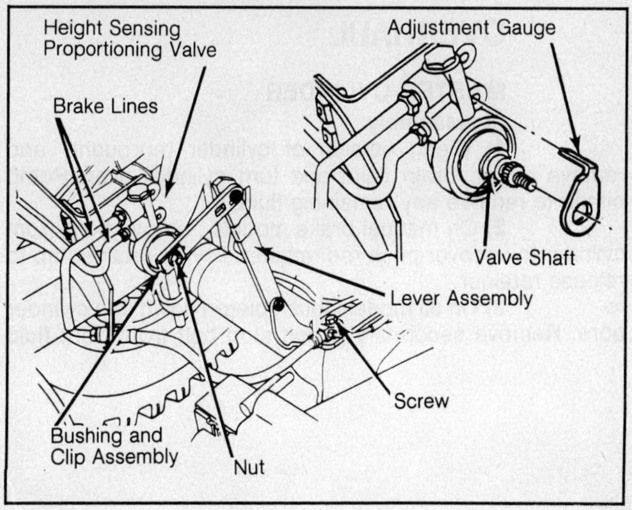

Master Cylinders

BENDIX/DELCO-MORAINE DUAL PISTON

Chevrolet, GMC, Jeep

DESCRIPTION

Bendix and Delco-Moraine tandem dual piston master cylinders are single casting type with front and rear pistons and a separate reservoir and outlet for each piston.

Rear piston is operated by push rod connected to brake pedal. Front piston is operated by rear piston. In a combination disc and drum system, reservoir which feeds disc brakes is larger to compensate for larger displacement of disc caliper cylinder.

ADJUSTMENT

BRAKE PEDAL

NOTE: **Adjustment for vehicles equipped with power boosters is accomplished at power booster. See POWER BRAKE UNITS in this section.**

Vehicles without power assisted brakes incorporate a nonadjustable push rod. Brake pedal push rod length is preset by manufacturer.

REMOVAL & INSTALLATION

MASTER CYLINDER

Removal

1) Disconnect front and rear hydraulic brake lines at master cylinder. Plug brake lines to prevent entry of foreign matter into brake system.

2) On vehicles without power assist units, disconnect brake pedal push rod at brake pedal. Remove master cylinder retaining nuts, and remove master cylinder.

Installation

1) To install master cylinder, position on vehicle and install retaining nuts. Connect front and rear hydraulic brake lines to cylinder.

2) Connect brake pedal push rod, if removed. Fill reservoir with clean brake fluid, and bleed hydraulic system. See HYDRAULIC BRAKE BLEEDING in this section.

OVERHAUL

MASTER CYLINDER

Disassembly

1) Clean outside of cylinder thoroughly and remove cover. Drain fluid, and turn cylinder over. Pump piston to remove any remaining fluid.

2) On manual brake models, remove boot from cylinder to uncover push rod retainer. Pry up retainer tab to release retainer.

3) On all models, push piston down into cylinder bore. Remove secondary piston stop bolt from front fluid reservoir (if equipped). Remove snap ring from groove in cylinder bore.

4) Remove both piston assemblies. Remove any internal parts remaining in bore. On Jeep CJ7 and Scrambler models, remove push rod from primary piston. Remove and discard all rubber parts from piston assemblies.

5) Enlarge holes in tube seats using a 13/64" drill. Place a large flat washer over outlet and thread a 1/4" x 20 x 3/4" screw into seat. Tighten screw until seat is loose. Remove seat, screw and washer.

Fig. 1: Removing Tube Seat from Master Cylinder

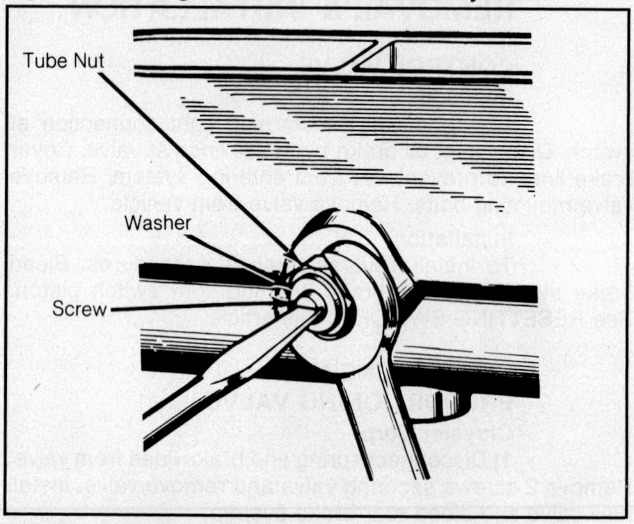

Tighten screw until tube seat is loose, then remove seat.

Inspection

Inspect cylinder bore for scoring or corrosion. Staining which has not pitted or roughened surface of cylinder can be removed with crocus cloth. If cylinder bore is scored, pitted or corroded, replace master cylinder.

Reassembly

1) Install replacement tube seats by threading a spare brake line tube nut into hole. Turn nut in until tube seat bottoms. Do not cock tube seat in hole.

2) Remove nut and check for burrs which may have been loosened by nut. Install piston cups on secondary piston, with cup lips facing away from each other.

3) Install seal protector, piston seal, spring retainer and return spring on secondary piston. Install seal so lip faces interior of master cylinder when installed.

4) Lubricate cylinder bore with clean brake fluid and install secondary piston assembly. Luricate primary piston seals and install primary piston assembly in bore.

5) Hold primary piston down in bore and install snap ring in groove in bore. Install secondary piston stop bolt (if equipped). Install master cylinder cover and new diaphragm.

6) On vehicles with manual brakes, assemble brake pedal push rod through retainer (if used), and push retainer over end of master cylinder. Install rubber boot over push rod.

BENDIX/DELCO-MORAINE DUAL PISTON (Cont.)

Fig. 2: Exploded View of Typical Delco-Moraine Master Cylinder

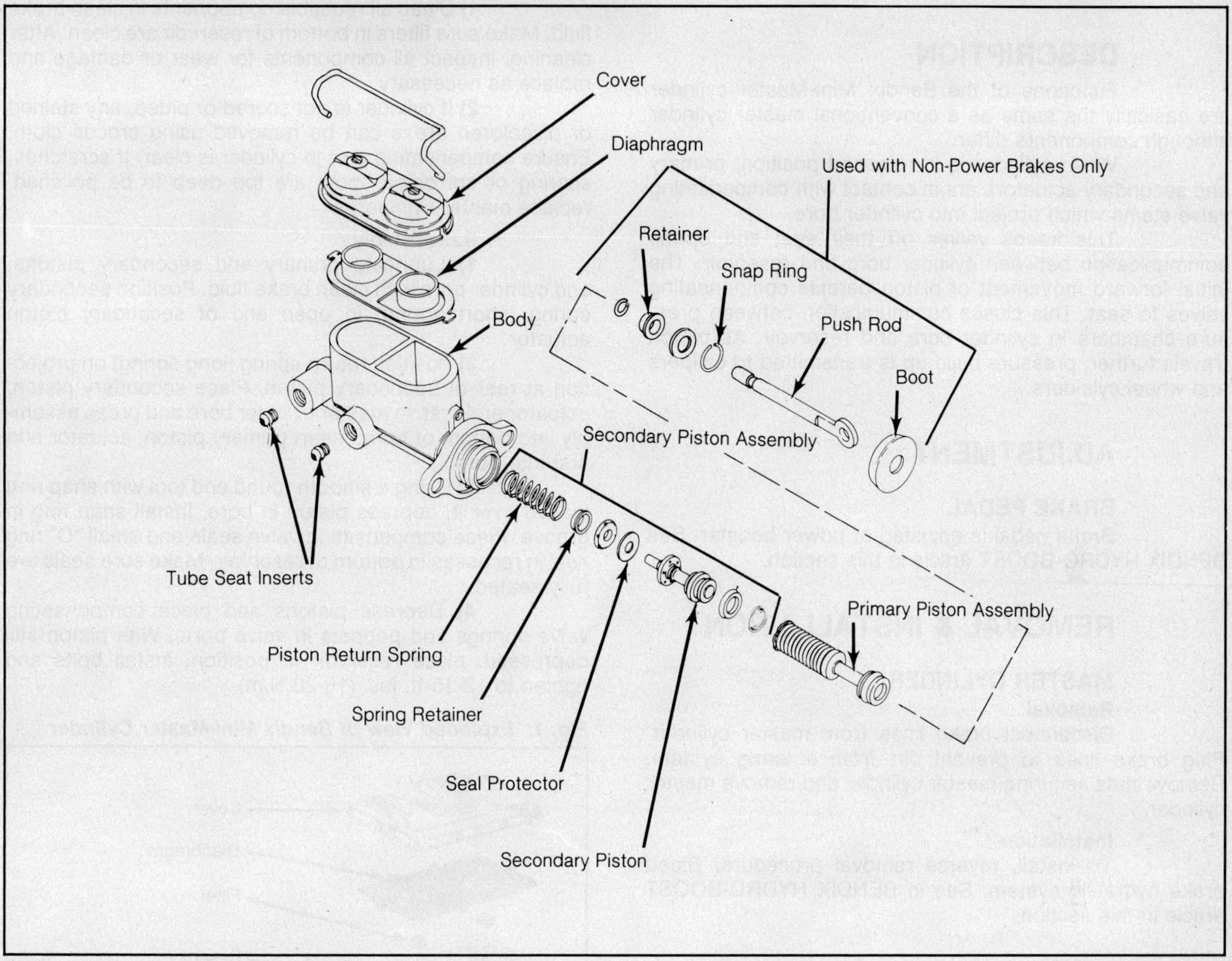

Bendix master cylinders are similar.

Master Cylinders

BENDIX MINI-MASTER

Chevrolet, GMC

DESCRIPTION

Functions of the Bendix Mini-Master cylinder are basically the same as a conventional master cylinder although components differ.

When cylinder is in released position, primary and secondary actuators are in contact with compensating valve stems which project into cylinder bore.

This keeps valves off their seat and opens communication between cylinder bore and reservoir. The initial forward movement of piston permits compensating valves to seat. This closes communication between pressure chambers in cylinder bore and reservoir. As piston travels further, pressure build up is transmitted to calipers and wheel cylinders.

ADJUSTMENT

BRAKE PEDAL

Brake pedal is adjusted at power booster. See BENDIX HYDRO-BOOST article in this section.

REMOVAL & INSTALLATION

MASTER CYLINDER

Removal

Disconnect brake lines from master cylinder. Plug brake lines to prevent dirt from entering system. Remove nuts securing master cylinder and remove master cylinder.

Installation

To install, reverse removal procedure. Bleed brake hydraulic system. See in BENDIX HYDRO-BOOST article in this section.

OVERHAUL

MASTER CYLINDER

Disassembly

1) Remove reservoir cover and diaphragm. Drain all brake fluid. Remove 4 reservoir bolts and separate reservoir and master cylinder body. Remove small "O" ring and compensating valve seals from bottom of reservoir.

2) Do not remove 2 filters from bottom of reservoir unless they are damaged. Push in primary piston and remove compensating valve poppets and springs from ports in master cylinder body.

3) Remove snap ring from master cylinder bore using a small screwdriver. Release primary and secondary pistons and remove from bore.

4) It may be necessary to plug front outlet port and apply low air pressure to front compensating valve port to remove secondary piston assembly.

Cleaning & Inspection

1) Clean all reusable components in clean brake fluid. Make sure filters in bottom of reservoir are clean. After cleaning, inspect all components for wear or damage and replace as necessary.

2) If cylinder is not scored or pitted, any stained or discolored areas can be removed using crocus cloth. Ensure compensating port in cylinder is clear. If scratches, scoring or corrosion spots are too deep to be polished, replace master cylinder.

Reassembly

1) Lubricate primary and secondary pistons, and cylinder bore with clean brake fluid. Position secondary spring (short spring) in open end of secondary piston actuator.

2) Position return spring (long spring) on projection at rear of secondary piston. Place secondary piston, actuator end first, in master cylinder bore and press assembly into bottom of bore. Insert primary piston, actuator end first into bore.

3) Using a smooth round end tool with snap ring placed over it, depress piston in bore. Install snap ring in groove. Place compensating valve seals and small "O" ring seal in recesses in bottom of reservoir. Make sure seals are fully seated.

4) Depress pistons and place compensating valve springs and poppets in valve ports. With piston still depressed, place reservoir in position. Install bolts and tighten to 12-15 ft. lbs. (16-20 N.m).

Fig. 1: Exploded View of Bendix Mini-Master Cylinder

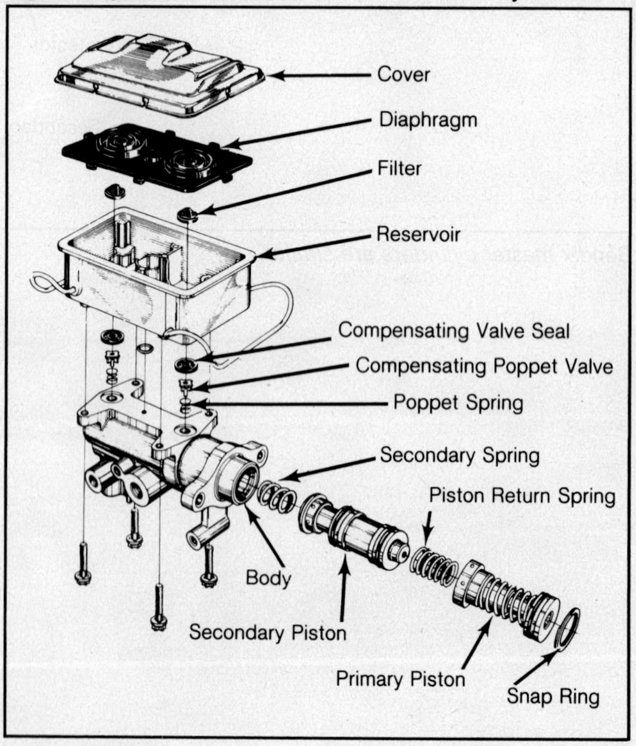

CHRYSLER CORP. DUAL PISTON - ALUMINUM

DESCRIPTION

The aluminum tandem dual piston master cylinder has a nylon reservoir and an anodized aluminum body. The front and rear pistons have separate reservoirs and outlets.

The reservoir may be filled from 1 cap, as reservoirs are connected at the top. Air entrapment is controlled by cup expanders in rear brake wheel cylinders. No residual pressure valves are installed on this master cylinder.

REMOVAL & INSTALLATION

POWER BRAKE MASTER CYLINDER

Removal

Disconnect primary and secondary brake lines from master cylinder and plug outlets. Remove nuts that retain cylinder to power brake unit. Slide master cylinder straight out and away from brake unit.

Installation

Position master cylinder over studs of power brake unit, aligning power cylinder brake push rod with cylinder piston. Install and tighten nuts. Connect both brake lines and bleed system. See HYDRAULIC BRAKE BLEEDING in this section.

MANUAL BRAKE MASTER CYLINDER

Removal

1) Disconnect primary and secondary brake lines from master cylinder and plug outlets. Disconnect stop light light switch mounting bracket under instrument panel.

2) Grasp brake pedal and pull back to disengage push rod from master cylinder. This will destroy push rod retention grommet. Remove nuts retaining master cylinder to cowl panel. Slide master cylinder straight out and away from cowl.

Installation

1) Install new push rod retention grommet. Position master cylinder to cowl panel. Install and tighten nuts. Connect and tighten brake lines.

2) From under instrument panel, moisten push rod grommet with water and align push rod with master cylinder piston. Using brake pedal, apply pressure to fully seat push rod into piston.

3) Install master cylinder boot and connect stop light switch mounting bracket. Bleed brake system. See HYDRAULIC BRAKE BLEEDING in this section.

OVERHAUL

MASTER CYLINDER

Disassembly

1) Clean outside of reservoir and cylinder body. Remove reservoir caps and empty brake fluid. Position cylinder body in vise and rock reservoir from side-to-side, to remove from cylinder. Remove grommets.

2) Using needle nose pliers, remove secondary piston retainer pin from inside master cylinder housing. Remove snap ring from end of master cylinder body. Slide primary piston out of bore.

3) Tap open end of cylinder on bench to remove secondary piston. If piston sticks, use air pressure to force piston from cylinder. If brass tube seats are damaged or worn, use screw extractor to remove seats.

Inspection

Wash master cylinder bore with clean brake fluid. Inspect bore for pitting, scratches or scoring. Inspect piston for corrosion and scoring, replace as necessary. During overhaul, all rubber parts must be replaced.

NOTE: Do not hone aluminum master cylinder. If bore is unserviceable, replace cylinder.

Fig. 1: Exploded View of Aluminum Master Cylinder

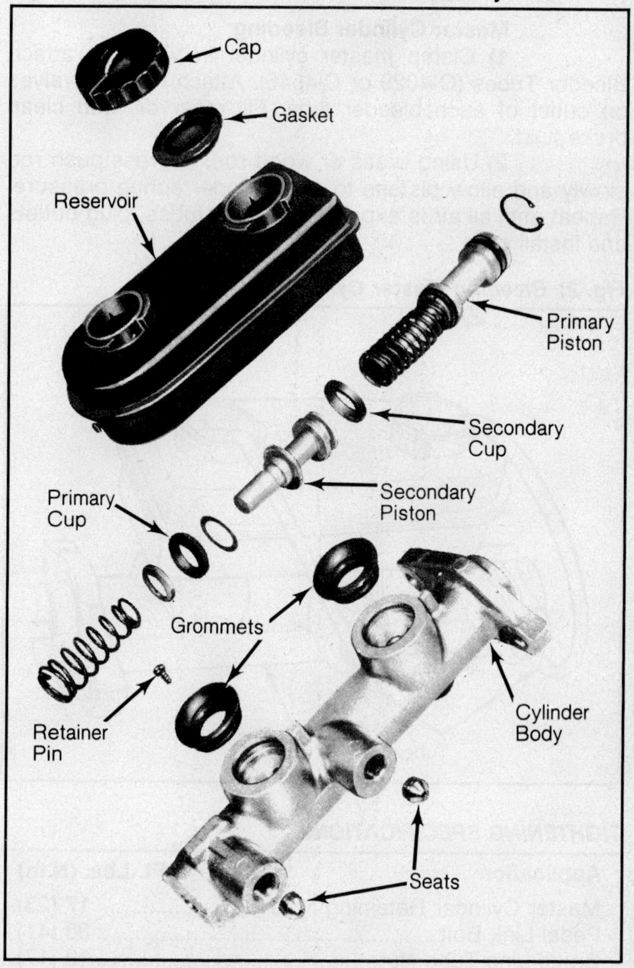

Reassembly

1) Dip master cylinder and all components in clean brake fluid. Assembling seals dry could ruin seals.

2) Install check flow washer on secondary piston and carefully work primary cup on end with lip facing away from piston. Slide cup retainer over front end of piston followed by spring.

3) Carefully work piston secondary cup into cylinder bore, with lip away from piston. Install secondary piston into bore. Be careful that lip of cups enters bore evenly in order not to damage sealing of cups.

4) Carefully work secondary cup over rear end of primary piston with larger lip of cup toward piston. Center spring retainer of primary piston on secondary piston. Push piston assemblies into bore up to primary piston cup.

Master Cylinders

CHRYSLER CORP. DUAL PISTON – ALUMINUM (Cont.)

5) Carefully work cup into bore and push piston into secondary seal. Work lip of primary cup into bore and push in on piston until seated. Depress piston with brass or wood rod and install snap ring.

6) Position secondary piston retainer pin in cylinder housing and tap or press in until firmly seated. Install tube seats. Install housing-to-reservoir grommets and, using rocking motion, install reservoir on master cylinder body.

NOTE: **Reservoir is keyed to prevent installation in wrong direction.**

Master Cylinder Bleeding

1) Clamp master cylinder in vise and attach Bleeder Tubes (C-4029 or C-4546). Attach residual valves on outlet of each bleeder tube. Fill reservoir with clean brake fluid.

2) Using brass or wood rod, depress push rod slowly and allow pistons to return under spring pressure. Repeat until all air is expelled. Remove tubes, plug outlets and install caps.

Fig. 2: Bleeding Master Cylinder

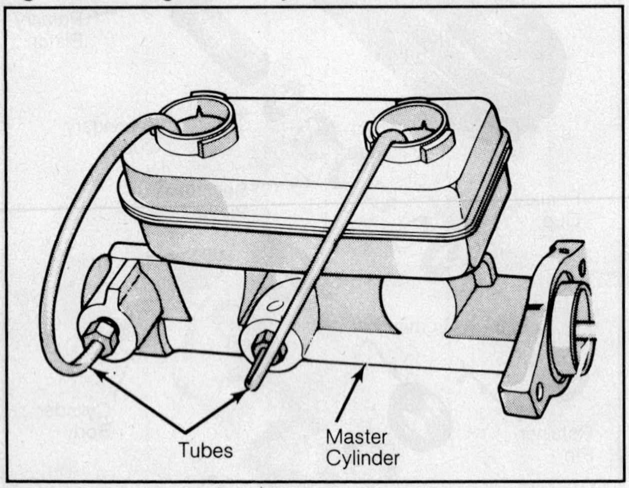

TIGHTENING SPECIFICATIONS

Application	Ft. Lbs. (N.m)
Master Cylinder Retaining Nuts	17 (23)
Pedal Link Bolt	30 (41)
Brake Line Tube Nuts	12 (17)

Master Cylinders

CHRYSLER CORP. DUAL PISTON - CAST IRON

DESCRIPTION

This tandem dual piston master cylinder is of the venting type, with two reservoirs in a single casting and one outlet for each reservoir. Rear piston is operated by push rod connected to brake pedal. Front piston is operated by rear piston.

REMOVAL & INSTALLATION

MASTER CYLINDER

Removal

Disconnect front and rear hydraulic brake lines at master cylinder. Remove nuts retaining nuts to power brake unit. Lift master cylinder from vehicle.

Installation

Position master cylinder on vehicle and install retaining nuts. Tighten to 200 INCH lbs. (23 N.m). Connect front and rear hydraulic brake lines. Fill reservoir with clean brake fluid and bleed brake system. See HYDRAULIC BRAKE BLEEDING in this section.

OVERHAUL

MASTER CYLINDER

Disassembly

1) Clean outside of cylinder and remove cover to drain brake fluid. Use screw extractor to remove tube seats. Remove snap ring from open end of cylinder and slide washer out.

2) Carefully remove primary piston assembly and slide secondary piston from cylinder. Clean all parts in alcohol and blow dry with compressed air.

Inspection

1) Inspect cylinder bore for scoring or pitting. Light scratches or minor corrosion can usually be removed by using crocus cloth.

2) Deep scratches or scoring may be honed, provided bore diameter is not increased more than .002" (.05 mm). If this limit is exceeded, master cylinder must be replaced.

3) Check pistons for scoring, scratches and corrosion. Pistons must be replaced if any of these conditions exist. Replace all rubber parts when overhauling master cylinder.

Reassembly

1) Dip all components in brake fluid before reassembly. Carefully slide secondary piston assembly into cylinder bore. Slide primary piston into bore, hold washer in position and install snap ring. Install tube seats.

2) Clamp master cylinder in a vise, being careful not to damage housing. Attach bleed tubes (C-4029) to outlet ports of cylinder, with ends of tubes placed in master cylinder reservoirs.

3) Fill reservoirs with clean brake fluid and depress push rod slowly. Allow pistons to return to normal position under spring pressure.

4) Repeat procedure until all air bubbles are expelled. Remove bleeding tubes, and install cylinder cover and diaphragm. Remove cylinder from vise.

Fig. 1: Exploded View of Cast Iron Master Cylinder

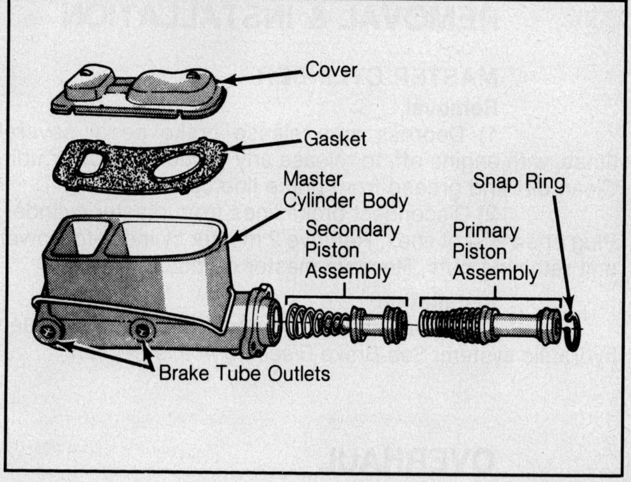

Master Cylinders

DELCO QUICK TAKE-UP

Chevrolet, GMC, Jeep

DESCRIPTION

The Delco Quick Take-Up master cylinder is a 2-piece unit with cast master cylinder body and plastic fluid reservoir. It is designed for use with systems utilizing low drag calipers.

This master cylinder includes a quick take-up valve. This valve delivers a large volume of fluid, at low pressure, upon initial application of brakes. The fluid quickly displaces retracted calipers, placing brake linings in contact with brake rotors and drums.

ADJUSTMENT

BRAKE PEDAL

Brake pedal is adjusted at power booster. See appropriate POWER BRAKE UNIT article in this section.

REMOVAL & INSTALLATION

MASTER CYLINDER

Removal

1) Depress and release brake pedal several times, with engine off, to release any vacuum in power unit. Clean dirt and grease from brake line connections.

2) Disconnect brake lines from master cylinder. Plug open end of lines. Remove 2 master cylinder-to-power unit retaining nuts. Remove master cylinder.

Installation

To install, reverse removal procedures. Bleed hydraulic system. *See Brake Bleeding in this Section.*

OVERHAUL

MASTER CYLINDER

Disassembly

1) Remove reservoir cover and diaphragm. Discard remaining brake fluid in reservoir. Push in on primary piston and remove snap ring.

2) Apply compressed air at forward brake line hole while plugging rear hole. Pistons will be forced out at open end of master cylinder.

3) Remove spring retainer and seals from secondary piston. Discard seals. Clamp mounting ear of master cylinder in vise and carefully pry off reservoir.

4) Do not attempt to remove take-up valve from master cylinder. It is not a serviceable component. Remove reservoir grommets and discard.

Inspection

1) Inspect cylinder bore for scoring or corrosion. If signs of corrosion are evident, replace master cylinder. No abrasives, of any kind, are to be used on cylinder bore.

2) Inspect reservoir cover and diaphragm for cuts, cracks or deformation. Replace damaged or defective parts.

Reassembly

1) Lubricate new reservoir grommets with silicone brake lube and press into master cylinder. Make sure grommets are properly seated. Lay reservoir on flat, hard surface. Rock master cylinder body onto reservoir until completely seated.

2) Lubricate new piston seals with clean brake fluid and install on secondary piston, with lip of seals toward ends of piston. Install spring retainer.

3) Install secondary piston spring and secondary piston assembly in master cylinder. Lubricate primary piston seals with clean brake fluid.

4) Install primary piston in master cylinder. Press in piston and install snap ring. Fit diaphragm in reservoir cover and install cover.

Fig. 1: Exploded View of Quick Take-Up Master Cylinder

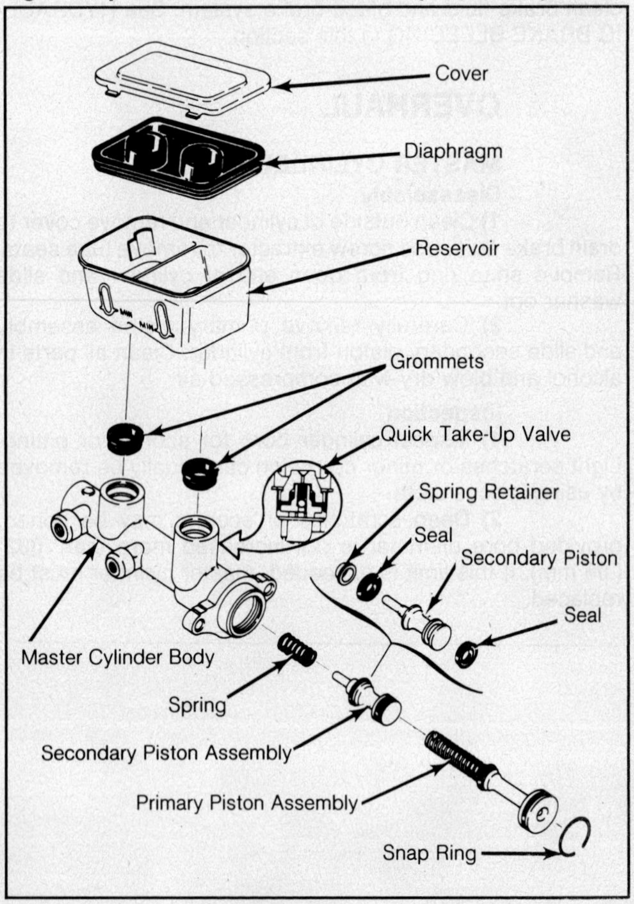

FORD DUAL PISTON MASTER CYLINDER

DESCRIPTION

Ford tandem dual piston master cylinder is a single casting with front and rear piston and a separate reservoir with an outlet for each piston.

Rear piston is operated by a push rod connected to brake pedal. Front, or floating, piston is operated by rear piston.

In a combination drum and disc system, reservoir which feeds disc brakes is larger, to correspond with larger size of disc brake caliper cylinders. Master cylinder outlet which feeds drum brake has a residual valve under tube seat. Disc brake outlet has no valve, since disc brakes must not have any residual pressure.

ADJUSTMENT

BRAKE PEDAL

Brake pedal adjustments are not required. Brake pedal free-travel will not be correct if power brake booster push rod clearance is not correct. See appropriate POWER BRAKE UNIT article in this section.

REMOVAL & INSTALLATION

POWER BRAKE MASTER CYLINDER

Removal

Depress brake pedal to expel vacuum from brake booster. Disconnect brake lines at master cylinder. Remove clutch master cylinder, if used. Remove nuts retaining master cylinder to brake booster. Remove master cylinder.

Installation

To install, reverse removal procedure. Center pressure differential valve and bleed system. See HYDRAULIC BRAKE BLEEDING in this section.

MANUAL BRAKE MASTER CYLINDER

Removal

1) Disconnect wires from stop light switch. Remove retaining pin, spacers, and bushing securing master cylinder push rod to brake pedal. Remove stop light switch.

2) Remove nuts securing master cylinder to firewall. Disconnect brake lines. Remove bolts and studs securing master cylinder to firewall and remove master cylinder. Remove boot and master cylinder push rod.

Installation

To install, reverse removal procedure. Center pressure differential valve and bleed system. See HYDRAULIC BRAKE BLEEDING in this section.

OVERHAUL

MASTER CYLINDER

Disassembly

1) Clean outside of master cylinder, remove filler cap and diaphragm. Drain any remaining fluid from cylinder. Depress primary piston and remove snap ring from end of master cylinder bore.

2) Remove primary piston assembly from cylinder bore. Apply air pressure to forward outlet port of cylinder and carefully blow secondary piston assembly out of bore.

Inspection

Clean all parts with isopropyl alcohol, and blow dry with compressed air. Ensure that all ports and vents are open and free of foreign matter. Inspect master cylinder bore and all parts for excessive wear or damage. If bore is damaged, replace master cylinder.

Reassembly

1) Lubricate all components including cylinder bore with clean brake fluid. Carefully insert secondary and primary piston assemblies into master cylinder bore. Depress primary piston and install snap ring in groove.

2) On vehicles with manual brakes, install push rod retainer onto push rod and install into primary piston. Ensure that retainer is properly seated and holding push rod securely.

Bleeding

1) Support master cylinder in a vise and fill both reservoirs with fluid. Install plugs in brake outlet ports. Loosen plug in rear outlet port and depress primary piston slowly to force air out of cylinder. Tighten plug while piston is depressed to prevent air from entering cylinder.

2) Repeat procedure until no air is evident. Proceed to front outlet port when rear is bled, ensuring that rear plug is tight. Piston travel will be greatly restricted when all air is expelled. Remove plugs, install cover and diaphragm.

Fig. 1: Exploded View of Master Cylinder Assembly

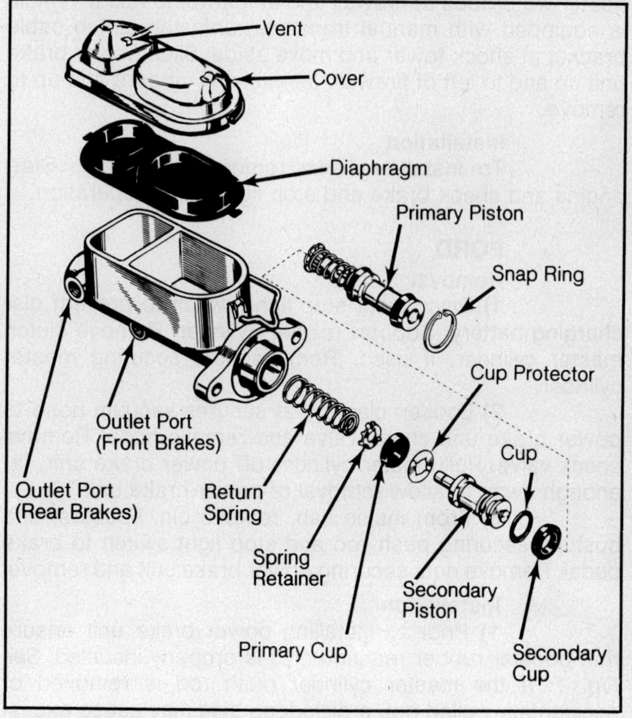

Power Brake Units

BENDIX SINGLE DIAPHRAGM

Chrysler Corp., Ford

DESCRIPTION

This unit uses engine manifold vacuum and atmospheric pressure to assist braking. The vacuum power chamber consists of a front and rear shell, diaphragm, diaphragm plate, push rod, and vacuum diaphragm return spring.

A mechanically actuated power brake unit check valve, integral with the vacuum power diaphragm, controls the degree of brake application and release in accordance with foot pressure applied to check valve operating rod through brake pedal linkage.

REMOVAL & INSTALLATION

CHRYSLER CORP.

Removal

1) Remove nuts attaching master cylinder to power brake unit. Carefully slide master cylinder off mounting studs and allow to rest on fender. Disconnect vacuum hose from power brake unit check valve.

2) From under instrument panel, position a small screwdriver between center tang on retainer clip and pin in brake pedal. Rotate screwdriver to allow retainer clip center tang to pass over end of brake pedal pin and pull retainer clip. Discard retainer clip.

3) Remove power brake unit attaching nuts. On RWD vehicles, remove power brake unit.

4) On FWD vehicles, unfasten brackets on steel heater water tube at firewall and at left frame rail. If vehicle is equipped with manual transaxle, unfasten clutch cable bracket at shock tower and move aside. Slide power brake unit up and to left of firewall, then tilt unit inboard and up to remove.

Installation

To install, reverse removal procedure. Start engine and check brake and stop light switch operation.

FORD

Removal

1) Disconnect stop light switch to prevent discharging battery. Support master cylinder. Remove clutch master cylinder, if used. Remove nuts securing master cylinder.

2) Loosen clamp that secures vacuum hose to power brake unit check valve and remove hose. Remove check valve. Pull master cylinder off power brake unit, far enough away to allow removal of power brake unit.

3) From inside cab, remove pin, spacers, and bushing securing push rod and stop light switch to brake pedal. Remove nuts securing power brake unit and remove.

Installation

1) Prior to installing power brake unit ensure that booster rubber reaction disc is properly installed. *See Fig. 1.* If the master cylinder push rod is removed or accidentally pulled out, a dislodged disc may cause excessive pedal travel.

2) The reaction disc is Black compared to the Silver-colored valve plunger that will be exposed if push rod and seat are removed. To install power brake unit, reverse removal procedure. Start engine and check brake operation.

OVERHAUL

The power brake unit is serviced as an assembly and must be replaced if it is found to be defective. On Ford vehicles, the unit must also be replaced if the rubber reaction disc (Black) cannot be properly aligned, installed or if it cannot be located within the unit. *See Fig. 1.*

Fig. 1: Bendix Single Diaphragm Assembly

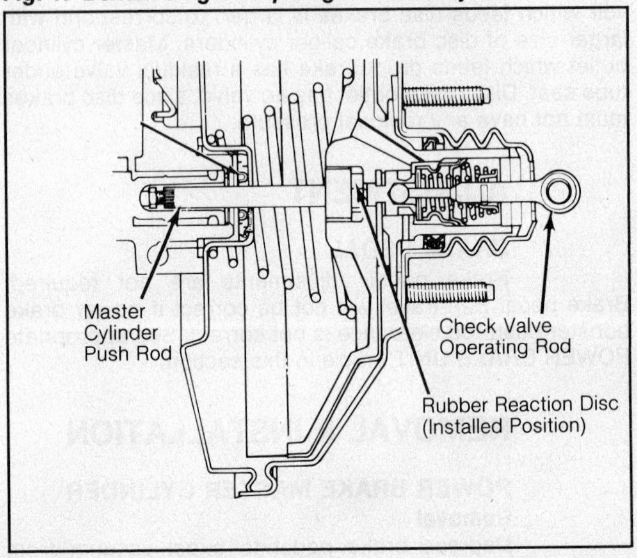

Checking reaction disc installation.

ADJUSTMENT

PUSH ROD

Ford Only

Check distance from outer end of push rod to front face of unit using a locally manufactured gauge. *See Fig. 2.* Turn push rod screw in or out until length is .980"-.995" (24.9-25.3 mm).

Fig. 2: Ford Push Rod Adjustment

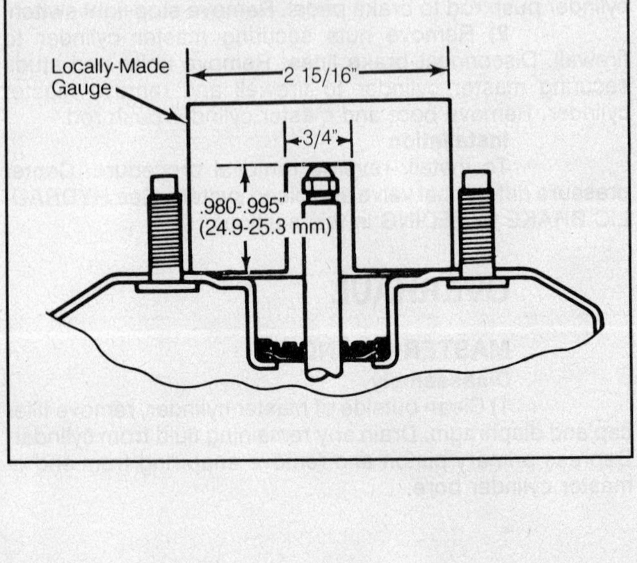

BENDIX TANDEM DIAPHRAGM

Chrysler Corp., Ford

DESCRIPTION

The power brake unit uses engine manifold vacuum and atmospheric pressure to provide power-assisted brake application. The vacuum power chamber includes front and rear shell, center plate, tandem front and rear diaphragms, push rod and a diaphragm return spring.

A mechanically actuated check valve, integral with diaphragms, controls the degree of power brake application and release in accordance with foot pressure applied to valve operating rod through brake pedal linkage.

REMOVAL & INSTALLATION

CHRYSLER CORP.

Removal

Disconnect vacuum hose from power brake unit check valve. Remove nuts securing master cylinder to unit. Remove master cylinder. Remove linkage bellcrank pivot bolt. Remove nuts securing power brake unit to mounting bracket and remove unit.

Installation

To install, reverse removal procedure. Start vehicle and check brake operation.

Fig. 1: Chrysler Corp. Transverse Mounted Tandem Diaphragm Power Brake Unit

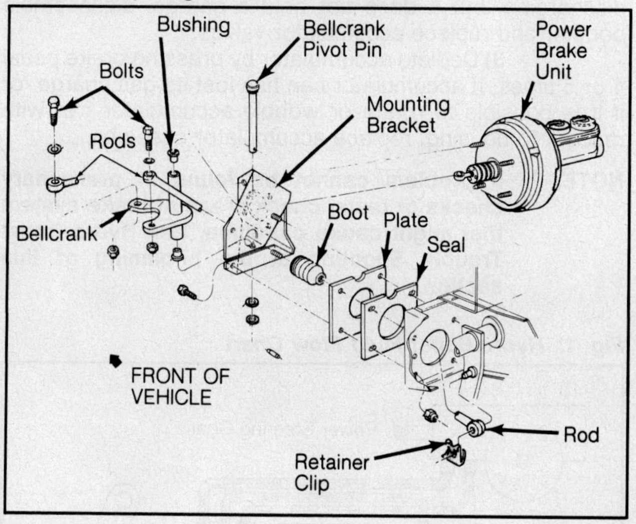

FORD

Removal

1) Disconnect stop light switch to prevent discharging battery. Support master cylinder. Remove clutch master cylinder, if used. Remove nuts securing master cylinder.

2) Loosen clamp that secures vacuum hose to power brake unit check valve and remove hose. Remove check valve. Pull master cylinder off power brake unit, far enough away to allow removal of power brake unit.

3) From inside cab, remove pin, spacers, and bushing securing push rod and stop light switch to brake pedal. Remove nuts securing power brake unit and remove.

Installation

To install, reverse removal procedure. Ensure that booster push rod is positioned on correct side of master cylinder. Start engine and check brake operation.

OVERHAUL

The power brake unit is serviced as an assembly and must be replaced if it is found to be defective.

ADJUSTMENT

PUSH ROD

Ford Only

Check distance from outer end of push rod to front face of unit using a locally manufactured gauge. *See Fig. 2*. Turn push rod screw in or out until length is .980"-.995" (24.9-25.3 mm).

Fig. 2: Ford Push Rod Adjustment

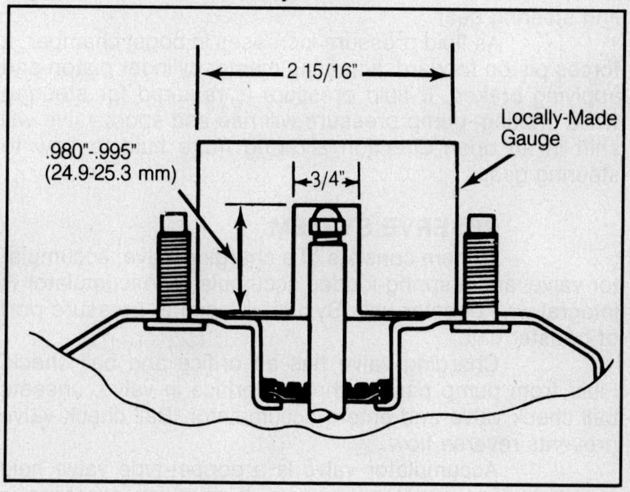

Power Brake Units

BENDIX HYDRO-BOOST

Chevrolet, Chrysler Corp., GMC

NOTE: **Bendix Hydro-Boost information not available from Chrysler Corp. at time of publication.**

DESCRIPTION

System utilizes power steering pump fluid pressure to operate booster. The assembly contains an open-center spool valve which controls pump pressure during braking. Also, a lever mechanism is used to control the position of the valve and a boost piston to operate master cylinder.

The unit also has a reserve system which stores sufficient fluid under pressure to provide at least 2 braking applications. Brakes can be applied manually if reserve system is depleted.

OPERATION

RELEASED POSITION (NO BRAKING)

With pedal released, spool valve return spring holds spool valve open. The spool valve allows fluid flow between power steering pump and power steering gear.

Fluid pressure is blocked from entering boost pressure chamber by lands on spool valve. Boost pressure chamber is vented through spool valve, to pump return port, and back to power steering pump.

BRAKING POSITION

As brake pedal is depressed, it moves pedal rod and spool valve. This closes fluid return to pump, and admits fluid into boost chamber from pressure port. Additional valve movement restricts flow between pump and steering gear.

As fluid pressure increases in boost chamber, it forces piston forward, actuating master cylinder piston and applying brakes. If fluid pressure is required for steering while braking, pump pressure will rise and spool valve will shift in an open direction allowing more fluid to flow to steering gear.

RESERVE SYSTEM

System consists of a charging valve, accumulator valve, and a spring-loaded accumulator. Accumulator is integral with booster unit. System is open to pressure port of booster unit.

Charging valve has an orifice and ball check. Fluid from pump passes through orifice in valve, unseats ball check valve and enters accumulator. Ball check valve prevents reverse flow.

Accumulator valve is a poppet-type valve held closed by accumulator pressure. If no pump pressure is available, an actuator on spool valve sleeve opens accumulator valve. Fluid pressure can also enter accumulator from boost chamber through accumulator valve, when boost chamber pressure exceeds accumulator pressure.

A pressure relief valve vents accumulator to pump return port when pressure in accumulator exceeds approximately 1600 psi (112 kg/cm^2).

TESTING

NOTE: **Hydro-Boost cannot cause noisy brakes, fading brake pedal, or pulling brakes. If one of these conditions exists, other components of brake system are at fault.**

PRELIMINARY CHECKS

1) Check engine idle speed. Check all power steering and brake lines for leaks or restrictions. Check and fill master cylinder with brake fluid. Check and fill power steering pump reservoir with power steering fluid.

2) Check for areated fluid (air mixed with fluid) in power steering pump. Check steering pump drive belt tension and condition. Check steering pump pressure.

BOOSTER FUNCTIONAL TEST

With engine off, apply brake several times to deplete accumulator reserve. Depress and hold brake pedal with 40 lbs. (18 kg) pressure. Start engine. Brake pedal should fall slightly, then push back against foot. If no action is felt, booster is not operating properly.

ACCUMULATOR LEAK-DOWN TEST

Start engine, and charge accumulator by either applying brake with heavy pedal force or turning steering wheel lock-to-lock. Turn off engine and wait 1 hour. After 1 hour, there should be 2 power-assisted brake applications with engine off.

CHECKING RESERVE SYSTEM

1) Perform accumulator leak-down test. If reserve system will not retain a charge for 1 hour, but functions normally immediately following charging, disassemble booster and replace accumulator valves.

2) If accumulator can be heard charging and discharging, but it does not hold a charge, disassemble booster and replace accumulator valves.

3) Deplete accumulator by pressing brake pedal 4 or 5 times. If accumulator can has lost its gas charge, or if it is possible to rotate or wobble accumulator can with respect to housing, replace accumulator assembly.

NOTE: **If problem cannot be found in preliminary checks or tests, check areas of brake system that might cause condition. See Hydro-Boost Trouble Shooting at the beginning of this section.**

Fig. 1: Hydro-Boost Fluid Flow Chart

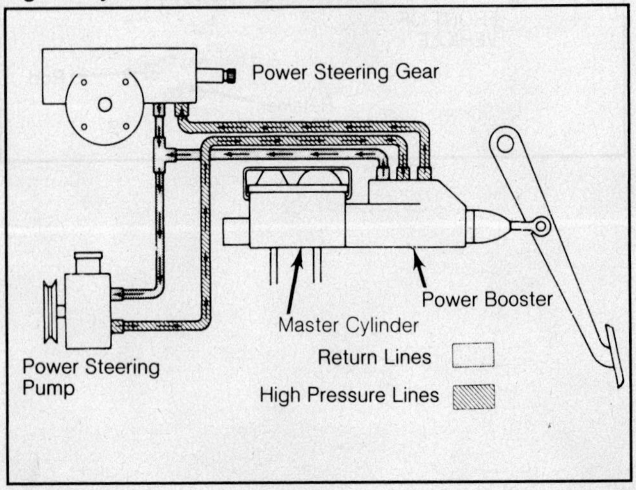

BENDIX HYDRO-BOOST (Cont.)

REMOVAL & INSTALLATION

HYDRO-BOOST UNIT

Removal

1) Depress and release brake pedal several times to exhaust pressure from accumulator. Clean dirt from hydraulic line connections at booster and at master cylinder.

2) Remove nuts that secure master cylinder and support bracket to booster. Support master cylinder, and cover exposed end with clean cloth. Disconnect hydraulic lines from booster, and plug all openings.

NOTE: **In most cases, it is not necessary to disconnect master cylinder brake lines to remove booster.**

3) Remove booster pedal push rod cotter pin and washer. Disconnect push rod from brake pedal (Blazer and Pickups) or booster bracket pivot lever (Vans).

4) On Blazer and Pickups, remove lower dash trim, then lower steering column. On forward control chassis, remove support brackets.

5) On all models, remove booster bracket-to-firewall or support bracket nuts. Remove booster assembly.

Installation

To install, reverse removal procedure. Lubricate pedal rod and linkage pivot bolts, pins, sleeves and bushings with Lubriplate. Bleed system. Check brake pedal and stop light switch adjustment.

OVERHAUL

HYDRO-BOOST UNIT

CAUTION: **To avoid personal injury, do not apply heat to, or attempt to repair accumulator. Before discarding inoperative accumulator, drill a 1/16" hole through end of accumulator can opposite the "O" ring.**

Disassembly

1) Secure unit in vise. Do not clamp accumulator. Remove pedal rod boot, if used. Remove mounting bracket by removing retaining ring and nut. Saw off pedal rod eyelet to enable removal of piston rod, lever and piston assembly from booster cover.

Fig. 3: Removing Booster Pedal Rod

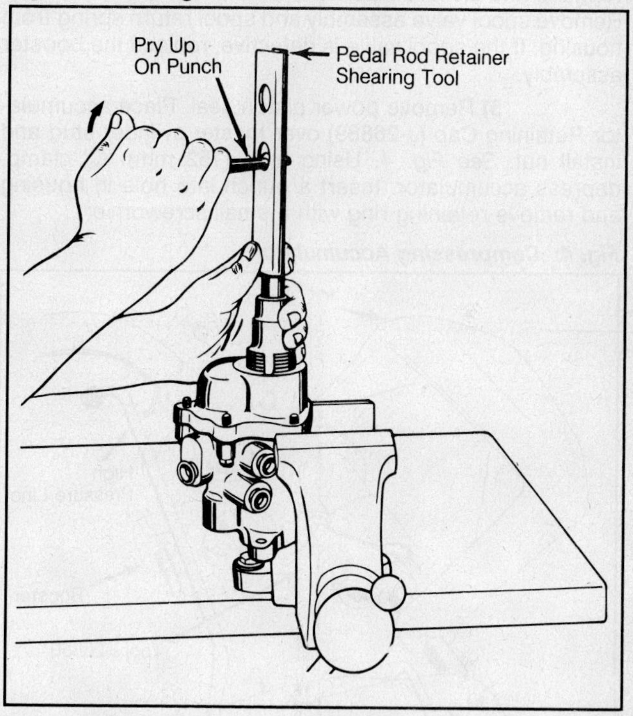

Fig. 2: Exploded View of Bendix Hydro-Boost Assembly Components

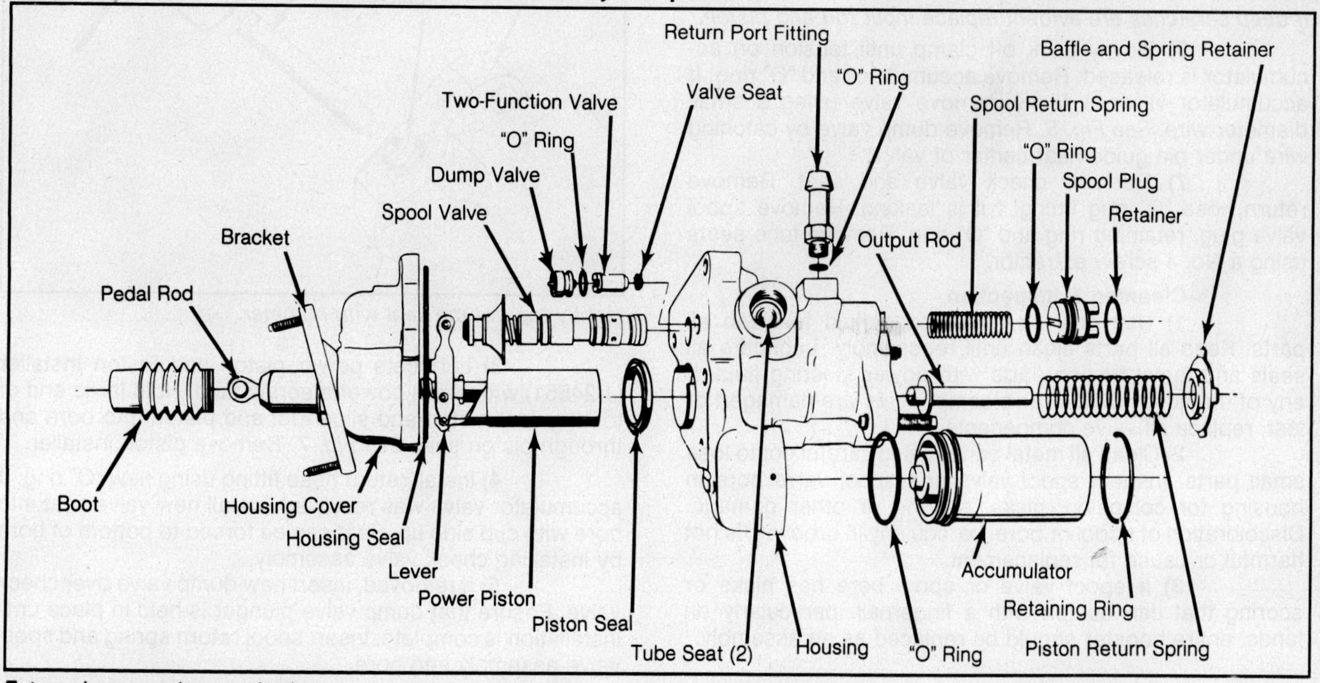

External accumulator unit shown.

Power Brake Units

BENDIX HYDRO-BOOST (Cont.)

2) Using a small screwdriver, pry plastic baffle out of spring retainer. Disengage tabs of spring retainer from ledge inside opening near master cylinder mounting flange of booster. Remove retainer, piston return spring, and output rod from opening.

3) Place booster cover in a soft-jawed vise and remove 5 screws retaining booster housing to cover. Remove booster assembly from vise. Hold booster over a pan and separate cover from housing.

4) Remove housing seal from cover and discard. Remove and discard input rod, lever and piston assembly. Remove spool valve assembly and spool return spring from housing. If the spool valve is defective, replace the booster assembly.

5) Remove power piston seal. Place accumulator Retaining Cap (J-26889) over master cylinder stud and install nut. *See Fig. 4*. Using a 6" (152 mm) "C" clamp, depress accumulator. Insert a punch into hole in housing and remove retaining ring with a small screwdriver.

Fig. 4: Compressing Accumulator

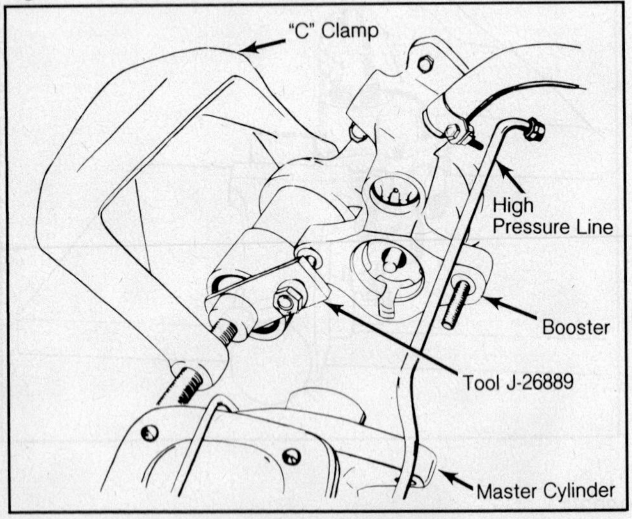

If deep scratches are evident replace input rod and piston.

6) Slowly back off clamp until tension on accumulator is released. Remove accumulator and "O" ring. If accumulator valve is faulty, remove valve using a small diameter wire. *See Fig. 5*. Remove dump valve by catching wire under pin guide near center of valve.

7) Remove check valve and seat. Remove return hose "O" ring fitting if it is leaking. Remove spool valve plug, retaining ring and "O" ring. Remove tube seats using a No. 4 screw extractor.

Cleaning & Inspection

1) Use only power steering fluid to clean all parts. Keep all parts clean until reassembly. Lubricate all seals and metal friction parts with power steering fluid. If any of the accumulator valve components are damaged or lost, replace all valve components.

2) Clean all metal parts, being careful not to lose small parts. Inspect spool valve and spool valve bore in housing for corrosion, nicks, scoring or other damage. Discoloration of spool or bore, particularly in grooves, is not harmful or cause for replacement.

3) If spool valve or spool bore has nicks or scoring that can be felt with a fingernail, particularly on lands, entire booster should be replaced as an assembly.

Fig. 5: Removing Accumulator Valves

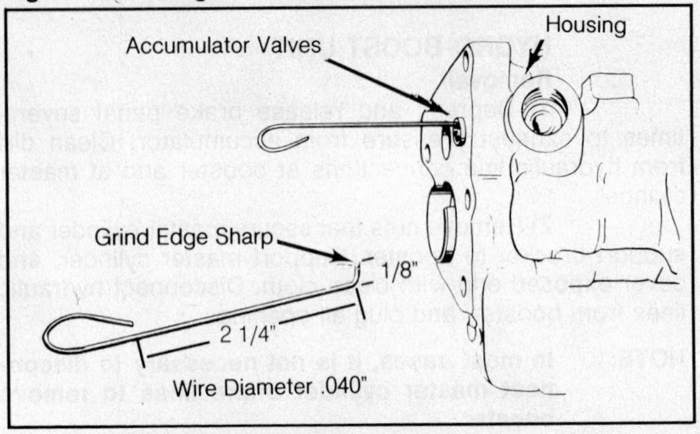

Use a short length of wire to fabricate removal tool.

Reassembly

1) Install tube seats using Tube Seat Installer (J-6217). *See Fig. 6*. Install "O" ring on spool plug. Push plug into housing and install retaining ring.

2) Coat power piston seal and bore with clean power steering fluid and place seal in bore. Lip of seal must face away from master cylinder mounting flange. Ensure that seal is fully seated in housing.

NOTE: **The piston counterbore on 4-wheel disc applications is of a different diameter than that of standard models. Remove pilot portion of power piston installer before installing power piston.**

Fig. 6: Installing Tube Seats

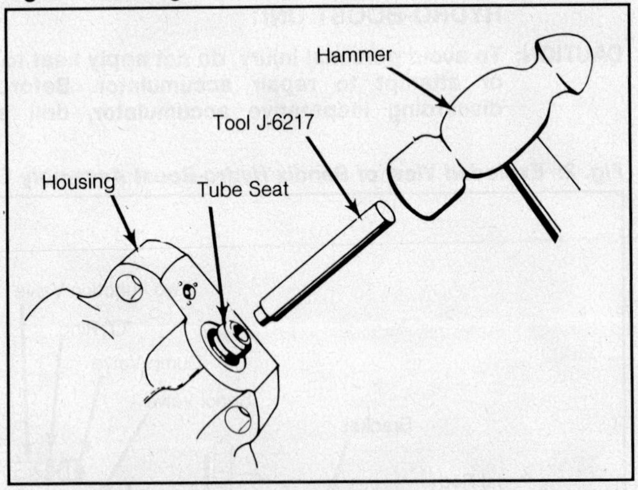

Lightly tap in tube seat with hammer.

3) Lubricate power piston and Piston Installer (J-24551) with clean power steering fluid. Hold large end of tool against piston and slide tool and piston into bore and through piston seal. *See Fig. 7*. Remove piston installer.

4) Install return hose fitting using new "O" ring. If accumulator valve was removed, install new valve seat into bore with cup side up. Seat can be forced to bottom of bore by installing check valve assembly.

5) If removed, insert new dump valve over check valve. Ensure that dump valve plunger is held in place until installation is complete. Insert spool return spring and spool valve assembly into bore.

BENDIX HYDRO-BOOST (Cont.)

Fig. 7: Installing Input Rod & Power Piston Assembly

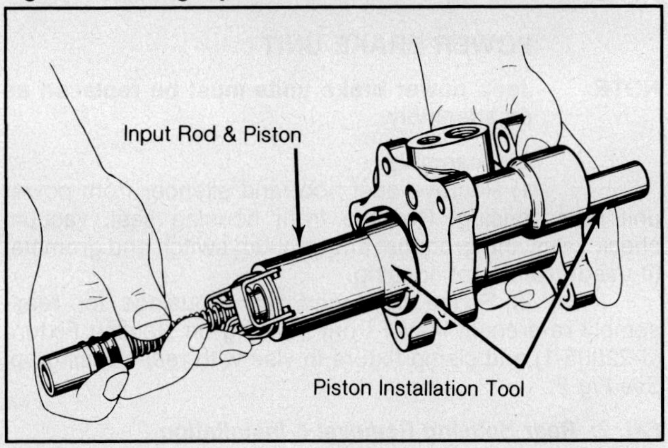

6) Extend power piston lever to accept sleeve on spool valve. Slide lever pins into slot in sleeve. Install new seal in groove in housing cover. Lubricate input rod seal(s) with clean power steering fluid.

7) Install input rod in cover, being careful not to damage cover bore. Join cover and housing. Install and tighten cover screws. Install output rod, spring, baffle and new spring retainer. Secure new baffle and spring retainer using a 7/8" socket.

8) Using clean power steering fluid, lubricate accumulator seal. Install seal and accumulator in housing, then place retaining ring over accumulator. Place accumulator Retaining Cap (J-26889) over master cylinder stud and install nut. *See Fig. 4*.

9) Using a 6" (152 mm) "C" clamp, depress accumulator making sure that it is straight. Snap retaining ring into housing groove. Remove retaining cap and "C" clamp. Ensure that retaining ring is properly installed.

10) Position mounting bracket on booster. Tab on inside diameter of large hole in bracket should fit into slot in threaded portion of booster hub. Install bracket nut with serrations toward bracket. Tighten nut. Install retaining ring.

11) If repair kit contains a staked 2-piece pedal rod, go to step **13)**. If kit contains a grommet retained pedal rod, install boot (if used) on pedal rod, then install new grommet in groove near end of pedal rod.

12) Moisten grommet with water and insert grommet end of pedal rod into input rod end of booster housing. Push on end of pedal rod to seat grommet in groove inside housing. When grommet is fully seated, pedal will rotate freely and without binding. Install boot, with open end of boot on hub of booster.

13) Install boot (if used) on externally threaded pedal rod. Slide open end of boot onto hub of booster. Install lock nut on pedal rod. Install eyelet pedal rod (internally threaded) onto pedal rod. Adjust pedal rod to 31" (790 mm). Tighten lock nut.

BLEEDING

HYDRO-BOOST SYSTEM

1) Fill reservoir with steering fluid and leave undisturbed for at least 2 minutes. Start engine and run momentarily. Add fluid if necessary. Repeat until fluid level remains constant with engine running.

2) Stop engine. Raise vehicle so that front wheels are off the ground. Turn steering wheel right and left, lightly contacting stops. Add fluid if necessary. Lower vehicle.

3) Start engine and depress brake pedal several times while turning steering wheel from stop-to-stop. Turn engine off and depress brake pedal several times to exhaust accumulator pressure. Add fluid if necessary.

4) If fluid is foamy, let vehicle stand for several minutes, then repeat procedure. The presence of air in the system will cause fluid level to rise with engine off. Continue to bleed system until all air is expelled.

TIGHTENING SPECIFICATIONS

Application	Ft. Lbs. (N.m)
Booster Housing Cover	20 (27)
Mounting Bracket Nut	110 (150)

Power Brake Units

DELCO-MORAINE SINGLE DIAPHRAGM

Chevrolet, GMC, Jeep

DESCRIPTION

Power brake unit uses a combination of intake manifold vacuum and atmospheric pressure to provide power assist. Reserve vacuum supply and vacuum check valve allow several brake applications, with vacuum assist, after engine has stopped.

Unit is composed of 2 main sections. The vacuum power cylinder and the dual master cylinder. Vacuum power cylinder contains power piston assembly, which houses control valve, reaction mechanism, and power piston return spring.

Fig. 1: Exploded View of Typical Delco-Moraine Single Diaphragm Power Brake Unit

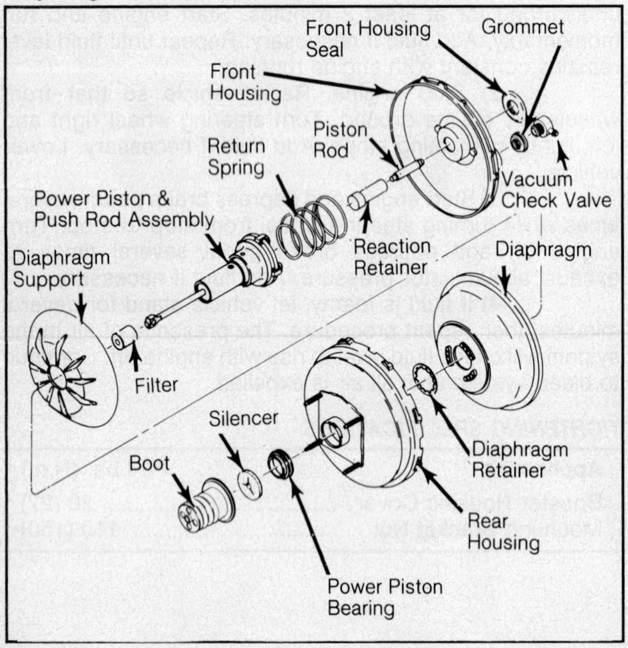

REMOVAL & INSTALLATION

POWER BRAKE UNIT

Removal

1) Disconnect push rod from brake pedal. Disconnect vacuum hose from vacuum check valve. Remove nuts retaining master cylinder to power unit and move master cylinder aside. Do not disconnect brake lines.

2) Remove nuts retaining power unit to dash panel. Disconnect booster push rod from brake pedal. On Jeep Grand Wagoneer and Trucks, discard pedal attaching bolt and nut. Remove power unit from vehicle.

Installation

To install, reverse removal procedure. On Jeep Grand Wagoneer and Trucks, install a new brake pedal-to-booster push rod bolt and nut. Tighten brake pedal attaching bolt and nut to 35 ft. lbs. (47 N.m).

OVERHAUL

POWER BRAKE UNIT

NOTE: **Jeep power brake units must be replaced as an assembly.**

Disassembly

1) Remove dust boot and silencer from power unit rear housing. Remove front housing seal, vacuum check valve and grommet and vacuum switch and grommet (if used) from front housing.

2) Scribe front and rear housings for reassembly reference. Install front housing on Holding Fixture (J-22805-1) and clamp fixture in vise with rear housing up. *See Fig 2.*

Fig. 2: Rear Housing Removal & Installation

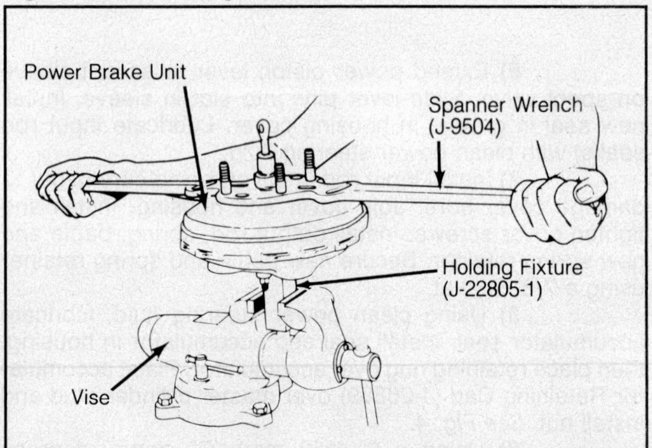

3) Place Spanner Wrench (J-9504) on studs of rear housing. Press down and turn wrench counterclockwise to unlock housing. *See Fig 2.* Remove power piston bearing, return spring and power piston group. Remove piston rod and reaction retainer.

4) Remove filter using an awl. Grasp assembly at outside edge of diaphragm support and diaphragm. Hold push rod down against a hard surface. Use a slight force or impact to dislodge diaphragm retainer. Do not disassemble power push rod assembly.

Cleaning & Inspection

1) Clean all metal, plastic, and rubber parts in denatured alcohol. Blow out all passages, orifices, and valve holes with clean, dry air. Air dry all parts.

2) Slight rust on inside of housings can be polished with crocus or emery cloth. There should not be any nicks or cuts on rubber parts. Replace any damaged part.

Reassembly

1) Lubricate inside diameter of diaphragm lip with silicone lubricant and fit in diaphragm support. Install support and diaphragm over power piston and push rod assembly.

2) Install new diaphragm retainer and seat using Retainer Installer (J-28458) and soft mallet. Install filter, reaction retainer, and piston rod. Install front housing in holding fixture and place in vise. Install return spring with White end toward front housing.

DELCO-MORAINE SINGLE DIAPHRAGM (Cont.)

Fig. 3: Diaphragm Retainer Installation

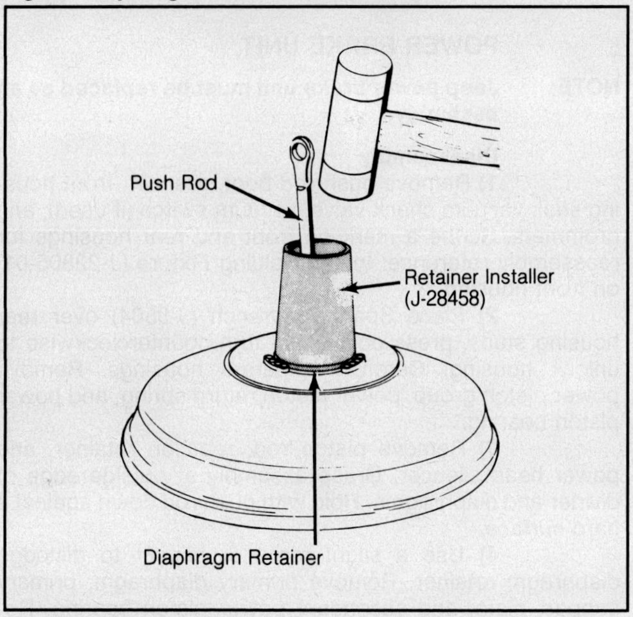

3) Insert power piston assembly through rear housing and place on top of front housing and return spring. Install rear housing, aligning scribe marks on front and rear housings. Install wrench, press down and turn clockwise to lock housings.

NOTE: Assembly can be aided by connecting a vacuum source to booster.

4) Using a screwdriver, stake 2 tabs 180° apart on housing. Lubricate inside and outside diameters of grommets and front housing seal. Install silencer, boot, seal, grommets, vacuum check valve and vacuum switch (if used).

ADJUSTMENT

PISTON ROD

NOTE: Chevrolet and GMC production piston rod is not adjustable. If production rod is reused, gauging is used to check proper assembly. If adjustable service rod is used to replace production rod, gauging is used to set to correct rod height.

Chevrolet & GMC

1) Place "Go/No-Go" Gauge (J-22647) over piston rod in a position which will allow gauge to be moved without touching studs. Center section of gauge has 2 levels. *See Fig. 4.*

2) Piston rod should always contact longer section (lower level), and never contact shorter section (higher lever). Any variation beyond these 2 limits would require replacement of production rod or adjustment of service rod.

Jeep

Push rod of replacement units is preset at factory and requires no field adjustment.

Fig. 4: Checking Piston Rod Height

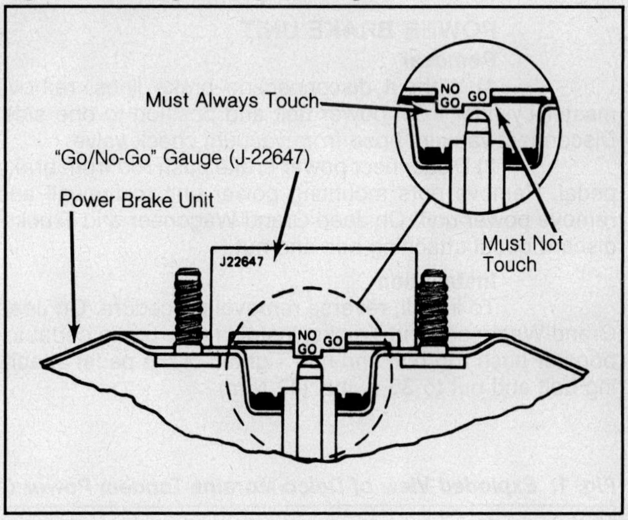

Nonadjustable production rod is shown

Power Brake Units

DELCO-MORAINE TANDEM DIAPHRAGM

Chevrolet, GMC, Jeep

DESCRIPTION

Power brake unit is mounted on firewall and connected directly to brake pedal. A combination of vacuum and atmospheric pressure is used to provide power assist.

Power cylinder houses power piston assembly, which contains primary and secondary diaphragms, pistons, floating control valve, reaction piston, and disc.

REMOVAL & INSTALLATION

POWER BRAKE UNIT

Removal

1) Without disconnecting brake lines, remove master cylinder from power unit and position to one side. Disconnect vacuum hose from vacuum check valve.

2) Disconnect power brake push rod from brake pedal. Remove nuts mounting power unit to firewall and remove power unit. On Jeep Grand Wagoneer and Trucks, discard pedal attaching bolt and nut.

Installation

To install, reverse removal procedure. On Jeep Grand Wagoneer and Trucks, install a new brake pedal-to-booster push rod bolt and nut. Tighten brake pedal attaching bolt and nut to 35 ft. lbs. (47 N.m).

OVERHAUL

POWER BRAKE UNIT

NOTE: **Jeep power brake unit must be replaced as an assembly.**

Disassembly

1) Remove push rod boot, silencer, front housing seal, vacuum check valve, vacuum switch (if used), and grommets. Scribe a mark on front and rear housings for reassembly reference. Install Holding Fixture (J-22805-01) on front housing.

2) Place Spanner Wrench (J-9504) over rear housing studs, press down, and turn counterclockwise to unlock housing. Carefully separate housings. Remove power piston group, power piston return spring, and power piston bearing.

3) Remove piston rod, reaction retainer, and power head silencer. Grasp assembly at outside edge of divider and diaphragms. Hold with push rod down against a hard surface.

4) Use a slight force or impact to dislodge diaphragm retainer. Remove primary diaphragm, primary support plate, and secondary power piston bearing. Remove housing divider, secondary support plate, diaphragm and power piston assembly.

5) To disassemble power piston assembly, pry tangs and remove reaction body retainer. Using No. 2 Truarc pliers, remove retaining ring from air valve push rod assembly. Remove air valve push rod assembly by inserting a screwdriver through eyelet and pulling rod out.

Fig. 1: Exploded View of Delco-Moraine Tandem Power Cylinder

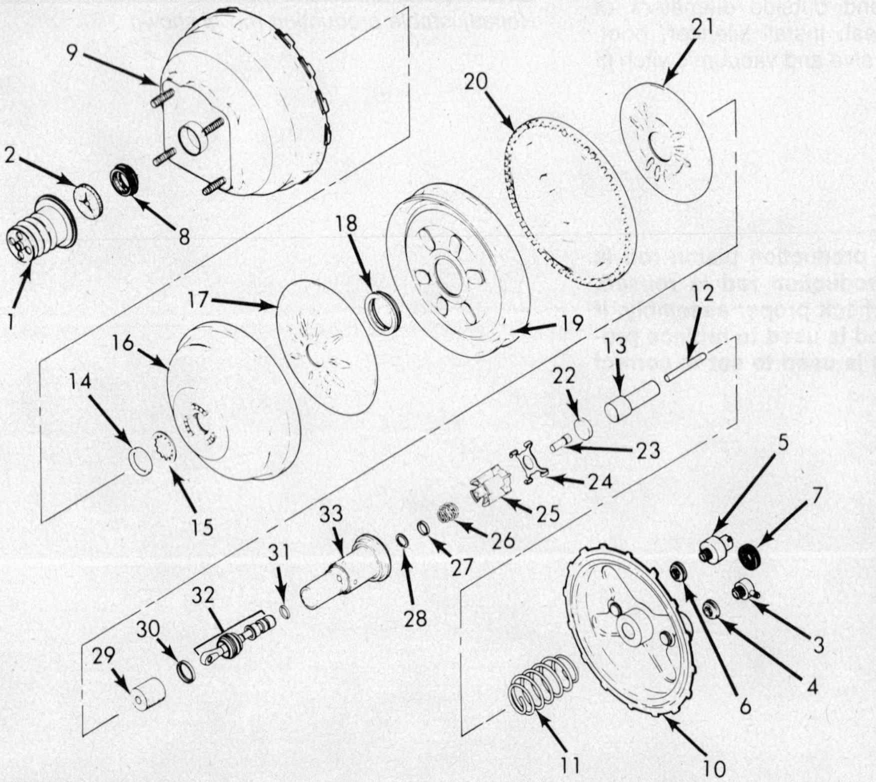

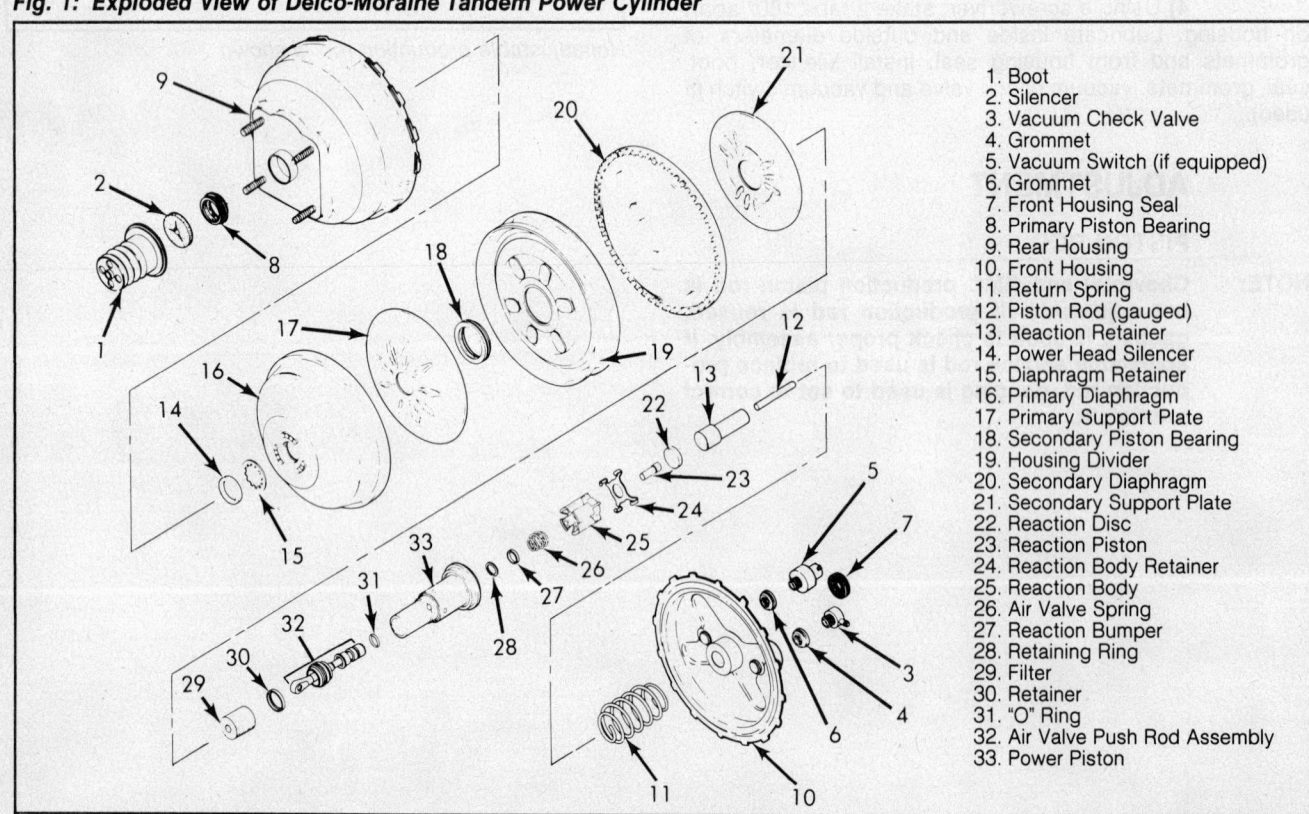

1. Boot
2. Silencer
3. Vacuum Check Valve
4. Grommet
5. Vacuum Switch (if equipped)
6. Grommet
7. Front Housing Seal
8. Primary Piston Bearing
9. Rear Housing
10. Front Housing
11. Return Spring
12. Piston Rod (gauged)
13. Reaction Retainer
14. Power Head Silencer
15. Diaphragm Retainer
16. Primary Diaphragm
17. Primary Support Plate
18. Secondary Piston Bearing
19. Housing Divider
20. Secondary Diaphragm
21. Secondary Support Plate
22. Reaction Disc
23. Reaction Piston
24. Reaction Body Retainer
25. Reaction Body
26. Air Valve Spring
27. Reaction Bumper
28. Retaining Ring
29. Filter
30. Retainer
31. "O" Ring
32. Air Valve Push Rod Assembly
33. Power Piston

DELCO-MORAINE TANDEM DIAPHRAGM (Cont.)

Cleaning & Inspection

1) Clean all plastic, metal and rubber parts in denatured alcohol. Blow out all passages, orifices and valve holes. Air dry all parts.

2) Slight rust on housing may be cleaned with crocus or emery cloth. Do not reinstall any rubber parts with cuts, nicks or distortion. If in doubt, replace parts.

Fig. 2: Air Valve Push Rod Retainer Installation

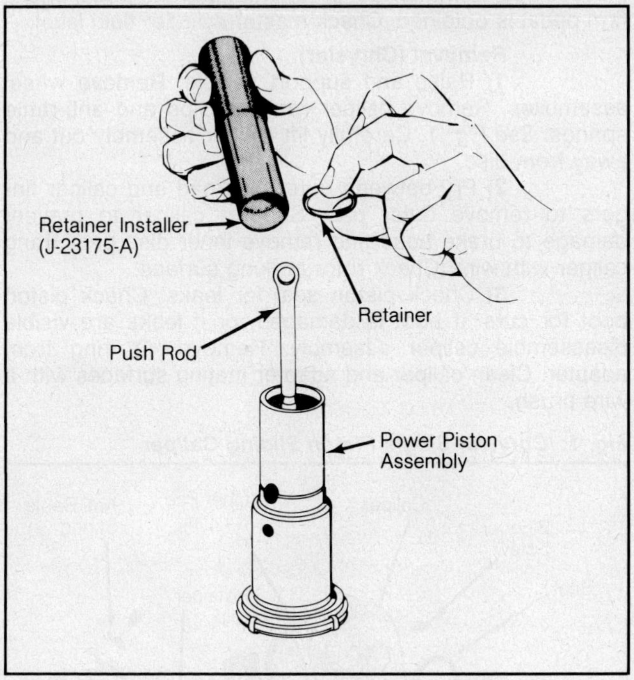

Reassembly

1) Place power piston on bench with large diameter down. Install air valve rod push assembly. Install retainer using Retainer Installer (J-23175-A). *See Fig. 2.*

2) Install Assembly Cone (J-28458) over push rod end of piston. Lubricate inside diameter of secondary diaphragm with silicone lubricant and fit in secondary support plate.

3) Install secondary diaphragm and support plate over power piston and push down until it bottoms. *See Fig. 3.* Lubricate inside diameter of secondary power piston bearing and install in housing divider with flat surface of bearing on same side as 6 raised lugs on divider.

4) Hold divider so that formed-over flange faces up. Press divider down over assembly cone and onto power piston to rest against secondary diaphragm. Lubricate inside diameter of primary diaphragm and install in primary support plate.

5) Remove assembly cone from power piston. Place primary support plate and diaphragm assembly over power piston and push down until it bottoms. Place diaphragm retainer over power piston and onto diaphragm.

6) Install assembly cone over power piston onto diaphragm retainer and strike with hammer until retainer is locked on neck of power piston. Remove assembly cone.

7) Install reaction retainer, piston rod, and power head silencer. Place primary power piston bearing in rear housing center hole. Lubricate with silicone lubricant on inner diameter.

8) Install holding fixture to front housing and place fixture in vise. Install power piston assembly to rear housing. Install power piston return spring over reaction retainer and lower rear housing onto front housing.

Fig. 3: Installing Secondary Diaphragm and Support Plate

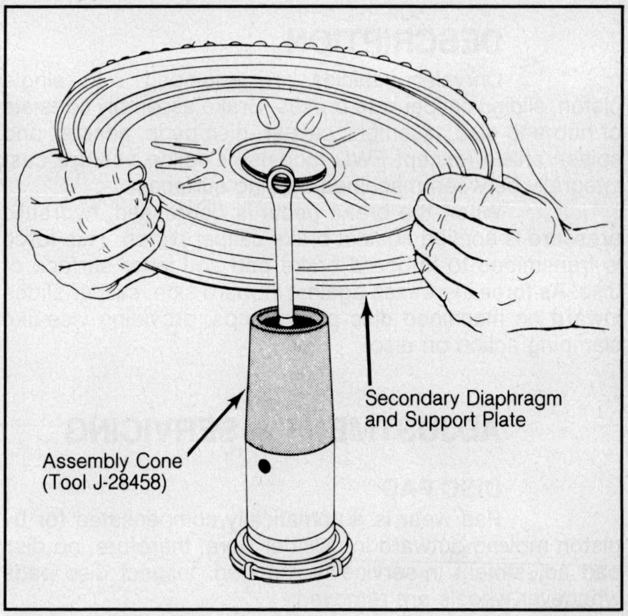

9) Align scribe marks and press down on spanner wrench, turning clockwise to lock housings. Stake 2 housing tabs into sockets 180° apart.

10) Lubricate inside and outside diameters of grommets and front housing seal. Install seal, grommets, vacuum check valve, vacuum switch (if used), silencer, and push rod boot.

PISTON ROD

NOTE: **This adjustment applies to Chevrolet and GMC only. Jeep push rod is not adjustable.**

1) Place "Go/No-Go" Gauge (J-22647) over piston rod so it can be moved without contacting studs. Piston rod should contact longer section of gauge.

3) Production rod is nonadjustable, and if out of limits, must be replaced with service rod. With service rod, adjust self-locking screw to meet gauging specifications.

Fig. 4: Adjusting Piston Rod

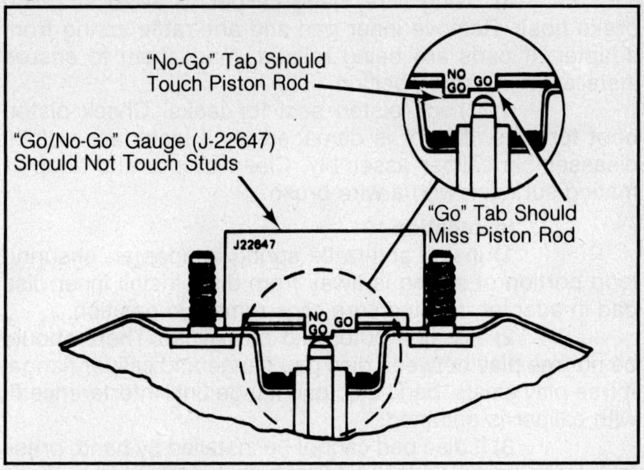

Chevrolet and GMC models only.

Brake Systems

CHRYSLER CORP. SLIDING CALIPER DISCS

All Models

DESCRIPTION

Chrysler vehicles are equipped with single piston, sliding caliper disc brakes. Brake assembly consists of hub and disc assembly, caliper, disc pads, adapter and splash shield (except FWD models). Cooling fins are cast integrally between machined braking surfaces.

When the brake pedal is depressed, hydraulic pressure is applied against brake caliper piston. This force is transmitted to in-board brake pad and inner surface of disc. As force increases against inboard side, caliper slides inward on machined disc plate ramps, providing vise-like clamping action on disc.

ADJUSTMENT & SERVICING

DISC PAD

Pad wear is automatically compensated for by piston moving outward in cylinder bore; therefore, no disc pad adjustment in-service is required. Inspect disc pads whenever wheels are removed.

Measure shoe and0 lining assembly at its thinnest part. When an assembly is worn to approximately 5/16" (8 mm), replace both inner and outer pads on both front wheels.

BLEEDING SYSTEM

See HYDRAULIC BRAKE BLEEDING in this section.

REMOVAL & INSTALLATION

DISC BRAKE PADS

Removal (Bendix)

1) Siphon fluid from master cylinder until cylinder is 1/3 full. Raise and support vehicle. Remove wheel assembly. Using a "C" clamp, bottom caliper piston in cylinder bore.

2) Remove clamp. Remove key retaining screw. Using brass punch, drive out caliper support key and spring. Remove caliper from adapter and pry outer disc pad from caliper.

3) Using wire, hang caliper to avoid straining brake hose. Remove inner pad and anti-rattle spring from adapter. If pads are being reused, mark them to ensure installation in same position.

4) Check piston seal for leaks. Check piston boot for cuts. If boot is damaged, or if leaks are visible, disassemble caliper assembly. Clean caliper and adapter mating surfaces with a wire brush.

Installation

1) Install anti-rattle spring in adapter, ensuring loop portion of spring is away from disc. Install inner disc pad in adapter, making sure clips remain in position.

2) Position outer pad on caliper. There should be no free play between disc pad flange and caliper flange. If free play exists, bend disc pad flange until interference fit with caliper is obtained.

3) If disc pad cannot be installed by hand, press into place using a block of wood and a "C" clamp. Place caliper into position over disc. Position brake caliper on adapter, making sure hose is not twisted.

4) Place spring over support key. Install assembly between adapter and lower caliper machined surfaces. Tap assembly into place using brass punch and hammer.

5) Install retaining screw, making sure boss on screw fits fully into cut-out on key. Install wheel assembly. Fill reservoir to within 1/4" of top. Pump brake pedal until a firm pedal is obtained. Check master cylinder fluid level.

Removal (Chrysler)

1) Raise and support vehicle. Remove wheel assemblies. Remove caliper retainer clips and anti-rattle springs. *See Fig. 1*. Carefully lift caliper assembly out and away from disc.

2) Pry between outer disc pad and caliper fingers to remove outer pad. Support caliper to prevent damage to brake hose and remove inner disc pad. Hang caliper with wire. Check rotor braking surface.

3) Check piston seal for leaks. Check piston boot for cuts. If boot is damaged, or if leaks are visible disassemble caliper assembly. Remove "O" ring from adapter. Clean caliper and adapter mating surfaces with a wire brush.

Fig. 1: Chrysler Single Piston Sliding Caliper

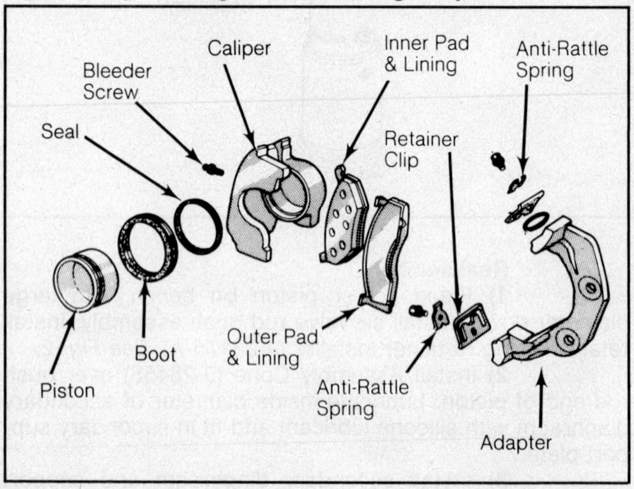

Installation

1) Install "O" ring on adapter. Slowly push piston back into caliper until bottomed. Care must be taken to ensure reservoir does not overflow while pushing in on piston. Slide outer disc pad into caliper.

2) There should be no free play between disc pad flange and caliper flange. If free play exists, bend disc pad flange until interference fit with caliper is obtained.

3) If necessary, install disc pad using a "C" clamp and wood block placed across disc pad. Place inner pad on adapter with disc pad flanges aligned with flange ways in adapter.

4) Slide caliper into position in adapter and over disc. Align caliper on adapter, taking care not to pull dust boot away from groove in piston. Install anti-rattle springs and retaining clips.

5) Ensure that anti-rattle spring is installed on top of retainer spring plate. Tighten retaining screws to 180 INCH lbs. (20 N.m). Pump brake pedal several times to obtain firm pedal.

CHRYSLER CORP. SLIDING CALIPER DISCS (Cont.)

6) If firm pedal cannot be obtained, bleed brake system. Check master cylinder fluid level. Install wheel assemblies. Tighten stud nuts, skipping every other nut, until all 5 are tightened to specification.

Removal (Kelsey-Hayes)

1) Raise and support vehicle. Remove front wheels. Remove caliper guide pin. Pry caliper away from adapter and pads to break gasket adhesive hold. Remove caliper. Hang caliper with wire, do not allow to hang by brake hose.

2) Remove outer pad. Remove rotor from hub and remove inner pad. Check rotor braking surface. Check piston seal for leaks. Check piston boot for cuts. If boot is damaged, or if leaks are visible, disassemble the caliper assembly.

Installation

1) Clean caliper and adapter mating surfaces with a wire brush. Lubricate mating surfaces with multi-purpose grease. Remove protective paper from noise suppression gasket on inner and outer pads.

2) Install anti-rattle clips on top of inner pad, on bottom of outer pad, and on top finger of caliper. Install inner pad, rotor, and outer pad. Install caliper assembly. Install guide pin and tighten.

3) Install wheel assemblies. Tighten stud nuts, skipping every other nut, until all 4 are tightened to half specification. Then repeat to full specification. Pump brake pedal to obtain firm pedal. Check master cylinder fluid level.

BRAKE CALIPER

Brake caliper removal and installation procedures are same as for disc brake pads, except it will be necessary to disconnect and plug hydraulic brake hose at caliper.

DISC ROTOR

Removal (FWD Models)

See Kelsey-Hayes disc brake pad removal in this article to remove and install disc brake rotor.

Removal (AW150, W150 & W250 With Model 44 Front Axle)

1) Raise and support vehicle. Remove brake caliper from adapter. Hang caliper out of way. Remove inner pad. Remove grease cap and driving hub snap ring. Remove driving hub and retaining spring.

2) Using Socket (C-4170), remove outer wheel bearing lock nut. Remove retaining washer and inner lock nut. Remove rotor. Outer wheel bearing and retainer spring plate will slide out as rotor is removed.

Installation

1) Mount rotor on spindle and install outer wheel bearing. Install inner wheel bearing lock nut using socket, tighten nut to 50 ft. lbs. (68 N.m) to seat bearings.

2) Loosen inner lock nut and, while rotating disc, retighten nut to 30-40 ft. lbs. (41-54 N.m). Back off inner lock nut 135°-150°. Install retaining washer making certain pin on lock nut enters nearest hole in locking washer.

3) Install outer lock nut and tighten to 50 ft. lbs. (68 N.m). Disc end play should be within .001"-.010" (.03-.25 mm). Install retaining spring plate, retaining spring (large end first), driving hub and snap ring.

4) Apply RTV to sealing edge of grease cap and install. Reverse removal procedure to complete installation.

Removal (W250 & W350 With Model 60 Front Axle)

1) Prop brake pedal in up position. Raise and support vehicle. Remove wheel assembly. Remove brake caliper. Remove grease cap and snap ring. Remove drive flange nuts and lock washers. Remove flange and discard gasket.

2) On models with locking hubs, turn locking hub shift knob to "ENGAGE" position. Apply pressure to face of shift knob. Remove 3 screws spaced 120° apart and nearest to flange. *See Fig. 2.*

3) Pull shift knob from mounting base. Remove snap ring from axle shaft. Remove cap screws and lock washers from mounting base flange. Separate and remove locking hub assembly from hub rotor. Remove and discard gasket.

Fig. 2: Locking Hub Assembly

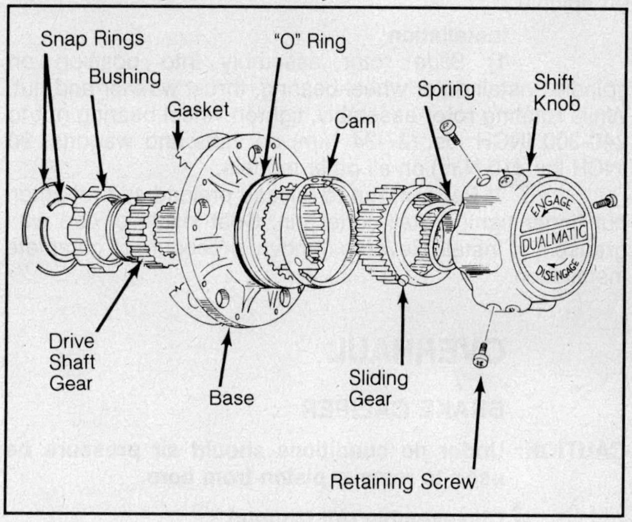

4) On all models, straighten lock tab on outer wheel bearing lock ring. Using Socket (DD-1241-JD), remove outer lock nut, lock ring, inner lock nut and outer wheel bearing.

5) Remove rotor assembly. Remove oil seal and inner bearing from hub. If bearing outer races are to be replaced, use a brass drift to remove races from hub. Remove grease and thoroughly clean hub.

6) Clean bearings, using cleaning solvent. Dry bearings with compressed air, but do not spin bearings. Lubricate bearings with engine oil and inspect. If bearings are suitable for further use, pack bearings with multi-purpose grease.

Installation

1) Install bearing outer races, if removed. Install inner bearing in greased hub and install oil seal. Install rotor assembly on spindle and install outer bearing. Install inner lock nut, using socket. Tighten nut to 50 ft. lbs. (68 N.m) to seat bearings.

2) Loosen lock nut and, while rotating disc, retighten nut to 30-40 ft. lbs. (41-54 N.m). Back off inner lock nut 135°-150°. Install lock ring and outer lock nut. Tighten lock nut to 65 ft. lbs. (88 N.m). Disc end play should be .001"-.010" (.03-.25 mm).

3) Bend one tang of lock ring over inner lock nut and one tang over outer lock nut. Install new gasket on hub.

CHRYSLER CORP. SLIDING CALIPER DISCS (Cont.)

Install drive flange, lock washers and nuts. Tighten nuts to 30-40 ft. lbs. (41-54 N.m). Install snap ring.

4) On models with locking hubs, lubricate parts with multi-purpose grease. Position new gasket and locking hub onto rotor hub. Install cap screws and lock washers. Tighten screws to 30-40 ft. lbs.(41-54 N.m). Install axle shaft snap ring.

5) Position shift knob on mounting base. Align splines by pushing in on shift knob and turning it clockwise to lock it in position. Install and tighten shift knob retaining screws. On all other models, reverse removal procedure to complete installation.

Removal (All Other RWD Models)

Raise and support vehicle. Remove wheel assembly. Remove brake caliper from adapter. Hang caliper with wire. Remove grease cap, cotter pin, nut lock, nut, thrust washer, and outer wheel bearing. Pull rotor assembly off spindle.

Installation

1) Slide rotor assembly into position on spindle. Install outer wheel bearing, thrust washer and nut. While rotating rotor assembly, tighten wheel bearing nut to 240-300 INCH lbs. (27-34 N.m) on vans and wagons, 90 INCH lbs. (10 N.m) on all other models.

2) Back off nut to release preload and retighten nut finger tight. Install cotter pin. Coat inside of cap with grease and install. Reverse removal procedure to complete installation.

OVERHAUL

BRAKE CALIPER

CAUTION: Under no conditions should air pressure be used to remove piston from bore.

Disassembly (All Models)

1) Remove brake caliper from adapter. Place caliper assembly on upper control arm and on top of shop towels. Place a small piece of wood between piston and caliper.

2) Carefully depress brake pedal to hydraulically force piston out of bore. Pedal will fall away when piston has passed bore opening. Prop pedal in any position below first inch of travel to prevent fluid loss.

3) Disconnect brake hose and remove caliper from vehicle. Remove dust boot. Work seal out of groove in piston bore with a wooden or plastic rod to prevent damage to cylinder. Discard piston seal and boot. Remove bushings from Kelsey-Hayes calipers.

Inspection (All Models)

1) Clean all parts with alcohol and blow dry with compressed air. Inspect piston bore for scoring or pitting. Light scratches or corrosion can be removed with crocus cloth.

2) Deep scratches or scoring should be honed, providing bore diameter is not increased more than .001" (.025 mm). on Chrysler and Kelsey-Hayes calipers, .002" (.050 mm) on Bendix calipers. If bore does not clean up, replace housing.

Reassembly (Bendix)

1) Lubricate new piston seal with clean brake fluid. Position seal in bore and gently work seal into groove with fingers until fully seated. Seal should not be twisted or rolled.

2) Lubricate new piston boot with brake fluid. Install boot into caliper by working into outer groove using fingers only. Plug inlet and bleeder screw hole.

3) Lubricate piston and, with fingers spreading boot, press piston into boot until boot is forced into groove around piston. Remove plug. Carefully push piston down until bottomed.

Fig. 3: Bendix Single Piston Sliding Caliper

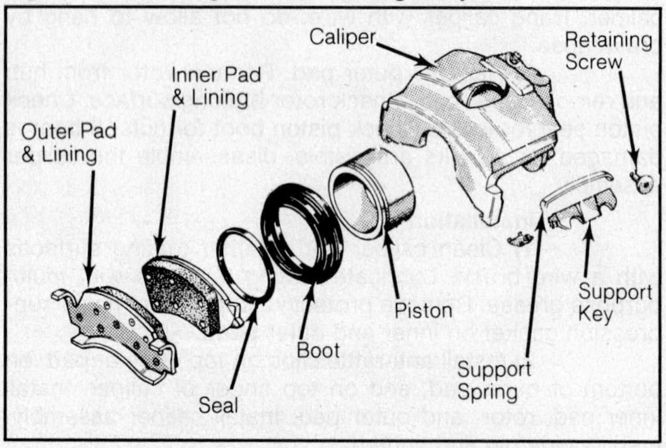

Reassembly (Chrysler)

1) Lubricate new piston seal with brake fluid. Position seal in bore and gently work seal into groove with fingers until fully seated. Seal should not be twisted or rolled.

2) Coat new piston boot with brake fluid, leaving generous amount inside boot. Position dust boot over piston. Install piston into bore, pushing past piston seal until it bottoms.

3) Position dust boot in counterbore. Using a hammer and Boot Installer (C-4690), drive boot into counterbore, being careful to avoid cocking seal.

Reassembly (Kelsey-Hayes)

1) Coat new piston seal with clean brake fluid. Position seal in bore and gently work seal into groove with fingers until fully seated. Seal should not be twisted or rolled.

2) Lubricate dust boot and piston with clean brake fluid. Position dust boot over piston. Install piston into bore. Push piston past seal until it bottoms. Position dust boot in counterbore. Using a hammer and Boot Installer (C-4842), drive boot into counterbore.

3) Compress flange of guide pin bushings with fingers and work bushings into position by pressing in on bushings until seated. Ensure flanges extend over caliper casting evenly on both sides.

DISC ROTOR

NOTE: Minimum rotor thickness after machining should not be less than .030" above minimum thickness specification cast on disc.

FWD Models

1) Remove wheel assembly. If disc is cracked, replace it. Install and tighten lug nuts. Mount dial indicator on steering arm with plunger contacting rotor approximately 1" (25 mm) from edge of disc. Slowly rotate disc and note runout.

CHRYSLER CORP. SLIDING CALIPER DISCS (Cont.)

Fig. 4: Kelsey-Hayes Single Piston Sliding Caliper

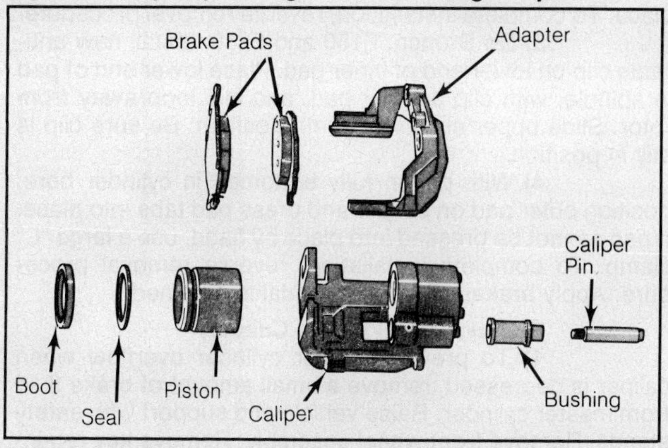

2) Runout on either side of disc should not exceed .005" (.13 mm). If runout exceeds specification, check runout of hub face. Before removing rotor, make a chalk mark across both disc and 1 wheel stud. Make mark on high side of runout.

3) Remove disc from hub. Install dial indicator on steering arm with stem contacting hub face near outer diameter. Place dial indicator stem outside stud circle but inside chamfer on hub rim. If runout exceeds .003" (.08 mm), hub must be replaced.

4) If hub runout is within specification, install rotor on hub with chalk marks 180° apart. Install wheel lug nuts and recheck rotor runout. If runout is still excessive, replace or reface rotor.

5) Measure thickness at 12 equal points with a micrometer at a radius approximately 1" (25 mm) from edge of rotor. If thickness varies by more than .0005" (.013 mm), rotor should be resurfaced or replaced.

RWD Models

1) With vehicle supported on safety stands and wheel assemblies removed, mount dial indicator on steering arm with indicator plunger against braking surface about 1" (25 mm) from edge of disc.

2) Temporarily adjust wheel bearings to zero end play. Measure runout on both sides of disc. If runout on either side exceeds .004" (.10 mm) on AD150, D150, vans and wagons, or .005" (.13 mm) on all other models, resurface or replace disc.

3) Using micrometer, measure thickness of disc at 12 equally spaced locations around disc about 1" (25 mm) from edge. If measurements vary more than .0005" (.013 mm) on AD150, D150, vans and wagons, or .001" (.025 mm) on all other models, resurface or replace disc.

4) Replace disc if it is badly scored or warped and machining does not correct defects. When refinishing, always remove equal amounts of material, to a maximum of .030" (.76 mm) total from both sides, .015" (.38 mm) from each face.

5) All disc assemblies have minimum thickness markings on unmachined surface between wheel studs. Markings include .030" (.76 mm) allowable wear, beyond recommended resurfacing limits of .030" (.76 mm) total, .015" (.38 mm) each side.

TIGHTENING SPECIFICATIONS

Application	Ft. Lbs. (N.m)
Caliper	
Guide Pin (Kelsey-Hayes)	25-35 (34-47)
Retaining Bolt (Chrysler)	14-22 (19-30)
Retaining Screw (Bendix)	15 (20)
Caliper Adapter Bolts	
All with 1/2" Bolts	95-125 (129-170)
All with 5/8" Bolts	140-180 (190-245)
Lug Nuts	
FWD Models	95 (129)
RWD Trucks	75 (101)
RWD Vans & Wagons	85 (115)

DISC BRAKE ROTOR SPECIFICATIONS

Application	Disc Diameter In. (mm)	Lateral Runout In. (mm)	Parallelism In. (mm)	Original Thickness In. (mm)	Min. Refinish Thickness In. (mm)	Discard Thickness In. (mm)
AD150, B150, B250 & D150	11.75 (298.5)	.004 (.10)	.0005 (.013)	1.25 (31.8)	1.21 (30.7)	1.18 (29.97)
AW150 & W150	11.63 (295.4)	.005 (.13)	.001 (.03)	1.25 (31.8)	1.21 (30.7)	1.18 (29.97)
B350 [1]	12.82 (325.6)	.004 (.10)	.0005 (.013)	1.19 (30.2)	1.16 (29.5)	1.125 (28.58)
B350 [2]	12.82 (325.6)	.004 (.10)	.0005 (.013)	1.25 (31.8)	1.21 (30.7)	1.18 (29.97)
D250 [3]	12.82 (325.6)	.005 (.13)	.001 (.03)	1.25 (31.8)	1.21 (30.7)	1.18 (29.97)
D250, D350 & W250 [4]	12.82 (325.6)	.005 (.13)	.001 (.03)	1.19 (30.2)	1.16 (29.5)	1.125 (28.58)
W250 & W350 [5]	12.88 (327.2)	.005 (.13)	.001 (.03)	1.19 (30.2)	1.16 (29.5)	1.125 (28.58)
FWD Models	10.6 (270)	.005 (.13)	.0005 (.013)	.870 (22.1)	.833 (21.2)	.803 (20.4)

1 – School bus and vehicles with 4000 lbs. front axle.
2 – Vehicles with 3600 lbs. front axle, except school bus.
3 – Vehicles with 3300 lbs. front axle.
4 – D250 vehicles with 4000 lbs. front axle.
5 – W250 vehicles with Model 60 front axle.

FORD SLIDING CALIPER DISCS

DESCRIPTION

All 250 Series (over 6900 GVW) and 350 Series trucks use a dual piston caliper. All other models use a single piston caliper. On all models, caliper is secured to anchor plate by a retaining key and spring. Ventilated rotor is cast with wheel hub. As brake pedal is depressed, fluid from master cylinder passes through the metering valve and into caliper cylinder.

ADJUSTMENT & SERVICING

DISC PADS

Pad wear is automatically compensated for by piston sliding outward in cylinder bore; therefore, no disc pad adjustment is required. Replace pads if lining thickness is 1/32" (.79 mm) or less. Always replace both sets of brake pads. Never service one wheel only.

BLEEDING SYSTEM

See HYDRAULIC BRAKE BLEEDING in this section.

REMOVAL & INSTALLATION

DISC BRAKE PADS

Removal (Single Piston Caliper)

1) To prevent master cylinder overflow when caliper is depressed, remove a small amount of brake fluid from master cylinder. Raise vehicle and support with safety stands.

2) Remove front wheel assembly. Place a large "C" clamp on caliper. Tighten clamp to bottom piston in cylinder bore. Remove clamp.

3) On Aerostar, Bronco II and Ranger, remove dirt from around caliper pin tabs. Tap upper caliper pin toward indboard side of vehicle, until pin tabs touch spindle face.

4) Insert a screwdriver into slot provided behind pin tabs on inboard side of pin. Using pliers, compress end of pin while prying with screwdriver until tabs slip into spindle groove.

5) Place a 7/16" punch on end of pin and drive caliper pin out of caliper slide groove. Repeat procedure for lower pin. Remove caliper from rotor. Remove outer brake pad. Compress anti-rattle clip and remove inner brake pad.

6) On Bronco, F150 and F250, remove key retaining screw. Using a brass rod, and light hammer, drive out caliper support spring.

7) Remove caliper from spindle by pushing it downward against spindle and rotating upper end upward and out of spindle. Support caliper out of the way.

8) Remove outer disc pad from caliper. It may be necessary to tap pad to loosen pad flange from caliper. Remove inner disc pad from spindle assembly. Remove pad anti-rattle clip from lower end of pad.

Installation

1) On Aerostar, Bronco II and Ranger, reverse removal procedure. Ensure that outer shoe torque buttons are solidly seated in caliper cut-outs. Install caliper pin until retention tabs on side of pin contact spindle face.

2) Do not allow tabs of caliper pin to to be tapped in too far into spindle groove. If this happens, it will be necessary to tap the other end of pin until tabs snap into place. To complete installation, reverse removal procedure.

3) On Bronco, F150 and F250, Install new anti-rattle clip on lower end of inner pad. Place lower end of pad in spindle, with clip against pad, and clip loop away from rotor. Slide upper end of pad into position. Be sure clip is still in position.

4) With piston fully bottomed in cylinder bore, position outer pad on caliper and press pad tabs into place. If pad cannot be pressed into place by hand, use a large "C" clamp. To complete installation, reverse removal procedure. Apply brakes until a firm pedal is obtained.

Removal (Dual Piston Caliper)

1) To prevent master cylinder overflow when caliper is depressed, remove a small amount of brake fluid from master cylinder. Raise vehicle and support with safety stands. Remove front wheel assembly. Remove key retaining screw.

2) Using a brass rod, and light hammer, drive out key and spring. Remove caliper by rotating key and spring end out and away from rotor.

3) Slide opposite end of caliper clear of slide in the support and off the rotor. Do not allow caliper to hang from brake line. Remove caliper disc pad anti-rattle spring. Remove inner and outer disc pads.

Installation

1) Make sure caliper pistons are fully bottomed in caliper. Install disc pads and anti-rattle spring. Place caliper rail into the slide on support and rotate caliper onto rotor.

2) Place key and spring into position and start inserting between caliper and support. Check that spring is between key and caliper, and that spring tangs overlap ends of key. Use a screwdriver if necessary to hold caliper up against support.

3) Drive key and spring into position aligning correct notch with existing hole in support. Install key retaining screw and tighten to 14-22 ft. lbs. (19-30 N.m). Check brake fluid level in master cylinder and fill as necessary. Apply brakes until firm pedal is obtained.

BRAKE CALIPER

Removal & Installation

Caliper removal and installation procedures are same as for disc pad replacement, except it will be necessary to disconnect brake hose. After caliper installation, bleed brake system.

DISC ROTOR

Removal & Installation (All 2WD Models)

Raise vehicle and support with safety stands. Remove wheel and caliper assemblies. Remove dust cap, cotter pin, nut, washer, and outer bearing. Carefully remove hub and rotor assembly. Remove inner bearing and seal. To install, reverse removal procedure. Adjust front wheel bearings. See WHEEL BEARING ADJUSTMENT in SUSPENSION section.

Removal (Bronco II & Ranger 4WD Models With Automatic Locking Hubs)

1) Raise vehicle and support with safety stands. Remove wheel assembly and caliper. Remove retainer washers from lug nut studs. Remove locking hub assembly from spindle. *See Fig. 1.* Remove snap ring from end of spindle shaft.

FORD SLIDING CALIPER DISCS (Cont.)

2) Remove axle shaft spacer, needle bearing, and bearing spacer. Being careful not to damage plastic moving cam, pull cam assembly off wheel bearing adjustment nut. Remove thrust washer and thrust (needle) bearing from adjustment nut.

3) Look into spindle keyway, under adjustment nut hole, and remove any portion of locking key that has separated from cam assembly. If this condition exists, replace entire cam assembly.

4) Remove adjustment nut using Socket (T7OT-4252-B). Remove hub and disc assembly, outer wheel bearing will slide out as hub is being removed. Remove grease seal and inner wheel bearing.

5) Inspect needle and wheel bearings for wear or damage. Inspect bearing cups for pits or cracks. Replace worn parts. If necessary, remove bearing cups with drift.

Fig. 1: Automatic Locking Hub Assembly

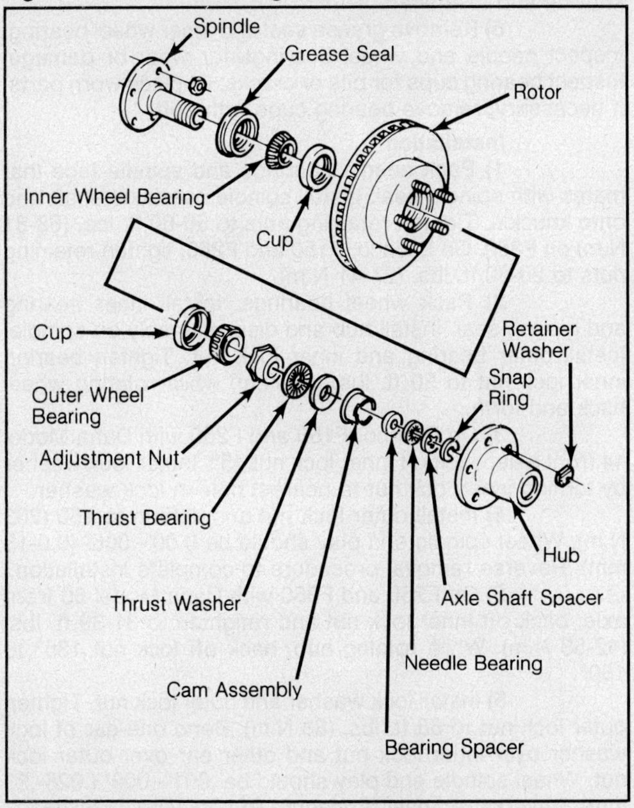

Illustration applies to Bronco II and Ranger.

Installation

1) Pack needle and wheel bearings. Install inner wheel bearing and grease seal. Install hub and disc assembly on spindle. Install outer wheel bearing and adjustment nut.

2) Spin rotor and tighten adjustment nut to 35 ft. lbs. (47 N.m). Back off nut 1/4 turn. Retighten adjustment nut to 16 INCH lbs. (1.8 N.m). Carefully align closest hole in adjustment nut with center of spindle keyway.

NOTE: **Extreme care must be taken when aligning nut with center of spindle keyway to prevent damage to cam assembly locking key.**

3) Install thrust (needle) bearing and thrust washer. Install cam assembly onto lock nut by lining up key in cam with spindle keyway. Install bearing spacer, needle bearing, and axle shaft spacer.

4) Install snap ring. End play should be .001"-.003" (.025-.076 mm). Install locking hub assembly over spindle by lining up 3 lugs on hub with cut-outs in cam assembly. Reverse removal procedure to complete installation.

Removal (All Other 4WD Models With Automatic Locking Hubs)

1) Raise vehicle and support with safety stands. Remove wheel assembly and caliper. Remove 5 cap screws using Torx "R" bit TX25. Remove cover. Do not drop ball bearing, bearing race, or retainer. *See Fig. 2*.

2) Remove rubber seal. Remove seal bridge retainer from retainer ring. Remove retainer ring by closing ends with needle nose pliers and at same time pulling hub lock away from wheel hub.

3) Remove "C" washer from stub shaft grooove. Remove splined spacer from shaft. Remove wheel bearing lock nuts and lock washers. To complete removal, see removal steps **3)** through **5)** of 4WD model manual locking hubs.

Fig. 2: Automatic Locking Hub Assembly

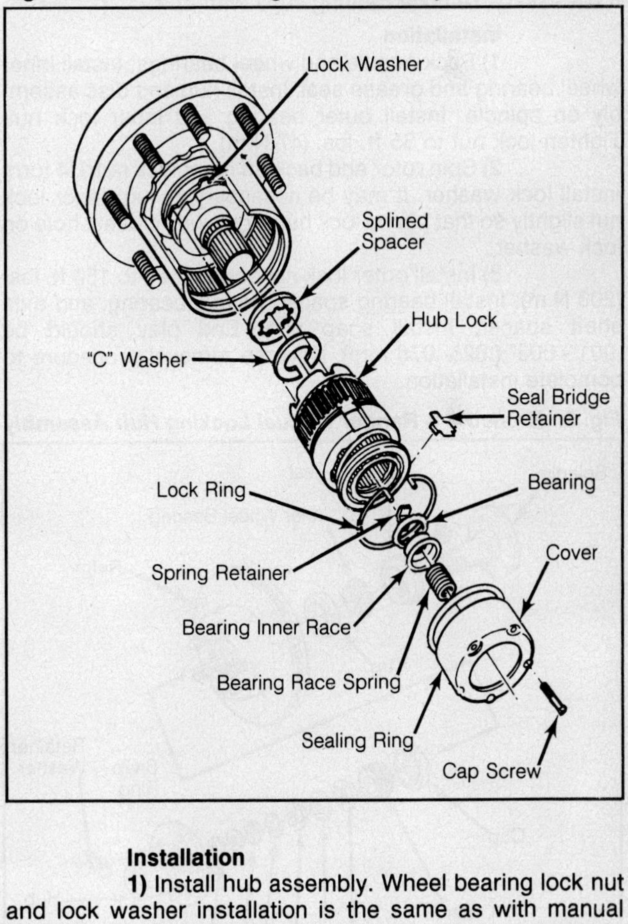

Installation

1) Install hub assembly. Wheel bearing lock nut and lock washer installation is the same as with manual locking hubs. Tighten outer wheel bearing lock nut to 150 ft. lbs. (203 N.m).

2) Install splined spacer and "C" washer on stub shaft. Start hub lock assembly into hub. Ensure that large tangs line up with lock washers. Ensure that outside and inside diameter splines line up with hub and stub shaft splines.

3) Install retainer ring by closing ends with needle nose pliers and at same time pushing hub lock into wheel hub. Install seal bridge retainer with narrow end first.

FORD SLIDING CALIPER DISCS (Cont.)

4) Install rubber seal over hub lock. Install cover, making sure that ball bearing, bearing race, and retainer are in place. Alternately tighten cap screws to 45 INCH lbs. (5 N.m). Reverse removal procedure to complete installation.

Removal (Bronco II & Ranger 4WD Models With Manual Locking Hubs)

1) Raise vehicle and support with safety stands. Remove wheel assembly and caliper. Remove retainer washers from lug nut studs. Remove locking hub assembly from spindle. *See Fig. 3*.

2) Remove snap ring from end of spindle shaft. Remove axle shaft spacer, needle bearing, and bearing spacer. Remove wheel bearing outer lock nut using Front Wheel Bearing Spanner (T38T-1197-A).

3) Remove lock nut washer. Remove wheel bearing inner lock nut using spanner. Remove hub and disc assembly, outer wheel bearing will slide out as hub is being removed.

4) Remove grease seal and inner wheel bearing. Inspect needle and wheel bearings for wear or damage. Inspect bearing cups for pits or cracks. Replace worn parts. If necessary, remove bearing cups with drift.

Installation

1) Pack needle and wheel bearings. Install inner wheel bearing and grease seal. Install hub and disc assembly on spindle. Install outer bearing and inner lock nut. Tighten lock nut to 35 ft. lbs. (47 N.m).

2) Spin rotor and back off inner lock nut 1/4 turn. Install lock washer. It may be necessary to turn inner lock nut slightly so that pin on lock nut aligns with closest hole on lock washer.

3) Install outer lock nut and tighten to 150 ft. lbs. (203 N.m). Install bearing spacer, needle bearing, and axle shaft spacer. Install snap ring. End play should be .001"-.003" (.025-.076 mm). Reverse removal procedure to complete installation.

Fig. 3: Bronco II & Ranger Manual Locking Hub Assembly

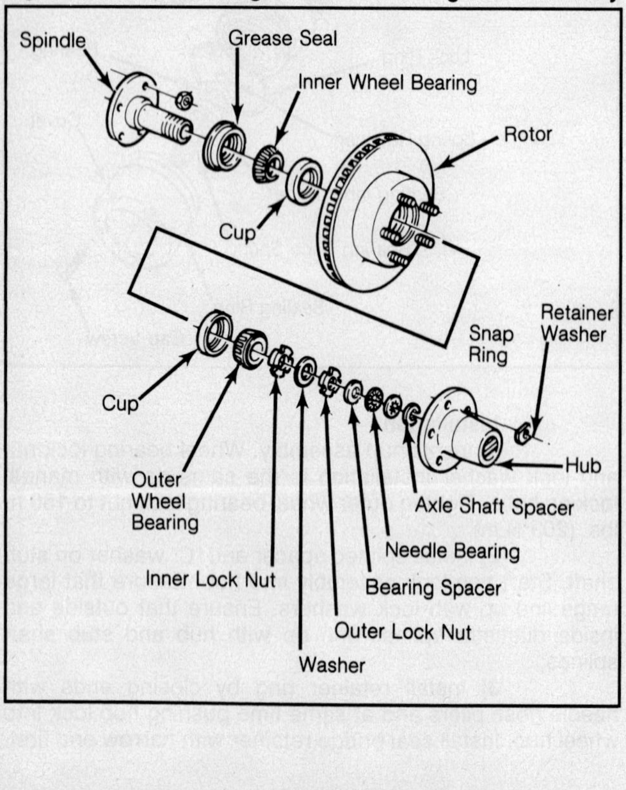

Removal (All Other 4WD Models With Manual Locking Hubs)

1) Raise vehicle and support with safety stands. Remove wheel assembly and caliper. Remove cap by removing 6 socket head cap screws from cap assembly and slip apart.

2) Remove snap ring from end of axle shaft. Remove lock ring from groove of wheel hub. Slide hub assembly out of wheel hub. If necessary, use a puller to remove hub assembly.

3) Remove wheel bearing lock nut, lock ring, and adjustment nut using Front Wheel Bearing Spanner (T59T-1197-B) for F100, F250 and Bronco; or (T78T-1197-A) for F250 (Over 6900 GVW) and F350.

4) Remove hub and disc assembly, outer wheel bearing will slide out as hub is being removed. Remove spindle retaining nuts, then carefully remove spindle from knuckle and axle shaft.

5) Remove grease seal and inner wheel bearing. Inspect needle and wheel bearings for wear or damage. Inspect bearing cups for pits or cracks. Replace worn parts. If necessary, remove bearing cups with drift.

Installation

1) Pack needle bearings and spindle face that mates with spindle seal. Install spindle over axle shaft and onto knuckle. Tighten retaining nuts to 50-60 ft. lbs. (68-81 N.m) on F350. On Bronco, F150 and F250, tighten retaining nuts to 20-30 ft. lbs. (27-41 N.m).

2) Pack wheel bearings. Install inner bearing and grease seal. Install hub and disc assembly on spindle. Install outer bearing and inner lock nut. Tighten bearing inner lock nut to 50 ft. lbs. (68 N.m) while rotating wheel back and forth.

3) On Bronco, F150 and F250 with Dana Model 44 front axle, back off inner lock nut 45°. Install lock washer by turning inner lock nut to nearest hole in lock washer.

4) Install outer lock nut and tighten to 150 (203 N.m). Wheel spindle end play should be 0.00"-.006" (0.0-15 mm). Reverse removal procedure to complete installation.

5) On F250 and F350 with Dana Model 50 front axle, back off inner lock nut and retighten to 31-39 ft. lbs. (42-53 N.m). While rotaing hub, back off lock nut 135° to 150°.

6) Install lock washer and outer lock nut. Tighten outer lock nut to 65 ft. lbs. (88 N.m). Bend one ear of lock washer over inner lock nut and other ear over outer lock nut. Wheel spindle end play should be .001"-.009" (.025-.23 mm). Reverse removal procedure to complete installation.

OVERHAUL

BRAKE CALIPER

Disassembly (All Models)

1) Remove caliper. Remove plug from inlet port (if used) and drain fluid from cylinders. Place a block of wood between caliper and cylinders. *See Fig. 4*. Apply low air pressure to brake hose inlet. Air pressure will force out piston(s).

2) If a piston is jammed or cocked and will not easily come out, tap end of piston sharply with a brass hammer to straighten. Do not pry piston from bore.

3) Reapply low air pressure to remove cocked piston. Remove seal and boot from grooves. Discard seals and boots.

FORD SLIDING CALIPER DISCS (Cont.)

Fig. 4: Using Compressed Air to Remove Caliper Piston

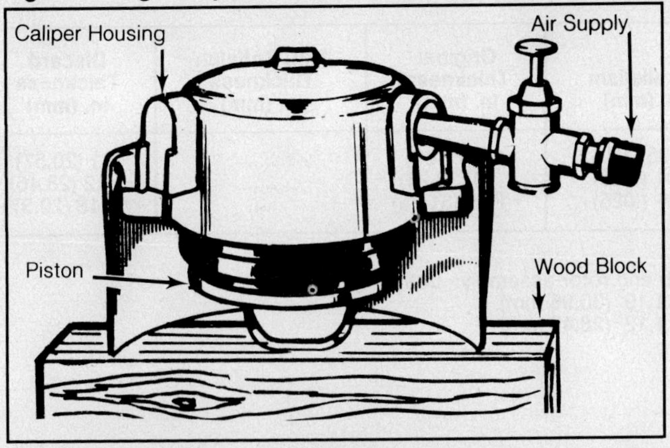

Use low pressure air to force out piston(s)

Cleaning & Inspection

1) Clean rust and corrosion from caliper machined surfaces with a wire brush, being careful not to get wire brush in cylinder bores. Clean all components with denatured alcohol and dry with compressed air.

2) Inspect cylinder bore, seal grooves, and boot grooves for wear or damage. If bores are scored, corroded or worn, replace caliper. Replace anti-rattle clip, caliper support spring and key.

Fig. 5: Aerostar, Bronco II & Ranger Single Piston Caliper

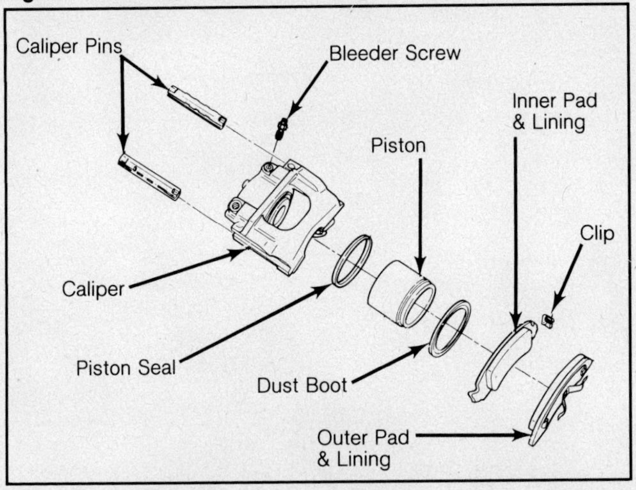

Reassembly (Single Piston)

1) Lubricate piston seal with clean brake fluid and install in cylinder bore groove. Lubricate cylinder with clean brake fluid. Coat piston and outside beads of dust boot with clean brake fluid.

2) Push piston through boot until boot is around bottom (closed end) of piston. Position piston and boot directly over cylinder bore. Work bead of dust boot into groove near top of cylinder bore.

3) With bead seated in groove, press straight down on piston until it bottoms in cylinder bore. Care must be taken not to cock or jam piston in cylinder. If necessary use a "C" clamp and a block of wood to bottom piston in cylinder.

Reassembly (Dual Piston)

1) Lubricate new piston seals with clean brake fluid and install seals in grooves in cylinders. *See Fig. 7.* Lubricate cylinders with clean brake fluid.

2) Lubricate retaining lips of boots with clean brake fluid and install in grooves in cylinders. Coat pistons

Fig. 6: Bronco, F150 & F250 Single Piston Caliper

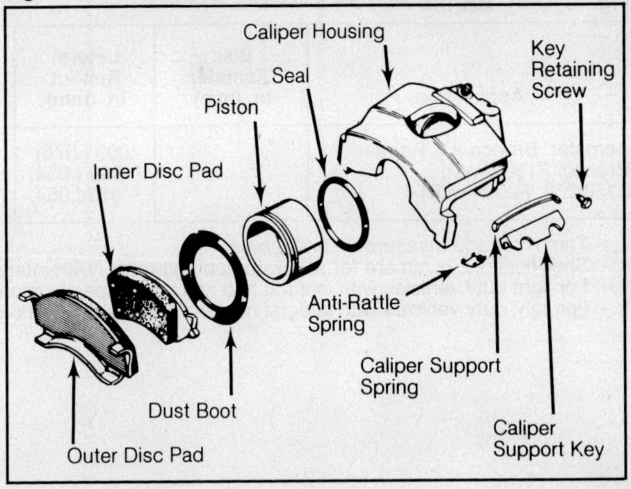

with clean brake fluid. Insert into cylinders by hand until they are beyond piston seals.

3) Position a wood block over one piston and press into cylinder, taking care not to cock piston. Install other piston in same manner.

Fig. 7: F350 Dual Piston Caliper

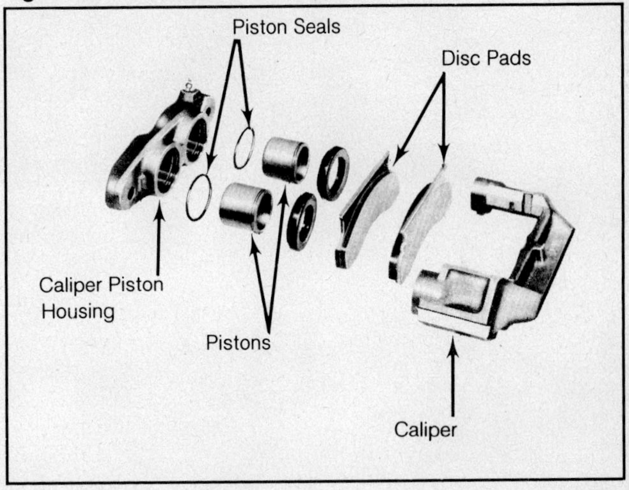

DISC ROTOR

Lateral Runout

1) Tighten spindle nut to eliminate bearing end play. Ensure that rotor can be turned. Install and tighten lug nuts. Attach dial indicator on suspension, with indicator tip on face of rotor.

2) Set dial indicator to zero, slowly turn rotor, and note high and low readings on dial. Runout must not exceed specifications.

3) Resurface or replace rotor as required. A maximum of .020" (.51 mm) material may be taken off each side of braking surface. Cuts must be of equal depth on both sides of rotor.

Parallelism

Using a micrometer, measure rotor thickness at 12 points approximately 30° apart, and at 1" (25 mm) from outer edge of rotor. Runout must not exceed specifications. Resurface or replace rotor as required

FORD SLIDING CALIPER DISCS (Cont.)

Fig. 8: DISC BRAKE ROTOR SPECIFICATIONS

Application	Disc Diameter In. (mm)	Lateral Runout In. (mm)	Parallelism In. (mm)	Original Thickness In. (mm)	Min. Refinish Thickness In. (mm)	Discard Thickness In. (mm)
Aerostar, Bronco II & Ranger	....	.003 (.076)	[1] .0006 (.0152)	.87 (22.09)	.....	.81 (20.57)
Bronco, F150 (4WD)	.....	[2] .010 (.054)	.001 (.025)	1.19 (30.26)	.....	1.12 (28.45)
F150/250, F250 (4WD)	.....	[2] .010 (.054)	.001 (.025)	[3] 1.25 (31.75)	.....	[4] 1.18 (29.97)

[1] – Turn rotor and measure on brake lathe.
[2] – Specifications given are for separate hub and rotor. With integral hub and rotor assembly: .003" (.076 mm).
[3] – For light duty vehicles with integral hub and rotor, specifications are 1.19" (30.96 mm).
[4] – For light duty vehicles with integral hub and rotor, specifications are 1.12" (28.45 mm)

GENERAL MOTORS FLOATING CALIPER DISCS

NOTE: Delco floating caliper disc brakes are used on all gasoline engine models except those equipped with Bendix Hydro-Boost power brake units and/or 4-wheel disc brakes. All other models use Bendix sliding caliper disc brakes.

DESCRIPTION

Delco floating caliper disc brake assembly uses a single piston caliper. The caliper is mounted to an anchor plate which is bolted to the steering knuckle. The caliper assembly floats through 4 rubber bushings on 2 steel guide pins.

The pins are threaded into caliper anchor plate. When brakes are applied, hydraulic pressure is passed to caliper piston. This force pushes inner brake pad against inner rotor braking surface.

Pressure then moves caliper inward on guide pins, thus forcing outer disc pad against outer rotor braking surface. When brakes are released, pressure is removed from cylinder. Rotor runout moves piston back off of rotor to maintain sufficient rotor-to-pad clearance.

Fig. 1: Exploded View of Floating Caliper Assembly

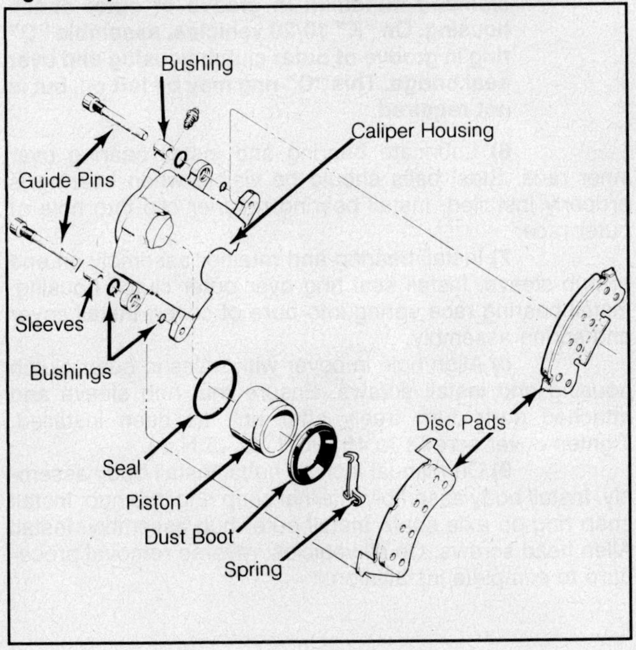

ADJUSTMENT & SERVICING

DISC BRAKE PADS

Pad wear is automatically compensated for by piston moving outward in cylinder bore. No disc pad adjustment in service is required.

Inspect condition of disc pads whenever wheels are removed. If any disc pad is worn to within 1/32" (0.8 mm) of rivet heads, replace all disc pad sets on that axle.

BLEEDING SYSTEM

See HYDRAULIC BRAKE BLEEDING in this section.

REMOVAL & INSTALLATION

DISC BRAKE PADS

Removal

1) Remove 2/3 of brake fluid from master cylinder. Raise vehicle and support with safety stands. Remove wheel assemblies. Place a large "C" clamp on caliper so that screw side of clamp rests against metal part of outer disc pad.

2) Tighten "C" clamp until caliper moves away from vehicle far enough to push piston to bottom of bore. Remove "C" clamp. Do not disconnect brake line to caliper. Remove 2 mounting bolts which retain caliper to support bracket.

3) Lift caliper off rotor and remove inner disc pad. Pry out outer disc pad. Hang caliper with wire from front suspension arm so that caliper weight is not supported by brake hose.

4) Remove shoe support spring from cavity in piston. Remove sleeves from inner ear in caliper. Remove rubber bushings from grooves in each of 4 caliper ears.

Installation

1) Lubricate new sleeves and bushings with silicone lubricant. Install bushings in 4 caliper ears. Install sleeves in bushings. Install shoe support spring on inner disc pad.

2) Install inner disc pad in caliper with wear sensor at leading edge of pad (forward wheel rotation). Install outer disc pad in caliper with ears of pad over caliper. Center tab on pad should be engaged in caliper cut-out.

3) Place caliper over rotor. Install mounting bolts and tighten. Check clearance between bracket stops and caliper. Clearance should be .005-.012" (0.13-0.30 mm).

4) Fill master cylinder with new brake fluid. Pump brake pedal several times to seat disc pads against rotor. Clinch ears of outer disc pad with channel lock pliers, placing 1 jaw on top of ear and other jaw on bottom of caliper.

5) After clinching, ears should be flat against caliper housing with no clearance. If clearance exists, repeat procedure. Install wheels and lower vehicle.

BRAKE CALIPER

Removal & Installation

Brake caliper removal and installation procedures are same as for disc brake pads, except that it will be necessary to disconnect brake hose at caliper. Tighten brake hose inlet fitting.

DISC ROTOR

Removal (2WD Models)

Raise vehicle and support with safety stands. Remove brake caliper (do not disconnect brake hose). Remove grease cap from end of hub. Remove cotter pin nut, washer, and outer bearing. Remove rotor and hub assembly.

Installation

Install rotor and hub assembly on spindle. Install outer bearing, washer, and nut. Adjust wheel bearings. See WHEEL BEARING ADJUSTMENT in SUSPENSION section.

Removal (4WD "S" Series)

Raise vehicle and support with safety stands. Remove wheel assembly. Remove brake caliper (do not disconnect brake hose). Remove rotor.

GENERAL MOTORS FLOATING CALIPER DISCS (Cont.)

Installation

To install, reverse removal procedure.

Removal (All Other 4WD Models)

1) Raise vehicle and support with safety stands. Remove wheel assemblies. On vehicles with automatic locking hubs, remove 5 screws, retaining hub cover to outer clutch housing.

2) Remove cover, seal, seal bridge, and bearing components. Use needle nose pliers to compress wire retaining ring. *See Fig. 2*. Pull remaining components from wheel.

3) On vehicles with manual locking hubs, remove Allen head screws. Remove outer locking hub locking assembly. Remove snap ring from end of axle shaft. Remove body assembly internal snap ring from hub. Remove body assembly.

4) On all vehicles, remove wheel bearing outer lock nut, retainer, and inner bearing adjustment nut using Wrench (J-6893) and Adapter (J-6893-01). Remove hub and disc assembly. Remove outer wheel bearing.

5) Remove oil seal and inner wheel bearing. Remove inner and outer wheel bearing cups (if necessary) using a brass drift and hammer. Clean and inspect all parts, as required.

Fig. 2: Automatic Locking Hub Assembly

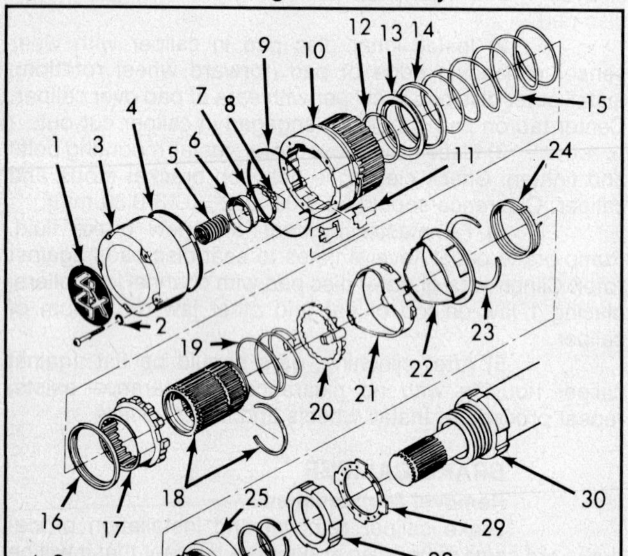

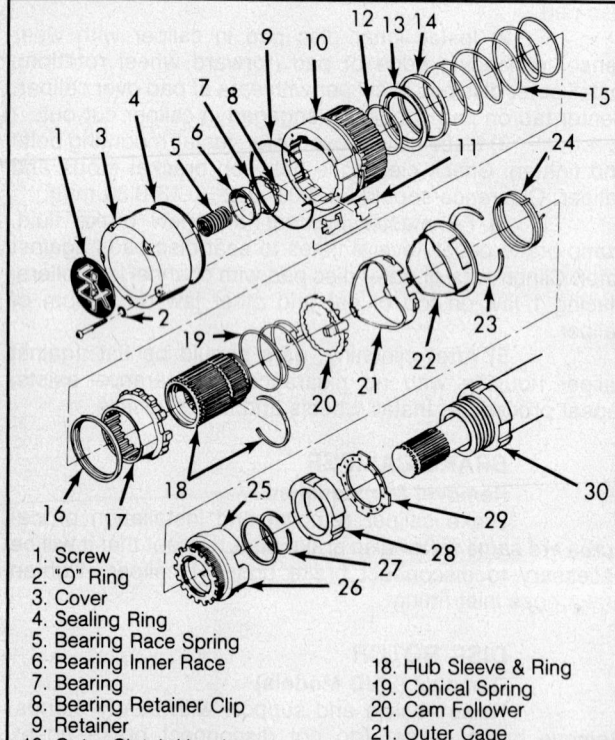

1. Screw
2. "O" Ring
3. Cover
4. Sealing Ring
5. Bearing Race Spring
6. Bearing Inner Race
7. Bearing
8. Bearing Retainer Clip
9. Retainer
10. Outer Clutch Housing
11. Seal Bridge Retainer ("K" 10/20) Assembly aid Retainer ("K" 30)
12. Retaining Ring
13. Spring Support Washer
14. Spring Retainer
15. Return Spring
16. Spring Retainer
17. Clutch Gear
18. Hub Sleeve & Ring
19. Conical Spring
20. Cam Follower
21. Outer Cage
22. Inner Cage
23. Snap Ring
24. Brake Band
25. Drag Sleeve & Detent
26. Spacer
27. Retaining Ring
28. Lock Nut
29. Drag Sleeve Washer
30. Adjustment Nut

Adjustment nut pin must pass through hole in drag sleeve washer.

Installation

1) Install bearing cups, if removed. Lubricate wheel bearings with high temperature wheel bearing grease. Install inner bearing and oil seal. Install hub and disc assembly. Install outer wheel bearing.

2) Tighten adjustment nut to 50 ft. lbs. (68 N.m) while rotating hub. Back off adjustment nut. On vehicles with automatic locking hubs, retighten nut to 35 ft. lbs. (47 N.m) while rotating hub. Back off adjustment nut 3/8 turn (maximum).

3) On vehicles with manual locking hubs, retighten nut to 50 ft. lbs. (68 N.m) while rotating hub. Back off adjustment nut just enough to free bearing. On all vehicles, install retainer. Tang on inside diameter of washer should fit into slot of spindle.

4) Move adjustment nut (if necessary) to align a hole in drag sleeve washer with pin on lock nut. Tighten lock nut to 160 ft. lbs. (217 N.m). Wheel bearing end play should be .001-.010" (.025-.254 mm).

5) On vehicles with automatic locking hubs, install retaining ring in groove of unsplined end of outer clutch housing, with tangs pointing away from housing. Hold tangs of retainer together and assemble seal bridge retainer over tangs.

NOTE: Seal bridge retainer holds retainer in a clamped condition in groove of outer clutch housing. On "K" 10/20 vehicles, assemble "O" ring in groove of outer clutch housing and over seal bridge. This "O" ring may be left on, but is not required.

6) Lubricate bearing and install bearing over inner race. Steel balls should be visible when bearing is properly installed. Install bearing retainer clip into hole of outer race.

7) Install bearing and retainer assembly on end of hub sleeve. Install seal ring over outer clutch housing. Install bearing race spring into bore of cover. Install cover and spring assembly.

8) Align hole in cover with holes in outer clutch housing and install screws. Ensure that hub sleeve and attached parts turn freely after unit as been installed. Tighten cover screws to 45 INCH lbs. (5 N.m).

9) On manual locking hubs, install body assembly. Install body assembly internal snap ring into hub. Install snap ring on axle shaft. Install outer hub assembly. Install Allen head screws. On all vehicles, reverse removal procedure to complete installation.

OVERHAUL

BRAKE CALIPER

Disassembly

1) Drain brake fluid from caliper. Use clean shop towels to pad interior of caliper and apply compressed air at caliper inlet to remove piston. *See Fig. 3*. Use just enough pressure to ease piston out of bore.

3) Use screwdriver to pry boot out of caliper housing. Pry piston seal from its groove in caliper bore with a piece of wood or plastic. Remove bleeder valve from housing.

GENERAL MOTORS FLOATING CALIPER DISCS (Cont.)

Inspection

1) Boot, seal, rubber bushings, and sleeves are to be replaced each time caliper is overhauled. Clean all other parts in denatured alcohol. Dry parts with dry compressed air.

2) Check guide pins for corrosion. If corroded, replace guide pins. Check outside diameter of piston for scoring, nicks, corrosion, wear or damaged plating. If surface defects exist, piston must be replaced.

3) Piston bore should be checked for similar defects. Bore is not plated, and may be polished with crocus cloth. Replace caliper housing if bore cannot be cleaned out.

Reassembly

1) Install bleeder valve. Lubricate bore in caliper housing and new piston seal with clean brake fluid. Position seal in caliper bore groove. Ensure seal is not twisted.

2) Lubricate piston with clean brake fluid and assemble new boot into groove in piston with fold facing open end of piston. Insert piston into caliper bore using care not to unseat seal.

3) Force piston to bottom of bore. Position outer diameter of boot in caliper counterbore. Using Boot Installer (J-26267), drive boot into housing until fully seated.

DISC ROTOR

Lateral Runout

Adjust wheel bearings until all end play is eliminated. Attach dial indicator with contact tip of indicator about 1" from rotor edge. Set indicator to zero and turn rotor through one complete revolution, noting indicator reading.

Fig. 3: Using Compressed Air to Remove Caliper Piston

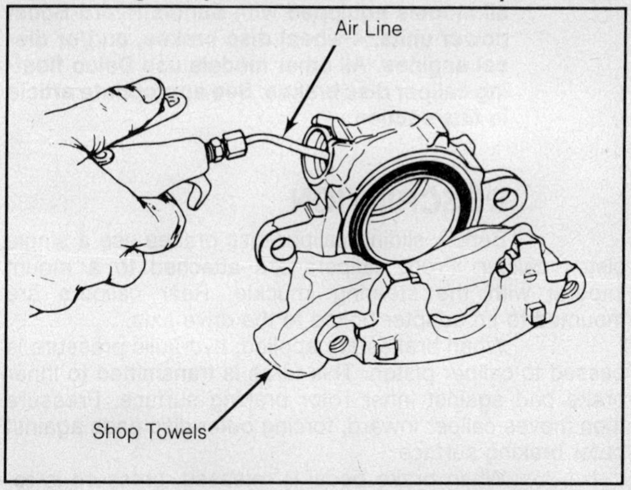

Compressed air must be filtered and dry.

Parallelism

Check thickness of rotor at 4 or more points around circumference of rotor. Make all measurements at same distance from edge of rotor. If thickness variation is excessive, refinish or replace rotor as necessary.

TIGHTENING SPECIFICATIONS

Application	Ft. Lbs. (N.m)
Brake Hose-to-Caliper	25 (34)
Caliper Mounting Bolts	35 (47)

DISC BRAKE ROTOR SPECIFICATIONS

Application	Disc Diameter In. (mm)	Lateral Runout In. (mm)	Parallelism In. (mm)	Original Thickness In. (mm)	Min. Refinish Thickness In. (mm)	Discard Thickness In. (mm)
"C" Series	11.86 (301.2)	.004 (.10)	.0005 (.013)	1.04 (26.4)	.980 (24.89)	.965 (24.51)
"G" Series	11.86 (301.2)	.004 (.10)	.0005 (.013)	1.28 (32.5)	1.23 (31.2)	1.22 (30.9)
"P" & "K" Series	12.50 (317.5)	.004 (.10)	.0005 (.013)	[1] 1.28 (32.5)	1.23 (31.2)	1.22 (30.9)
	14.25 (362.0)	.004 (.10)	.0005 (.013)	1.53 (38.9)	1.48 (37.6)	1.465 (37.21)
"S" Series	....	.004 (.10)	.0005 (.013)	....	.978 (24.84)	.965 (24.51)

[1] – On rotors that are 1.53" (38.9 mm) thick, minimum thickness is 1.48" (37.6 mm). Discard thickness is 1.465" (37.21 mm).

GENERAL MOTORS SLIDING CALIPER DISCS

NOTE: Bendix sliding caliper disc brakes are used on all models equipped with Bendix Hydro-Boost power units, 4-wheel disc brakes, and/or diesel engines. All other models use Delco floating caliper disc brakes. See appropriate article in this section.

DESCRIPTION

Bendix sliding caliper disc brakes use a single piston caliper. Front calipers are attached to a mount integral with the steering knuckle. Rear calipers are mounted to an adapter bolted to the drive axle.

When brakes are applied, hydraulic pressure is passed to caliper piston. This force is transmitted to inner brake pad against inner rotor braking surface. Pressure then moves caliper inward, forcing outer disc pads against outer braking surface.

When brake pedal is released, pressure is removed from caliper cylinder and rotor runout moves piston back into caliper cylinder to maintain sufficient rotor-to-pad clearance.

ADJUSTMENT & SERVICING

DISC PADS

Pad wear is automatically compensated for by piston moving outward in cylinder bore. No disc pad adjustment is required. Inspect condition of disc pads whenever wheels are removed. If any pad is worn to within 1/32" (0.8 mm) of rivet heads, replace all pad sets on axle.

BLEEDING SYSTEM

See HYDRAULIC BRAKE BLEEDING in this section.

Fig. 1: Rear Sliding Caliper Disc Brake Components

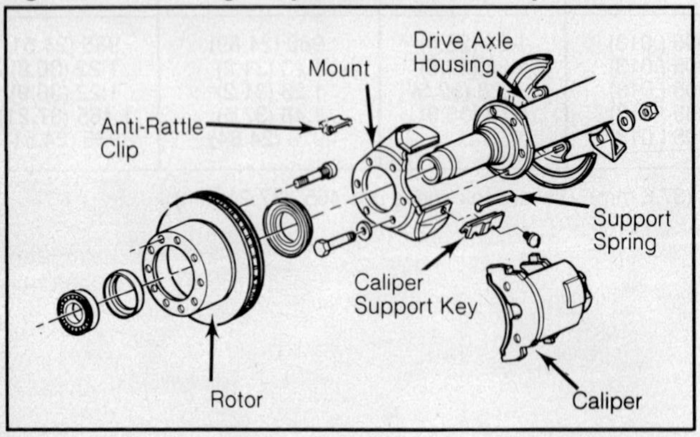

REMOVAL & INSTALLATION

DISC BRAKE PADS

Removal

1) Remove 2/3 of brake fluid from master cylinder. Raise vehicle and support with safety stands. Remove wheel assemblies. Place a large "C" clamp on caliper and tighten clamp to bottom piston in cylinder bore.

2) Remove clamp. Remove key retaining screw. Drive out caliper support key and spring with brass rod and light hammer. *See Fig. 2.* Remove caliper and support caliprer with wire.

3) Remove inner disc pad from caliper. Remove and discard clip. Remove outer disc pad from caliper. It may be necessary to tap pad to loosen it from caliper housing.

Fig. 2: Exploded View of Sliding Caliper Assembly

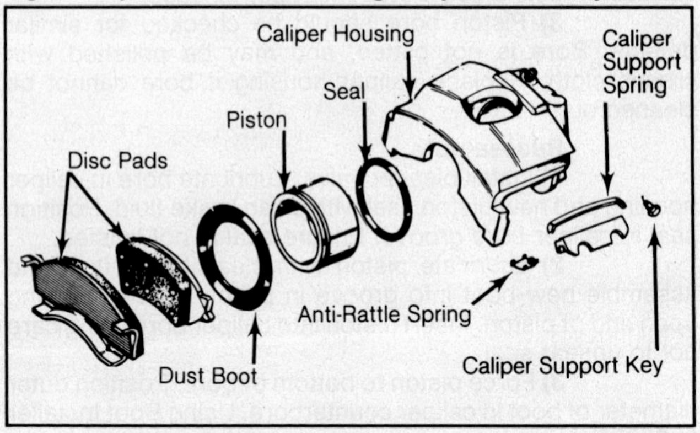

Installation

1) Lubricate caliper and mount sliding surfaces with silicone lubricant. Install new clip in mount. Place lower end of inner pad into mount and against clip.

2) Slide upper end of pad into place. Be sure clip is still in correct position. With caliper piston fully bottomed in cylinder bore. Position outer pad on caliper and press tabs into place.

3) If pad cannot be properly positioned by hand, use a large "C" clamp, taking care not to mar lining. With disc pads installed, lift caliper and rest bottom edge of outer pad on outer edge of rotor.

4) Check that there is no clearance between bottom tab of outer pad and caliper abutment. Outer pad should be tight in caliper housing. Postion caliper on mounting surface. Ensure brake hose is not twisted.

5) Place spring over support key and tap into place until key retaining screw can be installed. Tighten screw. Fill master cylinder with brake fluid. Apply brakes until pedal is firm. Install wheel assemblies and lower vehicle.

BRAKE CALIPER

Removal & Installation

Caliper removal and installation procedures are the same as those for disc pad replacement, except that it will be necessary to disconnect brake hose. Use new copper washers when connecting brake hose.

DISC ROTOR

Removal (2WD Models)

1) Raise vehicle and support with safety stands. Remove brake caliper without disconnecting brake line.

2) Remove grease cap from end of hub. Remove cotter pin, nut, washer, and outer bearing. Remove rotor and hub assembly.

Installation

Install rotor and hub assembly on spindle. Install outer bearing, washer, and nut. Adjust wheel bearings. See WHEEL BEARING ADJUSTMENT in SUSPENSION section.

GENERAL MOTORS SLIDING CALIPER DISCS (Cont.)

Removal (4WD Models)

1) Raise vehicle and support with safety stands. Remove wheel assemblies. On vehicles with automatic locking hubs, remove 5 screws, retaining hub cover to outer clutch housing.

2) Remove cover, seal, seal bridge, and bearing components. Use needle nose pliers to compress wire retaining ring. Pull remaining components from wheel.

3) On vehicles with manual locking hubs, remove Allen head screws. Remove outer locking hub locking assembly. Remove snap ring from end of axle shaft. Remove body assembly internal snap ring from hub. Remove body assembly.

4) On all vehicles, remove wheel bearing outer lock nut, retainer, and inner bearing adjustment nut using Wrench (J-6893) and Adapter (J-6893-01). Remove hub and disc assembly. Remove outer wheel bearing.

5) Remove oil seal and inner wheel bearing. Remove inner and outer wheel bearing cups (if necessary) using a brass drift and hammer. Clean and inspect all parts, as required.

Installation

1) Install bearing cups, if removed. Lubricate wheel bearings with high temperature wheel bearing grease. Install inner bearing and oil seal. Install hub and disc assembly. Install outer wheel bearing.

2) Tighten adjustment nut to 50 ft. lbs. (68 N.m) while rotating hub. Back off adjustment nut. On vehicles with automatic locking hubs, retighten nut to 35 ft. lbs. (47 N.m) while rotating hub. Back off adjustment nut 3/8 turn (maximum).

3) On vehicles with manual locking hubs, retighten nut to 50 ft. lbs. (68 N.m) while rotating hub. Back off adjustment nut just enough to free bearing. On all vehicles, install retainer. Tang on inside diameter of washer should fit into slot of spindle.

4) Move adjustment nut (if necessary) to align a hole in drag sleeve washer with pin on lock nut. Tighten lock nut to 160 ft. lbs. (217 N.m). Wheel bearing end play should be .001-.010" (.025-.254 mm).

5) On vehicles with automatic locking hubs, install retaining ring in groove of unsplined end of outer clutch housing, with tangs pointing away from housing. Hold tangs of retainer together and assemble seal bridge retainer over tangs.

NOTE: Seal bridge retainer holds retainer in a clamped condition in groove of outer clutch housing. On "K"10/20 vehicles, assemble "O" ring in groove of outer clutch housing and over seal bridge. This "O" ring may be left on, but is not required.

6) Lubricate bearing and install bearing over inner race. Steel balls should be visible when bearing is properly installed. Install bearing retainer clip into hole of outer race.

7) Install bearing and retainer assembly on end of hub sleeve. Install seal ring over outer clutch housing. Install bearing race spring into bore of cover. Install cover and spring assembly.

8) Align hole in cover with holes in outer clutch housing and install screws. Ensure that hub sleeve and attached parts turn freely after unit as been installed. Tighten cover screws to 45 INCH lbs. (5 N.m).

9) On manual locking hubs, install body assembly. Install body assembly internal snap ring into hub. Install snap ring on axle shaft. Install outer hub assembly. Install Allen head screws. On all vehicles, reverse removal procedure to complete installation.

Removal (Rear Wheel Disc Brakes)

1) Raise vehicle and support with safety stands. Remove brake caliper without disconnecting brake line. Support caliper out of way.

2) Remove axle shaft flange bolts. Remove axle shaft. Bend lock tab on bearing lock nut and remove lock nut. Remove lock tab assembly. Remove inner bearing adjusting nut and washer. Remove rotor and hub assembly.

Installation

1) Install rotor and hub assembly into position on axle housing. Install outer bearing and washer. Make sure tang on washer is aligned with groove in axle housing.

2) Install inner bearing nut and adjust wheel bearings. See WHEEL BEARING ADJUSTMENT in SUSPENSION section. Install axle shaft using a new flange gasket. Tighten bolts to 115 ft. lbs. (156 N.m). Install brake caliper.

OVERHAUL

BRAKE CALIPER

Disassembly

1) Clean brake caliper exterior. Drain fluid from caliper housing. Place caliper assembly on bench (piston side down). Place several shop towels between piston and outer legs of caliper housing.

2) Carefully apply low-pressure air at caliper inlet port until piston comes out of caliper housing. If piston is seized, lightly tap end of piston with soft-faced hammer.

3) Remove boot from piston and seal from cylinder bore. Clean caliper housing and piston with denatured alcohol. Check cylinder bore, seal groove, and boot groove for damage or excessive wear. Replace piston if pitted.

Reassembly

To assemble caliper, soak all parts in new brake fluid and reverse disassembly procedure. Install piston using Piston Installer (J-24548). Use large "C" clamp to seat piston in cylinder bore.

DISC ROTOR

Lateral Runout

Adjust wheel bearings until all end play is eliminated. Attach dial indicator with contact tip of indicator on braking surface approximately 1" from rotor edge. Set indicator to zero and turn rotor through one complete revolution, noting indicator reading.

Parallelism

Check thickness of rotor at 4 or more points around circumference of rotor. Make all measurements at same distance from edge of rotor. If thickness variation is excessive, refinish or replace rotor as necessary.

TIGHTENING SPECIFICATIONS

Application	Ft. Lbs. (N.m)
Brake Line-to-Caliper	32 (43)
Support Key Retaining Screw	18 (24)
Caliper Mounting Bolts	35 (47)
Hydraulic Line-to-Brake Hose	13 (18)
Bleeder Valve Screws	5 (7)

GENERAL MOTORS SLIDING CALIPER DISCS (Cont.)

DISC BRAKE ROTOR SPECIFICATIONS

Application	Disc Diameter In. (mm)	Lateral Runout In. (mm)	Parallelism In. (mm)	Original Thickness In. (mm)	Min. Refinish Thickness In. (mm)	Discard Thickness In. (mm)
"C" Series	11.86 (301.2)	.004 (.10)	.0005 (.013)	1.04 (26.4)	.980 (24.89)	.965 (24.51)
"G" Series & Vehicles With Diesel Engines	11.86 (301.2)	.004 (.10)	.0005 (.013)	1.28 (32.5)	1.23 (31.2)	1.22 (30.9)
"P" & "K" Series	12.50 (317.5)	.004 (.10)	.0005 (.013)	[1] 1.28 (32.5)	1.23 (31.2)	1.22 (30.9)
"P" & "K" Series	[2] 14.25 (362.0)	.004 (.10)	.0005 (.013)	1.53 (38.9)	1.48 (37.6)	1.465 (37.21)

1 – On rotors that are 1.53" (38.9 mm) thick, minimum thickness is 1.48" (37.6 mm). Discard thickness is 1.465" (37.21 mm).
2 – Rear disc diameter is 13.75" (349.3 mm) for "P"-30 models.

JEEP FLOATING CALIPER DISCS

DESCRIPTION

Floating caliper disc brake assembly uses a single piston caliper which "floats" on 2 bolts. As brake pedal is depressed, hydraulic pressure is passed through a proportioning valve to brake caliper piston.

This force is transmitted to inboard brake pad, forcing it against braking surface of rotor. Pressure then moves outer caliper housing and pad inward on caliper mounting bolts, thus forcing outer pad against outer braking surface of rotor.

When the brake is released, pressure is removed from the cylinders and inherent rotor runout moves pistons back into cylinders to maintain sufficient rotor-to-pad clearance.

ADJUSTMENT & SERVICING

BRAKE PADS

Automatic adjustment is provided by outward relocation of piston as lining wears.

BLEEDING SYSTEM

See HYDRAULIC BRAKE BLEEDING in this section.

REMOVAL & INSTALLATION

BRAKE PADS

Removal

1) Drain 2/3 of brake fluid from master cylinder reservoir. Raise vehicle and support with safety stands. Remove front wheel assembly.

2) Place "C" clamp on caliper. Solid end of clamp should contact back of caliper. Screw end should contact metal part of outboard shoes.

3) Tighten "C" clamp until caliper forces piston to bottom of bore. Remove both Allen head mounting bolts and lift caliper off rotor. Support caliper out of the way.

4) On Grand Wagoneer and Trucks, remove both brake pad from caliper. Note spring position and support spring from inboard shoe. Remove sleeves and bushings from caliper.

5) On all other models, hold anti-rattle clip against caliper adapter and remove outer brake pad. Remove inner brake pad and anti-rattle clip from caliper adapter. Clean caliper mating surfaces on adapter with a wire brush.

Installation

1) To install, reverse removal procedure. On Grand Wagoneer and Trucks, lubricate new bushings, sleeves, bushing grooves, and small ends of mounting bolts with silicone lubricant. Install rubber bushings in caliper mounting ears.

2) On all other models, lubricate caliper mating surfaces on caliper adapter. On all models, tighten mounting pins. Add brake fluid to reservoir. Apply brakes until brake pedal is firm. Check brake fluid level.

BRAKE CALIPER

Removal & Installation

Caliper removal and installation procedures are same as for disc pad replacement. To remove caliper from vehicle, disconnect brake line at caliper and cap hole to prevent contamination.

DISC ROTOR

Removal (Cherokee & Wagoneer)

Raise and support vehicle. Remove front wheel and caliper. Suspend caliper from frame or suspension. Remove rotor.

Installation

Clean hub and rotor mating surfaces. To install, reverse removal procedure.

Removal (CJ7 & Scrambler)

1) Raise and support vehicle. Remove front wheel and caliper. Suspend caliper from frame or suspension. Remove hub body attaching bolts and remove hub body.

2) Remove snap ring from axle shaft. Remove hub clutch and bearing assembly. Straighten lip of outer lock nut retaining washer. Remove outer and inner lock nuts and retaining washers. Remove hub and rotor. Remove wheel bearings from rotor.

Installation

1) Install wheel bearings and grease seal in rotor. Install rotor. Install tabbed washer and inner lock nut. Install wheel, but do not tighten lug nuts completely.

2) Tighten inner lock nut to 50 ft. lbs. (68 N.m) while rotating wheel. Back off inner lock nut 1/6 turn (45-65°). Install tabbed washer and outer lock nut. Tighten outer lock nut to 50 ft. lbs. (68 N.m).

3) Bend lip of tabbed washer over lock nut. Install hub clutch and bearing assembly on axle shaft. Install snap ring. Install hub body on bearing assembly with a new gasket.

4) Align bolt holes and install hub attaching bolts and tabbed lock washers. Tighten bolts to 30 ft. lbs. (41 N.m). Reverse removal procedure to complete installation.

Removal (Grand Wagoneer & Truck)

1) Raise vehicle and support with safety stands. Remove wheel and caliper. On models without front hubs, remove rotor hub cap, drive gear snap ring, drive gear, pressure spring and spring cup.

2) On models with front hubs, remove screws attaching hub body to hub clutch and remove hub body from clutch. Remove large and small retaining rings. Remove hub clutch from axle shaft.

3) On all models, remove wheel bearing outer and inner lock nuts and retaining ring using Socket (J-6893-D). Remove rotor. Remove wheel bearings from rotor.

Installation

1) Lubricate bearings with "EP" type water proof wheel bearing grease. Install bearings and seal in rotor. Install rotor and inner lock nut. Inner lock nut has a locating peg on one side. When installed, peg must face away from bearing.

2) Install wheel, but do not tighten lug nuts completely. Tighten inner lock nut to 50 ft. lbs. (68 N.m) while rotating wheel. Back of inner lock nut 1/6 turn (45-65°).

3) Install retaining washer. Ensure that inner lock nut locating peg is engaged with retaining washer. Install outer lock nut and tighten to 50 ft. lbs. (68 N.m).

4) On models without front hubs, install pressure spring cup, pressure spring, drive gear and snap ring. Coat rim of chrome hub cover with Permatex No. 3 and install cap in rotor hub.

JEEP FLOATING CALIPER DISCS (Cont.)

NOTE: Recessed side of spring cup faces outer bearing and flat side faces pressure spring.

5) On models with front hubs, install hub clutch on axle. Install large and small hub retaining rings. Install hub body on clutch and tighten to 30 INCH lbs. (3 N.m). Reverse removal procedure to complete installation.

OVERHAUL

CALIPER

Disassembly

1) Clean caliper exterior with brake cleaning solvent. Drain residual fluid from caliper and place caliper on a clean working surface.

2) Remove piston from caliper by applying compressed air to inlet port. Use just enough pressure to ease piston out of bore. Protect piston from damage with folded shop towels. Do not try to catch piston by hand.

3) Pry dust boot out of bore with screwdriver. Do not scratch bore. Using a small plastic or wooden stick, pry piston seal from bore. *See Fig. 1*. Remove bleeder screw, sleeves, and bushings.

Cleaning & Inspection

1) Clean all parts with brake cleaning solvent. Blow dry parts with dry, filtered air. Examine parts for rust, corrosion, pitting, scratches, or cracks. Replace piston if it is damaged or corroded.

2) Minor stains on piston bore can be polished with crocus cloth. Do not use emery cloth or any other abrasive. Wash bore thoroughly with brake fluid after using crocus cloth. Replace caliper if bore is damaged or corroded.

Fig. 1: CJ7, Cherokee, Scrambler & Wagoneer Caliper Assembly

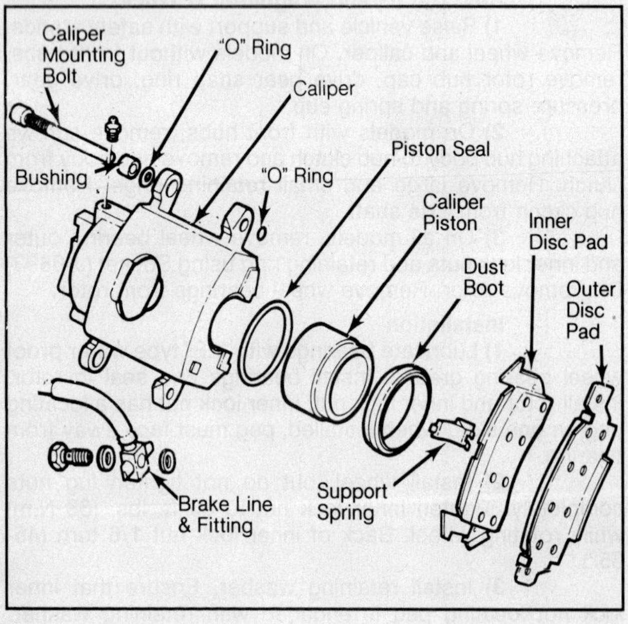

Reassembly

1) Lubricate bore and new seal with brake fluid. Install seal in groove using fingers. Lubricate piston with brake fluid. Slide metal retainer portion of dust boot over over open end of piston. Pull boot rearward until boot lip seats in piston groove.

2) Push retainer portion of dust boot forward until boot is flush with rim at open end of piston and boot fold snaps into place. Insert piston in bore being careful not to unseat piston seal.

3) Push piston to bottom of bore using hammer handle. Position dust boot retainer in counterbore at top of piston bore. Seat dust boot retainer with Dust Boot Installer (J-22904 or J-33028).

4) Metal retainer portion of boot must be evenly seated in counterbore and must fit below face of caliper. Install bleeder screw. Install new sleeves and bushings in caliper. Connect brake line to caliper using new copper gaskets.

Fig. 2: Grand Wagoneer & Truck Caliper Assembly

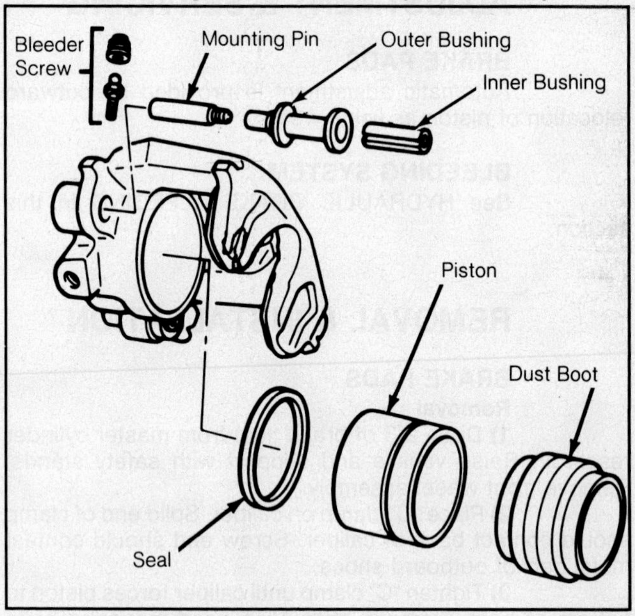

ROTOR

Runout

1) Measure rotor lateral runout by mounting a dial indicator on support stand or steering spindle. Position indicator stylus so it contacts center of rotor braking surface.

2) Zero indicator and turn rotor 1 revolution. Note indicator reading. Runout must not exceed specification. Refinish or replace rotor as necessary.

Parallelism

Measure rotor parallelism with a micrometer. Measure thickness at 4 or more equally spaced points around rotor at approximately 1" (25.4 mm) from edge of rotor. Variation must not exceed specification. Refinish or replace rotor as necessary.

NOTE: Thickness of machined rotor must not be below minimum thickness specification.

TIGHTENING SPECIFICATIONS

Application	Ft. Lbs. (N.m)
Caliper Mounting Bolts	35 (47)
Bleeder Screw	12 (16)
Brake Line-to-Caliper	13 (18)

JEEP FLOATING CALIPER DISCS (Cont.)

DISC BRAKE ROTOR SPECIFICATIONS

Application	Disc Diameter In. (mm)	Lateral Runout In. (mm)	Parallelism In. (mm)	Original Thickness In. (mm)	Min. Refinish Thickness In. (mm)	Discard Thickness In. (mm)
Cherokee & Wagoneer	11.02 (279.9)	.005 (.13)	.001 (.03)	.88 (22.4)	.....	.815 (20.70)
CJ7 & Scrambler	11.70 (297.2)	.005 (.13)	.001 (.03)	.88 (22.4)	.....	.815 (20.70)
Grand Wagoneer & Truck	[1] 12.00 (304.8)	.005 (.13)	.001 (.03)	.....	.....	1.215 (30.86)

[1] – Disc diameter on "J"-20 truck is 12.50" (317.5 mm).

Brake Systems

CHRYSLER CORP. SINGLE ANCHOR

DESCRIPTION

Chrysler Corp. vehicles use both Chrysler and Bendix single anchor brake assemblies. Chrysler brake design is used on all 9" and 11" diameter brake applications. Bendix brake design is used on all 12" brake applications.

Both types of brake assemblies consist of a support plate, 2 brake shoes, return springs, wheel cylinder, and a cable type adjuster assembly. The automatic adjuster assembly consists of a cable (with hook and anchor fitting), cable guide, adjuster lever, adjusting screw, pivot, socket, and spring.

ADJUSTMENT & SERVICING

BRAKE SHOES

1) Raise and support vehicle. Ensure parking brake lever is fully released and back off parking brake cable adjustment to ensure cable has slack. Remove adjusting hole cover.

2) Using Brake Adjuster (C-3784), expand brake shoes until slight drag is felt when wheel assembly is rotated. Using thin screwdriver, hold automatic adjusting lever away from adjustment star wheel.

3) Back off adjustment star wheel just until wheel assembly rotates freely and brake shoe drag is eliminated. Repeat adjustment for remaining wheels. Adjustment must be equal at all wheels. Replace adjusting hole covers and adjust parking brake.

BLEEDING SYSTEM

See HYDRAULIC BRAKE BLEEDING in this section.

PARKING BRAKE

FWD Models

1) Adjust service brakes. Release parking brake and loosen cable adjusting nut to allow slack in cable. Tighten cable adjusting nut until a slight drag is felt while rotating rear wheels.

2) Loosen cable adjusting nut until both rear wheels can be rotated freely. Back off adjusting nut an additional 2 turns. Apply and release parking brake several times, checking for free rotation at rear wheels.

RWD Models

1) Raise vehicle high enough to gain access to equalizer and cable adjuster. Make sure parking brake cable adjuster is fully released. Loosen adjuster so there is slack in both cables.

2) Make sure rear brakes are correctly adjusted. Tighten cable adjusting nut at adjuster until a slight drag is felt while rotating wheel.

3) Loosen adjusting nut until both wheels can be rotated freely. Apply and release parking brake. Ensure wheels rotate freely without any brake drag. Lower vehicle.

REMOVAL & INSTALLATION

BRAKE SHOES

Removal (Chrysler)

1) Remove drum. Note how secondary spring overlaps primary spring. Remove brake shoe return springs using Spring Remover (C-3785). Slide automatic adjuster cable off anchor. Disconnect cable from adjusting lever.

Fig. 1: Exploded View of Chrysler Brake Assembly

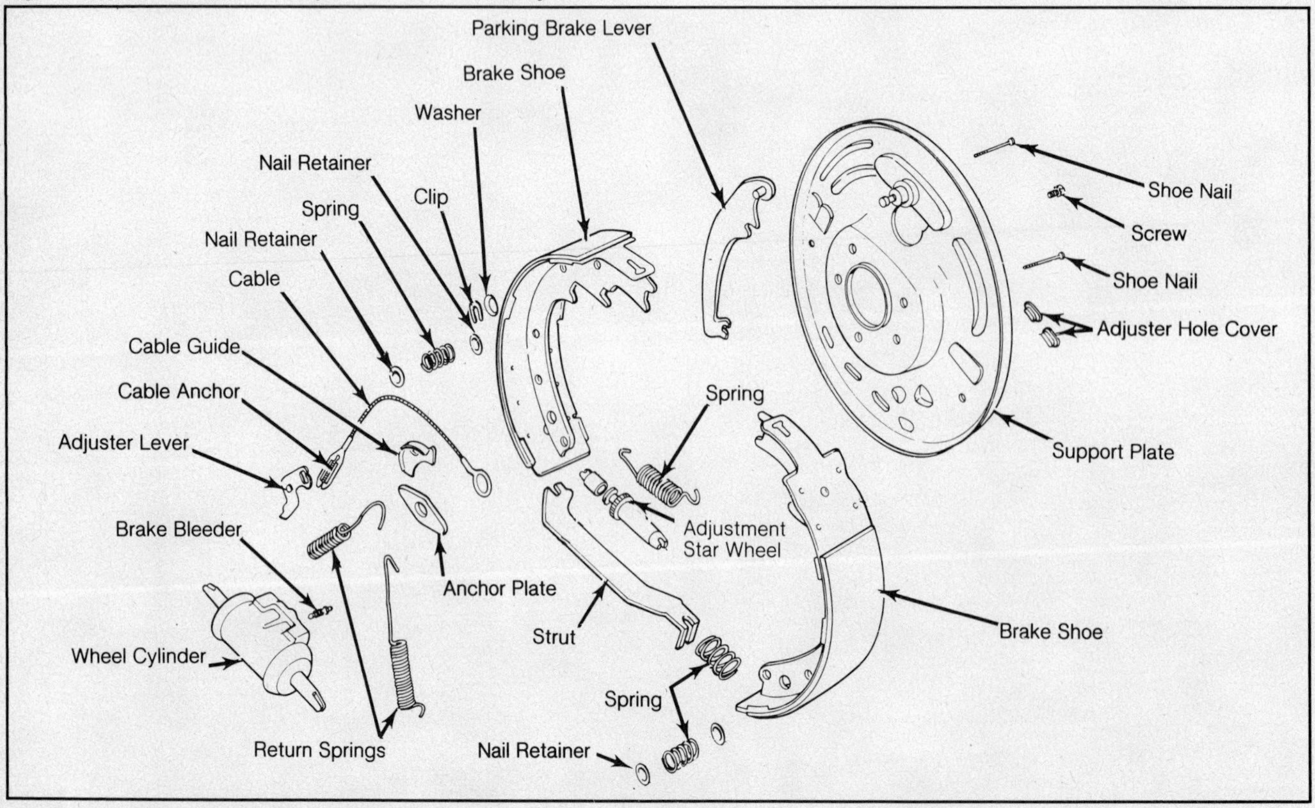

CHRYSLER CORP. SINGLE ANCHOR (Cont.)

Fig. 2: Exploded View of Bendix Brake Assembly

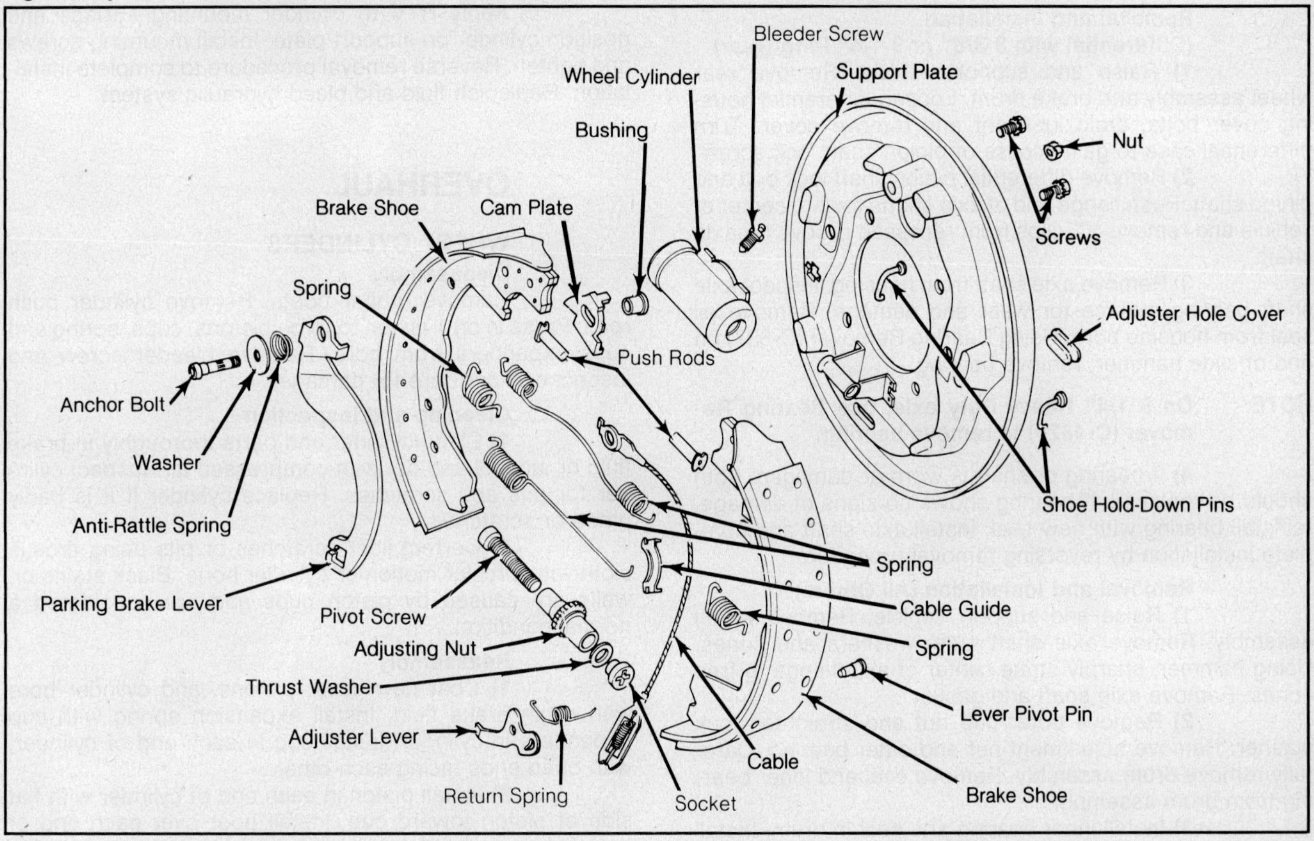

2) Remove cable, overload spring, cable guide, and anchor plate. Disengage adjusting lever from spring and remove spring and lever from pivot. Remove shoe-to-shoe spring, spread shoes and remove adjustment star wheel.

3) Remove shoe retainers, springs and nails. Remove parking brake lever from secondary shoe. Remove shoes and strut with anti-rattle springs. Detach parking brake lever from cable.

Installation

1) Apply thin coat of multi-purpose grease to 6 shoe contact pads on support plate. Attach parking brake lever to cable and install lever in rectangular hole in secondary shoe.

2) Place secondary shoe against support plate ensuring push rod and anchor are properly positioned. Insert strut into slot in parking brake lever. Slide anti-rattle spring over free end of strut.

3) Ensure tab on anti-rattle spring is located behind web of shoe and pointed forward and down. Install primary shoe, ensuring push rod and strut are properly positioned.

4) Install anchor plate and eye of adjusting cable over anchor. Install primary return spring. Position cable guide over hole in secondary shoe and install secondary return spring.

NOTE: **Left adjustment star wheel is stamped "L" and cadmium plated, right is stamped "R" and is Black.**

5) Install adjustment star wheel with wheel next to secondary shoe. Install shoe-to-shoe spring, engaging in primary shoe first with coil on opposite side of adjusting lever. Install adjusting lever spring over pivot pin.

6) Install adjusting lever under spring and over pivot. Slide lever rearward to lock in position. Install shoe nails, springs and retainers. Thread adjuster cable over guide and hook end of overload spring in lever.

Removal (Bendix)

1) Remove drum. Disconnect adjusting lever return spring from lever. Remove lever and return spring from pivot pin. Disconnect adjusting lever from cable. Remove upper shoe-to-shoe spring.

2) Disconnect and remove shoe retainers, springs and nails. Disconnect parking brake cable from lever. Remove lower shoe-to-shoe spring. Remove shoes and adjustment star wheel as an assembly.

Installation

NOTE: **Adjustment star wheel on left brake assembly has left-hand threads, right side assembly has right-hand threads.**

1) Lubricate and assemble adjustment star wheel. Apply thin film of multipurpose grease to shoe contact pads on support plate. Assemble lower shoe-to-shoe spring, adjustment star wheel and both shoes.

2) Position shoe assembly on support plate. Attach parking brake cable to lever. Install shoe nails, springs and retainers. Install upper shoe-to-shoe spring.

3) Position adjusting lever return spring on pivot. Ennsure that Yellow spring is on left brakes and Black spring is on right. Install adjusting lever. Route cable and connect to adjuster.

CHRYSLER CORP. SINGLE ANCHOR (Cont.)

AXLE BEARING & SEAL

Removal and Installation

(Differential with 8 3/8" or 9 1/4" Ring Gear)

1) Raise and support vehicle. Remove rear wheel assembly and brake drum. Loosen differential housing cover bolts, drain lubricant and remove cover. Turn differential case to gain access of pinion shaft lock screw.

2) Remove differential pinion shaft lock bolt and pinion shaft. Push flange end of axle shafts toward center of vehicle and remove "C" clips from recessed groove on axle shaft.

3) Remove axle shaft from housing. Inspect axle shaft bearing surface for wear and damage. Remove oil seal from housing bore. Using Bearing Remover (C-637) on end of slide hammer, remove bearing.

NOTE: **On 9 1/4" Heavy Duty axle, use Bearing Remover (C-4828) to remove bearing.**

4) If bearing or shaft is worn or damaged, both should be replaced. If bearing shows no signs of damage, reinstall bearing with new seal. Install axle shaft and complete installation by reversing removal procedure.

Removal and Installation (All Others)

1) Raise and support vehicle. Remove wheel assembly. Remove axle shaft nuts, washers and cones. Using hammer, sharply strike center of axle flange to free cones. Remove axle shaft and gasket.

2) Remove outer hub nut and straighten lock washer. Remove adjustment nut and outer bearing. Carefully remove drum assembly. Remove seal and inner bearing from drum assembly.

3) Install inner bearing and seal in drum. Install drum assembly, outer bearing, and adjustment nut. Tighten adjustment nut to 120-140 ft. lbs. (163-190 N.m) while rotating drum.

4) Back off adjustment nut approximately 1/3 turn (120°) to obtain .001-.008" (0.03-0.20 mm) end play. Tap lock washer into spindle keyway. Install gasket and axle shaft. Install wheel assembly and lower vehicle.

WHEEL CYLINDERS

Removal

Remove wheel, drum, and brake shoes. Inspect boots for damage and signs of leakage. Disconnect hydraulic brake line from wheel cylinder. Remove attaching bolts and remove cylinder.

Installation

Apply RTV to cylinder mounting surface and position cylinder on support plate. Install mounting screws and tighten. Reverse removal procedure to complete installation. Replenish fluid and bleed hydraulic system.

OVERHAUL

WHEEL CYLINDERS

Disassembly

Remove rubber boots. Remove cylinder push rods. Press in on 1 piston to force pistons, cups, spring and cups expanders from bore. Remove bleeder screw and inspect cylinder bore for damage.

Cleaning and Inspection

1) Clean cylinder and parts thoroughly in brake fluid or alcohol and dry with compressed air. Inspect cylinder for pits and scratches. Replace cylinder if it is badly pitted or scratched.

2) Correct light scratches or pits using crocus cloth with circular motion or cylinder hone. Black stains on walls are caused by piston cups and are considered a normal condition.

Reassembly

1) Coat new cups, pistons, and cylinder bore with clean brake fluid. Install expansion spring with cup expanders in cylinder. Install cup in each end of cylinder, with open ends facing each other.

2) Install piston in each end of cylinder with flat side of piston toward cup. Install boot over each end of cylinder ensuring boot seats properly against cylinder shoulder. Lubricate push rods and insert into each boot.

TIGHTENING SPECIFICATIONS

Application	Ft. Lbs. (N.m)
Axle Shaft Flange or	
Support Plate Mounting Nuts	
3/8"	35-55 (47-75)
7/16"	40-70 (54-95)
1/2"	65-105 (88-142)
Durlock	70 (95)
Differential Cover Bolts	21 (28)
Wheel Cylinder Mounting Bolts	11-19 (15-26)

DRUM BRAKE SPECIFICATIONS

Application	Drum Diam. In. (mm)	Drum Width In. (mm)	Max. Drum Refinish Diam. In. (mm)	Wheel Cyl. Diam. In. (mm)	Master Cyl. Diam. In. (mm)
Chrysler (FWD Models)	9 (229)	....	[1] 9.06 (230.1)	.75 (19.1)	.95 (24.1)
Chrysler (RWD Models)	11 (279)	2.50 (63.5)	[1] 11.06 (280.9)	.938 (23.8)	1.125 (28.6)
Bendix	12 (305)	[2] 3.00 (76.2)	[1] 12.06 (306.3)	[3] 1.00 (25.4)	1.125 (28.6)

[1] – Maximum diameter stamping on drum exceeds recommended maximum drum refinishing specification. Stamping includes .030" (.76 mm) allowable drum wear beyond recommended maximum specification.

[2] – All models except: D250 and D350 with Spicer 44 front axle; B-350 w/3600 front axle and B-350 with 8510 GVWR and 4000 front axle. These have 2.50" (63.5 mm) width.

[3] – All models with 2.50" (63.5 mm) drum width only. Wheel cylinder diameter on models with 3.00" (76.2 mm) drum width are 1.125" (28.6 mm) on trucks, 1.06" (26.9 mm) on vans and wagons.

FORD SINGLE ANCHOR

DESCRIPTION

The single anchor dual servo brake assembly is used on the rear of all 2WD trucks and on all 4 wheels of the 4WD vehicles (without disc brakes). This assembly consists of a support plate, 2 brake shoes, return springs, automatic adjuster components, and a wheel cylinder.

The automatic adjuster consists of a cable (with hood and anchor fitting), a cable guide, adjusting lever, adjusting screw, pivot nut, socket and spring.

The adjuster uses movement of the secondary shoe during reverse brake application to turn brake adjusting screw and maintain proper lining-to-drum clearance.

ADJUSTMENT & SERVICING

BRAKE SHOES

All Models

1) Adjustment is made with brake drums at room temperature and parking brakes correctly adjusted. Measure inside diameter of brake drum with brake shoe adjustment gauge. *See Fig. 1.*

Fig. 1: Measuring Brake Drum Diameter

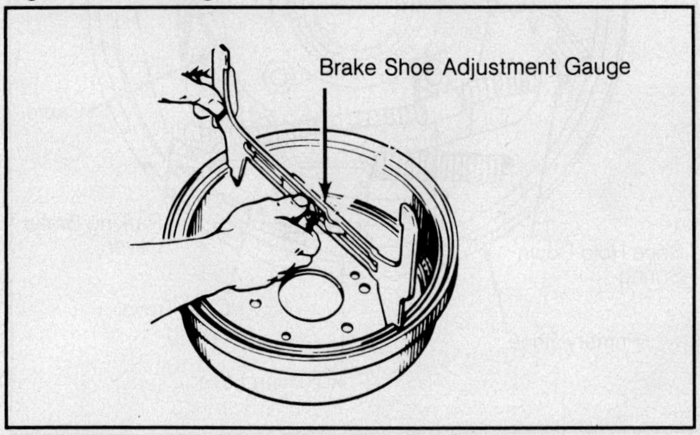

Check diameter with drum at room temperature.

2) Reverse tool and apply to brake shoes on a line parallel to ground, and through center of axle. Hold automatic adjuster lever away from adjusting screw and turn screw until outside diameter of shoes contacts gauge. *See Fig. 2.*

Fig. 2: Measuring Brake Shoe Diameter

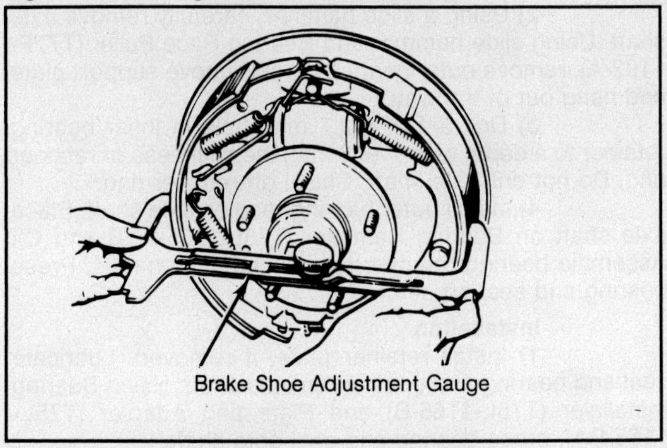

Shoes should just make contact with gauge.

3) Install brake drum and wheel assembly. Complete adjustment by applying brakes several times while driving vehicle in reverse. Check brake operation by making several stops while driving forward.

PARKING BRAKE

NOTE: Aerostar parking brake system is self-adjusting and requires no adjustment. On all other models, if front brake cable tension limiting device is replaced, initial adjustment procedures must be performed before adjusting cable. If tensioner is not replaced, initial adjustment is not required.

Initial Adjustment (Foot Pedal Actuated)

Depress parking brake pedal. Grip tension limiter bracket to prevent it from spinning. Tighten equalizer nut 2 1/2" up the rod. Check to make sure the cinch strap has slipped so that less than 1 3/8" remains exposed.

Final Adjustment

1) Adjust service brakes before adjusting parking brake cable. Ensure brake drums are cold.

2) Position parking brake pedal to the fully depressed position. Grip tension limiter housing to prevent it from spinning. Tighten equalizer nut 6 full turns past its original position.

3) Check cable tension at rear of equalizer assembly using Cable Tension Gauge (021-00018). Bronco II and Ranger tension should be 400-600 lbs. (182-272 kg) and 350 lbs. (159 kg) for all others. If tension is low, repeat step **2)**.

4) Release pedal and check rear wheel drag. If drag is noted on all models, except Bronco II and Ranger, remove drums and check for clearance between parking brake lever and cam plate.

5) Clearance should be .015" (.38 mm) with brakes fully released. If clearance is incorrect, readjust parking brake cable.

Initial Adjustment (Orscheln Lever Acutated)

1) Adjust service brakes before adjusting parking brake cables. Turn parking brake handle adjustment knob fully clockwise and apply parking brake.

2) Grip tension limiter housing to prevent it from spinning. Tighten equalizer nut 2 1/2" up the rod. Check to make sure the cinch strap has slipped so that less than 1 3/8" remains exposed.

3) Release parking brake lever. Turn adjustment knob counterclockwise. Install Cable Tension Gauge (021-00018) on cable, 2 1/2" behind equalizer. Apply parking brake, cable tension should be a minimum of 350 lbs. (159 kg). If tension is incorrect, repeat procedure.

Final Adjustment

1) Adjust service brakes and ensure brake drums are cold. Apply parking brake. Grip tension limiter housing to prevent it from spinning. Tighten equalizer nut until front cable tension measures 350 lbs. (159 kg).

2) Release and reapply parking brake. Check that front cable tension is at least 310 lbs. (141 kg). Release pedal and check rear wheel drag.

3) If drag is noted, remove drums and check for clearance between parking brake lever and cam plate. Clearance should be .015" (.38 mm) with brakes fully released. If clearance is incorrect, readjust parking brake cable.

BLEEDING SYSTEM

See HYDRAULIC BRAKE BLEEDING in this section.

FORD SINGLE ANCHOR (Cont.)

REMOVAL & INSTALLATION

BRAKE SHOES

Removal (E & F250/350)

1) Remove wheel assembly and brake drum. Remove parking brake assembly retaining nut from backing plate. Remove parking brake assembly. Remove adjusting cable assembly from anchor pin, cable guide, and adjusting lever.

2) Remove brake shoe return springs, hold down springs, and brake shoes. *See Fig. 3*. Remove and disassemble adjusting screw assembly.

Installation

To install, reverse removal procedure. Before installing brake shoes, apply a thin coat of multipurpose grease to contact points of brake assembly.

Fig. 3: Rear Brake Assembly (E & F250/350)

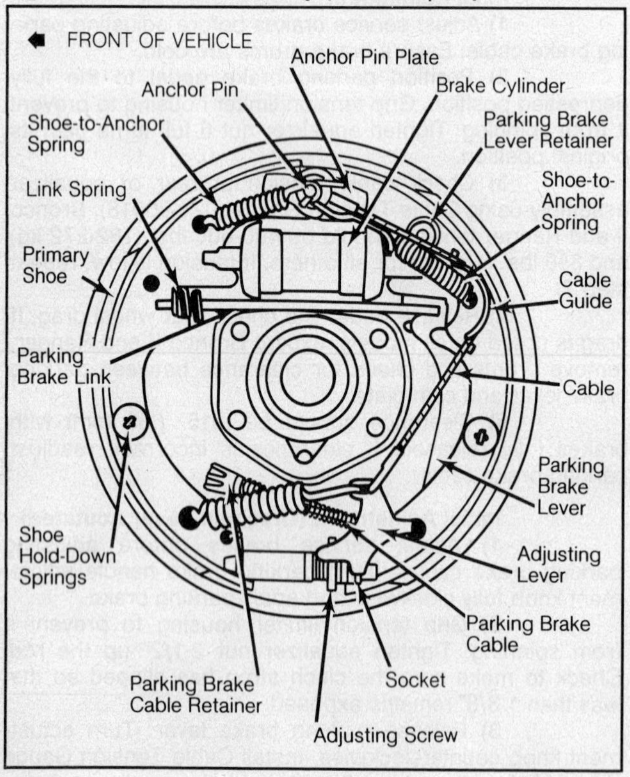

Removal (All Other Models)

1) Remove wheel assembly and drum. Place a clamp over ends of wheel cylinder. Disengage adjusting lever from adjusting screw by pulling backwards on lever.

2) Move outboard side of adjusting screw up, and back off pivot nut as far as possible. Pull adjusting lever, cable, and automatic adjuster spring down, and toward rear to unhook pivot hook from large hole in secondary shoe. Do not pry pivot hook from hole.

3) Remove automatic adjuster spring and adjusting lever. Remove shoe to anchor springs, cable anchor, and anchor pin plate. *See Fig. 4*.

4) Remove cable guide, shoe hold-down springs, shoes adjusting screw, pivot nut, and socket. Remove parking brake spring and link. Note color and position of springs for reassembly.

5) Disconnect parking brake cable from lever. Remove secondary shoe and disassemble parking brake lever from shoe by removing retaining clip and spring washer.

Installation

To install, reverse removal procedure. Make sure adjusting cable is in groove of cable guide. Check that cable does not bind on anchor pin, and adjusting screw is mounted on correct side. If adjuster screw is mounted on wrong side, adjuster will operate incorrectly.

Fig. 4: Rear Brake Assembly (Except E & F250/350)

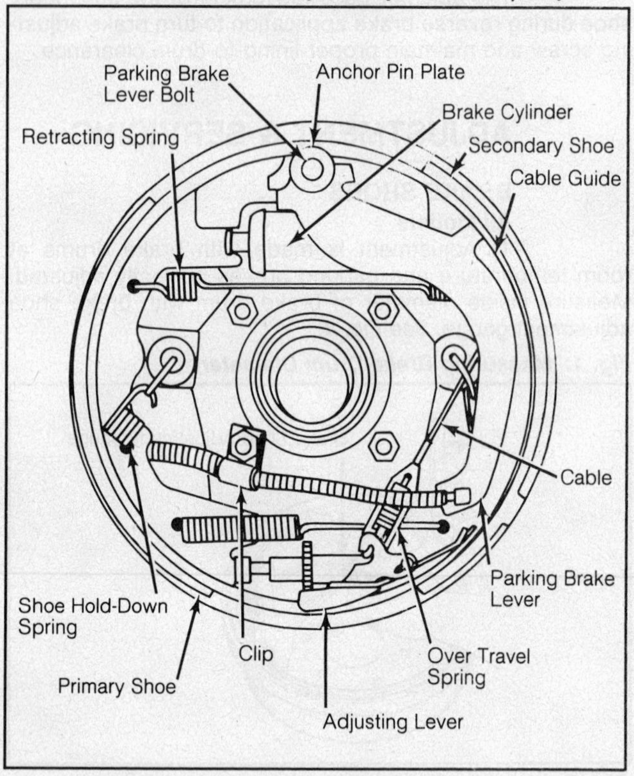

AXLE BEARING & SEAL

Removal (Bronco 4WD & F150)

1) Raise vehicle and support with safety stands. Remove wheel assembly and brake drum. Remove support plate mounting nuts through hole provided in axle shaft flange.

2) Using a slide hammer, carefully remove axle shaft. Using slide hammer and Bearing Race Puller (T77F-1102-A), remove outer bearing race. Remove support plate and hang out of the way.

3) Drill a 1/2" (12.7 mm) hole in inner bearing retainer to a depth of 3/8" (9.5 mm) the thickness of retainer ring. Do not drill axle shaft. Chisel off retainer ring.

4) Install outer bearing race on axle shaft. Place axle shaft on Bearing Remover (T75L-1165-A, B and C). Assemble bearing remover halves and tighten nuts. Press bearing and seal off shaft.

Installation

1) Install retainer plate, if removed. Lubricate seal and bearing and position on axle shaft. Using Bearing Installaler (T75L-1165-B) and Plate and Adapter (T75L-1165-DA), press bearing and seal onto shaft.

2) Position new inner bearing retainer on shaft. Press retainer firmly against bearing. Apply multipurpose grease to outer diameter of cup and seal. Install support plate and attaching bolts.

FORD SINGLE ANCHOR (Cont.)

3) Ensure that outer seal is installed on bearing. Carefully slide axle shaft into housing. Start axle shaft splines into side gear, and push in on shaft until bearing bottoms in housing. Install retainer plate. Tighten nuts to 20-40 ft. lbs. (27-54 N.m). Reverse removal procedure to complete installation.

Removal (All Other Models)

1) Raise vehicle and support with safety stands. Remove wheel assembly and brake drum. Loosen differential cover plate and drain lubricant from axle. Remove cover plate and discard gasket.

2) Remove differential pinion shaft lock bolt (lock pin) and discard. Remove differential pinion shaft. Push flanged end of axle toward center of vehicle and remove "C" clip from end of shaft. Do not lose or damage "O" ring (if used) under "C" clip.

3) Pull axle shaft from axle tube, being carefull not to damage oil seal. When removing axle shaft, do not rotate differential side gears. Rotating side gears causes pinion gears and thrust washers to fall out.

4) On E/F250 with Model 60 rear axle, remove oil seal from axle tube. Pull bearing from axle tube using Puller (T81P-1104-C), Adapters (T81P-1104-B Coarse Thread or D81T-1104-A Fine Thread), and Wheel Bearing Remover (T81T-1225-A).

5) On Aerostar, Bronco II and Ranger, insert Slide Hammer (T50T-100-A) and Axle Bearing Remover (T85L-1225-AH) behind bearing. On all other models (8.8" ring gear), insert Slide Hammer (T50T-100-A) and Seal Remover (T83T-1225-A) behind bearing. Remove seal and bearing.

Installation

1) On Aerostar, Bronco II and Ranger, lubricate bearing with axle lubricant and install bearing using Wheel Bearing Replacer (T78P-1225-A). Lubricate lips of seal with multi-purpose grease. Install seal with Seal Replacer (T78P-1177-A).

2) On all models with 8.8" ring gear, lubricate bearing with axle lubricant and install bearing using Wheel Bearing Replacer (T83T-1225-B). Lubricate lips of seal with multi-purpose grease. Install seal with Seal Replacer (T83T-1175-A).

3) On E/F250 with Model 60 rear axle, ensure that bearing bore is free of nicks and burrs. If necessary, wipe bore with emery cloth to obtain a smooth surface. Coat bearing with differential lube.

4) Press bearing into bore using Puller (T81P-1104-C), Adapters (T81P-1104-B or D81T-1104-A), Step Plate (D80L-630-1), and Rear Axle Bearing Replacer (T80T-4000-X). Ensure that bearing is not cocked.

5) Using Rear Oil Seal Installer ((T80T-4000-Y) and Handle (T80T-4000-X), drive oil seal into bore. Lubricate lips of seal with multipurpose, lithium base grease.

6) On all models, install axle shaft. Make sure that splined shaft engages side gears. Push flanged end of axle shaft toward center of axle and install "C" clip. Pull axle shaft outward until "C" clips locks into side gear.

7) Install pinion shaft, making sure that hole in shaft is lined up with hole in case. Ensure that pinion thrust washers are in position. Ensure that threads in case and lock screw are free of dirt and oil.

8) Install new lock bolt (lock pin). Tighten lock bolt to 20-25 ft. lbs. (27-34 N.m). Add RTV or silicone sealer to cover plate and install. Reverse removal procedure to complete installation.

HUB BEARINGS & SEAL

Removal (E & F250 H.D., E & F350)

1) Set parking brake and loosen axle shaft attahing bolts. Raise vehicle and support with safety stands. Release parking brakes. Remove axle shaft attaching bolts and lock washers. *See Fig. 5.* Discard bolts and washers.

2) Remove axle shaft and gasket. Discard gasket. Pry out locking wedge. Using a wheel dolly, raise wheel to remove all weight from bearings. Remove bearing adjustment nut and outer bearing. Remove wheel assembly from axle.

3) Remove inner bearing and seal out of hub with brass drift. Avoid damage to bearing cage. Clean and inspect bearings and races. If bearings need replacement, remove bearing outer races from hub with a brass drift.

Installation

1) If bearings are replaced, press new bearing outer races into hub with Bearing Race Replacer (T75T-1225-A and T75T-1225-B). Make sure bearing race is seated correctly. A feeler gauge .0015" (.038 mm) thick should not fit between hub and bearing race.

2) Pack bearings with multipurpose, lithium base grease. Place inner bearing in hub and install new seal with bearing race replacer. Tape over threads on end of spindle. Slide hub assembly over spindle, using care to avoid damaging seal lips.

3) Remove tape and install outer bearing and adjustment nut. Using Hex Lock Nut Wrench (T70T-4252-D) or Octal Lock Nut Wrench (T70T-4252-E), tighten adjustment nut to 120-140 ft. lbs. (163-190 N.m) while rotating wheel.

4) Back off adjustment nut until hub bearing end play is .001-.010" (.03-.25 mm). This should require 1/8 to 3/8 turn of adjustment nut. If end play is correct, place locking wedge into keyway in spindle and pound wedge into nylon retainer ring.

NOTE: **Locking wedge must cut new groove in nylon retainer. Nut and wedge must be replaced if nut cannot be positioned within correct end play range so that new groove is cut in nylon retainer.**

Fig. 5: Hub Bearing Installation

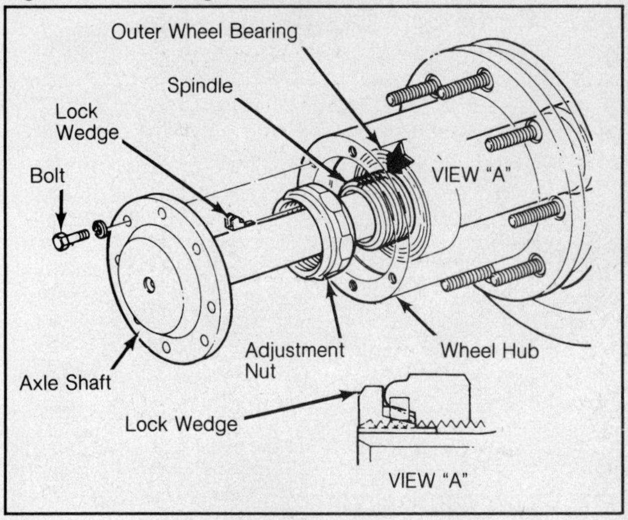

Wedge must cut new groove in nylon retainer.

FORD SINGLE ANCHOR (Cont.)

5) Install axle shaft with new flange gasket, lock washers, and new axle shaft retaining bolts. Tighten bolts to 40-50 ft. lbs. (54-68 N.m). Adjust brakes if necessary.

WHEEL CYLINDER

Removal & Installation

Remove wheel assembly, drum, and brake shoes. Remove cylinder connecting links and disconnect hydraulic brake line from cylinder. Remove brake cylinder retaining bolts. Remove cylinder from backing plate. To install, reverse removal procedure. Adjust brakes and bleed hydraulic system.

OVERHAUL

WHEEL CYLINDERS

Disassembly

With the wheel cylinder removed from vehicle, remove rubber boots from ends of cylinders. Remove piston return spring, cylinder cups, and piston from cylinder. Remove bleeder screw and inspect cylinder bore for damage.

Reassembly

If bore of cylinder is lightly pitted or scratched, hone or replace as necessary. Soak all parts in brake fluid or assembly lube, and reverse disassembly procedures. Clamp brake cylinder pistons against ends of cylinder.

TIGHTENING SPECIFICATIONS

Application	Ft. Lbs. (N.m)
Hydraulic Tube Nuts	
3/8" & 7/16"	10-15 (14-20)
1/2" & 9/16"	10-17 (14-23)
Support Plate-to-Axle	
7/16"	35-45 (47-61)
1/2 x 13"	75-105 (102-142)
1/2 x 20"	50-70 (68-95)
9/16"	135-165 (183-224)

DRUM BRAKE SPECIFICATIONS

Application	Drum Diam. In. (mm)	Drum Width In. (mm)	Max. Drum Refinish Diam. In. (mm)	Wheel Cyl. Diam. In. (mm)	Master Cyl. Diam. In. (mm)
Aerostar, Bronco II & Ranger	9.00 (228.6)	1.75 (44.5)	9.06 (230.1)	.....	.938 (23.8)
Bronco, E150 & F150	11.03 (280.2)	2.25 (57.2)	11.09 (281.7)	.....	1.00 (25.4)
E250, E350 & F250 (Exc. H.D.)	12.00 (304.8)	2.50 (63.5)	12.06 (306.3)	.....	1.062 (26.9)
E350 H.D, F250 H.D. & F350	12.00 (304.8)	3.00 (76.2)	12.06 (306.3)	.....	1.062 (26.9)

GENERAL MOTORS SINGLE ANCHOR

DESCRIPTION

Delco single anchor, duo-servo type brake assemblies are used on the rear of all models. The assemblies consist of a support plate, 2 brake shoes, return springs, automatic adjuster components and a duo-servo wheel cylinder.

Automatic adjusters consist of a connecting link, override lever, override spring, return spring, actuating lever and an adjusting screw. Normal adjustment is accomplished through movement of actuating lever and secondary shoe during application of brakes when vehicle is operated in reverse.

ADJUSTMENT & SERVICING

BRAKE SHOES

1) Knock out lanced area in brake drum with a punch. If drum is installed, it must be removed and all metal removed from brake area.

2) Turn adjusting screw, through hole, until brake shoes expand and brake drums can just be turned by hand. The drag should be equal at all wheels.

3) Back off adjusting screw 30 notches at each wheel. If drum still drags, back off an additional 1 or 2 notches. Install hole cover in drum.

PARKING BRAKE

Foot Pedal Actuated

1) With service brakes correctly adjusted, raise vehicle until both rear wheels are off ground. Loosen equalizer adjusting nut. Apply parking brake 3 notches from fully released position.

2) Tighten adjusting nut until a slight drag is felt when wheels are rotated forward. Tighten lock nut. Release parking brake and wheels should rotate forward freely. Lower vehicle.

Orscheln Lever Actuated

1) With service brakes in proper adjustment, turn adjusting knob on lever counterclockwise to stop. Apply parking brake and raise vehicle until both rear wheels are off ground.

2) Loosen intermediate cable equalizer lock nut and adjust front nut until slight drag is felt when rear wheels are rotated forward. Tighten lock nut. Readjust lever adjusting knob to obtain definite snap-over-center feel. Release parking brake, check that wheels rotate freely.

Transmission Mounted (Internal Shoe)

1) With at least 1 rear wheel raised off ground, block wheels and release parking brake. Remove cotter pin and clevis pin connecting pull rod and relay lever.

2) Rotate drum to bring one access hole into line with adjuster screw at bottom of brake shoes (manual transmission) or top of shoes (automatic transmission). Knock out plug in drum for access hole, if necessary.

3) Rotate adjusting screws with a screwdriver to expand shoes until tight against drum. Drum should not be able to be rotated by hand. Back off adjuster screw 10 notches. Place parking brake lever in full released position.

4) Pull on brake cable enough to take up slack in brake linkage. Adjust pull rod clevis to line up with hole in relay lever. Insert clevis pin and roller pin. Tighten clevis lock nut. Install a new plug in access hole in drum and lower vehicle.

BLEEDING SYSTEM

See HYDRAULIC BRAKE BLEEDING in this section.

REMOVAL & INSTALLATION

BRAKE SHOES

Removal

1) Raise vehicle and support with safety stands. Remove wheel assembly and brake drum. It may be neces-

Fig. 1: Exploded View of Single Anchor Brake Assembly

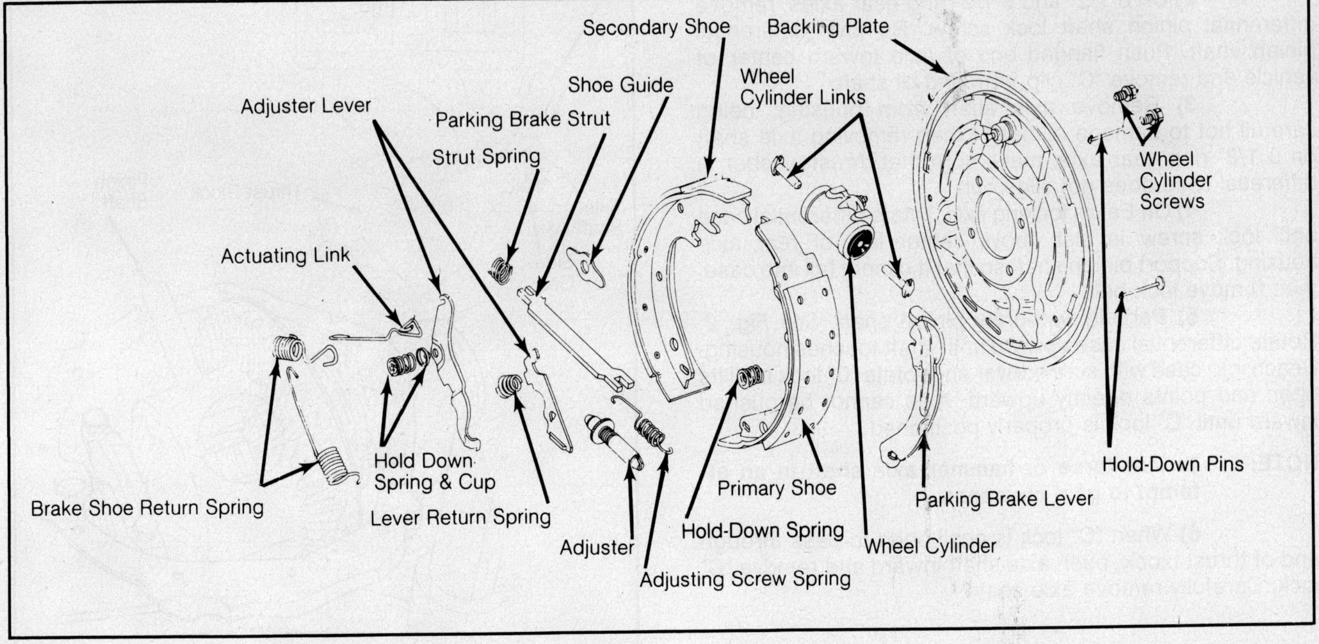

GENERAL MOTORS SINGLE ANCHOR (Cont.)

sary to back off brake shoe adjustment before removing drum. Unlock primary and secondary shoe springs. Remove shoe hold-down springs.

NOTE: On some vehicles, it may be necessary to remove axle shafts to remove hub and drum.

2) Lift up on actuator, unhook actuating link from anchor pin and remove link. Spread shoes enough to clear wheel cylinder links. Remove parking brake strut and spring. Disconnect cable from lever. Remove brake shoes.

Installation

1) Lubricate fulcrum end of parking brake lever with brake lubricant. Attach lever to secondary shoe. Make sure lever moves free. Connect brake shoes together with adjuster spring.

2) Place adjuster screw in postion. Make sure spring does not contact starwheel portion of adjusting screw. Right-hand thread adjusting screw should be on left side.

3) Make sure star wheel lines up with hole in backing plate. Apply a thin coating of brake lubricant to contact surface on backing plate. Position brake shoes on backing plate.

4) Primary shoe (short lining) is to front. Connect cable to parking brake lever. Install strut between shoes. Install actuator, return spring and actuator link. Install shoe hold-down springs.

5) Install both primary and secondary shoe springs. Measure inside diameter of brake drum with Adjustment Gauge (J-21177). Expand brake shoes to dimension obtained on outside caliper portion of tool.

6) Install brake drum and wheel assembly. Bleed system if any portion of hydraulic system was opened. Check fluid level in master cylinder and add as necessary.

AXLE BEARING & SEAL

Removal (Semi-Floating Axle)

1) Raise vehicle and support with safety stands. Remove wheel assembly and brake drum. Loosen differential cover plate and drain lubricant from axle. Remove cover plate.

2) On 8 1/2" and 9 1/2" ring gear axles, remove differential pinion shaft lock screw. Remove differential pinion shaft. Push flanged end of axle toward center of vehicle and remove "C" clip from end of shaft.

3) Remove axle shaft from housing, being carefull not to damage oil seal. When removing axle shaft on 9 1/2" ring gear axle, make sure that thrust washer in differetial case does not slide out.

4) On Eaton locking axle, rotate differential case until lock screw is just above center line of rear axle housing. Support pinion shaft so that it cannot fall into case, then remove lock bolt.

5) Partially withdraw pinion shaft. *See Fig. 2.* Rotate differential case upward until shaft touches housing. Reach into case with screwdriver and rotate "C" lock until its open end points directly upward. Axle cannot be pushed inward until "C" lock is properly positioned

NOTE: Do not force or hammer axle shaft in an attempt to gain clearance.

6) When "C" lock is positioned to pass through end of thrust block, push axle shaft inward and remove "C" lock. Carefully remove axle shaft.

7) On 8 1/2" ring gear axle, insert Bearing Remover (J-23689) behind bearing. Tighten nut finger tight against washer. Attach Slide Hammer (J-2619-01) to remover, remove bearing and seal.

8) On Eaton and 9 1/2" ring gear axles, insert Wobble Plate (J-29712) into axle tube so that it graps behind bearing. Center receiver on axle tube and tighten nut. Back off nut, remove bearing and seal.

Installation

1) Lubricate bearing and seal lips with wheel bearing grease. Install bearing using Bearing Installer (J-23690) for 8 1/2" ring gear axle; (J-29709) on Eaton and 9 1/2" ring gear axles. Install bearing until installer bottoms against tube.

2) Install oil seal using Oil Seal Installer (J-21128) for 8 1/2" ring gear axle; (J-29713) on Eaton and 9 1/2" ring gear axles. Install seal until it is flush with end of tube.

3) Carefully install axle shaft. Ensure that splines on shaft engage splines on side gear. On 8 1/2" and 9 1/2" ring gear axles, push flanged end of axle shaft toward center of axle and install "C" clip.

4) Pull axle shaft outward until "C" clips seats in side gear. Install pinion shaft, making sure that hole in shaft is lined up with lock screw hole. Install new lock screw and tighten to 25 ft. lbs. (34 N.m).

5) On Eaton locking ring gear axle, install "C" lock while keeping pinion shaft partially withdrawn. Place "C" lock in thrust block. *See Fig. 2.* Carefully withdraw axle shaft until "C" lock is clear of thrust block.

6) When both locks are installed, install pinion shaft. Align hole in shaft with lock screw hole. Install new lock screw and tighten to 25 ft. lbs. (34 N.m).

7) On all models, install cover plate using a new gasket. Fill axle with lubricant to a level even with bottom of

Fig. 2: Axle Shaft "C" Lock Installation

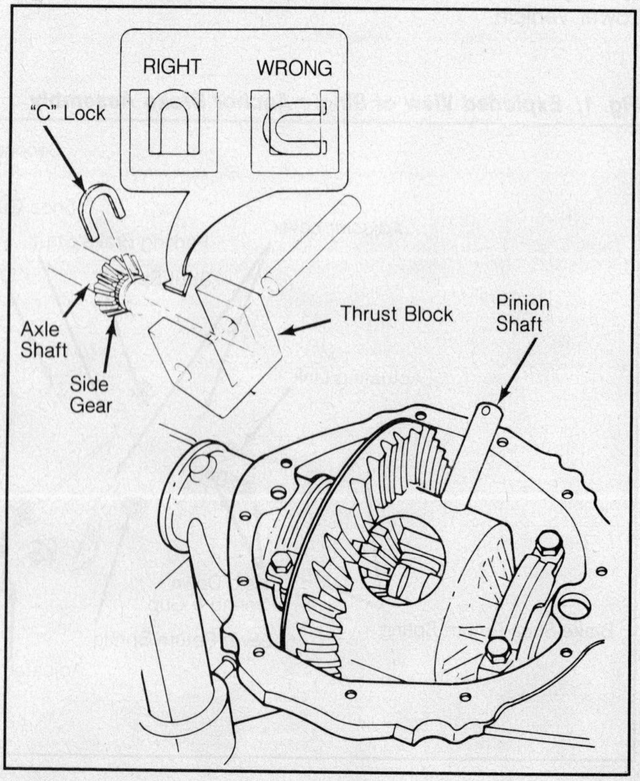

GENERAL MOTORS SINGLE ANCHOR (Cont.)

filler hole. Reverse removal procedure to complete installation.

HUB BEARINGS & SEAL

Removal (Full-Floating Axle)

1) Remove bolts that attach axle shaft flange to wheel hub. Stike flange with hammer to loosen shaft. Grip rib on end of flange with locking pliers and twist shaft to start shaft removal.

2) Remove axle shaft from tube. Starighten tang of retainer from slot or flat of lock nut. Using Socket (J-2222), remove lock nut from tube. Straighten tang of retainer from slot or flat of adjustment nut. Remove adjustment nut. Remove thrust washer and hub/drum assembly.

3) If necessary use a long drift and hammer, to remove inner bearing, race, and oil seal from hub. Remove outer bearing snap ring. Using Bearing Remover (J-24426) and handle, remove outer bearing and race from hub.

Installation

1) Pack wheel bearings. Place outer bearing into hub. Install race of outer bearing into hub using handle and Bearing Installer (J-8608). Drive race beyond snap ring groove.

2) Install snap ring. Press race of outer bearing against snap ring using bearing remover. Using Bearing Installer (J-24427), install inner bearing race. Install race until it seats agaist shoulder of hub bore. Install new oil seal.

3) Install hub/drum assembly on axle housing. Install thrust washer so that tang on inside diameter of washer is key way on axle housing. Install adjustment nut and tighten to 50 ft. lbs. (68 N.m) while rotating hub. Back off adjustment nut until loose.

4) If adjustment nut is aligned with keyway in spindle, insert square key into slot. If adjustment nut is not aligned, slightly back off nut and insert square key in slot. Do not back off nut more than one slot to align key. Reverse removal procedure to complete installation.

WHEEL CYLINDER

Removal & Installation

Remove wheel assembly, drum, and brake shoes. Remove cylinder connecting links and disconnect hydraulic brake line from cylinder. Remove brake cylinder retaining bolts and remove cylinder from support plate. To install, reverse removal procedure.

OVERHAUL

WHEEL CYLINDER

Disassembly

Remove rubber boots from ends of cylinder. Remove pistons, cylinder cups, and piston return spring from cylinder. Remove bleeder screw and inspect bore for damage.

Reassembly

If bore of cylinder is pitted and/or scratched, hone or replace as needed. Soak rubber cylinder cups in brake fluid or assembly lube and reverse disassembly procedure.

TIGHTENING SPECIFICATIONS

Application	Ft. Lbs. (N.m)
Brake Hose Attaching Nut	13 (18)
Rear Brake Anchor Pin	140 (190)
Bleeder Valves	5 (7)
Brake Line Nut	13 (18)
Wheel Cylinder Attaching Bolts	4 (6)
Brake Line Clips	13 (18)

DRUM BRAKE SPECIFICATIONS

Application	Drum Diam. In. (mm)	Drum Width In. (mm)	Max. Drum Refinish Diam. In. (mm)	Wheel Cyl. Diam. In. (mm)	Master Cyl. Diam. In. (mm)
Astro/Safari	9.50 (241.3)	2.0 (50.8)	9.56 (242.8)	.812 (20.6)	[1] 1.0 (25.4)
"C"10 & "G"10					
to 4900 GVW	11.00 (279.4)	2.00 (50.8)	11.06 (280.9)	1.06 (26.9)	1.00 (25.4)
to 5600 GVW	11.00 (279.4)	2.00 (50.8)	11.06 (280.9)	1.00 (26.9)	1.12 (28.5)
"C"10 5200-6100 GVW	11.15 (283.2)	2.75 (69.9)	11.21 (284.7)	1.00 (25.4)	[2] 1.12 (28.4)
"C", "G", & "K"10; "C", "G", "K", & "P"20 6250-7300 GVW	11.15 (283.2)	2.75 (69.9)	11.21 (284.7)	[3] .937 (23.8)	[2] 1.12 (28.4)
"C", "K", & "P"20; "G" & "P"30 to 8600 GVW	13.00 (330.2)	2.50 (63.5)	13.06 (331.7)	1.06 (26.9)	1.25 (31.8)
"C", "G", "K", & "P"30	13.00 (330.2)	3.50 (88.9)	13.06 (331.7)	1.19 (30.2)	[4] 1.33 (33.8)
"S" Series	9.5 (241.3)	2.0 (50.8)	9.56 (242.8)	[5] .875 (22.2)	.94 (23.9)

[1] – Master cylinder diameter is 1.25" (31.7 mm) on vehicles with a payload rating over 1000.
[2] – Master cylinder diameter is 1.25" (31.7 mm) on vehicles with diesel engine and Hydro-Boost.
[3] – Wheel cylinder diameter is 1" (25.4 mm) on 20 series vehicles without heavy duty option.
[4] – Master cylinder diameter is 1.31" (33.3 mm) on "C"30, on "P"30 with heavy duty brakes, and on motor home chassis.
[5] – Wheel cylinder diameter is 0.75" (19.1 mm) on models with power assisted brakes.

JEEP SINGLE ANCHOR – CABLE ADJUSTER

CJ7, Cherokee, Scrambler, Wagoneer

DESCRIPTION

Automatic adjuster brakes are 2 shoe, self-centering type with brake shoe anchor at upper end of shoes above wheel cylinder. Single cylinder is double acting. Automatic adjuster device is cable operated.

ADJUSTMENTS & SERVICING

AXLE SHAFT END PLAY

CJ7 & Scrambler

1) Strike ends of axle shafts with lead hammer to seat bearing cups against support plates. Install Axle Shaft End Play Measurement Bar (J-2092) onto axle shaft. *See Fig. 1.*

2) Mount dial indicator on support plate or on bar. Measure end play while pushing and pulling on axle shaft. End play should be .004-.008" (0.10-0.20 mm). Adjust end play by removing or adding shims as necessary.

Fig. 1: Checking Axle Shaft End Play

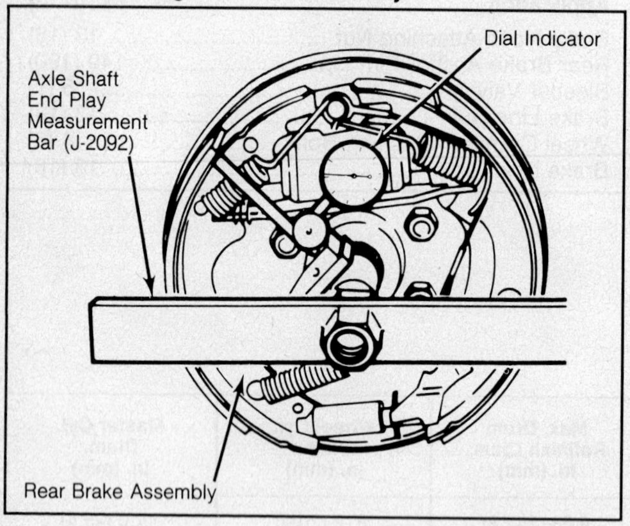

BRAKE SHOES

Brake shoes adjust automatically as brakes are applied while vehicle is operated in reverse. Brake shoes can be manually adjusted by rotating adjuster screw.

Remove access slot cover. Using a small blade screwdriver, push in on adjustment lever to separate from adjustment screw. Turn adjustment screw until brake drum is locked tight, then back screw off until wheel rotates freely. It may also be necessary to back shoes off a few notches to remove drum.

PARKING BRAKE

1) Adjust service brakes. Check cable for binds, kinks or frayed condition. Replace damaged cable. On CJ7 and Scrambler, release parking brake. Loosen lock nuts at parking brake cable equalizer under vehicle.

2) Tighten equalizer until wheels drag slightly when rotated by hand. Loosen equalizer until wheels rotate freely and no drag is felt. Tighten lock nuts and check operation of parking brake.

3) On Cherokee and Wagoneer, apply and release parking brake 5 times. Place parking brake lever in 5th notch. Raise vehicle. Using Adjustment Gauge (J-34651), apply a torque of 45-50 INCH Lbs. (5-6 N.m). *See Fig. 2.*

4) Adjust nut on parking brake cable equalizer until pointer is in Green section of gauge. Apply and release parking brake cable 5 times. Check adjustment, readjust cable if necessary.

Fig. 2: Parking Brake Adjustment

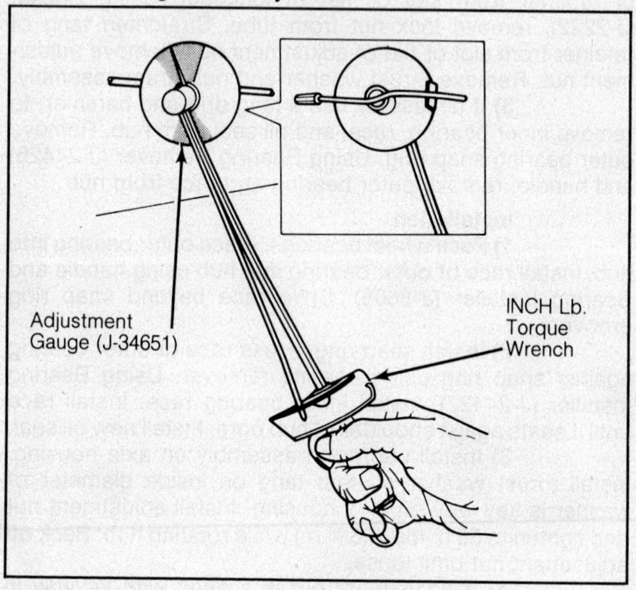

BLEEDING SYSTEM

See HYDRAULIC BRAKE BLEEDING in this section.

REMOVAL & INSTALLATION

BRAKE SHOES

Removal

1) Raise vehicle and support with safety stands. Remove wheel assembly and drum. Remove "U" clip and washer from parking brake lever pivot pin. Place Wheel Cylinder Clamp (J-8002) over wheel cylinder.

2) Remove primary and secondary return springs, spring retainers, hold-down springs and retaining pins. Remove adjuster lever, adjuster screw and spring from brake shoes. Remove brake shoes.

Installation

1) Lubricate support plate ledges, anchor pin, adjuster cable guide, adjuster screw assembly, parking brake lever and lever pivot pin with molydisulphide grease.

2) Connect parking brake lever to secondary brake shoe with washer and "U" clip. Crimp ends of clip to retain it on pivot. Remove wheel cylinder clamp. Position brake shoes on brake support plate and install hold-down springs.

3) Install parking brake lever strut and spring. Install adjuster cable guide plate and adjuster cable on anchor pin. Install primary return spring. Install guide to secondary brake shoe and install secondary return spring.

JEEP SINGLE ANCHOR – CABLE ADJUSTER (Cont.)

Fig. 3: Exploded View of Jeep Brake Assembly With Cable Operated Adjuster

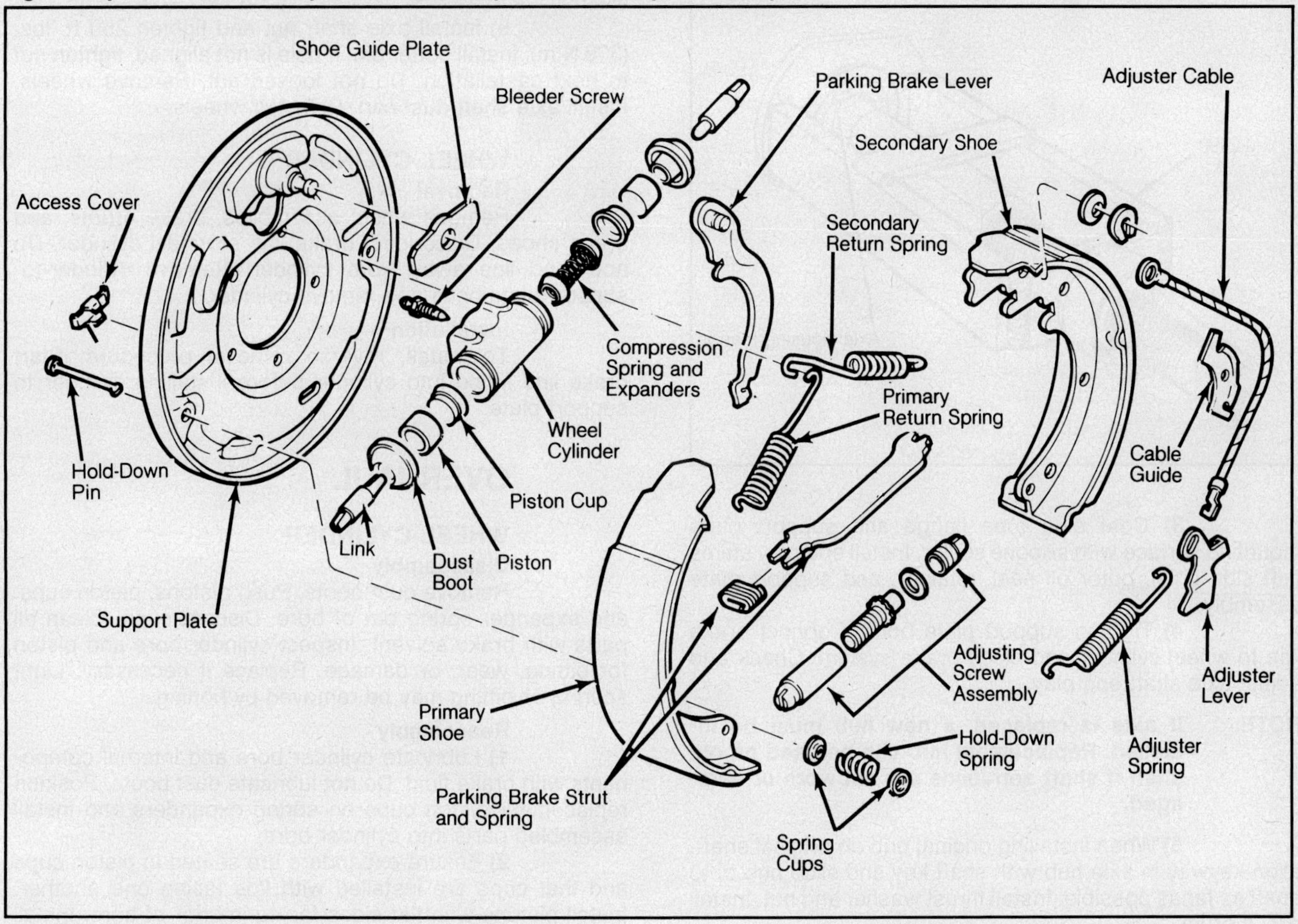

4) Install adjuster screw, spring and lever and connect to cable. Using Brake Gauge (J-21177-01), preset brake shoe adjustment. Install brake drums. Adjust brake shoes with drum in place.

5) Install wheels and lower vehicle. Apply and release brakes 10-15 times while driving forward and backward. This adjusts and balances brake system. Road test vehicle.

AXLE BEARING & SEAL

Removal (Cherokee & Wagoneer)

1) Raise vehicle and support with safety stands. Remove wheel assembly and drum. Remove support plate attaching nuts. Using a slide hammer, remove axle shaft.

2) Place axle shaft in a vise. Drill a 1/4" (6.35 mm) hole 3/4 of the way through bearing retaining ring. Chisel off bearing retaining ring. Press bearing off of axle. Remove seal and retainer plate.

Installation

Lubricate bearing and seal lip. Install retainer plate and seal over axle. Press axle shaft bearing and retaining ring onto shaft simultaneously. Ensure that bearing and ring are seated against axle shaft shoulder. Reverse removal procedure to complete installation.

Removal (CJ7 & Scrambler)

1) Raise and support vehicle. Remove rear wheels. Remove rear axle shaft dust cap, cotter pin, and axle shaft nut. Remove brake drums. Remove axle hub using Puller (J-25109-01).

NOTE: **Do not use knock-out type puller to remove hub. This type of puller may damage rear wheel bearings and differential thrust block.**

2) Disconnect parking brake cable at equalizer. Disconnect brake line at wheel cylinder. Remove support plate assembly, axle shaft oil seal, and retainer. If left axle shaft is being removed, remove axle shaft end play shims.

3) Remove axle shaft and bearing using Puller (J-2498). *See Fig. 4*. Remove axle shaft inner oil seal. Axle bearing must be pressed off shaft. Do not remove by any other method.

NOTE: **On models with Trac-Loc differential, do not rotate differential gears unless both axle shafts are in place. The side gear splines will become misaligned and prevent shaft replacement.**

Installation

1) Pack new wheel bearing with high temperature bearing grease. Press bearing onto shaft. Small diameter of bearing must face toward outer tapered end of shaft.

2) Lubricate lip of inner oil seal and coat outer circumference with non-hardening sealant. Install inner oil seal using Seal Installer (J-21788). Install axle shaft aligning splines with side gear splines. Install axle shaft outer bearing cup.

Brake Systems

JEEP SINGLE ANCHOR – CABLE ADJUSTER (Cont.)

Fig. 4: Removing CJ7 & Scrambler Axle Shaft

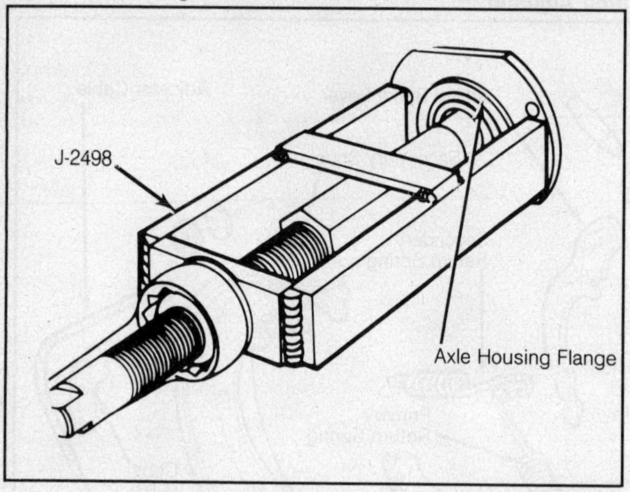

3) Coat axle tube flange and support plate mounting surface with silicone sealer. Install end play shims (left side only), outer oil seal, retainer, and support plate assembly.

4) Tighten support plate bolts. Connect brake line to wheel cylinder and bleed brake system. Check and adjust axle shaft end play.

NOTE: **If axle is replaced, a new hub must be installed. Replacement hub can be used on old shaft if shaft serrations are not worn or damaged.**

5) When installing original hub on original shaft, align keyway in axle hub with shaft key and slide hub onto shaft as far as possible. Install thrust washer and nut. Install brake drum.

6) Install wheels and lower vehicle. Apply parking brake. Tighten axle shaft nut to 250 ft. lbs. (339 N.m). Install cotter pin. If hole is not aligned, tighten nut to next castellation. Do not loosen nut. Remove wheels. Install axle shaft dust cap. Reinstall wheels.

7) When installing new hub on shaft, align keyway in axle hub with shaft key and slide hub onto shaft as far as possible. Lubricate 2 thrust washers with chassis grease and install washers on end of axle shaft. Install axle shaft nut.

8) Install brake drum. Install wheels and lower vehicle. Apply parking brake. Tighten axle shaft nut until distance from hub outer face to axle shaft outer end is 1 5/16" (33.34 mm). Remove axle shaft nut and 1 thrust washer.

9) Install axle shaft nut and tighten 250 ft. lbs. (339 N.m). Install cotter pin. If hole is not aligned, tighten nut to next castellation. Do not loosen nut. Remove wheels. Install axle shaft dust cap. Reinstall wheels.

WHEEL CYLINDER

Removal

Remove wheel assemblies, brake drums, and brake shoes. Disconnect brake line at wheel cylinder. Do not bend line away from cylinder. Remove cylinder-to-support plate bolts and remove cylinder.

Installation

To install, reverse removal procedure. Start brake line fitting into cylinder before installing cylinder to support plate.

OVERHAUL

WHEEL CYLINDER

Disassembly

Remove dust boots. Push pistons, piston cups, and expander spring out of bore. Discard cups. Clean all parts with brake solvent. Inspect cylinder bore and piston for pitting, wear, or damage. Replace if necessary. Light scoring or pitting may be removed by honing.

Reassembly

1) Lubricate cylinder bore and internal components with brake fluid. Do not lubricate dust boots. Position replacement piston cups on spring expanders and install assembled parts into cylinder bore.

2) Ensure expanders are seated in piston cups and that cups are installed with lips facing one another. Install pistons with flat sides facing interior of bore. Install dust boots.

TIGHTENING SPECIFICATIONS

Application	Ft. Lbs. (N.m)
Axle Shaft Nut	
CJ7 & Scrambler	250 (339)
Brake Cylinder-to-Support Plate	11 (15)
Bleeder Screw 1/4"	4-5 (5-7)
Bleeder Screw 3/8"	4-12 (5-16)
Brake Line	10-17 (14-23)
Support Plate	30-35 (41-47)

DRUM BRAKE SPECIFICATIONS

Application	Drum Diam. In. (mm)	Drum Width In. (mm)	Max. Drum Refinish Diam. In. (mm)	Wheel Cyl. Diam. In. (mm)	Master Cyl. Diam. In. (mm)
CJ7, Cherokee, Scrambler & Wagoneer	10.00 (254.0)	1.75 (44.5)	10.06 (255.5)	.875 (22.2)	1.00 (25.4)

JEEP SINGLE ANCHOR – LEVER ADJUSTER

Grand Wagoneer, Pickups

DESCRIPTION

Single anchor brake assembly consists of a support plate, 2 brake shoes, brake shoe return springs, adjuster lever and single wheel cylinder.

ADJUSTMENTS & SERVICING

HUB BEARINGS

J20 Pickup

1) Remove axle shaft attaching nuts, lock washers, and cone washers. Remove axle shaft and gasket. Discard gasket. Straighten lip of lock washer. Remove lock nut and lock washer. Raise vehicle and support with safety stands.

2) Rotate wheel assembly and tighten adjustment nut to 50 ft. lbs. (68 N.m). Back off adjustment nut 1/6 turn or until wheel assembly rotates freely and without side-to-side movement.

3) Install and tighten lock nut to 50 ft. lbs. (68 N.m). Bend lock washer lip over lock nut. Check bearing adjustment and correct if necessary. Install gasket and axle shaft. Install cone washers, lock washers, and nuts. Lower vehicle.

Fig. 1: J20 Pickup Hub Bearing Adjustment

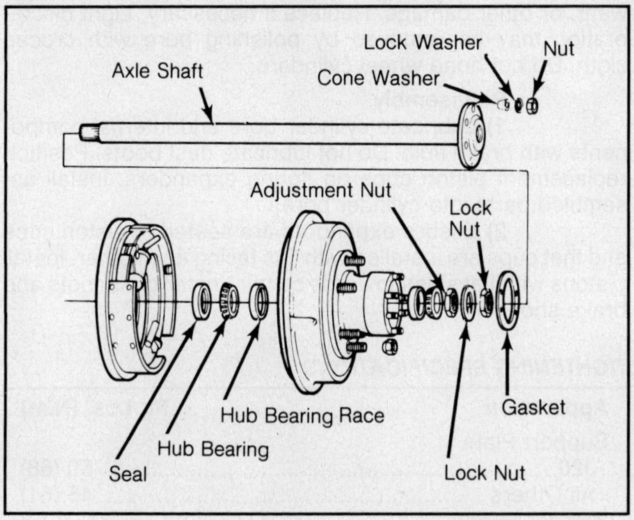

BRAKE SHOES

Brake shoes adjust automatically when brakes are applied while vehicle is operated in reverse. Manual adjustment is required if shoes have been removed and reinstalled.

During overhaul it is sometimes necessary to back off shoes to remove brake drums. This is done by turning star wheel adjuster which is accessible through a hole in brake backing plate. A thin blade screwdriver or similar tool must be used to disengage automatic adjuster lever while making manual adjustment.

PARKING BRAKE

1) Adjust service brakes. Check for binding, kinked, or frayed cables. Replace as necessary. Release parking brake. Loosen lock nuts at equalizer under vehicle.

2) Tighten cables until wheels drag slightly when rotated by hand. Loosen cables until wheels rotate freely and no drag is felt. Tighten lock nut and check operation of parking brake.

BLEEDING SYSTEM

See HYDRAULIC BRAKE BLEEDING in this section.

REMOVAL & INSTALLATION

BRAKE SHOES

Removal

1) Raise vehicle and support with safety stands. Remove wheels. On models with full-floating rear axle, remove 2 screws that locate drum on hub.

2) On all models, remove primary shoe return spring, automatic adjuster actuator spring and secondary shoe return spring. Remove hold-down springs and brake shoe assemblies. *See Fig. 2.*

3) Disengage parking brake cable from parking brake lever, (parking brake strut is removed with brake shoe assembly). Place wheel cylinder clamps over wheel cylinders to retain pistons.

4) Inspect all springs, parking brake lever, automatic adjuster lever and pivot, and actuating lever. Replace weak springs, bent levers, or parts that are worn or broken.

Fig. 2: Exploded View of Drum Brake Assembly

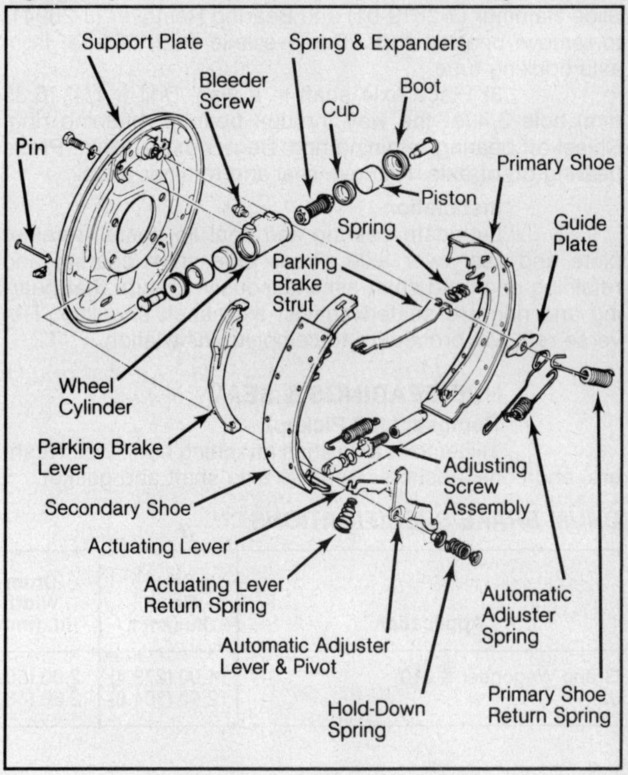

JEEP SINGLE ANCHOR – LEVER ADJUSTER (Cont.)

Installation

1) Clean support plate. Apply a thin film of molydisulphide grease or chassis lubricant to support plate ledges, anchor pin, adjuster screw threads, and pivot.

2) Apply grease to adjuster lever-to-secondary brake shoe contact surface, parking brake lever pivot, and portion of lever that contacts secondary brake shoe.

3) Attach parking brake cable to parking brake lever on secondary shoe. Pinch "U" clip to retain lever on shoe. Install secondary brake shoe, automatic adjuster lever, and lever pivot as an assembly.

4) Install brake shoe hold-down spring. Install return spring on actuating lever tang. Large end of tapered spring should rest on brake shoe.

5) Install primary shoe and hold-down spring. Install guide plate on anchor pin. Install parking brake strut and spring on brake shoes.

6) Install adjusting screw and spring. Short end of hooked spring goes on the primary brake shoe. Long hooked end goes on secondary brake shoe.

7) Install the secondary shoe return spring, adjuster spring, and primary return spring. Install brake drums. Adjust brakes and bleed system.

8) Install wheels and lower vehicle. Apply and release brakes 10-15 times while driving forward and backward. This adjusts and balances brake system. Road test vehicle.

AXLE BEARING & SEAL

Removal (Grand Wagoneer & J10 Pickup)

1) Raise vehicle and support with safety stands. Remove wheel assembly and brake drum. Remove support plate retaining nuts through hole provided in axle flange. Using slide hammer, remove axle shaft.

2) If wheel bearing cup remains in housing, use Slide Hammer (J-2619-01) and Bearing Remover (J-26941) to remove bearing cups. Remove axle shaft oil seal from axle housing tube.

3) Place axle shaft in a vise. Drill a 1/4" (6.35 mm) hole 3/4 of the way through bearing retaining ring. Chisel off bearing retaining ring. Do not use a torch. Press bearing off of axle. Remove seal and retainer plate.

Installation

Lubricate bearing and seal lip. Install retainer plate and seal over axle. Press axle shaft bearing and retaining ring onto shaft simultaneously. Ensure that bearing and ring are seated against axle shaft shoulder. Reverse removal procedure to complete installation.

HUB BEARINGS & SEAL

Removal (J20 Pickup)

1) Remove axle shaft attaching nuts, lock washers, and cone washers. Remove axle shaft and gasket. Discard gasket. Straighten lip of lock washer. Remove lock nut and lock washer. Raise vehicle and support with safety stands.

2) Support wheel and drum assembly. Remove bearing adjustment nut. Carefully remove wheel and drum assembly. Outer hub bearing will slide out as assembly is being removed. Remove seal and inner hub bearing.

Installation

To install, reverse removal procedure. Lubricate bearings and seal lip with high temperature bearing grease. Adjust hub bearings.

WHEEL CYLINDER

Removal & Installation

Remove wheels, drums and brake shoes. Disconnect brake line, but do not bend it away from cylinder. Remove cylinder mounting bolts and remove cylinder. To install, reverse removal procedure.

OVERHAUL

WHEEL CYLINDER

Disassembly

1) Remove brake shoe links and dust boots. Push pistons, piston cups, and expander spring out of bore. Discard piston cups. Clean all cylinder parts with clean brake solvent.

2) Inspect cylinder bore and piston for pitting, wear, or other damage. Replace if necessary. Light discoloration may be removed by polishing bore with crocus cloth. Do not hone wheel cylinders.

Reassembly

1) Lubricate cylinder bore and internal components with brake fluid. Do not lubricate dust boots. Position replacement piston cups on spring expanders. Install assembled parts into cylinder bore.

2) Ensure expanders are seated in piston cups and that cups are installed with lips facing each other. Install pistons with flat sides towards center. Install dust boots and brake shoe links.

TIGHTENING SPECIFICATIONS

Application	Ft. Lbs. (N.m)
Support Plate	
J20	50 (68)
All Others	45 (61)
Bleeder Screw	7 (9)
Brake Line-to-Wheel Cylinder	13 (18)
Wheel Cylinder-to-Support Plate	18 (24)

DRUM BRAKE SPECIFICATIONS

Application	Drum Diam. In. (mm)	Drum Width In. (mm)	Max. Drum Refinish Diam. In. (mm)	Wheel Cyl. Diam. In. (mm)	Master Cyl. Diam. In. (mm)
Grand Wagoneer & J10	11.00 (279.4)	2.00 (50.8)	11.06 (280.9)	.937 (23.80)	1.125 (28.58)
J20	12.00 (304.8)	2.50 (63.5)	12.06 (306.3)	1.125 (28.58)	1.125 (28.58)

SECTION 11

WHEEL ALIGNMENT

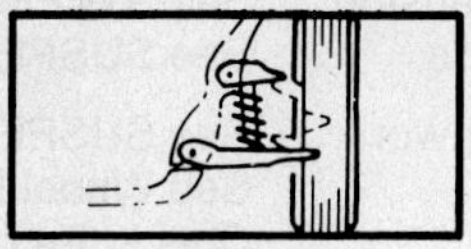

CONTENTS

NOTE: **ALSO SEE GENERAL INDEX.**

IMPORTANT: **Because of the many model names used by vehicle manufacturers, accurate identification of models is important. See Model Identification at the front of this publication.**

Wheel Alignment

TROUBLE SHOOTING

CONDITION	POSSIBLE CAUSE	CORRECTION
Premature Tire Wear	Improper tire inflation or balance	Check tire pressure and balance
	Front alignment out of tolerance	See Adjustments in WHEEL ALIGNMENT
	Steering or suspension worn	See SUSPENSION or STEERING
	Improper standing height	See RIDING HEIGHT SPECIFICATIONS
	Bent wheel	See WHEEL ALIGNMENT
	Improper torsion bar adjustment	See SUSPENSION
	Loose or worn wheel bearings	See Wheel Bearing Adj. in SUSPENSION
	Worn or defective shock absorbers	Replace shock absorbers
Pulls to One Side	Improper tire inflation/mismatched tires	Check tires and tire pressure
	Brakes dragging	See BRAKES
	Broken or sagging spring	See SUSPENSION
	Broken torsion bar	See SUSPENSION
	Power steering valve not centered	See STEERING
	Front alignment out of tolerance	See Adjustments in WHEEL ALIGNMENT
	Defective wheel bearing	See Wheel Bearings in SUSPENSION
	Uneven sway bar links	See SUSPENSION
	Frame bent	Check for frame damage
	Steering system bushing worn	See STEERING
	Idler arm bushing too tight	See STEERING LINKAGE
Hard Steering	Idler arm bushing too tight	See STEERING LINKAGE
	Ball joint tight or seized	See Ball Joint Checking in SUSPENSION
	Steering linkage too tight	See STEERING LINKAGE
	Power steering fluid low	Add proper amount of fluid
	Power steering drive belt loose	See STEERING
	Power steering pump defective	See STEERING
	Steering gear out of adjustment	See STEERING
	Incorrect wheel alignment	See WHEEL ALIGNMENT
	Damaged steering gear or suspension	See STEERING or SUSPENSION
	Bent steering knuckle or supports	See SUSPENSION
Vehicle "Wanders"	Strut rod or control arm bushing worn	See SUSPENSION
	Loose or worn wheel bearings	See Wheel Bearings in SUSPENSION
	Improper tire inflation	Check tire pressure
	Stabilizer bar missing or defective	See SUSPENSION
	Wheel alignment out of tolerance	See Adjustment in WHEEL ALIGNMENT
	Broken spring or bad shocks	See SUSPENSION
	Worn steering & suspension components	See SUSPENSION
Front End Shimmy	Tire out of balance/round	Check tire balance
	Excessive wheel runout	See WHEEL ALIGNMENT
	Insufficient or improper caster	See WHEEL ALIGNMENT
	Worn suspension or steering components	See SUSPENSION
	Wheel bearings worn or loose	See Wheel Bearing Adj. in SUSPENSION
	Power steering reaction bracket loose	See STEERING
	Steering gear box (rack) mounting loose	See STEERING
	Steering gear adjustment loose	See STEERING
	Worn spherical joints	See SUSPENSION
Toe-In Not Adjustable	Lower control arm bent	See SUSPENSION
	Frame bent	Check frame for damage
Camber Not Adjustable	Control arm bent	See SUSPENSION
	Frame bent	Check frame for damage
	Hub & bearing not seated properly	See SUSPENSION

Radial Tire Lead

Some alignment problems involing "lead" or pull to one side have been caused by off-center belts on radial tires. To diagnose this problem inflate tires to recommended pressure and drive vehicle both directions on an uncrowned road. Observe and note any "lead", then switch front tires and road test again. If lead is corrected without roughness, leave tires in position. If roughness results, replace tires. If lead reverses, install a known good tire on one side and repeat road test. If lead remains, install a known good tire in place of other front tire. If lead remains, recheck alignment. It may be necessary to adjust caster so that leading side is 1° more positive than other side.

WHEEL ALIGNMENT SPECIFICATIONS

CHRYSLER CORP.

WHEEL ALIGNMENT SPECIFICATIONS

Application	Axle Gap (Inches)	Caster (Degrees)	Camber (Degrees)	Toe-In (Inches)	Steering Axis Inclination (Degrees)
"AD" 150 & "D" Series	.....	-1/2 to +1 1/2	0 to +1	0 to 1/2	.....
"B" Series	.....	+1 1/4 to +3 3/4	-1/4 to +1	0 to 1/4	.....
"W" Series	.....	+1/2 to +3 1/2	+1/2 to +1 1/2	1/8 to 3/8	.....
Mini Ram Van, Caravan & Voyager					
Front	.....	.....	-1/4 to +3/4	7/32 Out to 1/8 In	.....
Rear	.....	.....	-1 1/8 to-1/8	1/2 Out to 1/2 In [1]	.....

[1] – Toe out when backed onto alignment rack is toe in when driving.

FORD

WHEEL ALIGNMENT SPECIFICATIONS

Application	Axle Gap (Inches)	Caster (Degrees)	Camber (Degrees)	Toe-In (Inches)	Steering Axis Inclination (Degrees)
Aerostar	.....	4	2/10	3/32 Out to 5/32 In	.....
E150	4 to 4 1/4	4 1/2 to 6	-3/4 to 3/4	1/32	7.5
	4 1/4 to 4 1/2	4 to 5 1/2	-1/2 to 1	1/32	7.5
	4 1/2 to 4 3/4	3 1/4 to 4 1/2	1/4 to 1 3/4	1/32	7.5
	4 3/4 to 5	2 1/2 to 4	1/2 to 2	1/32	7.5
	5 to 5 1/4	2 to 3 1/4	3/4 to 2 1/2	1/32	7.5
	5 1/4 to 5 1/2	1 1/2 to 2 3/4	1 1/4 to 3	1/32	7.5
	5 1/2 to 5 3/4	1 to 2 1/4	1 3/4 to 3 1/2	1/32	7.5
	5 3/4 to 6	1/4 to 1 1/2	2 1/4 to 4	1/32	7.5
E250/350	3 3/4 to 4	7 1/2 to 9	-3/4 to 3/4	1/32	8
	4 to 4 1/4	7 to 8 1/2	-1/2 to 1 1/4	1/32	8
	4 1/4 to 4 1/2	6 1/4 to 7 3/4	0 to 1 3/4	1/32	8
	4 1/2 to 4 3/4	5 1/2 to 7 1/4	1/2 to 2 1/4	1/32	8
	4 3/4 to 5	5 to 6 1/4	1 to 2 3/4	1/32	8
	5 to 5 1/4	4 1/2 to 5 3/4	1 1/2 to 3 1/4	1/32	8
	5 1/4 to 5 1/2	3 3/4 to 5 1/4	2 to 3 3/4	1/32	8
F150 (2WD)	3 1/4 to 3 1/2	5 to 6	-3/4 to 1 1/2	1/32	13
	3 1/2 to 4	4 1/4 to 5 1/4	1/4 to 2 1/2	1/32	13
	4 to 4 1/4	3 1/4 to 4 1/4	1 to 3 1/2	1/32	13
	4 1/4 to 4 3/4	2 1/2 to 3 1/2	2 to 4 1/4	1/32	13
F250/350 (2WD)	2 1/2 to 2 7/8	5 to 6	-3/4 to 1 3/4	1/32	8
	2 7/8 to 3 1/4	4 1/4 to 5 1/4	0 to 2 1/2	1/32	8
	3 1/4 to 3 5/8	3 1/4 to 4 1/4	1 to 3 1/4	1/32	8
	3 5/8 to 4	2 1/2 to 3 1/4	2 to 4 1/4	1/32	8
F150 (4WD) & Bronco	3 1/4 to 3 1/2	6 to 7	-1 to 1/2	1/32	13
	3 1/2 to 4	5 to 6	-1/2 to 1 1/2	1/32	13
	4 to 4 1/4	4 to 5	1/4 to 2 1/2	1/32	13
	4 1/4 to 4 3/4	3 to 4	1 1/4 to 3 1/2	1/32	13
F250/350 (4WD)	5 to 5 1/2	3 to 5 1/8	-1 3/4 to 3/4	1/32	13
	5 1/2 to 6	3 1/8 to 5 1/4	-3/4 to 1 3/4	1/32	13
	6 to 6 1/4	3 1/4 to 5 3/8	1/2 to 2 3/4	1/32	13
	6 1/4 to 6 3/4	3 1/2 to 5 1/2	1 1/2 to 4	1/32	13
Ranger (2WD)	3 1/8	4 1/2 to 7 1/2	-1 1/4 to 1/4	1/32	13
	3 3/8	4 to 7	-3/4 to 3/4	1/32	13
	3 1/2	3 1/2 to 6 1/2	-1/4 to 1 1/4	1/32	13
	3 3/4	3 to 6	1/4 to 1 3/4	1/32	13
	3 7/8	2 1/2 to 5 1/2	3/4 to 2 1/4	1/32	13
	4 1/8	2 to 5	1 1/4 to 2 3/4	1/32	13
	4 3/8	1 1/2 to 4 1/2	1 3/4 to 3 1/4	1/32	13

Wheel Alignment

WHEEL ALIGNMENT SPECIFICATIONS (Cont.)

FORD (Cont.)

WHEEL ALIGNMENT SPECIFICATIONS

Application	Axle Gap (Inches)	Caster (Degrees)	Camber (Degrees)	Toe-In (Inches)	Steering Axis Inclination (Degrees)
Ranger (4WD) & Bronco II	3 1/8	4 to 7	-3/4 to 3/4	1/32	13
	3 3/8	3 1/2 to 6 1/2	-1/4 to 1 1/4	1/32	13
	3 1/2	3 to 6	1/4 to 1 3/4	1/32	13
	3 3/4	2 1/2 to 5 1/2	3/4 to 2 1/4	1/32	13
	3 7/8	2 to 5	1 1/4 to 2 3/4	1/32	13
	4 1/8	1 1/2 to 4 1/2	1 3/4 to 3 1/4	1/32	13
	4 3/8	1 to 4	2 1/4 to 3 3/4	1/32	13

GENERAL MOTORS

WHEEL ALIGNMENT SPECIFICATIONS

Application	Axle Gap (Inches)	Caster (Degrees)	Camber (Degrees)	Toe-In (Inches)	Steering Axis Inclination (Degrees)
Astro/Safari	.....	2.2 to 3.2	1.4 to 0.4	[4]	.....
C10	2 1/2	3.7	0.7	3/16	.....
	2 3/4	3.5	0.7	3/16	.....
	3	3.2	0.7	3/16	.....
	3 1/4	2.9	0.7	3/16	.....
	3 1/2	2.6	0.7	3/16	.....
	3 3/4	2.4	0.7	3/16	.....
	4	2.0	0.7	3/16	.....
	4 1/4	1.8	0.7	3/16	.....
	4 1/2	1.5	0.7	3/16	.....
	4 3/4	1.3	0.7	3/16	.....
	5	1	0.7	3/16	.....
	5 1/4	0.8	0.7	3/16	.....
	5 1/2	0.5	0.7	3/16	.....
	5 3/4	0.3	0.7	3/16	.....
	6	0	0.7	3/16	.....
C20/30	2 1/2	1.5	0.3	3/16	.....
	2 3/4	1.2	0.3	3/16	.....
	3	0.9	0.3	3/16	.....
	3 1/4	0.6	0.3	3/16	.....
	3 1/2	0.3	0.3	3/16	.....
	3 3/4	0.1	0.3	3/16	.....
	4	0	0.3	3/16	.....
	4 1/4	-0.2	0.3	3/16	.....
	4 1/2	-0.7	0.3	3/16	.....
	4 3/4	-1	0.3	3/16	.....
	5	-1.2	0.3	3/16	.....
	5 1/4	-1.4	0.3	3/16	.....
	5 1/2	-1.6	0.3	3/16	.....
	5 3/4	-1.8	0.3	3/16	.....
G10/20	1 1/2	3.4	0.5	3/16	.....
	1 3/4	3.2	0.5	3/16	.....
	2	3.0	0.5	3/16	.....
	2 1/4	2.9	0.5	3/16	.....
	2 1/2	2.7	0.5	3/16	.....
	2 3/4	2.5	0.5	3/16	.....
	3	2.3	0.5	3/16	.....
	3 1/4	2.2	0.5	3/16	.....
	3 1/2	2.0	0.5	3/16	.....
	3 3/4	1.8	0.5	3/16	.....
	4	1.7	0.5	3/16	.....
	4 1/4	1.5	0.5	3/16	.....
	4 1/2	1.4	0.5	3/16	.....

WHEEL ALIGNMENT SPECIFICATIONS (Cont.)

GENERAL MOTORS (Cont.)

WHEEL ALIGNMENT SPECIFICATIONS

Application	Axle Gap (Inches)	Caster (Degrees)	Camber (Degrees)	Toe-In (Inches)	Steering Axis Inclination (Degrees)
G30	1 1/2	3.1	0.3	3/16	.....
	1 3/4	3.0	0.3	3/16	.....
	2	2.7	0.3	3/16	.....
	2 1/4	2.4	0.3	3/16	.....
	2 1/2	2.1	0.3	3/16	.....
	2 3/4	1.8	0.3	3/16	.....
	3	1.5	0.3	3/16	.....
	3 1/4	1.2	0.3	3/16	.....
	3 1/2	0.9	0.3	3/16	.....
	3 3/4	0.7	0.3	3/16	.....
	4	0.5	0.3	3/16	.....
	4 1/4	0.2	0.3	3/16	.....
	4 1/2	0	0.3	3/16	.....
K10/20/30	.....	8 [1]	1.5 [1]	0	.....
P20/30	2	3.0 [2,3]	0.3	3/16	.....
	2 1/4	2.6 [2,3]	0.3	3/16	.....
	2 1/2	2.3 [2,3]	0.3	3/16	.....
	2 3/4	2 [2,3]	0.3	3/16	.....
	3	1.7 [2,3]	0.3	3/16	.....
	3 1/4	1.4 [2,3]	0.3	3/16	.....
	3 1/2	1.2 [2,3]	0.3	3/16	.....
	3 3/4	0.9 [2,3]	0.3	3/16	.....
	4	0.6 [2,3]	0.3	3/16	.....
	4 1/4	0.4 [2,3]	0.3	3/16	.....
	4 1/2	0.2 [2,3]	0.3	3/16	.....
	4 3/4	-0.1 [2,3]	0.3	3/16	.....
S10/15 & T10/15	.....	1 1/2 to 2 1/2	0.3 to 1.3	[4]	.....

[1] – Not adjustable.
[2] – Add 0.3° on vehicles with hydroboost brake system.
[3] – Subtract 0.4° on vehicles with dual rear wheels.
[4] – Toe-in on these vehicles is 0.1° to 0.2° per wheel.

JEEP

WHEEL ALIGNMENT SPECIFICATIONS

Application	Axle Gap (Inches)	Caster (Degrees)	Camber (Degrees)	Toe-In (Inches)	Steering Axis Inclination (Degrees)
Cherokee & Wagoneer	.....	7 to 8	-1/2 to +1/2	1/32 In to 1/32 Out	.....
CJ7 & Scrambler	.....	6	0 [1]	0 to 3/32	10
Grand Wagoneer & Truck	.....	4 to 5	0 to +1/2 [1]	3/64 to 3/32	8 1/2

[1] – Not adjustable.

Wheel Alignment

WHEEL ALIGNMENT PROCEDURES

PRE-ALIGNMENT

VEHICLE CHECKS

Before making wheel alignment adjustment, perform the following checks:

1) Tires should be equal in size and runout must not be excessive. Tires and wheels should be in balance, and inflated to manufacturer's specifications.

2) Wheel bearings must be properly adjusted. Steering linkage and suspension must not have excessive looseness. Check for wear in tie rod ends and ball joints.

3) Steering gear box must not have excessive play. Check and adjust to manufacturer's specifications.

4) Vehicle must be at curb height with full fuel load and spare tire in vehicle. No extra load should be on vehicle.

5) Vehicle must be level with floor and with suspension settled. Jounce front and rear of vehicle several times and allow it to settle to normal curb height.

6) If steering wheel is not centered with front wheels in straight-ahead position, correct by shortening one tie rod adjusting sleeve and lengthening opposite sleeve equal amounts.

7) Ensure wheel lug nuts are tightened to torque specifications.

WHEEL LUG NUT TIGHTENING SPECIFICATIONS

Application	Ft. Lbs. (N.m)
Chevrolet & GMC	
Astro/Safari	90 (122)
C10, G10/20	100 (136)
K10	90 (122)
C20/30, G30, P20/30, K20	
W/Single Rear Wheels	120 (163)
C30, G30, K30, P30	
W/Dual Rear Wheels 9/16" Studs	140 (190)
W/Dual Rear Wheels 5/8" Studs	200 (271)
S10/15	
2WD	80 (109)
4WD	100 (136)
Chrysler Corp.	
All FWD Models	95 (129)
All RWD Models	
1/2"-20	105 (142)
5/8"-18	200 (271)
W/Flanged Type Nut	325 (441)
Ford	
All Models	
1/2"-20	90 (122)
9/16"-18	145 (197)
Jeep	
CJ7 & Scrambler	85 (115)
J20 Truck	130 (176)
All Other Models	75 (102)

DESCRIPTION

CAMBER

Camber is the tilting of the wheel, outward at either top or bottom, as viewed from front of vehicle. When wheels tilt outward at top from centerline of vehicle, camber is said to be positive. When wheels tilt inward at top, camber is said to be negative. Amount of tilt or camber angle, is measured in degrees from vertical.

Fig. 1: Camber Angle

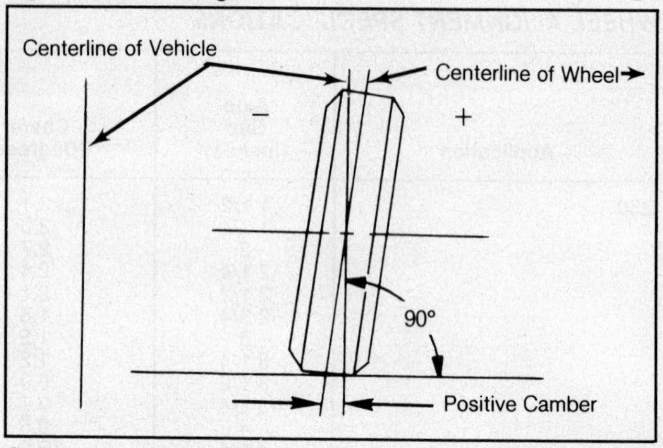

Camber is amount of tilt inward or outward from vertical.

CASTER

Caster is the tilting of front steering axis. This forward or backward tilt from vertical is viewed from side of vehicle. When axis is tilted backward from vertical, caster is said to be positive, creating a trailing action on front wheels. When axis is tilted forward, caster is negative, causing a leading action on front wheels.

Fig. 2: Caster Angle

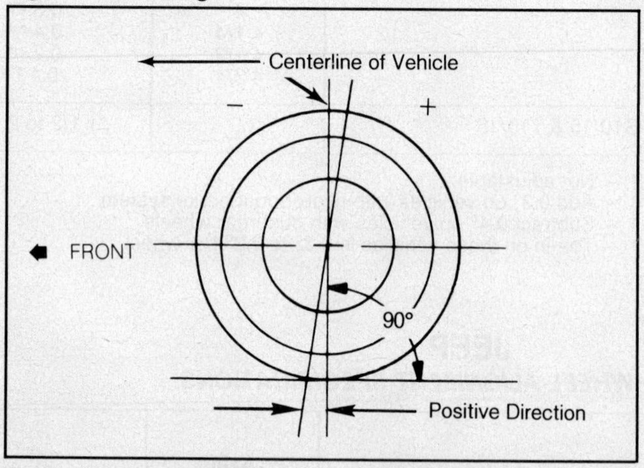

Caster is amount of tilt forward or backward from vertical.

TOE-IN

Toe-in is the turning in of the front wheels. Amount of toe-in is generally only a fraction of an inch. The toe specification ensures a parallel rolling of the front wheels.

ADJUSTMENT

TOE-IN

1) Measure toe-in with front wheels in straight-ahead position and steering wheel centered. Adjust toe-in by loosening clamps and adjusting sleeve or adjusting ends on right and left tie rods equally and in opposite directions to maintain steering wheel in centered position.

2) When tightening clamps, make sure that clamp bolts are positioned so there will be no interference with other parts throughout entire travel of steering linkage.

Wheel Alignment

WHEEL ALIGNMENT PROCEDURES (Cont.)

NOTE: Face of tie rod end must be parallel with machined surface of steering rod end.

Fig. 3: Determining Corrected Caster Angle

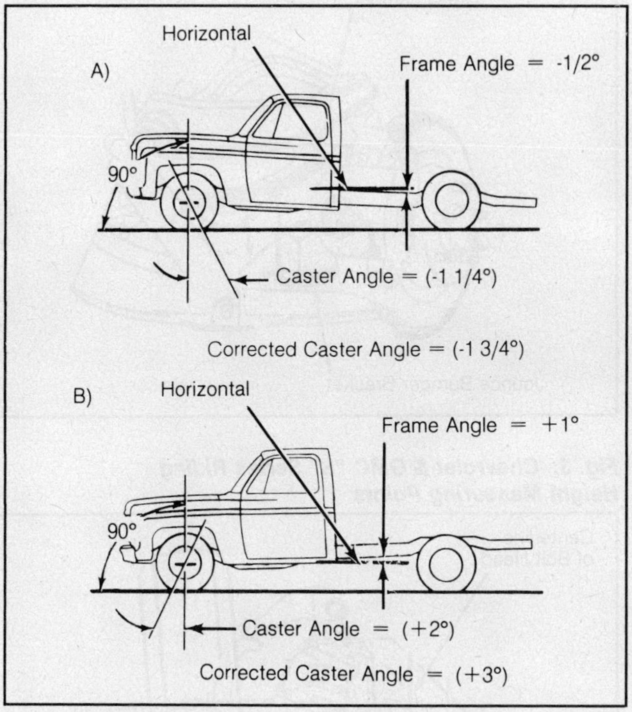

When caster is tilted backward from vertical, caster is positive; when tilted forward, caster is negative.

Fig. 4: Wheel Toe-In

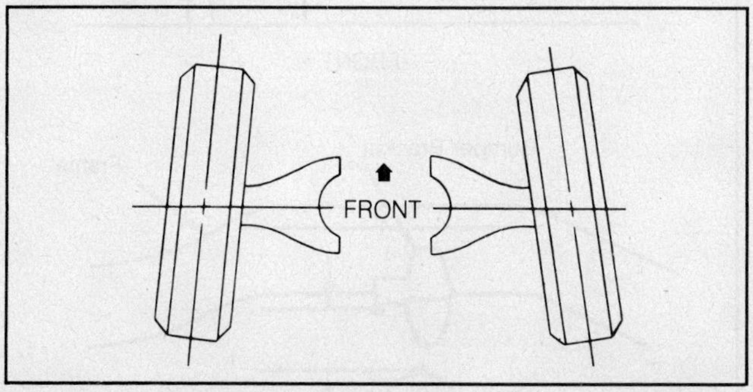

To adjust, turn sleeve on right and left tie rods an equal amount in opposite directions.

TOE-OUT ON TURNS

1) This is a check for bent or damaged parts, and not a service adjustment. With caster, camber and toe-in properly adjusted, check toe-out with weight of vehicle on wheels.

2) Use full-floating turn table under each wheel and repeat test with each wheel positioned for right and left turns.

3) Incorrect toe-out generally indicates a bent steering arm. Replace arm and recheck wheel alignment adjustments. Do not attempt to correct by straightening parts.

Fig. 5: Wheel Toe-Out on Turns

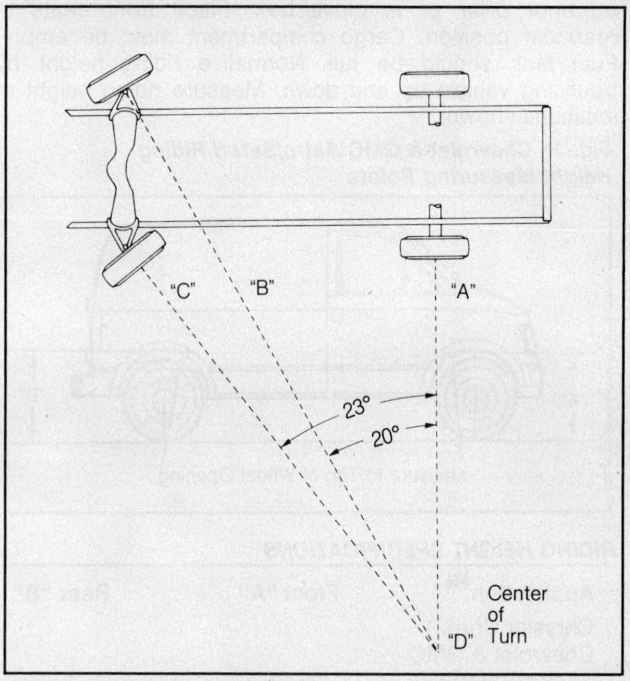

Test each wheel in right and left turn positions.

STEERING AXIS INCLINATION

1) This is a check for bent or damaged parts, and not a service adjustment. Vehicle must be level, both crosswise and lengthwise. Camber should be properly adjusted.

2) If camber cannot be brought within limits and steering axis inclination is correct, steering knuckle is bent. If camber and steering axis inclination are both incorrect by approximately the same amount, upper and lower control arms are bent.

3) Replace parts and recheck all wheel alignment adjustments. Do not attempt to correct by straightening parts.

Fig. 6: Steering Axis Inclination

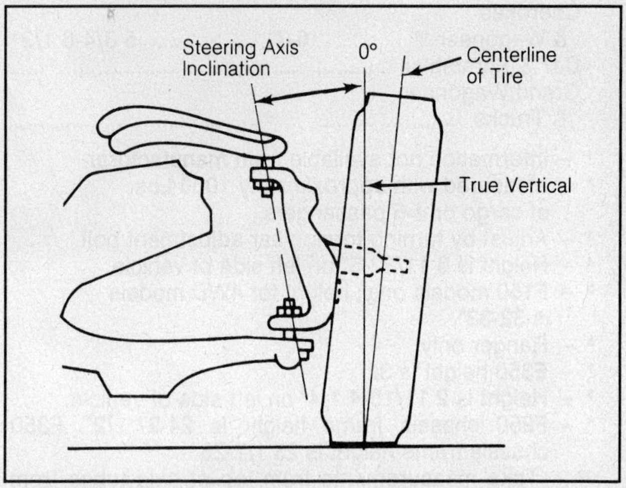

If axis and camber inclination are incorrect, check upper and lower control arms for bends.

Riding Height Specifications

ALL MANUFACTURERS

Check tire pressure. Specifications are found on door pillar or in glove box. Place front seats in rearmost position. Cargo compartment must be empty. Fuel tank should be full. Normalize riding height by bouncing vehicle up and down. Measure riding height at locations shown.

Fig. 1: Chevrolet & GMC Astro/Safari Riding Height Measuring Points

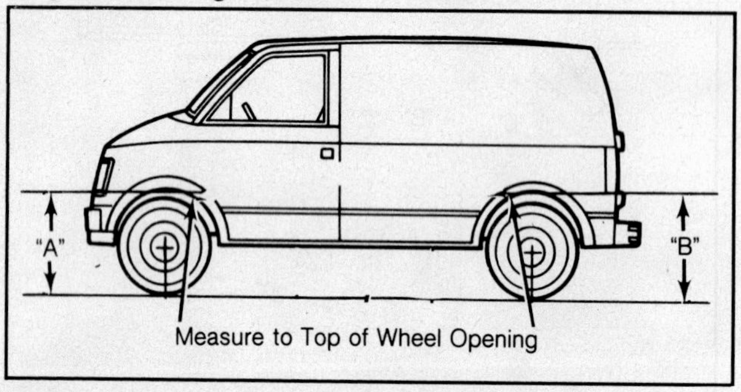

RIDING HEIGHT SPECIFICATIONS

Application	Front "A"	Rear "B"
Chrysler Corp. [1]		
Chevrolet & GMC		
Astro/Safari [2]	29-30"	30-31"
C10/20 & C30	2 1/2-5 3/4"	.....
G10/20/30	1 1/2-4 1/2"	.....
K10/20/30	.....	.....
P20/30	2-4 3/4"	.....
S10/15 [3]	4 5/8-5"	6 1/2-7"
Ford		
Aerostar	.....	.....
Bronco & F150	[4] 3 1/4-4 3/4"	[5] 29-30"
Bronco II & Ranger	3 1/8-4 3/8"	[6] 21"
E150	4-6"	26 1/2-27 1/2"
E250/350	3 3/4-5 1/2"	[7] 29"
F250/350		
2WD	[8] 2 1/2-4"	[9] 31-34"
4WD	5-6 3/4"	[9] 32-34"
Jeep		
Cherokee & Wagoneer [10]	6-7"	5 3/4-6 1/2"
CJ7 & Scrambler	.....	.....
Grand Wagoneer & Trucks	.....	.....

1 – Information not available from manufacturer.
2 – Measured with approximately 1000 Lbs. of cargo or 4-5 passengers.
3 – Adjust by turning torsion bar adjustment bolt.
4 – Height is 3 11/32-5" on left side of vehicle.
5 – F150 models only; height for 4WD models is 32-33".
6 – Ranger only.
7 – E350 height is 32".
8 – Height is 2 11/16-4 1/4" on left side of vehicle.
9 – F250 chassis frame height is 24-27 1/2". F350 chassis frame height is 23 1/2-26".
10 – Take measurements from top of axle tubes from frame sill directly above the tubes. Add 11/32" to all dimensions if vehicle is equipped with P 205/75 R15 tires. Add 3/4" to all dimensions if vehicle is equipped with P 215/75 R15 tires.

Fig. 2: Chevrolet & GMC "C", "G", & "P" Series Riding Height Measuring Points

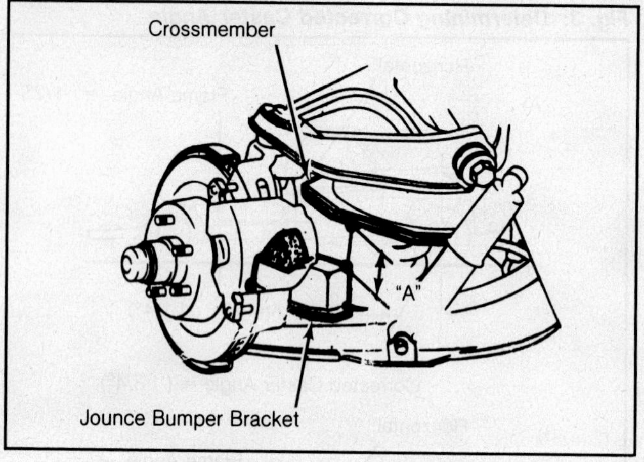

Fig. 3: Chevrolet & GMC "S" Series Riding Height Measuring Points

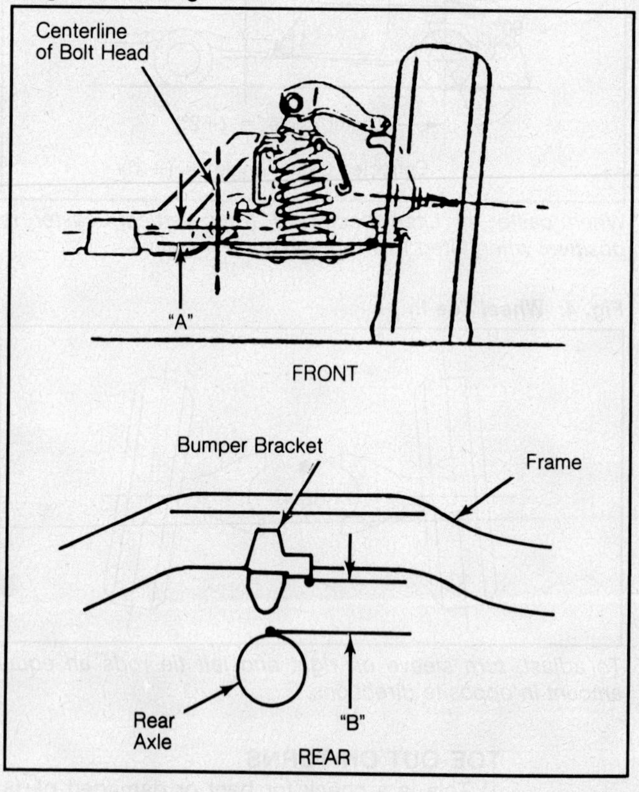

ALL MANUFACTURERS (Cont.)

Fig. 4: Ford Bronco & "F" Series 4WD Riding Height Measuring Points

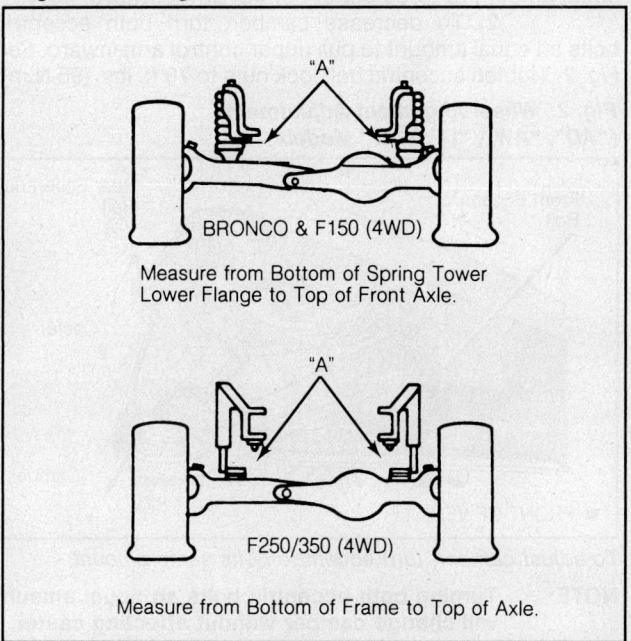

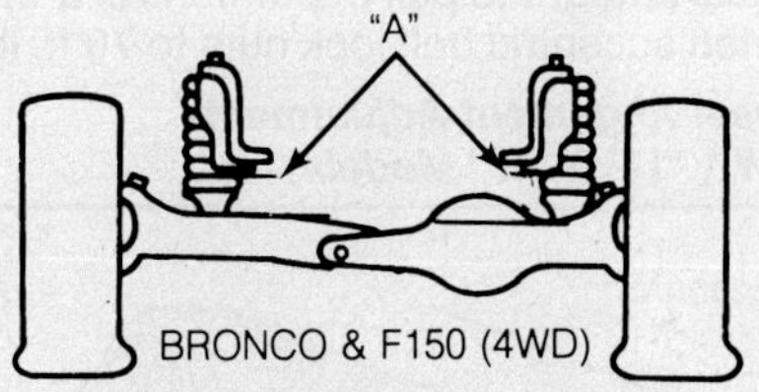

Measure from Bottom of Spring Tower Lower Flange to Top of Front Axle.

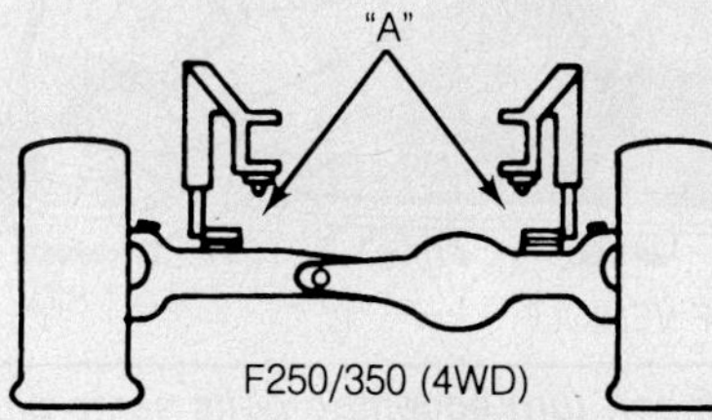

Measure from Bottom of Frame to Top of Axle.

Fig. 5: Ford Bronco II & Ranger Riding Height Measuring Points

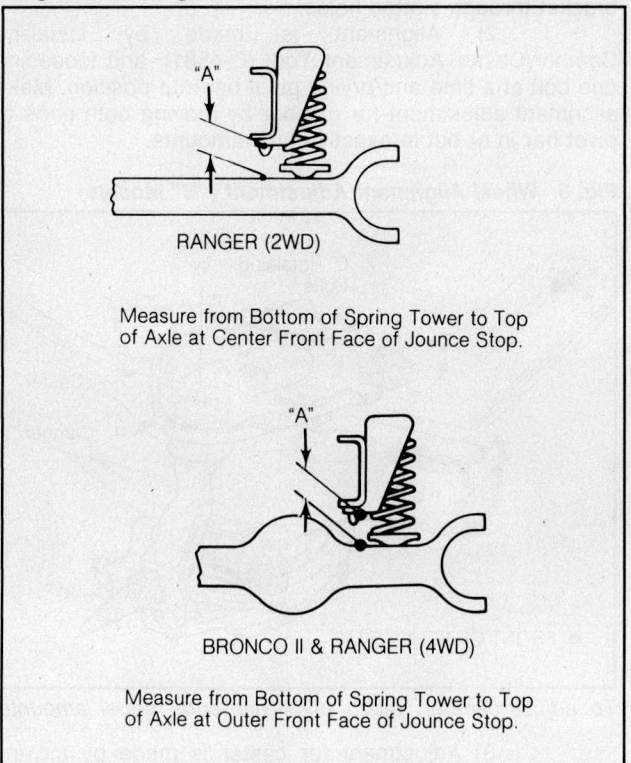

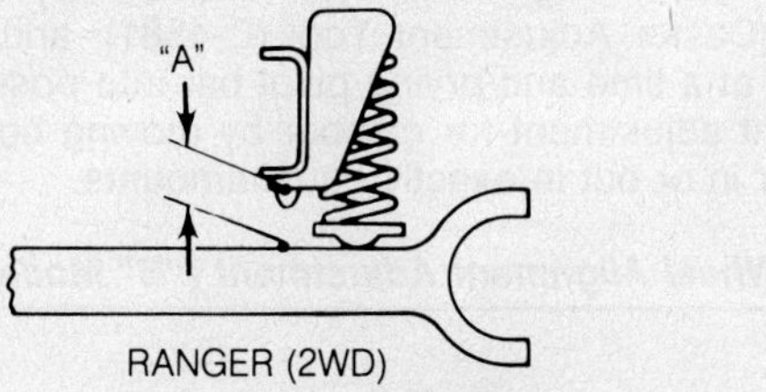

Measure from Bottom of Spring Tower to Top of Axle at Center Front Face of Jounce Stop.

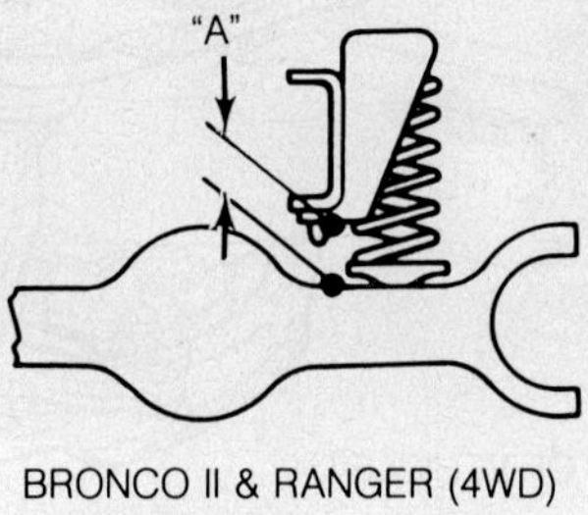

Measure from Bottom of Spring Tower to Top of Axle at Outer Front Face of Jounce Stop.

Fig. 6: Ford "E" Series Riding Height Measuring Points

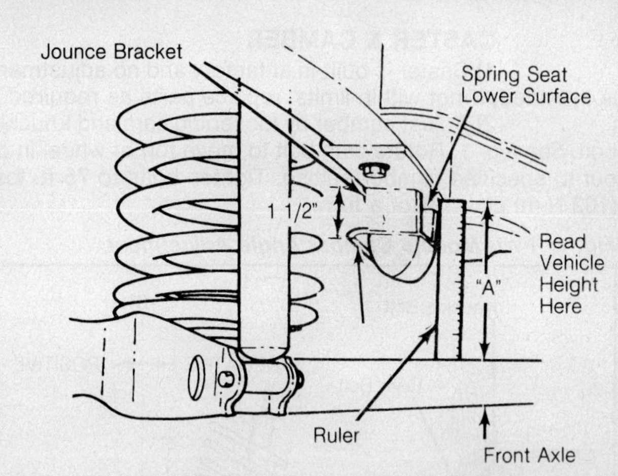

Fig. 7: Ford "F" Series 2WD Riding Height Measuring Points

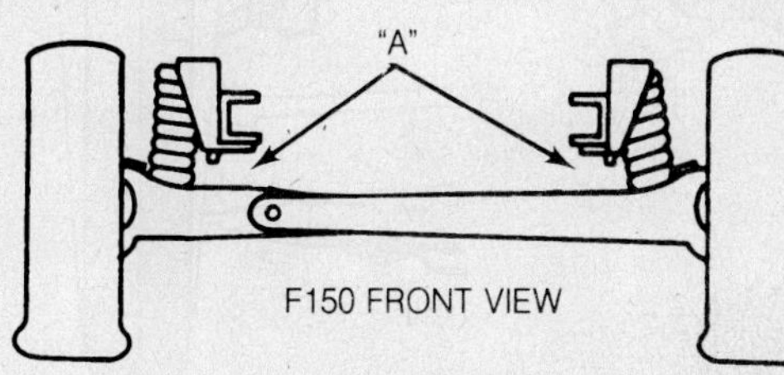

Measure from Bottom of Spring Tower to Top of Axle.

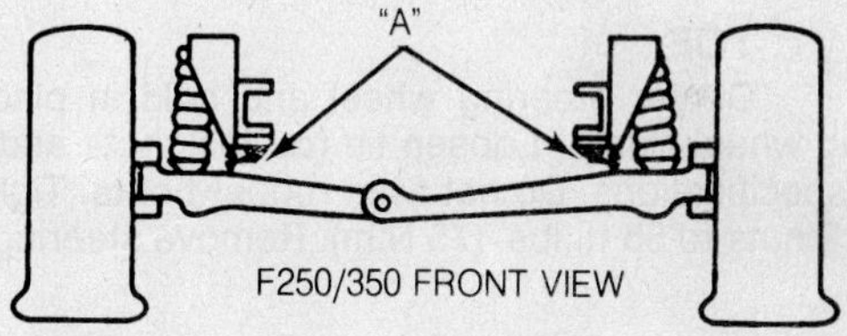

Measure from Bottom of Spring Tower to Top of Axle.

Fig. 8: Ford Rear Riding Height Measuring Points

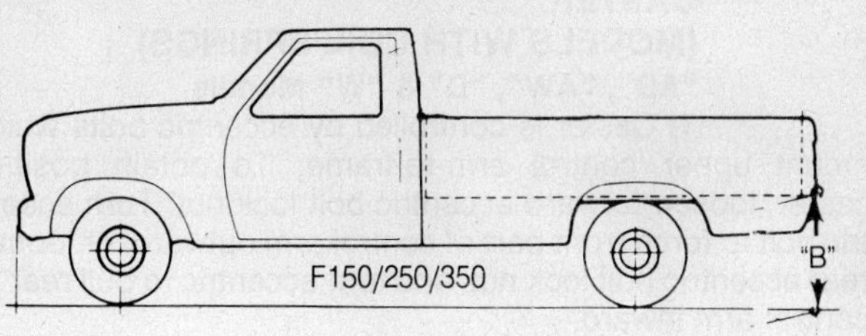

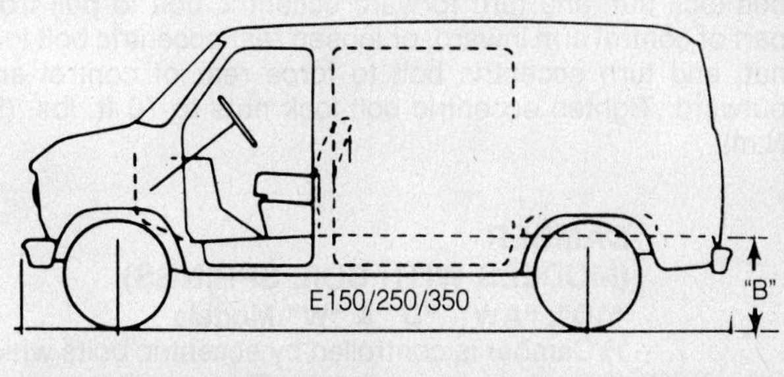

CASTER, CAMBER & TOE-IN ADJUSTMENTS CHRYSLER CORP.

FWD MODELS

CASTER & CAMBER

1) Caster is built-in at factory and no adjustment is provided. If not within limits, replace parts as required.

2) Adjust camber by loosening cam and knuckle bolt. *See Fig. 1*. Rotate cam bolt to move top of wheel in or out to specified camber setting. Tighten bolts to 75 ft. lbs. (102 N.m) plus 1/4 of a turn.

Fig. 1: FWD Models Camber Angle Adjustment

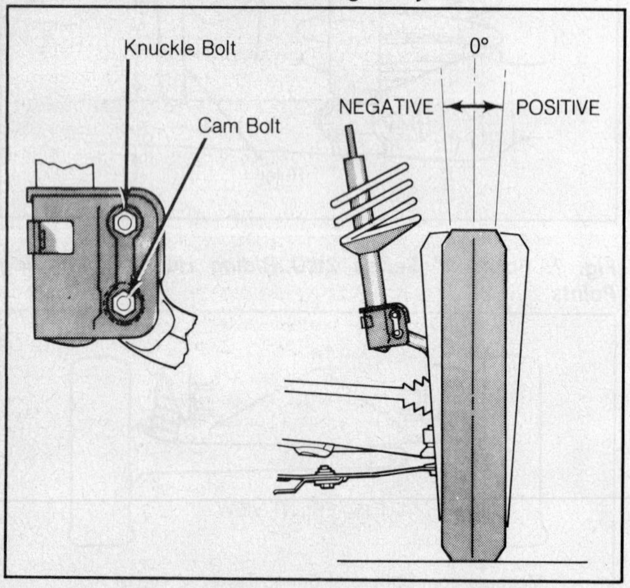

TOE

Center steering wheel and hold in place with steering wheel clamp. Loosen tie rod lock nuts and adjust toe to specifications. Do not twist rubber boots. Tighten tie rod lock nuts to 55 ft. lbs. (75 N.m). Remove steering wheel clamp.

RWD MODELS

CASTER
(MODELS WITH COIL SPRINGS)
"AD", "AW", "D" & "W" Models

1) Caster is controlled by eccentric bolts which mount upper control arm-to-frame. To obtain positive caster, loosen forward eccentric bolt lock nut. Turn eccentric bolt to force front part of control arm outward, or loosen rear eccentric bolt lock nut, and turn eccentric to pull rear of control arm inward.

2) To obtain negative caster, loosen eccentric bolt lock nut, and turn forward eccentric bolt to pull front part of control arm inward, or loosen rear eccentric bolt lock nut, and turn eccentric bolt to force rear of control arm outward. Tighten eccentric bolt lock nuts to 70 ft. lbs. (95 N.m).

CAMBER
(MODELS WITH COIL SPRINGS)
"AD", "AW", "D" & "W" Models

1) Camber is controlled by eccentric bolts which mount upper control arm-to-frame. To increase camber, loosen eccentric bolt lock nuts. Turn both eccentric bolts an equal amount to force upper control arm outward.

2) To decrease camber, turn both eccentric bolts an equal amount to pull upper control arm inward. *See Fig. 2*. Tighten eccentric bolt lock nuts to 70 ft. lbs. (95 N.m).

Fig. 2: Wheel Alignment Adjustment ("AD", "AW", "D" & "W" Models)

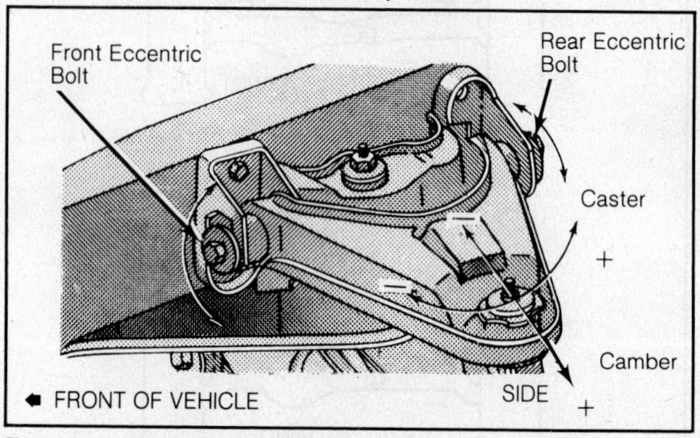

To adjust camber, turn eccentric bolts same amount.

NOTE: Turning both eccentric bolts an equal amount will change camber without affecting caster.

"B" Models

1) Caster and camber are controlled by upper control arm pivot bar. Bar is bolted to frame mounted bracket through slotted holes. *See Fig. 3*.

2) Alignment is made by installing Camber/Caster Adjustment Tool (C-4581), and loosening one bolt at a time and prying pivot bar into position. Make alignment adjustment for camber by moving both ends of pivot bar in or out in exactly equal amounts.

Fig. 3: Wheel Alignment Adjustment ("B" Models)

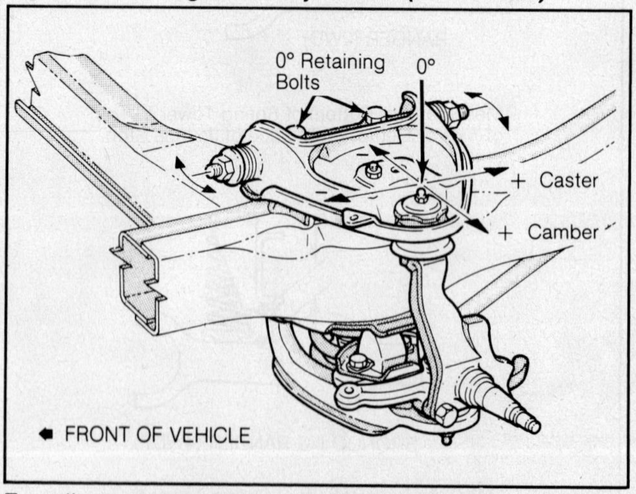

To adjust camber, move pivot bar ends equal amounts.

3) Adjustment for caster is made by moving each end of bar in exactly equal amounts in opposite directions. Increase positive caster by moving front of pivot bar away from engine and rear of bar toward engine an equal amount. Tighten retaining bolts to 195 ft. lbs. (265 N.m).

NOTE: Caster should be held as nearly equal as possible on both wheels.

CASTER, CAMBER & TOE-IN ADJUSTMENTS CHRYSLER CORP. (Cont.)

CASTER & CAMBER (MODELS WITH LEAF SPRINGS)

1) Caster should be checked after camber and steering axis inclination have been checked. Caster adjustment is accomplished by inserting wedge between spring and axle. *See Fig. 4*.

2) To increase caster, insert wedge with thick portion toward rear of vehicle. To decrease caster, insert wedge with thick portion of wedge toward front of vehicle.

3) No adjustment is provided for camber. Camber is preset at factory, if not within limits, axle or steering knuckle is bent and should be replaced.

Fig. 4: Caster Angle Adjustment for Leaf Spring Models

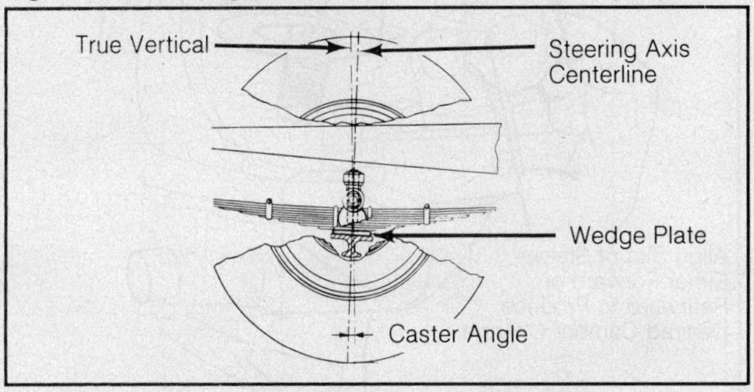

To adjust, insert wedge between spring and axle.

TOE

"AD", "AW", "D" & "W" Models

1) Loosen tie rod clamp bolts. Adjust toe by turning tie rod sleeves. To avoid binding tie rods, rotate both tie rods in direction of sleeve travel.

2) Position clamps on sleeves so that bolt and clamp opening is in line with slot in sleeves. Tighten sleeve clamps to 160 INCH lbs. (18 N.m).

"B" Models

1) Secure steering wheel in straight-ahead position. On vehicles equipped with power steering, start engine before centering wheel and maintain engine running while adjusting toe.

2) Loosen tie rod clamp bolts. Adjust toe by turning tie rod sleeves. To avoid binding tie rods, rotate both tie rods in direction of sleeve travel. Shut engine off.

3) Position sleeve clamps so ends do not rest in sleeve slots. Tighten clamps to 26 ft. lbs. (35 N.m) on H.D. models. Tighten sleeve clamps to 200 INCH lbs. (23 N.m) on all other models. Ensure that clamp bolts are indexed at or near bottom.

TURNING ANGLE

4WD Models Only

1) The turning angle stop screws are located on back side of steering knuckle, just above axle shaft centerline. To adjust, loosen stop screw lock nut.

2) Using full-floating turn table under each wheel, adjust turning angle by adjusting stop screw IN to increase and OUT to decrease turning angle.

TURNING ANGLE ADJUSTMENT 4WD ONLY

Application	Left Wheel	Right Wheel
W150	37°	27°
W250	35°	[1] 29°
W350	45°	20°

[1] – If equipped with 8.7 x 16.5" tires, turning angle is 26°. If equipped with 9.5 x 16.5" tires, turning angle is 24°.

CASTER, CAMBER & TOE-IN ADJUSTMENTS
FORD

CASTER

MODELS WITH COIL SPRINGS

1) Caster on Aerostar is adjusted by removing shims from front leg of upper control arm and installing them on rear leg, or vice-versa. If same amount is switched from one leg to another, caster will be adjusted but camber will not be affected.

2) Caster on all other models is built-in at factory and no adjustment is provided. If not within limits, replace parts as required.

MODELS WITH LEAF SPRINGS

1) Caster angle is adjusted by inserting a shim between the spring and axle. Shims are available in 0°, 1° and 2° increments. If possible, caster adjustment should always be done on right front axle to avoid changing fron driveshaft alignment.

2) To adjust caster, raise vehicle and support front axles on safety stands. Loosen "U" bolt nuts and spring from axle. Install caster shims between spring and axle.

3) Position thin edge of shim toward front of vehicle to increase caster, thin edge toward rear of vehicle to decrease caster. After alignment tighten "U" bolt nuts to 105 ft. lbs. (142 N.m).

NOTE: **Caster shims installed on left axle will change front driveshaft angle. If shims are used on left axle, drive shaft angle must be checked. Correct side-to-side caster variations by adjusting right axle caster.**

CAMBER

The forged twin "I" beam suspension design used on E150/250/350 and F250/350 2WD models has camber angle built-in at factory and no adjustment is provided. If not within limits, replace parts as necessary.

AEROSTAR

Camber adjustment is obtained by removing or installing an equal number of shims from front and rear legs of upper control arm. *See Fig. 1.*

Fig. 1: Aerostar Wheel Alignment Adjustment

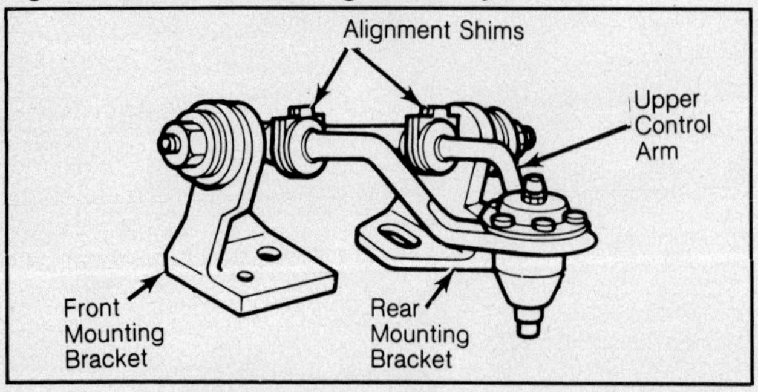

BRONCO & F150/250/350 4WD

1) Camber angle is built into axle and no adjustment is necessary under normal loading conditions. For unusual loading conditions, adjustments can be made by a series of interchangeable sleeves. *See Fig. 2.*

2) Sleeves are available in 4 ranges of 1/2° increments from 1 1/2° negative to 1 1/2° positive. Sleeves are installed on threaded end of upper ball joint. To adjust camber, see procedure described in BRONCO II & RANGER 4WD.

Fig. 2: Installing Camber Adjustment Sleeve

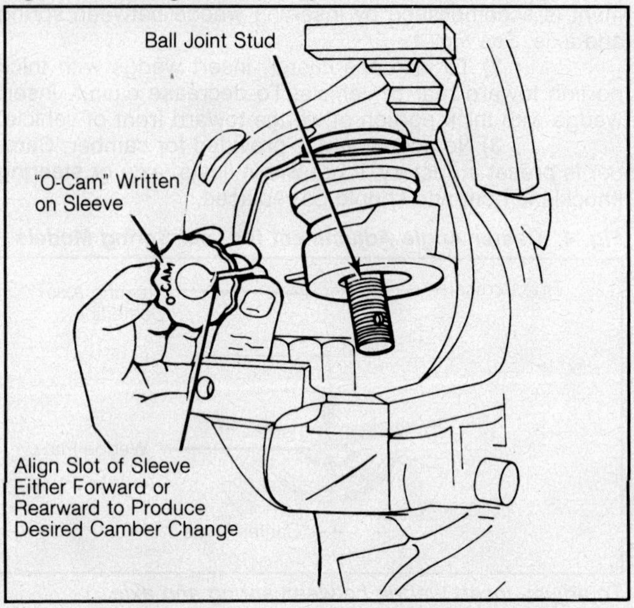

BRONCO II, RANGER & F150 2WD

1) Raise vehicle on hoist. Remove front wheel assemblies. Remove upper ball joint nut. Remove cotter pin on lower ball stud. Back nut down to end of stud.

2) Strike spindle near upper and lower ball joints to break spindle loose from ball joint studs. Use Camber Adjuster Remover (D81T-3010-B) to wedge camber adjuster out of spindle.

3) Replace adjuster with desired camber adjuster. Camber adjusters are available in 0°, 1/2°, 1° and 1 1/2°.

4) To increase camber (more positive), align slot as follows: On drivers side, point slot rearward. On passenger side, point slot forward.

5) To decrease camber (more negative), align slot as follows: On drivers side, point slot forward. On passenger side, point slot rearward.

6) Apply Loctite or equivalent to upper ball stud and hand start upper ball stud. Hand start lower ball nut. Partially tighten lower ball stud nut to 35 ft. lbs. (47 N.m). Tighten upper ball stud to 85-110 ft. lbs. (115-150 N.m).

7) Finish tightening lower ball stud to 104-146 ft. lbs. (141-198 N.m). Advance nut to the next castellation and install cotter pin. Install front wheel assemblies and lower vehicle.

BRONCO II & RANGER 4WD

1) Raise vehicle on hoist and remove wheel assemblies. Remove upper ball joint cotter pin and nut. Loosen lower ball joint nut and back off nut to end of stud.

2) Strike inside of spindle near upper and lower ball joints to break loose from ball joint studs. Remove camber adjustment sleeve. If required, use Pitman Arm Puller (T64P-3590-F), to remove sleeve from spindle.

3) Install camber adjustment sleeve on top ball joint stud with arrow pointing outboard for positive camber and the arrow pointing inboard for negative camber. *See Fig. 3.*

CASTER, CAMBER & TOE-IN ADJUSTMENTS
FORD (Cont.)

NOTE: Zero camber sleeves will not have an arrow and may be rotated in either direction as long as lugs on yoke engage slots in bushing.

4) Remove lower ball joint stud nut and discard. Install a new nut on lower ball joint stud nut and tighten to 40 ft. lbs. (54 N.m). Install new nut on top ball joint stud and tighten to 85-100 ft. lbs. (115-136 N.m).

5) Advance nut until castellation aligns with cotter pin hole and install cotter pin. Finish tightening lower nut to 95-110 ft. lbs. (129-149 N.m). Reinstall wheel assemblies and lower vehicle. Check camber and adjust toe.

Fig. 3: Camber Adjustment

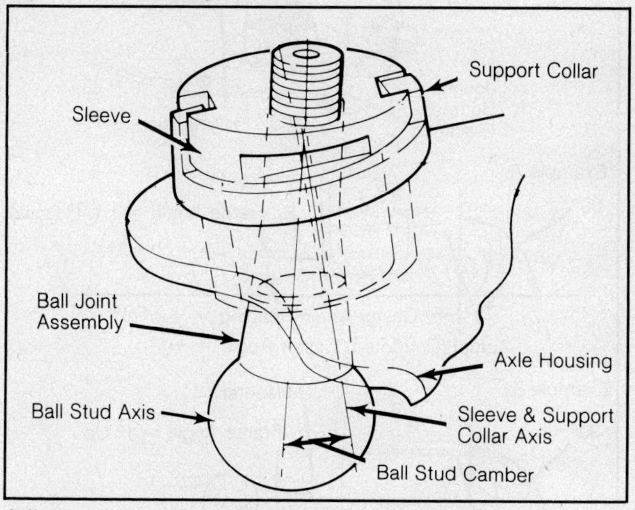

Adjust using upper ball joint mounting sleeves.

TOE

AEROSTAR

1) Start engine and move steering wheel back and forth several times until it is in the straight-ahead position. Turn engine off, and lock steering wheel in centered position.

2) Check toe reading. If toe is not within specifications, remove bellows seal clamp (if used) and free boot from rod before adjusting toe. Do not allow boot to twist.

3) Loosen jam nuts and adjust toe to specifications. Hold tie rod with wrench and tighten jam nut to 45 ft. lbs. (61 N.m). Replace bellows and seal clamp (if used) after tightening jam nut.

BRONCO II & RANGER

1) Loosen clamp bolts at each end of spindle connecting rod tube. Rotate sleeve until correct toe alignment is obtained.

2) With clamps centered between adjustment sleeve lock ring nibbs, position clamp bolts horizontally on bottom of tube and with nuts toward front (rear) of vehicle. *See Fig 3*. Tighten sleeve to 35 ft. lbs. (47 N.m).

3) Recheck toe alignment to ensure no changes have occured when clamps were tightened. Check that steering wheel is centered.

ALL OTHER MODELS

1) Loosen adjusting sleeve clamp bolts on each end of tie rod (left side only on "E" series). Rotate sleeve(s) until correct toe alignment is obtained.

2) With clamps 3/16" (5 mm) from end of sleeve on 4WD models, position clamp bolts horizontally and with nuts toward front (rear) of vehicle. *See Fig. 4*. Tighten sleeve to 35 ft. lbs. (47 N.m).

3) With clamps centered between the adjustment sleeve lock ring nibbs on all other models, position clamp bolts horizontally (vertically) and with nuts pointing downward or toward front (rear) of vehicle. Tighten sleeve to 35 ft. lbs. (47 N.m).

NOTE: Steering wheel misalignment on "E" series vehicles can only be corrected by removing and recentering steering wheel after toe has been adjusted.

Fig. 4: Toe Adjustment Sleeve Clamp Positions

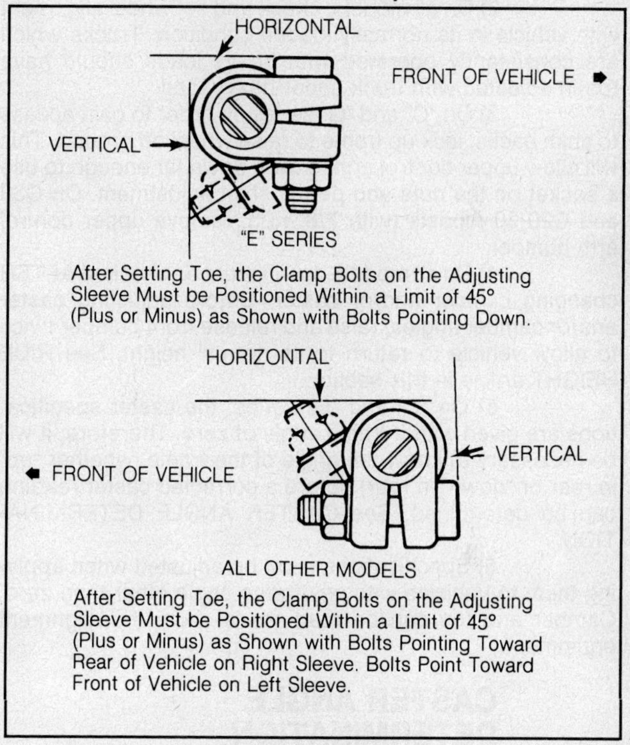

HORIZONTAL
FRONT OF VEHICLE
VERTICAL
"E" SERIES
After Setting Toe, the Clamp Bolts on the Adjusting Sleeve Must be Positioned Within a Limit of 45° (Plus or Minus) as Shown with Bolts Pointing Down.
HORIZONTAL
VERTICAL
FRONT OF VEHICLE
ALL OTHER MODELS
After Setting Toe, the Clamp Bolts on the Adjusting Sleeve Must be Positioned Within a Limit of 45° (Plus or Minus) as Shown with Bolts Pointing Toward Rear of Vehicle on Right Sleeve. Bolts Point Toward Front of Vehicle on Left Sleeve.

TURNING ANGLE

"E" & "F" SERIES

1) All "E" and "F" series models have built in steering stops which cannot be altered. E250/350 models have non-adjustable steering stop pins which are pressed into axle. These pins are matched to tire size and may require replacement if tire size is changed.

2) F150/250/350 4WD models use a welded screw and lock nut which is not adjustable. A spacer cap is used with wide tread tires on F150.

TURNING ANGLE SPECIFICATIONS

Application	Kingpin	Ball Joint
F150	36.8°	36.8°
F250/350	35.0°	35.0°
F150 4WD		[1] 36°
F250 4WD [2]		33.4°
F350 4WD		30.3°

[1] – 34.0 with 10 X 15 size tires.
[2] – 30.3° for F250 4WD Heavy Duty trucks.

CASTER, CAMBER & TOE-IN ADJUSTMENTS GENERAL MOTORS

PRE-ALIGNMENT INFORMATION

NOTE: A normal shim pack will leave at least 2 threads of bolt exposed beyond the nut. Difference between front and rear shim packs must not exceed .40" (10.32 mm) on "S", "T" and "M" series or .30" (7.62 mm) on "C" and "G" series. On "C" and "G" series, ensure front shim pack is at least .10" (2.52 mm) thick.

1) On all models except "K" series, caster and camber can be adjusted in 1 operation. On "K" series, caster and camber is designed into the front axle assembly and is not adjustable.

2) On all models, check and set wheel alignment with vehicle in its normally loaded condition. Trucks which are consistantly operated with heavy loads should have toe-in adjusted with truck under heavy load.

3) On "C" and "G" series, in order to gain access to shim packs, jack up frame to raise wheel off ground. This will allow upper control arm to drop down far enough to use a socket on the nuts and permit shim adjustment. On G30 and C20/30 models (with 7/8" nut), remove upper control arm bumper.

4) On all models, toe-in must be checked AFTER changing camber and/or caster. Before adjusting caster and/or camber angles, raise and release front bumper twice to allow vehicle to return to its normal height. See RIDE HEIGHT article in this section.

5) On "C" and "G" series, the caster specifications are given with a frame angle of zero. Therefore, it will be necessary to know the angle of the frame (whether "up" in rear or "down" in rear) before a corrected caster reading can be determined. See CASTER ANGLE DETERMINATION.

6) Specifications must be adjusted when applying them to vehicles with any frame angle other than zero. Camber and toe can be read "as is" from the alignment equipment.

CASTER ANGLE DETERMINATION

"C" & "G" SERIES

1) With vehicle on level surface, determine frame angle using bubble protractor or inclinometer. Determine caster angle reading from the alignment equipment.

2) To determine an actual (corrected) caster angle with various frame angles and caster angle readings from the alignment equipment, one of the following rules applies:

- A "down in rear" frame angle must be subtracted from a positive caster angle reading. *See Fig. 1, Example A.*
- An "up in rear" frame angle must be added to positive caster angle reading. *See Fig. 1, Example B.*
- A "down in rear" frame angle must be added to a negative caster angle reading. *See Fig. 1, Example C.*
- An "up in rear" frame angle must be subtracted from a negative caster angle reading. *See Fig. 1, Example D.*

3) The dimension "BC" is measured 90° from lower surface of crossmember to inboard rear corner of jounce bumper bracket. *See Fig. 1, View A.* Using dimension "BC" and the appropriate CASTER, CAMBER & TOE-IN table, find the recommended caster angle.

4) If an actual (corrected) caster angle (step 2) does not correspond to a recommended caster angle (step 3) within F1°, make necessary shim changes to bring actual (corrected) caster angle in line with recommended caster angle.

Fig. 1: Determining Caster Angle For "C" & "G" Series

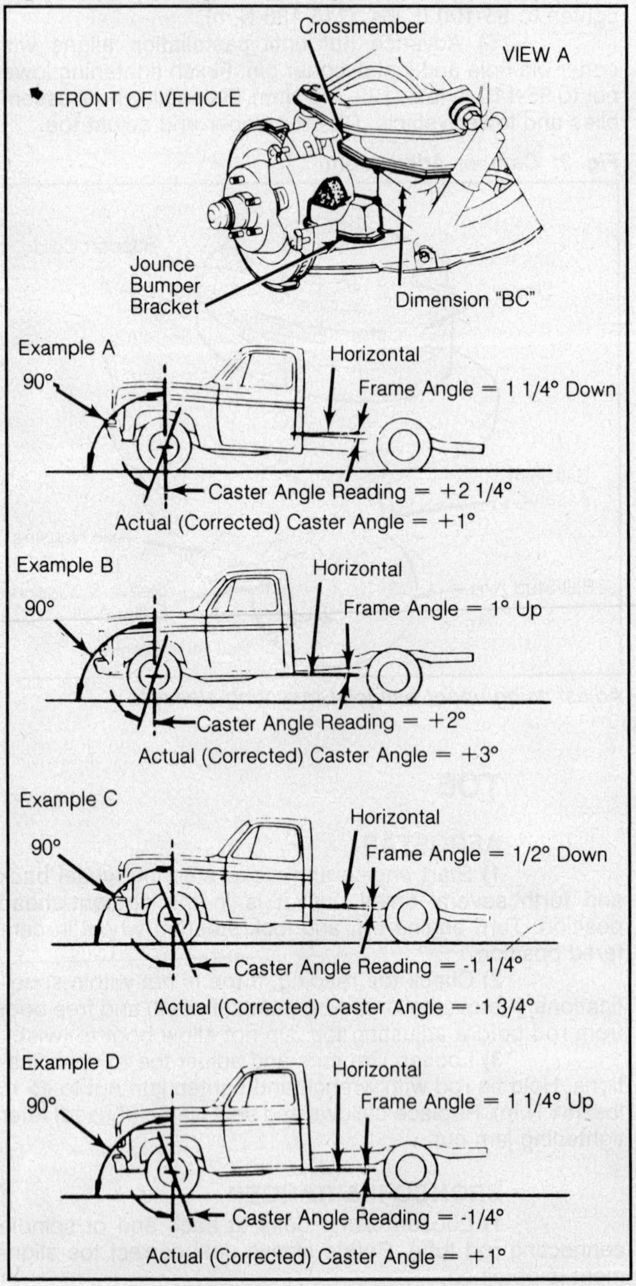

The "C" series is shown. Caster angle for "G" series also may be determined using this chart.

CASTER

2WD MODELS

Determine caster angle from alignment machine and adjust as necessary. To decrease positive caster,

CASTER, CAMBER & TOE-IN ADJUSTMENTS GENERAL MOTORS (Cont.)

transfer 1 or more shims from between rear upper control arm retaining bolt and frame to front retaining bolt and vise versa. *See Fig. 2*. If a normal shim pack will not bring vehicle within specifications, check for damaged control arms and related parts.

4WD MODELS

Determine caster angle from alignment machine and correct (if adjustable) as necessary. To adjust caster on "T" models, loosen upper control arm-to-frame mounting nuts. Rotate either cam (depending on adjustment needed) by rotating bolt head. To increase positive caster, move front cam lobe inward and rear cam outward and vise versa. If vehicle front end alignment specifications are not within limits, check for damaged control arms and related parts.

CAMBER

NOTE: **Adding an equal number of shims at both front and rear of cross shaft will decrease positive camber. By adding or subtracting equal amounts of shims, camber may be corrected without affecting caster.**

2WD MODELS

Determine camber angle from alignment machine and adjust as necessary. Camber is changed by adding or subtracting shims from between upper control arm shaft and frame bracket. Adding an equal number of shims at both front and rear of cross shaft will decrease positive camber and vice versa. *See Fig. 2*. If a normal shim pack will not bring vehicle within specifications, check for damaged control arms and related parts.

4WD MODELS

Determine camber angle from alignment machine and correct (if adjustable) as necessary. To adjust camber on "T" models, loosen upper control arm-to-frame nuts. To increase positive camber, move both front and rear cam lobes inward. If alignment specification is not within limits, check for damaged control arms and related parts.

NOTE: **Wheel runout must be checked and, if necessary, compensated for before checking and/or adjusting toe-in. Maximum steel wheel radial runout is .040" (1.02 mm) and lateral runout is .045" (1.14 mm). Maximum aluminum wheel radial and lateral runout is .030" (.76 mm). Replace wheel if beyond specifications.**

TOE-IN

NOTE: **Toe-in can be increased or decreased by turning the threaded sleeve to change the length of the tie rods. When tie rods are mounting ahead of the steering knuckle, they must be decreased in length in order to increase toe-in.**

1) Determine toe-in and adjust as necessary. Inspect tie rod adjuster sleeve clamp bolts and nuts for rust. If in good condition, loosen nuts and bolts. If excessively rusted, measure nut removal torque after breakaway. If more than 7 ft. lbs. (9 N.m), replace nut(s) and bolt(s).

2) Apply penetrating oil to adjuster sleeve and clamps, then rotate sleeve until free on tie rods. Center steering wheel and lock in position with steering wheel holder.

3) With clamp bolts and nuts of each adjusting sleeve loose, turn adjuster sleeves to obtain proper toe-in adjustment. After adjustment, check that the number of threads showing on each end of sleeve are equal (within 3 threads) and tie rod end housings are at right angles to steering arm.

4) Position clamps with bolt centerlines horizontal (within 60° of each other). Ensure adjuster sleeve slot is not within clamp jaws. With clamps between and clear of dimples, tighten clamp bolts and nuts.

5) Clamp ends may touch when nuts are tightened to specification but gap adjacent to adjuster sleeve must not be less than .0050" (.127 mm). Replace clamp and/or sleeve if not to specification.

REAR WHEEL & AXLE HOUSING ALIGNMENT

1) If rear tire wear indicates that axle housing may be bent, check alignment. Back vehicle squarely onto an alignment machine. Compensate for wheel runout the same as for checking front wheel toe-in.

Fig. 2: Adjusting Caster & Camber

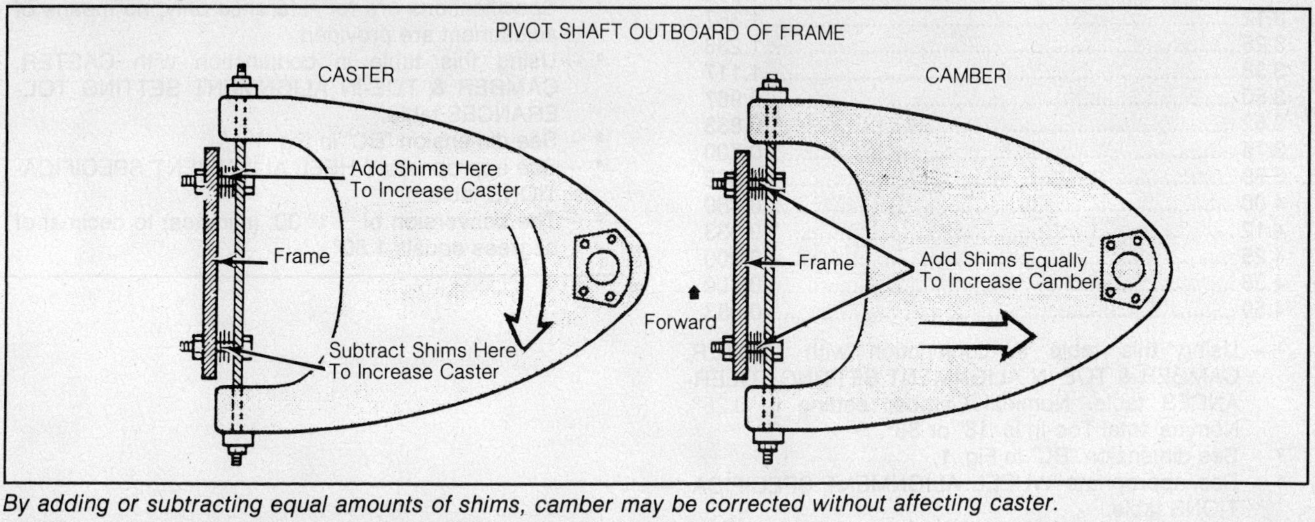

By adding or subtracting equal amounts of shims, camber may be corrected without affecting caster.

CASTER, CAMBER & TOE-IN ADJUSTMENTS GENERAL MOTORS (Cont.)

an alignment machine. Compensate for wheel runout the same as for checking front wheel toe-in.

NOTE: **Due to the fact the vehicle is backed onto alignment machine, the actual toe-out will be read on the scale as toe-in. If tram (scuff) gauge is used to check toe-out, disregard this note.**

2) Check camber. Camber reading should be 3° negative to 5° positive. Check toe-in. Proper toe-in is 0° to .05° (0" to 1/16"). If vehicle is not within specification, check and straighten frame and/or related components as necessary.

NOTE: **Equipment used to straighten frame must allow rechecking of camber and toe-in without removing axle housing from vehicle.**

TIGHTENING SPECIFICATIONS

Application	Ft. Lbs. (N.m)
Tie Rod Adjuster Sleeve Clamp Bolt/Nut	
Astro & Safari	14 (19)
"C" & "G" Series	12 (16)
"S" & "T" Series	15 (20)
Upper Control Arm Pivot Shaft Nut	
Astro & Safari	66 (90)
C10 & G10/20 Series	70 (95)
C20/30 & G30 Series	105 (142)
"S" & "T" Series	70 (95)

G30 SERIES CASTER, CAMBER & TOE-IN TABLE [1]

Dimension "BC" [2]	Caster° [3]
1.50	3.094
1.62	3.034
1.75	2.967
1.88	2.800
2.00	2.667
2.12	2.500
2.25	2.367
2.38	2.233
2.50	2.100
2.62	1.967
2.75	1.833
2.88	1.633
3.00	1.500
3.12	1.367
3.25	1.233
3.38	1.117
3.50	0.967
3.62	0.833
3.75	0.700
3.88	0.583
4.00	0.450
4.12	0.333
4.25	0.200
4.38	0.100
4.50	-0.033

1 – Using this table in conjunction with CASTER, CAMBER & TOE-IN ALIGNMENT SETTING TOLERANCES table. Nominal Camber setting is 0.25°. Nominal total Toe-In is .18" or 36°.
2 – See dimension "BC" in Fig. 1.
3 – See appropriate WHEEL ALIGNMENT SPECIFICATIONS table.

G10/20 SERIES CASTER, CAMBER & TOE-IN TABLE [1]

Dimension "BC" [2]	Caster° [3]
1.50	3.417
1.62	3.317
1.75	3.217
1.88	3.100
2.00	3.000
2.12	2.950
2.25	2.850
2.38	2.750
2.50	2.667
2.62	2.567
2.75	2.480
2.88	2.400
3.00	2.330
3.12	2.317
3.25	2.150
3.38	2.066
3.50	2.000
3.62	1.880
3.75	1.800
3.88	1.730
4.00	1.667
4.12	1.600
4.25	1.530
4.38	1.467
4.50	1.400

1 – Using this table in conjunction with CASTER, CAMBER & TOE-IN ALIGNMENT SETTING TOLERANCES table. Nominal Camber setting is 0.50°. Nominal total Toe-In setting is .18" or 36°.
2 – See dimension "BC" in Fig. 1.
3 – See appropriate WHEEL ALIGNMENT SPECIFICATIONS table.

K10/30 SERIES CASTER [1]***, CAMBER*** [1] ***& TOE-IN TABLE*** [2]

Dimension "BC" [3]	Caster° [4]	Camber° [4]	Total Toe-In [4]
2.50 Through 5.88	+8° (Nominal)	+1° 30' [5] (Nominal)	0' (Nominal)

1 – Specifications are for reference only, no means of adjustment are provided.
2 – Using this table in conjunction with CASTER, CAMBER & TOE-IN ALIGNMENT SETTING TOLERANCES table.
3 – See dimension "BC" in Fig. 1.
4 – See appropriate WHEEL ALIGNMENT SPECIFICATIONS table.
5 – The conversion of +1° 30' (minutes) to decimal of degrees equals 1.50°.

CASTER, CAMBER & TOE-IN ADJUSTMENTS
GENERAL MOTORS (Cont.)

C10 SERIES CASTER, CAMBER & TOE-IN TABLE [1]

Dimension "BC" [2]	Caster° [3]
2.50	3.65
2.62	3.55
2.75	3.45
2.88	3.30
3.00	3.15
3.12	3.00
3.25	2.85
3.38	2.75
3.50	2.60
3.62	2.45
3.75	2.35
3.88	2.20
4.00	2.05
4.12	1.90
4.25	1.75
4.38	1.65
4.50	1.50
4.62	1.35
4.75	1.25
4.88	1.10
5.00	1.00
5.12	0.90
5.25	0.75
5.38	0.60
5.50	0.50
5.62	0.35
5.75	0.25
5.88	0.15
6.00	0

[1] – Using this table in conjunction with CASTER, CAMBER & TOE-IN ALIGNMENT SETTING TOLERANCES table. Nominal Camber setting is 0.70°. Nominal total Toe-In setting is .18" OR .36°.
[2] – See dimension "BC" in Fig. 1.
[3] – See appropriate WHEEL ALIGNMENT SPECIFICATIONS table.

CASTER, CAMBER & TOE-IN ALIGNMENT SETTING TOLERANCES TABLE [1]

	Check	Re-Set
Caster [2]	±1.00° [3]	±0.50° [4]
Camber [2]	±0.75° [3]	±0.50° [4]
Total Toe-In [2]	±.12" ±.232°	±.06" ±.116°

[1] – Using this table in conjunction with appropriate CASTER, CAMBER & TOE-IN tables.
[2] – See appropriate WHEEL ALIGNMENT SPECIFICATIONS table.
[3] – Left and right to be equal within 1.00°.
[4] – Left and right to be equal within 0.50°.

C20/30 SERIES CASTER, CAMBER & TOE-IN TABLE [1]

Dimension "BC" [2]	Caster° [3]
2.50	1.507
2.62	1.370
2.75	1.224
2.88	1.061
3.00	0.928
3.12	0.766
3.25	0.612
3.38	0.474
3.50	0.328
3.62	0.186
3.75	0.114
3.88	0.046
4.00	-.011
4.12	-.084
4.25	-.152
4.38	-.605
4.50	-.746
4.62	-.866
4.75	-.999
4.88	-1.126
5.00	-1.246
5.12	-1.350
5.25	-1.440
5.38	-1.542
5.50	-1.638
5.62	-1.747
5.75	-1.849
5.88	-1.944

[1] – Using this table in conjunction with CASTER, CAMBER & TOE-IN ALIGNMENT SETTING TOLERANCES table. Nominal Camber setting is 0° 15' (.25°). Nominal total Toe-In setting is .36".
[2] – See dimension "BC" in Fig. 1.
[3] – See appropriate WHEEL ALIGNMENT SPECIFICATIONS table.

CASTER, CAMBER & TOE-IN ADJUSTMENTS
JEEP

CAMBER

Correct camber angle of 0° for all models is preset at time of manufacture and cannot be adjusted. It is important that camber be the same on both front wheels. If not within limits, replace parts as necessary.

CASTER

CHEROKEE & WAGONEER

Caster adjustment is made by adding or removing shims at rear of lower control arms.

ALL OTHER MODELS

Caster adjustment is made by inserting shims between spring and axle. To increase caster, insert thick portion of shim toward rear of vehicle. To decrease caster, insert thick portion of shim toward front of vehicle.

Fig. 1: Caster Adjustment

To adjust, insert shim between spring and axle.

TOE

CHEROKEE & WAGONEER

1) Find steering gear center pivot point by counting steering wheel turns (lock-to-lock). Turn steering wheel 1/2 the total lock-to-lock turns. Lock steering wheel in centered position.

2) Loosen adjuster tube clamp bolts and adjust the center link which connects the pitman arm to right wheel. Set right wheel toe to specifications. Position clamps with nut toward front of vehicle. Tighten clamp bolts to 12 ft. lbs. (16 N.m).

3) Loosen adjuster tube clamp bolts and adjust the tie rod which connects center link to left wheel. Set left wheel toe to specifications. Position clamps with nut toward rear of vehicle. Tighten clamp bolts to 12 ft. lbs. (16 N.m).

ALL OTHER MODELS

Loosen adjuster tube clamp bolts. Turn tie rod in or out. Tie rods have both right and left-hand threads to provide equal adjustment at each wheel. After adjustment, tighten clamp bolts to 30 ft. lbs. (41 N.m).

TURNING ANGLE

1) The turning angle stop screws are located on back side of steering knuckle, just above axle centerline. To adjust, loosen lock nut on stop screw.

2) Using full-floating turn table under each wheel, adjust stop screw IN to increase turning angle and OUT to decrease turning angle. Tighten lock nut.

TURNING ANGLE ADJUSTMENT

Application	Left Wheel	Right Wheel
Cherokee & Wagoneer [1]	32-33°	32-33°
CJ7 & Scrambler	30-31°	30-31°
Grand Wagoneer & Pickups	36-37°	36-37°

[1] – This angle may be reduced to allow 1/2" (13 mm) minimum clearance between front sway bar bracket and tire at full turn.

CHRYSLER CORP.

HOISTING

FRAME CONTACT HOIST

Ram, Power Ram & Ramcharger

Vehicle may be raised on single or twin-post swiveling arm, or ramp-type drive hoists. If using swiveling arm hoist, ensure that lifting arms or pads are positioned evenly on the frame rails, and that adequate clearance is maintained for transfer case (4WD models) or skid plate.

If a twin-post hoist is used, a 4" x 4" x 12" wooden spacer may be required to maintain a level lifting attitude. Place the wooden spacer under the front axle tube (opposite differential housing) and secure to hoist. All hoists must be equipped with adapters to support vehicle properly.

CAUTION: Do not raise vehicle by hoisting or jacking against front lower control arms. If the rear axle, fuel tank, spare tire and liftgate will be removed for service, place additional weight on the rear end of the vehicle. This will prevent tipping as the center of gravity changes.

Caravan, Mini Ram Van & Voyager

To raise vehicle on single, and twin-post type hoists, assure that hoist pads contact the vehicle frame behind the front control arm pivots and inside the rear wheels on the rear axle housing. Always use appropriate hoist adapters.

Ram Van & Wagon

To raise vehicle on single, and twin-post type hoists, assure that hoist pads contact the vehicle frame behind the front control arm pivots and inside the rear wheels on the rear axle housing. Always use appropriate hoist adapters.

Fig. 1: Chrysler Truck Hoist Precautions

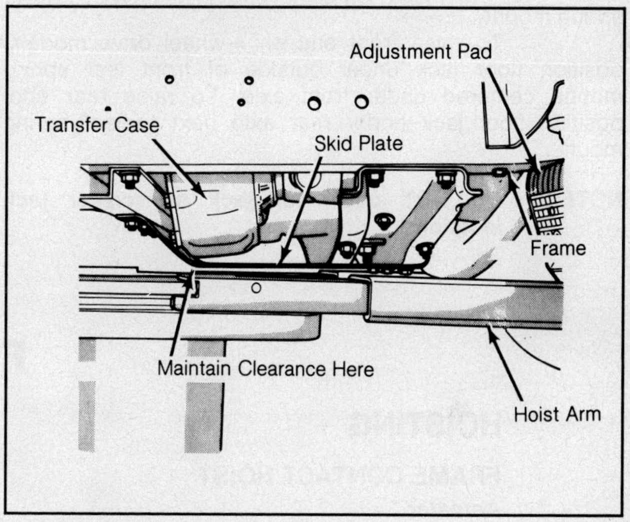

Typical single-post hoist is shown.

Fig. 2: Hoisting & Jacking Support Locations: Caravan, Mini Ram Van & Voyager

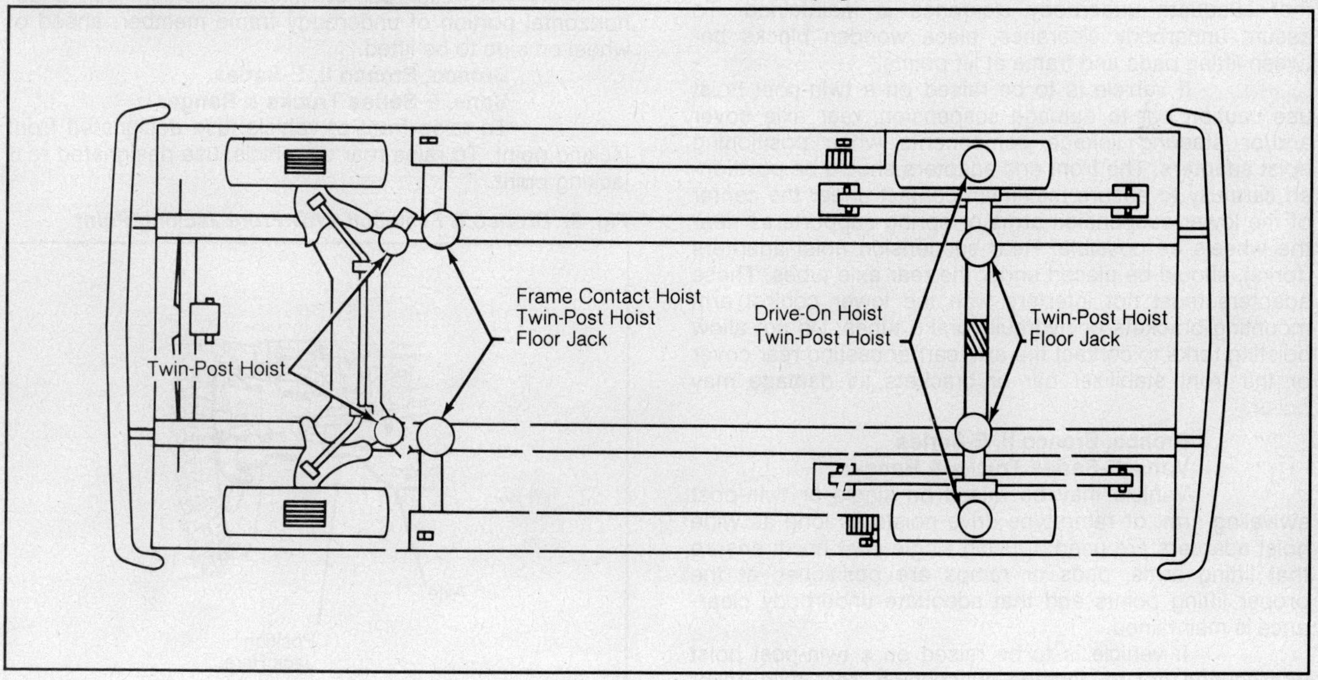

CHRYSLER CORP. (Cont.)

JACKING

FLOOR JACK

Ram, Power Ram & Ramcharger

To raise front end of 2-wheel drive models, place and center the floor jack under the inner edge of the lower control arm pivot bolt mounting bracket. To raise rear end, position floor jack under rear axle next to leaf spring mount.

To raise front end on 4-wheel drive models, position floor jack under outside of front leaf spring mount, centered under front axle. To raise rear end, position floor jack under rear axle next to leaf spring mount.

NOTE: DO NOT use floor jack at scissor jack locations.

Caravan, Mini Ram Van, & Voyager

To raise front end, place floor jack under front crossmember forward flange, inboard of the lower control arm pivot. To raise rear end, place floor jack under the rear axle, next to the leaf spring mount.

Ram Van & Wagon

To raise front end, place floor jack under front crossmember forward flange, inboard of the lower control arm pivot. To raise rear end, place floor jack under the rear axle, next to the leaf spring U-bolt mount.

CAUTION: Never place jack under any part of the vehicle underbody. Do not attempt to raise one entire side of the vehicle by placing a jack midway between the front and rear wheels as permanent body damage could occur.

FORD

HOISTING

FRAME CONTACT HOIST

Aerostar

Vehicle may be raised on single or twin-post swiveling arm, or ramp-type drive hoists. If using single post hoist, ensure that lifting arms, pads or ramps are positioned at the proper lifting points as shown below, and that adequate underbody clearance is maintained. To assure underbody clearance, place wooden blocks between lifting pads and frame at lift points.

If vehicle is to be raised on a twin-post hoist use caution not to damage suspension, rear axle cover and/or steering linkage components when positioning hoist adapters. The front end adapters should be positioned carefully to ensure maximum contact under the center of the lower suspension arms or spring supports as near the wheels as possible. Rear suspension hoist adapters (forks), should be placed under the rear axle tubes. These adapters must not interfere with the lower control arm mounting brackets or hydraulic brake tubes. Do not allow hoisting forks to contact the axle carrier casting rear cover or the front stabilizer bar or brackets as damage may occur.

Bronco, Bronco II, E-Series Vans, F-Series Trucks & Ranger

Vehicle may be raised on single or twin-post swiveling arm, or ramp-type drive hoists as long as wide hoist adapters are used. If using single post hoist, ensure that lifting arms, pads or ramps are positioned at the proper lifting points and that adequate underbody clearance is maintained.

If vehicle is to be raised on a twin-post hoist use caution not to damage suspension, rear axle cover and/or steering linkage components when positioning hoist adapters.

JACKING

FLOOR JACK

Aerostar

To raise front of vehicle, position jack under horizontal portion of underbody frame member, behind front wheel of side to be lifted.

To raise rear of vehicle, position jack under horizontal portion of underbody frame member, ahead of wheel on side to be lifted.

Bronco, Bronco II, E-Series Vans, F-Series Trucks & Ranger

To raise front of vehicle, use designated front jacking point. To raise rear of vehicle, use designated rear jacking point.

Fig. 3: Bronco & F150-350 4WD Front Jacking Point

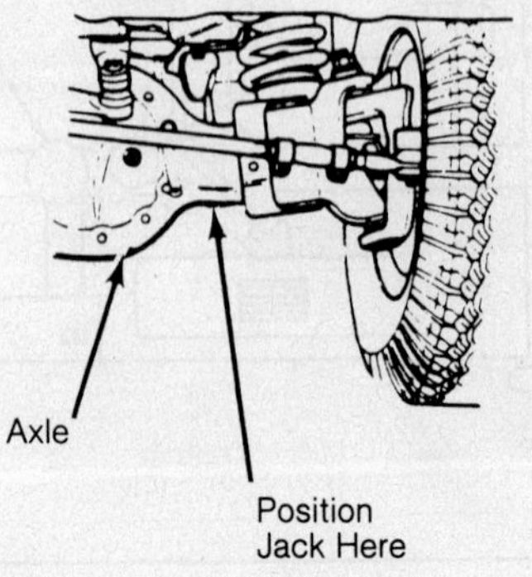

Jacking & Hoisting

FORD (Cont.)

Fig. 4: Aerostar Hoisting & Jacking Contact Points

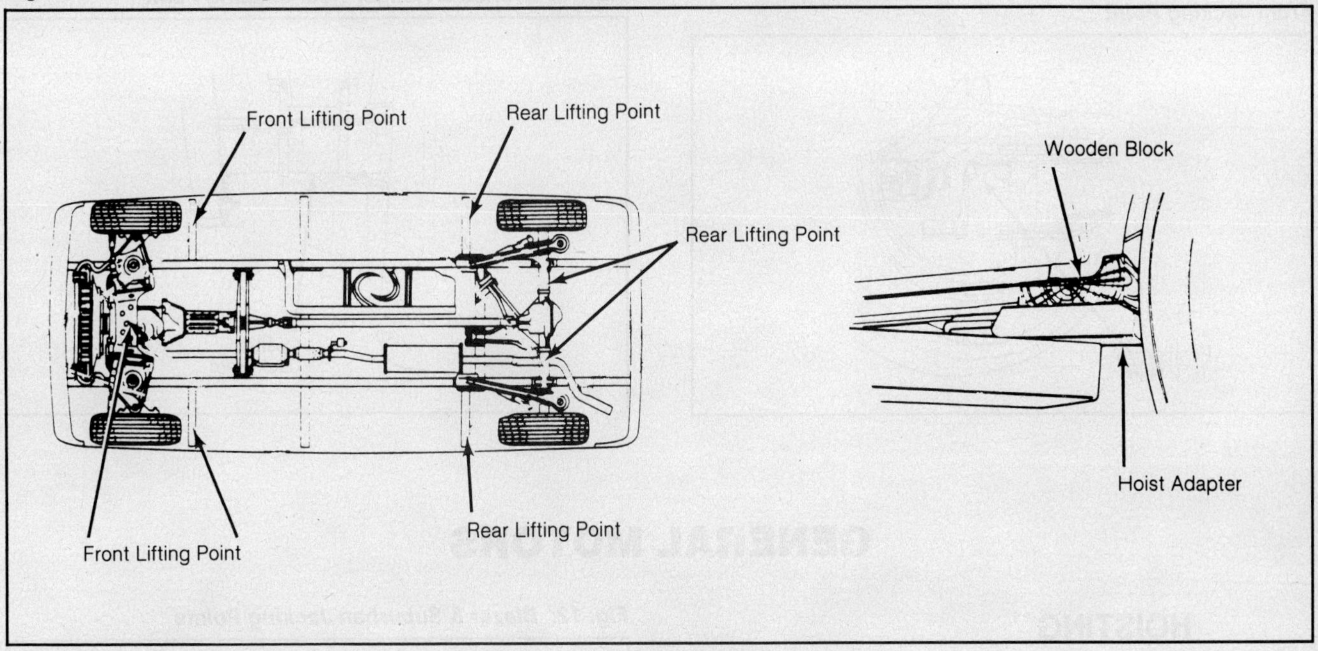

Wooden blocks must be used to maintain necessary underbody clearance.

Fig. 5: E150 Front Jacking Point

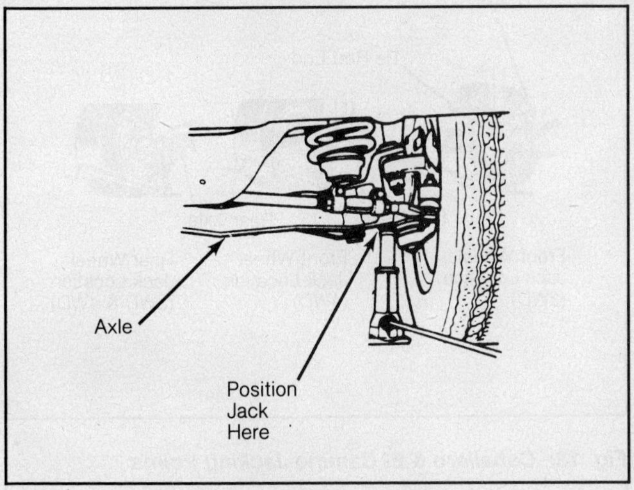

Fig. 6: E & F250-350 2WD Front Jacking Point

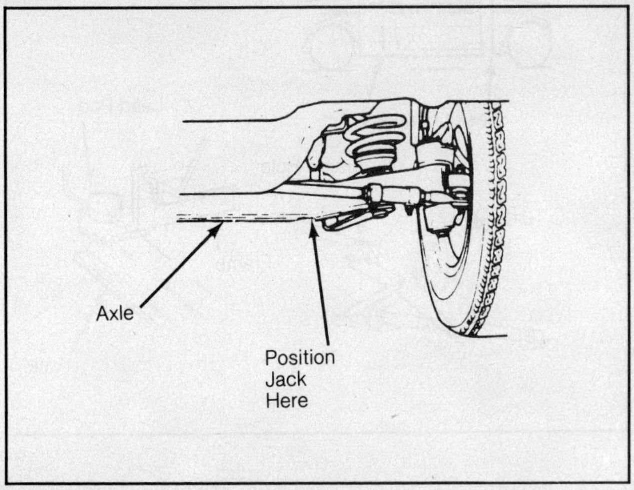

Fig. 7: Bronco, E & F150-350 2WD & 4WD Rear Jacking Point

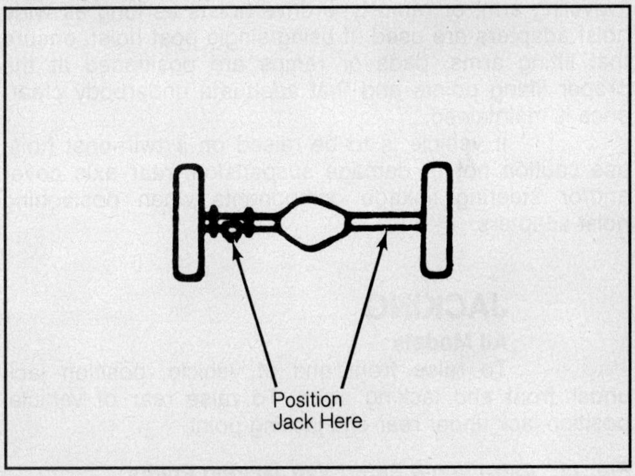

Fig. 8: Ranger 2WD Front Jacking Point

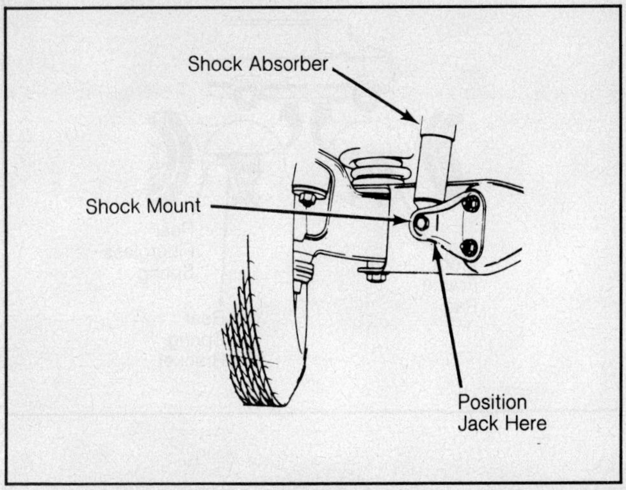

Jacking & Hoisting

FORD (Cont.)

Fig. 9: Bronco II & Ranger 4WD Front Jacking Point

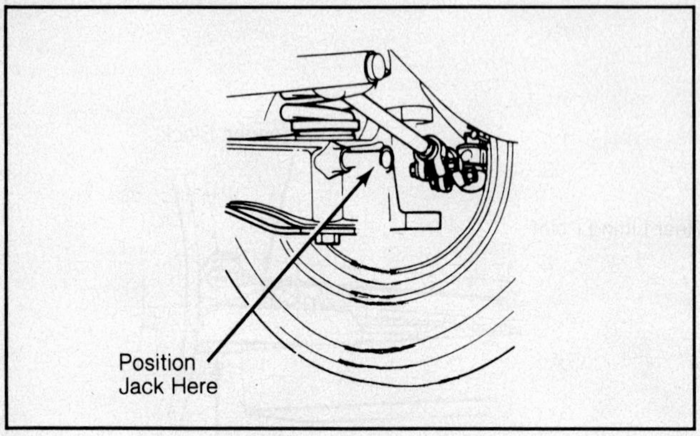

Fig. 10: Bronco & Ranger Rear Jacking Point

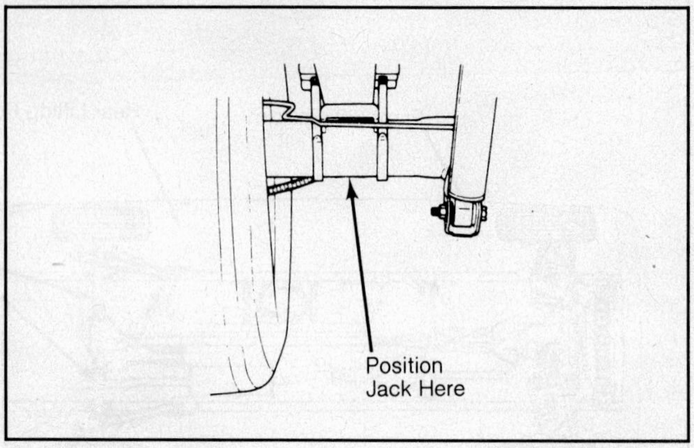

GENERAL MOTORS

HOISTING

FRAME CONTACT HOIST

All Models

Vehicle may be raised on single or twin-post swiveling arm, or ramp-type drive hoists as long as wide hoist adapters are used. If using single post hoist, ensure that lifting arms, pads or ramps are positioned at the proper lifting points and that adequate underbody clearance is maintained.

If vehicle is to be raised on a twin-post hoist use caution not to damage suspension, rear axle cover and/or steering linkage components when positioning hoist adapters.

JACKING

All Models

To raise front end of vehicle, position jack under front end jacking point. To raise rear of vehicle, position jack under rear end jacking point.

Fig. 11: Astro Van & Safari Van Jacking Points

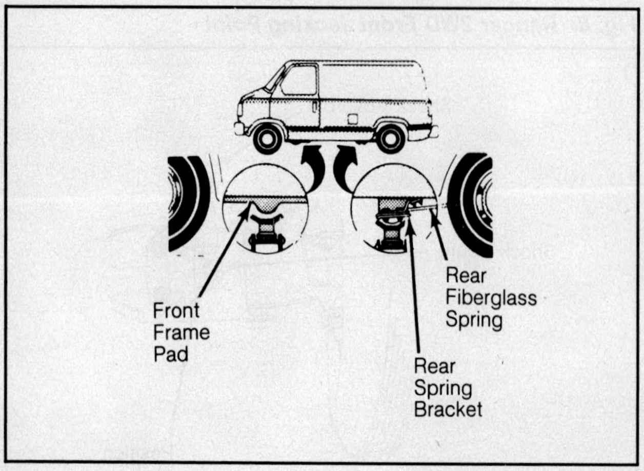

Fig. 12: Blazer & Suburban Jacking Points

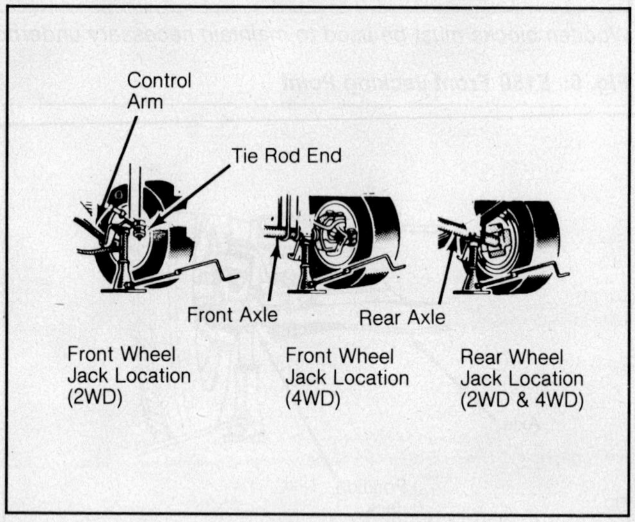

Fig. 13: Caballero & El Camino Jacking Points

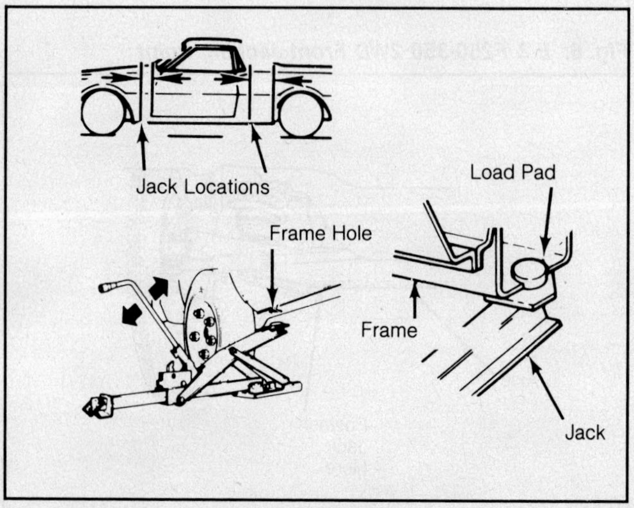

GENERAL MOTORS (Cont.)

Fig. 14: Chevy & GMC Van Jacking Points

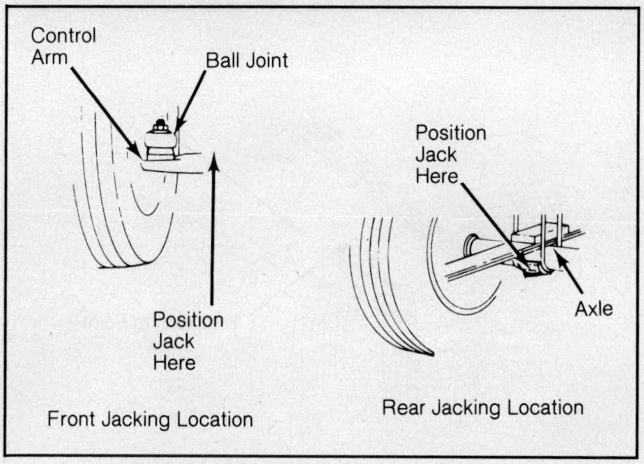

Fig. 16: S-10 & S-15 Jacking Points

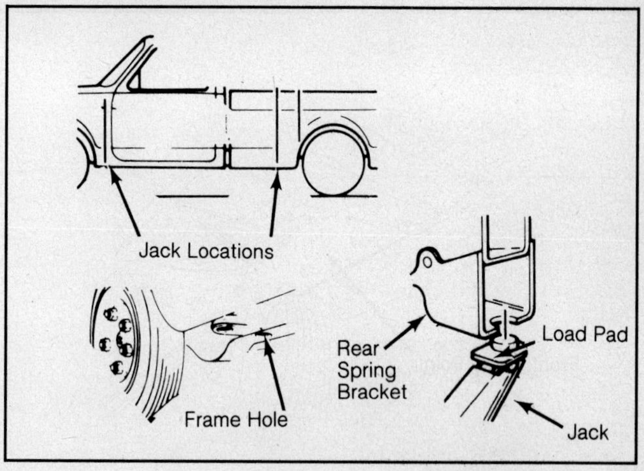

Fig. 15: Chevy & GMC Truck Jacking Points

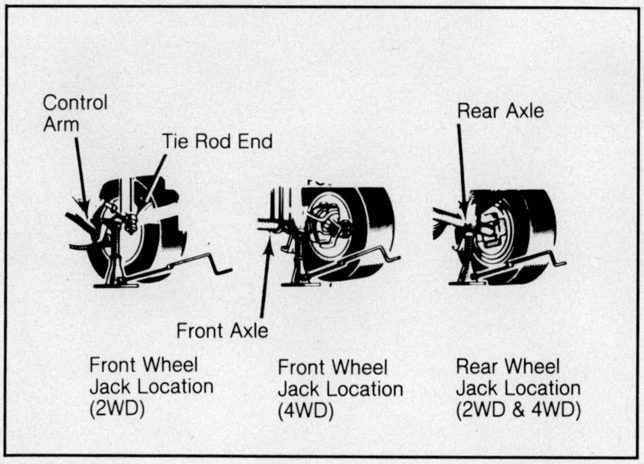

Fig. 17: S-10 Blazer Jacking Points

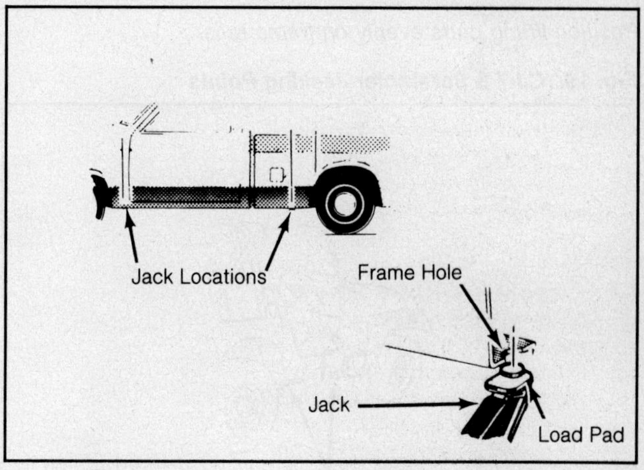

JEEP

HOISTING

FRAME CONTACT HOIST

Cherokee, Comanche & Wagoneer

Vehicle may be raised on single or twin-post swiveling arm, or ramp-type drive hoists. If using swiveling arm hoist, ensure that lifting pads are positioned evenly on the frame rails at point "A" and "B". Ensure that the lifting pads are not contacting the transfer case or skid plate. All hoists should be equipped with proper adapters to support vehicle at frame rails only.

CJ-7, Grand Wagoneer
Scrambler & Truck

Vehicle may be raised on single or twin-post swiveling arm, or ramp-type drive hoists. If using swiveling arm hoist, ensure that lifting pads are positioned evenly on the frame rails and that the lifting pads are not contacting the transfer case or skid plate. All hoists should be equipped with proper adapters to support vehicle at frame rails only.

JACKING

FLOOR JACK

Cherokee, Comanche & Wagoneer

Vehicle may be raised by positioning jack at points "A" and "B" only. Never attempt to raise the vehicle with the jack positioned under the axle tubes, body side sills or front suspension arms. Use the sub frame rail lift points only.

CJ-7 & Scrambler

Vehicle may be raised by positioning jack under the leaf-spring pivot nearest point to be raised. Align the jack with the axle so that the saddle of the jack is beneath the spring eye pivot end.

Grand Wagoneer & Truck

Vehicle may be raised by positioning jack under the front or rear frame rails. Never place jack under front or rear axle tubes, or under shock absorber mounting brackets

Jacking & Hoisting

JEEP (Cont.)

Fig. 18: Cherokee, Comanche, Grand Wagoneer, Wagoneer & Truck Hoisting & Jacking Points

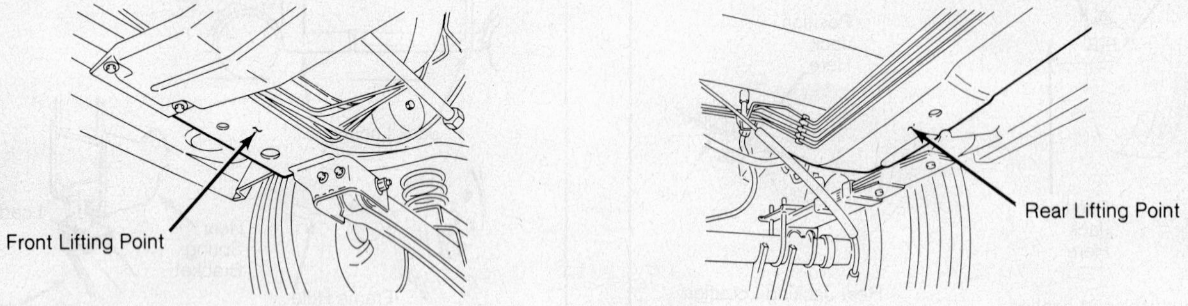

Position lifting pads evenly on frame rails.

Fig. 19: CJ-7 & Scrambler Jacking Points

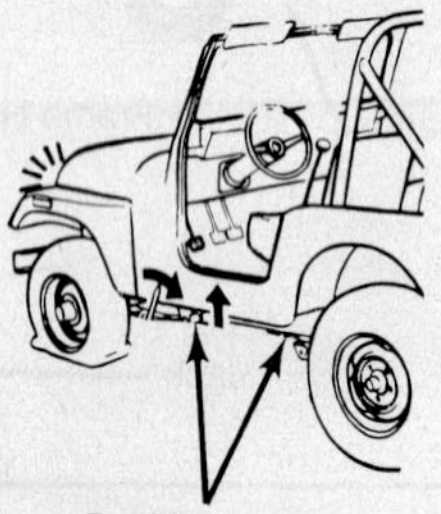

Towing Procedures

ALL MANUFACTURERS

American vehicle manufacturers use an anti-theft steering column lock. The system locks steering, shift mechanisms and ignition systems together. Special provisions are necessary when switch is in the "LOCK" position and key is not available.

GENERAL TOWING INFORMATION

1) Remove loose or protruding parts of damaged vehicle such as hoods, doors, fenders, trim, etc. Remove exhaust tips and any other optional equipment that may interfere with towing sling.

2) Operator should refrain from from going under vehicle while it is lifted by towing equipment. Support vehicle with safety stands if it is necessary to go underneath vehicle.

3) Padding should be placed between tow sling and any painted surfaces. When using tow hooks on rear suspension, position hooks so as not to damage brake lines. Do not allow towing equipment to rest on fuel tank.

4) Do not hook vehicle by front or rear shock absorber or coil springs (if used). Do not lift or tow the vehicle by attaching to or securing to the bumper energy absorber units (if used).

5) Towed vehicle should be raised 4-6 inches from ground. Ensure that there is adequate clearance at opposite end of vehicle. If necessary, remove wheels from end being lifted and carry lifted end closer to ground. An 8 inch clearance must be maintained between drums (rotors) and ground.

6) A safety chain completely independent of the primary towing attachment must be used. Never allow passengers to ride in a towed vehicle. State and local rules and regulations must be followed when towing a vehicle.

CAUTION: To prevent drive train damage, shift the transmission and transfer case (if used) into the positions outlined under specific towing instructions.

TOWING (WITH IGNITION KEY)

NOTE: Information not available for Chevrolet and GMC vehicles.

CHRYSLER CORP.

1) All RWD vehicles (except 4WD) may be towed if the selector lever is in Neutral and the distance to be travelled does not exceed 15 miles or towing speed does not exceed 30 MPH.

2) If transmission is inoperative or if the vehicle is to be towed more than 15 miles, the propeller shaft must be disconnected or the vehicle towed with rear wheels off the ground.

3) On 4WD models with manual locking hubs, place both transmission and transfer case in Neutral. Place manual locking hubs if "FREE" position. Turn the ignition key to the "OFF" position, not the "LOCK" position.

4) On 4WD models with vacuum operated locking hubs, place transmission in Neutral and transfer case in the "2H" position. Remove propeller shaft from end of vehicle that remains on ground or place wheels on towing dolly. Turn the ignition key to the "OFF" position, not the "LOCK" position.

JEEP

1) On CJ7, Grand Wagoneer, Scrambler and Trucks, turn ignition key to the "OFF" position. Shift transmission into Park (Neutral) and transfer case into Neutral. Turn locking hubs into "LOCK" position, if equipped.

2) On Grand Wagoneer or Truck with Select-Trac, shift the transmission into Neutral with the vehicle moving slowly (2-3 MPH). Using a firm, positive movement, shift the transfer case selector lever into Neutral.

3) When the selector lever is in the Neutral position, both axles are disconnected from the drive train. This will permit the vehicle to be towed without removing the propeller shafts.

Fig. 1: Typical 2WD Front Towing Hookup

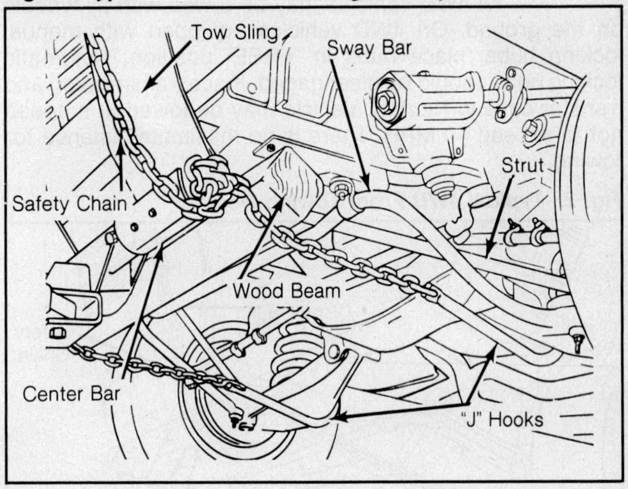

TOWING (WITHOUT IGNITION KEY)

NOTE: Information not available for Chevrolet and GMC vehicles.

CHRYSLER CORP.

1) All FWD vehicles may be lifted and towed from the front, provided the parking brake is released. If parking brake is not released, the rear wheels should be placed on a tow dolly.

2) All RWD vehicles, may be towed with the front wheels off the ground provided the parking brake is released. The propeller shaft must be removed or the rear wheels placed on a tow dolly. See TOWING (WITH IGNITION KEY) for vehicles using a floor mounted gear selector or 4WD.

FORD

If the ignition key is not available, place the rear wheels on a tow dolly and tow the vehicle with the front wheels raised. If vehicle is towed on its front wheels, the steering wheel must be clamped in the straight-ahead position with a steering wheel clamping device designed for towing. Do not use steering column lock.

JEEP

1) On CJ7, Grand Wagoneer, Scrambler and Trucks that are unlocked and equipped with manual transmission, shift transmission and transfer case into Neutral. Tow vehicle with front wheels raised.

2) If vehicle is locked, place a tow dolly under rear wheels or disconnect propeller shaft and secure to underside of vehicle. Tow vehicle with front wheels raised.

TOWING (RECREATIONAL)

CHRYSLER CORP.

1) All FWD vehicles equipped with a manual transaxle may be towed with all wheels on the ground at

Towing Procedures

ALL MANUFACTURERS (Cont.)

legal highway speeds and for any distance. Automatic transaxle equipped vehicles may be towed at 25 MPH and for a distance not to exceed 15 miles.

2) All 4WD vehicles may be towed with all wheels on the ground at legal highway speeds and for any distance. Place transmission and transfer case in Neutral. Turn ignition key to the "OFF" position. Remove propeller shafts.

FORD

All 4WD vehicles may be towed with all wheels on the ground. On 4WD vehicles equipped with manual locking hubs, place hubs in "FREE" position. Automatic locking hubs should be disengaged. Place transmission and transfer case in Neutral. Vehicle may be towed at a speed not to exceed 40 MPH. There is no maximum distance for towing.

Fig. 2: Typical 4WD Front Towing Hookup

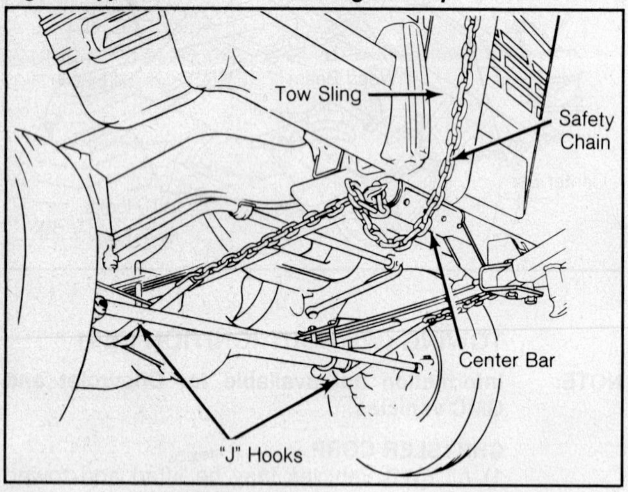

GENERAL MOTORS

1) The "S" series 4WD vehicles may be towed on all four wheels provided the automatic transmission is in Park or the manual transmission is in the highest gear. Place transfer case in Neutral. It is not necessary to remove the propeller shaft.

2) If 4WD vehicles (except "S" series) are to be towed with all wheels on the ground, place tranfer case in "2H" position and transmission in Neutral. Tow vehicle at speeds less than 35 MPH and for a maximum distance of 50 miles.

3) For speeds and distances greater than specified, disconnect the rear propeller shaft at rear axle carrier. Secure propeller shaft to underside of vehicle. Tape "U" joint bearing journal caps. Remove front propeller shaft and store in vehicle.

JEEP

1) On CJ7, Grand Wagoneer, Scrambler or Truck with the model 208 or 300 transfer case and automatic (manual) transmission, turn ignition switch to the "OFF" position to unlock the steering wheel.

2) Shift automatic (manual) transmission into Park (gear) and transfer case into Neutral position. Place locking hubs in the "LOCK" position to provide axle lubrication.

3) On Grand Wagoneer or Truck with Select-Trac, shift the transmission into Neutral with the vehicle moving slowly (2-3 MPH). Using a firm, positive movement, shift the transfer case selector lever into Neutral.

4) When the slector lever is in the Neutral position, both axles are disconected from the drive train. This will permit the vehicle to be towed without removing the propeller shafts.

TOWING PRECAUTIONS

CHRYSLER CORP.

1) All FWD vehicles may be towed on their rear wheels for extended distances provided the parking brake is released. It is recommended that vehicles be towed with "J" hooks and front wheels off the ground whenever possible.

2) All FWD vehicles may be towed on front wheels at speeds not to exceed 25 MPH for a distance not greater than 15 miles. The steering wheel must be clamped in the straight-ahead position.

3) On FWD manual tranxaxle equipped vehicles, the tranaxle must be in Neutral and the drive axles must not be damaged. If any of these limits cannot be met, the front wheels must be placed on a tow dolly.

4) Automatic transaxle equipped vehicles may not be towed with all 4 wheels on ground. Manual transaxle vehicles may be towed with no distance restrictions provided the transaxle is in Neutral and the parking brake is released.

Fig. 3: Typical Rear Towing Hookup

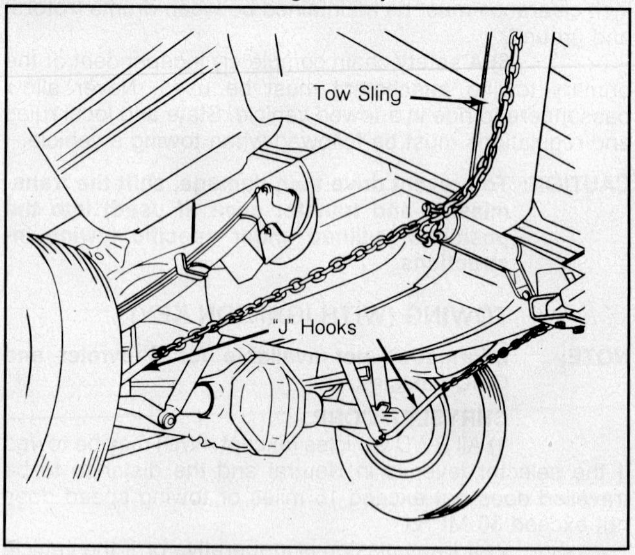

FORD

1) Release parking brake and place transmission in Neutral. As a general rule, towed vehicle should be pulled with drive wheels off the ground. If driving wheels cannot be raised off ground, either place them on a tow dolly or disconnect propeller shaft.

2) If vehicle is towed on its front wheels, the steering wheel must be clamped in the straight-ahead position with a steering wheel clamping device designed for towing. Do not use steering column lock.

3) If vehicle being towed has an inoperative rear axle, raise the rear wheels. If vehicle's transmission is inoperative, the propeller shaft must be removed or the rear wheels raised.

4) Use "T" hooks if Aerostar will be towed with the rear wheels off the ground. If vehicle is equipped with an under vehicle spare tire carrier, remove tire and store in a secure area.

Towing Procedures

ALL MANUFACTURERS (Cont.)

5) When towing 2WD vehicles on rear wheels, vehicle may be towed at a speed not to exceed 35 MPH and for a maximum distance of 50 miles. When towing vehicle with front wheels on the ground, vehicle may be towed at a speed not to exceed 50 MPH. There is no maximum distance for towing.

6) On 4WD vehicles equipped with manual locking hubs, place hubs in "FREE" position. Automatic locking hubs should be disengaged. Place transmission and transfer case in Neutral. Vehicle may be towed at a speed not to exceed 40 MPH. There is no maximum distance for towing.

GENERAL MOTORS

1) All 2WD vehicles with automatic transmissions may be towed at speeds less than 35 MPH for distances up to 50 miles. These speed and distance restrictions do not apply to vehicles equipped with manual transmissions.

2) The steering wheels must be unlocked, transmission in Neutral, and parking brake released. Connect towing equipment to main structural parts of vehicle, not bumpers or brackets, follow the instructions of wrecker manufacturer.

NOTE: **If 2WD or 4WD vehicles are to be towed with the rear wheels off the ground, the steering wheel should be locked in the straight-ahead position. Do not use steering lock mechanism.**

3) If 4WD vehicles (except "S" series) are to be towed with the front wheels off the ground, place tranfer case in "2H" position and transmission in Neutral. Tow vehicle at speeds less than 35 MPH and for a maximum distance of 50 miles.

4) For speeds and distances greater than specified, disconnect the rear propeller shaft at rear axle carrier. Secure propeller shaft to underside of vehicle. Tape "U" joint bearing journal caps.

5) If 4WD vehicles are to be towed with the rear wheels off the ground, place the tranfer case in "2H" position and transmission in Neutral. For speeds and distances greater than specified, remove front propeller shaft and store in vehicle.

JEEP

1) Jeep vehicles may be towed with front or rear wheels off the ground, towing speeds should be limited to 30 MPH for a distance not to exceed 15 miles.

2) If CJ7, Grand Wagoneer, Scrambler or Truck with the model 208 or 300 transfer case is to be towed over 200 miles; stop towing vehicle, place transfer case in Neutral, and start engine. Place automatic transmission in drive and run engine for 1-2 minutes to lubricate transfer case.

3) On Cherokee and Wagoneer equipped with the model 207 transfer case and automatic (manual) transmission, shift transmission into Park (Neutral) and transfer case into Neutral.

4) On Cherokee and Wagonner equipped with the model 229 transfer case and automatic transmission, turn ignition switch to the "OFF" position to unlock the steering wheel. Shift transmission into Park and transfer case into Neutral.

SECTION 12

SUSPENSION

CONTENTS

NOTE: **ALSO SEE GENERAL INDEX.**

IMPORTANT: **Because of the many model names used by vehicle manufacturers, accurate identification of models is important. See MODEL IDENTIFICATION at the front of this publication.**

Suspension

TROUBLE SHOOTING

CONDITION	POSSIBLE CAUSE	CORRECTION
Front End Noise	Loose or worn wheel bearings	See Wheel Bearing Adjustment in SUSPENSION
	Worn shocks or shock mountings	Replace shocks or mountings.
	Worn struts or strut mountings	Replace struts or strut mountings
	Loose or worn lower control arm	See Lower Control Arm Removal & Installation in SUSPENSION
	Loose steering gear-to-frame bolts	See Steering Gear Removal & Installation in STEERING
	Steering knuckle contacts lower control arm wheel stop	See Steering Knuckle in STEERING or Lower Control Arm in SUSPENSION
	Worn control arm bushings	See Control Arms in SUSPENSION
	Ball joints not lubricated	Lubricate ball joints & see Ball Joint Checking in SUSPENSION
Front Wheel Shake, Shimmy or Vibration	Tires or wheels out of balance	Check tire balance
	Incorrect wheel alignment	See Adjustment in WHEEL ALIGNMENT
	Propeller Shaft Unbalanced	See Propeller Shaft in DRIVE AXLES
	Loose or worn wheel bearings	See Wheel Bearing Adjustment in SUSPENSION
	Loose or worn tie rod ends	See Tie Rod Removal & Installation in SUSPENSION
	Worn upper ball joints	See Ball Joint Checking in SUSPENSION
	Worn shock absorbers	Replace shock absorbers
	Worn strut bushings	Replace strut bushings
Car Pulls to One Side	Mismatched or uneven tires	Check tire condition
	Broken or sagging springs	See Coil Spring Removal & Installation in SUSPENSION
	Loose or worn strut bushings	See Strut Removal & Installation in SUSPENSION
	Improper wheel alignment	See Adjustment in WHEEL ALIGNMENT
	Improper rear axle alignment	See DRIVE AXLES
	Power steering gear unbalanced	See STEERING
	Front brakes dragging	See BRAKES
Abnormal Tire Wear	Unbalanced tires	Check tire balance & rotation
	Sagging or broken springs	See Coil Spring in SUSPENSION
	Incorrect front end alignment	See Adjustment in WHEEL ALIGNMENT
	Faulty shock absorbers	Replace shock absorbers
Scuffed Tires	Toe-In incorrect	See Adjustment in WHEEL ALIGNMENT
	Suspension arm bent or twisted	See appropriate SUSPENSION article
Springs Bottom or Sag	Bent or broken springs	See Coil Spring in SUSPENSION
	Leaking or worn shock absorbers	Replace shock absorbers
"Dog" Tracking	Broken leaf spring	Replace leaf spring
	Bent rear axle housing	See DRIVE AXLES
	Frame misalignment	Check frame for damage
Spring Noises	Loose "U" Bolts	See SUSPENSION
	Loose or worn bushings	See SUSPENSION
	Worn or missing interliners	See SUSPENSION
Shock Absorber Noise	Loose shock mountings	Check & tighten mountings
	Worn bushings	Replace bushings
	Air in system	Bleed air from system
	Undercoating on shocks	Remove undercoating
Car Leans or Sways on Corners	Loose stabilizer bar	See SUSPENSION
	Faulty shocks or mountings	Replace shocks or mountings
	Broken or sagging springs	See Coil Spring in SUSPENSION
Shock Absorbers Leaking	Worn seals or reservoir tube crimped	See SUSPENSION
Broken Springs	Loose "U" bolts	See Coil Spring in SUSPENSION
	Inoperative shock absorbers	Replace shock absorbers

Front Suspension

CHRYSLER CORP. – FWD

DESCRIPTION

The front suspension is MacPherson type with vertical shock absorbing struts. The struts attach to upper fender reinforcements and steering knuckle to provide upper steering knuckle position. Lower control arms attach outboard to steering knuckle and inboard to a crossmember through a ball joint to provide lower steering knuckle position.

Working through a pivot bearing in upper retainer, the upper strut and steering knuckle turn as an assembly during steering maneuvers. Coil springs, around struts, support system.

ADJUSTMENT

WHEEL ALIGNMENT SPECIFICATIONS & PROCEDURES

See Wheel Alignment Specifications & Procedures in WHEEL ALIGNMENT section.

WHEEL BEARING ADJUSTMENT

The front wheel bearings are permanently sealed, no lubrication or adjustment is necessary. Replace hub nuts, washers and pins when removed, as they are not reusable. With brakes applied, tighten new hub nuts to 180 ft. lbs. (245 N.m). Always install new bearings any time hub is removed.

BALL JOINT CHECKING

NOTE: **The lower ball joint operates with no free play.**

Lower Ball Joint

With weight of vehicle resting on wheels in normal driving position, hold grease fitting and attempt to move it. If fitting moves easily, ball joint is worn and should be replaced.

REMOVAL & INSTALLATION

FRONT WHEEL BEARING

NOTE: **Service procedures requiring front hub removal require that a new bearing be installed.**

Removal

1) Remove cotter pin, nut lock and spring washer. Loosen hub nut with vehicle on floor and brakes applied. Raise and support vehicle. Remove front wheel and tire.

2) Remove hub nut, making sure splined drive shaft is free to separate from spline in hub. Detach brake hose retainer from strut. Detach brake caliper from steering knuckle. Using wire, support caliper out of the way. Remove rotor from hub studs.

3) Remove cotter pin and castellated nut from tie rod. Using Ball Joint Remover (C-3894-A), disconnect tie rod end from steering arm. Remove clamp bolt securing ball joint stud in steering knuckle. Pull knuckle away from driveshaft.

4) Separate knuckle from hub using Remover/Installer (C-4811). To separate, back out 3 bearing retainer screws from the knuckle until hub is unseated from the installed position. Insert adapter screw into rear retainer screw threads.

5) Position thrust button inside hub bore. Position tool and install 2 screws firmly into tapped brake adapter extensions. Put nut and washer on adapter screw. Tighten screw on tool to remove hub from bearing.

6) Remove tool and attaching screws from steeering knuckle. Remove 3 screws and bearing retainer from knuckle. Carefully pry bearing seal from machined recess in knuckle. Clean recess. Press bearing out of knuckle with removal tool. Discard bearing and seal.

Installation

1) Press new bearing into knuckle using Remover/Installer (C-4811). Install new seal and retainer. Tighten retainer screws to 20 ft. lbs. (27 N.m). Press hub into bearing with Remover/Installer (C-4811).

2) Position new seal in recess. Using Seal Installer (C-4698) install seal. Lubricate full circumference of seal and wear sleeve with multi-purpose grease. Install knuckle to suspension. Complete installation by reversing removal procedure.

3) Tighten caliper adapter bolts to 160 ft. lbs. (216 N.m). Tighten ball joint clamp bolts to 70 ft. lbs. (95 N.m). Tighten tie rod castellated nut to 35 ft. lbs. (47 N.m). Tighten wheel nuts to 95 ft. lbs. (129 N.m).

LOWER BALL JOINT

NOTE: **Ball joints that are welded to the control arm must be serviced by replacement of the complete control arm assembly.**

Removal

1) Raise and support vehicle. Remove wheel and tire. Detach sway bar bushing retainer bolts from lower control arm. Remove stub strut bushing retainer nuts. Detach pivot bushing mount bolts from lower control arm and crossmember.

2) Remove clamp bolt, separate lower ball joint from steering knuckle and remove lower control arm assembly from vehicle. Pry off ball joint dust seal. Mount control arm assembly in hydraulic press.

3) Position Receiving Cup (C-4699-2) to support lower control arm while removing ball joint. Install 1 1/16" deep socket over stud and against joint upper housing. Press to remove ball joint assembly from arm.

Installation

1) Position ball joint housing into control arm cavity. Position assembly in press with Installer (C-4699-1) supporting control arm. Align and press assembly until ball joint housing ledge stops against control arm cavity down flange.

2) Support ball joint housing with Receiving Cup (C-4699-2). Position new seal over stud, against housing. With 1 1/2" socket, press seal onto joint housing with seat against control arm.

STRUT DAMPER

NOTE: **Where service procedure includes use of original strut and knuckle, mark cam adjusting bolt for reassembly reference.**

Removal

1) Raise and support vehicle. Remove wheel and tire. Remove cam adjusting bolt and knuckle bolt from strut assembly. Remove brake hose-to-damper bracket retaining screw and position brake hose out of work area.

Front Suspension

CHRYSLER CORP. – FWD (Cont.)

2) Remove strut damper-to-fender shield mounting nut washer assemblies. Remove strut assembly from vehicle.

Disassembly

1) Compress spring with Spring Compressor (C-4838). Put 5 coils between compressor jaws. *See Fig. 1.*

2) Hold strut rod while loosening strut rod nut. Remove nut. Remove strut mount. Remove coil spring. Mark spring for reinstallation on same side of vehicle.

NOTE: **Coil springs are rated separately for each side of vehicle depending on optional equipment and type of service. If removed, ensure springs are marked for installation in original positions.**

Inspection

Inspect and replace all components showing signs of leakage, damage or excessive wear. If leakage is found, replace strut damper as an assembly.

Reassembly

1) Install dust shield, jounce bumper, spacer and spring seat to top of spring. Install mount to strut rod, ensuring lower washer is in position.

2) Position upper spring retainer alignment tab parallel to damper lower attaching bracket. *See Fig. 1.* Install rebound retainer and rod nut.

3) Using Strut Rod Nut Holder (L-4558), tighten rod nut to 60 ft. lbs. (81 N.m) before releasing spring compressor. Remove spring compressor.

Fig. 1: Spring Seat and Retainer Position

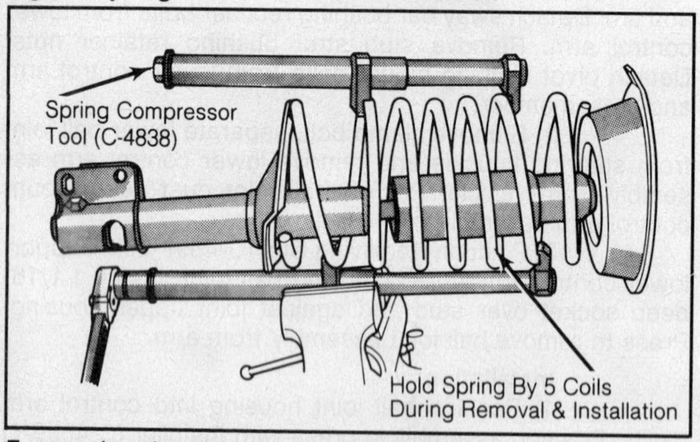

Ensure that the strut rod assembly mount nut is properly tightened before releasing the spring compressor.

Installation

1) Install unit into fender reinforcement and install retaining nuts and washers. Tighten nuts to 20 ft. lbs. (27 N.m). Position knuckle neck into strut. Position washer plate and install cam and knuckle bolts.

2) Attach brake hose retainer to damper. Tighten retainer bolt to 10 ft. lbs. (13 N.m). Index cam bolt to original mark. Place a 4" (112 mm) "C" clamp on the strut and knuckle.

3) Tighten the clamp just enough to eliminate any looseness between the knuckle and the strut. Check alignment of the index marks. Tighten the bolts to 75 ft. lbs. (100 N.m) plus 1/4 turn. Remove "C" clamp.

4) Install wheel and tire. Tighten wheel nuts to 95 ft. lbs. (129 N.m). Adjust camber and toe settings if strut was replaced.

LOWER CONTROL ARM

Removal

1) Raise and support vehicle. Remove front inner pivot through bolt. Remove rear stub strut nut, retainer and bushings. Remove ball joint-to-steering knuckle clamp bolt. Separate ball joint from steering knuckle.

NOTE: **Use care not to pull steering knuckle out from vehicle after release from ball joint or the inner constant velocity joint will separate.**

2) Remove sway bar-to-control arm end bushing retainer nuts and rotate control arm over sway bar. Remove rear stub strut bushing, sleeve and retainer. Check lower control arm for distortion and bushings for deterioration. Replace components as necessary.

3) If pivot bushings need replacement, position Support (C-4700) between flanges of lower control arm and around bushing to prevent control arm distortion. Install 1/2" x 2 1/2" bolt into bushing.

4) With Receiving Cup (C-4669-2) on press base, position control arm inner flange against cup wall to support flange while pressing out bushing. Remove bushing by pressing against bolt head.

Installation

1) To install bushing, install bushing inner sleeve and insulator into cavity of Receiving Cup (C-4699-2). Position assembly onto press base and align control arm to receive bushing.

2) Position Installer (C-4699-1) to support control arm outer flange while receiving bushing. Press bushing into control arm until bushing flange seats against control arm.

3) To complete installation, reverse removal procedure. Ensure control arm mount bolts are tightened with suspension supporting vehicle.

STEERING KNUCKLE

Removal

1) Remove cotter pin, nut lock and spring washer. Loosen hub nut with vehicle on floor and brakes applied. Raise vehicle and remove wheel. Remove hub nut, making sure splined drive shaft is free to separate from spline in hub. If necessary, driveshaft may be tapped lightly with soft brass punch. *See Fig. 2.*

2) Remove tie rod end from steering knuckle with Remover (C-3894-A). Remove brake hose retaining clamp from strut damper. Remove ball joint clamp stud bolt and caliper adapter bolts with washers. Remove caliper and support with wire. DO NOT hang by brake flex hose. Remove rotor.

3) Mark camber position on upper cam adjusting bolt, then remove both bolts. Remove knuckle from strut damper and off of ball joint stud. Be sure drive shaft is supported during removal of knuckle to prevent damage to constant velocity joints.

Installation

To install, reverse removal procedure.

SWAY BAR

Removal

1) Raise and support vehicle. Remove nuts, bolts and retainers from lower control arms. Remove bolts at crossmember clamps. Remove clamps and sway bar from vehicle.

Fig. 2: Exploded View of Strut Damper Assembly

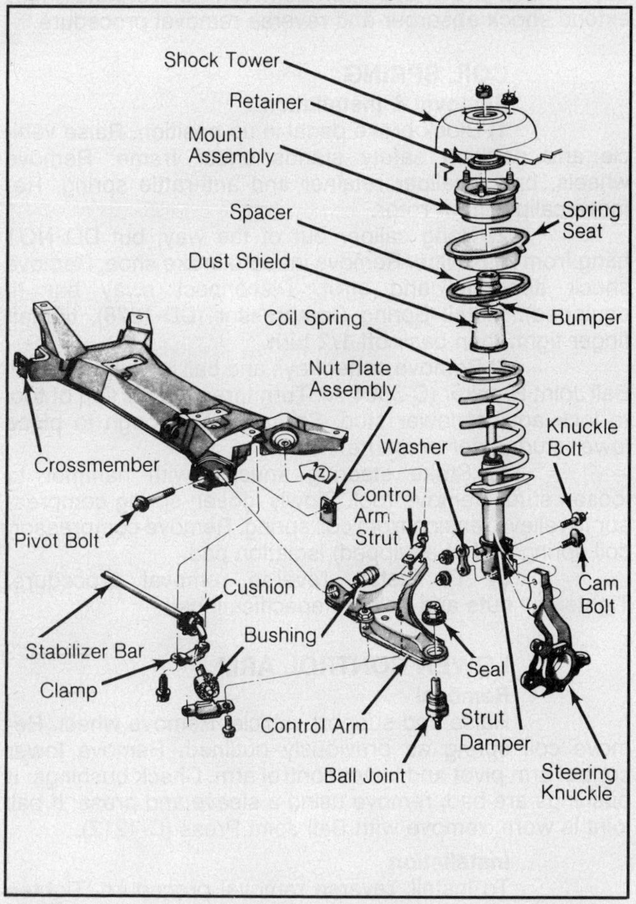

Use caution removing steering knuckle so that drive shaft does not pull out, separating inner constant velocity joint.

2) Inspect components for cracks, damage or rubber deterioration. Replace parts as necessary.

Installation

1) If bushing replacement is required, the inner bushing can be removed by opening split. The outer bushing must be cut or hammered off. If replaced, outer bushing should be forced on until 1/2" of stabilizer bar protrudes.

NOTE: The control arm retainers are symmetrical and bend slightly upon installation.

2) Position crossmember bushings on bar with curved surface up and split to front. Set lower clamps on crossmember bushings, lift bar into crossmember and install lower bolts and clamps.

3) Position retainers at control arms, insert bolts and install nuts. With lower control arms raised to design height, tighten bolts.

TIGHTENING SPECIFICATIONS

Application	Ft. Lbs. (N.m)
Strut Rod Nut	60 (81)
Strut-to-Steering Knuckle	
Cam & Knuckle Bolts	[1] 75 (100)
Ball Joint Clamp Bolt	70 (95)
Brake Caliper Adapter Bolt	160 (216)
Brake Hose-to-Strut Retainer Screw	10 (13)
Lower Control Arm Pivot Bolt	105 (143)
Sway Bar Bushing	
Control Arm Retainer Bolt	25 (34)
Crossmember Retainer Bolt	25 (34)
Tie Rod End Nut	35 (47)
Wheel Hub Mount Nut	180 (245)

[1] – Tighten 1/4 turn beyond specified torque.

Front Suspension

CHRYSLER CORP. – RWD

DESCRIPTION

Independent front suspension consists of upper and lower control arms, steering knuckles, coil springs, and hydraulic shock absorbers. Upper control arms are mounted to frame side rails, while lower control arms are mounted to crossmember.

Steering knuckles are mounted between upper and lower control arms by conventional ball joints. Coil springs are mounted between seat in frame and lower contol arm. Double-acting shock absorbers mount inside coil springs and are fastened to lower control arms and frame.

ADJUSTMENT & CHECKING

WHEEL ALIGNMENT SPECIFICATIONS & PROCEDURES

See WHEEL ALIGNMENT SPECIFICATIONS & PROCEDURES in WHEEL ALIGNMENT section.

WHEEL BEARING ADJUSTMENT

2WD Models

1) Tighten wheel bearing adjusting nut to 360-480 INCH lbs. (40-53 N.m) while rotating wheel. Stop rotation and back off adjusting nut to release all preload. Retighten nut finger tight.

2) End play should be .0001-.003" (.0025-.0760 mm). Install nut lock and cotter pin. Coat grease cap lightly with grease and install.

4WD Models

1) Using Spanner (C-4170) on Model 44 axles, or DD-1241-JD and C-3952 on Model 60 front axles, tighten inner lock nut to 50 ft. lbs. (68 N.m). Loosen lock nut and retighten to 30-40 ft. lbs. (41-54 N.m) while rotating hub. Back off lock nut 135-150°.

2) Install retaining washer (lock ring). Install and tighten outer lock nut to 50 ft. lbs. (70 N.m) for Model 44 axle or 65 ft. lbs. for Model 60 axle. On all models, end play should be within .001-.010" (.03-.25 mm).

BALL JOINT CHECKING

Ball joints are preloaded. If up and down movement exceeds .02" (.5 mm), replace ball joint.

REMOVAL & INSTALLATION

WHEEL BEARINGS

Removal & Installation

1) Block brake pedal in up position. Raise vehicle and remove wheel. Remove caliper and separate from rotor. Insert block of wood between brake pads to prevent brake fluid leakage.

2) Remove grease cap, cotter pin, lock nut, nut, thrust washer and outer wheel bearing. Carefully slide rotor from spindle. Remove oil seal and inner bearing. To install, clean bearings, inspect for damage and replace if necessary. Reverse removal procedure. Adjust bearing preload.

SHOCK ABSORBER

Removal & Installation

Raise and support vehicle. Remove upper mounting nut and retainer. Remove lower mounting bolts and remove shock absorber from vehicle. To install, fully extend shock absorber and reverse removal procedure.

COIL SPRING

Removal & Installation

1) Block brake pedal in up position. Raise vehicle and position safety stands under frame. Remove wheels, brake caliper retainer and anti-rattle spring. Remove caliper from rotor.

2) Hang caliper out of the way, but DO NOT hang from brake line. Remove inboard brake shoe. Remove shock absorber and strut. Disconnect sway bar (if equipped). Install Spring Compressor (DD-1278), tighten finger tight, then back off 1/2 turn.

3) Remove cotter keys and ball joint nuts. Install Ball Joint Breaker (C-3564-A). Turn threaded portion of tool to lock against lower stud. Spread tool enough to place lower stud under pressure.

4) Strike steering knuckle with hammer to loosen stud. Remove tool. Slowly loosen spring compressor to relieve tension from coil spring. Remove compressor, coil spring and (if equipped) isolation pad.

5) To install, reverse removal procedure. Tighten all nuts and bolts to specifications.

LOWER CONTROL ARM

Removal

Raise and support vehicle. Remove wheel. Remove coil spring as previously outlined. Remove lower control arm pivot and lower control arm. Check bushings. If bushings are bad, remove using a sleeve and press. If ball joint is worn, remove with Ball Joint Press (C-4212).

Installation

To install, reverse removal procedure. Tighten all nuts and bolts with vehicle resting on ground. Check wheel alignment. See WHEEL ALIGNMENT SPECIFICATIONS & PROCEDURES in WHEEL ALIGNMENT section.

UPPER CONTROL ARM

Removal

1) Raise and support vehicle. Remove wheel. On 2WD models, block brake pedal in up position and remove brake caliper retainer and anti-rattle spring. Remove caliper from rotor.

2) Remove inboard brake shoe. On all models, remove shock absorber and install Spring Compressor (DD-1278). Finger tighten compressor, then back-off 1/2 turn.

3) Remove cotter keys and ball joint nuts. Position Ball Joint Breaker (C-3564-A), with threaded portion of tool locking against upper stud.

4) Spread tool to place stud under pressure. Strike knuckle with hammer to loosen. Remove tool. Remove mount bolts and control arm. Check bushings. If worn, remove bushing with a sleeve and press.

Installation

To install, reverse removal procedure. Do not tighten control arm pivot bolts until vehicle weight is supported by front suspension. Check wheel alignment.

LOWER BALL JOINT

Removal & Installation

Remove coil spring as previously outlined. Support lower control arm with a jack stand. Remove ball joint

Front Suspension

CHRYSLER CORP. – RWD (Cont.)

seal. Using Ball Joint Press (C-4212), remove ball joint from lower control arm. Using Ball Joint Press (C-4212), press new ball joint into lower control arm. Install seal with Adapter (C-4034). Install control arm.

UPPER BALL JOINT

Removal & Installation

Raise and support vehicle under outer end of lower control arm. Remove wheel. Remove upper ball joint nuts. Using Ball Joint Breaker (C-3564-A), free upper ball joint. Using Wrench (C-3561), unscrew ball joint from control arm. To install, reverse removal procedure. Tighten ball joint and all nuts and bolts to specifications.

STEERING KNUCKLE

Removal & Installation

1) Block brake pedal in up position. Raise and support vehicle. Position safety stands at the extreme front of frame rail. Remove wheel. Remove caliper retainer and anti-rattle spring assemblies. Remove caliper and hang out of way. Remove inboard shoe.

2) Remove hub cap, cotter key, nut, washer and outer bearing. Remove brake rotor and splash shield. Place jack under outer end of lower control arm. Disconnect tie rod at steering knuckle. See STEERING LINKAGE in STEERING section.

3) Separate ball joint studs from steering knuckle. Remove steering knuckle from vehicle and separate components. To install, reverse removal procedure, and tighten all nuts and bolts to specifications.

Fig. 1: Exploded View of 2WD Pickup & Ramcharger Front Suspension Assembly

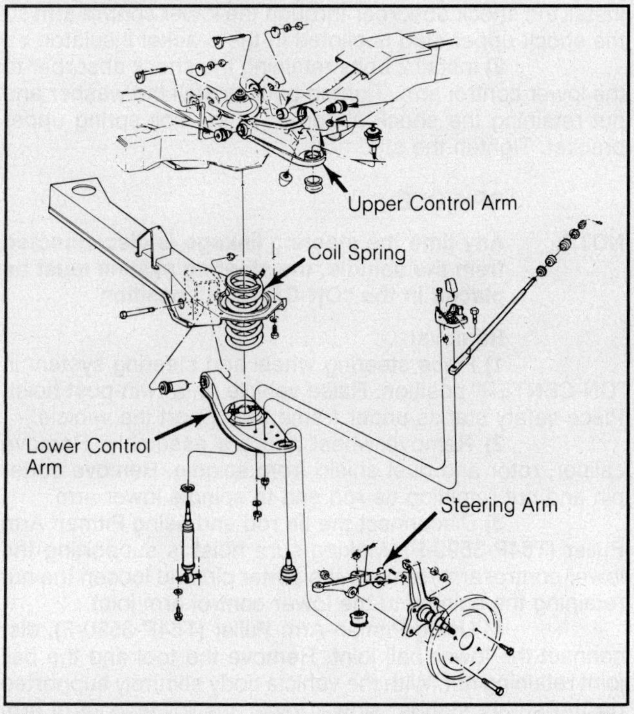

When separating steering knuckle/ball joint assembly, DO NOT attempt to force stud out of knuckle with tool alone.

Fig. 2: Exploded View of Van Front Suspension Assembly

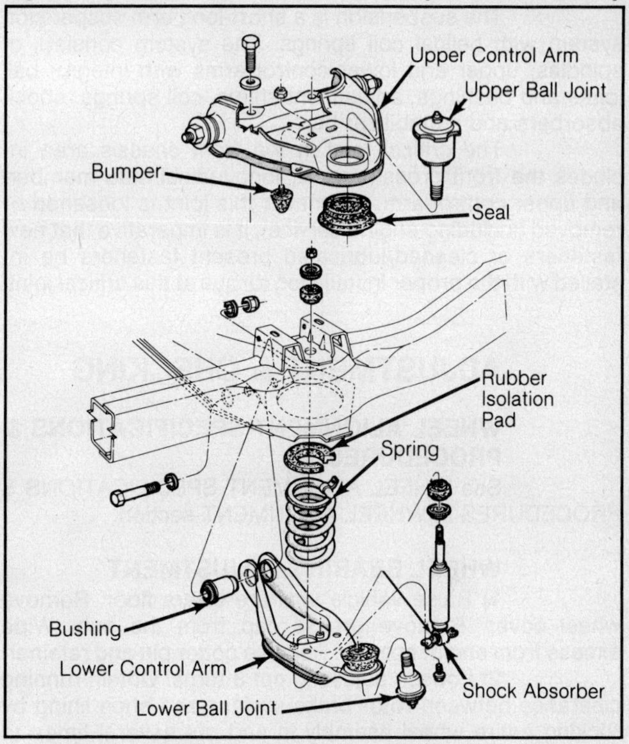

To separate steering knuckle/ball joint assembly, mount tool (in tension) and hit knuckle with hammer to jar loose.

TIGHTENING SPECIFICATIONS

Application	Ft. Lbs. (N.m)
Ball Joint Nuts	
Ram Van & Wagon	
Lower	
11/16"	135 (183)
3/4"	175 (237)
Upper	135 (183)
D150 & 250 Models	
Lower & Upper	135 (183)
D350 Model	
Lower & Upper	175 (237)
Front Strut Mounting	
Ram Van & Wagon	100 (135)
D150-350	50 (68)
Lower Control Arm-to-Crossmember	
Ram Van & Wagon	175 (237)
D150-350 Models	210 (285)
Lower Shock Absorber Mount	
All 2WD Models	17 (23)
All 4WD Models	55 (75)
Rear Strut Nut	
Ram Van & Wagon	52 (70)
D150-350	85 (115)
Sway Bar	
Link End	8 (11)
Frame End	22 (30)
Upper Ball Joint-to-Control Arm	
Ram Van & Wagon	125 (170)
D150-350	125 (170)
Upper Control Arm (Eccentric) Bolt	70 (95)
Upper Shock Absorber Mount	
All 2 WD Models	25 (34)
All 4WD Models	55 (75)

Front Suspension

FORD COIL SPRING – AEROSTAR

DESCRIPTION

The suspension is a short-long arm suspension system with helical coil springs. The system consists of spindles, upper and lower control arms with integral ball joints and bushings, adjustment shims, coil springs, shock absorbers and a stabilizer bar.

The critical joint in the front chassis area includes the front crossmember, longitudinal side member, and upper control arm. Whenever this joint is loosened or removed (including engine service), it is imperative that new fasteners or cleaned/lubricated present fasteners be installed with the proper installation torque at this critical joint.

ADJUSTMENT & CHECKING

WHEEL ALIGNMENT SPECIFICATIONS & PROCEDURES

See WHEEL ALIGNMENT SPECIFICATIONS & PROCEDURES in WHEEL ALIGNMENT section.

WHEEL BEARING ADJUSTMENT

1) Raise vehicle until tire clears floor. Remove wheel cover. Remove grease cap from the hub. Wipe excess from end of spindle. Remove cotter pin and retainer.

2) Loosen adjusting nut 3 turns. Obtain running clearance between rotor brake surface and shoe lining by rocking entire wheel asembly in and out several times to push caliper and brake pads away from rotor.

3) An alternate method to obtain the proper running clearance may be done by lightly tapping on the caliper housing. Be sure not to tap on any other area that may damage the rotor and the lining surfaces. DO NOT pry on the phenolic caliper piston.

4) The running clearance must be maintained throughout bearing adjustment procedure. If proper clearance cannot be maintained, caliper must be removed.

5) While rotating wheel assembly, tighten adjusting nut to 17-25 ft. lbs. (23-34 N.m). Loosen adjusting nut 1/2 turn. Retighten to 18-20 INCH lbs. (2.0-2.3 N.m).

6) Place retainer on adjusting nut. The castellations on the retainer must be aligned with cotter pin hole in the spindle. DO NOT turn adjuster nut to make castellations line up with hole in spindle.

7) Remove retainer from the nut and reindex retainer without moving nut. Repeat until castellations line up with hole in spindle. Install a new cotter pin. Check front wheel rotation. If wheel rotates properly, reinstall the grease cap and wheel cover.

8) If rotation is noisy or rough, remove, inspect and lubricate the bearing cones and cups. Before driving the vehicle, pump the brake pedal several times to restore normal brake travel.

BALL JOINT CHECKING

Lower Ball Joint

1) Raise and support vehicle. Grasp the lower edge of the tire and move the wheel in and out. While the wheel is being moved, observe the lower spindle jaw and lower control arm.

2) A 1/32" (0.79 mm) or greater movement between the lower control arm and the lower spindle jaw indicates that the lower ball joint must be replaced. Inspect the rubber bushings at the lower control arm attachments for wear or looseness. Repair or replace as necessary.

Upper Ball Joint

1) When checking upper ball joints, grasp the upper edge of the tire and move the wheel in and out. A 1/32" (0.79 mm) or greater movement between the upper spindle arm and the upper control arm indicates that the upper ball joint must be replaced.

2) Inspect the rubber bushings at the upper control arm attachments for wear or looseness. Repair or replace as necessary.

REMOVAL & INSTALLATION

FRONT WHEEL BEARINGS

Removal & Installation

1) Raise vehicle until tire clears floor. Remove wheel from hub and rotor. Remove caliper from spindle and wire it to the underbody to prevent damage to brake hose.

2) Remove grease cap from hub. Remove the cotter pin, lock nut, adjusting nut and flat washer from spindle. Remove outer bearing. Pull hub and rotor off spindle. Remove grease seal and inner bearing.

3) To install, clean bearings, inspect for damage and replace as necessary. Reverse removal procedure.

SHOCK ABSORBER

Removal

Remove nut and washer retaining shock absorber to coil spring upper bracket. Remove 2 bolts retaining shock absorber to bottom of lower control arm.

Installation

1) Inspect the insulator in the coil spring upper bracket. If required, remove and replace the insulator. Install the shock absorber through the lower control arm so the shock upper stud is piloted in the bracket insulator.

2) Install 2 bolts retaining the shock absorber to the lower control arm. Tighten bolts. Install the washer and nut retaining the shock absorber to the coil spring upper bracket. Tighten the stud nut.

SPINDLE

NOTE: **Any time the steering linkage is disconnected from the spindle, the steering system must be placed in the "ON-CENTER" position**

Removal

1) Place steering wheel and steering system in "ON-CENTER" position. Raise vehicle on a twin-post hoist. Place safety stands under frame to support the vehicle.

2) Remove wheel and tire assembly. Remove caliper, rotor and dust shield from spindle. Remove cotter pin and nut retaining tie rod end to spindle lower arm.

3) Disconnect the tie rod end using Pitman Arm Puller (T64P-3590-F). Making sure hoist is supporting the lower control arm, remove the cotter pin and loosen the nut retaining the spindle to the lower control arm joint.

4) Using Pitman Arm Puller (T64P-3590-F), disconnect the lower ball joint. Remove the tool and the ball joint retaining nut. With the vehicle body securely supported on the safety stands, slowly lower the lower control arm until lower ball joint is disengaged from the spindle.

CAUTION: **Use extreme caution when lowering the lower control. The coil spring may quickly expand with dangerous force.**

FORD COIL SPRING – AEROSTAR (Cont.)

Fig. 1: Exploded View Of Front Suspension

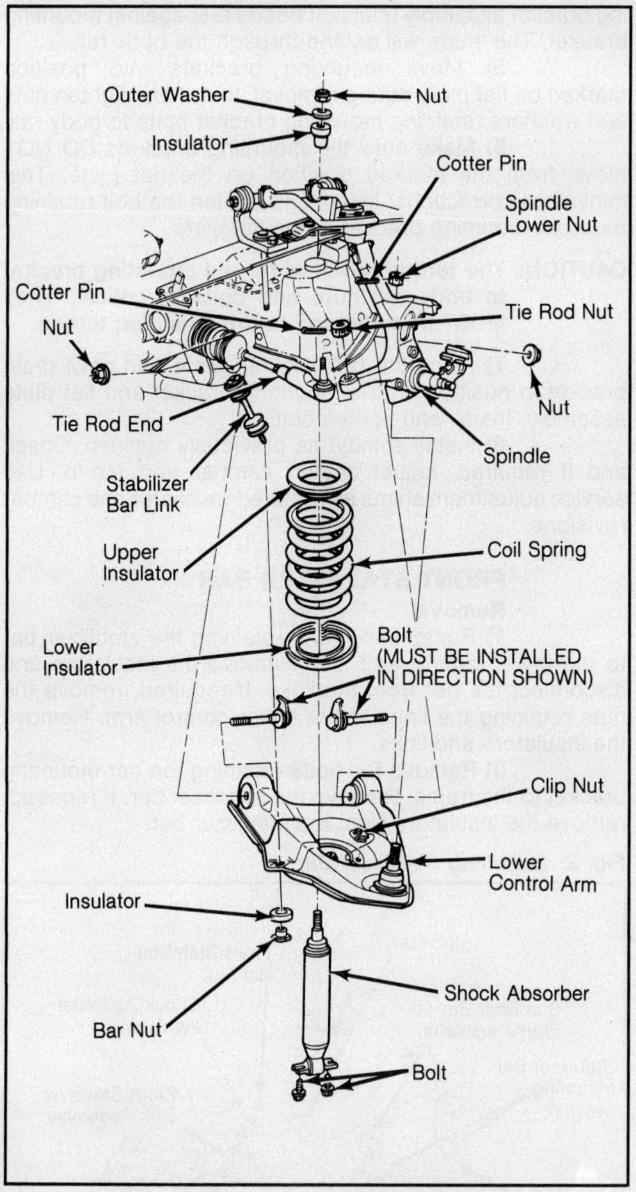

5) Remove bolt and nut retaining spindle to upper control arm ball joint. Remove spindle from vehicle.

Installation

1) Position the spindle upper arm on the upper ball joint. Install and tighten the nut and bolt. Inspect upper and lower ball joint boot seals for damage and replace if required.

2) Position the spindle lower arm over the ball joint stud. With the hoist, slowly raise the lower control arm until the ball joint stud extends through the spindle arm and is seated in the spindle.

3) Install and tighten the nut. If required, advance the nut to the next castellation and install the cotter pin. Connect the tie rod end to the spindle arm.

4) Firmly seat the tie rod end stud into the tapered hole to prevent rotation while tightening. Install and tighten nut. If required, advance the nut to next castellation and install cotter pin.

5) Install dust shield, rotor and caliper. Install wheel and tire assembly. Remove safety stands and lower the vehicle.

COIL SPRING

Removal

1) Place the steering wheel and steering system in the "ON-CENTER" position. Raise vehicle on a hoist. Remove tire and wheel assembly. Disconnect stabilizer bar link bolt from lower control arm.

2) Remove 2 bolts attaching the shock absorber to the lower control arm. Remove the upper nut and washer retaining the shock absorber. Remove shock absorber. Remove steering center link from pitman arm.

3) Support vehicle with safety stands under jacking pads. Lower hoist, but maintain working room. Using Spring Compressor (D78P-5310-A), install 1 plate with pivot ball seat facing downward into coils of spring.

4) Rotate the plate, so that it is flush with upper surface of lower control arm. Install other plate with pivot ball seat facing downward into coils of spring.

5) Insert the upper ball nut through the coils of the spring, so the nut rests in upper plate. Insert compression rod into the upper and lower plate and upper ball nut.

6) Insert the securing pin through the upper ball nut and compression rod. Due to stepped design, pin can only be installed 1 way.

7) With the upper ball nut secured, turn the upper plate so that it "WALKS UP" the coil until it contacts the upper spring seat; then, back off 1/2 turn. Install the lower ball nut and thrust washer on the compression rod, and screw on the forcing nut.

8) Tighten forcing nut until spring is compressed enough so that it is free in its seat. Loosen 2 lower arm pivot bolts. Remove cotter pin and loosen but DO NOT remove, nut attaching lower ball joint to spindle.

9) Using Pitman Arm Puller (T64P-3590-F), loosen lower ball joint. Remove the puller tool. Support the lower control arm with a jack and remove the ball joint nut. Lower the control arm and remove the spring.

10) If a new spring is to be installed, mark position of upper and lower plates on spring with caulk. Compress a new spring for installation. Measure compressed length of the old spring. Loosen forcing nut to relieve spring tension, and remove tools from spring.

Installation

1) Assemble the spring compressor, and locate in the same position as indicated in step **10)** of removal procedure. Before compressing the coil spring, be sure that the upper ball nut securing pin is inserted properly.

2) Compress coil spring until spring height reaches the dimension obtained in step **10)** of removal procedure. Position the coil spring assembly into the lower control arm. To install coil spring, reverse the remaining removal procedure.

LOWER CONTROL ARM

Removal

1) Place steering wheel and steering system in "ON-CENTER" position. Raise vehicle on a twin-post hoist. Place safety stands under the frame to support the vehicle.

2) During service procedures, the front post hoist is lowered to release coil spring tension. Remove coil spring as outlined in COIL SPRING. Remove bolts and nuts retaining lower control arm to No. 1 crossmember.

Front Suspension

FORD COIL SPRING – AEROSTAR (Cont.)

NOTE: Prior to removing lower control arm, front post of hoist should be rotated to support vehicle under No. 1 crossmember.

3) Replace entire lower control arm assembly to service bushings.

Installation

1) Position lower control arm in No. 1 crossmember. Install bolts in proper direction. *See Fig. 1*. Install nut and tighten until snug. DO NOT tighten to specified torque at this time.

2) Inspect lower ball joint boot seal for damage and replace if required. Install the coil spring. With the vehicle in the "NORMAL RIDE" position, tighten nuts and bolts retaining lower control arm to No. 1 crossmember.

UPPER CONTROL ARM, BALL JOINT & MOUNTING BRACKETS

Removal

1) Place steering wheel and steering system in "ON-CENTER" position. Raise vehicle on a twin-post hoist. Place safety stands under body rail to support vehicle.

2) During the service procedure, the front hoist is lowered to release coil spring compression.

NOTE: When servicing any component in the upper control arm and ball joint system, only 1 side of the vehicle is serviced at a time. NEVER service both sides at the same time.

3) Remove spindle as previously outlined. Remove bolt retaining cowl drain bracket and bolt retainer plate. Remove the bracket and plate. Mark position of control arm mounting brackets on the flat plate.

4) Remove the bolt and washer retaining the front mounting bracket to the flat plate. From beneath the rail, remove the 3 nuts from the bolts retaining the 2 upper control arm mounting brackets to the body rail.

5) Remove the 3 long bolts retaining the mounting brackets to the body rail by rotating the upper control arm out of position in order to remove the bolts. Remove the upper control arm, upper ball joint, mounting bracket and flat plate from the vehicle.

6) If required to service the upper control arm and upper ball joint assembly or the mounting brackets and adjusting arm assembly, remove the nuts retaining the upper control arm to the adjusting arm.

7) Note the exact position and number of shims on each control arm stud. These shims control caster and camber. Remove the upper control arm from the adjusting arm. The adjusting arm and mounting brackets are serviced as an assembly. The upper control arm and ball joint are serviced as an assembly.

Installation

1) If removed, install the upper control arm in the adjusting arm. install the shims on the control arm studs with the same number of shims in the exact position as marked during removal. Install and tighten the nuts retaining the shims to the control arm.

2) If removed, install the boot seal on the upper and/or lower ball joint. Place the flat plate for the mounting brackets in position on the body rail. Install and tighten bolt.

3) Place mounting brackets and upper control arm assembly in position on flat plate. Install 3 long bolts and washers retaining mounting brackets to body rail.

4) Rotate or rock upper control arm and mounting bracket assembly until bolt heads rest against mounting bracket. The studs will extend through the body rail.

5) Move mounting brackets into position marked on flat plate during removal. Install and tighten nuts and washers retaining mounting bracket bolts to body rail.

6) Make sure the mounting brackets DO NOT move from the marked position on the flat plate. This minimizes corrections. Install and tighten the bolt retaining the front mounting bracket to the flat plate.

CAUTION: The torque required for the mounting bracket to body rail nuts and bolts is critical. They MUST be tightened to the specified torque.

7) Place the bolt retainer plate and cowl drain bracket in position on the mounting bracket and flat plate assembly. Install and tighten bolt.

8) Install spindle as previously outlined. Check and if required, adjust caster, camber and toe-in. Use service adjustment shims as required for caster and camber revisions.

FRONT STABILIZER BAR

Removal

1) Remove the nuts retaining the stabilizer bar to the lower control arm link. Remove the insulators and disconnect the bar from the links. If required, remove the nuts retaining the links to the lower control arm. Remove the insulators and links.

2) Remove the bolts retaining the bar mounting bracket to the frame. Remove the stabilizer bar. If required, remove the insulators from the stabilizer bar.

Fig. 2: Installing Stabilizer Bar

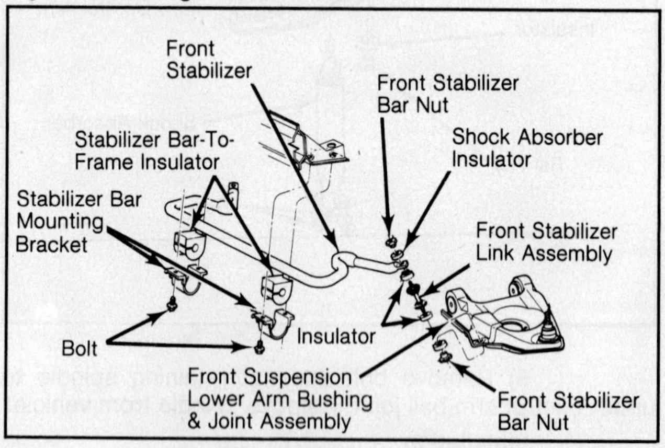

Installation

1) If removed, install the insulators on the stabilizer bar. Place the bar, insulators and mounting bracket on the frame. Install and tighten the bolts.

2) If removed, connect the link and insulators to the lower control arm. Install and tighten the nut. Connect the links and insulators to the stabilizer bar. Install and tighten the nuts.

JOUNCE BUMPER

Removal & Installation

To remove jounce bumper, remove the bolt retaining the jounce bumper to the No. 1 crossmember. Remove the jounce bumper. To install, place the jounce bumper in position on the crossmember. Install and tighten the bolt.

FORD COIL SPRING – AEROSTAR (Cont.)

Fig. 3: Removing & Installing Jounce Bumper

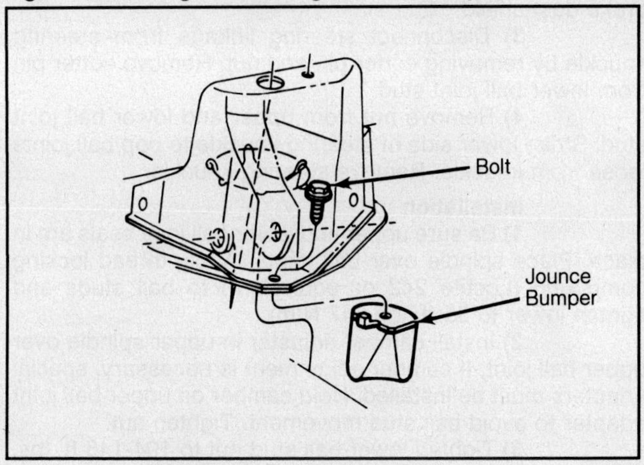

REBOUND BUMPER

Removal & Installation

Remove the bolt retaining the rebound bumper to the shock tower portion of the crossmember. Remove the rebound bumper. To install, place the rebound bumper in position on the shock tower. Install and tighten the bolt.

TIGHTENING SPECIFICATIONS

Application	Ft. Lbs. (N.m)
Crossmember-to-Frame Rail Bolts	
Front	135-145 (100-107)
Rear & Center	145-155 (107-114)
Cowl Drain Bracket & Bolt Plate-to-Frame Nut & Bolt	10-14 (14-18)
Jounce Bumper-to-Frame Bolt	30 (22)
Rebound Bumper-to-Frame Bolt	30 (22)
Lower Control Arm-to-No. 1 Crossmember Nut and Bolt	[1] 187-260 (254-352)
Shock-to-Lower Control Arm Bolts	16-24 (22-33)
Shock-to-Upper Spring Seat Stud Nut	25-35 (34-48)
Spindle-to-Lower Ball Joint Nut	[2] 80-120 (108-163)
Spindle-to-Upper Ball Joint Nut	27-37 (37-50)
Stabilizer Bar-to-Lower Control Arm Bar Nut	12-18 (16-24)
Stabilizer Bar Mounting Bracket-to-Frame Bolts	16-24 (22-33)
Stabilizer Link-to-Stabilizer Bar Nut	12-18 (16-24)
Tie Rod End-to-Spindle Arm Nut	[2] 52-74 (70-100)
Upper Control Arm-to-Adjusting Arm Nuts	70-100 (95-135)
Wheel Lug Nuts	85-115 (116-155)

[1] – Tighten to specified torque with vehicle in "NORMAL RIDE" position with all other fasteners tightened to specified torque.

[2] – Tighten to specified torque and if required, advance to next castellation to install cotter pin.

Front Suspension

FORD 2WD COIL SPRING – RANGER

DESCRIPTION

Front suspension is coil spring, twin "I" Beam-type. Suspension is comprised of coil spring, "I" beam axle arm, radius arm, upper and lower ball joint, steering knuckle, tie rod, shock absorber and optional stabilizer bar. One end of each axle is attached to a steering knuckle and radius arm assembly. Other end is attached to a frame pivot bracket. Knuckle is connected to axle by upper and lower ball joints. Ball joints never require lubrication. Steering knuckle movement is controlled by tie rods and steering linkage.

ADJUSTMENT & CHECKING

WHEEL ALIGNMENT SPECIFICATIONS & PROCEDURES

See WHEEL ALIGNMENT SPECIFICATIONS & PROCEDURES in WHEEL ALIGNMENT section.

WHEEL BEARING ADJUSTMENT

With wheel rotating, tighten adjusting nut to 17-25 ft. lbs. (23-34 N.m). Back off adjusting nut 1/2 turn. Tighten adjusting nut to 10-15 INCH lbs. (1.1-1.7 N.m). Install lock and new cotter pin.

BALL JOINT CHECKING

Raise and support vehicle. Move lower edge of tire in and out while watching lower steering knuckle. If movement exceeds 1/32" (0.79 mm), replace lower ball joint. To check upper ball joint, move upper edge of tire in and out. If movement between upper steering knuckle and upper axle exceeds 1/32" (0.79 mm), replace upper ball joint.

REMOVAL & INSTALLATION

FRONT WHEEL BEARINGS

Removal & Installation

1) Raise vehicle until tire clears floor. Remove wheel from hub and rotor. Remove caliper from spindle and wire it to the underbody to prevent damage to brake hose.

2) Remove grease cap from hub. Remove the cotter pin, lock nut, adjusting nut and flat washer from spindle. Remove outer bearing. Pull hub and rotor off spindle. Remove grease seal and inner bearing. To install, clean bearings, inspect for damage and replace as necessary. Reverse removal procedure.

SHOCK ABSORBER

Removal & Installation

Remove nut and washer attaching shock absorber to spring seat. Remove nut and bolt retaining shock to radius arm and lower shock. Compress and remove shock absorber. To install, extend shock absorber and reverse removal procedure.

SPINDLE

Removal

1) Raise and support front of vehicle. Remove wheel and tire assembly. Remove caliper assembly from rotor and support aside.

2) Remove dust cap, cotter pin, nut, nut retainer, washer and outer bearing. Remove rotor from spindle. Remove inner bearing cone and seal. Discard seal. Remove brake dust shield.

3) Disconnect steering linkage from steering knuckle by removing cotter pin and nut. Remove cotter pin from lower ball joint stud.

4) Remove nut from upper and lower ball joint stud. Strike lower side of steering knuckle to pop ball joints loose from knuckle. Remove steering knuckle.

Installation

1) Be sure upper and lower ball joint seals are in place. Place spindle over ball joints. Apply thread locking compound (Loctite 242 or equivalent) to ball studs and tighten lower to 35 ft. lbs. (47 N.m).

2) Install camber adjuster in upper spindle over upper ball joint. If camber adjustment is necessary, special adapters must be installed. Hold camber on upper ball joint adapter to avoid ball stud movement. Tighten nut.

3) Tighten lower ball stud nut to 104-146 ft. lbs. (141-197 N.m). and install cotter pin. Install dust shield. Pack bearings with bearing grease. Install inner seal cone and seal.

4) Install hub and rotor on spindle. Install outer bearing cone, washer and nut. Adjust bearing end play and install cotter pin and dust cap. Install caliper. Connect steering linkage to spindle. Tighten nut.

CAMBER ADAPTER

Removal

1) Remove nut from upper ball joint stud. Strike inside of the spindle to pop upper ball joint taper loose from knuckle.

2) If upper ball joint does not loosen, back lower ball joint nut 1/2 way down lower ball joint stud and strike

Fig. 1: Spindle Removal

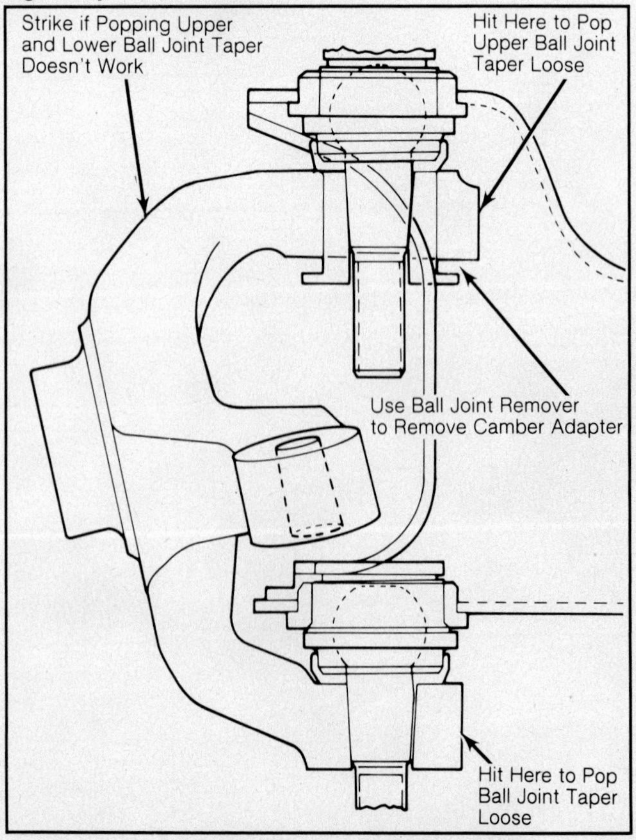

Strike inside of spindle to remove upper ball joint.

FORD 2WD COIL SPRING – RANGER (Cont.)

side of lower spindle. *See Fig. 1.* Remove camber adjusting sleeve using Camber Adjuster Remover (D81T-3010-B).

Installation

1) Install adapter in spindle. On right spindle, adapter slot must point forward in vehicle for camber change or rearward for negative camber change.

2) On left spindle, adapter slot must point rearward for positive camber change and forward for negative camber change.

3) To complete installation, reverse removal procedure. Apply thread locking compound (Threadlock and Sealer E0AZ-19554-A or equivalent) to stud threads before installing nut.

UPPER AND LOWER BALL JOINT

Removal

1) Remove spindle. Remove snap ring from ball joints. Assemble "C" Frame (T74P-4635-C) and Receiving Cup (D81T-3010-A). *See Fig. 2.*

2) Turn forcing screw clockwise until ball joint is removed from axle. Remove upper ball joint first. Assemble "C" frame and receiving cup on lower ball joint. Turn forcing screw clockwise until ball joint is removed.

Installation

Lower ball joint must be installed first. To install, reverse removal procedure. DO NOT heat ball joint or axle to aid in installation.

Fig. 2: Upper Ball Joint Removal

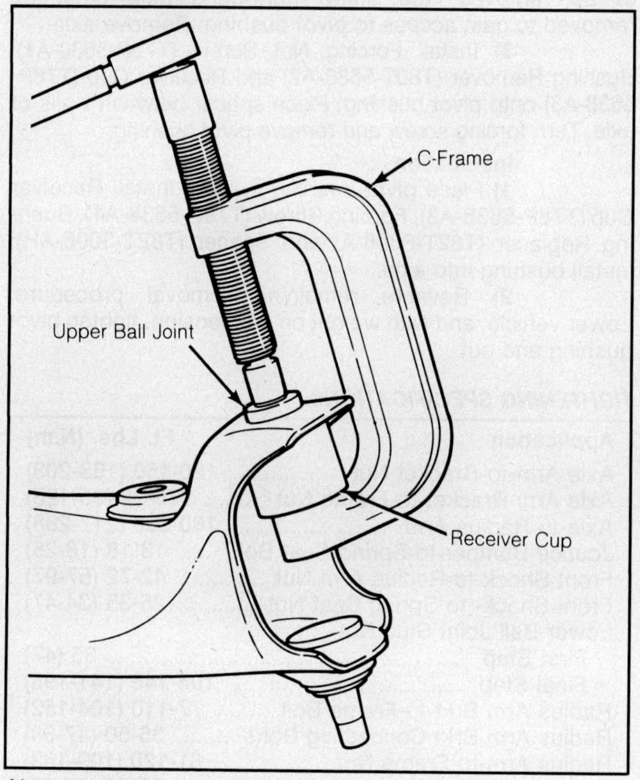

Always remove upper ball joint first.

COIL SPRING

Removal & Installation

1) Raise and support front of vehicle. Disconnect shock absorber from lower bracket. Remove nut holding lower retainer to spring slot. Remove lower retainer.

NOTE: **Axle must be supported by jack during removal and installation procedure. If brake hose length does not permit adequate clearance, caliper must be removed from spindle.**

2) Lower axle without stretching brake hose and tube assembly. Remove coil spring using long pry bar. Insert pry bar between 2 axles. Force "I" beam axle down far enough to lift spring over bolt that passes through lower spring seat. *See Fig. 3.*

3) Rotate spring so built-in retainer on upper spring seat is cleared. Remove spring. To install, reverse removal procedure. Tighten all nuts and bolts.

Fig. 3: Coil Spring Assembly

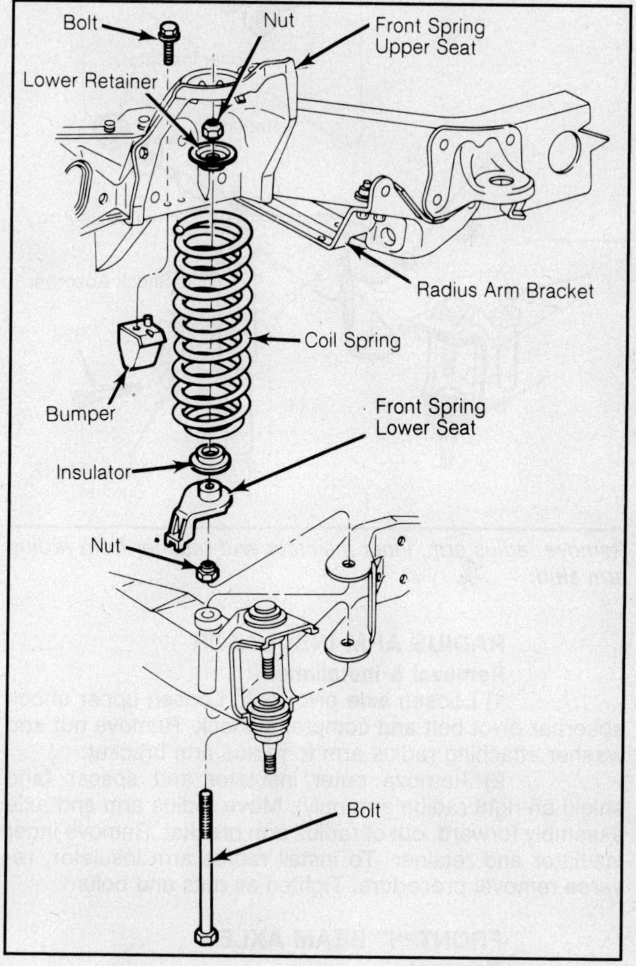

RADIUS ARM

Removal & Installation

1) Raise and support front of vehicle. Disconnect lower end of shock absorber from lower bracket. Remove front spring. Loosen axle pivot bolt.

NOTE: **Axle must be supported by jack during removal and installation procedure. If brake hose length does not permit adequate clearance, caliper must be removed from spindle.**

2) Remove spring lower seat from radius arm and remove bolt and nut attaching radius arm to axle and front bracket.

Front Suspension

FORD 2WD COIL SPRING – RANGER (Cont.)

3) Remove nut, rear washer and insulator from rear side of radius arm rear bracket. Remove radius arm, inner insulator and retainer from radius arm stud. *See Fig. 4*. To install radius arm, reverse removal procedure. Tighten all nuts and bolts.

Fig. 4: Radius Arm Removal and Installation

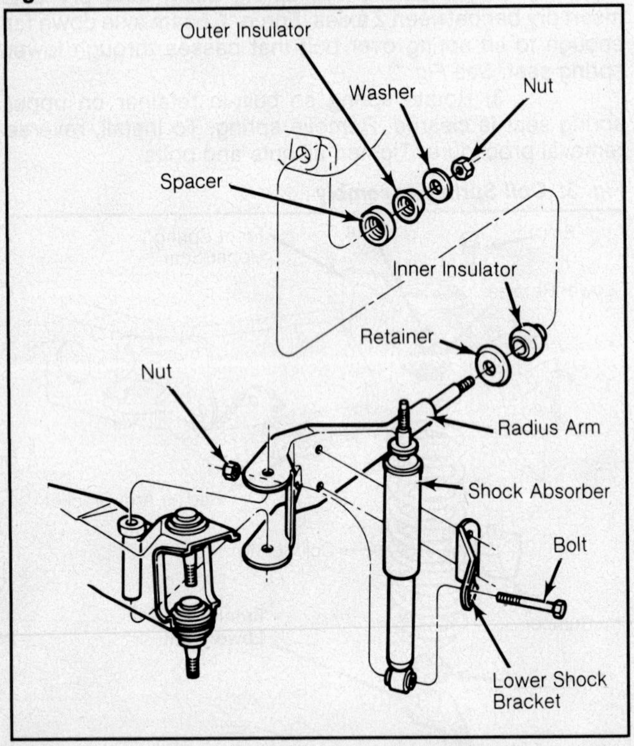

Remove radius arm, inner insulator and retainer from radius arm stud.

RADIUS ARM INSULATOR

Removal & Installation

1) Loosen axle pivot bolt. Loosen upper shock absorber pivot bolt and compress shock. Remove nut and washer attaching radius arm to radius arm bracket.

2) Remove outer insulator and spacer (and shield on right radius arm only). Move radius arm and axle assembly forward, out of radius arm bracket. Remove inner insulator and retainer. To install radius arm insulator, reverse removal procedure. Tighten all nuts and bolts.

FRONT "I" BEAM AXLE

Removal

Remove front wheel spindle and front spring. Remove spring lower seat from radius arm. Remove nut and bolt attaching radius arm to front axle. Remove axle-to-frame pivot bracket bolt and nut.

Installation

1) Position axle on frame pivot bracket and install bolt and nut finger tight. Position opposite end of axle to radius arm.

2) Install bolt from underneath bracket, radius arm and axle. Position axle against jounce bumper to place pivot bushing in proper position. Tighten axle-to-frame pivot bracket bolt. Reverse removal procedure to complete front axle installation.

AXLE PIVOT BRACKET

Removal

Remove front spring. Remove radius arm and spindle. Remove axle. Remove fasteners and retainer. Remove axle pivot bracket.

Installation

Position axle pivot bracket to frame. Install forward and rearward bolts and retainers from inside of pivot bracket out through crossmember. Loosely install the nuts on outside of crossmember. Tighten nuts.

NOTE: The proper nuts for this application have an undercut to provide clearance to bolt knurl. Use proper nuts or install one 0.20" (5 mm) thick hardened washer under each nut if a standard nut is used.

AXLE PIVOT BUSHING

Removal

1) Remove front coil spring. If pivot bushing in left-hand "I" beam axle is to be removed, remove axle pivot nut and bolt. Pull pivot end of axle down until bushing is exposed.

2) If pivot bushing in right-hand "I" beam axle is to be removed, the entire right-hand axle must be removed to gain access to pivot bushing. Remove axle.

3) Install Forcing Nut Screw (T78P-5638-A1), Bushing Remover (T80T-5638-A2) and Receiver Cup (T78P-5638-A3) onto pivot bushing. Place spacer between walls of axle. Turn forcing screw and remove pivot bushing.

Installation

1) Place pivot bushing in axle. Install Receiver Cup (T78P-5638-A3), Forcing Screw (T78P-5638-A1), Bushing Replacer (T82T-3006-A) and Spacer (T82T-3006-AH); install bushing into axle.

2) Reverse remaining removal procedure. Lower vehicle, and with weight on suspension, tighten pivot bushing and nut.

TIGHTENING SPECIFICATIONS

Application	Ft. Lbs. (N.m)
Axle Arm-to-Bracket Nut	120-150 (163-203)
Axle Arm Bracket-to-Frame Nut	70-92 (95-125)
Axle-to-Radius Arm	160-220 (217-298)
Jounce Bumper-to-Spring Seat Bolt	13-18 (18-25)
Front Shock-to-Radius Arm Nut	42-72 (57-97)
Front Shock- to-Spring Seat Nut	25-35 (34-47)
Lower Ball Joint Stud Nut	
First Step	35 (47)
Final Step	104-146 (141-198)
Radius Arm Brkt-to-Frame Bolt	77-110 (104-152)
Radius Arm Brkt Connecting Bolts	35-50 (47-68)
Radius Arm-to-Frame Nut	81-120 (109-163)
Stabilizer Bar-to-Bracket Bolt	35-50 (47-68)
Stabilizer Bar-to-Radius Arm Nut	48-64 (65-88)
Upper Ball Joint Stud Nut	85-110 (115-150)

FORD 2WD COIL SPRING – EXCEPT AEROSTAR & RANGER

Pickup & Van

DESCRIPTION

Front suspension is a coil spring, twin "I" Beam-type. "I" beams are mounted to a frame pivot bracket at one end, and to the steering knuckle and a radius arm at the other. Forged axles are used on F-250/350 and Vans. The F-150 series may be equipped with either a stamped or forged front axle.

On forged axles, steering knuckle is mounted to the axle by a solid, constant diameter kingpin. Bronze bushings are pressed into steering knuckles to provide bearing surfaces for kingpin. On stamped axles, ball joints are used.

Radius arm runs rearward from axle, to a bracket mounted on frame side rail. Coil spring is seated on top of radius arm and in a bracket mounted to frame. Hydraulic shock absorber is mounted between frame and radius arm to dampen road shock. A stabilizer bar is located in front of the axles.

ADJUSTMENTS & CHECKING

WHEEL ALIGNMENT SPECIFICATIONS & PROCEDURES

See WHEEL ALIGNMENT SPECIFICATIONS & PROCEDURES in WHEEL ALIGNMENT section.

WHEEL BEARING ADJUSTMENT

Tighten nut to 22-25 ft. lbs. (30-33 N.m) while turning rotor. Back off adjusting nut 1/8 turn. Install retainer and cotter pin without loosening nut any more. Bearing end play should be .001-.010" (.025-.254 mm).

BALL JOINT OR KINGPIN CHECKING

Raise vehicle. Adjust wheel bearings. Grab each wheel and shake in and out while watching front spindle assembly. Assembly must not move more than 1/32" (0.79 mm) at the upper or lower arms, relative to the axle. If worn beyond limits, replace ball joints or install new kingpins and bushings.

REMOVAL & INSTALLATION

FRONT WHEEL BEARINGS

Removal & Installation

1) Raise vehicle until tire clears floor. Remove wheel from hub and rotor. Remove caliper from spindle and wire it to the underbody to prevent damage to brake hose.

2) Remove grease cap from hub. Remove the cotter pin, lock nut, adjusting nut and flat washer from spindle. Remove outer bearing. Pull hub and rotor off spindle. Remove grease seal and inner bearing.

3) To install, clean bearings, inspect for damage and replace as necessary. Reverse removal procedure. See WHEEL BEARING ADUSTMENT in ADJUSTMENT & CHECKING section of this article.

SPINDLE

Removal (Forged Front "I" Beam Axle)

1) Raise vehicle and support under front axle. Remove wheel and tire assembly. Remove brake caliper from mount and wire it up out of the way. Remove brake rotor and brake dust shield. Disconnect tie rod end from spindle using Tie Rod Remover (3290-C).

2) Remove nut and lock washer from locking pin. Tap out locking pin. Remove upper and lower pin grease plugs. Drive kingpin out from the top of the axle using pin punch and modified plug as a guide. Remove spindle and thrust bearing. Knock out the kingpin seal.

Installation

1) Ensure kingpin bore is free of nicks, burrs and corrosion. Lightly coat the bore surface with a lithium-based grease. Install kingpin seal with the metal backing facing up toward the bushing.

2) Gently press seal into position being careful not to distort the casing. Install a new thrust bearing with the lip flange facing down toward the lower bushing. Press until the bearing is firmly seated against the surface of the spindle.

3) Lightly coat the bushing surface with grease and place spindle in position on the axle. Install the kingpin with the "T" stamped on 1 end toward the top, and the notch in the pin aligned with the lock pin hole in the axle.

4) Drive the pin through the bushings and axle from the top until the kingpin notch and axle lock pin hole are aligned. Install the lock pin with the threads pointing forward and the wedge groove facing the kingpin notch.

5) Firmly drive the lock pin into position and mount the lock washer and nut. Tighten the nut to 38-62 ft. lbs. (52-84 N.m). Install the king pin plugs into the threads at the top and bottom of the spindle. Tighten the plugs to 35-50 ft. lbs. (48-67 N.m).

6) Lubricate the kingpin and bushings through both fittings until grease is visible seeping past the upper seal at the top and from the thrust bearing slip joint at the bottom. If grease does not appear, recheck installation procedure.

7) To complete installation, reverse the remaining removal procedure. Tighten tie rod castellated nut to 70-100 ft. lbs. (94-135 N.m). Check, and if necessary, adjust the toe setting.

Fig. 1: F-250/350 (2WD) Twin "I" Beam Suspension

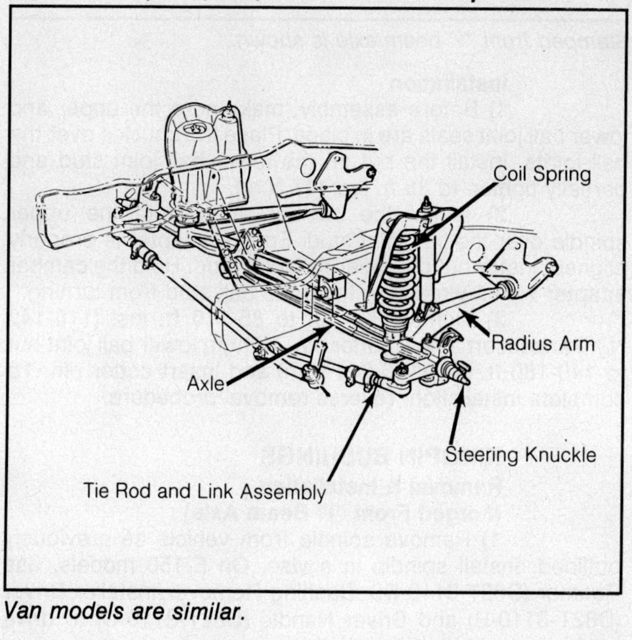

Van models are similar.

Front Suspension

FORD 2WD COIL SPRING – EXCEPT AEROSTAR & RANGER (Cont.)

Removal (Stamped Front "I" Beam Axle)

1) Raise vehicle and support vehice on safety stands. Remove wheel and tire assembly. Remove brake caliper and wire it up out of the way. Remove brake rotor and dust shield. Disconnect steering linkage from spindle using Tie Rod Remover (3290-C).

2) Remove the cotter pin and nuts from upper ball joint. Remove the cotter pin and loosen the lower ball joint nut from the stud. Strike knuckle as shown to remove from axle. *See Fig. 2.* Remove spindle from vehicle.

NOTE: DO NOT use a pickle fork to separate the ball joint from the spindle as this will damage the seal and ball joint socket.

Fig. 2: Removing Spindle

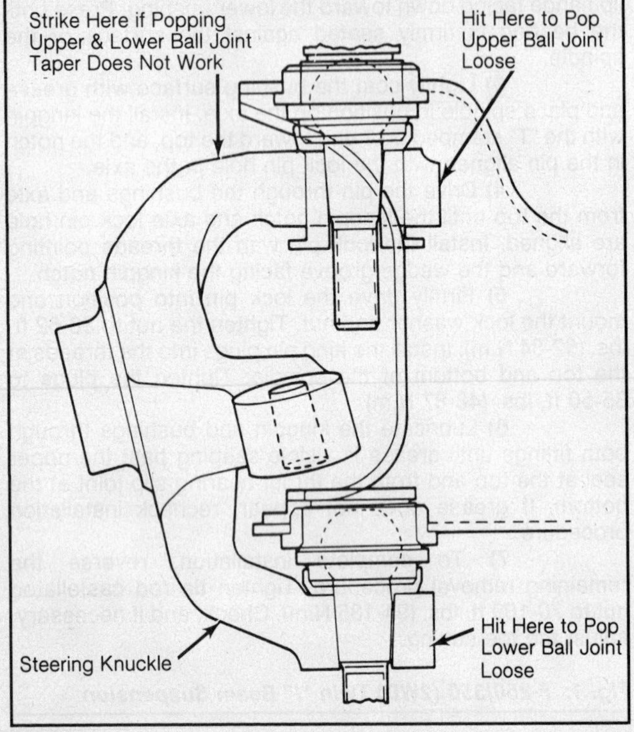

Stamped front "I" beam axle is shown.

Installation

1) Before assembly, make sure the upper and lower ball joint seals are in place. Place the knuckle over the ball joints. Install the nut on the lower ball joint stud and partially tighten to 35 ft. lbs. (47 N.m).

2) Install the camber adapter in the upper spindle over the ball joint stud. Ensure adapter is properly aligned. Install nut on upper ball joint stud. Hold the camber adapter with a wrench to keep the ball stud from turning.

3) Tighten the nut to 85-110 ft. lbs. (116-149 N.m) and insert a new cotter pin. Tighten lower ball joint nut to 140-180 ft. lbs. (190-244 N.m) and insert cotter pin. To complete installation, reverse removal procedure.

KINGPIN BUSHINGS

Removal & Installation
(Forged Front "I" Beam Axle)

1) Remove spindle from vehicle as previously outlined. Install spindle in a vise. On E-150 models, use Reamer (D82T-3110-D0, Bushing Remover/Installer Driver (D82T-3110-B) and Driver Handle (D82T-3110-C) to drive bushing out of bore in spindle.

2) On E-250/350 and F-250/350 models, use Reamer (T53T-3110-DA), Bushing Remover/Installer Driver (D82T3110-B) and Driver Handle (D82T-3110-C) to drive bushings out of bore in spindle.

3) Each side of the bushing remover/installer driver tool is marked with a "T" or a "B". Use the side with the "T" stamping to install the top spindle bushing. Use the side with the "B" to install the bottom spindle bushing.

4) Remove and discard the seal from the bottom of the top bushing bore. Remove and install the top spindle bushing first. Install the driver handle through the bottom bore.

5) Position a new bushing on the "T" side stamping of the bushing remover/installer driver. The bushing must be installed on the tool so the open end grooves will face outward when installed.

6) Position the new bushing and driver over the old bushing. Insert the handle into the driver and drive the old bushing out while the new bushing is driven in. Drive until the tool is seated.

7) The bushing will then be seated at the the proper depth 0.080" (2 mm) minimum from the bottom of upper spindle boss. Using the "B" side stamping, repeat steps **5)** and **6)** to install the bottom bushing.

8) Proper depth of bottom bushing is 0.130" (3.5 mm). Ream the new bushings to .001-.003" (.025-.076 mm) larger than the diameter of a new kingpin. Ream the top bushing first with the reamer tool.

9) Install the smaller diameter of the tool through the top bore and into the bottom bore until the reaming threads are in position in the top bushing. Rotate the tool until the threads exit the top bushing.

10) The larger diameter portion of the tool will act as a pilot in the top bushing to properly ream the bottom bushing. Clean all metal shavings and lubricate bushings and kingpins.

11) Install a new seal on bushing remover/installer driver tool on the side with the "T" stamping. Install the handle into the driver and push the seal into position in the bottom of the top bushing bore.

12) Reverse the remaining removal procedure to complete installation.

BALL JOINTS

Removal (Stamped Front "I" Beam Axle)

Remove spindle from vehicle as previously outlined. Remove snap ring from ball joints. Using "C" Frame (T74P-4635-C) and Receiver Cup (D81T-3010-A), press upper ball joint out of axle. Repeat procedure and press out lower ball joint.

CAUTION: Do not use heat on ball joint or axle during removal and installation procedures.

Installation

Seat the lower ball joint squarely in the hole by hand. Using Ball Joint Receiver Cup (D81T-3010-A5) and Installation Cup (D81T-3010-A1) inside Cup (D81T-3010-A4), press the ball joint in until firmly seated. Repeat the same procedure for pressing in the upper ball joint. Install snap rings. To complete installation, reverse removal procedure.

COIL SPRING

Removal

1) Raise front of vehicle. Place safety stands under frame and a floor jack under axle. Disconnect lower

FORD 2WD COIL SPRING – EXCEPT AEROSTAR & RANGER (Cont.)

shock absorber mount. Remove bolts securing upper spring retainer and remove retainer.

2) Remove nut securing lower spring retainer to spring seat and axle. Slowly lower jack under axle and remove spring.

Installation

Place spring in position and raise front axle with jack. Place lower spring retainer over stud and lower seat, and tighten attaching nut. Place upper retainer over the spring and upper seat and tighten bolts. Connect lower shock absorber mount. Lower vehicle.

FRONT AXLE

Removal

1) Remove front spindle, coil spring and the stabilizer bar. Remove lower spring seat from the radius arm.

2) Remove the bolt and nut that attaches the stabilizer bar bracket and radius arm to the "I" beam front axle. Remove the axle-to-frame pivot bolt and nut.

Fig. 3: Stamped Front "I" Beam Axle Assembly

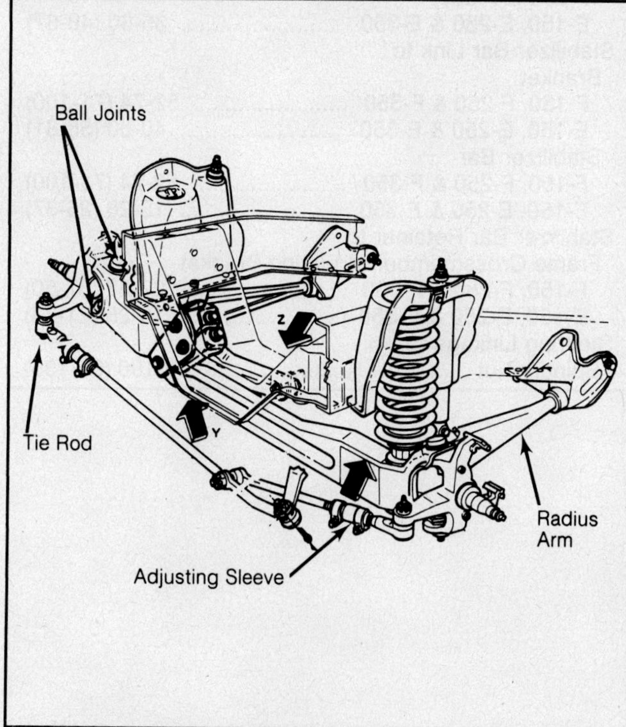

F150 model shown.

Installation

1) Position axle to the frame pivot bracket and install pivot bolt and nut finger tight. Connect radius arm and front bracket, then install and tighten bolt. Install lower spring seat, making sure it aligns over radius arm bolt.

2) Install coil spring. Tighten axle pivot bolt. Install steering knuckle, and stabilizer bar.

RADIUS ARM

Removal

1) Raise vehicle and position safety stands under frame. Place a floor jack under axle. Disconnect lower shock absorber mount. Remove front spring. Remove lower spring seat from radius arm.

2) Remove bolt holding radius arm and stabilizer bracket to axle. Remove nut, rear washer, insulator and spacer from rear radius arm mount. Remove radius arm.

Installation

To install the radius arm, reverse removal procedure. Tighten all fasteners to specifications.

STABILIZER BAR

Removal

1) Disconnect left and right ends of front stabilizer bar from the link assembly attached to "I" beam bracket.

2) Disconnect the retainer bolts and remove the stabilizer bar. Disconnect the stabilizer link assembly by loosening left and right lock nuts from "I" beam brackets.

Installation

1) Loosely assemble the entire assembly with both links outboard of the stabilizer bar. Pull stabilizer bar rearward and install bar ends to the links and install link bolts with threads pointing outward.

2) Install link-to-stabilizer bar washers and tighten retaining nuts. Tighten stabilizer bar-to-frame mounting nuts while pushing bar forward to swing the links away from the axle mounting brackets.

Fig. 4: Identification of Suspension Details

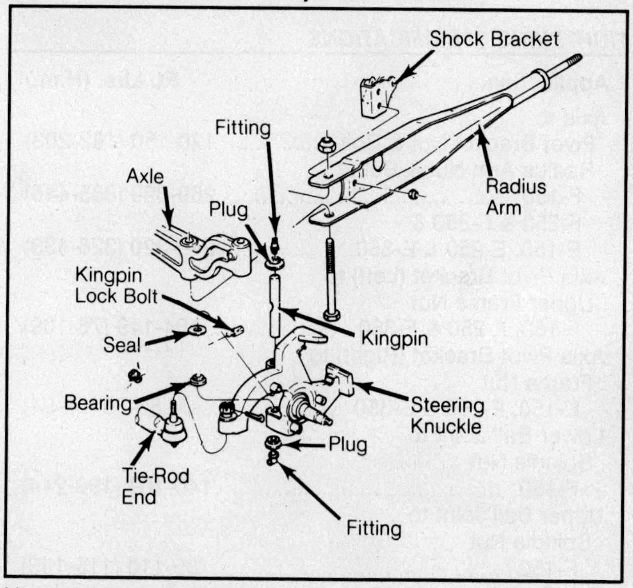

Van models, except E-250/350 spindle, are shown.

SHOCK ABSORBER

Removal

1) Insert a wrench from the rear side of the spring upper seat to hold shock upper retaining nut. Loosen the stud by turning the hex on the exposed lower part of the stud.

2) Disconnect the lower end of the shock absorber from the lower bracket bolt and nut. Remove shock absorbers, washers and rubber insulators.

Installation

To install, reverse removal procedure. Install NEW rubber insulators. Install lower shock mounting bolt with head facing tire.

Front Suspension

FORD 2WD COIL SPRING – EXCEPT AEROSTAR & RANGER (Cont.)

Fig. 5: Identification of Suspension Details

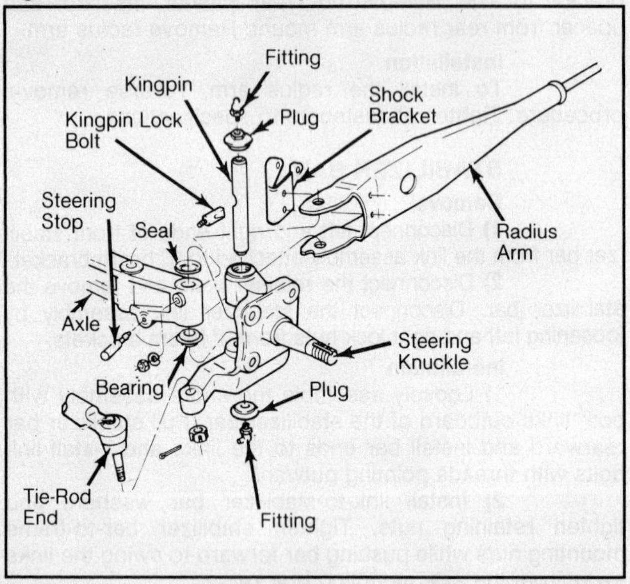

E-250/350 Van models spindles are shown.

TIGHTENING SPECIFICATIONS

Application	Ft. Lbs. (N.m.)
Axle to	
Pivot Bracket Nut & Bolt	120-150 (162-203)
Radius Arm Nut & Bolt	
F-150	269-329 (365-446)
F-250 & F-350 &	
E-150, E-250 & E-350	240-320 (326-433)
Axle Pivot Bracket (Left) to	
Upper Frame Nut	
F-150, F-250 & F-350	104-149 (76-109)
Axle Pivot Bracket (Right) to	
Frame Nut	
E-150, E-250 & E-350	50-70 (58-94)
Lower Ball Joint to	
Spindle Nut	
F-150	140-180 (190-244)
Upper Ball Joint to	
Spindle Nut	
F-150	85-110 (116-149)
Coil Spring to	
Lower Retainer Nut	
F-150 &	
E-150, E-250 & E-350	70-100 (95-135)
F-250 & 350	30-70 (41-94)
Coil Spring Upper Retainer to	
Spring Seat Nut	
F-150, F-250 & F-350	13-18 (18-24)
E-150, E-250 & E-350	20-30 (28-40)
Jounce Bumper to Frame Bolt	14-22 (19-29)
Lock Pin to Spindle Nut	
F-250 & F-350 &	
E-150, E-250 & E-350	38-62 (52-84)

TIGHTENING SPECIFICATIONS (Cont.)

Application	Ft. Lbs. (N.m)
Radius Arm to	
Rear Bracket Nut	80-120 (109-162)
Radius Arm Rear Bracket	
to Frame	
F-150, F-250 & F-350	77-100 (105-135)
E-150, E-250 & E-350	75-105 (102-142)
Shock Absorber to	
Lower Bracket Nut & Bolt	40-60 (55-81)
Upper Spring Seat Nut	
F-150	25-35 (34-47)
F-250 & F-350	15-25 (21-33)
E-150, E-250 & E-350	18-28 (25-37)
Shock Absorber Bracket to	
Radius Arm Nut & Bolt	
F-150, F-250 & F-350	27-37 (37-50)
E-150, E-250 & E-350	70-95 (95-128)
Spindle Pin Plug to	
Spindle Nut	
F-250 & F-350	
E-150, E-250 & E-350	35-50 (48-67)
Stabilizer Bar Link to	
Bracket	
F-150, F-250 & F-350	52-74 (71-100)
E-150, E-250 & E-350	40-60 (55-81)
Stabilizer Bar	
F-150, F-250 & F-350	52-74 (71-100)
E-150, E-250 & E-350	18-28 (25-37)
Stabilizer Bar Retainer to	
Frame Crossmember Mounting Bracket	
F-150, F-250 & F-350	27-37 (37-50)
E-150, E-250 & E-350	15-25 (21-33)
Steering Linkage to	
Spindle Nut	70-100 (94-135)

Front Suspension

FORD 4WD COIL SPRING

Bronco, Bronco II, F-150, Ranger

DESCRIPTION

Independent front suspension consists of a 2-piece front driving axle assembly, 2 coil springs and 2 radius arms. Front driving axle consists of 2 independent axle arm assemblies. One end of each axle arm assembly is anchored to the frame. The other end of each axle arm assembly is supported by coil spring and radius arm. Hydraulic shock absorbers are direct, double-acting type.

ADJUSTMENTS & CHECKING

WHEEL ALIGNMENT SPECIFICATIONS & PROCEDURES

See WHEEL ALIGNMENT SPECIFICATIONS & PROCEDURES in WHEEL ALIGNMENT section.

WHEEL BEARING ADJUSTMENT

Bronco II & Ranger

1) Raise the vehicle and support with safety stands. Remove wheel lug nuts and remove the wheel and tire. Remove retainer washers from the lug studs and remove the manual locking hub from the spindle.

2) Remove the axle shaft spacer, needle thrust bearing and the bearing spacer. Remove the outer wheel bearing lock nut from the spindle using Four-Prong Spindle Nut Spanner Wrench (T83T-1197-A). Ensure the tabs on the wrench engage the slots in the lock nut.

3) Remove the lock nut washer from the spindle. Loosen the inner wheel bearing lock nut using spanner wrench. Ensure that the tabs of the wrench engage the slots in the lock nut and that the slot in the wrench is over the pin on the lock nut.

4) Tighten the inner lock nut to 35 ft. lbs. (47 N.m) to seat the bearings. Spin the rotor and back-off the inner lock nut 1/4 turn. Install the lock washer on the spindle. It may be necessary to turn the inner lock nut so the pin on the lock nut aligns with the closest hole in the lock washer.

5) Install the outer wheel bearing lock nut using spanner wrench. Tighten lock nut to 150 ft. lbs (203 N.m). Install the bearing thrust spacer, needle bearing and axle shaft spacer.

6) Clip the snap ring onto the end of the spindle. Install the manual hub over the spindle. Install the retainer washers. Install the tire and wheel and tighten lug nuts to 85-115 ft. lbs. (115-155 N.m).

7) Check the end play of the wheel and tire on the spindle. End play should be 0.001-0.003" (0.02-0.08 mm). *See Fig. 1*. Install locking hub as outlined in MANUAL LOCKING HUB.

Bronco & F-150

1) Raise and support vehicle on safety stands. Remove hub lock assembly from spindle. See LOCKING HUBS in this article.

2) Using Spanner Socket (T59T-1197-B), and a torque wrench, tighten the bearing inner adjusting nut to 50 ft. lbs. (68 N.m). while rotating the wheel back and forth to seat the bearing.

3) Back-off adjusting nut approximatley 45°. Assemble lock washer by turning inner lock nut to nearest

Fig. 1: Bronco II & Ranger Wheel Bearing Adjusting Nut Assembly

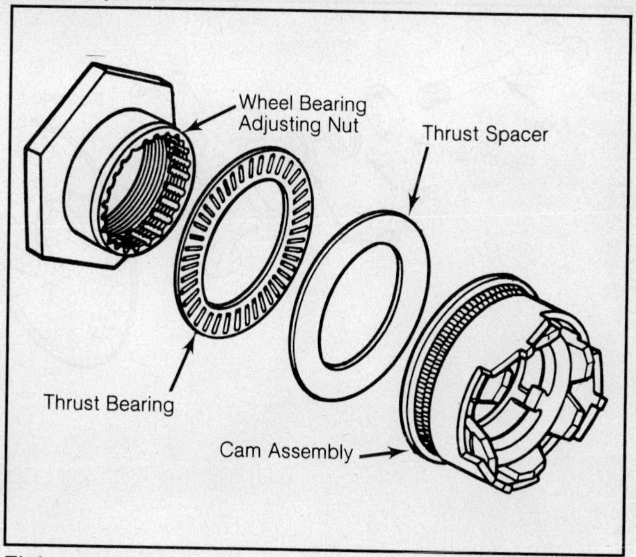

Tighten innerlock nut to 35 ft. lbs (47 N.m).

hole in the lock washer. To lock, install the outer lock nut and tighten to 150 ft. lbs. (203 N.m).

4) Final end play of the wheel on the spindle should be 0.00-0.006" (0.00-0.15 mm). Install automatic hubs as outlined in AUTOMATIC LOCKING HUB. Remove safety stands and lower vehicle. *See Fig. 2*.

BALL JOINT CHECKING

Raise vehicle. Adjust wheel bearings. Grab each wheel and shake in and out while watching front spindle assembly. Assembly must not move more than 1/32" (0.79 mm) at the upper or lower arms, relative to the axle. If worn beyond limits, replace ball joints.

REMOVAL & INSTALLATION

WHEEL BEARINGS

Removal

1) Remove locking hubs. Remove wheel bearing lock nut, lock ring and adjusting nut. Remove hub/disc assembly. Outer bearing will slide out.

2) Remove spindle nuts, then remove spindle from knuckle studs and axle shaft. Clean all parts, then remove spindle bore seal, "V" block seal and thrust washer from outer axle shaft. Replace any worn parts.

3) Remove inner bearing cone and grease seal from hub with slide puller. Check bearing cups and drive out with punch if worn.

Installation

1) Lubricate needle bearing and spindle face. Assemble "V" block seal next to needle bearing. Place spindle bore seal and thrust washer on axle shaft. Place spindle on knuckle studs and tighten nuts.

2) Place inner bearing cone and roller in cup, then install grease seal. Place hub/disc assembly on spindle. Install outer bearing cone and roller with adjusting nut. Adjust wheel bearings and install locking hubs.

Front Suspension

FORD 4WD COIL SPRING (Cont.)

Fig. 2: Exploded View of Bronco & F-150 Wheel Bearing Assembly

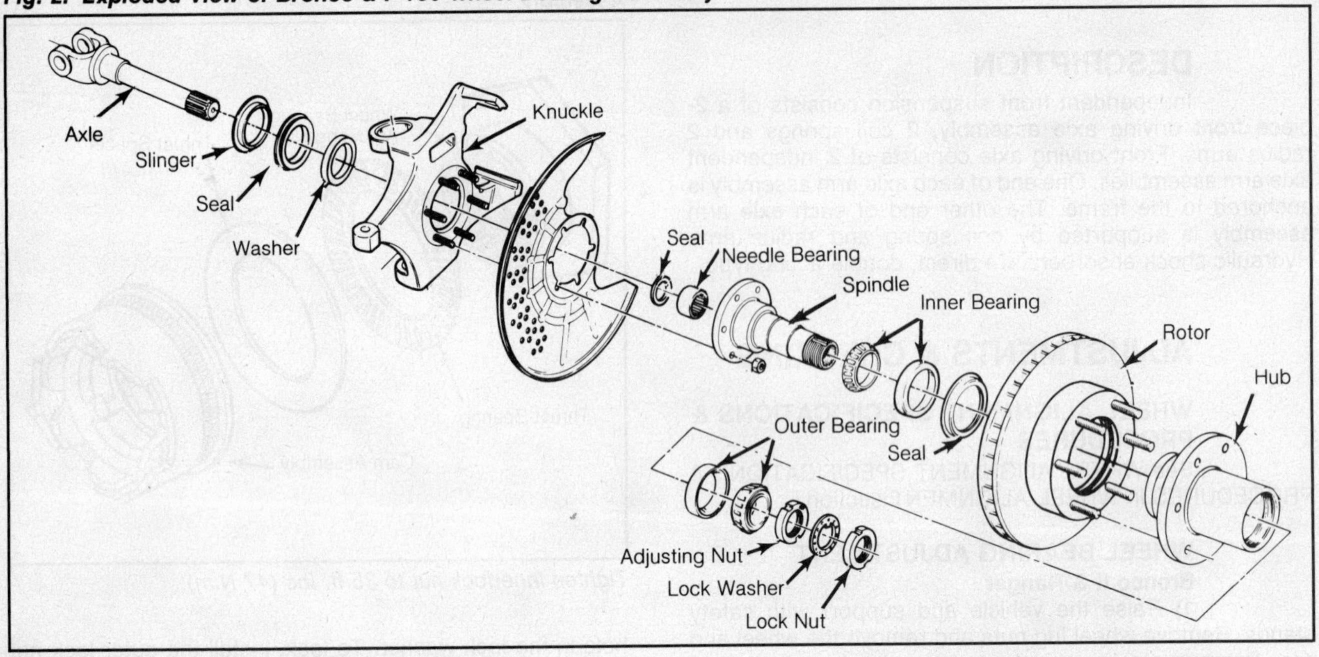

Clean all parts and use new grease for reassembly.

Fig. 3: Exploded View of Automatic Locking Hubs

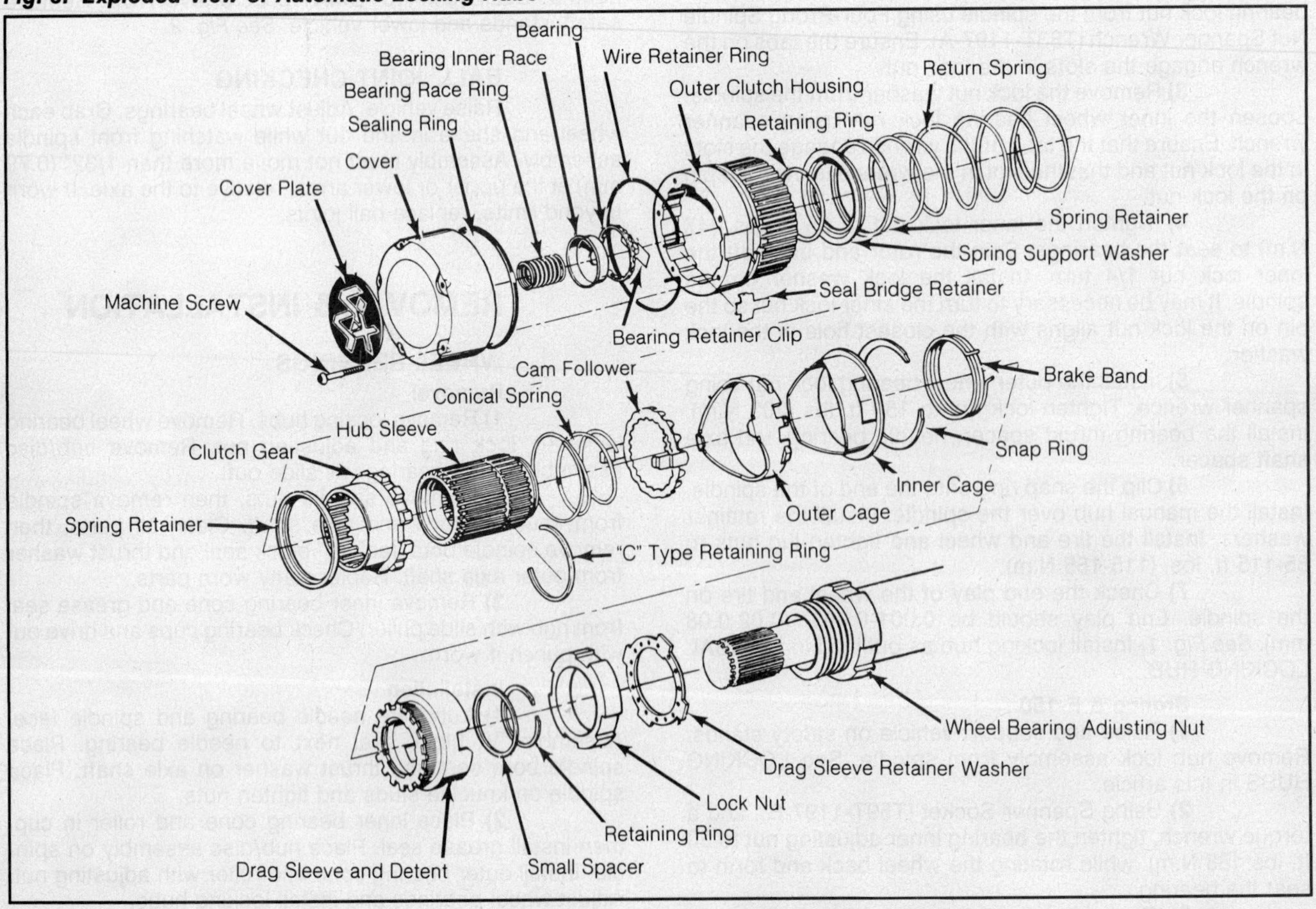

FORD 4WD COIL SPRING (Cont.)

AUTOMATIC LOCKING HUB

Removal

1) Remove 5 cap screws, and remove cover. Remove bearing race spring assembly. Remove sealing ring and seal bridge retainer. Remove bearing components.

2) Squeeze tangs of wire retaining ring together with needle nose pliers. Pull remaining components of automatic hub from wheel. *See Fig. 3.*

Installation

1) Make sure that drag sleeve retainer washer is in position, between wheel bearing adjusting nut and lock nut. Torque wheel bearing adjusting nut to specifications.

2) Make sure that spacer and retaining ring are in position on axle shaft. Install automatic locking hub into wheel hub. Align drag sleeve slots with tabs on drag sleeve retainer washer. *See Fig. 4 .*

3) Align outer clutch housing splines with splines of wheel hub. Loosen cover screws 3 or 4 turns, and push in on cover to allow retaining ring to expand into rotor hub groove.

Fig. 4: Drag Sleeve Retainer Washer

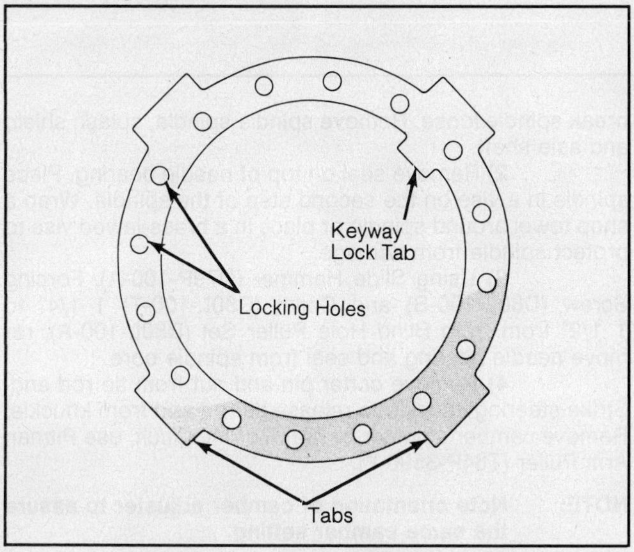

MANUAL LOCKING HUB

Removal

1) Remove hub screws and washers, noting how washers are installed on screws. Loosen gear hub housing, and slide away from hub and drum assembly.

2) Remove inner metal gasket, and discard. Remove gear hub housing. Remove outer gasket, and discard. Wipe clean all exposed components. Apply pressure on clutch gear, and remove snap ring.

3) Remove clutch gear and pressure spring from assembly, while knob is in "LOCK" position. Turn knob to "FREE" position. Usng a drift punch, drive cam lock pin out of assembly.

4) Remove actuating cam from knob. Remove knob from knob retainer. Using a cap screw, pull out on axle shaft. Remove snap ring, bushing, and inner clutch assembly. If wear is shown on either the inner or outer clutch gear, replace both as a set.

Installation

1) Before assembling hub, check splines on axle shaft. Make sure threaded screw holes in wheel hub are clean. Apply Moly X-L hi-speed grease to thrust face of bushing and to splines of inner clutch gear.

2) Install inner clutch gear on bushing. Install bushing and inner clutch gear on axle shaft. Make sure splines on inner clutch gear are aligned with splines on axle.

3) Install a new snap ring. Make sure snap ring is fully seated. Apply Parker "O" Ring Lubricant to "O" ring area of control knob. Install "O" ring.

4) Place actuating knob into knob retainer with arrow pointing to "FREE" position. Install knob retainer snap ring. It may be necessary to use a small screwdriver to position snap ring in groove.

5) Place actuating cam on knob, making sure ears of cam are aligned with retainer slots. Install cam lock pin through cam groove and holes in actuator knob.

6) Make sure ends of pin are flush with outside diameter of cam. Turn actuator knob to "LOCK" position. Apply a small amount of Moly X-L hi-speed lubricant to cam grooves.

7) Install spring and outer clutch gear. Press down on clutch gear to compress spring. With spring compressed, install snap ring. Turn actuator knob to "FREE" position.

8) Install 2 retaining screws and washers into knob retainer to align hub components. Apply a small amount of lubricant to outer splines of outer clutch gear.

9) Remove excess lubricant from retainer gasket surface. Install a new outer retainer gasket. Assemble housing by aligning splines of housing with outer clutch gear splines.

10) Install a new inner metal gasket on hub housing. Install hub assembly to axle, using retainer screws as pilots to align gasket holes and wheel hub holes.

11) Tighten retainer screws to secure hub in place. Turn actuator knob to "LOCK" position. Install the 4 remaining screws. Tighten screws evenly to 30-35 ft. lbs. (41-48 N.m).

NOTE: **It may be difficult to engage and disengage hub, until it has been used several times.**

SHOCK ABSORBER

Removal

Remove nut and washer holding shock absorber to upper spring seat. Remove bolt and nut from lower bracket retaining shock absorber to radius arm. Slide shock out of lower bracket. Compress shock and remove.

Installation

Extend shock absorber through spring seat, install washer and nut and tighten. Reverse removal procedures to complete installation.

QUAD SHOCK ABSORBERS

Removal (Bronco & F-150)

Remove self-locking nut, steel washer and rubber bushings from upper end of shock absorbers. Remove self-locking nut from lower end of shocks. Remove shock absorbers.

Installation

Replace rubber bushings when replacing shock absorbers. Place shock absorbers on mounting brackets with large diameter on top. Install bushings, steel washers and self-locking nuts and tighten.

SPINDLE

Removal (Bronco II & Ranger)

1) Raise and support vehicle. Remove wheel and tire. Remove caliper. Remove hub locks, wheel bear-

Front Suspension

FORD 4WD COIL SPRING (Cont.)

Fig. 5: Exploded View of Spicer (Dana) External Locking Hub

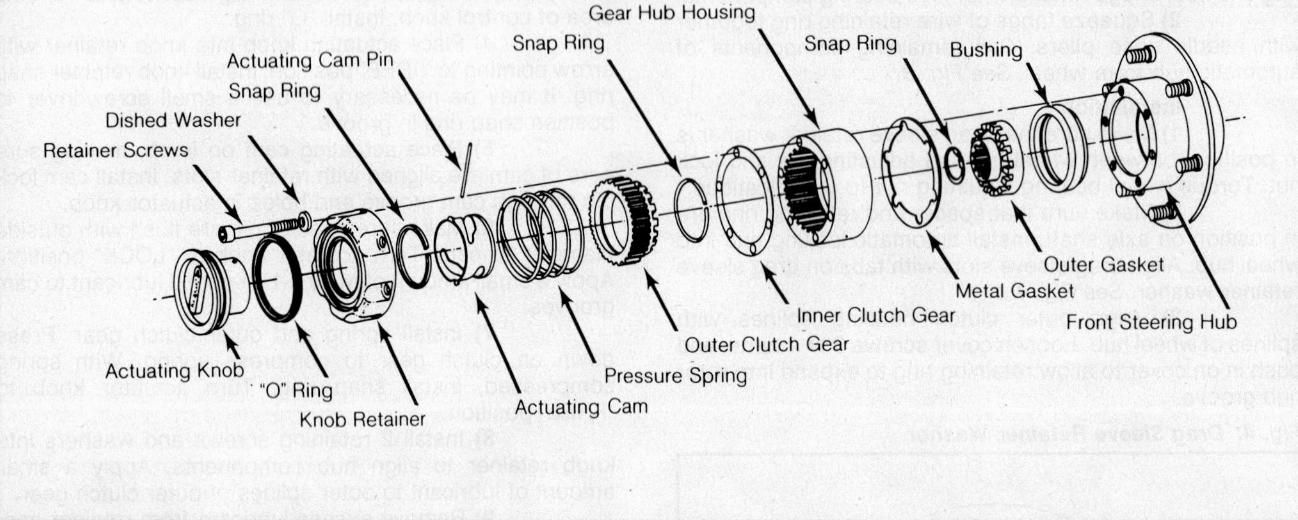

ings and lock nuts. Remove hub and rotor. Remove outer wheel bearing cone.

2) Remove grease seal from rotor with Seal Remover (T50T-100-A). Discard seal. Remove inner wheel bearing. Remove inner and outer bearing cups from rotor.

3) Remove nuts holding tie rod to spindle. Tap spindle with plastic hammer to jar tie rod from spindle. Remove splash shield.

4) On vehicle right-hand side, remove shaft and joint assembly by pulling assembly out of carrier. On right-hand side of carrier, remove and discard keystone clamp from shaft and joint assembly and stub shaft.

5) Slide rubber boot onto stub shaft and pull shaft and joint assembly from splines of stub shaft. Wrap spindle in protective cloth and place 2nd step of spindle in vise.

6) Remove oil seal and needle bearing from spindle. If necessary, remove seal from shaft by driving off with a hammer.

Installation

1) Place bearing in bore with manufacturer identification facing outward. Drive bearing into bore. Install grease seal in bearing bore with lip side of seal facing upwards. Coat bearing seal lip with multi-purpose grease.

2) If removed, install new shaft seal. On right-hand side of carrier, install rubber boot and new keystone clamps on stub shaft slip shaft.

3) To assemble right shaft and joint into slip yoke, align missing spline in slip yoke barrel with gapless spline on shaft and joint assembly.

4) Slide right shaft and joint into slip yoke. Be sure splines are fully engaged. Slide boot over assembly and tighten keystone clamp.

5) On left side of carrier, slide shaft and joint assembly through spindle and engage splines onto spindle. Tighten spindle nuts.

6) To complete spindle installation, reverse removal procedure.

Removal (Bronco & F-150)

1) Remove spindle nuts and spindle. It may be necessary to tap spindle with rawhide or plastic hammer to break spindle loose. Remove spindle spindle, splash shield and asle shaft.

2) Remove seal on top of needle bearing. Place spindle in a vise on the second step of the spindle. Wrap a shop towel around spindle or place in a brass-jawed vise to protect spindle from damage.

3) Using Slide Hammer (D79P-100-A), Forcing Screw (D80L-100-B) and Collet (D80L-100-T) 1 1/4" to 1 1/2" from from Blind Hole Puller Set (D80L-100-A), remove needle bearing and seal from spindle bore.

4) Remove cotter pin and nut from tie rod end. Strike steering knuckle to release tie rod end from knuckle. Remove camber adjuster by hand, or if difficult, use Pitman Arm Puller (T64P-3590-F).

NOTE: Note orientation of camber adjuster to assure the same camber setting.

5) Place knuckle in vise and remove snap ring from bottom ball joint socket, if so equipped. Remove plug from "C" Frame (T74P-4635-C) and replace with Plug (T80T-3010-A4).

6) Assemble "C" frame and Receiving Cup (D79P-3010-BG) on upper ball joint and turn forcing screw clockwise until ball joint is removed. ALWAYS remove bottom ball joint first.

Installation

To install, reverse removal procedure. Tighten all bolts and nuts. Replace any safety or self-locking nuts.

BALL JOINT

Removal

1) Remove spindle. If tie rod has not been removed, remove cotter pin from tie rod nut and remove nut. Tap tie rod to free from spindle steering arm.

2) Remove upper ball joint cotter pin and nut. Loosen lower ball joint nut. Strike inside of spindle near upper and lower ball joints to break spindle loose from ball joint studs.

3) Remove camber adjuster sleeve. If necessary use Pitman Arm Puller (T64P-3590-F). Place spindle in vise

FORD 4WD COIL SPRING (Cont.)

and remove snap ring from bottom ball joint socket, if equipped.

4) Assemble "C" Frame (T74P-5635-C), Forcing Screw (D79T-3010-B) and Ball Joint Remover (T83T-3050-A) on lower ball joint. Turn forcing screw clockwise until lower ball joint is removed from spindle.

5) Repeat step **4)** to remove upper ball joint. Turn forcing screw clockwise until upper ball joint is removed from spindle.

Installation

1) To install ball joint, reverse removal procedure. Always install lower ball joint first. Lower ball joint does not have a cotter pin hole in the stud.

2) Install camber adjuster on top ball joint stud with arrow pointing outward for positive camber and pointing inward for negative camber.

3) Zero camber bushings will not have an arrow and may be rotated in either direction as long as lugs on yoke engage slots in bushing.

4) Camber adjuster will seat itself into spindle at a predetermined position. DO NOT attempt to alter position of camber adjuster.

COIL SPRING

Removal (Bronco II & Ranger)

1) Raise and support vehicle. Position jack under spring located beneath axle. Remove bolt and nut holding shock absorber to radius arm. Slide shock out from bracket.

2) Remove nut holding spring to axle and radius arm. Remove retainer. Lower axle until spring tension is removed and clearance is adequate to remove spring.

Fig. 6: Bronco II & Ranger Coil Spring Installation

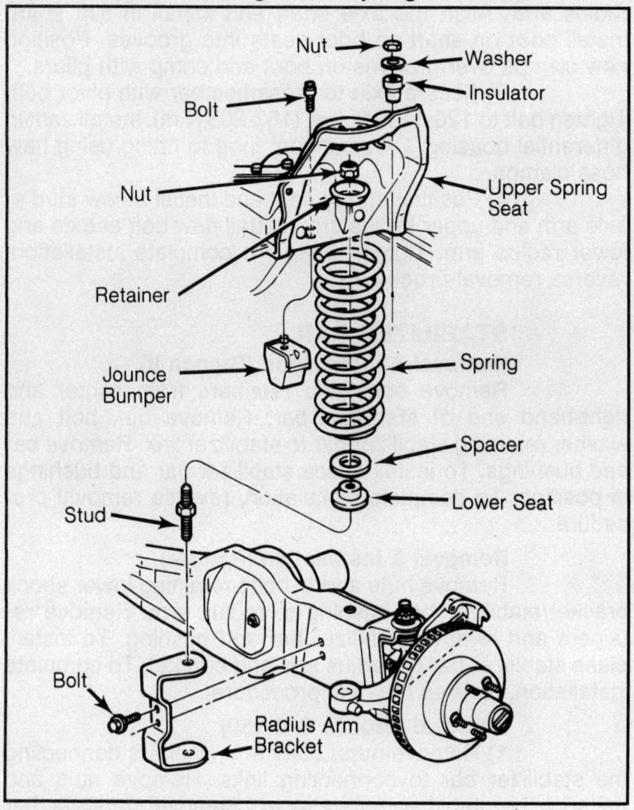

Position spring in upper spring seat and retainer.

3) Remove spring by rotating upper coil out of tabs in upper spring seat. Remove spacer and seat. Remove stud from axle if necessary.

Installation

Position upper end of spring so coil fits into spring stop in upper spring seat and top coil fits over upper spring retainer. To complete installation, reverse removal procedures.

Removal & Installation (Bronco & F-150)

1) Raise vehicle. Remove shock absorber-to-lower bracket bolt and nut. Remove lower spring retainer bolt. Remove upper spring retainer bolt. Remove upper spring attaching screw and upper retainer.

2) Place safety stands under frame rails and lower axle enough to relieve tension on spring. Remove spring and lower retainer from vehicle. To install, reverse removal procedure.

RADIUS ARM

Removal (Bronco II & Ranger)

1) Raise and support front of vehicle. Place jack under axle. Disconnect lower end of shock absorber from shock lower bracket.

NOTE: **Axle must be supported by jack during removal and installation procedure. If brake hose length does not permit adequate spring removal clearance, caliper must be removed from steering knuckle.**

2) Remove front spring. Loosen axle pivot bolt. Remove spring lower seat and stud from radius arm. Remove bolts attaching radius arm-to-axle and front bracket.

3) Remove nut, rear washer and insulator from rear side of radius arm rear bracket. Remove radius arm from vehicle. Remove inner insulator and retainer from radius arm stud.

Installation

Position front end of radius arm front bracket to axle. Install bolts and stud in bracket. Install bolts and stud finger tight. To complete installation, reverse removal procedures.

Removal (Bronco & F-150)

1) Raise vehicle and place safety stands under frame side rails. Remove shock absorber attaching bolts and remove shock absorber from radius arm. Remove lower spring attaching bolt. Loosen axle pivot bolt.

2) Remove radius arm rear insulator. Lower axle and allow axle to move forward. Remove the 2 self-tapping screws attaching the front axle to radius arm bracket to axle housing.

3) Remove bolt and stud attaching radius arm to axle. Move axle forward and remove radius arm from axle. Pull radius arm from frame brackets.

Installation

1) Position washer and insulator on rear of radius arm and place radius arm into the frame bracket. Install attaching nut. Position radius arm to axle. Install new bolts and stud, using Locktite No. 242.

2) Attach radius arm to axle. Attach lower spring seat, insulator and retainer to spring and axle. Tighten rear radius rod attaching nut. Install shock absorber and tighten nuts.

FORD 4WD COIL SPRING (Cont.)

RADIUS ARM INSULATOR

Removal (Bronco II & Ranger)

1) Loosen axle pivot bolt. Loosen upper shock absorber pivot bolt and compress shock.

2) Remove nut and washer attaching radius arm to radius arm bracket. Remove outer insulator and spacer.

3) Move radius arm and axle assembly forward out of radius arm bracket. Remove inner insulator and retainer.

Installation

To install radius arm insulator, reverse removal procedure and tighten all nuts and bolts.

FRONT AXLE

Removal (Bronco II & Ranger)

1) Raise and support vehicle under radius arm brackets. Disconnect driveshaft from front axle yoke. Remove wheel and tire.

2) Remove disc brake calipers. Remove cotter pin and nut retaining tie rod to spindle. Disconnect linkage from spindle.

3) Position jack under axle arm and compress coil spring. Remove nut retaining lower part of spring to axle arm. Lower jack and remove coil spring, spacer, seat and stud.

4) Remove bolt and nut and disconnect shock absorber from radius arm bracket. Remove stud and bolts connecting radius arm bracket and radius arm to axle arm. Remove bracket and radius arm.

5) Remove pivot bolt securing right hand axle arm assembly to crossmember. Remove keystone clamps securing axle shaft boot from axle shaft slip yoke and axle shaft. Slide over rubber boot.

6) Disconnect right driveshaft from slip yoke assembly. Lower jack and remove right axle arm assembly. Position another jack under differential housing.

7) Remove bolt connecting left axle arm to crossmember. Lower jacks and remove left axle arm assembly.

Installation

To complete front axle installation, reverse removal procedures.

Bronco & F-150

1) Raise vehicle on a hoist or jack and install safety stands under radius arm brackets. Remove wheel and tire and brake caliper. Position jack under axle arm and remove the upper coil spring retainers.

2) Lower the jack and remove the coil spring, spring cushion and lower spring seat. Disconnect the shock absorber at the radius arm and upper mounting bracket.

3) Remove the stud and spring seat at radius arm and axle arm. Remove bolt securing upper attachment to axle arm radius arm to lower attachment axle arm. Disconnect the vent tube at the differential housing and discard hose clamps.

4) Remove the vent fitting and install a 1/8" pipe plug. Remove the pivot bolt securing the right-hand axle arm to crossmember. Remove and discard the keystone clamps and remove the boot frm the shaft.

5) Remove the right-hand drive axle and pull the axle shaft from the slip shaft. Position a jack under the differential housing. Remove the bolt securing the left-hand axle to the crossmember. Remove the left-hand drive axle.

Installation

To install front axles, reverse removal procedure.

DRIVE AXLES

Removal Bronco & F-150

1) Raise vehicle on a hoist or jack and install safety stands under radius arm brackets. Remove wheel and tire. Remove caliper. Position jack under axle arm and remove upper coil spring retainers. Lower jack and remove coil spring, cushion and lower spring seat.

NOTE: **Axle arm must be supported on jack throughout spring removal. Hang caliper to frame. DO NOT hang by brake hose.**

2) Disconnect shock absorber at radius arm and upper mounting bracket. Remove stud and spring seat at radius arm and axle arm. Remove bolt securing upper attachment to axle arm radius to lower attachment axle arm.

3) Disconnect vent tube at differential housing. Discard hose clamps. Remove vent fitting and instll a 1/8" pipe plug. Remove pivot bolt securing right-hand axle arm to crossmember.

4) Remove and discard keystone clamps and remove boot from shaft. Remove right drive axle and pull axle shaft from the slip shaft. Position a jack under differential housing. Remove bolt securing left-hand axle to crossmember. Remove left-hand drive axle.

Installation

1) Raise vehicle on a hoist or jack and position left drive axle at radius arm. Secure drive axle to crossmember with pivot bolt. Tighten bolt to 120-150 ft. lbs. (163-203 N.m).

2) Position right-hand axle at crossmember and radius arm. Align the axle shaft and install in slip shaft. Install boot on shaft so boot seats into grooves. Position new clamps over grooves on boot and crimp with pliers.

3) Secure axle to crossmember with pivot bolt. Tighten bolt to 120-1150 ft. lbs. (163-203 N.m). Install vent in differential housing. Connect vent tube to fitting using new hose clamps.

4) Position spring seat and install a new stud at axle arm and upper radius arm. Install new bolt at axle and lower radius arm. Tighten bolts. To complete installation, reverse removal procedure.

STABILIZER BAR

Removal & Installation (Bronco II)

Remove bolts and retainers from center and right-hand end of stabilizer bar. Remove nut, bolt and washer retaining stabilizer bar to stabilizer link. Remove bar and bushings. To install, place stabilizer bar and bushings in position. To complete installation, reverse removal procedure.

Removal & Installation (Ranger)

Remove nuts and U-bolts retaining lower shock bracket/stabilizer bar bushing to radius arm. Remove retainers and remove stabilizer bar and bushing. To install, place stabilizer bar on radius arm and bracket. To complete installation, reverse removal procedure.

Removal (Bronco & F-150)

1) Remove nuts, bolts and washers connecting the stabilizer bar to connecting links. Remove nuts and bolts of the stabilizer bar retainer. Remove stabilizer bar insulator assembly.

FORD 4WD COIL SPRING (Cont.)

2) To remove the stabilizer bar mounting bracket, the coil spring must be removed. See COIL SPRING. (The bracket to frame assembly may be removed but not the crossmember). Remove the lower spring seat. The bracket attaching stud and bracket can now be removed.

Installation

1) To install the stabilizer bar mounting brackets, locate the brackets to that the locating tang is position in the radius arm notch, or quad shock bracket, if equipped.

2) Install a NEW stud. Tighten stud to 240-260 ft. lbs. (325-353 N.m). Reposition the spring lower seat and install the spring and retainers. To install the stabilizer bar insulator assembly, assemble all nuts, bolts and washers to the bar, brackets, retainers and links loosely.

3) With the bar positioned correctly, tighten the retainer nut to 27-37 ft. lbs. (37-50 N.m) with retainer around the insulator. Then tighten all remaining nuts at the link assemblies to 71-100 ft. lbs. (52-74 N.m).

4) To install the F-150 Regular Cab brackets to crossmember, tighten the 6 carriage bolt nuts to 27-37 ft. lbs. (37-50 N.m). For the F-150 Super Cab, tighten the nuts for the frame bracket to 71-100 ft. lbs. (52-74 N.m). On the F-150 Snow-Fiter, tighten the bolts for the frame bracket to 27-37 ft. lbs. (37-50 N.m).

BRONCO II & RANGER TIGHTENING SPECIFICATIONS

Application	Ft. Lbs. (N.m)
Axle Pivot Bolt	120-150 (163-203)
Radius Arm-to-Rear Bracket Nut	80-120 (109-162)
Radius Arm Front Bracket	160-220 (217-298)
Radius Arm Bracket Front Bolts	27-37 (37-50)
Radius Arm Bracket Lower Bolts	160-220 (217-298)
Shock-to-Radius Arm Nut & Bolt	42-72 (57-97)
Shock-to-Upper Seat	25-35 (34-47)
Spring Retainer Nut	70-100 (95-135)
Stabilizer Bar Retainer Bolts	77-110 (104-150)
Stabilizer Bar U-Bolt Nuts	48-68 (66-92)
Tie Rod Adjusting Sleeve	30-42 (40-57)

BRONCO & F-150 TIGHTENING SPECIFICATIONS

Application	Ft. Lbs. (N.m)
Lower Spring Retainer	71-100 (90-134)
Radius Arm-to-Axle	
Lower Bolt	320-340 (434-461)
Upper Stud	240-260 (326-352)
Rear Radius Arm Nut	80-100 (109-134)
Shock Absorber Mounting Bolt	
Lower	40-60 (54-81)
Upper	25-35 (34-37)
Stabilizer Bar Link-to-Bracket	52-74 (71-100)
Stabilizer Bar Retaining Nuts	27-37 (37-50)
Upper Spring Retainer	13-18 (18-24)

FORD LEAF SPRING – IFS 4WD TRUCKS

F-250 & F-350

DESCRIPTION

The 4WD independent front suspension (IFS) system has a 2-piece drive axle attached to frame with 2 semi-elliptic leaf-type springs. Each spring assembly is clamped to axle arm assembly with 2 "U" bolts. Rear spring eye is attached to hanger bracket and front spring eye is attached to shackle bracket. The 2 direct, double-action hydraulic shock absorbers are attached to each frame bracket at top and to "U" bolt spring spacer plate at bottom. *See Fig. 1*.

Either manual or automatic hub locks are installed on 4WD vehicles to activate the front drive axle. When actuated, hub lock body assembly locks hub and wheel assembly to front drive axle shaft. When released, axle shaft is disengaged from hub body assembly and hub is allowed to rotate freely on spindle. Two tapered roller bearings are mounted in hub with a hub grease seal installed inboard of inner bearing.

CAUTION: **Do not attempt to use past model lug nuts (cone-shaped, 1-piece) to replace integral 2-piece swiveling lug nuts. If used, 1-piece lug nuts can come loose during vehicle operation. Do not attempt to use past model wheels, which have cone-shaped lug nut seats, on these vehicles. Do not use new design wheels on past model wheel hubs or wheels could come loose during operation.**

ADJUSTMENTS & CHECKING

WHEEL ALIGNMENT SPECIFICATIONS & PROCEDURES

All F-250/350 models use a stamped axle housing, independent front suspension design with adjustable camber angle. On front leaf spring suspensions, caster angles are adjustable by placing shims between the leaf springs and the axle housing arm assembly. Toe-in is checked and set in the conventional manner. See RIDE HEIGHT and WHEEL ALIGNMENT SPECIFICATIONS & PROCEDURES in WHEEL ALIGNMENT section.

WHEEL BEARING ADJUSTMENT

NOTE: **If bearing adjustment does not eliminate looseness or rough and/or noisy operation, remove, clean, inspect and repack hub and bearings with specified grease. If bearing races or roller assemblies are worn or damaged, they must be replaced.**

Dana 50 Series Front Drive Axle (With IFS)

1) Raise and support vehicle on safety stands. Hold tire at front and rear, then push tire inward and outward. If any free play is noticed between hub/rotor assembly and spindle, adjust wheel bearings.

2) Remove manual or automatic hub lock assembly and outer lock nut with washer. See REMOVAL & INSTALLATION. Using Front Wheel Bearing Spanner (D78T-1197-A) and a torque wrench, tighten inner adjusting nut to 50 ft. lbs. (68 N.m).

3) Back-off inner adjusting nut, then retighten to 31-39 ft. lbs. (41-54 N.m). While rotating hub, back-off adjusting nut 135° to 150°. Assemble outer lock nut and new lock washer, then tighten nut to 65 ft. lbs. (88 N.m).

4) Bend 1 ear of lock washer over inner nut and the other ear of lock washer over outer nut. Install a dial indicator and check hub end play. Final end play should be .001-.009" (.02-.25 mm).

5) If end play is beyond limits, remove hub and bearing assembly and inspect components for excessive wear or damage. Replace hub and/or bearing assemblies as necessary. Reinstall components and adjust wheel bearings. Install hub lock assembly. Remove safety stands and lower vehicle.

BALL JOINT CHECKING

1) Raise and support vehicle on frame hoist. Hold tire at top and bottom, then shake wheel while watching for movement of disc brake support or spindle assembly.

2) If front spindle assembly is loose and moves more than 1/32" (.79 mm) at upper or lower arms (relative to axle), replace upper and/or lower ball joint as necessary.

REMOVAL & INSTALLATION

AUTOMATIC LOCKING HUB ASSEMBLY

Removal (F-250 Models)

1) Raise and support vehicle. To remove locking hub assembly, first separate locking hub cap assembly from body assembly. Using a Torx-R bit (TX25), detach 5 cap screws from cap assembly, then remove locking hub cap and bearing components.

CAUTION: **Do not drop ball bearing, race, spring retainer or spring during disassembly.**

2) Remove rubber sealing ring. Remove seal bridge retainer (small metal stamping) from spring retainer ring space. Detach lock ring retainer by closing ends with needle-nose pliers while pulling locking hub body assembly from wheel hub. *See Fig. 1*.

3) If wheel hub and spindle are to be removed, detach "C" washer from stub shaft groove. Remove splined spacer from shaft. Remove wheel bearing lock nuts and lock washer. *See Fig. 1*. Disassemble, clean and inspect locking hub assembly components.

4) Detach snap ring and flat washer from inner end of locking hub assembly. *See Fig. 3*. Pull hub sleeve and attached parts out of drag sleeve, then cock drag sleeve to unlock tangs of brake band. Remove drag sleeve assembly. *See Fig. 3*.

CAUTION: **Do not remove brake band from drag sleeve.**

5) Wash drag sleeve/brake band assembly in clean solvent and thoroughly blow dry. Lubricate brake band/drag sleeve assembly with lubricant meeting specification ESL-M1C93A (Darmex Spec. DX-123-LT). Work lubricant over spring and area of drag sleeve under spring.

6) Dip locking hub body assembly (except cap assembly and brake band/drag sleeve assembly) in Dexron II Automatic Transmission Fluid and permit to drip dry for a few minutes before proceeding with assembly.

FORD LEAF SPRING – IFS 4WD TRUCKS (Cont.)

Fig. 1: Exploded View Of Warner Gear Automatic Locking Hub Assembly

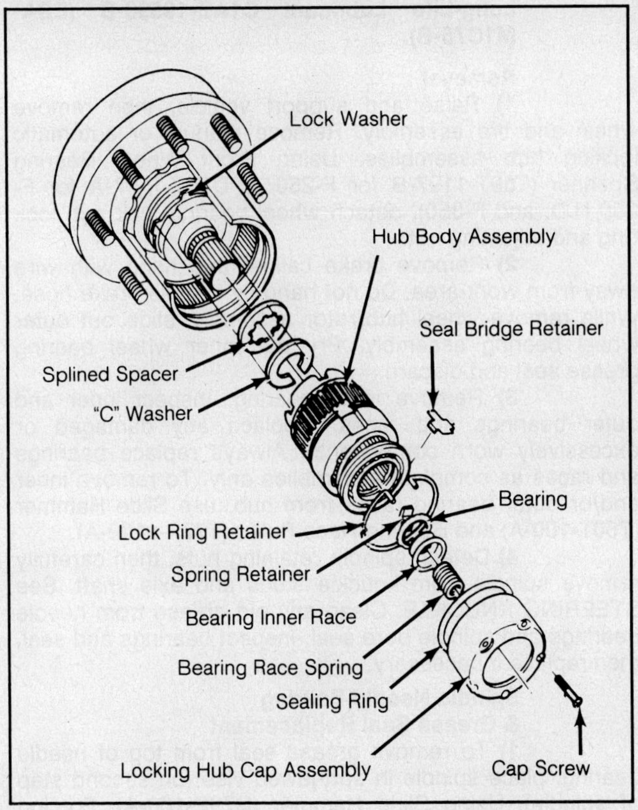

Inspection

Wash locking hub cap bearing, race and retainer in clean solvent, then inspect for excessive wear or damage. Replace components as needed. Thoroughly blow dry parts with compressed air. Do not spin bearings with air or damage can result. Repack bearing with lithium grease, then properly position bearing assembly in race. *See Fig. 2.*

Installation

1) To install locking hub components, first assemble 1 of 2 brake band tangs on each side of outer cage (plastic), which is located in window of inner cage

Fig. 2: Positioning Locking Hub Cap Bearing, Race & Spring Retainer

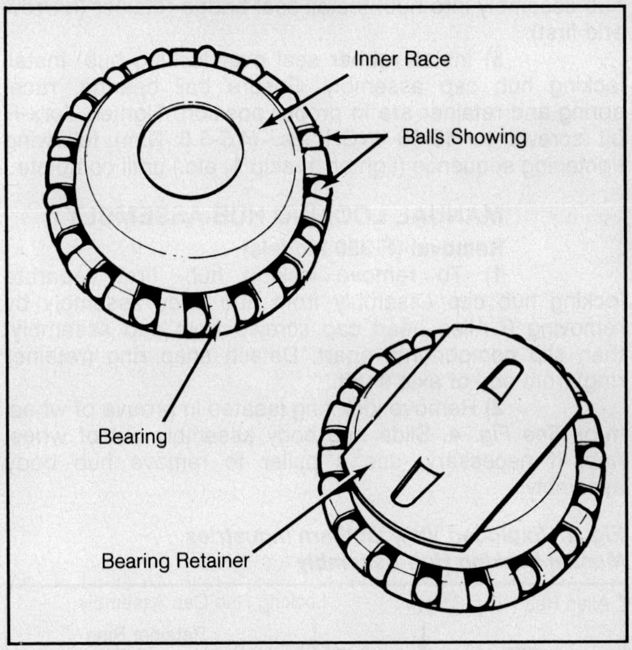

Position inner race into bearing assembly, then install bearing retainer as shown.

(steel). It is necessary to cock these parts to engage tangs in this position as the drag sleeve is positioned against cam follower face. Install washer and snap ring. *See Fig. 3.*

2) If removed, install wheel bearing inner adjusting nut and lock washer. Tighten outer lock nut to 150 ft. lbs. (203 N.m). Install splined spacer and "C" washer onto axle shaft.

NOTE: **Remove excess grease from hub lock and hub splines before installation.**

3) Start locking hub assembly into hub. Ensure large tangs are lined up with lock washer and outside diameter and inside diameter splines are in line with hub and axle shaft splines.

Fig. 3: Checking Position Of Brake Band & Drag Sleeve Assembly To Locking Hub Body Assembly

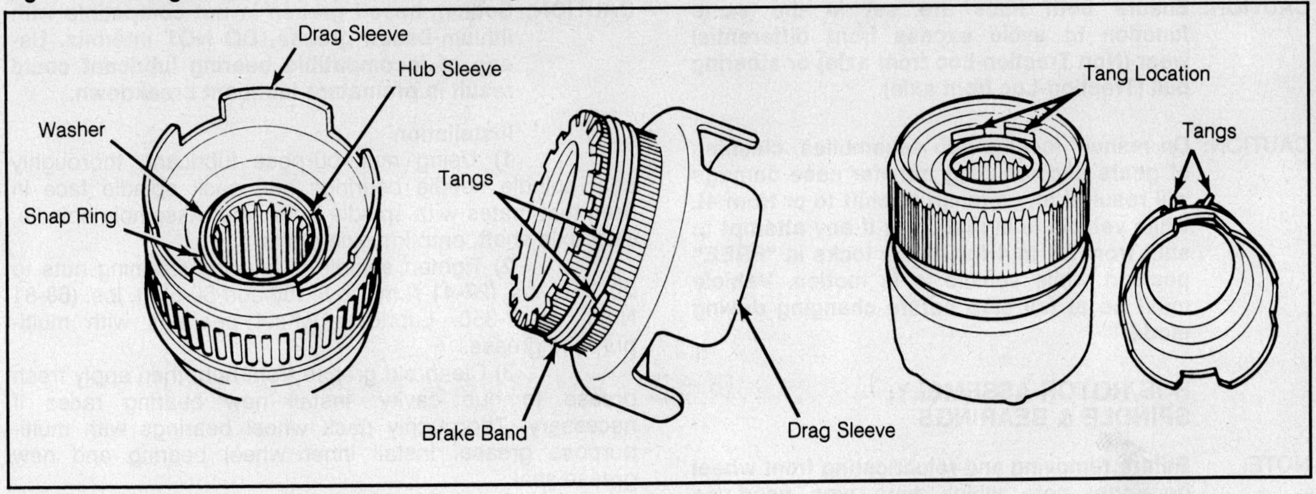

FORD LEAF SPRING – IFS 4WD TRUCKS (Cont.)

4) Install retainer ring by closing ring ends with needle-nose pliers and, at the same time, push locking hub assembly into hub. Install seal bridge retainer (narrow end first).

5) Install rubber seal over locking hub. Install locking hub cap assembly. Ensure ball bearing, race, spring and retainer are in proper position. Tighten Torx-R bit screws to 40-50 INCH lbs. (4.5-5.6 N.m) following tightening sequence (tighten 1, skip 1, etc.) until complete.

MANUAL LOCKING HUB ASSEMBLY

Removal (F-350 Models)

1) To remove locking hub, first separate locking hub cap assembly from hub body assembly by removing 6 Allen head cap screws from cap assembly, then slip components apart. Detach snap ring (retainer ring) from end of axle shaft.

2) Remove lock ring (seated in groove of wheel hub). *See Fig. 4.* Slide hub body assembly out of wheel hub. If necessary, use a puller to remove hub body assembly.

Fig. 4: Exploded View Of Warn Industries Manual Locking Hub Assembly

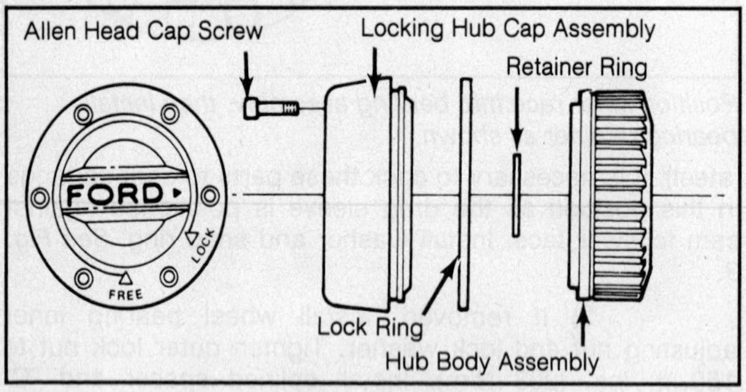

NOTE: **Do not pack grease into locking hub cap. To much grease can cause excessive dialing effort.**

Installation

To install locking hub assembly components, reverse removal procedure. Install locking hub cap assembly and tighten cap screws to 35-55 INCH lbs. (4.0-6.2 N.m).

CAUTION: **Ensure both hubs are set in the same function to avoid excess front differential wear (Non Traction-Loc front axle) or steering pull (Traction-Loc front axle).**

CAUTION: **On manual locking hub assemblies, clashing of gears and resulting transfer case damage will result if any attempt to shift to or from 4L while vehicle is in motion or if any attempt to shift from 2H to 4H with hub locks in "FREE" position while vehicle is in motion. Vehicle must be at full stop before changing driving mode.**

HUB/ROTOR ASSEMBLY, SPINDLE & BEARINGS

NOTE: **Before removing and relubricating front wheel bearings, note which type was used as original wheel bearing lubricant. The recommended wheel and spindle bearing lubricant is a lithium-based grease; Multi-Purpose Long-Life Lubricant C1AZ-19590-B (ESA-M1C75-B).**

Removal

1) Raise and support vehicle, then remove wheel and tire assembly. Remove manual or automatic locking hub assemblies. Using Front Wheel Bearing Spanner (T59T-1197-B for F-250 or D78T-1197-A for F-250 H.D. and F-350), detach wheel bearing lock nut, lock ring and adjusting nut.

2) Remove brake caliper and hang with wire away from work area. Do not hang by flexible brake hose. While remove wheel hub/rotor assembly, slide out outer wheel bearing assembly. Pry out inner wheel bearing grease seal and discard.

3) Remove inner bearing. Inspect inner and outer bearings and races. Replace any damaged or excessively worn components. Always replace bearings and races as complete assemblies only. To remove inner and/or outer bearing races from hub, use Slide Hammer (T50T-100-A) and Bearing Race Puller (T77F-1102-A).

4) Detach spindle retaining nuts, then carefully remove spindle from knuckle studs and axle shaft. See STEERING KNUCKLE. Clean any old grease from needle bearings and spindle bore seal. Inspect bearings and seal, then replace if necessary.

Spindle Needle Bearing & Grease Seal Replacement

1) To remove grease seal from top of needle bearing, place spindle in soft-jawed vise (on second step of spindle). Using Slide Hammer (D79P-100-A), Forcing Screw (D80L-100-B) and 1 1/4-1 1/2" Collet (D80L-100-T) from Blind Hole Puller Set (D80L-100-A), remove needle bearing and bearing seal from spindle bore, then discard seal.

2) Install new needle bearing (writing facing outward) in spindle bore using Driver Handle (T80T-4000-W) and Spindle Bearing Installer (T80T-4000-S for F-250 or T80T-4000-R for F-350).

3) Install new needle bearing grease seal (with seal lip directed away from spindle) using Hub Seal Installer (T80T-4000-T for F-250 or T80T-4000-U for F-350) and Driver Handle (T80T-4000-W). Tap in seal until fully seated. Pack bearing and hub seal with grease.

CAUTION: **Sodium-based grease is not compatible with lithium-based grease, DO NOT intermix. Usage of incompatible bearing lubricant could result in premature lubricant breakdown.**

Installation

1) Using multi-purpose lubricant, thoroughly coat spindle needle bearings and pack spindle face in area that mates with spindle bore seal. Assemble spindle, over axle shaft, onto knuckle studs.

2) Tighten spindle-to-knuckle retaining nuts to 20-30 ft. lbs. (27-41 N.m) on F-250 and 50-60 ft. lbs. (68-81 N.m). on F-350. Lubricate wheel bearings with multi-purpose grease.

3) Clean old grease from hub, then apply fresh grease to hub cavity. Install new bearing races if necessary. Thoroughly pack wheel bearings with multi-purpose grease. Install inner wheel bearing and new grease seal.

FORD LEAF SPRING – IFS 4WD TRUCKS (Cont.)

4) If necessary, clean rotor surface with high-flash point cleaner. Position hub/rotor assembly on spindle, then install outer bearing and adjusting nut. Adjust wheel bearings. Install lock washer, lock nut and locking hub assembly. To complete installation, reverse removal procedure.

SHOCK ABSORBERS

Removal

1) Insert wrench from rear side of upper shock bracket to hold shock absorber upper retaining nut. Loosen the stud by turning hex provided on exposed (lower) part of stud. Remove nut and washer.

2) Disconnect lower end of shock from "U" bolt spring plate spacer. Compress shock and remove from vehicle. On 1-piece shock mounting grommet, cut grommet from upper shock bracket.

Installation

1) Insert a new 1-piece rubber insulator into the top surface of shock bracket using a soap/water solution to aid in installation. Insert shock stud through insulator.

2) Install steel washer and hand tighten nut. While holding nut, turn hex to tighten nut to 25-35 ft. lbs. (34-47 N.m). Attach lower shock mount to "U" bolt plate with mounting bolt and nut, then tighten to 52-74 ft. lbs. (70-100 N.m).

LEAF SPRING ASSEMBLY

Removal

1) Raise and support vehicle, on frame hoist, until weight is off front springs (wheels must still touching floor). Support drive axle assembly (and secure if necessary) to prevent rotation.

2) Disconnect lower end of shock absorber from "U" bolt spring plate spacer. Detach "U" bolt nuts, then remove "U" bolts, "U" bolt spacer and spring plate spacer. Detach nut from leaf spring eye bolt at rear hanger bracket. Drive bolt out of hanger bracket.

3) Detach nut from spring eye bolt at front shackle. Drive out eye bolt from spring and shackle, then remove leaf spring assembly. Detach spring clip, separate spring leafs and check for broken leafs, loss of arc or other damage. Replace components as necessary.

Installation

1) Position front of leaf spring assembly in front spring shackle, then install eye bolt through spring and shackle. Tighten eye bolt nut to 120-150 ft. lbs. (163-203 N.m).

2) Position rear of spring assembly in rear bracket. Install eye bolt through spring and hanger bracket. Install eye bolt nut and tighten to 120-150 ft. lbs. (163-203 N.m).

3) Position "U" bolt spring plate spacer on top of spring assembly. Position lower spring spacer below spring assembly, then install "U" bolts in saddles on upper plate spacer and through holes in lower spring spacer. Install "U" bolt nuts finger tight.

4) Connect lower end of shock absorber to "U" bolt spring plate spacer bracket and tighten mounting bolt to specification. Lower vehicle and tighten "U" bolt nuts to 85-120 ft. lbs. (115-163 N.m). Remove axle restrains.

STEERING KNUCKLE & AXLE SHAFT ASSEMBLY

Removal

1) Detach spindle retainer nuts. If necessary, tap with soft-faced hammer to break spindle loose from knuckle. Remove spindle, brake rotor splash shield and axle shaft assembly.

2) If necessary, remove grease seal from top of spindle needle bearing. If tie rod has not been removed, detach cotter pin from stud. Loosen top ball joint stud nut

Fig. 5: Exploded View OF IFS Front Drive Axle Assembly

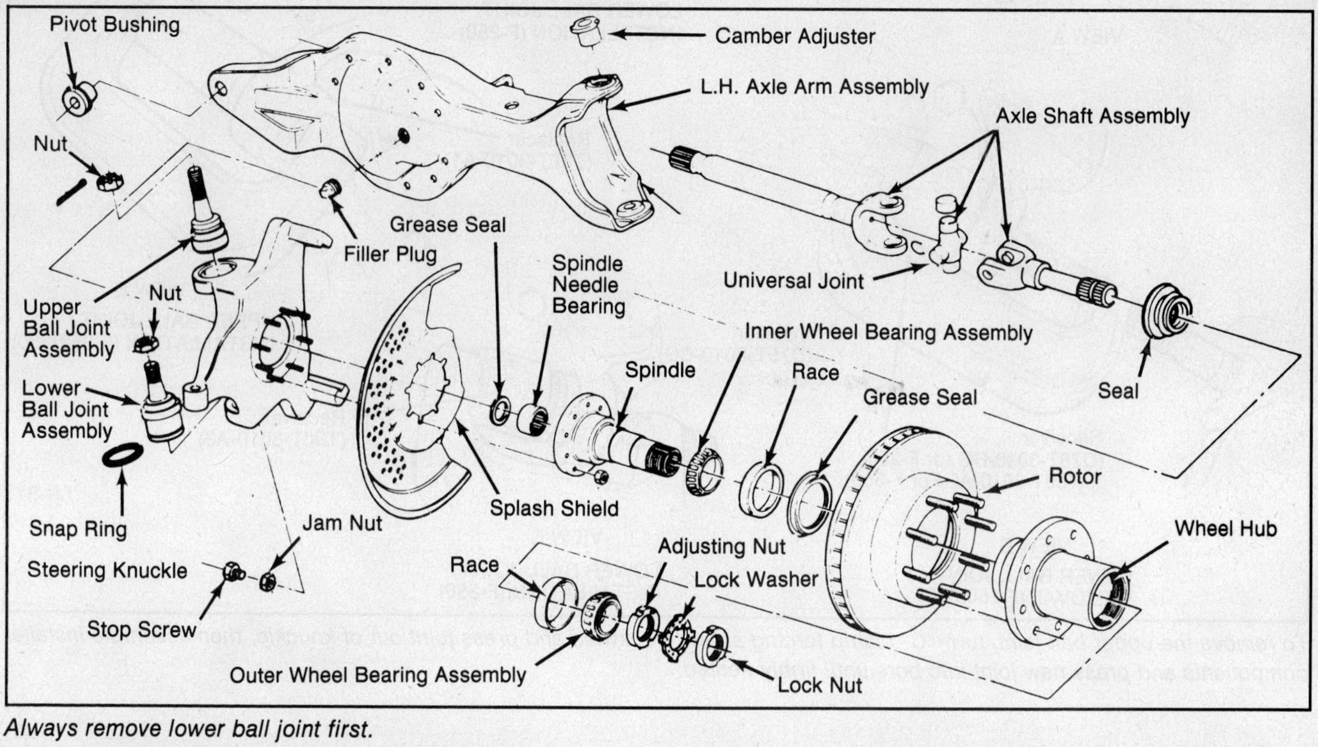

Always remove lower ball joint first.

FORD LEAF SPRING – IFS 4WD TRUCKS (Cont.)

and bottom ball joint stud nut (inside of knuckle). Remove top nut. Sharply hit top stud with soft-faced hammer to free knuckle from axle arm. Remove and discard bottom nut.

NOTE: **Check orientation of camber adjuster to ensure the same camber setting during assembly.**

3) Remove camber adjuster by hand or, if necessary, use Pitman Arm Puller (T64P-3590-F). Place knuckle in vise and remove snap ring from bottom ball joint socket (if equipped).

NOTE: **Always remove lower ball joint first.**

4) Remove plug from "C" Clamp (T74P-4635-C) and replace with Plug (T80T-3010-A4). Assembly "C' clamp and Receiver (D79T-3010-A4 for F-250 or T80T-3010-A2 for F-350) onto bottom ball joint.

5) Turn forcing screw clockwise until ball joint is removed from knuckle. Install "C" clamp and Receiver (D79P-3010-BG) on upper ball joint and turn forcing screw clockwise to remove.

Installation

1) Clean steering knuckle bore and install lower ball joint as straight as possible. On F-250 models, assemble "C" clamp, Ball Joint Receiver Cup (T80T-3010-A3) and Installer Cup (D79T-3010-BF) onto lower joint, then turn forcing screw clockwise until joint is firmly seated. Install snap ring on lower joint (if equipped).

2) On F-350 models, assemble "C" clamp, ball joint receiver cup and Installer Cup (D79T-3010-BG) onto lower joint, then turn forcing screw clockwise until joint is firmly seated. Install snap ring on lower joint (if equipped).

NOTE: **If either ball joint cannot be installed to the proper depth, realignment of Receiver Cup (T80T-3010-A3) will be necessary.**

3) Position upper ball joint in knuckle bore. To install F-250/350 upper joint, assemble "C" clamp, Receiver Cup (T80T-3010-A3) and Ball Joint Replacer (T80T-3010-A1) onto upper joint. then turn forcing screw clockwise until joint is firmly seated.

Fig. 6: Upper & Lower Ball Joint Removal & Installation

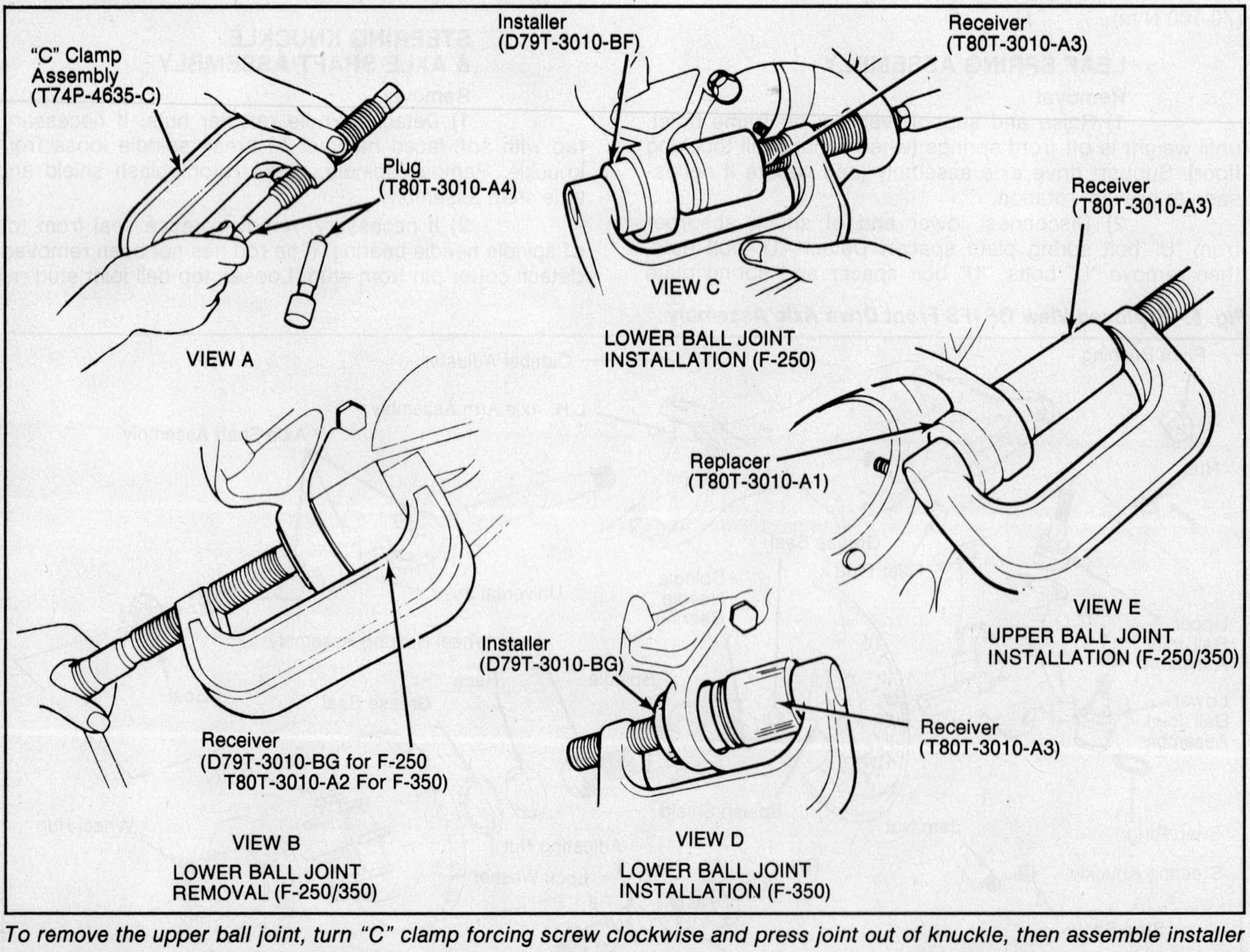

To remove the upper ball joint, turn "C" clamp forcing screw clockwise and press joint out of knuckle, then assemble installer components and press new joint into bore until firmly seated.

FORD LEAF SPRING – IFS 4WD TRUCKS (Cont.)

4) Assemble knuckle to axle arm assembly. Install camber adjuster on top ball joint stud with arrow pointing outboard for positive camber or inboard for negative camber. Install new nut on bottom stud finger tight. Install and tighten top stud nut finger tight.

5) Tighten bottom nut to 80 ft. lbs. (109 N.m). Tighten top nut to 100 ft. lbs. (136 N.m). Only tighten top nut to align cotter pin hole, do not back off. Retighten bottom nut to 90-110 ft. lbs. (123-150 N.m).

6) Install new needle bearing (writing facing outward) in spindle bore using Driver Handle (T80T-4000-W) and Spindle Bearing Installer (T80T-4000-S for F-250 or T80T-4000-R for F-350). Install new needle bearing grease seal with seal lip directed away from spindle.

7) Pack bearing and hub seal with grease. Install seal using Seal Installer (T80T-4000-T) and driver handle. Install seal on top of needle bearing. Apply light coat of grease to seal lip. Place thrust washer on axle shaft.

8) Install left hand shaft assembly into differential side gear. Install right hand shaft assembly into slip yoke, giving special attention that wide tooth space in slip yoke spline is aligned with wide tooth on axle shaft spline.

9) Lubricate splines with multi-purpose grease. Install splash shield and spindle. Install and tighten spindle retainer nuts to 50-60 ft. lbs. (68-81 N.m).

AXLE HOUSING ARM ASSEMBLY, PIVOT BRACKET & BUSHING

CAUTION: Ensure axle arms are securely supported during removal. If not, the axle arms will suddenly drop 4-6 inches when pivot bolts are removed.

Removal

1) Remove manual or automatic locking hub assembly, hub/rotor assembly, spindle, splash shield and axle shaft assembly. Place supports securely under axle housing arms, then remove pivot bolts. If necessary, pry axle housing arm out of bracket and remove from vehicle.

2) If necessary, raise engine to provide access to vertical bracket fasteners in top of crossmember by loosening right and left engine mounting bolts. Align fan blade to clear shroud and rasie engine 2 inches.

3) Ensure air cleaner does not touch firewall. Block engine securely in place. Remove and discard all axle pivot bracket-to-crossmember fasteners, then remove pivot brackets.

4) Install Forcing Screw (T78P-5638-A1), Pivot Bushing Remover (T80T-5638-A1) and Receiver Cup (T78P-5638-A3) onto pivot bushing. Turn forcing screw and remove pivot bushing.

Installation

1) Place new pivot bushing in axle housing bore. Install Receiver Cup (T78P-5638-A2), forcing screw and Pivot Bushing Replacer (T80T-5638-A2) onto axle housing. Turn forcing screw to press bushing into bore.

2) Position axle pivot bracket to crossmember and loosenly install bolts, bolts/retainer assembly and nuts. Do not tighten at this time. Ensure new vertical fasteners for each pivot bracket are installed with bolt heads adjacent to engine oil pan to maintain required clearance.

3) New horizontal fasteners must be installed with bolt heads on inside surface of pivot brackets. To ensure correct positioning of axle pivot brackets, first tighten horizontal fasteners in side of crossmember to 110 ft. lbs. (149 N.m).

4) Tighten vertical fasteners in top of crossmember to 110 ft. lbs. (149 N.m). Position axle housing in pivot brackets. Install pivot bolt and tighten nut to 150 ft. lbs. (200 N.m). Remove blocks supporting engine and lower engine into position. Install and tighten mount bolts. To complete installation, reverse removal procedure.

STABILIZER BAR

Removal

1) Raise and support vehicle. Detach bolts, washers and nuts securing links to spring seat caps on both sides. Remove nuts, washers and rubber insulator grommets connecting links to stabilizer bar. Remove link assemblies.

Fig. 7: Removing & Installing Axle Housing Pivot Bushing

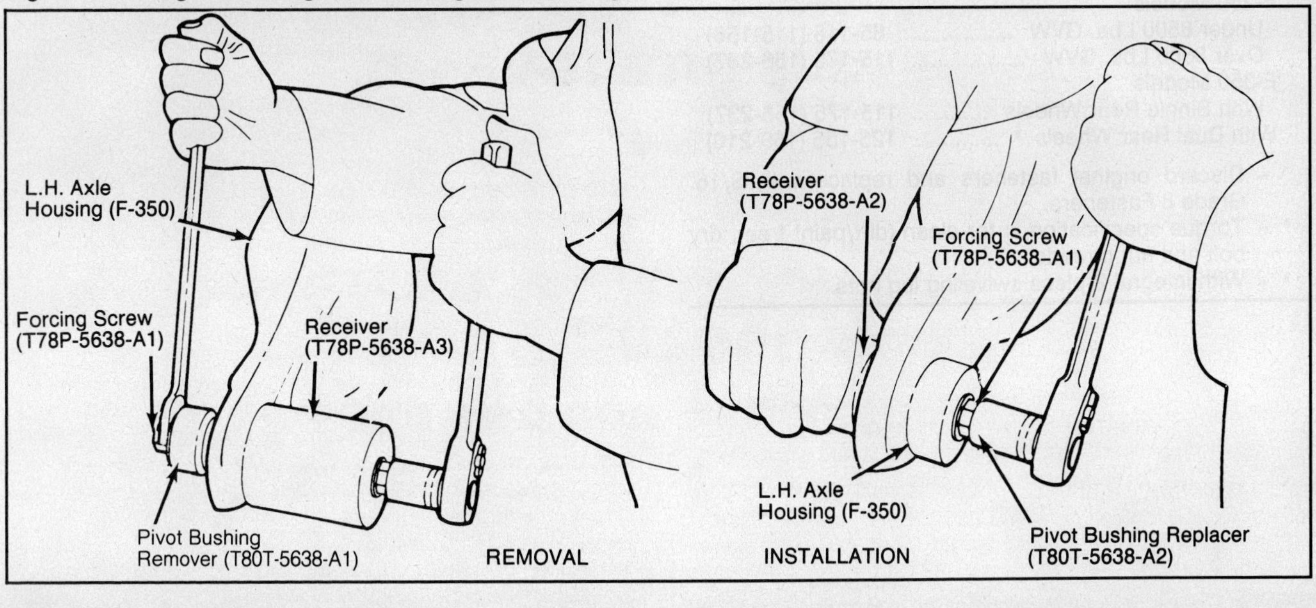

FORD LEAF SPRING – IFS 4WD TRUCKS (Cont.)

2) Detach nuts and bolts securing stabilizer bar retainer brackets to mounting bracket and remove retainers. Remove stabilizer bar.

3) If necessary, detach stabilizer bar mount bracket mounting bolts and nuts, then remove bracket from frame rails. Inspect insulator bushings, grommets and bar for excessive wear or damage. Replace components as needed.

Installation

1) Apply rubber grease to insulator area of bar, then install new insulators onto bar (if split-type insulator, ensure slit is toward front). To install stabilizer bar and components, replace components in reverse of removal procedure (without tightening bolts).

2) Tighten nuts connecting stabilizer bar links to spring seat caps, on both sides, to 48-65 ft. lbs. (65-88 N.m). Tighten nuts connecting links to stabilizer bar to 15-25 ft. lbs. (21-33 N.m). Tighten nuts and bolts connecting retainers to mounting bracket to 25-35 ft. lbs. (34-48 N.m). Lower vehicle.

TIGHTENING SPECIFICATIONS

Application	Ft. Lbs. (N.m)
Axle Pivot Bracket-To-Frame [1]	125-130 (170-180)
Front Leaf Spring Assembly	
To-Axle "U" Bolt	85-120 (115-163)
To-Hanger Bracket	120-150 (163-203)
Shackle-To-Shackle Bracket	150-210 (203-285)
To-Shackle	120-150 (163-203)
Front Jounce Bumper	
To-Bumper Bracket	19-30 (26-41)
Bumper Bracket-To-Frame	48-65 (65-88)
Front Shock Absorber	
Bracket-To-Frame	48-65 (65-88)
Upper Stud Nut	25-35 (34-47)
"U" Bolt Spacer	15-25 (21-33)
Stabilizer Bar	
Link-To-Bar Nut	15-25 (21-33)
Link-To-Spring Seat Cap Bolt/Nut	48-65 ()65-88
Retainer Bracket	
To-Mount Bracket Bolt/Nut	27-37 (37-50)
Mount Bracket-To-Frame Rail Bolt/Nut	27-37 (37-50)
Wheel Lug Bolt (8 Lug Wheel) [2]	
F-250 Models	
Under 8500 Lbs. GVW	85-115 (115-156)
Over 8500 Lbs. GVW	115-175 (156-237)
F-350 Models	
With Single Rear Wheels	115-175 (156-237)
With Dual Rear Wheels [2]	125-155 (169-210)

[1] – Discard original fasteners and replace with 9/16" Grade 8 Fasteners.

[2] – Torque specification is for clean (dirt/paint free), dry bolt and nut threads.

[2] – With integral 2-piece swiveling lug nuts.

GENERAL MOTORS COIL SPRING
ASTRO, SAFARI & "S" SERIES TRUCKS

DESCRIPTION

Independent front suspension consists of upper and lower control arms with steering knuckle mounted by ball joints. The upper control arms are mounted with pivot shafts, through rubber bushings. The lower control arms have pressed-in bushings and are mounted by bolts which thread through the frame. Coil springs are mounted between lower control arm and a formed seat in suspension crossmember. Hydraulic fluid filled (or gas-charged) shock absorbers fit inside coil spring, between lower control arm and upper control arm frame bracket. A stabilizer bar is bracket mounted to frame side rails and connected to lower control arms by link bolts.

ADJUSTMENTS & CHECKING

WHEEL ALIGNMENT SPECIFICATIONS & PROCEDURES

See WHEEL ALIGNMENT SPECIFICATIONS & PROCEDURES in WHEEL ALIGNMENT section.

Fig. 1: Exploded View of Front Suspension Assembly

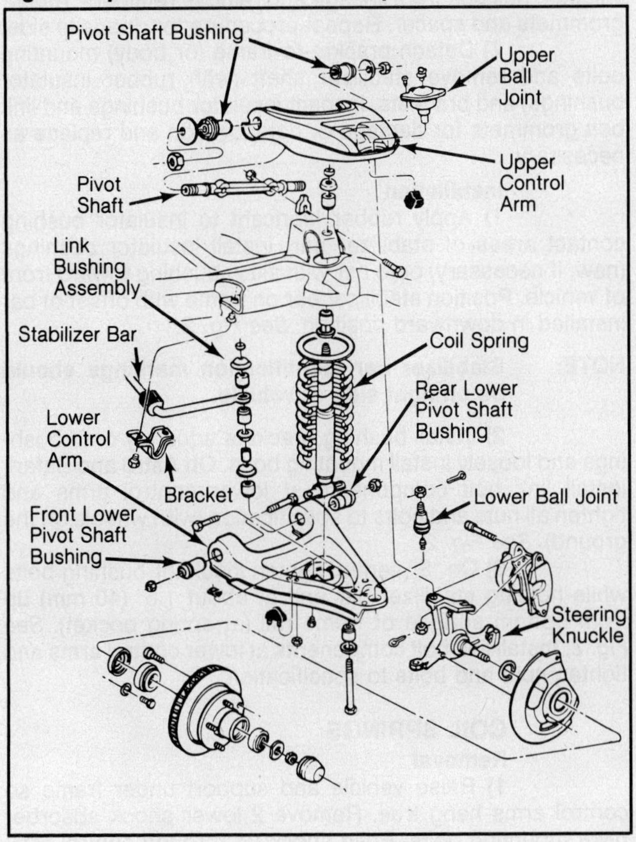

WHEEL BEARING ADJUSTMENT

CAUTION: Never preload tapered roller bearings or damage to roller ends will result. Bearings are designed to have a slightly loose feel when properly adjusted.

1) Raise and support vehicle. Remove wheel cover, then spin wheel by hand to check bearings for excessive tightness, looseness, noise or roughness.

2) To check for tight or loose bearings, grip wheel assembly at top and bottom. Move assembly in and out while measuring hub movement. If movement is less than .0010" (.025 mm) or more than .0050" (.127 mm), adjust bearings.

NOTE: Bearings should be cleaned, inspected, replaced (if necessary) and lubricated before adjustment.

3) With hub dust cap and cotter pin removed, tighten spindle bearing nut to 12 ft. lbs. (16 N.m) while turning wheel forward by hand. Back off nut until it is just loose.

4) Hand-tighten nut until snug, then loosen slightly (no more than 1/2 a flat) until new cotter pin can be inserted. Hub play (in and out) should be .0010-.0050" (.025-.127 mm) when properly adjusted. Install dust cap and wheel cover.

BALL JOINT CHECKING

NOTE: Ensure wheel bearings are adjusted before checking ball joints for excessive wear. If ball joint rubber grease seal is cut or damaged, it must be replaced.

Upper Ball Joint

1) Upper ball joint is internally spring-loaded and riveted to upper control arm. Raise vehicle and support with jack stands under lower control arms, as close as possible to each lower ball joint.

2) Ensure upper control arm bumper does not contact frame. Place dial indicator against lower part of wheel rim, then push in on bottom of tire while pulling out at the top. Read gauge, then reverse push/pull procedure.

3) Lateral (horizontal) deflection should not exceed .125" (3.18 mm). If dial indicator reading is excessive, continue inspection by disconnecting ball joint from knuckle and check for any looseness. Attempt to twist stud with fingers. If any of these conditions exist, replace ball joint.

Lower Ball Joint

1) Lower ball joint is a press fit into the control arm. A wear indicator is built into the ball joint and wear inspection is done by visual observation only.

2) Wear is indicated by the position of the 1/2" (12.7 mm) diameter round boss that the grease fitting is threaded into. A new ball joint has a boss projection of .050" (1.27 mm) beyond cover surface.

3) With vehicle weight on wheels, check to see that wear indicator protrudes beyond surface of ball joint cover. If wear indicator is flush or recessed, replace ball joint.

REMOVAL & INSTALLATION

WHEEL BEARINGS

Removal

1) Detach brake caliper mounting bolts and wire caliper aside, out of work area. Do not hang by flexible hose. Detach hub dust cap. Remove cotter pin, retainer nut and washer from steering knuckle spindle, then pull hub and rotor assembly from spindle.

CAUTION: Use care not to drop outer wheel bearing during hub and rotor assembly removal.

GENERAL MOTORS COIL SPRING ASTRO, SAFARI & "S" SERIES TRUCKS (Cont.)

2) Remove outer wheel bearing. Pry out inner bearing grease seal and discard. Remove inner bearing. Inspect bearings for damage or excessive wear and replace as needed. If necessary, drive out bearing outer races using hammer and Wheel Bearing Race Remover (J-29117).

Inspection

Wash wheel bearings and hub in solvent and blow dry with compressed air. Do not spin bearings with air or damage can result. Check bearings for cracked cages and worn or pitted rollers. Inspect bearing outer races for cracks, scores, looseness in hub or a brinelled condition.

Installation

1) If bearing races were removed, drive inner bearing race into position using hammer, Driver Handle (J-8092) and Front Hub Bearing Race Installer (J-8850). Use hammer, driver handle and Front Hub Bearing Race Installer (J-8457), install inner bearing race.

2) Using an approved high temperature wheel bearing grease, lubricate each bearing assembly thoroughly. Apply grease to spindle, hub cavity and outer races. Install inner bearing into hub. Using a flat plate, drive in new grease seal until seal is flush with hub.

3) Lubricate seal lip with thin film of grease, then carefully install hub and rotor assembly onto spindle. Install outer bearing, washer and nut, then initially tighten nut to 12 ft. lbs. (16 N.m) while turning hub assembly by hand. Complete installation by reversing removal procedure. Check and final adjust bearings as necessary.

SHOCK ABSORBERS

Removal

1) Raise and support vehicle. Using an open end wrench, hold upper stem from turning while detaching upper stem retaining nut, retainer and rubber grommet at top of shock absorber.

2) Remove 2 bolts retaining lower shock absorber pivot to lower control arm. Pull shock absorber down and out from bottom, then remove from vehicle.

NOTE: **Two types of shock absorber are available as standard equipment, a hydraulic fluid filled (spiral-groove reservoir) standard unit and a gas-charged (smooth-body reservoir) "Firm Ride" shock.**

CAUTION: **Hydraulic fluid filled shock will develop an air void if not kept in a vertical position (top end up). Faulty diagnosis can result if air is not purged from unit.**

Inspection

1) On hydraulic fluid filled shock, purge air from pressure chamber by mounting in vise (top end up) and fully extending unit. Reverse position (top end down) and fully collapse unit. Repeat procedure several times.

2) Bench check shock unit by mounting in vise with top end up (top end down on gas-charged shocks). Do not clamp on reservoir tube or mounting threads. Check rubber grommets for damage or deterioration and replace as needed. Stroke shock by hand at various rates of speed and note resistance.

3) Rebound (up) resistance is normally stronger than compression (down) by about 2:1. Ensure resistance is smooth and constant for each stroking rate. It is normal to detect a hissing noise (orifice swish).

4) Check shock for a skip or lag near mid-stroke, a sieze (except at extreme end of travel), a noise (squeal or grunt) after completing 1 full stroke in both directions, a clicking noise at fast reversal or fluid leakage. Replace shock if any of these conditions exist.

5) Check gas-charged "Firm Ride" shocks in the same manner as hydraulic fluid filled type by following steps **2)** through **4)**. Also note that if a lag is noticed when shock is stroked, the gas-filled cell has ruptured and the shock must be replaced.

Installation

1) With lower retainer and rubber grommet in place, position shock absorber (with shaft extended) through lower control arm and into mounting hole in upper control arm frame bracket.

2) Install upper grommet and retainer, then hold shaft and tighten upper nut. Install bolts connecting lower shock pivot to control arm and tighten to specification. Lower vehicle.

STABILIZER BAR

Removal

1) Raise and support vehicle. Detach nut from link bolt, pull bolt from linkage and remove retainers, rubber grommets and spacer. Repeat procedure for opposite side.

2) Detach bracket-to-frame (or body) mounting bolts and remove stabilizer shaft (with rubber insulator bushings) and brackets. Inspect insulator bushings and link bolt grommets for damage or deterioration and replace as necessary.

Installation

1) Apply rubber lubricant to insulator bushing contact areas of stabilizer bar. Install insulator bushings (new, if necessary) onto bar with slit in bushing toward front of vehicle. Position stabilizer bar on frame with offset of bar installed in downward position. *See Fig. 2.*

NOTE: **Stabilizer bar identification markings should be on right side of vehicle.**

2) Install bushing brackets squarely onto bushings and loosely install mounting bolts. On Astro and Safari, install link bolt components at lower control arms and tighten all nuts and bolts to specification (with wheels on the ground). *See Fig. 2.*

3) On "S" series, tighten insulator bushing bolts while holding stabilizer bar end at about 1.6" (40 mm) up from bottom surface of frame rail (at spring pocket). *See Fig. 2.* Install link bolt components at lower control arms and tighten nuts and bolts to specification.

COIL SPRINGS

Removal

1) Raise vehicle and support under frame so control arms hang free. Remove 2 lower shock absorber pivot mounting bolts. Push shock up through control arm, into coil spring.

2) Securely install Front Coil Spring Compressor (J-23028-01) onto an adjustable jack stand. Place compressor tool into position cradling lower control arm inner bushings.

3) Remove stabilizer bar-to-lower control arm link bolt components. Raise jack to remove tension on lower control arm pivot bolts. Install a safety chain around spring and through lower control arm.

GENERAL MOTORS COIL SPRING ASTRO, SAFARI & "S" SERIES TRUCKS (Cont.)

Fig. 2: Installing Stabilizer Bar Brackets & Link Bolt Components

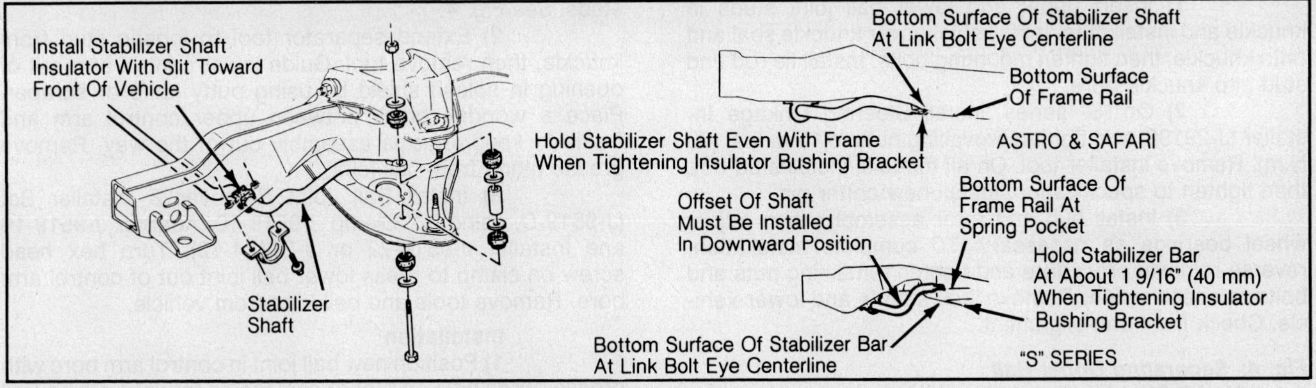

Ensure stabilizer bar insulator bracket mounting bolts are tighten with bar in proper position (depending on model).

4) Detach lower control arm mounting bolts (rear bolt first). Carefully lower jack until all tension is released from coil spring, then remove safety chain. Remove spring from vehicle.

NOTE: **Do not apply force on lower control arm and ball joint to remove spring. Proper maneuvering of the spring will allow for easy removal.**

Installation

1) Position spring on control arm making sure that spring insulator is in place. Lift control arm with compressor tool and jack stand. Ensure spring is properly positioned.

NOTE: **Coil spring must be positioned with tape at lowest position. Bottom of spring is coiled helical and the top is coiled flat with a gripper notch near end of spring coil.**

2) Position lower control arm in frame and install pivot bolts (front bolt first). In order to maintain steering linkage clearance, install pivot bolts with nuts toward the rear of vehicle. *See Fig. 10*. Complete installation by reversing remove procedure, then tighten all nuts and bolts to specification.

STEERING KNUCKLE

Removal

1) Raise and support vehicle with jack stands, at front lift points. Remove wheel and tire assembly. Detach brake caliper mounting bolts, then remove caliper and hang out of work area with wire. Do not hang by flexible brake hose.

NOTE: **Spring tension is needed to assist in breaking ball joint studs loose from steering knuckle. Do not place stands under lower control arm at this time.**

2) Remove hub and rotor assembly. Detach 3 splash shield-to-knuckle mounting bolts, then remove splash shield. Separate tie rod end stud from steering knuckle using Tie Rod Remover (J-6627).

3) Carefully remove knuckle grease seal if knuckle will be replaced. Using Ball Joint Separator (J-23742), separate ball joint studs from knuckle. Position floor jack under lower control arm, near spring seat. Raise jack until lower control arm is just supported.

CAUTION: **Floor jack must remain under control arm spring seat during removal and installation to retain spring and control arm in position.**

4) Raise upper control arm to disengage ball joint stud from knuckle. Raise knuckle from lower ball joint stud and remove from vehicle. Clean knuckle thoroughly. Inspect steering knuckle for damage and/or deformation.

Inspection

With ball joints and tie rod end detached, clean all dirt from steering knuckle. Inspect tapered holes in knuckle for out-of-round, deformation or damage. Replace steering knuckle if any of these conditions exist.

Fig. 3: Positioning Coil Spring For Installation

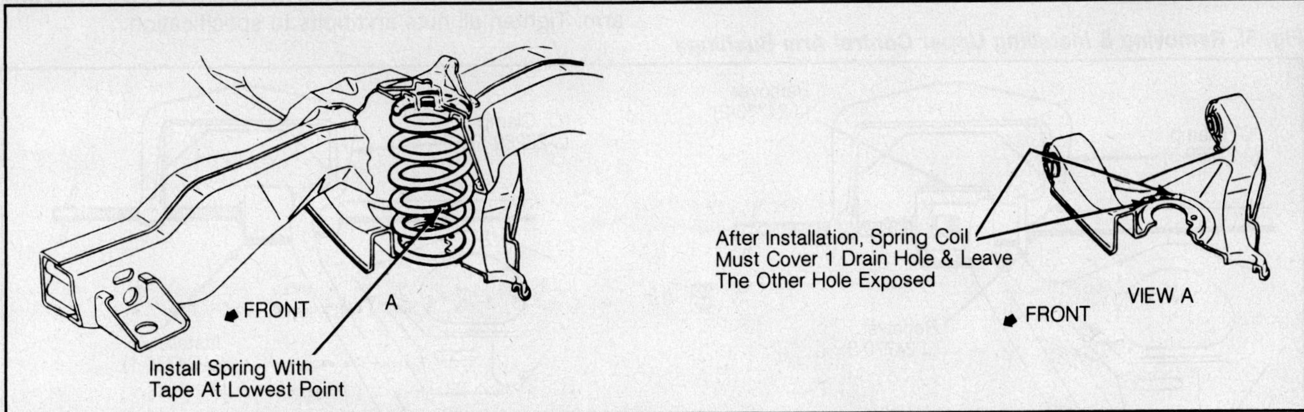

End of lower spring coil must cover all or part of one drain hole in control arm, leaving the other open.

GENERAL MOTORS COIL SPRING ASTRO, SAFARI & "S" SERIES TRUCKS (Cont.)

Installation

1) Insert upper and lower ball joint studs in knuckle and install nuts. Install shield over knuckle seal and onto knuckle, then tighten mounting bolts. Install tie rod end stud into knuckle bore.

2) On "S" series, install Steering Linkage Installer (J-29193) and tighten prevailing nuts to 15 ft. lbs. (20 N.m). Remove installer tool. On all models, install stud nut, then tighten to specification. Install new cotter pin.

3) Install hub and rotor assembly, then adjust wheel bearings as necessary. To complete installation, reverse removal procedure and tighten remaining nuts and bolts to specification. Remove jack stands and lower vehicle. Check front end alignment.

Fig. 4: Separating Upper Ball Joint Stud & Steering Knuckle

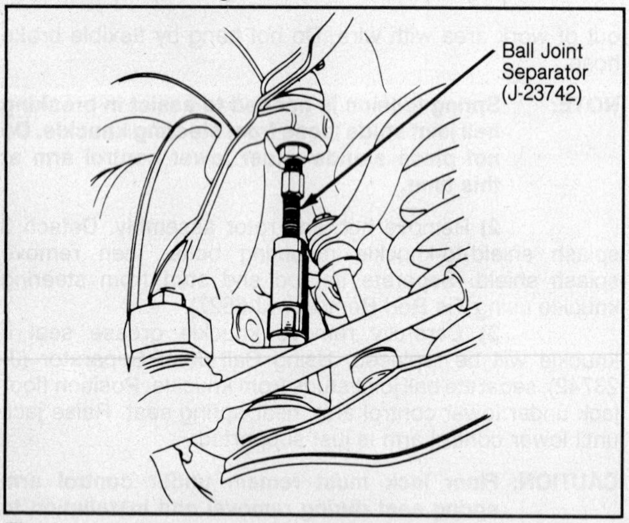

The lower ball joint is detached from knuckle using the same separator tool (mounted in the opposite position).

LOWER BALL JOINT

CAUTION: Floor jack must remain under control arm spring seat during removal and installation to retain spring and control arm in position.

Removal

1) Raise and support vehicle with safety stands positioned under frame. Place adjustable jack stand under lower control arm spring seat. Remove tire and wheel assembly. Remove lower ball joint stud cotter pin and stud nut. Position Ball Joint Separator (J-23742) between the ball studs. *See Fig. 4*.

2) Extend separator tool to loosen stud from knuckle, then remove tool. Guide lower control arm out of opening in splash shield by using putty knife or scraper. Place a wooden block between upper control arm and frame to keep knuckle assembly out of the way. Remove grease fitting from ball joint.

3) Install Ball Joint Remover & Installer Set (J-9519-D, using "C" Clamp J-9519-10, Adapter J-9519-16 and Installer J-9519-22 or J-21474-13). Turn hex head screw on clamp to press lower ball joint out of control arm bore. Remove tools and ball joint from vehicle.

Installation

1) Position new ball joint in control arm bore with grease purge hole on rubber seal facing forward. Using Ball Joint Remover & Installer Set (J-9519-D, using "C" Clamp J-9519-10 and Installer J-9519-9), press joint into bore until it bottoms on control arm. Remove installer tools.

2) Reverse removal procedure to complete installation. Tighten all bolts and nuts to specification. Lubricate ball joint fitting until grease appears at seal purge hole.

3) Check and adjust front alignment as necessary. See WHEEL ALIGNMENT SPECIFICATIONS & PROCEDURES in WHEEL ALIGNMENT section.

UPPER BALL JOINT

Removal

1) Raise and support front of vehicle with jack stands positioned under lower control arms, between spring seat and ball joint. Jacks must remain under lower control arm to retain spring and control arm in position.

NOTE: Since vehicle weight is used to relieve spring tension on upper control arm, jack stand must be positioned between spring seat and ball joint for maximum leverage.

2) Remove wheel and tire assembly. Remove cotter pin and upper ball joint stud nut. Install Ball Joint Separator (J-23742) between the ball studs. Extend separator tool to loosen ball stud from knuckle. *See Fig. 4*.

3) Remove separator tool and pull stud free from knuckle. Support knuckle assembly to prevent weight of assembly from damaging brake line. With control arm in raised position, drill off 4 rivet heads. Using a hammer and small punch, drive out rivets and remove ball joint assembly.

Installation

1) To install, reverse removal procedure. Use nuts and bolts in place of rivets to attach ball joint to control arm. Tighten all nuts and bolts to specification.

Fig. 5: Removing & Installing Upper Control Arm Bushings

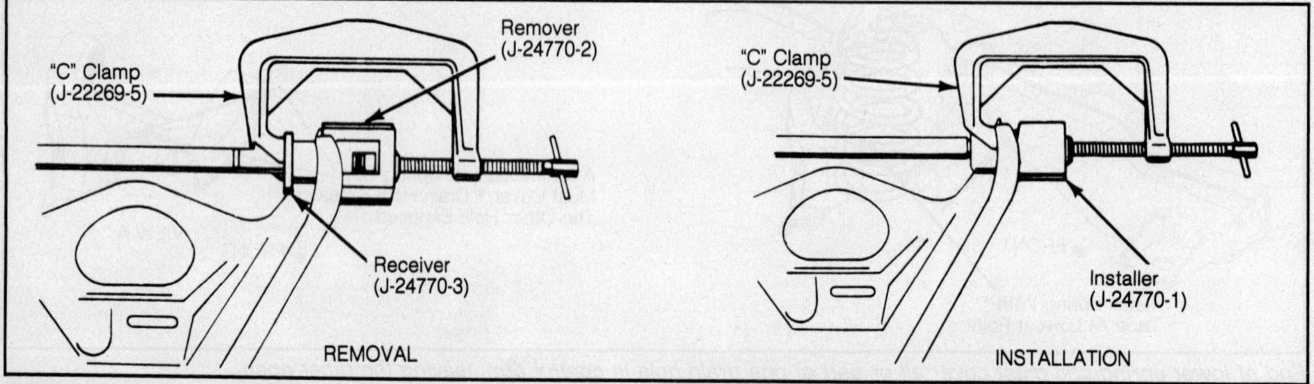

Position control arm and bushing remover tools as shown, then press each bushing out of control arm bore.

GENERAL MOTORS COIL SPRING ASTRO, SAFARI & "S" SERIES TRUCKS (Cont.)

2) Lubricate new ball joint with proper chassis grease. Check wheel bearing adjustment. Adjust front end alignment as necessary. See WHEEL ALIGNMENT SPECIFICATIONS & PROCEDURES in WHEEL ALIGNMENT section.

UPPER CONTROL ARM & PIVOT SHAFT BUSHINGS

Removal

1) Note location of alignment shims for reinstallation. Remove control arm mounting nuts and shims. Raise and support front end of vehicle under lower control arms, between spring seats and ball joints.

2) Remove wheel. Loosen, then remove upper ball joint from steering knuckle. Support rotor and hub assembly to prevent weight from damaging brake hose. It is necessary to remove upper control arm mounting bolts for clearance. Remove upper control arm.

Pivot Shaft Bushing Replacement

1) With upper control arm assembly removed from vehicle, remove nuts from ends of pivot shaft. Position control arm assembly and Upper Control Arm Bushing Service Set (which must include Remover J-24770-2, Receiver J-24770-3, Installer J-24770-1 and "C" Clamp J-22269-5) in vise. *See Fig. 5.*

Fig. 7: Positioning Upper Control Arm Bushing

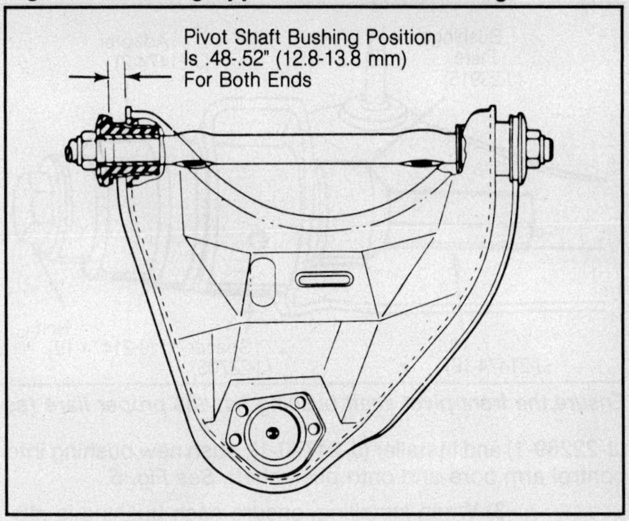

2) Press bushing out of control arm bore, then repeat procedure for opposite side bushing. To install bushings, place pivot shaft in control arm. Using "C" Clamp

Fig. 6: Removing & Installing Lower Control Arm Front Pivot Shaft Bushings

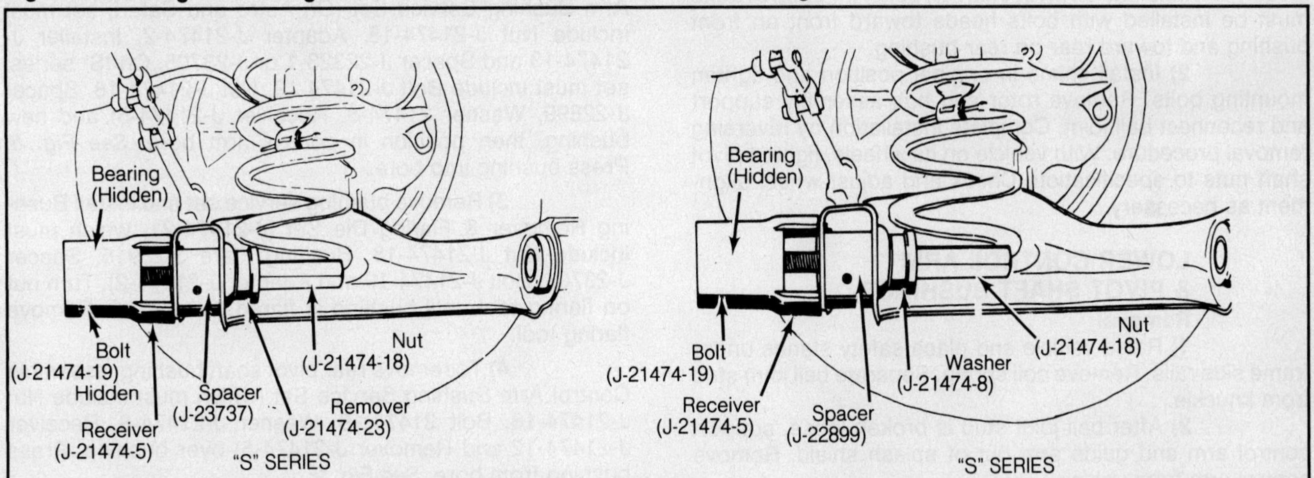

Depending on vehicle, ensure proper bushing remover set components are used to press out front bushing or damage to control arm can result.

GENERAL MOTORS COIL SPRING
ASTRO, SAFARI & "S" SERIES TRUCKS (Cont.)

Fig. 8: Flaring Front Pivot Shaft Bushing

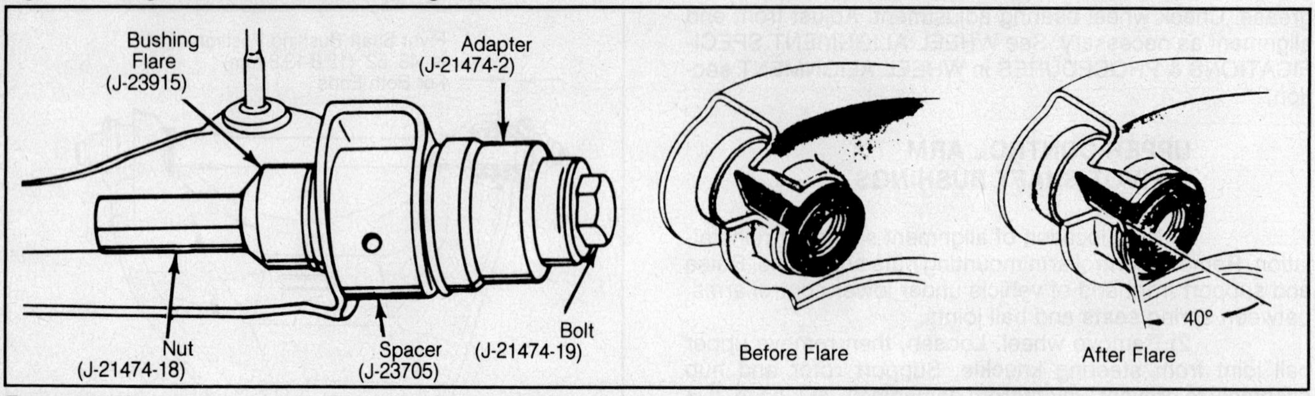

Ensure the front pivot shaft bushing has the proper flare (as shown) after flaring operation is performed.

(J-22269-1) and Installer (J-24770-1), push new bushing into control arm bore and onto pivot shaft. *See Fig. 5*.

3) When installing, ensure each bushing is .48-.52" (12.8-13.8 mm) from face of control arm to bushing outer sleeve. *See Fig. 7*. Repeat procedure of opposite side bushing. Install nuts onto pivot shaft ends, then install control arm assembly on vehicle.

Installation

1) To install, position upper control arm bolts loosely in frame. Install pivot shaft on bolts. Inner pivot bolts must be installed with bolts heads toward front on front bushing and toward rear on rear bushing.

2) Install shims in original position and tighten mounting bolts. Remove rotor and hub assembly support and reconnect ball joint. Complete installation by reversing removal procedure. With vehicle on its wheels, tighten pivot shaft nuts to specification. Check and adjust wheel alignment as necessary.

LOWER CONTROL ARM & PIVOT SHAFT BUSHINGS

Removal

1) Raise vehicle and place safety stands under frame side rails. Remove coil spring. Separate ball joint stud from knuckle.

2) After ball joint stud is broken loose, support control arm and guide arm out of splash shield. Remove control arm from vehicle.

Pivot Shaft Bushing Replacement

1) Using a blunt chisel, drive front bushing flare down flush with rubber of bushing. Install Control Arm Bushing Service Set (On Astro and Safari, set must include Receiver J-21474-5, Washer J-21474-8, Bolt J-21474-19 and Spacer J-22323-1 or J-23705. On "S" series, set must include Bolt J-21474-19, Receiver J-21474-5, Spacer J-23737, Remover J-21474-23 and Nut J-21474-18). Press out front bushing. *See Fig. 6*.

2) To install front bushing, assemble Control Arm Bushing Service Set (On Astro and Safari, set must include Nut J-21474-18, Adapter J-21474-2, Installer J-21474-13 and Spacer J-22323-1 or J-23705. On "S" series, set must include Bolt J-21474-19, Nut J-21474-18, Spacer J-22899, Washer 21474-8, Receiver J-21474-5) and new bushing, then position in control arm bore. *See Fig. 6*. Press bushing into bore.

3) Remove bushing service set and install Bushing Remover & Flaring Die Set (J-21474-21, which must include Nut J-21474-18, Bushing Flare J-23915, Spacer J-23705, Bolt J-21474-19 and Adapter J-21474-2). Turn nut on flaring tool until bushing is flared. *See Fig. 8*. Remove flaring tool.

4) To remove rear pivot shaft bushing, assemble Control Arm Bushing Service Set (which must include Nut J-21474-18, Bolt 21474-19, Washer J-21474-8, Receiver J-21474-12 and Remover J-21474-5) over bushing. Press bushing from bore. *See Fig. 9*.

Fig. 9: Removing & Installing Lower Control Arm Rear Pivot Shaft Bushing

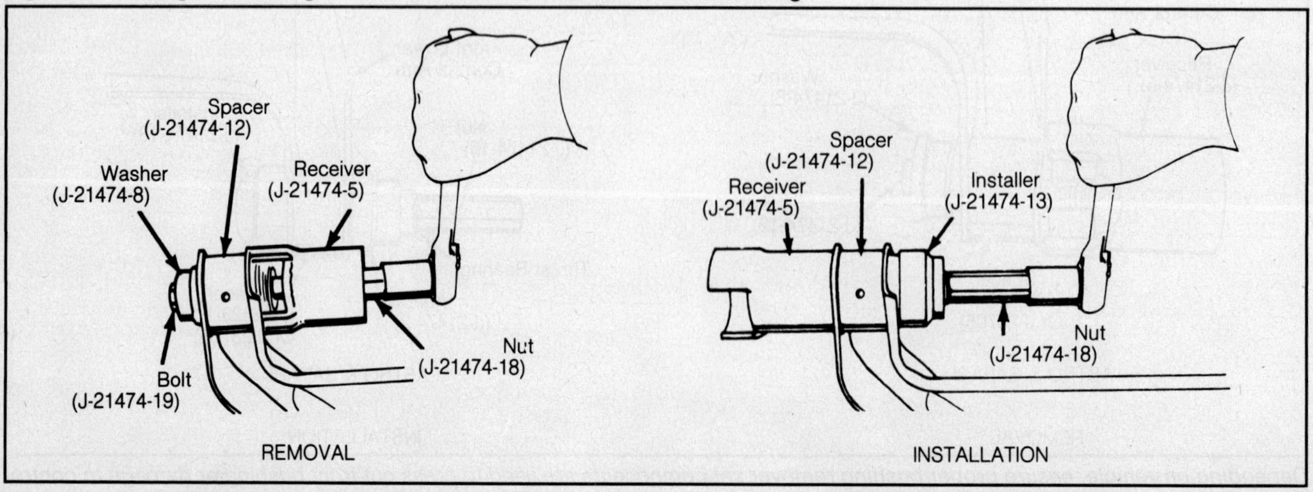

GENERAL MOTORS COIL SPRING ASTRO, SAFARI & "S" SERIES TRUCKS (Cont.)

5) Assemble Control Arm Bushing Service Set (which must include Nut J-21474-18, Installer J-21474-13, Spacer J-21474-12 and Receiver J-21474-5) over new bushing positioned in bore. *See Fig. 9.* Press bushing into position until bottomed against control arm.

Installation

1) To install, reverse removal procedure. Ensure front leg of lower control arm is installed into crossmember before installing rear leg. *See Fig. 10.*

2) Tighten lower control arm pivot bushing nuts with weight of vehicle on the wheels. Tighten all remaining nuts and bolts to specification. Check wheel alignment and adjust as necessary.

Fig. 10: Lower Control Arm Pivot Bolt Installation

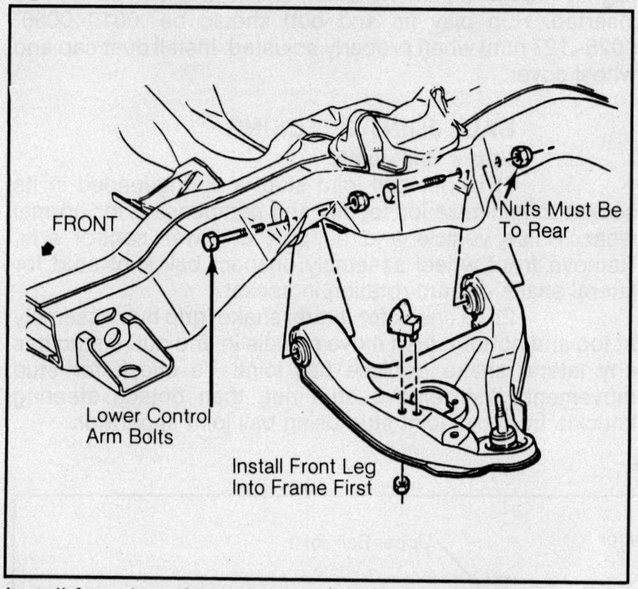

Install front leg of lower control arm into crossmember before installing rear leg into frame bracket.

TIGHTENING SPECIFICATIONS

Application	Ft. Lbs. (N.m)
Brake Rotor Splash Shield Mounting Bolt	10 (14)
Lower Ball Joint Stud Nut	90 (120)
Lower Control Arm	
To-Frame Pivot Bolt & /Nut	
Astro & Safari [1]	96 (130)
"S" Series [1]	65 (90)
Bumper Mounting Bolt	
Astro & Safari	22 (30)
"S" Series	20 (27)
Shock Absorber	
To-Lower Control Arm Mounting Bolt	
Astro & Safari	18 (25)
"S" Series	20 (27)
Upper Mounting Nut	
Astro & Safari	15 (20)
"S" Series	8 (11)
Stabilizer Bar	
Insulator Bracket-To-Frame Mounting Bolt	
Astro & Safari [2]	22 (30)
"S" Series [3]	24 (33)
Link Mounting Bolt/Nut	13 (18)
Tie Rod End Stud Nut	
Astro & Safari	33 (45)
"S" Series	40 (54)
Upper Ball Joint	
Stud Nut	
Astro & Safari	52 (70)
"S" Series	65 (90)
To-Control Arm Mounting Bolt/Nut	
Astro & Safari	[4]
"S" Series	8 (11)
Upper Control Arm	
To-Frame Mounting Bolt/Nut	
Astro & Safari	65 (90)
"S" Series	45 (60)
Pivot Mounting Nuts	85 (115)
Wheel Lug Nut	90 (120)

[1] – Tighten pivot bolts and nuts with weight of vehicle on its wheels.

[2] – Tighten mounting bolts with bottom surface of stabilizer bar end (at eye centerline) even with bottom surface of frame rail and weight of vehicle on its wheels.

[3] – Tighten mounting bolts with bottom surface of stabilizer bar end (at eye centerline) at 1.6" (40 mm) up from bottom of frame rail (at spring pocket) and vehicle weight on suspension.

[4] – Tighten service ball joint-to-upper control arm mounting bolts and nuts to specification listed in manufacturers instructions.

GENERAL MOTORS COIL SPRING EXCEPT ASTRO, SAFARI & "S" SERIES TRUCKS

DESCRIPTION

Independent front suspension consists of upper and lower control arms with steering knuckle mounted in between by ball joints. Control arms mount on inner pivot shafts by either rubber or threaded steel bushings. Coil springs are mounted between lower control arm and a formed seat in suspension crossmember. Some models have front suspension equipped with urethane air cylinders inside the coil springs.

Hydraulic or gas-charged shock absorbers fit between lower control arm and frame. A stabilizer bar is mounted to frame side rails and is connected to lower control arms by links.

ADJUSTMENTS & CHECKING

WHEEL ALIGNMENT SPECIFICATIONS & PROCEDURES

See WHEEL ALIGNMENT SPECIFICATIONS & PROCEDURES in WHEEL ALIGNMENT section.

WHEEL BEARING ADJUSTMENT

CAUTION: Never preload tapered roller bearings or damage to roller ends will result. Bearings are designed to have a slightly loose feel when properly adjusted.

1) Raise and support vehicle. Remove wheel cover, then spin wheel by hand to check bearings for excessive tightness, looseness, noise or roughness.

2) To check for tight or loose bearings, grip wheel assembly at top and bottom. Move assembly in and out while measuring hub movement. If movement is less than .0010" (.025 mm) or more than .0050" (.127 mm), adjust bearings.

NOTE: Bearings should be cleaned, inspected, replaced (if necessary) and lubricated before adjustment.

3) With hub dust cap and cotter pin removed, tighten spindle bearing nut to 12 ft. lbs. (16 N.m) while turning wheel forward by hand. Back off nut until it is just loose.

4) Hand-tighten nut until snug, then loosen slightly (no more than 1/2 a flat) until new cotter pin can be inserted. Hub play (in and out) should be .0010-.0050" (.025-.127 mm) when properly adjusted. Install dust cap and wheel cover.

BALL JOINT CHECKING

Upper Ball Joint

1) Upper ball joint stud is spring-loaded in its socket to minimize looseness and compensate for normal wear. Raise vehicle and support at lower control arm. Remove front wheel assembly. Inspect ball joint stud for lateral shake or stud rotation in socket.

2) To check for lateral shake, grip hub assembly at top and bottom, then move spindle in and out. If stud has any lateral shake, replace ball joint. To check for stud movement, first remove stud nut, then detach steering knuckle from ball joint stud using ball joint separator.

Fig. 1: Exploded View of Front Suspension Assembly

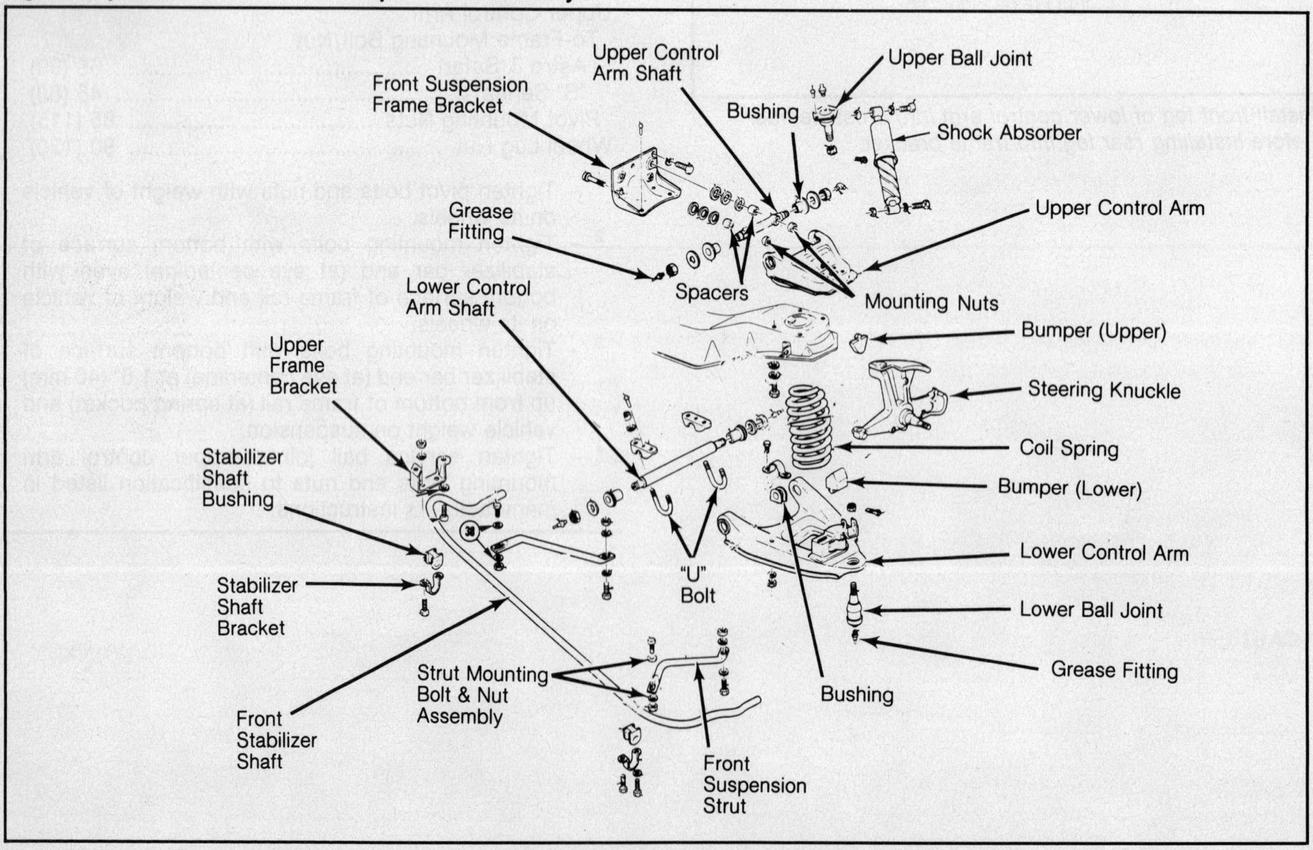

The "G" series front suspension is shown, "C" series is similar (except for front suspension struts).

GENERAL MOTORS COIL SPRING EXCEPT ASTRO, SAFARI & "S" SERIES TRUCKS (Cont.)

3) With finger pressure only, attempt to twist stud in its socket. Replace ball joint if stud can be twisted. Inspect upper ball joint rubber grease seal for cuts or tears. Replace ball joint if damage is found.

Lower Ball Joint

1) Lower ball joints are a loose fit when not connected to steering knuckle. Wear may be checked without ball stud disassembly. To check lower ball joint, first lift vehicle.

2) Support weight of control arms at wheel and hub with jack stand. Measure distance between top of ball joint stud and tip of lower grease fitting. *See Fig. 2*. Move support to control arm and allow wheel and hub to hang free.

3) Remeasure distance. If distance exceeds 3/32" (2.38 mm), replace ball joint. Inspect lower ball joint rubber grease seal for cuts or tears. Replace ball joint if damage is found.

Fig. 2: Checking Lower Ball Joint Wear Measurement

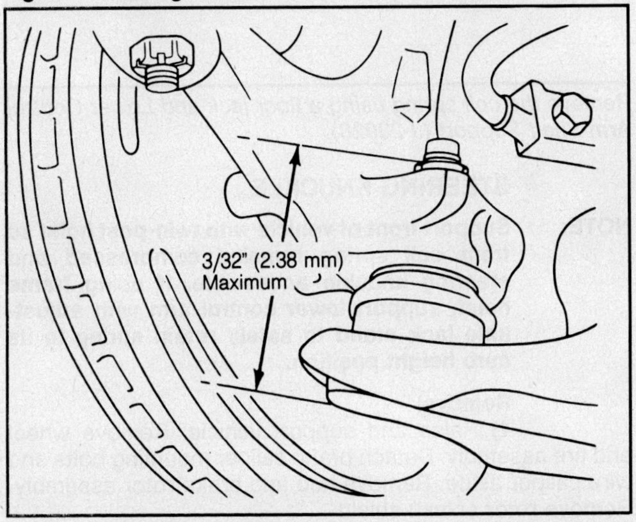

Check difference in length between loaded and unload ball joint and replace if measurement is beyond specification.

REMOVAL & INSTALLATION

NOTE: Front wheel bearings should be cleaned, inspected, repacked and adjusted at every brake relining or 12,000 miles, whichever comes first.

WHEEL BEARINGS

1) Raise and support vehicle, then remove wheel and tire assembly. Detach dust cap and remove cotter pin. Detach brake caliper mounting bolts and hang caliper out of work area with wire.

CAUTION: Do not hang brake caliper by flexible hose or severe hose damage can result.

2) Detach spindle nut, then remove hub and rotor assembly. Remove outer bearing from hub. Pry out inner grease seal and discard, then remove inner bearing. Wash bearings in cleaning solvent and inspect for cracked bearing cages and worn or pitted rollers.

3) Wash out hub and inspect bearing races for cracks, scoring or looseness in hub. If bearing(s) and/or race(s) need replacement, drive old race out of hub. Insert brass drift, through hub, behind race (in notches in hub). Using hammer, strike drift (alternating on each side of race) until race is removed.

4) Depending on vehicle, drive in new inner and/or outer race using a hammer and the proper bearing race installer. On vehicles with 1 3/4" (44.5 mm) diameter bearings, use Bearing Race Installer (J-8849); 1 15/16" (49.2 mm) diameter bearings use Bearing Race Installer (J-8457); 2 5/16" (58.7 mm) diameter bearings use Bearing Race Installer (J-8850) and 2 1/2" (63.5 mm) diameter bearings use Bearing Race Installer (J-8458).

5) Before installing, thoroughly pack each wheel bearing with GM Wheel Bearing Grease (1051344). With bearings and races replaced, install new inner grease seal (using a flat plate) until seal is flush with hub.

6) Lubricate seal lip (moderately) and hub cavity (liberally) with wheel bearing grease. To complete installation, reverse removal procedure, then adjust wheel bearings. See ADJUSTMENTS & CHECKING.

SHOCK ABSORBERS

Removal

Raise and support vehicle. If equipped, detach air shock pressure line fitting(s). Remove nuts and eye bolts securing upper and lower ends of shock absorber. Remove shock absorber from vehicle.

Inspection

1) On hydraulic fluid filled shock absorber (spiral-groove reservoir), check for binding, excessive noise, missing bump stops, worn or damaged rubber mounting grommets and hydraulic fluid leaks around seal cover area.

NOTE: A slight trace of hydraulic fluid (Dark Brown tint with a characteristic odor) around seal cover area is not a cause for replacement.

CAUTION: Ensure all hydraulic shocks that have been stored horizontally are purge of air before inspection or misdiagnosis may result. See step 5).

2) Check shock for proper dampening and internal noise by stroking unit (with top of shock held vertical) through full rebound (up) and compression (down). Movement should be smooth and consistent with the most resistance (by approximately 2:1) during extension.

3) If shock has an internal noise, check for loose piston by extending shock fully, then exert an extra pull. If noisy, shock should be replaced. Also replace shock if a squeal or grunt is heard after 1 full stroke in both directions, a clicking noise on fast reverse, or a skip or lag at reversal near midstroke.

4) On gas-charged shock absorber (smooth-bodied reservoir), ensure bench checking is done with shock inverted (top end down). If, when stroked, a lag is noticed, it indicates that the gas-filled cell is ruptured and shock should be replaced. If no lag is noticed, continue to check unit by following steps **1)** through **3)** for hydraulic shocks.

5) Purge shock by mounting unit in vise (with top in vertical position), then fully extend shock. Next, hold top of shock down and fully collapse unit. Repeat procedure several times to purge air void. After purging air, clamp lower shock mounting ring vertically in vise (large diameter tube up). Pump unit by hand at different rates of speed.

GENERAL MOTORS COIL SPRING EXCEPT ASTRO, SAFARI & "S" SERIES TRUCKS (Cont.)

6) Smooth resistance should be felt through the length of the stroke. Since unit is normally pressurized, the sound of air bubbles or a gurgling noise is normal. To complete inspection, continue to check unit by following steps **1)** through **3)** for hydraulic shocks.

Installation

Position shock absorber over mounting bolts or into mounting brackets and install eye bolts. Tighten all bolts and nuts to specification. Lower vehicle.

STABILIZER BAR

Removal

1) Raise vehicle. Remove nuts and bolts attaching stabilizer bar brackets to frame. Remove bracket bolts and nuts at bushings on lower control arm.

2) Remove stabilizer bar from vehicle. Check all rubber bushings for excessive wear, damage or aging and replace as necessary.

NOTE: **When installing, ensure slit in bar-to-frame bushing faces forward.**

Installation

1) Lubricate bushings with rubber grease when installing on stabilizer bar. Position stabilizer bar on frame, then install frame brackets over bushings.

2) Install bracket mounting nuts and bolts loosely. Install brackets over bushings at lower control arms. Tighten all nuts and bolts to specification. Lower vehicle.

COIL SPRINGS

Removal

1) Raise vehicle and support under frame so that control arms hang free. Disconnect shock absorber and stabilizer bar bracket at lower control arm. Bolt Lower Control Arm Shaft Support (J-23028) onto a suitable jack, then position assembly under lower control arm shaft so shaft seats in grooves of support tool. *See Fig. 3.*

CAUTION: **Install a safety chain through lower control arm and coil spring before detaching lower control arm shaft bolts. Only control arm shaft and lower control arm hold spring in place once bolts are removed. Lower jack slowly.**

2) Raise jack to relieve tension on lower control arm shaft, then remove 2 "U" bolts mounting control arm shaft to crossmember. Carefully lower jack until all tension is released from spring. If equipped with urethane air cylinder, deflate unit and remove from within spring, then remove spring from vehicle.

NOTE: **On models with urethane air cylinders within the coil springs, check for leaks and damage before installation. Air pressure in these cylinders may be increased or decreased (to adjust vehicle trim) through valve located at bottom of cylinder.**

Installation

To install coil spring (and air cylinder if equipped), reverse removal procedure. When positioning lower control arm shaft to crossmember, ensure front indexing hole in shaft is aligned with crossmember attaching saddle stud. Install and tighten all mounting bolts. Remove support tool and safety chain, then lower vehicle.

Fig. 3: Front Coil Spring Removal

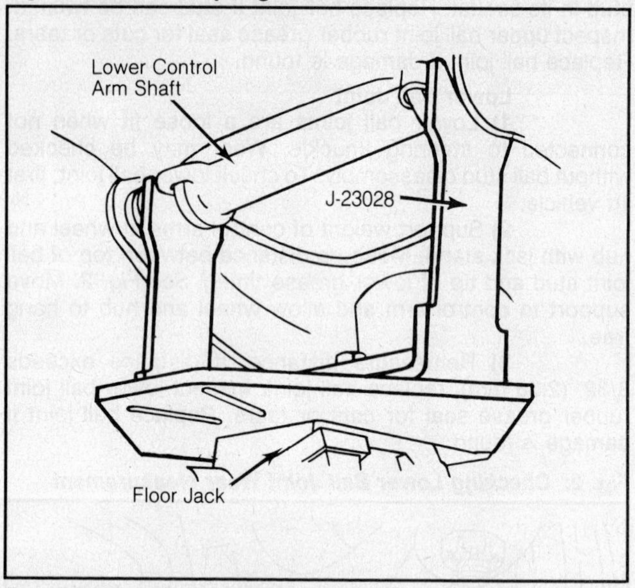

Remove the coil spring using a floor jack and Lower Control Arm Shaft Support (J-23028).

STEERING KNUCKLE

NOTE: **Support front of vehicle with twin-post hoist so front coil spring remains compressed and steering knuckle accessible. If using frame hoist, support lower control arm with adjustable jack stand to safely retain spring in its curb height position.**

Removal

1) Raise and support vehicle. Remove wheel and tire assembly. Detach brake caliper mounting bolts and wire caliper aside. Remove hub and brake rotor assembly. Remove rotor splash shield.

2) Remove outer tie rod end ball stud cotter pin and nut. Remove stud from steering knuckle arm by striking arm (at tie rod end) with hammer while using heavy hammer as a backing. Pull tie rod end stud from arm.

3) Remove upper and lower ball joint cotter pins and loosen nuts. Using Ball Joint Separator (J-23742), free steering knuckle from ball joint studs. *See Fig. 5.* Remove stud nuts and withdraw steering knuckle.

Inspection

With ball joints and tie rod end detached, clean all dirt from steering knuckle. Inspect tapered holes in knuckle for out-of-round, deformation or damage. Replace steering knuckle if any of these conditions exist.

Installation

To install, reverse removal procedure and tighten all nuts and bolts. If necessary, tighten ball joint and/or tie rod end stud nut 1 more notch to insert cotter pin. After installation, adjust wheel bearings as necessary. See ADJUSTMENTS & CHECKING.

UPPER BALL JOINT

Removal

1) Raise and support vehicle. If frame hoist is used, support lower control arm with adjustable jack stand. Remove cotter pin from upper ball stud. Loosen nut 2 turns (but do not remove at this time).

GENERAL MOTORS COIL SPRING EXCEPT ASTRO, SAFARI & "S" SERIES TRUCKS (Cont.)

2) Remove brake caliper and suspend it from frame with wire. Do not hang caliper by flexible brake hose. Install Ball Joint Separator (J-23742) between the ball studs. *See Fig. 5.*

3) Extend bolt on separator tool to loosen ball stud from knuckle. Remove separator tool and stud nut. Center punch rivet heads, then drill out rivets and remove ball joint assembly.

CAUTION: When installing upper and lower ball joint nuts, do not loosen nut to install cotter pin. If necessary, tighten 1 extra notch.

Installation

1) To install, reverse removal procedure. Using new nuts and bolts in place of rivets to attach new ball joint to control arm, tighten to specification.

2) Install new cotter pin, tightening nut as necessary to align stud hole. Install grease fitting and lubricate new ball joint with chassis lubricant equal to GM-6031-M Chassis Grease (1051344).

NOTE: Lubricate ball joints (and tie rod ends) every 4 months or 5000 miles on C20 and G30 models and every 12 months or 5000 miles on all other vehicles. For severe driving conditions, lubricate every 3 months or 2500 miles on all models.

LOWER BALL JOINT

Removal

1) Raise and support vehicle. If frame hoist is used, support lower control arm with adjustable jack stand. Remove wheel and tire assembly. Remove lower ball joint stud cotter pin. Loosen stud nut 2 turns but do not remove at this time.

2) Remove brake caliper and suspend out of way with wire. Do not hang by flexible brake hose. Install Ball Joint Separator (J-23742) between the ball studs. Extend bolt on separator tool to loosen ball stud. *See Fig. 5.*

Fig. 5: Separating Upper & Lower Ball Joints

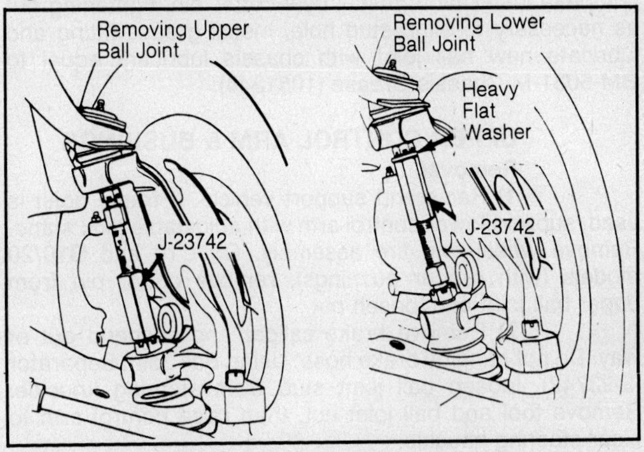

Ensure the separator tool is placed in the proper position depending on the ball joint being separated.

3) Remove tool and ball stud nut. Pull brake rotor/hub assembly and steering knuckle assembly up off ball stud and support upper control arm with block of wood.

4) Install Ball Joint Remover & Installer Set (J-9519-D, which must include "C" Clamp J-9519-10, Installer J-9519-9, Adapter J-9519-16 and Receiver J-9519-22 or J-21474-13). Turn hex head screw on clamp to press lower ball joint out of control arm bore. Remove tools and ball joint from vehicle. *See Fig. 4.*

Fig. 4: Removing & Installing Lower Ball Joint

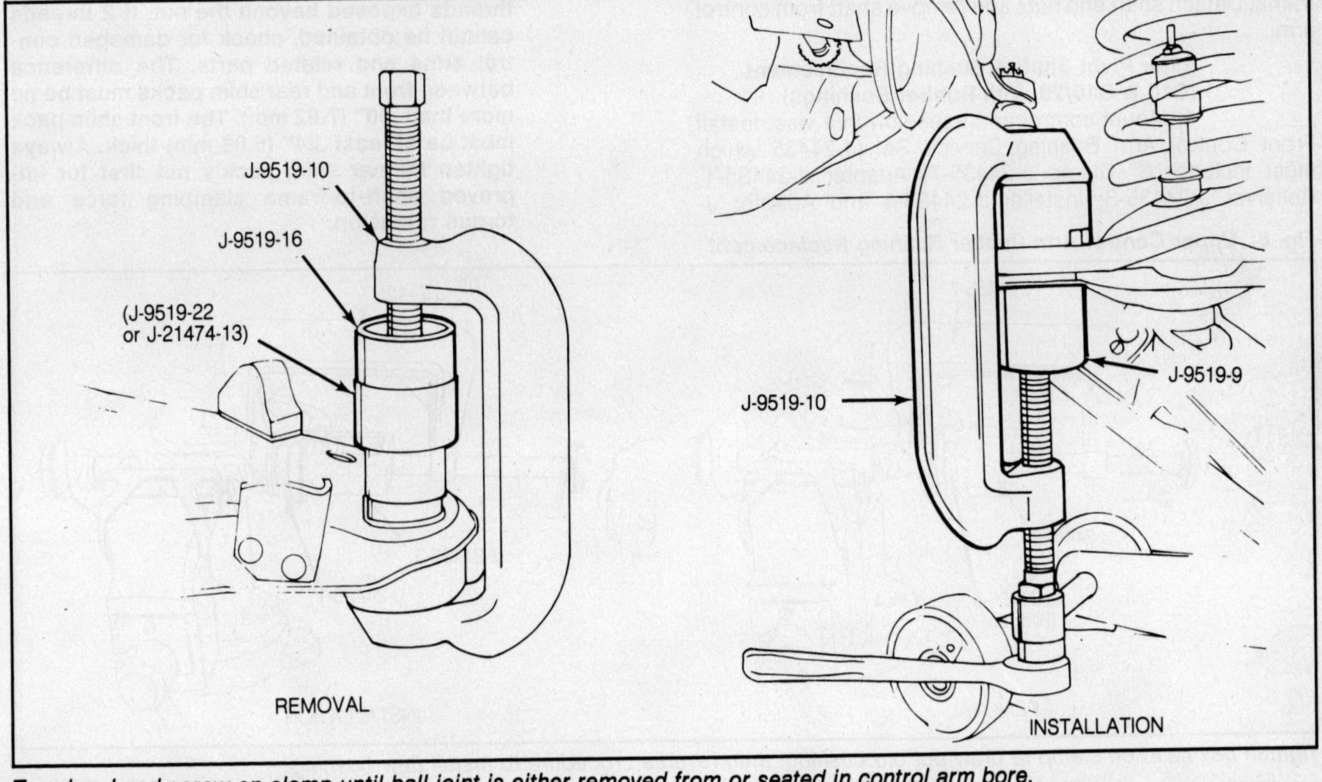

Turn hex head screw on clamp until ball joint is either removed from or seated in control arm bore.

GENERAL MOTORS COIL SPRING
EXCEPT ASTRO, SAFARI & "S" SERIES TRUCKS (Cont.)

Installation

1) Start new ball joint in control arm bore, then install ball joint remover & installer set. *See Fig. 4*. Ensure bleed vent in rubber boot is positioned facing forward.

2) Turn hex head screw on clamp until ball joint is seated in control arm. Reverse removal procedure to complete installation. Install new cotter pin, tightening nut as necessary to align stud hole. Install grease fitting and lubricate new ball joint with chassis lubricant equal to GM-6031-M Chassis Grease (1051344).

UPPER CONTROL ARM & BUSHINGS

Removal

1) Raise and support vehicle. If frame hoist is used, support lower control arm with adjustable jack stand. Remove wheel and tire assembly. On C10 and G10/20 models (with rubber bushings), remove cotter pin from upper ball joint and loosen nut.

2) Remove brake caliper and suspend out of way. Do not hang by brake hose. Using Ball Joint Separator (J-23742), loosen ball joint stud from steering knuckle. Remove tool and ball joint nut, then raise control arm to clear steering knuckle.

3) Detach nuts and bolts attaching control arm shaft to frame member, then remove control arm from vehicle. Tape shims together and tag for proper location when control arm is reinstalled.

4) On C20/30 and G30 models (with steel bushings), loosen upper control arm shaft end nuts before loosening shaft-to-frame attaching nuts. Loosen shaft-to-frame nuts and remove caster and camber shims. Tape shims together and tag for proper location when control arm is reinstalled.

5) Detach pivot shaft-to-frame nuts but do not allow control arm to swing too far away from frame. Use a safety chain to retain control arm in close relationship to frame. Detach shaft end nuts and remove shaft from control arm.

Inner Pivot Shaft & Bushing Replacement (C10 & G10/20 With Rubber Bushings)

1) Mount control arm assembly in a vise. Install Front Control Arm Bushing Service Set (J-24435 which must include "C" Clamp J-24435-7, Adapter J-24435-1, Receiver J-24435-3, Installer J-24435-4 and Adapter J-24435-5) onto control arm bushing using "C" clamp and proper adapters. *See Fig. 6*.

2) Tighten clamp to draw out old bushing, then discard bushing. Remove pivot shaft from control arm if necessary. Reposition control arm in vise and remove opposite side bushing.

3) Lubricate new bushing with rubber grease and position into control arm bore. Install "C" clamp and proper adapters over bushing, then tighten clamp to press bushing into position. *See Fig. 6*.

4) Install pivot shaft into inside diameter of first installed bushing. Install remaining bushing as described in step **3)**. Remove bushing service tools and install control arm on vehicle. Tighten all fasteners to specification.

Inner Pivot Shaft & Bushing Replacement (C20/30 & G30 With Steel Bushings)

1) Remove grease fittings from bushing outer ends and unscrew bushings from control arm and shaft. Remove and discard old seals. Slide new seal onto each end of shaft and insert shaft into control arm.

2) Adjust shaft until centered in control arm, then turn bushings in and tighten to specification. *See Fig. 7*. Check shaft for free rotation. Install grease fittings and lubricate with proper chassis grease.

CAUTION: When installing upper control arm, ensure special aligning washers are positioned onto pivot shaft with concave and convex sides together.

Installation

1) Place control arm in position on bracket and install mounting nuts. On C10 and G10/20 models (with rubber bushings), before tightening nuts, insert caster and camber shims in the same order as removed. Tighten mounting nuts to specification.

NOTE: A normal shim pack will leave at least 2 bolt threads exposed beyond the nut. If 2 threads cannot be obtained, check for damaged control arms and related parts. The difference between front and rear shim packs must be no more than .30" (7.62 mm). The front shim pack must be at least .24" (6.09 mm) thick. Always tighten thinner shim pack's nut first for improved shaft-to-frame clamping force and torque retension.

Fig. 6: Upper Control Arm Rubber Bushing Replacement

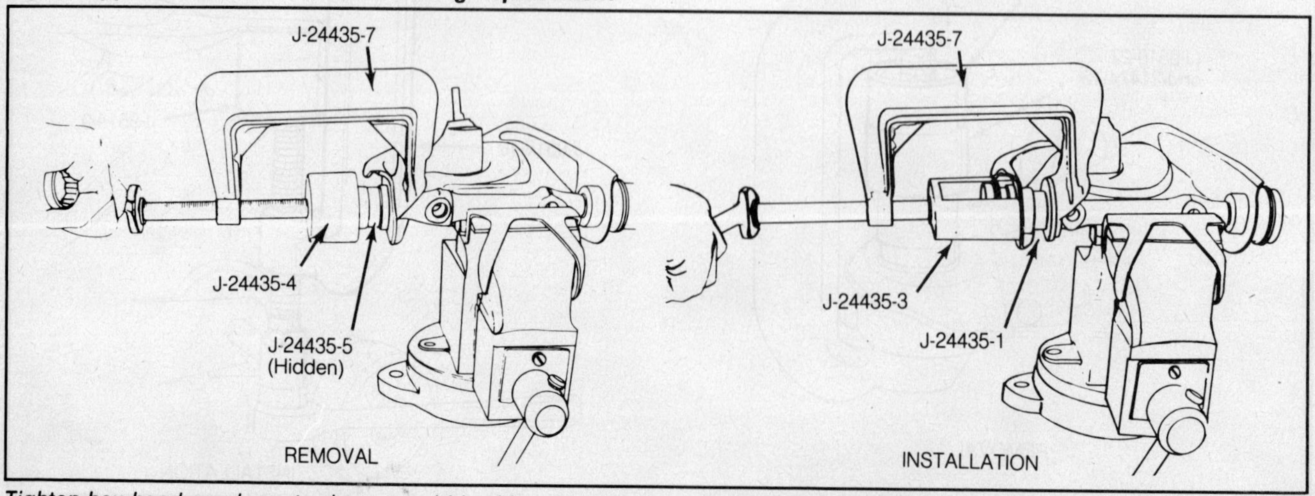

Tighten hex head on clamp to draw out old bushing, then reverse procedure to install new bushing.

GENERAL MOTORS COIL SPRING EXCEPT ASTRO, SAFARI & "S" SERIES TRUCKS (Cont.)

2) On C20/30 and G30 models (with steel bushings), position pivot shaft-to-frame bolts and start pivot shaft nuts. Tighten shaft end nuts. Check for proper spacing. *See Fig. 7*. The shaft should rotate by hand after tightening nuts.

Fig. 7: Positioning Upper Control Arm Pivot Shaft (With Steel Bushings)

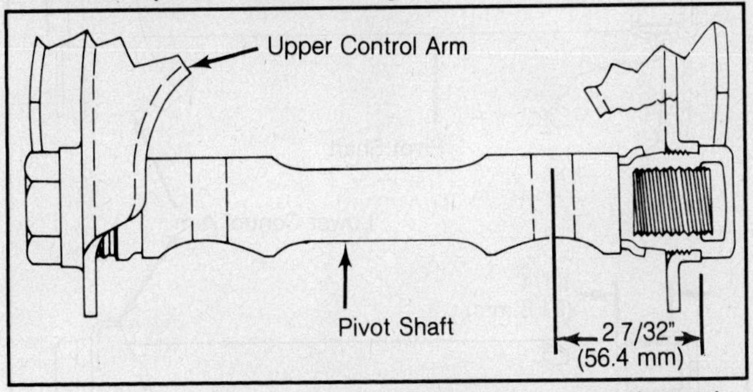

Ensure shaft rotates by hand after end nuts are tightened.

3) Install caster and camber shims in the same order as removed and tighten pivot shaft-to-frame mounting nuts. Remove safety chain and install wheel and tire assembly. Lower vehicle.

4) On C10 and G10/20 models, insert ball joint stud into steering knuckle and install nut. Tighten stud nut to specification and install new cotter pin. To complete installation, reverse removal procedure. After installation, check front end alignment.

LOWER CONTROL ARM & BUSHINGS

Removal

1) Raise vehicle and place safety stands under frame side rails. Remove wheel and tire assembly. Remove brake caliper and suspend out of way with wire. Do not hang from flexible brake hose. Remove coil spring. See COIL SPRINGS. Support inboard end of control arm after spring removal.

NOTE: On C10 models (with rubber bushings) and C20/30 and G30 models (with steel bushings), if just control arm bushings or pivot shaft are to be replaced, lower control arm does not have to be removed from vehicle.

2) Remove cotter pin from lower ball joint stud, then loosen stud nut 1 turn. Using Ball Joint Separator (J-23742), position large cupped end of tool over upper ball stud nut and pilot threaded end of tool onto lower ball stud.

3) Extend bolt of tool to loosen ball stud from steering knuckle, then remove tool and stud nut. Detach nuts attaching control arm to frame, then lower jack stand and remove control arm from vehicle.

Inner Pivot Shaft & Bushings On-Vehicle Replacement (C10 With Rubber Bushings)

1) Raise vehicle on hoist and support frame so control arms hang free. Position adjustable jack stand under lower control arm, inboard of spring, and into control arm depression.

2) Install safety chain over upper control arm, inboard of stabilizer and outboard of shock absorber. Disconnect shock and stabilizer bar attachments at lower control arm. Loosen shaft end nuts.

3) Detach "U" bolts retaining inboard end of lower control arm. Lower jack SLOWLY to release spring tension and gain clearance to remove bushings. Ensure all tension is released from spring before proceeding.

4) Using Lower Control Arm Bushing Stake Remover (J-22717), remove stakes on front bushing. Using Front Control Arm Bushing Service Set (J-24435 which must include "C" Clamp J-24435-7, Remover J-24435-2, Receiver J-24435-3, Installer J-24435-4 and Spacer J-24435-6), tighten hex head on "C" clamp to remove old bushings. *See Fig. 8*.

5) Remove tools and discard old bushing. Remove stakes on opposite side bushing, then install remover tools and press out bushing (leave pivot shaft in to guide tool). Remove pivot shaft if necessary.

6) Coat each new bushing with rubber grease before installation. Position 1 bushing in control arm bore. Install "C" clamp and proper service tools, then press bushing into position until seated firmly in control arm. *See Fig. 8*. Insert pivot shaft, then install second bushing.

7) Stake front bushing in at least 2 places after installation. To complete installation, reverse removal procedure. Tighten all fasteners to specification. After installation, check front end alignment as needed.

Inner Pivot Shaft & Bushings Replacement (G10/20 With Rubber Bushings)

1) With lower control arm removed from vehicle, detach pivot shaft nuts. Place control arm in an arbor press. Press front end of pivot shaft to remove rear bushing and pivot shaft assembly.

Fig. 8: Lower Control Arm Rubber Bushing Replacement

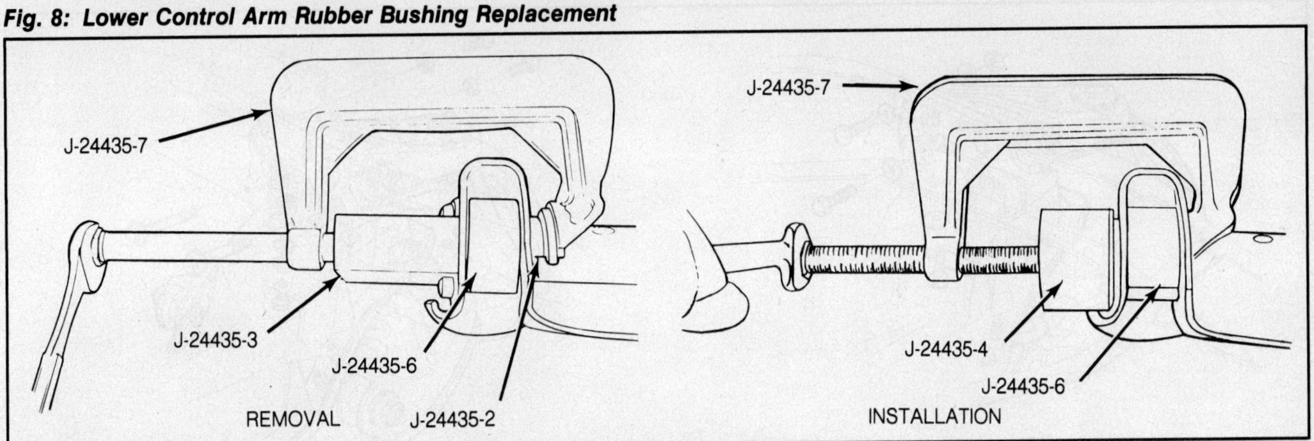

Ensure Spacer (J-24435-6) is in position as shown to aviod collapsing control arm during assembly.

GENERAL MOTORS COIL SPRING EXCEPT ASTRO, SAFARI & "S" SERIES TRUCKS (Cont.)

2) Using Lower Control Arm Bushing Stake Remover (J-22717), remove stakes on front bushing. Using "C" Clamp (J-24435-7), Receiver (J-24435-3), Remover (J-24435-2) and Spacer (J-24435-6), tighten hex head on "C" clamp to press out old bushing.

3) Install new front bushing using "C" clamp, spacer and Installer (J-24435-4). Ensure outer tube hole is to the front (or forward to the staked bushing) and spacer is between parallel sides of control arm bushing bore. *See Fig. 8.* Stake front bushing in at least 2 places after installation. Insert pivot shaft and second bushing.

Inner Pivot Shaft & Bushings Replacement (C20/30 & G30 With Steel Bushings)

1) Raise vehicle on hoist and support frame so control arms hang free. Position adjustable jack stand under lower control arm, inboard of spring, and into control arm depression.

2) Install safety chain over upper control arm, inboard of stabilizer and outboard of shock absorber. Disconnect shock absorber attachments at lower control arm. Loosen shaft end nuts.

3) Remove "U" bolts. Lower jack stand just enough to gain access to pivot shaft. Detach shaft end nuts and remove shaft. Remove grease fittings from ends of bushings, then unscrew bushings from shaft and control arm. Remove shaft and discard seals.

4) Slide new seal onto each end of shaft and insert shaft into control arm. Start new bushings on shaft and into control arm. Adjust shaft until it is centered in control arm. *See Fig. 9.* Once centered, turn bushings in and tighten to specification. Check shaft for free rotation. Install grease fittings and lubricate bushings.

5) Install shaft end nuts but do not tighten at this time. Raise jack and position shaft into crossmember saddle. Ensure hole in shaft is indexed to mate with bolt head in saddle.

6) Install "U" bolts but do not tighten nuts at this time. Tighten pivot shaft end nuts. Ensure shaft rotates by hand after tightening. Tighten "U" bolt nuts. Remove safety chain and lower vehicle.

Installation

1) If removed, place control arm in position and install ball joint stud into steering knuckle bore. Tighten stud nut to specification and install new cotter pin. Install coil spring and control arm.

Fig. 9: Positioning Lower Control Arm Pivot Shaft (With Steel Bushings)

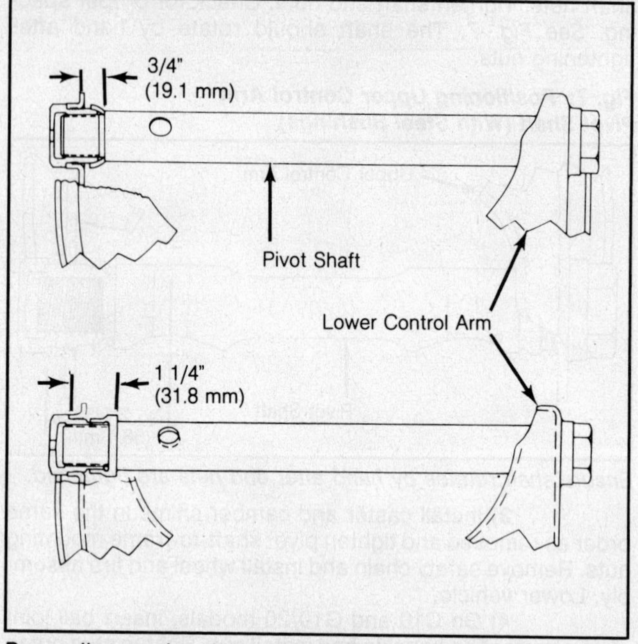

Depending on the pivot shaft and bushing configuration, position pivot shaft as shown.

2) To complete installation, reverse removal procedure. Tighten all nuts and bolts to specification and check wheel alignment as necessary. See WHEEL ALIGNMENT section for procedures and specifications.

CROSSMEMBER & SUSPENSION UNIT

NOTE: **Front suspension components may be serviced separately as previously outlined or, if extensive repairs are needed, crossmember and suspension unit can be removed as an assembly.**

Removal

1) Raise hood and disconnect negative battery cable. Raise and support vehicle on twin-post hoist. Remove both front wheel and tire assemblies. Disconnect front brake hose clip from each upper control arm.

Fig. 10: Front Suspension Unit-To-Frame Mounting Bolts

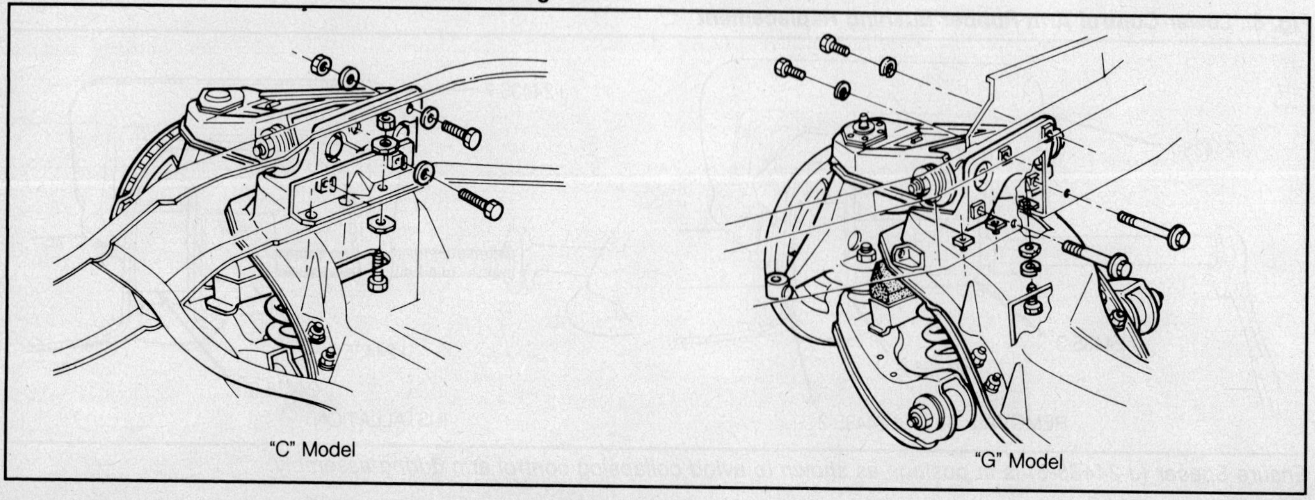

GENERAL MOTORS COIL SPRING EXCEPT ASTRO, SAFARI & "S" SERIES TRUCKS (Cont.)

2) Support front of vehicle with jack stands at frame side rails and lower front hoist. Clean area around front brake hose fittings, then detach hoses from calipers and plug openings.

3) Disconnect tie rod ends from steering knuckles. Disconnect front stabilizer bar (if equipped) and shocks from lower control arms. Remove brake line clip bolts from front suspension crossmember. On "C" models, the clip is located under right hand engine mount support bracket.

CAUTION: Brake line clips must be disconnected from front suspension unit or severe damage to brake line will result when unit is lowered from vehicle.

4) Detach engine mount support bracket-to-front suspension crossmember bolts. *See Fig. 10.* Detach crossmember-to-lower frame rail bolts. Raise front hoist to support front suspension member. Support engine.

NOTE: Engine must be supported adequately before front suspension unit is lowered from vehicle.

5) Detach upper control arm bracket-to-frame side rail bolts. Suspension unit is now disconnected from vehicle. Lower front hoist to lower front suspension unit from vehicle.

Installation

1) With front suspension unit positioned on hoist, raise hoist to align unit with frame rail holes. Assemble upper control arm bracket bolts and crossmember bolts to frame rails finger tight.

NOTE: Control arm bracket bolts must be tightened before crossmember bolts. Ensure crossmember is in contact with frame side rails.

2) Tighten upper control arm bracket bolts to frame side rails. Remove engine support at this time and lower hoist. Assemble engine mount support bracket-to-front suspension crossmember bolts and tighten to specification. To complete installation, reverse removal procedure. Lubricate suspension components. Bleed brake system.

TIGHTENING SPECIFICATIONS

Application	INCH Lbs. (N.m)
Brake Line Clip-To-Crossmember Mounting Bolt	
"C" Models	150 (17)
"G" Models	100 (12)
Brake Line Clip	
To-Upper Control Arm Mounting Bolt	150 (17)
Brake Splash Shield-To-Knuckle Bolt	120 (14)

TIGHTENING SPECIFICATIONS (Cont.)

Application	Ft. Lbs. (N.m)
Ball Joint	
Upper Nut	
C10 & G10/20 [1]	50 (68)
C30 & G30 [2]	90 (122)
Lower Nut	
All Models [2]	90 (122)
Brake Caliper Mounting Bolt	35 (48)
Control Arm (Rubber Bushings)	
C10 & G10/20	115 (156)
Crossmember	
Brake Support Strut	60 (81)
To-Bottom Rail	
All (Except Forward Control Chassis)	90 (122)
Forward Control Chassis	
Motorhome	215 (292)
Conventional [3]	130 (176)
To-Frame Side Rail	
All (Except Forward Control Chassis)	65 (88)
Forward Control Chassis	
Motorhome & Conventional [3]	100 (136)
Engine Mount Support Bracket Mntg. Bolt	35 (48)
Lower Control Arm (Steel Bushings)	
New	
C20/30 & G30	280 (380)
Used	
C20/30 & G30	130 (176)
Lower Control Arm Shaft	
"U" Bolt-to-Frame	
G10/20	65 (88)
C10/30 & G30	85 (115)
Shock Absorber	
Upper Nut	
C10/30	140 (190)
G10/30	75 (102)
Lower Nut	
C10/30	60 (81)
G10/30	75 (102)
Stabilizer Bar Bracket-To-Spring Plate	
C20/30	13 (18)
Stabilizer Bar Bracket	
To-Lower Control Arm Mounting Bolt	25 (34)
To-Frame Mounting Bolt/Nut	25 (34)
Suspension Bumper	
C10 & G10/30	15 (20)
C20/30	19 (26)
Tie Rod End-To-Steering Knuckle Mounting Nut	
All Models	41 (55)
Upper Control Arm (Steel Bushings)	
New	
C30 & G30	190 (256)
Used	
C30 & G30	115 (156)
Upper Control Arm	
Pivot Shaft Nut	
C10 & G10/20	70 (95)
C20/30 & G30	105 (142)
Bracket-To-Frame Side Rail Mntg. Bolts	65 (90)
Wheel Lug Nuts	75 (100)

1 – Additional torque required to align cotter pin must not exceed 90 ft. lbs. (122 N.m) maximum.
2 – Additional torque required to align cotter pin must not exceed 130 ft. lbs. (176 N.m) maximum.
3 – With 4-wheel power disc brakes.

Front Suspension

GENERAL MOTORS 4WD TORSION BAR "S" SERIES TRUCKS

DESCRIPTION

The front suspension consists of upper and lower control arms, stabilizer bar, shock absorbers and left and right torsion bars. Torsion bars are used instead of coil springs. The front end of torsion bar is connected to lower control arm. The rear end of torsion bar is mounted to an adjustable arm at crossmember support. The vehicle ride height is controlled by this adjustment.

There are two types of shock absorbers available, "Firm Ride" (smooth-body reservoir) hydraulic fluid filled-type, and "Extra Firm Ride" (spiral groove reservoir) gas charged-type. These 4WD models have sealed front wheel bearings which are pre-adjusted and require no lubrication maintenance.

ADJUSTMENTS & CHECKING

WHEEL ALIGNMENT SPECIFICATIONS & PROCEDURES

See WHEEL ALIGNMENT SPECIFICATIONS & PROCEDURES in WHEEL ALIGNMENT section.

WHEEL BEARING ADJUSTMENT

The front wheel bearings are pre-adjusted and require no maintenance unless the wheel hub and bearing carrier is removed. See REMOVAL & INSTALLATION.

BALL JOINT CHECKING

1) Raise vehicle and support with jack stands under lower control arms (or stabilizer bar bracket). Stands should be as close as possible to each lower ball joint. Upper control arm bumper must not contact frame.

2) To check upper ball joint, place Dial Indicator (J-8001) against low side of wheel rim, then rock wheel in and out. Horizontal deflection should not exceed .125" (3.20 mm). Replace upper ball joint if beyond limit.

3) To check lower ball joint, place dial indicator on center of wheel hub dust cover. Pry between the lower control arm and the outer wheel bearing race portion of the hub assembly. *See Fig. 1*. Horizontal deflection should not exceed .125" (3.20 mm).

4) If dial indicator reading is excessive, or ball stud has been disconnected from knuckle and any looseness is detected or stud can be twisted with fingers, replace ball joint.

REMOVAL & INSTALLATION

WHEEL HUB & BEARING ASSEMBLY

Removal

1) Raise and support vehicle. Remove wheel and tire assembly. Depress brake caliper piston (using "C" clamp if necessary), detach brake caliper mounting bolts and wire caliper aside, out of work area. Remove disc brake rotor.

2) Detach dust cover and remove cotter pin, hub retainer nut cover, hub retainer nut and washer. Slide hub/bearing carrier off front axle shaft splines. Inspect steering knuckle grease seal and hub bearing for excessive wear or damage. Replace as necessary.

3) If hub wheel stud must be replaced, press old stud from hub using Wheel Stud Remover (J-5504). Do not hammer on stud to remove or damage to hub can result.

Installation

1) To install new wheel stud, lubricate stud bore, then install stud. Place 4 washers on stud and install stud nut reversed (flat side to washers). Tighten stud nut to draw stud into hub bore. Remove nut and washers. Install hub and bearing assembly onto axle shaft if removed.

2) With hub/carrier installed, tighten hub retainer nut to 174 ft. lbs. (235 N.m). Install hub retainer nut cover,

Fig. 1: Checking Upper & Lower Ball Joints

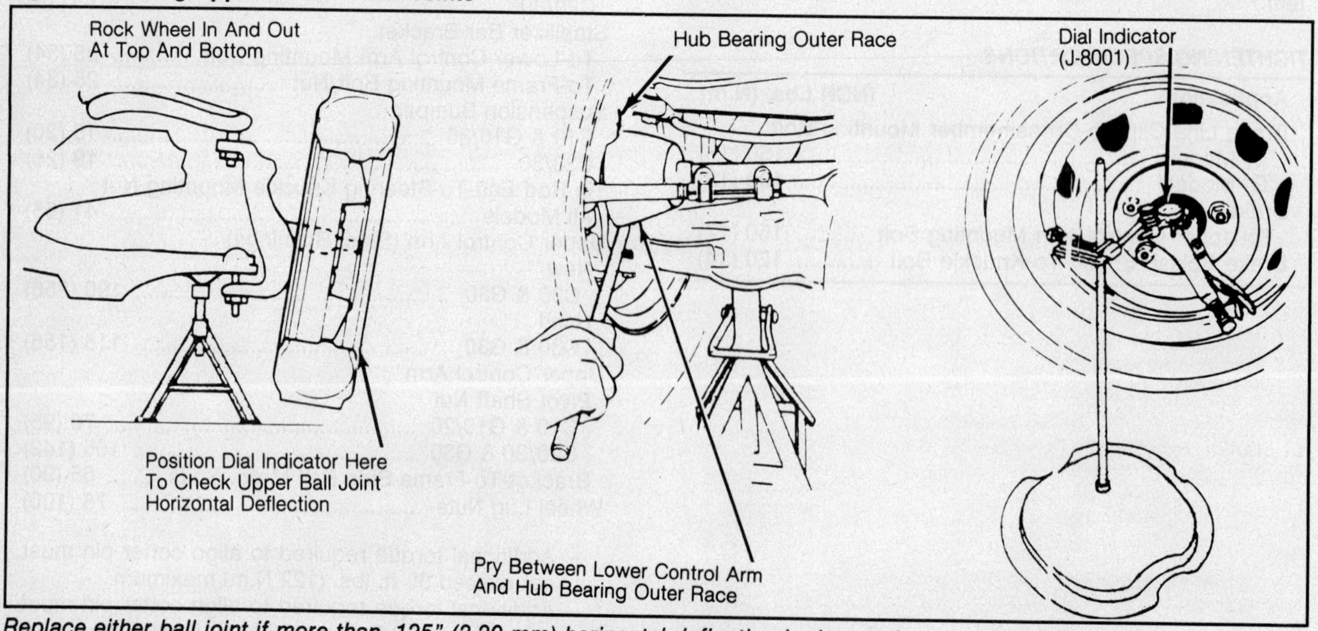

Replace either ball joint if more than .125" (3.20 mm) horizontal deflection is detected.

Front Suspension

GENERAL MOTORS 4WD TORSION BAR "S" SERIES TRUCKS (Cont.)

new cotter pin and dust cover. DO NOT back off nut to install cotter pin.

3) Install brake rotor and caliper. To complete installation, reverse removal procedure. Depress brake pedal several times to extend caliper piston after installation is complete.

SHOCK ABSORBER

Removal

Raise and support vehicle. Remove wheel and tire assembly. Detach upper and lower shock mounting bolts and nuts. Remove shock absorber from vehicle. Check for fluid leakage and/or bushing deterioration or deformation. Replace shocks, in pairs only, as necessary.

Inspection

1) On hydraulic fluid filled shock absorber (spiral groove reservoir), check for binding, excessive noise, missing bump stops, worn or damaged rubber mounting grommets and hydraulic fluid leaks around the seal cover area.

NOTE: **A slight trace of hydraulic fluid (Dark Brown tint with a characteristic odor) around the seal cover area is not a cause for replacement.**

CAUTION: **Ensure all hydraulic shocks that have been stored horizontally are purge of air before inspection or misdiagnosis may result. See step 5).**

2) Check shock for proper dampening and internal noise by stroking unit (with top of shock held vertical) through full rebound (up) and compression (down). Movement should be smooth and consistent with the most resistance (by approximately 2:1) during extension.

3) If shock has an internal noise, check for loose piston by extending shock fully, then exert an extra pull. If noisy, shock should be replaced. Also replace shock if a squeal or grunt is heard after 1 full stroke in both directions, a clicking noise on fast reverse, or a skip or lag at reversal near midstroke.

4) On gas-charged shock absorber (smooth-bodied reservoir), ensure bench checking is done with the shock inverted (top end down). If, when stroked, a lag is noticed, it indicates that the gas-filled cell is ruptured and shock should be replaced. If no lag is noticed, continue to check unit by following steps **1)** through **3)** for hydraulic shocks.

5) Purge hydraulic fluid filled shock by mounting unit in vise (with top in vertical position), then fully extend shock. Next, hold top of shock down and fully collapse unit. Repeat procedure several times to purge air void.

6) After purging air, clamp lower shock mounting ring vertically in vise (large diameter tube up). Pump unit by hand at different rates of speed. Smooth resistance should be felt through the length of the stroke.

Installation

Extend new shock to its limit. Install shock, mounting bolts and nuts. Ensure nuts are positioned at rear of shock mounts. Tighten mounting bolts to 66 ft. lbs. (90 N.m) and mounting nuts to 52 ft. lbs. (70 Nm).

STEERING KNUCKLE

Removal

1) Raise and support vehicle. Remove wheel and tire assembly. Install Axle Shaft Boot Seal Protector (J-28712) to protect drive axle boot during repairs. Depress caliper piston, detach brake caliper and wire aside, out of work area. Remove brake rotor.

2) Remove dust cover, hub retainer nut cover, retainer nut and washer. Slide hub/bearing carrier off axle shaft. Detach tie rod end nut. Using Steering Linkage Puller (J-24319), disconnect tie rod end from steering knuckle.

3) If necessary, use Torsion Bar Unloader (J-22517-02) to unload torsion bar, then back off torsion bar adjusting screw to ease steering knuckle removal. *See Fig. 2.* If backed off, count exact number of turns of adjusting screw for reassembly reference.

Fig. 2: Unloading Torsion Bar

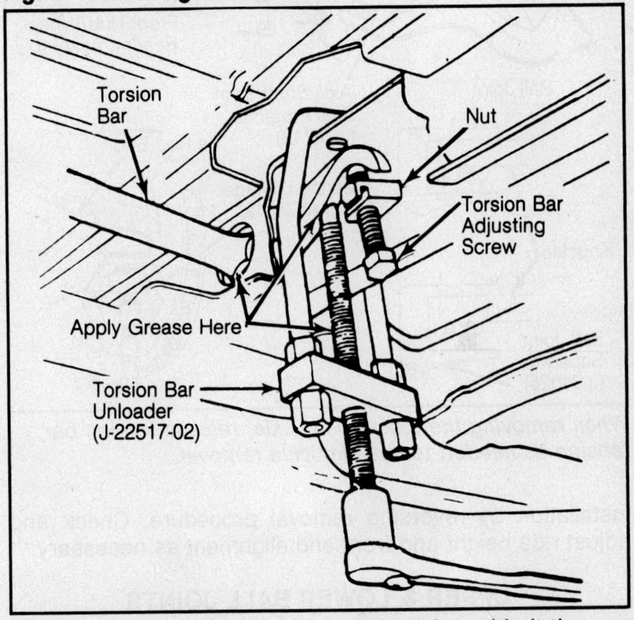

Apply grease to unloader tool bolt threads and bolt tip before unloading torsion bar.

4) Place Ball Joint Separator (J-34026) over upper or lower ball joint. *See Fig. 3.* Loosen ball joint retainer nut. Back off until nut contacts tool. Continue backing off nut until nut forces ball stud out of knuckle. Detach opposite ball joint in same manner.

NOTE: **There are darkened areas on the wheel bearing assembly caused by a heat treatment process. Do not replace bearings due to discoloration only.**

5) Remove steering knuckle from vehicle without damaging or moving axle shaft. Inspect knuckle grease seal for cuts, distortion and wear. Check steering knuckle, hub/bearing carrier and wheel bearing for damage. Replace components as necessary. *See Fig. 3.*

Installation

1) Install new knuckle grease seal using hammer and Front Hub Knuckle Inner Seal Installer (J-28574). Slide axle shaft assembly through steering knuckle. Install knuckle onto ball joint studs.

2) Attach ball joint mounting nuts. Tighten upper stud nut to 50 ft. lbs. (68 N.m) and lower stud nut to 83 ft. lbs. (113 N.m). Install tie rod nut and tighten to 35 ft. lbs. (48 N.m).

3) Install hub/bearing carrier assembly onto axle shaft and into knuckle, then tighten mounting bolts to 78 ft. lbs. (105 N.m). Install washer, hub retainer nut, cover and new cotter pin.

4) Tighten hub retainer nut to 174 ft. lbs. (235 N.m). DO NOT back off nut to install cotter pin. Complete

Front Suspension

GENERAL MOTORS 4WD TORSION BAR "S" SERIES TRUCKS

Fig. 3: Exploded View of Steering Knuckle & Hub/Bearing Carrier Assembly

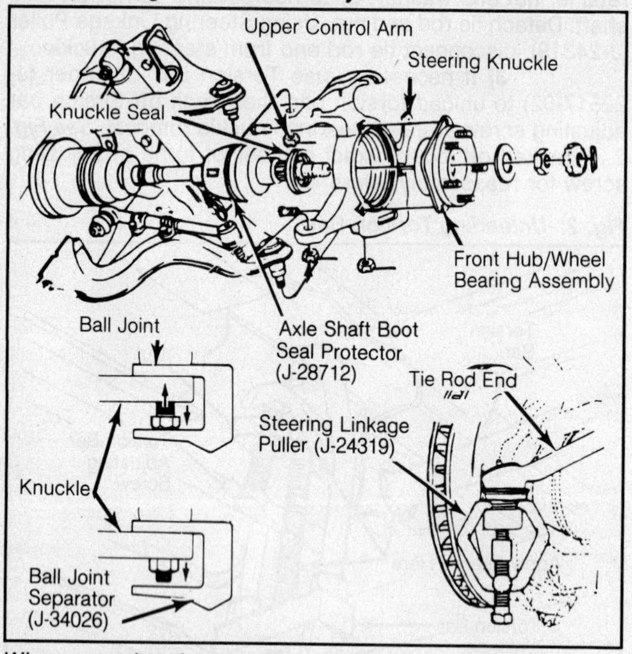

When removing the steering knuckle, release torsion bar tension as needed to ease knuckle removal.

installation by reversing removal procedure. Check and adjust ride height and front end alignment as necessary.

UPPER & LOWER BALL JOINTS

Removal

1) Raise and support vehicle. Remove wheel and tire assembly. Depress piston, detach brake caliper and wire aside, out of work area. Remove brake rotor. Remove dust cover, cotter pin, hub retainer nut cover, retainer nut and washer.

2) Slide hub/bearing carrier off axle shaft. Detach tie rod end and ball joints from steering knuckle. *See Fig. 3*. Remove steering knuckle as previously described. To remove upper and/or lower ball joint, original mounting rivets must be removed.

3) Using 1/8" drill bit, drill ball joint rivets 1/4" deep, in center of rivets. Using 1/2" drill bit, drill rivets just enough to remove rivet head. Using hammer and punch, drive rivets out of control arm. Remove ball joint.

Installation

1) Install new ball joint using new bolts and nuts in place of rivets. Tighten upper and lower ball joint mounting nuts to 15 ft. lbs. (20 N.m). If necessary, install grease fittings.

2) Lubricate ball joints and tie rod with grease. To complete installation, reverse removal procedure. After installation, check and adjust ride height and front end alignment as necessary.

UPPER CONTROL ARM & BUSHINGS

Removal

1) Raise and support vehicle. Remove wheel and tire assembly. Remove disc brake components and hub/bearing carrier assembly. Disconnect ball joints and tie rod end. Remove steering knuckle as previously described.

2) Index mark alignment adjustment cams for realignment reference. Remove upper control arm pivot bolts, cams and nuts. Note component locations for reassembly reference. Remove control arm. *See Fig. 4*.

3) Inspect control arm bushings and bumper for excessive wear, distortion and/or deterioration. Replace bushings and/or bumper as needed. Mount control arm in vise and note bushing installed position for reassembly reference.

4) Using Control Arm Bushing Service Set (J-33793-1, 2 and 3) with Nut (J-21474-18) and Bolt (J-21474-19), press bushing out of control arm. *See Fig. 4*. If necessary, detach bumper mounting bolt. Remove bumper.

Installation

1) If upper control arm bumper is deteriorated or damaged, install new bumper and tighten mounting nut to 20 ft. lbs. (27 N.m). To install upper control arm bushings, assemble bushing service set with adapters and position new bushing in control arm bore. *See Fig. 4*. Press in bushing until properly seated in control arm.

Fig. 4: Removing & Installing Upper Control Arm & Bushings

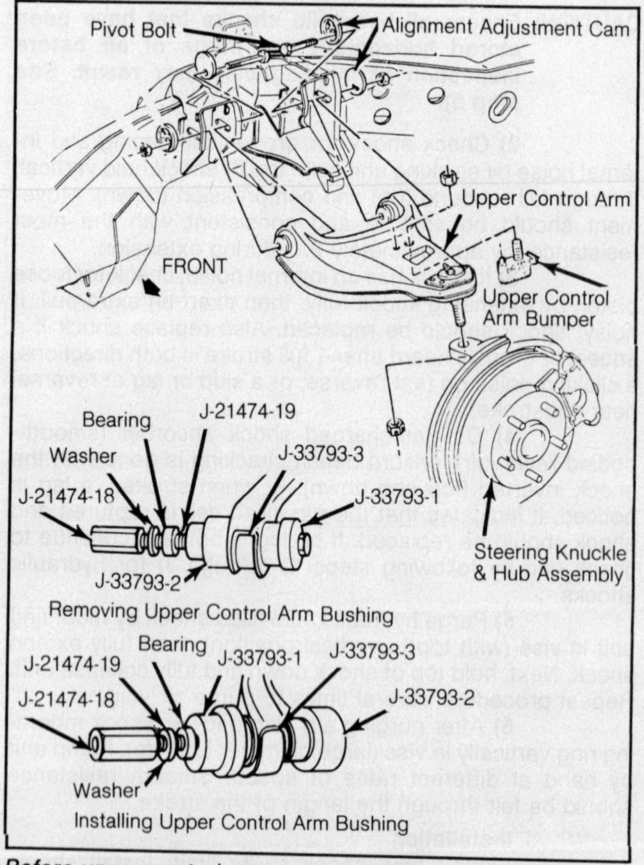

Before upper control arm removal, index mark alignment adjustment cams for realignment reference.

2) Repeat installation procedure for opposite end bushing. Mount control arm on vehicle and install pivot bolts, alignment adjustment cams and pivot nuts in their proper locations.

3) Connect steering knuckle to ball joints and tie rod end. Tighten all mounting bolts. Complete installation by reversing removal procedure. After all components are installed, check front end alignment and adjust as needed.

Front Suspension

GENERAL MOTORS 4WD TORSION BAR "S" SERIES TRUCKS (Cont.)

Fig. 5: Removing & Installing Lower Control Arm & Pivot Bushings

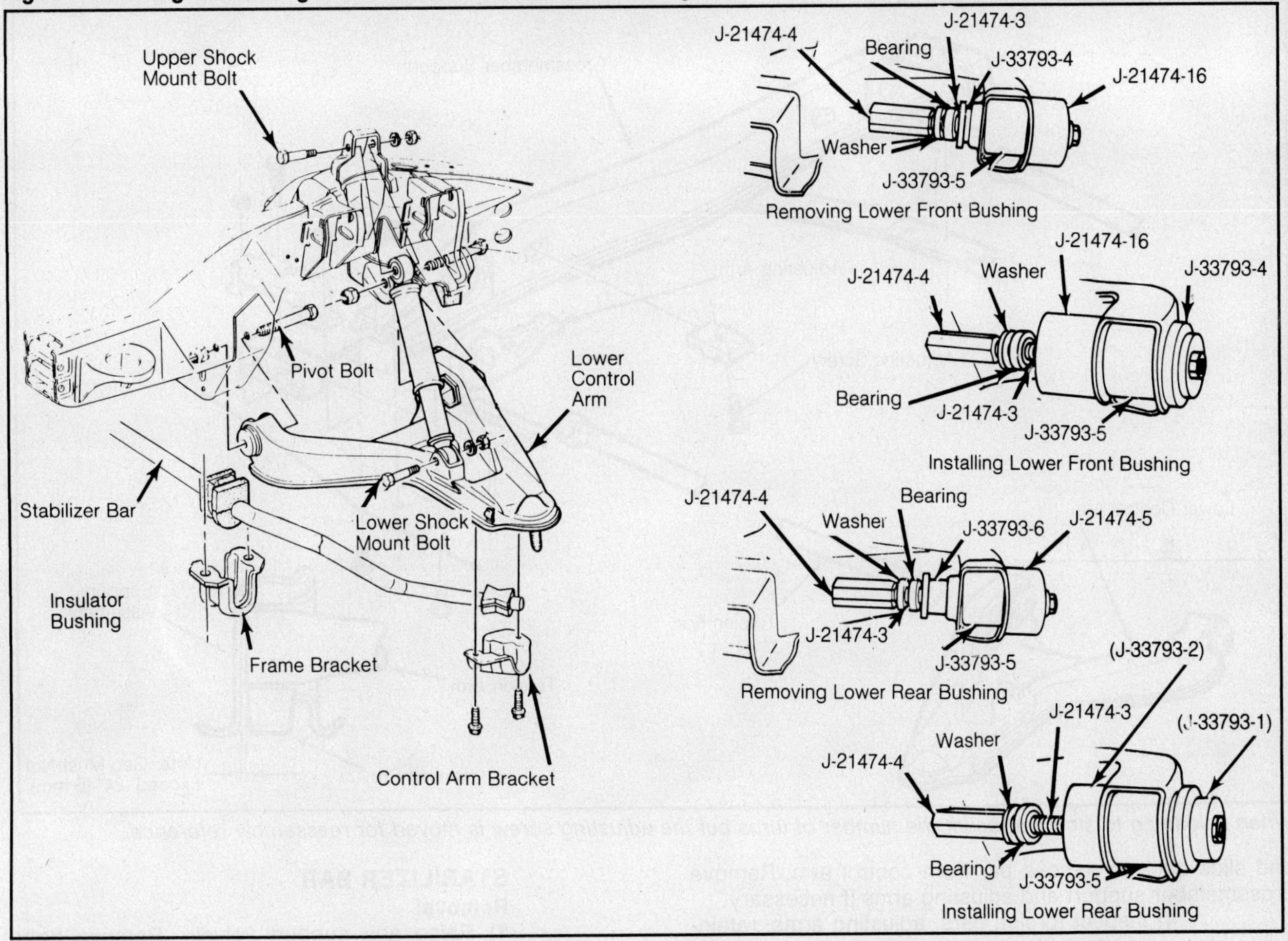

When installing lower control arm bushings, ensure installer presses bushing into control arm until fully seated.

LOWER CONTROL ARM & BUSHINGS

Removal

1) Raise and support vehicle. Remove wheel and tire assembly. Remove disc brake components and hub/bearing carrier assembly. Disconnect ball joints and tie rod end, then remove steering knuckle as previously described. Before control arm removal, unload torsion bar (remove if necessary).

2) Disconnect upper and lower shock mounting bolts and remove shock. Detach stabilizer bar-to-lower control arm bracket mounting bolts (both sides). Rotate bar down and out of work area. Disconnect and remove lower control arm pivot mounting bolts with nuts.

3) Remove lower control arm from vehicle. Inspect control arm, bumper and pivot bushings for excessive wear, damage, deformation and/or deterioration. Replace components as needed.

4) To remove lower front bushing, install Control Arm Bushing Service Set (J-21474-3, 4 and 16) with Adapters (J-33793-4 and 5) on control arm, over bushing. *See Fig. 5*. Turn hex on bushing remover (J-21474-4) and press bushing out of control arm.

5) To remove lower rear bushing, install bushing service set and adapters on control arm, over bushing. Turn bushing remover hex and press bushing out of control arm. *See Fig. 5*.

Installation

1) To install lower front and/or rear bushing in control arm, assembly service set tools and adapters. Position bushing in control arm bore. Turn installer tool hex and draw bushing into control arm until properly seated. *See Fig. 5*.

2) To complete lower control arm installation, reverse removal procedures. After installation, set ride height and check front end alignment as necessary.

TORSION BARS & CROSSMEMBER SUPPORT

Removal

1) Raise and support vehicle. Remove wheel and tire assembly. To unload torsion bar, install Torsion Bar Unloader (J-22517-02). Lubricate unloader bolt threads and tip with grease, then tighten in position.

2) When removing torsion bar adjusting screw, count the number of turns out the screw moves, for reassembly reference. Remove adjusting screw and nut. Release unloader slowly until torsion bar is completely unloaded. Remove unloader tool.

3) Detach torsion bar support retainer mounting bolts and nuts, then remove retainers and rubber support cushions. *See Fig. 6*. Slide torsion bar forward in lower control arm until clear of crossmember support. Pull down

Front Suspension

GENERAL MOTORS 4WD TORSION BAR "S" SERIES TRUCKS (Cont.)

Fig. 6: Exploded View Of Torsion Bars & Crossmember Support Assembly

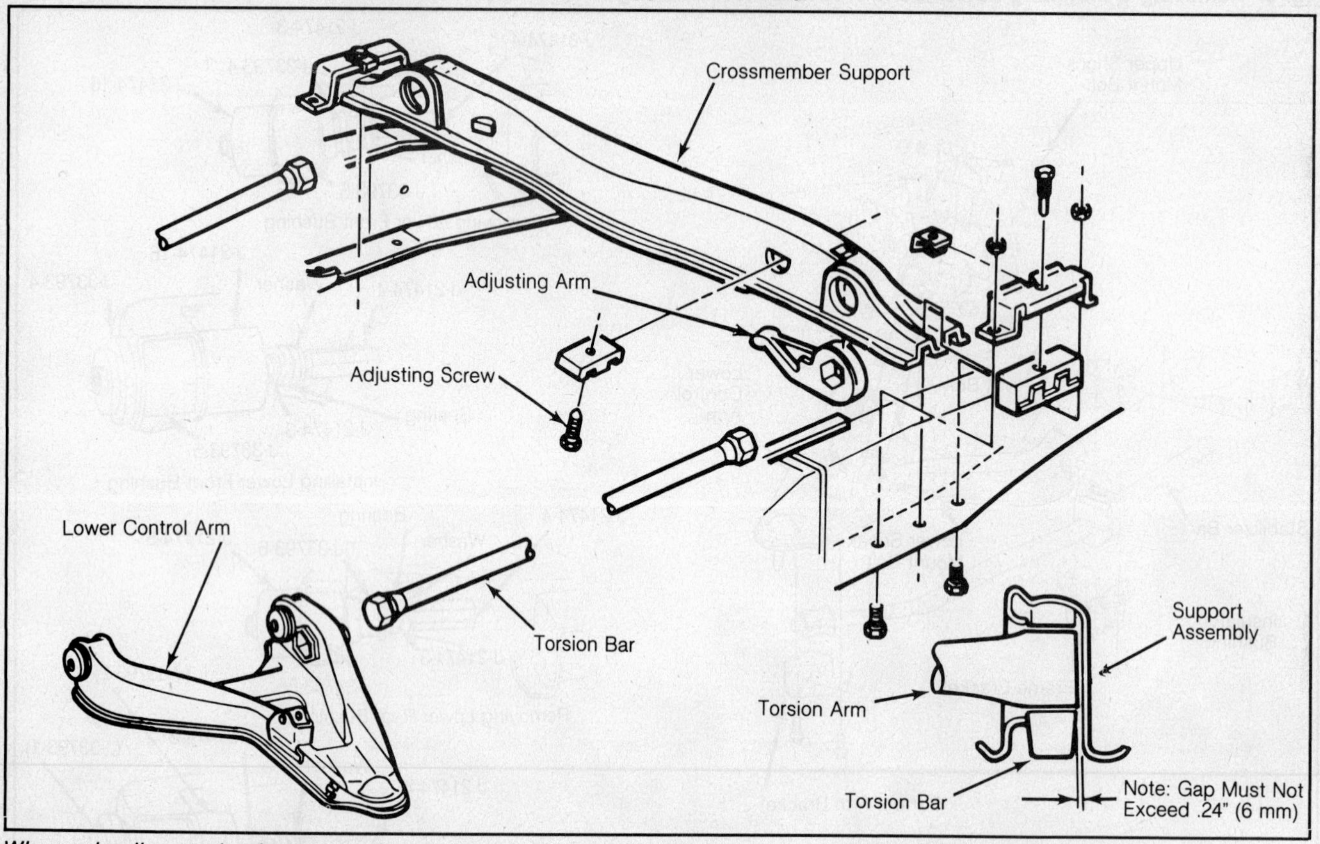

When unloading torsion bar, count the number of turns out the adjusting screw is moved for reassembly reference.

and slide back to remove bar from control arm. Remove crossmember support and adjusting arms if necessary.

4) Inspect torsion bars, adjusting arms, retainers, rubber support cushions and crossmember support for bend, cracks, deterioration or damage. Check adjusting screw and nut for damage or stripped threads. Replace components as necessary.

Installation

1) If removed, install crossmember support, cushions and retainers. Apply grease to hex ends of torsion bar, adjusting arm-to-torsion bar hex area, adjusting screw threads and unloader bolt threads (and tip) to aid in reassembly. Slide torsion bar forward into control arm, lift and pull bar back into position in adjusting arm and crossmember support.

2) Torsion bar is in proper position when there is no more than .24" (6 mm) between rear end of bar and rear wall of crossmember support. *See Fig. 6.* Install unloader tool and tighten to proper tension for adjusting screw and nut installation.

3) Install adjusting nut and turn screw the same number of turns in as were turned out. Release unloader tool. Install remaining components in reverse of removal procedure. After installation, check and adjust ride height and front end alignment as needed.

STABILIZER BAR

Removal

1) Raise and support vehicle. Remove both wheel and tire assemblies. Unload and remove torsion bar as previously described. Detach stabilizer bar frame bracket mounting bolts. Detach bar-to-lower control arm bracket mounting bolts.

2) Remove stabilizer bar with brackets and rubber insulator bushings. Inspect bushings for deformation and/or deterioration. Check stabilizer bar and brackets for cracks, damage and wear. Replace components as necessary.

Installation

1) Install new insulator bushings on stabilizer bar (with split toward front) and brackets onto bushings. Position bar and partially start lower control arm bracket mounting bolts.

2) Install frame bracket mounting bolts and tighten to specification. Tighten remaining mounting bolts. Install torsion bars. Complete installation by reversing removal procedure.

Front Suspension

GENERAL MOTORS 4WD TORSION BAR "S" SERIES TRUCKS (Cont.)

TIGHTENING SPECIFICATIONS

Application	Ft. Lbs. (N.m)
Ball Joint-to-Control Arm Mounting Bolt	15 (20)
Hub/Bearing Carrier Assembly	
To-Drive Axle Retainer Nut [1]	174 (235)
To-Steering Knuckle Mounting Bolt	78 (105)
Lower Control Arm	
Bumper Mounting Bolt	22 (30)
To-Frame Pivot Bolt & Nut	92 (125)
Lower Ball Joint Stud	
To-Steering Knuckle Mounting Nut	83 (113)
Shock Absorber [2]	
Upper Mounting Nut	52 (70)
Lower Mounting Nut	52 (70)
Lower Mounting Bolt	66 (90)
Stabilizer Bar-to-Frame Bracket Mounting Bolt	30 (40)
Stabilizer Bar-to-Lower Control Arm Insulator Bracket Mounting Bolt	23-26 (32-35)
Tie Rod End-to-Steering Knuckle Mounting Nut	35 (48)
Torsion Bar Crossmember Support Retainer Mounting Bolt	25 (34)
Upper Ball Joint Stud	
To-Steering Knuckle Mounting Nut	50 (68)
Upper Control Arm-to-Frame Pivot Bolt & Nut	70 (95)

[1] - Do not back off retainer nut to install new cotter pin. After reaching proper torque, tighten nut only enough to align slot.

[2] - Install shock absorber mounting bolts with nuts to the rear of vehicle.

Front Suspension

GENERAL MOTORS – 4WD LEAF SPRING "K" SERIES TRUCKS

K10/30 Pickup, Blazer, Jimmy

DESCRIPTION

At the wheel ends of the axle tubes, 2 types of steering knuckle attachments are used. The K10/20 series knuckle is attached with ball joints. The K30 series use a king pin type attachment. The tapered upper king pin fits in a tapered nylon bushing. The lower king pin is part of the bearing cap and rides in a tapered roller bearing.

Hydraulic or gas-charged shock absorbers are attached to brackets on frame rails and front axle assembly. The Z75 option features 2 shocks per side. Leaf springs mount to frame rail brackets and shackles, providing support for axle assembly. A stabilizer bar is mounted to frame rail by brackets and to front axle assembly by pivot bolts. *See Fig. 1*.

An automatic locking hub is used on all models. This system automatically engages the hubs whenever four-wheel drive is selected. A manual locking hub is also used on K30 series (only). This system must be engaged manually whenever four-wheel drive is selected.

ADJUSTMENTS & CHECKING

WHEEL ALIGNMENT SPECIFICATIONS & PROCEDURES

On "K" series, caster and camber is designed into the front axle assembly and is not adjustable. Toe-in is adjusted using the same procedure as 2WD vehicles with 0° (nominal) as the standard setting. See WHEEL ALIGNMENT SPECIFICATIONS & PROCEDURES in WHEEL ALIGNMENT section.

NOTE: **Front axle ball joint adjustment is generally necessary only when there is excessive play in the steering, irregular wear on tires or persistant loosening of the tie rod is observed.**

BALL JOINT TURNING EFFORT CHECK

1) Raise and support vehicle on frame hoist, then position adjustable jack stands just inside of front springs. Disconnect connecting rod and tie rod to allow independent movement of each steering knuckle.

2) Attach a spring-type pull scale (fish scale), which reads in Lb. (kg) increments, to the tie rod mounting hole of the steering knuckle arm. With knuckle assembly in the straight-ahead position, determine the right angle pull required to keep knuckle turning after initial breakaway.

3) The turning pull tension should not exceed 25 lbs. (11.3 kg) for each knuckle assembly, in either direction. If pull tension is not to specification, see REMOVAL & INSTALLATION section of this article for ball joint stud sleeve adjustment.

NOTE: **Spindle needle bearings should be checked and lubricated at the same time as the front wheel bearings. The lubrication interval should be 12,000 miles under normal conditions, off road use (such as in mud or water) will require shorter intervals. Spindle bearings are accessible after removing the spindle.**

WHEEL BEARING ADJUSTMENT

Warner Gear Automatic Hub

1) After lubricating wheel and spindle bearings, install hub/rotor assembly and outer wheel bearing onto spindle. Using Wheel Bearing Nut Wrench (J-6893-D) and Torque Wrench Adapter (J-23446 or J-6893-01 for K10/20 and J-26878-A for K30), tighten inner adjusting nut to 50 ft. lbs. (60 N.m) while rotating hub (by hand) to seat bearings.

2) Back off inner adjusting nut, then retighten to 35 ft. lbs. (47 N.m) while hub is being rotated. Back off inner adjusting nut again, no more than 3/8 turn maximum. Assemble drag sleeve retainer washer, over axle shaft, against bearing adjusting nut. *See Fig. 2*.

NOTE: **When installing drag sleeve retainer washer, ensure tang (on inside diameter of washer) fits keyway properly and pin on inner nut passes through 1 hole in retainer washer.**

3) Assemble and tighten outer lock nut to 160-205 ft. lbs. (217-310 N.m). Check hub/rotor assembly end play with a dial indicator. Standard end play is .0010-.0100" (.025-.254 mm). If not to specification, repeat steps **1)** through **3)**. If end play is within limits, install locking hub assembly.

REMOVAL & INSTALLATION

AUTOMATIC & MANUAL LOCKING HUB & BRAKE ROTOR ASSEMBLY

Removal (Warner Gear Automatic Hub)

1) Detach 5 Allen head screws (with "O" rings) retaining hub cover plate to outer clutch housing. Remove cover plate, sealing ring, seal bridge retainer (K10/20) or assembly aid retainer (K30), bearing race spring, inner bearing race, ball bearing assembly and bearing retainer clip.

2) Using needle-nose pliers, compress wire retaining ring and pull remaining components from the wheel hub. Remove snap ring from hub sleeve groove. *See Fig. 2, No. 28*. Turn clutch gear until it drops into engagement with outer clutch housing.

NOTE: **Do not remove brake band from drag sleeve. Brake band spring tension can be changed if coils are over expanded and this could affect hub operation.**

3) Lift and cock drag sleeve to unlock brake band tangs from window of inner cage, then remove drag sleeve and brake assembly. Remove snap ring from outer clutch housing groove. *See Fig. 2, No. 24*.

4) Using a small screwdriver, pry outer cage (plastic) free from inner cage while inner cage is being removed. Using small screwdriver, pry outer cage tabs free from outer clutch housing groove. Remove outer cage.

5) Remove clutch sleeve and attached components from outer clutch housing. Compress return spring and hold in position with "C" clamps. Clamps may have to be fabricated if necessary. *See Fig. 2, View A*.

NOTE: **The 2 "C" shaped clamps may be fabricated from 3/8" (9.5 mm) wide by 3/32" (2.4 mm) or 1/8" (3.2 mm) thick stock. The distance between the 2 clamp legs should be about 1 1/4" (31.8 mm).**

Front Suspension

GENERAL MOTORS – 4WD LEAF SPRING "K" SERIES TRUCKS (Cont.)

Fig. 1: Exploded View Of Front Suspension System

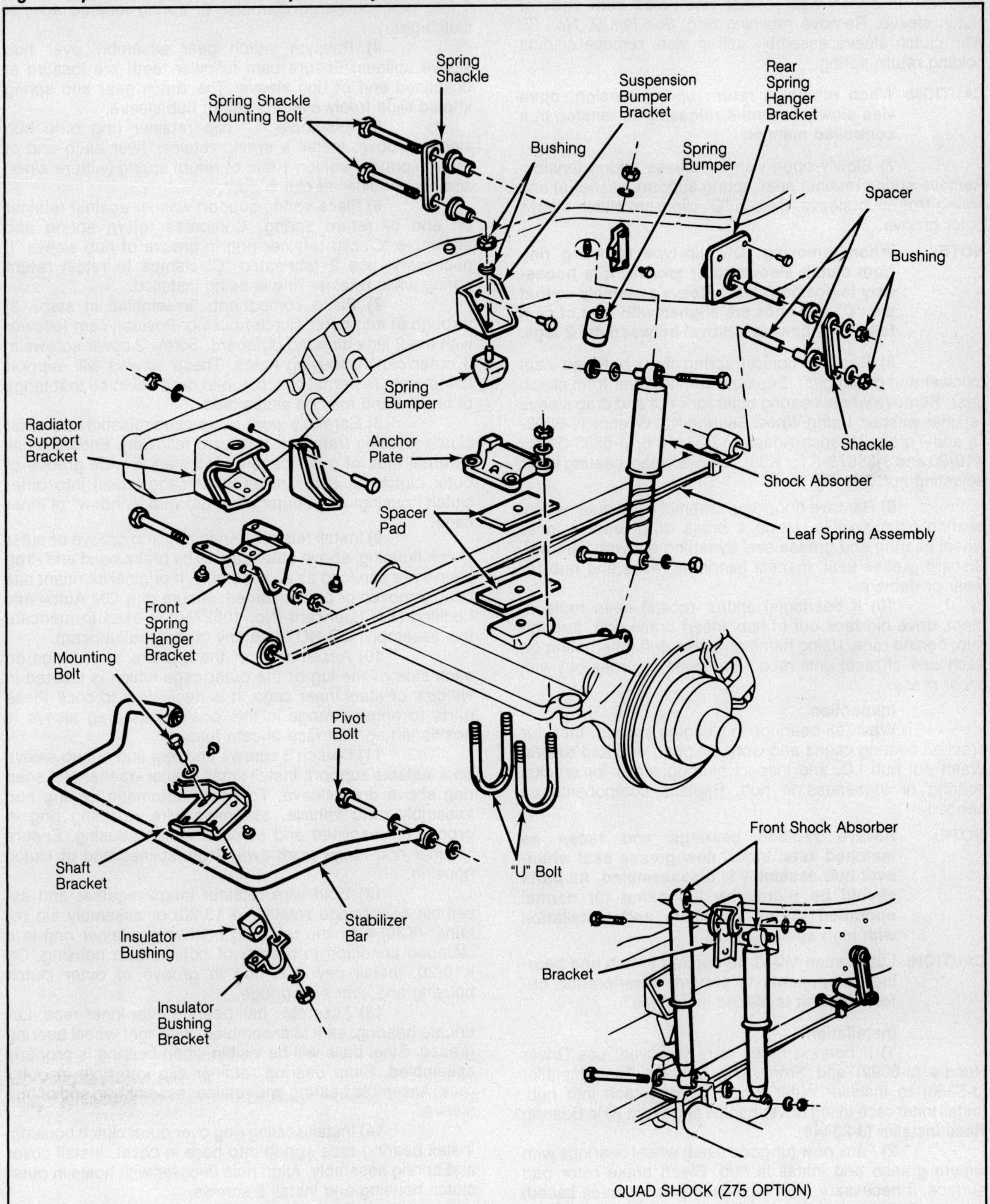

Front Suspension

GENERAL MOTORS – 4WD LEAF SPRING "K" SERIES TRUCKS (Cont.)

6) After clamps are installed, position entire assembly in bench vise so that vise holds both ends of clutch sleeve. Remove retaining ring. *See Fig. 2, No. 12*. With clutch sleeve assembly still in vise, remove clamps holding return spring.

CAUTION: When releasing return spring tension, open vise slowly to permit releasing of tension in a controlled manner.

7) Slowly open vise to release spring tension. Remove spring retainer seat, spring support washer(s) and spring from hub sleeve. Detach "C" clip from clutch sleeve outer groove.

NOTE: When removing "C" clip-type retaining ring from clutch sleeve outer groove, it is necessary to position clutch sleeve assembly so that the "C" clip ends are aligned with legs of cam follower, allowing removal between the 2 legs.

8) Remove conical spring from between cam follower and clutch gear. Separate cam follower from clutch gear. Remove wheel bearing outer lock nut and drag sleeve retainer washer. Using Wheel Bearing Nut Wrench (J-6893-D) and Torque Wrench Adapter (J-23446 or J-6893-01 for K10/20 and J-26878-A for K30), remove wheel bearing inner adjusting nut. *See Fig. 2*.

9) Remove hub/rotor assembly and outer wheel bearing from spindle. Using a brass drift, remove inner wheel bearing and grease seal by taping out with hammer. Discard grease seal. Inspect bearings, races and hub for wear or damage.

10) If bearing(s) and/or race(s) need replacement, drive old race out of hub. Insert brass drift, through hub, behind race. Using hammer, strike drift (alternating on each side of race) until race is removed or press out with arbor press.

Inspection

Wash all bearings in cleaning solvent, then for cracked bearing cages and worn, chipped or pitted rollers. Wash out hub I.D. and inspect bearing races for cracks, scoring or looseness in hub. Replace components as needed.

NOTE: Always replace bearings and races as matched sets. Install new grease seal whenever hub assembly is disassembled. All parts should be thoroughly lubricated for normal operation during assembly and installation with high speed grease.

CAUTION: Lubrication MUST be applied to hub and bearing components to prevent deterioration before the unit is placed in service.

Installation

1) If bearing races were removed, use Driver Handle (J-8092) and Front Axle Bearing Race Installer (J-6368) to installer outer wheel bearing race into hub. Install inner race using driver handle and Front Axle Bearing Race Installer (J-23448).

2) Pack new (or good used) wheel bearings with lithium grease and install in hub. Clean brake rotor pad surface, if necessary, with high-flash point (non-oil based) cleaner. Position hub/rotor assembly onto spindle. Install adjusting nut and adjust wheel bearings. See ADJUSTMENTS & CHECKING.

3) After wheel bearing adjustment, install automatic locking hub assembly. Snap the cam follower tangs over flats of clutch gear. Compress conical spring and slide it into position (large diameter of spring located against clutch gear).

4) Position clutch gear assembly over hub sleeve splines. Ensure cam follower teeth are located at unsplined end of hub sleeve. The clutch gear and spring should slide freely over splines of hub sleeve.

5) Assemble "C" clip retainer ring onto hub sleeve groove. Install a spring retainer over each end of return spring. Position 1 end of return spring (with retainer) against shoulder of clutch gear.

6) Place spring support washer against retainer on end of return spring. Compress return spring and assemble "C" clip retainer ring in groove of hub sleeve. If necessary, use 2 fabricated "C' clamps to retain return spring while retainer ring is being installed.

7) Place components assembled in steps **3)** through **6)** into outer clutch housing. Position cam follower with the 2 legs directed outboard. Screw 3 cover screws in 3 outer clutch housing holes. These screws will support component to permit clutch hub to drop down so that tangs of brake band may be assembled.

8) Carefully work outer cage (plastic) into outer clutch housing (ramps facing cam follower). Ensure small external tabs of outer cage are located in wide groove of outer clutch housing. Install inner cage (steel) into outer clutch housing. Align outer cage tab with "window" of inner cage.

9) Install retaining snap ring into groove of outer clutch housing, above outer cage. The brake band and drag sleeve are serviced as an assembly. If original lubricant has been removed or contaminated, ensure only GM Automatic Locking Hub Lubricant (No. 1052750) is used to lubricate this assembly. DO NOT use any other type lubricant.

10) Assemble 1 of the 2 brake band tangs on each side of the lug of the outer cage which is located in window of steel inner cage. It is necessary to cock these parts to engage tangs in this position as drag sleeve is positioned against face of cam follower.

11) Detach 3 screws and rest end of hub sleeve on a suitable support. Install small spacer washer and snap ring above drag sleeve. To install automatic locking hub assembly onto vehicle, assemble wire retaining ring in groove in unsplined end of outer clutch housing. Ensure retainer ring tangs point away from splined end of clutch housing.

12) Hold wire retainer tangs together and assemble seal bridge retainer (K10/20) or assembly aid retainer (K30) over the tangs to hold wire retainer ring in a clamped condition in groove of outer clutch housing. On K10/20, install new "O" ring in groove of outer clutch housing and over seal bridge.

13) Assemble ball bearing over inner race. Lubricate bearing, as it is assembled, with light wheel bearing grease. Steel balls will be visible when bearing is properly assembled. Snap bearing retainer clip into hole in outer race. Assemble bearing and retainer assembly in end of hub sleeve.

14) Install sealing ring over outer clutch housing. Install bearing race spring into bore in cover. Install cover and spring assembly. Align hole in cover with holes in outer clutch housing and install 5 screws.

NOTE: On K10/20 models, assemble "O" ring over seal bridge to prevent it from jumping out of position during handling before hub bearing is assembled onto vehicle. This "O" ring may be left on but is not required.

Front Suspension

GENERAL MOTORS – 4WD LEAF SPRING "K" SERIES TRUCKS (Cont.)

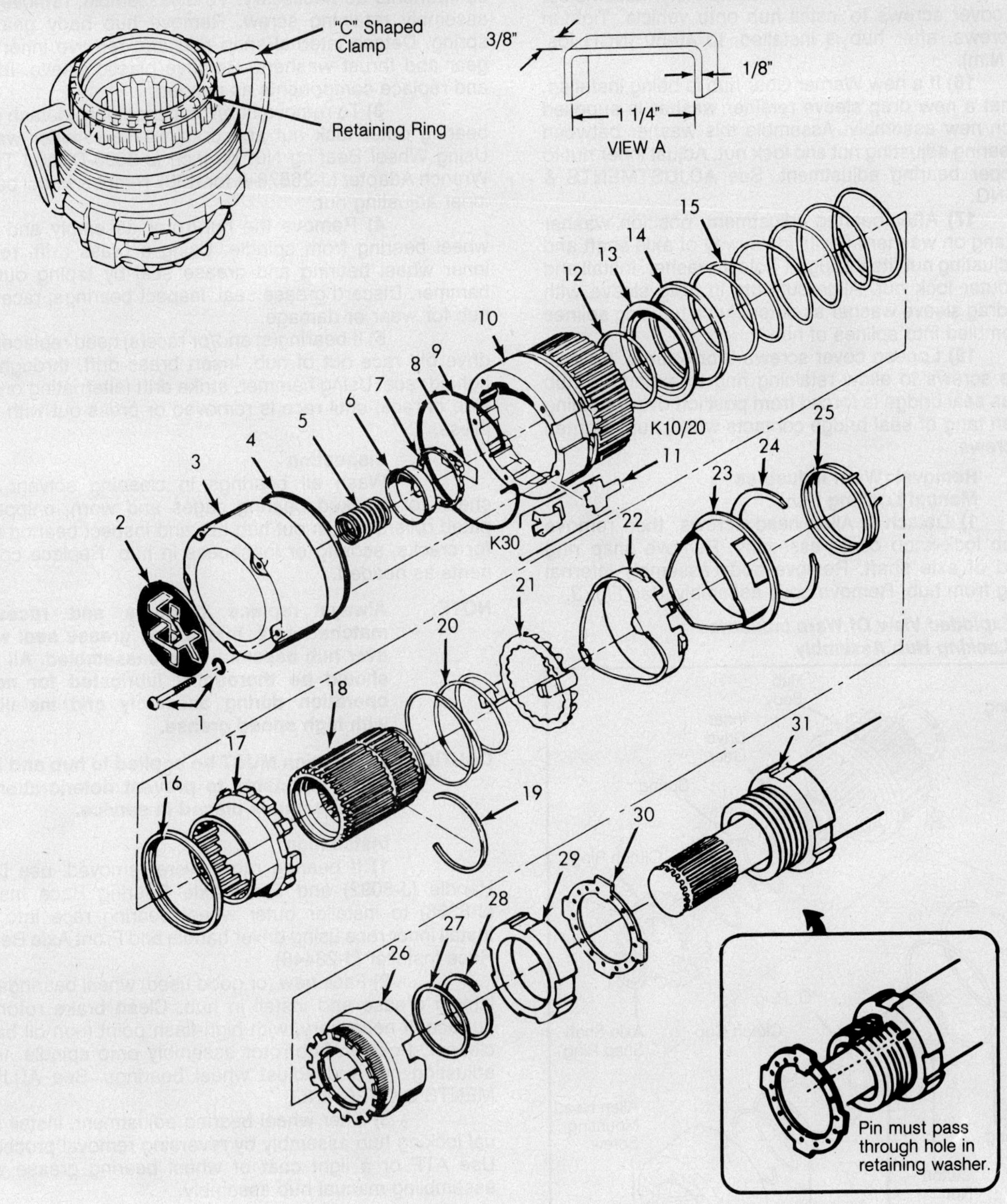

Fig. 2: Exploded View Of Warner Gear Automatic Hub

1. Allen Head Machine Screw & "O" Ring
2. Cover Plate
3. Automatic Hub Cover
4. Sealing Ring
5. Bearing Race Spring
6. Bearing Inner Race
7. Bearing
8. Bearing Retainer Clip
9. Wire Retaining Ring
10. Outer Clutch Housing
11. Seal Bridge Retainer (K10/20) Or Assembly Aid Retainer (K30)
12. Retaining Ring
13. Spring Support Washer
14. Spring Retainer
15. Return Spring
16. Spring Retainer
17. Clutch Gear
18. Hub Sleeve
19. "C" Type Retaining Ring
20. Conical Spring
21. Cam Follower
22. Outer Cage
23. Inner Cage
24. Snap Ring
25. Brake Band
26. Drag Sleeve & Detent
27. Small Spacer
28. Retaining Ring
29. Lock Nut
30. Drag Sleeve Retainer Washer
31. Wheel Bearing Adjusting Nut

Front Suspension
GENERAL MOTORS – 4WD LEAF SPRING "K" SERIES TRUCKS (Cont.)

15) Check that hub sleeve and attached parts turn freely after unit has been completely assembled. Loosen cover screws to install hub onto vehicle. Tighten cover screws, after hub is installed, to 40-50 INCH lbs. (4.5-5.6 N.m).

16) If a new Warner Gear hub is being installed, check that a new drag sleeve retainer washer is supplied with each new assembly. Assemble this washer between wheel bearing adjusting nut and lock nut. Adjust inner nut to give proper bearing adjustment. See ADJUSTMENTS & CHECKING.

17) After bearing adjustment, position washer so that tang on washer I.D. fits in keyway of axle shaft and pin on adjusting nut fits through 1 hole in washer. Install and tighten outer lock nut. Align cut-outs in drag sleeve with tabs on drag sleeve washer as outer clutch housing splines are assembled into splines of hub.

18) Loosen cover screws 3 or 4 turns. Push in on these screws to allow retaining ring to expand in hub groove as seal bridge is forced from position over retaining ring when tang of seal bridge contacts wheel hub. Tighten cover screws.

Removal (Warn Industries Manual Locking Hub)

1) Detach 6 Allen head screws, then remove outer hub lock-knob cover assembly. Remove snap ring from end of axle shaft. Remove body assembly internal snap ring from hub. Remove body assembly. *See Fig. 3.*

Fig. 3: Exploded View Of Warn Industries Manual Locking Hub Assembly

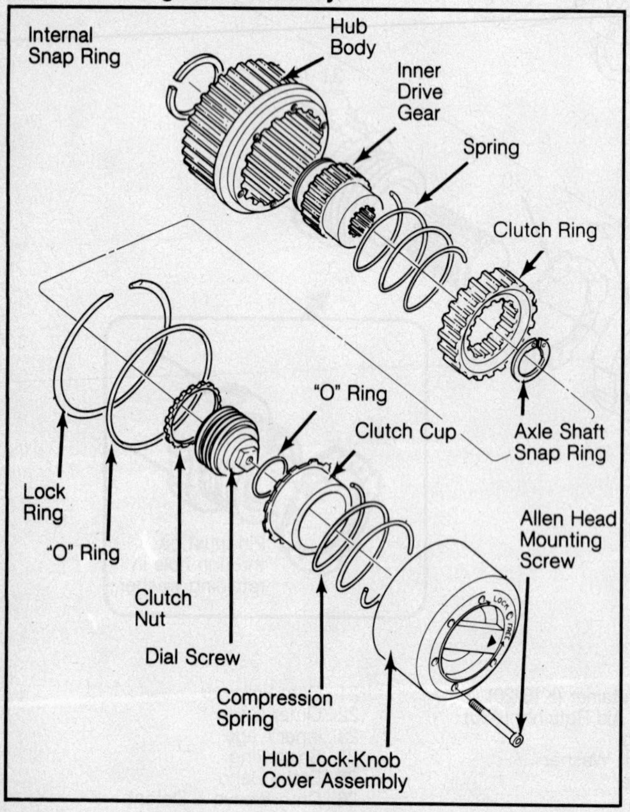

NOTE: **Do not disassemble outer hub lock-knob cover assembly. If disassembled, timing relationships will be difficult to restore. Replace unit as an assembly only.**

2) Disassemble inner body and clean or replace components as necessary. To disassemble, remove body assembly retaining screw. Remove hub body gear and spring. Detach internal snap ring and remove inner drive gear and thrust washers. Remove plastic sleeve. Inspect and replace components as needed.

3) To remove hub/rotor assembly, detach wheel bearing outer lock nut and drag sleeve retainer washer. Using Wheel Bearing Nut Wrench (J-6893-D) and Torque Wrench Adapter (J-26878-A for K30), remove wheel bearing inner adjusting nut.

4) Remove the hub/rotor assembly and outer wheel bearing from spindle. Using a brass drift, remove inner wheel bearing and grease seal by taping out with hammer. Discard grease seal. Inspect bearings, races and hub for wear or damage.

5) If bearing(s) and/or race(s) need replacement, drive old race out of hub. Insert brass drift, through hub, behind race. Using hammer, strike drift (alternating on each side of race) until race is removed or press out with arbor press.

Inspection

Wash all bearings in cleaning solvent, then check for cracked bearing cages and worn, chipped or pitted rollers. Wash out hub I.D. and inspect bearing races for cracks, scoring or looseness in hub. Replace components as needed.

NOTE: **Always replace bearings and races as matched sets. Install new grease seal whenever hub assembly is disassembled. All parts should be thoroughly lubricated for normal operation during assembly and installation with high speed grease.**

CAUTION: **Lubrication MUST be applied to hub and bearing components to prevent deterioration before the unit is placed in service.**

Installation

1) If bearing races were removed, use Driver Handle (J-8092) and Front Axle Bearing Race Installer (J-6368) to installer outer wheel bearing race into hub. Install inner race using driver handle and Front Axle Bearing Race Installer (J-23448).

2) Pack new (or good used) wheel bearings with lithium grease and install in hub. Clean brake rotor pad surface, if necessary, with high-flash point (non-oil based) cleaner. Position hub/rotor assembly onto spindle. Install adjusting nut and adjust wheel bearings. See ADJUSTMENTS & CHECKING.

3) After wheel bearing adjustment, install manual locking hub assembly by reversing removal procedure. Use ATF or a light coat of wheel bearing grease when assembling manual hub assembly.

SPINDLE

Removal

1) Raise and support vehicle. Remove wheel and tire assembly. Detach automatic or manual locking hub components. Remove hub/rotor assembly. Detach spindle retaining bolts.

2) Remove spindle and thrust washer by tapping end of spindle lightly with soft-faced hammer. *See Fig. 4, VIEW A.* Inspect thrust washer and replace if excessive wear has occurred. With spindle removed from vehicle, install assembly in vise (on high step diameter).

Front Suspension

GENERAL MOTORS – 4WD LEAF SPRING "K" SERIES TRUCKS (Cont.)

Fig. 4: Front Spindle Removal & Component Inspection

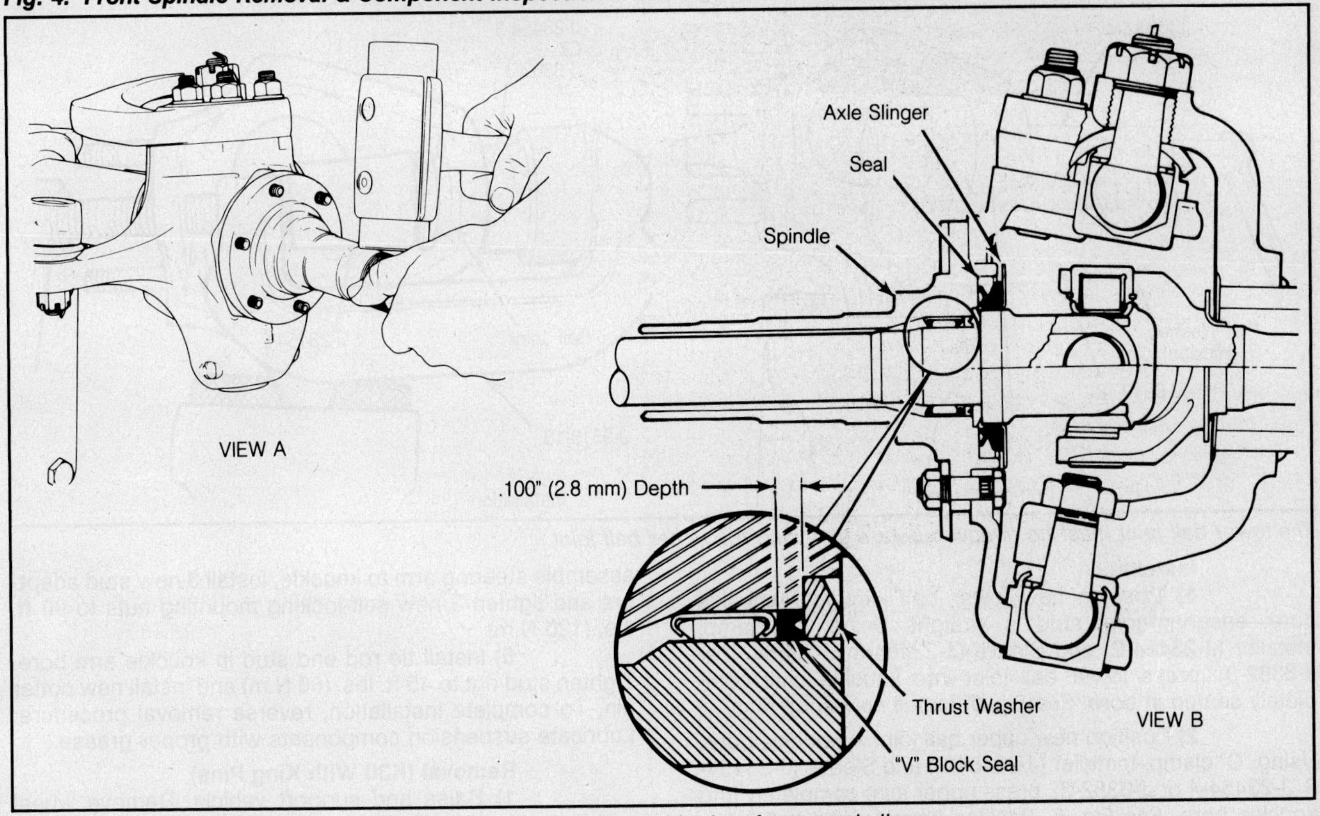

Replace worn thrust washer as needed and reinstall washer with chamfer toward slinger.

3) Ensure machined surface of spindle will not be damaged by vise jaws. Remove grease seals and discard. Remove needle roller bearing and inspect for excessive wear or damage.

Installation

1) If necessary, install new bearing assembly into spindle using Driver Handle (J-8092 for K10/20 or J-21465-17 for K30) and Needle Bearing Installer (J-23445).

2) Install new grease seal onto slinger with lip toward spindle. Install new "V" block oil seal with "V" block portion facing thrust washer. *See Fig. 4, VIEW B*. Relubricate needle bearing and spindle with lithium grease. Install new thrust washer over axle shaft (with chamfer toward slinger).

3) Install spindle over axle shaft, then position spindle onto knuckle. Using new spindle nuts, tighten to 65 ft. lbs. (88 N.m). Install hub/rotor assembly and automatic or manual locking hub in reverse of removal procedure. Lubricate suspension components as necessary.

STEERING ARM, KNUCKLE, BALL JOINTS & KING PINS

NOTE: **The lower ball joint must be removed before servicing the upper ball joint. Left-hand knuckle steering arm must be removed to service upper ball joint.**

Removal (K10/20 With Ball Joints)

1) Detach automatic locking hub, hub/rotor assembly and spindle components. If steering arm must be removed, detach tie rod. Remove cotter pin and loosen tie rod stud nut. Tap on nut with soft-faced hammer to loosen from knuckle steering arm.

2) Remove nuts and disconnect tie rod. If steering arm must be removed (to service left-hand knuckle upper ball joint), detach and discard self-locking mounting nuts, then remove arm. Remove cotter pin from upper ball joint stud.

3) Remove stud retaining nuts. To remove knuckle assembly from yoke, insert a wedge-shaped tool between lower ball joint stud and yoke. Tap on knuckle assembly to release. Repeat procedure on upper ball joint.

NOTE: **Do not remove yoke upper ball joint stud adjusting sleeve unless new ball joints are being installed. If it is necessary to loosen sleeve to remove knuckle, do not loosen more than 2 threads using Ball Stud Nut Wrench (J-23447).**

CAUTION: **Use caution during removal as the non-hardened threads in yoke can be easily damaged by the hardened threads of the adjusting sleeve.**

4) Before removing ball joints, detach snap ring from lower ball joint. Lower ball joint must be removed before service to upper ball joint can be performed. Install knuckle assembly in vise.

5) Using "C" Clamp (J-9519-10), Receiver (J-23454-1) and Sleeve (J-23454-4), remove lower ball joint from knuckle. *See Fig. 5*. Remove upper ball joint using "C" clamp, Receiver, flat washer and Sleeve (23454-3, J-23454-4 or J-6382-3). *See Fig. 5*.

NOTE: **If sleeve is not available, fabricate a remover tool from 2 3/8" O.D. steel tubing with minimum 2 1/16" I.D. Cut tubing 2 1/2" (63.5 mm) long.**

Front Suspension

GENERAL MOTORS – 4WD LEAF SPRING "K" SERIES TRUCKS (Cont.)

Fig. 5: Removing & Installing Lower Ball Joint In Steering Knuckle

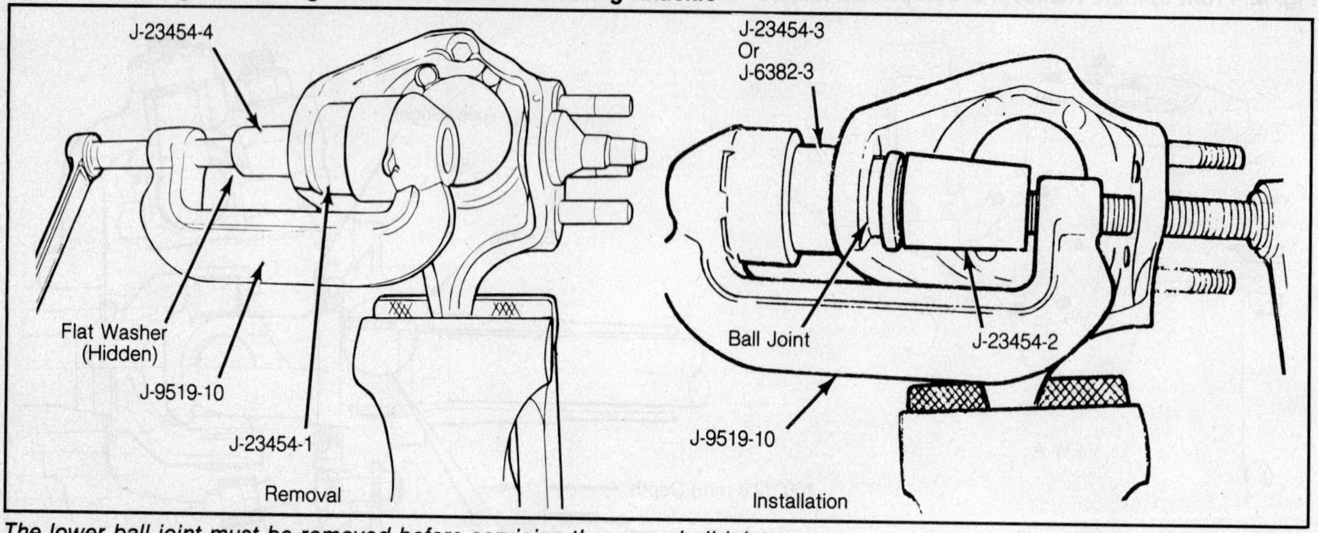

The lower ball joint must be removed before servicing the upper ball joint.

Installation

1) Position new lower ball joint into knuckle bore, ensuring joint stud is straight. Using "C" clamp, Installer (J-23454-2) and Sleeve (J-23454-3, J-23454-4 or J-6382-3), press lower ball joint into knuckle until completely seated in bore. *See Fig. 5*. Install new snap ring.

2) Position new upper ball joint in knuckle bore. Using "C" clamp, Installer (J-23454-2) and Sleeve (J-23454-3, J-23454-4 or J-6382-3), press upper joint completely into knuckle bore. *See Fig. 6*. Position knuckle and ball joints into yoke. Install new retainer nuts (finger tight) onto studs.

3) Push up on knuckle (to keep stud from turning) while partially tightening lower ball joint retainer nut to 30 ft. lbs. (40 N.m). Tighten yoke upper ball joint stud adjusting sleeve to 50 ft. lbs. (70 N.m) using Spanner Wrench (J-23447).

4) Tighten upper ball joint stud retainer nut to 100 ft. lbs. (136 N.m). Install new cotter pin. Do not loosen stud nut to insert cotter pin, tighten only enough to align slot in nut to stud hole.

5) Apply final torque of 70 ft. lbs. (95 N.m) to lower stud nut. If tie rod and steering arm were removed, assemble steering arm to knuckle, install 3 new stud adapters and tighten 3 new self-locking mounting nuts to 90 ft. lbs. (120 N.m).

6) Install tie rod end stud in knuckle arm bore. Tighten stud nut to 45 ft. lbs. (60 N.m) and install new cotter pin. To complete installation, reverse removal procedure. Lubricate suspension components with proper grease.

Removal (K30 With King Pins)

1) Raise and support vehicle. Remove wheel and tire assembly. Remove hub/rotor assembly and spindle. If necessary, tap spindle with soft-faced hammer to free it from knuckle. Inspect bronze spacer (located between axle shaft joint assembly and bearing). If excessive wear is evident, replace spacer.

2) Detach 4 nuts from upper king pin cap. Remove nuts alternately (compression spring will force cap up). Remove cap, compression spring and gasket. Discard gasket. From underside of knuckle, detach 4 cap screws from lower king pin bearing cap.

3) Remove bearing cap and lower king pin. Remove upper king pin tapered bushing and knuckle from yoke. Remove king pin felt seal. Remove knuckle. With yoke

Fig. 6: Removing & Installing Upper Ball Joint In Steering Knuckle

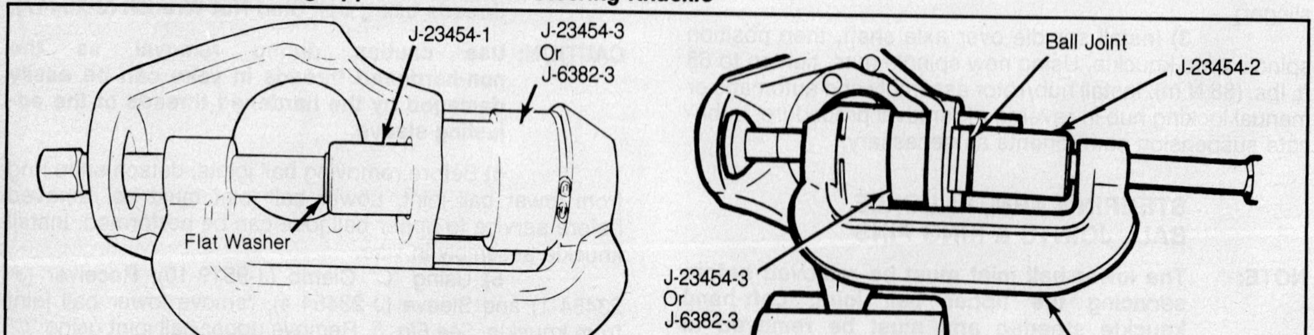

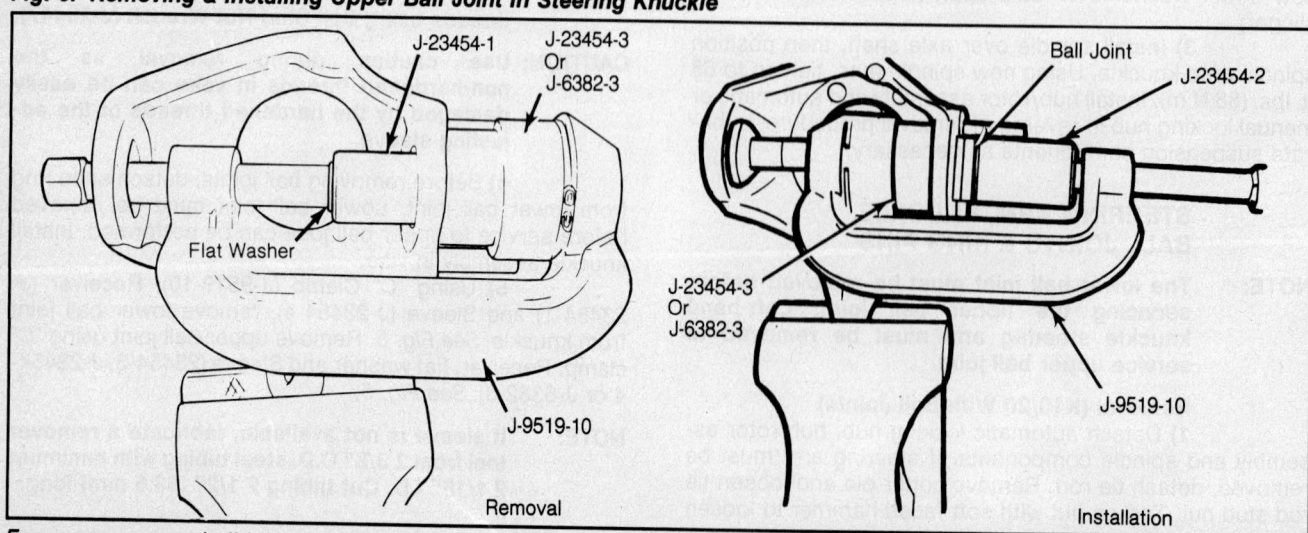

Ensure new upper ball joint is pressed completely into knuckle bore during installation.

mounted in vise, remove upper king pin with large breaker bar and King Pin Socket (J-26871).

NOTE: Upper king pin may require extreme effort to remove. Torque specification is 500-600 ft. lbs. (678-813 N.m).

4) Using hammer and Front King Pin Bearing Race Remover/Installer (J-7817), remove lower king pin bearing race, bearing, grease retainer and seal (all at the same time). *See Fig. 7.* Discard seal. Inspect grease retainer for damage and replace as needed.

Fig. 7: Removing K30 King Pin Bearing, Race, Grease Retainer & Seal

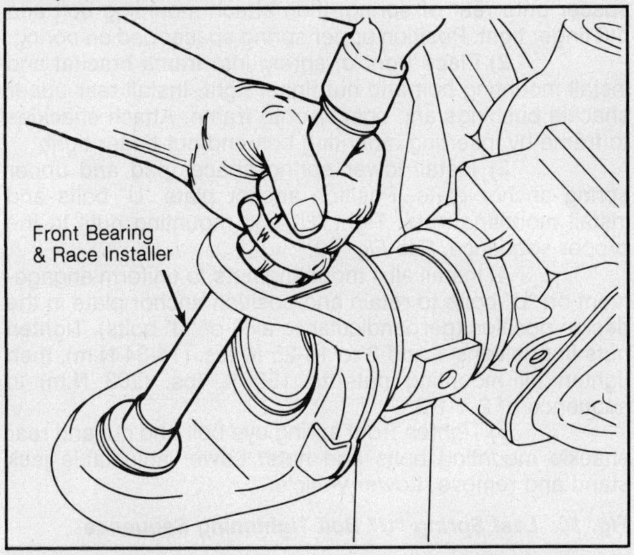

Use hammer and remover/installer tool to drive bearing components from knuckle (all at the same time).

Installation

1) Install new grease retainer and lower king pin bearing race using hammer and Front King Pin Bearing Race Remover/Installer (J-7817). Fill grease retainer with specified grease, then lubricate bearing and install.

2) Using hammer and King Pin Bearing Oil Seal Installer (J-22301), tap in seal until properly seated. Do not distort seal, it will protrude slightly from surface of yoke flange when fully installed.

3) Using hammer and King Pin Socket (J-26871), install upper king pin. Tighten to 500-600 ft. lbs. (678-813 N.m). Install new felt seal onto king pin. Assemble knuckle. Install tapered bushing over king pin. Install lower bearing cap and king pin with 4 cap screws, then tighten (alternately and evenly) to 70-90 ft. lbs. (95-120 N.m).

4) Install compression spring onto upper king pin bushing. Install bearing cap, with new gasket, over 4 studs. Tighten nuts (alternately and evenly) to 70-90 ft. lbs. (95-120 N.m). To complete installation, reverse removal procedure. Lubricate suspension components with proper grease.

SHOCK ABSORBER

Removal

Raise and support vehicle. Detach nuts and eye bolts retaining upper and lower shock absorber mounts. Remove shock from vehicle. Inspect rubber mounting bushings for excessive wear or deterioration. Check shock body for damage or fluid leakage.

Inspection

1) On hydraulic fluid filled shock absorber (spiral-groove reservoir), check for binding, excessive noise, missing bump stops, worn or damaged rubber mounting grommets and hydraulic fluid leaks around seal cover area.

NOTE: A slight trace of hydraulic fluid (Dark Brown tint with a characteristic odor) around seal cover area is not a cause for replacement.

CAUTION: Ensure all hydraulic shocks that have been stored horizontally are purged of air before inspection or misdiagnosis may result. See step 5).

2) Check shock for proper dampening and internal noise by stroking unit (with top of shock held vertical) through full rebound (up) and compression (down). Movement should be smooth and consistent with the most resistance (by approximately 2:1) during extension.

3) If shock has an internal noise, check for loose piston by extending shock fully, then exert an extra pull. If noisy, shock should be replaced. Also replace shock if a squeal or grunt is heard after 1 full stroke in both directions, a clicking noise on fast reverse, or a skip or lag at reversal near midstroke.

4) On gas-charged shock absorber (smooth-bodied reservoir), ensure bench checking is done with shock inverted (top end down). If, when stroked, a lag is noticed, it indicates that the gas-filled cell is ruptured and shock should be replaced. If no lag is noticed, continue to check unit by following steps **1)** through **3)** for hydraulic shocks.

5) Purge shock by mounting unit in vise (with top in vertical position), then fully extend shock. Next, hold top of shock down and fully collapse unit. Repeat procedure several times to purge air void. After purging air, clamp lower shock mounting ring vertically in vise (large diameter tube up). Pump unit by hand at different rates of speed.

6) Smooth resistance should be felt through the length of the stroke. Since unit is normally pressurized, the sound of air bubbles or a gurgling noise is normal. To complete inspection, continue to check unit by following steps **1)** through **3)** for hydraulic shocks.

Installation

Place shock absorber in position over mounting bolts or into mounting brackets. Install eye bolts and nuts, then tighten to specification. Lower vehicle.

STABILIZER BAR

Removal

1) Raise and support vehicle on frame hoist. Detach nuts and bolts attaching stabilizer brackets and bushings at frame locations. Detach pivot bolts and washers at lower spring anchor plates. *See Fig. 8.*

2) Remove stabilizer bar from vehicle. Inspect rubber bushings for excessive wear or deterioration. Check bar for damage. Replace components as necessary.

Installation

1) Apply rubber grease to stabilizer bar bushing locations. Position bar-to-frame bushings with slit toward front of vehicle. Place stabilizer bar in position on frame and install frame brackets over bushings. Ensure brackets are positioned properly over bushings.

2) Install bolts and nuts finger tight. Install pivot bolts and washers through stabilizer bar bushings and into

Front Suspension

GENERAL MOTORS – 4WD LEAF SPRING "K" SERIES TRUCKS (Cont.)

lower spring anchor plates. *See Fig. 8*. Tighten all nuts and bolts. Lower vehicle.

Fig. 8: Typical Stabilizer Bar Mounting Attachments

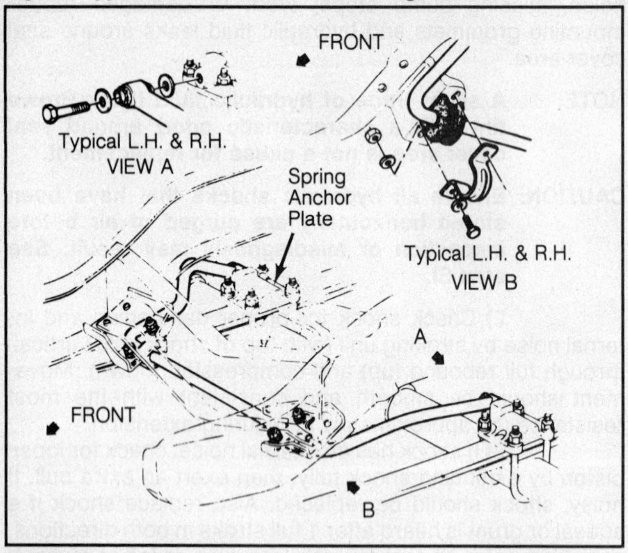

Replace any bushing showing signs of deterioration or damage.

LEAF SPRING & BUSHINGS

Removal

1) Raise and support vehicle on frame hoist. Place adjustable jack stand under axle. Lift axle until all tension is relieved from leaf spring assembly. Detach shackle-to-frame upper mounting nut and bolt. Detach front spring eye bolt and nut.

2) Detach "U" bolt mounting nuts and remove spring-to-axle "U" bolts. Remove spring leafs, upper anchor plate and spring spacer pads. Detach shackle-to-spring lower mounting nut and bolt.

3) Remove bushings, spacers and shackles. *See Fig. 9*. Inspect bushings for excessive wear or deterioration. Check spring leafs for cracks, damage or loss of arc. Replace components as necessary.

Fig. 9: Leaf Spring Assembly & Mount Components

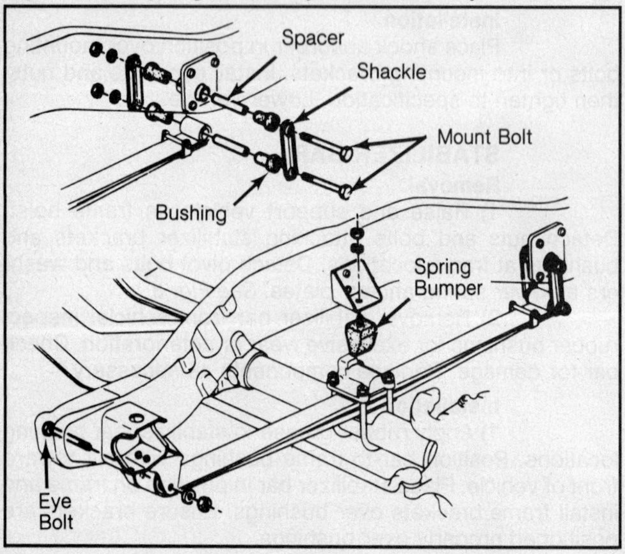

Bushing Replacement

Place spring leaf on hydraulic press and press out bushing using proper sized rod, pipe or remover tool. Press in new bushing. Ensure installer tool presses on steel outer shell of bushing. Install bushing until it protrudes an equal amount on each side of spring.

Spring Inserts (Liners) Or Leaf Replacement

Place spring assembly in vise and detach clips. Remove center bolt. Open vise slowly, allowing spring to expand. Wire brush components and inspect for broken leafs. Replace leaf(s) and/or liners as necessary.

Installation

1) Install spring shackles, lower bushings and spacer onto rear of spring, then attach mounting bolt and nut finger tight. Position upper spring spacer pad on spring.

2) Place front of spring into frame bracket and install mounting bolt and nut finger tight. Install rear upper shackle bushings and spacer onto frame. Attach shackles to frame by inserting mounting bolt and nut finger tight.

3) Install lower spring spacer pad and upper spring anchor plate. Position anchor plate "U" bolts and install mounting nuts. Tight "U" bolt mounting nuts in the proper sequence. *See Fig. 10*.

4) Install all 4 mounting nuts to uniform engagement on "U" bolts to retain and position anchor plate in the design position (perpendicular to axis of "U" bolts). Tighten nuts in positions 1 and 3 to 10-25 ft. lbs. (14-34 N.m), then tighten all mounting nuts to 150 ft. lbs. (203 N.m) in sequence of 2-4-1-3.

5) Tighten front spring eye bolt and nut and rear shackle mounting bolts and nuts. Lower adjustable jack stand and remove. Lower vehicle.

Fig. 10: Leaf Spring "U" Bolt Tightening Sequence

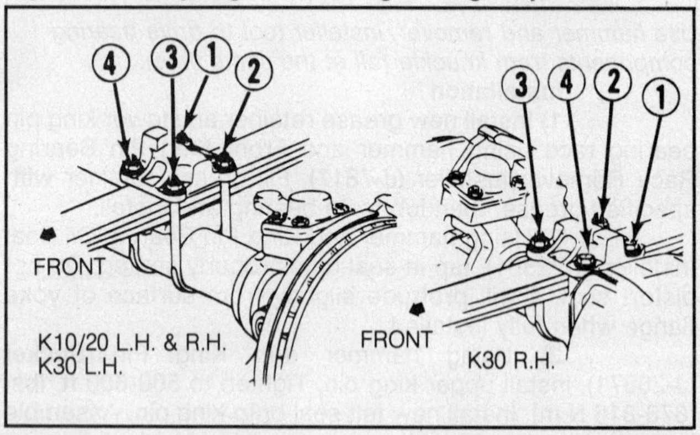

Ensure "U" bolt mounting nuts are tightened in the proper sequence for vehicle application.

Front Suspension
GENERAL MOTORS – 4WD LEAF SPRING "K" SERIES TRUCKS (Cont.)

TIGHTENING SPECIFICATIONS

Application	Ft. Lbs. (N.m)
Automatic Hub	
Inner Wheel Bearing Adjusting Nut [1]	50 (60)
Outer Lock Nut	160-205 (217-310)
Leaf Spring	
Front Eye Bolt	90 (122)
Rear Eye Bolt	50 (68)
To Rear Shackle Bolt	50 (68)
To Axle "U" Bolt	150 (203)
Front Support-To-Frame	25 (34)
Lower Ball Joint Nut [2]	80 (109)
Shock Absorber Mounting Bolt/Nut	65 (88)
Spindle-To-Knuckle Mounting Nut [3]	65 (88)
Stabilizer Bar	
To Control Arm Anchor Plate	130 (176)
To Frame Bracket	55 (75)
Suspension Bumper	15 (20)
Tie Rod End Stud Nut	45 (60)
Upper Ball Joint Nut [4]	100 (136)
	INCH Lbs. (N.m)
Automatic Hub Cover Allen Screw	40-50 (4.5-5.6)
Brake Splash Shield-To-Knuckle Bolt	120 (13.5)

[1] – Initial adjusting torque shown. After first adjustment, back off nut and retighten to 35 ft. lbs. (47 N.m) while rotating wheel. Back off adjusting nut 3/8 turn maximum. Install lock nut and tighten.

[2] – Plus additional torque to align cotter pin.

[3] – Use new mounting nuts whenever spindle is removed from knuckle.

[4] – Plus additional torque to align cotter pin, not to exceed 130 ft. lbs. (176 N.m).

Front Suspension

JEEP COIL SPRING

Cherokee, Wagoneer

DESCRIPTION

Both 2WD and 4WD front suspensions consist of a solid axle (tubular axle on 2WD), four control arms, two coil springs and a track bar. The track bar is used to minimize front axle side-to-side movement. A stabilizer bar and two hydraulic dual-action shock absorbers control suspension spring movement.

On 4WD models, the steering knuckle attaches to ball joints pressed into axle housing bracket bores and serves as a housing for front hub/driveshaft assembly. The front hub consists of conventional tapered roller bearings with inner and outer wheel bearing/seal assemblies, retained in hub by nut lock and axle hub nut.

On 2WD models, the front hub and rotor assembly mounts onto steering knuckle spindle with tapered roller bearings and uses an inner grease seal only. Bearings are held to spindle with thrust washer and hub nut.

ADJUSTMENT

WHEEL ALIGNMENT SPECIFICATIONS & PROCEDURES

See WHEEL ALIGNMENT SPECIFICATIONS & PROCEDURES in WHEEL ALIGNMENT section.

WHEEL BEARING ADJUSTMENT

NOTE: Bearings should be cleaned, inspected, replaced (if necessary) and lubricated before adjustment.

CAUTION: Never preload tapered roller bearings or damage to roller ends will result. Bearings are designed to have a slightly loose feel when properly adjusted.

2WD Models

1) Raise and support vehicle, then remove wheel and tire assembly. Detach brake caliper mounting bolts and suspend caliper away from work area with wire. Turn hub and rotor assembly by hand and check for smooth rotation and/or excessive bearing end play.

2) If excessive end play movement and/or rough or notchy rotation exists, remove hub dust cap, cotter pin, nut retainer, retainer nut, thrust washer and outer wheelbearing. Pull hub and rotor assembly from spindle, pry out grease seal and remove inner wheel bearing. *See Fig. 1*. Inspect components for excessive wear or damage and replace as necessary.

3) If bearings are in good condition, replace hub dust cover, cotter pin and nut retainer. Ensure bearings are thoroughly packed with lithium grease. While rotating hub and rotor assembly by hand, tighten hub retainer nut to 17-25 ft. lbs. (23-34 N.m) to seat bearings.

4) Loosen retainer nut 1/2 turn (while rotating hub), then retighten nut to 19 INCH lbs. (2 N.m). Install nut retainer and new cotter pin. Clean hub dust cap and coat inside with clean grease (do not fill). Reverse removal procedure to complete installation.

4WD Models

1) Raise and support vehicle, then remove wheel and tire assembly. Detach brake caliper mounting bolts and suspend caliper away from work area with wire. Turn hub and bearing carrier assembly by hand and check for smooth rotation and/or excessive bearing end play.

2) If excessive end play movement or rough and/or notchy rotation exists, remove hub/carrier assembly from steering knuckle. *See Fig. 1*. Inspect bearings and seals for wear or damage. Replace as necessary. If bearings are in good condition, remove dust cover, cotter pin and nut lock, then loosen and remove axle hub nut.

3) Ensure hub, bearing carrier and wheel bearings are packed with clean lithium grease. Install components and tighten axle hub nut to 175 ft. lbs. (237 N.m). Install nut lock and new cotter pin.

REMOVAL & INSTALLATION

WHEEL BEARINGS

Removal (2WD Models)

1) Raise and support vehicle. Remove wheel and tire assembly. Detach brake caliper mounting bolts and hang caliper out of work area by wire. DO NOT hang by flexible brake hose.

CAUTION: Use care not to drop outer wheel bearing during hub and rotor assembly removal.

2) Remove hub dust cap, cotter pin, retainer nut, spindle nut, washer and outer wheel bearing. Remove hub and rotor assembly from spindle. Pry grease seal from hub and discard. Remove inner wheel bearing. *See Fig. 1*. Inspect bearings and races for excessive wear or damage.

Fig. 1: Exploded View Of 2WD Hub/Rotor Assembly & 4WD Hub/Bearing Carrier Assembly

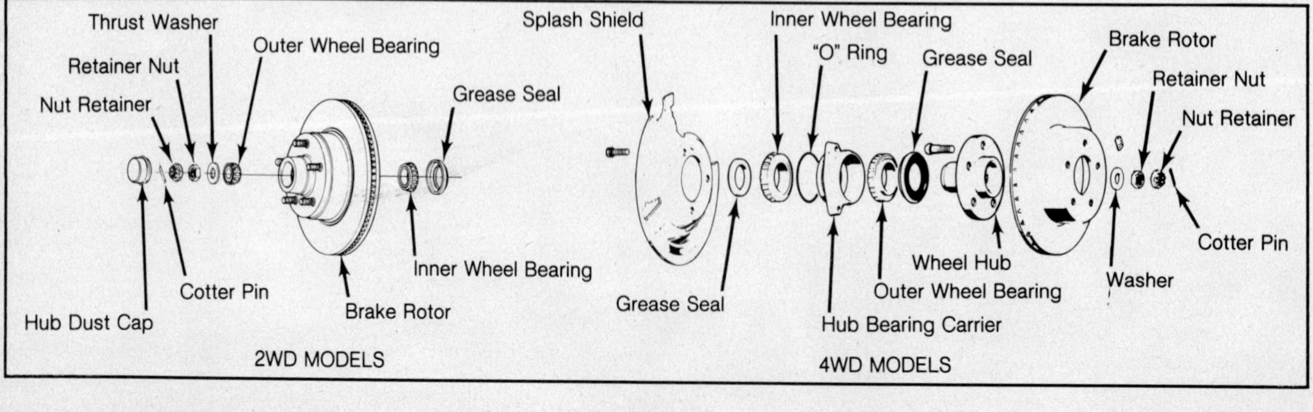

Inspection

1) Wash wheel bearings and hub in solvent and blow dry with compressed air. Do not spin bearings with air or damage to rollers can result. Check bearings for cracked cages and worn or pitted rollers.

2) Inspect inner and outer bearing races for cracks, scores, looseness in hub or a brinelled condition. Replace bearings and races, in matched sets only, as necessary.

Installation (2WD Models)

1) If bearing(s) and/or race(s) need replacement, drive old race out of hub. Insert brass drift, through hub, behind race. Using hammer, strike drift (alternating on each side of race) until race is removed.

2) Position new bearing race in hub bore. Place old race on top of new race, then drive new inner and/or outer race into hub bore until seated. Thoroughly pack good used or new wheel bearings with clean lithium grease.

3) Place a small amount of grease in hub cavity and on spindle. Install inner bearing in hub. Install new grease seal until flush with hub, then apply thin coat of grease to sealing lip.

4) Position hub and rotor assembly onto spindle and install outer bearing and spindle nut. Adjust wheel bearings as previously described. To complete installation, reverse removal procedure.

Removal (4WD Models)

1) Raise and support vehicle. Remove wheel and tire assembly. Detach brake caliper mounting bolts and hang caliper out of work area by wire. DO NOT hang by flexible brake hose. Remove brake rotor from hub.

2) Remove cotter pin, nut lock and axle hub nut. Remove hub-to-steering knuckle mounting bolts. Pull hub assembly from knuckle. Remove splash shield if necessary.

3) Press hub out of bearing carrier. Remove bearings and discard grease seals. *See Fig. 1*. Inspect roller bearings for chipped or broken rollers and cages. Check bearing races for cracks, chips or excessive wear.

4) Replace bearing races by tapping from hub with brass drift or press out with arbor press. Always replace bearings and races as matched sets. Install new seals whenever hub assembly is disassembled.

Installation (4WD Models)

1) Partially fill cavities in steering knuckle, hub and bearing carrier with lithium wheel bearing grease. Thoroughly pack tapered roller bearings with grease. Install bearings in hub.

2) Install new grease seals into bearing carrier. Press hub through bearings in carrier. Install splash shield onto hub/carrier assembly. Install assembly onto steering knuckle.

3) Tighten hub mounting bolts to 75 ft. lbs. (101 N.m). Install hub washer and nut. Tighten hub nut to 175 ft. lbs. (237 N.m). Install nut lock and new cotter pin. Complete installation by reversing removal procedure.

SHOCK ABSORBER

Removal

1) With vehicle on the ground, at normal ride height, remove top shock absorber bayonet nut, washer and rubber grommet from inside engine compartment, at shock tower. Note component locations for reassembly reference.

2) Raise and support vehicle on frame hoist. Detach two lower shock mounting nuts and bolts from axle housing bracket. Remove shock absorbers from vehicle. Inspect units for damage or leakage. Replace shock absorbers in pairs only.

Installation

1) Assemble new washer and grommet onto top stud of shock absorber. Position shock through shock tower. Install lower mounting bolts, with nuts, onto axle housing bracket and tighten to 12-16 ft. lbs. (16-22 N.m).

2) Lower vehicle. Install new grommet, washer and top nut onto shock absorber at shock tower. Tighten bayonet nut to 5-14 ft. lbs. (7-19 N.m).

STEERING KNUCKLE

Removal

1) Raise and support vehicle. Remove wheel and tire assembly. Remove brake caliper and support with wire, away from work area. Detach brake rotor and set aside. Remove hub dust cover, cotter pin, nut lock and axle hub nut.

2) Detach hub-to-knuckle mounting bolts. Remove hub/bearing carrier assembly and splash shield from steering knuckle. Remove axle shaft from left side of axle housing.

3) To remove right side axle shaft, first disconnect vacuum harness from shift motor (on right side of axle housing). Remove shift motor and axle shaft from housing. Remove caliper anchor plate from steering knuckle.

4) Remove each ball joint stud cotter pin and retaining nut. Using brass hammer, strike steering knuckle (at ball joint stud bore area) to dislodge knuckle from ball joint/axle housing bracket assembly. Inspect split ring seat in steering knuckle ball joint stud bore and replace if worn or damaged. *See Fig. 2*.

Fig. 2: Checking Steering Knuckle Split Ring Seat Replacement Position

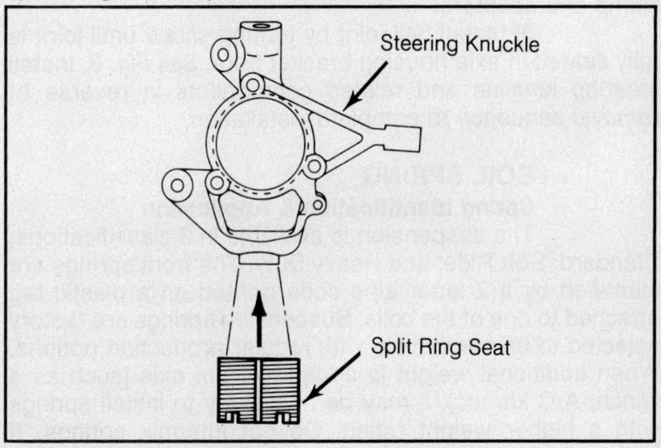

Split ring seat is located in ball joint stud bore of the steering knuckle.

Installation

1) If split ring seat is replaced, ensure seat is set to proper depth into steering knuckle ball joint stud bore. Using Ball Stud Nut Wrench (J-23447), set split ring seat depth to .206" (5.23 mm).

2) Measure the depth from knuckle surface to top (notched edge) of split ring seat. When installing right side axle shaft, ensure shift collar is in position on intermediate shaft and axle shaft is fully engaged over intermediate shaft end.

Front Suspension

JEEP COIL SPRING (Cont.)

3) Install shift motor, being certain that fork engages with collar. Tighten mounting bolts. Partially fill hub cavity of steering knuckle with chassis lubricant. Install hub assembly and splash shield.

4) Position steering knuckle/hub assembly over ball joint studs. Install and tighten mounting nuts. Install new cotter pins. Install caliper anchor plate. Tighten mounting bolts. To complete installation, reverse removal procedure.

UPPER & LOWER BALL JOINTS

Removal

1) Raise and support vehicle. Remove wheel and tire assembly. Inspect upper and lower ball joints for damage, torn grease seals or excessive wear. Replace as necessary.

2) Remove steering knuckle assembly. Position Ball Joint Receiver (J-34503-1) over top of upper ball joint. Set Remover (J-34503-3) in "C" Clamp (J-34503). Position clamp and adapter with receiver tool. Tighten "C" clamp screw to remove ball joint from axle housing bracket bore. *See Fig. 3.*

3) To remove lower ball joint, position Ball Joint Receiver (J-34503-1) onto "C" clamp screw and Remover (J-34503-3) at base of clamp. Invert clamp and adapters and remove lower ball joint by tightening clamp screw. *See Fig. 3.*

Installation

1) Place Upper Ball Joint Installer (J-34503-5) over new upper ball joint. Set Angled Receiver (J-34503-2) in "C" clamp. Position clamp and adapter against axle housing bracket, over installer and ball joint. Turn "C" clamp screw and fully seat ball joint into axle housing bracket bore. *See Fig. 3.*

2) To install lower ball joint, position Lower Ball Joint Installer (J-34503-4) on "C" clamp screw. Position Angled Receiver (J-34503-2) in base of "C" clamp. Invert "C" clamp and adapters.

3) Install ball joint by turning screw until joint is fully seated in axle housing bracket bore. *See Fig. 3.* Install steering knuckle and related components in reverse of removal sequence to complete installation.

COIL SPRING

Spring Identification & Application

The suspension is available in 3 classifications; Standard; Soft Ride; and Heavy Duty. The front springs are identified by a 2 letter alpa code printed on a plastic tag attached to one of the coils. Suspension springs are factory selected to be compatible with regular production options. When additional weight is added to front axle (such as a winch, A/C kit, etc), it may be necessary to install springs with a higher weight rating. Do not intermix springs. If spring upgrade is required, use only the same type of spring.

The slight forward rake of Cherokee/Wagoneer vehicles is by design and is not to be misdiagnosed as a front spring problem. In addition, a side-to-side body height variance of about 3/4" (19 mm) at the sill (measured from sill to ground) and 1" (25.4 mm) at fender flares (measured from flare to ground) is acceptable.

Removal

1) Raise and support vehicle. Remove wheel and tire assembly. Index mark driveshaft, then disconnect at front axle. Position adjustable jack stand under axle housing, then disconnect lower control arms (at axle housing).

Fig. 3: Removing and Installing Upper and Lower Ball Joints

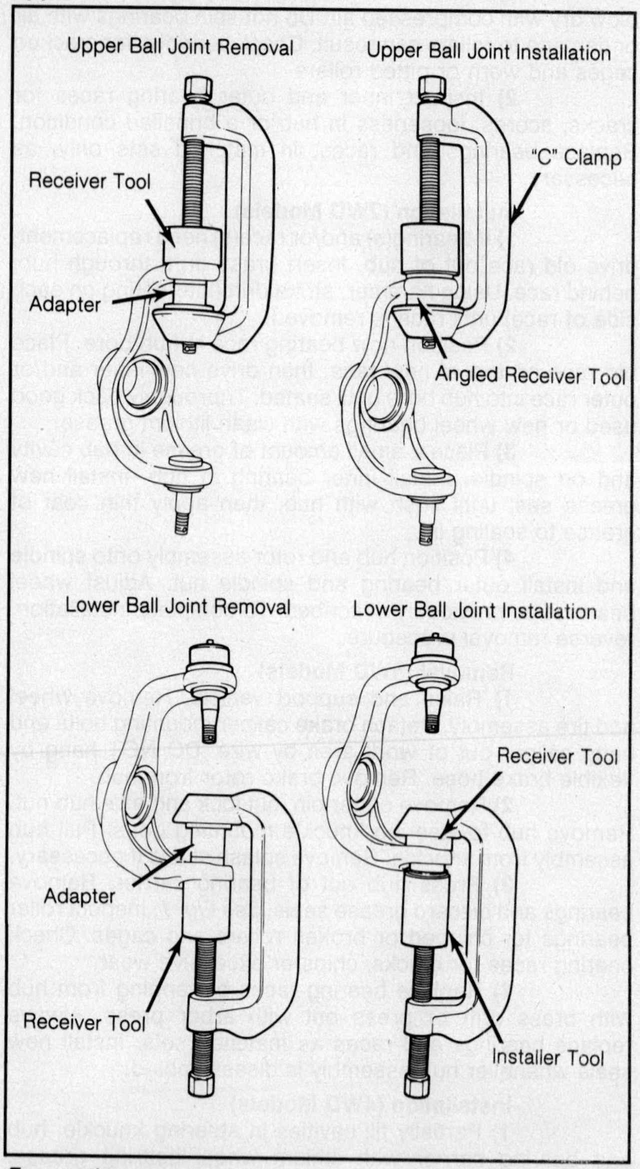

Ensure the upper and lower ball joints are pressed into the axle housing bracket until fully seated in bore.

2) Disconnect stabilizer bar links and lower shock absorber mounting bolts and nuts at axle housing. Disconnect track bar at the sill bracket. Disconnect center link at pitman arm.

3) Gradually lower axle housing to relieve spring pressure. Detach spring retainer mounting bolt, then remove retainer and coil spring. Note component locations for reassembly reference.

NOTE: **Coil springs are rated separately for each side of vehicle depending on optional equipment and type of service. If removed, ensure springs are marked for installation in original positions.**

Installation

1) Install original or replacement spring, position spring retainer and tighten retainer mounting bolt. Raise axle housing into position. Connect lower control arms to axle housing.

Front Suspension

JEEP COIL SPRING (Cont.)

Fig. 4: Removing & Installing Upper Control Arm Bushing

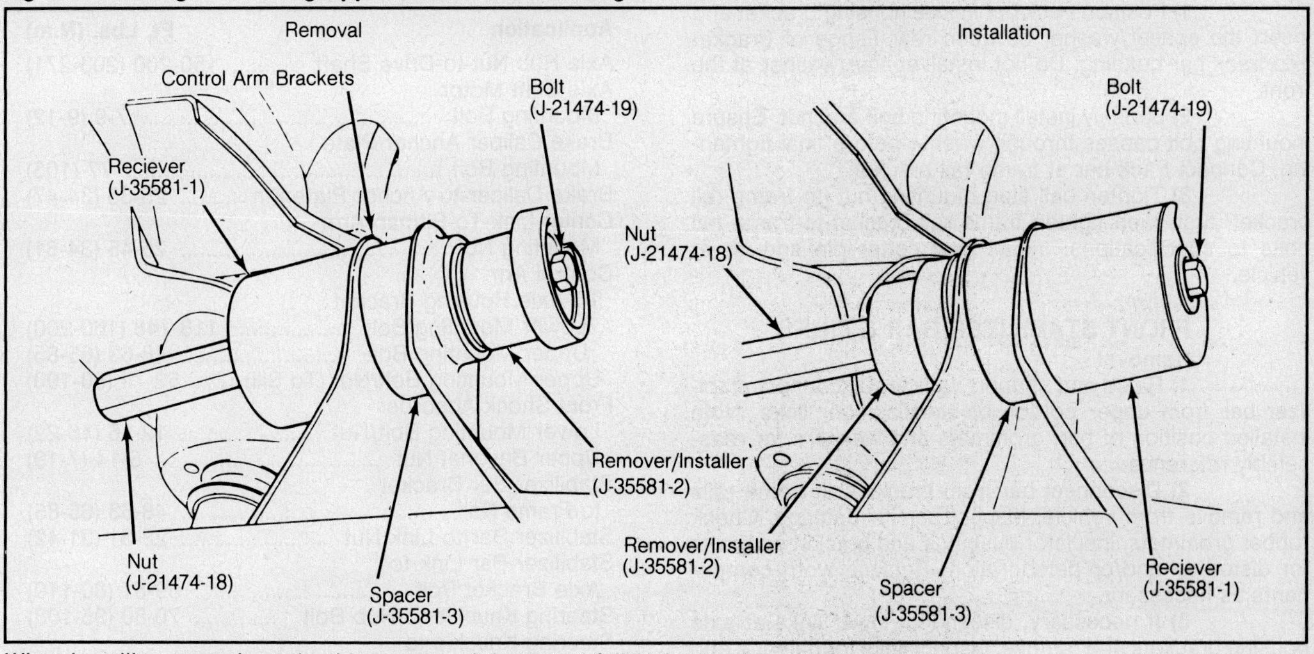

When installing control arm bushing, ensure it is seated fully into axle housing bracket.

2) Install lower shock absorber mounting bolts, center link-to-pitman arm, track bar-to-frame bracket and stabilizer bar links-to-axle housing. To complete installation, reverse removal procedure.

UPPER CONTROL ARM & AXLE HOUSING PIVOT BUSHING

Removal

1) To remove right side upper control arm for 6-cylinder equipped vehicles, first disconnect right side engine mount. Raise and support engine enough so rear control arm mounting bolt clears exhaust pipe. On all models, raise and support vehicle.

2) Remove upper control arm mounting bolt and nut from axle housing. Disconnect mounting bolt and nut at frame rail. Remove upper control arm. Repeat procedure for opposite control arm, if necessary. Inspect control arm for damage or distortion and replace as needed.

3) Check pivot bushings for excessive distortion, deterioration or wear. If bushing replacement is necessary, install Spacer (J-33581-3) between ears of control arm bracket on axle housing. *See Fig. 4*.

NOTE: **Spacer is not used on axle housings with solid control arm brackets.**

CAUTION: **Do not attempt to remove upper control arm pivot bushing without spacer. Tool is designed to support bracket and prevent distortion during bushing removal.**

4) Install Upper Control Arm Pivot Bushing Remover/Installer Set (J-35581 which must include Spacer J-35581-3, Remover/Installer J-35581-2, Reciever J-35581-1, Bolt J-21474-19 and Nut J-21474-18) onto pivot bushing. *See Fig. 4*.

5) Turn nut to press bushing out of axle housing and into receiver tool. *See Fig. 4*. Once bushing is removed, detach bushing remover/installer set but leave spacer in position for new bushing installation.

Installation

1)To install new upper control arm bushing into bracket bore on axle housing, first position bushing on Remover/Installer (J-35581-2) and Nut (J-21474-18). Position tools and bushing in control arm bracket, then assemble remaining installer tools. *See Fig. 4*.

2) Turn nut to press bushing into housing until fully seated in bore. *See Fig. 4*. Detach remover/installer tools (and spacer), then connect upper control arm at frame and axle housing brackets. Tighten mounting bolts. To complete installation, reverse removal procedure.

LOWER CONTROL ARM & BUSHING

Removal

1) Raise and support vehicle. Disconnect lower control arm mounting bolts and nuts at axle housing and frame brackets. Remove lower control arm.

2) Inspect control arm for damage and bushings for excessive distortion or wear. Replace control arm and/or bushings as necessary.

Installation

Position lower control arm in front and rear brackets. Install mounting bolts and nuts. Tighten mounting bolts to 118-148 ft. lbs. (160-200 N.m). To complete installation, reverse removal procedure.

TRACK BAR

Removal

1) Raise and support vehicle. Remove cotter pin and mounting nut at frame rail bracket. Remove bolt and nut at axle housing bracket. Remove bar. Inspect track bar for damage and bushing for excessive distortion or wear. Replace as needed.

2) If a snapping noise has been heard from the front of vehicle, inspect track bar bushing inner sleeve for signs of wear. If sleeve has been touching axle bracket, spread bracket flanges about 1/8" (3.5 mm) to provide space for a hardened spacer/washer (G2436163).

Front Suspension

JEEP COIL SPRING (Cont.)

Installation

1) Position track bar in axle housing bracket and insert the spacer/washer between rear flange of bracket and track bar bushing. Do not install spacer/washer at the front.

2) Loosely install mounting bolt and nut. Ensure mounting bolt passes through washer before final tightening. Connect track bar at frame rail bracket.

3) Tighten ball stud mounting nut (to frame rail bracket) first, then tighten frame rail bracket-to-frame rail bolts to specifications. Install new cotter pin and lower vehicle.

FRONT STABILIZER BAR & LINKS

Removal

1) Raise and support vehicle. Disconnect stabilizer bar from upper portion of stabilizer bar links. Note installed position of bar, grommets and washers for reassembly reference.

2) Disconnect bar from brackets at frame rails and remove from vehicle. Inspect bar for damage. Check rubber grommets, insulator bushings and bracket supports for distortion and/or deterioration. Replace worn components as necessary.

3) If necessary, disconnect lower links at axle housing brackets and remove. Inspect links for damage and rubber grommets for excessive wear, distortion and/or deterioration. Replace components as necessary.

Installation

1) Lubricate stabilizer bar bushings and link grommets with rubber grease. Connect links to axle housing brackets. Install washers and rubber grommets on links.

2) Install rubber bushings and brackets onto stabilizer bar and connect components to frame rails. Connect bar to stabilizer links with washers, grommets and mounting nuts in correct positions.

3) Tighten mounting bolts and nuts to specifications. Complete installation by reversing removal procedure.

TIGHTENING SPECIFICATIONS

Application	Ft. Lbs. (N.m)
Axle Hub Nut-to-Drive Shaft	150-200 (203-271)
Axle Shift Motor	
Mounting Bolt	7-9 (9-12)
Brake Caliper Anchor Plate	
Mounting Bolt	77 (105)
Brake Caliper-to-Anchor Plate Pin	25-35 (34-47)
Center Link-To-Pitman Arm	
Mounting Nut	25-45 (34-61)
Control Arm	
To-Axle Housing Bracket	
Lower Mounting Bolt	118-148 (160-200)
Upper Mounting Bolt	48-63 (65-85)
Upper Mounting Bolt/Nut (To Sill)	59-74 (80-100)
Front Shock Absorber	
Lower Mounting Bolt/Nut	12-16 (16-22)
Upper Bayonet Nut	5-14 (7-19)
Stabilizer Bar Bracket	
to Frame Rail	48-63 (65-85)
Stabilizer Bar-to-Link Nut	23-31 (31-42)
Stabilizer Bar Link-to	
Axle Bracket Bolt	59-81 (80-110)
Steering Knuckle-to-Hub Bolt	70-80 (95-108)
Steering Knuckle-to	
Ball Joint Mounting Nut	65-85 (88-115)
Steering Knuckle-to	
Tie Rod Nut	25-45 (34-61)
Track Bar	
Ball Stud Nut	30-40 (41-54)
Bracket-To-Frame Rail Bolt	66-81 (90-110)
To-Axle Housing Bolt	66-81 (90-110)

SECTION 13

STEERING

CONTENTS

NOTE: ALSO SEE GENERAL INDEX.

IMPORTANT: Because of the many model names used by vehicle manufacturers, accurate identification of models is important. See Model Identification at the front of this publication.

Steering

STANDARD STEERING COLUMN TROUBLE SHOOTING

CONDITION	POSSIBLE CAUSE	CORRECTION
Noise in Column	Coupling pulled apart	See STEERING COLUMNS
	Column not correctly aligned	See STEERING COLUMNS
	Broken lower joint	Replace joint
	Horn contact ring not lubricated	See Removal in STEERING WHEEL
	Bearings not lubricated	See STEERING COLUMNS
	Bearing worn or broken	Replace bearing and lubricate
	Shaft snap ring not properly seated	Reseat or replace snap ring
	Plastic spherical joint not lubricated	See STEERING COLUMNS
	Shroud or housing loose	Tighten holding screws
	Lock plate retaining ring not seated	See STEERING COLUMNS
	Loose sight shield	Tighten holding screws
High Steering Shaft Effort	Column assembly misaligned	See STEERING COLUMNS
	Improperly installed dust shield	Adjust or replace
	Damaged upper or lower bearing	Replace bearings
	Tight steering universal joint	See STEERING COLUMNS
High Shift Effort	Column is out of alignment	See STEERING COLUMNS
	Improperly installed dust shield	Adjust or replace
	Seals or bearings not lubricated	See STEERING COLUMNS
	Ignition switch screws too long	Replace with new shorter screws
	Neutral switch screws too long	Replace with new shorter screws
	Mounting bracket screws too long	Replace with new shorter screws
	Burrs on shift tube	Remove burrs or replace tube
	Lower bowl bearing assembled wrong	See STEERING COLUMNS
	Shift tube bent or broken	Replace as necessary
	Improper adjustment of shift levers	See STEERING COLUMNS
Improper Trans. Shifting	Sheared shift tube joint	Replace as necessary
	Sheared lower shaft lever weld joint	Replace as necessary
	Improper shift lever adjustment	See STEERING COLUMNS
	Improper gate plate adjustment	See STEERING COLUMNS
Excess Play in Column	Instrument panel bracket bolts loose	Tighten bolts and check bracket
	Broken weld nut on jacket	See STEERING COLUMNS
	Instrument bracket capsule sheared	See STEERING COLUMNS
	Column bracket/jacket bolts loose	Tighten bolts and check bracket
Steering Locks in Gear	Release lever mechanism damaged	See STEERING COLUMNS

TILT STEERING COLUMN TROUBLE SHOOTING

CONDITION	POSSIBLE CAUSE	CORRECTION
Steering Wheel Loose	Excess clearance in support	Check and replace if necessary
	Excess clearance in housing/pivot pin	Check and replace if necessary
	Damaged anti-lash spring in spheres	See TILT STEERING COLUMNS
	Upper bearing not seated properly	See TILT STEERING COLUMNS
	Upper bearing inner race seal missing	Replace if necessary
	Improperly adjusted tilt/telescopic lock	See adjustment in STEERING COLUMNS
	Loose support screws	Tighten and check bracket
	Bearing preload spring missing/broken	Replace spring
	Housing loose on jacket	Tighten and/or replace screws
Play in Column Mount	Loose support screws	Tighten and check bracket
	Loose shoes in housing	See TILT STEERING COLUMNS
	Loose tilt head pivot pins	See TILT STEERING COLUMNS
	Loose shoe lock pin in support	See TILT STEERING COLUMNS
Housing Scraping on Bowl	Bowl bent or out of round	See STEERING WHEEL removal
Wheel Will Not Lock	Shoe seized on its pivot pin	See TILT STEERING COLUMNS
	Shoe may have burrs/dirt in them	Clean or replace
	Shoe lock spring weak/broken	Replace if necessary

TILT STEERING COLUMN TROUBLE SHOOTING (Cont.)

CONDITION	POSSIBLE CAUSE	CORRECTION
Wheel Fails to Return	Pivot pins are bound up	Clean or replace
	Wheel tilt spring is damaged	See TILT STEERING COLUMNS
	Turn signal switch wires too tight	Loosen and check operation
Noise When Tilting	Upper tilt bumpers worn	Replace if necessary
	Tilt spring rubbing in housing	Adjust and check operation
Hard Steering	Incorrect tire pressure	Inflate to proper pressure
	Lack of lubricant in steering linkage	Service Steering, Suspension and Linkage
	Improper front end alignment	See WHEEL ALIGNMENT
	Improper steering gear adjustment	See STEERING

MANUAL STEERING GEAR TROUBLE SHOOTING

CONDITION	POSSIBLE CAUSE	CORRECTION
Rattle or Chucking Noise in Rack and Pinion	Rack and pinion mounting bracket loose	Tighten all mounting bolts
	Lack of/or incorrect lubricant	See RACK & PINION STEERING
	Pitman arm loose on shaft	See STEERING
	Steering gear mounting bolts loose	Tighten all mounting bolts
Excessive Play	Front wheel bearing improperly adjusted	See FRONT SUSPENSION
	Loose or worn steering linkage	See STEERING LINKAGE
	Loose or worn ball joints	See FRONT SUSPENSION
	Loose or worn steering gear shaft	See STEERING
	Steering arm loose on gear shaft	See STEERING
	Incorrect front wheel alignment	See WHEEL ALIGNMENT
	Steering gear housing bolts loose	Tighten all mounting bolts
	Steering gear adjustment too loose	See adjustment in STEERING
	Steering arms loose on knuckles	Tighten and check steering linkage
	Rack and pinion mounting loose	Tighten all mounting bolts
	Rack and pinion out of adjustment	See adjustment in STEERING
	Tie rod end loose	Tighten and check steering linkage
	Steering wheel loose	See STEERING
	Excessive Pitman shaft-to-ball nut lash	See STEERING
Poor Returnability	Lack of lubricant in ball joint or linkage	Lubricate and service systems
	Binding in linkage or ball joints	See STEERING LINKAGE and SUSPENSION
	Improper front end alignment	See WHEEL ALIGNMENT
	Improper steering gear adjustment	See STEERING
	Improper tire pressure	Inflate to proper pressure
Excessive Vertical Motion	Improper tire pressure	Inflate to proper pressure
	Tires, wheels or rotors out of balance	Balance tires then check wheels and rotors
	Worn or faulty shock absorbers	Check and replace if necessary
	Loose tie rod ends or steering	Tighten or replace if necessary
	Improper wheel alignment	See WHEEL ALIGNMENT
	Loose or worn wheel bearings	See SUSPENSION
Steering Pulls to One Side	Improper tire pressure	Inflate to proper pressure
	Mismatched front tires	Rotate or replace if necessary
	Wheel bearings not adjusted properly	See FRONT SUSPENSION
	Bent or broken suspension components	See FRONT SUSPENSION
	Improper wheel alignment	See WHEEL ALIGNMENT
	Brakes dragging	See BRAKES
Instability	Low or uneven tire pressure	Inflate to proper pressure
	Loose or worn wheel bearings	See FRONT SUSPENSION
	Loose or worn idler arm bushing	See FRONT SUSPENSION
	Loose or worn strut bushings	See FRONT SUSPENSION
	Incorrect front wheel alignment	See WHEEL ALIGNMENT
	Steering gear not centered	See STEERING
	Springs or shock absorbers inoperative	Check and replace if necessary
	Improper cross shaft	See STEERING

Steering

POWER STEERING TROUBLE SHOOTING

CONDITION	POSSIBLE CAUSE	CORRECTION
Rattle or Chucking Noise in Steering	Pressure hoses touching engine parts	Adjust to proper clearance
	Loose Pitman shaft	Adjust or replace if necessary
	Tie rods ends or Pitman arm loose	Tighten and check system
	Rack and pinion mounts loose	Tighten all mounting bolts
	Free play in worm and piston assembly	See STEERING
	Loose sector shaft or thrust bearing adjustment	See STEERING
	Free play in pot coupling	See STEERING
	Worn shaft serrations	See STEERING
Growl in Steering Pump	Excessive pressure in hoses	Restriction in hoses see POWER STEERING
	Scored pressure plates	See POWER STEERING
	Scored thrust plates or rotor	See POWER STEERING
	Extreme wear of cam ring	See POWER STEERING
Rattle in Steering Pump	Vanes not installed properly	See POWER STEERING PUMPS
	Vanes sticking in rotor slots	See POWER STEERING PUMPS
Swish Noise in Pump	Defective flow control valve	See POWER STEERING PUMPS
Groan in Steering Pump	Air in fluid	See POWER STEERING PUMPS
	Poor pressure hose connection	Tighten and check, replace if necessary
Squawk When Turning	Damper "O" ring on valve spool cut	See POWER STEERING PUMPS
Moan or Whine in Pump	Pump shaft bearing scored	Replace bearing and fluid
	Air in fluid or fluid level low	See POWER STEERING PUMPS
	Hose or column grounded	Check and replace if necessary
	Cover "O" ring missing or damaged	See POWER STEERING PUMPS
	Valve cover baffle missing or damaged	See POWER STEERING PUMPS
	Interference of components in pump	See POWER STEERING PUMPS
	Loose or poor bracket alignment	Correct or replace if necessary
Hissing When Parking	Internal leakage in steering gear	Check valve assembly first
Chirp in Steering Pump	Loose or worn power steering belt	Adjust or replace if neceesary
Buzzing When Not Steering	Noisy pump	See POWER STEERING PUMPS
	Free play in steering shaft bearing	See STEERING
	Bearing loose on shaft serrations	See STEERING
Clicking Noise in Pump	Pump slippers too long	See POWER STEERING PUMPS
	Broken slipper springs	See POWER STEERING PUMPS
	Excessive wear or nicked rotors	See POWER STEERING PUMPS
	Damaged cam contour	See POWER STEERING PUMPS
Poor Return of Wheel	Wheel rubbing against turn signal	See STEERING WHEEL SWITCHES
	Flange rubbing steering gear adjuster	See STEERING
	Tight or frozen steering shaft bearing	See STEERING
	Steering Gear out of adjustment	See Adjustment in STEERING
	Sticking or plugged spool valve	See POWER STEERING PUMPS
	Improper front end alignment	See WHEEL ALIGNMENT
	Wheel bearings worn or loose	See FRONT SUSPENSION
	Ties rods or ball joints binding	Check and replace if necessary
	Intermediate shaft joints binding	See STEERING
	Kinked pressure hoses	Correct or replace if necessary
	Loose housing head spanner nut	See POWER STEERING
	Damaged valve lever	See POWER STEERING
	Sector shaft adjusted too tight	See adjustment in POWER STEERING
	Worm thrust bearing adjusted too tight	See adjustment in POWER STEERING
	Reaction ring sticking in cylinder	See POWER STEERING
	Reaction ring sticking in housing head	See POWER STEERING
	Steering pump internal leakage	See POWER STEERING PUMPS
	Steering gear-to-column misalignment	See STEERING COLUMNS
	Lack of lubrication in linkage	Service front suspension
	Lack of lubrication in ball joints	Service front suspension

Steering

POWER STEERING TROUBLE SHOOTING (Cont.)

CONDITION	POSSIBLE CAUSE	CORRECTION
Increased Effort When Turning Wheel Fast Foaming, Milky Power Steering Fluid, Low Fluid Level or Low Pressure	High internal pump leakage	See POWER STEERING PUMPS
	Power steering pump belt slipping	Adjust or replace if necessary
	Low fluid level	Check and fill to proper level
	Engine idle speed to low	Adjust to correct setting
	Air in pump fluid system	See POWER STEERING PUMPS
	Pump output low	See POWER STEERING PUMPS
	Steering gear malfunctioning	See STEERING
Wheel Surges or Jerks	Low fluid level	Check and fill to proper level
	Loose fan belt	Adjust or replace if necessary
	Insufficient pump pressure	See POWER STEERING PUMPS
	Sticky flow control valve	See POWER STEERING PUMPS
	Linkage hitting oil pan at full turn	See STEERING LINKAGE
Kick Back or Free Play	Air in pump fluid system	See POWER STEERING PUMPS
	Worn poppet valve in steering gear	See POWER STEERING
	Excessive over center lash	See POWER STEERING
	Thrust bearing out of adjustment	See POWER STEERING
	Free play in pot coupling	See POWER STEERING PUMPS
	Steering gear coupling loose on shaft	See POWER STEERING PUMPS
	Steering disc mounting bolts loose	Tighten or replace if necessary
	Coupling loose on worm shaft	Tighten or replace if necessary
	Improper sector shaft adjustment	See POWER STEERING
	Excessive worm piston side play	See POWER STEERING
	Damaged valve lever	See POWER STEERING
	Universal joint loose	Tighten or replace if necessary
	Defective rotary valve	See POWER STEERING
No Power When Parking	Sticking flow control valve	See POWER STEERING PUMPS
	Insufficient pump pressure output	See POWER STEERING PUMPS
	Excessive internal pump leakage	See POWER STEERING PUMPS
	Excessive internal gear leakage	See POWER STEERING PUMPS
	Flange rubs against gear adjust plug	See STEERING COLUMN
	Loose pump belt	Adjust or replace if necessary
	Low fluid level	Check and add proper amount of fluid
	Engine idle too low	Adjust to correct setting
	Steering gear-to-column misaligned	See STEERING
No Power Left Turns	Left turn reaction seal "O" ring worn	See POWER STEERING
	Left turn reaction seal damaged/missing	See POWER STEERING
	Cylinder head "O" ring damaged	See POWER STEERING PUMPS
No Power Right Turns	Column pot coupling bottomed	See STEERING
	Right turn reaction seal "O" ring worn	See POWER STEERING
	Right turn reaction seal damaged	See POWER STEERING
	Internal leakage through piston end plug	See STEERING
	Internal leakage through side plugs	See STEERING
Lack of Effort in Turning	Left and/or right reaction seal worn	Replace, see POWER STEERING
	Left and/or right reaction oil passageway not drilled	Check housing and cylinder head
	Left and/or right reaction seal sticking in cylinder head	See POWER STEERING
Wanders to One Side	Front end alignment incorrect	See WHEEL ALIGNMENT
	Unbalanced steering gear valve	See STEERING
Low Pressure Due to Steering Pump	Flow control valve stuck or inoperative	See POWER STEERING
	Pressure plate not flat against cam ring	See POWER STEERING PUMPS
	Extreme wear of cam ring	Replace and check adjustments
	Scored plate, thrust plate or rotor	See POWER STEERING PUMPS
	Vanes not installed properly	See POWER STEERING PUMPS
	Vanes sticking in rotor slots	See POWER STEERING PUMPS
	Cracked/broken thrust or pressure plate	See POWER STEERING PUMPS

Horn Button & Steering Wheel Removal

ALL MANUFACTURERS

CAUTION: Do not hammer on puller to aid in steering wheel removal. Steering column collapsible parts will be damaged.

NOTE: For removal and installation procedures of column mounted switches, see STEERING COLUMN SWITCHES article in this section.

CHRYSLER CORP.

HORN BUTTON

Removal & Installation

1) Disconnect battery negative cable. If equipped with horn button, pull outward on button until it comes off. If equipped with horn pad, remove 2 retaining screws from behind steering wheel.

2) Lift the pad from steering wheel. Disconnect horn wire from switch terminal. To install, reverse removal procedure.

STEERING WHEEL

Removal & Installation

Remove steering wheel retaining nut. Remove steering wheel using Puller (C 3428B). To install, reverse removal procedure.

FORD

HORN BUTTON

Removal & Installation

1) Disconnect battery negative cable. Remove one screw from behind each steering wheel spoke. Remove horn pad switch assembly from steering wheel after disconnecting wire connector.

2) On vehicles with sport wheel option, pry button cover off with screwdriver. On vehicles with speed control, squeeze "J" clip ground wire terminal firmly and remove through hole in steering wheel. To install, reverse removal procedure.

STEERING WHEEL

Removal & Installation

1) Set wheels in straight ahead position and drive forward a short distance. Index mark steering wheel and steering column.

2) Remove steering wheel retaining nut. Pull off steering wheel using steering wheel Puller (T67L 3600 A). To install, reverse removal procedure. Ensure alignment marks made during disassembly are aligned.

GENERAL MOTORS

HORN BUTTON

Removal & Installation

Disconnect battery negative cable. Remove horn button or pad. To install, reverse removal procedure.

STEERING WHEEL

Removal

Disconnect battery negative cable. Remove horn button or pad. Remove snap ring and steering wheel nut. Index mark steering wheel and shaft. Use steering wheel puller to remove steering wheel. *See Fig. 1.*

Fig. 1: Removing GM Steering Wheel

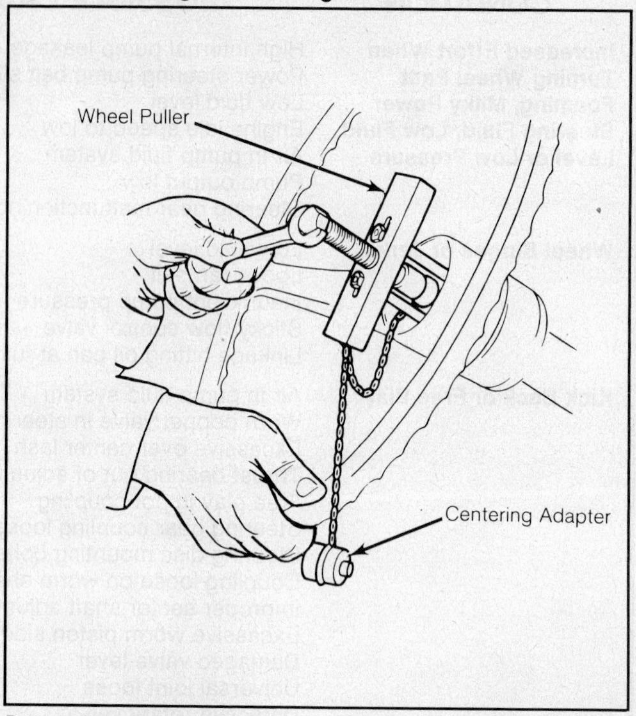

Do not hammer on puller.

Installation

To install, reverse removal procedure. Install snap ring after steering wheel retaining nut has been tightened.

NOTE: Directional signal switch must be in neutral position while installing steering wheel to prevent damage to canceling cam and switch assembly.

JEEP

HORN BUTTON

Removal & Installation

1) Disconnect battery negative cable and place front wheels in straight ahead position. If equipped with standard steering wheel, remove horn cover attaching screws from underside of wheel. Remove cover.

2) On vehicles with sport steering wheel, remove horn button by pulling button upward. On vehicles with standard steering wheel, remove horn wire by disconnecting at steering wheel switch. To install, reverse removal procedure.

STEERING WHEEL

CAUTION: Some steering wheel shaft nuts have metric threads. Metric threads have an identifying groove cut perpendicular to steering wheel splines. Standard American threads do not have groove.

Removal & Installation

1) On vehicles with standard steering wheel, unseat retainer that holds horn wire and spring in canceling cam yoke. Remove wire retainer and spring as an assembly. Remove steering wheel nut.

ALL MANUFACTURERS (Cont.)

Fig. 2: Exploded View of Jeep Steering Wheel Assembly

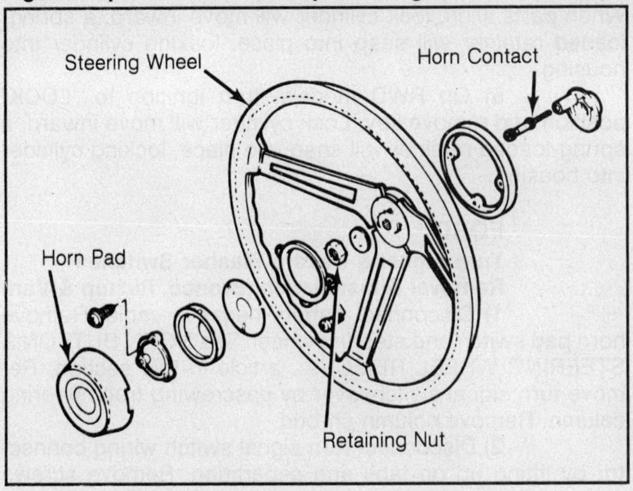

Cherokee and Wagoneer models are shown.

2) On vehicles with sport steering wheel, remove receiver bushing attaching screws and remove bushing, horn button receiver and contact plate. On vehicles, index mark steering wheel and shaft. Remove steering wheel using Puller (J 21232). To install, reverse removal procedure.

TIGHTENING SPECIFICATIONS

Application	Ft. Lbs. (N.m)
Steering Wheel Retaining Nut	
Chrysler Corp.	45 (61)
Ford	
Aerostar	22-34 (30-46)
All Others	30-42 (41-57)
GM/GMC	30 (41)
Jeep	
Cherokee & Wagoneer	25 (34)
All Others	22-28 (30-38)

Steering Column Switches

ALL MANUFACTURERS

REMOVAL & INSTALLATION

CHRYSLER

Turn Signal & Hazard Flasher Switches
Removal & Installation (All Models)

1) Disconnect battery negative cable. Remove horn button (or horn pad) and steering wheel. See HORN BUTTON & STEERING WHEEL REMOVAL article in this section. On models with tilt column, remove lock plate and cam assembly.

2) Remove turn signal lever screw to remove lever. On vehicles equipped with cruise control, do not completely disconnect turn signal lever but allow to hang loose. Remove switch retainer screws, retainer, wire cover clips and cover.

3) Pry out wiring through retainers and remove wiring. Disconnect switch harness from main harness, lift switch from column, guiding wires and insulator through column opening. Remove switch. To install, reverse removal procedure.

NOTE: **Some FWD vehicles require removal of lower steering column cover, silencer and lower column reinforcement before removing wiring.**

Lock Cylinder
Removal & Installation (All Models)

1) Remove horn assembly and steering wheel. See HORN BUTTON & STEERING WHEEL REMOVAL article in this section. Remove turn signal switch. Remove snap ring from upper end of steering shaft. Remove retaining screws and lock lever guide plate which exposes lock cylinder release hole. Turn ignition to "LOCK" position and remove key.

2) Insert a small screwdriver into lock cylinder release hole and push in to release spring-loaded lock retainer. Pull lock cylinder from housing bore while depressing retainer. *See Fig. 1.*

Fig. 1: Removing Chrysler Lock Cylinder

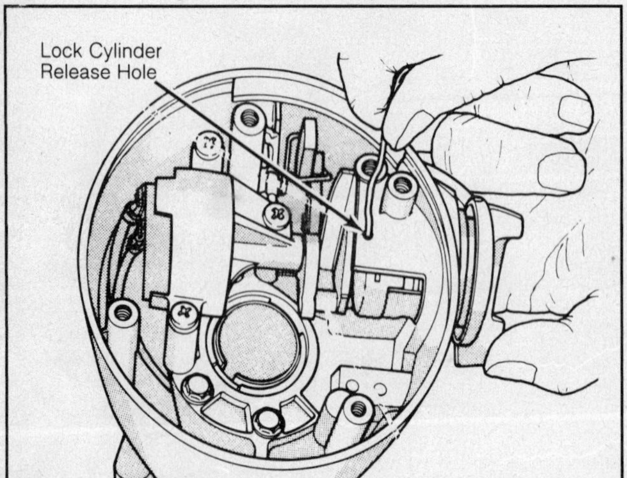
Lock Cylinder
Release Hole

3) On FWD models, turn ignition to "LOCK" position and remove key. Insert cylinder into lock housing. Place cylinder into place until contact is made with switch actuator.

4) Insert key into lock, press inward and rotate. When parts align, lock cylinder will move inward, a spring-loaded retainer will snap into place, locking cylinder into housing.

5) On RWD models, turn ignition to "LOCK" position and remove key. Lock cylinder will move inward, a spring-loaded retainer will snap into place, locking cylinder into housing.

FORD

Turn Signal & Hazard Flasher Switches
Removal & Installation (Bronco, Pickup & Van)

1) Disconnect battery negative cable. Remove horn pad switch and steering wheel. See HORN BUTTON & STEERING WHEEL REMOVAL article in this section. Remove turn signal switch lever by unscrewing from steering column. Remove column shroud.

2) Disconnect turn signal switch wiring connector by lifting up on tabs and separating. Remove screws securing switch assembly to column. On fixed columns, remove switch assembly from vehicle by guiding switch and connector plug through opening in shaft socket.

3) On models with tilt column, disconnect connector plug from wiring connector by using a wire terminal remover. *See Fig. 2.* Record color code and location of each wire as it is removed.

Fig. 2: Removing Wires from Ford Connector

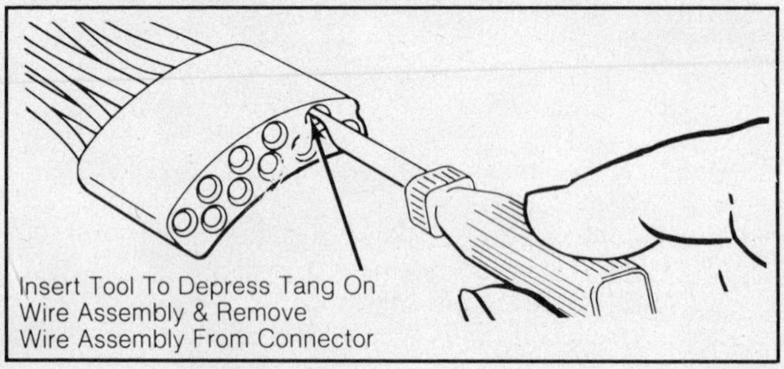
Insert Tool To Depress Tang On
Wire Assembly & Remove
Wire Assembly From Connector

Wiring must be removed from connector on models with tilt column.

4) Guide switch assembly from column though shift socket hole. On Vans with A/T, disconnect lamp wire from turn signal switch harness before removing switch. To install, reverse removal procedure.

Removal & Installation
(Aerostar, Bronco II & Ranger)

1) On models with tilt column, remove upper extension shroud by squeezing it at 6 and 12 o'clock positions and popping it free of retaining plate. Remove trim shroud.

2) On all models, remove turn signal switch lever by and by pulling and twisting lever straight out form switch. Remove foam sight shield from switch. Disconnect electrical connectors.

3) Remove screws attaching turn signal switch to lock cylinder housing. Lift switch away from housing. To install, reverse removal procedure.

Lock Cylinder
Removal & Installation (Bronco, Pickup & Van)

1) Disconnect battery negative cable. On models with standard column, remove horn pad and steering wheel. See HORN BUTTON & STEERING WHEEL REMOVAL article in this section. Place A/T in Park, or M/T in Neutral.

Steering Column Switches

ALL MANUFACTURERS (Cont.)

2) Turn lock cylinder to "RUN" position. Insert a 1/8" (3.18 mm) diameter wire pin or punch in access hole and depress retaining pin. Pull out on lock cylinder.

3) On models with standard column, access hole is located inside column near base of lock cylinder housing. On models with tilt column, hole is located on column housing adjacent to hazard flasher button. To install, reverse removal procedure.

Removal & Installation (Aerostar, Bronco II & Ranger)

1) Disconnect battery negative cable. Remove trim shroud. Remove electrical connector from key warning switch. Turn lock cylinder to "RUN" position.

2) Place 1/8" (3.18 mm) drill or small drift punch in hole located at 4 o'clock and 1 1/4" from outer edge of lock cylinder housing. Depress retaining pin and pull out lock cylinder.

3) To install lock cylinder, turn cylinder to "RUN" position. Depress retaining pin and insert cylinder into lock cylinder housing. To complete installation, reverse removal procedure.

GENERAL MOTORS

Turn Signal & Hazard Flasher Switches
Removal ("G" & "P" Series)

1) Remove steering wheel. See HORN BUTTON & STEERING WHEEL REMOVAL article in this section. Remove turn signal switch canceling cam and spring. Remove column-to-panel trim plate, if present. Disconnect signal switch wiring harness at half-moon connector. Pry wiring harness protector from column retaining slots.

2) Mark location of each wire in half-moon connector, then remove each individual wire from connector using Wire Remover (J 22727). Insert remover into connector, then push in until remover bottoms.

3) Pull wire from connector and withdraw remover. Remove directional signal lever screw and remove lever. Push in on hazard warning knob and unscrew to remove knob.

4) On models with tilt column and A/T, remove selector dial screws (if equipped) and remove dial and indicator. Remove cap and dial illumination light from housing cover. Unscrew and remove tilt release lever.

5) Use Puller (J 22708) to remove signal housing cover. *See Fig. 3*. On all columns, remove 3 signal switch mounting screws. Carefully remove switch assembly from column while guiding wire harness through opening in shift lever housing.

Fig. 3: Pulling GM Directional Signal Housing Cover

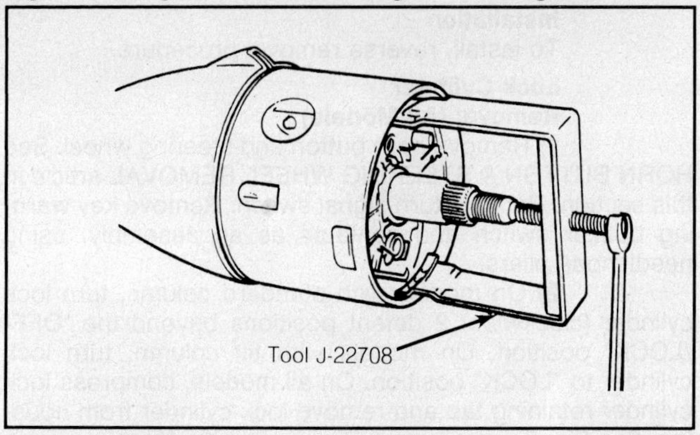

Puller is used for "G" & "P" series tilt column.

Installation

1) To install switch, wrap ends of signal switch wires with tape and guide them through opening at lower left side of bearing housing (tilt column) and out lower end of shift lever housing and under dash seal.

2) Place directional signal switch in position and install screws. Tighten screws to 25 INCH lbs. (2.8 N.m). On models with tilt column, align openings in signal switch cover with proper lever positions and tap cover into place using plastic hammer.

3) Install tilt release lever. Install A/T selector dial, pointer, dial illumination light and cap (if equipped). On all models, install signal switch lever and hazard warning knob.

4) Bend wire harness connector tabs from each wire before installing in half moon connector. Install each wire in its marked position and reconnect signal switch harness.

5) Snap wire harness protector into column retaining slots and install signal canceling cam and spring. Install steering wheel and column-to-instrument panel trim plate (if equipped).

Removal (All Others)

1) Remove steering wheel. See HORN BUTTON & STEERING WHEEL REMOVAL article in this section. Remove column-to-instrument panel trim cover screw and cover. Compress lock plate with Plate Compressor (J 23653). *See Fig. 4.*

Fig. 4: Removing GM Lock Plate & Snap Ring

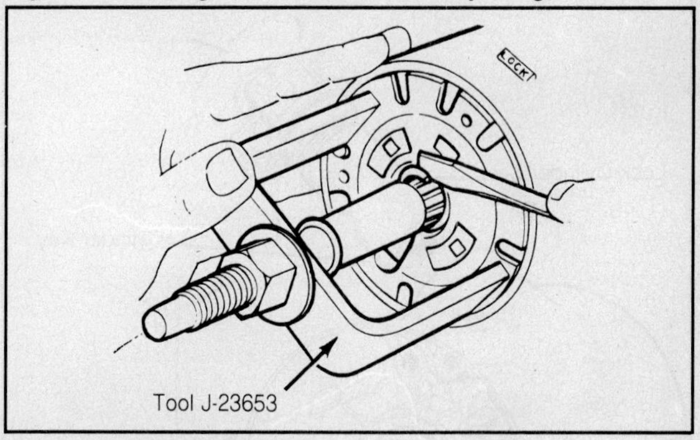

Do not reuse old snap ring.

2) Pry snap ring from groove and discard. Lift off lock plate, directional signal canceling cam, upper bearing preload spring and thrust washer from end of shaft.

3) Remove directional signal warning lever. Depress and unscrew hazard warning knob. Remove 3 switch mounting screws. On models with standard column, pull switch connector from bracket on column.

4) Pull switch straight up, guiding wiring harness through column housing and protector. Remove wire protector by pulling downward out of column with pliers using tab provided.

5) On models with tilt column, steering column must be in "LOW" position to remove directional signal switch. Removal procedure is same as for standard column.

Installation

1) On models with standard column, feed connector and protector cover down through housing and under mounting bracket. On models with tilt column, feed connector down through housing and then install protector cover.

Steering Column Switches

ALL MANUFACTURERS (Cont.)

CAUTION: It is extemely important that only specified screws, bolts and nuts be used during reassembly. Use of overlength screws could prevent column from compressing under impact.

2) On all columns, install 3 switch mounting screws and clip connector to bracket. Install trim panel, hazard warning knob and directional signal lever.

3) Ensure switch is in neutral position and hazard warning switch is out. Install thrust washer, upper bearing preload spring and canceling cam. Place lock plate onto end of shaft. Depress lock plate using Depressor (J 23653).

4) Install new snap ring on steering shaft. Install cover on lock plate and snap into position. Install steering wheel.

Lock Cylinder
Removal & Installation (All Models)

1) Remove steering wheel. See HORN BUTTON & STEERING WHEEL REMOVAL article in this section. Remove lock plate. Lift directional signal switch up far enough to slip over end of shaft. It is not necessary to remove switch completely.

2) Place key in lock cylinder and turn to "RUN" position. Remove lock retaining screw being carefull not to drop screw down column. Rotate lock cylinder to align cylinder key with keyway in housing. *See Fig. 5*. Pull cylinder from housing.

Fig. 5: Removing GM Lock Cylinder Assembly

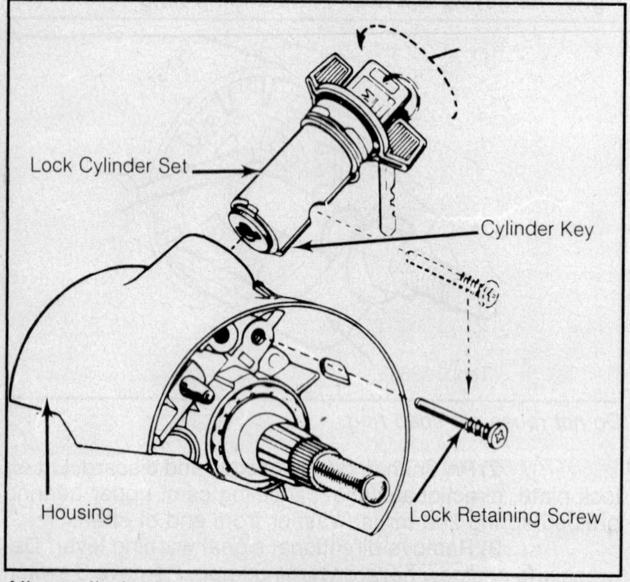

Align cylinder key with keyway in housing.

3) To install, hold lock cylinder and rotate key clockwise to stop. Align cylinder key and housing keyway and insert cylinder. To complete installation, reverse removal procedure.

Ignition Switch
Removal & Installation (All Models)

1) To remove ignition switch, steering column must be lowered, but it is not necessary to remove steering wheel. See STEERING COLUMN REMOVAL article in this section. If steering is not removed from vehicle, support column.

2) Turn ignition to "LOCK" position. If lock cylinder has already been removed, pull up on actuating rod of switch until it stops, then push down one detent. Switch is now in "LOCK" position. Remove 2 screws, then remove ignition switch.

3) To install, switch and lock cylinder should be in "LOCK" position. Install activating rod in switch. Install switch on column and tighten mounting screws. Install steering column and check system operation.

NOTE: Use only specified screws. Using screws that are too long may prevent a portion of column from compressing under impact.

JEEP

Turn Signal & Hazard Flasher Switches
Removal (All Models)

1) Place front wheels in straight-ahead position. Disconnect battery negative cable. Remove steering wheel. See HORN BUTTON & STEERING WHEEL REMOVAL article in this section.

2) On models with A/T, place selector lever in Park position. Remove selector lever retaining pin and lever. Using 2 screwdrivers, remove lock plate cover. On models with tilt column, remove tilt lever.

3) Compress lock plate using Plate Compressor (J23653 A). If shaft has metric threads, use Metric Forcing Screw (J 23653 4) prior to installing compressor on shaft. Remove and discard lock plate snap ring. Remove compressor.

NOTE: The lock plate is under strong spring tension, do not attempt to remove snap ring without using lock plate compressor.

4) Remove lock plate, canceling cam, upper bearing preload spring, spring seat and bearing race (thrust washer on some models). Depress hazard warning switch and unscrew from column.

5) On vehicles with A/T, use a paper clip to compress lock tab retaining shift quadrant light wire in connector block and disconnect wire. On all models, remove turn signal lever attaching screw and lever.

6) On vehicles with cruise control, disconnect 2 of 4 wires at switch connector. Fold wires back along harness. Tape wires to harness and tape a string to harness to aid in removal.

7) Disconnect turn signal switch wire harness at bottom of steering column. Tape around turn signal switch harness connector to aid in removal. Remove turn signal switch attaching screws and remove switch.

Installation

To install, reverse removal procedure.

Lock Cylinder
Removal (All Models)

1) Remove horn button and steering wheel. See HORN BUTTON & STEERING WHEEL REMOVAL article in this section. Remove turn signal switch. Remove key warning buzzer switch and contacts as an assembly, using needlenose pliers.

2) On models with standard column, turn lock cylinder (clockwise) 2 detent positions beyond the "OFF-/LOCK" position. On models with tilt column, turn lock cylinder to "LOCK" position. On all models, compress lock cylinder retaining tab and remove lock cylinder from housing. *See Fig. 6*.

Fig. 6: Removing Jeep Lock Cylinder

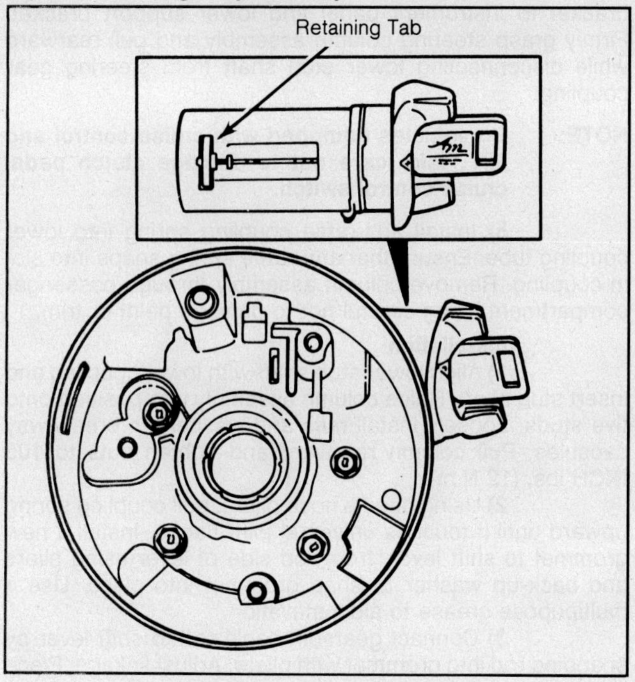

Installation

1) To install, insert key in lock cylinder. Hold cylinder sleeve and turn key clockwise until key stops. Align lock cylinder retaining tab with keyway in housing and insert cylinder into housing.

2) Push cylinder inward until it contacts lock sector. Rotate cylinder to engage it with lock sector. Push cylinder inward until cylinder retaining tab engages in housing groove. To complete installation, reverse removal procedure.

Ignition Switch

Removal (Cherokee & Wagoneer)

Remove lower instrument panel trim panel. Insert key in lock cylinder and turn cylinder to "OFF-UNLOCK" position. Disconnect switch from remote rod. Disconnect harness connectors at switch and remove switch.

Installation

Move switch slider to "ACC" position. Engage remote rod in switch slider and position switch on column. Do not move slider while positioning. Hold key in "ACC" position and push switch down slightly to remove slack in actuator rod. Install attaching screws. Connect harness connectors.

Removal (All Other Models)

Remove ignition switch from bottom of steering column.

Installation

Move switch slider to "ACC" position. Move switch slider back 2 clicks to "OFF-UNLOCK" position. Engage remote rod in switch slider and position switch on column. Do not move slider while positioning. Install attaching screws. Connect harness connectors.

Steering Columns

CHRYSLER CORP.

DESCRIPTION

All models use collapsible steering columns. All columns have integral ignition switch and locking device. Optional tilt wheel is available with both A/T and M/T. Transmission shift linkage is integral on all models except those with floor shift.

REMOVAL & INSTALLATION

FWD MODELS (COLUMN SHIFT)

Removal

1) Disconnect battery negative cable. On models with column shift, disconnect cable rod by prying rod from grommet in shift lever. Remove cable clip and remove cable from lower bracket.

2) Disconnect the wiring connectors at column jacket. Remove steering wheel center pad and steering wheel. See HORN BUTTON & STEERING WHEEL article in this section. On models with A/T, remove damper assembly.

3) Expose steering column bracket. Remove instrument panel steering column cover and lower reinforcement. Disconnect bezel. Remove indicator set screw and gearshift indicator pointer from shift housing.

4) Remove nuts attaching steering column bracket to instrument panel and lower support bracket. Firmly grasp steering column assembly and pull rearward while disconnecting lower stub shaft from steering gear coupling.

NOTE: **On vehicles equipped with cruise control and M/T, take care not to damage clutch pedal cruise control switch.**

5) Install anti-rattle coupling spring into lower coupling tube. Ensure that anti-rattle spring snaps into slot in coupling. Remove column assembly through passenger compartment being careful not to damage paint or trim.

Installation

1) Align lower stub shaft with lower coupling and insert stub shaft. Raise column assembly into position onto five studs. Loosely install nuts and washers in breakaway capsules. Pull column rearward and tighten nuts to 105 INCH lbs. (12 N.m).

2) Using needle nose pliers, pull coupling spring upward until it touches universal joint flange. Install a new grommet to shift lever, from rod side of lever using pliers and back-up washer to snap grommet into place. Use a multipupose grease to aid installation.

3) Connect gearshift cable rod to shift lever by snapping rod into grommet with pliers. Adjust linkage. Place steering wheel on shaft with master splines aligned. Place

Fig. 1: Exploded View of Front Wheel Drive Steering Column

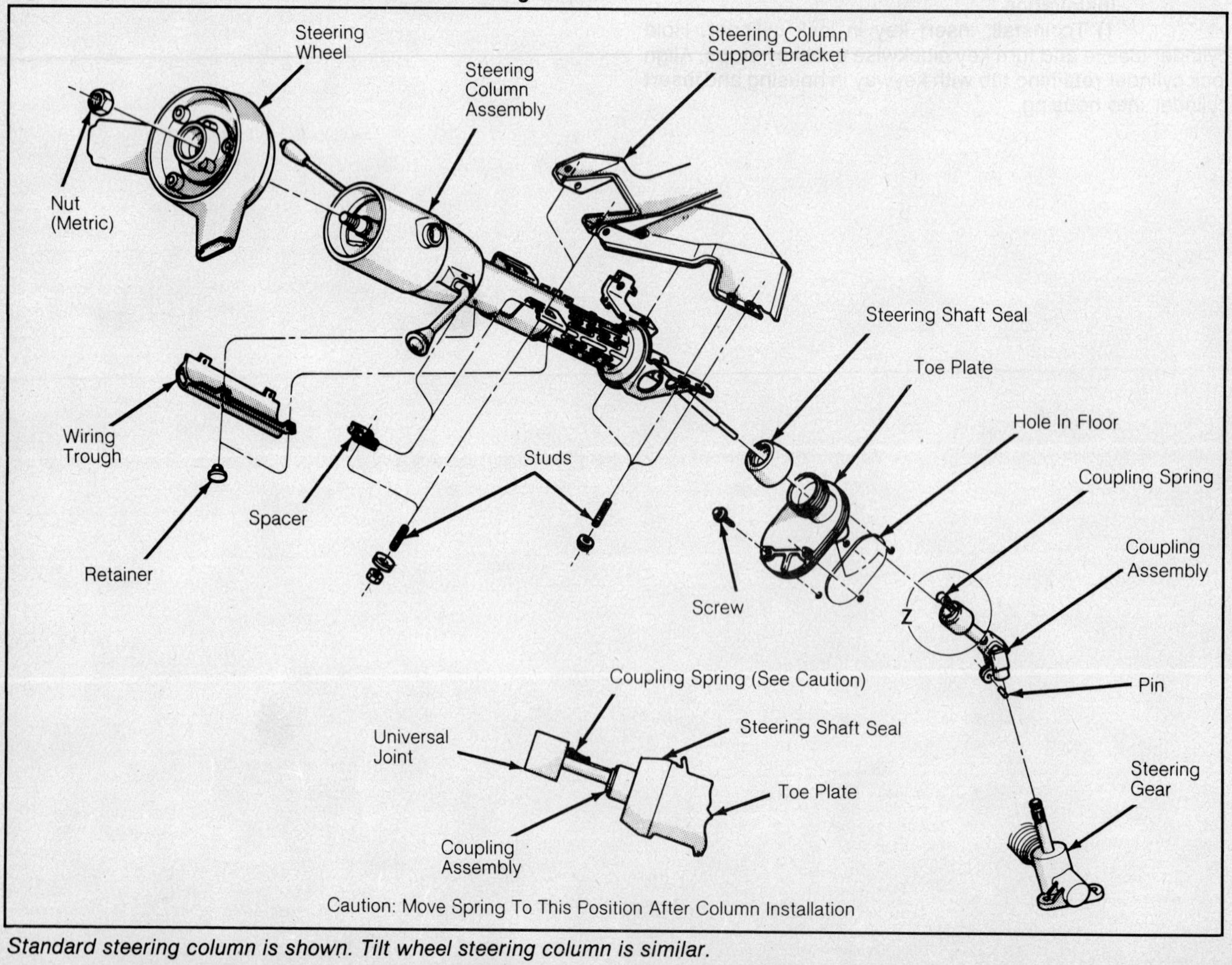

Standard steering column is shown. Tilt wheel steering column is similar.

damper assembly inside steering wheel, if vehicle is equipped with A/T. Install retaining nut and tighten to 45 ft. lbs. (61 N.m).

4) Install horn switch parts and connect switch wire. Connect wiring connectors at steering column jacket. Connect battery negative cable and test operation of lights and horn.

5) On models with A/T, install gearshift indicator pointer. Slowly move gearshift lever from "LOW" (1) to "PARK", pausing briefly at each selector position. If necessary, loosen and readjust to align pointer with each position. Install instrument panel steering column cover.

FWD MODELS (FLOOR SHIFT)

The steering column with a floor mounted gearshift is basically same as previously described. Standard columns and service procedures are identical except as described below.

- In place of rotating shift housing, there is a plastic shroud which is fixed to lock housing. Shroud covers jacket and lock inhibitor assembly. It is held in place by a tab that fits under side cover and one screw. Shroud can only be replaced by removing lock housing from jacket.
- The lock inhibitor assembly consist of a lever that engages lock levers (preventing locking of steering shaft), a button to operate lever and a return spring. Assembly is attached to lock housing in same location as shift gate is on column shift. Lower steering shaft bearing is mounted in an aluminum support.

RWD MODELS (COLUMN SHIFT)

Removal

1) Disconnect battery negative cable. On models with column shift, disconnect link rod(s) by prying rod from grommet in shift lever. Remove steering shaft lower coupling to worm shaft roll pin. *See Fig. 2.*

2) Disconnect wiring connectors at column jacket. Remove steering wheel center pad (or horn switch) and steering wheel See HORN BUTTON & STEERING WHEEL article in this section.

NOTE: **Do not bump or hammer on steering shaft to remove steering wheel.**

3) Remove turn signal lever. Remove floor plate-to-floor pan attaching screws. Remove cluster bezel and panel lower reinforcement to expose steering column bracket. If equipped with A/T, disconnect shift indicator pointer cable from shift housing.

Fig. 2: Exploded View of A/T Steering Column

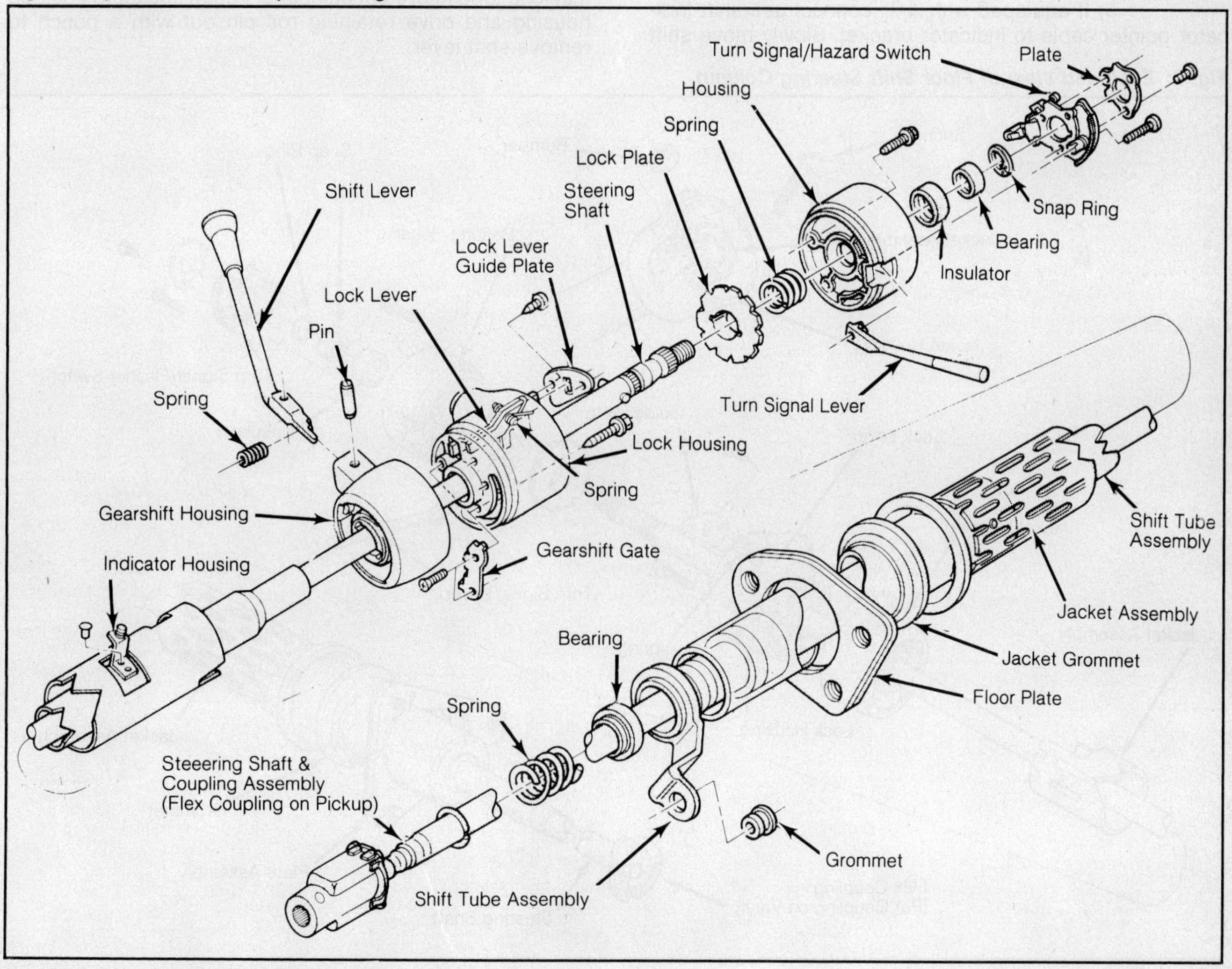

Van is shown. Pickup is similar.

Steering Columns

CHRYSLER CORP. (Cont.)

4) On all models, remove nuts attaching steering column bracket to instrument panel support. Carefully remove lower coupling from steering gear worm shaft.

5) Steering shaft may be equipped with either flexible coupling or a "Pot" coupling. Remove column assembly out through passenger compartment.

Installation

1) Install ground clip on left capsule slot. Plastic capsules should be preassembled in bracket slot. Insert column through floor pan opening. With front wheels straight-ahead and splines on wormshaft and coupling aligned, engage coupling and install roll pin.

CAUTION: Do not apply end load to steering shaft.

2) Hold column assembly with bracket slots on mounting studs. Loosely install 2 upper bracket washers and nuts. Be sure both capsules are fully seated in slots in support bracket and tighten nuts.

3) Position floor plate over floor pan opening, centering it around column, then install retaining bolts. Place steering wheel on shaft with splines aligned. Install and tighten nut. DO NOT drive wheel onto shaft, draw it down with retaining nut.

4) Install horn switch and connect wiring connector at column jacket. Before connecting link rod to column shift lever, a new grommet MUST be installed.

5) If equipped with A/T, connect gearshift indicator pointer cable to indicator bracket. Slowly move shift lever from "LOW" (1) to "PARK", pausing briefly at each position.

6) If necessary, bend indicator bracket to align pointer with each position. Reinstall panel lower reinforcement and cluster bezel. Connect battery negative cable and test horn and lights.

RWD MODELS (FLOOR SHIFT)

The steering column with a floor mounted gearshift is basically same as previously described. Standard columns and service procedures are identical except as described below.

- Lower steering shaft bearing is mounted in an aluminum support.
- A spring is attached between shift housing and column jacket. This spring keeps housing rotated counterclockwise against rubber bumper. *See Fig. 3.*

OVERHAUL

STANDARD COLUMN

Disassembly (FWD Models)

1) Pry out wiring trough retainers and lift off trough. New retainers may be required for reassembly. Use masking tape to protect paint and a deep socket to back-up housing and drive retaining roll pin out with a punch to remove shift lever.

Fig. 3: Exploded View of Floor Shift Steering Column

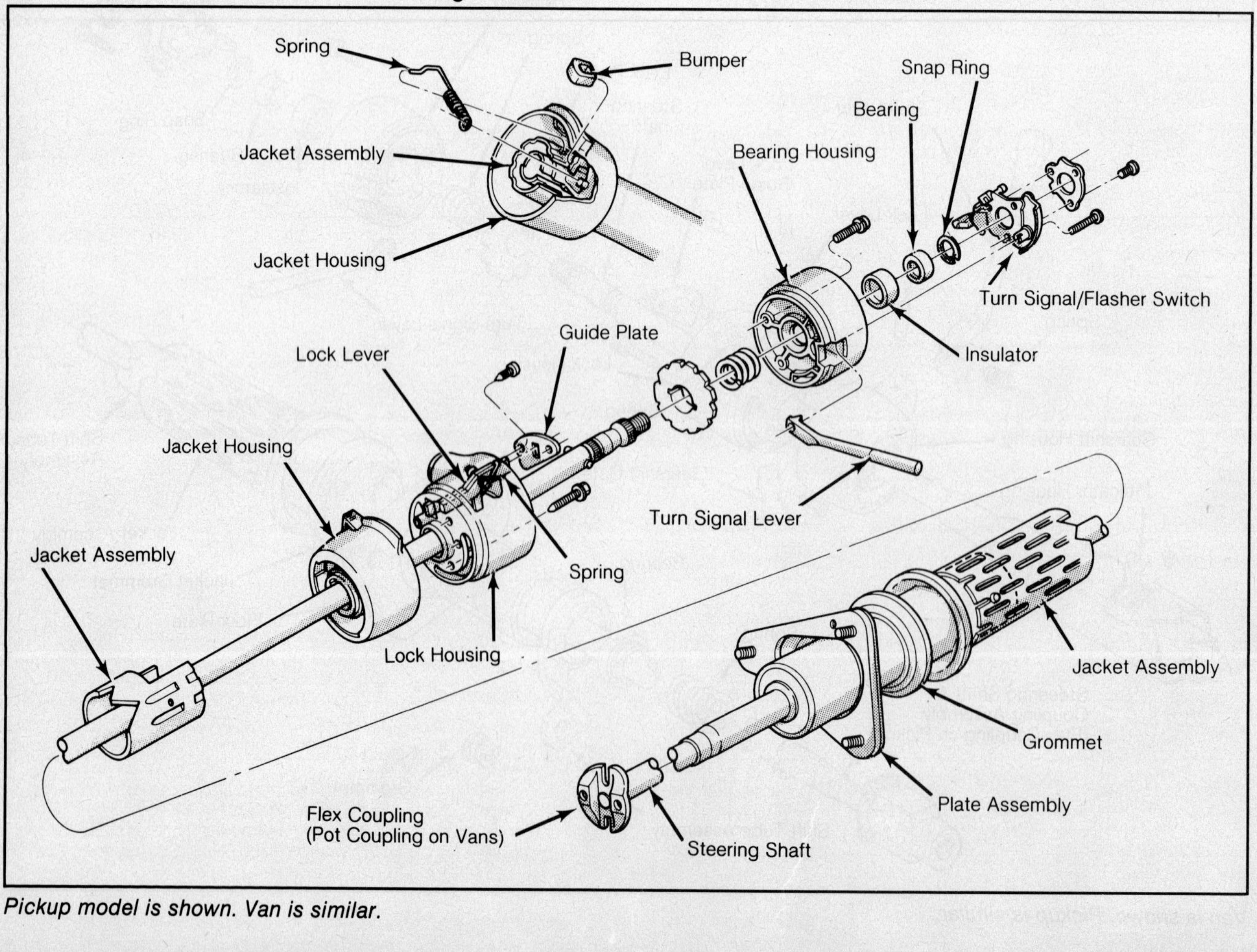

Pickup model is shown. Van is similar.

2) Remove breakaway capsules. Secure column in vise by clamping at column bracket. Do not distort column. Remove 2 screws that attach turn signal lever cover to lock housing and remove cover. Remove wipe/wash switch assembly. Pull hider up wipe/wash lever and remove 2 screws that attach lever sleeve to switch.

3) Rotate wipe/wash shaft to full clockwise position and remove shaft from switch. Remove turn signal switch and upper bearing retaining screws. Remove retainer and lift switch upward out of way. Unclip horn ground wire. Remove retaining screw and lift ignition key lamp assembly out of way.

4) Remove 4 screws holding bearing housing to lock housing. Remove snap ring from upper end of steering shaft. Remove bearing housing from shaft. Remove lock plate spring and lock plate from shaft. Remove shaft through lower end of column.

5) Remove ignition key. Remove screw and lift out key warning switch. Remove 2 screws attaching ignition switch to column jacket. Remove ignition switch by rotating switch 90° on actuator rod. Remove 2 screws from dimmer switch and disengage switch from rod.

6) Remove 2 screws that mount bellcrank and slide bellcrank up in slide housing until it can be disconnected from ignition switch rod. Place cylinder in "LOCK" position and remove key.

7) Insert a small diameter screwdriver or similar tool into lock cylinder release hole. Push inward to release spring-loaded lock retainer while pulling lock cylinder from housing bore.

8) Grasp lock lever and spring assembly and pull straight out of housing. Remove 4 lock housing-to-column jacket hex head retaining screws and remove housing from jacket. Loosen shift tube set screw, in shaft housing, from column shift models with A/T. On all models, remove shift tube through lower end of jacket.

Reassembly

1) During reassembly, coat all friction surfaces with multipurpose grease. Clamp column in vise so that both ends of column are accessible. Check column tube-to-mandrel rivets for tightness.

2) If replacement is necessary, use 1/8" diameter by 1/4" long (1/8" grip) aluminum blind rivets. Do not use steel rivets as rivets must shear upon impact. Position crossover load spring and shift lever in gearshift housing and tap pivot pin into place.

3) Assemble key cylinder plunger spring and install assembly on lock housing. Install shift lever gate on lock housing. Place shift lever in mid position and seat lock housing on top of jacket by indexing keyway in housing with slot in jacket. Install housing-to-jacket screws and tighten alternately to 90 INCH lbs. (10 N.m).

4) Install dimmer switch by firmly pushing rod into switch. Compress switch until 2 .093" drill shanks can be inserted into alignment holes. Reposition upper end of push rod in pocket of wipe/wash switch. Remove lower column cover, if necessary. Remove drills.

5) Switch should click when lever is lifted and again as lever returns, just before it reaches stop in down position. Grease and assemble 2 lock levers, lock lever spring and pin. Install assembly into lock housing. Seat pin firmly in bottom of slots. Ensure that lock lever spring leg is firmly in place in lock casting notch.

6) Install ignition switch actuator rod from bottom through oblong hole in lock housing and attach to bellcrank. Position bellcrank assembly into lock housing while pulling ignition switch and rod down column. Install bellcrank onto its mounting surface. Gearshift lever should be in "PARK" position.

7) Place ignition switch on actuator rod and rotate 90° to lock rod into position. Install ignition lock by turning key to "LOCK" position and removing key. Insert cylinder into housing far enough to contact switch actuator. Insert key, press inward and rotate cylinder.

8) When parts align, cylinder will move inward and spring loaded retainers will snap into place, locking cylinder in housing. With cylinder and ignition switch in "LOCK" position (second detent from top) tighten ignition switch mounting screws.

9) Feed key warning switch wires behind wiring post and down through space between housing and jacket. Remove ignition key and position switch in housing and tighten mounting screws. Install lower bearing support (floor shift), bearing and spring on steering shaft.

10) Install and lubricate rubber "O" ring in lower groove on upper end of steering shaft. Completely insert steering shaft assembly into column assembly. Press upper bearing into upper bearing housing. Bearing must be fully seated.

11) Push up on steering shaft to compress bearing and spring, hold shaft in this position until snap ring is installed. Install lock plate on steering shaft. Install upper bearing spring. Install upper bearing housing with bearing previously installed.

12) Install upper bearing snap ring on steering shaft, locking assembly into position. Install 4 screws attaching bearing housing to lock housing. Install ignition key lamp assembly in bearing housing. Install turn signal switch in bearing housing.

13) Feed turn signal switch and ignition key lamp wires through opening between bearing housing and lock housing and down along bottom of jacket. Install bearing retainer plate and tighten screws. Ensure that ground wires from turn signal switch are positioned toward ground clips before tightening.

14) Attach horn ground wire to bearing retaining plate. Assemble wiper switch, shaft, cover or speed control switch, hider and knob. Place wipe/wash switch assembly into lock housing, feeding wires through lock housing and shift and fasten to turn signal switch.

15) Install dimmer switch actuator rod up through housings and into pocket of wipe/wash switch. compress dimmer switch until 2 .093" drill shanks can be inserted into alignment holes.

16) With one end of rod in wipe/wash switch and other end in dimmer switch apply a slight upward pressure and fasten dimmer switch to bracket. Remove drills. Switch should click when lever is lifted and again as lever returns, just before it reaches stop in down position.

17) Install turn signal lever cover. Install breakaway capsules. Install wiring trough in place, being carefull not to pinch wires. Install new retainers if required.

Disassembly (RWD Models)

1) Pry out wiring trough retainers and lift off trough. New retainers may be required for reassembly. Use masking tape to protect paint and a deep socket to back-up housing and drive retaining roll pin out with a punch to remove shift lever.

2) Secure column in vise by clamping at column bracket. Do not distort column. Remove turn signal switch and upper bearing retaining screws. Remove retainer and lift switch upward out of way.

CHRYSLER CORP. (Cont.)

3) Remove retaining screw and lift ignition key lamp assembly out of way. Remove snap ring from upper end of steering shaft. Remove screws attaching bearing housing to lock housing.

NOTE: Screws attaching bearing housing to lock housing must be removed before steering shaft removal.

4) Remove bearing housing from shaft. Remove coil spring and lock plate from shaft. Remove shaft through lower end of column.

5) Remove 2 retaining screws and lock lever guide plate. This will expose lock cylinder release hole. Place cylinder in "LOCK" position and remove key.

6) Insert a small diameter screwdriver or similar tool into lock cylinder release hole. Push in to release spring-loaded lock retainer. At same time, pull lock cylinder from housing bore. Remove 3 retaining screws and ignition switch assembly. *See Fig. 4.*

Fig. 4: Removing Lock Cylinder

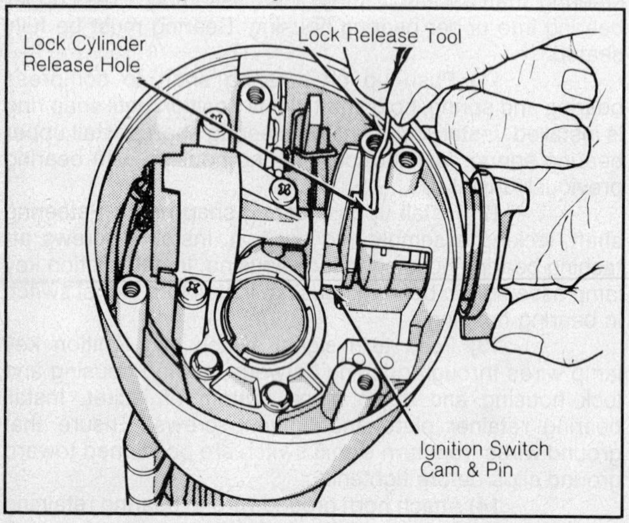

Cylinder must be in lock position.

7) Grasp lock lever and spring assembly and pull straight out of housing. Remove 4 lock housing-to-column jacket hex head retaining screws and remove housing from jacket.

8) Loosen shift tube set screw, in shaft housing, from column shift models with A/T. Remove shift tube through lower end of jacket. Remove floor plate and grommet from jacket.

9) To disassemble flexible coupling, remove 4 bolts and 2 cross straps. Remove flexible coupling. "Pot" coupling is removed by prying cover tangs from coupling body and lifting seal and cover from body. Drive dowel pin down into coupling and discard. Pull body off shaft and shoe assembly.

Reassembly

1) During reassembly, coat all friction surfaces with multipurpose grease. Clamp column in vise so that both ends of column are accessible.

2) Check column tube-to-mandrel rivets for tightness. If replacement is necessary, use 3/8" diameter by 3/4" long (3/8" grip) steel blind rivets. Do not use aluminum rivets.

3) Install floor plate and grommet on lower end of jacket. On models with A/T, position gearshift housing on column jacket. Install dust seal and shift tube support on shift tube. Slide shift tube into jacket.

4) Guide key on upper end of tube into slot in gearshift housing. Position crossover load spring and shift lever in gearshift housing and tap pivot pin into place. Install shift lever gate on lock housing.

5) Place shift lever in mid position and seat lock housing on top of jacket by indexing keyway in housing with slot in jacket. Install housing-to-jacket screws and tighten alternately. Install A/T indicator bracket.

6) Grease and assemble 2 lock levers, lock lever spring and pin. Install assembly into lock housing. Seat pin firmly in bottom of slots. Ensure that lock lever spring leg is firmly in place in lock casting notch. *See Fig. 5.*

Fig. 5: Installing Lock Lever and Spring Assembly

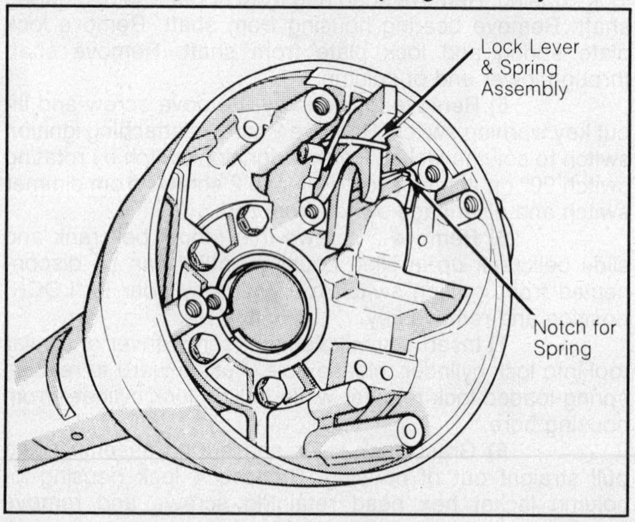

Lock lever spring must be fully seated in casting notch.

7) Install lock lever guide plate and retaining screws. Turn ignition to "OFF" (center detent) position. Place hand lever in "PARK" position. Feed wires down through space between housing and jacket. Position switch in housing and tighten mounting screws.

8) To install ignition lock, turn key to "LOCK" position and remove key. Lock cylinder will move inward and a spring loaded retainer will snap into place, locking cylinder into housing.

9) Fill coupling body 1/4" full with multipurpose grease and place cover and seal on shaft. Press shoe pin into steering shaft so it protrudes an equal distance on each side of shaft.

10) Place spring on side of shaft so that it straddles shoe pin. Place shoes on pin ends with flat side toward spring, engaging tangs. Squeeze shoes together and push assembly into coupling body.

11) Align master spline mark of coupling body with master spline on upper shaft. Drive in a new dowel pin flush to coupling body outer surface. Position seal and cover on body and crimp cover tangs on body.

12) Move shaft in and out of "Pot" body several times to distribute lubricant. Install bearing support (floor shift), bearing and spring on steering shaft and insert steering shaft into column assembly.

13) Install lock plate and new groove pin on steering shaft. Ensure pin is centered. Install steering column shaft lock plate sleeve over shaft lock plate pin and against lock plate.

14) Install bearing lower snap ring on steering shaft. Install coil spring on "B" models. Install ignition key lamp assembly in bearing housing. Place rubber insulator

with grounding staple over column upper bearing and install into bearing housing bore.

15) Use soap solution or rubber lubricant to ease installation. Install turn signal switch in bearing housing. Feed turn signal switch and ignition key lamp wires through opening in housing.

16) Install retaining plate over switch and tighten screws. Install turn signal/speed control lever on turn signal switch. If speed control, feed wires through opening provided in bearing housing.

17) Position housing assembly on steering shaft, feeding wires through space between housing and jacket. Install bearing and snap ring on shaft.

18) Install bearing housing-to-lock housing screws and tighten. Install wiring trough in place over wires, being careful not to pinch wires. Install new retainers if required.

TILT WHEEL COLUMN

Disassembly (FWD Models)

1) Remove 4 bolts attaching bracket assembly to column jacket. With column shift, remove shift housing cover. With floor shift, unsnap and remove shroud extensions. Remove wiring protector from column jacket. Mount column in vise by clamping on capsule bracket.

2) Remove tilt lever. Push hazard warning knob in and unscrew to remove. Remove ignition key lamp assembly. Pull knob off wipe/wash switch assembly. Pull hider up switch lever and remove 2 screws that attach sleeve to wipe/wash switch and remove sleeve.

3) Rotate shaft in wiper switch to fully clockwise position, and remove shaft by pulling straight out of wipe/wash switch. Carefully remove plastic cover from lock plate. Depress lock plate using Lock Plate Depressor (C4156), and pry retaining ring from groove.

4) Remove lock plate, canceling cam and upper bearing plate. Remove switch actuator screw and arm. Remove 3 turn signal switch attaching screws, place shift bowl in "LOW" (1) position. Wrap a piece of tape around and wires to prevent snagging when removing switch. Remove switch and wiring.

5) Remove key lamp. Place lock cylinder in "LOCK" position. Insert a small screwdriver into slot next to switch mounting screw boss and depress spring latch at bottom of slot and remove lock.

6) Remove key warning switch by using a paper clip. Bend one end of clip into a hook and insert into exposed loop of wedge spring. Pull wire and remove spring and switch. Do not allow spring to fall into steering column.

7) Remove 3 housing cover screws and remove housing cover. Remove wipe/wash switch. If required, press out wiper switch pivot pin witch a punch. If required, tilt lever opening shield and dimmer switch actuator rod may be removed from cap.

8) Place column in fully upright position. Remove tilt spring retainer using a large Phillips screwdriver. Insert screwdriver in opening, press in approximately 3/16" and turn approximately 1/8 clockwise until ears align with grooves in housing and remove spring and guide.

9) Remove dimmer switch mounting screws and remove dimmer switch. Separate dimmer switch from rod by pulling. Push upper steering shaft in far enough to remove steering shaft inner race seat and inner race. Place Pivot Pin Remover (C 4016) over pivot pin and thread small portion of screw firmly into pin.

10) Hold screw from turning with one wrench, turn nut clockwise with a second wrench to withdraw pivot pin from support. Remove opposite pivot pin in same manner. Use tilt release lever to disengage lock shoes. Remove bearing housing assembly by pulling upward to extend rack fully.

11) Move housing assembly left to disengage rack from actuator. Rotate housing clockwise to free dimmer switch actuator rod. Remove activator assembly. Remove coupling from lower end of steering shaft. Double coupling is retained to shaft with a roll pin. Remove shaft assembly from upper end.

CAUTION: Do not drop or bump steering shaft as plastic pins may shear.

12) Disassemble steering shaft assembly by removing center spheres and anti-lash springs. Remove 4 bolts securing support to lock plate and remove support from end of column jacket. If necessary, remove 2 attaching screws and shift gate from support. Dimmer switch is removed with support.

13) Remove shift tube retaining ring with screwdriver. Remove thrust washer. Remove 2 screws from lower bearing and remove lower bearing from jacket. Remove shift tube from bowl using Puller (C 4120). Insert bushing on end of puller in in shift tube to force tube from bowl. Do not hammer shift tube as plastic joints may shear.

14) Remove shift tube from jacket from lower end. Remove jacket mounting plate by sliding from jacket notches and tipping down toward bowl hub at 12 o'clock position and under jacket opening. Remove wave washer. Remove bowl from jacket. Remove shift lever spring from bowl by winding spring up with pliers and pulling out.

15) Remove lock bolt spring by removing spring retaining screw and moving spring clockwise. Using a hammer and punch lightly tap drive shaft from sector. Remove drive shaft, sector and bolt. Remove rack, spring and shim (if used). Remove tilt release lever pin.

16) Relieve load on lever release by holding shoes inward and wedge block between top of shoes and bearing housing. Remove lever and release lever spring. Remove lock shoe pin with punch and hammer. Remove lock shoes and lock shoe springs.

17) Remove bearings from bearing housing only if they are to be replaced. Remove separator and ball from bearing. Place housing on work bench. Using a punch againts back surface of race, hammer race from housing. Do not reuse bearings.

Reassembly

1) During reassembly, coat all friction surfaces with multipurpose grease. Clamp column in vise so that both ends of column are accessible.

2) Install bearings in bearing housing, if they were removed. Install lock shoe springs, lock shoes and shoe pin in bearing housing. Use a .180" rod to line up shoes for pin installation. With tilt lever opening on left side, shoes facing up, 4 slot shoe is facing up.

3) Install spring, release lever and pin in bearing housing. Install drive shaft in housing. Lightly tap sector onto drive shaft far enough to bottom on shaft. Install lock bolt and engage with sector cam surface. Install rack and spring. Block tooth on rack to engage block tooth on sector.

4) Install external tilt release lever. Install bolt spring and spring retaininginng screw. Tighten to 34 INCH lbs. (4 N.m). Install shift lever spring in bowl by winding up with pliers and pushing in. Slide bowl into jacket. Install wave washer and jacket mounting plate.

5) Work jacket mounting plate into jacket notches by tipping jacket mounting plate toward bowl hub at

12 o'clock position and under jacket opening. Slide jacket mounting plate in jacket notches. Carefully install shift tube in lower end of jacket.

6) Align key in tube with keyway in bowl and use Puller (C 4119) to pull shift tube into bowl. Do not push or tap on end of shift tube. Install thrust washer and retaining pin. by pulling bowl up to compress wave washer. Slide dimmer switch actuator rod through hole in support. Feed rod between bowl and jacket.

7) Install support by aligning "U" in support with "U" notch in jacket. Insert 4 screws through support into jacket mounting plate. Tighten screws to 60 INCH lbs. (7 N.m). Install lower bearing, if removed, on lower end of jacket.

8) Install centering spheres and anti-lash spring in upper steering shaft. Install lower steering shaft from same side of spheres that spring ends protrude. Perform a trial fit of assembly to ensure that master serration of upper shaft is on same side as master serration of lower shaft assembly.

9) Position shift bowl fully counterclockwise until it reaches stop. Install ignition switch actuator rod between bowl and jacket, from bottom. Guide back of coupling into support slot. Assemble bearing housing over steering shaft and engage rack over end of ignition switch actuator rod.

10) Position access hole of bearing housing over end of dimmer switch actuator rod. Rotate housing counterclockwise to assemble. Holding lock shoes in disengaged position, assemble bearing housing over steering shaft until pivot holes line up with holes in support.

11) Install pivot pins. Assemble as far as possible, using palm pressure of hand to prevent enlarging support pivot hole. Once started tap pins home with a small hammer and punch. Replace wipe/wash pivot assembly and press pivot pin in cover, if removed. Check pivot assembly for ease of movement.

12) If movement is restricted, tap other end of pin for clearance. Install wipe/wash switch. Replace tilt lever opening shield in cover, if removed. Position cap over dimmer switch actuator rod. Guide end of actuator rod into pivot slot during cover assembly. Hold cap so that cover will slide over it.

13) Place housing in full upward position, install guide after making sure there is grase between guide and peg on support, tilt spring and tilt spring retainer. Using a screwdriver in retaining slot, turn retainer clockwise to engage. Install bearing inner race and seat.

14) Install lock housing cover and tighten 3 screws to 100 INCH lbs. (11 N.m). Assemble key warning switch to spring clip with formed end of clip under end of switch and spring bowed away from switch on side opposite contact. Push switch and spring into hole in lock housing cover with contacts toward lock cylinder bore.

15) Install key lamp. Install turn signal switch wires and connector through cover, bearing housing and shift bowl. Push in hazard plunger. Install turn signal switch and tighten screws to 25 INCH lbs. (3 N.m). Install hazard warning knob and screw. Pull knob out.

16) Install canceling cam spring, canceling cam (carrier assembly) and lock plate. Using Lock Plate Depressor (C 4156), depress lock plate and install a new retaining ring. Install tilt release lever (if removed) and turn signal switch lever.

17) Install ignition lock by turning key to "LOCK" position and remove key. Insert cylinder into housing far enough to contact drive shaft. Press inward and move ignition switch actuator rod up and down to align parts.

18) When parts align, cylinder will move inward and a spring loaded retainer will snap into place locking cylinder in housing. When replacing ignition switch, position key cylinder in "LOCK" and remove key. Place ignition switch in "LOCK" position (second detent from bottom).

19) Fit ignition switch actuator rod into slider hole and loosely install on column with 2 screws. Push switch lightly toward lock housing to take out slack in actuator rod and tighten screws to 34 INCH lbs. (4 N.m). Do not move switch out of detent position.

20) Install dimmer switch by firmly seating push rod into switch. Compress switch until 2 .093" drill shanks can be inserted into alignment holes. Reposition upper end of push rod in pocket of wipe/wash switch. Remove lower column cover, if necessary.

21) With a light upward pressure on switch, install 2 screws. Remove drills. Switch should click when lever is lifted and again as lever returns, just before it reaches stop, in down position. Install wire protector over wires on column jacket, being carefull not to pinch wires.

22) Remove column from vise. Position lower bracket assembly on steering column. Install and tighten 2 bolts to 105 INCH lbs. (12 N.m). Align master splines and install coupling assembly on steering shaft. Support coupling under joint and drive in retaining roll pin.

Disassembly (RWD Models)

1) Remove steering wheel and column from vehicle. Remove bracket assembly-to-column jacket bolts. Remove wiring protector from jacket. Attach Holding Fixture (C 4132) to jacket and mount column in vise.

2) Remove tilt lever and turn signal or speed control lever. Push hazard warning knob in and unscrew to remove. Remove ignition key lamp assembly. Move tilt mechanism to full down tilt. Carefully remove plastic cover from lock plate.

3) Depress lock plate with finger and pry ring from groove with screwdriver. Remove lock plate, canceling cam and upper bearing spring. Remove three turn signal switch screws, place shift bowl in "LOW" (1) position.

4) Tie up wires and connectors to prevent snagging, remove switch and wiring. To remove lock cylinder, place in "LOCK" position. Insert a thin tool into slot next to switch mounting screw boss (right hand slot) and depress spring latch at bottom of slot to remove lock.

5) Remove housing cover screws and remove housing cover. Reinstall tilt lever and place column in full upward position. Remove tilt spring retainer with a phillips screwdriver.

6) Insert screwdriver in opening and press in 3/16". Turn about 1/8 turn counterclockwise until ears align with groove in housing and remove spring and guide.

7) Push upper steering shaft in sufficiently to remove steering shaft inner race seat and inner race. Turn ignition to "ACC" position and remove.

8) Place Pivot Pin Remover (C 4016) over pivot pin, thread small portion of screw into pin. Hold screw in position, turn nut clockwise and remove pivot pin from support. Remove opposite pivot pin. Use tilt release lever to disengage lock shoes.

9) Remove bearing housing by pulling upward to extend rack fully. Move housing to left to disengage rack from actuator. Remove actuator assembly. Remove roll pin and coupling assembly from lower end of steering shaft.

10) Remove shaft from upper end of column. Disassemble steering shaft by removing center spheres and anti-lash springs. Remove bolts securing support to lock plate and remove support from end of column jacket. If needed remove attaching screws and shift gate from support.

11) Using screwdriver remove shift tube retaining ring and thrust washer. With a small screwdriver disengage plastic shift tube support from lower end of jacket.

12) Remove shift tube from bowl using Puller (C 4120). Insert bushing on end of tool in shift tube and force tube from bowl. *See Fig. 6.*

Fig. 6: Removing Shift Tube from Bowl on Tilt Wheel

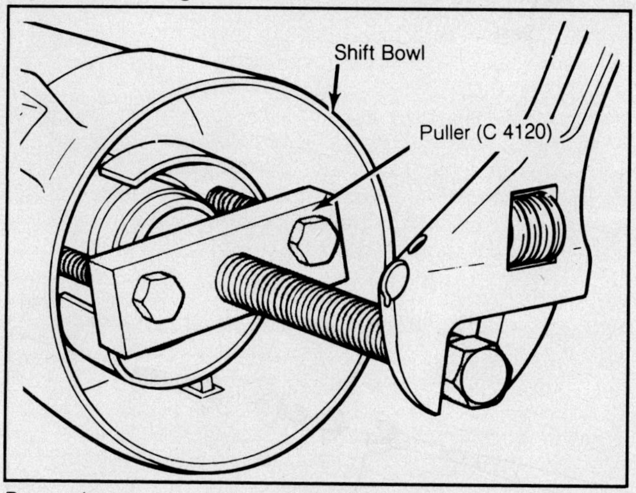

Do not hammer or pull on shift tube.

13) Remove shift tube from jacket at lower end. Remove lock plate by sliding from jacket notches and tapping down toward hub at 12 o'clock position and under jacket opening.

14) Remove wave washer and bowl from jacket. Remove shift lever spring from bowl by winding spring up with pliers and pulling out. Remove tilt lever opening shield and turn signal lever opening shield from housing.

15) Remove lock bolt spring by removing spring retaining screw and moving spring clockwise. Remove snap ring from sector drive shaft. Use a small punch to tap drive shaft from sector. Remove drive shaft, sector and bolt.

16) Remove rack and spring, and also shim if one is used. Using a punch and hammer remove tilt release lever pin. Remove lever and release lever spring.

17) To relieve load on release lever, hold shoes inward and wedge block between top of shoes (over slots) and bearing housing. Remove lock shoe pin with punch and hammer, remove lock shoes and lock shoe springs.

NOTE: **Do not remove bearings from housing unless they are to be replaced. Never reuse old bearings.**

Reassembly

1) Install bearings in housing, if removed. Install lock shoe springs, lock shoes and shoe pin. Use a rod about .180" diameter to line up shoes. With tilt lever opening on left side, and shoes facing up, 4 slot shoe is on left.

2) Install spring, release lever and pin in bearing housing. Relieve load on release lever as outlined in step **17)** of disassembly procedure. Install drive shaft and tap sector on shaft far enough to install snap ring. Install lock bolt and engage with sector cam surface.

3) Install rack and spring. Block tooth on rack must engage block tooth on sector. Install external tilt release lever, bolt spring and retainer. Install shift lever spring in bowl by winding up with pliers and pushing in.

4) Slide bowl into jacket, install wave washer and lock plate. Work lock plate into notches in jacket and carefully install shift tube in lower end of jacket.

5) Align key in tube with keyway in bowl and use Puller (C 4119) to pull tube into bowl. *See Fig. 7.* Install thrust washer and retaining ring by pulling bowl up to compress wave washer. Do not push hard or tap on end of tube.

Fig. 7: Installing Shift Tube on Models With Tilt Wheel

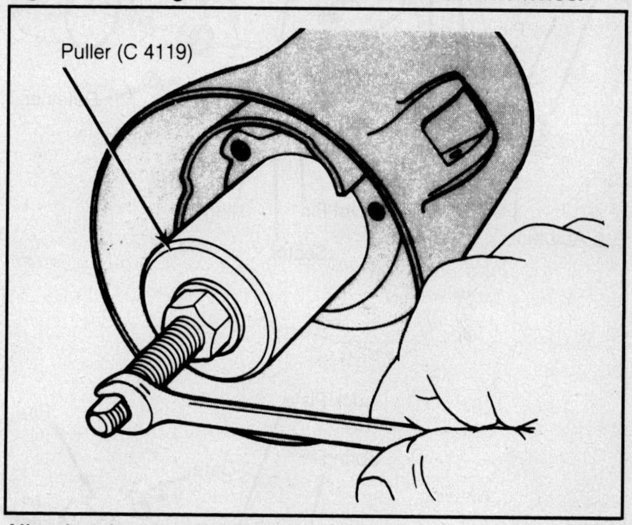

Align key in tube with keyway in bowl.

6) Install support by aligning "V" notch in support with notch in jacket, and install retaining screws. Install lower bearing at end of shift tube. Locate about 3/16" inside tube (use lubricant to ease installation).

7) Install centering spheres and anti-lash spring in upper steering shaft and lower steering shaft from same side of spheres that spring ends protrude.

8) Check double coupling assembly that master serration of upper shaft will align with master serration of pot coupling. Place housing in full upward position, install guide, tilt spring and tilt spring retainer using screwdriver.

9) Turn retainer clockwise to engage. Install steering shaft in shift tube from upper end. Place ignition switch actuator rod through bowl from bottom and insert slot in support.

10) Extend rack downward from bearing housing, assemble housing over steering shaft, and engage rack over end of actuator rod. Install external tilt release lever.

11) While holding lock shoes in disengaged position, assemble bearing housing over steering shaft until pivot pin holes line up. Install pivot pins.

12) With housing in full upward position, install guide. Ensure there is grease between guide and peg on support, tilt spring and spring retainer. Using a screwdriver in retainer slot, turn retainer clockwise to engage.

13) Install bearing inner race and tilt lever opening shield. Remove tilt release lever, install housing cover and tighten screws. Install signal switch wires and connector.

14) Push hazard warning plunger in, install switch and tighten screws. Install hazard warning knob and pull out. Install canceling cam spring, canceling cam and shift lock plate.

15) Using Depressor (C 4156), depress shift lock plate and install new retaining ring. *See Fig. 9*. Install tilt

Steering Columns

CHRYSLER CORP. (Cont.)

Fig. 8: Exploded View of Tilt Wheel Column Upper Half

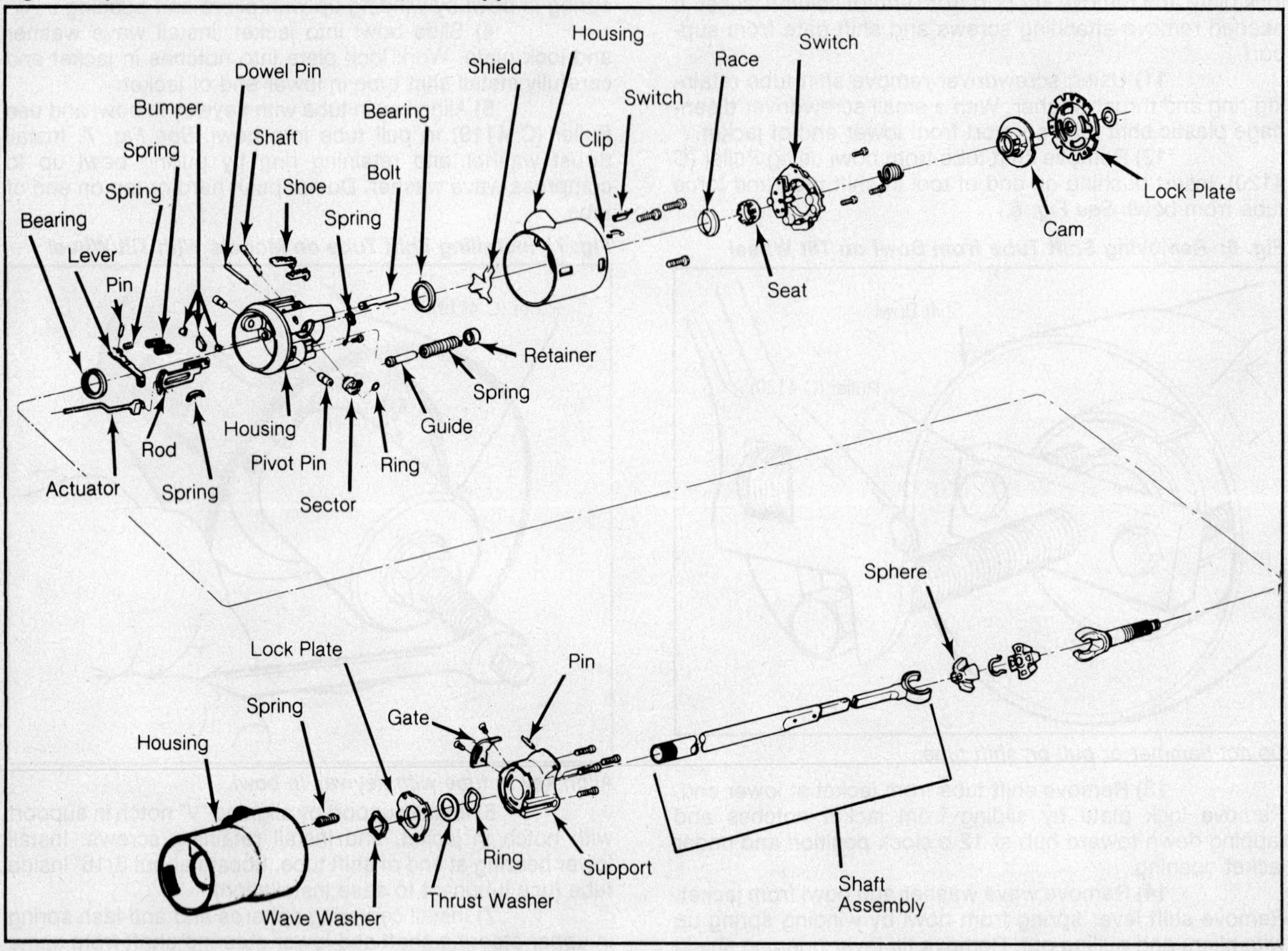

Rear wheel drive models are shown. Front wheel drive column is similar.

release lever and turn signal switch lever. To install ignition lock, turn key to "LOCK" position and remove key.

16) Insert cylinder into housing enough to contact switch actuator. Press inward to move switch actuator rod up and down to align parts. When aligned, cylinder will move inward and spring loaded retainer will snap into place.

17) When replacing ignition switch, position key cylinder in "ACC" detent (full counterclockwise).

18) Spring loaded position at one end is "START" position. Top place switch in "ACC" position, move slider to extreme opposite end. Fit actuator rod into slide hole and assemble loosely to column.

19) Push switch lightly down column to remove lash in actuator rod and tighten mounting screws. Do not move switch out of detent position. Install wire protector over wires on column jacket.

20) Remove column from vise. Remove holding fixture. Position bracket assembly on steering column. Tighten bolts. Align master splines and install coupling assembly on steering shaft. Drive in retaining roll pin. Install column and steering wheel.

Fig. 9: Installing Lock Plate Retaining Ring

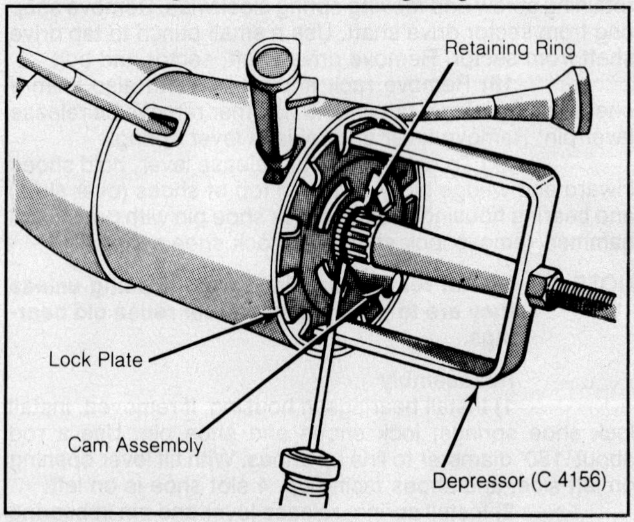

Depress lock plate for access to retaining ring groove.

CHRYSLER CORP. (Cont.)

TIGHTENING SPECIFICATIONS

Application	Ft. Lbs. (N.m)
Bracket-to-Column Bolt	10 (14)
Column Clamp Stud Nut	9 (12)
Flexible Coupling Bolts	17 (23)
Steering Wheel Retaining Nut	45 (61)
Support Plate Bolts	17 (23)
Upper Bracket Nuts	9 (12)
	INCH Lbs. (N.m)
Bearing Housing-to-Lock Housing Screws	35 (4)
Column Clamp Stud	20 (2)
Hazard Switch	27 (3)
Housing Cover Screws	100 (11)
Ignition Switch Screws	35 (4)
Lock Housing-to-Jacket	90 (10)
Shift Tube Support Screws	60 (7)
Tilt Release Spring Retaining Screw	35 (4)
Turn Signal Retaining Plate	27 (3)

Steering Columns

FORD AEROSTAR, BRONCO II & RANGER

DESCRIPTION

Steering columns are available in standard and tilt column models. Both models are of modular design. Wiper/Washer, turn signal/hazard, horn/dimmer and ignition switches are mounted on column. Switches can be serviced by removing upper column shroud.

Energy absorbing steering column collapses upon frontal impact. A cylindrical impact bumper is used on upper bracket to absorb impact loads.

Key release button prevents inadvertent locking of steering wheel. Ignition switch is operated by a pin, mounted on lock actuator rack, and is pinion-driven by rotating ignition.

REMOVAL & INSTALLATION

STEERING COLUMNS

Removal

1) Disconnect battery negative cable. Remove upper-to-lower steering shaft attaching bolt. Disengage pot-joint from column shaft by collapsing intermediate shaft assembly.

2) Remove steering wheel. See HORN BUTTON & STEERING WHEEL REMOVAL article in this section. Remove steering column trim shrouds. On tilt columns, remove upper extension shroud by squeezing it at 6 and 12 o'clock positions.

3) Remove steering column cover on instrument panel. Disconnect all electrical connections to steering column switches. Loosen bolts attaching steering column to brake pedal support.

4) Remove 3 screws attaching steering column toeplate to dash. Remove steering column-to-brake pedal support bolts. Lower steering column and pull from vehicle.

Installation

Insert lower end of steering column through opening in dash panel. To complete installation, reverse removal procedure.

OVERHAUL

STANDARD COLUMNS

Disassembly

1) Remove steering wheel, column shrouds, turn signal and wiper/washer switches. Remove steering column from vehicle. Remove upper bearing retainer plate and bearing snap ring.

2) Insert blades of 2 screwdrivers under bearing and pry it off steering shaft. Using a screwdriver, pry out lower bearing retainer and discard it.

3) Pull lower end of shaft assembly downward through tube until lower bearing/sleeve with lower shaft clears lower end of tube. Slide lower bearing/sleeve off of steering shaft.

4) Pull steering shaft assembly out of outer tube from bottom of tube. Scribe a mark on upper steering shaft where upper and lower steering shaft sections form a joint line.

5) Also scribe marks on upper and lower shafts to indicate shaft relationship. Separate upper and lower steering shaft sections. Remove and discard insulator clips.

6) Remove 2 bolts holding lock cylinder housing to outer tube flange bracket. Turn ignition key to "START" position. Pull actuator interlock out of clearance hole in tube. Lift casting off steering shaft.

Reassembly

1) Turn ignition switch to "START" position to locate actuator interlock through clearance hole in outer tube. Install and tighten 2 cylinder housing-to-bracket bolts.

2) Install new steel insulator clips on flats on steering column upper shaft. Lubricate lower 6" of steering column upper shaft with chassis lube.

3) Assemble upper and lower shafts. Align index marks made during disassembly. Slide lower bearing, with sleeve, up into outer tube as far as possible. Use a length of pipe to seat bearing retaining ring against bearing.

4) Pin punch steering column upper shaft serration diameter to ensure an interference fit between bearing inner race and steering column upper shaft. Slide upper bearing and insulator as far as possible down shaft.

5) Place a 3.25" (82.5 mm) length of 3/4" (19 mm) diameter pipe over end of shaft. Install steering wheel nut and tighten until bearing is fully seated. Remove steering wheel nut and pipe and install bearing snap ring.

6) Install upper bearing retainer plate. Install column shrouds, turn signal and wiper/washer switches. Install steering column in vehicle.

TILT COLUMNS

Disassembly

1) Remove steering wheel, column shrouds, turn signal and wiper/washer switches. Remove steering column from vehicle. Remove conical coil spring and upper bearing plate.

2) Remove upper bearing "C" clip. Move tilt casting to upper position to unload tilt spring. Use Pin Remover (T67P-3D739-C) to remove pivot pins. Lift off tilt casting.

3) Tilt casting bearings may be removed with a drift punch. Using a screwdriver, pry out lower bearing retainer and discard it.

4) Pull lower end of shaft assembly downward through tube until lower bearing/sleeve with lower shaft clears lower end of tube. Slide lower bearing/sleeve from steering shaft.

5) Pull steering shaft assembly out of outer tube from bottom of tube. Scribe a mark on upper steering shaft where upper and lower steering shaft sections form a joint line.

6) Also scribe marks on upper and lower shafts to indicate shaft relationship. Separate upper and lower steering shaft sections. Remove and discard insulator clips.

7) Remove 2 bolts connecting lock cylinder housing to outer tube flange bracket. Turn ignition key to "START" position, and pull actuator interlock out of clearance hole in tube.

Reassembly

1) Place lock cylinder housing onto upper steering column flange bracket. Turn ignition key to "START" position to locate actuator interlock through clearance hole in outer tube. Install and tighten cylinder housing-to-bracket bolts.

2) Install new steel insulator clips on flats of steering column upper shaft. Lubricate lower 6" of steering column upper shaft with chassis lube.

3) Assemble upper and lower shafts. Align index marks made during disassembly. Slide lower bearing, with

FORD AEROSTAR, BRONCO II & RANGER (Cont.)

Fig. 1: Exploded View of Aerostar, Bronco II & Ranger Standard Steering Column

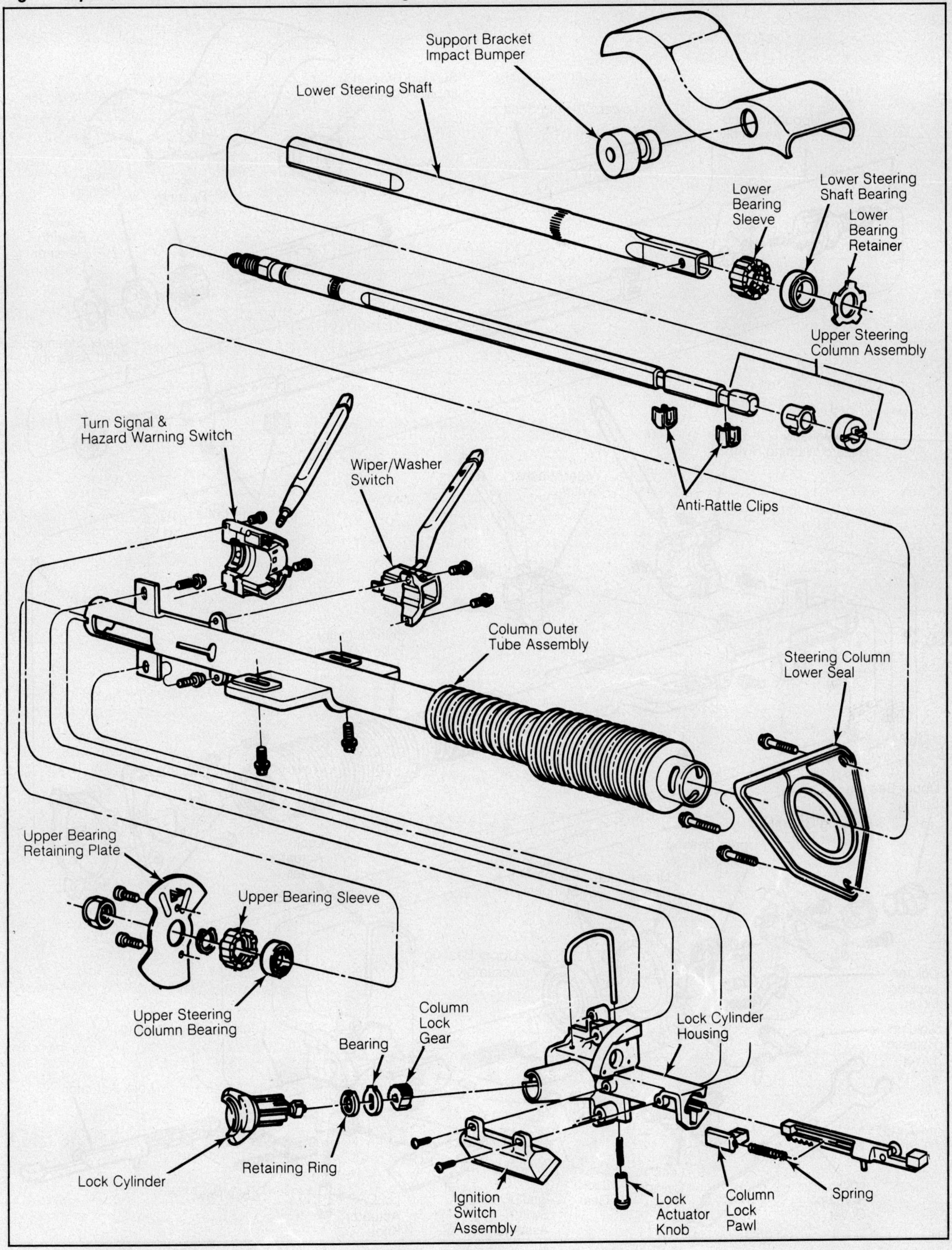

Steering Columns

FORD AEROSTAR, BRONCO II & RANGER (Cont.)

Fig. 2: Exploded View of Aerostar, Bronco II & Ranger Tilt Steering Column

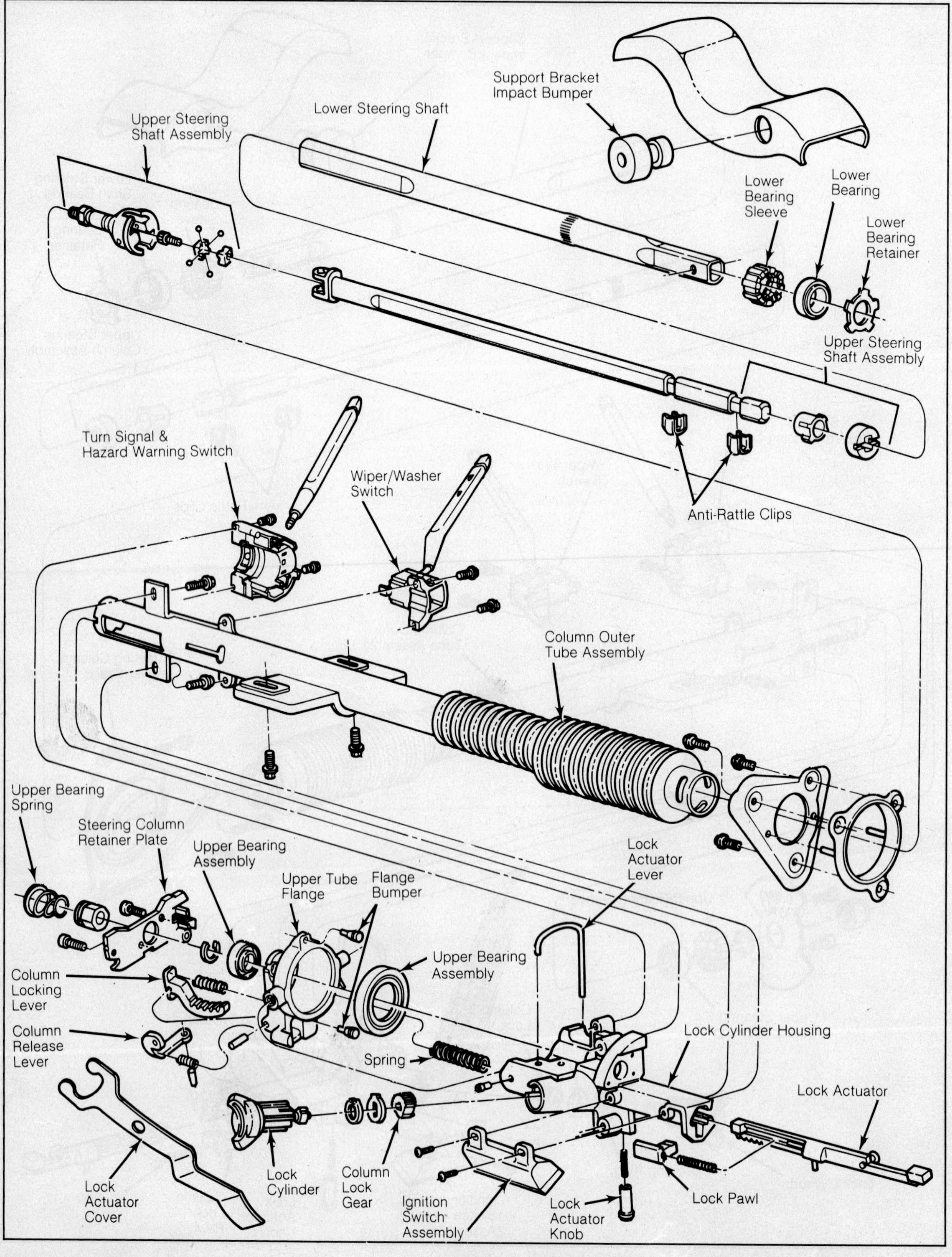

FORD AEROSTAR, BRONCO II & RANGER (Cont.)

sleeve, up into outer tube as far as possible. Use a length of pipe to seat bearing retaining ring against bearing.

4) Install upper tilt casting bearings into housing, using care not to press on inner race. Install tilt spring between upper and lower tilt castings. Latch tilt release lever in upper position.

5) Align two castings and install pivot pins using a "C" clamp. Assemble upper bearing snap ring, retainer plate and conical coil spring.

6) Spring should be seated in upper groove in steering shaft. Install column shrouds, turn signal and wiper/washer switches. Install steering column in vehicle.

TIGHTENING SPECIFICATIONS

Application	Ft. Lbs. (N.m)
Column-to-Brake Pedal Support	15-22 (20-30)
Column Toeplate-to-Dash Screws	12 (16)
Cylinder Housing-to-Bracket Bolts	12-21 (17-28)
Flex Coupling-to-Steering Gear Bolt	25-34 (34-47)
Intermediate Shaft-to-Column Shaft Bolt	40-50 (54-68)
Steering Wheel Retaining Nut	
Aerostar	22-34 (30-46)
All Others	30-42 (41-57)

FORD BRONCO, ECONOLINE & "F" PICKUPS

DESCRIPTION

All series use steering columns that have shift control rod within column tube. Directional signal switch and lever, hazard warning control knob and ignition switch are column-mounted.

Columns are equipped with anti-theft locking device, and A/T models have transmission linkage in column. Two types of columns are available, a standard column and a 5-position tilt column.

REMOVAL & INSTALLATION

BRONCO & PICKUPS

Removal

1) Disconnect battery negative cable. Remove steering wheel. See HORN BUTTON & STEERING WHEEL REMOVAL article in this section. Remove bolt and nut attaching intermediate shaft to steering column. Disconnect shift linkage rods from column.

2) Remove steering floor opening cover plate screws. Place shift lever in first gear (M/T), or "1" position (A/T). Spread shroud open and pull it up and away from instrument panel and column.

Fig. 1: Steering Column Installation

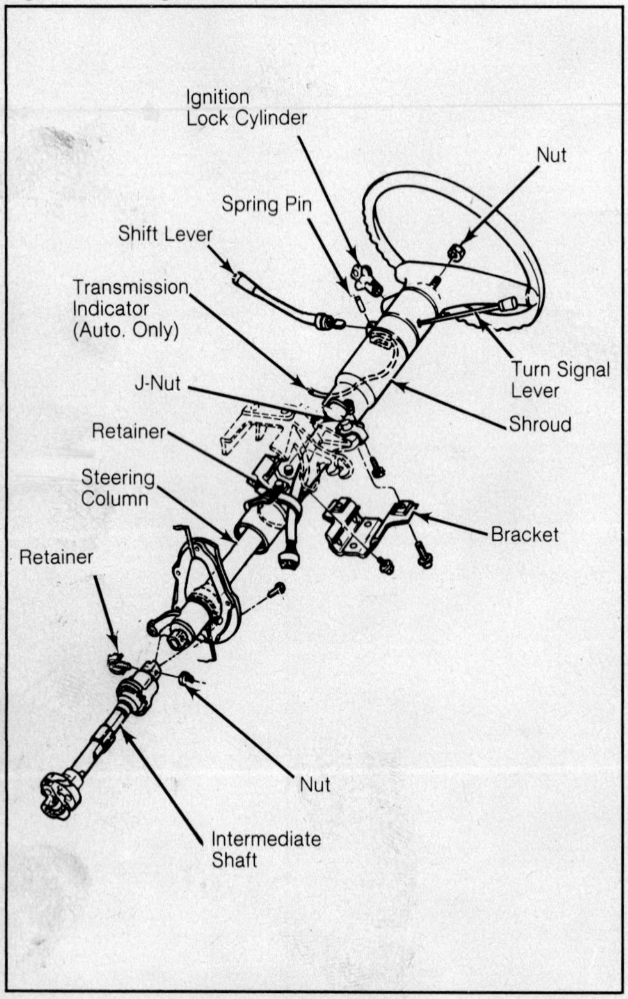

Bronco and Pickups are shown.

3) Remove A/T indicator actuation cable. Remove instrument panel column opening cover. Remove column support bracket-to-pedal support bracket bolts.

4) Disconnect turn signal and hazard flasher warning switch and ignition switch wiring harnesses. Remove column from vehicle. Remove support bracket from column.

Installation

Install column by reversing removal procedure. Adjust A/T indicator cable.

VANS

Removal

1) Disconnect battery negative cable. Remove nuts attaching flexible coupling to steering shaft flange. Remove shift linkage rods from column. Remove steering wheel.

2) Place transmission in first gear and remove steering column floor opening cover plate. Remove shroud by pulling shroud tabs out of clip at bottom of column.

3) Remove instrument panel column opening cover. Remove bolts attaching column bracket to pedal support bracket. Disconnect turn signal, hazard warning and ignition switch wiring harnesses. Remove steering column.

Installation

Install steering column by reversing removal procedure. Align steering column and flexible coupling. See ADJUSTMENT in this article.

OVERHAUL

STANDARD COLUMN

Disassembly (All Series)

1) Remove steering wheel and column. Remove turn signal lever. On 3-speed M/T and A/T, drive out shift lever pivot pin and remove lever.

2) Remove turn signal and hazard switch retaining screws and partially withdraw switch from upper flange. Remove snap ring from upper steering shaft. Remove lower bearing retainer.

3) Using a small hammer, gently drive steering shaft out bottom of steering column. Retain ignition switch in "LOCK" position and remove ignition switch and actuation rod.

4) On A/T, drill out shift tube retaining rivet from bottom of shift socket. On M/T and A/T, withdraw shift tube assembly from bottom of column.

5) Remove shift indicator and lens assembly from "E" series only. Loosen upper flange retaining nuts. Pinch nuts toward each other and withdraw upper flange from outer tube.

6) Remove shift socket from outer tube on 3-speed M/T and A/T. Remove flange extension, on 4-speed M/T, from outer tube.

7) On all series, remove upper bearing and insulator cover from upper flange by gently tapping opposite side of flange with a small hammer.

Reassembly

1) On 3-speed M/T, place bushing in socket retainer in outer tube. Place bushing on upper hub and wave washer on lower hub of shift socket.

FORD BRONCO, ECONOLINE & "F" PICKUPS (Cont.)

Fig. 2: Steering Column Installation

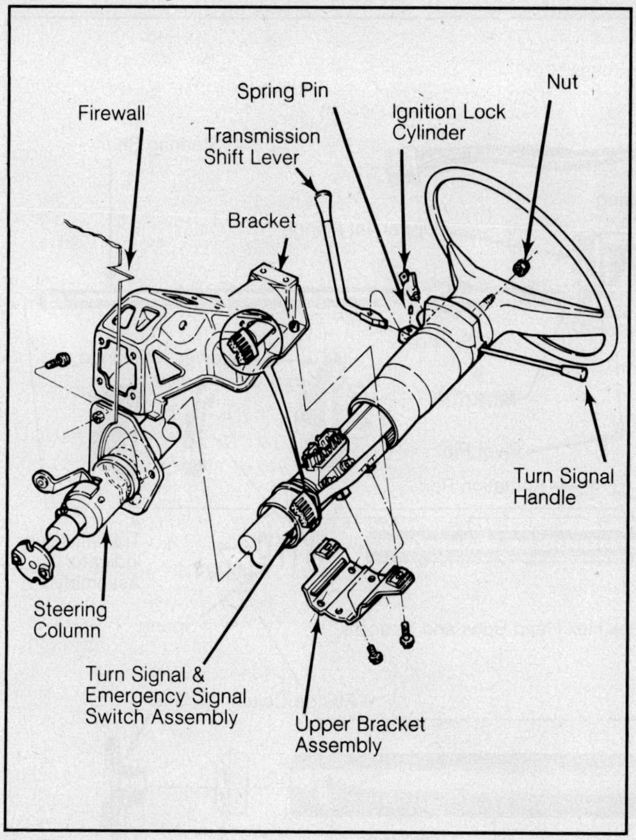

Vans are shown.

2) On A/T, install shift socket on outer tube and place wave washer in flange hub. On 4-speed M/T, install flange extension on outer tube.

3) On all series, install flange onto outer tube by pinching nuts together and pressing flange in place. Retaining bolt "T" head will engage cut-outs in outer tube as nuts are tightened.

4) Insert assembled shift tube assembly through lower column opening. Install shift tube retaining rivet through bottom of shift socket on A/T. Install steering shaft clip below knurl for upper bearing.

5) On Bronco and Pickups, check assembled shaft length. It should be 35.6" (.9 mm). Adjust by gently tapping in appropriate direction.

6) On all series, load shaft up through bottom of column taking care not to collapse steering shaft. Place cover insulator onto upper bearing. Press onto knurl on steering shaft until snap ring groove is visible above bearing.

7) Install snap ring. Install turn signal and hazard warning switch. Install lower bearing retainer. On Bronco and Pickups, ensure that centerline of coupling shaft attachment hole extends .8" (20.3 mm) below lower face of retainer.

8) Minor adjustments can be made by gently tapping shaft in appropriate direction. On vans, install lower bearing retainer and ensure that lower steering shaft is fully seated against upper shaft.

9) Install ignition switch actuation rod. Mount ignition switch and hand start retaining nuts with lock cylinder in "LOCK" position.

10) Tighten retaining nuts and remove clip. Install shift lever. Install turn signal switch lever.

TILT COLUMN

Disassembly (All Series)

1) Remove steering wheel. Remove column from vehicle. Remove turn signal lever. Drive out pivot pin and remove shift lever on A/T. Remove steering shaft lower flange and retaining clamp.

2) Remove lower bearing retainer. On A/T, remove shift tube retaining rivet from bottom of shift socket and withdraw shift tube from bottom of column.

3) On all series, remove lock drive gear. Remove turn signal switch screws, wiring harness to column clips and switch and wiring harness from column.

4) Remove cover casting screws. Remove casting from column. Unhook upper actuator from lower actuator and remove.

5) Remove and discard screws attaching lower flange to outer tube. Loosen ignition switch retaining screws and remove ignition rod from switch end.

6) Withdraw tilt mechanism, steering shaft and ignition actuation rod from steering column upper end. On A/T, remove shift socket. Remove key release lever mechanism-to-tilt mechanism on 4-speed M/T columns.

Reassembly

1) Attach "PRND21" ring to tilt mechanism on A/T. Attach flange extension and key release mechanism to tilt mechanism on 4-speed M/T.

2) Install shift socket on A/T. Install tilt mechanism, feeding steering shaft down center of column and ignition switch actuation rod through shift socket/flange extension along top of column outer tube.

NOTE: **Care must be taken not to change length of steering shaft on all models because of telescoping feature.**

3) Install flange retainer assemblies using new hex screws. Install lower bearing retainer. Attach ignition switch loosely to outer tube.

4) Connect upper and lower actuators. Install cover on column. Install turn signal switch and wiring harness in steering column. Attach wiring harness-to-steering column clips.

5) Install 2 screws attaching turn signal switch to flange casting and one screw attaching warning buzzer terminal. Install turn signal lever. Install lock drive gear. Install lock cylinder with key turned on.

6) Install retaining pin flush with cylinder. With ignition switch mounting nuts loose, clip switch through opening in side of switch casting. Center switch on actuation rod.

7) Tighten retaining nuts and remove clip. Install shift lever and pivot pin. Install turn signal lever. Install steering column and steering wheel.

FLANGE & LOCKING MECHANISM

Disassembly (All Non-Tilt Columns)

1) Remove flange retaining bolts. On M/T, remove snap ring and spring from lock release lever assembly. On A/T, remove shift indicator insert from front of flange.

2) With lock cylinder turned on, depress retaining pin and remove lock cylinder from flange. On all series, remove lock bearing snap ring and lock bearing.

FORD BRONCO, ECONOLINE & "F" PICKUPS (Cont.)

Fig. 3: Exploded View of Tilt Column Assembly

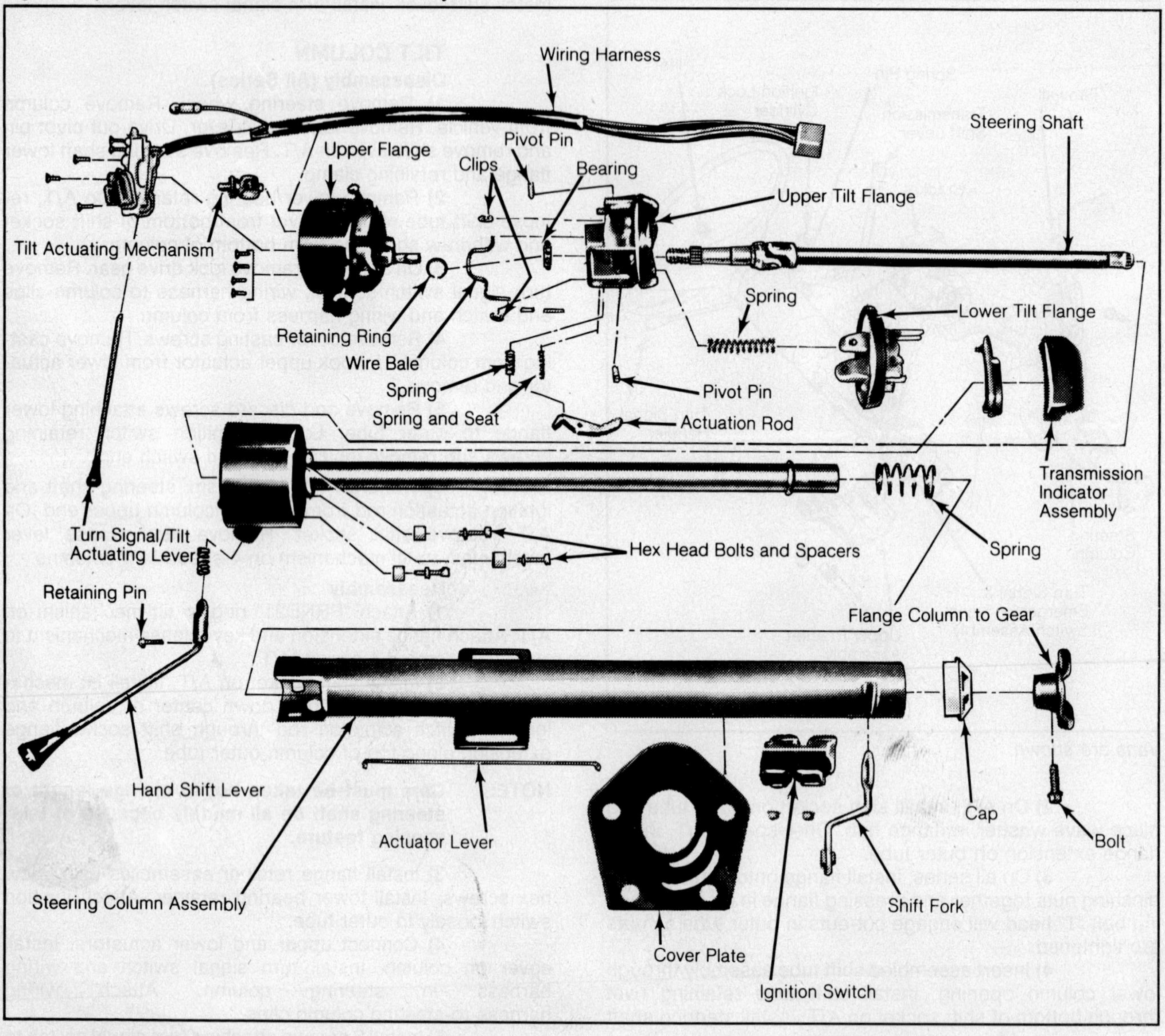

3) Remove lock drive gear and actuator assembly. Remove lock actuator insert screw and lock actuator through opening in front of flange.

Reassembly

1) Install lock actuator insert in rear of flange and tighten screw. Insert lock actuator assembly through opening in front of flange until it bottoms against insert.

2) Install lock drive gear through lock cylinder opening such that last gear tooth aligns with last tooth in actuator assembly when actuator is fully rearward.

3) Install lock bearing and snap ring. With cylinder turned on, and retaining pin depressed, insert lock cylinder into flange. On A/T, attach shift indicator insert to front of flange.

4) On M/T, position spring on lock release lever assembly through hole in front of flange and install snap ring on lock release lever assembly. On all series, install retaining bolt through holes in flange and hand start nuts on rear side.

Disassembly (All Tilt Columns)

1) Remove steering column from vehicle. Remove spring clips holding wire bale. Lift off wire bale. With a small drift, drive out pin holding locking lever. *See Fig. 4*.

2) Remove lever and spring. Remove column upper shaft snap ring. Separate upper and lower flange castings by removing 2 pivot pins located in side of casting.

3) Pivot pins may be removed by using Pin Remover (T67P-3D739-C). Do not reuse pivot pins if press fit is loose in flange. Upper flange bearings may be replaced by tapping lightly on outer race of bearing.

Reassembly

1) Install lower actuator with ignition switch rod attached. Assemble upper and lower flange and press in pivot pins with a "C" clamp.

2) Ensure column position spring is properly seated between upper and lower flange. Wavy thrust washer must be positioned between lower flange and socket.

FORD BRONCO, ECONOLINE & "F" PICKUPS (Cont.)

3) Install upper column snap ring, Assemble locking lever, spring and lever pin. Install wire bale and spring clips.

Fig. 4: Tilt Mechanism Flange Sub-Assembly

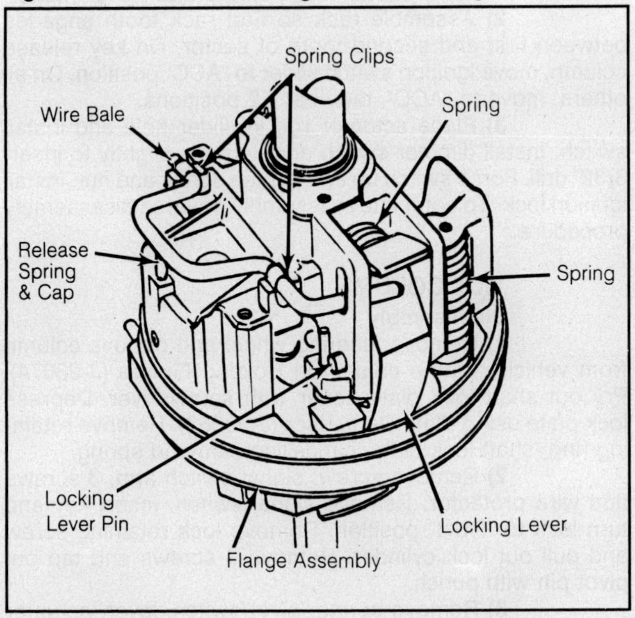

ADJUSTMENT

STEERING COLUMN ALIGNMENT

Bronco & Pickups

Alignment is automatically maintained by slip-joint coupling shaft attaching steering column to steering gear.

Check flexible coupling for clearance between slots on coupling shaft flange and flexible coupling safety pins. Pin-to-flange clearance should be .010" (.25 mm).

NOTE: **If it is determined that coupling has been driven in a non-flat position for more than 12,000 miles, coupling should be replaced.**

Vans

1) Remove steering column trim panel. Loosen bolts securing steering column to brake and clutch pedal support. Loosen steering column trim panel. Loosen steering column opening cover plate-to-dash panel bolts. Loosen lower column clamp.

2) Ensure flexible coupling nuts are tight. With front wheels in straight ahead position, pull up on steering column until flex coupling is in a flat to a 0.1" (2.5 mm) concaved position, pointing toward steering wheel.

3) Tighten steering column-to-support bracket bolts. Tighten steering column opening cover bolts. Insert a .160" (4.06 mm) shim between right flex coupling safety pin and slot. Now turn steering wheel one revolution clockwise.

Fig. 5: Aligning Steering Column on Vans

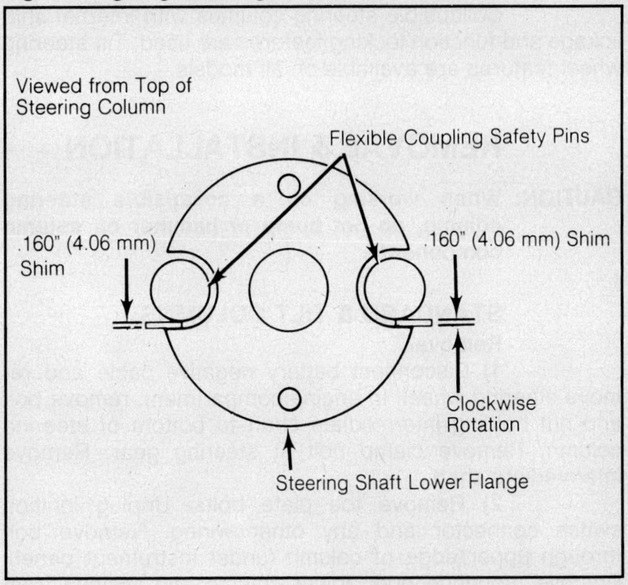

4) Check tightness of shim. If shim cannot be removed, loosen cover plate clamp and plate attaching bolts. Realign column until shim remains loose enough to be removed when rotating steering wheel.

5) Insert a .160" (4.06 mm) shim between left flex coupling safety pin and slot. Now turn steering wheel one revolution counterclockwise. Check shim tightness and adjust as described in step **4)**.

6) Tighten column-to-support bracket bolts. Tighten steering column opening cover, and install trim panel.

TIGHTENING SPECIFICATIONS

Application	Ft. Lbs. (N.m)
Cover Plate Clamp Bolt	8-18 (11-24)
Floor Opening Cover Plate	5-15 (7-20)
Intermediate Shaft to-Steering Column	45-59 (61-80)
Lower Bearing Retainer Clamp	10-14 (14-18)
Steering Column Support Bracket	13-38 (18-52)
Steering Shaft-to-Steering Gear	40-60 (55-81)
Steering Wheel Retaining Nut	30-42 (41-57)
	INCH Lbs. (N.m)
Ignition Switch Retaining Nuts	40-65 (4.5-7.3)
Shroud	10-15 (1.2-1.6)
Turn Signal/Hazard Warning Switch	15-25 (1.6-2.8)

GENERAL MOTORS – ASTRO, SAFARI & "S" SERIES TRUCKS

DESCRIPTION

Collapsible steering columns with internal shift linkage and function locking features are used. Tilt steering wheel features are available on all models.

REMOVAL & INSTALLATION

CAUTION: When working on a collapsible steering column, do not bump or hammer on column components.

STANDARD & TILT COLUMNS

Removal

1) Disconnect battery negative cable and remove steering wheel. In engine compartment, remove bolt and nut holding intermediate shaft to bottom of steering column. Remove clamp bolt at steering gear. Remove intermediate shaft.

2) Remove toe plate bolts. Unplug ignition switch connector and any other wiring. Remove bolt through upper edge of column (under instrument panel). Remove mounting nuts, lower column and remove from vehicle.

Installation

1) Place column in vehicle. Install column nuts loosely. Install and tighten toe plate bolts (starting with bolts toward center of vehicle). Tighten column nuts. Connect wiring. Position intermediate shaft on steering gear and tighten pinch bolt to 35-45 ft. lbs. (48-60 N.m).

2) Lock steering shaft and wheels in straight-ahead position. Connect intermediate shaft joint to lower end of steering column. Install clamp bolt and tighten nut. Install steering wheel. Connect battery negative cable.

OVERHAUL

STANDARD COLUMN

Disassemby

1) Remove column from vehicle and mount in vise or Holding Fixture (J-23074). Use screwdriver to pry out shaft lock cover. Depress lock plate using Plate Depressor (J-23653). Remove retaining ring. Remove lock plate, cancelling cam and spring.

2) Remove screw and turn signal switch arm. Remove 3 screws and wire protector, then switch assembly. Insert key and turn lock to "RUN" position. Remove lock retaining screw from top, then pull cylinder out of side. Remove ignition and dimmer switches.

3) Remove thrust washer and 4 Allen screws. Remove sector from housing. Pull off housing. Remove wave washer, lever and spring from key release. Remove 3 screws and plate from bottom of housing.

4) Remove cap, switch pivot pin and switch. If equipped with bearing retainer, remove retainer, bushing, horn contact and bearing. If no retainer, housing must be replaced to replace bearing.

5) Remove spring and bolt assembly, spring thrust washer, rack actuator and rack spring. Remove shift lever bowl and shroud. Remove shift bowl lower bearing.

6) Remove back-up light switch. Remove retaining ring from top of shaft. Remove retainer clip at bottom of column. Remove retainer, bearing, spring, shift column (if equipped) and steering shaft.

Reassembly

1) Assemble steering shaft and shift tube. Install back-up light switch. Position gear shift bowl assembly. Assemble housing and tap sector into place with punch. On key release column, install lever, spring and wave washer.

2) Assemble rack so first rack tooth engages between first and second tooth of sector. On key release column, move ignition switch slider to "ACC" position. On all others, move to "ACC", then back 2 positions.

3) Place actuator rod in slider hole and install switch. Install dimmer switch and depress slightly to insert 3/32" drill. Force switch up and tighten screw and nut. Install ignition lock. To complete reassembly, reverse disassembly procedure.

TILT COLUMN

Disassembly

1) Remove steering wheel and remove column from vehicle. Clamp column in Holding Fixture (J-23074). Pry out shaft lock plate cover with screwdriver. Depress lock plate using Plate Depressor (J-23653). Remove retaining ring, shaft lock plate, cancelling cam and spring.

2) Remove screw, signal switch arm, 3 screws and wire protector. Remove signal switch. Insert key and turn lock to "RUN" position. Remove lock retaining screw and pull out lock cylinder. Remove 3 screws and tap out pivot pin with punch.

3) Remove spring, pivot/switch, lever, actuator and column cover. Reinstall lever and move column to fully upward position. Remove tilt spring retainer by pressing in on and turning retainer with screwdriver. *See Fig. 2*. Remove pivot pin with Puller (J-21854).

4) Remove housing by pulling upward on tilt lever. Pull housing until it stops. Move housing to right to disengage rack from actuator. Remove tilt lever and all parts from top of column.

5) Remove steering column shaft from housing. Remove ignition, dimmer and backup light switches from column. Remove screws, support, retaining rings, thrust washer, lock plate and wave washer.

6) Remove gearshift bowl and shroud. At bottom of column, remove clip, retainer, bearing and spring. Remove gear shift tube assembly with Puller (J-23072). *See Fig. 3*.

Reassembly

1) To assemble, reverse disassembly procedure. When installing ignition switch, move slider to "ACC" position (non-key release) or to "OFF/LOCK" position.

2) Position rod and install switch. Position dimmer switch and depress slightly to insert 3/32" (2.4 mm) drill. Force switch up and tighten screw and nut. Reassemble housing.

3) While holding up on lever to disengage lock shoes, install housing over column. Move rack downward and hold. Tip housing to left until rack engages pin on ignition switch actuator rod.

4) Push housing down until pivot pin holes are in alignment. To complete reassembly, reverse disassembly procedure.

TIGHTENING SPECIFICATIONS

Application	Ft. Lbs. (N.m)
Flexible Coupling Pinch Bolts	30 (40)
Column Support Bolts	30 (40)

GENERAL MOTORS – ASTRO, SAFARI & "S" SERIES TRUCKS (Cont.)

Fig. 1: Exploded View of Standard Steering Column

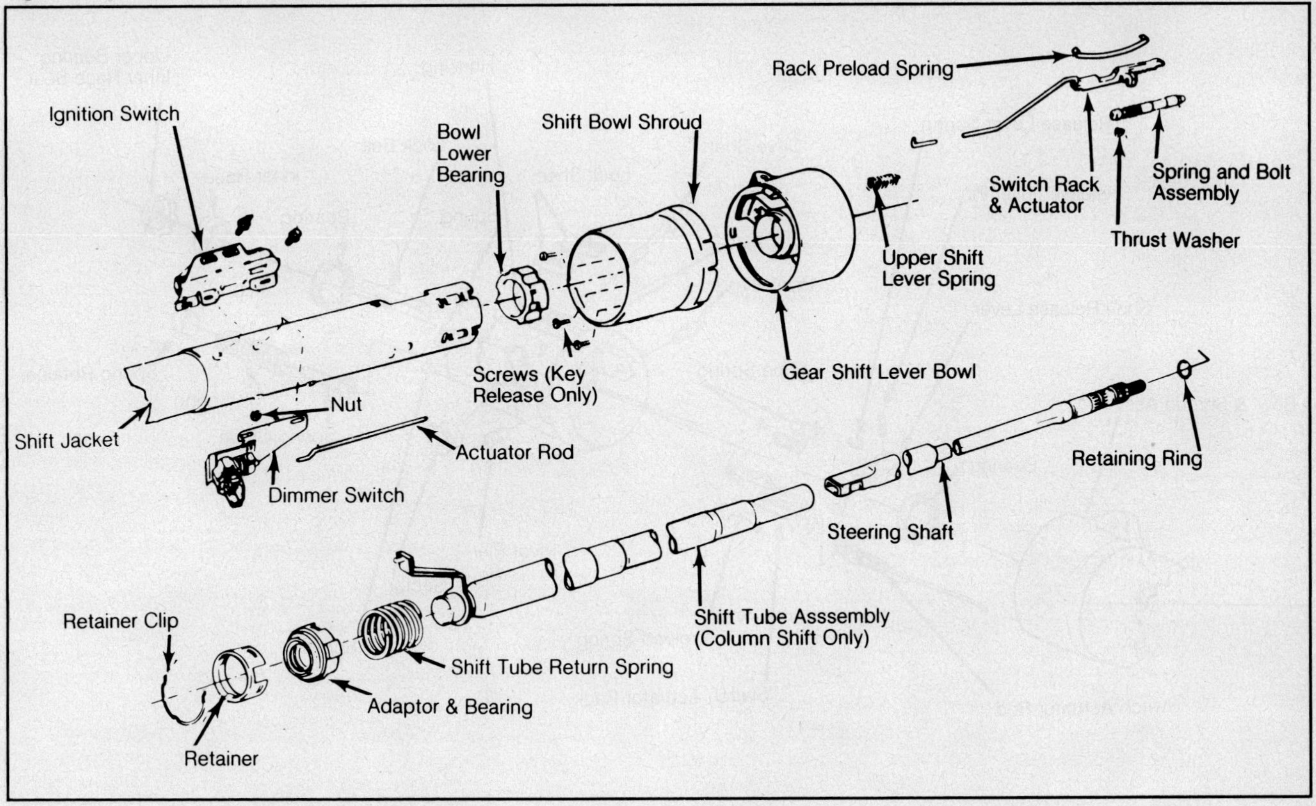

Fig. 2: Removing Tilt Lever Spring Retainer

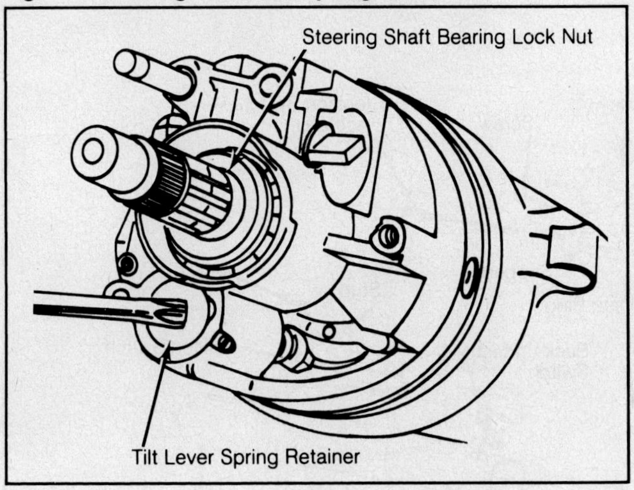

Fig. 3: Removing Shift Tube

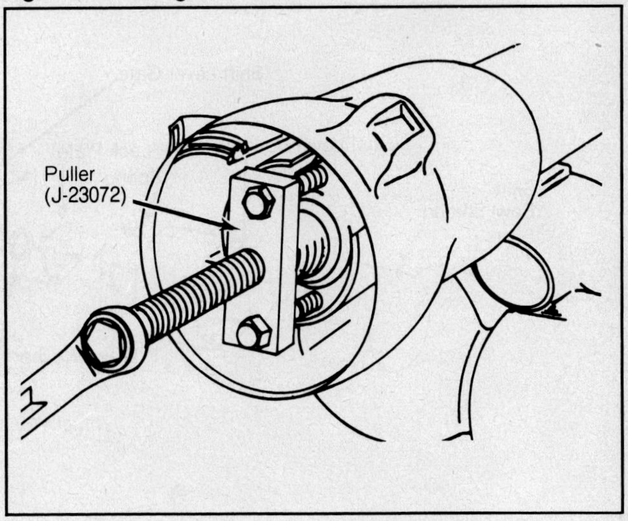

Screws must be fully engaged in lock plate.

GENERAL MOTORS – ASTRO, SAFARI & "S" SERIES TRUCKS (Cont.)

Fig. 4: Exploded View of Tilt Steering Column

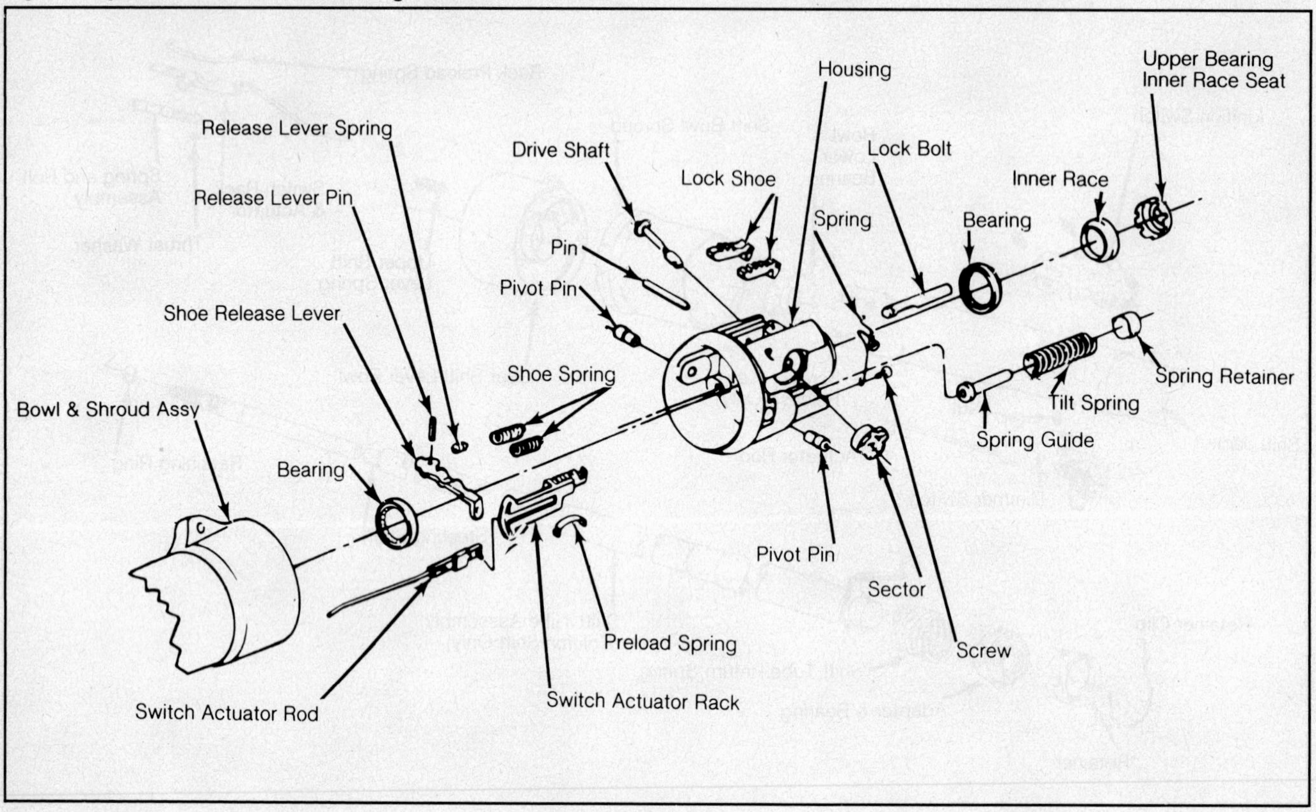

Fig. 5: Exploded View of Tilt Steering Column Lower Assembly

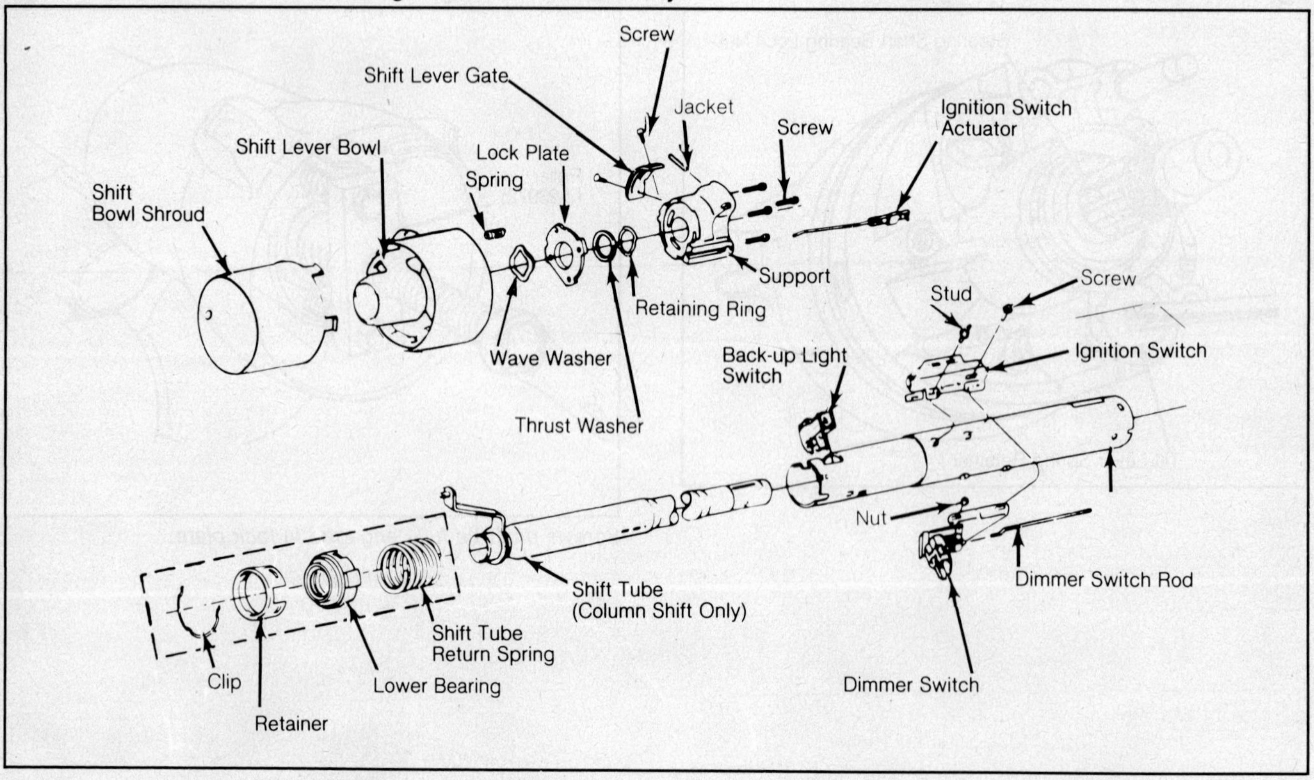

GENERAL MOTORS – EXCEPT ASTRO, SAFARI & "S" SERIES

DESCRIPTION

Collapsible steering columns with internal shift linkage and function locking features are used. Tilt steering wheel features are available on all models.

REMOVAL & INSTALLATION

CAUTION: When working on a collapsible steering column, do not bump or hammer on column components. Correct column installation is important to prevent stress on components during mounting. Using improper screws, nuts and bolts could prevent assembly from compressing under impact.

"C" & "K" SERIES

Removal

1) Loosen front of dash mounting plates. Disconnect battery negative cable. Remove steering wheel. Remove nuts and washers securing flanged end of steering shaft to flexible coupling.

2) Disconnect transmission control linkage from column shift tube levers. Disconnect steering column harness and wiring. Remove floor pan trim cover screws and remove cover.

3) Remove screws securing 2 halves of floor pan cover, then remove screws securing halves and seal to floor pan and remove covers. Remove transmission indicator cable (if equipped).

4) Move front seat as far back as possible to provide maximum working clearance. Remove 2 column bracket-to-instrument panel nuts and carefully remove column from vehicle, rotating column so that shift levers will clear hole in floor pan.

Installation

1) Assemble upper and lower dash covers to seal. Attach bracket to steering column. Tighten 4 retaining bolts.

NOTE: If flexible joint coupling was removed from steering gear shaft, it must be installed before steering column is installed.

2) Position steering column in vehicle. Assemble flange and flexible coupling. Install lock washers and nuts. Tighten nuts. Loosely install 2 bracket nuts to dash studs.

3) Install lower clamp (engine side of firewall) and tighten nuts. Install seal, upper and lower covers to cab side of firewall. Tighten 2 upper bracket nuts.

4) Remove plastic spacers from flexible coupling. Install automatic transmission indicator cable (if equipped).

5) Install instrument panel trim cover. Connect transmission control linkage. Install steering wheel. Connect battery negative cable.

"G" & P" SERIES

Removal

1) Disconnect battery negative cable. On column shift models, disconnect shifter rods at lower end of column. On "G" series, remove steering shaft flange-to-flexible coupling bolts.

2) On "P" series, remove intermediate steering shaft upper universal pinch bolt and mark coupling-to-shaft relationship. On all models, remove column clamp screws

Fig. 1: "C" & "K" Series Steering Column Installation

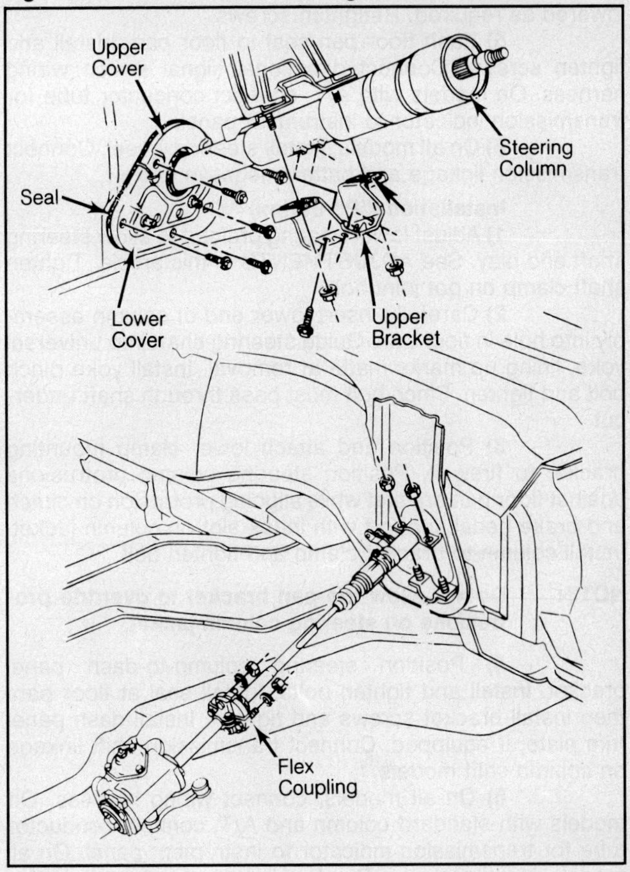

on engine side of firewall. Slide cover and seal down on column.

3) From inside vehicle, remove screws from floor pan cover and slide cover and seal up column. Remove steering wheel, then reinstall retaining nut and washer to prevent dislocation of steering shaft.

4) Disconnect wiring harness. On models with standard column and A/T, disconnect tube for transmission indicator at instrument panel. On models with tilt column and A/T, disconnect single wire at fuse block and unclip it from parking brake bracket.

5) On all models, remove cap screws from column support bracket at dash panel. Carefully withdraw column assembly, rotating it so that shift levers clear hole in floor pan.

Installation ("G" Series)

1) Adjust column lower bearing preload. See ADJUSTMENTS in this article. Install plastic spacers onto flexible coupling alignment pins.

2) From inside vehicle, carefully insert lower end of column through floor pan opening, guiding steering shaft flange onto flexible coupling. Install and tighten flange-to-coupling bolts.

3) Locate index slot in column jacket with protrusion on clutch band brake pedal support. Loosely install column-to-dash bracket and screws. Push column down until steering shaft flange bottoms on plastic spacers on flexible coupling and tighten bracket screws.

4) Remove plastic spacer from alignment pins. Check that flexible coupling-to-steering shaft flange clearance is .250-.325" (6-8 mm). If not within specifications,

GENERAL MOTORS – EXCEPT ASTRO, SAFARI & "S" SERIES (Cont.)

bracket screws must be loosened and column raised or lowered as required. Retighten screws.

5) Push floor pan seal to floor pan. Install and tighten screws. Connect directional signal switch wiring harness. On models with A/T, connect conductor tube for transmission indicator to instrument panel.

6) On all models, install steering wheel. Connect transmission linkage and battery negative cable.

Installation ("P" Series)

1) Adjust lower bearing preload to allow steering shaft end play. See ADJUSTMENTS in this article. Tighten shaft clamp on pot joint bolt.

2) Carefully insert lower end of column assembly into hole in floor pan. Guide steering shaft into universal yoke, lining up marks made at removal. Install yoke pinch bolt and tighten. Pinch bolt must pass through shaft undercut.

3) Position and attach lower clamp mounting bracket to firewall. Position steering column protrusions against floor pan bracket while aligning protrusion on clutch and brake pedal support with index slot on column jacket. Install column-to-bracket clamp and tighten bolt.

NOTE: Do not allow toe pan bracket to override protrusions on steering column jacket.

4) Position steering column-to-dash panel bracket. Install and tighten bolts. Install seal at floor pan, then install bracket screws and tighten. Install dash panel trim plate, if equipped. Connect transmission shift linkage on column shift models.

5) On all models, connect wiring harness. On models with standard column and A/T, connect conductor tube for transmission indicator to instrument panel. On all models, install steering wheel and connect battery negative cable.

OVERHAUL

"C" & "K" SERIES
STANDARD COLUMN

Disassembly

1) Remove 4 dash panel bracket-to-column screws and place bracket in safe place to prevent damage to mounting capsules. Place column in a vise using both weld nuts of set "A" or "B". *See Fig. 2.*

CAUTION: Ensure column is clamped correctly to avoid damage.

2) Remove directional signal switch, lock cylinder, and ignition switch. Drive out upper shift lever pivot pin and remove shift lever on column shift models.

3) Remove upper bearing thrust washer. Remove 4 screws attaching directional signal and ignition lock housing to column and remove housing assembly. Remove thrust cap from lower side of housing.

4) Lift ignition switch actuating rod and rack assembly, rack preload spring, and shaft lock bolt and spring assembly out of housing. Remove shift lever detent plate (shift gate).

5) Remove ignition switch actuator sector through lock cylinder hole by pushing firmly on block tooth of sector with punch. Remove gearshift lever housing and shroud from jacket assembly. Remove shift lever spring from gearshift lever housing

Fig. 2: Correct Installation of Steering Column in Vise

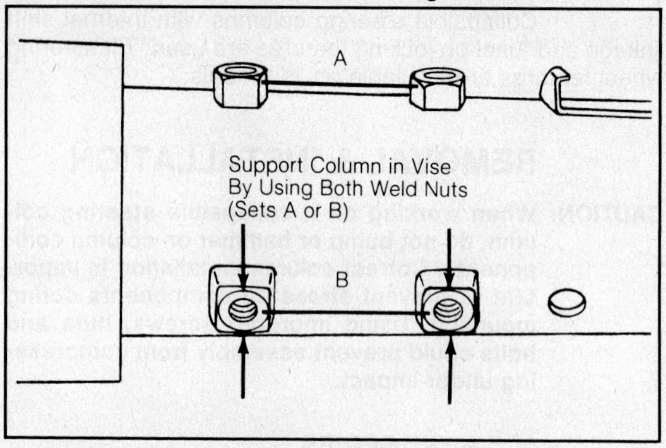

The vise jaws must clamp onto sides of weld nuts indicated by arrows shown on set "B".

6) On floor shift models, remove transmission control lock tube housing and shroud. Remove lock tube spring. On all models, pull steering shaft from lower end of jacket assembly.

7) Remove 2 screws holding back-up switch or neutral start switch to column and remove switch. Remove lower bearing retainer clip. *See Fig. 3.*

Fig. 3: Removing Lower Bearing Retaining Clip

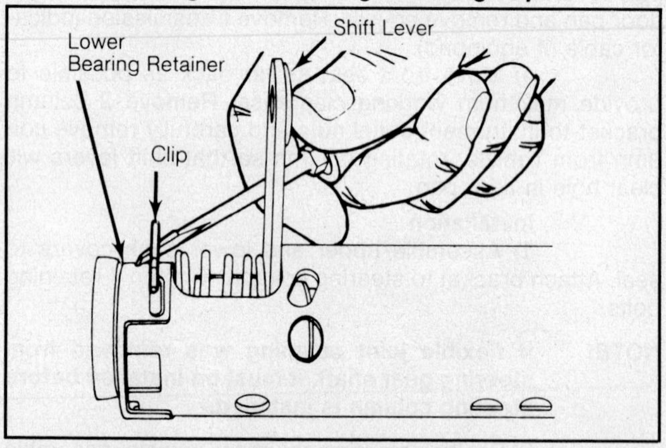

"C" & "K" series standard column is shown.

8) On models with A/T or floor shift, remove lower bearing retainer, bearing adapter assembly, shift tube thrust spring and washer.

9) Lower bearing may be removed from adapter by light pressure on bearing outer race. Slide out shift tube assembly. On vehicles with M/T and column shift, remove lower bearing adapter, bearing and 1st-Reverse shift lever.

10) Lower bearing may be removed from adapter by light pressure on bearing outer race. Remove 3 screws from bearing at lower end and slide out shift tube assembly.

11) On all models with column shift, remove gearshift housing lower bearing from upper end of column.

Reassembly

1) Apply a thin coat of lithium grease to all friction surfaces. Install sector into directional signal and lock cylinder housing. Install sector in lock cylinder hole over sector shaft with tang end to outside of hole.

2) Press sector over shaft with blunt tool. Install shift lever detent plate onto housing. Insert rack preload

GENERAL MOTORS – EXCEPT ASTRO, SAFARI & "S" SERIES (Cont.)

spring into housing from bottom side. Long section should be toward handwheel and hook onto edge of housing.

3) Assemble locking bolt onto crossover arm on rack. Insert rack and lock bolt assembly into housing from bottom with teeth up (toward handwheel) and toward center line of column.

4) Align first tooth on sector with last tooth on rack; if aligned properly, block teeth will line up when rack assembly is pushed in completely.

5) Install thrust cup on bottom hub of housing. Install gearshift housing lower bearing from very end of jacket, while aligning indentations in bearing with projections on jacket.

CAUTION: If bearing is not properly installed, it will not rest on all stops provided.

6) Install shift lever spring into gearshift lever (or lock tube) housing. Install housing and shroud assemblies onto upper end of mast jacket. Rotate housing to verify that it is seated in bearing.

7) With shift lever housing in place, install directional signal and lock cylinder housing onto jacket. Gearshift housing should be in "P" position and rack pulled downward. Ensure directional signal housing is seated on jacket. Install and tighten 4 screws.

8) Press lower bearing into adapter assembly. Insert shift tube assembly into lower end of jacket and rotate until upper shift tube key slides into housing keyway.

9) On models with A/T or floor shift, assemble spring, lower bearing and adapter assembly into bottom of jacket. Holding adapter in place, install lower bearing reinforcement and retainer clip. Ensure clip snaps into jacket and reinforcement slots.

10) On vehicles with M/T and column shift, loosely attach 3 screws in jacket and shift tube bearing. Assemble 1st-Reverse shift lever and lower bearing and adapter assembly into bottom of jacket.

11) Holding adapter in place, install bearing reinforcement and retaining clip. Ensure clip snaps into jacket and reinforcement slots. Adjust lower bearing. See ADJUSTMENTS in this article.

Fig. 4: Exploded View of Steering Column Assembly

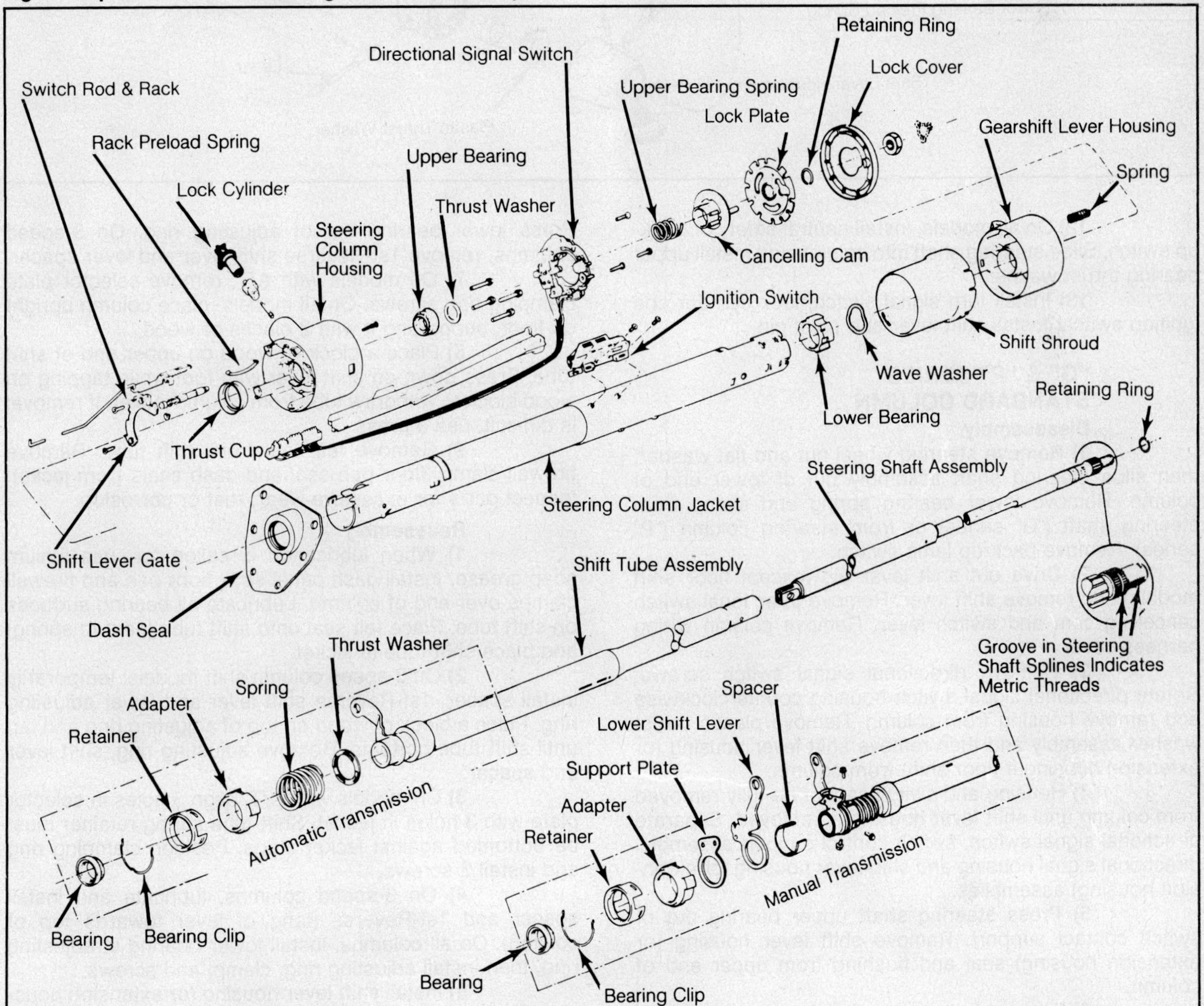

"C" & "K" series with column switch shown.

GENERAL MOTORS – EXCEPT ASTRO, SAFARI & "S" SERIES (Cont.)

Fig. 5: Exploded View of Steering Column Assembly for "G" & "P" Series

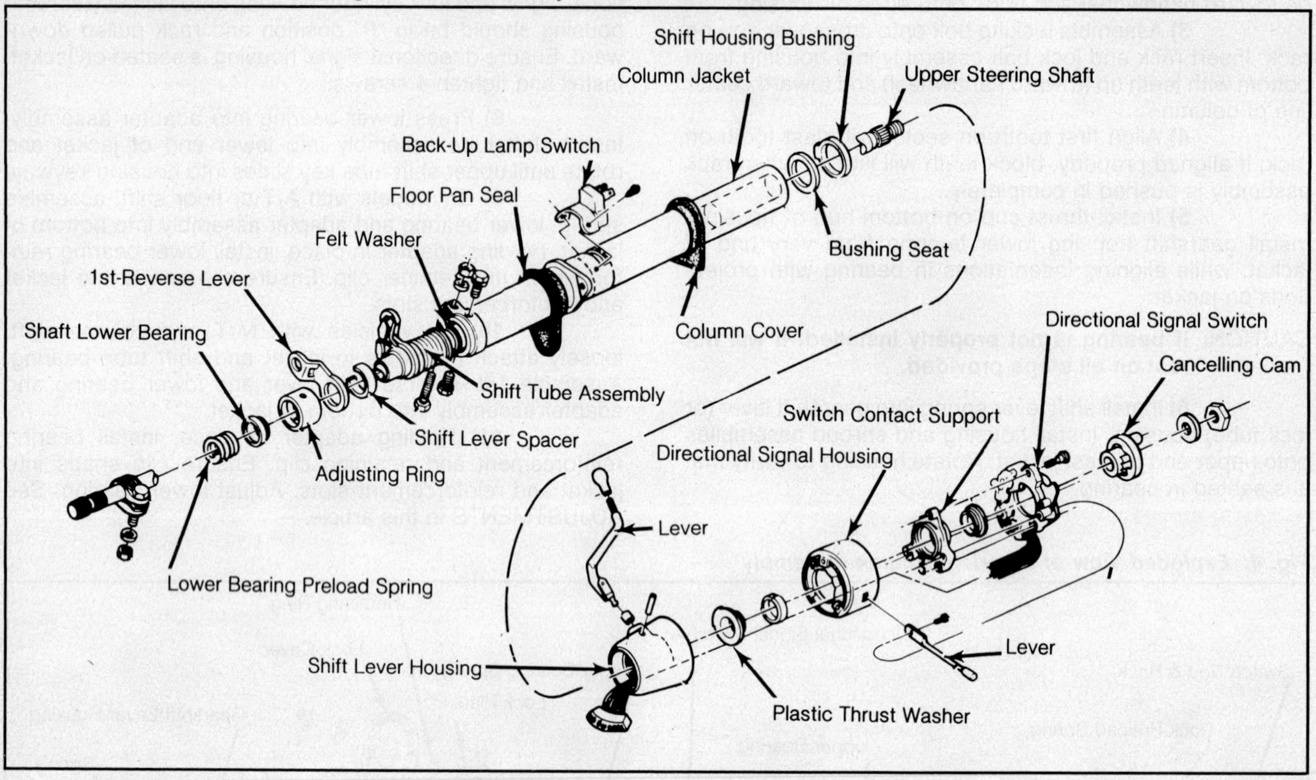

12) On all models, install neutral safety or back-up switch. Slide steering shaft into column and install upper bearing thrust washer.

13) Install turn signal switch, lock cylinder and ignition switch. Install shift lever and pivot pin.

"G" & "P" SERIES STANDARD COLUMN

Disassembly

1) Remove steering wheel nut and flat washer, then slide steering shaft assembly out of lower end of column. Remove lower bearing spring and clamp from steering shaft ("G" series) or from steering column ("P" series). Remove back-up lamp switch.

2) Drive out shift lever pin (except floor shift models) and remove shift lever. Remove directional switch cancelling cam and switch lever. Remove column wiring harness cover.

3) Remove directional signal switch screws. Rotate directional signal switch housing counterclockwise and remove housing from column. Remove plastic thrust washer assembly and then remove shift lever housing (or extension housing if floor shift) from column.

4) Housing and switch cannot be fully removed from column until shift lever housing is removed. Separate directional signal switch, switch control support assembly, directional signal housing and shift lever housing (or extension housing) assemblies.

5) Press steering shaft upper bearing out of switch contact support. Remove shift lever housing (or extension housing) seal and bushing from upper end of column.

6) Remove bolt and screws from adjusting ring clamp and remove clamp, adjusting ring, and lower bearing. Press lower bearing out of adjusting ring. On 3-speed columns, remove 1st-Reverse shift lever and lever spacer.

7) On models with A/T, remove selector plate clamping ring screws. On all models, place column upright on floor, supporting it with 2 pieces of wood.

8) Place a block of wood on upper end of shift tube. Press down on shift lever with foot while tapping on wood block to withdraw tube from column jacket. If removal is difficult, use a press.

9) Remove felt seal from shift tube. Remove firewall clamp, floor pan seal and dash seals from jacket. Inspect parts for excessive wear, rust or corrosion.

Reassembly

1) When lubrication is called for, use lithium soap grease. Install dash panel seal, floor pan and firewall clamps over end of column. Lubricate all bearing surfaces on shift tube. Place felt seal onto shift tube (next to spring) and place shift tube in jacket.

2) On 3-speed column shift models, temporarily install spacer, 1st-Reverse shift lever and lower adjusting ring. Place a block of wood on top of adjusting ring and tap until shift tube bottoms. Remove adjusting ring, shift lever and spacer.

3) On models with A/T, align 3 holes in selector plate with 3 holes in jacket. Shift tube spring retainer must be bottomed against jacket stops. Position clamping ring and install 3 screws.

4) On 3-speed columns, lubricate and install spacer and 1st-Reverse (tang of lever towards top of column). On all columns, install lower bearing in adjusting ring, then install adjusting ring, clamp, and screws.

5) Install shift lever housing (or extension housing) seat and bushing to upper end of housing. Thread directional signal switch wiring harness through switch and shift lever (or extension) housings.

GENERAL MOTORS – EXCEPT ASTRO, SAFARI & "S" SERIES (Cont.)

6) Lubricate inner diameter of shift (extension) housing and install onto upper end of column. Install switch housing plastic washer assembly. Press upper bearing into switch contact support.

7) Install directional signal switch housing, contact support, bearing, and switch. Torque screws to 25 INCH lbs. (2.8 N.m). Install column wiring harness cover and back-up lamp switch. Install directional signal and gearshift levers.

8) Loosely install lower bearing preload spring and clamp. Slide steering shaft assembly through column assembly. Install directional signal cancelling cam, steering shaft nut and lock washer.

"C" & "K" SERIES
TILT WHEEL
Disassembly

1) Remove 4 dash panel bracket-to-column screws. Set bracket aside to protect mounting capsules. Place column in a vise using both weld nuts of set "A" and "B". *See Fig. 2.*

CAUTION: Do not place column in vise by clamping onto only one nut or by clamping onto sides of nut not indicated by arrows.

2) Remove directional signal switch, lock cylinder, and igniton switch. Remove tilt release lever, then drive out shift lever pivot pin and remove shift lever and housing. Remove 3 directional signal housing screws and remove housing.

3) Install tilt release lever and place column in fully upward position. Remove tilt lever spring retainer.

4) Insert Phillips screwdriver into slot, press in approximately 3/16", then rotate 1/8" turn counterclockwise until retainer ears align with grooves in housing then remove retainer, spring, and guide. *See Fig. 6.*

Fig. 6: Removing Tilt Lever Spring Retainer

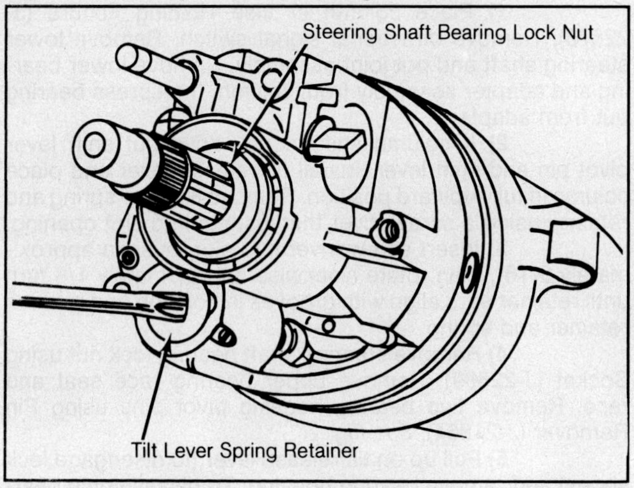

5) Remove pot joint-to-steering shaft clamp bolt, then remove intermediate shaft and pot joint assembly. Push upper steering shaft in enough to remove steering shaft upper bearing inner race and seat.

6) Pry off lower bearing retainer clip, then remove bearing reinforcement, bearing and bearing adapter assembly from lower end of mast jacket. Remove upper bearing housing pivot pins using Pin Remover (J-21854-1). *See Fig. 7.*

Fig. 7: Removing Bearing Housing Pivot Pins

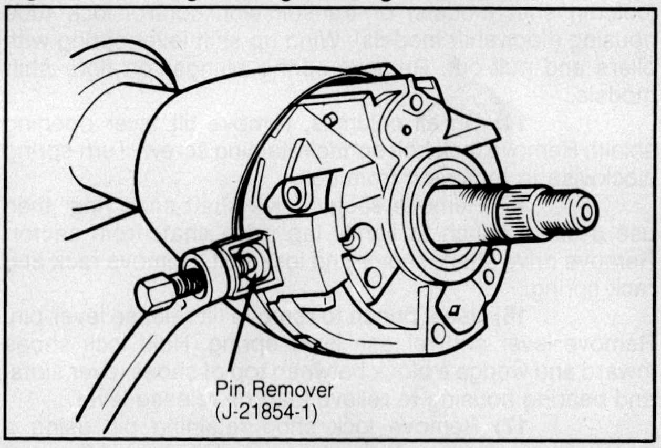

Tilt column models only are shown.

7) With tilt release lever installed, disengage lock shoes. Remove bearing housing by pulling upward to extend rack full down, then move housing to left to disengage ignition switch race from actuator rod.

8) Remove steering shaft assembly from upper end of column. Remove centering spheres and anti-lash spring to disassemble steering shaft. Remove transmission indicator wire, if equipped.

9) Remove steering shaft bearing housing support-to-gearshift housing screws, then remove bearing housing support. Remove ignition switch actuator rod. Use a screwdriver to remove shift tube retaining ring, then remove thrust washer.

10) Install Puller (J-23072) to lock plate, then turn center screws of puller clockwise to force shift tube from housing. *See Fig. 8.*

Fig. 8: Removing Shift Tube

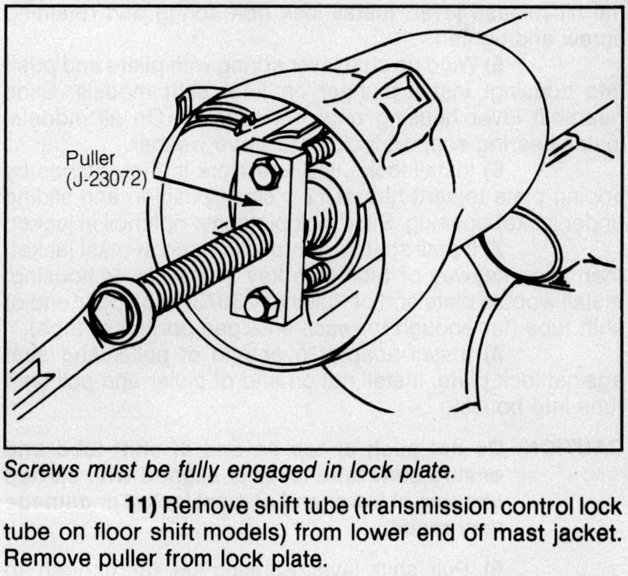

Screws must be fully engaged in lock plate.

11) Remove shift tube (transmission control lock tube on floor shift models) from lower end of mast jacket. Remove puller from lock plate.

CAUTION: Guide lower end of shift tube through slotted opening in mast jacket. If tube is allowed to interfere with jacket, damage may result.

12) Remove housing support lock plate by sliding out of jacket notches, then tipping it down toward housing hub at 12 o'clock position and sliding it under jacket opening. Remove wave washer.

GENERAL MOTORS - EXCEPT ASTRO, SAFARI & "S" SERIES (Cont.)

13) Remove shift lever housing from mast jacket (column shift models) or transmission control lock tube housing (floor shift models). Wind up shift lever spring with pliers and pull out. Remove spring plunger on floor shift models.

14) On all columns, remove tilt lever opening shield. Remove lock bolt spring retaining screw. Turn spring clockwise to remove it from bolt.

15) Remove sector drive shaft snap ring, then use a small punch to lightly tap drive shaft from sector. Remove drive shaft, sector and lock bolt. Remove rack and rack spring.

16) Use a punch to remove tilt release lever pin. Remove lever and release lever spring. Hold lock shoes inward and wedge a block between top of shoes (over slots) and bearing housing to relieve load on release lever.

17) Remove lock shoe retaining pin using a punch, then remove lock shoes and springs. Remove bearings from housing only if replacement is necessary.

Reassembly

1) Apply a thin coat of lithium grease or equivalent to all friction surfaces. If bearing was not disassembled, go to step **5)**. To reassemble bearing housing, press bearings into housing (if removed).

2) Install lock shoe springs, lock shoes, and shoe pin in housing. Use a .180" (4.6 mm) diameter rod to line up shoes for pin installation. Install shoe release lever, spring and pin.

3) If necessary to relieve load on release lever, hold shoes inward and wedge a block between top of shoes (over slots) and bearing housing. Install sector drive shaft into housing and lightly tap sector onto shaft far enough to allow installation of snap ring. Install snap ring.

4) Install lock bolt and engage it with sector cam surface. Install rack and spring while noting that block tooth on rack should engage block tooth on sector. Install external tilt release lever. Install lock bolt spring and retaining screw and tighten.

5) Wind up shift lever spring with pliers and push into housing. Install plunger on floor shift models. Slide gearshift lever housing onto mast jacket. On all models, install bearing support lock plate wave washer.

6) Install lock plate and work it into notches by tipping plate toward hub at 12 o'clock position and sliding under jacket opening. Slide lock plate into notches in jacket.

7) Install shift tube into lower end of mast jacket, then align keyway of tube with key in shift lever housing. Install wobble plate end of Puller (J-23073) into upper end of shift tube (far enough to reach enlarged portion of tube).

8) Install adapter over end of puller and seat against lock plate. Install nut on end of puller and pull shift tube into housing.

CAUTION: Do not push or tap on end of shift tube and ensure shift tube lever is aligned with slotted opening at lower end of mast jacket or damage may result.

9) Pull shift lever housing up far enough to compress wave washer, then install bearing support thrust washer and retaining ring. Install bearing support while ensuring "V" notch in support is in line with "V" in jacket.

10) Install attaching screws through support and into lock plate, then tighten. Align lower bearing adapter with notches in jacket and push adapter into lower end of mast jacket. Install lower bearing, bearing reinforcement and retaining clip.

NOTE: Clip must be aligned with slots in reinforcement, jacket and adapter.

11) Install centering spheres and anti-lash spring into upper shaft. Install lower shaft from same side of spheres that spring ends protrude. Install steering shaft assembly into shift tube from upper end and carefully guide shaft through shift tube and bearing.

12) Install ignition switch actuator rod through shift lever housing and insert into slot in bearing support. Extend rack downward from bearing housing, then assemble bearing housing over steering shaft and engage rack over end of actuator rod.

13) Install tilt release lever, then hold lock shoes in disengaged position and position bearing housing over steering shaft until pivot pin holes line up. Install pivot pins.

14) Place bearing housing in fully upward position. Install tilt lever spring guide, spring and spring retainer. Using a Phillips screwdriver, push retainer in and turn clockwise to engage in housing. Install upper bearing inner race and seat, then install tilt lever opening shield.

15) Remove tilt release lever, then install directional signal housing and tighten screws. Install tilt release lever and shift lever, then drive shift lever pin in.

16) Install lock cylinder, directional signal switch, and ignition switch. Install intermediate shaft assembly to upper shaft after aligning groove across upper end of pot joint with flat on steering shaft.

17) Install and tighten clamp while noting that clamp bolt must pass through shaft undercut. Install neutral safety switch or back-up switch.

18) Install dash panel bracket-to-column attaching screws and tighten. Slotted openings in bracket must face upper end of steering column.

"G" & "P" SERIES TILT WHEEL

Disassembly

1) Place column in Vise Holding Fixture (J-22573). Remove directional signal switch. Remove lower steering shaft and pot joint assembly. Remove lower bearing and adapter assembly from column, then press bearing out from adapter.

2) If column shift model, drive out shift lever pivot pin and shift lever. Install tilt release lever and place column in fully upward position. Remove tilt lever spring and retainer using a screwdriver that just fits into slot opening.

3) Insert screwdriver into slot, push in approximately 3/16", then rotate clockwise approximately 1/8 turn until retainer ears align with grooves in housing and remove retainer and spring.

4) Remove steering shaft bearing lock nut using Socket (J-22599). Remove upper bearing race seat and race. Remove two bearing housing pivot pins using Pin Remover (J-21854). *See Fig. 7.*

5) Pull up on tilt release lever (to disengage lock shoes) and remove bearing housing. To disassemble bearing housing, press upper and lower bearings out of housing. Use a slide hammer to remove bearing races from housing. Remove tilt release lever.

6) Drive out shoe release lever pivot pin using a punch. Remove lever spring and remove wedge. Drive out lock shoe retaining pin with a punch and remove shoes and shoe springs.

7) Remove steering shaft assembly through upper end of column. If disassembly of shaft is necessary,

GENERAL MOTORS – EXCEPT ASTRO, SAFARI & "S" SERIES (Cont.)

Fig. 9: Exploded View of Tilt Wheel Steering Column on "C" & "K" Series with Column Shift

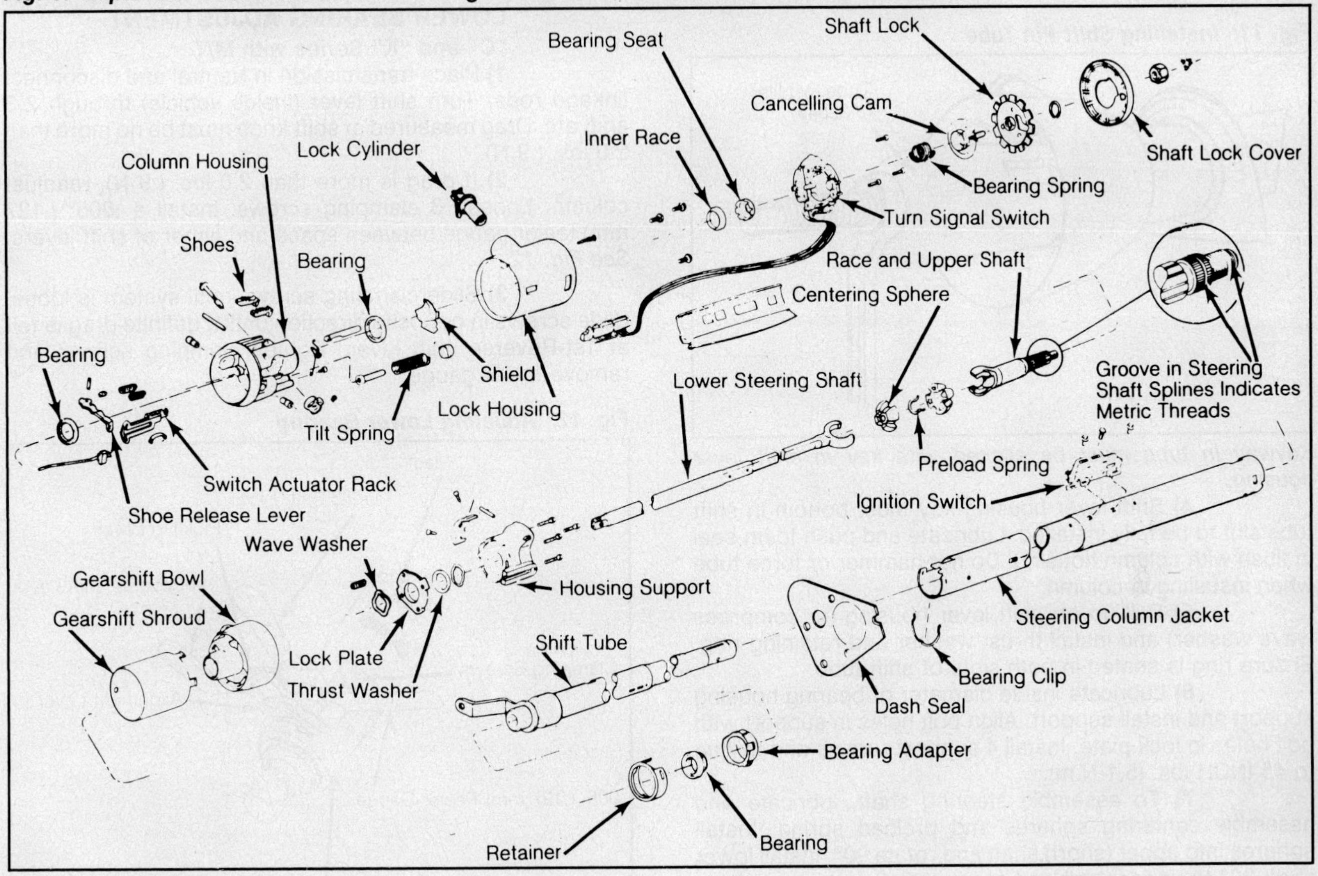

turn upper shaft 90° to lower shaft and slide upper shaft and centering spheres from lower shaft.

8) Rotate centering spheres 90° and remove centering spheres and preload spring from upper shaft. Remove 4 bearing housing support screws and remove support. If shift tube index plate (column shift only) must be removed, remove 2 retaining screws and remove plate.

9) Remove shift tube retaining ring with screwdriver. Remove thrust washer. Remove neutral start switch or back-up lamp switch retaining screws and remove switch.

10) Alter Shift Tube Remover (J-22551) by removing 1/2" from pilot end. *See Fig. 10.*

Fig. 10: Reworked Shift Tube Remover

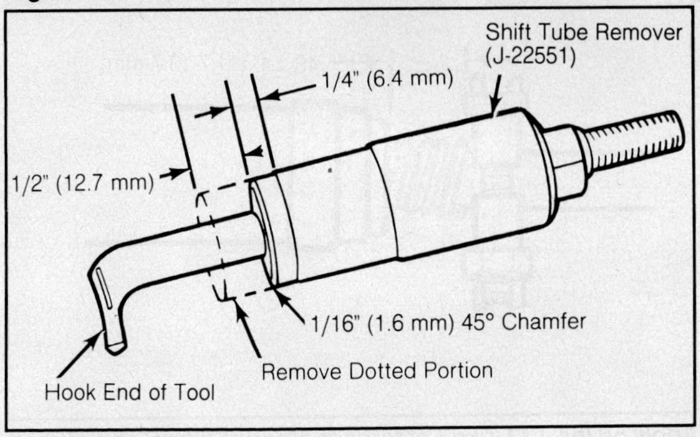

Do not hammer on shift tube during removal.

11) To remove shift tube assembly (using altered shift tube remover), insert hooked end of remover into notch in shift tube just below shift lever housing key. Pilot sleeve over threaded end of remover and into upper end of shift tube.

12) Force shift tube out of housing by turning nut onto remover. If shift tube is not completely free when nut is bottomed on its threads, complete removal by hand.

13) On column shift models, guide lower shift lever though slotted opening in column to prevent damage to tube or column. On all models, remove lock plate by sliding out of column notches, tipping plate downward toward housing to compress wave washer and then removing wave washer and lock plate.

14) Remove shift lever housing. On column shift models, remove shift lever spring by winding it up with pliers. On all models, remove dash panel seal mounting plate and instrument panel seal from column jacket.

Reassembly

1) Install dash panel seal, mounting plate and instrument panel seal on column. On column shift models, press a new shift lever spring into shift lever housing. Slide shift lever housing over upper end of column.

2) Place wave washer and lock plate in position. Work lock plate into notches by tipping plate toward housing (compressing wave washer) at open side of column. Lubricate lock plate and upper end of shift tube.

3) Carefully install shift tube into lower end of column (ensure foam seal is at lower end of shift tube). Align keyway in tube with key in shift lever housing and complete

GENERAL MOTORS – EXCEPT ASTRO, SAFARI & "S" SERIES (Cont.)

installation of shift tube using Tube Installer (J-22549). *See Fig. 11.*

Fig. 11: Installing Shift Pin Tube

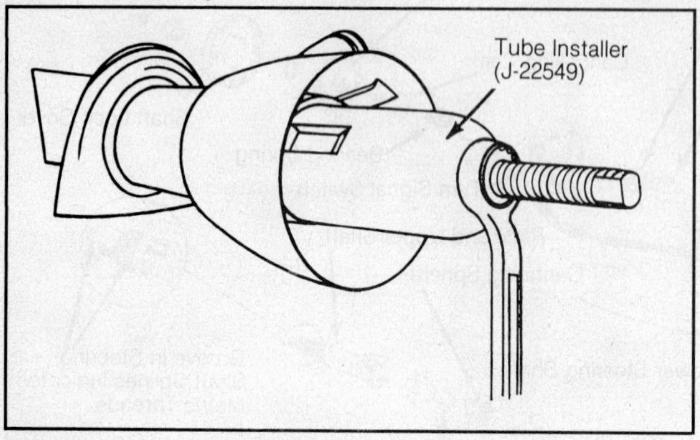

Keyway in tube must be aligned with key in shift lever housing.

4) Shift lever housing key must bottom in shift tube slot to be fully installed. Lubricate and push foam seal in flush with column housing. Do not hammer or force tube when installing in column.

5) Pull up on shift lever housing (to compress wave washer) and install thrust washer and retaining ring. Ensure ring is seated in both slots of shift tube.

6) Lubricate inside diameter of bearing housing support and install support. Align bolt holes in support with bolt holes in lock plate. Install 4 support screws and torque to 45 INCH lbs. (5.1 N.m).

7) To assemble steering shaft, lubricate and assemble centering spheres and preload spring. Install spheres into upper (short) shaft and rotate 90°. Install lower shaft 90° to upper shaft and over centering spheres.

8) Slowly straighten shafts while compressing preload spring. Install shaft assembly into housing from upper end. Install lower bearing and adapter, bearing reinforcement, wire clip, pot joint coupling and lower shaft.

9) To assemble bearing housing, press new upper and lower bearing races into bearing housing. Lubricate and install bearings into races. Place lock shoe springs in position in housing.

10) Install each shoe in place and compress spring until a straight punch can be used to hold shoes in position. Once shoes are in place, install retaining pin. Install shoe release lever and drive in pivot pin.

11) Install tilt release lever. Lubricate shoes and release lever. Install bearing housing assembly to support. Hold tilt release lever up until shoes have fully engaged support. Lubricate and install bearing housing pivot pins. Press pins in flush with housing.

12) Place housing in fully upward position then install tilt spring and retainer (tapered end of spring first). Push into housing approximately 3/16" and rotate counterclockwise 1/8 turn.

13) Lubricate and install upper bearing upper race, race seat and lock nut. Tighten lock nut to remove lash and then further tighten 1/16 to 1/8 turn (column must be in straight-ahead position). Remove tilt release lever.

14) Install directional signal switch. Install shift lever and pivot pin if column shift model. Install neutral start or back-up lamp switch.

ADJUSTMENTS

LOWER BEARING ADJUSTMENT

"C" and "K" Series with M/T

1) Place transmission in Neutral and disconnect linkage rods. Turn shift lever (inside vehicle) through 2-3 shift arc. Drag measured at shift knob must be no more than 2.0 lbs. (.9 N).

2) If drag is more than 2.0 lbs. (.9 N), readjust column. Loosen 3 clamping screws. Install a .005" (.127 mm) feeler gauge between space and either of shift levers. *See Fig. 12.*

3) Slide clamping screws until system is loose. Slide screws in opposite direction until a definite drag is felt at 1st-Reverse shift lever. Tighten clamping screws and remove feeler gauge.

Fig. 12: Adusting Lower Bearing

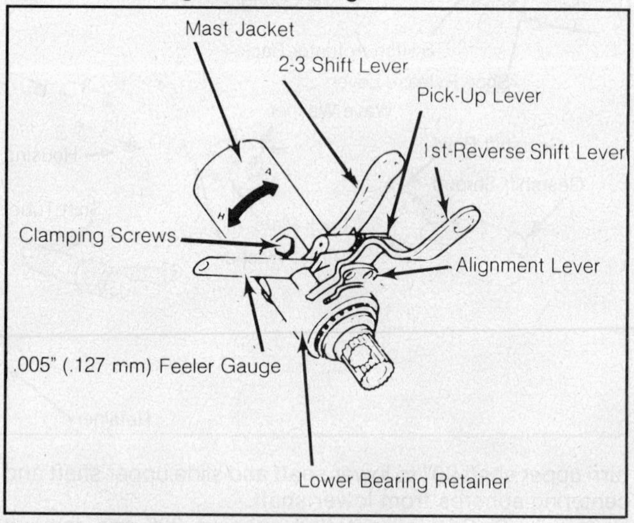

"C" and "K" series are shown.

"G" & "P" Series with M/T

Loosen clamp on steering shaft. Apply 50 lbs. (22.7 kg.) force to steering wheel end of shaft. Adjust clamp to obtain clearance of .46"-.54" (11.7-13.7 mm) for "G" series and 1.24"-1.28" (31.5-32.5 mm) for "P" series. *See Figs. 13 and 14.* Tighten clamp bolts.

Fig. 13: Adjusting Steering Column Lower Bearing for "G" Series

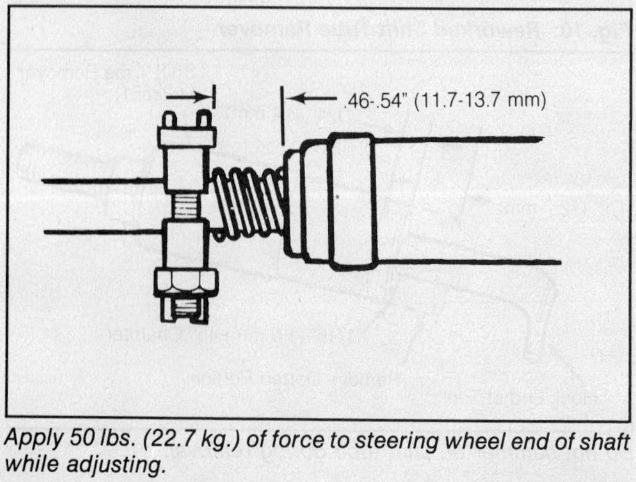

Apply 50 lbs. (22.7 kg.) of force to steering wheel end of shaft while adjusting.

GENERAL MOTORS – EXCEPT ASTRO, SAFARI & "S" SERIES (Cont.)

SHIFTER TUBE ADJUSTMENT

"G" & "P" Series with M/T

Loosen adjusting ring attaching screws and clamp bolt. Rotate adjusting ring to give .005" (.127 mm) end play between adjusting ring and 1st-Reverse shift lever. Tighten attaching screws and clamp bolt. *See Fig. 15.*

"G" & "P" Series with A/T

Place shift tube lever in "N" or "D" position. Loosen adjusting ring clamp screws and rotate adjusting ring to obtain .33-.36" (8.4-9.1 mm) end play between shift tube lever and adjusting ring. Tighten adjusting ring clamp screws. *See Fig. 16.*

Fig. 14: Adjusting Steering Column Lower Bearing for "P" Series

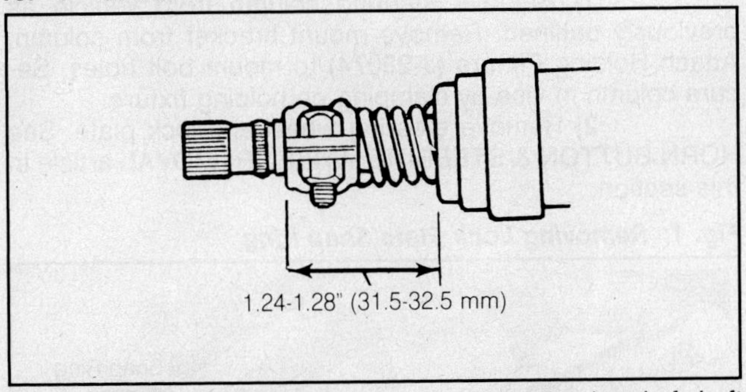

Apply 50 lbs. (22.7 kg.) of force to steering wheel end of shaft while adjusting.

Fig. 15: Adjusting Shift Tube for M/T on "G" & "P" Series

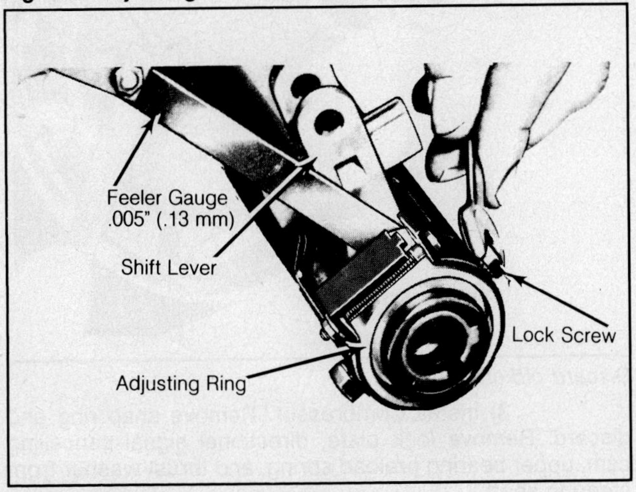

Rotate adjusting change clearance.

ADJUSTMENT SPECIFICATIONS

Application	INCHES (mm)
Lower Bearing Adjustment	
"G" Series	.46-.54 (12-13)
"P" Series	1.24-1.28 (31.5-32.5)
Shift Tube Adjustment	
A/T	.33-.36 (8.4-9.1)
M/T	.005 (.13)

Fig. 16: Adjusting Shift for A/T on "G" & "P" Series

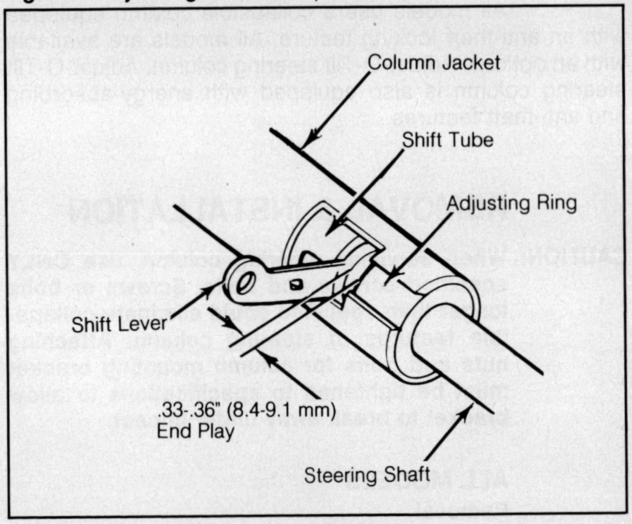

Rotate adjusting ring to change clearance.

TIGHTENING SPECIFICATIONS

Application	Ft. Lbs. (N.m)
Flexible Coupling Bolt & Studs	
"P" Series	20 (27)
All Others	18 (24)
Lower Coupling-to-Worm Shaft Clamp	
"P" Series	75 (102)
All Others	30 (41)
Lower Jacket Bearing Clamp	30 (41)
	INCH Lbs. (N.m)
Bearing Housing Support Screw (Tilt Wheel)	60 (6.8)
Column Lock Plate Cover	20 (2.3)
Column-to-Dash Panel	125 (14.2)
Firewall Bracket Clamp	
"G" Series	150 (17.0)
"P" Series	98 (11.1)
All Others	90 (10.2)
Floor Pan Cover Plate	
"G" Series	30 (3.4)
"P" Series	24 (2.7)
Ignition Switch Screws	35 (4.0)
Lock Bolt Spring Screw (Tilt Wheel)	35 (4.0)
Lower Bearing Adjusting Ring Bolt	70 (7.9)
Turn Signal Housing	45 (5.1)

Steering Columns

JEEP

DESCRIPTION

All models use a collapsible column equipped with an anti-theft locking feature. All models are available with an optional Adjust-O-Tilt steering column. Adjust-O-Tilt steering column is also equipped with energy-absorbing and anti-theft features.

REMOVAL & INSTALLATION

CAUTION: When servicing steering column, use ONLY specified screws and bolts. Screws or bolts longer than specified could eliminate collapsible features of steering column. Attaching nuts and bolts for column mounting bracket must be tightened to specifications to allow bracket to break away under impact.

ALL MODELS

Removal

1) Disconnect battery negative cable. On models with A/T, disconnect shift rod at steering column shift lever.

2) On Grand Wagoneer and Trucks with A/T and power brakes, place transmission in "LOW" (1) detent position to gain access to shift rod retaining clip at shift lever.

3) Remove upper steering shaft to intermediate shaft "U" joint pinch bolt. DO NOT attempt to separate upper steering shaft and intermediate shaft at this point.

4) On Grand Wagoneer and trucks with A/C, remove left duct extension. On all models, remove steering column to instrument panel bezel. On Grand Wagoneer and Trucks, bezel screws are located behind lower bezel half.

5) Remove bolts securing steering column mounting bracket to instrument panel. Remove bolts securing mounting bracket to steering column and remove bracket.

CAUTION: Store bracket in a safe place to prevent damage to breakaway capsules.

6) Remove upper and lower toe-plates. Disconnect wiring harness at ignition switch, removing black connector first.

7) On models with cruise control, disconnect electrical connector. Separate steering shaft from intermediate "U" joint and remove steering column assembly.

CAUTION: Handle steering column with care after removal. Blows on end of steering shaft or shift levers, leaning on column assembly, or dropping unit may cause damage to energy absorbing components.

Installation

1) Position steering column in vehicle. Connect upper steering shaft to intermediate shaft "U" joint. Install and tighten "U" joint pinch bolt.

2) On models with cruise control, connect electrical connector. Connect ignition switch connectors, connecting White connector first. Install upper and lower toe plates. Install bolts but do not tighten.

3) Install mounting bracket on steering column. Align column with instrument panel. Install bracket to instrument panel bolts but do not tighten.

4) Pull upward on column and tighten bolts. Ensure bolts are tightened while pulling upward on column. Tighten toe plate bolts.

5) Install both halves of instrument panel bezel. Install left A/C duct extension (if removed). Connect shift rod to shift lever.

6) Connect battery negative cable. Check A/T shift linkage operation and adjust as necessary. Check for correct operation of all electrical components.

OVERHAUL

STANDARD COLUMN (ALL MODELS)

Disassembly (M/T)

1) Remove steering column from vehicle as previously outlined. Remove mount bracket from column. Attach Holding Fixture (J-23074) to mount bolt holes. Secure column in vise by clamping on holding fixture.

2) Remove steering wheel and lock plate. See HORN BUTTON & STEERING WHEEL REMOVAL article in this section.

Fig. 1: Removing Lock Plate Snap Ring

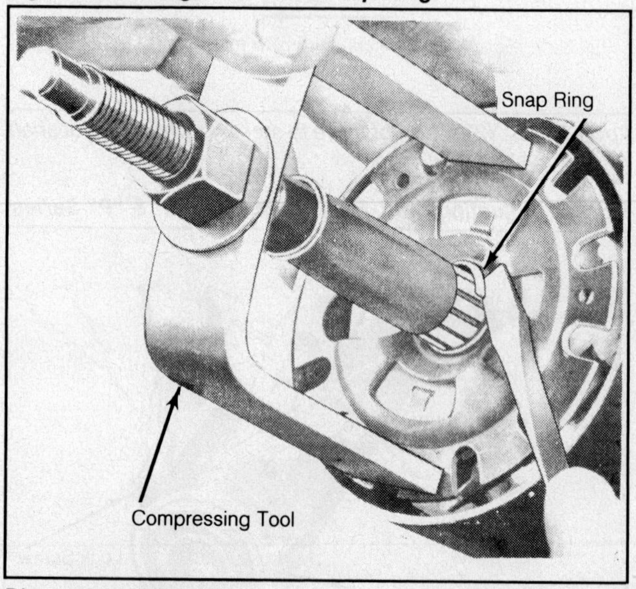

Discard old snap ring.

3) Install Compressor. Remove snap ring and discard. Remove lock plate, directional signal cancelling cam, upper bearing preload spring, and thrust washer from steering shaft.

CAUTION: After snap ring is removed from shaft, steering shaft is free in column. Do not allow shaft to fall out end of column.

4) Remove hazard warning switch knob by pressing inward and unscrewing. On models without cruise control, remove directional signal switch lever.

5) On models with cruise control, disconnect 2 of 4 wires at switch connector. Fold wires back along harness. Tape wires and a length of string to harness to aid removal.

6) Remove directional switch connector from bracket at lower end of column. Separate connector by lifting plastic lock tab on connector. Wrap tape around connector and harness to prevent snagging during removal. Remove directional signal switch screws.

JEEP (Cont.)

Fig. 2: Exploded View of Steering Column

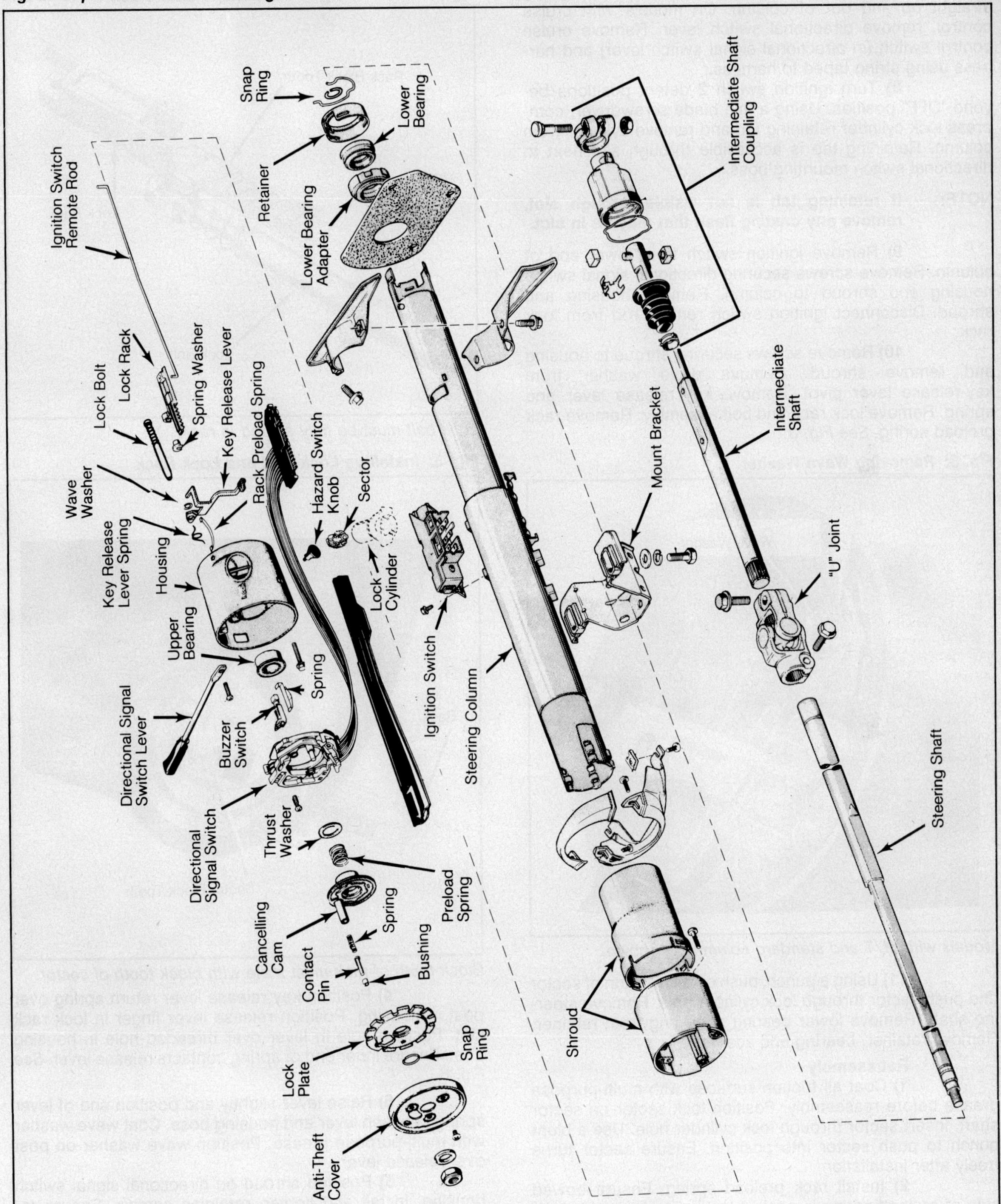

Models with M/T and standard column are shown.

Steering Columns

JEEP (Cont.)

7) Remove switch and harness by pulling straight up and out of column. On models with cruise control, remove directional switch lever. Remove cruise control switch (in directional signal switch lever) and harness using string taped to harness.

8) Turn ignition switch 2 detent positions beyond "OFF" position. Using a thin blade screwdriver, compress lock cylinder retaining tab and remove cylinder from column. Retaining tab is accessible through slot next to directional switch mounting boss.

NOTE: If retaining tab is not visible through slot, remove any casting flash that may be in slot.

9) Remove ignition switch from lower end of column. Remove screws securing directional signal switch housing and shroud to column. Remove housing and shroud. Disconnect ignition swtich remote rod from lock rack.

10) Remove screws securing shroud to housing and remove shroud. Remove wave washer from key-release lever pivot. Remove key release lever and spring. Remove lock rack and bolt assembly. Remove rack preload spring. *See Fig. 3.*

Fig. 3: Removing Wave Washer

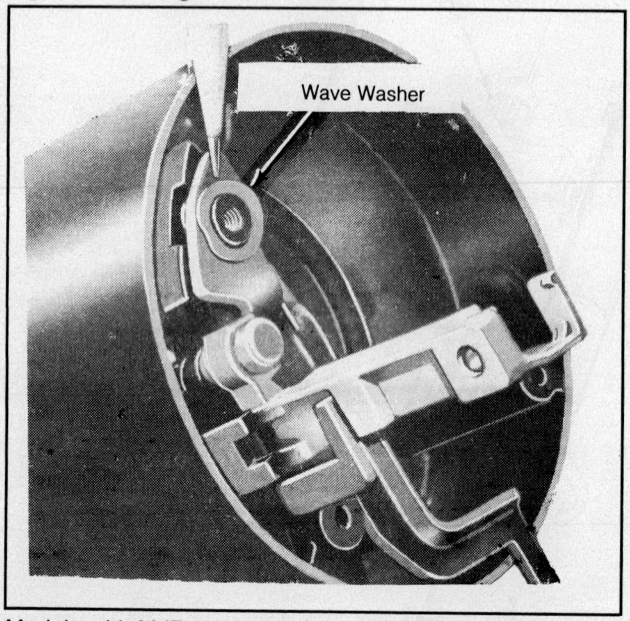

Models with M/T and standard column are shown.

11) Using a punch, push on block tooth of sector and push sector through lock cylinder hole. Remove steering shaft. Remove lower bearing snap ring from retainer. Remove retainer, bearing and adapter.

Reassembly

1) Coat all friction surfaces with multi-purpose grease before reassembly. Position lock sector on sector shaft. Insert sector through lock cylinder hole. Use a blunt punch to push sector into position. Ensure sector turns freely after installation.

2) Install rack preload spring. Ensure bowed side of preload spring is against lock rack. Assemble lock rack and lock spring. *See Fig. 4.*

3) Install assembled lock bolt and lock rack in housing. Ensure block tooth of lock rack is mated with block tooth of sector. *See Fig. 5.*

Fig. 4: Assembling Lock Bolt and Lock Rack

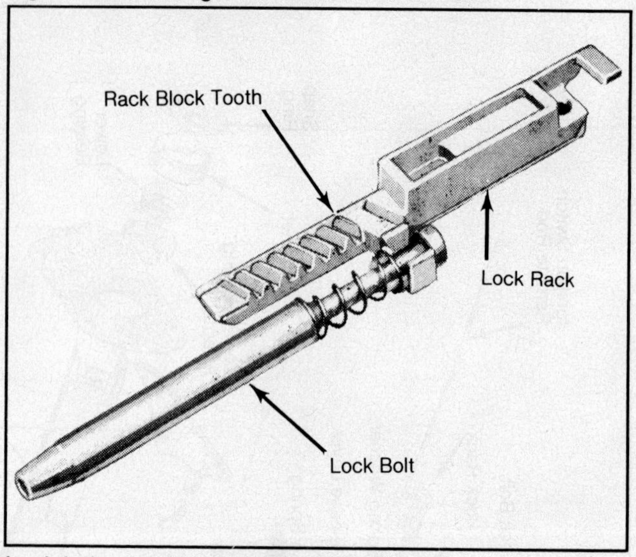

Lock bolt must be fully seated in rack.

Fig. 5: Installing Lock Bolt and Lock Rack

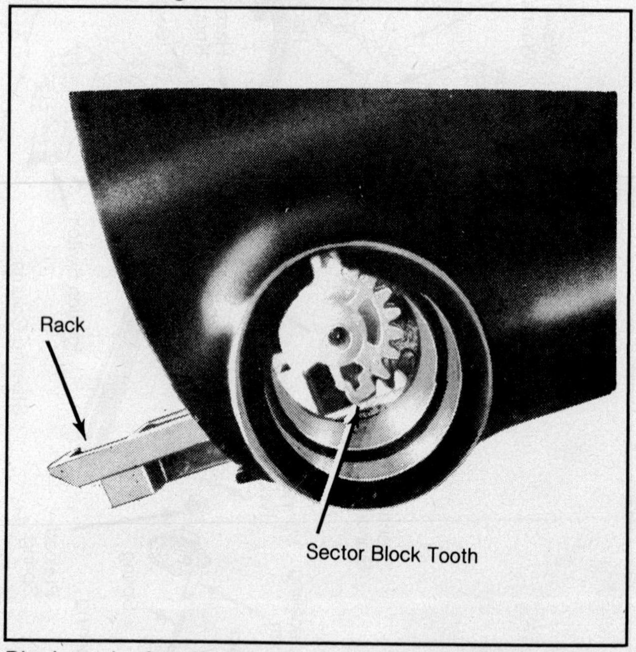

Block tooth of rack must mate with block tooth of sector.

4) Position key release lever return spring over post in housing. Position release lever finger in lock rack slot. Position hole in lever over threaded hole in housing post. Ensure inner end of spring contacts release lever. *See Fig. 6.*

5) Raise lever slightly and position end of lever spring between lever and housing boss. Coat wave washer with multi-purpose grease. Position wave washer on post over release lever.

6) Position shroud on directional signal switch housing. Install and tighten retaining screws. Ensure release lever wave washer is not dislodged when shroud is installed. Install remote rod on lock rack with short end of rod in rack.

7) Position assembled housing and shroud on column. Install and tighten retaining screws. Install lock

Fig. 6: Installing Release Lever and Spring

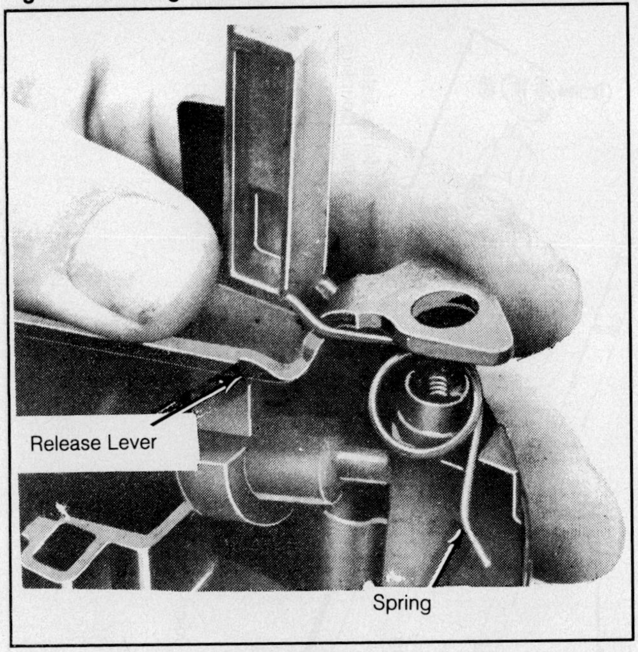

Inner end of spring must contact release lever.

Fig. 7: Installing Directional Signal Switch Cancelling Cam

Cam must be positioned as shown for proper operation of turn signal switch.

cylinder to housing. Insert key in lock cylinder. Hold cylinder sleeve and rotate key clockwise until key stops.

8) Position lock cylinder in housing bore making sure cylinder tab is aligned with keyway in housing. Push cylinder inward until it bottoms. Rotate key counterclockwise until drive section of cylinder mates with sector. Push cylinder in fully until tab engages in housing groove.

9) Turn cylinder clockwise to stop, then counterclockwise to stop at "OFF-UNLOCK" position. Position ignition switch on jacket. Move switch to extreme left position ("ACC"). Move slider 2 positions to right ("OFF-UNLOCK"). Insert remote rod into switch slider hole.

10) Position switch on column. Install and tighten retaining screws. Install lower bearing, bearing adapter, retainer and snap ring in lower end of column. Insert steering shaft in column through lower end.

11) Bend directional signal switch wires against connector. Feed connector and harness through housing and shroud. Align switch in housing. Install and tighten retaining screws.

12) On models without cruise control, install directional signal switch lever. On models with cruise control, install lever and switch assembly. Use string taped to harness during disassembly to help feed wires into housing.

13) Remove string and tape. Connect wires to switch terminal and install lever. Install thrust washer, upper bearing preload spring, and cancelling cam on steering shaft.

14) Position cancelling cam. *See Fig. 7.* Place directional signal switch in neutral position and install hazard warning switch knob.

15) Position lock plate on steering shaft. Position new snap ring on sleeve of Lock Plate Compressor (J-23653 for American threads; J-23653-4 for metric threads). Thread tool sleeve onto end of steering shaft. Compress lock plate and install snap ring in steering shaft groove.

16) Install anti-theft cover. Remove support tool from steering column. Install mounting bracket and torque bolts. Connect directional signal switch wire connector to column bracket Install steering wheel. Install column in vehicle.

Disassembly (A/T)

1) Remove steering column from vehicle as previously outlined. Remove mounting bracket from column. Attach Holding Fixture (J-23074) to mount bolt holes. Secure column in a vise by clamping holding fixture.

2) Remove steering wheel. Pry anti-theft cover off lock plate. Compress lock plate using Lock Plate Compressor (J-23653 for American threaded steering shaft nut; J-23653-4 for metric nut). Remove snap ring from steering shaft.

3) Remove compressor tool. Remove snap ring and discard. Remove lock plate, directional signal cancelling cam, upper bearing preload spring, and thrust washer from steering shaft.

CAUTION: After snap ring is removed from steering shaft, shaft is free in column. Do not allow shaft to fall out end of column.

4) Remove steering shaft from lower end of column. Remove hazard warning switch knob by pressing inward and unscrewing. On models without cruise control, remove directional signal switch lever.

5) On models with cruise control remove wires from switch terminal. Disconnect 2 of 4 wires at switch connector. Fold wires back along harness. Tape wires and a length of string to harness to aid removal.

6) Place gearshift lever into "P" position. Drive out gearshift lever pin using a small drift punch. Remove gearshift lever. Disconnect directional signal switch connector from bracket at lower end of column.

Steering Columns

JEEP (Cont.)

Fig. 8: Exploded View of Steering Column

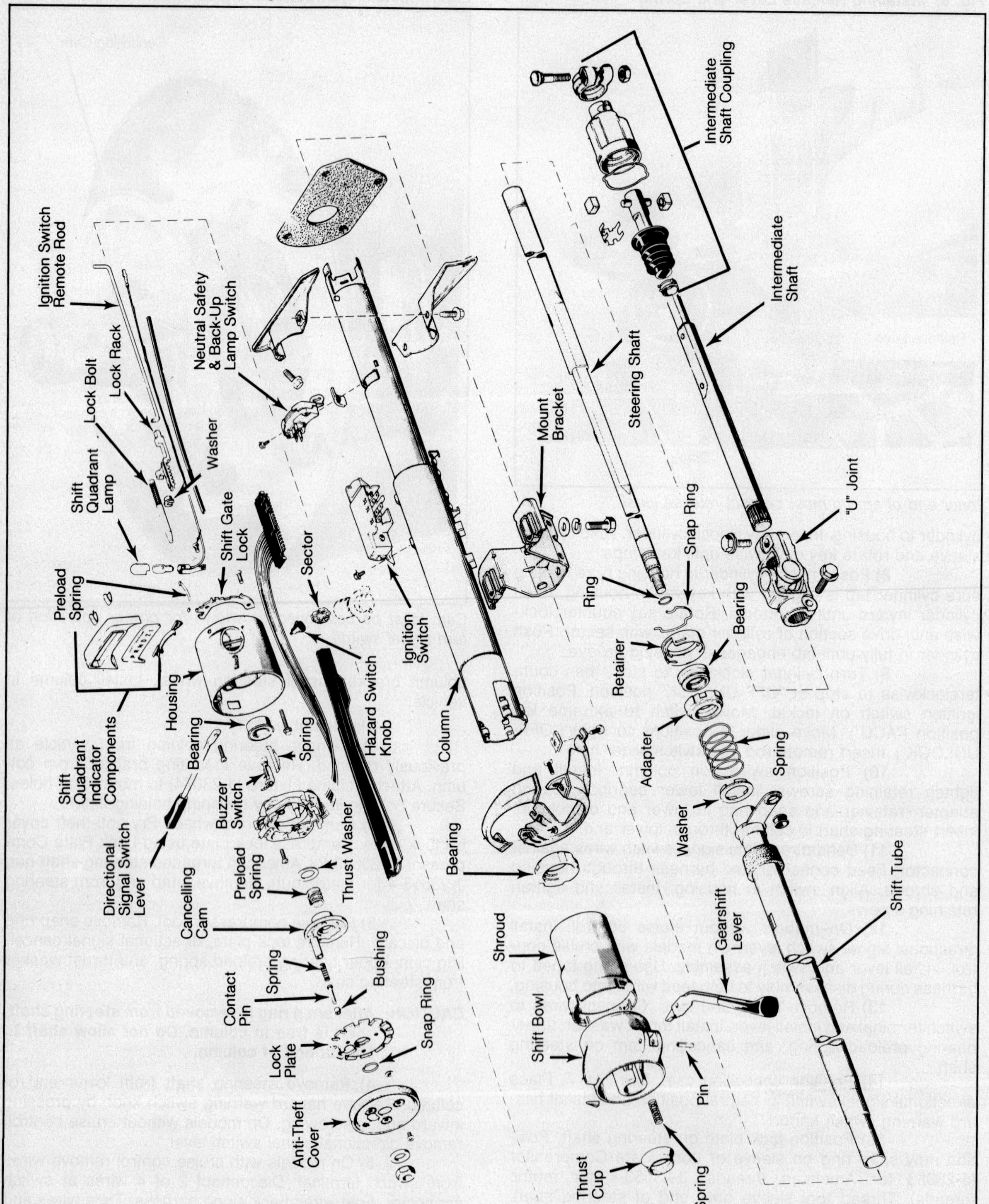

Models with A/T and standard column are shown.

Steering Columns

JEEP (Cont.)

7) Using stiff wire, compress lock tab holding shift light wire in connector and remove wire. Remove lower bracket and plastic wiring harness protector. Wrap tape around directional switch connector and wiring harness to prevent snagging during removal.

8) Pull switch straight up and out of column to remove. On models with cruise control, remove directional signal switch lever. Remove cruise control switch (in directional signal switch lever) and harness using string taped to harness.

9) Place lock cylinder in "LOCK" position. Compess cylinder retaining tab and remove lock cylinder. Retaining tab is accessible through slot next to directional signal boss in housing.

NOTE: **If retaining tab is not visible through slot, remove any casting flash that may be in slot.**

10) Remove ignition switch from lower end of column. Remove screws securing upper housing to column and remove housing. Ignition switch remote rod and shift quadrant light wire will be removed with upper housing.

11) Remove thrust cup from upper housing. Remove lock bolt and rack. Remove rack and preload spring. Using a blunt punch, remove sector from sector shaft. Note position of sector for reassembly. Remove sector through lock cylinder hole.

12) Remove shift gate lock from upper housing. Inspect shift gate lock detents for wear and replace as necessary. Remove shift quadrant by prying out 2 clips with a small punch. Remove quadrant light cover and socket assembly.

13) Remove shift bowl from column. Remove lower nylon bowl bearing from upper end of column. Remove lower bearing retainer, retaining ring, preload spring and nylon washer. Remove shift tube and nylon bearing from tube.

Reassembly

1) Apply multipurpose grease to all friction surfaces. In stall shift tube. Install nylon thrust washer in lower end of shift tube, making sure flat side of washer faces upper end of tube.

2) Install preload spring and lower bearing making sure bearing metal face is toward retainer. Install retainer and retainer clip.

3) Install lower nylon bearing in upper end of column. Ensure smaller inside diameter faces toward lower end of tube and bearing notches engage 3 locator crimps in column.

4) Align shift bowl with shift tube spline and install bowl. Install rack preload spring in upper housing. Position large end of sector on sector shaft. Tap sector into position using a blunt punch.

5) Install shift gate lock and retaining screws. Tighten screws. Install shift quadrant lamp and cover. Install quadrant indicator by pressing retainer clips into position with flat side toward bowl.

6) Assemble lock bolt and lock rack. *See Fig. 4*. Install lock bolt and lock rack in shift bowl. *See Fig. 9*. Ensure block tooth of lock rack engages block tooth of sector. *See. Fig. 5*.

7) Install nylon thrust cup in upper housing, making sure flared end of cup faces outward. Rotate shift bowl as far as possible counterclockwise and install upper housing. Tighten screws.

8) Guide shift quadrant lamp wire and remote lock rod into position between shift bowl and column. Install

Fig. 9: Installing Lock Rack and Bolt into Shift Bowl

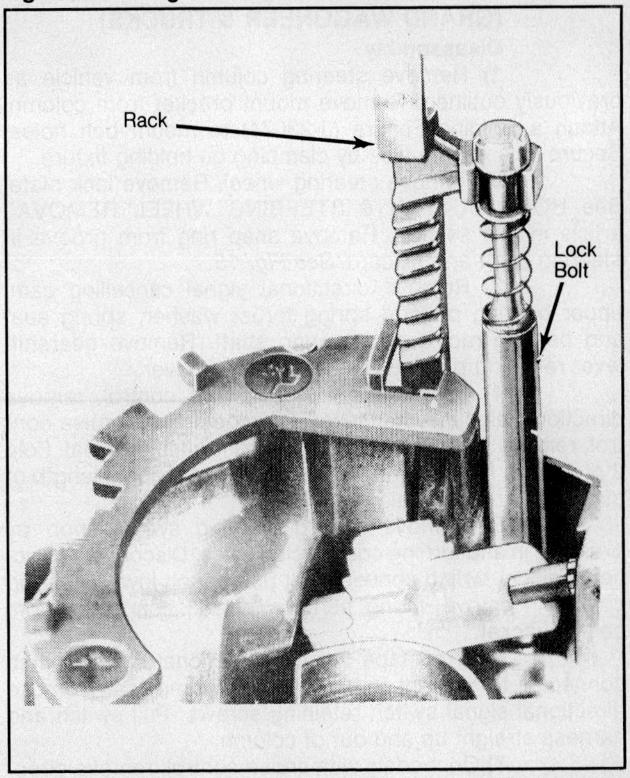

Block tooth of lock rack must engage block tooth of sector.

directional signal switch and harness. Remove tape from harness and connector. Position harness in plastic protector. Install and tighten switch retaining screws.

NOTE: **Ensure switch actuating lever pivot is correctly aligned and seated in upper housing boss.**

9) On models without cruise control, install directional signal switch lever. On models with cruise control, install directional signal switch lever and cruise control switch using string taped to harness. Remove string and tape. Connect wires to terminals.

10) Intall steering shaft from lower end of column. Install thrust washer, upper bearing preload spring and cancelling cam on steering shaft. Install lock plate, making sure lock plate splines are aligned with steering shaft splines.

11) Ensure cancelling cam shaft protrudes through lock plate opening. Install a new steering shaft snap ring on Lock Plate Compressor (J-23653 for American threaded steering shaft nut; J-23653-4 for metric threaded nut). Compress lock plate with tool.

12) Install snap ring in groove in steering shaft. Remove compressor tool. Install anti-theft cover. Install steering wheel. Install gearshift lever. Install lock cylinder in housing. Install ingnition switch on column.

13) Place shift bowl in any position but "P". Rotate bowl until lock rack bottoms against lower surface of bowl. Move ignition switch slider to left toward "ACC" position.

14) Move slide two positions to right toward "OFF-UNLOCK" position. Insert remote rod into slider hole. Attach ignition switch to steering column. Move switch out of "OFF-UNLOCK" position. Install column in vehicle as previously outlined.

Steering Columns

JEEP (Cont.)

TILT WHEEL
(GRAND WAGONEER & TRUCKS)

Disassembly

1) Remove steering column from vehicle as previously outlined. Remove mount bracket from column. Attach a Holding Fixture (J-23074) to mount bolt holes. Secure column in a vise by clamping on holding fixture.

2) Remove steering wheel. Remove lock plate. See HORN BUTTON & STEERING WHEEL REMOVAL article in this section. Remove snap ring from groove in steering shaft and discard. *See Fig. 15.*

3) Remove directional signal cancelling cam, upper bearing prelaod spring thrust washer, spring seat and bearing race from steering shaft. Remove gearshift lever retaining pin and remove gearshift lever.

4) On models without cruise control, remove directional signal switch lever. On models with cruise control, remove wires from cruise control switch terminal. Fold 2 of 4 wires back and tape along harness. Tape a length of string to harness to aid removal.

5) Remove hazard warning switch knob by pressing in and turning counterclockwise. Disconnect directional signal switch connector at bracket on lower steering column. Remove wiring harness plastic connector from column jacket.

6) Wrap tape around directional signal switch connector to prevent snagging when removing. Remove directional signal switch retaining screws. Pull switch and harness straight up and out of column.

7) On models with cruise control, remove directional switch lever. Remove cruise control switch (in directional signal switch lever) and harness using string taped to harness.

8) Insert igniton key in lock cylinder. Turn key to "LOCK" position. Compress cylinder retaining tab and remove lock cylinder. Retaining tab is accessible through slot next to directional signal switch boss in housing.

NOTE: **If retaining tab is not visible through slot, remove any casting flash that may be in slot.**

9) Remove shift quadrant by prying 2 spring clips out of column. remove mounting bracket and light socket. Remove tilt release handle. Remove cover retaining screws and remove cover.

10) Remove lock sector tension spring screw. Unlock sector spring from sector shaft. Remove snap ring from sector shaft. Remove sector, shaft and retaining ring. Install tilt release handle. Place column in fully upward tilt position.

11) Insert a screwdriver in tilt release spring retainer slot and compress retainer approximately 3/16". Rotate retainer 1/8 turn and remove retainer and spring.

CAUTION: **Tilt spring is under strong tension.**

12) Place housing in center position. Using Puller (J-21854-1) remove tilt pivot pins. *See Fig. 10.* Lift tilt release lever to disengage lock shoes and remove housing. Remove both ball bearing assemblies from housing if bearings are to be replaced.

13) Remove tilt release lever. Using a punch, drive out release lever pin. Compress lock shoe spring to release spring tension on pin. *See Fig. 11.*

14) Remove lock shoe pin from housing using pin punch. Remove lock shoes and lock shoe springs. Disconnect steering shaft at intermediate coupling. Remove shaft through upper end of columm. *See Fig. 12.*

Fig. 10: Removing Tilt Pivot Pins

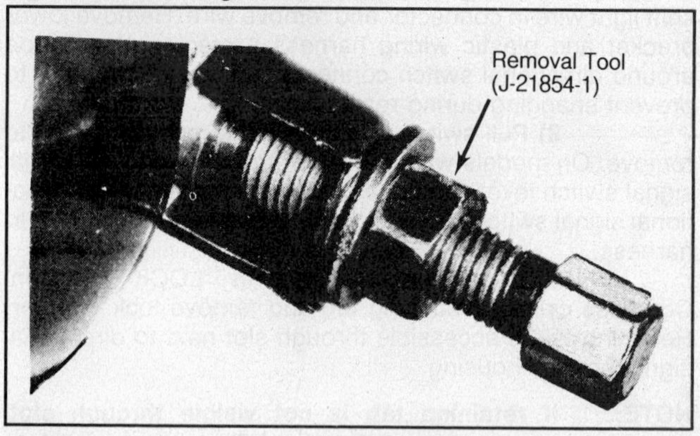

Housing must be in center (neutral) position.

Fig. 11: Removing Release Lever Pin

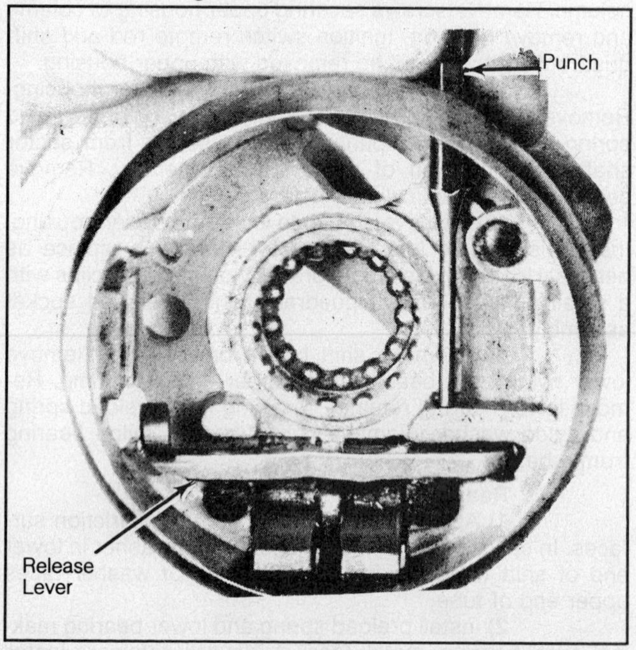

Compress lock shoe spring to release spring tension on pin.

15) Fold shaft at 90° and separate upper and lower halves at flex joint. Remove ignition switch. Remove lock rack and remote rod. Remove lower bearing retainer snap ring, retainer, bearing and adapter.

16) Remove screws securing support shift bowl. Remove shift gate screws and remove shift gate from support. Remove support and shift tube retaining ring and thrust washer. Using Puller (J-23072), pull shift tube from column.

17) Rotate shift bowl clockwise while sliding retainer plate out of jacket notches. Tip plate down toward shift bowl hub at 12 o'clock position and remove plate, bottom side first.

18) Remove wave washer and shift tube spring. Remove shift bowl from column jacket. Remove lower bearing retainer spring clip. Remove retainer, lower bearing and bearing adapter.

Reassembly

1) Coat all friction surfaces with multi-purpose grease before reassembly. Mount shift bowl on column. Position shift tube spring, wave washer, and retainer plate in shift bowl.

Fig. 12: Removing Lock Shoe Pin

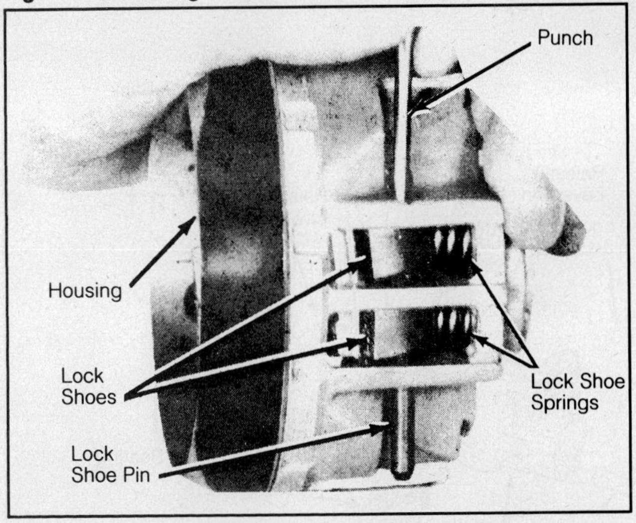

Compress lock springs to relieve tension on pin.

2) Install shift tube through lower end of column. Ensure tube spline is aligned with shift bowl keyway. Position Shift Tube Installers (J-23073-2 and J-23073-4) in shift tube.

3) Ensure spring loaded lower foot of tool is engaged with shift tube inner shoulder and tool guide is seated in shift tube. *See Fig. 13.*

Fig. 13: Positioning Shift Tube Installer Tools

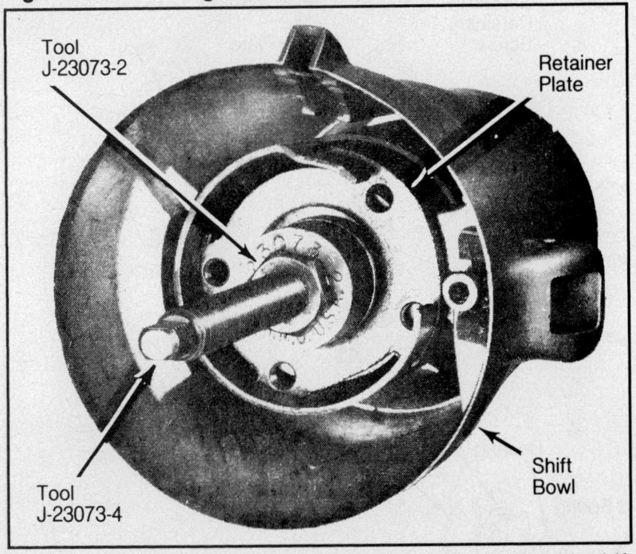

Spring loaded lower foot of tool must be engaged with shift tube inner shoulder.

4) Tighten tool spring tension nut until snug. Position Installers (J-23073-3 and J-23073-4) over puller stud. Tighten Installer Nut (J-23073-2) and pull tube into position in shift bowl. Remove shift tube installer tools. *See Fig. 14.*

5) Install shift tube thrust washer and retainer plate snap ring. Install lower bearing adapter, making sure notched end of adapter faces lower end of column. Install lower bearing in column. Ensure metal face of bearing faces lower end of column.

6) Install lower bearing retainer and retainer spring clip. Install shift gate in support and install attaching screws. Install support in shift bowl. Ensure "V" notch in support is aligned with "V" notch in column. Install support to shift bowl screws.

Fig. 14: Pulling Shift Tube into Shift Bowl

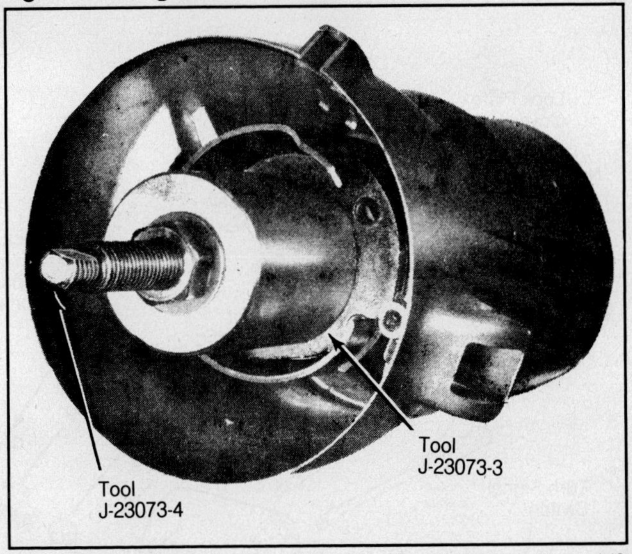

Shift tube retainer plate must be installed before pulling shift tube into bowl.

7) Assemble upper and lower steering shaft at flexible joint. Install steering shaft through upper end of column. Install ball bearings in housing if removed. Ensure there are 14 balls in each bearing.

8) Install tilt release handle. Insert ignition switch remote rod between shift bowl and column jacket, and into guide channel in left side of support. Engage lock rack in remote rod.

9) Guide housing over steering shaft and lock rack, making sure lock shoes align with teeth in support. Align housing and support pivot pin holes and drive in pivot pins using a soft faced mallet.

10) Install lock shoe spring, tilt bumpers and lock pin in housing. Install sector shaft in housing and lock sector in on shaft. Large block tooth of sector must engage large slot in rack.

11) Install sector shaft snap ring. Hook lock sector tension spring on lock bolt. Engage spring with sector and install spring retaining screw. Place housing in fully upward tilt position. Install tilt spring and guide in housing.

12) Push tilt spring retainer into housing 3/16" and rotate retainer 1/8 turn clockwise to secure retainer tabs in housing lugs. Place housing in center tilt position. Remove tilt release handle. Install cover on housing and install retaining screws.

13) Insert shift quadrant light wire upward through housing and between shift bowl and column jacket. Install shift quadrant mounting bracket and connect light socket. Hook base of shift quadrant over tabs on left side of quadrant and place in position.

14) Install quadrant pointer in shift bowl and engage in quadrant. Install quadrant retainer clip with flat side of clip facing downward. Install tilt release handle. Position directional signal switch and harness in column. Guide harness between cover and column.

15) On models without cruise control, install directional signal lever. On models with cruise control, install directional signal lever and cruise control switch assembly. Use string taped to connector during disassembly to install connector.

JEEP (Cont.)

Fig. 15: Exploded View of Tilt Wheel Steering Column for Grand Wagoneer & Trucks

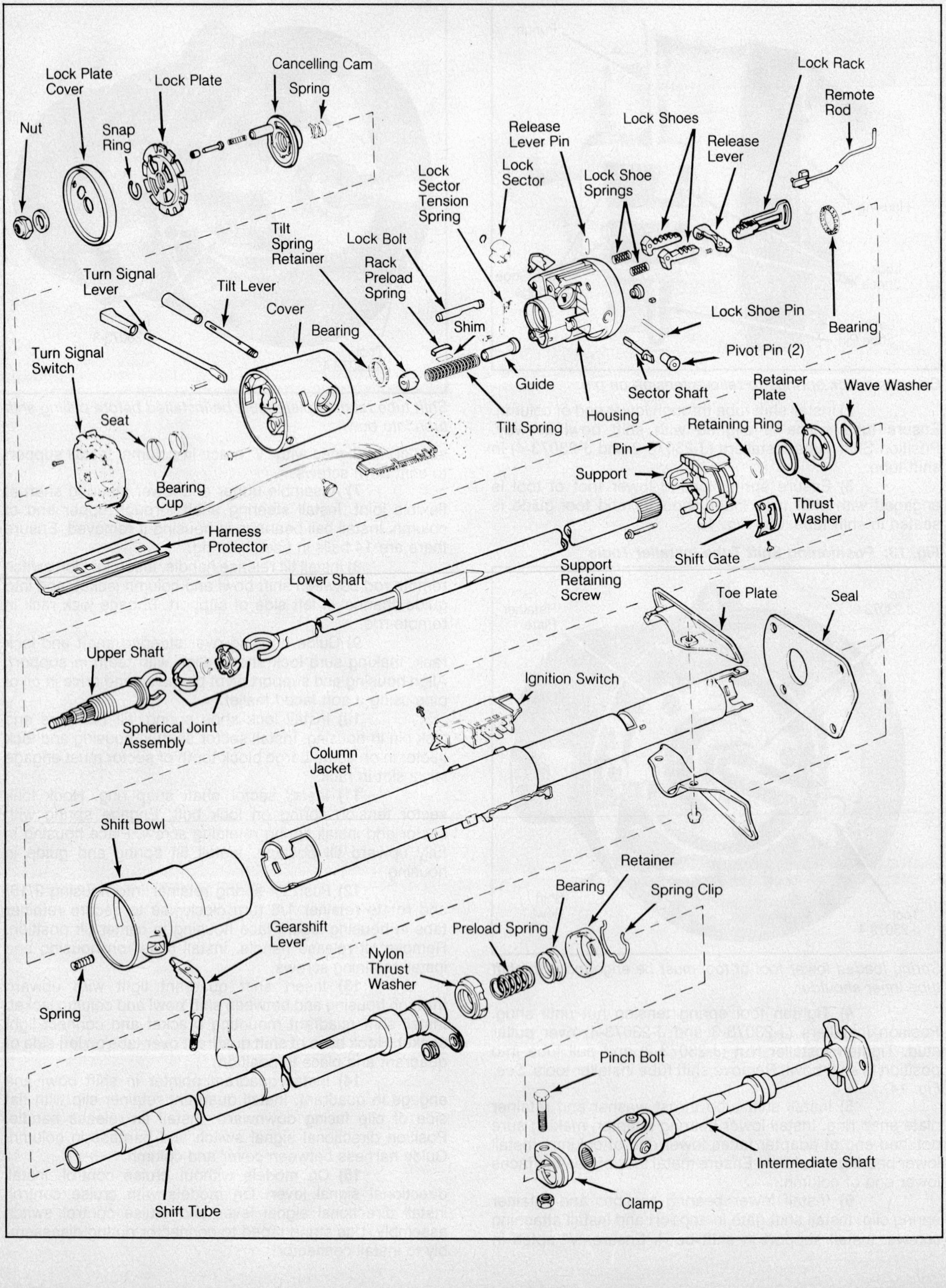

JEEP (Cont.)

16) Remove tape and string from connector. Connect 4 wires to switch terminal. Install and tighten lever screw. Position directional signal switch harness in plastic protector. Align directional signal switch in cover. Install and tighten retaining screws.

NOTE: **Ensure switch actuating lever pivot is correctly aligned and seated in housing pivot boss before installing switch attaching screws.**

17) Install bearing race, bearing race seat, preload spring, and cancelling cam on steering shaft. Align lock plate splines with steering shaft splines. Install lock plate. Ensure cancelling cam shaft protrudes through hole in lock plate.

18) Install new steering shaft snap ring on Lock Plate Compressor (J-23653 for American threaded steering shaft nut, (J-23653-4 for metric threaded nut). Position tool on steering shaft. Compress lock plate with tool. Install new snap ring in groove in steering shaft.

19) Position gearshift lever in shift bowl. Guide gearshift lever over lock sector tension spring and into bowl. Align retaining pin holes with a punch. Drive retaining pin into position using a soft faced hammer.

20) Insert ignition key into lock cylinder. Hold lock cylinder and turn key clockwise to stop. Align cylinder locking lug with keyway in cover and insert cylinder in cover.

21) Push cylinder against lock sector. Rotate cylinder counterclockwise until it engages sector. Push cylinder inward until retainer tab snaps into position.

22) Install steering column as previously outlined. Install steering wheel. Adjust gearshift linkage, and neutral safety and back-up lamp switch.

TILT WHEEL (CHEROKEE, CJ7, SCRAMBLER & WAGONEER MODELS)

Disassembly

1) Remove steering column as previously outlined. Remove mount bracket from column. Attach Holding Fixture (J-23074) to mount bolt holes. Secure column in vise by clamping on holding fixture.

2) Remove steering wheel. Remove gearshift lever retaining pin and remove lever (if equipped). Remove lock plate cover. Remove tilt and turn signal levers. Remove hazard warning knob by pressing in and turning counterclockwise.

3) Compress lock plate using Compressor (J-23653 for American threaded steering shaft nut; J-23653-4 for metric threaded nut). Remove snap ring from groove in steering shaft. Remove tool and discard snap ring.

4) Remove lock plate, cancelling cam and upper bearing preload spring. Disconnect turn signal switch harness at lower end of column. Remove wire harness protector from column. Wrap tape around harness to prevent snagging on removal.

5) Remove turn signal switch attaching screws and remove switch and harness. Pull switch straight up out of column. Insert ignition key in lock cylinder and turn key to on. Compress lock cylinder retaining tab with small screwdriver and remove cylinder.

NOTE: **Retaining tab is accessible through slot next to turn signal switch mounting boss. If tab is not visible, remove any casting flashing that may be in slot.**

6) Remove cover retaining screws and remove cover. Remove upper bearing race and bearing seat from steering shaft. Reinstall tilt lever and place column in fully upward position.

7) Remove tilt spring, guide and retainer with screwdriver. Press retainer inward and turn counterclockwise until retainer tabs align with housing lugs.

8) Place housing in center position. Remove housing pivot pins using tool J-21854-1 *See Fig. 10.* Raise tilt lever to disengage lock shoes and remove housing. Pull housing upward to disengage shoes, and turn housing to one side to separate lock rack from remote rod.

9) Remove tilt lever and shield from housing. Remove lock sector spring retaining screw and spring. Rotate spring clockwise to remove.

10) Remove lock sector retaining ring, lock sector and sector shaft. Tap shaft through sector and out of housing with a hammer and punch. *See Fig. 16.*

Fig. 16: Removing Lock Sector and Sector Shaft

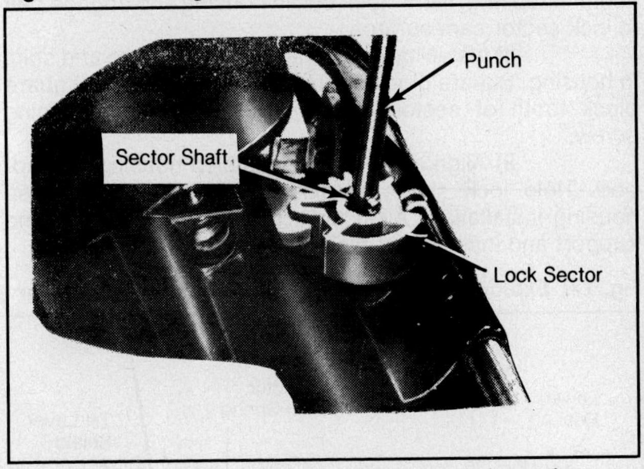

Remove shaft from sector with a hammer and punch.

11) Remove lock bolt, lock rack, rack preload spring, shim and remote rod from housing. Insert wedge between lock shoes and housing to relieve spring tension on tilt and lock shoe pins.

12) Remove tilt lever pin from housing with pin punch. Remove lock shoe pin from housing with pin punch, and remove lock shoes, springs and wedge.

13) Remove upper and lower housing bearings and races, if damaged or worn. If removed, discard and replace with new races and bearings. Disconnect steering shaft at coupling.

14) Remove steering shaft though upper end of column. Remove support attaching bolt and remove support. Remove retainer plate. Tip upper end of plate rearward and turn plate counterclockwise to remove.

15) Remove shroud using twisting-pulling motion. Remove key release lever and lever spring from shroud. Tip lever forward and lift upward to remove.

16) Disconnect ignition switch wire harness connector and remove switch. Remove snap ring, retainer and bearing assembly from lower end of column.

Reassembly

1) Coat all friction surfaces with multipurpose grease before reassembly. Install bearing assembly, bearing retainer and snap ring in lower end of column.

2) Install key release lever spring on lever and install assembled lever and spring in shroud. Align and install shroud on column jacket.

3) Install retainer plate by tipping plate to 12 o'clock position and sliding it under jacket opening. Align

Steering Columns

JEEP (Cont.)

column jacket "V" notch with notch on support and install support in column. Press key release lever down while pressing support into position.

4) Install support attaching screws finger tight then tighten alternately. Install remote rod in support by guiding rod through upper end of shroud and into rod slot in support.

5) Install steering shaft in column. Install bearings (if removed). Install lock shoe, springs and lock shoe pin in housing. Use .18" (4.6mm) diameter rod to align lock shoes and pin.

6) Install release lever, lever spring and lever pin in housing. Insert wedges between housing and lever to relieve spring tension. Install sector shaft in housing. Lightly tap shaft into housing using punch.

7) Install lock sector on shaft. Lightly tap sector onto shaft until shaft snap ring groove is exposed. Install sector snap ring. Install lock bolt in housing and engage bolt in lock sector cam surface.

8) Install lock rack, rack preload spring and shim in housing. Square block tooth of rack must engage square block tooth of sector. Install lock spring and retaining screw.

9) Align and install assembled housing on support. Hold lock shoes in disengaged position to ease housing installation. Align pivot pin holes in housing and support and install pivot pins.

10) When started in holes, seal pins fully using a hammer and punch. Press housing downward when first installing pins to avoid damage to pin holes.

11) Insert tilt lever in housing and position housing in fully upward tilt position. Lubricate tilt guide and spring and install tilt spring on guide. Insert assembled tilt spring and guide in housing and install guide retainer on spring.

12) Install tilt lever shield. Remove tilt lever. Install cover on housing. Install turn signal switch. Guide switch harness and connector through column and into housing. Do not install switch attaching screws at this time.

13) Install hazard warning switch knob in turn signal switch and align and install switch attaching screws. Ensure turn signal switch is properly aligned before tightening screws. Pull out on hazard warning knob.

14) Install upper bearing race and seat in housing. Install upper bearing preload spring, cancelling cam and lock plate.

15) Install new steering shaft snap ring on Compressor (J-23653 for American threaded steering shaft nut; J-23653-4 for metric threaded nut) and install tool on steering shaft. Compress lock plate and seat snap ring. Remove tool.

Fig. 17: Exploded View of Tilt Wheel Steering Column for Chreokee, CJ7, Scrambler & Wagoneer Models

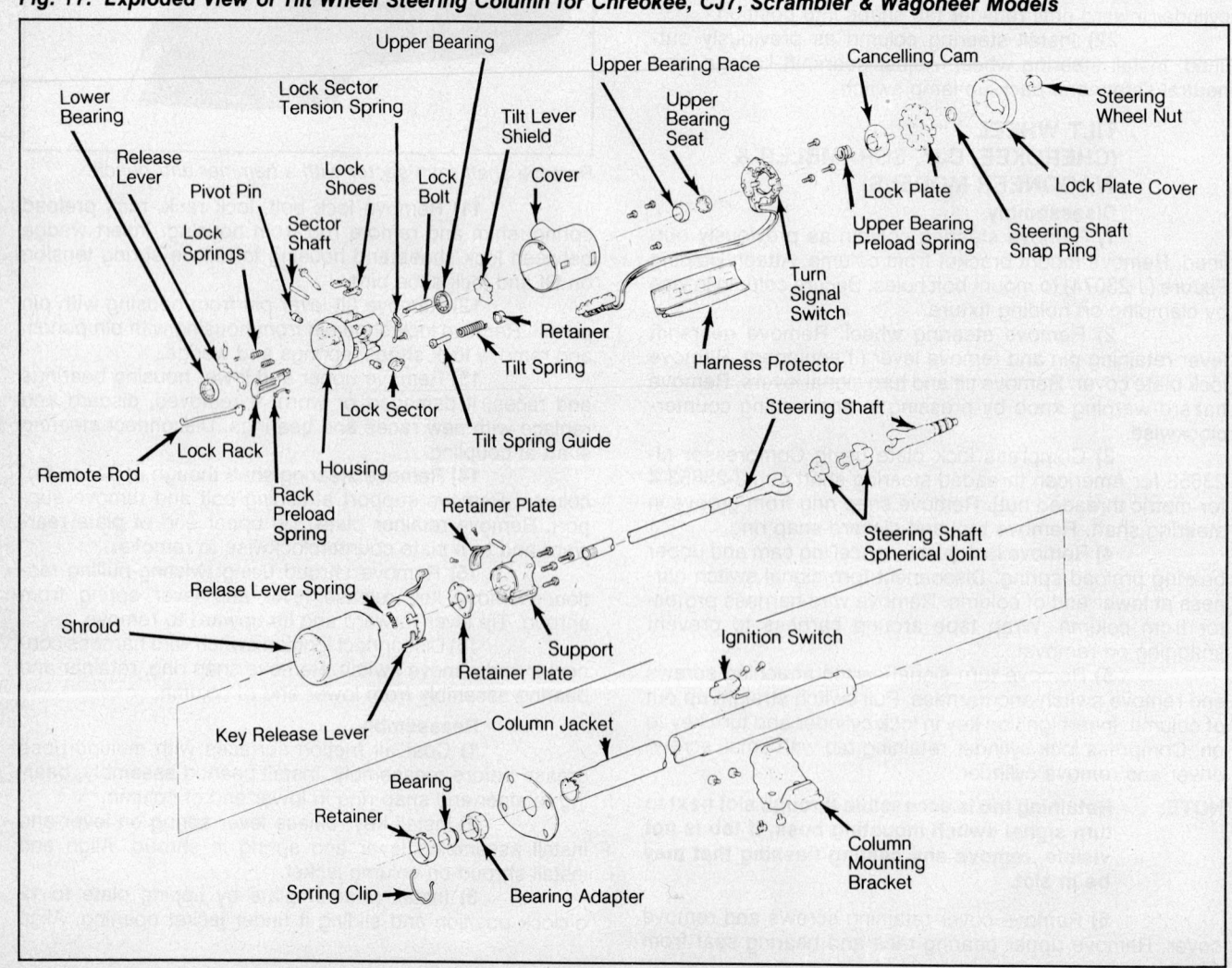

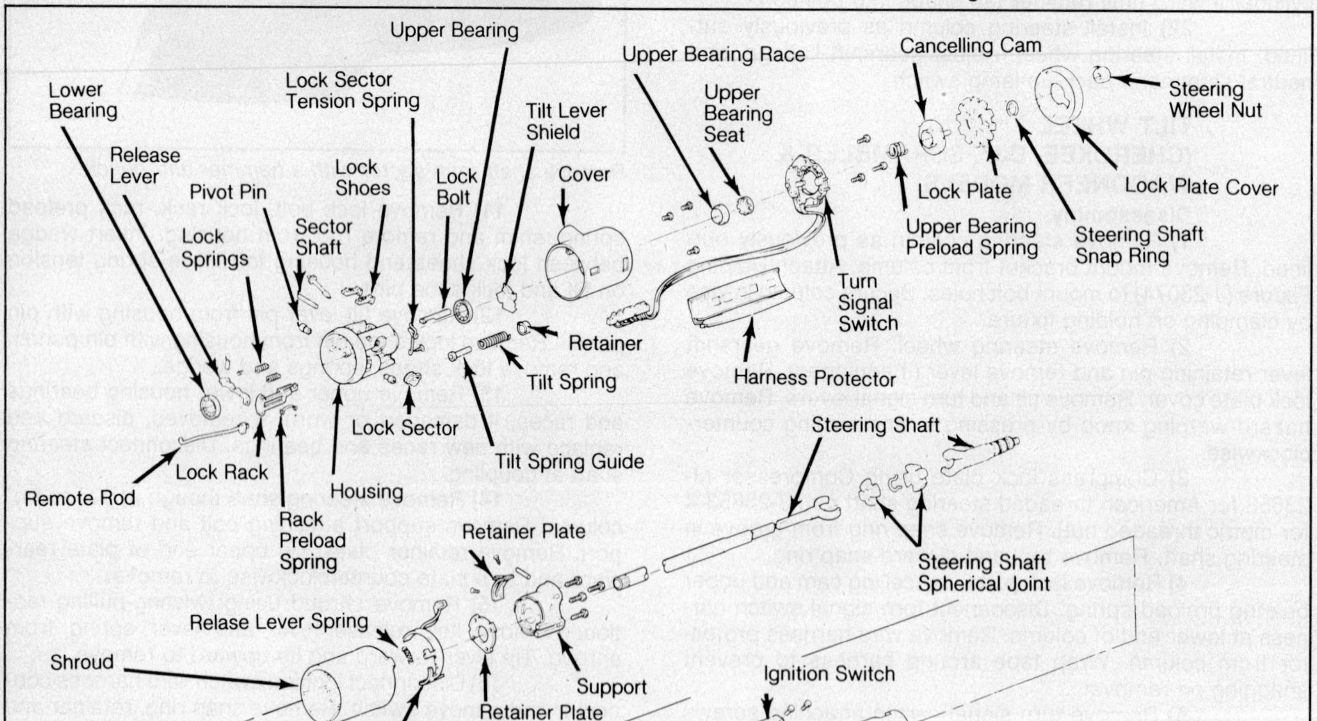

Steering Columns

JEEP (Cont.)

16) Install tilt and turn signal levers. Install shift lever and retaining pin. Install ignition lock cylinder. Hold cylinder sleeve, turn knob clockwise against stop, align cylinder tab with housing keyway and install cylinder in housing.

17) Turn cylinder knob counterclockwise until cylinder mates with lock sector and push cylinder in until retainer snaps into position. Insert key in cylinder and turn cylinder to "OFF" position. Install ignition switch.

18) Move switch to "ACC" position then back off 2 clicks to "OFF" position. Remote rod hole should be almost on center.

19) Insert remote rod into hole and install switch on column jacket. Move switch down to eliminate lash and tighten attaching screws. Place switch harness protectors over harness and snap into position.

20) Install lock plate cover. Install steering wheel. Install column in vehicle.

TIGHTENING SPECIFICATIONS

Application	Ft. Lbs. (N.m)
Column Mounting Bracket Bolt	20 (27)
Intermediate Shaft Pinch Bolt	45 (61)
Mounting Bracket-to-Instrument Panel Bolt	20 (27)
Steering Wheel Nut	30 (41)
Toe Plate Bolt	10 (14)
	INCH Lbs. (N.m)
Housing Screw	
Standard	60 (7)
Tilt	100 (11)
Ignition Switch Mounting Screw	35 (4)
Lock Sector Tension Spring Screw	35 (4)
Shroud Screw (M/T)	18 (2)
Support Screw (Tilt Column)	60 (7)
Tilt Lever Screw	35 (4)
Turn Signal Lever Screw	15 (2)
Turn Signal Switch Screw	35 (4)

Steering Linkage

CHRYSLER CORP.

SERVICE PROCEDURES

FWD MODELS

Tie Rod Replacement

Remove cotter pin and castle nut from tie rod. Separate tie rod from steering knuckle. Loosen jam nut. Unscrew tie rod end, noting number of turns required to remove it. Install new tie rod.

2WD MODELS

Tie Rod Replacement

1) Remove cotter pin and nut from tie rod end. Install Tie Rod End Puller (C-3894-A) and remove tie rod end from center link. Loosen sleeve clamping bolt. Unscrew tie rod end, noting number of turns required to remove it.

NOTE: **Removal of tie rod ends from steering arm or center link without using Tie Rod End Puller (C-3894-A) will damage tie rod end seal.**

2) Screw new tie rod end onto sleeve. Connect rod end to knuckle arm or center link and tighten. Install

Fig. 1: Disassembled View of Steering Linkage

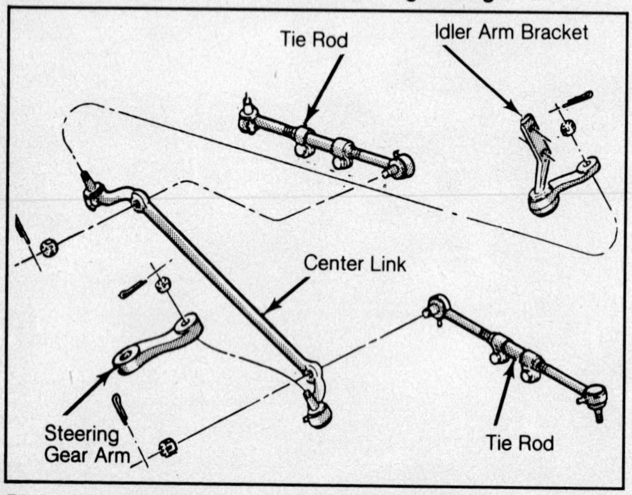

Pickup and Ramcharger models are shown.

Fig. 2: Disassembled View of Steering Linkage

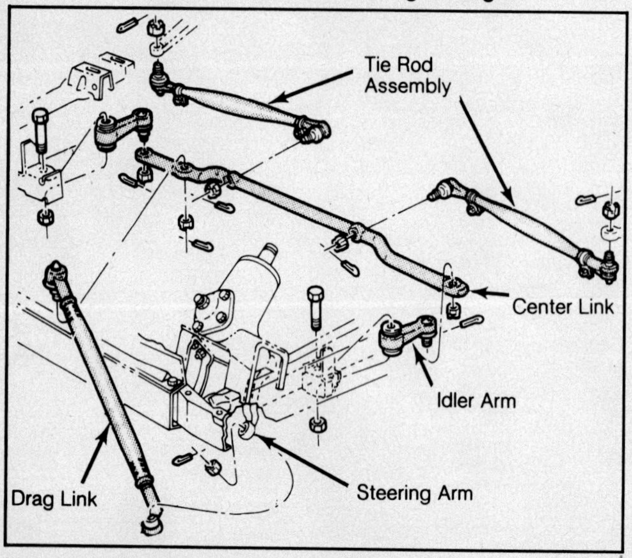

Vans and Wagon models are shown.

cotter pin. Check and adjust toe-in. See WHEEL ALIGNMENT SPECIFICATIONS & PROCEDURES article in WHEEL ALIGNMENT section.

3) Position clamp sleeve with bolt on bottom. Clamp opening should be aligned with slot in sleeve.

Ball Joints

Tension-type lower ball joints are used on all models. Ball joints and tie rod ends are semilubricated-type except on vehicles for off-highway use. Ball joints should be replaced if axial end play exceeds .020" (.5 mm).

4WD MODELS

Tie Rod Replacement

Procedure is same as for 2WD models.

Drag Link

Drag link must be installed to steering knuckle arm with short half (distance "A") attaching to knuckle arm. *See Fig. 3.*

Fig. 3: Installing Drag Link on 4WD Models

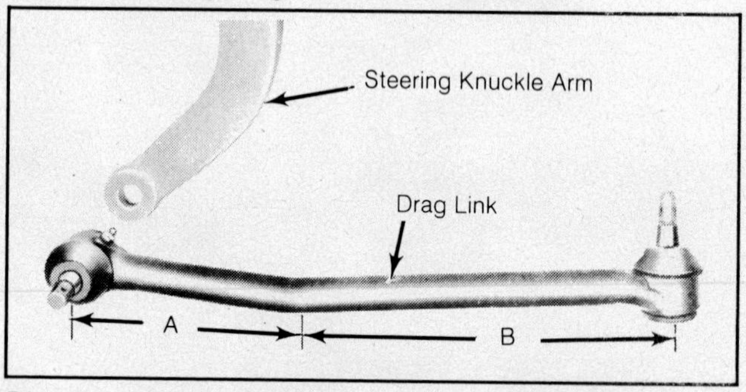

Distance "A" is measured from bend in drag link.

Ball Joints

Servicing ball joints used on steering knuckles requires dismantling of knuckles. See STEERING KNUCKLES article in SUSPENSION section. Ball joints with end play or looseness must be replaced.

TIGHTENING SPECIFICATIONS

Application	Ft. Lbs. (N.m)
Tie Rod Clamping Bolts	
Pickup & Van	[1] 13 (18)
Tie Rod End Nuts	
FWD	38 (52)
2WD Pickup	40 (54)
4WD Pickup	60 (82)
Van	
9/16" Nut	55 (75)
5/8" Nut	75 (102)

[1] – 26 Ft. Lbs. (35 N.m) for Heavy Duty models.

Steering Linkage

FORD

SERVICE PROCEDURES

DRAG LINK REPLACEMENT

Bronco II & Ranger

1) Raise and support vehicle with wheels in a straight-ahead position. Remove cotter pins and nuts from ball stud at pitman arm and steering connecting rod. Disconnect ball stud from linkage using Puller (3290-C).

2) Loosen tie rod adjusting sleeve bolts. Note number of turns required to remove drag link. To complete installation, reverse removal procedure. Check and adjust toe-in. See WHEEL ALIGNMENT SPECIFICATIONS & PROCEDURES article in WHEEL ALIGNMENT section.

PITMAN ARM REPLACEMENT

Bronco, Pickup & Van

1) Replace pitman arm if bent. Remove cotter pin and nut from drag link ball stud. Remove drag link ball stud from pitman arm. Remove pitman arm attaching nut and washer.

2) Remove pitman arm from steering gear sector shaft using Pitman Arm Remover (T64P-3590-F). Install new pitman arm on sector shaft with wheels in straight-ahead position.

3) Install pitman arm nut and washer. Install drag link ball stud on pitman arm, and install cotter pin.

Bronco II & Ranger

1) Remove cotter pin and nut fron drag link ball stud at pitman arm. Remove drag link ball stud from pitman arm using Puller (3290-C). Remove pitman arm attaching nut and washer.

2) Remove pitman arm from steering gear using Puller (T64P-3590-F). Install new pitman arm. To complete installation, reverse removal procedure. Tighten pitman arm and drag link nut.

Fig. 2: Disassembled View of Steering Linkage

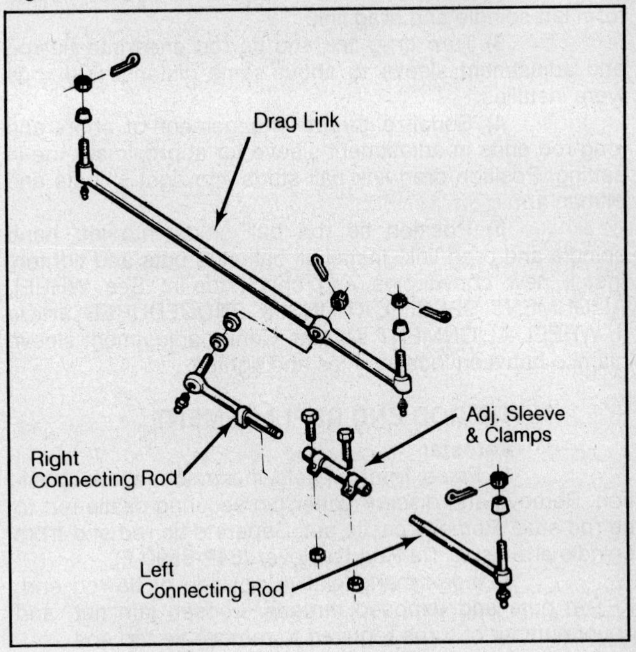

Van model is shown.

TIE ROD & DRAG LINK REPLACEMENT

Bronco, Pickup & Van

1) Replace drag link or connecting rods if ball studs are excessively loose, components are bent or threads are stripped. Never try to straighten drag link or connecting rods.

2) Remove cotter pins and nuts from drag link and tie rod ball studs. Remove drag link ball studs from

Fig. 1: Steering Linkage & Tie Rod Clamp Positioning

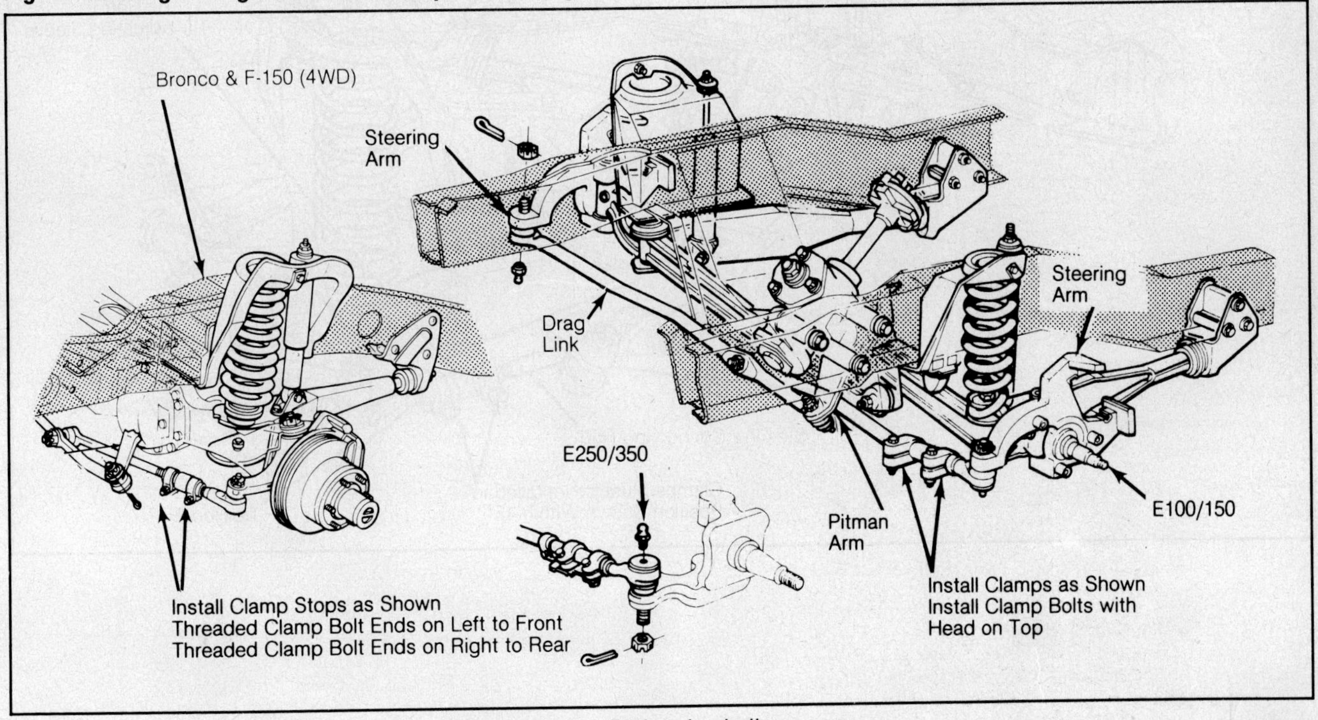

Bronco, "F" 150 Series 4WD and Van models are shown, Pickup is similar.

Steering Linkage

FORD (Cont.)

right spindle and pitman arm. Remove tie rod ball studs from left spindle and drag link.

3) Turn drag link and tie rod ends into tie rod end adjustment sleeve to about same distance old rods were installed.

4) Equalize thread engagement of short and long rod ends in adjustment sleeve for approximate toe-in setting. Position drag link ball studs into right spindle and pitman arm.

5) Position tie rod ball studs into left hand spindle and drag link. Install all ball stud nuts and tighten. Install new cotter pins and check toe-in. See WHEEL ALIGNMENT SPECIFICATIONS & PROCEDURES article in WHEEL ALIGNMENT section. Center adjustment sleeve clamps between locating nibs and tighten.

TIE ROD END REPLACEMENT

Aerostar

1) Place front wheels in straight-ahead position. Remove and discard cotter pin securing castle nut to tie rod stud. Remove castle nut. Separate tie rod end from spindle arm using Tie Rod Remover (64P-3590-F).

2) Index mark relative position of tie rod end, to jam nuts and exposed threads. Loosen jam nut, and count number of turns required to remove tie rod end.

3) To install, position tie rod end on inner ball joint assembly. Tighten jam nut. Place front wheels in straight-ahead position. Insert tie rod stud through spindle arm. Install and tighten castle nuts. Install new cotter pin.

Bronco II & Ranger

1) Place wheels in straight-ahead position. Remove cotter key and nut from tie rod ball stud. Loosen bolts on tie rod adjusting sleeve.

2) Remove tie rod ball stud from spindle using Puller (3290-C). Count number of turns it takes to remove sleeve from ball stud. Install new tie rod end.

3) To complete installation, reverse removal procedure. Ensure adjusting sleeves are in correct position. *See Fig. 3.* Check and adjust toe-in. See WHEEL ALIGNMENT SPECIFICATIONS & PROCEDURES article in WHEEL ALIGNMENT section.

TIGHTENING SPECIFICATIONS

Application	Ft. Lbs. (N.m)
Drag Link Ball Stud Nuts	50-75 (68-101)
Pitman Arm-to-Steering Gear Nut	170-230 (230-310)
Rod Clamps	30-42 (41-57)
Steering Gear-to-Frame	70 (95)
Tie Rod Adjusting Sleeve Nuts	29-41 (40-57)
Tie Rod Ball Stud Nuts	50-75 (68-101)
Steering Connecting Rod Nut	50-75 (68-101)

Fig. 3: Bronco II & Ranger Steering System

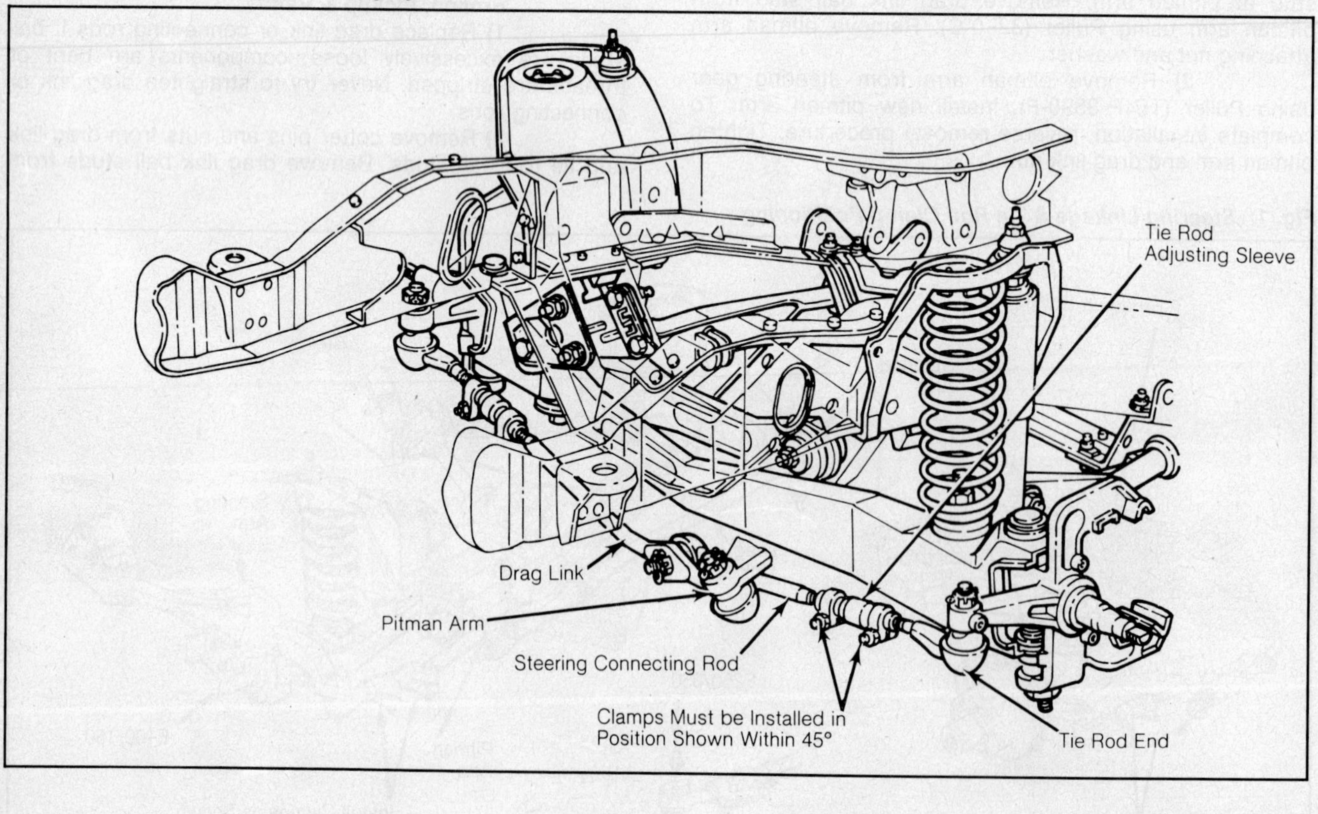

Steering Linkage

GENERAL MOTORS

STEERING SERVICE PRECAUTIONS

All steering component fasteners are made of special quality materials. Replacement fasteners must be of same part number or equivalent. Torque all fasteners to specification and install new cotter pins. When installing cotter pins, do not back off castle nuts to align cotter pin hole, tighten nut to next slot that lines up with hole.

Do not hammer on ball studs or damage to threads may result. If threads are not clean and smooth, ball studs may turn in joint when nuts are tightened. Sleeve clamps must always be positioned as specified before tightening bolts.

SERVICE PROCEDURES

Tie Rod Replacement

1) Remove tie rod fasteners. Use Tie Rod Remover (J-6627), or remove outer ball stud by tapping on steering arm at tie rod end. Use a light hammer with a heavy hammer as backing. Remove inner ball stud from relay rod in same manner.

2) To remove tie rod ends from tie rod, loosen clamp bolts and unscrew end assemblies. If tie rod adjuster clamp bolts are rusted, new nuts and bolts must be used

3) Apply penetrating oil between clamps and tube. Rotate clamps until they move freely. Use new fasteners to assure proper clamping force.

4) Lubricate tie rod threads with chassis lube and install tie rod ends. Ensure both are threaded an equal distance from tie rod. Check that threads on ball studs and nuts are clean and smooth.

5) Check condition of ball stud seals and replace if necessary. Install ball studs in steering arms and relay rod.

6) Install ball stud nuts and new cotter pins. Adjust toe-in. See WHEEL ALIGNMENT SPECIFICATIONS & PROCEDURES article in WHEEL ALIGNMENT section.

7) Before tightening tie rod adjusting sleeve clamp bolt, ensure clamps are between locating dimples at either end of sleeve. Adjuster sleeve slot must not be within open area of clamp jaw opening. *See Figs. 7 and 8.*

Fig. 1: "C" Series Steering Linkage

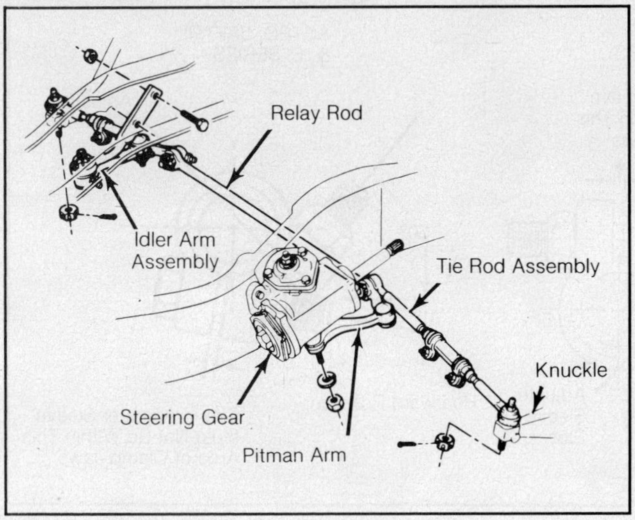

Fig. 2: "G" Series Steering Linkage

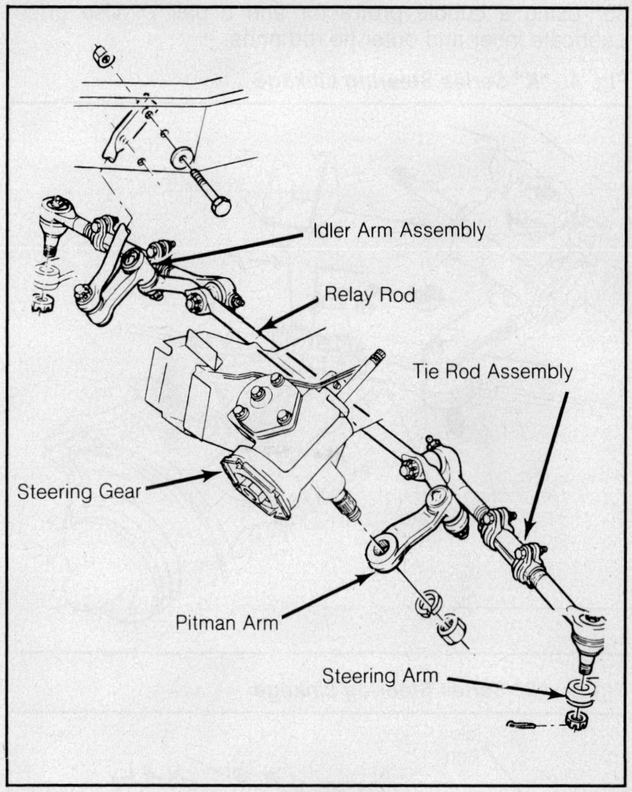

Fig. 3: "P" Series Steering Linkage

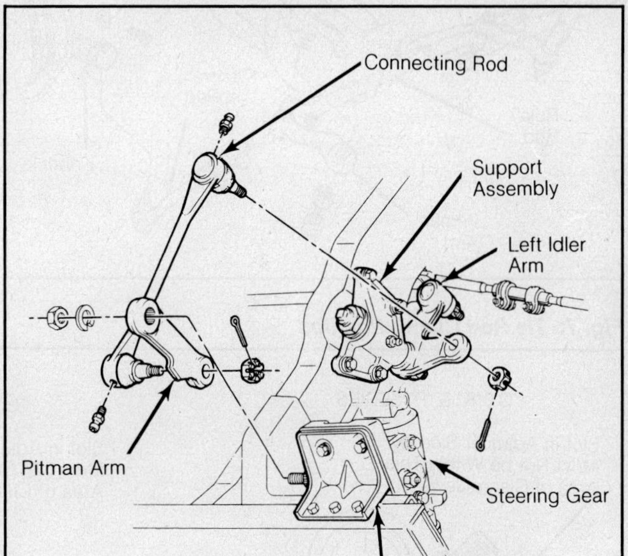

8) Rotate both inner and outer tie rod housings rearward to limit of ball joint travel before tightening clamps. After tightening clamps, return tie rod assembly to center of travel.

Steering Linkage

GENERAL MOTORS (Cont.)

9) Check each tie rod for a rotation of at least 35° using a bubble protractor and a pair of vise grips. Lubricate inner and outer tie rod ends.

Fig. 4: "K" Series Steering Linkage

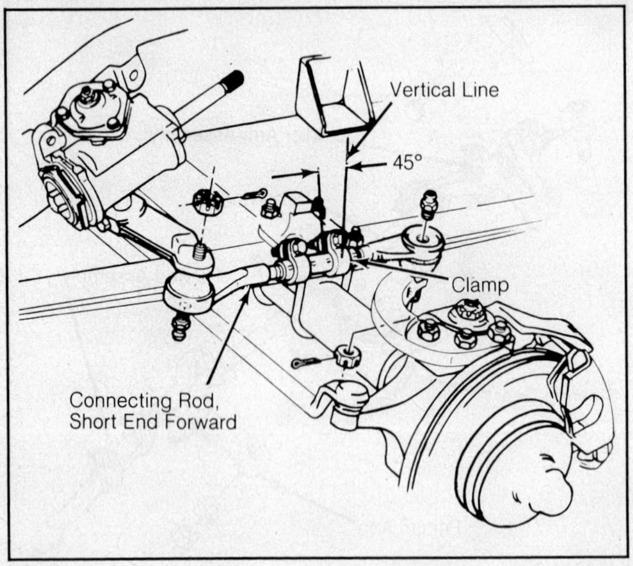

Fig. 5: "S" Series Steering Linkage

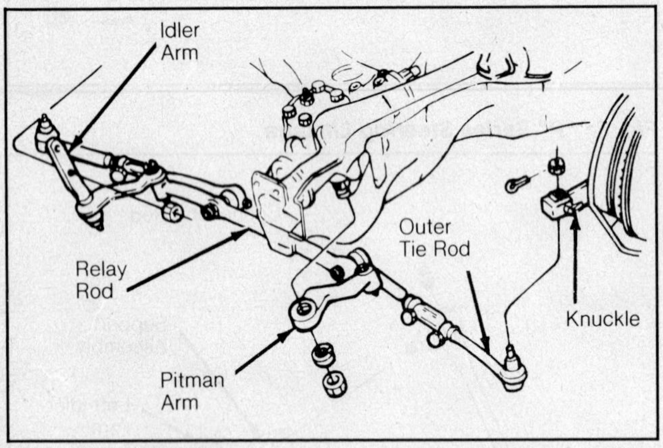

Fig. 6: Astro & Safari Steering Linkage

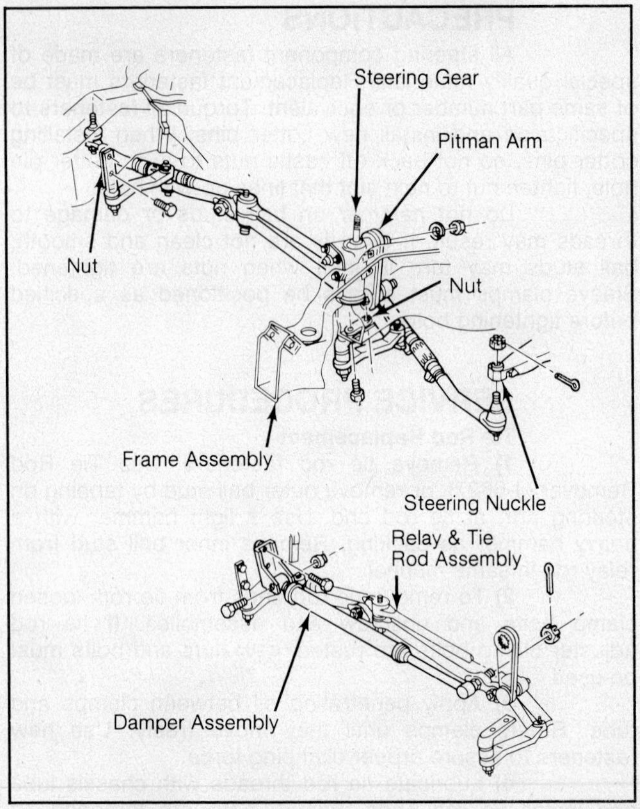

Relay Rod Replacement

1) Remove inner ends of tie rods from relay rod. Remove nuts from pitman arm and idler arm ball studs at relay rod. Remove relay rod from pitman and idler arms by tapping on relay rod ball stud bosses.

2) Use a light hammer with heavy hammer as a backing. Remove relay rod. To install, reverse removal procedure. Check ball studs and nuts for clean and smooth threads. Check stud seals and replace if necessary. Torque nuts and install new cotter pins.

Fig. 7: Tie Rod Clamp Position

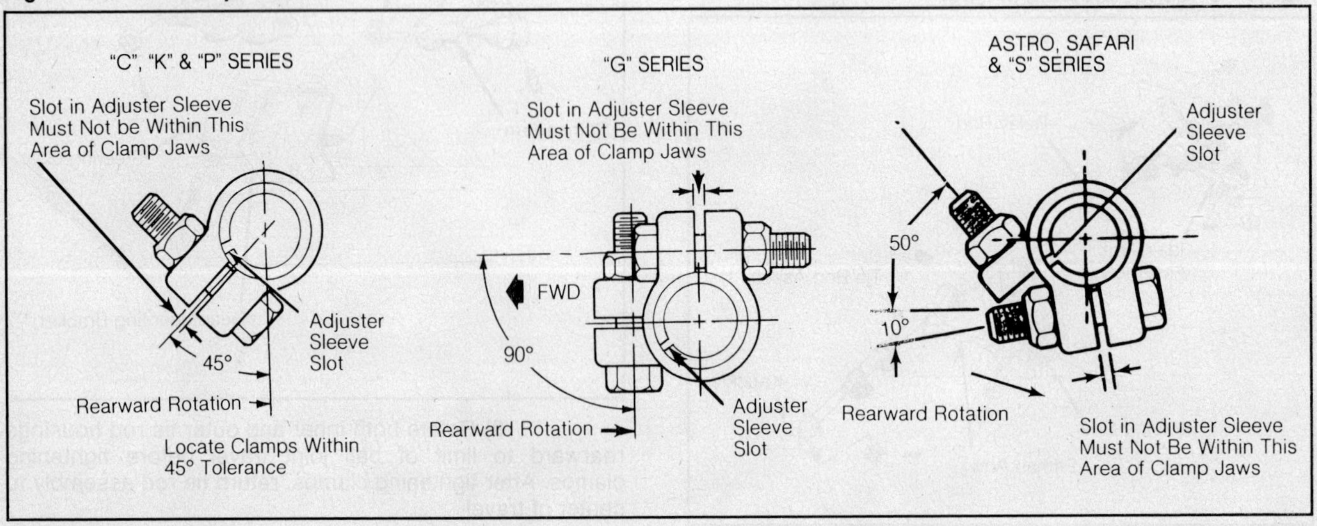

GENERAL MOTORS (Cont.)

Idler Arm Replacement

1) Place vehicle on hoist. Remove fasteners from ball stud and relay rod. Remove ball stud from relay rod by tapping on relay rod boss with a light hammer (use heavy hammer as a backing). Remove idler arm-to-frame bolts and remove idler arm assembly.

NOTE: Idler arm assembly should always be replaced if an up and down force of 25 lbs. (11 kg), applied at relay rod end of idler arm, produces a lash of more than 1/8" (3 mm) in straight-ahead position.

2) Ensure that threads on studs and nuts are clean and smooth. Check ball stud seals and replace if necessary. To install, reverse removal procedure.

3) Install connecting rod. Ensure long end of rod is toward pitman arm. Check for proper alignment of connecting rod clamps. *See Figs. 7 and 8* .

Fig. 8: Tie Rod Clamp Tightness

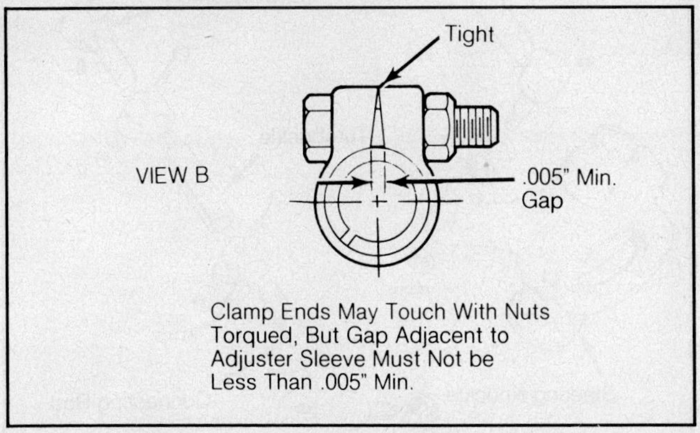
Tight
VIEW B
.005" Min. Gap
Clamp Ends May Touch With Nuts Torqued, But Gap Adjacent to Adjuster Sleeve Must Not be Less Than .005" Min.

Pitman Arm Replacement

1) Remove cotter pin from pitman arm ball stud and remove nut. Remove pitman arm or relay rod from ball stud by tapping on side of rod or arm (in which stud mounts) with a hammer while using heavier hammer as a backing.

2) Remove pitman arm nut from shaft or clamp bolt from pitman arm, and index mark arm-to-shaft position. Remove pitman arm from shaft using Puller (J-6632). To install, reverse removal procedure.

3) If a clamp-type pitman arm is used, spread pitman arm with a wedge just enough to slip arm onto shaft by hand pressure. Do not hammer on or damage to steering gear may result. Be sure to reinstall the hardened steel washer before installing nut.

Steering Connecting Rod Replacement (4WD Models)

1) Remove cotter pins from ball studs and remove castle nuts. Remove ball studs from steering arm and pitman arm boss by tapping with a light hammer while using a heavy hammer as a backing.

2) To install, reverse removal procedure. Ensure threads on studs and nuts are clean and smooth. Check ball stud seals and replace if necessary.

3) Install connecting rod on steering components, tighten nuts and install new cotter pins. Ensure connecting rod clamps are properly aligned. *See Fig. 7.*

TIGHTENING SPECIFICATIONS

Application	Ft. Lbs. (N.m)
Idler Arm Mounting Bolt	30 (41)
Idler Arm-to-Relay Rod Nut	[1] 66 (90)
Pitman Arm-to-Pitman Shaft Nut	
Astro & Safari	177 (240)
"C" & "G" Series	192 (260)
"K" Series	92 (125)
"P" Series	132 (180)
Pitman Arm-to-Relay Rod Nut	[1] 66 (90)
Steering Connecting Rod Clamps	40 (54)
Steering Connecting Rod Nut	
"K" Series	[2] 70 (95)
Tie Rod Ball Stud Nuts [3]	
Astro & Safari	130 (40)
All Others	50 (68)
Tie Rod Clamps	
Astro & Safari	13 (18)
"S" Series	16 (22)
All Others	22 (30)

[1] – Seat the taper using a free-spinning nut, then install lock nut.

[2] – If necessary, apply up to 100 ft. lbs. (136 N.m) of torque to advance nut to align with cotter pin hole.

[3] – If necessary, advance nut to align cotter pin with hole.

JEEP

SERVICE PROCEDURES

Tie Rod Replacement

1) Remove cotter pins and retaining nuts at both ends of tie rod and from end of connecting rod where it attaches to tie rod. Disconnect steering damper push rod at tie rod bracket. Remove tie rod ends from steering arms and connecting rod using a puller or expansion fork.

2) To install, attach tie rod ends to steering arms. Tighten nuts and install new cotter pins. Attach connecting rod, tighten nuts, and install new cotter pin. Attach steering damper. Check and adjust toe-in. See WHEEL ALIGNMENT SPECIFICATIONS & PROCEDURES article in WHEEL ALIGNMENT section.

Steering Damper Replacement (All Models)

1) With front wheels in straight-ahead position, remove lock nut securing damper to bracket on tie plate. Lift damper off stud. Remove lock nut securing push rod end to tie rod bracket and remove damper assembly.

2) To install, install rubber bushings in damper eyelets, then secure eyelet at push rod end to stud on tie rod bracket with attaching hardware. Install rubber bushings in damper body eyelet.

3) Extend push rod by pulling back on damper body until eyelet can be located on, and secured to, stud on damper bracket. Tighten all lock nuts.

Steering Linkage

JEEP (Cont.)

Fig. 1: Disassembled View of Steering Linkage

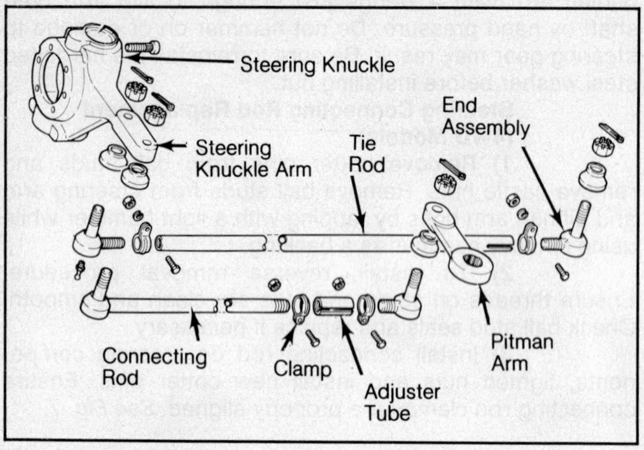

CJ7 and Scrambler are shown.

Fig. 2: Steering Damper Assembly

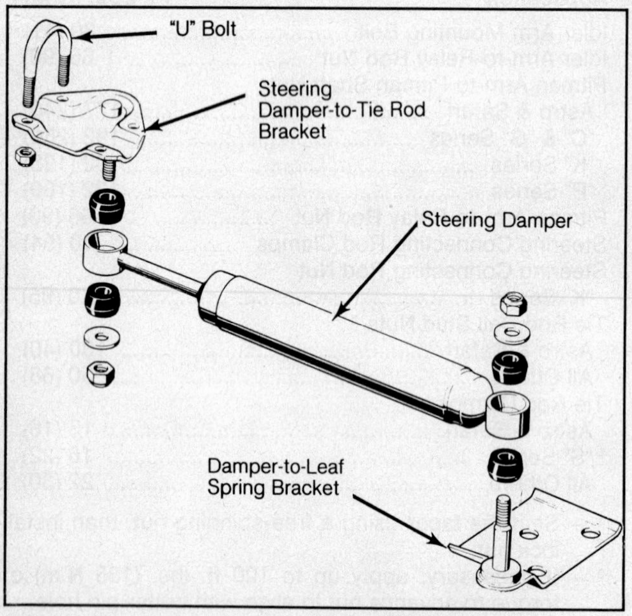

Grand Wagoneer and Trucks are shown.

Fig. 3: Steering Damper Assembly

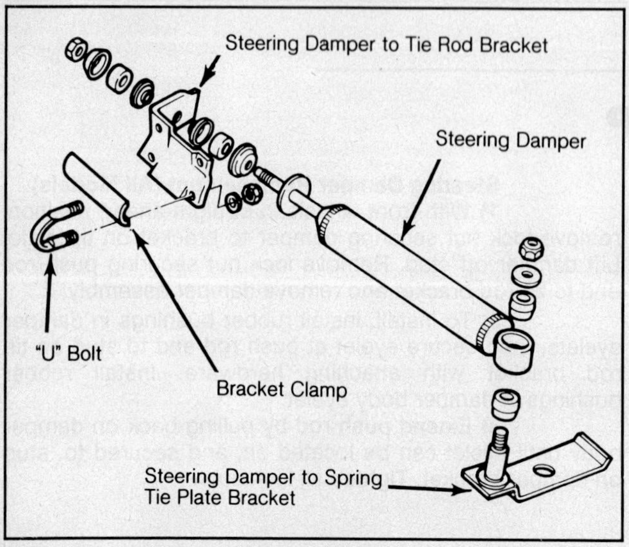

CJ7 and Scrambler models are shown.

Fig. 4: Disassembled View of Steering Linkage

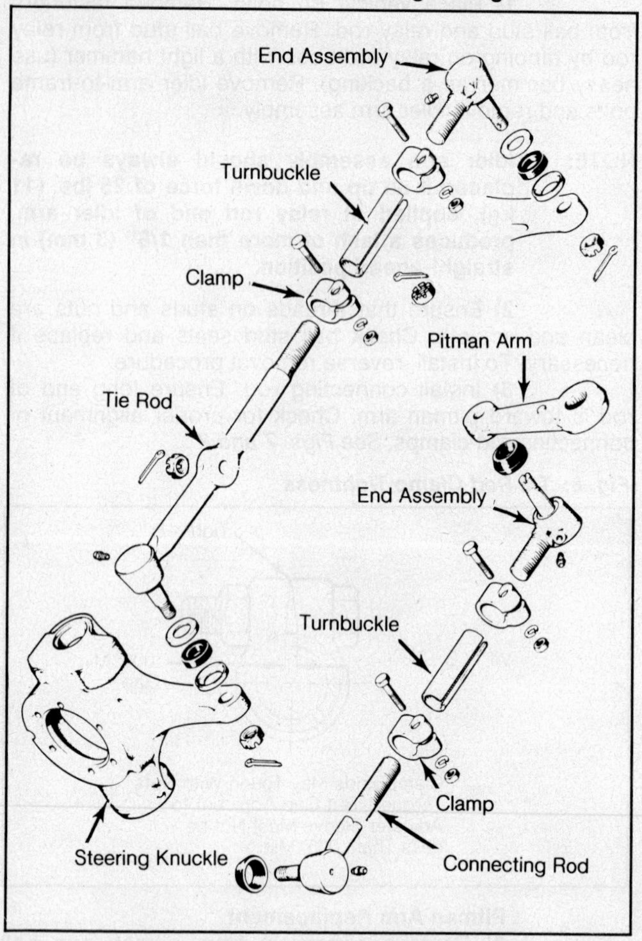

Grand Wagoneer and Trucks are shown.

Connecting Rod Replacement

1) Remove cotter pins and nuts from both ends of connecting rod, then remove rod. When installing, ensure wheels are in straight-ahead position and steering arm is parallel to center line of vehicle.

2) Ensure steering gear arm is properly indexed. Align marks on steering arm and gear shaft at center of high point. Install connecting rod.

TIGHTENING SPECIFICATIONS

Application	Ft.Lbs. (N.m)
Connecting Rod Clamp Bolt	
CJ7 & Scrambler	15 (20)
All Others	30 (41)
Connecting Rod 5/8"	
(To Castellated Nut Slot)	70 (95) Min.
Connecting Rod 9/16"	
(To Castellated Nut Slot)	60 (82) Min.
Pitman Arm-to-Shaft	185 (251)
Steering Damper Lock Nut	
CJ7 & Scrambler	22 (30)
All Others	35 (47)
Tie Rod Clamp Bolt	
CJ7 & Scramblers	12 (16)
All Others	30 (41)
Tie Rod Stud Nuts	
CJ7 & Scrambler	40 Min. (54)
Cherokee & Wagoneer	35 (47)
Grand Wagoneer & Trucks	60 (82)

Manual Steering Gears

CHRYSLER CORP. RACK & PINION

FWD Vans

DESCRIPTION

Rack and pinion-type gear mounts on front frame crossmember, behind drive axle. Lock-to-lock travel is four turns. Gear is permanently lubricated and cannot be adjusted or serviced. Service is limited to replacement of outer tie rod ends or bellows-type oil seal boots. If steering gear is defective, replace as an assembly.

REMOVAL & INSTALLATION

OUTER TIE ROD END

Removal

Loosen jam nut. Remove castle nut and cotter pin. Disconnect tie rod end from steering knuckle. Remove tie rod end by unscrewing from inner rod.

Installation

To install, reverse removal procedure. Set toe-in. See WHEEL ALIGNMENT SPECIFICATIONS & PROCEDURES article in WHEEL ALIGNMENT section.

BOOT SEAL

Removal

With outer tie rod end removed, remove jam nut. Remove boot outer clamp. Cut and discard boot inner clamp. Index mark breather tube location before removing boot. Lift boot inner lip from groove with a small screwdriver and remove boot.

Installation

To install, reverse removal procedure. Use silicone lubricant on boot lips.

STEERING GEAR

Removal

1) Remove front wheels and separate tie rod ends from steering knuckles. Remove steering column assembly. See STEERING COLUMNS article in this section. Drive coupling pin from pinion shaft universal joint. Remove anti-rotational link from crossmember and diverter valve bracket from left side of crossmember.

2) Remove front crossmember attaching bolts. Using a transmission jack, lower crossmember so steering gear can be removed from crossmember. Remove splash shields and boot seal shields. Remove bolts attaching gear to crossmember. From left side of vehicle, remove gear and pinion shaft universal joint.

Installation

To install, reverse removal procedure. Ensure master serrations are in line. Tighten mounting bolts and set toe-in. See WHEEL ALIGNMENT SPECIFICATIONS & PROCEDURES article in WHEEL ALIGNMENT section.

Fig. 1: Steering Gear and Mounting Bracket

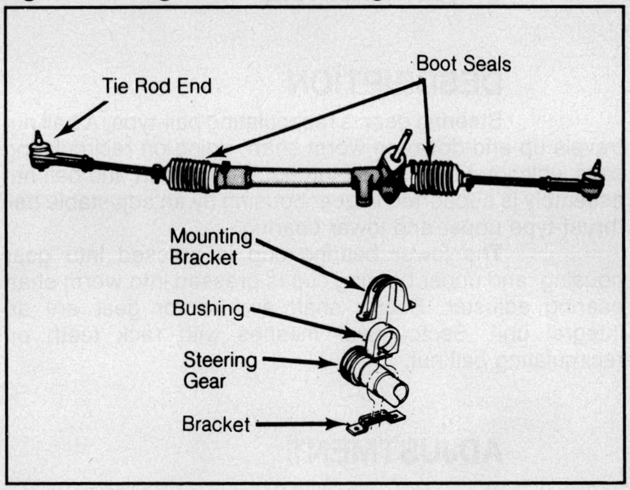

TIGHTENING SPECIFICATIONS

Application	Ft. Lbs. (N.m)
Tie Rod Ends	35 (47)
Tie Rod Jam Nuts	55 (75)
Mounting Bracket Bolts	21 (28)

Manual Steering Gears

CHRYSLER RECIRCULATING BALL

Chrysler Corp. Vans

DESCRIPTION

Steering gear is recirculating ball-type. A ball nut travels up and down on worm shaft, riding on recirculating balls which act as a screw thread. Worm shaft and ball nut assembly is supported in gear housing by an adjustable ball thrust-type upper and lower bearing.

The lower bearing cup is pressed into gear housing, and upper bearing cup is pressed into worm shaft bearing adjuster. Sector shaft and sector gear are an integral unit. Sector gear meshes with rack teeth on recirculating ball nut.

ADJUSTMENT

WORM BEARING PRELOAD

1) Disconnect steering gear arm from sector shaft with Gear Arm Remover (C-4150). Remove horn pad from steering wheel. Loosen sector shaft adjusting screw lock nut 2 turns.

2) Turn steering wheel 2 complete turns from straight-ahead position. Place torque wrench on steering shaft nut. Rotate steering shaft at least 1 turn toward straight-ahead position. While turning note rotating torque.

3) If reading is not within specifications, loosen adjuster lock nut. Use Spanner Wrench (C-3884) to turn adjuster clockwise to increase preload, or counterclockwise to decrease preload. Hold adjuster from turning and tighten lock nut. Retest worm bearing preload.

BALL NUT RACK & SECTOR MESH

1) With worm bearing preload properly adjusted, turn steering wheel gently from one stop to other, counting number of turns. Turn steering back half-way to center position.

2) Turn sector shaft adjusting screw clockwise to remove lash between ball nut rack and sector gear teeth, then torque adjusting screw lock nut. Turn steering wheel about 1/4 turn away from center position.

3) Measure torque required to rotate steering wheel through high spot at center position. See ADJUSTMENT SPECIFICATIONS table. If reading is not to specifications, readjust sector shaft adjusting screw to obtain proper torque reading.

4) Place front wheels in straight-ahead position. With steering gear and steering wheel centered, install steering arm on sector and torque retaining nut.

REMOVAL & INSTALLATION

NOTE: **Steering column must be completely detached from floor and instrument panel before removing steering gear.**

Removal

Disconnect battery negative cable. Remove steering column. From under vehicle remove steering arm retaining nut and lock washer. Remove steering arm with Gear Arm Remover (C-4150). Remove steering gear-to-frame retaining nuts and remove gear.

Fig. 1: Steering Gear Adjustment Locations

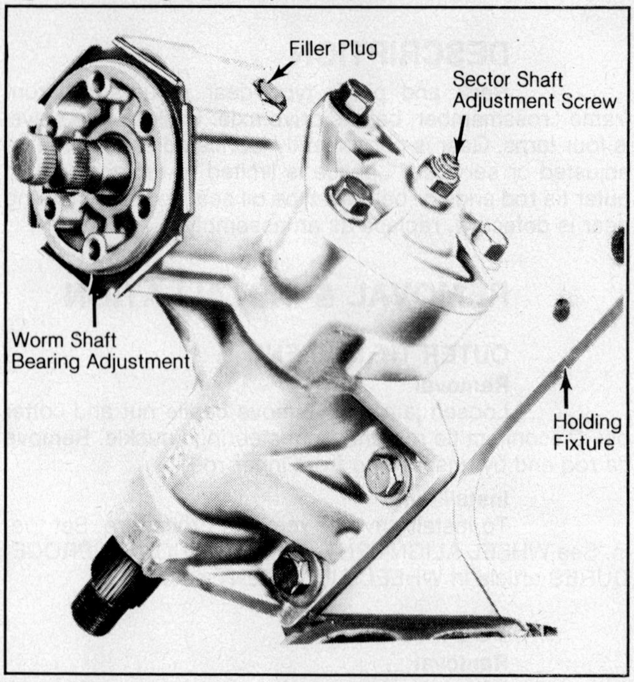

Worm bearing preload must be adjusted before sector shaft adjustment.

Installation

1) Position gear on frame and install retaining nuts. Rotate worm shaft by hand and center sector shaft to mid-point of its travel. Align master serrations on sector shaft with splines in steering arm.

2) Install steering arm lock washer and nut and tighten. Install steering column. Connect battery negative cable.

OVERHAUL

STEERING GEAR ASSEMBLY

NOTE: **Thoroughly clean entire outside surface of steering gear before disassembly to avoid contaminating worm shaft and ball nut assembly with dirt.**

Disassembly

1) Loosen sector shaft adjusting screw lock nut and back out screw 2 turns. Remove sector shaft oil seal. Position worm shaft in straight-ahead position.

2) Remove sector shaft cover bolts and remove sector shaft. Remove lock nut from sector shaft adjusting screw and remove screw. Slide adjustment screw and shim from slot in end of sector shaft.

3) Loosen worm shaft bearing adjuster lock nut with a soft drift punch and remove lock nut. Hold worm shaft from turning while unscrewing adjuster. Slide worm shaft adjuster off shaft.

NOTE: **Handle adjuster carefully to avoid damaging threads. Be sure that ball nut does not run down to either end of worm shaft as ball guide ends can be damaged.**

4) Carefully remove worm and ball nut assembly. Remove sector shaft needle bearing by placing gear

Manual Steering Gears

CHRYSLER RECIRCULATING BALL (Cont.)

housing in an arbor press and insert (C-3786) in lower end of housing. Press both bearings through housing.

5) Sector shaft cover assembly, including a needle bearing and bushing, is serviced as an assembly. Remove worm shaft oil seal with a blunt punch. Remove worm shaft spacer and upper bearing cup in same manner, being careful not to cock bearing cup.

6) Remove lower bearing cup by positioning locking head jaws of Bearing Cup Remover (C-3868) behind bearing cup and expanding remover head. Withdraw bearing cup by turning remover screw nut in a clockwise direction while holding center screw.

Cleaning and Inspection

1) Wash all parts in clean solvent and dry with compressed air. Test operation of ball nut assembly on worm shaft. If it does not travel smoothly or there is roughness, assembly must be replaced.

2) Inspect sector shaft for wear and check fit of shaft in housing bearings. DO NOT screw worm shaft adjuster into housing without lubrication, or when threads are dirty or damaged. Replace sector shaft and worm shaft oil seals whenever unit is disassembled.

Reassembly

1) Press lower sector shaft bearing into housing to 1/2" below end of bore. Press upper needle bearing into housing bore so it is flush with end of bore surface.

2) Press worm shaft bearing cup and spacer into adjuster nut. Install worm shaft oil seal in adjuster with metal retainer UP. Drive seal into place with sleeve so seal is slightly below end of bore in adjuster.

3) Lubricate all moving parts and seals with steering gear lubricant. Clamp housing in vise with worm bearing adjuster opening UP. Place a thrust bearing in lower cup in housing.

4) Hold ball nut from turning and insert worm shaft and ball nut assembly into housing with end of worm resting in thrust bearing. Place upper thrust bearing on worm shaft. Lubricate threads on adjuster and threads in housing.

5) Place tape over worm shaft splines and slide adjuster assembly over shaft. Thread adjuster into housing torque adjuster nut to 50 ft. lbs. (68 N.m) while rotating wormshaft. Loosen adjuster so no bearing preload exists.

6) Adjust worm shaft bearing preload to 1-4.5 INCH lbs. (.1-.5 N.m). Tighten bearing adjuster lock nut and retest preload. Pack worm shaft cavities in housing with steering gear lubricant. Slide sector shaft adjusting screw and shim into slot in end of shaft.

7) Sector shaft adjusting screw must have .004" (.102 mm) maximun end play. If clearance is not within specifications, shims are available in 3 thicknesses. Start sector shaft and adjuster screw into bearing housing cover.

8) Using a screwdriver through hole in cover, turn screw counterclockwise to pull shaft into cover. Install adjusting screw lock nut, but do not tighten. Rotate worm shaft to centralize ball nut. Place new cover gasket on housing cover.

9) Lubricate sector shaft and sector teeth and carefully install shaft and cover assembly into housing. Ensure that some lash exists between sector shaft teeth and ball nut rack. Install and tighten cover bolts.

10) Press sector shaft seal into gear housing with lip of seal facing housing. Adjust worm bearing preload. Adjust ball nut rack and sector mesh.

SECTOR SHAFT OIL SEAL REPLACEMENT

1) Sector shaft oil seal can be replaced with steering gear in vehicle or on bench. If replacement is done in vehicle, clean exposed portion of sector shaft before replacing oil seal.

2) Remove steering gear arm retaining nut and lock washer. Remove steering gear arm. Replace oil seal using Seal Installer (C-3880). Install steering arm and torque nut.

ADJUSTMENT SPECIFICATIONS

Application	INCH Lbs. (N.m)
Ball Nut Rack & Sector Mesh	
Gear in Vehicle	8.2-11.3 (.9-1.3)
Gear Removed From Vehicle	7.5-11.5 (.8-1.3)
Worm Bearing Preload	1.0-4.5 (.1-.5)

TIGHTENING SPECIFICATIONS

Application	Ft. Lbs. (N.m)
Sector Shaft Adj. Screw Lock Nut	35 (48)
Steering Arm Retaining Nut	175 (238)
Housing Cover Bolts	25 (34)
Steering Gear-to-Frame Bolts	100 (136)

Manual Steering Gears

FORD RACK & PINION

Aerostar

DESCRIPTION

Variable ratio manual steering gear is standard on Aerostar. Varying ratios are acheived by using a curved pinion tooth surface, and rack spacing that varies as wheel is turned from "on center" to "lock" positions.

A fast ratio ("on center" position) provides quick response for highway driving and lane changes. A slow ratio (between "on center" and "stop" positions) reduces steering effort while cornering and parking.

REMOVAL & INSTALLATION

OUTER TIE ROD END

Removal

1) Place front wheels in straight-ahead position. Remove and discard cotter pin securing castle nut to tie rod stud. Remove castle nut. Separate tie rod end from spindle arm using Tie Rod End Remover (64P-3590-F).

2) Index mark relative position of tie rod end to jam nuts and exposed threads. Loosen jam nut, and count number of turns required to remove tie rod end.

Installation

To install, position tie rod end on inner ball joint assembly. Tighten jam nut. Place front wheels in straight-ahead position. Insert tie rod stud through spindle arm. Install and tighten castle nuts. Install new cotter pin.

NOTE: Ensure tie rod studs are seated properly in taper of spindle arm.

BOOT

Removal

1) Remove steering gear. Clean exterior of gear. Place steering gear in soft-jawed vise, gripping it near center. Rotate pinion shaft to align White index mark on steering gear housing with mark on pinion shaft ("on center" position).

2) Index mark position of tie rod end to jam nuts and exposed threads. Loosen jam nut, and count number of turns required to remove tie rod end. Remove boot retaining clamps and boot.

Installation

Apply silicone gasket sealer to boot inner contact area of gear housing. Slide boot over inner ball joint assembly. Install new clamp at each end of boot.

STEERING GEAR

Removal

Remove tie rod ends from spindle arms. Support steering gear assembly. Remove gear assembly mounting bracket nuts, bolts and washers. Remove steering gear. If necessary, remove front and rear insulators from steering gear housing.

Installation

If removed, install front and rear insulators. Position steering gear on crossmember. Ensure that steering gear, steering wheel and front wheels are in straight-ahead position. To complete installation, reverse removal procedure.

Fig. 1: Exploded View of Steering Gear and Housing

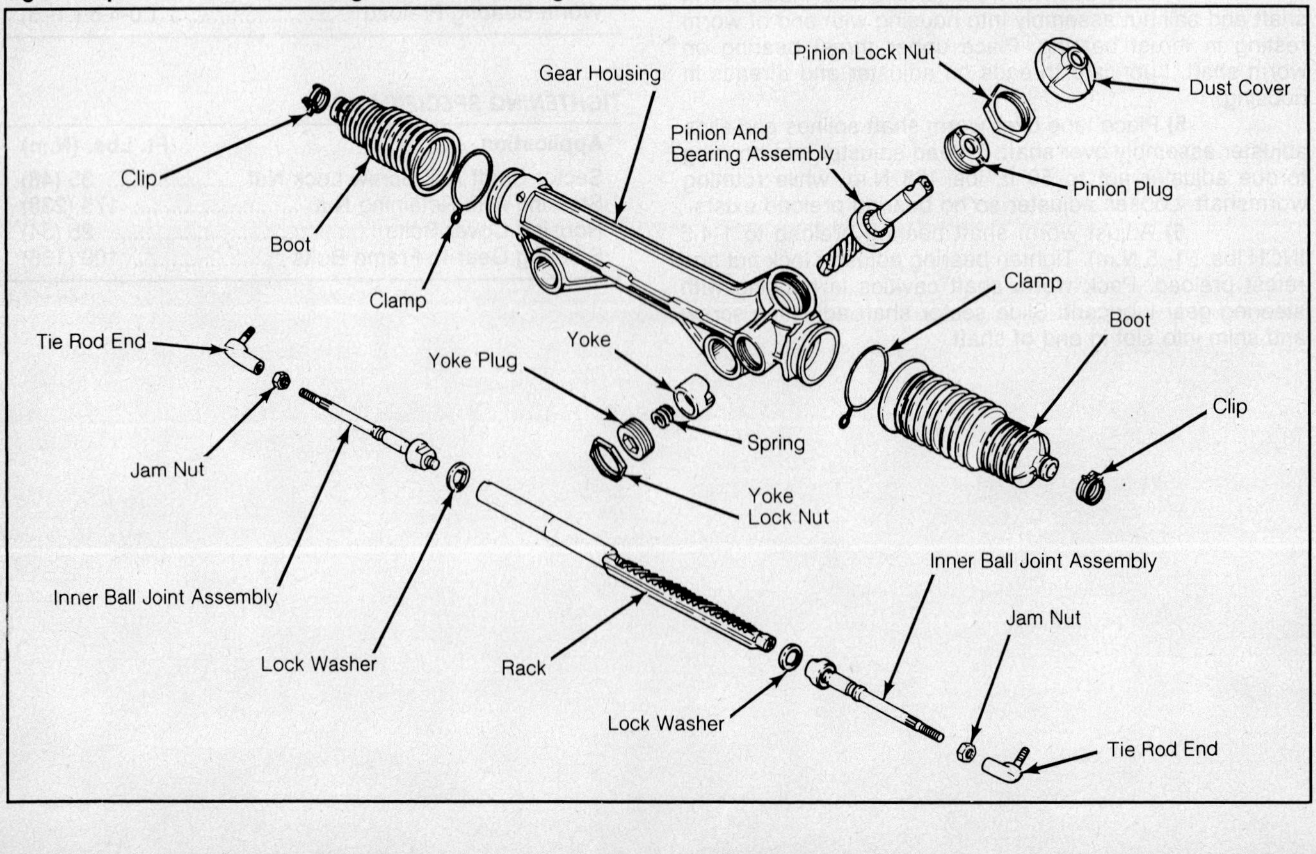

Manual Steering Gears

FORD RACK & PINION (Cont.)

OVERHAUL

STEERING GEAR

NOTE: **Clean exterior of steering gear before disassembly to avoid contaminating rack and pinion assembly with dirt.**

Disassembly

1) Remove steering gear from vehicle. Manually rotate pinion shaft from left lock to right lock position. Record number of pinion shaft rotations. Divide number of rotations by 2. This is "on center" position.

2) Turn pinion shaft to left lock position. Turn pinion shaft to "on center" position by rotating shaft number of turns required. White index marks on steering gear housing and pinion shaft should now be aligned.

3) Using Yoke and Pinion Plug Wrench (T85T-3504-AH), hold yoke plug in position, and remove yoke lock nut using Yoke and Pinion Lock Nut Wrench (T74P-3504-U). *See Fig. 2.*

Fig. 2: Removing Yoke Plug and Yoke Lock Nut

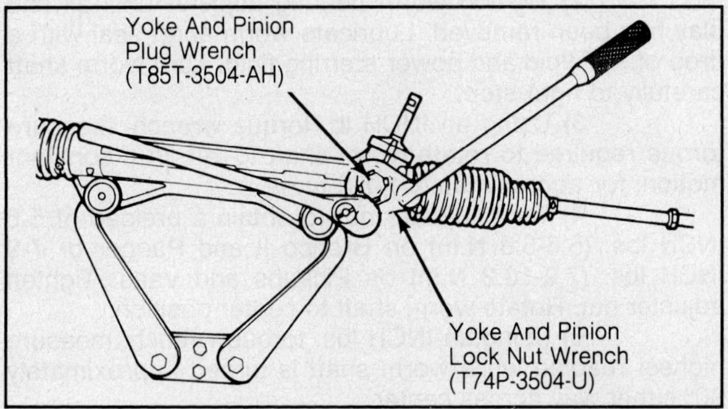

4) Remove yoke plug. Remove spring from yoke. Gently remove yoke from housing using external snap ring pliers. Remove pinion shaft dust cover.

5) Using yoke and pinion plug wrench, hold pinion plug in position. Remove pinion plug lock nut using yoke and pinion lock nut wrench. Remove pinion and bearing assembly from housing.

Cleaning & Inspection

Examine parts for wear and contamination. Inspect yoke to ensure that insert is seated flush with yoke body. If pinion teeth are pitted or worn, or if upper bearing is damaged or binding, replace entire steering gear assembly as a unit.

Reassembly

1) Coat pinion teeth and upper bearing with grease. Install pinion and bearing assembly into housing. Ensure pinion is seated in lower bearing. Slide pinion plug and seal assembly over pinion shaft.

2) Hand start pinion plug and seal into housing. Tighten pinion plug by hand to apply a light bearing preload. Apply Loctite to exposed threads of pinion plug. Hand start, and tighten pinion plug lock nut.

3) Pack pinion dust cover with grease and install over pinion shaft. Inspect yoke to ensure that insert is seated flush with yoke body. Coat plastic yoke insert and rack bar sliding surface with grease.

4) Install yoke in housing bore against "Y" section of rack. Coat both ends of yoke spring and install. Hand start yoke plug into housing, and tighten to 65 INCH lbs. (7.35 N.m).

5) Locate triangle symbol and bar marking on yoke plug. *See Fig. 3.* Scribe a mark on gear housing next to triangle symbol. Turn yoke plug counterclockwise to line up bar marking with scribed line on gear housing (about 1/10 of a turn).

Fig. 3: Setting Yoke Plug Preload

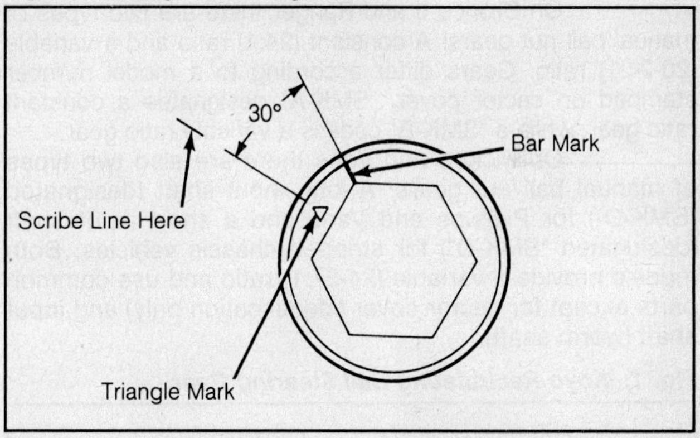

6) Apply Loctite to exposed threads of yoke plug. Hand start yoke plug lock nut. While holding yoke plug in position (using yoke and pinion plug wrench), tighten yoke lock nut (using yoke and pinion lock nut wrench).

7) Verify that bar marking (on yoke plug) and scribed mark (on steering gear housing) are still aligned. Install steering gear assembly.

TIGHTENING SPECIFICATIONS

Application	Ft. Lbs. (N.m)
Inner Ball Joint Assembly	50-65 (68-88)
Mounting Bracket Nut & Bolt	65-90 (80-122)
Tie Rod End Castle Nut	[1] 52-73 (70-100)
Tie Rod Jam Nut	36-50 (48-68)
Yoke Plug Lock Nut	43-58 (58-78)
	INCH Lbs. (N.m)
Pinion Plug	[2]
Yoke Plug	65 (7.35)

[1] – Stake lock washer after tightening.

[2] – Hand tighten to apply a light bearing preload.

Manual Steering Gears

KOYO RECIRCULATING BALL

Ford (Bronco II, "F" Series 2WD Pickup, Ranger & Van)

DESCRIPTION & OPERATION

The steering gear is worm and recirulating ball-type. A ball nut is used which has threads that mate to threads of worm shaft via continuous rows of ball bearings. As steering wheel is rotated, worm shaft rotates, causing ball nut to move up or down worm shaft.

The gear teeth on ball nut are meshed with gear teeth on sector shaft. Thus, movement of ball nut causes sector shaft to rotate and swing pitman arm.

Proper mesh engagement between sector and ball nut is obtained by an adjusting screw which moves sector shaft axially. Worm thrust bearing adjuster can be turned to provide proper preloading of worm thrust bearings.

On Bronco II and Ranger there are two types of manual ball nut gears: A constant (24:1) ratio and a variable (20-24:1) ratio. Gears differ according to a model number stamped on sector cover. "SMK-A" designates a constant ratio gear, while a "SMK-B" code is a variable ratio gear.

On Pickup and Vans there are also two types of manual ball nut gears: A long input shaft (designated "SMK-C") for Pickups and Vans and a short input shaft (designated "SMK-D") for stripped chassis vehicles. Both models provide a variable (24-27:1) ratio and use common parts except for sector cover (identification only) and input shaft (worm shaft).

Fig. 1: Koyo Recirulating Ball Steering Gear

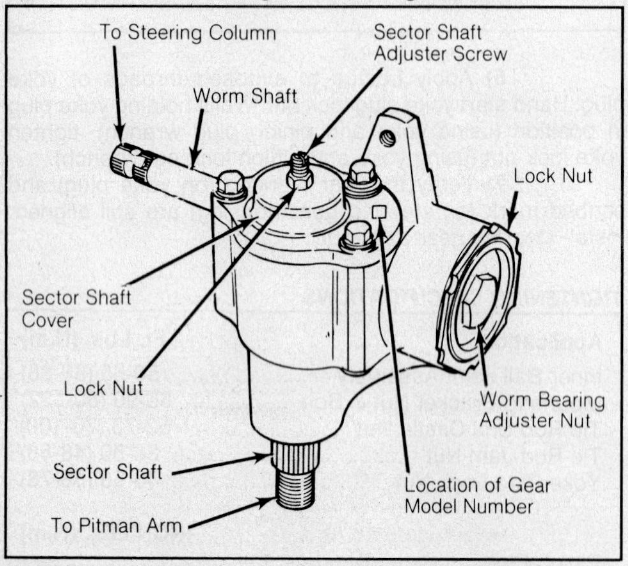

Bronco II and Ranger are shown, Pickup and Van are similar.

ADJUSTMENTS

PRELIMINARY

1) Worm bearing preload must be adjusted before meshload. While meshload may be adjusted with steering gear installed, worm preload cannot be adjusted in vehicle.

2) Disconnect pitman arm at ball stud. Lubricate worm shaft seal with a drop of A/T fluid. Remove horn pad. Turn steering wheel slowly to one stop.

3) Measure amount of torque required to rotate steering wheel at a constant speed for approximately 1 1/2 turns. If preload is not within 2-6 INCH lbs. (2.2-6.8 N.m) on Bronco II and Ranger or 5-9 INCH lbs. (6.0-10.0 N.m) on Pickups and Vans, readjust preload.

4) If preload is within specifications, check meshload. Measure highest torque required to rotate steering wheel back and forth approximately 90° either way across center position.

5) Meshload must be 4-10 INCH lbs. (4.5-11.3 N.m) on Bronco II and Ranger or 9-14 INCH lbs. (10.2-15.8 N.m) on Pickups and Vans. Meshload must also be at least 2 INCH lbs. (2.3 N.m) over preload. Meshload can be adjusted in vehicle.

WORM BEARING PRELOAD & MESHLOAD

1) Remove steering gear from vehicle. See REMOVAL & INSTALLATION in this article. Tighten sector cover bolts to 40 ft. lbs. (53 N.m). Loosen preload adjuster locknut and screw.

2) Tighten worm bearing adjuster until all end play has been removed. Lubricate worm shaft seal with a drop of A/T fluid and power sterring fluid. Turn worm shaft carefully to right stop.

3) Using an INCH lb. torque wrench, measure torque required to rotate worm shaft to left, in a constant motion, for approximately 1 1/2 turns.

4) Turn adjuster nut to obtain a preload of 5-6 INCH lbs. (5.6-6.8 N.m) on Bronco II and Ranger or 7-9 INCH lbs. (7.9-10.2 N.m) on Pickups and Vans. Tighten adjuster nut. Rotate worm shaft to center position.

5) Using an INCH lbs. torque wrench, measure highest reading while worm shaft is turned approximately 90° either way across center.

6) If highest reading is not within 9-10 INCH lbs. (10.2-11.3 N.m) on Bronco II and Ranger or 12-14 INCH lbs. (136-158 N.m) on Pickups and Vans, turn sector shaft adjusting screw as required.

7) Meshload must be at least 4 INCH lbs. (4.5 N.m) over preload. Hold sector shaft adjusting screw and torque locknut to 25 ft. lbs. (34 N.m).

REMOVAL & INSTALLATION

STEERING GEAR

Removal

1) Disengage flex coupling shield from steering gear input shield and slide it up intermediate shaft. Remove flex coupling-to-steering gear bolt.

2) Remove steering gear input shaft shield. Remove pitman arm nut and washer. Remove pitman arm using Puller (T64P-3590-F). Remove steering gear-to-frame attaching bolts and remove gear.

Installation

1) Center worm shaft in steering gear. Ensure that flat on gear input shaft is facing straight up and aligns with flat on flex coupling. Install steering gear to side rail and tighten bolts.

2) Align two blocked teeth on pitman arm with four missing teeth on sector shaft. Install nut and tighten. Install flex coupling-to-steering gear bolt. Snap flex coupling shield to steering gear input shaft shield.

Manual Steering Gears

KOYO RECIRCULATING BALL (Cont.)

Fig. 2: Exploded View of Steering Gear

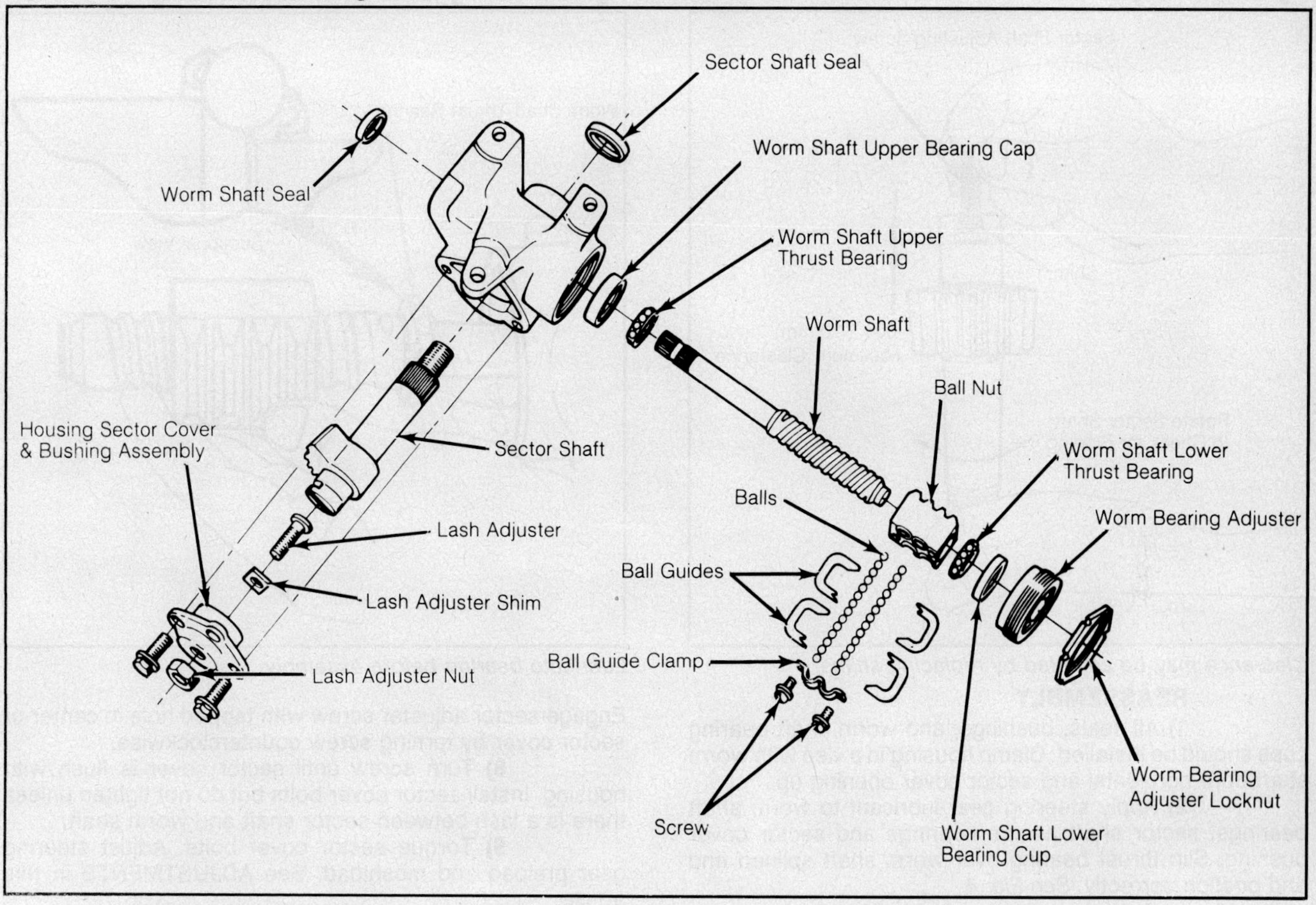

OVERHAUL

DISASSEMBLY

1) Place steering gear in a vise, clamping onto one mounting tab or a holding fixture. Worm shaft should be in a horizontal position, and centered in steering box.

2) Remove sector shaft cover bolts. Lift sector shaft and cover out of gear. Remove cover from shaft by turning screw clockwise. Keep shim with screw.

3) Loosen lock nut on worm shaft adjuster with Lock Nut Wrench (T83T-3504-AH), and remove adjuster plug and worm shaft thrust bearing. Pull worm shaft and ball nut assembly from housing.

4) DO NOT allow ball nut to run down to either end of worm shaft as ball guide ends may be damaged. Pry out and discard both sector shaft and worm shaft seals.

NOTE: **Individual parts are not available for service. If worm cannot rotate freely in ball nut, replace entire assembly.**

5) Remove worm shaft adjuster nut bearing cup with a slide hammer. Remove bearing cup from housing using a bearing driver or socket.

6) Sector shaft cover bushing is not serviceable. Entire sector cover assembly is serviced as a unit. Sector shaft needle bearing is serviced only as a unit with housing. DO NOT attempt to remove sector needle assembly.

CLEANING & INSPECTION

1) Wash parts with clean solvent and blow dry with air. Inspect bearings and races for signs or wear. Any parts that show signs of wear should be replaced.

2) Inspect sector shaft fit at side cover bushing. If bushing is worn, a new side cover and bushing assembly should be installed. Check ball nut and worm shaft assembly for wear and straightness.

3) Inspect worm shaft and ball nut for tightness or binding by turning worm shaft in ball nut. If ball nut and worm shaft is defective, replace as an assembly.

4) Inspect housing for cracks or damage. Inspect needle bearing inside housing for defects. Replace housing if any defects are found. Inspect steering gear teeth for chipping, excessive wear and surface breakdown.

5) Check clearance between sector adjusting screw head and bottom of sector shaft "T" slot. If clearance is more than .004" (.10 mm), replace shim to obtain desired clearance.

6) Steering gear lash adjuster shims are available in .078" (1.95 mm), .080" (2.00 mm), .082" (2.05 mm), .084" (2.10 mm) and .086" (2.15 mm). Hold sector adjuster screw and turn sector shaft.

7) Sector must turn freely. If sector does not turn freely, increase "T" slot clearance by replacing shims. *See Fig. 3.*

Manual Steering Gears

KOYO RECIRCULATING BALL (Cont.)

Fig. 3: Checking Sector Shaft "T" Slot Clearance

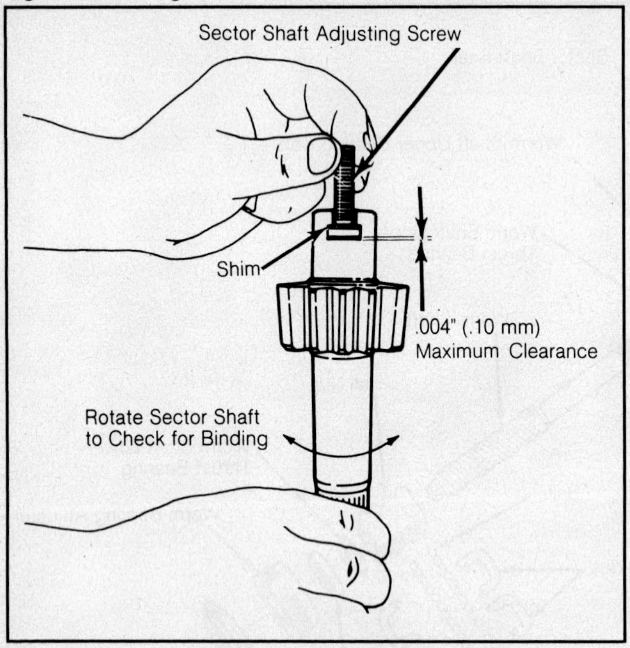

Clearance may be adjusted by replacing shims.

Fig. 4: Installing Worm Shaft Thrust Bearing

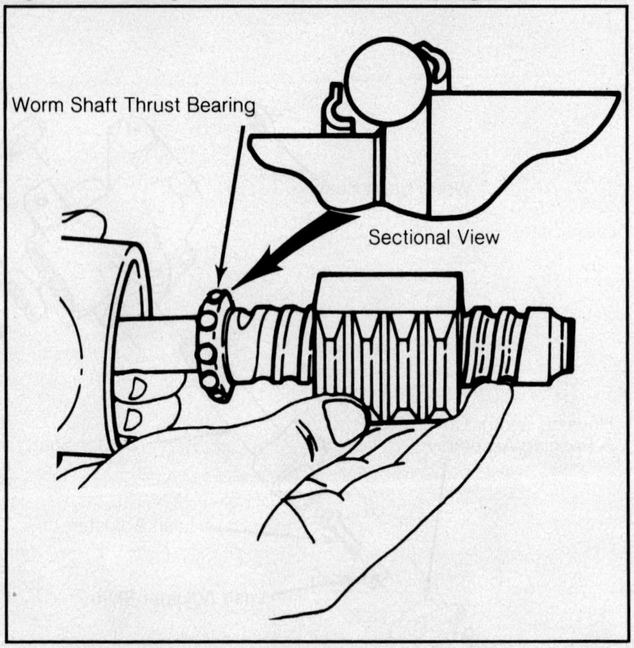

Lubricate bearing before assembly.

REASSEMBLY

1) All seals, bushings, and worm shaft bearing cups should be installed. Clamp housing in a vise with worm shaft bore horizontal and sector cover opening up.

2) Apply steering gear lubricant to worm shaft bearings, sector shaft needle bearings and sector cover bushing. Slip thrust bearing over worm shaft splined end and postion correctly. *See Fig. 4*

3) Install worm shaft nut, splined end first, into housing. *See Fig. 4.* Place remaining worm shaft bearing into adjuster plug bearing cup. Install adjuster plug and lock nut into housing.

4) Screw adjuster nut down until nearly all end play has been removed. Lubricate steering gear by rotating worm shaft until ball nut is end of its travel.

5) Pack as much grease as possible into housing without losing it out sector shaft opening. Rotate ball nut to other end of its travel and pack more grease into housing.

6) Rotate ball nut until it is in center of its travel. Insert sector shaft assembly, containing adjusting screw, into housing. Center tooth of sector gear must engage center rack tooth space in ball nut.

7) Pack housing with grease. Apply a thin bead of sealant to sector shaft cover and install on housing. Engage sector adjuster screw with tapped hole in center of sector cover by turning screw counterclockwise.

8) Turn screw until sector cover is flush with housing. Install sector cover bolts but do not tighten unless there is a lash between sector shaft and worm shaft.

9) Torque sector cover bolts. Adjust steering gear preload and meshload. See ADJUSTMENTS in this article.

TIGHTENING SPECIFICATIONS

Application	Ft. Lbs. (N.m)
Flex Coupling-to-Steering Gear Shaft Bolt	
Bronco II & Ranger	25-35 (34-47)
Pickup & Van	14-21 (18-28)
Pitman Arm-to-Sector Shaft Nut	170-230 (230-312)
Sector Cover Bolts	32-40 (43-54)
Sector Shaft Lock Nut	25 (34)
Steering Gear-to-Frame Bolts	54-66 (74-89)
Worm Bearing Adjuster Nut	166-187 (225-253)

Manual Steering Gears

SAGINAW RECIRCULATING BALL

Chrysler Corp. (Except Vans); General Motors; Jeep

DESCRIPTION & OPERATION

Steering gear is a recirculating ball-type and consists of a ball nut connected to steering worm and in mesh with sector gear. Gears are basically same for all models and service procedures will apply to all gears unless noted otherwise.

Precision finished helical grooves within ball nut match helical grooves in worm. Ball bearings roll within grooves when steering wheel is turned. There are two complete circuits using tubular ball guides to deflect balls away from their helical path at one end of groove and guide them back to other end.

When steering wheel is turned to right, nut moves upward; when turned to left, nut moves downward. Teeth on sector (forged as part of pitman shaft) and ball nut are so designed that a tighter fit exists between two when front wheels are straight ahead.

Proper engagement between sector and ball nut is obtained by adjusting screw, which moves pitman shaft endwise, permitting desired engagement of tapered teeth of ball nut and sector gear. Worm bearing adjuster can be turned to provide proper preloading of upper and lower bearings.

ADJUSTMENT

PRELIMINARY

Worm bearing preload adjustment MUST be made first; then, make over-center preload adjustment. DO NOT reverse order of adjustment. Adjustment of steering gear can be made on or off vehicle in most cases.

When making worm bearing preload adjustment with gear on vehicle, pitman arm must be disconnected or steering linkage disconnected from pitman arm.

The torque wrench can be connected directly to worm shaft (input shaft) or to steering wheel retaining nut (steering column drag is negligible). When making over-center preload adjustment, torque wrench is attached to sector shaft (after removing pitman arm) or steering wheel nut.

WORM BEARING PRELOAD

1) Loosen over-center preload adjuster screw. Tighten worm bearing adjuster until all end play has been removed; then loosen 1/4 turn and tighten lock nut. Turn worm shaft carefully to either stop. Do not jam into stop as damage to gear could result.

2) Rotate worm shaft back from stop about 1/2 turn. Using an INCH lb. torque wrench, measure torque required to keep worm shaft in motion about one revolution.

3) Adjust rotating torque to specifications, using worm bearing adjuster. Tighten lock nut, and recheck turning torque. Adjust as necessary. See OVER-CENTER PRELOAD.

WORM BEARING PRELOAD

Application	INCH Lbs. (N.m)
All Manufacturers	5-8 (.6-.9)

Fig. 1: Adjustment Points for Steering Gear

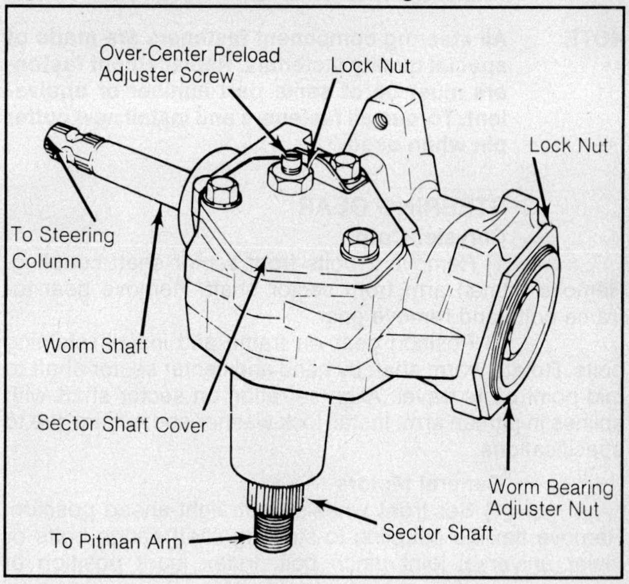

Worm bearing preload must be adjusted before over-center preload.

OVER-CENTER PRELOAD

1) With worm bearing preload adjusted, turn worm shaft slowly from stop-to-stop while counting total number of turns. Turn shaft back to exact center position.

2) Loosen lock nut and turn over-center adjustment screws in until all lash is taken out of shaft. Tighten lock nut. Rotate worm shaft slightly off center (45-90°), then attach an INCH lbs. torque wrench to worm shaft.

3) Using torque wrench as a lever, rotate worm shaft back through center position and record rotating torque. If rotating torque is not to specifications, repeat procedure.

OVER-CENTER ADJUSTMENT INCH LBS. (N.m)

Application	Preload
Chrysler Corp.	14 (1.6)
All Other Manufacturers	16 (1.8)

Fig. 2: Cross Section of Steering Gear

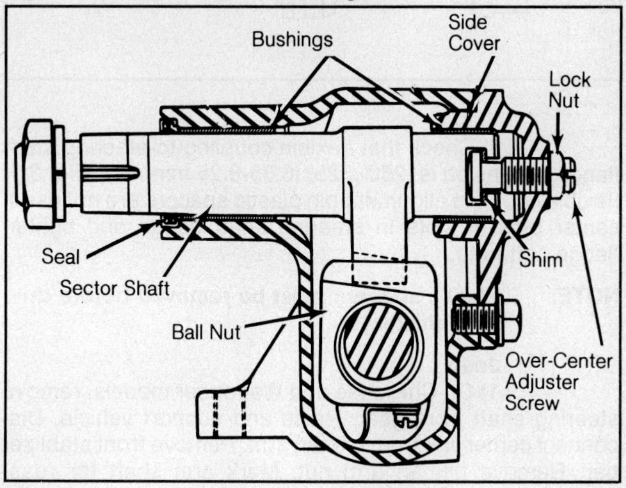

Manual Steering Gears

SAGINAW RECIRCULATING BALL (Cont.)

REMOVAL & INSTALLATION

NOTE: All steering component fasteners are made of special quality materials. Replacement fasteners must be of same part number or equivalent. Torque all fasteners and install new cotter pin when used.

STEERING GEAR

Chrysler Corp.

1) Remove 2 bolts from sector shaft coupling. Remove pitman arm from sector shaft. Remove gear-to-frame bolts and remove gear.

2) Position gear on frame and install retaining bolts. Rotate worm shaft by hand and center sector shaft to mid point of its travel. Align serration on sector shaft with splines in pitman arm. Install lock washer and nut, torque to specifications.

General Motors

1) Set front wheels in straight-ahead position. Remove flexible coupling-to-steering shaft flange bolts or lower universal joint pinch bolt. Index mark position of universal yoke-to-worm shaft.

2) Mark relationship of pitman arm-to-sector shaft. Remove pitman arm using Puller (J-6632). Remove steering gear mounting bolts and remove gear assembly.

3) Install flexible coupling on worm shaft aligning flat on coupling with flat on shaft. Push coupling on shaft until shaft hits shoulder and install pinch bolt. Pinch bolt must pass through shaft undercut.

4) Place gear in position, guiding coupling bolt into steering shaft flange. Install gear-to-frame bolts and torque to specification.

5) If flexible coupling alignment pin plastic spacers are used, ensure they are bottomed on pins, then tighten flange bolt nuts and remove plastic spacers. Spacers aid in centering pins and maintain correct coupling-to-flange dimension.

Fig. 3: Adjusting Flexible Coupling (General Motors)

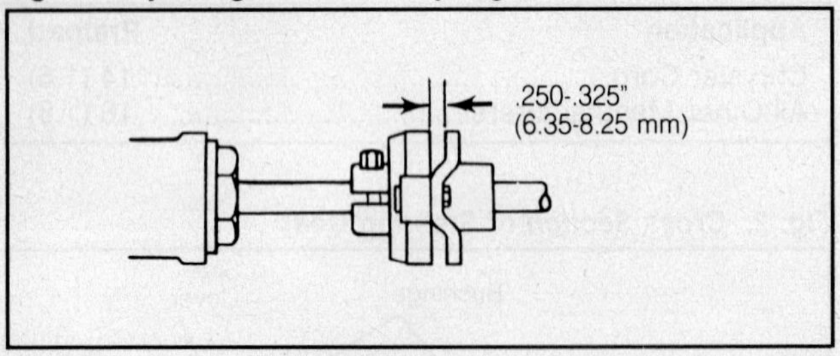

6) Check that flexible coupling-to-steering shaft flange dimension is .250-.325" (6.35-8.25 mm). *See Fig. 3.* If flexible coupling alignment pin plastic spacers are not used, center pins in slots in steering shaft flange and tighten flange bolt nuts.

NOTE: Plastic spacers must be removed before driving vehicle.

Jeep

1) On Cherokee and Wagoneer models, remove steering shaft from gear. Raise and support vehicle. Disconnect center link from pitman arm. Remove front stablizer bar. Remove pitman arm nut. Mark arm shaft for reassembly reference. Using Pitman Arm Remover (J-6632), remove pitman arm. Remove gear.

2) On CJ7 and Scrambler models, remove intermediate shaft-to-worm shaft coupling clamp bolt and disconnect intermediate shaft. Remove pitman arm nut and washer. Pull pitman arm off shaft using Puller (J-6632).

3) Raise left side of vehicle slightly to release tension from left front spring. Place safety stand under frame. Remove bolts securing steering gear lower bracket to frame. Remove bolts securing steering gear upper bracket to crossmember. Remove steering gear from vehicle.

4) On Grand Wagoneer and Trucks, remove intermediate shaft-to-worm shaft coupling clamp bolt and disconnect intermediate shaft. Remove pitman arm nut and washer. Pull pitman arm off shaft using Puller (J-6632). Remove steering gear-to-frame rail bolts and remove steering gear from vehicle.

5) Apply Loctite to frame end crossmember bolts. To install, reverse removal procedure.

SECTOR SHAFT SEAL

NOTE: For models not listed, seal replacement procedure was not available from manufacturer.

General Motors

1) On 4WD models, gear must be removed from vehicle to replace seal. On all others, remove pitman arm from sector shaft. Rotate steering wheel from stop-to-stop while counting number of turns. Turn wheel back half way, placing gear at center of travel.

2) Remove bolts attaching side cover to housing, and lift sector shaft and side cover assembly from housing. Pry sector shaft seal from housing using a screwdriver. Be careful not to scratch housing bore.

3) Inspect gear lubricant for contamination, if lubricant is contaminated in any way, gear should be completely overhauled. Lubricate new sector shaft seal with Steering Gear Lubricant (GM 4673M). Position seal in sector shaft bore, and tap it into place using a socket.

4) Remove over-center adjuster lock nut. Remove side cover from sector shaft assembly by turning over-center adjuster screw clockwise. Install sector shaft in gear so center tooth of sector enters center tooth space of ball nut.

5) Fill gear housing with lubricant and install new side cover gasket on gear housing. Install side cover over sector shaft by reaching through cover hole with a screwdriver.

6) Turn over-center adjuster screws counterclockwise until screw bottoms; then back off screw 1/4 turn. Install over-center adjuster lock nut. Adjust worm bearing and over-center preload.

Jeep

1) Mark pitman arm and sector shaft for reassembly reference. Remove pitman arm using puller. Remove seal from sector shaft using a pointed tool or small bladed screwdriver.

2) Inspect condition of gear lubricant. If contaminated, remove overhaul gear. Wrap pitman arm shaft splines with shim stock to protect replacement seal during installation.

3) Lubricate lip of replacement seal with chassis lubricant, slide seal over shim stock and seat seal in gear housing. Tap seal into place with small plastic hammer. Align index marks, install pitman arm and tighten.

OVERHAUL

DISASSEMBLY

All Models

1) Place steering gear in a vise, clamping onto one mounting tab. Worm shaft should be in a horizontal position. Loosen over-center preload adjuster lock nut, and turn adjuster a few turns out.

2) Loosen lock nut on worm shaft adjuster, and turn adjuster out a few turns. Rotate worm shaft from stop-to-stop, counting number of turns. Then turn shaft back 1/2 number of turns to center sector shaft.

3) Place a pan under assembly to catch oil, and remove 3 self-locking bolts holding side cover to housing. Tap on end of sector shaft with a mallet and lift side cover and sector shaft assembly from gear housing.

4) If sector does not clear opening easily, turn worm shaft by hand until sector can be removed. Remove worm shaft adjuster and lock nut assembly with lower worm shaft bearing.

CAUTION: DO NOT allow ball nut to run down to either end of wormshaft as ball guide ends may be damaged.

5) Remove worm shaft and ball nut assembly from housing while housing is in a horizontal position to prevent ball nut from running down worm shaft. Remove upper bearing from worm guide.

6) Using screwdriver, pry lower bearing retainer from worm adjuster assembly and remove bearing. Remove over-center adjuster lock nut and screw.

7) Slide screw and shim out slot in end of sector shaft. Pry out and discard both sector shaft and worm shaft seals.

CLEANING & INSPECTION

Wash parts with clean solvent and blow dry with compressed air. Inspect bearings and races for signs or wear. Any parts that show signs of wear should be replaced.

Inspect sector shaft fit at side cover bushing. If bushing is worn, a new side cover and bushing assembly should be installed. Check ball nut and worm shaft assembly for wear and straightness.

COMPONENT SERVICE

Sector Shaft & Worm Shaft Seals

Pry out seals using a screwdriver. Before installing new seals, check condition of sector shaft bushings and upper worm shaft bearing race. Use a socket (pressing outer diameter of seal) to replace seal. Avoid cocking seal in bore.

Sector Shaft Bushing

Support steering gear in a arbor press and drive sector shaft bushing from housing. Press new bushing into position reversing removal procedure. Replacement bushings are machined to size and need no reaming.

Worm Shaft Bearing Race (In Adjuster)

Remove worm shaft bearing race using a slide hammer or a hammer and punch. Press bearing in place using an arbor press.

Fig. 4: Removing Worm Shaft Bearing Race From Adjuster

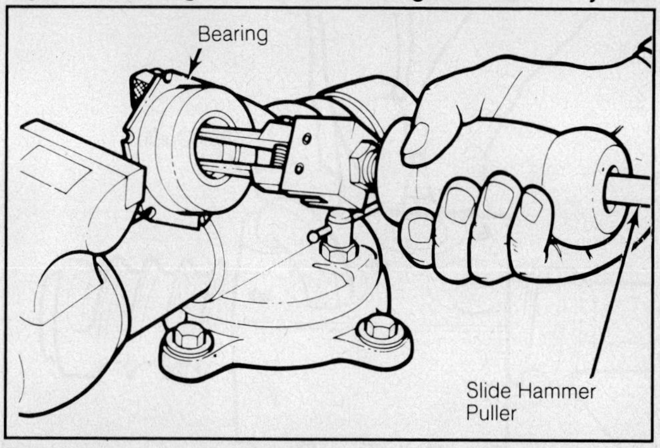

Install new race using arbor press.

Worm Shaft Bearing Race (In Housing)

Drive out housing bearing race with a hammer and punch. Press new race in using an arbor press.

Ball Nut & Worm Shaft Assembly

Ball nut disassembly is necessary only if an indication of binding or tightness (while rotating worm) is present. If disassembly is required, go to step **1)**.

1) This step will let loose about 50 ball bearings; be ready to catch them ALL. Remove clamp that retains ball guides and pull guides from ball nut while catching balls in clean pan. Turn nut over and rotate worm until all balls have fallen into pan.

2) Note relation of worm to ball nut and remove worm from ball nut. Wash parts and inspect worm, nut grooves, and ball bearings for indentations. Check ball guides for damage at ends where they deflect or pick up balls from helical path on worm.

3) To reassemble ball nut and worm shaft, insert ball nut over worm so that shallow end of ball nut teeth are on left side (looking from steering wheel end of worm shaft). Align grooves in worm and nut by sighting through ball guide holes.

4) There are 2 types of ball guides: those with a hole in the middle and those without a hole. If ball guides have hole in middle, insert ball guides into holes in ball nut. Divide balls into 2 equal groups and insert each group into a ball guide, while slowly turning worm shaft.

5) If guides have no hole, separate halves and fill half of each set with balls. Cover with remaining half and plug ends with grease to prevent balls from falling out.

6) Fill each circuit in ball nut with half of remaining balls in one circuit, and half in other. Do not turn worm shaft while installing. Insert ball guides. On both types, install ball guide retainer.

REASSEMBLY

All Models

1) Place gear housing in a vise with worm shaft bore horizontal and side cover opening facing up. All seals, bushings, and worm shaft bearing races should be installed.

2) Slip upper ball bearing over worm shaft and insert worm and nut assembly into housing feeding end of shaft through upper ball bearing race and seal. Place ball bearing in adjuster race and press stamped retainer into place with a socket.

Manual Steering Gears

SAGINAW RECIRCULATING BALL (Cont.)

Fig. 5: Filling Ball Circuits Through Holes in Ball Guides

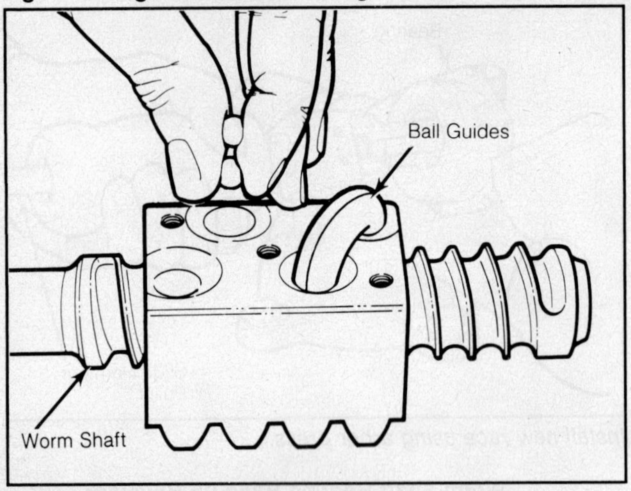

Rotate worm while installing balls.

3) Install adjuster and lock nut into housing carefully guiding worm shaft into bearing until nearly all end play is removed from worm shaft. Position over-center adjuster (with shim) in slotted end of sector shaft.

4) Check end clearance, which should not exceed .002" (.05 mm). If clearance is greater than specified, a steering gear over-center adjuster shim kit is available.

5) To lubricate gear, rotate worm shaft until ball nut is at end of travel, while forcing as much grease as possible into housing without losing it out sector shaft opening. Rotate worm until ball is at other end, and apply more lubricant.

Fig. 7: Filling Ball Circuits Through Holes in Ball Nut

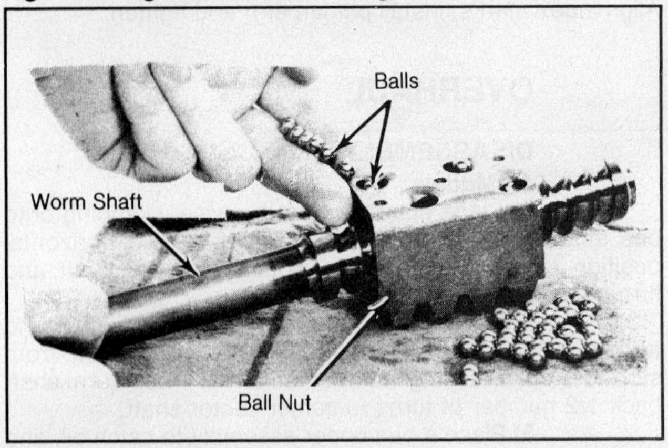

Do not rotate worm while installing balls.

6) Rotate worm until ball is at center. This will help sector and ball nut engage properly. Insert sector shaft and over-center adjuster screw (without side cover) into housing so center tooth of sector teeth enters center tooth space in ball nut.

7) Apply more lubricant into housing. Install side cover gasket. Install side cover over sector shaft by reaching through cover with a screwdriver.

8) Turn over-center adjuster screw counterclockwise until screw bottoms; then back off screw 1/2 turn. Loosely install a new lock nut onto adjuster screw.

9) Install and tighten side cover bolts to specifications. Adjust worm bearing preload and over-center preload as previously outlined. See ADJUSTMENTS in this article.

Fig. 6: Exploded View of Recirculating Ball Steering Gear

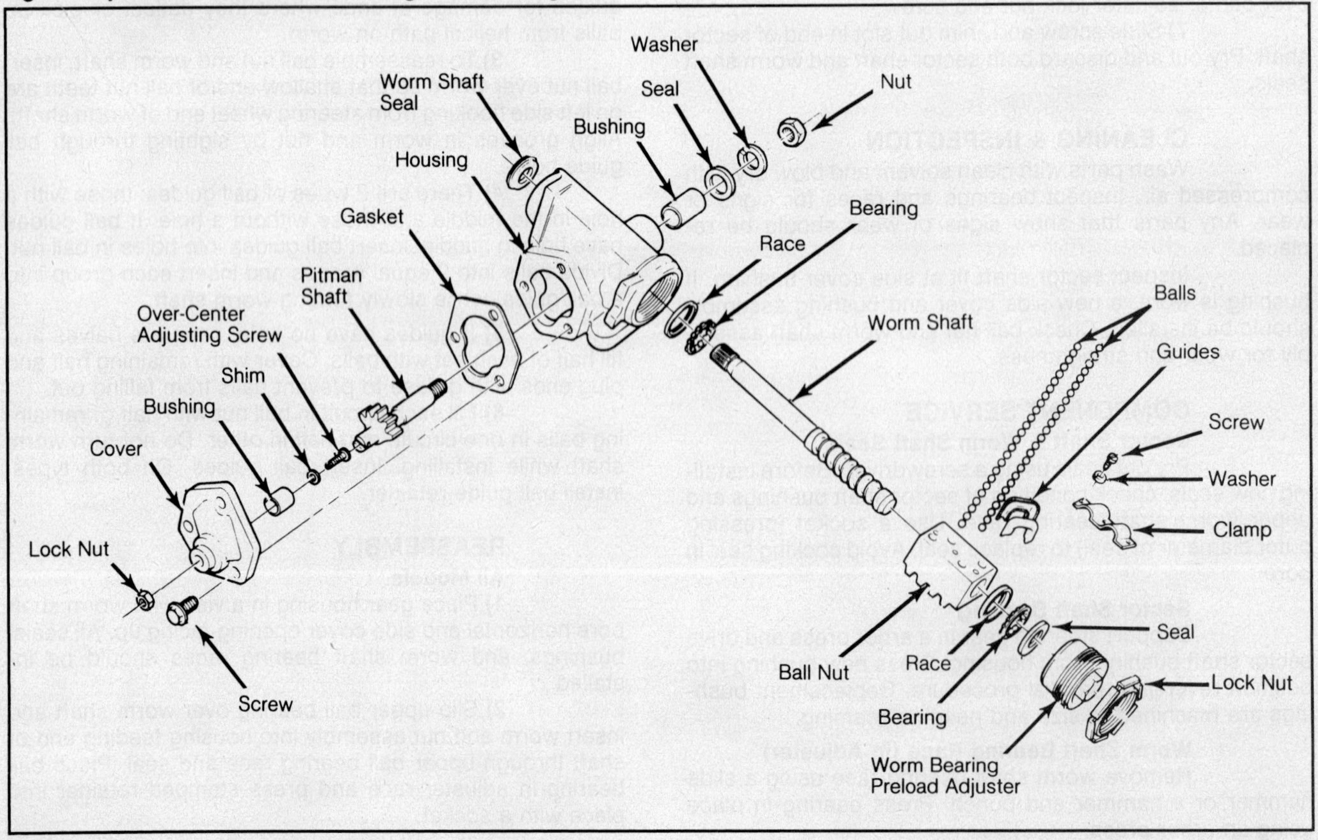

General Motors model is shown, all others are similar.

SAGINAW RECIRCULATING BALL (Cont.)

Fig. 8: Checking Over-Center Adjuster Clearance

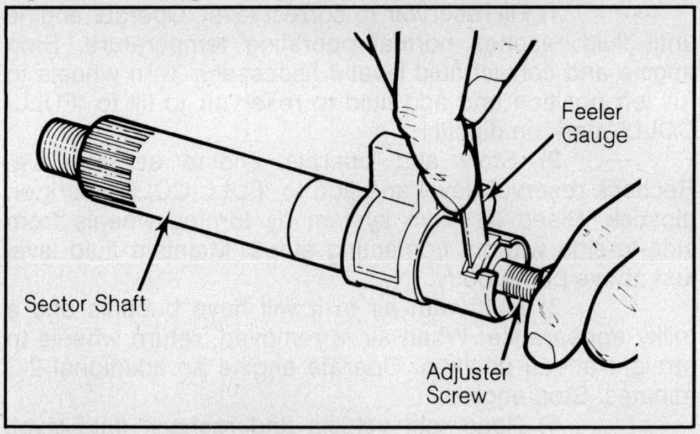

Clearance should be .002" (.05 mm).

TIGHTENING SPECIFICATIONS

Application	Ft. Lbs. (N.m)
Worm Bearing Preload Adj. Lock Nut	
Jeep	
Cherokee & Wagoneer	50 (68)
All Others	90 (122)
All Other Manufacturers	85 (116)
Over-Center Preload Adj.Lock Nut	
Chrysler Corp.	35 (48)
Jeep	23 (31)
All Other Manufacturers	25 (34)
Side Cover Bolts	
Chrysler Corp.	25 (34)
All Other Manufacturers	30 (41)
Flexible Coupling Bolts	
Jeep	45 (61)
All Other Manufacturers	30 (41)
Pitman Arm-to-Sector Shaft	
Chrysler Corp.	175 (238)
All Other Manufacturers	185 (252)
Steering Gear-to-Frame	
Chrysler Corp.	100 (136)
General Motors	70 (95)
Jeep	
Cherokee & Wagoneer	65 (88)
Grand Wagoneer & Truck	70 (95)
Steering Bracket-to-Frame	
CJ7 & Scrambler	
Bracket-to-Toe Plate	55 (75)
Bracket-to-Gear	70 (95)

Power Steering General Servicing

ALL MANUFACTURERS

LUBRICATION

SERVICE INTERVALS

Chrysler Corp.
Check fluid at every oil change.

Ford
Check during normal maintenance.

General Motors
Check at each oil change.

Jeep
Check every 5,000 miles or 5 months.

CHECKING FLUID LEVEL

Chrysler Corp.

On FWD models, check fluid with engine cold. Fluid level should be at "FULL-COLD" mark. On RWD models, check fluid with engine at normal operating temperature. Fluid level should read "FULL" on dipstick.

Ford

With fluid at normal operating temperature, and system bled, shut off engine. Fluid level on dipstick should read between "HOT" mark and end of dipstick.

General Motors & Jeep

Check fluid level with engine stopped and fluid hot or cold. Fluid level must be at "FULL-HOT" or "FULL-COLD" mark on dipstick. On models with remote reservoir, keep fluid level 0.5-1.0" from top of reservoir with wheels turned fully to left.

RECOMMENDED FLUID

Application	Power Steering Fluid Type
Chrysler Corp.	[1] Chrysler P/N (4318055)
Ford	ATF Type "F"
General Motors	GM P/N (P1050017)
Jeep	AMC/Jeep/Renault P/N (8993342)

[1] - Do not use ATF.

REFILLING & BLEEDING SYSTEM

Chrysler Corp. & Ford

Fill pump reservoir with power steering fluid. Start engine and run until fluid reaches 170°F (77°C). Bleed system by turning wheels from stop-to-stop several times. Shut off engine and check fluid level.

General Motors

1) Fill reservoir to correct level. Let oil settle for 2 minutes. Start engine and run for 4-5 seconds. Check reservoir and add oil if necessary. Repeat procedure until level in reservoir remains constant.

2) Raise front of vehicle so that both wheels are off ground. Start engine and increase engine speed to 1500 RPM. Turn wheels right and left, lightly contacting stops. Check fluid and add if necessary.

3) Lower vehicle. Turn wheels right and left. Check fluid level and add if necessary. If oil is foamy, go to next step.

4) Allow vehicle to stand for a few minutes with engine off. Repeat steps **1)** through **3)**, with front of vehicle raised. Again check fluid level and for air in system. If level is low or there is air in system, repeat complete procedure.

Jeep

1) Fill reservoir to correct level. Operate engine until fluid reaches normal operating temperature. Stop engine and correct fluid level if necessary. Turn wheels to full left position and add fluid to reservoir to fill to "FULL-COLD" mark on dipstick.

2) Start and operate engine at fast idle. Recheck reservoir level and add to "FULL-COLD" mark on dipstick. Bleed air from system by turning wheels from side-to-side without contacting stops. Maintain fluid level just above pump body.

3) Fluid with air in it will have bubbles and a milky appearance. When air is removed, return wheels to straight ahead position. Operate engine an additional 2-3 minutes. Stop engine.

4) Road test vehicle and recheck fluid level. Level should be at "FULL-HOT" position after system has stabilized. Add as necessary but do not overfill.

SERVICE

BELT TENSION
Tension in Lbs. (Kg.) Using Borroughs Tension Gauge

Application	New Belt	Used Belt
Chrysler Corp.		
RWD	120	65
	(54)	(30)
FWD	95	80
	(43)	(36)
Ford		
Aerostar, Bronco II		
& Ranger	[1] 80	[1] 60
	(36)	(27)
All Others	140	120
	(64)	(54)
General Motors		
5/16" Belt	80 Max.	50 Min.
	(36 Max.)	(23 Min.)
3/8" Belt	140 Max.	[2] 70 Min.
	(63 Max.)	(32 Min.)
15/32" Belt	165 Max.	90 Min.
	(75 Max.)	(41 Min.)
Jeep	[3] 125-155	90-115
	(57-70)	(41-52)

[1] - Tension for "V" ribbed belt.
[2] - Tension for used 3/8" cogged belt is 60 lbs. (27 kg). New cogged belt tension is same as standard 3/8" belt.
[3] - Cherokee & Wagoneer is 120-140 lbs. (54-64 kg).

TESTING

PREPARATION

All Vehicles

1) With belt tension correct, disconnect power steering pump pressure hose. Keep hose end raised to prevent fluid loss. Connect pressure hose of gauge (or Ford analyzer) to power steering pump fitting. Connect other hose from valve side of tester to steering gear inlet.

2) Open valve and run engine until fluid reaches normal operating temperature of 170°F (77°C). Check fluid level and add if necessary.

Power Steering General Servicing

ALL MANUFACTURERS (Cont.)

NOTE: For testing Ford vehicles, use Power Steering Analyzer D79-33610-A with flow meter.

PRESSURE TEST

Chrysler Corp., GM & Jeep

1) If testing Chrysler Corp. RWD vehicles, go to step **7)**. On GM, Jeep, and Chrysler Corp. FWD, note pressure reading with valve open and engine idling. Pressure should be 80-125 psi (5.6-8.8 kg/cm²) on GM and Jeep. Chrysler Corp. FWD vehicles should be 30-50 psi (2.1-3.5 kg/cm²).

2) If pressure is above 100 psi (7.0 kg/cm²) on Chrysler Corp. FWD, or 200 psi (14.1 kg/cm²) on all other vehicles, check hoses for restrictions and poppet valve (Saginaw gears) for proper assembly.

3) Close gate valve completely and reopen 3 times. Record highest reading each time. DO NOT close valve for more than 5 seconds. If pressure is less than specification, clean or replace flow control valve in pump. If pressures are still low, replace pump.

4) If readings are within specifications and within 50 psi (3.5 kg/cm²) of each other, pump is operating properly. See PRESSURE TEST SPECIFICATIONS table. If pressures are high, but do not repeat within 50 psi (3.5 kg/cm²), flow control valve in pump is sticking. Remove flow control valve and clean or replace.

5) If pump checks within specifications, open valve and turn steering wheel from right-to-left stops and record pressure. DO NOT hold wheel against stops more than 5 seconds. Pressure should be same as specified. See PRESSURE TEST SPECIFICATIONS table.

6) If pressure is low, steering gear is leaking internally and must be overhauled. Go to OVERHAUL in this article.

7) Turn steering wheel from left-to-right with engine idling at 600-800 RPM. There should be at least 900 psi (63.3 kg/cm²) of pressure.

8) If pressure is low, momentarily close valve. If pressure is less than 900 psi (63.3 kg/cm²), pump is faulty. If pressure is 900 psi (63.3 kg/cm²) but was low at previous reading, steering gear is at fault.

Ford

1) Start engine and record flow. If flow is below 1.6 gals./min. (6.1 L/min.) on Aerostar, Bronco II and Ranger (2 gals./min. (7.6 L/min.) on all others), pump may require repair. At this point, however, continue test.

2) If pressure is above 150 psi (10.5 kg/cm²), check hoses for restrictions. Partially close valve to build up pressure to 740 psi (51.8 kg/cm²) for Ford pumps and 620 psi (43.6 kg/cm²) for Saginaw pumps.

FORD POWER STEERING FLOW SPECIFICATIONS

Application	Minimum Flow Gals./Min. (L/Min.)
Ford Pump	
Aerostar,	
Bronco II & Ranger	1.4 (5.3)
All Others	1.7 (6.4)
Saginaw Pump	1.8 (6.8)

3) If flow drops below specifications, disassemble pump and replace cam pack. See POWER STEERING GEARS article in this section. If pressure plates are cracked or worn, they must be replaced.

4) Completely close and partially open gate valve 3 times. Do not close valve more than 5 seconds. Record highest reading each time. If pressure is higher or lower than specified, repair or replace flow control valve. See PRESSURE TEST SPECIFICATIONS table.

5) Set engine speed at 1500 RPM. Record flow. If flow varies more than 1 gal./min. (3.8 L/min.), flow control valve in pump must be repaired or replaced.

6) Turn steering wheel to left and right stops. Pressure should be nearly same as maximum relief pressure. Flow should drop below .5 gals./min. (1.9 L/min.).

7) If pressure and flow are not as specified, steering gear is leaking internally. Remove steering gear. Remove flow control valve. Repair or replace damaged parts. Check rack piston and valve seals for damage.

8) If pressure and flow is good, turn steering wheel slightly in both directions and release quickly while watching pressure gauge. Needle should move from normal backpressure reading and snap back as wheel is released.

9) If gauge reacts slowly, or sticks, rotary valve in steering gear is sticking. Repair or replace rotary valve. If system is severly contaminated, both hoses, control valve, and pump must be disassembled and cleaned.

NOTE: If problem still exists, check ball joints, linkage, and other front suspension members.

PRESSURE TEST SPECIFICATIONS

Application	Idle Pressure psi (kg/cm²)	Relief Pressure psi (kg/cm²)
Chrysler Corp.		
FWD Models	30-50	1000-1100
	(2.1-3.5)	(70.3-77.3)
RWD Models	[1] 900	1200-1300
	[1] (63.3)	(84.4-91.4)
Ford		
Saginaw Pump	80-125	1350-1450
	(5.6-8.8)	(94.9-101.9)
Ford Pump		
Aerostar, Bronco II & Ranger	80-125	950-1130
	(5.6-8.8)	(66.8-79.4)
All Others	80-125	1400-1500
	(5.6-8.8)	(98.4-105.5)
General Motors [2]		
Astro, Safari, C10/30 & P20/30	80-125	[3] 1225-1325
	(5.6-8.8)	(84.4-91.4)
G10/35	80-125	[3] 900-1000
	(5.6-8.8)	(63.3-70.3)
K10/35	80-125	1350-1450
	(5.6-8.8)	(94.9-101.9)
Jeep		
CJ7 & Scrambler [4]	80-125	1100-1200
	(5.6-8.8)	(77.3-84.4)
All Others	80-125	1400-1500
	(5.6-8.8)	(98.4-105.5)

[1] – Measure with steering wheel turned to extreme right or left position.

[2] – "T" Series pressure relief specification is not available from manufacturer.

[3] – On G30 series and motorhomes with hydroboost, pressure is 1350-1450 psi (94.9-101.9 kg/cm²).

[4] – Also for Cherokee and Wagoneer with 6-cyl. engine.

Power Steering Gears

CHRYSLER CORP. CONSTANT CONTROL

Vans & Wagons (RWD)

DESCRIPTION

Constant ratio power steering gear consists of a gear box housing containing a sector shaft with forged sector gear, a rack/piston with gear teeth broached into side of piston, and a worm shaft. Piston teeth and sector gear are in constant mesh with each other.

Worm shaft connects rack/piston to steering shaft through a flexible coupling. Worm shaft is geared to rack/piston through recirculating ball contact. Steering control valve, mounted to top of steering gearbox, directs flow of fluid through system.

LUBRICATION TROUBLE SHOOTING & TESTING

See POWER STEERING GENERAL SERVICING article in this section.

ADJUSTMENT

SECTOR SHAFT PRELOAD

1) Disconnect steering center link from pitman arm. Start engine and run at idle speed, while turning steering wheel from stop to stop, counting number of turns from one stop to other. Turn wheel back exactly 1/2 number of turns to center gear.

2) Loosen sector shaft adjuster screw until backlash is evident in pitman arm. Tighten adjuster until backlash just disappears, then continue tightening 3/8-1/2 turn from this position. Hold adjuster in position and torque lock nut.

CONTROL VALVE CENTERING

1) Loosen control valve mounting screws. Torque screws to 7 ft. lbs. (10 N.m) to prevent fluid leakage during centering operation. Start engine.

2) Tap on head or end plug of control valve assembly until unit is not self steering. Turn steering wheel from stop-to-stop severel times to bleed air from system. Check pump reservoir fluid level.

3) With front wheels in straight-ahead position, start and stop engine several times. Tap on valve end plug or valve head until there is no movement of steering wheel when engine is started or stopped.

4) When steering wheel movement no longer exists, valve is centered. Torque valve body attaching screws.

REMOVAL & INSTALLATION

STEERING GEAR

NOTE: **To avoid damage to collapsible steering column, it is recommended that column be completely detached from floor and instrument panel before steering gear is removed. See STEERING COLUMNS article in this section.**

Fig. 1: Cutaway View of Steering Gear Assembly

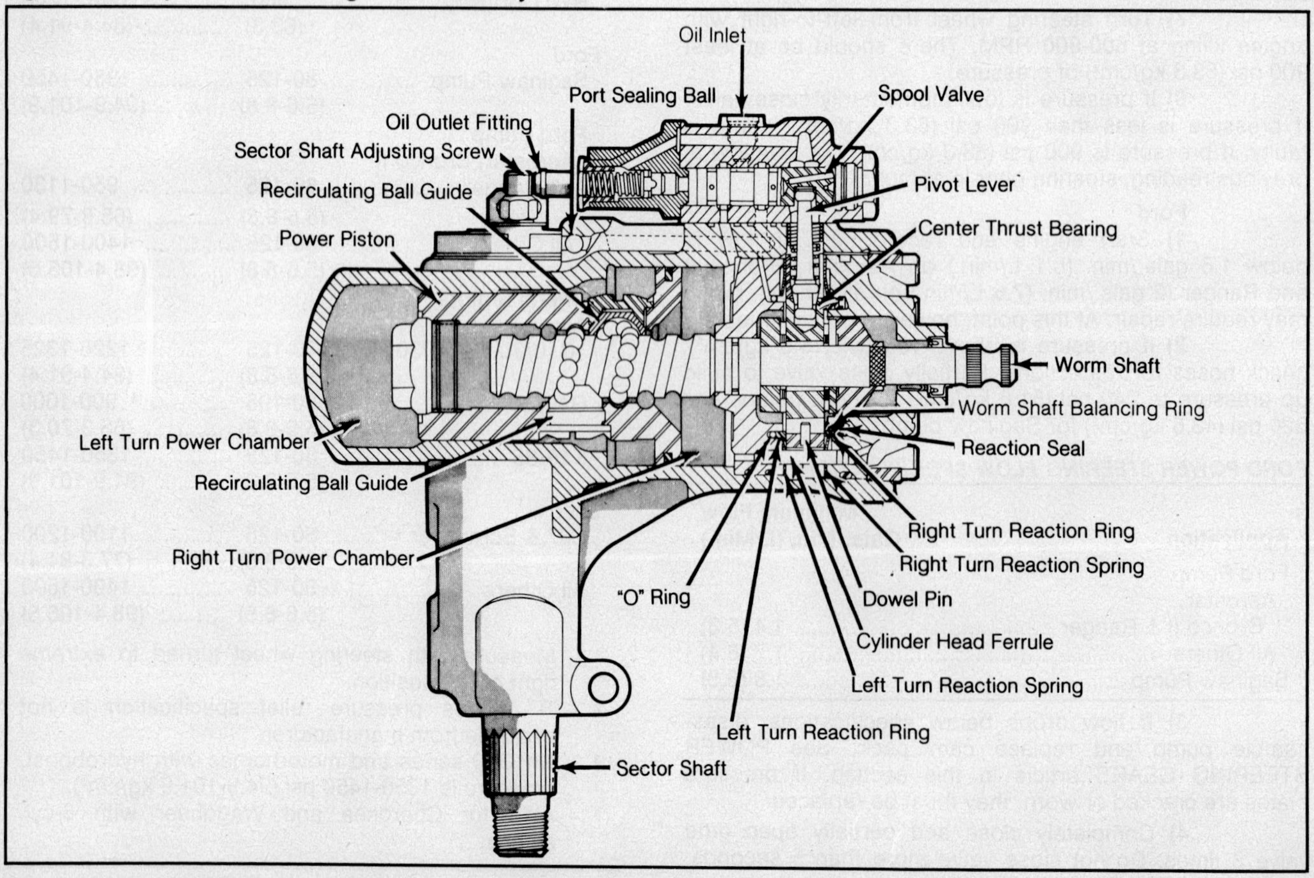

Power Steering Gears

CHRYSLER CORP. CONSTANT CONTROL (Cont.)

Removal

Remove battery negative cable and steering column. Disconnect power steering lines and cap all lines and fittings. Remove pitman arm with Pitman Arm Remover (C-4150). Remove bolts or nuts from steering gear and remove gear.

Installation

1) Position gear on frame and install retaining nuts or bolts. Rotate worm shaft by hand to center sector shaft. Align serrations on sector shaft with splines in pitman arm and install pitman arm.

2) Install and align steering column. Connect power steering lines and fill steering pump with fluid. Start engine and turn wheel from stop-to-stop to bleed system of air. Stop engine and fill steering pump if necessary.

OVERHAUL

STEERING GEAR

Disassembly

1) Clean exterior of gear, then clamp in a soft-jawed vise. Rotate input shaft from stop-to-stop several times to drain fluid.

2) Remove attaching screws, control valve, and "O" rings from housing. Remove pivot lever and spring by prying carefully under spherical head with a screwdriver.

CAUTION: Use care not to collapse slotted end of valve lever as this will destroy bearing tolerances of spherical head.

3) Loosen sector shaft adjuster lock nut, then use a spanner wrench to remove sector shaft cover spanner nut. Rotate input shaft until sector teeth are in center position.

4) Loosen steering power train retaining nut with a spanner wrench. Position Holder (C-3786) on threaded end of sector shaft. Slide holder into housing until both holder and shaft are engaged with bearings.

5) Rotate input shaft to full left turn position in order to compress power train components. Remove power train retaining nut and housing end tang washer.

6) Compress power train fully. Pry on rack/piston teeth with a screwdriver, using sector shaft as a fulcrum, and remove complete power train assembly. *See Fig. 2.*

CAUTION: It is important that cylinder head, center race and spacer assembly, and housing head be maintained in close contact with each other to eliminate possibility of reaction rings becoming disengaged from grooves in cylinder head and housing head, and to prevent center spacer from separating from center race and becoming cocked in housing.

7) Position power train assembly vertically in a soft-jawed vise. Raise housing head until input shaft oil seal just clears end of input shaft. Position Arbor (C-3929) on top of input shaft and extending into oil seal.

8) Keeping arbor in position, pull up on housing head until arbor is fully positioned in bearing. Remove head and arbor as a unit.

CAUTION: If input shaft oil seal is to be replaced, perform operation with housing head assembled in steering gear housing.

Fig. 2: Removing Powertrain Assembly

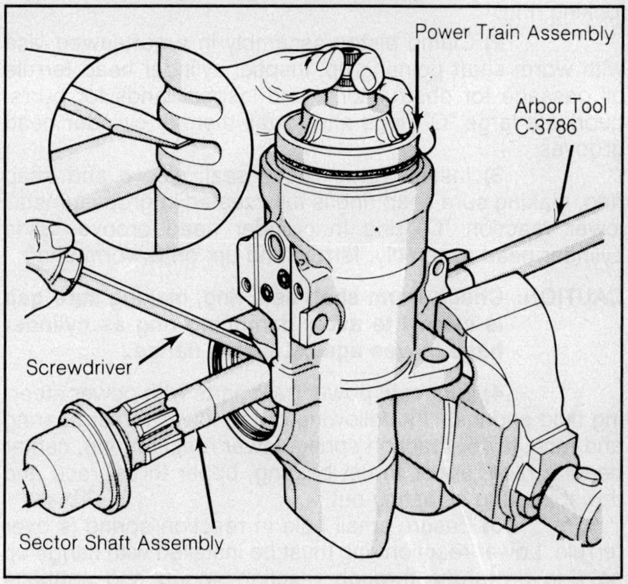

Turning wormshaft to left will compress powertrain components.

9) Remove large "O" ring from groove in housing head. Remove reaction seal by directing compressed air into ferrule chamber. Inspect all grooves for burrs. Ensure passage from ferrule chamber to upper reaction chamber is unobstructed.

10) Remove reaction spring, reaction ring, worm balancing ring, and spacer. While holding worm shaft from turning, turn nut to release staked portions from knurled section of shaft.

11) Wire brush knurled section, and blow out nut and worm shaft to remove metal particles. Remove nut, upper thrust bearing race and upper thrust bearing.

12) Remove center bearing race, lower thust bearing and lower thrust bearing race. Remove lower reaction ring and spring. Remove cylinder head assembly.

13) Remove "O" rings from outer grooves in cylinder head. Remove reaction "O" ring from groove in face of cylinder head by directing compressed air into oil hole between two "O" ring grooves.

14) Remove snap ring, sleeve, and rectangular oil seal ring from cylinder head counterbore. Test operation of worm shaft. Torque required to rotate worm shaft through its travel in or out of rack piston must not exceed 1 1/2 INCH lbs. (.2 N.m).

NOTE: Worm and piston are serviced as an assembly and should not be disassembled.

Inspection

1) Place piston in a soft-jawed vise with rack teeth facing up. Worm should be in center of its travel.

2) Vertical side play must be measured at a point 2 5/16" (59 mm) from piston flange. When end of worm is lifted with a force of 1 lb. (2.2 kg), side play should not exceed .008" (.2 mm).

3) Inspect condition of teflon piston ring for wear and cuts. Replace with new rubber sealing ring and cast iron piston ring if necessary. To install, slide new ring into place in piston groove.

Reassembly

1) Then place piston and ring assembly into Holding Fixture (C-3676), with lower part of piston and ring resting against land of fixture. Press down on piston to seat ring in groove, forcing open ends of ring out for ease of locking ring.

2) Clamp piston assembly in a soft-jawed vise with worm shaft pointing up. Inspect cylinder head ferrule oil passage for obstructions, and inspect lands for burrs. Lubricate large "O" rings and install them in cylinder head grooves.

3) Install worm sleeve seal, sleeve and snap ring, making sure snap ring is fully seated in groove. Install lower reaction "O" ring in cylinder head groove. Slide cylinder head assembly, ferrule end up, onto worm shaft.

CAUTION: Check worm shaft seal ring, making sure gap is closed to avoid damaging ring as cylinder head moves against piston flange.

4) Lubricate power train parts with power steering fluid and install in following order; lower thrust bearing and race, lower reaction spring, lower reaction ring, center bearing race, upper thrust bearing, upper thrust race and thrust bearing adjusting nut.

5) Ensure small hole in reaction spring is over ferrule. Lower reaction ring must be installed with flange up so ring protrudes through reaction spring and contacts reaction "O" ring in cylinder head.

6) Turn worm shaft 1/2 turn clockwise. Hold shaft in this position using Splined Nut (C-3637), and socket wrench. Tighten adjusting nut to 50 ft. lbs. (68 N.m) to pre-stretch threads. Hold shaft in position as outlined while performing following adjustment.

7) Loosen adjusting nut. Place several rounds of cord around center bearing race and attach a spring scale. Pull on cord causing bearing race to rotate.

8) Tighten adjusting nut while pulling on cord with spring scale. Adjusting nut is properly tightened when reading on spring scale is 16-24 oz. (4.4-6.7 N) with bearing race turning.

9) Stake upper part of worm shaft bearing adjusting nut into knurled area of shaft. Hold a 1/4" flat end punch on centerline of worm shaft end at a slight angle to nut flange. If adjusting nut moves, strike it in opposite direction to regain proper preload.

10) After retesting for proper preload, stake nut at 3 more locations 90° apart around upper part of nut. To test total staking, apply 20 ft. lbs. (27 N.m) of torque in each direction. If nut does not move, staking operation is correct.

11) Position spacer assembly over center race, engaging dowel pin of spacer in slot of race, and slot of spacer centered over cylinder head ferrule. This aligns valve pivot lever hole in center bearing race with valve pivot lever hole in center bearing spacer assembly.

NOTE: The small "O" ring for ferrule groove should not be installed until after upper reaction spring and spacer have been installed.

12) Install upper reaction ring on center race, and spacer, with flange down against spacer. Install upper reaction spring over reaction ring, with cylinder head ferrule through hole in reaction spring. Install worm balancing ring (without flange) inside upper reaction ring.

13) Lubricate ferrule "O" ring, and install in groove on cylinder head ferrule. If oil seal was removed from housing head, install new seal using Seal Installer (C-3650) to drive seal in until installer bottoms on support.

14) Lubricate and install reaction seal in groove in face of housing head with flat side of seal out. Install "O" ring in groove in housing head.

Fig. 3: Exploded View of Reaction Seal and Ring

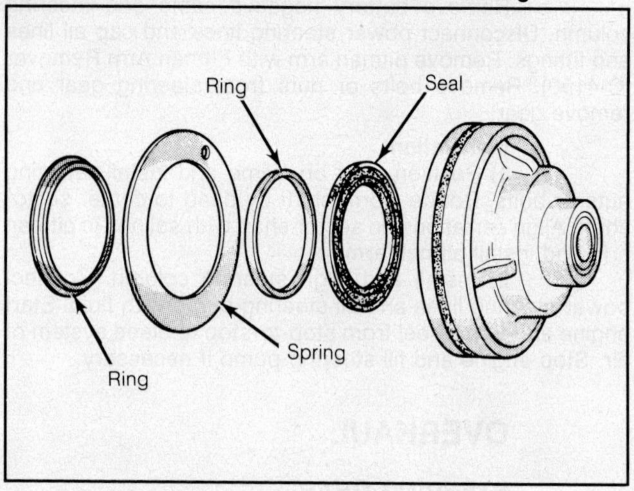

15) Slide housing head and arbor assembly over worm shaft, engaging cylinder head ferrule and "O" ring and making sure reaction rings enter circular groove in housing head.

16) Lubricate power train bore of housing and install power train assembly while noting the following: Keep worm turned fully counterclockwise to keep reaction rings from coming out of their grooves.

17) Piston teeth must be facing to right, and valve lever hole in center race and spacer must be in "up" position. Ensure cylinder head is bottomed on housing shoulder.

18) Align valve lever hole in center bearing race and center spacer with lever hole in gear housing. Install valve pivot lever, double bearing end first, through hole in housing until engaged in center race and spacer.

CAUTION: Slots in valve lever must be parallel to worm shaft in order to engage anti-rotation pin in center race.

19) Lightly tap on end of lever to seat lower pivot pin in center race. Center lever in hole by turning housing head by tapping on a reinforcing rib with a hammer and drift. Install housing head tang washer to index with groove in housing.

20) Install and torque spanner nut. Ensure valve lever remains centered in hole in housing. Turn worm shaft until piston bottoms in both directions, and note valve lever action.

21) Lever must center in hole and snap back to its center position when worm tension is relieved. Install valve lever spring, small end first.

22) Set power piston at center of travel, install sector shaft and cover assembly, and center sector teeth with piston rack teeth. Ensure "O" ring is properly installed on cover. Install sector cover lock nut.

23) Install control valve body on housing, making sure valve pivot lever enters hole in valve spool. Be sure "O" ring seals are in place. Torque control valve attaching screws. Install new sector shaft seal, seal back-up washer and snap ring. Install new grease retainer.

SECTOR SHAFT OIL SEAL

NOTE: Sector shaft oil seal may be replaced without removing steering gear from vehicle.

Power Steering Gears

CHRYSLER CORP. CONSTANT CONTROL (Cont.)

Fig. 4: Exploded View of Steering Gear Components

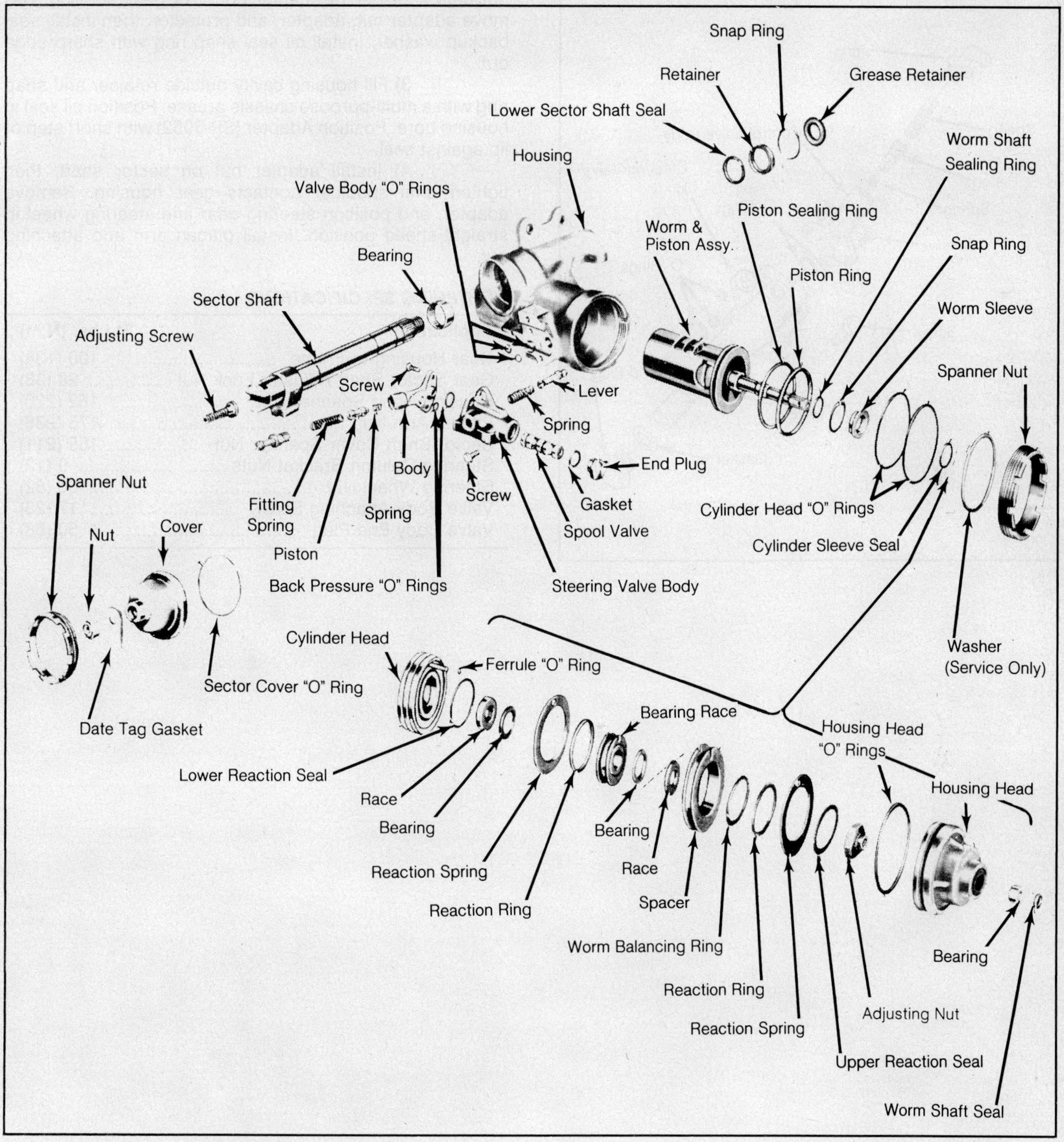

Disassembly

1) Remove pitman arm attaching nut. Disconnect pitman arm from sector shaft. Slide Adapter (SP-3056) over end of sector shaft, and thread adapter nut onto sector shaft.

2) Maintain pressure on threaded adapter with adapter nut while screwing adapter far enough to engage metal portion of grease retainer. Place 2 Half Rings (SP-1932) and retainer ring over both portions of adapter.

3) Turn adapter nut counterclockwise to remove retainer. Remove oil seal snap ring, and seal back-up washer. Remove inner seal in same manner using same tools as for grease retainer removal.

Reassembly

1) Place new seal, lip facing down, on flat surface and lubricate inner diameter with power steering fluid. Insert seal protective sleeve in seal, and position seal on sector shaft with lip of seal toward housing. Place Adapter (S-3052) with long step against new seal.

Power Steering Gears

CHRYSLER CORP. CONSTANT CONTROL (Cont.)

Fig. 5: Disassembled View of Control Valve Assembly

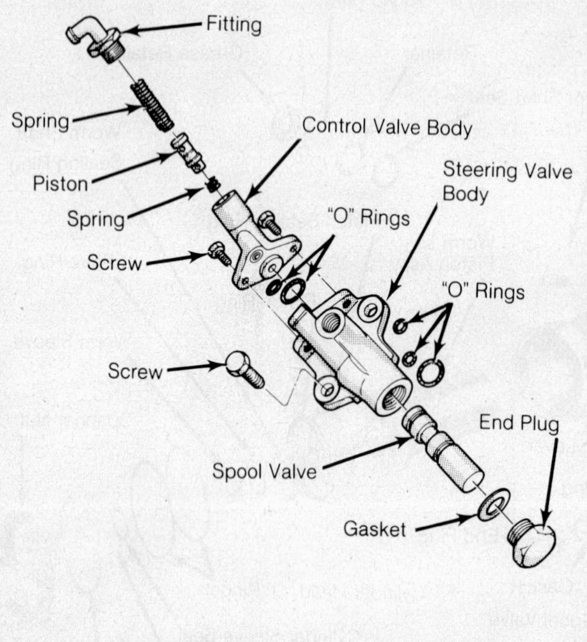

2) Install adapter nut on sector shaft and tighten nut until shoulder of adapter contacts gear housing. Remove adapter nut, adapter, and protector, then install seal backup washer. Install oil seal snap ring with sharp edge out.

3) Fill housing cavity outside retainer and snap ring with a multi-purpose chassis grease. Position oil seal in housing bore. Position Adapter (SP-3052) with short step of lip against seal.

4) Install adapter nut on sector shaft, then tighten until shoulder contacts gear housing. Remove adapter, and position steering gear and steering wheel in straight-ahead position. Install pitman arm and attaching nut.

TIGHTENING SPECIFICATIONS

Application	Ft.Lbs. (N.m)
Gear Housing-to-Frame	100 (136)
Gear Sector Shaft Adjuster Lock Nut	28 (38)
Housing Head Spanner Nut	162 (220)
Pitman Arm Nut	175 (238)
Sector Shaft Cover Spanner Nut	155 (211)
Steering Column Bracket Nuts	9 (12)
Steering Wheel Nut	60 (82)
Valve Body Attaching Screw	17 (23)
Valve Body End Plug	50 (68)

Power Steering Gears

CHRYSLER CORP. POWER RACK & PINION

Caravan, Mini Ram Van, Voyager

DESCRIPTION

A TRW power rack and pinion steering unit is used. A rotary valve in pinion assembly directs fluid to either side of integral rack piston, which is permanently secured to rack. Steering effort will increase if drive belt or pump breaks, or if pinion drive tangs are loosely attached to stub shaft.

LUBRICATION SERVICING & TESTING

See POWER STEERING GENERAL SERVICING article in this section.

REMOVAL & INSTALLATION

Power rack and pinion removal and installation is same as for manual rack and pinion steering except for tubes to pump. See MANUAL RACK & PINION STEERING GEAR article in this section.

INNER TIE RODS

Removal

Remove roll pin. Hold rack gear flat side with wrench and unscrew housing until tie rod separates from rack.

Installation

Bottom inner tie rod assembly on rack. Tighten housing using wrench on rack housing. Install roll pin.

OVERHAUL

INPUT SHAFT & VALVE ASSEMBLY

Stub Shaft Seal Removal

1) Remove snap ring. Remove lower bearing cap using Socket (C 4832). Hold stub shaft splined end with 12 point socket and remove pinion lock nut.

CAUTION: Pinion teeth will be damaged if stub shaft is not held.

2) Press on pinion shaft threaded (bottom) end until flush with ball bearing assembly. Remove stub shaft dust seal, seal and if required, needle bearing and race from shaft splined end. Complete removal of valve and pinion assembly is not necessary.

Installation

Lubricate all seals with power steering fluid before assembly. To install, reverse removal procedure. Install seal using Installer (C 4667) and Protector (C 4668).

Valve Pinion Removal

Turn stub shaft until rack extends equal distance from both sides of housing. Mark location of stub shaft flat on housing and press on pinion threaded end to remove valve and pinion assembly. Carefully remove rings from valve body (if replacement is needed).

Bearing & Seal Replacement

1) To remove lower ball bearing assembly, remove or bearing cap. Tap out bearing with a drift. Use a socket to press on new bearing outer race. Ensure that bearing does not tilt when installing in housing. Install bearing cap.

2) Remove pinion seal with Seal Remover (C 4694). Install new seal with lip facing inward using Seal Installer (C 4833).

Fig. 1: Exploded View of TRW Power Rack and Pinion Steering Assembly

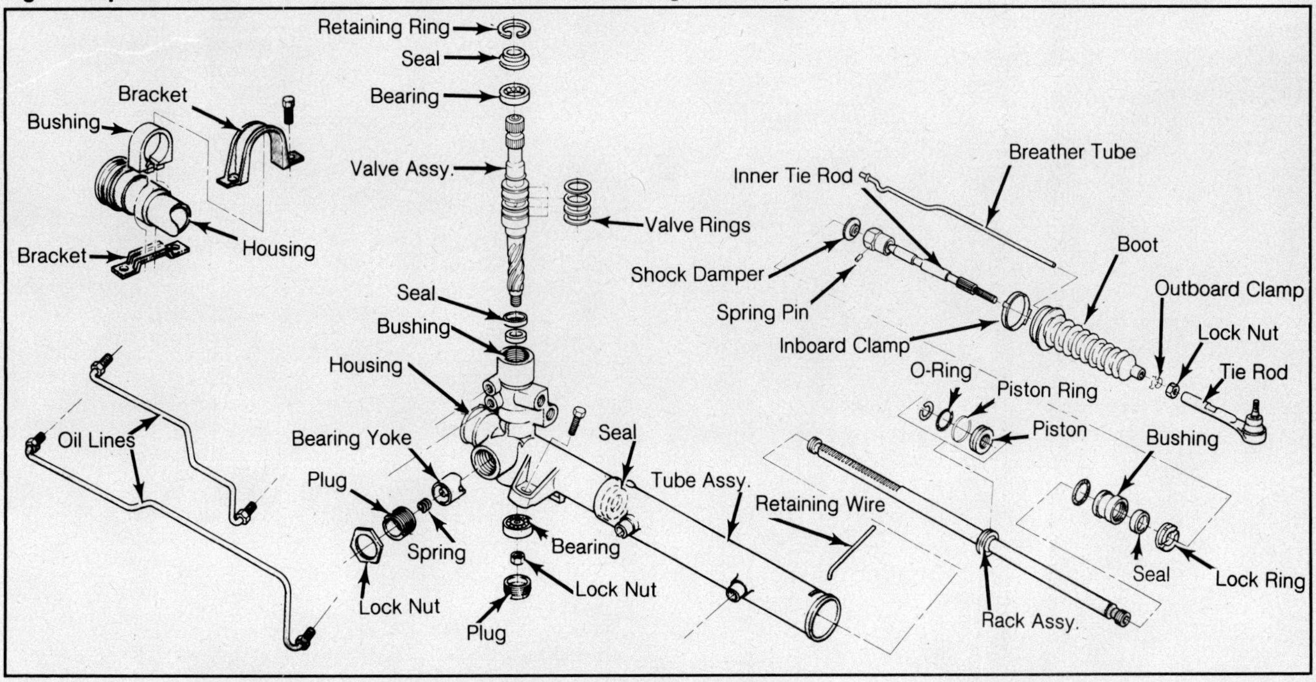

Power Steering Gears

CHRYSLER CORP. POWER RACK & PINION (Cont.)

Valve Pinion Installation

1) Lubricate valve body rings with power steering fluid and install rings on Ring Expander (C 4791). DO NOT soak rings in hot water. Slide rings off expander and into their proper grooves in valve body. Lubricate Ring Protector (C 4789) with power steering fluid and insert protector over valve body for 10 minutes to resize rings.

2) Center rack in housing. Lubricate valve body with power steering fluid and install valve and pinion assembly with ring protector in place. Do not damage lower pinion seal. When valve and pinion assembly is seated, shaft flat and housing mark must line up. Tighten pinion lock nut and install bearing cover.

GEAR HOUSING & RACK

Disassembly

1) Use punch to rotate retaining wire clockwise and expose end. Pull out wire with pliers. Remove fluid lines and install plugs finger tight in cylinder line holes. Remove adjuster plug and lock nut, spring and rack bearing.

2) Turn stub shaft, moving rack to right and force bulkhead out of housing. Remove rack from housing. Remove and discard piston "O" ring. Use Seal Driver (C 4665) to remove inner rack oil seal. Discard seal and plastic insert.

NOTE: **Coat seals with power steering fluid and apply lithium grease to rack teeth before assembly.**

Reassembly

1) Install new piston "O" ring on rack, using care not to cut ring. Install Seal Protector (C 4666) over rack gear end. Slide seal, with lip facing piston, over protector. Remove protector and bottom seal on rack piston.

2) Slide plastic retaining ring on rack and onto seal. Slide rack and seal into housing. Tap rack with mallet to seat seal.

3) Install bulkhead outer oil seal into bulkhead using Seal Installer (C 4669). Install bulkhead onto rack using Seal Protector (C 4670). Seat bulkhead assembly in rack tube using Installer Cup (C 4675) and install retaining wire by rotating bulkhead assembly counterclockwise.

4) Coat adjuster plug with lithium grease and install rack bearing, spring, adjuster plug and lock nut. Tighten adjuster plug until it bottoms, then back off 40°-60°. Tighten lock nut while holding adjuster plug stationary. Install fluid lines. Finger tighten both ends of lines before final tightening.

TIGHTENING SPECIFICATIONS

Application	Ft. Lbs. (N.m)
Tie Rod End-to-Steering Arm	38 (52)
Tie Rod Jam Nuts	55 (75)
Steering Gear Mounting Bolts	21 (29)

Power Steering Gears

FORD RACK & PINION

Aerostar

DESCRIPTION

Integral rack and pinion steering gear is optional on Aerostar. Gear and valve housings are uni-cast into a one piece aluminum unit. Steering gear is hydraulic/mechanical-type, and uses internal valving to direct hydraulic fluid flow and pressure.

Pressure and return lines are fitted with quick-connect fittings to minimize breakage caused by vehicle and engine vibration. Tie rod ends are rubber encapsulated and require no lubrication.

OPERATION

STEERING GEAR

Rotary Valve

Rotary-type control valve senses relative rotational motion of input shaft to direct and control fluid flow. When steering wheel is turned, resistance of front wheels, combined with weight of vehicle, cause a torsion bar to deflect.

When torsion bar is deflected, relative position of input shaft to sleeve ports is changed, and pressurized fluid is directed to appropriate end of power cylinder. Pressure from power cylinder causes piston to help move rack in proper direction.

ADJUSTMENTS

RACK YOKE PLUG PRELOAD

Gear In Vehicle

1) Place front wheels in straight-ahead position. Clean exterior of gear housing in yoke plug area. Loosen yoke plug lock nut 1/4 turn, using Lock Nut Wrench (T78P-3504-H). Loosen yoke plug.

2) Tighten yoke plug to 45-50 INCH lbs. (5.0-5.6 N.m). Back off yoke plug 1/8 turn (44-50°). Place lock nut wrench over lock nut. While holding yoke plug in position, tighten lock nut.

NOTE: **Do not allow yoke plug to move while tightening yoke plug lock nut.**

Gear Removed From Vehicle

1) Clean exterior of gear housing in yoke plug area. Insert an INCH lb. torque wrench into Pinion Shaft Torque Adapter (T74P-3504-R). Place adapter and torque wrench over input shaft.

2) Turn pinion from one lock to the other, counting total number of turns required. Turn pinion back halfway ("on center" position). Loosen yoke plug lock nut 1/4 turn, using Lock Nut Wrench (T78P-3504-H).

3) Loosen yoke plug. Tighten yoke plug to 45-50 INCH lbs. (5.0-5.6 N.m). Back off yoke plug 1/8 turn (44°-50°). Place lock nut wrench over lock nut. While holding yoke plug in position, tighten yoke plug lock nut.

Fig. 1: Exploded View of Steering Gear and Housing

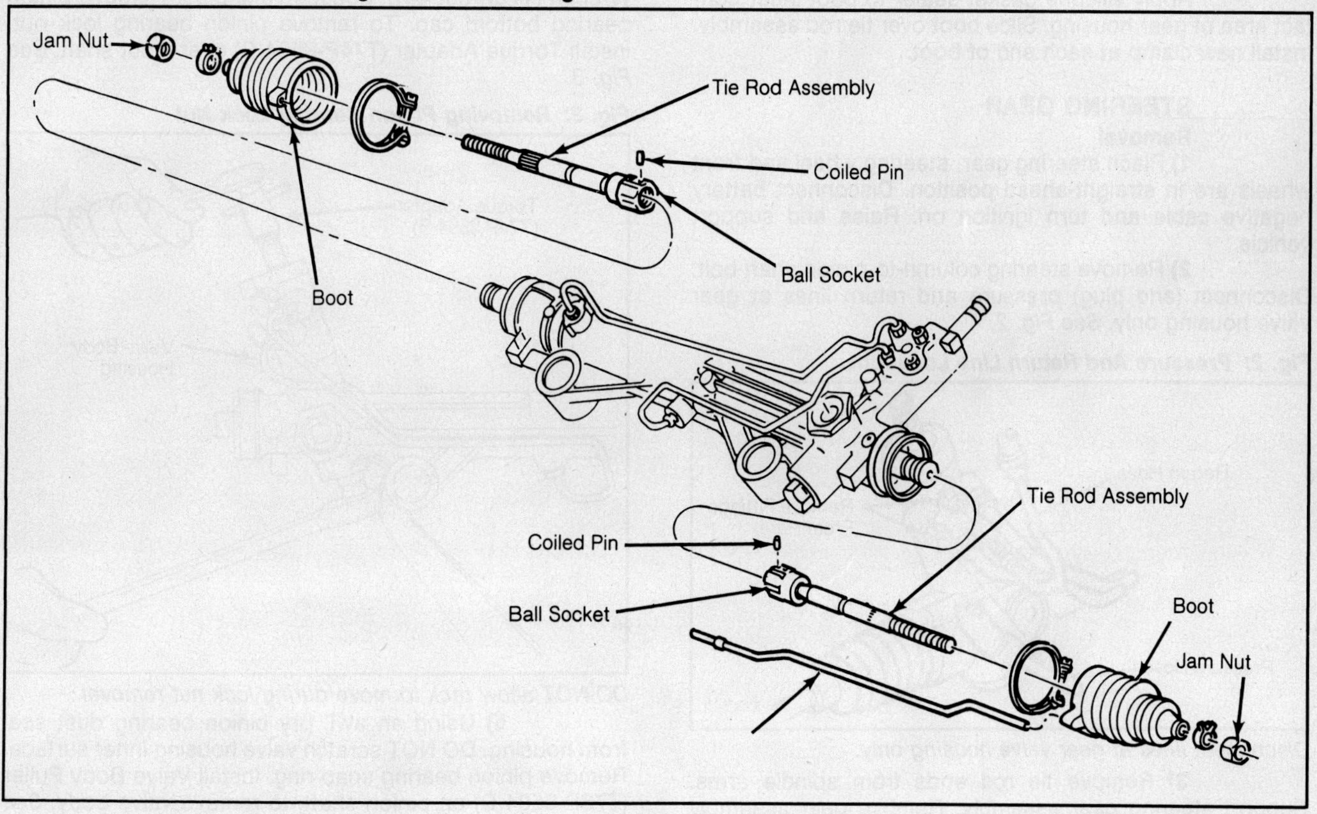

Power Steering Gears

FORD RACK & PINION (Cont.)

REMOVAL & INSTALLATION

OUTER TIE ROD END

Removal

1) Place front wheels in straight-ahead position. Remove and discard cotter pin securing castle nut to tie rod stud. Remove castle nut. Separate tie rod end from spindle arm using Tie Rod End Remover (64P-3590-F).

2) Index mark relative position of tie rod ends, to jam nuts and exposed threads. Loosen jam nut, and count number of turns required to remove tie rod end.

Installation

To install, position tie rod end on tie rod assembly. Tighten jam nut. Place front wheels in straight-ahead position. Insert tie rod stud through spindle arm. Install and tighten castle nuts. Install new cotter pin.

NOTE: **Ensure tie rod studs are seated properly in taper of spindle arm.**

BOOT

Removal

1) Remove steering gear. Clean exterior of gear. Place steering gear in soft-jawed vise, gripping it near center. Rotate pinion shaft to align white index mark on steering gear housing with mark on pinion shaft ("on center" position).

2) Index mark position of tie rod end, to jam nuts and exposed threads. Loosen jam nut, and count number of turns required to remove tie rod end. Remove boot retaining clamps and boot.

Installation

Apply silicone gasket sealer to boot inner contact area of gear housing. Slide boot over tie rod assembly. Install new clamp at each end of boot.

STEERING GEAR

Removal

1) Place steering gear, steering wheel and front wheels are in straight-ahead position. Disconnect battery negative cable and turn ignition on. Raise and support vehicle.

2) Remove steering column-to-pinion shaft bolt. Disconnect (and plug) pressure and return lines at gear valve housing only. *See Fig. 2.*

Fig. 2: Pressure And Return Line Locations

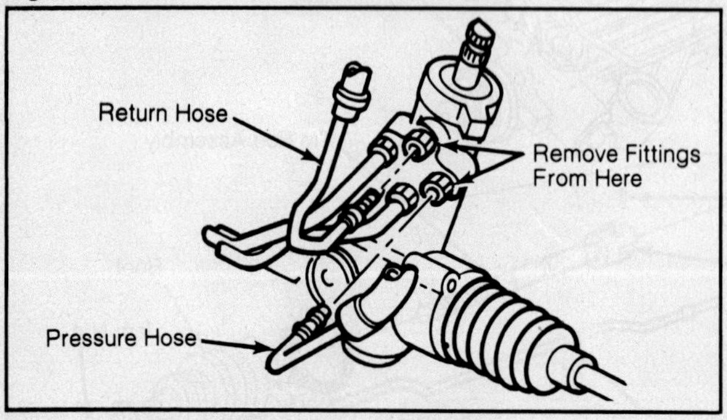

Disconnect lines at gear valve housing only.

3) Remove tie rod ends from spindle arms. Support steering gear assembly. Remove gear assembly mounting bracket nuts, bolts and washers. Remove steering gear. If necessary, remove front and rear insulators from steering gear housing.

Installation

If removed, install front and rear insulators. Position steering gear on crossmember. Ensure that steering gear, steering wheel and front wheels are in straight-ahead position. To complete installation, reverse removal procedure.

OVERHAUL

STEERING GEAR

NOTE: **Clean exterior of steering gear before disassembly to avoid contaminating rack and pinion assembly with dirt.**

Disassembly

1) Remove steering gear from vehicle. Mount gear in Holding Fixture (T57L-500-B). Manually rotate pinion shaft from left lock, to right lock position. Record number of pinion shaft rotations. Divide number of rotations by 2. This is "on center" position.

2) Turn pinion shaft to left lock position, and then back to "on center" position. White index marks on steering gear housing and pinion shaft should now be aligned.

3) Index mark position of tie rod end, to jam nuts and exposed threads. Loosen jam nut, and record number of turns required to remove tie rod end. Remove boot retaining clamps, boots, jam nuts and breather tube.

4) Loosen yoke plug lock nut using Lock Nut Wrench (T78P-3504-H). Loosen yoke plug. Remove pinion bearing bottom cap. To remove pinion bearing lock nut, install Torque Adapter (T74P-3504-R) over input shaft. *See Fig. 3.*

Fig. 3: Removing Pinion Bearing Lock Nut

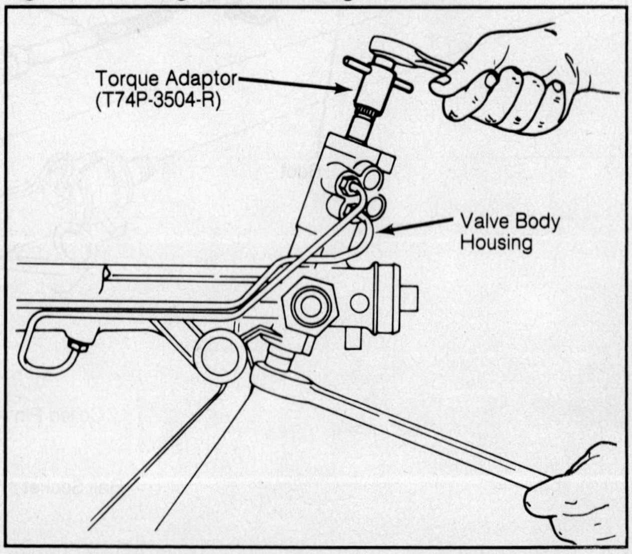

DO NOT allow rack to move during lock nut removal.

5) Using an awl, pry pinion bearing dust seal from housing. DO NOT scratch valve housing inner surface. Remove pinion bearing snap ring. Install Valve Body Puller (T78P-3504-B) on pinion shaft, to remove valve body. *See Fig. 4.*

Power Steering Gears

FORD RACK & PINION (Cont.)

Fig. 4: Removing Valve Body

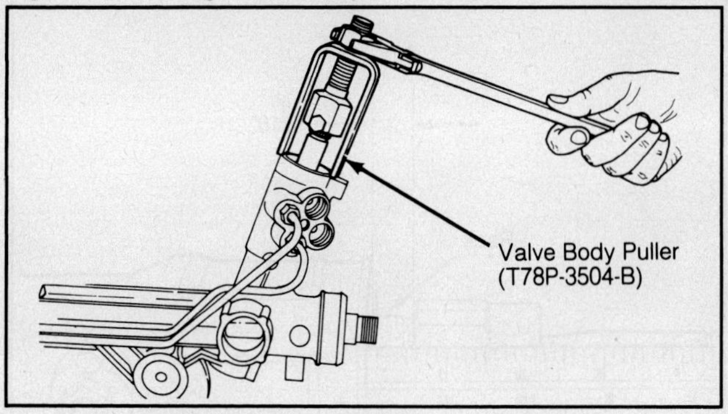

6) To remove lower pinion shaft seal, insert Seal Remover (T78P-3504-E2) and Spacer Collet (D82P-3504-E1) until spacer and remover bottom. Hold larger nut, and tighten smaller nut, until expander tightens. *See Fig. 5.*

Fig. 5: Removing Lower Pinion Shaft Seal

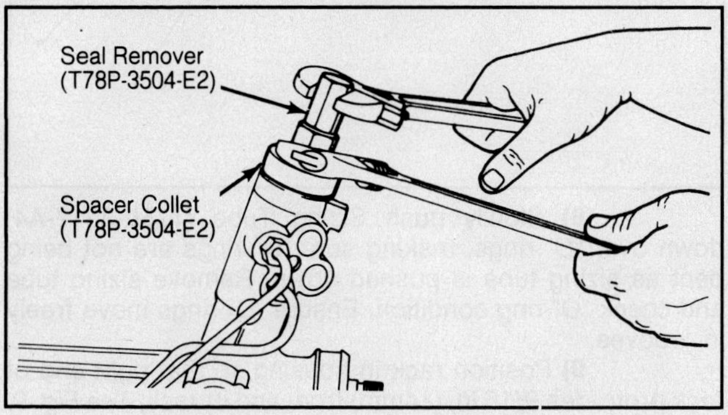

7) Insert end of slide hammer into rear of seal remover, and pull seal from housing. Inspect lower pinion bearing. If relacement is necessary, use slide hammer and Puller Attachment (T58L-101-A) to pull bearing from valve housing.

8) Thread point of Lock Nut Pin Remover (D81P-3504-N) into coiled pin in ball socket. Finger tighten remover. Tighten nut on lock nut remover. Remove and discard coiled pin. *See Fig. 6.*

9) Pull rack out to expose several teeth. Hold rack with adjustable pliers and remove both tie rod ball joint sockets using Socket Wrench (T74P-3504-U).

Cleaning & Inspection

Examine parts for wear and contamination, and replace as necessary. Inspect yoke to ensure that insert is seated flush with yoke body. If pinion teeth are pitted or worn, or if upper bearing is damaged or binding, replace entire steering gear assembly as a unit.

Reassembly

1) Hold rack with adjustable pliers and remove both tie rod ball joint sockets. Rest ball joint socket on wooden block. To install new coiled pin, hold pin with needle-nose pliers, and tap pin in lightly with plastic hammer.

2) If pinion bearing was removed, Install new bearing using Pinion Bearing Driver (T78P-3504-G). Ensure bearing is seated against shoulder in bore. Coat lower pinion oil seal with steering gear grease.

Fig. 6: Removing Coiled Pin

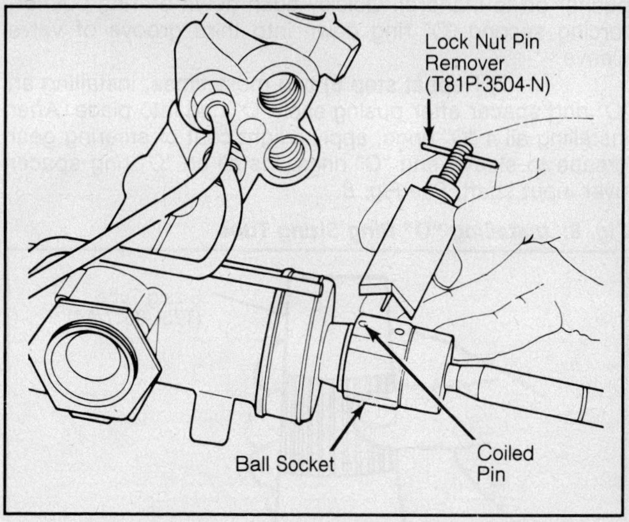

3) Place seal on Seal Installer (T78P-3504-G), with lip of seal facing toward installer. Support housing on clean surface, and drive seal in until seal is seated against shoulder.

4) If valve "O" rings were not removed, go to step **9)**. If "O" rings were removed, mount pinion end of valve assembly in soft-jawed vise. Lubricate Mandrel (T75L-3517-A1) with Type F transmission fluid. Install mandrel over valve assembly.

5) Slide 1 valve "O" ring over mandrel. Slide Ring Pusher (T75L-3517-A2) on to mandrel. Quickly push down on ring pusher, forcing "O" ring down into fourth groove of valve sleeve. *See Fig. 7.*

Fig. 7: Installing Valve "O" Rings

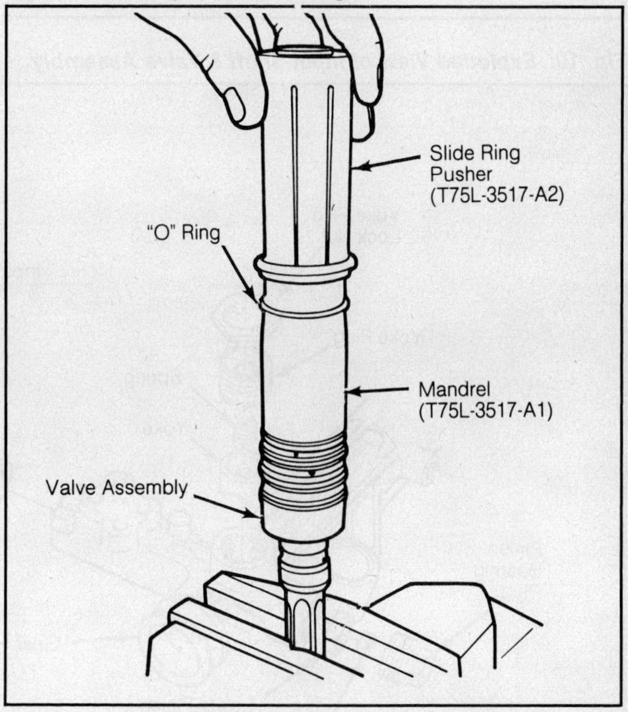

6) Install 1 "O" Ring Spacer (T75L-3517-A3) to keep next "O" ring from going past third groove of valve sleeve. Slide second "O" ring over mandrel. Slide ring pusher on to mandrel. Quickly push down on ring pusher, forcing second "O" ring down into third groove of valve sleeve.

7) Repeat step **6)** two more times, installing an "O" ring spacer after pusing each "O" ring into place. After installing all 4 "O" rings, apply a light coat of steering gear grease to sleeve and "O" rings. Install an "O" ring spacer over input shaft. *See Fig. 8.*

Fig. 8: Installing "O" Ring Sizing Tube

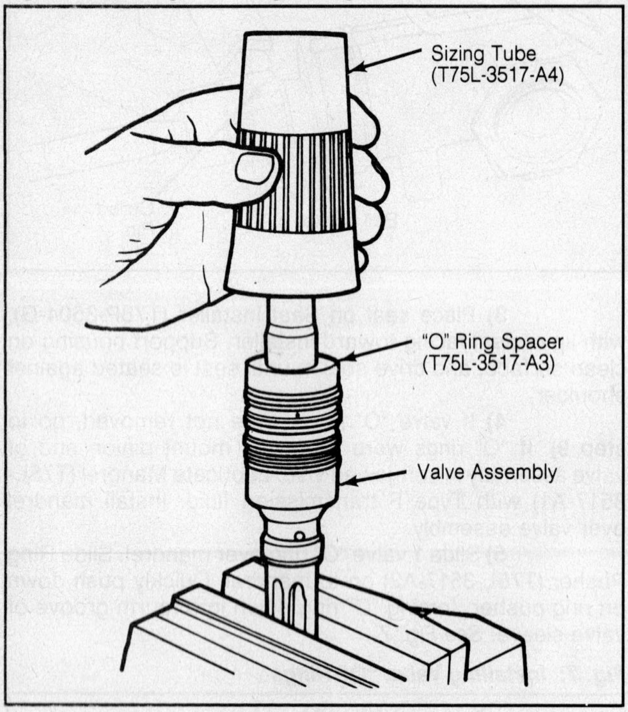

Fig. 9: Aligning Rack With Rack Housing

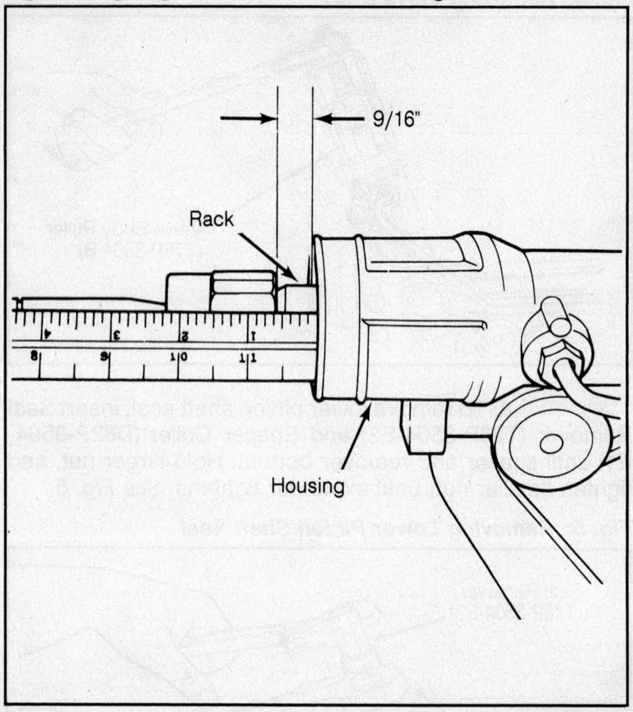

8) Slowly push Sizing Tube (T75L-3517-A4) down over "O" rings, making sure "O" rings are not being bent as sizing tube is pushed down. Remove sizing tube and check "O" ring condition. Ensure "O" rings move freely in grooves.

9) Position rack in housing so that right end of rack protrudes 9/16 in. (14mm) from end of rack. *See Fig. 9.* Place Valve Body Inserter (T78P-3504-C) into top of valve housing. Align flat spot of "D" shaped shaft 180° from yoke

Fig. 10: Exploded View of Input Shaft & Valve Assembly

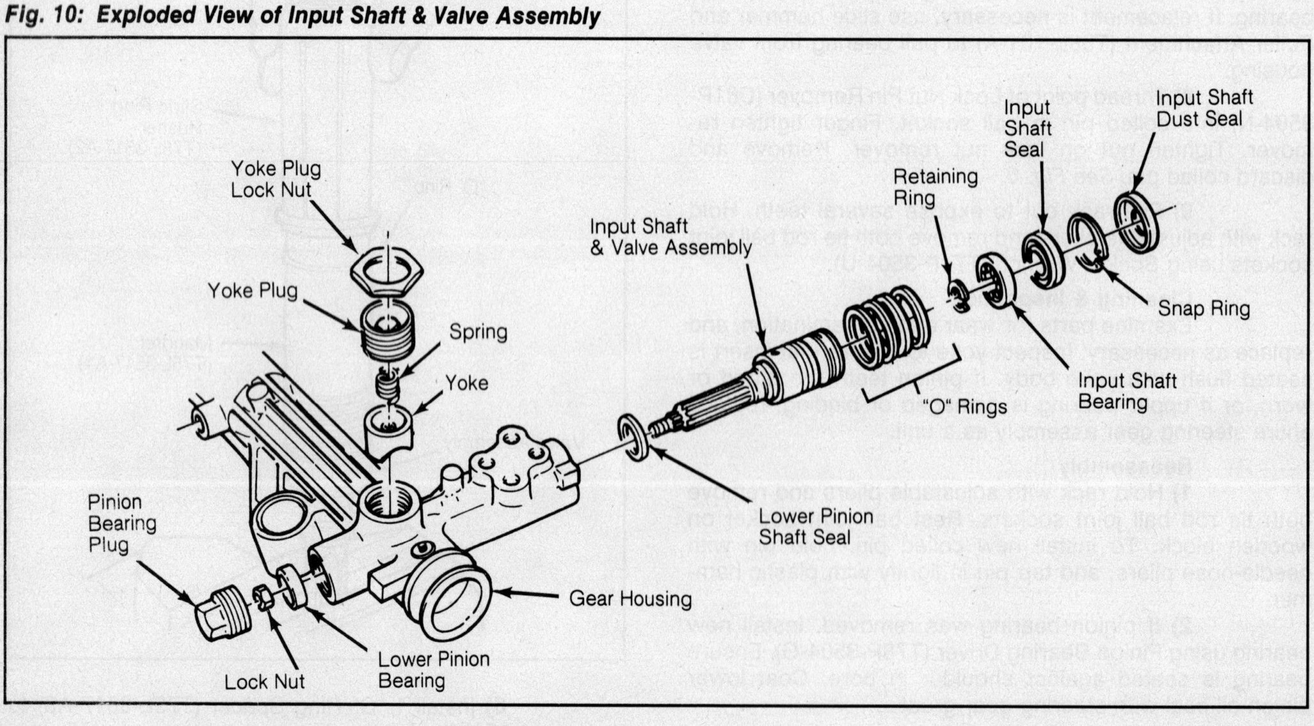

Power Steering Gears

FORD RACK & PINION (Cont.)

plug hole center (flat spot of "D" shaped shaft should be facing backward).

10) If necessary, rotate input shaft slightly to mesh shaft teeth with rack teeth. Push valve assembly in by hand until fully seated. Install pinion shaft torque adapter onto input shaft. Install nut onto pinion end of valve assembly.

11) Hold pinion shaft with torque adapter, and tighten nut. Slide pinion shaft bearing over shaft, and into valve bore. Firmly seat bearing into bore using Bearing Installer (T78P-3504-D).

12) Lightly coat input shaft seal with steering gear grease. Install input shaft over bearing installer, with lip toward gear housing. Drive seal in until fully seated. Install snap ring in valve bore.

13) Coat upper end of input shaft with grease. Slide Input Shaft Seal Aligner (T85T-3504-CH1) over input shaft. Drive input shaft seal in to position using Input Shaft Seal Installer (T85T-3504-CH2). Remove input shaft seal aligner from shaft.

14) Install and tighten bearing cap. Adjust rack yoke plug preload. See ADJUSTMENTS in this article. To complete reassembly, reverse disassembly procedure. Apply steering gear grease to section of tie rod where rubber boot is fastened.

TIGHTENING SPECIFICATIONS

Application	Ft. Lbs. (N.m)
Pinion Bearing Bottom Cap	50 (67)
Pinion Bearing Lock Nut	30-40 (45-55)
Mounting Bracket Nut & Bolt	65-90 (80-122)
Steering Column-To-Pinion Shaft Bolt	30-42 (41-56)
Tie Rod Assembly	55-65 (75-88)
Tie Rod End Castle Nut	52-73 (70-100)
Tie Rod Jam Nut	36-50 (48-68)
Pinion Plug Lock Nut	44-66 (60-89)
Pressure And Return Line Fittings [1]	10-15 (15-20)
Yoke Plug Lock Nut	44-66 (60-89)
	Inch Lbs. (N.m)
Yoke Plug [2]	45-50 (5.0-5.6)

[1] – Remove only at gear valve housing.
[2] – Tighten, then back off 1/8 turn.

Fig. 11: Exploded View of Rack Assembly

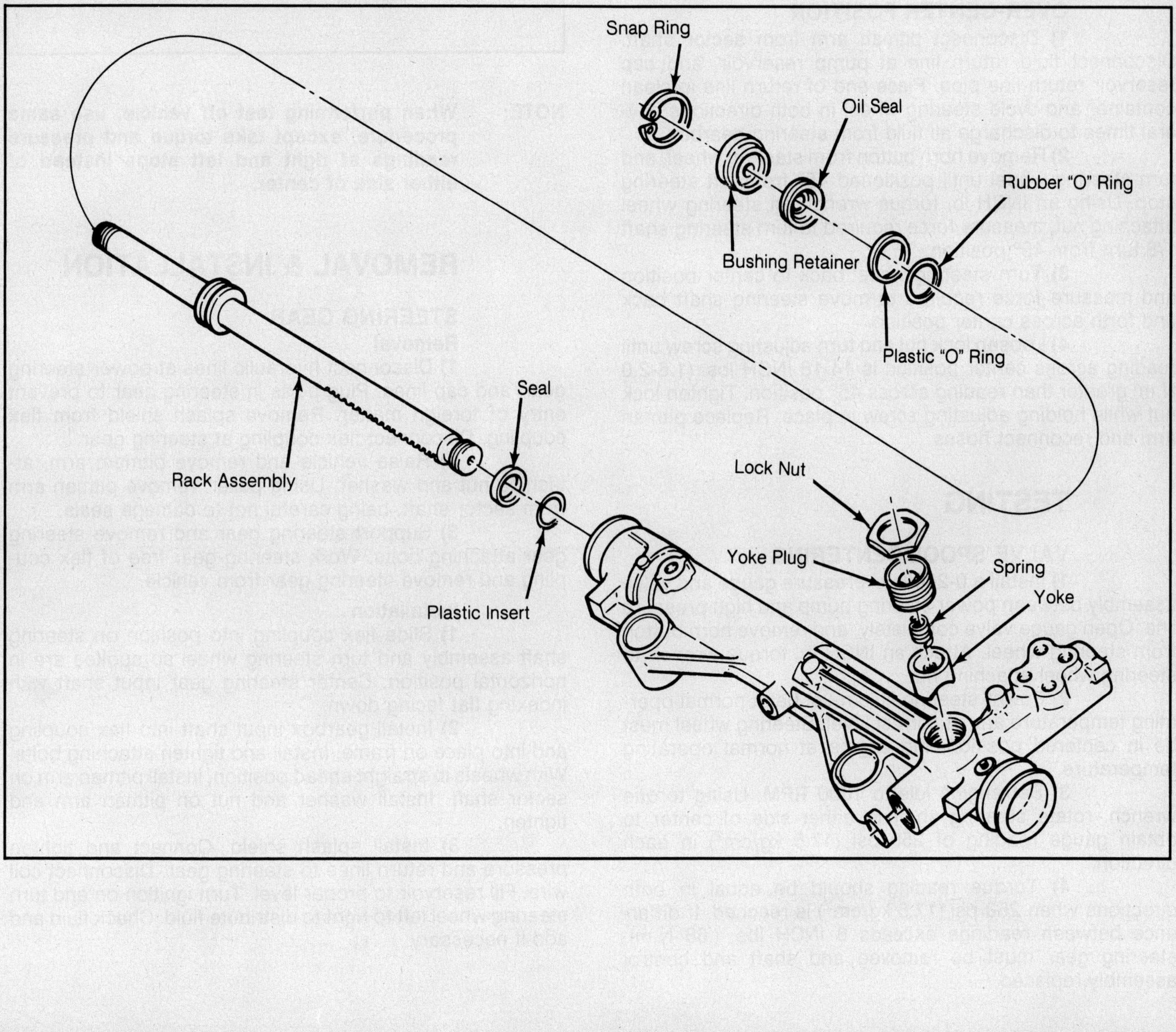

Power Steering Gears

FORD TORSION BAR

All Except Aerostar

DESCRIPTION

Torsion bar-type power steering unit consists of a worm and one-piece rack/piston, which is meshed to gear teeth on sector shaft. Hydraulic control valve, input shaft, and torsion bar assembly are mounted to end of worm shaft and operated by twisting action of torsion bar.

One-piece rack/piston, worm and sector shaft are mounted in one housing, while valve spool is mounted in an attached housing. This allows internal passage of fluid between valve and cylinder, thus eliminating all external lines and hoses, except for pressure and return hoses between pump and gearbox assembly.

LUBRICATION

Check fluid level in pump reservoir (with engine at normal operating temperature) every 5000 miles.

ADJUSTMENT

OVER-CENTER POSITION

1) Disconnect pitman arm from sector shaft. Disconnect fluid return line at pump reservoir, and cap reservoir return line pipe. Place end of return line in clean container and cycle steering wheel in both directions several times to discharge all fluid from steering gearbox.

2) Remove horn button from steering wheel, and turn steering wheel until positioned 45° from left steering stop. Using an INCH lb. torque wrench on steering wheel attaching nut, measure force required to turn steering shaft 1/8 turn from 45° position.

3) Turn steering wheel back to center position and measure force required to move steering shaft back and forth across center position.

4) Loosen lock nut and turn adjusting screw until reading across center position is 14-18 INCH lbs. (1.6-2.0 N.m) greater than reading across 45° position. Tighten lock nut while holding adjusting screw in place. Replace pitman arm and reconnect hoses.

TESTING

VALVE SPOOL CENTERING

1) Install a 0-2000 psi pressure gauge and valve assembly between power steering pump and high pressure line. Open gauge valve completely, and remove horn button from steering wheel. Attach an INCH lb. torque wrench to steering wheel attaching nut.

2) Power steering fluid must be at normal operating temperature and at correct level. Steering wheel must be in centered position and engine at normal operating temperature.

3) Set engine idle to 1000 RPM. Using torque wrench, rotate steering shaft to either side of center to obtain gauge reading of 250 psi (17.5 kg/cm^2) in each direction.

4) Torque reading should be equal in both directions when 250 psi (17.5 kg/cm^2) is reached. If difference between readings exceeds 6 INCH lbs. (.68 N.m), steering gear must be removed and shaft and control assembly replaced.

Fig. 1: Ford Torsion Bar Steering Gear Assembly

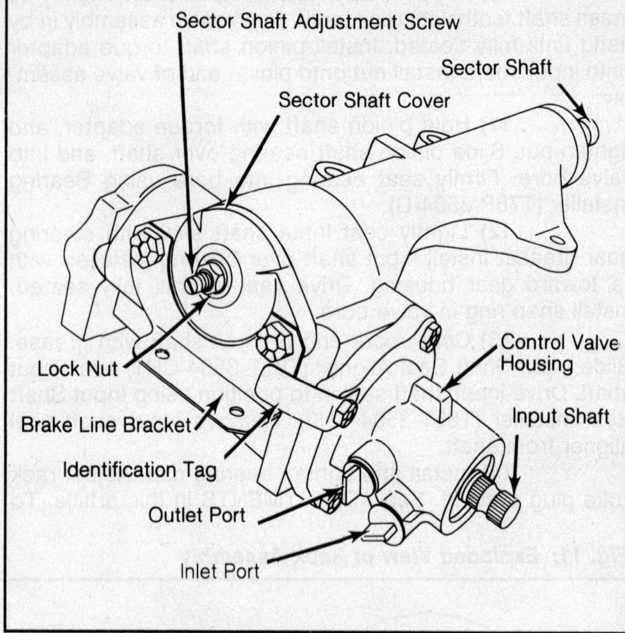

NOTE: When performing test off vehicle, use same procedure, except take torque and pressure readings at right and left stops instead of either side of center.

REMOVAL & INSTALLATION

STEERING GEAR

Removal

1) Disconnect hydraulic lines at power steering gear, and cap lines. Plug ports in steering gear to prevent entry of foreign matter. Remove splash shield from flex coupling. Disconnect flex coupling at steering gear.

2) Raise vehicle and remove pitmam arm, attaching nut and washer. Using puller, remove pitman arm from sector shaft, being careful not to damage seals.

3) Support steering gear and remove steering gear attaching bolts. Work steering gear free of flex coupling and remove steering gear from vehicle.

Installation

1) Slide flex coupling into position on steering shaft assembly and turn steering wheel so spokes are in horizontal position. Center steering gear input shaft with indexing flat facing down.

2) Install gearbox input shaft into flex coupling and into place on frame. Install and tighten attaching bolts. With wheels in straight ahead position, install pitman arm on sector shaft. Install washer and nut on pitman arm and tighten.

3) Install splash shield. Connect and tighten pressure and return lines to steering gear. Disconnect coil wire. Fill reservoir to proper level. Turn ignition on and turn steering wheel left to right to distribute fluid. Check fluid and add if necessary.

Power Steering Gears

FORD TORSION BAR (Cont.)

OVERHAUL

NOTE: **If complete gearbox assembly is not to be overhauled, remove unit to be overhauled and proceed to disassembly and reassembly of that unit.**

STEERING GEAR

Disassembly

1) Drain steering gear completely, and mount gear in a soft-jawed vise. Remove lock nut and washer from adjusting screw. Turn input shaft to either stop, then turn shaft back 2 turns to center gear.

2) Remove sector shaft cover attaching bolts. Tap lower end of sector shaft with a soft faced hammer to loosen shaft in bore, then lift shaft and cover assembly from housing. Discard cover "O" ring.

3) Turn sector shaft cover counterclockwise to remove it from adjusting screw. Remove valve housing attaching bolts and identification tag. Lift valve housing from steering gear housing while holding piston to prevent it from rotating off worm shaft.

4) Remove valve housing and control valve gasket. Discard gasket. With piston held so that ball guide faces up, remove ball guide clamp screws and ball guide clamp.

5) Over a clean container, place finger over opening in ball guide, turn piston so ball guide faces down and let guide tubes fall into container.

6) Rotate input shaft stop to stop until all balls fall from piston into container. Remove valve assembly from piston. Inspect piston bore to ensure all balls have been removed.

7) Install valve body assembly in bench mounted Holding Fixture (T57L-500-B) or vise. Loosen hex head race nut screw from bearing race nut. *See Fig. 2.* Carefully slide input shaft, worm and valve assembly out of valve housing.

CAUTION: **Due to tight clearance, cocking of spool may cause it to jam in housing.**

Reassembly

1) Mount valve housing in a holding fixture with flanged end upward. Apply a light coat of lubricant to Teflon rings on valve sleeve, then carefully install worm and valve in housing.

2) Install race nut in housing and tighten securely. Install Allen head race nut set screw through housing and tighten. Place piston on bench with ball guide holes facing up.

3) Insert worm shaft into piston so that first groove is in line with hole nearest center of piston. Place ball guide in piston. Place a minimum of 27 ball bearings in ball guide while turning worm counterclockwise as viewed from input end of shaft.

4) If all balls have not been fed into guide upon reaching left stop, rotate input shaft in one direction and then other while inserting remaining balls. DO NOT rotate input shaft more than 3 turns from left stop or balls will fall out of circuit.

5) Secure guides in ball nut with guide clamp. Apply petroleum jelly to Teflon seal on piston and place a new "O" ring on valve housing. Slide piston and valve into gear housing, using care not to damage piston ring.

6) Align oil passage in valve housing with passage in gear housing. Place new "O" ring in oil passage hole of gear housing. Install identification tag on housing on upper right valve housing bolt.

7) Loosely install housing attaching bolts, rotate ball nut so that teeth are in same place as sector teeth and tighten valve housing bolts. Position sector shaft cover "O" ring in steering gear housing. Turn input shaft as necessary to center piston.

8) Apply petroleum jelly to sector shaft journal, and position sector shaft and cover assembly in gear

Fig. 2: Removing Worm Bearing Race Nut

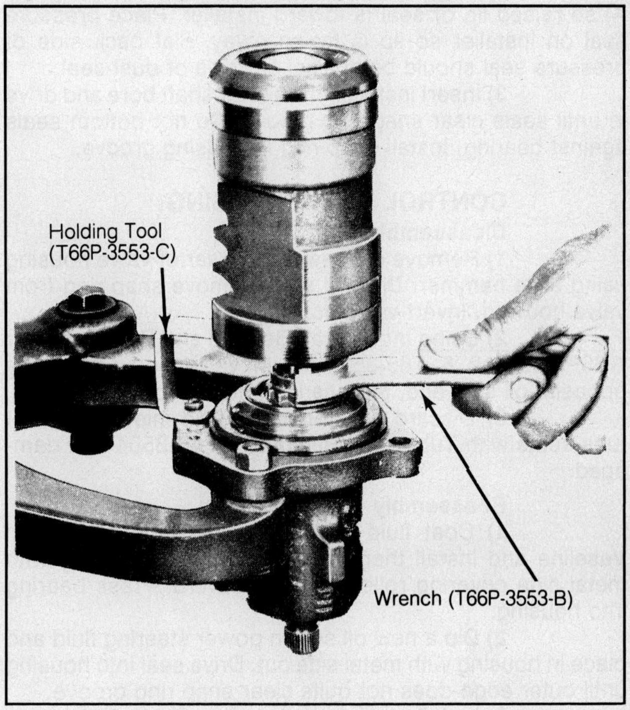

Fig. 3: Installing Piston on Worm Shaft

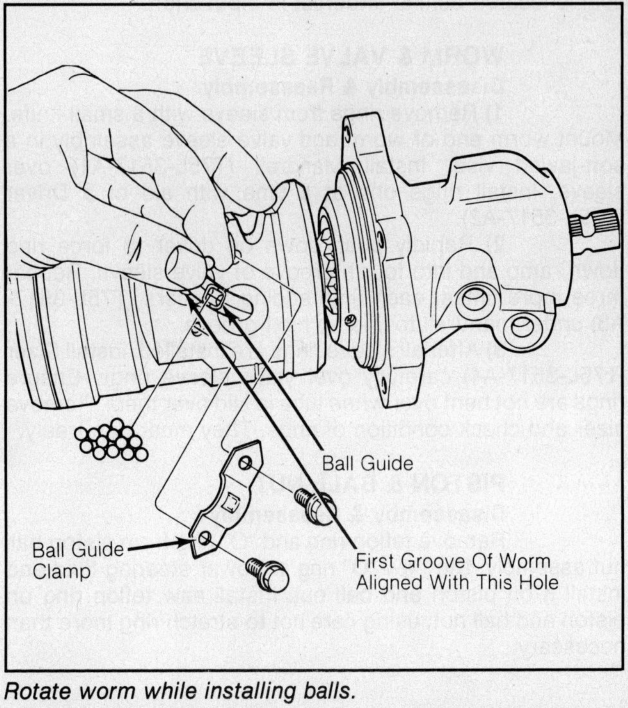

Rotate worm while installing balls.

Power Steering Gears

FORD TORSION BAR (Cont.)

housing. Install and tighten cover attaching bolts. Adjust steering over-center position. See OVER-CENTER POSITION in this article.

STEERING GEAR HOUSING

Disassembly & Reassembly

1) Remove snap ring from lower end of housing. Using a puller or slide hammer, remove dust seal and pressure seal from housing. Lubricate new seals and sector shaft seal bore with Lubriplate.

2) Place dust seal on Seal Installer (T77L-3576-A) so raised lip of seal is toward installer. Place pressure seal on installer so lip is facing away. Flat back side of pressure seal should be against flat side of dust seal.

3) Insert installer into sector shaft bore and drive in until seals clear snap ring groove. Do not bottom seals against bearing. Install snap ring in housing groove.

CONTROL VALVE HOUSING

Disassembly

1) Remove dust seal from rear of valve housing using slide hammer. Discard seal. Remove snap ring from valve housing. Invert valve housing.

2) Using Input Shaft Bearing and Seal Remover (T65P-3524-A2 & T65-3524-A3) in valve body assembly opposite oil seal end, tap bearing and seal out of housing.

3) Discard seal. Remove fluid inlet and outlet tube seats with Tube Seat Remover (T74P-3504-L) if damaged.

Reassembly

1) Coat fluid inlet and outlet tube seats with Vaseline and install them in housing. Install bearing with metal side covering rollers facing outward. Press bearing into housing.

2) Dip a new oil seal in power steering fluid and place in housing with metal side out. Drive seal into housing until outer edge does not quite clear snap ring groove.

3) Install snap ring in housing. Place dust seal in housing with dished rubber side out. Drive into place until seal is located behind undercut in input shaft.

WORM & VALVE SLEEVE

Disassembly & Reassembly

1) Remove rings from sleeve with a small knife. Mount worm end of worm and valve sleeve assembly in a soft-jawed vise. Install Mandrell (T75L-3517-A1) over sleeve. Install rings one at a time with aid of a Driver (T75L-3517-A2).

2) Rapidly push down on driver to force ring down ramp and into fourth groove of valve sleeve. Repeat three more times, each time adding Spacers (T75L-3517-A3) under mandrell to line up next groove.

3) After all sleeve rings are installed, install Sizer (T75L-3517-A4) carefully over valve sleeve rings. Ensure rings are not bent over when tube is slid over them. Remove sizer and check condition of rings. They must turn freely.

PISTON & BALL NUT

Disassemby & Reassembly

Remove teflon ring and "O" ring from piston ball nut assembly. Dip new "O" ring in power steering fluid and install it on piston and ball nut. Install new teflon ring on piston and ball nut, using care not to stretch ring more than necessary.

Fig. 4: Disassembled View of Control Valve Housing

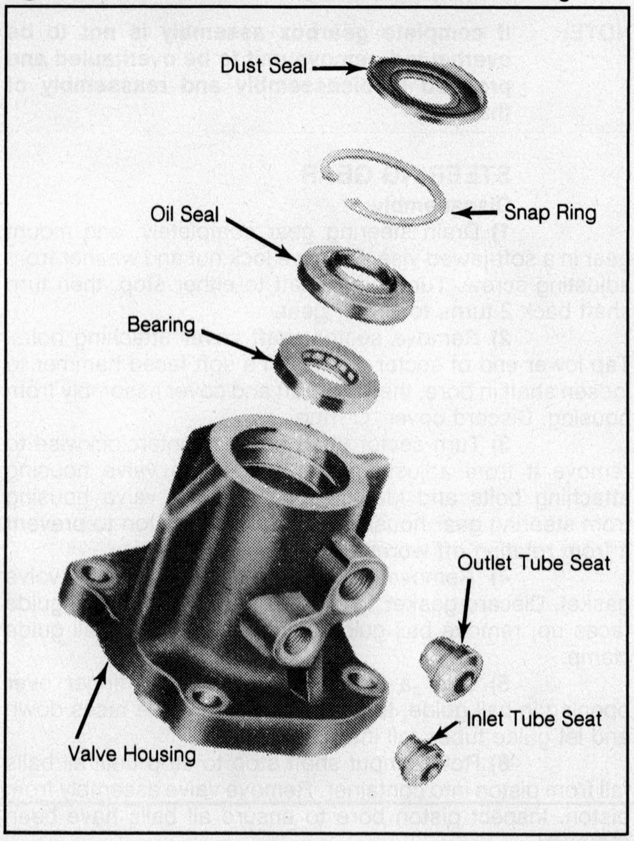

TIGHTENING SPECIFICATIONS

Application	Ft. Lbs. (N.m)
Piston End Cap	70-110 (95-150)
Flex Coupling Bolt	25-34 (34-46)
Mesh Load Adj. Screw Lock Nut	35-45 (48-61)
Pitman Arm Nut	190-230 (230-310)
Race Retaining Nut	[1]
Sector Shaft Cover Bolts	55-70 (75-95)
Valve Housing-to-Gear Bolts	35-45 (48-61)
	INCH Lbs. (N.m)
Allen Head Race Nut Set Screw	15-25 (1.6-2.8)
Ball Return Guide Clamp Screw	42-70 (4.7-7.9)

[1] - Tool used with torque wrench will affect observed reading at torque wrench. To obtain required torque, multiply length of torque wrench by desired torque (72 ft. lbs.; 98 N.m), and divide this product by total length of torque wrench and tool (5.5").

Power Steering Gears

FORD TORSION BAR (Cont.)

Fig. 5: Disassembled View of Ball Nut & Housing

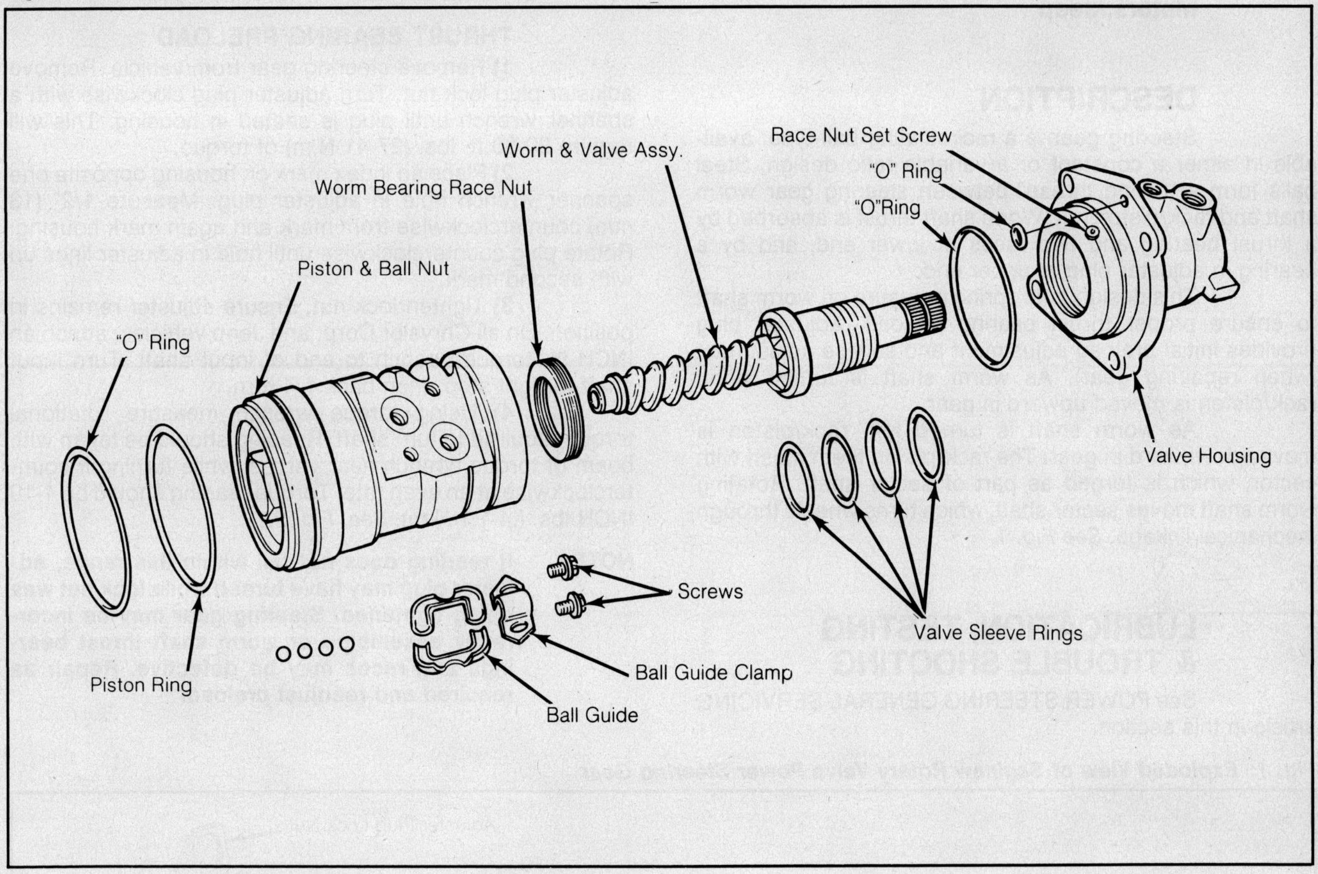

Power Steering Gears

SAGINAW ROTARY VALVE

Chrysler Corp. (Exc. Van), General Motors, Jeep

DESCRIPTION

Steering gear is a recirculating ball-type, available in either a constant or a variable ratio design. Steel balls form a "rolling thread" between steering gear worm shaft and rack/piston nut. Worm shaft thrust is absorbed by a thrust bearing and two races at lower end, and by a bearing in adjuster plug at upper end.

This design puts spring pressure on worm shaft to ensure proper thrust bearing preload. Adjuster plug provides initial preload adjustment and service adjustment (when repairing gear). As worm shaft is turned right, rack/piston is moved upward in gear.

As worm shaft is turned left, rack/piston is moved downward in gear. The rack/piston teeth mesh with sector, which is forged as part of sector shaft. Rotating worm shaft moves sector shaft, which turns wheels through mechanical linkage. *See Fig. 1*.

LUBRICATION, TESTING & TROUBLE SHOOTING

See POWER STEERING GENERAL SERVICING article in this section.

ADJUSTMENT

THRUST BEARING PRELOAD

1) Remove steering gear from vehicle. Remove adjuster plug lock nut. Turn adjuster plug clockwise with a spanner wrench until plug is seated in housing. This will require 20-30 ft. lbs. (27-41 N.m) of torque.

2) Place an index mark on housing opposite one spanner wrench hole in adjuster plug. Measure 1/2" (13 mm) counterclockwise from mark and again mark housing. Rotate plug counterclockwise until hole in adjuster lines up with second mark.

3) Tighten lock nut. Ensure adjuster remains in position. On all Chrysler Corp. and Jeep vehicles, attach an INCH lb. torque wrench to end of input shaft. Turn input shaft to right stop, then back 1/4 turn.

4) Using torque wrench measure rotational torque required to turn shaft. Reading should be taken with beam of torque wrench near vertical while turning it counterclockwise at an even rate. Torque reading should be 4-10 INCH lbs. (.4-1.1 N.m). *See. Fig. 2*.

NOTE: **If reading does not fall within this range, adjuster plug may have turned while lock nut was being tightened. Steering gear may be incorrectly assembled or worm shaft thrust bearings and races may be defective. Repair as required and readjust preload.**

Fig. 1: Exploded View of Saginaw Rotary Valve Power Steering Gear

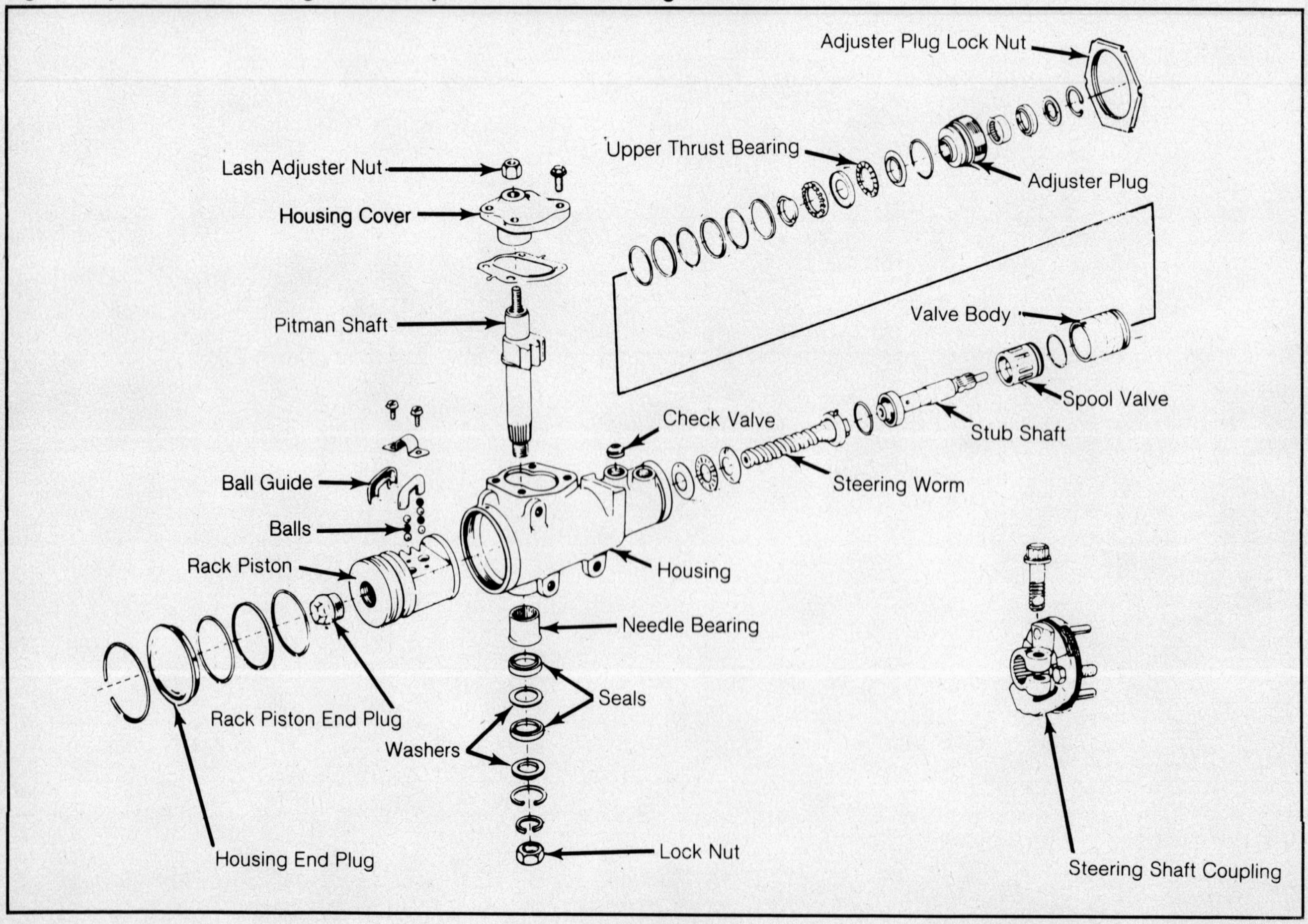

SAGINAW ROTARY VALVE (Cont.)

Fig. 2: Measuring Thrust Bearing Preload

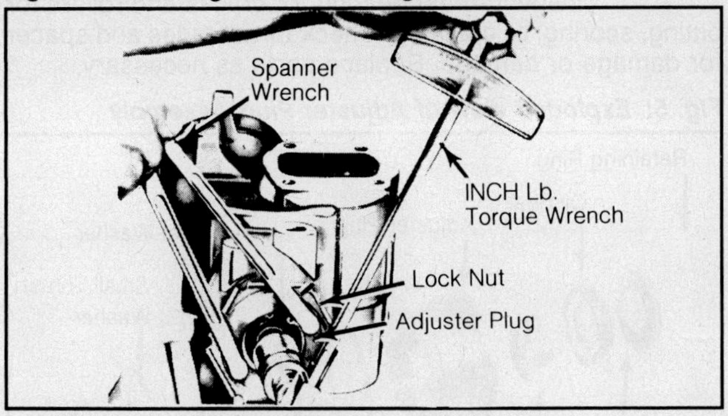

Preload should be 4-10 INCH lbs. (.4-1.1 N.m).

Fig. 3: Adjusting Over-Center Preload

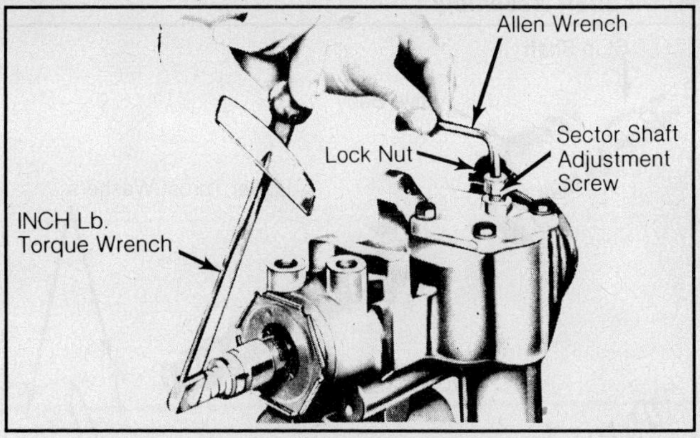

Adjust thrust bearing preload before over-center preload.

OVER-CENTER PRELOAD TORQUE

1) Loosen adjuster screw lock nut. Back off adjuster screw until stopped, then turn in 1 full turn. Rotate input shaft from stop to stop counting number of turns. Turn shaft half way back to center position.

2) Attach an INCH lb. torque wrench to input shaft. Turn shaft from side to side through specified arc on each side of center. See OVER-CENTER PRELOAD chart. Note torque reading going over center. *See Fig. 3.*

OVER-CENTER PRELOAD INCH LBS. (N.m)

Application	Arc	Over-Center	[1] Total
Chrysler Corp.			
New Gears	90°	4-8 (.5-.9)	14 (1.5)
Used Gears [2]	90°	4-5 (.5-.6)	14 (1.5)
General Motors			
New Gears	20°	6-10 (.7-1.1)	18 (2)
Used Gears	20°	4-5 (.5-.6)	18 (2)
Jeep			
New Gears	45°	4-8 (.4-.9)	14 (1.5)
Used Gears	45°	4-5 (.5-.6)	14 (1.5)

[1] - Total preload is sum of thrust bearing and over-center preload.
[2] - In service for more than 400 miles (640 km.).

REMOVAL & INSTALLATION

STEERING GEAR

Removal

1) Remove collapsible steering column. Raise and support vehicle. Place drain pan under steering gear assembly. Center steering gear. Disconnect hydraulic hoses from gear and cap ends. Disconnect steering linkage from pitman arm. Remove pitman arm from gear.

2) Remove flexible coupling clamp bolt and bolts retaining steering gear to frame. Disconnect gear from flexible coupling and remove gear from vehicle. On Jeep CJ7 and Scrambler models, remove steering gear and mounting bracket as an assembly.

Installation

To install, reverse removal procedure. Fill pump reservoir and bleed air from system. See POWER STEERING GENERAL SERVICING article in this section.

OVERHAUL

STEERING GEAR

Disassembly

1) Cap all openings in gear and clean gear exterior throughly. Mount gear in vise so that pitman shaft points downward. Rotate housing end plug retainer ring until one end of plug is over hole in housing.

2) Force end of ring from groove in housing and remove. Rotate input shaft counterclockwise to force housing end plug out of housing. Rotate input shaft clockwise 1/2 turn to draw rack/piston inward. Remove piston end plug.

CAUTION: Do not rotate shaft more than is necessary to remove plug as ball bearings will fall out of worm and rack piston assembly.

3) Remove lock nut from sector shaft adjuster. Remove sector shaft cover. Remove and discard "O" ring from cover. Turn input shaft until sector shaft teeth are centered in housing.

4) Tap end of sector shaft with a soft-faced hammer to free shaft from housing, then remove sector shaft. Remove adjuster plug lock nut. Remove adjuster plug with a spanner wrench.

5) Insert a rack/piston arbor into end of rack/piston until arbor just contacts worm shaft. Turn stub shaft counterclockwise to force rack/piston onto arbor. Remove rack/piston and arbor as an assembly.

6) Take care to keep arbor fully inserted so ball bearings will not fall out. Remove input shaft and control valve assembly from housing. Remove worm, wormshaft lower thrust bearing, and races from housing.

Reassembly

1) Lubricate all parts with clean power steering fluid before reassembly. Install lower thrust bearing and races on worm. *See Fig. 4.*

NOTE: If conical thrust races are used, ensure tapered surfaces are parallel to each other and that cupped sides face toward stub shaft.

Power Steering Gears

SAGINAW ROTARY VALVE (Cont.)

Fig. 4: Reassembly of Valve Body & Worm Shaft Assembly

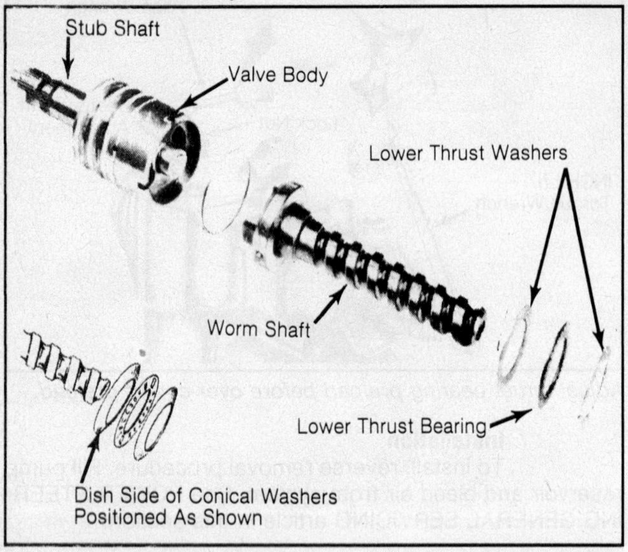

Cupped side of thrust washers must face toward stub shaft.

2) Install stub shaft cap "O" ring in valve body. Align valve body drive pin on worm with narrow pin slot in valve body. Worm drive lugs must engage in stub shaft cap.

3) Install valve body and worm assembly into housing. Perform installation by pressing directly on valve body only. This will prevent stub shaft "O" ring from disengaging from valve body.

4) Valve body is correctly seated when fluid return port in housing is fully visible. Ensure worm locating pin is fully engaged in valve body. Place seal protector over input shaft, install a new adjuster plug "O" ring, then install adjuster plug.

5) Remove seal protector from housing and loosely install adjuster plug lock nut. Insert arbor and rack/piston into housing. Align worm and rack/piston and turn stub shaft clockwise to engage worm. Maintain pressure on arbor until worm is fully engaged.

6) Turn input shaft clockwise until middle rack groove in rack/piston is aligned with center of sector shaft roller bearing. Remove arbor. Install a new sector shaft cover gasket.

7) Thread sector shaft cover onto adjuster screw until bottomed. Back off 1 1/2 turns. Install sector shaft so that center gear tooth meshes with center groove in rack/piston. Install cover attaching bolts.

8) Install adjuster lock nut halfway onto sector shaft. Install piston and plug in rack/piston. Install housing end plug "O" ring, end plug and retainer ring. Adjust worm bearing preload and over-center preload at this time.

ADJUSTER PLUG

Disassembly

1) Remove thrust bearing retainer ring with a screwdriver, taking care not to score needle bearing bore. Discard retainer ring. Remove thrust bearing spacer, thrust bearing and bearing races.

2) Remove and discard adjuster plug "O" ring, then remove input shaft seal retainer. Remove and discard dust seal. Pry input shaft seal from adjuster plug.

3) Inspect needle bearing in adjuster plug. If necessary, remove bearing by pressing out from spacer end. *See Fig. 5.*

Inspection

Inspect thrust bearing for cracks and rollers for pitting, scoring, or cracking. Check thrust races and spacer for damage or damage. Replace parts as necessary.

Fig. 5: Exploded View of Adjuster Plug Assembly

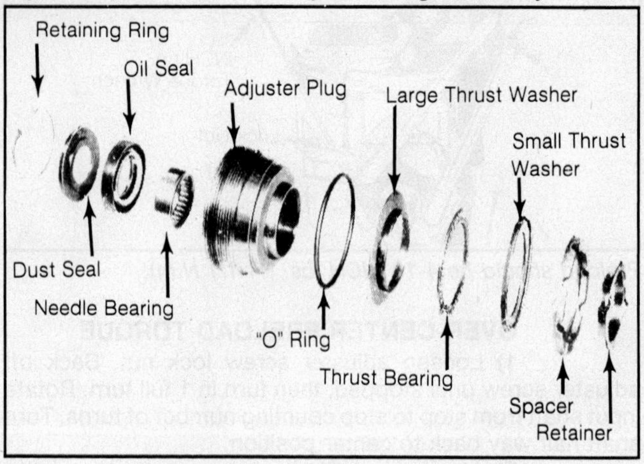

Reassembly

1) Press roller bearing into adjuster plug (identification end facing arbor) until bearing bottoms on input shaft seal bore. Install input shaft seal with spring in seal facing adjuster plug.

2) Install dust seal into adjuster plug. Rubber face of seal must face away from plug. Install retainer ring. Install adjuster plug "O" ring.

3) Assemble thrust bearing, thrust bearing race, and thrust bearing spacer on adjuster plug. Using a brass or wooden dowel, press bearing retainer into needle bearing bore.

RACK/PISTON & WORM

Disassembly

Remove worm, lower thrust bearing and bearing races from rack piston. Remove piston ring and back-up "O" ring from rack/piston. Remove ball return guide clamp, ball return guide and all ball bearings from rack/piston.

Inspection

1) Clean and dry all parts. Inspect worm and rack/piston grooves for scoring. Inspect ball bearings for damage. If any ball bearings are damaged, replace entire set. Check ball guides for pinching of ends.

2) Inspect lower thrust bearing races for cracking, scoring, or pitting. Replace wormshaft and rack/piston as an assembly if either part is damaged. Inspect rack/piston teeth for chips, cracks, dents or scoring.

Reassembly

1) Install "O" ring and piston ring onto rack/piston using care not to twist them. Install worm into rack/piston until worm is against piston shoulder. Install ball bearings into rack/piston while slowly rotating worm counterclockwise.

NOTE: **See RACK PISTON & WORM ASSEMBLY BALL BEARINGS table for number of balls to be installed. BE SURE to install light and dark colored balls alternately, as Black balls are .0005" smaller than Silver balls.**

SAGINAW ROTARY VALVE (Cont.)

2) Install correct number of balls in ball guide. Bearings in guide must be in sequence with bearings in rack/piston. Hold balls in place with chassis lubricant and install return ball guide assembly into position.

3) Install clamp and tighten attaching bolts. *See Fig. 6.* Insert rack/piston arbor into rack/piston until it contacts worm. Maintain pressure on arbor, and back worm out of rack/piston. DO NOT allow ball bearings to drop out of circuits.

RACK PISTON & WORM ASSEMBLY BALL BEARINGS

Application	Rack/Piston	Guide
Chrysler Corp.	19	5
General Motors	17	7
Jeep	18	6

Fig. 6: Installing Ball Bearing into Rack/Piston Assembly

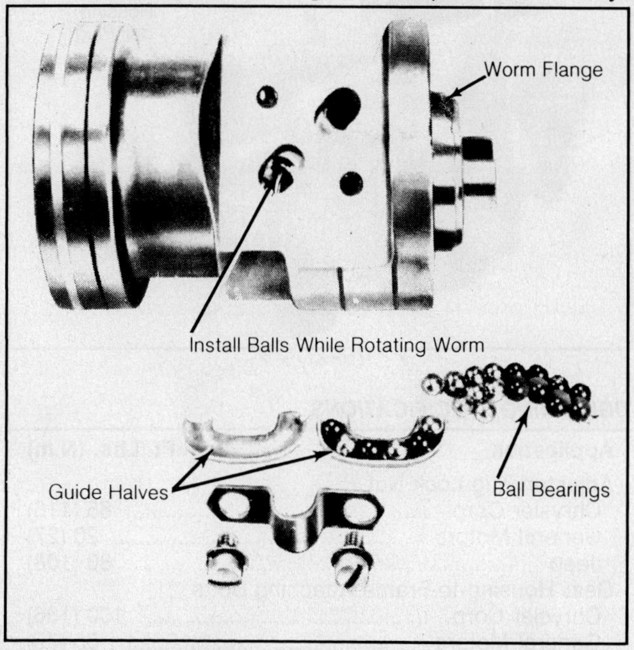

Alternate light and dark colored balls when installing.

ROTARY VALVE

NOTE: Complete valve assembly is balanced during assembly. If replacement of any part other than rings or seals is necessary, replace complete assembly.

Disassembly

1) Remove and discard stub shaft cap "O" ring. Invert valve and lightly tap end of stub shaft against wood block until shaft cap is free of valve body. Pull stub shaft outward until drive pin hole is visible. *See Fig. 7.*

NOTE: Do not pull shaft any further than 1/4" (6 mm) or spool valve may become cocked in valve body.

2) Disengage drive pin and carefuly remove stub shaft from valve body and spool assembly with a twisting motion. If binding occurs, realign valve and try removal again.

CAUTION: Do not force stub shaft or spool out of valve body.

Fig. 7: Pulling Shaft from Valve Assembly

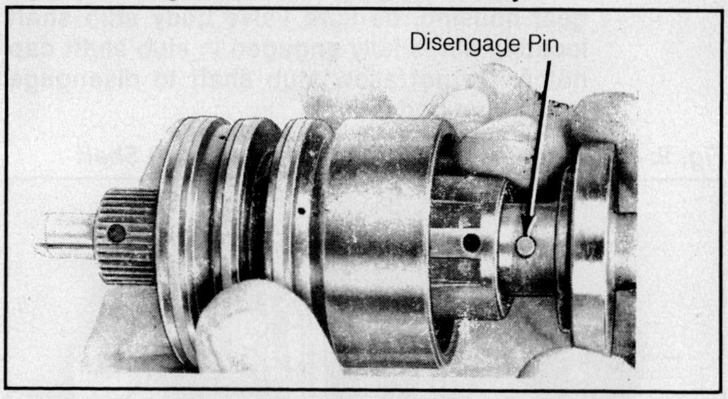

Depress pin to remove stub shaft from valve body.

3) Remove spool valve from valve body with twisting motion. Remove and discard all "O" rings and Teflon rings.

Fig. 8: Exploded View of Valve Body Assembly

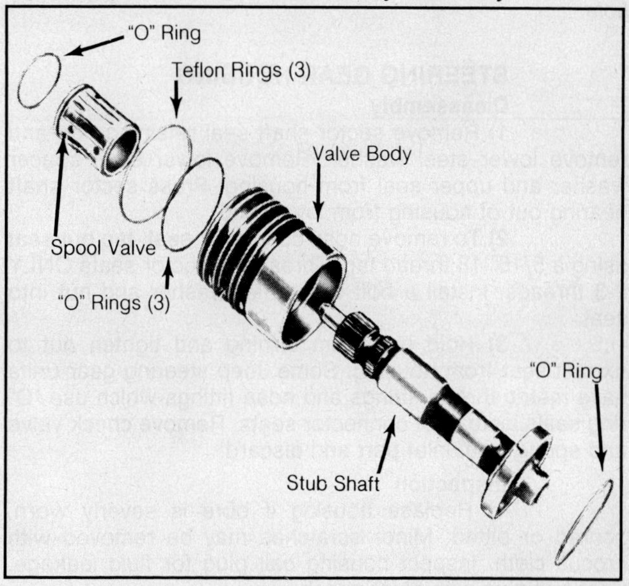

Reassembly

1) Lubricate all valve body components with power steering fluid. Install replacement back-up "O" rings in seal grooves and install replacement seal rings over back-up rings. Take care not to damage seal rings during installation.

NOTE: Teflon seal rings may appear to be distorted after installation. However, heat of operation will straighten them.

2) Lubricate replacement spool valve damper "O" ring with petroleum jelly. Install on spool valve. Carefully insert spool valve into valve body.

3) Push spool valve through valve body until locating pin hole is visible at opposite end of valve body and spool valve is flush with notched end of valve. Install stub shaft in spool valve and valve body.

4) Be sure stub shaft locating pin is aligned with spool valve locating hole. Align notch in stub shaft cap with stub shaft locating pin and press sub shaft and spool valve into valve body. Install stub shaft cap "O" ring into valve body. *See Fig. 9.*

Power Steering Gears

SAGINAW ROTARY VALVE (Cont.)

CAUTION: Before installing assembled valve body into gear housing, be sure valve body stub shaft locating pin is fully engaged in stub shaft cap notch. Do not allow stub shaft to disengage from valve body pin.

Fig. 9: Aligning Pin and Notch for Input (Stub) Shaft

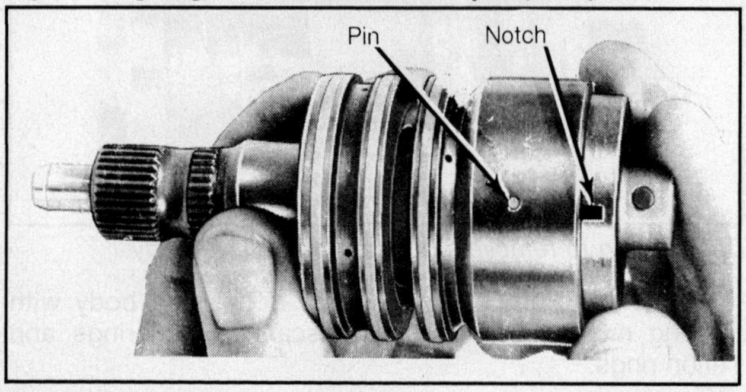

Stub shaft locating pin must align with spool valve locating hole.

STEERING GEAR HOUSING

Disassembly

1) Remove sector shaft seal retaining ring and remove lower steel washer. Remove lower seal, spacer washer and upper seal from housing. Press sector shaft bearing out of housing from lower end.

2) To remove hose connector seat, tap out seat using a 5/16"-18 thread tap. Thread connector seats ONLY 2-3 threads. Install a bolt with a flat washer and nut into seat.

3) Hold bolt from turning and tighten nut to extract seat from housing. Some Jeep steering gear units have metric thread fittings and hose fittings which use "O" ring seals instead of connector seats. Remove check valve and spring from inlet port and discard.

Inspection

1) Replace housing if bore is severly worn, scored or pitted. Minor scratches may be removed with crocus cloth. Inspect housing ball plug for fluid leakage. Seat ball plug with blunt punch.

2) Spray ball area with Loctite Solvent 7559 and dry with compressed air. Cover ball area with Loctite Sealant 290. Allow sealant to cure for 2 hours before assembling gear.

3) Inspect all retaining ring, bearing and seal surfaces in housing. Replace housing if any surface is worn or damaged.

Reassembly

1) Working from upper end, press a new bearing into housing until it is seated .030" (.76 mm) below shoulder in housing bore. Lubricate new seal with power steering fluid.

2) Install single lipped seal and spacer washer only far enough to provide clearance for next seal, washer and retaining ring. DO NOT bottom seal against housing counterbore.

3) Install double lipped seal and steel washer. Install retaining ring. DO NOT allow seals to contact one another. To ensure proper seal action, be sure there is clearance between them.

4) If port seat was removed, position new spring, check valve, and a new seat over opening in housing. Drive into place using a brass drift.

Fig. 10: Gear Housing Seals and Bearing

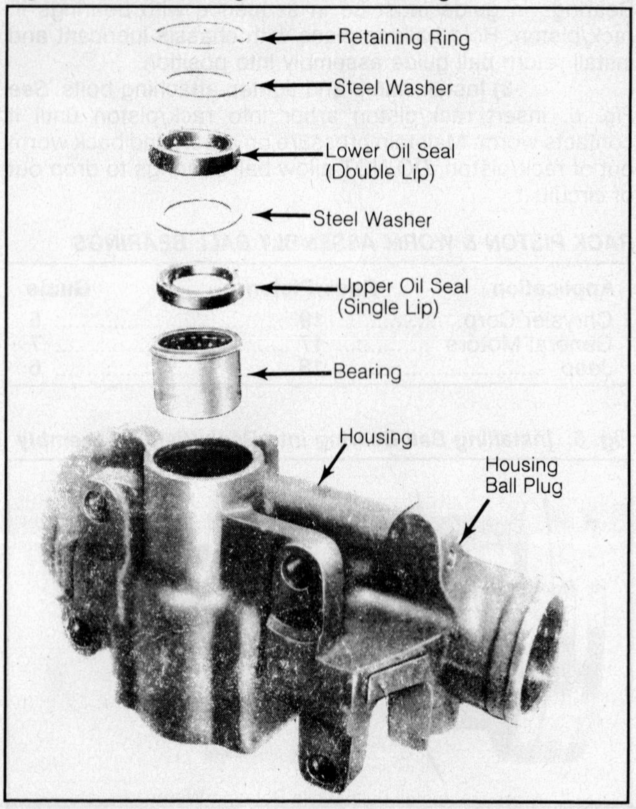

TIGHTENING SPECIFICATIONS

Application	Ft. Lbs. (N.m)
Adjuster Plug Lock Nut	
Chrysler Corp.	85 (116)
General Motors	20 (27)
Jeep	80 (108)
Gear Housing-to-Frame Attaching Bolts	
Chrysler Corp.	100 (136)
General Motors	55 (75)
Jeep	
CJ7 & Scrambler	55 (75)
Cherokee & Wagoneer	65 (88)
Grand Wagoneer & Trucks	70 (95)
Pitman Arm Attaching Nut	
Chrysler Corp.	175 (237)
General Motors	185 (250)
Jeep	185 (251)
Rack Piston End Plug	
Chrysler Corp.	50 (68)
General Motors	75 (102)
Jeep	
All Except Cherokee & Wagoneer	75 (102)
Cherokee & Wagoneer	50 (68)
Sector Shaft Adjuster Lock Nut	
Chrysler Corp.	28 (38)
General Motors	20 (27)
Jeep	33 (45)

Power Steering Pumps

FORD C-II

Aerostar, Bronco, Bronco II, "F" Series, Ranger

DESCRIPTION

C-II power steering pump is a belt driven, slipper-type integral pump with a fiber glass nylon reservoir. Reservoir is attached to rear side of pump housing front plate. Pump body is encased within housing and reservoir.

Hoses are attached with quick disconnect fittings, located below filler neck at outboard side of reservoir. A pressure sensitive identification tag is attached to reservoir, indicating basic model number.

LUBRICATION, TROUBLE SHOOTING & TESTING

See POWER STEERING GENERAL SERVICING article in this section.

REMOVAL & INSTALLATION

Removal

1) Disconnect fluid return hose at reservoir and drain fluid. Remove pressure hose from pump. Remove bolts from pump adjustment bracket and loosen pump enough to remove drive belt.

2) Remove pump and adjustment bracket from support bracket. Remove pulley from pump with appropriate pulley puller and remove adjustment bracket attaching bolts. Remove pump.

Installation

1) Install adjustment bracket on pump and tighten bolts. Install pulley on pump with appropriate pulley installer. Place pump with adjustment bracket and pulley on support bracket. Install and tighten adjustment bracket-to-support bracket bolts.

2) Install and adjust belt on pulley, then tighten adjustment bracket bolts. Install hoses to pump, fill reservoir and start engine, turning wheel from stop-to-stop to remove air from system.

OVERHAUL

Disassembly

1) Remove pulley from pump using Pulley Remover (T69L-10300-A). Remove outlet fitting, flow control valve, spring and reservoir. Place a "C" clamp in vise.

2) Install Lower Support Plate (T78P-3733-A1) over pump rotor shaft. Install Upper Compressor Plate (T78P-3733-A2) into upper portion of "C" clamp. Place pump assembly into "C" clamp with rotor shaft facing down. *See Fig. 1.*

3) Tighten "C" clamp until slight bottoming of valve cover is felt. Insert small drift through hole in side of pump housing plate and push inward on valve cover retaining ring. Remove retaining ring. *See Fig. 2.*

4) Remove pump from clamp. Remove valve cover and "O" ring seal. Push on rotor shaft and remove. Remove upper plate, rotor and slippers. Remove cam insert and two dowel pins.

5) Remove lower plate and Belleville spring by lightly tapping housing on flat surface, remove "O" ring. Remove rotor shaft seal and seal retainer with a screwdriver.

Fig. 1: Installing Compressor Plate Tools

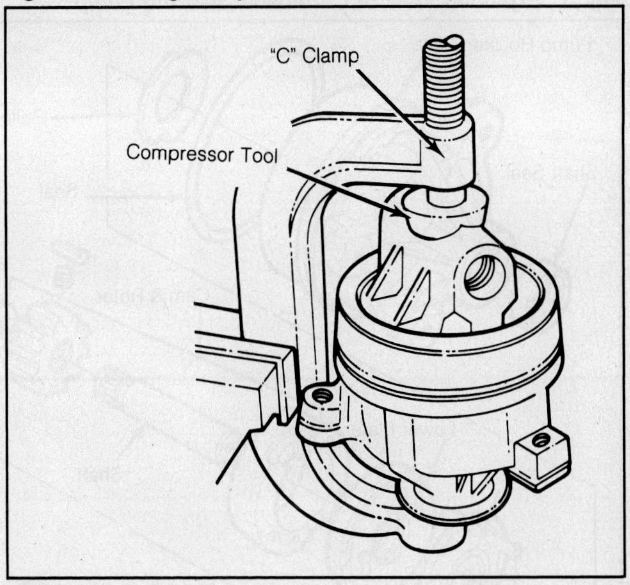

DO NOT overtighten "C" clamp.

Fig. 2: Removing Retaining Ring

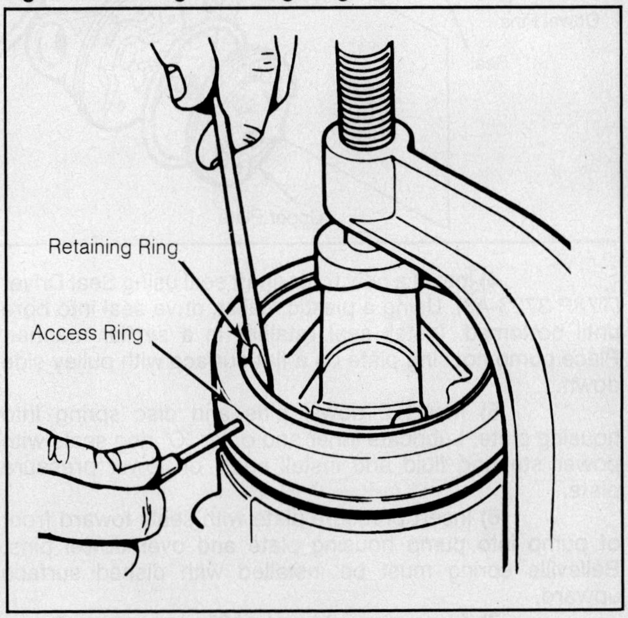

Use screwdriver to pry out retaining ring.

Reassembly

1) Place rotor on rotor shaft splines, with large rotor counterbore facing upward. Install retaining ring in groove in end of rotor shaft. Place insert cam over rotor with recessed flat toward reservoir.

2) With rotor extended half way out of cam, insert a spring into a rotor spring pocket. Work in rotor cavity directly below recessed flat on cam. Use one of slippers to compress spring and install slipper with groove facing upward.

3) Hold cam stationary and turn rotor either direction one space at a time and install another spring and slipper until all 10 rotor cavities have been filled. Be careful when turning rotor that springs and slipper do not fall out.

Power Steering Pumps

FORD C-II (Cont.)

Fig. 3: Exploded View of C-II Power Steering Pump

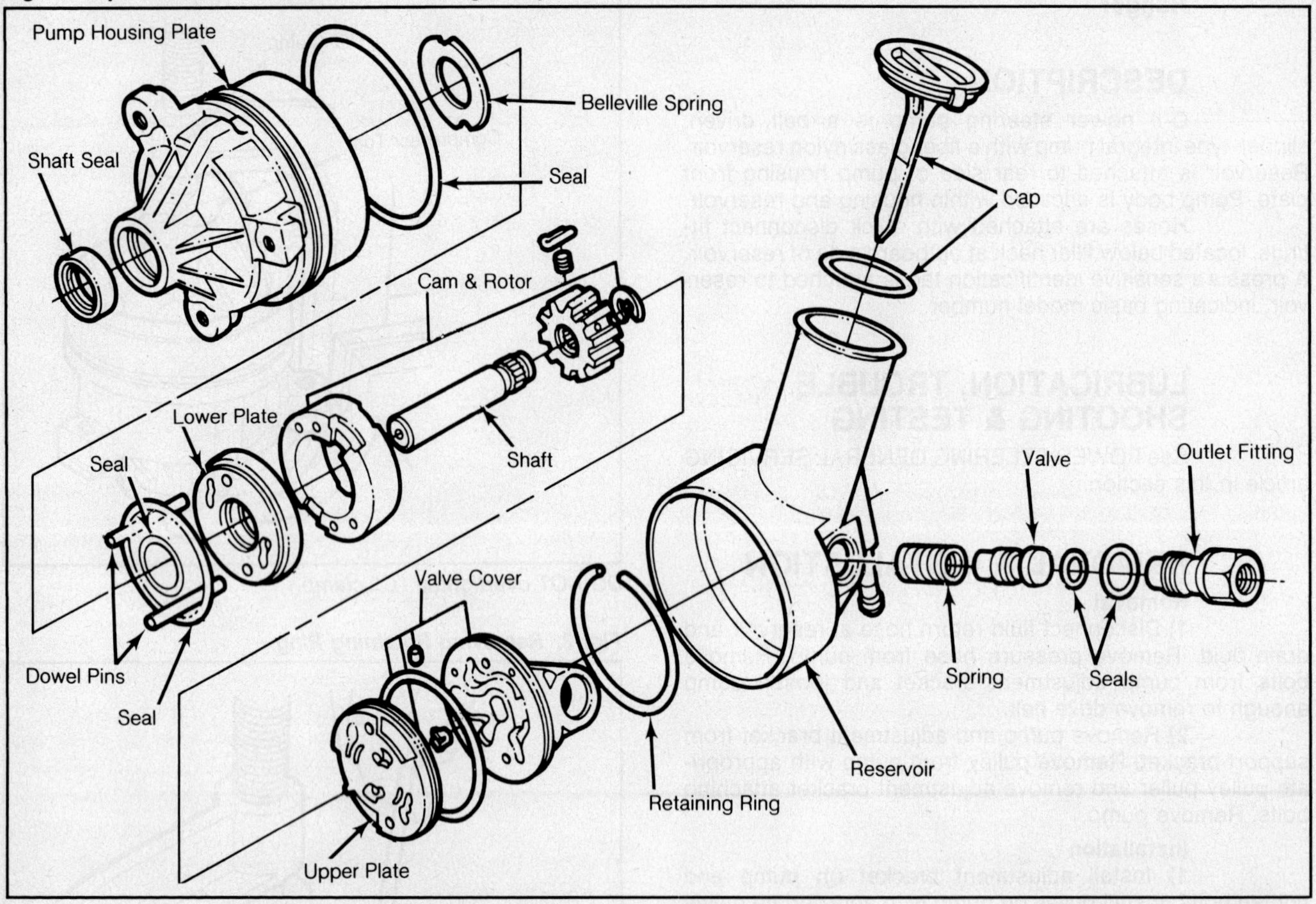

4) Install a new rotor shaft seal using Seal Driver (T78P-3733-A3). Using a plastic mallet, drive seal into bore until bottomed. Install seal retainer in a similar manner. Place pump housing plate on a flat surface with pulley side down.

5) Insert 2 dowel pins and disc spring into housing plate. Lubricate inner and outer "O" ring seals with power steering fluid and install seals on lower pressure plate.

6) Insert pressure plate with seals toward front of pump into pump housing plate and over dowel pins. Belleville spring must be installed with dished surface upward.

7) Place assembly into "C" clamp. Use Driver (T78P-3733-A3) in rotor shaft hole and press lower plate lightly until bottomed in pump plate housing. This will seat "O" ring. Install cam, rotor and slippers, and rotor shaft assembly into pump housing plate over dowel pins.

NOTE: **When installing this assembly, stepped holes must be used for dowel pins, and recessed notch in cam insert must face reservoir and be approximatly 180° opposite square pump mounting boss.**

8) Place upper pressure plate over dowel pins. Side of plate with square recessed notch must face toward reservoir and be positioned 180° opposite square pump mounting boss.

9) Place a new "O" ring seal on valve cover and lubricate with power steering fluid. Insert valve cover over dowel pins. Ensure outlet fitting hole in valve cover is directly in line with square mounting boss of pump housing plate.

10) Place entire assembly in "C" clamp tool. Compress valve cover into pump housing plate, until retaining ring groove is exposed in pump housing plate.

NOTE: **Ensure plastic baffle is securely in place in valve cover. If not, apply petroleum jelly to baffle and install.**

11) Install valve cover retaining ring with ends near access hole in pump housing plate. Remove pump assembly from "C" clamp. Place a new "O" ring seal on pump housing plate. Lubricate seal with power steering fluid. Install power steering reservoir.

12) Install flow control spring and flow control valve in valve cover. Place new "O" ring seals on outlet fitting and lubricate with power steering fluid. Install outlet fitting into valve cover and tighten. Install pulley using Pulley Installer (T65P-3A733-C).

TIGHTENING SPECIFICATIONS

Application	Ft. Lbs. (N.m)
Adjustment Bracket-to-Support	30-45(41-61)
Pressure Hose-to-Rear Fitting	14-29 (19-39)
Pump-to-Adjusting Bracket	30-45 (41-61)
Pump Outlet-to-Pump Valve Cover	25-34 (34-46)
Return Hose-to-Gear Fitting	17-32 (23-44)
Return Line-to-Frame	11-16 (15-22)

Power Steering Pumps

SAGINAW VANE-TYPE

Chrysler Corp.; Ford ("E" Series); General Motors; Jeep

DESCRIPTION

The Saginaw vane-type power steering pump can be identified by "ham-shaped" fluid reservoir can. Internally, rectangular pumping vanes carried by a shaft driven rotor move fluid from intake to pressure cavities of cam ring.

As rotor begins to rotate, centrifugal force throws vanes against inside surface of cam ring to pick up residual oil, which is then forced into high pressure area. As more oil is picked up by vanes, oil is forced into cavities of thrust plate and through 2 cross-over holes in cam ring and pressure plate (which empty into high pressure area between pressure plate and housing end plate).

Filling high pressure area causes oil to flow under vanes in slots of rotor, forcing vanes to follow inside oval surface of cam ring. As vanes rotate to small area of cam ring, oil is forced out from between vanes.

LUBRICATION, TROUBLE SHOOTING & TESTING

See POWER STEERING GENERAL SERVICING article in this section.

REMOVAL & INSTALLATION

POWER STEERING PUMP

Loosen pump adjusting bolt (or nut) and pump mounting bolts, then withdraw pump drive belt. Disconnect pressure and return hoses from pump and cap ends to prevent loss of fluid and entry of dirt.

Remove bolts attaching pump mounting bracket to engine, and withdraw pump, pulley and mounting bracket as an assembly. To install, reverse removal procedure and bleed hydraulic system.

OVERHAUL

CAUTION: When clamping pump in vise, be careful not to exert excessive force on front hub or pump as bushing may become distorted.

Disassembly

1) Do not use a hammer to remove pulley. Drain pump reservoir, clean exterior of unit and remove mounting bracket(s). Using a puller, withdraw pulley from shaft. *See Fig. 1.*

2) Clamp pump (with shaft pointing downward) in a soft jawed vise. Ensure vise grips pump at square boss and shaft housing. Remove pressure line union and "O" ring seal. Remove reservoir retaining studs.

3) Tap against filler tube with plastic hammer to loosen reservoir on pump body. Remove reservoir from body, then withdraw and discard "O" ring seals.

4) Using a 1/8" diameter punch, tap end plate retaining ring around until one end of ring is near hole in pump body. Insert punch in hole far enough to disengage ring from groove in pump bore, then use a screwdriver and pry ring out of body. *See Fig. 2.*

Fig. 1: Removing Pump Pulley

DO NOT use hammer to remove pulley.

Fig. 2: Removing Retaining Ring for Pump End Plate

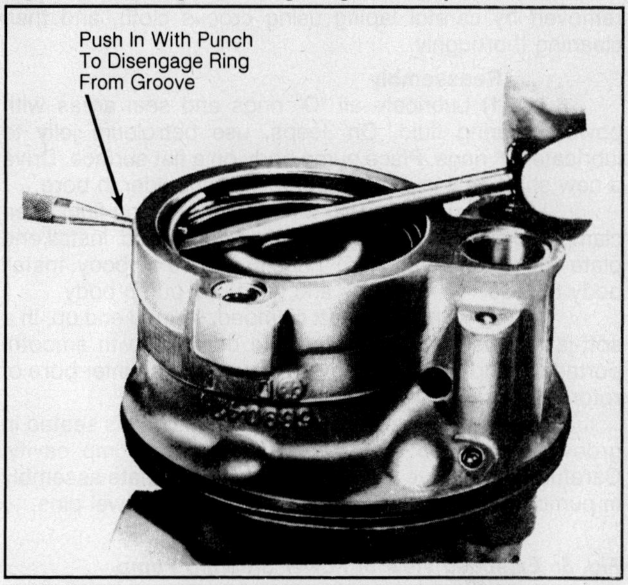

Tap end plate with a soft-faced hammer to break it loose from housing.

5) Tap end plate with a soft faced hammer to break it loose. Spring tension should push plate up. Remove spring. Remove pump from vise.

6) Place pump in inverted position on flat surface, and tap end of drive shaft with soft-faced hammer to loosen pressure plate, rotor, and thrust plate assembly from body.

7) Lift pump body off rotor assembly (flow control valve and spring should also slide out of bore). Remove and discard end plate and pressure plate "O" rings. Pry drive shaft oil seal from body using a screwdriver.

8) Inspect seal bore in housing for burrs, nicks, or score marks that would allow oil to by-pass outer seal surface. Lift pressure plate and cam ring from rotor, then remove rotor vanes.

9) Clamp drive shaft in soft-jawed vise, with rotor and thrust plate facing up, and remove rotor lock ring from shaft. Use care not to nick shaft or rotor. Slide rotor and thrust plate off shaft, and remove shaft from vise.

Cleaning & Inspection

1) Clean all pump components (except drive shaft seal) in clean solvent and blow dry. Inspect flow control valve assembly for wear, scoring, burrs or other damage.

2) Check all machined surfaces of body for scratches or burrs which might allow leaks. Mating surfaces

Power Steering Pumps

SAGINAW VANE-TYPE (Cont.)

on "O" rings require special attention. Inspect pump body drive shaft bushing for excessive wear.

3) If replacement is required, replace pump body and bushing as an assembly. Inspect end cover for nicks and burrs on surface for "O" ring, then polish with a fine oil stone if necessary.

4) Inspect rotor ring for roughness or irregularities. Use a small oil stone to correct minor irregularities and replace ring if outside cam surface is badly worn or scored. Check thrust plate and pressure plate for scoring and wear.

5) To remove light scoring, carefully lap with crocus cloth until surface is smooth and flat. Clean surface thoroughly. Check fit of vanes in rotor to ensure that they slide freely but fit snugly into slots.

6) If vanes are excessively loose in slots, rotor and/or vanes require replacement. Scoring on rotor may be removed by careful laping using crocus cloth, and then cleaning thoroughly.

Reassembly

1) Lubricate all "O" rings and seal areas with power steering fluid. On Jeeps, use petroleum jelly to lubricate "O" rings. Place pump body on a flat surface. Drive a new shaft seal in until it bottoms on shoulder in bore.

2) Lubricate seal with power steering fluid, then clamp body in vise with shaft pointing downward. Install end plate and pressure plate "O" rings in groove on body. Install body to reservoir "O" rings and install on pump body.

3) With drive shaft clamped, splined end up, in a soft-jawed vise, install thrust plate on shaft with smooth, ported side up. Slide rotor over splines with counter bore of rotor facing down.

4) Install rotor lock ring. Ensure ring is seated in groove. Install two dowel pins in holes in pump cavity. Carefully insert drive shaft, rotor, and thrust plate assembly in pump cavity, indexing location holes with dowel pins.

NOTE: Always use a new full diameter locking ring.

5) Slide cam ring over rotor and onto dowel pins, with arrow on ring facing toward rear of housing. Install vanes in rotor slots with radius edge facing out towards cam ring inner surface. Position pressure plate on dowel pins with circular spring depression toward rear of housing.

6) Place a 1 1/4" socket in groove of pressure plate, and seat entire assembly on "O" ring in pump cavity by pressing down on socket with both thumbs. Place spring in groove in pressure plate and position end cover lip edge up over spring.

7) Press end cover down below retaining ring groove with thumb or arbor press. Install retaining ring. Ensure ring is seated in groove. Care should be taken to prevent cocking end cover in bore or distorting assembly.

8) Using a punch, tap retaining ring ends around in groove until opening is opposite flow control valve bore. This is necessary for maximium retention of retaining ring.

9) Install new reservoir "O" ring, mounting stud "O" rings, and flow control valve "O" ring on pump body, then carefully position reservoir on pump body. Align mounting stud holes until studs can be started in threads.

10) Using a soft-faced hammer, tap reservoir down on pump and install flow control valve spring and valve assembly slotted end up. Install new "O" ring seal on pressure hose fitting. Ensure ring is installed on UPPER groove.

CAUTION: It is possible to install pressure hose "O" ring in lower groove. This will restrict relief outlet orifice.

11) Install pressure hose fitting and tighten mounting studs. Tighten hose fitting and rear mounting studs. Remove pump assembly from vise and install mounting bracket and drive pulley.

Fig. 3: Exploded View of Power Steering Pump

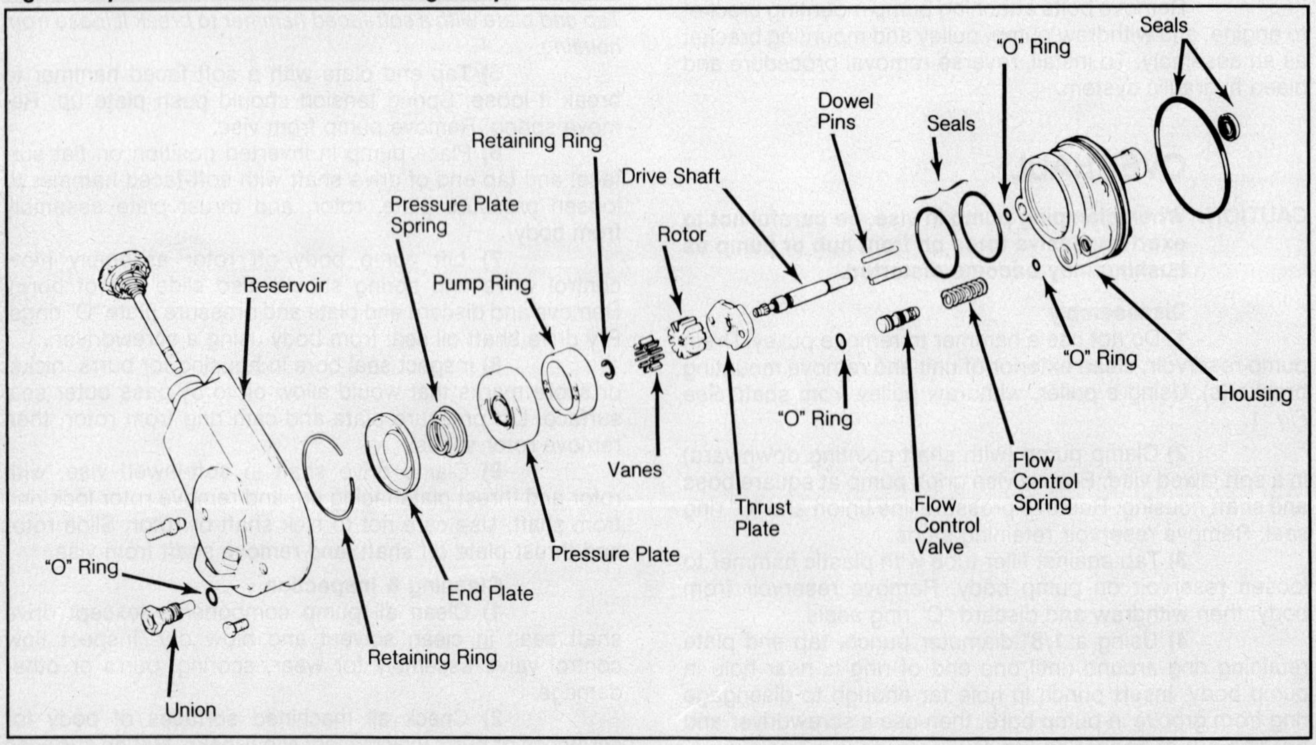

Power Steering Pumps

SAGINAW VANE-TYPE (Cont.)

Fig. 4: Installing Pump Pulley

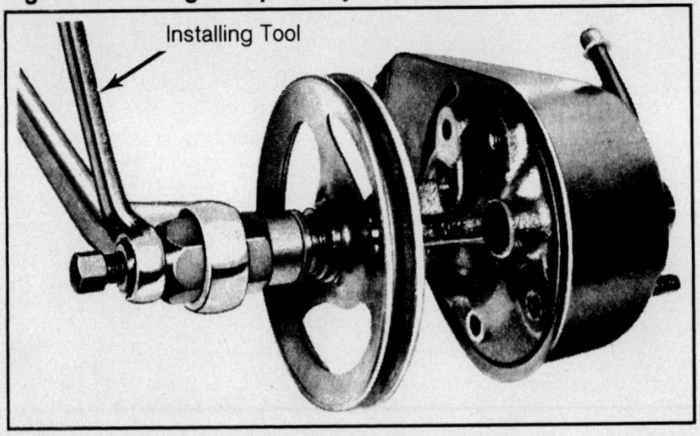

DO NOT hammer pulley onto shaft.

TIGHTENING SPECIFICATIONS

Application	Ft. Lbs. (N.m)
Hose Fittings	
Gear End	
Chrysler Corp.	25 (34)
Ford	20-30 (27-41)
Jeep	20 (27)
Pump End	
Chrysler Corp.	35 (48)
Ford	20-35 (27-48)
Jeep	20 (27)
Bracket Bolts	
All Manufacturers	35 (48)

SECTION 14

TRANSMISSION SERVICING

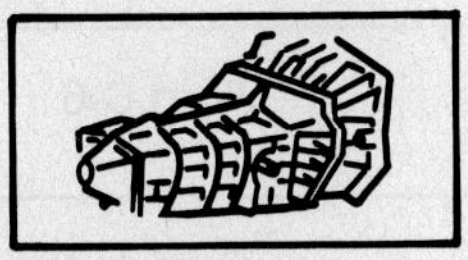

CONTENTS

TRANSMISSION APPLICATIONS — Page

AUTOMATIC TRANSMISSION OIL PAN GASKET IDENTIFICATION

AUTOMATIC TRANSMISSION SERVICING

MANUAL TRANSMISSION SERVICING

AUTOMATIC TRANSMISSION REMOVAL

MANUAL TRANSMISSION REMOVAL

NOTE: ALSO SEE GENERAL INDEX.

IMPORTANT: Because of the many model names used by vehicle manufacturers, accurate identification of models is important. See Model Identification at the front of this publication.

Transmission Application

AUTOMATIC TRANSMISSIONS

MANUFACTURER & MODEL	TRANSMISSION MODEL
CHRYSLER CORP. Ram Van/Wagon, 2WD/4WD Pickup, 4WD Ramcharger	Chrysler Corp. Loadflite A-727
Ram Van/Wagon, 2WD/4WD Pickup	Chrysler Corp. Loadflite A-904T
Ram Van/Wagon, 2WD/4WD Pickup, 2WD/4WD Ramcharger	Chrysler Corp. Loadflite A-999
Caravan, Mini Ram Van, Voyager	Chrysler Corp. Torqueflite A-413
Caravan, Mini Ram Van, Voyager	Chrysler Corp. Torqueflite A-470
FORD Aerostar Van	Ford A4LD Automatic Overdrive
2WD/4WD Ranger, Bronco II	Ford A4LD Automatic Overdrive
F-150 Pickup (4.9L & 5.0L)	Ford C-5
Bronco, E-150/350 Van, 2WD/4WD F-150/350 Pickup	Ford C-6
Bronco, E-150/250 Van, 2WD/4WD F-150/250 Pickup	Ford Automatic Overdrive
GENERAL MOTORS "C" Series, "G" Series, "K" Series	Turbo Hydra-Matic 350C
"C" Series, "G" Series, "K" Series, "P" Series	Turbo Hydra-Matic 400
Astro/Safari Van, "C" Series, "G" Series, "K" Series, "S" Series	Turbo Hydra-Matic 700-R4
JEEP CJ7, J10 Pickup, Scrambler, Grand Wagoneer	Chrysler Corp. Loadflite 999
J10/20 Pickup	Chrysler Corp. Loadflite 727
Cherokee, Wagoneer	Chrysler Corp. Loadflite 904

Transmission Application

MANUAL TRANSMISSIONS

MANUFACTURER & MODEL	TRANSMISSION MODEL
CHRYSLER CORP. 2WD/4WD Pickups, Ramcharger	New Process 435 4-Speed
Ram Van/Wagon, 1/2 Ton 2WD Pickup	Overdrive-4
Caravan, Yoyager, Mini Ram Van	Chrysler A-460 4-Speed
Caravan, Voyager, Mini Ram Van	Chrysler A-525 5-Speed Close Ratio
FORD Aerostar Van	Mazda 5-Speed Manual Overdrive
Bronco II, Ranger	Toyo Kogyo 5-Speed
Bronco II, Ranger	Mitusbishi 5-Speed
E-150 Van, F-150 Pickup	Ford 3.03 3-Speed
Bronco, F-150/350 Pickup	New Process 435 4-Speed
Bronco, F-150/350 Pickup	Warner T-18 4-Speed
Bronco, F-150/250 2WD Pickup, F-150 4WD Pickup	Ford Top Shifter (TOD) 4-Speed Overdrive
F-250/350 Pickup (6.9L Diesel & 7.5 Gas)	Warner T-19B/19D 4-Speed
E-150 Van	Ford 4-Speed Overdrive
GENERAL MOTORS Astro/Safari Van	GM 76 MM 4-Speed
"S" Series	GM 77 MM 4-Speed
"S" Series	GM 77.5 MM 4-Speed
Astro/Safari Van, "S" Series	GM 77 MM 5-Speed
"C" Series, "G" Series, "K" Series, "P" Series	Muncie 76 MM 3-Speed
"C" Series, "G" Series, "K" Series, "P" Series	New Process 89 MM 4-Speed Overdrive
"C" Series, "G" Series, "K" Series, "P" Series	GM 117 MM 4-Speed
JEEP CJ7, Scrambler	Borg-Warner T4 4-Speed
CJ7, Scrambler	Borg-Warner T5 5-Speed Overdrive
J10 Pickup, Grand Wagoneer (Fleet)	Borg-Warner T176 4-Speed
Cherokee, Wagoneer	Aisin AX4 4-Speed
Cherokee, Wagoneer	Aisin AX5 5-Speed Overdrive

OIL PAN GASKET IDENTIFICATION

Fig. 1: Chrysler Corp. & Jeep A727

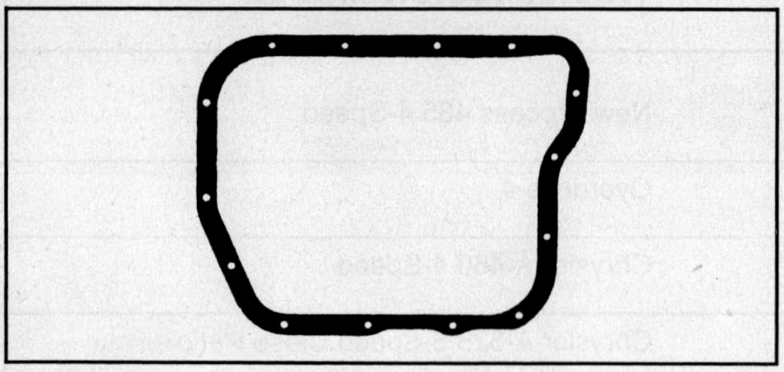

Fig. 2: Chrysler Corp. & Jeep A904T & A999

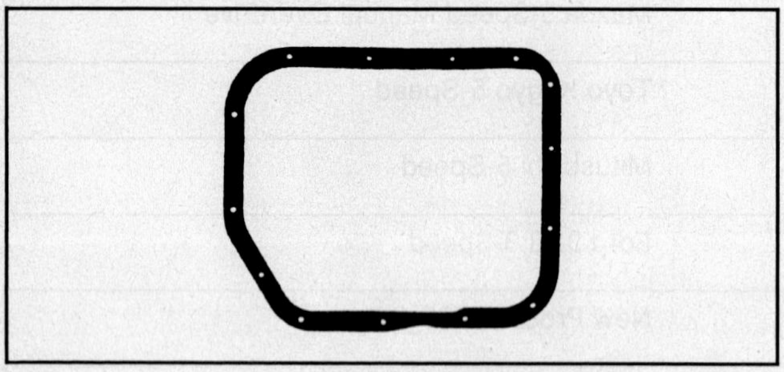

Fig. 3: Ford A4LD

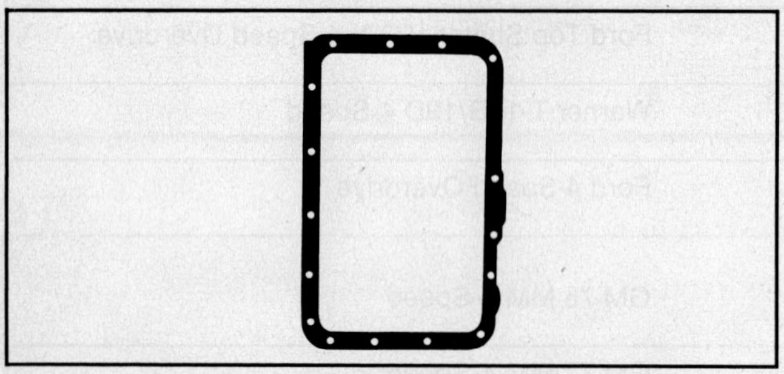

Fig. 4: Ford C5

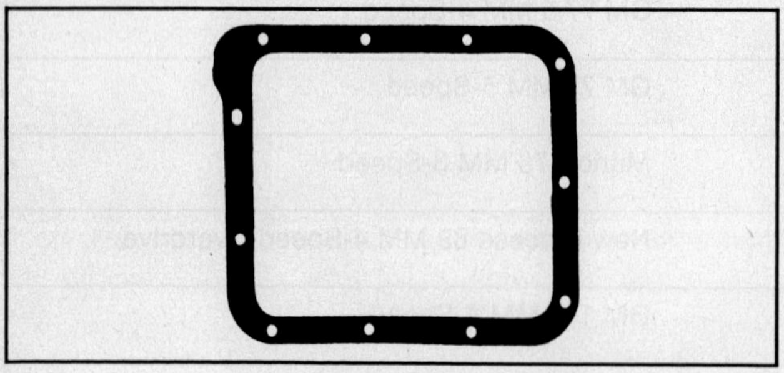

Fig. 5: Ford C6

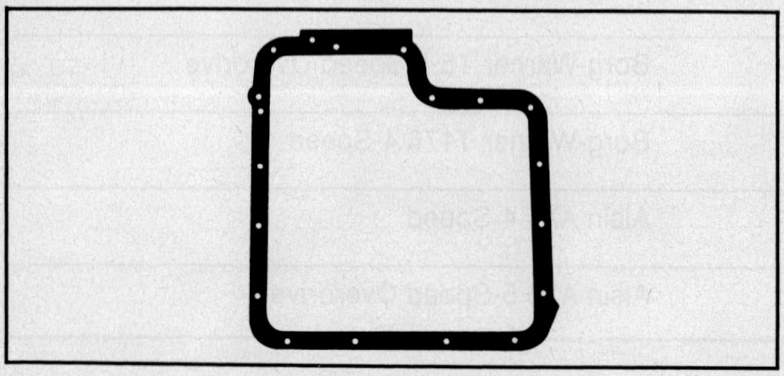

Fig. 6: Ford AOD

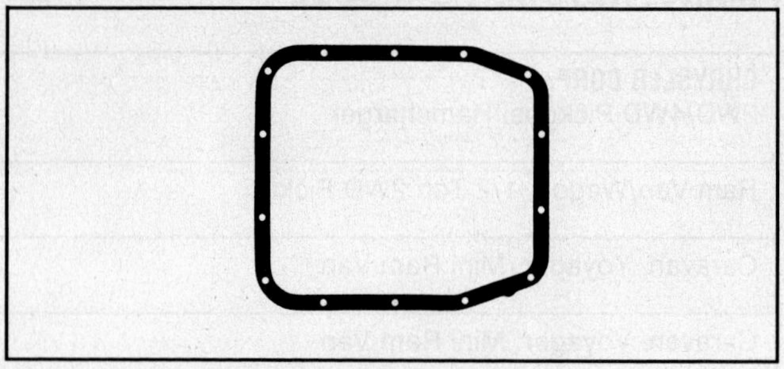

Fig. 7: General Motors THM 350C

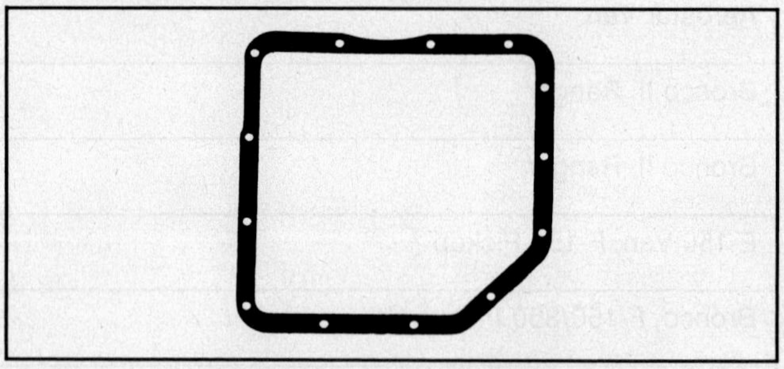

Fig. 8: General Motors THM 400

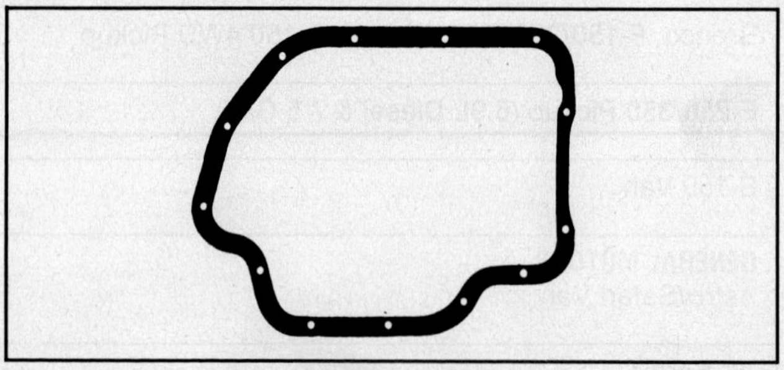

Fig. 9: General Motors THM 700-R4

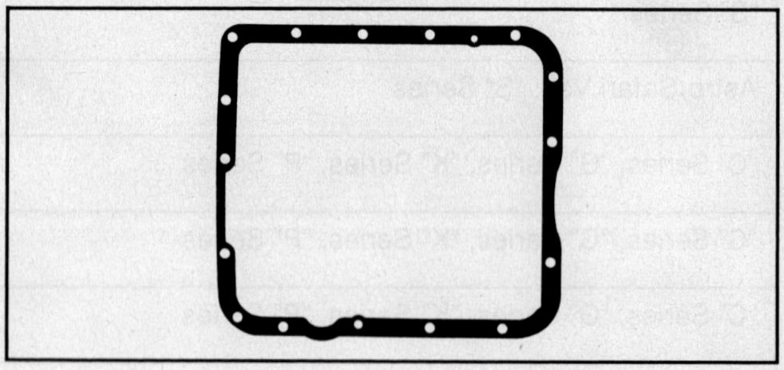

CHRYSLER CORP. FWD LIGHT TRUCKS

LUBRICATION

SERVICE INTERVALS

Under normal operating conditions, the fluid installed at the factory will give satisfactory lubrication for the life of the vehicle. Fluid changes are not necessary unless the lubricant has become contaminated with water.

If the vehicle is operated at sustained high speed during hot weather, above 90°F (32°C), the transmission fluid should be changed and the magnet, attached to the inside of the differential pan, cleaned every 15,000 miles.

CHECKING FLUID LEVEL

All Models

1) Check fluid level with vehicle parked on level surface, parking brake applied, engine at curb idle speed and at normal operating temperature. Move selector lever through all gear ranges, ending in "P".

2) Fluid level should be between the "ADD" mark and the cross-hatched area marked "OK" (between the two holes in the dipstick). Because damage may result, never overfill transaxle. Make sure dipstick seats properly to keep out water and dirt.

RECOMMENDED FLUID

Use only Dexron II automatic transmission fluid when topping off or refilling transmission.

CAPACITY

NOTE: **When filling transmission, use capacities listed in table only as guidelines. Correct fluid level should always be determined by marks on dipstick, rather than by amount of fluid added.**

TRANSMISSION REFILL CAPACITIES

Application	Refill Quantity	Dry Fill Quantity
A413/A470	4 qts. (3.8L)	8.9 qts. (8.4L)
A413/A470 (Fleet)	4 qts. (3.8L)	9.2 qts. (8.7L)

DRAINING & REFILLING

All Models

1) Raise vehicle on hoist. Place drain container with large opening, under transaxle oil pan. Loosen pan bolts and tap pan at one corner to break it loose allowing fluid to drain, then remove oil pan. Install new filter and gasket on bottom of valve body and tighten retaining screws to 44 INCH lbs. (5 N.m).

2) Clean oil pan and reinstall using new RTV sealant. Tighten oil pan bolts to 165 INCH lbs. (19 N.m). Remove differential cover. Using a clean dry cloth, clean magnet found on inside surface of differential cover. Using RTV sealant for a gasket, reinstall differentail cover.

3) Pour 4 quarts of "Dexron II" automatic transmission fluid through dipstick opening. Start engine and idle for at least one minute. Then, with parking and service brakes applied, move selector lever momentarily to each position, ending in park or neutral position.

4) Add sufficient fluid to bring level to 1/8 inch below "ADD" mark. Recheck fluid level after transaxle is at normal operating temperature. Level should be in "HOT" region. To prevent dirt from entering transaxle, make certain dipstick is fully seated into dipstick opening.

ADJUSTMENT

KICKDOWN (FRONT) BAND

All Models

1) Kickdown band adjusting screw is located on left side (top front) of transaxle case. Loosen lock nut and back off nut about 5 turns. Test adjusting screw for free turning in the transaxle case.

2) Using wrench (C 3380 A) with adapter (C 3705), tighten band adjusting screw to 47-50 INCH lbs. (5.3-5.6 N.m). If adapter is not used, tighten adjusting screw to 72 INCH lbs. (8 N.m) which is the true torque. Back off adjusting screw 2 1/2 turns. Hold adjusting screw in position and tighten lock nut to 35 ft. lbs. (47 N.m).

LOW-REVERSE (REAR) BAND

All Models

To adjust band, proceed as follows: Loosen and back off lock nut approximately 5 turns. Using an inch-pound torque wrench, tighten adjusting screw to 44 INCH lbs. (5 N.m) true torque. Back off adjusting screw 3 1/2 turns. Tighten lock nut to 10 ft. lbs. (14 N.m).

THROTTLE PRESSURE CABLE

All Models

1) Perform transaxle throttle pressure cable adjustment while engine is at normal operating temperature, otherwise make sure carburetor is not on fast idle cam by disconnecting choke. Loosen adjustment bracket lock screw.

2) To insure proper adjustment, bracket must be free to slide on its slot. If necessary, disassemble and clean or repair bracket and case boss sliding surface to assure free action.

3) Slide bracket to left (toward engine) to limit of its travel. Release bracket and move throttle lever fully to right against its internal stop and tighten the adjusting bracket lock screw to 106 INCH lbs. (12 N.m).

Fig. 1: Typical Throttle Control

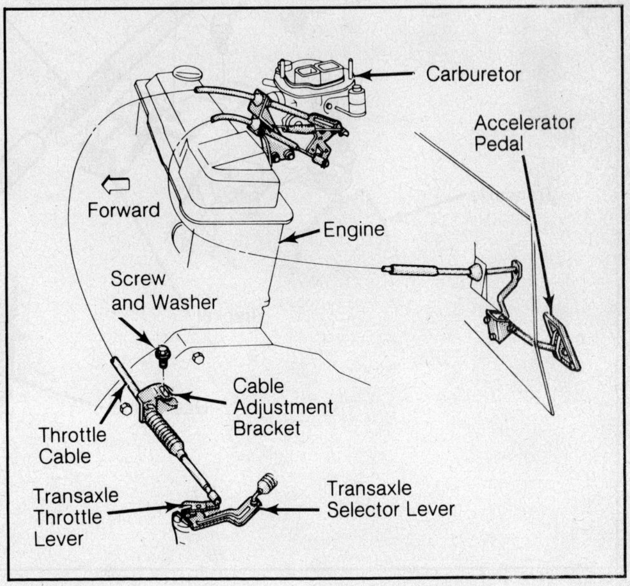

CHRYSLER CORP. FWD LIGHT TRUCKS (Cont.)

4) The adjustment is complete and transaxle throttle cable backlash was automatically removed. Reconnect choke if disconnected. Test cable freedom of operation by moving transaxle throttle lever forward and slowly release it to confirm it will return fully rearward.

GEARSHIFT LINKAGE

NOTE: **When it is necessary to disassemble linkage cable from levers, which use plastic grommets as retainers, the grommets should be replaced with new ones.**

1) Use a prying tool to force rod from grommet in lever, then cut away old grommet. Use pliers to snap new grommet into lever and rod into grommet. Place gear shift lever in "P". Loosen clamp bolt on gearshift cable bracket.

2) Pull shift lever by hand fully forward to front detent position (Park) and tighten clamp screw to 106 INCH lbs. (12 N.m). Gearshift linkage should now be properly adjusted.

3) Check adjustment as follows: Detent position for "N" and "D" should be within limits of hand lever gate stops. Key start must occur only when shift lever is in "P" or "N" positions.

NEUTRAL SAFETY SWITCH

All Models

1) The neutral safety switch is the center terminal of the 3 terminal switch. It provides the ground for the starter solenoid circuit through the selector lever in only "P" and "N" positions.

2) To test switch, remove wiring connector from switch and test for continuity between center pin of switch and transaxle case. Continuity should exist only when transaxle is in "P" or "N".

3) Check gearshift cable adjustment before replacing a switch which tests bad. Unscrew switch from transaxle case allowing fluid to drain into a container. Move selector lever to "P" and then to "N" positions, and inspect to see that switch operating lever fingers are centered in switch opening in case.

4) Screw switch, with a new seal, into transaxle case and tighten to 24 ft. lbs. (33 N.m). Retest switch with test lamp. Add fluid to transaxle to bring up to proper level.

5) Back-up light switch circuit is through two outside terminals of 3 terminal switch. To test switch, remove wiring connector from switch and test for continuity between two outside pins. Continuity should exist only with transaxle in "R" position. No continuity should exist from either pin to case.

Fig. 3: Back-Up Light/Neutral Safety Switch

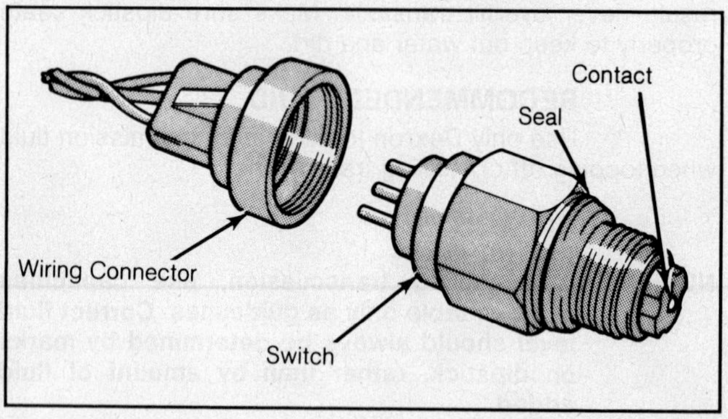

Fig. 2: Gearshift Linkage Adjustment

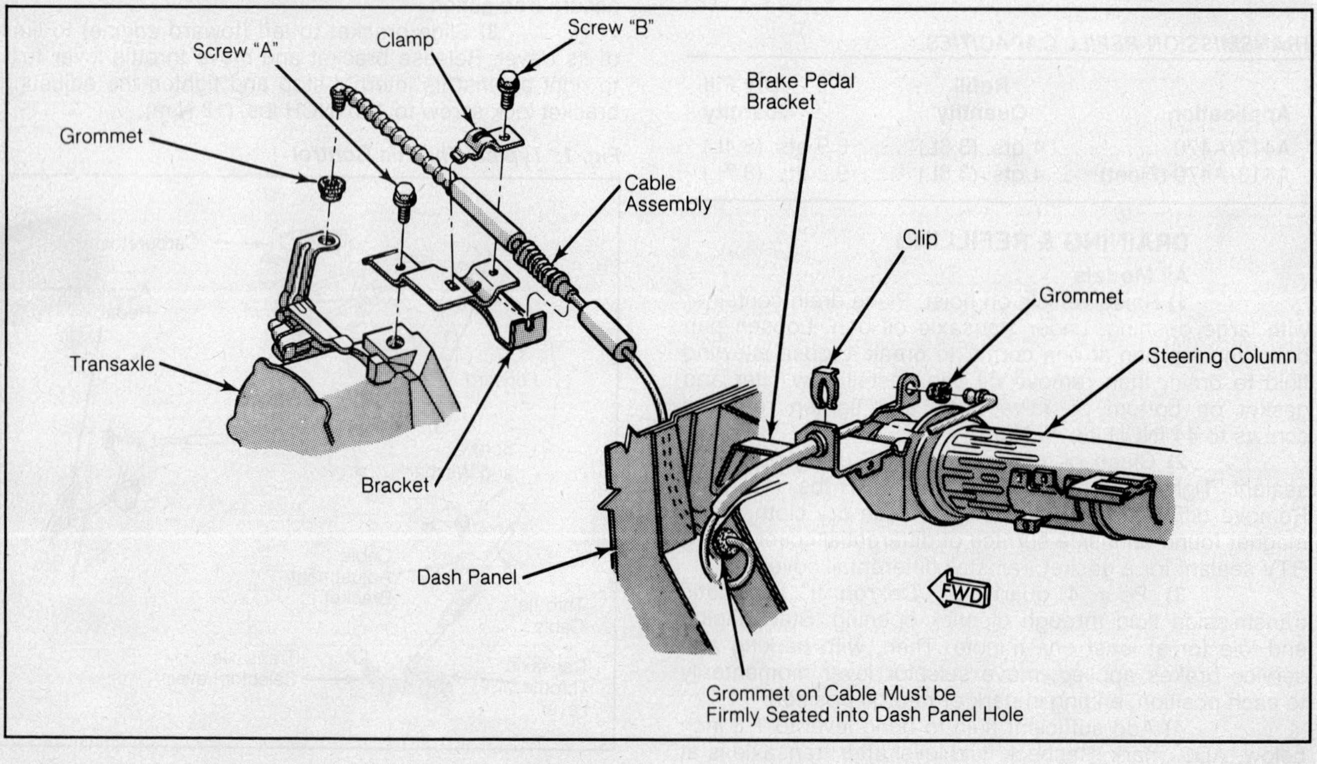

CHRYSLER CORP. RWD LIGHT TRUCKS

LUBRICATION

SERVICE INTERVALS

Check fluid level at each engine oil change. Under normal light duty service conditions, service transmission (change fluid, replace filter, and adjust bands) every 37,500 miles. Under normal heavy duty service conditions, service transmission every 24,000 miles. Under severe heavy duty service conditions, transmission should be serviced every 12,000 miles.

CHECKING FLUID LEVEL

All Models

1) Check fluid level with vehicle parked on level surface, parking brake applied, engine at curb idle speed and at normal operating temperature. Move selector lever through all gear ranges, ending in Neutral.

2) Fluid level should be between "FULL" and "ADD ONE PINT" marks on dipstick. Fluid level should never be above "FULL" mark. Make sure dipstick seats properly to seal out water and dirt.

RECOMMENDED FLUID

Use only Dexron II automatic transmission fluid when topping off or refilling transmission.

CAPACITY

NOTE: **When filling transmission, use capacities listed in table only as guidelines. Correct fluid level should always be determined by marks on dipstick, rather than by amount of fluid added.**

TRANSMISSION REFILL CAPACITIES

Application	Quantity
A-727	
Lock-Up Converter	8.3 qts. (7.9L)
Non Lock-Up Converter	8.5 qts. (8.1L)
A-904T & A-999	8.5 qts. (8.1L)

DRAINING & REFILLING

All Models

1) Loosen oil pan bolts. Tap lightly at one corner to break loose and allow fluid to drain. Remove pan. Install new filter on bottom of valve body and tighten retaining screws. Clean oil pan and install with new gasket.

2) Pour 4 quarts of transmission fluid through filler tube. Start engine and allow to run at idle for 2 minutes. With engine at curb idle and parking brake applied, move shift selector lever through all ranges, ending in Neutral. Add fluid up to "ADD ONE PINT" mark on dipstick. Do not overfill.

3) Reseat dipstick fully to seal out water and dirt. Recheck fluid level when transmission reaches normal operating temperature.

ADJUSTMENT

KICKDOWN (FRONT) BAND

All Models

1) Locate kickdown band adjusting screw at left side of transmission case, near throttle lever shaft. *See Fig. 1.* Loosen adjusting screw lock nut and back off approximately 5 turns. Make sure adjusting screw turns freely in case. Using special wrench (C 3380 A) with adapter (C 3705), tighten adjusting screw to 48 INCH lbs. (5 N.m). If adapter is not used, tighten adjusting screw to 72 INCH lbs. (8 N.m) which is the true torque.

2) Back off adjusting screw 2 1/2 turns. Hold adjusting screw in position and tighten lock nut to 35 ft. lbs. (47 N.m).

Fig. 1: Adjusting Kickdown Band

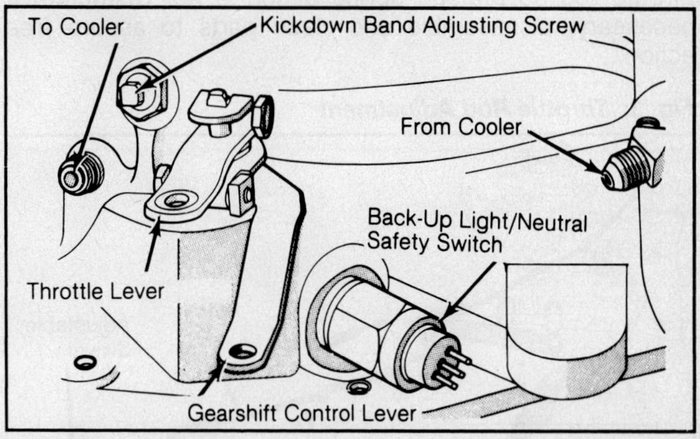

With band properly adjusted, tighten lock nut to 35 ft. lbs. (47 N.m).

LOW-REVERSE (REAR) BAND

All Models

1) Transmission pan must be removed to adjust band. Remove transmission oil pan and locate low-reverse band adjusting screw on rear servo lever. *See Fig. 2.* Loosen adjusting screw lock nut and back off nut approximately 5 turns. Test adjusting screw for free turning in lever. Using special wrench (C3380 A), tighten adjusting screw to 72 INCH lbs. (8 N.m).

2) Back off adjusting screw specified number of turns as given in *Low-Reverse Band Adjustment Table.* Hold adjusting screw in position and tighten lock nut to 35 ft. lbs. (47 N.m). Clean oil pan, install new gasket with pan and refill transmission with fluid.

LOW-REVERSE BAND ADJUSTMENT TABLE

Application	Back Off Screw
Models A-904T and A-999	4 Turns
Model A-727	2 Turns

Fig. 2: Low-Reverse Band Adjusting Screw Location

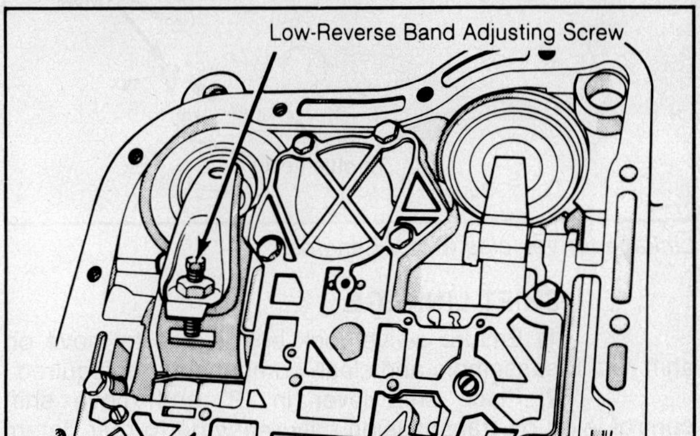

CHRYSLER CORP. RWD LIGHT TRUCKS (Cont.)

TRANSMISSION THROTTLE ROD

All Models

1) With engine at normal operating temperature and carburetor off fast idle cam, adjust idle speed to specifications. Turn off engine and disconnect choke at carburetor or block choke valve in full open position. Open throttle slightly to release fast idle cam and return throttle to curb idle position.

2) Raise vehicle on hoist. Loosen swivel lock screw. Be sure swivel is free to slide along flat end of throttle rod so preload spring action is not restricted. If necessary, disassemble and clean parts to assure free action.

Fig. 3: Throttle Rod Adjustment

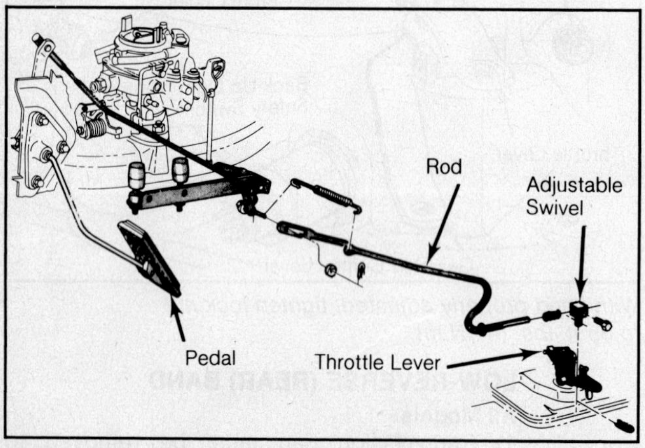

Linkage for vehicles with 6-cylinder engine.

3) Hold transmission lever firmly forward against internal stop and tighten swivel lock screw to 100 INCH lbs. (11 N.m). Adjustment is complete. Linkage backlash is automatically removed by preload spring.

4) Lower vehicle and reconnect choke. To test linkage, move throttle rod rearward and release slowly to confirm full forward return.

Fig. 4: Throttle Rod Adjustment

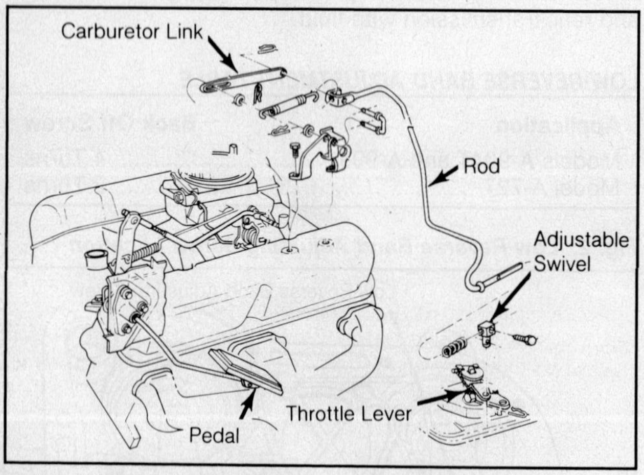

Linkage for vehicles with V8 engines.

SHIFT LINKAGE

1) Ensure swivel lock bolt is free to move on shift rod. Disassemble and clean components as required.

2) Place shift lever in "P" and move shift control lever on transmission fully rearward to rear detent position (Park). Tighten swivel lock bolt.

3) When linkage is properly adjusted, detent positions for Neutral and Drive will be within limits of shift lever gate stops. Engine must crank in "P" and "N", only.

Fig. 5: Column Shift Linkage Adjustment

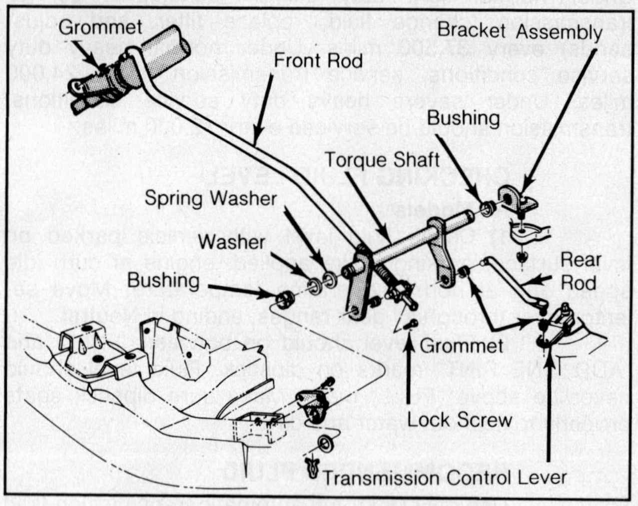

NEUTRAL SAFETY SWITCH

All Models

1) With transmission linkage properly adjusted, switch should allow starter operation in Park and Neutral only. To test switch, remove wire connector and test for continuity between center pin of switch and case. Continuity should exist only when transmission is in Park or Neutral.

2) Check for continuity between 2 outer pins. Continuity should exist with transmission in Reverse, only. There should be no continuity between either outside pin and the transmission case.

NOTE: **Be sure gearshift linkage is properly adjusted before replacing a switch which tests bad.**

3) To replace, remove switch from case and allow fluid to drain. Move selector lever to Park and Neutral positions and check that switch operating fingers are centered in switch opening. Install new switch and seal. Retest switch for continuity and add transmission fluid.

Fig. 6: Location of Back-Up Light/Neutral Safety Switch

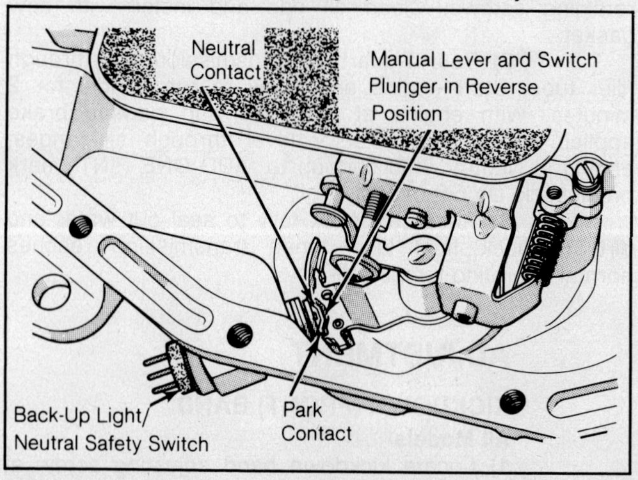

When installing new switch, tighten to 24 ft. lbs. (33 N.m).

FORD LIGHT TRUCKS

LUBRICATION

SERVICE INTERVALS

Vehicles used in normal service do not require regularly scheduled maintenance. Fluid level should be checked whenever underhood maintenance is performed, or if leakage is detected. Clutch bands on C-5 and C-6 transmissions should be adjusted when the quality of shifts deteriorates or otherwise indicates improper band adjustment.

On vehicles used for fleet service, or those operated under severe conditions, drain and refill transmission at 30,000 mile intervals.

CHECKING FLUID LEVEL

1) With transmission at normal operating temperature, place vehicle on level ground. Apply parking brake, and run engine at curb idle. Shift selector through all positions, ending in Park.

2) With transmission at normal operating temperature, fluid level should be between "ADD" and "DON'T ADD" marks on dipstick. If transmission is at room temperature, fluid level should be between middle and top holes on dipstick.

3) If fluid level is correct at room temperature, it will be between "ADD" and "DON'T ADD" marks on dipstick when normal operating temperature is reached. Do not overfill. Check condition of fluid for contamination or burned smell. Fully reseat dipstick.

RECOMMENDED FLUID

The C-6, AOD and A4LD transmissions require "Dexron II" type transmission fluid. The C-5 requires Ford "Type H" (Ford Specification ESP-M2C166-H).

CAPACITY

NOTE: **Transmission and converter assembly capacities listed are approximate. Determine correct fluid level by mark on dipstick rather than by amount of fluid added.**

TRANSMISSION REFILL CAPACITIES

Application	Quantity
AOD Transmission	12.3 qts. (11.6L)
A4LD Transmission	9.0 qts. (8.5L)
C-5 Transmission	11.0 qts. (10.4L)
C-6 Transmission	
2WD Models	12.0 qts. (11.4L)
4WD Models	13.5 qts. (12.7L)

DRAINING & REFILLING

1) On C-5 models, disconnect fluid filler tube from oil pan to drain fluid, then remove pan. On all other models, loosen oil pan bolts and tap pan to break gasket seal. Allow fluid to drain, then remove oil pan bolts and oil pan. On all models, clean pan and reinstall with new filter, gasket and pan gasket. On C-5 models, install filler tube.

2) Add 3 quarts (2.8L) transmission fluid through filler tube. Check fluid level as described. When filling a dry transmission and converter, refer to *Transmission Refill Capacity chart*. Recheck fluid level when transmission is at normal operating temperature. Do not overfill.

ADJUSTMENT

INTERMEDIATE (FRONT) BAND

C-5 & C-6 Only

Clean dirt from band adjusting screw area. Remove and discard band adjusting screw lock nut. Install new lock nut. Tighten adjusting screw to 120 INCH lbs. (14 N.m). Back off screw exact number of turns as indicated in *Intermediate (Front) Band Adjustment* table. Hold adjusting screw in position and tighten new lock nut to 40 ft. lbs. (54 N.m).

INTERMEDIATE (FRONT) BAND ADJUSTMENT

Application	Back Off (Turns)
C-5	4 1/4
C-6	1 1/2

Fig. 1: Adjusting Intermediate Band

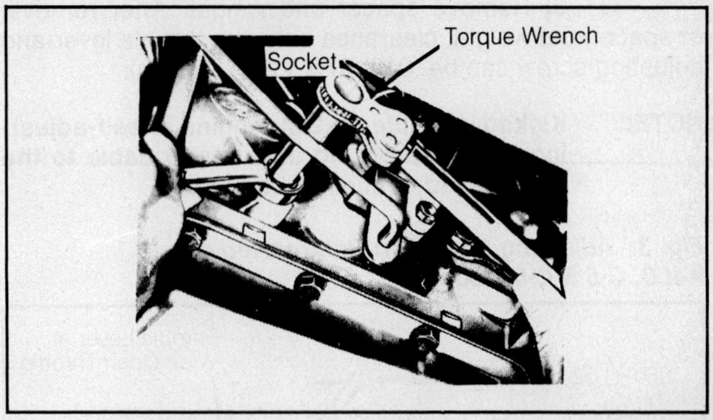

Ford C-5 models shown; C-6 similar.

LOW-REVERSE (REAR) BAND

C-5 Only

Clean all dirt from band adjusting screw area, then remove and discard band adjusting screw lock nut. Install new lock nut on adjusting screw. Tighten screw tighten adjusting screw to 120 INCH lbs. (14 N.m), then back off 3 full turns. Hold screw in position and tighten lock nut to 40 ft. lbs. (54 N.m).

Fig. 2: Adjusting Low-Reverse Band (C-5 Only)

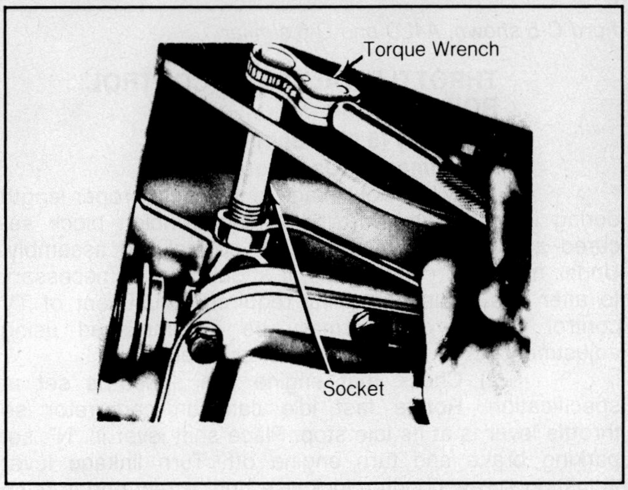

FORD LIGHT TRUCKS (Cont.)

KICKDOWN CONTROL

NOTE: **Linkage must be free and must return to idle when released. Throttle linkage must be properly adjusted before attempting to make kickdown control adjustment.**

A4LD, C-5 & C-6

1) Check for wide-open carburetor and linkage travel at full throttle. Carburetor full-throttle stop must be contacted by throttle linkage and there must be a slight amount of movement left in downshift linkage. Be sure downshift linkage return spring is connected and downshift lever returns to closed position.

2) Apply 6 lb. (2.7 kg) to transmission kickdown lever. Rotate throttle to wide open throttle position. Insert a .060" (1.52 mm) spacer between throttle lever and adjusting screw. *See Fig. 3*. Loosen lock nut and rotate adjusting screw until contact is made between screw and spacer.

3) Remove spacer and weight. After removal of spacer and weight, clearance between throttle lever and adjusting screw can be .010-.070" (.25-1.78 mm).

NOTE: **Kickdown cable on 2.3L engine is self-adjusting after depressing accelerator cable to the floor. No adjustment is required.**

Fig. 3: Adjusting Kickdown Control Rod on A4LD, C-5 & C-6 Models

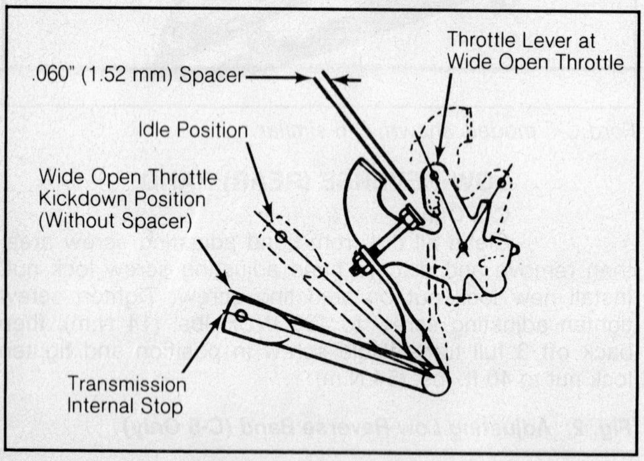

Ford C-5 shown, A4LD and C-6 similar.

THROTTLE VALVE (TV) CONTROL ROD LINKAGE

AOD Only (5.0L 2-Bbl.)

Adjustment at Carburetor

1) TV control linkage is set to its proper length during initial assembly using sliding trunnion block secured at transmission end of TV control rod assembly. Under normal circumstances, it should not be necessary to alter this adjustment. Any required adjustment of TV control linkage can normally be accomplished using adjustment screw on linkage lever at carburetor.

2) Check that engine idle speed is set at specification. Rotate fast idle cam on carburetor so throttle lever is at its idle stop. Place shift lever in "N", set parking brake and turn engine off. Turn linkage lever adjusting screw counterclockwise until screw end is flush with lever face. *See Fig. 4*.

3) Turn adjusting screw clockwise to obtain .005" (.12 mm) clearance between end of screw and throttle lever. Open and close throttle to eliminate friction and recheck clearance. DO NOT apply any load on levers while checking. Turn adjusting screw clockwise 4 full turns.

4) If screw travel is limited, 2 turns minimum are permitted, however 4 turns are preferred. If idle speed requires adjustment of more than 50 RPM, turn adjustment screw on linkage lever.

NOTE: **If adjustment of linkage lever screw is not possible, adjustment of the TV control rod at transmission is required. This adjustment is also required when a new TV control rod is installed.**

Fig. 4: Adjusting TV Linkage at Carburetor

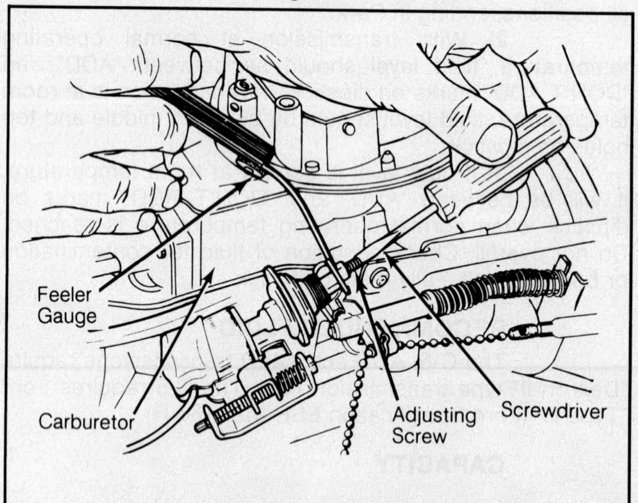

Adjustment at Transmission

1) Ensure engine idle speed is properly set. Rotate fast idle cam on carburetor so throttle lever is at its idle stop. Place transmission selector lever in Neutral and set parking brake.

2) Set linkage lever adjustment screw about mid-range. Raise vehicle and allow exhaust system to cool. Loosen bolt on TV control rod trunnion block at transmission lever. Ensure that trunnion block is free to slide on rod.

3) Push upward on lower end of TV rod (at transmission) to ensure that carburetor linkage is held firmly against throttle lever. Control rod should stay in position when released.

4) Firmly hold TV control lever on transmission upward against internal stop and tighten trunnion block bolt in position. Lower vehicle. Check that throttle lever is against idle stop.

THROTTLE VALVE (TV) CONTROL CABLE SYSTEM

AOD Only (4.9L & 5.0L EFI)

Adjustment at Carburetor/Throttle Body

1) TV control cable is set and locked to its proper length during initial assembly by pushing in locking tab at carburetor/throttle body end of cable assembly. When tab is unlocked, cable is released for adjustment.

FORD LIGHT TRUCKS (Cont.)

Under normal circumstances, it should not be necessary to alter or readjust initial setting of TV control cable.

2) On 4.9L engine, Idle Speed Control (ISC) plunger automatically extends when engine is shut off and moves throttle lever to fast idle in preparation for next time engine is started. The ISC plunger must be retracted as follows:

3) In engine compartment, near right fender well, locate self test connector and self test input (STI) connector. These 2 connectors are located next to each other. *See Fig. 5.* Connect a jumper wire between STI connector and Signal Return (ground) of Self Test Connector. *See Fig. 6.*

Fig. 5: Location of Self Test Connectors

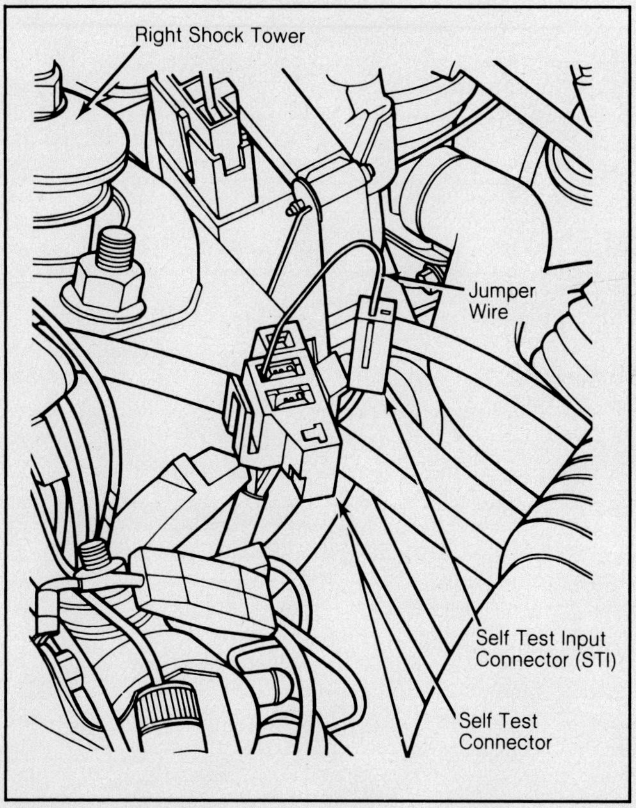

Note location of jumper wire.

Fig. 6: Connecting Ground on Self Test Connectors

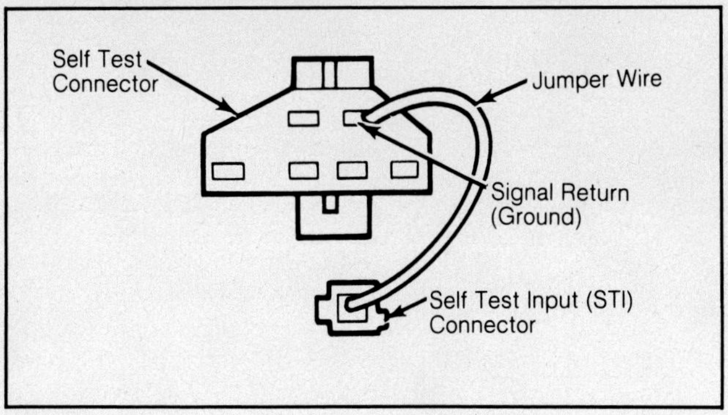

4) Turn ignition to "Run" position but DO NOT start engine. ISC plunger will retract. Wait until plunger is fully retracted (about 10 seconds). Turn key off. Remove jumper wire and air cleaner.

5) On 4.9L and 5.0L EFI engines, set parking brake and put selector in "N". Ensure that throttle lever is resting against idle stop. Verify cable routing is free of sharp bends or pressure points and cable operates freely. Unlock locking tab at carburetor/throttle body end by pushing up from below, and prying up rest of way to free cable.

6) A retention spring must be installed on TV contol lever to hold it in idle position (as far to rear as lever will travel) with about 10 lbs. (4.5 kg) of force. If a suitable single spring is not available, 2 throttle return springs may be used. Attach retention spring(s) to transmission TV lever and hook rear end of spring to transmission case.

7) On 4.9L engines, rotate fast idle cam on carburetor so throttle lever is at its idle stop. Carburetor throttle lever must be in anti-diesel idle position.

8) Verify take-up spring (carburetor/throttle body end of cable) properly tensions cable. If spring is loose or bottomed out, check for bent cable brackets. Push down on locking key until flush. Remove retention spring(s) from transmission TV lever. On 4.9L engines, reconnect ISC motor.

SHIFT LINKAGE

All Models (Exc. Aerostar)

1) With engine off and parking brake applied, place shift lever in "D" (Overdrive on AOD). On models with column-mounted shift levers, hold against stop by hanging an 8 lb. (3.6 kg) weight from selector lever.

2) Loosen nut on slotted shift rod at transmission. Move shift lever at transmission all the way to the rear, then forward 2 steps (4 steps on Bronco II and Ranger). This places lever in "D" position.

3) On Bronco II and Ranger, apply light forward pressure on shifter control lever. On all models, tighten nut at slotted lever to 144-216 INCH lbs. (16-24 N.m). Remove weight from shift lever. Mover lever through all positions making sure transmission is at full detent in each position.

Aerostar A4LD

1) From inside vehicle, place shift lever in "D" (Overdrive) position. From below vehicle, loosen adjustment screw on shift cable and remove end fitting from manual lever ball stud.

2) Position manual lever at transmission in "D" (Overdrive) position by moving lever all the way rearward, and then moving it 3 detents forward. Connect cable end fitting to manual lever.

NOTE: **Too much pressure on shift control lever lower arm can move shifter to "D" (Drive) position. Apply pressure only until resistance of detent notch is felt.**

3) Tighten adjustment screw to 45-60 INCH lbs. (5-7 N.m). After adjustment, be sure selector lever positively engages in "P" (Park) position. Control lever must move to right when engaged in "P" (Park) detent. Check transmission control lever in all detent positions with engine running to ensure correct detent/transmission action. Re-adjust, if required.

FORD LIGHT TRUCKS (Cont.)

NEUTRAL START SWITCH

NOTE: **Automatic Overdrive and A4DL switches are not adjustable.**

1) With transmission shift linkage properly adjusted, loosen the 2 switch attaching bolts.

2) Place transmission manual lever in Neutral position, then rotate switch and insert a gauge pin (No. 43 drill shank) into gauge pin holes of switch.

3) Gauge pin must be inserted to a full 31/64" into the 3 holes of the switch. Tighten switch attaching bolts and remove gauge pin.

4) Check operation of switch. Engine should start in Neutral and Park positions only.

Fig. 7: Location of Neutral Start Switch

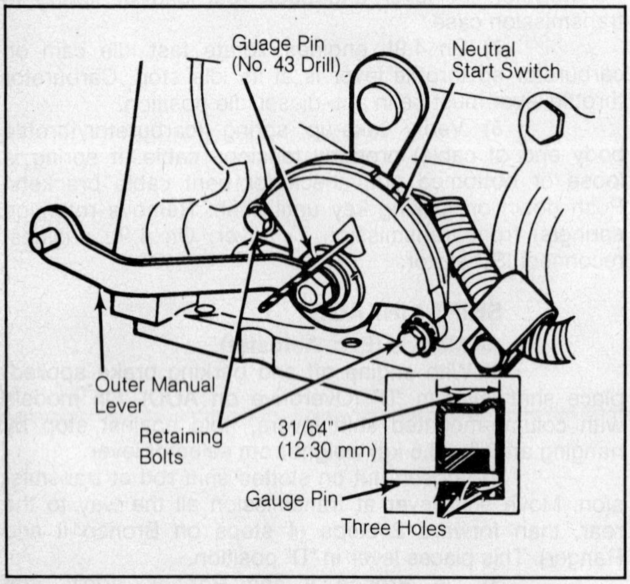

Note the location of the No. 43 Drill.

GENERAL MOTORS LIGHT TRUCKS

LUBRICATION

SERVICE INTERVALS

Check transmission fluid level at each engine oil change. Change transmission fluid and filter at 100,000 mile intervals on vehicles in normal use. If used in severe service conditions (commercial use, trailer pulling, constant stop and go city traffic), change fluid and filter every 15,000 miles.

CHECKING FLUID LEVEL

NOTE: **One pint of fluid will raise level from "ADD" mark to "FULL" mark on dipstick in a hot transmission. Do not overfill.**

With engine at curb idle, move selector lever through all positions, ending in "P". Remove dipstick and touch end cautiously to find out if fluid is cool, warm or hot. Wipe dipstick clean and check level, by temperature, as follows:

COOL (65-85°F)

Fluid level should check between the 2 dimples below "ADD" mark on dipstick.

WARM

Fluid level should check close to the "ADD" mark (either above or below) on dipstick.

HOT

Fluid is hot when it cannot be touched comfortably. Fluid level should check between "ADD" and "FULL" marks on dipstick. If vehicle has been operated for an extended period of time at high speed, in city traffic, or pulling a trailer, an accurate fluid level cannot be immediately determined. Transmission must cool for about 30 minutes, after vehicle is parked, before fluid level is checked.

RECOMMENDED FLUID

Use only DEXRON II automatic transmission fluid, or equivalent.

CAPACITY

NOTE: **Transmission refill capacities given below are approximations. Correct fluid level should always be determined by marks on dipstick, rather than by amount added. DO NOT overfill transmission.**

CAPACITY

TRANSMISSION REFILL CAPACITIES

Application	Refill Quantity	Dry Fill Quantity
THM 200C	3.5 qts. (3.3L)	9.5 qts. (9.0L)
THM 350C	3.2 qts. (3.0L)	10.0 qts. (9.5L)
THM 400	4.5 qts. (4.3L)	11.0 qts. (10.4L)
THM 700-R4	5.0 qts. (4.7L)	11.5 qts. (10.9L)

DRAINING & REFILLING

With engine at normal operating temperature, loosen transmission oil pan bolts. Pry pan loose with a large screwdriver and allow fluid to drain. Remove oil pan and gasket. Replace old filter. Install oil pan with new gasket. Add fluid to proper mark on dipstick.

ADJUSTMENT

DETENT (DOWNSHIFT) OR THROTTLE VALVE (TV) CABLE

Diesel Engines

1) Remove cruise control rod (if equipped). Disconnect cable terminal at throttle assembly. Loosen lock nut on pump rod and back off several turns.

2) Rotate throttle lever assembly (at valve body) to full open position and hold. Lengthen pump rod until injection pump lever contacts full throttle stop. Release throttle lever and tighten pump rod lock nut.

Fig. 1: Detent/TV Cable Adjustment Components

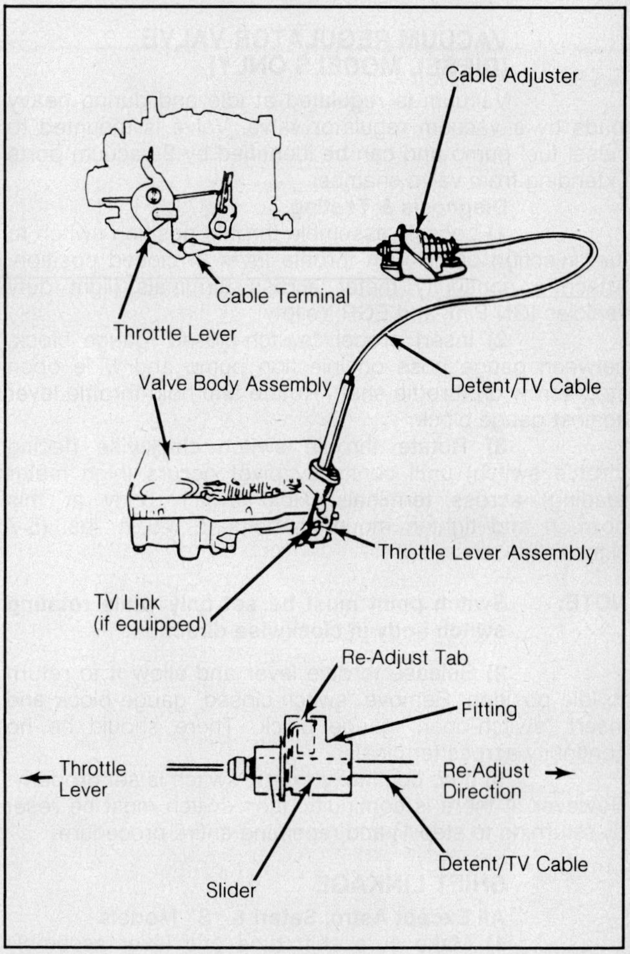

TV cable is used on 200C and 700-R4 transmissions, only. All other models use detent cable.

3) Remove pump rod from lever assembly. Reconnect cable terminal at throttle lever. Depress and hold metal adjusting tab on cable adjuster. Move slider through fitting, away from throttle lever, until slider stops against fitting. Release tab.

4) Rotate lever assembly to full throttle position and release. Reconnect pump rod. If equipped with cruise control, reconnect rod and adjust servo throttle rod to minimum slack with engine off. Put clip in free hole nearest to bellcrank, within servo bail.

Gas Engines

1) Gasoline engine equipped vehicles use "self-adjusting" cables. A brief procedure is required, however, to allow cable to adjust.

GENERAL MOTORS LIGHT TRUCKS (Cont.)

2) Press tab in cable re-adjuster and move slider back through fitting, away from throttle lever, until slider stops against fitting. Release tab. Move throttle lever to full open position. This automatically adjusts cable. Release lever.

DETENT (DOWNSHIFT) SWITCH

THM 400 Only

With engine off, push detent switch plunger as far forward as possible. This presets switch for adjustment. Depress accelerator pedal to wide open position; switch will self adjust. Operation of detent switch circuit can be checked by connecting a test lamp across switch terminals.

VACUUM REGULATOR VALVE (DIESEL MODELS ONLY)

Vacuum is regulated at idle and during heavy loads by a vacuum regulator valve. Valve is mounted to diesel fuel pump and can be identified by 2 vacuum ports extending from valve chamber.

Diagnosis & Testing

1) Loosely assemble throttle position switch to fuel injection pump with throttle lever in closed position. Attach a continuity meter across terminals (light duty vehicles IGN Pink and EGR Yellow).

2) Insert proper "switch-closed" gauge block, between gauge boss on injection pump and wide open stop screw on throttle shaft. Rotate and hold throttle lever against gauge block.

3) Rotate throttle switch clockwise (facing throttle switch) until continuity pivot occurs (high meter reading) across terminals. Hold switch body at this position and tighten mounting bolts to 4-5 ft. lbs. (5-7 N.m).

NOTE: **Switch point must be set only while rotating switch body in clockwise direction.**

4) Release throttle lever and allow it to return to idle position. Remove "switch-closed" gauge block and insert "switch-open" gauge block. There should be no continuity across terminals.

5) If no continuity exists, switch is set properly. However, if there is continuity, then switch must be reset by returning to step **1)** and repeating entire procedure.

SHIFT LINKAGE

All Except Astro, Safari & "S" Models

1) Make sure shift tube and lever assembly are free in steering column. Disconnect shift lever rod from swivel at lower column lever. Move transmission lever clockwise to stop, then counterclockwise 2 detents. This is Neutral position. Place selector lever in Neutral. Locate position using mechanical stops, NOT indicator pointer.

2) Slide swivel and clamp onto shift lever rod. Install grommets, washers and nut (as needed) but do not tighten nut. Hold lower column lever against Neutral stop on Park side. Tighten swivel nut to 20 ft. lbs. (27 N.m).

Astro, Safari & "S" Models

1) Make sure shift tube and lever are free in steering column. To adjust linkage, remove screw and spring washer from swivel. Turn transmission lever clockwise to stop, then counterclockwise 2 detents. This is Neutral position.

2) Place selector lever in Neutral. Locate proper position using mechanical stops, NOT indicator pointer. Hold swivel against shift lever, install spring washer and screw and tighten finger tight. Avoid applying force in either direction (along shift rod or lever) while tightening screw to 20 ft. lbs. (27 N.m).

NEUTRAL SAFETY SWITCH

All Models With Column Mounted Switch

Place gearshift selector lever in neutral position and loosen switch attaching screws. Rotate switch on column until a .095" (2.5 mm) gauge pin can be inserted into switch gauge hole to a depth of 3/8" (10 mm). Tighten switch attaching screws and remove gauge pin. Check for engine starting in Neutral and Park only.

All Models With Trans. Mounted Switch

Raise and support vehicle and loosen switch mounting bolts. Align hole in switch lever with hole in switch assembly. Insert a .095" (2.5 mm) gauge pin through switch holes to hold switch in neutral position. With selector lever on transmission in neutral detent position, tighten switch mounting bolts and remove gauge pin. Lower vehicle and check operation of switch.

JEEP

LUBRICATION

SERVICE INTERVALS

Check fluid level and condition of fluid at each engine oil change. Under light duty service conditions, change fluid, replace filter and adjust bands every 28 months or 27,500 miles. Under heavy duty service conditions, change fluid, replace filter and adjust bands every 12 months or 12,500 miles.

CHECKING FLUID LEVEL

1) Park vehicle on level surface and apply parking brake. With engine at normal operating temperature and idling, move transmission selector lever through all gear ranges, ending in Neutral. Check fluid level.

2) Fluid level should be between "FULL" and "ADD ONE PINT" marks on dipstick. Fluid level should never be above "FULL" mark. Make sure dipstick seats properly to seal out water and dirt.

RECOMMENDED FLUID

Use only Dexron II type automatic transmission fluid.

CAPACITY

NOTE: **Transmission and converter capacities are approximate only. Fluid level should always be determined by reading on dipstick, rather than amount of fluid added.**

TRANSMISSION REFILL CAPACITIES

Application	Quantity
All Models	
Including Converter	8.5 qts. (8.0L)
Without Converter	4.3 qts. (4.0L)

DRAINING & REFILLING

1) Loosen oil pan bolts, tap pan to break it loose and allow fluid to drain. Remove pan. Install new filter on bottom of valve body and tighten retaining screws. Install new "O" ring on fluid pickup pipe (if needed). Clean oil pan and install with a new gasket.

2) Pour 4 quarts of transmission fluid through filler tube. Start engine and allow to run at curb idle for a few minutes. With engine idling and parking brake applied, move shift selector lever through all ranges, ending in neutral. Add fluid up to "ADD ONE PINT" mark on dipstick.

3) With transmission at normal operating temperature, check fluid level. Fluid should be between "ADD" and "FULL" marks on dipstick. Transmission must NOT be overfilled. Seat dipstick fully to seal out water and dirt.

ADJUSTMENT

KICKDOWN (FRONT) BAND

1) Locate kickdown band adjusting screw on left side of case, near throttle lever shaft. Loosen adjusting screw lock nut and back off approximately 5 turns. Make sure adjusting screw turns freely in case.

2) Using adapter tool (J-24063) and 5/16" square socket, tighten screw to 36 INCH lbs. (4 N.m). If adapter is not used, tighten screw to 72 INCH lbs. (8 N.m). Back off screw 2 1/2 turns. Hold adjusting screw in position and tighten lock nut to 35 ft. lbs. (48 N.m).

Fig 1: Kickdown Band Adjusting Screw Location

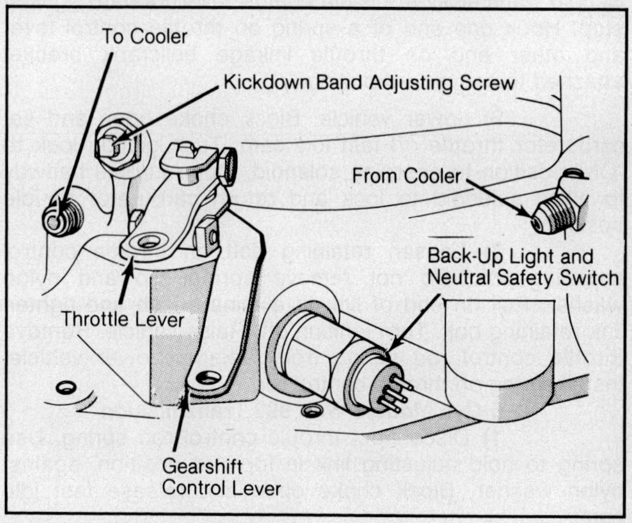

Adjust band every 27,500 miles in light duty service, every 12,500 miles for heavy duty service.

LOW REVERSE (REAR) BAND

1) Raise vehicle, drain transmission fluid and remove oil pan. Locate adjusting screw on rear servo lever. Loosen adjusting screw lock nut and back off about 5 turns. Tighten screw to 41 INCH lbs. (4.6 N.m).

2) Back off screw specified number of turns. *See Low-Reverse Band Adjustment Table*. Hold adjusting screw in position and tighten lock nut to 35 ft. lbs. (48 N.m). Install oil pan and fill transmission with fluid.

LOW-REVERSE BAND ADJUSTMENT TABLE

Application	Back Off Screw
Model 727	2 Turns
Model 904	7 Turns
Model 999	4 Turns

Fig. 2: Adjusting Low-Reverse Band

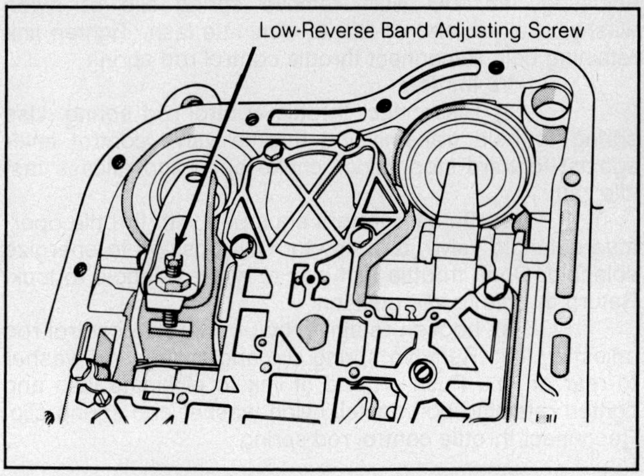

Band should be adjusted whenever oil pan is removed.

JEEP (Cont.)

TRANSMISSION THROTTLE LINKAGE

4-Cyl. Models With 904 Transmission

1) Disconnect throttle control rod spring at carburetor. Raise vehicle. Use throttle control rod spring to hold transmission throttle control lever forward against stop. Hook one end of a spring on throttle control lever and other end on throttle linkage bellcrank bracket attached to converter housing.

2) Lower vehicle. Block choke open and set carburetor throttle off fast idle cam. Turn ignition lock to "ON" position to energize solenoid. Open throttle halfway to allow solenoid to lock and return carburetor to idle position.

3) Loosen retaining bolt on throttle control adjusting link. Do not remove spring clip and nylon washer. Pull on end of link to eliminate lash and tighten link retaining bolt. Turn ignition off. Raise vehicle. Remove throttle control rod spring from linkage. Lower vehicle. Install spring on throttle control rod.

6-Cyl. Models With 999 Transmission

1) Disconnect throttle control rod spring. Use spring to hold adjusting link in forward position, against nylon washer. Block choke open and release fast idle cam.

2) Raise vehicle. Loosen both retaining bolts on adjusting link clamp. DO NOT remove spring clip or nylon washer.

3) Use a spare spring to hold transmission throttle lever against forward stop.

4) Push adjusting link to eliminate lash and pull clamp to rear so bolt in rod bottoms in rear of slot in rod. Tighten forward clamp retaining bolt.

5) Pull throttle control rod to rear so bolt in rod bottoms in front of slot and tighten rear retaining bolt. Remove spare spring. Lower vehicle and reconnect throttle control rod spring.

6-Cyl. Models With 727 Transmission

1) Disconnect throttle control rod spring. Use spring to hold transmission throttle control lever forward, against stop. Block choke open and release fast idle cam.

2) On carburetors equipped wih throttle operated solenoid valve, turn key to "ON" position to energize solenoid. Open throttle half-way to allow solenoid to lock. Return throttle to idle position.

3) Loosen retaining bolt on throttle control adjusting link. DO NOT remove spring clip or nylon washer. Pull on end of link to eliminate lash. Tighten link retaining bolt. Reconnect throttle control rod spring.

V8 Models

1) Disconnect throttle control rod spring. Use spring to hold transmission throttle valve control lever against forward stop. Block choke open and release fast idle cam.

2) On carburetors equipped with throttle operated solenoid valve, turn key to "ON" position to energize solenoid. Open throttle half-way to allow solenoid to lock. Return throttle to idle position.

3) Loosen retaining bolt on throttle control rod adjusting link. Remove spring clip and slide nylon washer to rear of link. Push on end of link to eliminate lash and tighten retaining bolt. Install nylon washer and spring clip. Reconnect throttle control rod spring.

NEUTRAL SAFETY SWITCH

1) Switch combines functions of neutral safety switch and back-up light switch. With transmission linkage properly adjusted, switch should allow starter operation in "P" and "N" only.

2) To test switch, remove wire connector and test for continuity between center pin of switch and case. Continuity should only exist when transmission is in "P" or "N". Check for continuity between 2 outer pins. Continuity should exist with transmission in "R" only. There should be no continuity between either outer pin and transmission case. If these conditions are not met, the switch should be replaced.

3) Remove switch from case and allow fluid to drain into a container. Move selector lever to "P" and "N" positions and check that switch operating fingers are centered in switch opening. Install switch and new seal and tighten. *See Fig. 3.*

Fig. 3: Back-Up Light/Neutral Safety Switch Location

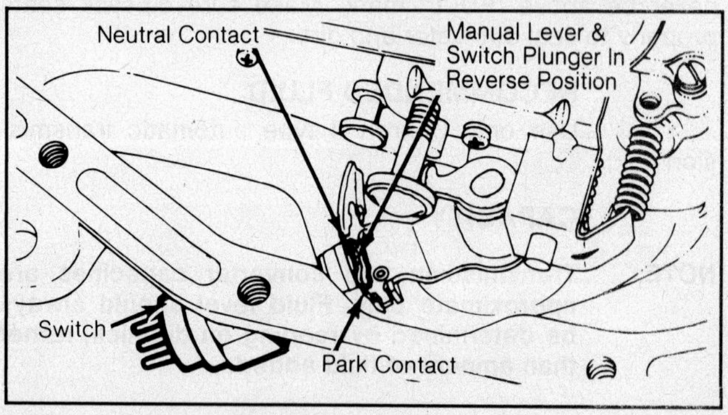

When installing switch, tighten to 24 ft. lbs. (33 N.m).

SHIFT LINKAGE

1) Loosen shift rod trunnion jam nuts at transmission lever. Remove lock pin retaining shift rod to bellcrank. Disengage trunnion and shift rod. Place selector lever in "P" position and lock steering column. Move transmission shift lever to full rear (Park) position.

2) Adjust shift rod trunnion to obtain free pin fit in bellcrank arm. Tighten jam nuts. Make sure gearshift linkage lash is eliminated by pulling downward on shift rod and pushing upward on outer bellcrank when tightening jam nuts.

3) Check steering column lock for ease of operation. Check that engine starts in "N" or "P", only. If starter engages in any drive gear, or does not work in "N" or "P", check for proper shift linkage adjustment or faulty neutral safety switch.

CHRYSLER CORP. FWD LIGHT TRUCKS

LUBRICATION

SERVICE INTERVALS

All Models

1) Under normal operating conditions, fluid installed at factory will give satisfactory lubrication for life of vehicle. Fluid changes are not necessary unless lubricant has become contaminated with water.

2) If vehicle is operated at sustained high speed during hot weather, above 90°F (32°C), transmission fluid should be changed and magnet, attached to inside of differential pan, cleaned every 15,000 miles.

Shift & Clutch Linkage

1) If linkage begins to squeak or grunt, pivot hole in adjuster and teeth of adjusting positioner should be lubricated with a thin film of multipurpose grease.

2) Gearshift control mechanism should be lubricated whenever high shift effort or noise (mechanism rattling) is apparent. A multipurpose grease is suitable for this application.

CHECKING FLUID LEVEL

Check lubricant level at filler plug hole on side of transmission. Lubricant should be level with bottom of filler plug hole. Add lubricant as needed to bring to correct level.

RECOMMENDED FLUID

FWD vehicles may be equipped with the A-460 or A-525 manual transaxles. If it becomes necessary to add fluid, use only fluids of the type labeled Dexron II automatic transmission fluid.

TRANSMISSION REFILL CAPACITIES

Application	Quantity
All Models [1]	2.1 qts. (2.0L)

[1] – Measure given is approximate.

ADJUSTMENT

SHIFT LINKAGE

All Models

1) Working over left front fender, remove lock pin from transaxle selector shaft housing. Reverse lock pin, long end down, and insert lock pin into same threaded hole while pushing selector shaft into selector housing. A hole in selector shaft will align with lock pin, allowing lock pin to be screwed into housing. This operation locks selector shaft in 1-2 neutral position.

2) Remove gearshift knob, retaining nut, and pull-up ring. Remove boot from console and remove console. Install 2 cable adjusting pins. Torque selector cable adjusting screw to 55 INCH lbs. (6 N.m). Torque crossover cable adjusting screw to 55 INCH lbs. (6 N.m). *See Fig. 1.*

3) Install console, boot, pull-up ring, retaining nut and gearshift knob. Remove lock pin from selector shaft housing and reinstall lock pin (so long end is up) in selector shaft housing. Tighten lock pin to 106 INCH lbs. (12 N.m). Check for shift into first and reverse. Check for blockout into reverse.

Fig. 1: Adjusting Gearshift Linkage

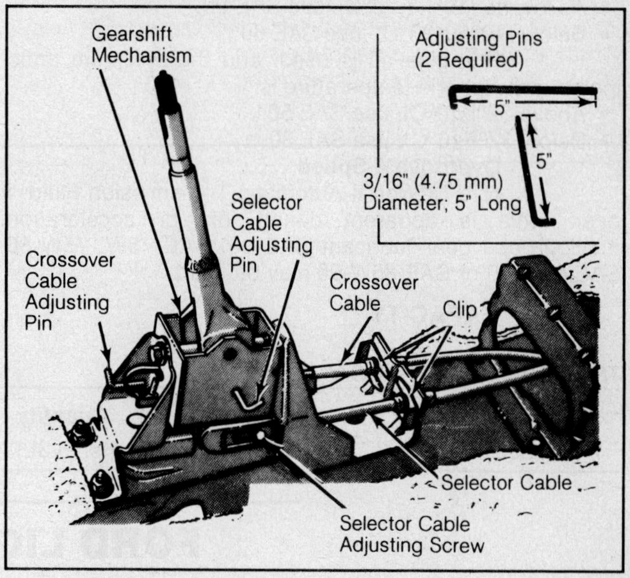

CHRYSLER CORP. RWD LIGHT TRUCKS

LUBRICATION

SERVICE INTERVALS

NOTE: **There are 2 light duty truck emission control standards classifications: Light Duty and Heavy Duty. Light Duty refers to vehicles up to 8500 lbs. GVW; Heavy Duty refers to vehicles over 8500 lbs. GVW.**

All Models

1) Check fluid level whenever vehicle is serviced. On vehicles used in normal service with heavy duty emissions, transmission should be drained and refilled every 36,000 miles.

2) On vehicles containing light duty emissions, transmission should be drained and refilled every 37,500 miles. On vehicles used under severe conditions, drain and refill transmission every 18,000 miles.

Shift Linkage

1) Gearshift control mechanism should be lubricated every 22,500 miles or every 2 years. Lubricate more frequently if shift effort or noise is apparent. The 4-speed gearshift linkage has a grease fitting located on left side of mechanism. Lubricate linkage from under vehicle.

2) Use a high pressure grease gun to lubricate linkage with multipurpose grease. Lubricate until grease is visible on operating levers.

CHRYSLER CORP. RWD LIGHT TRUCKS (Cont.)

NOTE: Vehicle must be in reverse gear position, engine OFF, when lubricating gearshift control mechanism.

CHECKING FLUID LEVEL

Check lubricant level at filler plug hole on side of transmission. Lubricant should be level with bottom of filler plug hole. Add lubricant as needed to bring to correct level.

RECOMMENDED FLUID

New Process 435 4-Speed

Either multipurpose gear lubricants meeting API specification GL-5 or engine oils labeled for API Service "SF" may be used.

If multipurpose gear lubricant is used and the minimum anticipated atmospheric temperature is:

- Above 90°F (32°C), use SAE 140.
- As low as -10°F (-23°C), use SAE 90.
- Below -10°F (-23°C), use SAE 80.

If engine oil is used, and the minimum anticipated atmospheric temperature is:

- Above 32°F (0°C), use SAE 50.
- Below 32°F (0°C), use SAE 30.

Overdrive 4-Speed

Use Dexron II Automatic Transmission Fluid. If gear rattle is apparent during idle or acceleration, multipurpose gear lubricant SAE 90, SAE 75W, 75W-80, SAE 80W-90 or SAE 85W-90 may be used.

CAPACITY

TRANSMISSION REFILL CAPACITIES

Application	Quantity
All Models	3.5 qts. (3.3L)

ADJUSTMENT

SHIFT LINKAGE

Overdrive 4-Speed

1) Install floor shift lever aligning tool to hold levers in neutral crossover position. *See Fig. 1.* Remove all rods from transmission shift levers and place levers in neutral detent positions.

2) Rotate shift rods until they are centered in transmission lever mounting holes, starting with 1st-2nd shift rod. Replace all washers and clips. Remove aligning tool and test shifting action.

Fig. 1: Overdrive 4-Speed Gearshift Linkage Adjustment

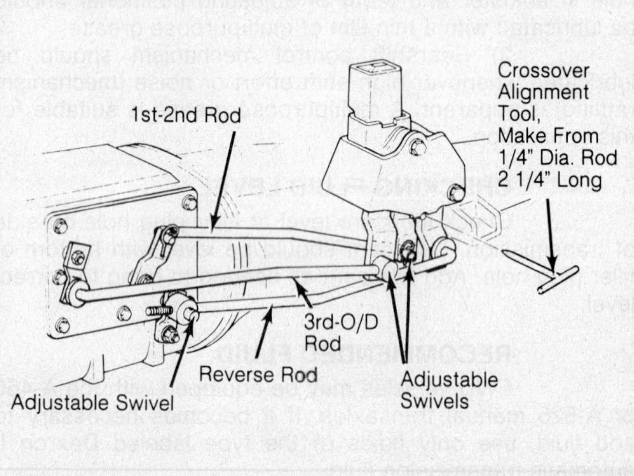

FORD LIGHT TRUCKS

LUBRICATION

SERVICE INTERVALS

Check fluid level whenever malfunction is suspected, leakage is observed, or after vehicle operation in water. Periodic draining and refilling is not required.

CHECKING FLUID LEVEL

Check lubricant level at transmission filler plug hole. It should be level with bottom of filler hole. Add lubricant as needed.

RECOMMENDED FLUID

All transmissions except Warner T19B should use 80W multi-purpose gear lubricant meeting Ford specification ESP-M2C83-C, or equivalent. Warner T19B transmissions use SAE 30 or SAE 50 engine oil, depending upon ambient air temperatures. If vehicle will be operated at temperatures below 0°F (-18°C), SAE 30 should be used. SAE 50 should be used if temperatures are consistently above 0°F (-18°C).

CAPACITY

NOTE: Capacities given below are approximate. Correct fluid level should be determined by level at filler plug hole, rather than by amount added.

TRANSMISSION REFILL CAPACITIES

Application	Quantity
Pickup, Van, Bronco	
Ford 3.03 3-Speed	3.5 pts. (1.6L)
Warner T-18 4-Speed	7.0 pts. (3.3L)
Warner T-19B 4-Speed	7.0 pts. (3.3L)
New Process 435 4-Speed	
With Extension	7.0 pts. (3.3L)
Without Extension	6.5 pts. (3.0L)
Ford Top Shifter (TOD)	
4-Speed Overdrive	4.5 pts. (2.1L)
Ford 4-Speed Overdrive	4.5 pts. (2.1L)
Bronco II & Ranger	
Mitsubishi 5-Speed	4.9 pts. (2.3L)
Toyo Kogyo 5-Speed Overdrive	3.0 pts. (1.4L)
Aerostar	
Mazda 5-Speed Overdrive	3.0 pts. (1.4L)

FORD LIGHT TRUCKS (Cont.)

ADJUSTMENT

SHIFT LINKAGE

Shift linkage may be adjusted on the 3-Speed and 4-Speed Overdrive transmissions, only. All other models use internal shift linkage which cannot be adjusted.

3-Speed

1) Insert a 3/16" gauge pin through steering column shift levers and plastic spacer.

2) Loosen shift rod lock nuts at transmission shift levers. Place both shift levers in Neutral position. Tighten lock nuts and remove gauge pin. Check shift linkage operation for smoothness.

4-Speed Overdrive

1) Disconnect all 3 shift rods and insert a 1/4" diameter pin in alignment hole in shifter assembly. Align 1-2 (rear) and 3-4 (front) shift levers in Neutral position. Turn Reverse (middle) lever counterclockwise to Neutral position.

2) Rotate transmission output shaft to be sure all levers are in Neutral. Then turn reverse lever fully clockwise to reverse position. This causes the interlock system to align 1-2 and 3-4 rails in precise neutral positions. Install 1-2 and 3-4 shift rods on shift levers and tighten lock nuts.

3) Rotate reverse lever back to Neutral position. Install reverse shift rod and lock nut. Remove alignment pin and check for proper linkage operation.

GENERAL MOTORS LIGHT TRUCKS

LUBRICATION

SERVICE INTERVALS

NOTE: **There are 2 light duty truck emission control standards classifications: Light Duty and Heavy Duty. Light Duty refers to vehicles up to 8500 lbs. GVW; Heavy Duty refers to vehicles over 8500 lbs. GVW.**

On "S" models with 4-speed transmission, change transmission fluid after the first 7500 miles and at 30,000 mile intervals thereafter. On all other light duty vehicles, check transmission fluid level every 12 months or 7500 miles. On heavy duty vehicles, check fluid level every 12 months or 6000 miles. Periodic draining and refilling is not required.

CHECKING FLUID LEVEL

Check lubricant level at transmission filler plug hole. Lubricant should be level with bottom of hole. Add as needed.

RECOMMENDED FLUID

All manual transmissions except 4-Speed Overdrive, Astro/Safari 5-Speed and those in the "S" Series, use SAE 80W, GL-5 or SAE 80W-90 GL-5 multipurpose gear lubricant. The 4-Speed Overdrive, Astro/Safari 5-Speed and "S" Series manual transmissions use Dexron II automatic transmission fluid.

CAPACITY

NOTE: **Capacities listed in the following chart are approximations only. Correct fluid level should be determined by level at filler plug hole, rather than by amount added.**

TRANSMISSION REFILL CAPACITIES

Application	Quantity
3-Speed (76 MM)	3.0 pts. (1.4L)
4-Speed (76 MM)	4.0 pts. (1.9L)
4-Speed (117 MM)	8.0 pts. (3.7L)
4-Speed w/Overdrive (89 MM)	4.5 pts. (2.1L)
Astro/Safari & "S" Models	[1]

[1] – Add fluid to bottom of filler plug hole.

ADJUSTMENT

SHIFT LINKAGE

All With Shifter on Column

1) Place gear selector lever in reverse position. Turn transmission shift lever fully clockwise to forward stop. Turn ignition switch to "LOCK" position. Attach primary shift rod to column shift lever with retainer.

2) Slide swivel on to end of shift rod and insert swivel into transmission shift lever. Loosely assemble with bolt and washer. Turn column shift lever down as far as possible and tighten bolt.

3) Turn ignition switch to "UNLOCK" position and move gear selector lever to neutral. Turn transmission shift lever and cross shaft lever clockwise to full forward positions, then back 1 detent to Neutral.

4) Align gauge holes in column shift levers (3) and insert 1/4" gauge pin through holes. Repeat adjustment procedure with secondary shift rod. Remove gauge pin and check for proper linkage operation. Ignition switch should turn to "LOCK" position with shifter in reverse position, only.

All With Floor-Mounted Shifter

1) Disconnect all shift rods from transmission shift levers. With shift selector lever in neutral position, insert a 1/4" diameter pin through alignment holes in shifter assembly.

2) Align all shift levers at transmission in Neutral position. Rotate transmission output shaft to be sure all levers are in neutral. Loosen lock nuts on shift rod ends and align rod ends with shift lever holes. Install shift rods in levers, tighten lock nuts and install lock pins.

3) Remove alignment pin and check for proper linkage operation.

Astro/Safari 5-Speed & "S" Series

On Astro/Safari 5-Speed and "S" Series vehicles, the shift control lever mounts directly to the transmission. Therefore no adjustment is necessary.

Manual Transmission Servicing

JEEP

LUBRICATION

SERVICE INTERVALS

Under normal driving conditions, check fluid level every 5000 miles or when serviced. Under severe driving conditions, check fluid level every 3000 miles. Transmission lubricant should be changed at 27,500 mile intervals.

CHECKING FLUID LEVEL

Check lubricant level at transmission filler plug hole. Lubricant should be level with bottom of hole. Add lubricant as needed.

RECOMMENDED FLUID

The only recommended lubricant for Jeep with manual transmission is AMC/Jeep Manual Transmission Fluid, Part No. 89 83 000 000.

CAPACITY

NOTE: **Capacities given below are approximate. Correct fluid level should be determined by level at filler plug hole.**

TRANSMISSION REFILL CAPACITIES

Application	Quantity
4-Speed	
AX4	7.4 pts. (3.5L)
T4	3.5 pts. (1.7L)
T-176	3.5 pts. (1.7L)
5-Speed	
AX5	7.0 pts. (3.3L)
T5	4.0 pts. (1.9L)

SHIFT LINKAGE

NOTE: **All Jeep models use transmission shift linkage which does not require external adjustment.**

CHRYSLER CORP. – RWD

TRANSFER CASE

MODEL NP-205

Removal

1) Raise vehicle, remove plug and drain transfer case. Replace plug. Disconnect speedometer cable. Remove skid plate, crossmember and strut rods as needed. Disconnect propeller shafts and wire out of way. Do not allow propeller shafts to hang free, as damage to universal joints may result.

2) Disconnect shift lever rod from shift rail link. Support transfer case and remove transfer case-to-transmission adapter bolts. Move transfer case to rear until input shaft clears adapter. Lower transfer case from vehicle.

Installation

Reverse removal procedures to install transfer case. Ensure that all attaching bolts are tight. Fill transfer case with lubricant.

MODEL NP-208

Removal

1) Raise vehicle, remove plug and drain transfer case. Mark front and rear output shaft yokes and propeller shafts for reassembly reference. Disconnect speedometer cable and indicator switch wires. Disconnect shift lever link from operating lever.

2) Support transfer case with transmission jack and remove crossmember. Disconnect front and rear propeller shafts at yokes and wire to frame.

3) If necessary, disconnect parking brake cable guide from pivot on right frame rail. Remove bolts attaching exhaust pipe support bracket to transfer case. Remove transfer case-to-transmission bolts. Move assembly to the rear until clear of output shaft. Lower transfer case from vehicle.

4) Remove all gasket material from rear of transmission adapter housing.

Installation

Install new transmission-to-transfer case gasket with sealer on both sides. Align transfer case with transmission. Rotate transfer case output shaft until transmission output shaft engages transfer case input shaft. Move transfer case until case seats flush against transmission. Install transfer case attaching bolts. Reverse removal procedures to complete installation.

TRANSMISSION

ALL MODELS

NOTE: Transmission and converter must be removed and installed as an assembly to prevent damage to converter drive plate, front pump bushing, and oil seal. DO NOT allow weight of transmission to rest on plate during removal or installation.

Removal

1) Remove transfer case from 4WD vehicles. Disconnect negative battery cable. Disconnect lower exhaust system as needed for removal clearance. Remove engine-to-transmission struts (if equipped). Disconnect cooler lines at transmision. Remove starter, cooler line bracket and converter access cover.

2) Loosen oil pan bolts, tap pan to break loose and allow fluid to drain. Reinstall pan. Rotate crankshaft clockwise with socket on vibration damper bolt to gain access to converter-to-drive plate bolts. Remove bolts. Mark propeller shaft for reassembly reference and remove from vehicle.

NOTE: Crankshaft flange bolt circle, inner and outer circle of holes in drive plate and tapped holes in converter all have 1 hole offset so parts can only be installed in original position.

3) Disconnect wiring connector from back-up light/neutral safety switch. Disconnect gearshift rod and torque shaft assembly from transmission. Disconnect transmission throttle rod from lever. Remove linkage bellcrank assembly, if equipped. Remove oil filler tube. Disconnect speedometer cable.

4) Install an engine support fixture under rear of engine. Raise transmission with service jack to relieve load on suports. Remove bolts securing crossmember to transmission and frame, then remove crossmember. Remove all converter housing-to-engine attaching bolts.

5) Carefully work transmission and converter assembly rearward off engine block dowel pins, disengaging converter hub from end of crankshaft. Attach a small "C" clamp on edge of converter housing to hold converter in place while transmission is being removed. Lower transmission and remove from vehicle.

Installation

1) Before installing converter, rotate front pump rotors with alignment tool (C3881) until 2 small holes in tool handle are vertical. Slide torque converter over input and reaction shafts, making sure converter hub slots are vertical, and fully engage pump inner rotor lugs.

2) Test for full engagement by placing a straightedge across face of transmission case. Surface of converter front cover lug should be at least 1/2" to rear of straightedge when converter is fully engaged. Attach a small "C" clamp to edge of converter housing to hold converter in place while installing transmission.

3) Inspect converter drive plate for distortion or cracks and replace if necessary. Install drive plate and tighten bolts to 55 ft. lbs. (75 N.m).

4) Coat converter hub hole in crankshaft with multi-purpose grease. Place transmission assembly on jack and position under vehicle. Make sure marks on converter and drive plate (made during removal) are aligned. Carefully work transmission assembly into position over dowels. Install all converter housing-to-engine retaining bolts. Tighten bolts to 30 ft. lbs. (41 N.m).

5) To install reverse removal procedure. Adjust shift and throttle linkages and fill transmission with fluid. On 4WD models, install transfer case.

TIGHTENING SPECIFICATIONS

Application	Ft. Lbs. (N.m)
Converter Housing-to-Engine	30 (41)
Cooler Line Fitting	15 (20)
Drain & Fill Plugs	
NP-205 Transfer Case	30 (41)
NP-208 Transfer Case	18 (24)
Oil Pan Bolts	13 (18)
Torque Converter-to-Drive Plate Bolts	22 (30)
Transfer Case-to-Transmission	40 (54)

CHRYSLER CORP. – FWD

TRANSAXLE

ALL MODELS

NOTE: Transaxle removal does not require engine removal.

CAUTION: Transaxle and torque converter must be removed as an assembly; other wise, the torque converter drive plate, pump bushing or oil seal may be damaged. The drive plate will not support a load; therefore, none of the weight of the transaxle should be allowed to rest on the plate during removal.

Removal

1) Disconnect battery negative cable. Disconnect throttle linkage and shift linkage from transaxle. Remove upper and lower oil cooler hoses. Support engine using an engine support fixture. Remove bell housing upper bolts. Remove hub castle lock, nut and cotter pin.

2) Raise vehicle and remove front wheels. Remove wheel hub nut and driveshafts. Remove left splash shield. Remove speedometer adapter, cable and pinion as an assembly. Disconnect sway bar. Remove both lower ball joint-to-steering knuckle bolts.

3) Pry lower ball joint from steering knuckle. Remove driveshaft from hub. Remove both driveshafts. Remove dust cover, mark torque converter and drive plate, and remove torque converter mounting bolts. Remove access plug in right splash shield to rotate engine crankshaft.

4) Remove neutral safety switch connector. Remove engine mount bracket from front crossmember. Remove front mount insulator through-bolt and bell housing bolts. Position transmission jack under transaxle. Remove left engine mount. Remove starter and lower bell housing bolts.

5) Slowly lower transaxle. It may be necessary to pry at engine to provide for clearance.

Installation

To install, reverse removal procedure. Be sure to adjust gearshift and throttle cables. Refill transaxle with Dexron II type automatic transmission fluid.

TIGHTENING SPECIFICATIONS

Application	Ft. Lbs. (N.m)
Bell Housing Cover	9 (12)
Flex Plate-to-Crankshaft	
A-413	65 (88)
A-470	100 (136)
Flex Plate-to-Torque Converter	40 (54)
Transaxle-to-Cylinder Block	70 (95)
Lower Bell Housing Cover	9 (12)
Manual Control Lever	9 (12)
Speedometer-to-Extension	5 (7)
Starter-to-Transaxle Bell Housing	40 (54)
Throttle Cable-to-Transaxle Case	9 (12)
Throttle Lever-to-Transaxle Shaft	9 (12)
Manual Cable-to-Transaxle Case	21 (28)
Front Motor Mount	40 (54)
Left Motor Mount	40 (54)

FORD

TRANSFER CASE

NP-208 (BRONCO, F-150 & F-250)

Removal

1) Raise and support vehicle. Remove drain plug and drain fluid from transfer case. Replace plug. Disconnect 4WD indicator switch connector at transfer case. Disconnect speedometer driven gear from transfer case rear bearing retainer.

2) Remove transmission shift lever-to-transfer case retaining nut. Remove skid plate from frame. Support transfer case with transmission jack. Disconnect front and rear propeller shafts from transfer case output shaft yokes and wire out of way. Do not allow shafts to hang free as damage to universal joints may result.

3) Remove transfer case-to-transmission adapter bolts. Remove gasket between transfer case and adapter and lower transfer case out of vehicle.

Installation

To install transfer case, reverse removal procedures. Fill case with 7 pints (3.3 liters) of Dexron II type automatic transmission fluid.

BORG-WARNER 1345 (F-150–F350)

Removal

1) Raise vehicle. Remove drain plug and drain fluid from transfer case. Replace plug. Disconnect 4WD indicator switch connector at transfer case. If equipped, remove skid plate.

2) Disconnect front and rear propeller shafts from transfer case output shaft yokes, and wire out of way. Do not allow shafts to hang free as damage to universal joints may result.

3) Disconnect speedometer driven gear from rear bearing retainer. Remove retaining clips and shift rod from transfer case control and transfer case shift levers. Disconnect vent hose from case.

4) Remove heat shield. Support transfer case with transmission jack, remove transfer case-to-transmission adapter bolts and slide transfer case off of transmission output shaft (towards rear). Lower transfer case out of vehicle and remove gasket from between transfer case and adapter.

Installation

Reverse removal procedures to install transfer case. Fill case with 6.5 pints (3.1 liters) of Dexron II type automatic transmission fluid.

BORG-WARNER 1350 (BRONCO II & RANGER)

Removal

1) Raise vehicle. Remove skid plate (if equipped). Remove drain plug and drain fluid from case. Replace plug. Disconnect 4WD indicator switch connector at transfer case. Disconnect front propeller shaft from front axle. Loosen front shaft boot clamp and slide out propeller shaft and boot as an assembly.

FORD (Cont.)

2) Disconnect rear propeller shaft from transfer case. Disconnect speedometer driven gear from transfer case rear cover. Disconnect vent hose from control lever.

3) Loosen or remove large and small bolts (1 each) retaining shifter to extension housing. Pull on control lever until bushing slides off transfer case shift lever pin. Unscrew shift lever from control lever, as needed.

4) Remove heat shield from transfer case. Support transfer case with jack and remove transfer case-to-transmission extension housing bolts (5). Slide transfer case to the rear and off of transmission output shaft. Lower case from vehicle. Remove gasket from between transfer case and extension housing.

Installation

Reverse removal procedures to install transfer case, noting the following:

1) When installing shift lever assembly, tighten large bolt first, then small bolt.

2) When installing vent assembly, White marking on hose should be positioned in notch in shifter with upper end of hose 2 inches above top of shifter, inside of shift lever boot.

3) Before installing front propeller shaft into transfer case, lubricate female splines of transfer case input shaft with multi-purpose grease.

4) Fill transfer case to bottom of fill plug hole with Dexron-II automatic transmission fluid.

TRANSMISSION

A4LD (BRONCO II & RANGER)

Removal

1) Raise vehicle on hoist. Place drain pan under transmission fluid pan. Starting at rear of pan and working toward front, loosen attaching bolts and allow fluid to drain.

2) Remove all pan attaching bolts except 2 at front, to allow fluid to further drain. After all fluid has drained, install 2 bolts on rear side of pan to temporarily hold it in place.

3) Remove converter access cover and adapter plate bolts from lower end of converter housing. Remove 4 flywheel to converter attaching nuts. Crank engine to turn converter to gain access to nuts, using a wrench on crankshaft pulley attaching bolt.

NOTE: On belt driven overhead camshaft engines, never turn engine backwards.

4) Remove driveshaft and install extension housing seal replacer tool in extension housing. Remove speedometer cable from extension housing. Disconnect shift rod at manual lever and downshift rod at dowshift lever.

5) Remove starter-to-converter housing attaching bolts and position starter out of way. Disconnect neutral start switch wires from switch. Remove vacuum line from vacuum modulator.

6) Position a jack under transmission and raise slightly. Remove engine rear support-to-crossmember bolts. Remove crossmember-to-frame side support attaching bolts and remove crossmember insulator and support and damper.

7) Lower jack and allow transmission to hang. Position jack at front of engine and raise engine to gain access to 2 upper converter housing-to-engine attaching bolts. Disconnect oil cooler lines at transmission

8) Plug all openings to keep out dirt. Remove lower converter housing-to-engine attaching bolts. Remove transmission filler tube. Secure transmission to jack with a safety chain.

9) Remove 2 upper converter housing-to-engine attaching bolts. Move transmission to rear and down to remove it from under vehicle.

Installation

To install, reverse removal procedure. Ensure full converter engagement in transmission before installing it. During installation, keep transmission in a "nose-up" position at all times to prevent disengagement of the torque converter and pump gear.

A4LD (AEROSTAR)

Removal

1) Raise vehicle on hoist. Place drain pan under transmission. Starting at rear of pan and working toward front, loosen attaching bolts and allow fluid to drain.

2) Remove all bolts except the 2 at front to allow further draining. After all fluid has been drained, install 2 bolts on rear side of pan also to temporarily retain pan.

3) Remove converter access cover and adapter plate bolts from lower end of converter housing. Remove 4 flywheel-to-converter nuts by placing a 22 mm socket and breaker bar on crankshaft pulley attaching bolt. Rotate pulley clockwise to gain access to each of the nuts.

CAUTION: On belt driven overhead cam engines, never rotate pulley in a counterclockwise direction.

4) Scribe a mark indexing driveshaft to rear axle pinion flange. Remove "U" bolts and nuts retaining driveshaft to flange. Remove driveshaft. Install an extension housing seal replacer tool in housing to prevent fuel spillage.

5) Remove speedometer cable from extension housing. Disconnect neutral start switch wires and converter clutch solenoid. Remove kickdown cable from upper selector lever. Remove retaining clip from selector cable bracket.

6) Remove selector cable from ball stud on lower selector lever. Depress tab on retainer and remove kickdown cable from bracket. Disconnect vacuum hose from transmission vacuum modulator.

7) Disconnect relay-to-starter cable at starter terminal. Remove starter mounting bolts and ground cable. Remove starter. Remove filler tube from transmission. Position transmission jack under transmission. Place a safety chain around transmission. Slightly raise transmission.

8) Remove insulator crossmember retaining nuts. Remove crossmember-to-frame side support attaching nuts nad bolts. Remove crossmember. If required, remove bolts retaining insulator to transmission and remove insulator.

9) Remove converter housing-to-engine fasteners. Slightly lower jack to gain access to oil cooler lines. Disconnect oil cooler lines at transmission. Plug all openings to keep dirt and contamination out.

Automatic Transmission Removal

FORD (Cont.)

10) Move transmission to rear so it disengages from dowel pins and converter is disengaged from flywheel. Lower transmission from vehicle.

NOTE: If transmission is to be removed for a period of time, support engine with a safety stand and wood block.

Installation

To install, reverse removal procedure. Make sure torque converter rotates freely and is not bound up. Replace fluid and check for leaks.

C-5 (F-150)

Removal

1) Disconnect battery negative cable. On 4WD vehicles, remove filler tube bracket bolt from valve cover bracket. On all models, raise and support vehicle. Drain transmission fluid and replace pan. Remove converter drain plug access cover. On 2WD models, remove adapter plate bolts from lower end of converter housing.

2) On all models, remove converter-to-flex plate attaching nuts and converter drain plug. Allow fluid to drain from converter, then reinstall and tighten drain plug. On 2WD models, mark propeller shaft for reassembly. Disconnect shaft at rear axle and slide out of transmission.

3) On all models, disconnect battery cable from starter motor and remove starter. Disconnect neutral start switch wires at connector. Remove rear mount-to-crossmember nuts and 2 crossmember-to-frame bolts. Remove right and left gussets. On 4WD vehicles, remove rear insulator-to-extension housing bolts (2).

4) On all models, disconnect throttle valve (TV) linkage rod from transmission TV lever. Disconnect manual rod from manual lever at transmission. On 4WD models, disconnect downshift and manual linkage rods from levers on transmission. Remove vacuum hose from diaphragm unit. Remove vacuum line from retaining clip.

5) On all models, remove bellcrank housing-to-converter housing bolts (2). Remove transfer case (4WD models). Raise transmission enough to allow removal of crossmember. Remove rear mount from crossmember, then remove crossmember.

6) Lower transmission as needed to disconnect oil cooler lines. Disconnect cooler lines. Disconnect speedometer cable from extension housing. On 2WD models, remove transmission filler tube-to-engine bolt and lift filler tube out of transmission.

7) On all models, secure transmission to jack with safety chain. Remove converter housing-to-engine bolts. Carefully remove transmission and converter assembly from vehicle.

Installation

To install transmission, reverse removal procedures, noting the following:

1) Ensure that converter is fully engaged with pump gear before installation.

2) When installing filler tube, install a new "O" ring on bottom of tube.

3) On 2WD models, when installing damper assembly over engine rear support studs, make sure that the painted surface of the damper is facing forward when installed in vehicle.

4) Before installing rear propeller shaft, apply a small amount of multi-purpose grease to splines of yoke.

C-6 ("E" SERIES)

Removal

1) Working inside vehicle, remove engine compartment cover and disconnect electrical leads at plug connector. Remove flex hose from air cleaner heat tube (V8 models only), then remove upper converter housing-to-engine attaching bolts. Remove fluid filler tube-to-engine bolt.

2) Raise vehicle, drain transmission pan and remove converter drain plug access cover. Remove converter-to-flex plate attaching nuts and converter drain plug. Drain fluid and replace drain plug.

3) Disconnect propeller shaft. Remove filler tube. Disconnect starter cable and remove starter. Position an engine support bar to side rail and oil pan flanges. Disconnect oil cooler lines and vacuum lines from transmission.

4) Remove speedometer driven gear from extension housing and manual and downshift linkage rods from transmission control levers. Support transmission with transmission jack and secure with safety chain.

5) Remove bolts and nuts securing rear mount to crossmember and bolts retaining crossmember to side rails. Remove 2 support inserts, raise transmission with jack and remove crossmember. Remove remaining converter housing-to-engine bolts and lower assembly out of vehicle.

Installation

Reverse removal procedures to install, noting the following: Be sure that converter is fully engaged with pump gear during installation. Always use a new "O" ring on the end of the fluid filler tube. When installation is complete, fill transmission with Dexron II type automatic transmission fluid.

C-6 (BRONCO & "F" SERIES)

Removal

1) Disconnect negative cable from battery. Remove 2 upper converter housing-to-engine bolts. Raise vehicle, drain transmission pan and remove converter drain plug access cover.

2) Remove converter-to-flex plate attaching nuts and converter drain plug. Allow fluid to drain, then reinstall and tighten converter drain plug. On 2WD models, disconnect propeller shaft at rear axle and slide shaft out of transmission.

3) On all models, disconnect speedometer cable from extension housing. Disconnect downshift and manual linkage rods from levers at transmission. Disconnect oil cooler lines from transmission.

4) Remove vacuum line from vacuum unit. Remove vacuum line retaining clip. Disconnect starter cable from starter and remove starter. On 4WD models, remove transfer case.

5) On all models, remove 2 rear crossmember-to-frame attaching bolts. Remove 2 rear support-to-extension housing attaching bolts and 6 bolts securing second crossmember to frame side rails.

6) Raise transmission with a transmission jack and remove both crossmembers. Secure transmission to the jack with safety chain. Remove remaining converter housing-to-engine attaching bolts. Move transmission away from engine, lower the jack and remove converter and transmission assembly from vehicle.

FORD (Cont.)

Installation

Reverse removal procedure to install, noting the following: Make sure that torque converter is fully engaged in transmission before and during installation. When installing fluid filler tube, always use a new "O" ring on end of tube. When installation is complete, fill transmission with Dexron II type automatic transmission fluid.

AUTOMATIC OVERDRIVE (E-150/250, F-150/250 & BRONCO)

Removal

1) Disconnect negative battery cable. Raise vehicle and drain transmission fluid. Remove converter drain plug access cover. Remove converter-to-flex plate attaching nuts and torque converter drain plug. Drain converter, then reinstall and tighten converter drain plug.

2) Disconnect propeller shaft from rear axle and remove shaft from transmission. Disconnect starter cable and remove starter. Disconnect neutral start switch wires at connector.

3) Remove rear mount-to-crossmember bolts and crossmember-to-frame bolts. Remove bolts securing engine rear support to extension housing. Disconnect TV linkage rod and manual rod from transmission levers.

4) Remove bellcrank bracket-to-converter housing bolts (2). Raise transmission with jack and remove crossmember. Lower transmission enough to remove oil cooler lines.

5) Disconnect speedometer cable from extension housing. Remove bolt securing filler tube to engine and remove filler tube. Secure transmission to jack with safety chain. Remove converter housing-to-engine bolts. Move transmission to rear and down to remove from vehicle.

Installation

Reverse removal procedures to install transmission, noting the following: Ensure that converter is fully seated in transmission before and during installation procedure. Install new "O" ring on end of fluid filler tube before installing tube. When installation is complete, fill transmission with Dexron II type automatic transmission fluid.

TIGHTENING SPECIFICATIONS

Application	Ft. Lbs. (N.m)
Converter Housing-to-Engine	
C-5	40-50 (55-67)
C-6	
Gas Engine	40-50 (55-67)
Diesel Engine	50-65 (67-87)
AOT	40-50 (55-67)
A4LD	28-38 (38-51)
Converter-to-Flex Plate	
A4LD	20-34 (27-46)
All Others	20-30 (28-40)

GENERAL MOTORS

TRANSFER CASE

NP-205 (30 SERIES)

Removal

1) Raise and support vehicle on hoist. Drain transfer case. Disconnect speedometer cable. Remove skid plate and crossmember supports as necessary. Disconnect rear drive shaft from transfer case and tie up away from work area.

2) Disconnect front drive shaft from transfer case and tie up shaft away from work area. Disconnect shift lever rod from shift rail link. Support transfer case and remove bolts attaching transfer case to transmission adapter.

3) Move transfer case to rear until input shaft clears adapter and lower assembly from vehicle.

Installation

To install, reverse removal procedure.

NP-207 ("S" SERIES)

Removal

1) With transfer case shift lever in "4 Hi" position, disconnect negative battery cable. Raise vehicle and remove skid plate. Drain transfer case. Mark front and rear output shaft yokes and propeller shafts for reassembly reference and remove shafts.

2) Disconnect speedometer cable and vacuum harness from transfer case. Remove shift lever from case. Remove catalytic converter hanger bolts at converter. Raise transmission and transfer case assembly with jack and remove transmission mount bolts. Remove mount.

3) Lower complete assembly. Support transfer case alone and remove transmission-to-transfer case bolts. Remove shift lever bracket from transfer case adapter in order to reach upper left attaching bolt.

4) Separate transfer case from transmission adapter and remove from vehicle.

Installation

Reverse removal procedures to install. Always use a new gasket between the transfer case and adapter.

NP-208 (10 & 20 SERIES)

Removal

1) Place transfer case in "4H". Raise vehicle. Drain lubricant from transfer case. Remove cotter pin from shift lever swivel. Mark transfer case front and rear output shaft yokes and propeller shafts for assembly alignment reference.

2) Disconnect speedometer cable and indicator switch wires. Disconnect front drive shaft at transfer case yoke. Disconnect parking brake cable guide from pivot located on right frame rail, if necessary. Remove engine strut rod from transfer case.

3) Place support under transfer case and remove transfer case-to-transmission adapter bolts. Move transfer case assembly rearward until free of transmission output shaft and remove assembly. Remove all gasket material from rear of transmission adapter housing.

Installation

To install, reverse removal procedure.

Automatic Transmission Removal

GENERAL MOTORS (Cont.)

TRANSMISSIONS

ALL MODELS EXCEPT ASTRO/SAFARI VAN, "S" & "K" SERIES

Removal

1) Disconnect negative battery cable. Remove air cleaner and disconnect TV or detent cable at carburetor. Remove dipstick and filler tube support bracket bolt. Raise and support vehicle. Mark propeller shaft for reassembly reference and remove from vehicle.

2) Disconnect speedometer cable and shift linkage and all electrical leads from transmission. Remove transmission support brackets (if present) and flywheel inspection cover.

3) Mark flex plate and torque converter for reassembly in same position and remove torque converter-to-flex plate bolts. Disconnect catalytic converter support bracket (if equipped).

4) Remove transmission rear mount bolts. Support transmission with jack and raise slightly. Remove transmission support-to-frame bolts and insulators. Remove support.

5) Lower transmission enough to remove oil cooler lines and TV or detent cable from transmission. Disconnect lines and cable. Support engine with jack and remove transmission-to-engine bolts.

6) Disconnect transmission assembly from engine. Install torque converter retaining tool (J-21366) and remove transmission from vehicle.

Installation

To install, reverse removal procedure and note the following: Before installing flex plate-to-converter bolts, make certain that the weld nuts on converter are flush with the flex plate and the converter rotates freely by hand in this position. Install converter-to-flex plate bolts (3) and tighten finger tight before tightening to proper specification.

ASTRO/SAFARI VAN

Removal

1) Open hood and disconnect negative cable at battery. Remove engine cover. Disconnect T.V. cable at its upper end. Raise vehicle. Remove propeller shaft. Disconnect speedometer cable at transmission. Disconnect shift linkage at transmission.

2) Disconnect all electrical leads at transmission and any clips that retain leads to transmission case. Remove transmission support brace attaching bolts at converter. Disconnect exhaust crossover pipe from exhaust manifolds.

3) Remove converter cover and mark flywheel and torque converter to maintain original balance. Remove torque converter to flywheel bolts and/or nuts. Position a transmission jack under transmission and raise it slightly.

4) Remove transmission crossmember to mount bolts and crossmember to frame bolts (and insulator if used). Slide crossmember rearward and remove from vehicle. Lower transmission to gain access to oil cooler lines and T.V. Cable attachments. Disconnect oil cooler lines and T.V. cable. Cap all openings.

5) Support engine with a suitable tool and remove transmission to engine bolts. Disconnect transmission assembly, being careful not to damage any cables, lines or linkage. Install torque converter holding tool J-21366 and remove transmission assembly from vehicle.

Installation

To install, reverse removal procedure.

"K" SERIES

Removal

1) Disconnect negative battery cable. Remove air cleaner and disconnect TV or detent cable at carburetor. Remove transfer case shift lever knob and boot. Raise and support vehicle.

2) Mark propeller shafts for reassembly reference and remove from vehicle. Disconnect speedometer cable, shift linkage and all electrical leads from transmission and transfer case. Disconnect transfer case shift linkage.

3) Remove transmission support strut rods and flywheel inspection cover. Mark flex plate and converter for reassembly reference. Remove torque converter-to-flex plate retaining bolts.

4) Disconnect transmission oil cooler lines from transmission. Support transmission and transfer case assembly with a jack and remove transfer case-to-frame bracket bolts. Remove mount bolts and crossmember.

5) Remove transmission/transfer case assembly mounting bolts and remove assembly from vehicle. Separate transmission from transfer case.

Installation

Reverse removal procedures to install, noting the following: Before installing flex plate-to-converter bolts, make certain that the weld nuts on converter are flush with the flex plate and the converter rotates freely by hand in this position. Then, hand start all 3 bolts and tighten finger tight before tightening to specifications.

"S" SERIES

NOTE: **On 4WD models, refer to Transfer Case removal procedures to remove transfer case.**

Removal

1) Disconnect negative battery cable. Remove air cleaner and disconnect TV cable at carburetor. On models with 1.9L 4-cylinder engine, remove upper starter retaining nut. On all models, raise and support vehicle.

2) Mark propeller shaft for reassembly reference and remove shaft. Disconnect speedometer cable, shift linkage and all electrical leads from transmission. Remove brake line to crossmember clips and remove crossmember (4WD only).

3) Remove transmission support brace bolts and converter cover (if equipped). Remove exhaust crossover pipe and converter attaching bolts. Remove crossover and converter as an assembly.

4) Remove flywheel inspection plate and mark flex plate and torque converter for reassembly reference. Remove torque converter-to-flex plate bolts. Disconnect catalytic converter support bracket.

5) Place a jack under transmission and raise slightly. Remove transmission support-to-mount bolt and support-to-frame bolts and insulators. Remove left body mounting bolts and loosen radiator support mount bolt.

6) Raise cab on left side as needed to remove upper transmission-to-engine bolts. Support cab with wood block between body and frame. Slide transmission support towards rear and lower transmission enough to remove oil cooler lines and TV cable. Disconnect lines and cable.

GENERAL MOTORS (Cont.)

7) Support engine with jack and remove remaining transmission-to-engine bolts. Slide transmission away from engine and install torque converter retaining tool (J-21366) to prevent converter damage as transmission is removed from vehicle. Remove transmission.

Installation

Reverse removal procedures to install, noting the following: Before installing flex plate-to-converter bolts, make certain that the weld nuts on converter are flush with the flex plate and the converter rotates freely by hand in this position. Then, hand start all 3 bolts and tighten finger tight before tightening to specifications.

TIGHTENING SPECIFICATIONS

Application	Ft. Lbs. (N.m)
Transmission-to-Engine	
"S" Series	25 (34)
All Others	35 (47)

TIGHTENING SPECIFICATIONS

Application	Ft. Lbs. (N.m)
Converter-to-Flex Plate	
"S" Series	35 (47)
All Others	35 (47)
Transmission Mount-to-Crossmember	
"S" Series	25 (34)
All Others	35 (47)
Transmission-to-Mount	
"S" Series	35 (47)
All Others	35 (47)
Crossmember-to-Frame	
"S" Series	25 (34)
All Others	35 (47)
Transfer Case-to-Adapter	
"S" Series	20-25 (27-34)
All Others	25 (34)
Transmission-to-Adapter	25 (34)

JEEP

TRANSFER CASE

MODEL NP-207

Removal

1) Shift transfer case into "4H" position. Raise and support vehicle. Drain lubricant from transfer case. Mark rear axle yoke and drive shaft for installation reference. Remove rear drive shaft. Disconnect speedometer cable, vacuum hoses and vent hose from transfer case.

2) Raise transmission and transfer case and remove transmission crossmember attaching bolts. Remove crossmember and lower transmission and transfer case. Mark transfer case front output shaft flange and drive shaft for installation reference.

3) Disconnect front drive shaft from transfer case. Disconnect shift lever linkage rod at transfer case. Remove shift lever bracket bolts. Support transfer case and remove transfer case attaching bolts. Remove tranfer case assembly.

Installation

To intall, reverse removal procedure.

MODEL NP-208

Removal

1) Raise vehicle. Drain lubricant from transfer case. Disconnect speedometer cable and indicator switch wires and disconnect transfer case shift lever link at operating lever. Place a safety stand under transmission and remove the rear crossmember.

2) Mark transfer case front and rear output shaft yokes and drive shafts for assembly alignment reference. Disconnect front and rear drive shafts at transfer case yokes. Secure shafts to frame rails with wire. Disconnect parking brake cable guide from pivot located on right frame rail, if necessary.

3) Remove bolts attaching exhaust pipe support bracket-to-transfer case, if necessary. Remove transfer case-to-transmission bolts. Move transfer case assembly rearward until free of transmission output shaft and remove assembly. Remove all gasket material from rear of transmission adapter housing.

Installation

To install, reverse removal procedure.

MODEL NP-229

Removal

1) Raise and support vehicle. Drain lubricant from transfer case. Disconnect speedometer cable and vent hose. Disconnect transfer case shift lever link at operating lever. Place a safety stand under transmission and remove rear crossemmber.

2) Mark transfer case front and rear output shafts at transfer case yokes and drive shafts for installation alignment reference. Disconnect front and rear drive shafts at transfer case yokes. Secure Shafts. Disconnect shift motor vacuum hoses.

3) Disconnect transfer case shift linkage. Remove transfer case-to-transmission bolts. Move transfer case assembly rearward until clear of transmission oupput shaft and remove assembly. Remove all gasket material from rear of transmission adapter housing.

Installation

To install, reverse removal procedure.

MODEL NP-300

Removal

1) Remove floor covering, if equipped and remove transmission access cover from floorpan. Raise vehicle and drain lubricant from transfer case. Position support stand under clutch housing to support engine and transmission and remove rear crossmember.

2) Disconnect front and rear drive shafts at transfer case. Mark drive shaft yokes for assembly reference. Disconnect speedometer cable at transfer case. If necessary, disconnect parking brake cable at equalizer. Disconnect exhaust pipe support bracket at transfer case, if equipped. Remove bolts attaching transfer case to transmission and remove tranfer case.

Installation

To install, reverse removal procedure.

JEEP (Cont.)

TRANSMISSION

ALL MODELS

Removal

1) Disconnect fan shroud and transmission fill tube upper bracket. Raise vehicle. Remove converter inspection cover and fill tube. Remove starter.

2) Mark drive shafts for reassembly. Disconnect shafts at transfer case and wire to frame rails. DO NOT allow shafts to hang free as damage to universal joints may result. On V8 models, disconnect exhaust pipes from exhaust manifolds. Drain transfer case lubricant. Disconnect speedometer cable from transmission.

3) Disconnect all shift and throttle linkages and wiring from transmission and transfer case. Mark converter drive plate and converter for reassembly and remove torque converter-to-drive plate bolts. Rotate crankshaft to gain access to bolts.

4) Suport transmission/transfer case assembly with jack and secure with chain. Remove bolts and rear crossmember. Lower transmission enough to disconnect cooler lines at transmission. Remove transmission-to-engine retaining bolts and slowly slide transmission assembly away from engine.

5) Hold converter in position while lowering transmission assembly from vehicle. Separate transmission from transfer case.

Installation

Reverse removal procedures to install, noting the following: Do not tighten exhaust pipe attaching bolts until crossmember has been installed and transmission jack has been removed. Make sure all index marks made at removal are aligned. Tighten all bolts to specification and fill transmission and transfer case with fluid.

TIGHTENING SPECIFICATIONS

Application	Ft. Lbs. (N.m)
Cooler Line Nuts	25 (34)
Torque Converter-to-Drive Plate	22 (30)
Transfer Case-to-Transmission	40 (54)
Transmission-to-Engine	30 (41)

Manual Transmission Removal

CHRYSLER CORP. – RWD

TRANSFER CASE

MODEL NP-205

Removal

1) Raise and support vehicle. Remove plug and drain transfer case. Replace plug. Disconnect speedometer cable. Remove skid plate, crossmember and strut rods as needed. Disconnect propeller shafts and wire out of way. Do not allow propeller shafts to hang free, as damage to universal joints may result.

2) Disconnect shift lever rod from shift rail link. Support transfer case and remove transfer case-to-transmission adapter bolts. Move transfer case to rear until input shaft clears adapter. Lower transfer case from vehicle.

Installation

Reverse removal procedures to install transfer case. Ensure that all attaching bolts are tight. Fill transfer case with lubricant.

MODEL NP-208

Removal

1) Raise vehicle, remove plug and drain transfer case. Mark front and rear output shaft yokes and propeller shafts for reassembly reference. Disconnect speedometer cable and indicator switch wires. Disconnect shift lever link from operating lever.

2) Support transfer case with transmission jack and remove crossmember. Disconnect front and rear propeller shafts at yokes and wire to frame.

3) If necessary, disconnect parking brake cable guide from pivot on right frame rail. Remove bolts attaching exhaust pipe support bracket to transfer case. Remove transfer case-to-transmission bolts. Move assembly to the rear until clear of output shaft. Lower transfer case from vehicle.

4) Remove all gasket material from rear of transmission adapter housing.

Installation

1) Install new transmission-to-transfer case gasket with sealer on both sides. Align transfer case with transmission. Rotate transfer case output shaft until transmission output shaft engages transfer case input shaft.

2) Move transfer case until case seats flush against transmission. Install transfer case attaching bolts. Reverse removal procedures to complete installation.

TRANSMISSION

ALL MODELS

Removal

1) Disconnect negative battery cable. Remove retaining screws from floor pan and slide boot up and off shift lever.

2) On models equipped with New Process 435 transmission, remove shift lever retainer by pressing down, rotating retainer clockwise and releasing.

3) On models equipped with Overdrive 4-Speed transmission, remove shift lever by inserting a .010" (.25 mm) feeler gauge between floor shift assembly and shift lever, and disengaging internal spring clip. *See Fig. 1.*

Fig. 1: Removing Overdrive 4-Speed Shift Lever

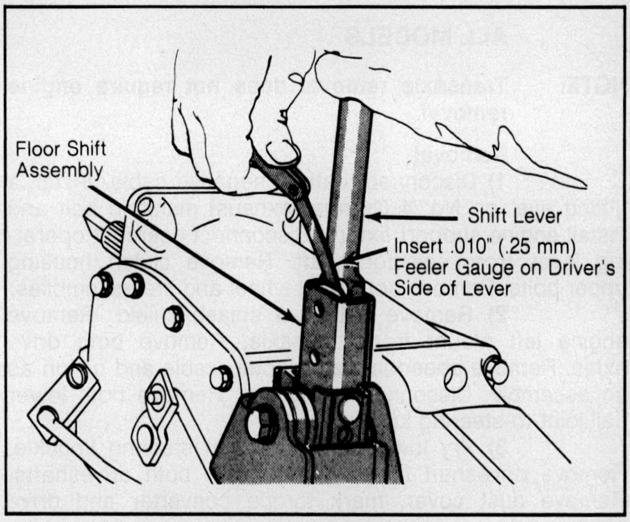

Insert feeler gauge to remove spring clip.

4) Remove bolts and washers securing shift lever to mounting plate on extension housing and remove.

5) On all models, drain fluid from transmission. On 4WD models, remove transfer case. On all vehicles, remove propeller shaft from transmission at rear universal joint. Disconnect speedometer cable and back-up light switch. Install engine support fixture (C-3487-A).

6) On models equipped with New Process 435 transmission, place adapters (DD-1279) firmly over frame rails. On all models, make sure support ends of engine fixture tool are up against underside of oil pan flange.

7) Raise engine slightly with support fixture. On models with Overdrive 4-Speed transmission, disconnect extension housing from removable center crossmember.

8) On all models, support transmission with a jack and remove crossmember. Remove transmission-to-clutch housing bolts. Slide transmission rearward until drive pinion shaft clears clutch disc, then lower and remove transmission.

Installation

1) To install reverse removal procedure. Apply a small amount of high-temperature grease to the pilot shaft bushing in the flywheel and on pinion bearing retainer release bearing sleeve area before installing transmission.

2) As transmission is installed, engage pinion shaft with clutch disc by slowly turning shaft to engage teeth. DO NOT allow transmission to hang free once clutch disc has been engaged.

TIGHTENING SPECIFICATIONS

Application	Ft. Lbs. (N.m)
Transfer Case-to-Transmission	40 (54)
Crossmember-to-Frame	30 (41)
Ext. Housing-to-Rear Mount Bolt	50 (68)
Transmission Case-to-Clutch Housing	
Overdrive 4-Speed	50 (68)
NP-435	105 (142)

CHRYSLER CORP. – FWD

TRANSAXLE

ALL MODELS

NOTE: Transaxle removal does not require engine removal.

Removal

1) Disconnect battery negative cable. Install a "lifting eye" on No. 4 Cylinder exhaust manifold bolt and install engine support fixture. Disconnect gearshift operating lever from selector shaft. Remove clutch housing upper bolts. Remove both front wheel and tire assemblies.

2) Remove left front splash shield. Remove engine left mount from transaxle. Remove both drive axles. Remove speedometer adapter, cable and pinion as an assembly. Disconnect sway bar. Remove both lower ball joint-to-steering knuckle bolts.

3) Pry lower ball joint from steering knuckle. Remove driveshaft from hub. Remove both driveshafts. Remove dust cover, mark torque converter and drive plate, and remove torque converter mounting bolts. Remove access plug in right splash shield to rotate engine crankshaft.

4) Remove neutral safety switch connector. Remove engine mount bracket from front crossmember. Remove front mount insulator through-bolt and bell housing bolts. Position transmission jack under transaxle. Remove left engine mount. Remove starter and lower bell housing bolts.

5) Slowly lower transaxle. It may be necessary to pry at engine to provide for clearance.

Installation

To install, reverse removal procedure. Be sure to adjust gearshift and throttle cables. Refill transaxle with Dexron II type automatic transmission fluid. When installing transaxle, it may be helpful to use two locating pins in place of the top two transaxle to engine block bolts. After transaxle is in place, install bolts and remove locating pins before removing jack.

TIGHTENING SPECIFICATIONS

Application	Ft. Lbs. (N.m)
Bell Housing Cover	9 (12)
Flex Plate-to-Crank	
A-413	65 (88)
A-470	100 (136)
Flex Plate-to-Torque Converter	40 (54)
Transaxle-to-Cylinder Block	70 (95)
Lower Bell Housing Cover	9 (12)
Manual Control Lever	9 (12)
Speedometer-to-Extension	5 (7)
Starter-to-Transaxle Bell Housing	40 (54)
Throttle Cable-to-Transaxle Case	9 (12)
Throttle Lever-to Transaxle Shaft	9 (12)
Manual Cable-to-Transaxle Case	21 (28)
Front Motor Mount	40 (54)
Left Motor Mount	40 (54)

FORD

TRANSFER CASE

NP-208 (BRONCO, F-150 & F-250)

Removal

1) Raise and support vehicle. Remove drain plug and drain fluid from transfer case. Replace plug. Disconnect 4WD indicator switch connector at transfer case. Disconnect speedometer driven gear from transfer case rear bearing retainer.

2) Remove transmission shift lever-to-transfer case retaining nut. Remove skid plate from frame. Support transfer case with transmission jack. Disconnect front and rear propeller shafts from transfer case output shaft yokes and wire out of way. Do not allow shafts to hang free as damage to universal joints may result.

3) Remove transfer case-to-transmission adapter bolts. Remove gasket between transfer case and adapter and lower transfer case out of vehicle.

Installation

To install transfer case, reverse removal procedures. Fill case with 7 pints (3.3 liters) of Dexron II type automatic transmission fluid.

BORG-WARNER 1345 (F-150 & F-350)

Removal

1) Raise vehicle. Remove drain plug and drain fluid from transfer case. Replace plug. Disconnect 4WD indicator switch connector at transfer case. If equipped, remove skid plate.

2) Disconnect front and rear propeller shafts from transfer case output shaft yokes, and wire out of way. Do not allow shafts to hang free as damage to universal joints may result.

3) Disconnect speedometer driven gear from rear bearing retainer. Remove retaining clips and shift rod from transfer case control and transfer case shift levers. Disconnect vent hose from case.

4) Remove heat shield. Support transfer case with transmission jack, remove transfer case-to-transmission adapter bolts and slide transfer case off of transmission output shaft (towards rear). Lower transfer case out of vehicle and remove gasket from between transfer case and adapter.

Installation

Reverse removal procedures to install transfer case. Fill case with 6.5 pints (3.1 liters) of Dexron II type automatic transmission fluid.

BORG-WARNER 1350 (BRONCO II & RANGER)

Removal

1) Raise vehicle. Remove skid plate (if equipped). Remove drain plug and drain fluid from case. Replace plug. Disconnect 4WD indicator switch connector at transfer case. Disconnect front propeller shaft from front axle. Loosen front shaft boot clamp and slide out propeller shaft and boot as an assembly.

FORD (Cont.)

2) Disconnect rear propeller shaft from transfer case. Disconnect speedometer driven gear from transfer case rear cover. Disconnect vent hose from control lever.

3) Loosen or remove large and small bolts (1 each) retaining shifter to extension housing. Pull on control lever until bushing slides off transfer case shift lever pin. Unscrew shift lever from control lever, as needed.

4) Remove heat shield from transfer case. Support transfer case with jack and remove transfer case-to-transmission extension housing bolts (5). Slide transfer case to the rear and off of transmission output shaft. Lower case from vehicle. Remove gasket from between transfer case and extension housing.

Installation

Reverse removal procedures to install transfer case, noting the following:

1) When installing shift lever assembly, tighten large bolt first, then small bolt.

2) When installing vent assembly, White marking on hose should be positioned in notch in shifter with upper end of hose 2 inches above top of shifter, inside of shift lever boot.

3) Before installing front propeller shaft into transfer case, lubricate female splines of transfer case input shaft with multi-purpose grease.

4) Fill transfer case to bottom of fill plug hole with Dexron-II automatic transmission fluid.

TRANSMISSION

5-SPEED TOYO KOGYO (BRONCO II & RANGER)

Removal

1) Place shift lever in neutral position. Remove boot retainer screws and bolts attaching retainer cover to gearshift lever retainer. Disconnect clutch master cylinder push rod from clutch pedal.

2) Pull gearshift lever assembly, shim and bushing straight up and away from lever retainer. Cover shift tower in extension housing with a cloth to avoid dropping dirt into transmission.

3) Disconnect clutch hydraulic system master cylinder push rod from clutch pedal. Open hood and disconnect battery negative cable from battery terminal. Raise vehicle. Disconnect drive shaft at rear axle drive flange.

4) Pull drive shaft rearward and disconnect from transmission. Install a suitable plug in extension housing to prevent lubricant leakage. Remove clutch housing dust shield and slave cylinder and secure it at one side.

5) Remove speedometer cable from extension housing. Disconnect starter motor and back-up lamp switch wires. Place jack under engine, protecting oil pan with a wood block.

6) On 4WD vehicles, remove transfer case. Remove starter motor. Position a transmission jack under transmission. Remove bolts, lock washers and flat washers attaching transmission to engine rear plate.

7) Remove nuts and bolts attaching transmission mount and damper to crossmember. Remove nuts attaching crossmember to frame side rails and remove crossmember.

8) Lower engine jack. Work clutch housing off locating dowels and slide transmission rearward until input shaft spline clears clutch disc. Remove transmission from vehicle.

Installation

To install, reverse removal procedure.

5-SPEED MITSUBISHI (BRONCO II & RANGER)

Removal

1) Place gearshift selector in neutral. Remove boot retainer bolts. Remove bolts attaching retainer cover to gearshift lever retainer. Pull gearshift lever assembly out of transfer case adapter. Cover opening in transfer case adapter with a cloth to prevent dirt from falling into adapter.

2) Open hood and disconnect battery negative cable from battery terminal. Raise vehicle. Index rear drive shaft to front axle flange and transfer case. Disconnect drive shaft at rear axle flange. Pull rear drive shaft rearward and disconnect drive shaft from transmission.

3) Install a suitable plug in transfer case adapter to prevent lubricant leakage. Remove clutch housing dust shield. Disconnect hydraulic fluid line from clutch slave cylinder. Plug line to prevent fluid leakage. Disconnect speedometer from transfer case adapter.

4) Disconnect starter motor cable, back-up lamp switch wire and shift indicator switch wire. Disconnect neutral position switch (2.3L EFI engine). Place jack under engine block, protecting oil pan with wood block. Remove transfer case from vehicle.

5) Remove starter. Place a transmission jack under transmission. Remove bolts, lock washers and flat washers attaching transmission to engine and plate. Remove nuts and bolts attaching transmission mount and damper to crossmember.

6) Remove nuts attaching crossmember to frame side rails and remove crossmember. Lower engine jack. Work clutch housing off locating dowels and slide transmission rearward until input shaft clears clutch disc. Remove transmission from vehicle.

Installation

To install, reverse removal procedure.

3.03 3-SPEED ("E" SERIES)

Removal

1) Raise and support vehicle. Remove lower extension housing-to-transmission bolt to drain lubricant. Disconnect propeller shaft from flange at transmission and wire out of way. Do not allow shaft to hang free as damage to universal joint may result.

2) Disconnect speedometer cable and shift control rods from transmission shift levers. Place jack under transmission and secure transmission to jack with safety chain.

3) Raise transmission slightly and remove 4 bolts retaining transmission extension housing to insulator and retainer assembly. Remove transmission-to-clutch housing bolts. Install engine support bar on frame, under engine, and lower transmission out of vehicle.

Installation

Reverse removal procedures to install. Fill transmission with lubricant. Adjust clutch and shift linkages.

Manual Transmission Removal

FORD (Cont.)

3.03 3-SPEED ("F" SERIES)

Removal

1) Raise vehicle and support on safety stands. Support engine with jack and wood block under oil pan. To drain fluid from transmission, remove lower extension housing-to-transmission bolt.

2) Place jack under transmission and secure transmission to jack with safety chain. Disconnect shift linkage at transmission. Disconnect speedometer cable and back-up switch wires.

3) Disconnect propeller shaft and wire out of way. Do not allow shaft to hang free as damage to universal joint may result. Raise transmission and remove rear support, insulator and retainer.

4) Remove transmission-to-clutch housing attaching bolts. Move transmission rearward until input shaft clears clutch housing. Lower transmission out of vehicle. Do not depress clutch pedal at any time while transmission is out of vehicle.

Installation

Reverse removal procedures to install, noting the following: Apply a thin film of multi-purpose grease to the release bearing inner hub surfaces, release lever fulcrum and fork, and the transmission front bearing retainer. With installation complete, fill transmission with lubricant. Adjust clutch and shift linkage.

4-SPEED OVERDRIVE ("E" SERIES)

Removal

1) Raise and support vehicle. Mark propeller shaft position for reassembly reference. Disconnect propeller shaft from rear axle and slide shaft out of transmission. Disconnect speedometer cable and shift rods. Remove bolts connecting shift control to transmission case.

2) Remove rear transmission support-to-crossmember bolts. Support engine with transmission jack and raise transmission enough to take weight off number 3 crossmember. Remove bolts holding crossmember to frame side supports. Remove crossmember.

3) Place jack under rear of engine and raise high enough to remove weight from forward crossmember. Remove crossmember. With transmission supported by and secured to transmission jack, remove clutch housing-to-transmission bolts.

4) Move transmission to the rear until input shaft clears clutch housing and remove transmission. Do not depress clutch pedal while transmission is out of vehicle.

Installation

Reverse removal procedures to install.

(T.O.D.) 4-SPEED OVERDRIVE ("F" SERIES 2WD)

Removal

1) Raise vehicle on hoist. Mark drive shaft to aid as reference at reassembly. Disconnect drive shaft from rear flange. Slide drive shaft off transmission output shaft and intall extension housing seal installation tool into extension housing to prevent lubrication leakage.

2) Disconnect speedometer cable from extension housing. Disconnect back-up lamp switch and high gear switch wires. Remove shift lever from transmission. Support engine with a transmission jack and remove extension housing-to-engine rear support attaching bolts.

3) Raise rear of engine high enough to remove weight from crossmember. Remove bolts retaining crossmember to frame side supports and remove crossmember. Support transmission on a jack and remove bolts attaching transmission to flywheel housing.

4) Move transmission and jack rearward until transmission input shaft clears flywheel housing. If necessary, lower engine enough to obtain clearance for transmission removal. DO NOT depress clutch pedal while transmission is removed.

Installation

To install, reverse removal procedure.

(T.O.D.) 4-SPEED OVERDRIVE (BRONCO & F-150 4WD)

Removal

1) Raise vehicle on a hoist. Drain transmission and transfer case. Disconnect 4WD indicator switch wire connector at transfer case. Disconnect back-up lamp switch wire connector at transmission. Remove skid plate, if equipped, from frame. Mark front and rear drive shafts for reference at reassembly.

2) Disconnect rear drive shaft from transfer case and wire it out of way. Disconnect front drive shaft from transfer case and wire out of way. Remove speedometer cable from transfer case. Remove retaining clips and shift rod from transfer case control lever and transfer case shift lever.

3) Disconnect vent hose from transfer case. Remove shift lever from transmission. Support transmission with a transmission jack and remove transmission housing-to-engine rear support bracket. Raise rear of transmission high enough to remove weight from crossmember.

4) Remove 2 nuts connecting upper gusset to frame on both sides of frame. Remove nut and bolt assembly connecting gusset to support. Remove gusset on left side. Remove bolts holding transmission to transmission support plate on crossmember. Raise transmission with a transmission jack.

5) Remove nut and bolt assemblies connecting support plate to crossmember. Remove support plate and right gusset. Remove nut and bolt assemblies connecting crossmember to frame. Remove crossmember. Remove heat shield from transfer case. Support transfer case with a transmission jack.

6) Remove 6 bolts retaining transfer case to transmission adapter. Slide transfer case rearward off of transmission output shaft and lower transfer case from vehicle and remove gasket between transfer case and adapter. Support transmission on a jack and remove bolts attaching transmission to flywheel housing.

7) Move transmission and jack rearward until transmission input shaft clears flywheel housing. If necessary, lower engine enough to obtain clearance for transmission removal. DO NOT depress clutch pedal while transmission is removed.

Installation

To install, reverse removal procedure.

NP 435 4-SPEED (BRONCO & "F" SERIES)

Removal

1) Remove floor mat. Remove shift lever, shift ball and boot as an assembly. On 4WD models, remove transfer case shift lever, shift ball and boot as an

FORD (Cont.)

assembly. Remove floor pan transmission cover or weather pad on F150-350 models. Remove seat if necessary.

2) To remove gearshift lever and knob, first remove inner cap with puller (T73T 7220 A or equivalent). Remove seat and spring. Remove gearshift lever. Disconnect back-up light.

3) Raise vehicle. Disconnect speedometer cable and rear propeller shaft. Wire shaft out of way. On 4WD models, drain transfer case, remove front propeller shaft from case and wire out of way.

4) Remove cotter pin holding shift link and remove link. Remove bolts holding bracket to transfer case. Position transmission jack under transfer case.

5) Remove transfer case-to-transmission bolts and remove transfer case. On all models, place transmission jack under transmission and lift slightly. Remove transmission-to-insulator, insulator-to-crossmember and crossmember-to-frame bolts. Remove insulator and crossmember.

6) Remove transmission-to-clutch housing bolts and lower transmission out of vehicle.

Installation

To install transmission, reverse removal procedures.

WARNER T-18 ("F" SERIES 2WD)

Removal

1) Working from inside vehicle, remove floor mat and body floor pan cover. Remove gearshift lever, shift ball and boot as an assembly. Remove weather pad. Raise and support vehicle. Disconnect speedometer cable.

2) Disconnect back-up light switch from rear of gear shift housing cover. Disconnect propeller shaft from transmission and wire out of way. Do not allow shaft to hang free as damage to universal joint may result. Disconnect clutch linkage.

3) Remove skid plate (if equipped) and heat shield. Support transmission with jack. Remove crossmember gusset-to-frame bolts and gusset-to-crossmember bolts. Remove transmission-to-insulator bolts. Raise transmission and remove insulator-to-crossmember bolts. Remove insulator

4) Remove right gusset, crossmember-to-frame bolts and crossmember. Remove transmission-to-clutch housing bolts. Move transmission away from clutch housing until input shaft clears housing. Lower transmission out of vehicle.

Installation

Reverse removal procedures to install, noting the following: When installing shift lever, shift ball and boot assembly, lubricate the spherical ball seat with multipurpose grease.

WARNER T-18 (BRONCO & "F" SERIES 4WD)

Removal

1) Working from inside vehicle, remove floor mat and access cover to floor pan. Place shift lever in reverse position and remove cover, insulator and dust cover. Remove transfer case shift lever, shift ball and boot as an assembly.

2) Remove transmission shift lever, shift ball and boot as an assembly. Raise vehicle. Remove drain plug and allow transmission to drain. Replace plug. Disconnect front and rear propeller shafts from transfer case and wire out of way. Do not allow shafts to hang free as damage to universal joint may result.

3) Remove shift link retainer ring and remove shift link from transfer case. Disconnect speedometer cable. Place transmission jack under transfer case. Remove transfer case-to-transmission bolts and lower transfer case out of vehicle.

4) Remove rear support bracket-to-transmission bolts (8), position transmission jack under transmission and remove rear support bracket and brace. Remove transmission-to-clutch housing bolts (4) and remove transmission.

Installation

Reverse removal procedures to install transmission.

WARNER T19B ("F" SERIES 2WD)

Removal

1) Working from inside vehicle, remove floor mat and body floor pan cover. Remove gearshift lever, shift ball and boot as an assembly. Remove weather pad.

2) Raise vehicle. Place transmission jack under transmission and disconnect speedometer cable. Disconnect back-up light switch from rear of gear shift housing cover. Disconnect propeller shaft and clutch linkage. Wire out of way.

3) Remove transmission rear insulator and lower retainer. Remove skid plate (if equipped) and heat shield. Remove upper gusset bolts and gusset-to-crossmember bolts. Remove left side gusset.

4) Remove transmission-to-support plate bolts, raise transmission slightly and remove support plate-to-crossmember bolts. Remove support plate and right gusset. Remove crossmember-to-frame bolts and remove crossmember.

5) Remove transmission-to-clutch housing bolts. Move transmission to the rear until input shaft clears housing and remove transmission.

Installation

Reverse removal procedures to install transmission, noting the following: When installing the shift lever, shift ball and boot assembly, lubricate spherical ball seat with multipurpose grease.

WARNER T19B & T19D ("F" SERIES 4WD)

Removal

1) Working from inside vehicle, remove floor mat and access cover to floor pan (shift lever in reverse when removing cover). Remove insulator and dust cover. Remove transfer case shift lever, shift ball and boot as an assembly.

2) Remove transmission shift lever, shift ball and boot as an assembly. Raise vehicle. Drain transmission and replace drain plug. Disconnect front and rear drive shafts from transfer case and wire out of way.

3) Remove shift link retainer ring and remove link from transfer case. Disconnect speedometer cable. Place transmission jack under transfer case and remove transfer case-to-transmission bolts (6). Lower transfer case out of vehicle.

4) Remove rear support bracket-to-transmission bolts (8). Place transmission jack under transmission and remove rear support bracket and brace. Remove transmission-to-clutch housing bolts (4) and remove transmission.

Installation

To install transmission, reverse removal procedures.

Manual Transmission Removal

FORD (Cont.)

5-SPEED MAZDA OVERDRIVE (AEROSTAR)

Removal

1) Disconnect negative battery cable from battery terminal. Place transmission in neutral. Remove 4 bolts attaching boot assembly to floor. Pull boot up shift lever. Remove 4 bolts retaining shift lever assembly to transmission remote shift rail adapter. Remove lever, knob and boot assembly.

2) Raise vehicle on hoist. Disconnect starter cable and wires. Remove starter retaining bolts and remove starter. Remove clip retaining tube to hydraulic clutch slave cylinder. Remove tube and fittng from slave cylinder to prevent entry of contaminants.

3) Disconnect back-up lamp switch and shift indicator and neutral position wires from senders on transmission. Remove cable (conventional speedometer) or disconnect wire (electronic speedometer) from fitting.

4) Scribe a mark on driveshaft and rear axle flange to index driveline position for installation and balance purposes. Remove "U" bolts and nuts from rear axle flange. Remove driveshaft. Cap transmission extension housing to prevent lubricant spillage.

5) Remove nuts retaining insulator to crossmember. Loosen nut and washer assemblies attaching front insulators to crossmember brackets. Position a transmission jack under transmission. Place jack safety chain around transmission. Slightly raise transmission.

6) Remove nuts and bolts retaining crossmember to frame and remove crossmember. Remove bolts retaining clutch housing to engine. Bring transmission rearward to separate clutch housing from dowel pins in rear of engine block. Slowly lower transmission from vehicle.

NOTE: **If transmission is to be removed from vehicle for an extended period, support rear of engine with safety stand and wood block.**

7) If required, remove nuts retaining clutch housing to transmission and remove housing and clutch slave cylinder.

Installation

To install, reverse removal procedure.

TIGHTENING SPECIFICATIONS

Application	Ft. Lbs. (N.m)
Transmission-to-Clutch Housing	
Bronco II & Ranger	30-40 (42-56)
All Others	
3-Speed	42-50 (59-70)
4-Speed	35-50 (49-70)
Transfer Case-to-Transmission	
NP-208	20-25 (28-35)
Borg-Warner 1345	25-43 (35-60)
Borg-Warner 1350	25-35 (35-49)
Insulator-to-Crossmember	
3-Speed	50-70 (70-98)
4-Speed Overdrive	50-70 (70-98)
Bronco II & Ranger	71-94 (98-132)
All Others	
2WD	50-70 (70-98)
4WD	35-45 (49-63)
Insulator-to-Transmission	
3-Speed ("E" Models)	50-70 (70-98)
4-Speed Overdrive	50-70 (70-98)
T19B 4-Speed	45-60 (63-84)
All Others	60-80 (84-112)

GENERAL MOTORS

TRANSFER CASE

NP-205 (30 SERIES)

Removal

1) Raise and support vehicle on hoist. Drain transfer case. Disconnect speedometer cable. Remove skid plate and crossmember supports as necessary. Disconnect rear drive shaft from transfer case and tie up away from work area.

2) Disconnect front drive shaft from transfer case and tie up shaft away from work area. Disconnect shift lever rod from shift rail link. Support transfer case and remove bolts attaching transfer case to transmission adapter.

3) Move transfer case to rear until input shaft clears adapter and lower assembly from vehicle.

Installation

To install, reverse removal procedure.

NP-207 ("S" SERIES)

Removal

1) With transfer case shift lever in "4 Hi" position, disconnect negative battery cable. Raise vehicle and remove skid plate. Drain transfer case. Mark front and rear output shaft yokes and propeller shafts for reassembly reference and remove shafts.

2) Disconnect speedometer cable and vacuum harness from transfer case. Remove shift lever from case. Remove catalytic converter hanger bolts at converter. Raise transmission and transfer case assembly with jack and remove transmission mount bolts. Remove mount.

3) Lower complete assembly. Support transfer case alone and remove transmission-to-transfer case bolts. Remove shift lever bracket from transfer case adapter in order to reach upper left attaching bolt.

4) Separate transfer case from transmission adapter and remove from vehicle.

Installation

Reverse removal procedures to install. Always use a new gasket between the transfer case and adapter.

NP-208 (10 & 20 SERIES)

Removal

1) Place transfer case in "4H". Raise vehicle. Drain lubricant from transfer case. Remove cotter pin from shift lever swivel. Mark transfer case front and rear output shaft yokes and propeller shafts for assembly alignment reference.

GENERAL MOTORS (Cont.)

2) Disconnect speedometer cable and indicator switch wires. Disconnect front drive shaft at transfer case yoke. Disconnect parking brake cable guide from pivot located on right frame rail, if necessary. Remove engine strut rod from transfer case.

3) Place support under transfer case and remove transfer case-to-transmission adapter bolts. Move transfer case assembly rearward until free of transmission output shaft and remove assembly. Remove all gasket material from rear of transmission adapter housing.

Installation

To install, reverse removal procedure.

TRANSMISSION

ASTRO/SAFARI VAN

Removal

1) Raise vehicle and drain lubricant from transmission. Remove drive shaft. Disconnect speedometer cable. Disconnect electrical connectors at transmission. Disconnect shift linkage at shifter. Remove shifter support attaching bolts at transmission.

2) Remove transmission mount attaching bolts. Support transmission and remove crossmember attaching bolts and crossmember from vehicle. Remove transmission attaching bolts and remove transmission from vehicle.

Installation

To install, reverse removal procedure. Apply a light coating of high temperature grease to main drive gear bearing retainer and splined portion of transmission drive gear shaft to assure free movement of clutch and transmission components during assembly.

ALL EXCEPT "K" & "S" SERIES

Removal

1) On models with 117 MM 4-speed, remove attaching screws from shift lever boot retainer. Slide boot assembly up shift lever and remove lever. To remove shift lever, push down on collar and turn counterclockwise.

2) On all models, raise and support vehicle under frame. Drain fluid from transmission. Disconnect speedometer cable at transmission. Remove shift controls from transmission (if not already removed). Remove parking brake lever, controls, and back-up switch wire as needed.

3) Disconnect propeller shaft at transmission and position support under transmission assembly. Disconnect exhaust pipes from exhaust manifolds as needed. Remove frame crossmember and flywheel inspection plate.

4) On 117 MM 4-speed, remove top 2 transmission-to-clutch housing bolts and install guide pins. On all models, remove all transmission-to-clutch housing attaching bolts, slide transmission rearward until input shaft is clear of clutch hub and remove assembly from vehicle. Remove guide pins if used.

NOTE: **Support clutch release bearing and support assembly when removing transmission main drive gear from flywheel housing. This will prevent release bearing from falling out of flywheel housing.**

Installation

Apply a light coating of high temperature grease to main drive gear bearing retainer and splined portion of transmission main drive gear shaft. Reverse removal procedures to complete installation.

ALL "K" SERIES

Removal

1) On models with 117 MM 4-speed, remove attaching screws from shift lever boot retainer. Slide boot assembly up shift lever and remove lever. To remove shift lever, push down on collar and turn counterclockwise.

2) On all models, raise and support vehicle under frame. Drain fluid from transmission and transfer case. Disconnect speedometer cable. Disconnect front and rear propeller shafts at transfer case and wire out of way. Disconnect transfer case shift lever.

3) Position support under transfer case. Remove transfer case-to-adapter bolts and remove transfer case. Disconnect shift control rods from shifter levers if not already removed. Separate exhaust pipes from exhaust manifolds as needed.

4) Support rear part of engine and remove 2 adapter bolts. Remove crossmember. Remove 2 top transmission-to-clutch housing cap screws. Insert 2 guide pins (J-1126 on 117 MM, J-2216 all others) in holes. Remove 2 lower transmission-to-clutch housing cap screws.

5) Slide transmission and adapter assembly rearward until clutch gear is free of splines in clutch disc. Guide pins will support transmission and prevent damage to clutch disc. Remove transmission and adapter as an assembly. Remove adapter from transmission.

Installation

Apply a light coating of high temperature grease to main drive gear bearing retainer and splined portion of transmission main drive gear shaft. Reverse removal procedures to complete installation.

ALL "S" SERIES

NOTE: **If vehicle is a 4WD model, refer to Transfer Case removal procedures and remove case.**

Removal

1) Disconnect negative battery cable. On 77.5 MM 4-speed, remove upper starter motor nut. On all models, remove shift lever boot screws and slide boot up shift lever. Shift transmission into neutral and remove shift lever bolts at transmission. Remove shift lever.

2) Disconnect electrical connector and clip at transmission, if present. Raise vehicle and remove propeller shaft. Disconnect exhaust pipe at manifold, if needed.

3) Disconnect speedometer cable, electrical connector and clutch cable at transmission. Support transmission on jack and remove mount attaching bolts. Remove catalytic converter hanger. Remove crossmember attaching bolts and crossmember. Remove flywheel inspection cover.

4) On 77.5 MM 4-speed, remove lower starter motor attaching bolt. Remove body mounting bolts on left side of body and loosen radiator support bolt. Raise cab on left side as needed to remove upper bell housing attaching bolts. Support cab with wood block between frame and cab.

GENERAL MOTORS (Cont.)

5) Remove transmission-to-engine bolts on all models. Remove transmission.

Installation

Reverse removal procedures to install transmission, noting the following: On 77 MM 4-speed, coat main drive gear bearing retainer and splined portion of transmission main drive gear with high temperature grease before installation.

TIGHTENING SPECIFICATIONS

Application	Ft. Lbs. (N.m)
Transmission-to-Clutch Housing	
All Except "S" Series	75 (102)
"S" Series	
1.9L 4-Cylinder	25 (35)
2.8L V6	55 (75)

TIGHTENING SPECIFICATIONS (Cont.)

Application	Ft. Lbs. (N.m)
Crossmember-to-Frame	
"S" Series	25 (30)
All Others	55-65 (75-88)
Crossmember-to-Mount	
"S" Series	25 (30)
All Others	40-45 (54-61)
Mount-to-Transmission Bolt	35 (50)
Radiator Support Mounting Bolt	45-60 (60-80)
Cab Mounting Bolts	45-60 (60-80)
Transfer Case-to-Extension Housing	
"S" Series	19-29 (26-40)
All Others	26-40 (36-56)
Adapter-to-Transmission	
"S" Series	
All Others	26-40 (36-56)

JEEP

TRANSFER CASE

MODEL NP-207

Removal

1) Shift transfer case into "4H" position. Raise and support vehicle. Drain lubricant from transfer case. Mark rear axle yoke and drive shaft for installation reference. Remove rear drive shaft. Disconnect speedometer cable, vacuum hoses and vent hose from transfer case.

2) Raise transmission and transfer case and remove transmission crossmember attaching bolts. Remove crossmember and lower transmission and transfer case. Mark transfer case front output shaft flange and drive shaft for installation reference.

3) Disconnect front drive shaft from transfer case. Disconnect shift lever linkage rod at transfer case. Remove shift lever bracket bolts. Support transfer case and remove transfer case attaching bolts. Remove transfer case assembly.

Installation

To install, reverse removal procedure.

MODEL NP-208

Removal

1) Raise vehicle. Drain lubricant from transfer case. Disconnect speedometer cable and indicator switch wires and disconnect transfer case shift lever link at operating lever. Place a safety stand under transmission and remove the rear crossmember.

2) Mark transfer case front and rear output shaft yokes and drive shafts for assembly alignment reference. Disconnect front and rear drive shafts at transfer case yokes. Secure shafts to frame rails with wire. Disconnect parking brake cable guide from pivot located on right frame rail, if necessary.

3) Remove bolts attaching exhaust pipe support bracket-to-transfer case, if necessary. Remove transfer case-to-transmission bolts. Move transfer case assembly rearward until free of transmission output shaft and remove assembly. Remove all gasket material from rear of transmission adapter housing.

Installation

To install, reverse removal procedure.

MODEL NP-229

Removal

1) Raise and support vehicle. Drain lubricant from transfer case. Disconnect speedometer cable and vent hose. Disconnect transfer case shift lever link at operating lever. Place a safety stand under transmission and remove rear crossmember.

2) Mark transfer case front and rear output shafts at transfer case yokes and drive shafts for installation alignment reference. Disconnect front and rear drive shafts at transfer case yokes. Secure shafts. Disconnect shift motor vacuum hoses.

3) Disconnect transfer case shift linkage. Remove transfer case-to-transmission bolts. Move transfer case assembly rearward until clear of transmission ouput shaft and remove assembly. Remove all gasket material from rear of transmission adapter housing.

Installation

To install, reverse removal procedure.

MODEL NP-300

Removal

1) Remove floor covering, if equipped and remove transmission access cover from floorpan. Raise vehicle and drain lubricant from transfer case. Position support stand under clutch housing to support engine and transmission and remove rear crossmember.

2) Disconnect front and rear drive shafts at transfer case. Mark drive shaft yokes for assembly reference. Disconnect speedometer cable at transfer case. If necessary, disconnect parking brake cable at equalizer. Disconnect exhaust pipe support bracket at transfer case, if equipped. Remove bolts attaching transfer case to transmission and remove tranfer case.

Installation

To install, reverse removal procedure.

JEEP (Cont.)

TRANSMISSION

ALL MODELS

Removal

1) Remove screws attaching shift lever boot to floorpan. Slide boot over lever. On models with T4 or T5 transmission, remove shift lever and lever housing from transmission.

2) On models with T-176 transmission, press and turn shift lever retainer counterclockwise to release lever. Remove lever, boot, spring and seat as an assembly.

3) On all models, raise vehicle and support with safety stands. Disconnect rear drive shaft from transfer case and wire out of way. DO NOT allow shaft to hang free, as damage to universal joint may result.

4) Disconnect front parking brake cable at equalizer. Remove rear cable clip from crossmember. Place a jack under clutch housing to support engine. Remove rear crossmember from frame.

5) Disconnect speedometer cable, back-up light switch wire and 4WD indicator switch wire. Disconnect transfer case vent hose. Disconnect front drive shaft and wire out of way.

6) On "CJ" and Scrambler models, remove transfer case shift lever by removing shifter shaft retaining nut. Remove cotter pins retaining shift control link pins in shift rods and remove pins. Remove shifter shaft and disengage shift lever from shift control links. Move lever out of the way.

NOTE: **On some models, shifter shaft must be unthreaded from shift lever in order to be removed. On other models, shaft can be removed by sliding it out of lever.**

7) Remove cotter pin and washers connecting link to shift lever. Separate link from lever. Support transmission and transfer case with jack.

8) Remove bolts securing transmission to clutch housing and remove transmission and transfer case. Separate transfer case and transmission.

Installation

Reverse removal procedures to install transmission. Adjust clutch and shift linkage.

TIGHTENING SPECIFICATIONS

Application	Ft. Lbs. (N.m)
Transmission-to-Clutch Housing	55 (75)
Transmission Cover Bolts	55-65 (75-88)
Housing-to-Transmission Case	40-45 (54-61)
Crossmember Attaching Bolts	34-40 (47-54)
Filler Plug	13-15 (18-20)

Latest Changes & Corrections

FOR 1985 AND PREVIOUS MODELS

NOTE: The Latest Changes and Corrections represent a collection of last minute 1985 information that arrived too late to be included into the regular data pages. In addition, we have included information on prior year models which we have received since last year's edition.

TUNE-UP SECTION 1

CHRYSLER CORP.

1 *1985 CHRYSLER CORP. CARAVAN, VOYAGER AND RAM VAN: NEW DISTRIBUTOR APPLICATION* – Some of the above models may exhibit cold engine sag during medium to heavy acceleration. The problem may be corrected by installing a new design distributor (part no. MD027695). Use the following repair procedure:

1) Remove distributor primary leads from the ignition coil terminals. Remove and plug the vacuum advance hose from the distributor vacuum diaphragm. Remove distributor cap.

2) Remove original distributor. Install new design distributor. Install distributor cap and attach coil leads. Start engine and warm it normal operating temperature.

3) Set basic ignition timing to 7° BTDC. Reconnect vacuum advance hose to distributor diaphragm.

FORD MOTOR CO.

2 *1981-83 FORD PICKUPS WITH 5.8L V8 & EEC-III IGNITION: FIRING ORDER CORRECTION* – In 1981-83 Mitchell Light Truck Service & Repair manual, firing order given for 5.8L V8 engines with EEC-III is incorrect. Actual firing order is 1-5-7-8-6-3-4-2. Number 1 spark plug is straight back on cap in spot where number 3 is in Fig. 2. Rotation shown is correct.

GENERAL MOTORS

3 *GENERAL MOTORS TRUCKS WITH V8 ENGINE: IGNITION TIMING PROCEDURE* – Ignition timing procedure at step **3)** for General Motors V8 in Tune-Up section was incorrect through 1984 edition. It should read as follows:

On California vehicles with HEI-EST and HEI-ESC distributors, disconnect the 4-wire plug connector at the distributor when checking ignition timing. Once timing has been set, reconnect connector and clear trouble code from computer. (On Federal vehicles, engine won't run with connector disconnected.)

COMPUTERIZED ENGINE CONTROL SECTION 1a

CHRYSLER CORP.

4 *1983-84 CHRYSLER CORP. FWD: ELECTRONIC FUEL CONTROL COMPUTER TEST* – The Electronic Fuel Control Computer Test in Mitchell's 1983-84 Domestic Cars Service & Repair manuals contains an error. Step **3)** should read as follows:

Hold the jumper wire with one hand and touch the battery positive terminal with your other hand. Engine speed should decrease at least 50 RPM and voltmeter should indicate less than 5 volts. If computer fails both tests, replace it. Reconnect oxygen sensor wire.

FORD MOTOR CO.

5 *1983-84 FORD 4-CYLINDER ENGINE WITH MCU: DIAGNOSTIC CODE 51 MCU PIN NUMBER CORRECTION* – In Mitchell's 1983-84 Domestic Light Truck Service and Repair manual, the 4-Cyl MCU engine control system Test 8 (Diagnostic Code 51-Low Temp. Switch) has an error. Step **4)** should read:

Disconnect harness from low temperature switch and measure resistance between wire leading to MCU pin 5 and engine ground. If resistance is less than 1000 ohms, repair wire leading to MCU pin 5. If resistance is greater than 1000 ohms, replace MCU.

EMISSIONS

FORD MOTOR CO.

6 *1984 BRONCO, E & F SERIES WITH 5.0L ENGINE: NEW VACUUM DELAY VALVE* – Some 1984 Bronco, E and F Series with 5.0L engine (calibration numbers 4-54E-R10-12, 4-54L-R10-12 and 4-54W-R10-11) may emit White smoke during prolonged idling.

This condition may be caused by the thermactor system not venting excess air. A new design vacuum delay valve (D8AZ-9E897-A) and revised vacuum hose routing should correct the problem. Use the following repair procedure:

1) Check engine and emission systems for proper operation. Ensure White smoke is not caused by something other than vacuum delay valve.

2) Remove air cleaner. Remove and discard Red and White retard delay valve, vacuum reservoir and hose between the Thermal Valve Switch (TVS) on the air cleaner and Air By-Pass Valve (BPV).

3) Connect a vacuum hose to new delay valve with Green end toward BPV. Connect another vacuum hose to TVS and White end of delay valve. Install vacuum hose harness to vehicle. Ensure there are no vacuum leaks or kinks. Reinstall air cleaner.

GENERAL MOTORS

7 *DECELERATION CONTROL VALVE OF AIR SYSTEM: TESTING PROCEDURE* – This valve is used on air injection systems to allow additional air flow into intake manifold from air cleaner. This leans out rich condition caused by high vacuum when throttle valve is closed during deceleration. Valve is actuated by manifold vacuum. This valve was not covered in 1984 and earlier articles on Chevrolet 4.1L 250" 6-Cylinder with Pulse-Air or AIR.

Latest Changes & Corrections

FOR 1985 AND PREVIOUS MODELS (Cont.)

1) To test deceleration valve, remove air cleaner. Plug air cleaner vauum source and connect tachometer. Disconnect small deceleration valve signal hose from manifold vacuum source while engine is running at idle speed.

2) Reconnect signal hose. Air should be heard flowing through valve intake hose (from air cleaner) and into valve. Idle speed should drop when vacuum hose is reconnected.

3) Check valve hoses for restrictions or leaks if air flow does not continue for minimum of 1 second or engine speed does not drop noticeably. Replace valve if no restrictions or leaks are found.

JEEP

8

1983-84 JEEP CJ, CHEROKEE, SCRAMBLER & WAGONEER: LOSS OF POWER, POOR MILEAGE AND/OR DIFFICULT HOT STARTING – Some 1983-84 Jeep models with 2.5L engine may experience loss of power, poor gas mileage and/or difficult hot starting. This condition may be caused by a vacuum leak at the EGR valve tube-to-exhaust manifold. Service procedures are now available to correct this condition.

1) Disconnect the EGR valve tube fastening nut. Remove the tube flange bolts from the exhaust manifold. Remove the tube and flange gasket.

2) Clean the gasket surface on the EGR valve tube. Check the EGR valve tube gasket surface for flatness.

3) If the surface is warped more than .020" (.50 mm), replace the EGR valve tube.

4) Clean all gasket surfaces and EGR valve tube fittings. Loosely connect the EGR valve tube to the intake manifold.

5) Using a new gasket, bolt the EGR valve tube to the exhaust manifold. Tighten the tube fitting nut to 30 ft. lbs. (40 N.m).

6) Tighten the tube flange bolts to 14 ft. lbs. (20 N.m).

FUEL SYSTEMS SECTION 2

CHRYSLER CORP.

9

1980-84 5.2L V8 FEDERAL MODELS WITH HOLLEY 2280 2-BARREL CARBURETOR: POWER VALVE NEEDLE IDENTIFICATION – In Mitchell's 1980-84 Domestic Light Truck Service & Repair manuals, a note in the OVERHAUL section for this carburetor incorrectly stated the mechanical power valve needle is longer than the vacuum one. It should read as follows:

NOTE: **Do not interchange the mechanical and vacuum power valve assemblies. Vacuum power valve needle is about .050" longer than mechanical power valve needle. The vacuum power valve needle has an undercut groove just above the needle stop. Mechanical power valve is located on choke side of carburetor. Do not mix up valve seats. Assemblies must be reinstalled in original locations, and must be kept with their respective needle and spring assembly.**

FORD MOTOR CO.

10

1983-84 RANGER & BRONCO II WITH 2.8L ENGINE: CARBURETOR ICING – Some models may experience hesitation and stalling in cold temperatures and high humidity. This condition may be caused by carburetor icing. To correct this condition, perform the following air cleaner modification:

1) Replace air cleaner shroud and tube assembly with a new assembly (part no. E5TZ-9A603-B).

2) Replace the duct and valve assembly with a new assembly (part no. E5TZ-9A626-A).

3) Replace the duct and valve assembly-to-air cleaner gasket (part no. E1SZ-9E691-A) if damaged.

11

1985 RANGER WITH 2.3L EFI ENGINE: STARTING/PRIMING PROCEDURE FOR DRAINED FUEL SYSTEM – If the fuel system becomes drained during service procedures, the system must be primed as follows:

1) Cycle the ignition between "ON" and "OFF". The ignition should be "ON" for 5 seconds, then turned "OFF".

2) Repeat this procedure 20 times before attempting to start the engine. If the engine does not start after 15 seconds, repeat priming procedure.

JEEP

12

1985 CJ7 & SCRAMBLER MODELS WITH 2.5L ENGINE: NEW CARBURETOR APPLICATION – This engine may be equipped with new YFA carburetor having Part No. 7704 or 7706. Correct carburetor adjustment specifications table as follows:

Application: 7704 and 7706. Float level: .600". Choke Unloader: .280". Choke Pull-Down: Not Applicable. Fast Idle: .175". Auto. Choke: TR

13

1985 GRAND WAGONEER & TRUCKS WITH 6.0L ENGINE: NEW CARBURETOR APPLICATION – This engine may be equipped with new Holley Model 2150 carburetor, Part No. 5RHA2. Correct carburetor adjustment specifications table as follows:

Application: 5RHA2. Float level (Dry Setting): 21/64". Accel. Pump. #3. Choke Pull-Down: .118". Fast Idle Cam: .076". Choke Unloader: .420". Auto. Choke: "Y" Notch. Bowl Vent Valve: Not Applicable.

ELECTRICAL SECTION 4

CHRYSLER CORP.

14

1981-84 MODELS WITH ELECTRONIC SPARK CONTROL SYSTEM: DISTRIBUTOR ILLUSTRATION MISLABELED – In Mitchell's 1981-84 Domestic Light Truck Service & Repair manuals, the exploded view of the distributor contains components from 6-cylinder and V8 applications. The correct distributor components are as shown in the 1985 edition.

Latest Changes & Corrections

FOR 1985 AND PREVIOUS MODELS (Cont.)

15 *1985 TRUCKS (ALL): NEW BATTERY STATE OF CHARGE INDICATOR* – All 1985 truck batteries now use a 4-color "state of charge" indicator. See BATTERY STATE OF CHARGE INDICATOR table.

BATTERY STATE OF CHARGE INDICATOR

Indicator Color	Specific Gravity	State Of Charge (%)
Green	1.220	75-100
Black	1.220-1.190	50-75
Red	1.190	50
Yellow	0	0

FORD MOTOR CO.

16 *1983-84 MODELS WITH & MOTORCRAFT TFI-IV IGNITION: IGNITION COIL PRIMARY CIRCUIT SWITCHING CHECK* – In Mitchell's 1983-84 Domestic Light Truck Service & Repair manuals, step **3)** of this check should direct you to the WIRING HARNESS CHECK, not the PRIMARY CURCUIT CONTINUITY CHECK. The step should read as follows:

If test light flashes, proceed to IGNITION COIL PRIMARY RESISTANCE CHECK. If test light comes on but does not flash, proceed to WIRING HARNESS CHECK. If test light does not come on at all or is very dim, proceed to WIRING HARNESS CHECK.

WIRING DIAGRAMS SECTION 5

GENERAL MOTORS & JEEP

17 *1984 BLAZER, JIMMY, PICKUP, SUBURBAN, CHEROKEE & WAGONEER: TRANSPOSED WIRING DIAGRAMS* – In Mitchell's 1984 Domestic Light Truck Service & Repair manual, the wiring diagrams on pages 5-33 and 5-49 are transposed with one another. The diagram on page 5-33 should be on page 5-49 and the diagram on page 5-49 should be on page 5-33.

ENGINE SECTION 7

CHRYSLER CORP.

18 *CARAVAN, MINI RAM VAN & VOYAGER WITH 2.6L ENGINES: ENGINE KNOCK DURING START-UP* – Engine may have knock during start-up. This condition may be caused by the timing chain tensioner retracting. A new design rubber Spacer (Part No. MD084945) is available to correct this condition.

Remove front timing chain cover. Remove timing chain tensioner and spring. Insert rubber spacer inside tensioner spring. Reinstall timing chain tensioner spring and tensioner. Reassemble engine.

FORD MOTOR CO.

19 *1983-84 RANGER WITH 2.0L ENGINE: NEW CHROME INTAKE AND EXHAUST VALVES* – Some 1983-84 Rangers with 2.0L engine may have inadequate power over 40 MPH. This may be caused by sticking valves or insufficient valve guide-to-stem clearance. New chrome valves intake valves (E5TZ-6507-F) and exhaust valves (E5TZ-6505-F) should solve this problem. Use the following repair procedure:

1) Remove cylinder head. Remove can followers and valves, keeping all parts in order. Inspect all valve stems for wear, galling or scoring. Replace damaged valves with new chrome valves.

2) Ensure valve guides are clean and reamed to .3433-.3443" (8.720-8.745 mm). Check valve guide-to-stem clearances. Clearance should be .001-.0027" (.025-.069 mm) on intake valves, .015-.032" (.038-.081 mm) on exhaust valves.

3) Replace valve stem seals. Clean or replace spark plugs. Reassemble cylinder head.

20 *1983-84 RANGER & BRONCO II WITH 2.8L ENGINES: REAR MAIN SEAL COLOR CHANGE* – When servicing rear main seal, note the color of the rear main seal. The original seal is Rust colored and has an engineering number (83BM-6701-A3A) stamped on it. A new design seal has been released with the same service part number, however this seal is Gray. The new Gray seal should be used when servicing the rear main seal.

21 *1984 E & F SERIES WITH 7.5L ENGINE: NEW WATER PUMP PULLEY* – A new reinforced water pump pulley (E3TZ-8509-S) was introduced for E and F series light duty trucks with 7.5L engine. The reinforced water pump pulley has the same part number as the previous design. The new design pulley has a daug of White paint on its face.

JEEP

22 *1984 CJ7, SCRAMBLER, GRAND WAGONEER & TRUCK WITH 4.2L ENGINES: NEW CAMSHAFT SPROCKET PRELOAD BOLT* – New camshaft sprocket bolt entered production in late October, 1984. This new bolt contains a spring loaded thrust pin in the head of the bolt to preload the camshaft. The bolt is used to stop light knocking sound caused by normal camshaft end thrust. New camshaft sprocket preload bolt may be installed in engines equipped with preload bolt,as follows:

1) Remove timing case cover. Remove original camshaft bolt and washer. Retain the washer. Install washer and replacement Camshaft Sprocket Preload Bolt (Part No. 324 3156). Tighten bolt to 80 ft. lbs. (108 N.m).

2) Lubricate Tension Spring (Part No. 324 3157), Thrust Pin (Part No. 324 3155) and pin bore with AMC/Jeep Super Oil Conditioner (Part No. 899 3431). Then install spring and thrust pin in bolt head. Reinstall timing case cover.

Latest Changes & Corrections

FOR 1985 AND PREVIOUS MODELS (Cont.)

23 *1985 CHEROKEE & WAGONEER WITH 2.1L TURBO DIESEL ENGINES: NEW DESIGN PISTON OIL COOLING JETS* – New design piston oil cooling jets are used in 2.1L Turbo Diesel engines starting with engine serial number 3800. The new system consists of a new design block and separate piston oil cooling jets. The early design consists of block, oil supply line and fittings, piston oil cooling jets and manifold. Components of the 2 systems ARE NOT interchangeable.

24 *1985 CHEROKEE & WAGONEER WITH 2.1L TURBO DIESEL ENGINES: DEACTIVATING OIL FILTER LIGHT* – The switch that activates the oil filter light is improperly calibrated and generates false readings. If not already deactivated, remove oil filter light bulb and disconnect the switch-to-bulb feed wire as follows:

Remove instrument cluster bezel. Remove lens covering oil filter light bulb and remove bulb. Disconnect and tape feed wire to harness, if necessary. Install oil filter light lens and instrument cluster bezel.

WHEEL ALIGNMENT SECTION 11

CHRYSLER CORP.

25 *1985 MINI RAM VAN, CARAVAN & VOYAGER: REAR WHEEL TOE SPECIFICATIONS* – The rear wheel toe-in specifications have been revised for these vehicles. Wheel alignment specifications table presently is 1/2" Out to 1/2" In. Rear toe-in should be 1/4" Out to 1/4" In.

"WE LISTEN"

Do you have any comments or recommended changes to this book?
We will appreciate receiving them so that we may continue to publish the world's best Service & Repair manuals. **Mail this card today. We'd like to hear from you!**

□ Domestic Cars □ Imported Cars & Trucks □ Domestic Light Trucks & Vans □ Medium & Heavy Duty Trucks
□ Tune-Up □ Mechanical □ Transmission □ Emission □ Air Conditioning □ Electrical

Section No.________ Page No. ________ Vehicle Model & Year ____________

Comments: ____________________

Name ____________ Company ____________

Address ____________ City ______ State _____ Zip _____

Phone ( ) __________ Date __________ THANK YOU

NOTE: This form must be filled out completely to be considered.

"WE LISTEN"

Do you have any comments or recommended changes to this book?
We will appreciate receiving them so that we may continue to publish the world's best Service & Repair manuals. **Mail this card today. We'd like to hear from you!**

□ Domestic Cars □ Imported Cars & Trucks □ Domestic Light Trucks & Vans □ Medium & Heavy Duty Trucks
□ Tune-Up □ Mechanical □ Transmission □ Emission □ Air Conditioning □ Electrical

Section No.________ Page No. ________ Vehicle Model & Year ____________

Comments: ____________________

Name ____________ Company ____________

Address ____________ City ______ State _____ Zip _____

Phone ( ) __________ Date __________ THANK YOU

NOTE: This form must be filled out completely to be considered.

"WE LISTEN"

Do you have any comments or recommended changes to this book?
We will appreciate receiving them so that we may continue to publish the world's best Service & Repair manuals. **Mail this card today. We'd like to hear from you!**

□ Domestic Cars □ Imported Cars & Trucks □ Domestic Light Trucks & Vans □ Medium & Heavy Duty Trucks
□ Tune-Up □ Mechanical □ Transmission □ Emission □ Air Conditioning □ Electrical

Section No.________ Page No. ________ Vehicle Model & Year ____________

Comments: ____________________

Name ____________ Company ____________

Address ____________ City ______ State _____ Zip _____

Phone ( ) __________ Date __________ THANK YOU

NOTE: This form must be filled out completely to be considered.

Name ____________________

Address ____________________

City __________ State ______ Zip ______

NO POSTAGE NECESSARY IF MAILED IN THE UNITED STATES

BUSINESS REPLY MAIL

FIRST CLASS PERMIT NO. 3701 SAN DIEGO, CA

POSTAGE WILL BE PAID BY ADDRESSEE

MITCHELL INFORMATION SERVICES, INC.
P.O. Box 26260
San Diego, California 92126

Name ____________________

Address ____________________

City __________ State ______ Zip ______

NO POSTAGE NECESSARY IF MAILED IN THE UNITED STATES

BUSINESS REPLY MAIL

FIRST CLASS PERMIT NO. 3701 SAN DIEGO, CA

POSTAGE WILL BE PAID BY ADDRESSEE

MITCHELL INFORMATION SERVICES, INC.
P.O. Box 26260
San Diego, California 92126

Name ____________________

Address ____________________

City __________ State ______ Zip ______

NO POSTAGE NECESSARY IF MAILED IN THE UNITED STATES

BUSINESS REPLY MAIL

FIRST CLASS PERMIT NO. 3701 SAN DIEGO, CA

POSTAGE WILL BE PAID BY ADDRESSEE

MITCHELL INFORMATION SERVICES, INC.
P.O. Box 26260
San Diego, California 92126

EASY-TO-USE … H MANUALS

Com…

Four much-needed editions available, covering all computerized engine control systems on all domestic models and nearly all imports using those systems. Easy-to-follow. Includes test procedures, diagnostic charts, specs and illustrations.

1985 Edition covers 1985 domestics & 1984 imports. **Price: only $22.00**
1984 Edition covers 1984 domestics & 1983 & 1983 imports. **Price: only $22.00**
1983 Edition covers 1983 domestics & 1982 imports. **Price: only $22.00**
1982 Edition covers 1981-82 domestics. **Price: only $15.00**
Combined Package: All 4 above, in binder. **Price: only $71.00**

Electronic Fuel Injection Manual

New 1985 edition. Now expanded to cover all 1975 through 1985 domestic fuel injection systems, plus most 1968 through 1984 imports as well. Outlines different types of systems, describes each system and specialized component, gives full make and model application, provides trouble shooting tables and shows steps for diagnosis and testing. All necessary specifications included. **Price: only $20.00**

Emission Control Training Manual

A great training manual, but even the old timers will benefit from this comprehensive book. Covers all emission systems, regardless of model or make – from positive crankcase ventilation to computerized engine controls. Even explains the state and federal government standards, and how governments regulate emissions. Plenty of helpful illustrations. 176 pages. **Price: only $15.00**

Electrical Component Locator – Domestic & Import Editions

Quickly locates those hidden and unidentified components. Very useful because the illustrations identify both the shape and location of each component (ideal for group of look-alike components that have no ID on them). Domestic Edition covers all 1978 through 1984 Domestic cars and light trucks. Import Edition covers 1977-1983 cars and light trucks.
Price: $71.00 each

Medium & Heavy-Duty Truck Service & Repair Manual

Now, a single source for service and repair information on most major medium and heavy duty trucks sold in the U.S.A. Divided into five separate parts for fast use: 1) Tune-up, fuel systems, engines, clutches; 2) Ignition, starters, alternators; 3) Brakes, suspension, steering; 4) Drive axles, transfer cases; 5) Transmissions. **Price: only $200.00**

Electronic Ignition Service Manual

Easy-to-follow step-by-step coverage of each electronic ignition system, including description, operation, and test procedures specs. You get: basic wiring diagrams, voltmeter & ohmmeter hook-up locations for testing and easy to understand instructions. Also includes cautions to help prevent errors and a history of ignition development. Cover '77-'85 Domestics and '77-'84 Imports. **Price: only $15.00**

Cut this form off at dashed line and mail to: **MITCHELL INFORMATION SERVICES, INC.**

YES!

I want to save time and increase my shop profits – at no risk to me at all for 30 days. Please send me the manuals I have checked off below. I understand that if I am not completely satisfied, I can return the books within 30 days of delivery for a full refund.

- □ Air Conditioning & Heating 1966-75 .... $35.00
- □ Air Conditioning & Heating 1976-80 .... $35.00
- □ Air Conditioning & Heating 1981-85 .... $71.00
- □ Air Conditioning & Heating 1976-85 .... $85.00
- □ Imported A/C & Heating 1976-84 .... $70.00
- □ Domestic Emission Control 1975-85 .... $71.00
- □ Domestic Older Model Emission $48.00
- □ Imported Emission Control 1975-84 .... $71.00
- □ Imported Older Model Emission $48.00
- □ Computerized Engine Controls Manual 1981-85 .... $71.00
- □ Electronic Fuel Injection Manual $20.00
- □ Emission Control Training Manual $15.00
- □ Domestic Electrical Component Locator, 1978-84 .... $71.00
- □ Imported Electrical Component Locator, 1977-83 .... $71.00
- □ Medium & Heavy-Duty Truck Service Manual $200.00
- □ Electronic Ignition Service Manual $15.00
- □ Imported Car Tune-Up Manual $115.00
- □ Imported Car Mechanical Manual $115.00
- □ Imported Car Transmission Manual $115.00
- □ Domestic Car Tune-Up Manual $115.00
- □ Domestic Car Mechanical Manual $115.00
- □ Domestic Car Transmission Manual $115.00

Sub-Total $ ______
State Sales Tax* $ ______
Shipping & Handling $ $6.50
If C.O.D. add $1.90 $ ______
FINAL TOTAL $ ______

*NOTE: Your appropriate state sales tax must be included to process your order.

Please check one:

- □ Check or money order enclosed
- □ Send my order C.O.D.
- □ Charge to Master Charge/Visa
- □ Please send me more information
- □ Please send a sales representative to see me

Account # ______ Expiration Date ______
Issuing Bank ______
Your Signature ______

Name ______
Company ______
Address ______
City ______ Phone ( )
State ______ Zip ______

IMPORTANT REMINDER!
The full cost of your manuals may be taken as a business tax deduction.
Save time. Call toll FREE 800-854-7030 (In CA call 800-421-0159) Ask for Eve Shaw.

Note: prices apply to USA only and are subject to change without notice. ADT 1985

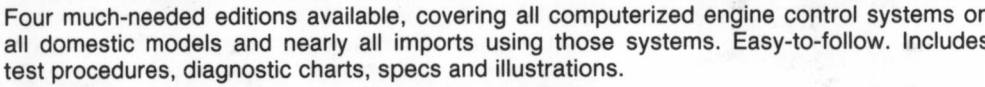

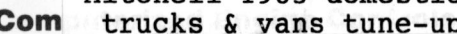